BASIC ALGEBRA FORMULAS

Arithmetic Operations

$$a(b + c) = ab + ac, \qquad \frac{a}{b} \cdot \frac{c}{d} = \frac{ac}{bd}$$

$$\frac{a}{b} + \frac{c}{d} = \frac{ad + bc}{bd}, \qquad \frac{a/b}{c/d} = \frac{a}{b} \cdot \frac{d}{c}$$

Laws of Signs

$$-(-a) = a, \qquad \frac{-a}{b} = -\frac{a}{b} = \frac{a}{-b}$$

Zero Division by zero is not defined.

$$\text{If } a \neq 0\text{: } \frac{0}{a} = 0, \quad a^0 = 1, \quad 0^a = 0$$

$$\text{For any number } a\text{: } a \cdot 0 = 0 \cdot a = 0$$

Laws of Exponents

$$a^m a^n = a^{m+n}, \qquad (ab)^m = a^m b^m, \qquad (a^m)^n = a^{mn}, \qquad a^{m/n} = \sqrt[n]{a^m} = \left(\sqrt[n]{a}\right)^m$$

If $a \neq 0$,

$$\frac{a^m}{a^n} = a^{m-n}, \qquad a^0 = 1, \qquad a^{-m} = \frac{1}{a^m}.$$

The Binomial Theorem For any positive integer n,

$$(a + b)^n = a^n + na^{n-1}b + \frac{n(n-1)}{1 \cdot 2} a^{n-2}b^2 + \frac{n(n-1)(n-2)}{1 \cdot 2 \cdot 3} a^{n-3}b^3 + \cdots + nab^{n-1} + b^n.$$

For instance,

$$(a + b)^2 = a^2 + 2ab + b^2, \qquad (a - b)^2 = a^2 - 2ab + b^2$$

$$(a + b)^3 = a^3 + 3a^2b + 3ab^2 + b^3, \qquad (a - b)^3 = a^2 - 3a^2b + 3ab^2 - b^3.$$

Factoring the Difference of Like Integer Powers, $n > 1$

$$a^n - b^n = (a - b)(a^{n-1} + a^{n-2}b + a^{n-3}b^2 + \cdots + ab^{n-2} + b^{n-1})$$

For instance,

$$a^2 - b^2 = (a - b)(a + b),$$
$$a^3 - b^3 = (a - b)(a^2 + ab + b^2),$$
$$a^4 - b^4 = (a - b)(a^3 + a^2b + ab^2 + b^3).$$

Completing the Square If $a \neq 0$,

$$ax^2 + bx + c = au^2 + C \qquad \left(u = x + (b/2a),\ C = c - \frac{b^2}{4a}\right)$$

The Quadratic Formula If $a \neq 0$ and $ax^2 + bx + c = 0$, then

$$x = \frac{-b \pm \sqrt{b^2 - 4ac}}{2a}.$$

GEOMETRY FORMULAS

A = area, B = area of base, C = circumference, S = lateral area or surface area, V = volume

Triangle

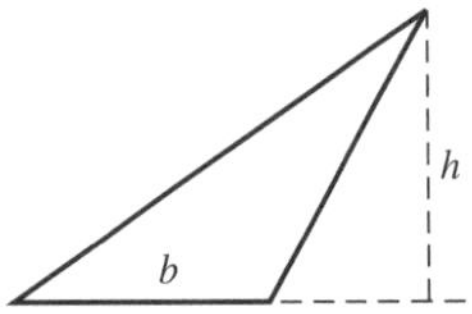

$A = \frac{1}{2}bh$

Similar Triangles

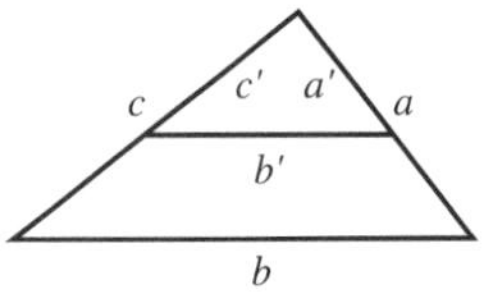

$\frac{a'}{a} = \frac{b'}{b} = \frac{c'}{c}$

Pythagorean Theorem

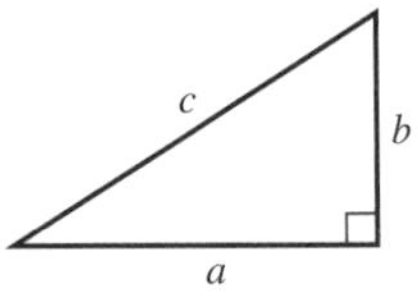

$a^2 + b^2 = c^2$

Parallelogram

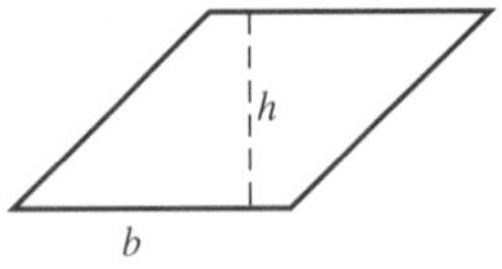

$A = bh$

Trapezoid

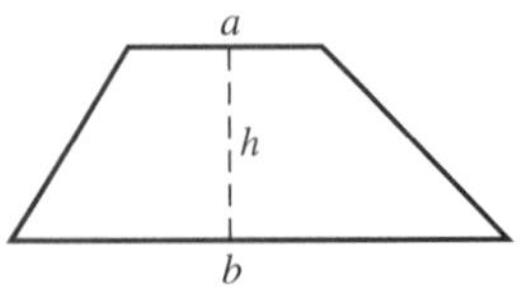

$A = \frac{1}{2}(a + b)h$

Circle

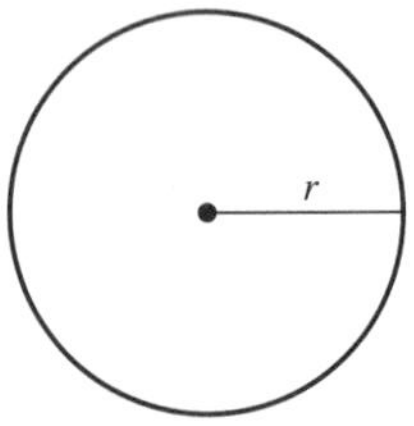

$A = \pi r^2$,
$C = 2\pi r$

Any Cylinder or Prism with Parallel Bases

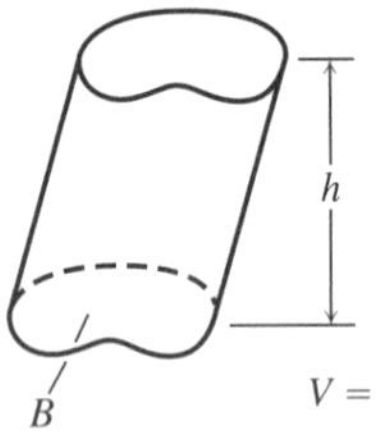

$V = Bh$

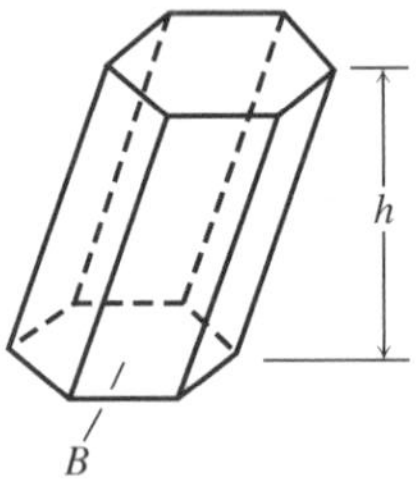

Right Circular Cylinder

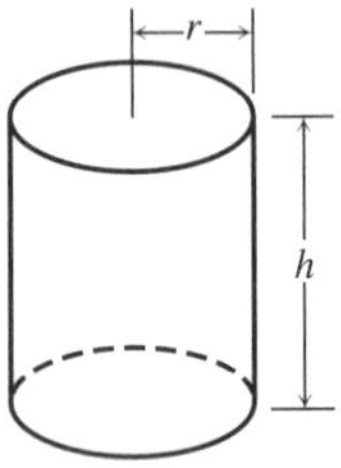

$V = \pi r^2 h$
$S = 2\pi rh$ = Area of side

Any Cone or Pyramid

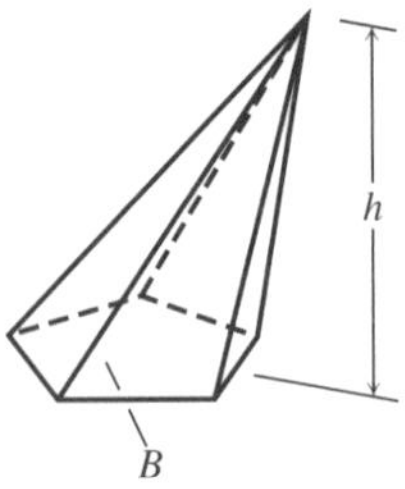

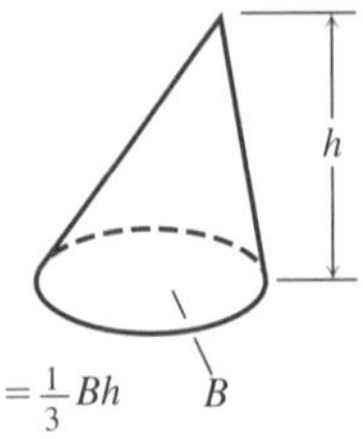

$V = \frac{1}{3}Bh$

Right Circular Cone

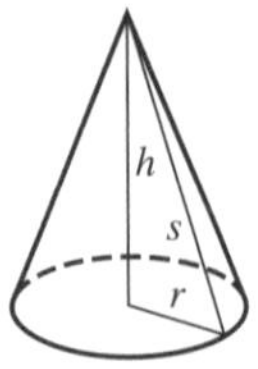

$V = \frac{1}{3}\pi r^2 h$
$S = \pi rs$ = Area of side

Sphere

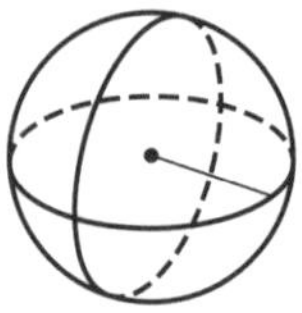

$V = \frac{4}{3}\pi r^3$, $S = 4\pi r^2$

UNIVERSITY CALCULUS

SINGLE VARIABLE WITH VECTORS

UNIVERSITY CALCULUS

SINGLE VARIABLE WITH VECTORS

Joel Hass
University of California, Davis

Maurice D. Weir
Naval Postgraduate School

George B. Thomas, Jr.
Massachusetts Institute of Technology

Addison-Wesley
Boston Columbus Indianapolis New York San Francisco Upper Saddle River
Amsterdam Cape Town Dubai London Madrid Milan Munich Paris Montréal Toronto
Delhi Mexico City São Paulo Sydney Hong Kong Seoul Singapore Taipei Tokyo

Publisher: Greg Tobin
Senior Acquisitions Editor: William Hoffman
Senior Project Editor: Rachel S. Reeve
Editorial Assistant: Lianna Kong
Managing Editor: Karen Wernholm
Senior Production Supervisor: Jeffrey Holcomb
Senior Designer: Barbara T. Atkinson
Supplements Supervisor: Emily Portwood
Software Development: Mary Durnwald and Bob Carroll
Marketing Manager: Phyllis Hubbard
Marketing Assistant: Celena Carr
Senior Author Support/ Technology Specialist: Joe Vetere
Senior Prepress Supervisor: Caroline Fell
Senior Manufacturing Buyer: Evelyn Beaton
Production Coordinator: Kathy Diamond
Composition: Nesbitt Graphics, Inc.
Illustrations: Techsetters, Inc.

Cover Image: "Flying Spinnakers," photographed by Morris and Stanley Rosenfeld on July 9, 1937 © Mystic Seaport, Rosenfeld Collection, image acquired in honor of Franz Schneider. The photograph is of the 70' Clinton Crane–designed, Henry B. Nevins–built 10-meter class sloop GLEAM and the 70' Sparkman & Stephens–designed, Henry B. Nevins–built 12-meter class sloop NORTHERN LIGHT, running down Long Island Sound on the NYYC Cruise. Visible in the image is the cropped port quarter view of GLEAM and the spinnaker and mainsail of NORTHERN LIGHT running before the wind under spinnakers and mainsails.

For permission to use copyrighted material, grateful acknowledgment is made to the copyright holders on page C-1, which is hereby made part of this copyright page.

1 2 3 4 5 6 7 8 9 10—CRK—12 11 10

Addison-Wesley
is an imprint of

PEARSON

www.pearsoned.com

ISBN-10: 0-321-74403-9
ISBN-13: 978-0-321-74403-6

Contents

Preface

OVERVIEW *University Calculus* offers a more streamlined and faster-paced text that maintains the high standards and focused applications that have been the hallmark of *Thomas' Calculus*.

Condensing material from a well-established book is a difficult task. We have preserved the careful development of the main ideas in *Thomas' Calculus*, and we have resisted the temptation to lower its level of rigor. We think that having high standards inspires students to seek excellence. On the other hand, a solid grounding in the various types of functions is essential to understanding calculus. In this vein, we have retained a shortened first chapter reviewing the basic functions. We understand that some professors will prefer to skip this review, but we also believe that many students need to see this material again. The first chapter is not an introduction to calculus, but rather a helpful aid for the average student.

Today, an increasing number of students become familiar with the terminology and operational methods of calculus in high school. However, their conceptual understanding of calculus is often quite limited when they enter college. We have acknowledged this reality by concentrating on concepts and their applications throughout.

To achieve the goals of *University Calculus*, we consulted with many colleagues and reviewers across the country. They helped us decide which topics to retain and which to remove or condense. We are grateful for their thoughtful advice, from which we can now offer this new text.

Pedagogical Features

EXERCISES Exercises and examples play a crucial role in learning calculus. We have included many of the exercises that appeared in previous editions of *Thomas' Calculus*, and which constituted a great strength of those editions. Within each section we have organized and grouped the exercises by topic, progressing from computational problems to applied and theoretical problems. This arrangement gives students the opportunity to develop skills in using the methods of calculus and to deepen their understanding of its applications.

RIGOR The level of rigor is consistent throughout. We give both formal and informal discussions, making clear the distinction between the two, and we include precise definitions and accessible proofs for the students. The text is organized so the material can be covered informally, giving the instructor a degree of flexibility. For example, while we do not prove that a continuous function on a closed and bounded interval has a maximum there, we do state this theorem carefully and use it to prove several subsequent results.

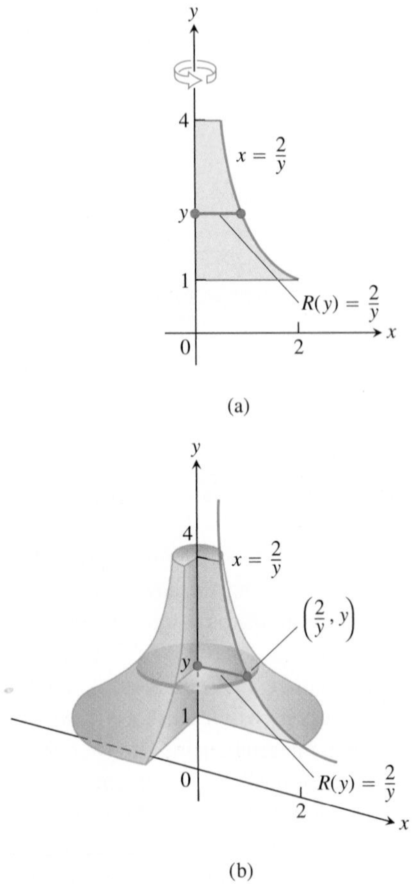

FIGURE 6.11, page 396
Finding the volume of the solid generated by revolving the region (a) about the y-axis.

ART We realize that figures and illustrations are a critical component to learning calculus. We paid special attention to the clarity with which the figures illustrate their associated concepts. This is especially evident with the three-dimensional graphics, where we were able to better indicate depth, layering, and rotation (see figures on this page).

END-OF-CHAPTER REVIEWS AND PROJECTS In addition to problems appearing after each section, each chapter culminates with review questions, practice exercises, and a series of Additional and Advanced Exercises. Student projects are available over the Internet at **www.aw-bc.com/thomas**.

WRITING EXERCISES Writing exercises placed throughout the text ask students to explore a variety of calculus concepts and applications. In addition, each chapter contains questions asking students to summarize what they have learned. Many of these questions ask for written descriptions that test conceptual understanding.

ANSWERS Answers are provided for all odd-numbered exercises when appropriate, and these have been carefully checked for correctness.

MATHEMATICAL CORRECTNESS We have been careful to say only what is true and mathematically sound. Every definition, theorem, corollary, and proof has been reviewed for clarity and mathematical correctness.

WRITING AND APPLICATIONS This text continues to be easy to read, conversational, and mathematically rich. Each new topic is motivated by clear, easy-to-understand examples and applications.

TECHNOLOGY Technology can be incorporated according to the taste of the instructor. Each section contains exercises requiring the use of technology; these are marked with a **T** if suitable for calculator or computer usage or are labeled **Computer Explorations** if a computer algebra system (CAS, such as *Maple* or *Mathematica*) is required.

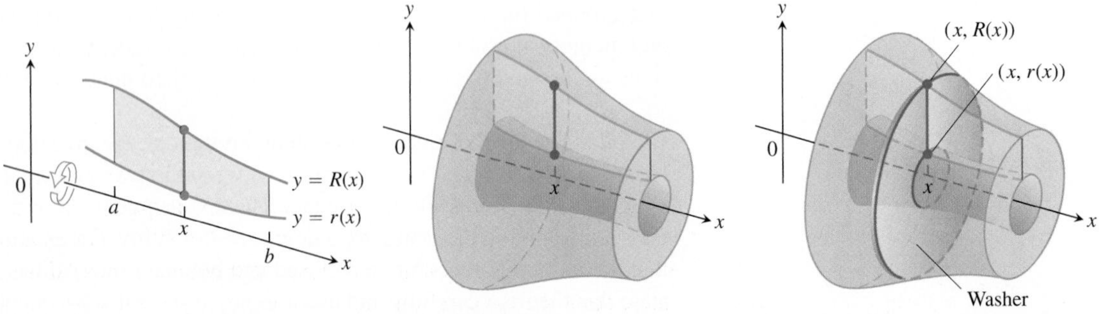

FIGURE 6.13, page 397
The cross-sections of the solid of revolution generated here are washers, not disks.

Print Supplements

STUDENT EDITION OF UNIVERSITY CALCULUS
ISBN 0-321-35014-6

INSTRUCTOR'S SOLUTIONS MANUAL
Part One (Chapters 1–9), ISBN 0-321-38848-8
Part Two (Chapters 10–14), ISBN 0-321-38698-1
The *Instructor's Solutions Manual* by William Ardis, et al., contains complete worked-out solutions to all of the exercises in the text.

ANSWER BOOK
ISBN 0-321-39423-2
The *Answer Book* by William Ardis, et al., contains short answers to most of the exercises in the text.

STUDENT OUTLINES
Part One (Chapters 1–9), ISBN 0-321-39551-4
Part Two (Chapters 8, 10–14), ISBN 0-321-39969-2
Organized to correspond to the text, the *Student Outlines* by Joseph Borzellino and Patricia Nelson reinforces important concepts and provides an outline of the important topics, theorems, and definitions, as well as study tips and additional practice problems.

STUDENT'S SOLUTIONS MANUAL
Part One (Chapters 1–9), ISBN 0-321-38849-6
Part Two (Chapters 8, 10–14), ISBN 0-321-38850-X
The *Student's Solutions Manual* by William Ardis, et al., is designed for the student and contains carefully worked-out solutions to all the odd-numbered exercises in the text.

JUST-IN-TIME ALGEBRA AND TRIGONOMETRY FOR EARLY TRANSCENDENTALS CALCULUS,
Third Edition
ISBN 0-321-32050-6
Sharp algebra and trigonometry skills are critical to mastering calculus, and *Just-in-Time Algebra and Trigonometry for Early Transcendentals Calculus,* Third Edition, by Guntram Mueller and Ronald I. Brent is designed to bolster these skills while students study calculus. As students make their way through calculus, this text is with them every step of the way, showing them the necessary algebra or trigonometry topics and pointing out potential problem spots. The easy-to-use contents has algebra and trigonometry topics arranged in the order in which students will need them as they study calculus.

ADDISON-WESLEY'S CALCULUS REVIEW CARD
The Calculus Review Card is a resource for students containing important formulas, functions, definitions, and theorems that correspond precisely to *University Calculus.* This card can work as a reference for completing homework assignments or as an aid in studying and is available bundled with a new text. Contact your Addison-Wesley sales representative for more information.

Media and Online Supplements

TECHNOLOGY RESOURCE MANUALS

Maple Manual by Donald Hartig, California Polytechnic State University

Mathematica Manual by Marie Vanisko, California State University Stanislaus, and Lyle Cochran, Whitworth College

TI-Graphing Calculator Manual by Luz DeAlba, Drake University

These manuals cover *Maple* 9, *Mathematica* 5, and the TI-83 Plus/TI-84 Plus, TI-85/TI-86, and TI-89/TI-92 Plus, respectively. Each manual provides detailed guidance for integrating a specific software package or graphing calculator throughout the course, including syntax and commands. These manuals are available to qualified instructors through **http://www.aw-bc.com/irc/**.

MYMATHLAB

MyMathLab is a series of text-specific, easily customizable online courses for Addison-Wesley textbooks in mathematics and statistics. Powered by CourseCompass™ (Pearson Education's online teaching and learning environment) and MathXL (our online homework, tutorial, and assessment system), MyMathLab gives you the tools you need to deliver all or a portion of your course online, whether your students are in a lab setting or working from home. MyMathLab provides a rich and flexible set of course materials, featuring free-response exercises that are algorithmically generated for unlimited practice and mastery. Students can also use online tools, such as video lectures, animations, multimedia textbook, and Maple/Mathematica projects, to independently improve their understanding and performance. Instructors can use MyMathLab's homework and test managers to select and assign online exercises correlated directly to the textbook, and they can also create and assign their own online exercises and import TestGen tests for added flexibility. MyMathLab's online gradebook—designed specifically for mathematics and statistics—automatically tracks students' homework and test results and gives the instructor control over how to calculate final grades. Instructors can also add offline (paper-and-pencil) grades to the gradebook. MyMathLab is available to qualified adopters. For more information, visit our Web site at **www.mymathlab.com** or contact your Addison-Wesley sales representative.

MATHXL®

MathXL is a powerful online homework, tutorial, and assessment system that accompanies Addison-Wesley textbooks in mathematics or statistics. With MathXL, instructors can create, edit, and assign online homework and tests using algorithmically generated exercises correlated at the objective level to the textbook. They can also create and assign their own online exercises and import TestGen tests for added flexibility. All student work is tracked in MathXL's online gradebook. Students can take chapter tests in MathXL and receive personalized study plans based on their test results. The study plan diagnoses weaknesses and links students directly to tutorial exercises for the objectives they need to study and retest. Students can also access supplemental animations and video clips directly from selected exercises. MathXL is available to qualified adopters. For more information, visit our Web site at **www.mathxl.com** or contact your Addison-Wesley sales representative.

TESTGEN

TestGen enables instructors to build, edit, print, and administer tests using a computerized bank of questions developed to cover all the objectives of the text. TestGen is algorithmically based, allowing instructors to create multiple but equivalent versions of the same question or test with the click of a button. Instructors can also modify test bank questions or add new questions. Tests can be printed or administered online. The software is available on a dual-platform Windows/Macintosh CD-ROM.

DIGITAL VIDEO TUTOR

The Digital Video Tutor features an engaging team of mathematics instructors who present comprehensive coverage of topics in the text. The lecturers' presentations include examples and exercises from the text and support an approach that emphasizes visualization and problem solving. The video lectures are available on CD-ROM, making it easy and convenient for students to watch the videos from a computer at home or on campus. The complete digitized video set, affordable and portable for students, is ideal for distance learning or supplemental instruction.

WEB SITE **www.aw-bc.com/thomas**

The *University Calculus* Web site provides the expanded historical biographies and essays referenced in the text. Also available is a collection of *Maple* and *Mathematica* modules that can be used as projects by individual students or groups of students.

ADDISON-WESLEY MATH TUTOR CENTER

The Addison-Wesley Math Tutor Center is staffed by qualified mathematics and statistics instructors who provide students with tutoring on examples and odd-numbered exercises from the textbook. Tutoring is available via toll-free telephone, toll-free fax, e-mail, and the Internet. Interactive, Web-based technology allows tutors and students to view and work through problems together in real time over the Internet. The Addison-Wesley Math Tutor Center is available to qualified adopters. For more information, please visit our Web site at **www.aw-bc.com/tutorcenter** or call us at 1-888-777-0463.

Acknowledgments

For their careful checking of this text for accuracy, we extend our gratitude to Marie Vanisko and Thomas Wegleitner. We also extend our sincere thanks for the suggestions and contributions made by the following reviewers:

Harry Allen, *Ohio State University*
Edoh Amiran, *Western Washington University*
Anthony Bedenikovic, *Bradley University*
Deborah Brandon, *Carnegie Mellon University*
Said Fariabi, *San Antonio College*
Krystyna Kuperberg, *Auburn University*
Paul Sacks, *Iowa State University*
Stephen Summers, *University of Florida*
Blake Thornton, *Washington University in St. Louis*
Ilie Ugarcovici, *Rice University*

Finally, we are grateful for the advice, suggestions, and encouragment provided by our development editor, David Chelton.

UNIVERSITY CALCULUS

SINGLE VARIABLE WITH VECTORS

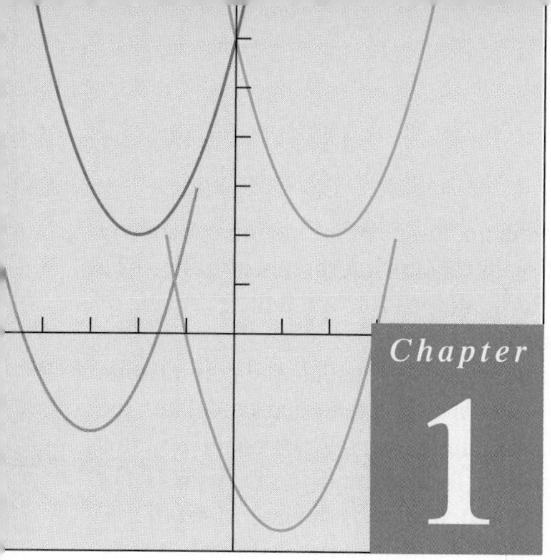

Chapter 1 FUNCTIONS

OVERVIEW Functions are fundamental to the study of calculus. In this chapter we review what they are and how they are pictured as graphs, how they are combined and transformed, and ways they can be classified. We look at the key function types occurring in calculus, including trigonometric, exponential, and logarithmic functions. We also discuss misrepresentations that can occur when using calculators and computers to obtain a function's graph. (The real number system, Cartesian coordinates, straight lines, parabolas, and circles are reviewed in the Appendices.)

1.1 Functions and Their Graphs

Functions are a tool for describing the real world in mathematical terms. A function can be represented by an equation, a numerical table, a graph, or by verbal description; we will use all four representations throughout this book. This section reviews these function ideas.

Functions; Domain and Range

The temperature at which water boils depends on the elevation above sea level (the boiling point drops as you ascend). The interest paid on a cash investment depends on the length of time the investment is held. The area of a circle depends on the radius of the circle. The distance an object travels at constant speed along a straight line path depends on the elapsed time.

In each case, the value of one variable quantity, say y, depends on the value of another variable quantity, which we might call x. We say that "y is a function of x" and write this symbolically as

$$y = f(x) \qquad (\text{"}y \text{ equals } f \text{ of } x\text{"}).$$

In this notation, the symbol f represents the function, the letter x is the **independent variable** representing the input value of f, and y is the **dependent variable** or output value of f at x.

> **DEFINITION** A **function** from a set D to a set Y is a rule that assigns a *unique* (single) element $f(x) \in Y$ to each element $x \in D$.

The set D of all possible input values is called the **domain** of the function. The set of all values of $f(x)$ as x varies throughout D is called the **range** of the function. The range may not include every element in the set Y. The domain and range of a function can be any sets of objects, but often in calculus they are sets of real numbers interpreted as points of a coordinate line. (In Chapters 11–14, we will encounter functions for which the elements of the sets are points in the coordinate plane or in space.)

Often a function is given by a formula that describes how to calculate the output value from the input variable. For instance, the equation $A = \pi r^2$ is a rule that calculates the area A of a circle from its radius r (so r, interpreted as a length, can only be positive in this formula). When we define a function $y = f(x)$ with a formula and the domain is not stated explicitly or restricted by context, the domain is assumed to be the largest set of real x-values for which the formula gives real y-values, the so-called **natural domain**. If we want to restrict the domain in some way, we must say so. The domain of $y = x^2$ is the entire set of real numbers. To restrict the domain of the function to, say, positive values of x, we would write "$y = x^2, x > 0$."

FIGURE 1.1 A diagram showing a function as a kind of machine.

Changing the domain to which we apply a formula usually changes the range as well. The range of $y = x^2$ is $[0, \infty)$. The range of $y = x^2, x \geq 2$, is the set of all numbers obtained by squaring numbers greater than or equal to 2. In set notation (see Appendix 1), the range is $\{x^2 | x \geq 2\}$ or $\{y | y \geq 4\}$ or $[4, \infty)$.

When the range of a function is a set of real numbers, the function is said to be **real-valued**. The domains and ranges of many real-valued functions of a real variable are intervals or combinations of intervals. The intervals may be open, closed, or half open, and may be finite or infinite. The range of a function is not always easy to find.

A function f is like a machine that produces an output value $f(x)$ in its range whenever we feed it an input value x from its domain (Figure 1.1). The function keys on a calculator give an example of a function as a machine. For instance, the $\sqrt{x}$ key on a calculator gives an output value (the square root) whenever you enter a nonnegative number x and press the $\sqrt{x}$ key.

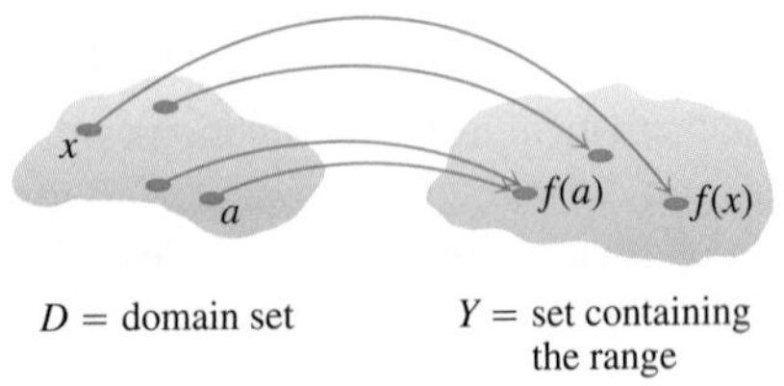

FIGURE 1.2 A function from a set D to a set Y assigns a unique element of Y to each element in D.

A function can also be pictured as an **arrow diagram** (Figure 1.2). Each arrow associates an element of the domain D to a unique or single element in the set Y. In Figure 1.2, the arrows indicate that $f(a)$ is associated with a, $f(x)$ is associated with x, and so on. Notice that a function can have the same *value* at two different input elements in the domain (as occurs with $f(a)$ in Figure 1.2), but each input element x is assigned a *single* output value $f(x)$.

EXAMPLE 1 Verify the natural domains and associated ranges of these functions.

Function	Domain (x)	Range (y)
$y = x^2$	$(-\infty, \infty)$	$[0, \infty)$
$y = 1/x$	$(-\infty, 0) \cup (0, \infty)$	$(-\infty, 0) \cup (0, \infty)$
$y = \sqrt{x}$	$[0, \infty)$	$[0, \infty)$
$y = \sqrt{4 - x}$	$(-\infty, 4]$	$[0, \infty)$
$y = \sqrt{1 - x^2}$	$[-1, 1]$	$[0, 1]$

Solution The formula $y = x^2$ gives a real y-value for any real number x, so the domain is $(-\infty, \infty)$. The range of $y = x^2$ is $[0, \infty)$ because the square of any real number is nonnegative and every nonnegative number y is the square of its own square root, $y = \left(\sqrt{y}\right)^2$ for $y \geq 0$.

The formula $y = 1/x$ gives a real y-value for every x except $x = 0$. For consistency in the rules of arithmetic, *we cannot divide any number by zero*. The range of $y = 1/x$, the set of reciprocals of all nonzero real numbers, is the set of all nonzero real numbers, since $y = 1/(1/y)$.

The formula $y = \sqrt{x}$ gives a real y-value only if $x \geq 0$. The range of $y = \sqrt{x}$ is $[0, \infty)$ because every nonnegative number is some number's square root (namely, it is the square root of its own square).

In $y = \sqrt{4 - x}$, the quantity $4 - x$ cannot be negative. That is, $4 - x \geq 0$, or $x \leq 4$. The formula gives real y-values for all $x \leq 4$. The range of $\sqrt{4 - x}$ is $[0, \infty)$, the set of all nonnegative numbers.

The formula $y = \sqrt{1 - x^2}$ gives a real y-value for every x in the closed interval from -1 to 1. Outside this domain, $1 - x^2$ is negative and its square root is not a real number. The values of $1 - x^2$ vary from 0 to 1 on the given domain, and the square roots of these values do the same. The range of $\sqrt{1 - x^2}$ is $[0, 1]$. ■

Graphs of Functions

If f is a function with domain D, its **graph** consists of the points in the Cartesian plane whose coordinates are the input-output pairs for f. In set notation, the graph is

$$\{(x, f(x)) \mid x \in D\}.$$

The graph of the function $f(x) = x + 2$ is the set of points with coordinates (x, y) for which $y = x + 2$. Its graph is the straight line sketched in Figure 1.3.

The graph of a function f is a useful picture of its behavior. If (x, y) is a point on the graph, then $y = f(x)$ is the height of the graph above the point x. The height may be positive or negative, depending on the sign of $f(x)$ (Figure 1.4).

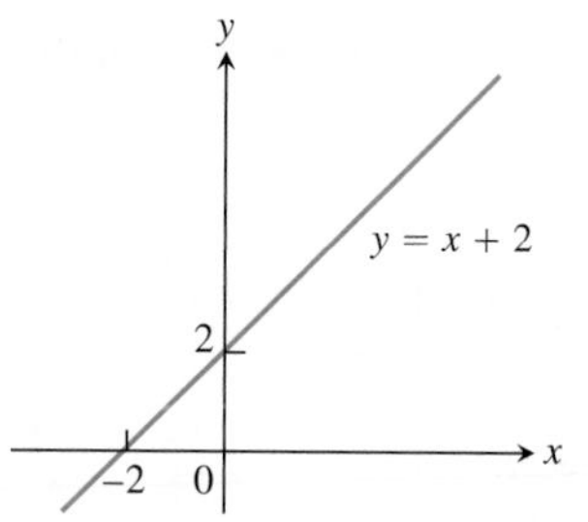

FIGURE 1.3 The graph of $f(x) = x + 2$ is the set of points (x, y) for which y has the value $x + 2$.

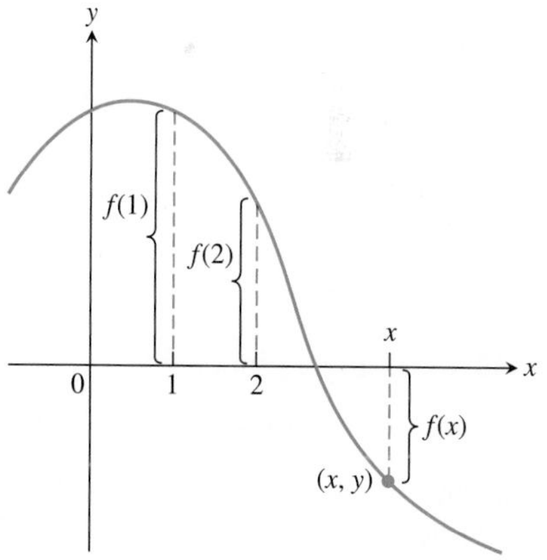

FIGURE 1.4 If (x, y) lies on the graph of f, then the value $y = f(x)$ is the height of the graph above the point x (or below x if $f(x)$ is negative).

x	$y = x^2$
-2	4
-1	1
0	0
1	1
$\frac{3}{2}$	$\frac{9}{4}$
2	4

EXAMPLE 2 Graph the function $y = x^2$ over the interval $[-2, 2]$.

Solution Make a table of xy-pairs that satisfy the equation $y = x^2$. Plot the points (x, y) whose coordinates appear in the table, and draw a *smooth* curve (labeled with its equation) through the plotted points (see Figure 1.5). ■

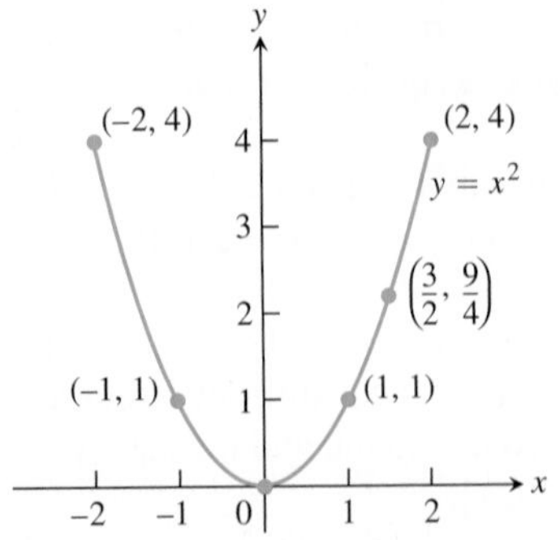

FIGURE 1.5 Graph of the function in Example 2.

How do we know that the graph of $y = x^2$ doesn't look like one of these curves?

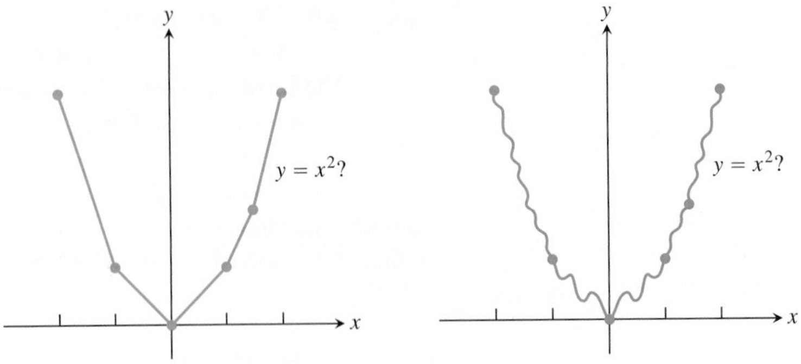

To find out, we could plot more points. But how would we then connect *them*? The basic question still remains: How do we know for sure what the graph looks like between the points we plot? The answer lies in calculus, as we will see in Chapter 4. Meanwhile we will have to settle for plotting points and connecting them as best we can.

Representing a Function Numerically

We have seen how a function may be represented algebraically by a formula (the area function) and visually by a graph (Example 2). Another way to represent a function is **numerically**, through a table of values. Numerical representations are often used by engineers and scientists. From an appropriate table of values, a graph of the function can be obtained using the method illustrated in Example 2, possibly with the aid of a computer. The graph of only the tabled points is called a **scatterplot**.

EXAMPLE 3 Musical notes are pressure waves in the air that can be recorded. The data in Table 1.1 give recorded pressure displacement versus time in seconds of a musical note produced by a tuning fork. The table provides a representation of the pressure function over time. If we first make a scatterplot and then connect the data points (t, p) from the table, we obtain the graph shown in Figure 1.6.

TABLE 1.1 Tuning fork data

Time	Pressure	Time	Pressure
0.00091	−0.080	0.00362	0.217
0.00108	0.200	0.00379	0.480
0.00125	0.480	0.00398	0.681
0.00144	0.693	0.00416	0.810
0.00162	0.816	0.00435	0.827
0.00180	0.844	0.00453	0.749
0.00198	0.771	0.00471	0.581
0.00216	0.603	0.00489	0.346
0.00234	0.368	0.00507	0.077
0.00253	0.099	0.00525	−0.164
0.00271	−0.141	0.00543	−0.320
0.00289	−0.309	0.00562	−0.354
0.00307	−0.348	0.00579	−0.248
0.00325	−0.248	0.00598	−0.035
0.00344	−0.041		

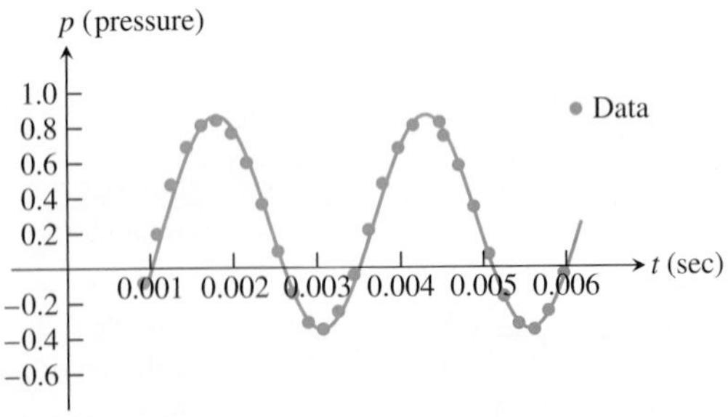

FIGURE 1.6 A smooth curve through the plotted points gives a graph of the pressure function represented by Table 1.1 (Example 3).

■

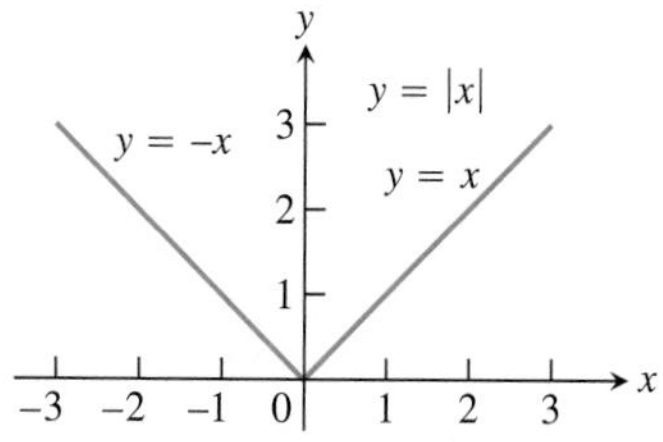

FIGURE 1.7 The absolute value function has domain $(-\infty, \infty)$ and range $[0, \infty)$.

Piecewise-Defined Functions

Sometimes a function is described by using different formulas on different parts of its domain. One example is the **absolute value function**

$$|x| = \begin{cases} x, & x \geq 0 \\ -x, & x < 0, \end{cases}$$

whose graph is given in Figure 1.7. The right-hand side of the equation means that the function equals x if $x \geq 0$, and equals $-x$ if $x < 0$. Here are some other examples.

EXAMPLE 4 The function

$$f(x) = \begin{cases} -x, & x < 0 \\ x^2, & 0 \leq x \leq 1 \\ 1, & x > 1 \end{cases}$$

is defined on the entire real line but has values given by different formulas depending on the position of x. The values of f are given by: $y = -x$ when $x < 0$, $y = x^2$ when $0 \leq x \leq 1$, and $y = 1$ when $x > 1$. The function, however, is *just one function* whose domain is the entire set of real numbers (Figure 1.8). ■

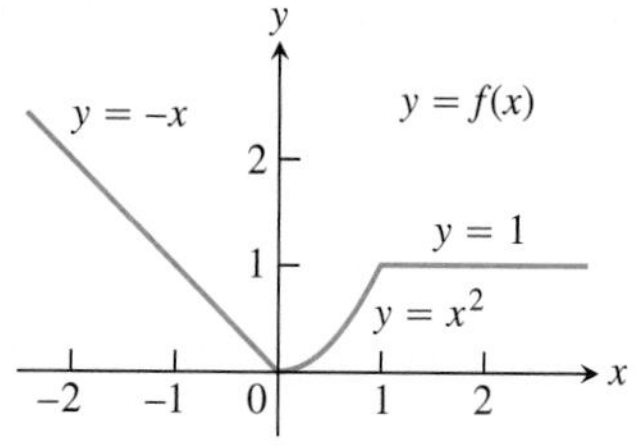

FIGURE 1.8 To graph the function $y = f(x)$ shown here, we apply different formulas to different parts of its domain (Example 4).

EXAMPLE 5 The function whose value at any number x is the *greatest integer less than or equal to* x is called the **greatest integer function** or the **integer floor function**. It is denoted $\lfloor x \rfloor$. Figure 1.9 shows the graph. Observe that

$$\lfloor 2.4 \rfloor = 2, \quad \lfloor 1.9 \rfloor = 1, \quad \lfloor 0 \rfloor = 0, \quad \lfloor -1.2 \rfloor = -2,$$
$$\lfloor 2 \rfloor = 2, \quad \lfloor 0.2 \rfloor = 0, \quad \lfloor -0.3 \rfloor = -1 \quad \lfloor -2 \rfloor = -2.$$ ■

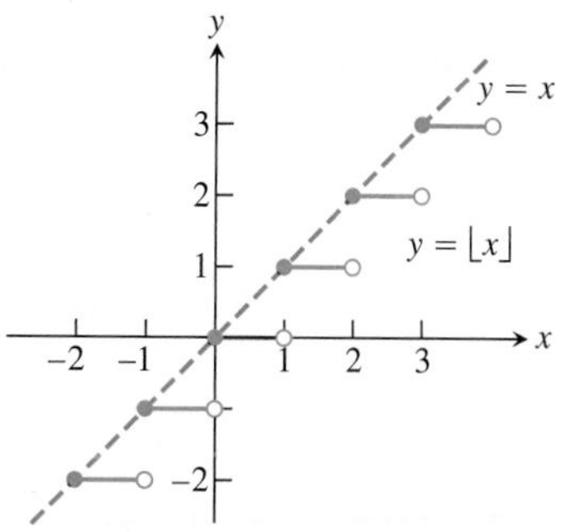

FIGURE 1.9 The graph of the greatest integer function $y = \lfloor x \rfloor$ lies on or below the line $y = x$, so it provides an integer floor for x (Example 5).

EXAMPLE 6 The function whose value at any number x is the *smallest integer greater than or equal to* x is called the **least integer function** or the **integer ceiling function**. It is denoted $\lceil x \rceil$. Figure 1.10 shows the graph. For positive values of x, this function might represent, for example, the cost of parking x hours in a parking lot which charges \$1 for each hour or part of an hour. ■

The Vertical Line Test

Not every curve you draw is the graph of a function. A function f can have only one value $f(x)$ for each x in its domain, so *no vertical* line can intersect the graph of a function more than once. Thus, a circle cannot be the graph of a function, since some vertical lines intersect the circle twice (Figure 1.11a). If a is in the domain of a function f, then the vertical line $x = a$ will intersect the graph of f in the single point $(a, f(a))$.

The circle in Figure 1.11a, however, does contain the graphs of *two* functions of x; the upper semicircle defined by the function $f(x) = \sqrt{1 - x^2}$ and the lower semicircle defined by the function $g(x) = -\sqrt{1 - x^2}$ (Figures 1.11b and 1.11c).

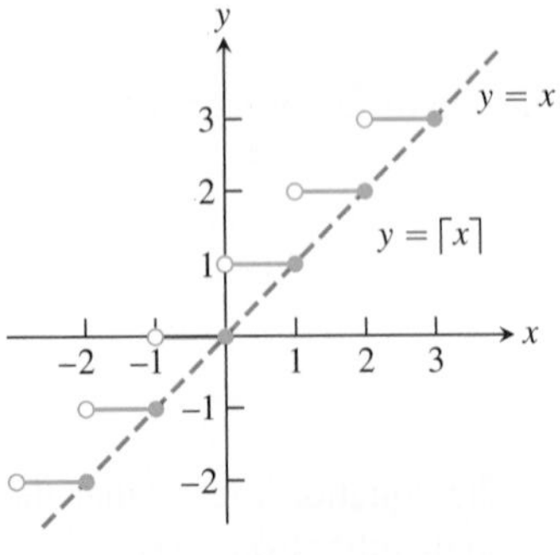

FIGURE 1.10 The graph of the least integer function $y = \lceil x \rceil$ lies on or above the line $y = x$, so it provides an integer ceiling for x (Example 6).

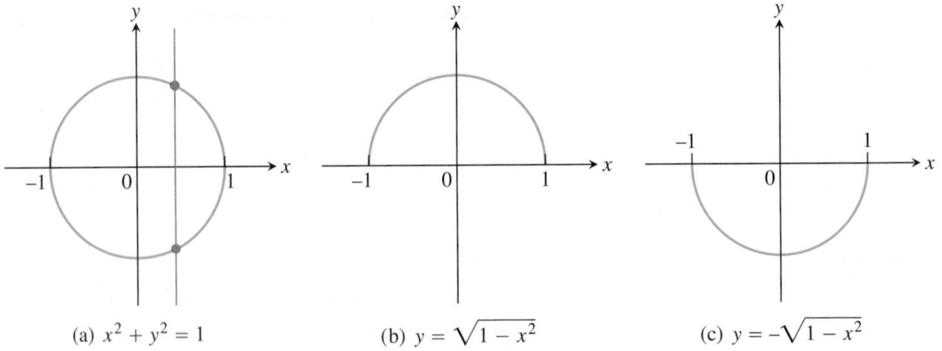

FIGURE 1.11 (a) The circle is not the graph of a function; it fails the vertical line test. (b) The upper semicircle is the graph of a function $f(x) = \sqrt{1 - x^2}$. (c) The lower semicircle is the graph of a function $g(x) = -\sqrt{1 - x^2}$.

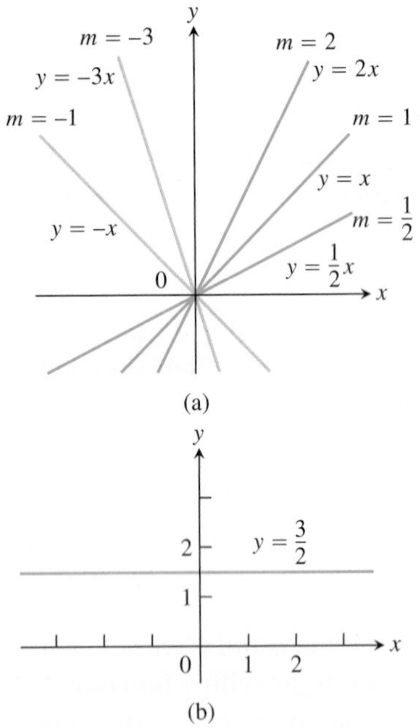

FIGURE 1.12 (a) Lines through the origin with slope m. (b) A constant function with slope $m = 0$.

Common Functions

There are a number of important types of functions frequently encountered in calculus. We identify and briefly describe them here.

Linear Functions A function of the form $f(x) = mx + b$, for constants m and b, is called a **linear function**. Figure 1.12a shows an array of lines $f(x) = mx$ where $b = 0$, so these lines pass through the origin. The function $f(x) = x$ where $m = 1$ and $b = 0$ is called the **identity function**. Constant functions result when the slope $m = 0$ (Figure 1.12b). A linear function with positive slope whose graph passes through the origin is called a *proportionality* relationship.

> **DEFINITION** Two variables y and x are **proportional** (to one another) if one is always a constant multiple of the other; that is, if $y = kx$ for some nonzero constant k.

Power Functions A function $f(x) = x^a$, where a is a constant, is called a **power function**. There are several important cases to consider.

(a) $a = n$, a positive integer.

The graphs of $f(x) = x^n$, for $n = 1, 2, 3, 4, 5$, are displayed in Figure 1.13. These functions are defined for all real values of x. Notice that as the power n gets larger, the curves

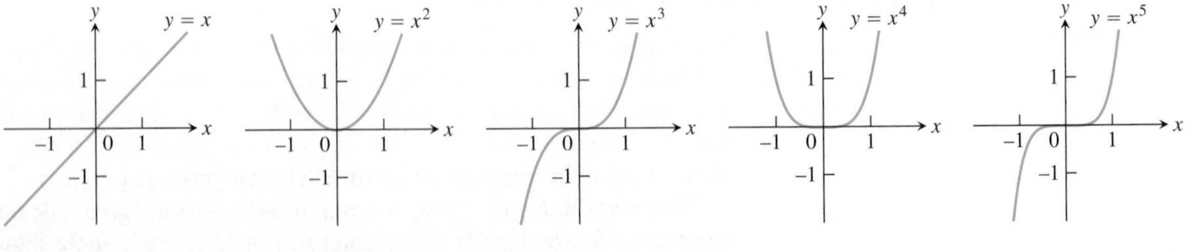

FIGURE 1.13 Graphs of $f(x) = x^n$, $n = 1, 2, 3, 4, 5$ defined for $-\infty < x < \infty$.

tend to flatten toward the x-axis on the interval $(-1, 1)$, and also rise more steeply for $|x| > 1$. Each curve passes through the point (1, 1) and through the origin.

(b) $a = -1$ or $a = -2$.

The graphs of the functions $f(x) = x^{-1} = 1/x$ and $g(x) = x^{-2} = 1/x^2$ are shown in Figure 1.14. Both functions are defined for all $x \neq 0$ (you can never divide by zero). The graph of $y = 1/x$ is the hyperbola $xy = 1$, which approaches the coordinate axes far from the origin. The graph of $y = 1/x^2$ also approaches the coordinate axes.

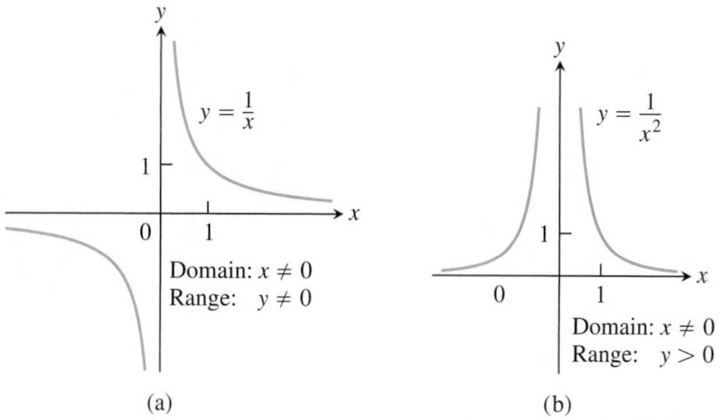

FIGURE 1.14 Graphs of the power functions $f(x) = x^a$ for part (a) $a = -1$ and for part (b) $a = -2$

(c) $a = \frac{1}{2}, \frac{1}{3}, \frac{3}{2}$, and $\frac{2}{3}$.

The functions $f(x) = x^{1/2} = \sqrt{x}$ and $g(x) = x^{1/3} = \sqrt[3]{x}$ are the **square root** and **cube root** functions, respectively. The domain of the square root function is $[0, \infty)$, but the cube root function is defined for all real x. Their graphs are displayed in Figure 1.15 along with the graphs of $y = x^{3/2}$ and $y = x^{2/3}$. (Recall that $x^{3/2} = (x^{1/2})^3$ and $x^{2/3} = (x^{1/3})^2$.)

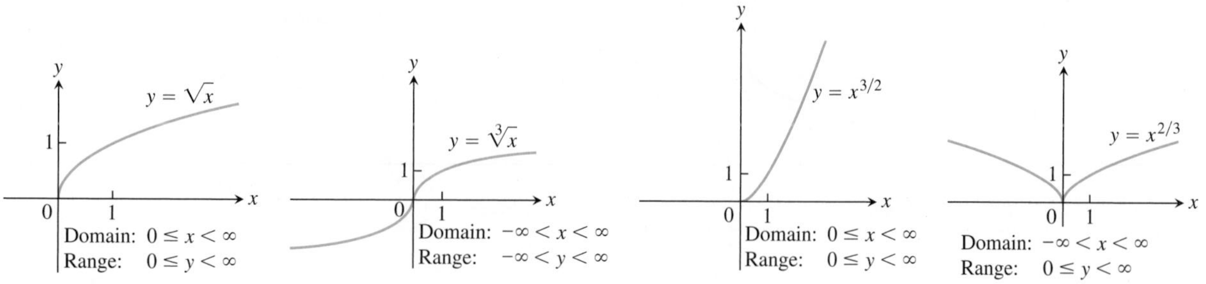

FIGURE 1.15 Graphs of the power functions $f(x) = x^a$ for $a = \frac{1}{2}, \frac{1}{3}, \frac{3}{2}$, and $\frac{2}{3}$.

Polynomials A function p is a **polynomial** if

$$p(x) = a_n x^n + a_{n-1} x^{n-1} + \cdots + a_1 x + a_0$$

where n is a nonnegative integer and the numbers $a_0, a_1, a_2, \ldots, a_n$ are real constants (called the **coefficients** of the polynomial). All polynomials have domain $(-\infty, \infty)$. If the leading coefficient $a_n \neq 0$ and $n > 0$, then n is called the **degree** of the polynomial. Linear functions with $m \neq 0$ are polynomials of degree 1. Polynomials of degree 2, usually written as $p(x) = ax^2 + bx + c$, are called **quadratic functions**. Likewise, **cubic functions** are polynomials $p(x) = ax^3 + bx^2 + cx + d$ of degree 3. Figure 1.16 shows the graphs of three polynomials. You will learn techniques to graph polynomials in Chapter 4.

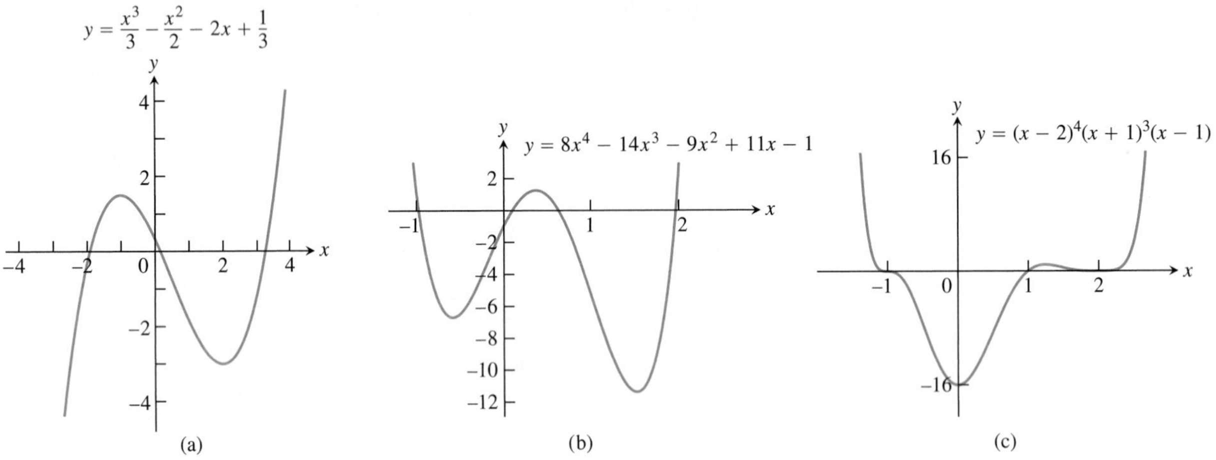

FIGURE 1.16 Graphs of three polynomial functions.

Rational Functions A **rational function** is a quotient or ratio $f(x) = p(x)/q(x)$, where p and q are polynomials. The domain of a rational function is the set of all real x for which $q(x) \neq 0$. The graphs of several rational functions are show in Figure 1.17.

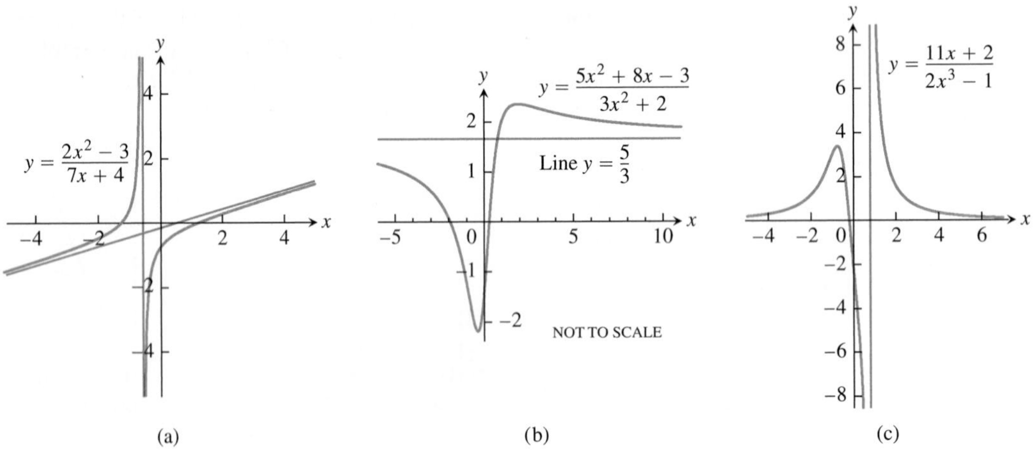

FIGURE 1.17 Graphs of three rational functions.

Algebraic Functions Any function constructed from polynomials using algebraic operations (addition, subtraction, multiplication, division, and taking roots) lies within the class of **algebraic functions**. All rational functions are algebraic, but also included are more complicated functions (such as those satisfying an equation like $y^3 - 9xy + x^3 = 0$, studied in Section 3.6). Figure 1.18 displays the graphs of three algebraic functions.

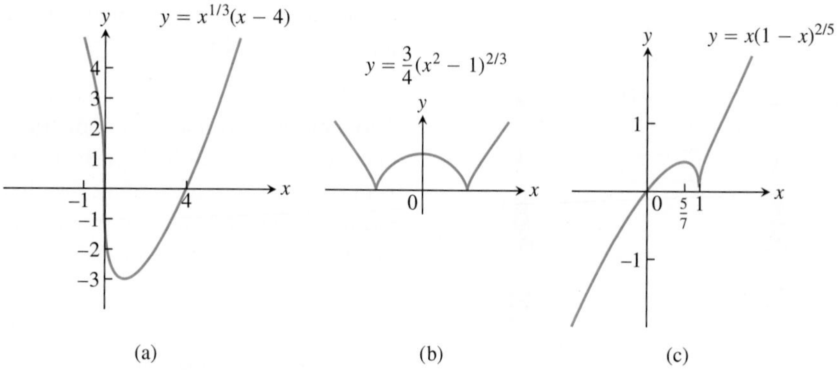

FIGURE 1.18 Graphs of three algebraic functions.

Trigonometric Functions We review trigonometric functions in Section 1.3. The graphs of the sine and cosine functions are shown in Figure 1.19.

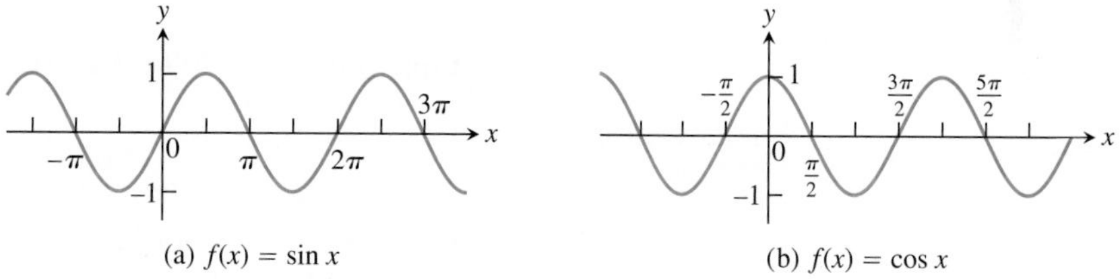

FIGURE 1.19 Graphs of the sine and cosine functions.

Exponential Functions Functions of the form $f(x) = a^x$, where the base $a > 0$ is a positive constant and $a \neq 1$, are called **exponential functions**. All exponential functions have domain $(-\infty, \infty)$ and range $(0, \infty)$, so an exponential function never assumes the value 0. We introduce exponential functions in Section 1.4. The graphs of some exponential functions are shown in Figure 1.20.

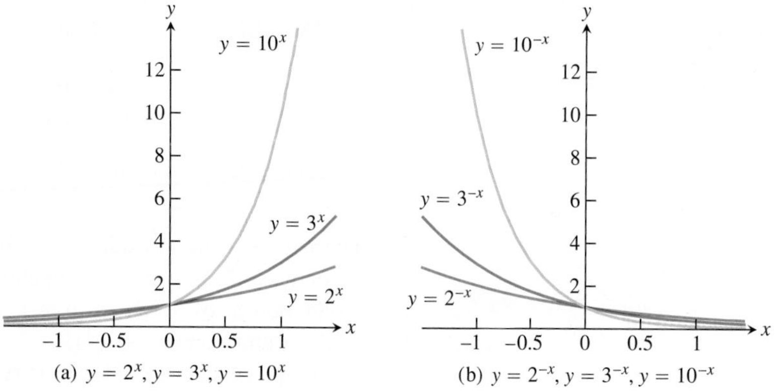

FIGURE 1.20 Graphs of exponential functions.

Logarithmic Functions These are the functions $f(x) = \log_a x$, where the base $a \neq 1$ is a positive constant. They are the *inverse functions* of the exponential functions, and the calculus of these functions is studied in Chapters 3 and 5. Figure 1.21 shows the graphs of

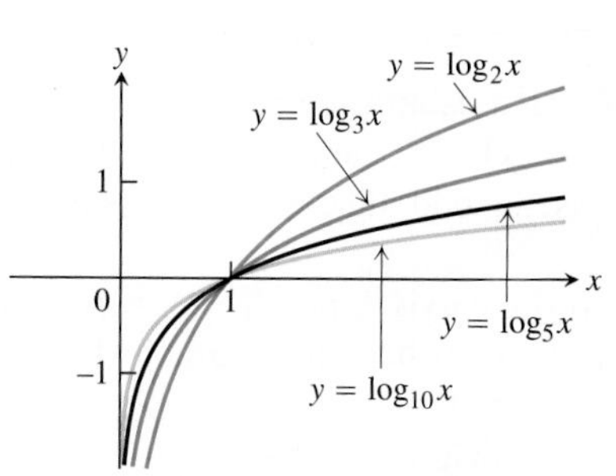

FIGURE 1.21 Graphs of four logarithmic functions.

four logarithmic functions with various bases. In each case the domain is $(0, \infty)$ and the range is $(-\infty, \infty)$.

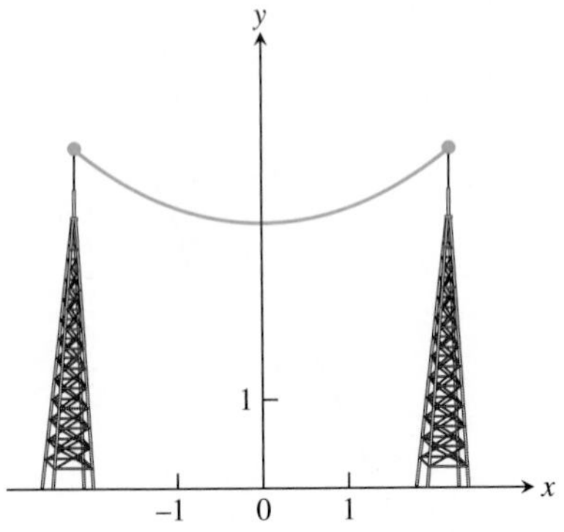

FIGURE 1.22 Graph of a catenary or hanging cable. (The Latin word *catena* means "chain.")

Transcendental Functions These are functions that are not algebraic. They include the trigonometric, inverse trigonometric, exponential, and logarithmic functions, and many other functions as well. A particular example of a transcendental function is a **catenary**. Its graph takes the shape of a cable, like a telephone line or TV cable, strung from one support to another and hanging freely under its own weight (Figure 1.22). The function defining the graph is discussed in Section 3.11.

Increasing Versus Decreasing Functions

If the graph of a function *climbs* or *rises* as you move from left to right, we say that the function is *increasing*. If the graph *descends* or *falls* as you move from left to right, the function is *decreasing*. We give formal definitions of increasing functions and decreasing functions in Section 4.3. In that section, you will learn how to find the intervals over which a function is increasing and the intervals where it is decreasing. Here are examples from Figures 1.13, 1.14, and 1.15.

Function	Where increasing	Where decreasing
$y = x^2$	$0 \le x < \infty$	$-\infty < x \le 0$
$y = x^3$	$-\infty < x < \infty$	Nowhere
$y = 1/x$	Nowhere	$-\infty < x < 0$ and $0 < x < \infty$
$y = 1/x^2$	$-\infty < x < 0$	$0 < x < \infty$
$y = \sqrt{x}$	$0 \le x < \infty$	Nowhere
$y = x^{2/3}$	$0 \le x < \infty$	$-\infty < x \le 0$

Even Functions and Odd Functions: Symmetry

The graphs of *even* and *odd* functions have characteristic symmetry properties.

> **DEFINITIONS** A function $y = f(x)$ is an
>
> **even function of x** if $f(-x) = f(x)$,
>
> **odd function of x** if $f(-x) = -f(x)$,
>
> for every x in the function's domain.

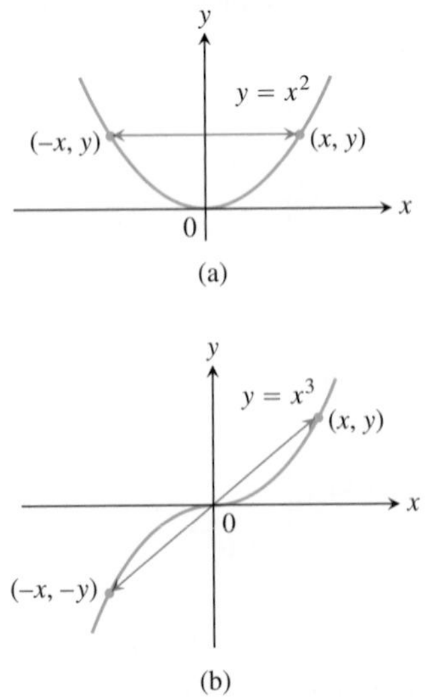

FIGURE 1.23 (a) The graph of $y = x^2$ (an even function) is symmetric about the y-axis. (b) The graph of $y = x^3$ (an odd function) is symmetric about the origin.

The names even and odd come from powers of x. If y is an even power of x, as in $y = x^2$ or $y = x^4$, it is an even function of x (because $(-x)^2 = x^2$ and $(-x)^4 = x^4$). If y is an odd power of x, as in $y = x$ or $y = x^3$, it is an odd function of x (because $(-x)^1 = -x$ and $(-x)^3 = -x^3$).

The graph of an even function is **symmetric about the y-axis**. Since $f(-x) = f(x)$, a point (x, y) lies on the graph if and only if the point $(-x, y)$ lies on the graph (Figure 1.23a). A reflection across the y-axis leaves the graph unchanged.

The graph of an odd function is **symmetric about the origin**. Since $f(-x) = -f(x)$, a point (x, y) lies on the graph if and only if the point $(-x, -y)$ lies on the graph (Figure 1.23b). Equivalently, a graph is symmetric about the origin if a rotation of 180° about the origin leaves the graph unchanged. Notice that the definitions imply both x and $-x$ must be in the domain of f.

EXAMPLE 7

$f(x) = x^2$	Even function: $(-x)^2 = x^2$ for all x; symmetry about y-axis.
$f(x) = x^2 + 1$	Even function: $(-x)^2 + 1 = x^2 + 1$ for all x; symmetry about y-axis (Figure 1.24a).
$f(x) = x$	Odd function: $(-x) = -x$ for all x; symmetry about the origin.
$f(x) = x + 1$	Not odd: $f(-x) = -x + 1$, but $-f(x) = -x - 1$. The two are not equal. Not even: $(-x) + 1 \neq x + 1$ for all $x \neq 0$ (Figure 1.24b).

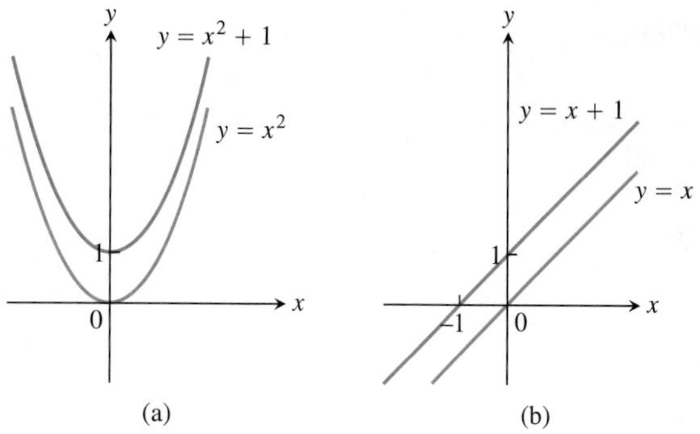

FIGURE 1.24 (a) When we add the constant term 1 to the function $y = x^2$, the resulting function $y = x^2 + 1$ is still even and its graph is still symmetric about the y-axis. (b) When we add the constant term 1 to the function $y = x$, the resulting function $y = x + 1$ is no longer odd. The symmetry about the origin is lost (Example 7) ■

EXERCISES 1.1

In Exercises 1–4, find the domain and range of each function.

1. $f(x) = 1 + x^2$

2. $f(x) = 1 - \sqrt{x}$

3. $F(t) = \dfrac{1}{\sqrt{t}}$

4. $g(z) = \dfrac{1}{\sqrt{4 - z^2}}$

In Exercises 5 and 6, which of the graphs are graphs of functions of x, and which are not? Give reasons for your answers.

5. **a.** 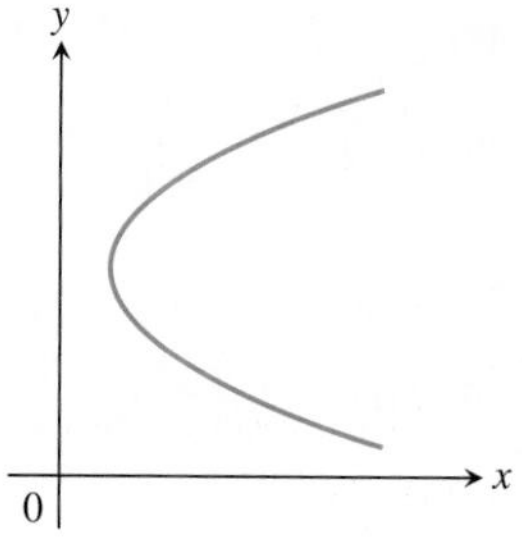

b. 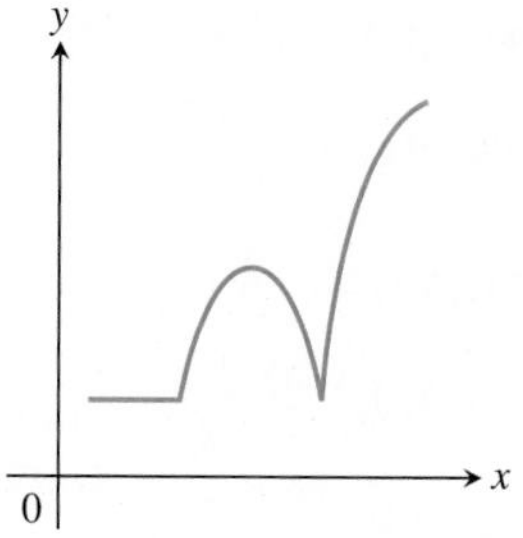

6. **a.** 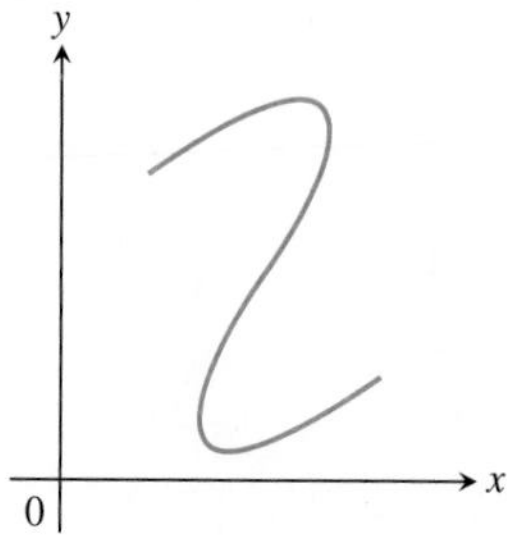

b. 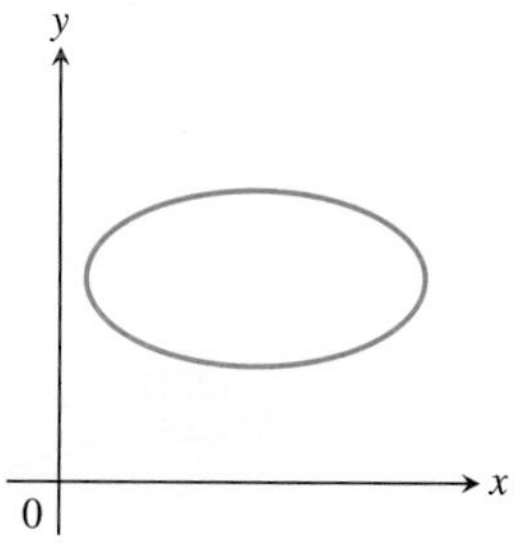

7. Express the area and perimeter of an equilateral triangle as a function of the triangle's side length x.

8. Express the side length of a square as a function of the length d of the square's diagonal. Then express the area as a function of the diagonal length.

9. Express the edge length of a cube as a function of the cube's diagonal length d. Then express the surface area and volume of the cube as a function of the diagonal length.

10. A point P in the first quadrant lies on the graph of the function $f(x) = \sqrt{x}$. Express the coordinates of P as functions of the slope of the line joining P to the origin.

Find the domain and graph the functions in Exercises 11–16.

11. $f(x) = 5 - 2x$ **12.** $f(x) = 1 - 2x - x^2$

13. $g(x) = \sqrt{|x|}$ **14.** $g(x) = \sqrt{-x}$

15. $F(t) = t/|t|$ **16.** $G(t) = 1/|t|$

17. Graph the following equations and explain why they are not graphs of functions of x.

a. $|y| = x$ **b.** $y^2 = x^2$

18. Graph the following equations and explain why they are not graphs of functions of x.

a. $|x| + |y| = 1$ **b.** $|x + y| = 1$

Graph the functions in Exercises 19–22.

19. $f(x) = \begin{cases} x, & 0 \le x \le 1 \\ 2 - x, & 1 < x \le 2 \end{cases}$

20. $g(x) = \begin{cases} 1 - x, & 0 \le x \le 1 \\ 2 - x, & 1 < x \le 2 \end{cases}$

21. $F(x) = \begin{cases} 3 - x, & x \le 1 \\ 2x, & x > 1 \end{cases}$

22. $G(x) = \begin{cases} 1/x, & x < 0 \\ x, & 0 \le x \end{cases}$

23. Find a formula for each function graphed.

a.

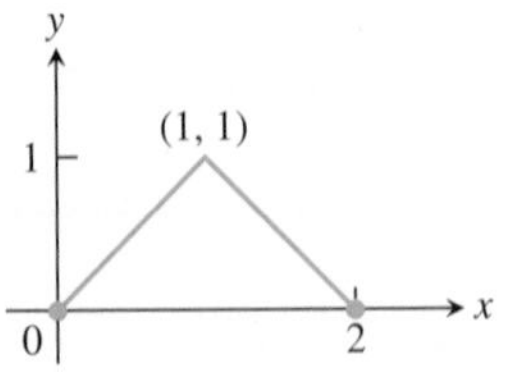

b.

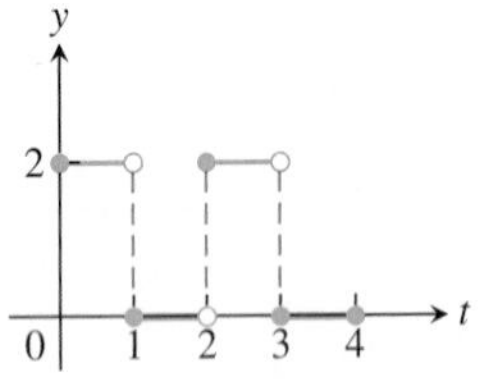

24. a.

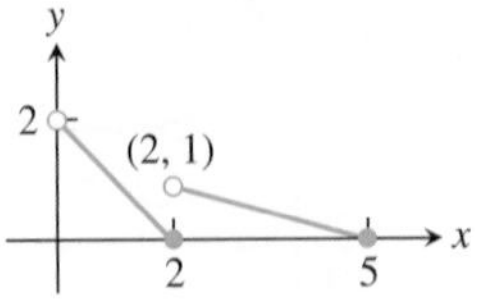

b.

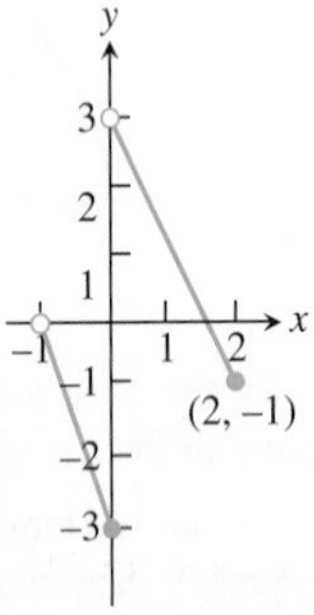

25. a.

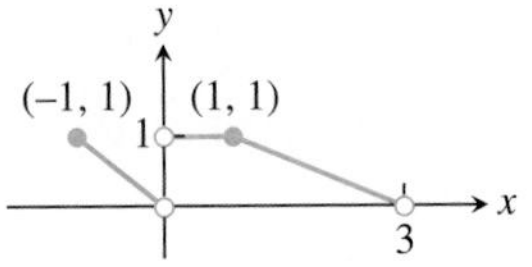

b.

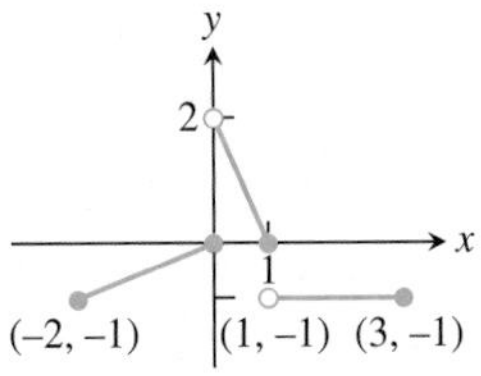

26. a.

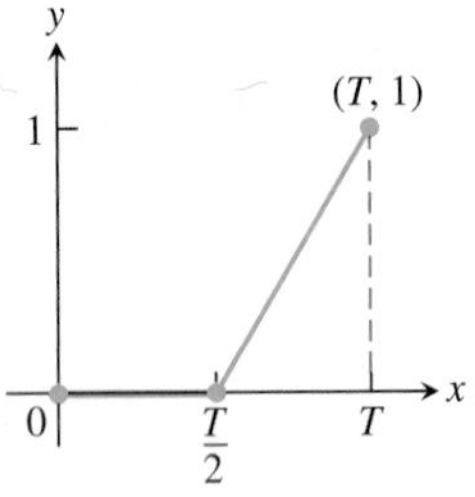

b.

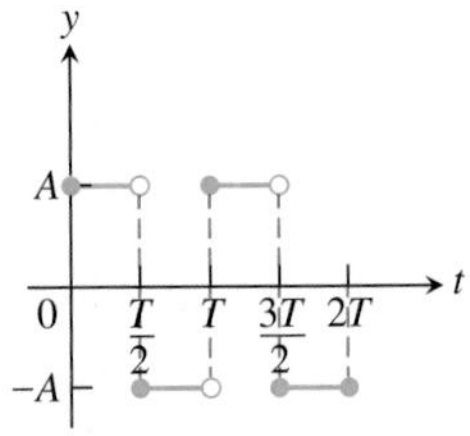

27. For what values of x is

a. $\lfloor x \rfloor = 0$? **b.** $\lceil x \rceil = 0$?

28. What real numbers x satisfy the equation $\lfloor x \rfloor = \lceil x \rceil$?

29. Does $\lceil -x \rceil = -\lfloor x \rfloor$ for all real x? Give reasons for your answer.

30. Graph the function

$$f(x) = \begin{cases} \lfloor x \rfloor, & x \ge 0 \\ \lceil x \rceil, & x < 0 \end{cases}$$

Why is $f(x)$ called the *integer part* of x?

Graph the functions in Exercises 31–42. What symmetries, if any, do the graphs have? Specify the intervals over which the function is increasing and the intervals where it is decreasing.

31. $y = -x^3$ **32.** $y = -\dfrac{1}{x^2}$

33. $y = -\dfrac{1}{x}$ **34.** $y = \dfrac{1}{|x|}$

35. $y = \sqrt{|x|}$ **36.** $y = \sqrt{-x}$

37. $y = x^3/8$ **38.** $y = -4\sqrt{x}$

39. $y = -x^{3/2}$ **40.** $y = (-x)^{3/2}$

41. $y = (-x)^{2/3}$ **42.** $y = -x^{2/3}$

In Exercises 43–54, say whether the function is even, odd, or neither. Give reasons for your answer.

43. $f(x) = 3$ **44.** $f(x) = x^{-5}$

45. $f(x) = x^2 + 1$ **46.** $f(x) = x^2 + x$

47. $g(x) = x^3 + x$ **48.** $g(x) = x^4 + 3x^2 - 1$

49. $g(x) = \dfrac{1}{x^2 - 1}$ **50.** $g(x) = \dfrac{x}{x^2 - 1}$

51. $h(t) = \dfrac{1}{t - 1}$ **52.** $h(t) = |t^3|$

53. $h(t) = 2t + 1$ **54.** $h(t) = 2|t| + 1$

55. A box with an open top is to be constructed from a rectangular piece of cardboard with dimensions 14 in. by 22 in. by cutting out equal squares of side x at each corner and then folding up the sides as in the figure. Express the volume V of the box as a function of x.

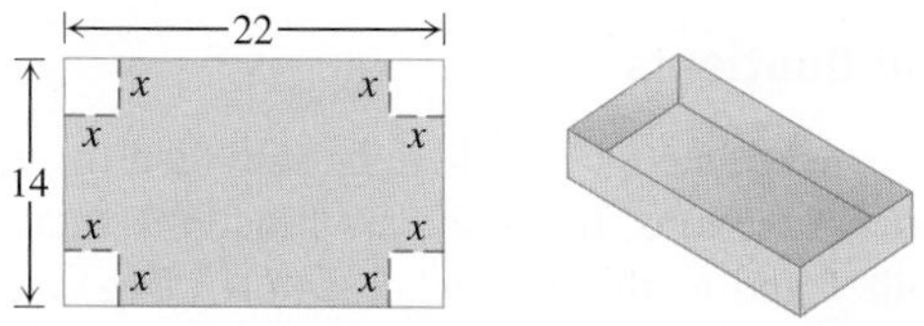

56. The figure shown here shows a rectangle inscribed in an isosceles right triangle whose hypotenuse is 2 units long.

a. Express the y-coordinate of P in terms of x. (You might start by writing an equation for the line AB.)

b. Express the area of the rectangle in terms of x.

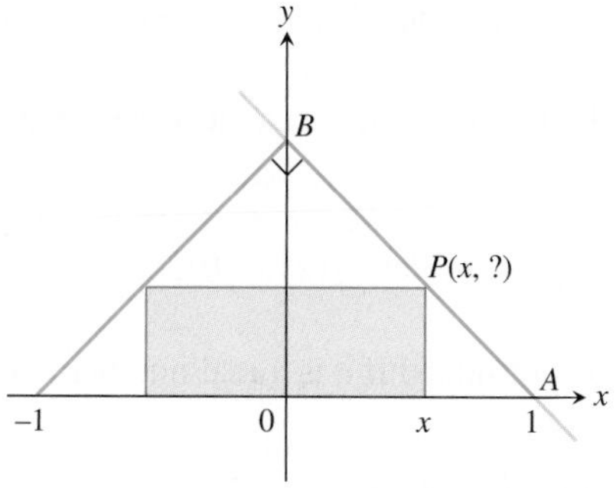

In Exercises 57 and 58, match each equation with its graph. Do not use a graphing device, and give reasons for your answer.

57. **a.** $y = x^4$ **b.** $y = x^7$ **c.** $y = x^{10}$

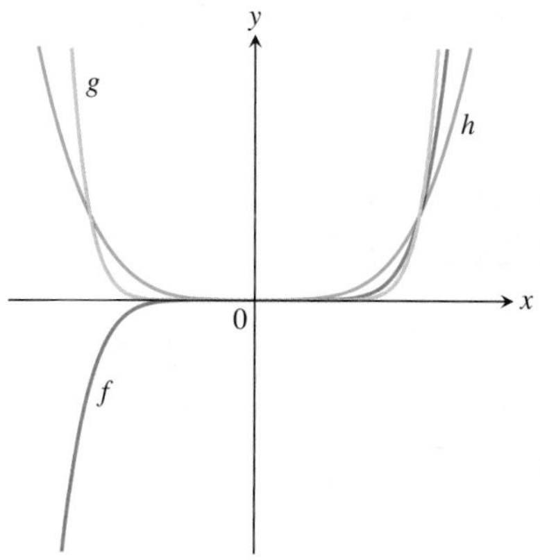

58. **a.** $y = 5x$ **b.** $y = 5^x$ **c.** $y = x^5$

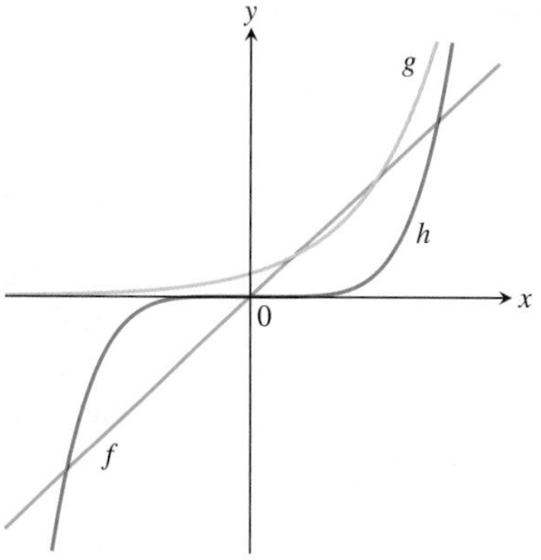

T 59. **a.** Graph the functions $f(x) = x/2$ and $g(x) = 1 + (4/x)$ together to identify the values of x for which

$$\frac{x}{2} > 1 + \frac{4}{x}.$$

b. Confirm your findings in part (a) algebraically.

T 60. **a.** Graph the functions $f(x) = 3/(x - 1)$ and $g(x) = 2/(x + 1)$ together to identify the values of x for which

$$\frac{3}{x - 1} < \frac{2}{x + 1}.$$

b. Confirm your findings in part (a) algebraically.

61. For a curve to be *symmetric about the x-axis*, the point (x, y) must lie on the curve if and only if the point $(x, -y)$ lies on the curve. Explain why a curve that is symmetric about the x-axis is not the graph of a function, unless the function is $y = 0$.

62. Industrial costs Dayton Power and Light, Inc., has a power plant on the Miami River where the river is 800 ft wide. To lay a new cable from the plant to a location in the city 2 mi downstream on the opposite side costs \$180 per foot across the river and \$100 per foot along the land.

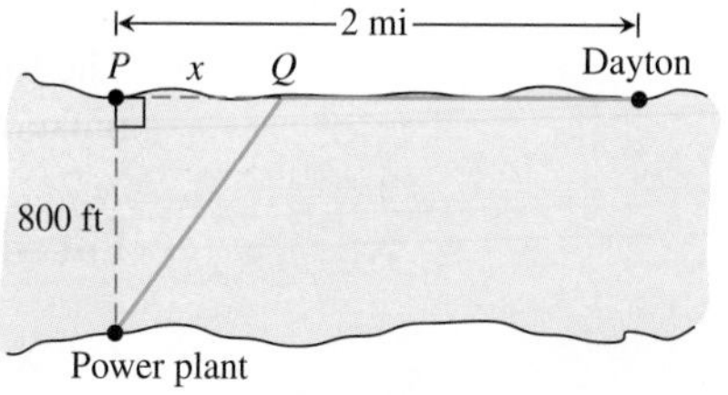

(Not to scale)

a. Suppose that the cable goes from the plant to a point Q on the opposite side that is x ft from the point P directly opposite the plant. Write a function $C(x)$ that gives the cost of laying the cable in terms of the distance x.

b. Generate a table of values to determine if the least expensive location for point Q is less than 2000 ft or greater than 2000 ft from point P.

1.2 Combining Functions; Shifting and Scaling Graphs

In this section we look at the main ways functions are combined or transformed to form new functions.

Sums, Differences, Products, and Quotients

Like numbers, functions can be added, subtracted, multiplied, and divided (except where the denominator is zero) to produce new functions. If f and g are functions, then for every x that belongs to the domains of both f and g (that is, for $x \in D(f) \cap D(g)$), we define functions $f + g$, $f - g$, and fg by the formulas

$$(f + g)(x) = f(x) + g(x).$$
$$(f - g)(x) = f(x) - g(x).$$
$$(fg)(x) = f(x)g(x).$$

Notice that the + sign on the left-hand side of the first equation represents the operation of addition of *functions*, whereas the + on the right-hand side of the equation means addition of the real numbers $f(x)$ and $g(x)$.

At any point of $D(f) \cap D(g)$ at which $g(x) \neq 0$, we can also define the function f/g by the formula

$$\left(\frac{f}{g}\right)(x) = \frac{f(x)}{g(x)} \qquad (\text{where } g(x) \neq 0).$$

Functions can also be multiplied by constants: If c is a real number, then the function cf is defined for all x in the domain of f by

$$(cf)(x) = cf(x).$$

EXAMPLE 1 The functions defined by the formulas

$$f(x) = \sqrt{x} \qquad \text{and} \qquad g(x) = \sqrt{1 - x},$$

have domains $D(f) = [0, \infty)$ and $D(g) = (-\infty, 1]$. The points common to these domains are the points

$$[0, \infty) \cap (-\infty, 1] = [0, 1].$$

The following table summarizes the formulas and domains for the various algebraic combinations of the two functions. We also write $f \cdot g$ for the product function fg.

Function	Formula	Domain
$f + g$	$(f + g)(x) = \sqrt{x} + \sqrt{1 - x}$	$[0, 1] = D(f) \cap D(g)$
$f - g$	$(f - g)(x) = \sqrt{x} - \sqrt{1 - x}$	$[0, 1]$
$g - f$	$(g - f)(x) = \sqrt{1 - x} - \sqrt{x}$	$[0, 1]$
$f \cdot g$	$(f \cdot g)(x) = f(x)g(x) = \sqrt{x(1 - x)}$	$[0, 1]$
f/g	$\frac{f}{g}(x) = \frac{f(x)}{g(x)} = \sqrt{\frac{x}{1 - x}}$	$[0, 1)$ ($x = 1$ excluded)
g/f	$\frac{g}{f}(x) = \frac{g(x)}{f(x)} = \sqrt{\frac{1 - x}{x}}$	$(0, 1]$ ($x = 0$ excluded)

■

The graph of the function $f + g$ is obtained from the graphs of f and g by adding the corresponding y-coordinates $f(x)$ and $g(x)$ at each point $x \in D(f) \cap D(g)$, as in Figure 1.25. The graphs of $f + g$ and $f \cdot g$ from Example 1 are shown in Figure 1.26.

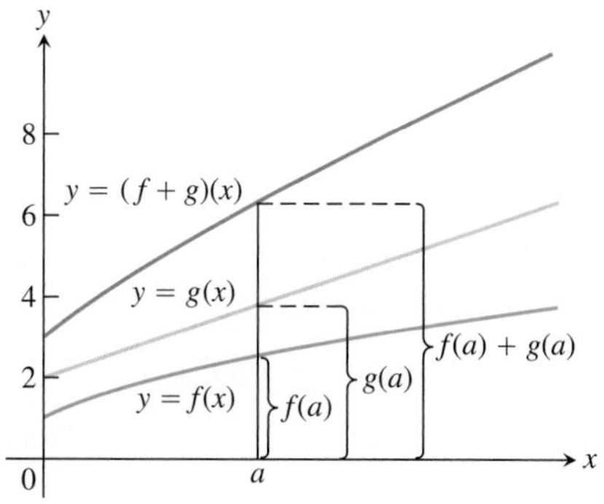

FIGURE 1.25 Graphical addition of two functions.

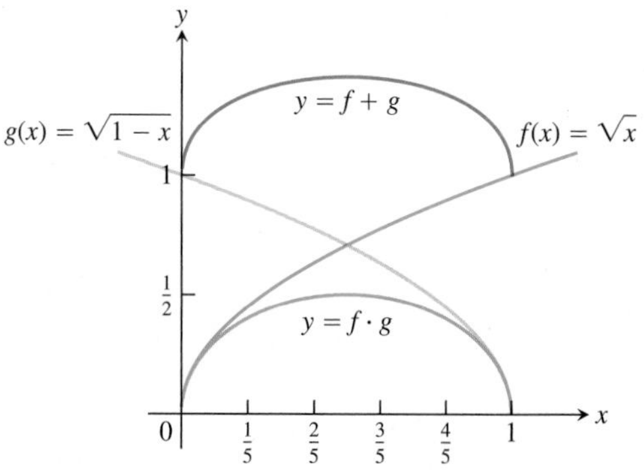

FIGURE 1.26 The domain of the function $f + g$ is the intersection of the domains of f and g, the interval [0, 1] on the x-axis where these domains overlap. This interval is also the domain of the function $f \cdot g$ (Example 1)

Composite Functions

Composition is another method for combining functions.

> **DEFINITION** If f and g are functions, the **composite** function $f \circ g$ ("f composed with g") is defined by
>
> $$(f \circ g)(x) = f(g(x)).$$
>
> The domain of $f \circ g$ consists of the numbers x in the domain of g for which $g(x)$ lies in the domain of f.

The definition says that $f \circ g$ can be formed when the range of g lies in the domain of f. To find $(f \circ g)(x)$, *first* find $g(x)$ and *second* find $f(g(x))$. Figure 1.27 pictures $f \circ g$ as a machine diagram and Figure 1.28 shows the composite as an arrow diagram.

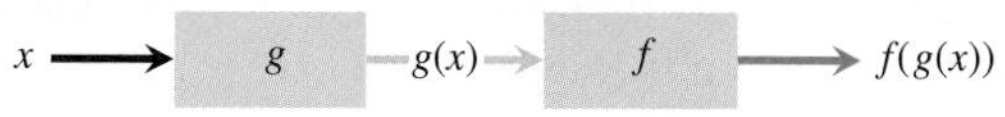

FIGURE 1.27 Two functions can be composed at x whenever the value of one function at x lies in the domain of the other. The composite is denoted by $f \circ g$.

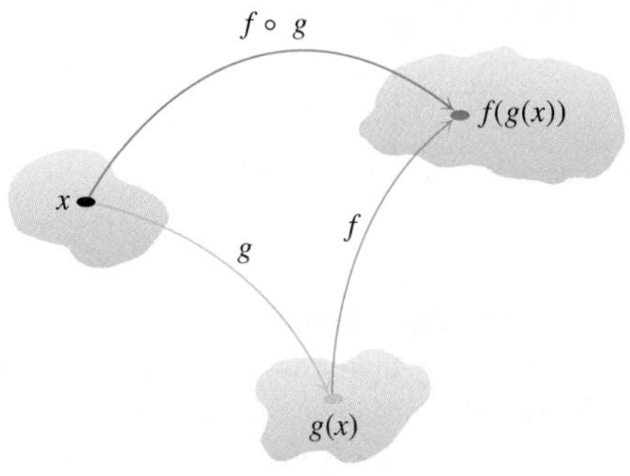

FIGURE 1.28 Arrow diagram for $f \circ g$.

To evaluate the composite function $g \circ f$ (when defined), we find $f(x)$ first and then $g(f(x))$. The domain of $g \circ f$ is the set of numbers x in the domain of f such that $f(x)$ lies in the domain of g.

The functions $f \circ g$ and $g \circ f$ are usually quite different.

EXAMPLE 2 If $f(x) = \sqrt{x}$ and $g(x) = x + 1$, find

(a) $(f \circ g)(x)$ **(b)** $(g \circ f)(x)$ **(c)** $(f \circ f)(x)$ **(d)** $(g \circ g)(x)$.

Solution

Composite	Domain
(a) $(f \circ g)(x) = f(g(x)) = \sqrt{g(x)} = \sqrt{x + 1}$	$[-1, \infty)$
(b) $(g \circ f)(x) = g(f(x)) = f(x) + 1 = \sqrt{x} + 1$	$[0, \infty)$
(c) $(f \circ f)(x) = f(f(x)) = \sqrt{f(x)} = \sqrt{\sqrt{x}} = x^{1/4}$	$[0, \infty)$
(d) $(g \circ g)(x) = g(g(x)) = g(x) + 1 = (x + 1) + 1 = x + 2$	$(-\infty, \infty)$

To see why the domain of $f \circ g$ is $[-1, \infty)$, notice that $g(x) = x + 1$ is defined for all real x but belongs to the domain of f only if $x + 1 \ge 0$, that is to say, when $x \ge -1$. ■

Notice that if $f(x) = x^2$ and $g(x) = \sqrt{x}$, then $(f \circ g)(x) = \left(\sqrt{x}\right)^2 = x$. However, the domain of $f \circ g$ is $[0, \infty)$, not $(-\infty, \infty)$, since $\sqrt{x}$ requires $x \ge 0$.

Shifting a Graph of a Function

A common way to obtain a new function from an existing one is by adding a constant to each output of the existing function, or to its input variable. The graph of the new function is the graph of the original function shifted vertically or horizontally, as follows.

Shift Formulas

Vertical Shifts

$y = f(x) + k$ Shifts the graph of f *up* k units if $k > 0$

Shifts it *down* $|k|$ units if $k < 0$

Horizontal Shifts

$y = f(x + h)$ Shifts the graph of f *left* h units if $h > 0$

Shifts it *right* $|h|$ units if $h < 0$

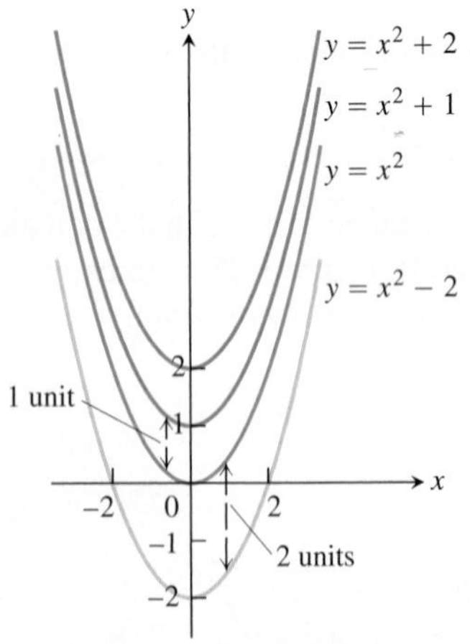

FIGURE 1.29 To shift the graph of $f(x) = x^2$ up (or down), we add positive (or negative) constants to the formula for f (Example 3a and b).

EXAMPLE 3

(a) Adding 1 to the right-hand side of the formula $y = x^2$ to get $y = x^2 + 1$ shifts the graph up 1 unit (Figure 1.29).

(b) Adding -2 to the right-hand side of the formula $y = x^2$ to get $y = x^2 - 2$ shifts the graph down 2 units (Figure 1.29).

(c) Adding 3 to x in $y = x^2$ to get $y = (x + 3)^2$ shifts the graph 3 units to the left (Figure 1.30).

(d) Adding -2 to x in $y = |x|$, and then adding -1 to the result, gives $y = |x - 2| - 1$ and shifts the graph 2 units to the right and 1 unit down (Figure 1.31). ■

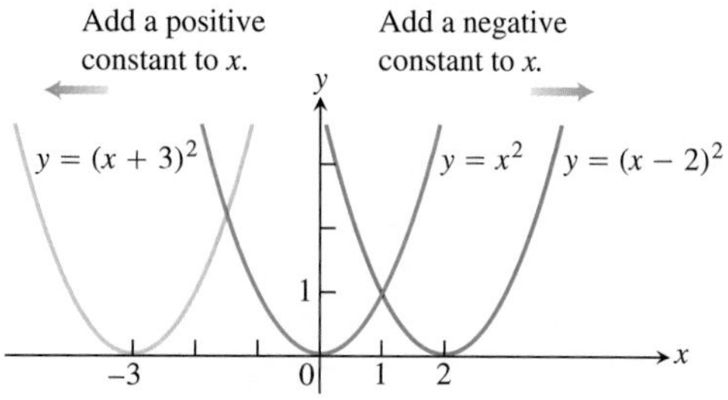

FIGURE 1.30 To shift the graph of $y = x^2$ to the left, we add a positive constant to x. To shift the graph to the right, we add a negative constant to x (Example 3c).

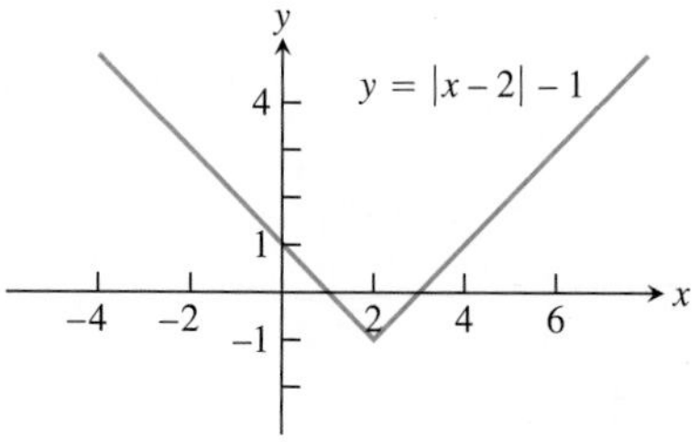

FIGURE 1.31 Shifting the graph of $y = |x|$ 2 units to the right and 1 unit down (Example 3d).

Scaling and Reflecting a Graph of a Function

To scale the graph of a function $y = f(x)$ is to stretch or compress it, vertically or horizontally. This is accomplished by multiplying the function f, or the independent variable x, by an appropriate constant c. Reflections across the coordinate axes are special cases where $c = -1$.

Vertical and Horizontal Scaling and Reflecting Formulas

For $c > 1$,

$y = cf(x)$	Stretches the graph of f vertically by a factor of c.
$y = \frac{1}{c}f(x)$	Compresses the graph of f vertically by a factor of c.
$y = f(cx)$	Compresses the graph of f horizontally by a factor of c.
$y = f(x/c)$	Stretches the graph of f horizontally by a factor of c.

For $c = -1$,

$y = -f(x)$	Reflects the graph of f across the x-axis.
$y = f(-x)$	Reflects the graph of f across the y-axis.

EXAMPLE 4 Here we scale and reflect the graph of $y = \sqrt{x}$.

(a) Vertical: Multiplying the right-hand side of $y = \sqrt{x}$ by 3 to get $y = 3\sqrt{x}$ stretches the graph vertically by a factor of 3, whereas multiplying by $1/3$ compresses the graph by a factor of 3 (Figure 1.32).

(b) Horizontal: The graph of $y = \sqrt{3x}$ is a horizontal compression of the graph of $y = \sqrt{x}$ by a factor of 3, and $y = \sqrt{x/3}$ is a horizontal stretching by a factor of 3 (Figure 1.33). Note that $y = \sqrt{3x} = \sqrt{3}\sqrt{x}$ so a horizontal compression *may* correspond to a vertical stretching by a different scaling factor. Likewise, a horizontal stretching may correspond to a vertical compression by a different scaling factor.

(c) Reflection: The graph of $y = -\sqrt{x}$ is a reflection of $y = \sqrt{x}$ across the x-axis, and $y = \sqrt{-x}$ is a reflection across the y-axis (Figure 1.34). ■

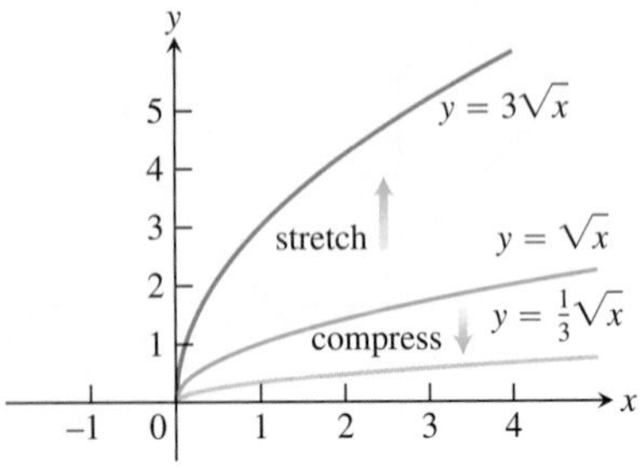

FIGURE 1.32 Vertically stretching and compressing the graph $y = \sqrt{x}$ by a factor of 3 (Example 4a).

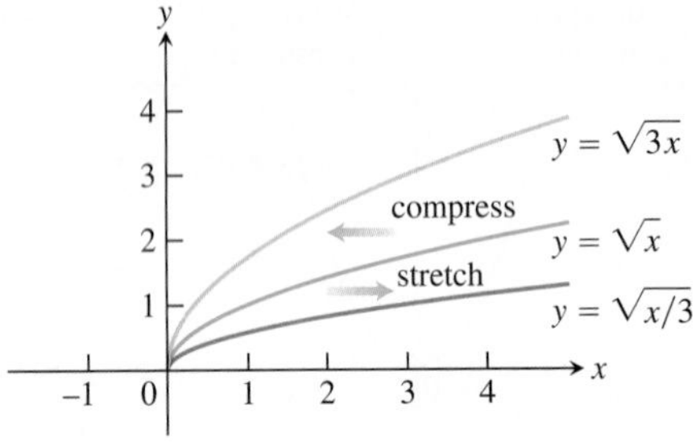

FIGURE 1.33 Horizontally stretching and compressing the graph $y = \sqrt{x}$ by a factor of 3 (Example 4b).

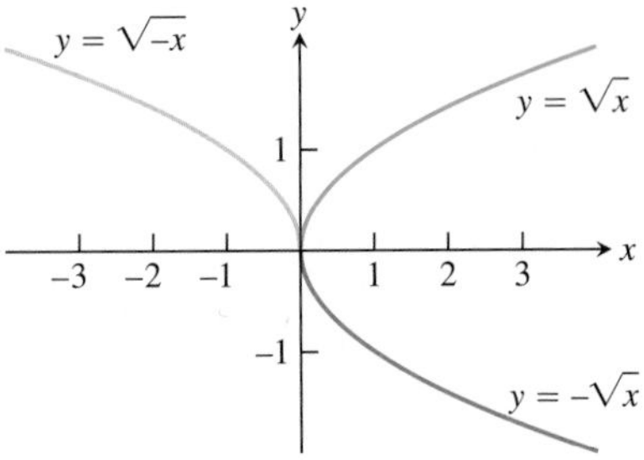

FIGURE 1.34 Reflections of the graph $y = \sqrt{x}$ across the coordinate axes (Example 4c).

EXAMPLE 5 Given the function $f(x) = x^4 - 4x^3 + 10$ (Figure 1.35a), find formulas to

(a) compress the graph horizontally by a factor of 2 followed by a reflection across the y-axis (Figure 1.35b).

(b) compress the graph vertically by a factor of 2 followed by a reflection across the x-axis (Figure 1.35c).

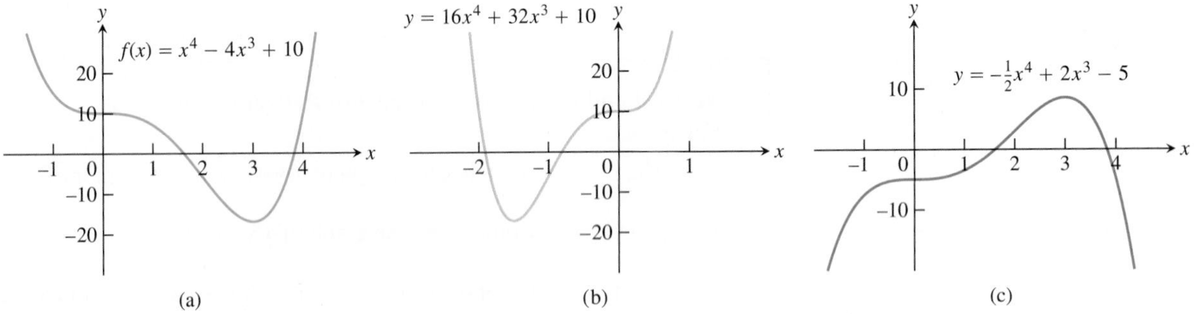

FIGURE 1.35 (a) The original graph of f. (b) The horizontal compression of $y = f(x)$ in part (a) by a factor of 2, followed by a reflection across the y-axis. (c) The vertical compression of $y = f(x)$ in part (a) by a factor of 2, followed by a reflection across the x-axis (Example 5).

Solution

(a) The formula is obtained by substituting $-2x$ for x in the right-hand side of the equation for f

$$\begin{aligned} y = f(-2x) &= (-2x)^4 - 4(-2x)^3 + 10 \\ &= 16x^4 + 32x^3 + 10. \end{aligned}$$

(b) The formula is

$$y = -\frac{1}{2}f(x) = -\frac{1}{2}x^4 + 2x^3 - 5.$$ ■

Ellipses

The standard equation for a circle is reviewed in Appendix 3. Substituting cx for x in the standard equation for a circle of radius r centered at the origin (Figure 1.36a) gives

$$c^2x^2 + y^2 = r^2. \tag{1}$$

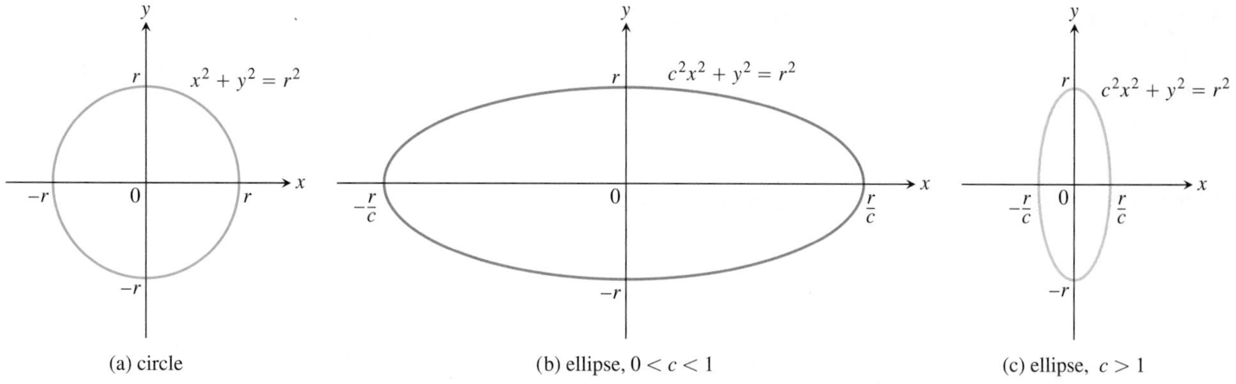

FIGURE 1.36 Horizontal stretchings or compressions of a circle produce graphs of ellipses.

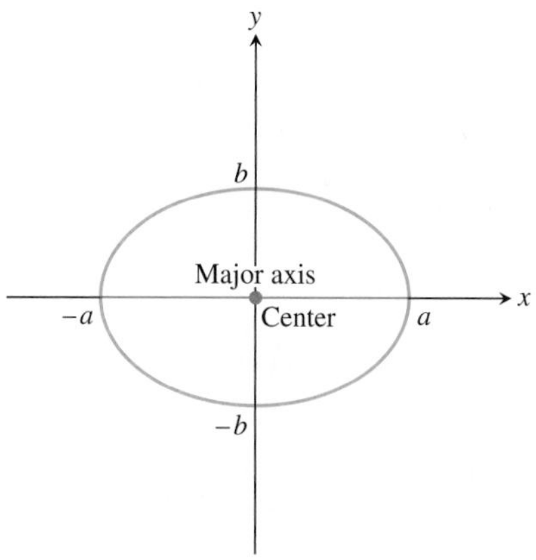

FIGURE 1.37 Graph of the ellipse $\frac{x^2}{a^2} + \frac{y^2}{b^2} = 1$, $a > b$, where the major axis is horizontal.

If $0 < c < 1$, the graph of Equation (1) horizontally stretches the circle; if $c > 1$ the circle is compressed horizontally. In either case, the graph of Equation (1) is an ellipse (Figure 1.36). Notice in Figure 1.36 that the y-intercepts of all three graphs are always $-r$ and r. In Figure 1.36b, the line segment joining the points $(\pm r/c, 0)$ is called the **major axis** of the ellipse; the **minor axis** is the line segment joining $(0, \pm r)$. The axes of the ellipse are reversed in Figure 1.36c: The major axis is the line segment joining the points $(0, \pm r)$, and the minor axis is the line segment joining the points $(\pm r/c, 0)$. In both cases, the major axis is the line segment having the longer length.

If we divide both sides of Equation (1) by r^2, we obtain

$$\frac{x^2}{a^2} + \frac{y^2}{b^2} = 1 \tag{2}$$

where $a = r/c$ and $b = r$. If $a > b$, the major axis is horizontal; if $a < b$, the major axis is vertical. The **center** of the ellipse given by Equation (2) is the origin (Figure 1.37).

Substituting $x - h$ for x, and $y - k$ for y, in Equation (2) results in

$$\frac{(x - h)^2}{a^2} + \frac{(y - k)^2}{b^2} = 1. \tag{3}$$

Equation (3) is the **standard equation of an ellipse** with center at (h, k). The geometric definition and properties of ellipses are reviewed in Section 9.4.

EXERCISES 1.2

In Exercises 1 and 2, find the domains and ranges of f, g, $f + g$, and $f \cdot g$.

1. $f(x) = x, \quad g(x) = \sqrt{x - 1}$
2. $f(x) = \sqrt{x + 1}, \quad g(x) = \sqrt{x - 1}$

In Exercises 3 and 4, find the domains and ranges of f, g, f/g, and g/f.

3. $f(x) = 2, \quad g(x) = x^2 + 1$
4. $f(x) = 1, \quad g(x) = 1 + \sqrt{x}$

5. If $f(x) = x + 5$ and $g(x) = x^2 - 3$, find the following.

a. $f(g(0))$ **b.** $g(f(0))$

c. $f(g(x))$ **d.** $g(f(x))$

e. $f(f(-5))$ **f.** $g(g(2))$

g. $f(f(x))$ **h.** $g(g(x))$

6. If $f(x) = x - 1$ and $g(x) = 1/(x + 1)$, find the following.

a. $f(g(1/2))$ **b.** $g(f(1/2))$

c. $f(g(x))$ **d.** $g(f(x))$

e. $f(f(2))$ **f.** $g(g(2))$

g. $f(f(x))$ **h.** $g(g(x))$

7. If $u(x) = 4x - 5$, $v(x) = x^2$, and $f(x) = 1/x$, find formulas for the following.

a. $u(v(f(x)))$ **b.** $u(f(v(x)))$

c. $v(u(f(x)))$ **d.** $v(f(u(x)))$

e. $f(u(v(x)))$ **f.** $f(v(u(x)))$

8. If $f(x) = \sqrt{x}$, $g(x) = x/4$, and $h(x) = 4x - 8$, find formulas for the following.

a. $h(g(f(x)))$ **b.** $h(f(g(x)))$

c. $g(h(f(x)))$ **d.** $g(f(h(x)))$

e. $f(g(h(x)))$ **f.** $f(h(g(x)))$

Let $f(x) = x - 3$, $g(x) = \sqrt{x}$, $h(x) = x^3$, and $j(x) = 2x$. Express each of the functions in Exercises 9 and 10 as a composite involving one or more of f, g, h, and j.

9. a. $y = \sqrt{x} - 3$ **b.** $y = 2\sqrt{x}$

c. $y = x^{1/4}$ **d.** $y = 4x$

e. $y = \sqrt{(x - 3)^3}$ **f.** $y = (2x - 6)^3$

10. a. $y = 2x - 3$ **b.** $y = x^{3/2}$

c. $y = x^9$ **d.** $y = x - 6$

e. $y = 2\sqrt{x - 3}$ **f.** $y = \sqrt{x^3 - 3}$

11. Copy and complete the following table.

	$g(x)$	$f(x)$	$(f \circ g)(x)$
a.	$x - 7$	$\sqrt{x}$	?
b.	$x + 2$	$3x$	?
c.	?	$\sqrt{x - 5}$	$\sqrt{x^2 - 5}$
d.	$\dfrac{x}{x - 1}$	$\dfrac{x}{x - 1}$	?
e.	?	$1 + \dfrac{1}{x}$	x
f.	$\dfrac{1}{x}$	?	x

12. Copy and complete the following table.

	$g(x)$	$f(x)$	$(f \circ g)(x)$
a.	$\dfrac{1}{x - 1}$	$\lvert x \rvert$	?
b.	?	$\dfrac{x - 1}{x}$	$\dfrac{x}{x + 1}$
c.	?	$\sqrt{x}$	$\lvert x \rvert$
d.	$\sqrt{x}$	?	$\lvert x \rvert$

In Exercises 13 and 14, **(a)** write a formula for $f \circ g$ and $g \circ f$ and find the **(b)** domain and **(c)** range of each.

13. $f(x) = \sqrt{x + 1}$, $g(x) = \dfrac{1}{x}$

14. $f(x) = x^2$, $g(x) = 1 - \sqrt{x}$

15. The accompanying figure shows the graph of $y = -x^2$ shifted to two new positions. Write equations for the new graphs.

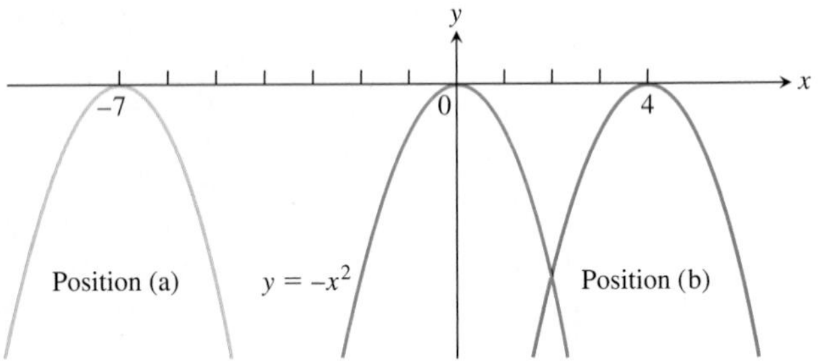

16. The accompanying figure shows the graph of $y = x^2$ shifted to two new positions. Write equations for the new graphs.

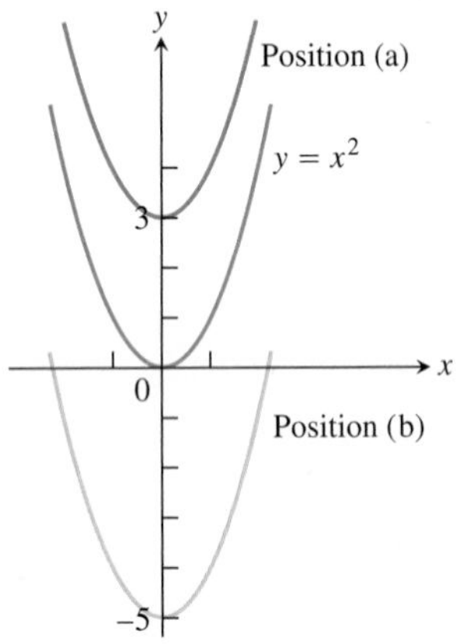

17. Match the equations listed in parts (a)–(d) to the graphs in the accompanying figure.

a. $y = (x - 1)^2 - 4$ **b.** $y = (x - 2)^2 + 2$

c. $y = (x + 2)^2 + 2$ **d.** $y = (x + 3)^2 - 2$

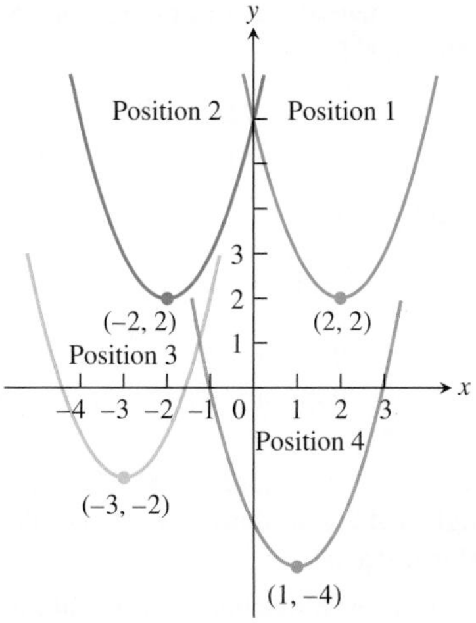

18. The accompanying figure shows the graph of $y = -x^2$ shifted to four new positions. Write an equation for each new graph.

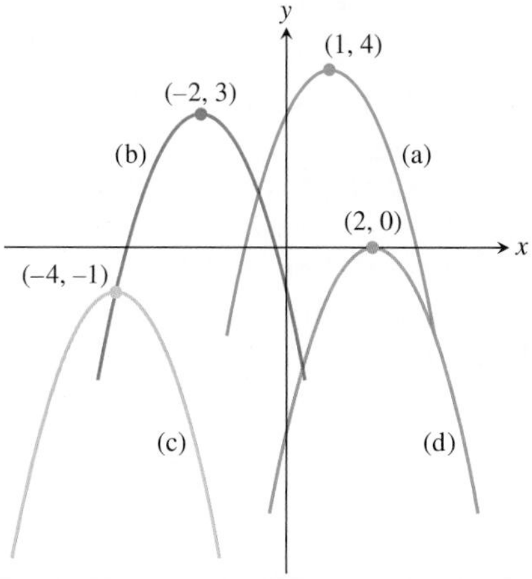

Exercises 19–28 tell how many units and in what directions the graphs of the given equations are to be shifted. Give an equation for the shifted graph. Then sketch the original and shifted graphs together, labeling each graph with its equation.

19. $x^2 + y^2 = 49$ Down 3, left 2

20. $x^2 + y^2 = 25$ Up 3, left 4

21. $y = x^3$ Left 1, down 1

22. $y = x^{2/3}$ Right 1, down 1

23. $y = \sqrt{x}$ Left 0.81

24. $y = -\sqrt{x}$ Right 3

25. $y = 2x - 7$ Up 7

26. $y = \frac{1}{2}(x + 1) + 5$ Down 5, right 1

27. $y = 1/x$ Up 1, right 1

28. $y = 1/x^2$ Left 2, down 1

Graph the functions in Exercises 29–48.

29. $y = \sqrt{x + 4}$

30. $y = \sqrt{9 - x}$

31. $y = |x - 2|$

32. $y = |1 - x| - 1$

33. $y = 1 + \sqrt{x - 1}$

34. $y = 1 - \sqrt{x}$

35. $y = (x + 1)^{2/3}$

36. $y = (x - 8)^{2/3}$

37. $y = 1 - x^{2/3}$

38. $y + 4 = x^{2/3}$

39. $y = \sqrt[3]{x - 1} - 1$

40. $y = (x + 2)^{3/2} + 1$

41. $y = \dfrac{1}{x - 2}$

42. $y = \dfrac{1}{x} - 2$

43. $y = \dfrac{1}{x} + 2$

44. $y = \dfrac{1}{x + 2}$

45. $y = \dfrac{1}{(x - 1)^2}$

46. $y = \dfrac{1}{x^2} - 1$

47. $y = \dfrac{1}{x^2} + 1$

48. $y = \dfrac{1}{(x + 1)^2}$

49. The accompanying figure shows the graph of a function $f(x)$ with domain $[0, 2]$ and range $[0, 1]$. Find the domains and ranges of the following functions, and sketch their graphs.

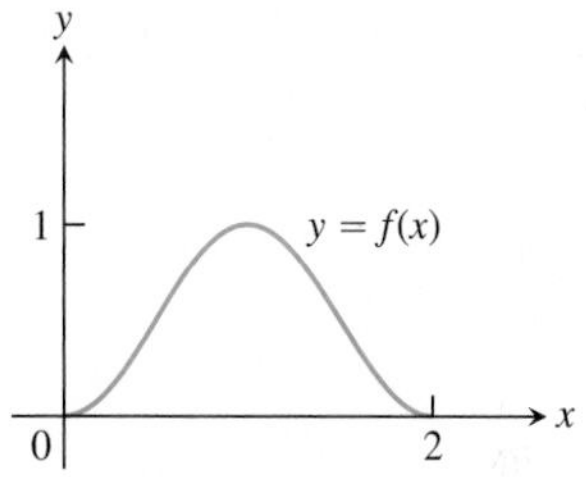

a. $f(x) + 2$ **b.** $f(x) - 1$

c. $2f(x)$ **d.** $-f(x)$

e. $f(x + 2)$ **f.** $f(x - 1)$

g. $f(-x)$ **h.** $-f(x + 1) + 1$

50. The accompanying figure shows the graph of a function $g(t)$ with domain $[-4, 0]$ and range $[-3, 0]$. Find the domains and ranges of the following functions, and sketch their graphs.

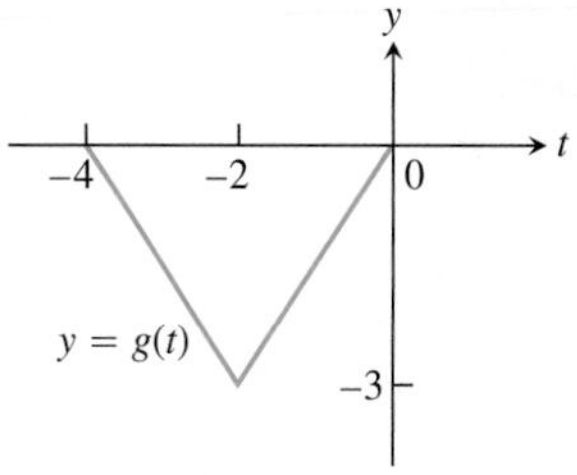

a. $g(-t)$ **b.** $-g(t)$

c. $g(t) + 3$ **d.** $1 - g(t)$

e. $g(-t + 2)$ **f.** $g(t - 2)$

g. $g(1 - t)$ **h.** $-g(t - 4)$

Exercises 51–60 tell by what factor and direction the graphs of the given functions are to be stretched or compressed. Give an equation for the stretched or compressed graph.

51. $y = x^2 - 1$, stretched vertically by a factor of 3

52. $y = x^2 - 1$, compressed horizontally by a factor of 2

53. $y = 1 + \dfrac{1}{x^2}$, compressed vertically by a factor of 2

54. $y = 1 + \dfrac{1}{x^2}$, stretched horizontally by a factor of 3

55. $y = \sqrt{x + 1}$, compressed horizontally by a factor of 4

56. $y = \sqrt{x + 1}$, stretched vertically by a factor of 3

57. $y = \sqrt{4 - x^2}$, stretched horizontally by a factor of 2

58. $y = \sqrt{4 - x^2}$, compressed vertically by a factor of 3

59. $y = 1 - x^3$, compressed horizontally by a factor of 3

60. $y = 1 - x^3$, stretched horizontally by a factor of 2

In Exercises 61–68, graph each function, not by plotting points, but by starting with the graph of one of the standard functions presented in Figures 1.13–1.15, and applying an appropriate transformation.

61. $y = -\sqrt{2x + 1}$

62. $y = \sqrt{1 - \dfrac{x}{2}}$

63. $y = (x - 1)^3 + 2$

64. $y = (1 - x)^3 + 2$

65. $y = \dfrac{1}{2x} - 1$

66. $y = \dfrac{2}{x^2} + 1$

67. $y = -\sqrt[3]{x}$

68. $y = (-2x)^{2/3}$

69. Graph the function $y = |x^2 - 1|$.

70. Graph the function $y = \sqrt{|x|}$.

Exercises 71–76 give equations of ellipses. Put each equation in standard form and sketch the ellipse.

71. $9x^2 + 25y^2 = 225$

72. $16x^2 + 7y^2 = 112$

73. $3x^2 + (y - 2)^2 = 3$

74. $(x + 1)^2 + 2y^2 = 4$

75. $3(x - 1)^2 + 2(y + 2)^2 = 6$

76. $6\left(x + \dfrac{3}{2}\right)^2 + 9\left(y - \dfrac{1}{2}\right)^2 = 54$

77. Write an equation for the ellipse $(x^2/16) + (y^2/9) = 1$ shifted 4 units to the left and 3 units up. Sketch the ellipse and identify its center and major axis.

78. Write an equation for the ellipse $(x^2/4) + (y^2/25) = 1$ shifted 3 units to the right and 2 units down. Sketch the ellipse and identify its center and major axis.

79. Assume that f is an even function, g is an odd function, and both f and g are defined on the entire real line $\mathbb{R}$. Which of the following (where defined) are even? odd?

a. fg **b.** f/g **c.** g/f

d. $f^2 = ff$ **e.** $g^2 = gg$ **f.** $f \circ g$

g. $g \circ f$ **h.** $f \circ f$ **i.** $g \circ g$

80. Can a function be both even and odd? Give reasons for your answer.

T **81.** (*Continuation of Example* 1.) Graph the functions $f(x) = \sqrt{x}$ and $g(x) = \sqrt{1 - x}$ together with their (a) sum, (b) product, (c) two differences, (d) two quotients.

T **82.** Let $f(x) = x - 7$ and $g(x) = x^2$. Graph f and g together with $f \circ g$ and $g \circ f$.

1.3 Trigonometric Functions

This section reviews radian measure and the basic trigonometric functions.

Angles

Angles are measured in degrees or radians. The number of **radians** in the central angle $A'CB'$ within a circle of radius r is defined as the number of "radius units" contained in the arc s subtended by that central angle. If we denote this central angle by θ when measured in radians, this means that $\theta = s/r$ (Figure 1.38), or

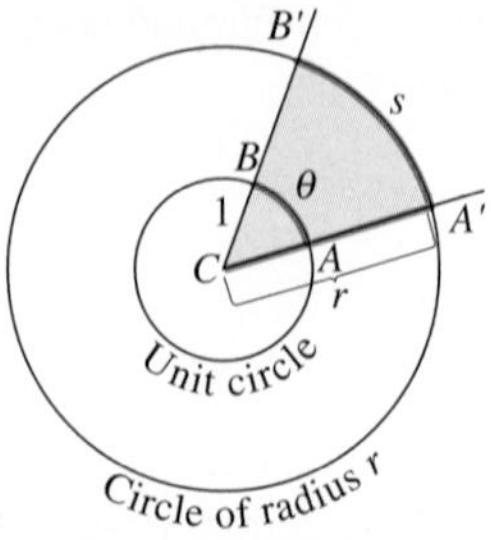

FIGURE 1.38 The radian measure of the central angle $A'CB'$ is the number $\theta = s/r$. For a unit circle of radius $r = 1$, θ is the length of arc AB that central angle ACB cuts from the unit circle.

$$s = r\theta \qquad (\theta \text{ in radians}). \tag{1}$$

If the circle is a unit circle having radius $r = 1$, then from Figure 1.38 and Equation (1), we see that the central angle θ measured in radians is just the length of the arc that the angle cuts from the unit circle. Since one complete revolution of the unit circle is 360° or 2π radians, we have

$$\pi \text{ radians} = 180^\circ \tag{2}$$

and

$$1 \text{ radian} = \frac{180}{\pi} (\approx 57.3) \text{ degrees} \qquad \text{or} \qquad 1 \text{ degree} = \frac{\pi}{180} (\approx 0.017) \text{ radians.}$$

Table 1.2 shows the equivalence between degree and radian measures for some basic angles.

TABLE 1.2 Angles measured in degrees and radians

Degrees	−180	−135	−90	−45	0	30	45	60	90	120	135	150	180	270	360
θ (radians)	$-\pi$	$\frac{-3\pi}{4}$	$\frac{-\pi}{2}$	$\frac{-\pi}{4}$	0	$\frac{\pi}{6}$	$\frac{\pi}{4}$	$\frac{\pi}{3}$	$\frac{\pi}{2}$	$\frac{2\pi}{3}$	$\frac{3\pi}{4}$	$\frac{5\pi}{6}$	π	$\frac{3\pi}{2}$	2π

An angle in the xy plane is said to be in **standard position** if its vertex lies at the origin and its initial ray lies along the positive x-axis (Figure 1.39). Angles measured counterclockwise from the positive x-axis are assigned positive measures; angles measured clockwise are assigned negative measures.

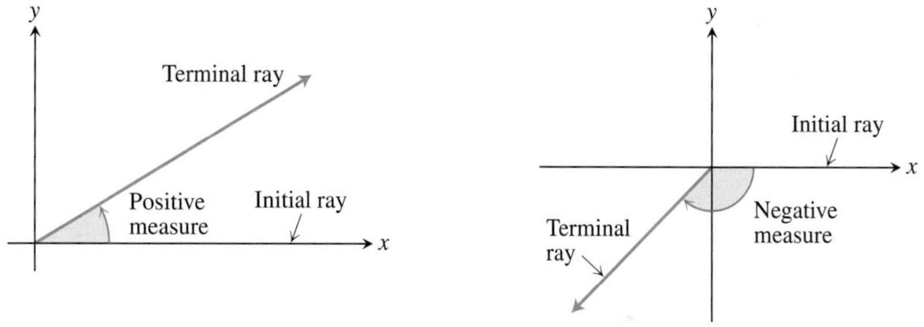

FIGURE 1.39 Angles in standard position in the xy-plane.

Angles describing counterclockwise rotations can go arbitrarily far beyond 2π radians or 360°. Similarly, angles describing clockwise rotations can have negative measures of all sizes (Figure 1.40).

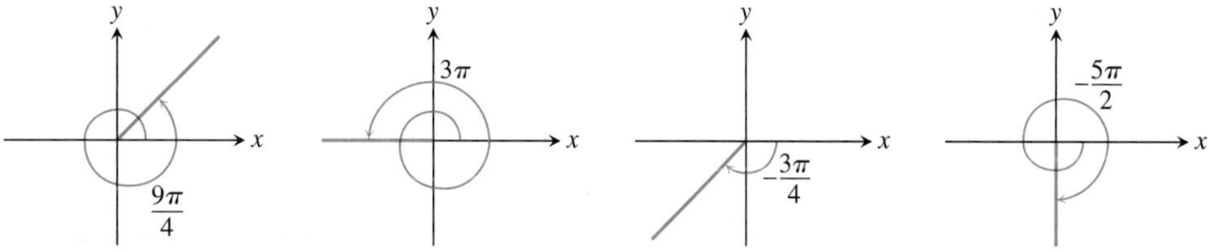

FIGURE 1.40 Nonzero radian measures can be positive or negative and can go beyond 2π.

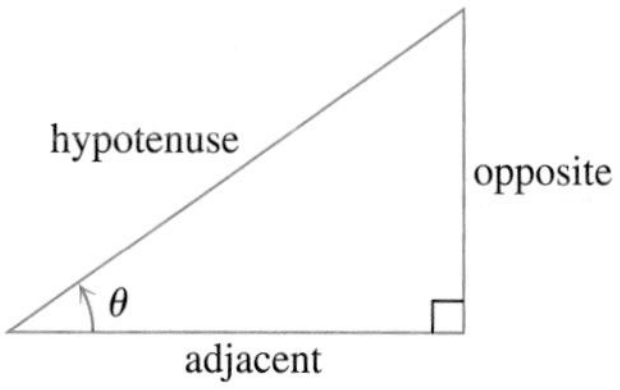

$$\sin\theta = \frac{\text{opp}}{\text{hyp}} \qquad \csc\theta = \frac{\text{hyp}}{\text{opp}}$$

$$\cos\theta = \frac{\text{adj}}{\text{hyp}} \qquad \sec\theta = \frac{\text{hyp}}{\text{adj}}$$

$$\tan\theta = \frac{\text{opp}}{\text{adj}} \qquad \cot\theta = \frac{\text{adj}}{\text{opp}}$$

FIGURE 1.41 Trigonometric ratios of an acute angle.

Angle Convention: Use Radians From now on, in this book it is assumed that all angles are measured in radians unless degrees or some other unit is stated explicitly. When we talk about the angle $\pi/3$, we mean $\pi/3$ radians (which is 60°), not $\pi/3$ degrees. When you do calculus, keep your calculator in radian mode.

The Six Basic Trigonometric Functions

You are probably familiar with defining the trigonometric functions of an acute angle in terms of the sides of a right triangle (Figure 1.41). We extend this definition to obtuse and negative angles by first placing the angle in standard position in a circle of radius r. We then define the trigonometric functions in terms of the coordinates of the point $P(x, y)$ where the angle's terminal ray intersects the circle (Figure 1.42).

$$\textbf{sine:}\quad \sin\theta = \frac{y}{r} \qquad \textbf{cosecant:}\quad \csc\theta = \frac{r}{y}$$

$$\textbf{cosine:}\quad \cos\theta = \frac{x}{r} \qquad \textbf{secant:}\quad \sec\theta = \frac{r}{x}$$

$$\textbf{tangent:}\quad \tan\theta = \frac{y}{x} \qquad \textbf{cotangent:}\quad \cot\theta = \frac{x}{y}$$

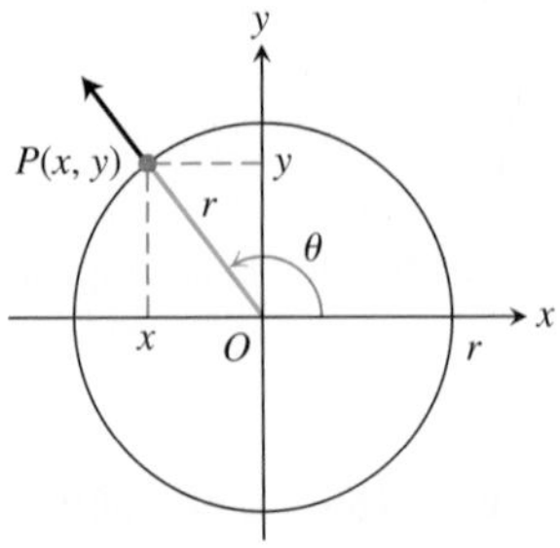

FIGURE 1.42 The trigonometric functions of a general angle θ are defined in terms of x, y, and r.

These extended definitions agree with the right-triangle definitions when the angle is acute.

Notice also the following definitions, whenever the quotients are defined.

$$\tan\theta = \frac{\sin\theta}{\cos\theta} \qquad \cot\theta = \frac{1}{\tan\theta}$$

$$\sec\theta = \frac{1}{\cos\theta} \qquad \csc\theta = \frac{1}{\sin\theta}$$

As you can see, $\tan\theta$ and $\sec\theta$ are not defined if $x = 0$. This means they are not defined if θ is $\pm\pi/2, \pm 3\pi/2, \ldots$. Similarly, $\cot\theta$ and $\csc\theta$ are not defined for values of θ for which $y = 0$, namely $\theta = 0, \pm\pi, \pm 2\pi, \ldots$.

The exact values of these trigonometric ratios for some angles can be read from the triangles in Figure 1.43. For instance,

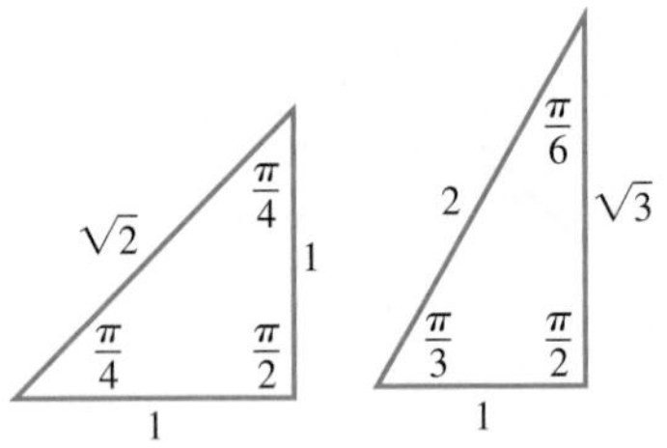

FIGURE 1.43 Radian angles and side lengths of two common triangles.

$$\sin\frac{\pi}{4} = \frac{1}{\sqrt{2}} \qquad \sin\frac{\pi}{6} = \frac{1}{2} \qquad \sin\frac{\pi}{3} = \frac{\sqrt{3}}{2}$$

$$\cos\frac{\pi}{4} = \frac{1}{\sqrt{2}} \qquad \cos\frac{\pi}{6} = \frac{\sqrt{3}}{2} \qquad \cos\frac{\pi}{3} = \frac{1}{2}$$

$$\tan\frac{\pi}{4} = 1 \qquad \tan\frac{\pi}{6} = \frac{1}{\sqrt{3}} \qquad \tan\frac{\pi}{3} = \sqrt{3}$$

The CAST rule (Figure 1.44) is useful for remembering when the basic trigonometric functions are positive or negative. For instance, from the triangle in Figure 1.45, we see that

$$\sin\frac{2\pi}{3} = \frac{\sqrt{3}}{2}, \qquad \cos\frac{2\pi}{3} = -\frac{1}{2}, \qquad \tan\frac{2\pi}{3} = -\sqrt{3}.$$

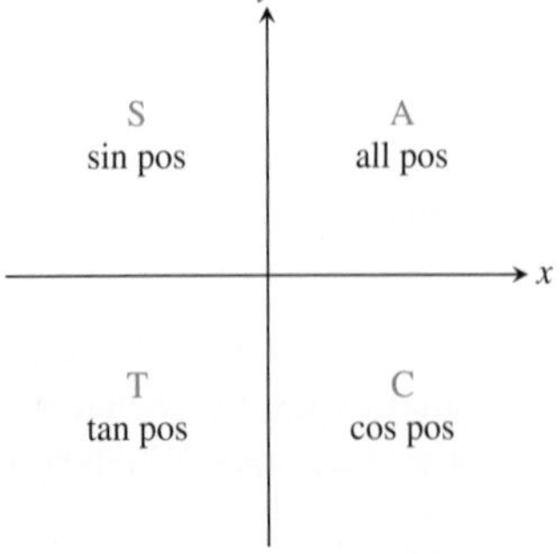

FIGURE 1.44 The CAST rule, remembered by the statement "All Students Take Calculus," tells which trigonometric functions are positive in each quadrant.

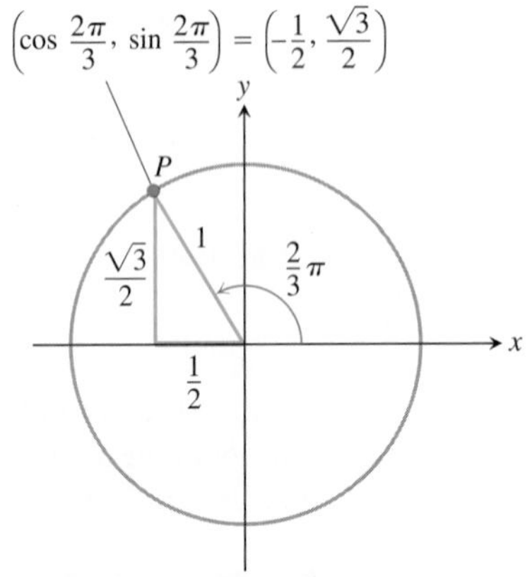

FIGURE 1.45 The triangle for calculating the sine and cosine of $2\pi/3$ radians. The side lengths come from the geometry of right triangles.

Using a similar method we determined the values of $\sin\theta$, $\cos\theta$, and $\tan\theta$ shown in Table 1.3.

TABLE 1.3 Values of $\sin\theta$, $\cos\theta$, and $\tan\theta$ for selected values of θ

Degrees	**−180**	**−135**	**−90**	**−45**	**0**	**30**	**45**	**60**	**90**	**120**	**135**	**150**	**180**	**270**	**360**
θ (radians)	$-\pi$	$\frac{-3\pi}{4}$	$\frac{-\pi}{2}$	$\frac{-\pi}{4}$	0	$\frac{\pi}{6}$	$\frac{\pi}{4}$	$\frac{\pi}{3}$	$\frac{\pi}{2}$	$\frac{2\pi}{3}$	$\frac{3\pi}{4}$	$\frac{5\pi}{6}$	π	$\frac{3\pi}{2}$	2π
$\sin\theta$	0	$\frac{-\sqrt{2}}{2}$	-1	$\frac{-\sqrt{2}}{2}$	0	$\frac{1}{2}$	$\frac{\sqrt{2}}{2}$	$\frac{\sqrt{3}}{2}$	1	$\frac{\sqrt{3}}{2}$	$\frac{\sqrt{2}}{2}$	$\frac{1}{2}$	0	-1	0
$\cos\theta$	-1	$\frac{-\sqrt{2}}{2}$	0	$\frac{\sqrt{2}}{2}$	1	$\frac{\sqrt{3}}{2}$	$\frac{\sqrt{2}}{2}$	$\frac{1}{2}$	0	$-\frac{1}{2}$	$\frac{-\sqrt{2}}{2}$	$\frac{-\sqrt{3}}{2}$	-1	0	1
$\tan\theta$	0	1		-1	0	$\frac{\sqrt{3}}{3}$	1	$\sqrt{3}$		$-\sqrt{3}$	-1	$\frac{-\sqrt{3}}{3}$	0		0

Periodicity and Graphs of the Trigonometric Functions

When an angle of measure θ and an angle of measure $\theta + 2\pi$ are in standard position, their terminal rays coincide. The two angles therefore have the same trigonometric function values: $\sin(\theta + 2\pi) = \sin\theta$, $\tan(\theta + 2\pi) = \tan\theta$, and so on. Similarly, $\cos(\theta - 2\pi) = \cos\theta$, $\sin(\theta - 2\pi) = \sin\theta$, and so on. We describe this repeating behavior by saying that the six basic trigonometric functions are *periodic*.

Periods of Trigonometric Functions

Period π: $\tan(x + \pi) = \tan x$
$\cot(x + \pi) = \cot x$

Period 2π: $\sin(x + 2\pi) = \sin x$
$\cos(x + 2\pi) = \cos x$
$\sec(x + 2\pi) = \sec x$
$\csc(x + 2\pi) = \csc x$

DEFINITION A function $f(x)$ is **periodic** if there is a positive number p such that $f(x + p) = f(x)$ for every value of x. The smallest such value of p is the **period** of f.

When we graph trigonometric functions in the coordinate plane, we usually denote the independent variable by x instead of θ. Figure 1.46 shows that the tangent and cotangent

Even

$\cos(-x) = \cos x$
$\sec(-x) = \sec x$

Odd

$\sin(-x) = -\sin x$
$\tan(-x) = -\tan x$
$\csc(-x) = -\csc x$
$\cot(-x) = -\cot x$

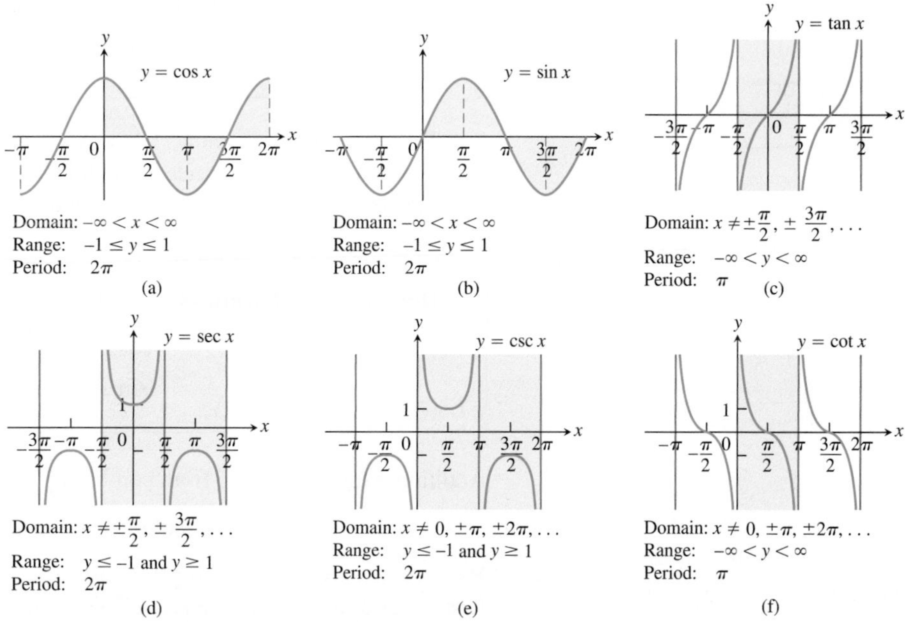

FIGURE 1.46 Graphs of the six basic trigonometric functions using radian measure. The shading for each trigonometric function indicates its periodicity.

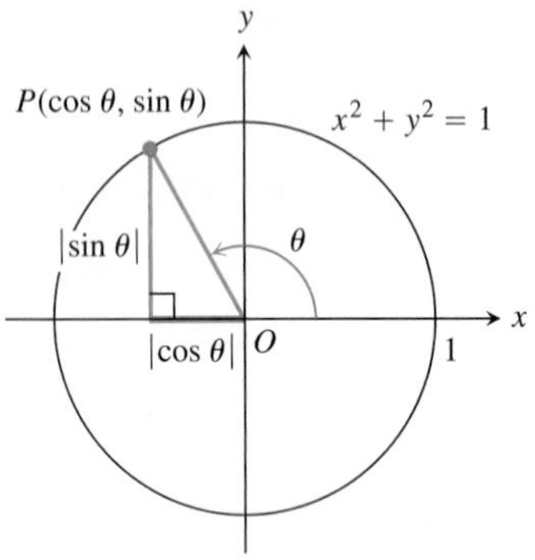

FIGURE 1.47 The reference triangle for a general angle θ.

functions have period $p = \pi$, and the other four functions have period 2π. Also, the symmetries in these graphs reveal that the cosine and secant functions are even and the other four functions are odd.

Trigonometric Identities

The coordinates of any point $P(x, y)$ in the plane can be expressed in terms of the point's distance r from the origin and the angle θ that ray OP makes with the positive x-axis (Figure 1.42). Since $x/r = \cos\theta$ and $y/r = \sin\theta$, we have

$$x = r\cos\theta, \qquad y = r\sin\theta.$$

When $r = 1$ we can apply the Pythagorean theorem to the reference right triangle in Figure 1.47 and obtain the equation

$$\cos^2\theta + \sin^2\theta = 1. \tag{3}$$

This equation, true for all values of θ, is the most frequently used identity in trigonometry. Dividing this identity in turn by $\cos^2\theta$ and $\sin^2\theta$ gives

$$1 + \tan^2\theta = \sec^2\theta.$$
$$1 + \cot^2\theta = \csc^2\theta.$$

The following formulas hold for all angles A and B (Exercises 53 and 54).

Addition Formulas

$$\begin{aligned} \cos(A + B) &= \cos A\cos B - \sin A\sin B \\ \sin(A + B) &= \sin A\cos B + \cos A\sin B \end{aligned} \tag{4}$$

There are similar formulas for $\cos(A - B)$ and $\sin(A - B)$ (Exercises 35 and 36). All the trigonometric identities needed in this book derive from Equations (3) and (4). For example, substituting θ for both A and B in the addition formulas gives

Double-Angle Formulas

$$\begin{aligned} \cos 2\theta &= \cos^2\theta - \sin^2\theta \\ \sin 2\theta &= 2\sin\theta\cos\theta \end{aligned} \tag{5}$$

Additional formulas come from combining the equations

$$\cos^2\theta + \sin^2\theta = 1, \qquad \cos^2\theta - \sin^2\theta = \cos 2\theta.$$

We add the two equations to get $2\cos^2\theta = 1 + \cos 2\theta$ and subtract the second from the first to get $2\sin^2\theta = 1 - \cos 2\theta$. This results in the following identities, which are useful in integral calculus.

Half-Angle Formulas

$$\cos^2 \theta = \frac{1 + \cos 2\theta}{2} \quad (6)$$

$$\sin^2 \theta = \frac{1 - \cos 2\theta}{2} \quad (7)$$

The Law of Cosines

If a, b, and c are sides of a triangle ABC and if θ is the angle opposite c, then

$$c^2 = a^2 + b^2 - 2ab \cos \theta. \quad (8)$$

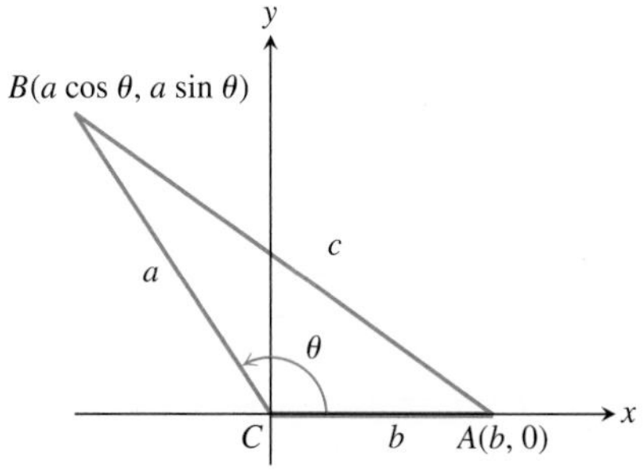

FIGURE 1.48 The square of the distance between A and B gives the law of cosines.

This equation is called the **law of cosines**.

We can see why the law holds if we introduce coordinate axes with the origin at C and the positive x-axis along one side of the triangle, as in Figure 1.48. The coordinates of A are $(b, 0)$; the coordinates of B are $(a \cos \theta, a \sin \theta)$. The square of the distance between A and B is therefore

$$\begin{aligned} c^2 &= (a \cos \theta - b)^2 + (a \sin \theta)^2 \\ &= a^2\underbrace{(\cos^2 \theta + \sin^2 \theta)}_{1} + b^2 - 2ab \cos \theta \\ &= a^2 + b^2 - 2ab \cos \theta. \end{aligned}$$

The law of cosines generalizes the Pythagorean theorem. If $\theta = \pi/2$, then $\cos \theta = 0$ and $c^2 = a^2 + b^2$.

Transformations of Trigonometric Graphs

The rules for shifting, stretching, compressing, and reflecting the graph of a function summarized in the following diagram, apply to the trigonometric functions we have discussed in this section.

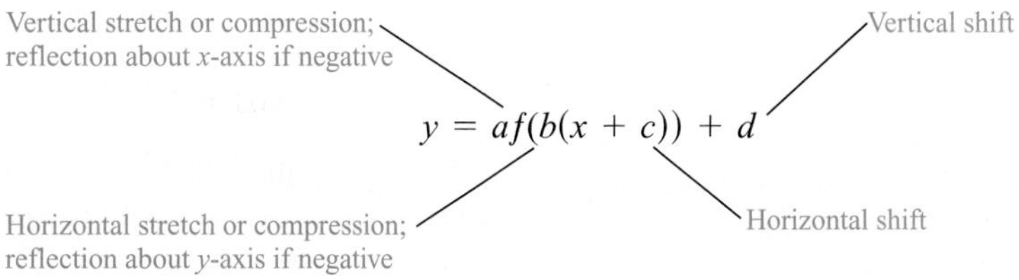

The transformation rules applied to the sine function give the **general sine function** or **sinusoid** formula

$$f(x) = A \sin\left[\frac{2\pi}{B}(x - C)\right] + D,$$

where $|A|$ is the *amplitude*, $|B|$ is the *period*, C is the *horizontal shift*, and D is the *vertical shift*. A graphical interpretation of the various terms is revealing and given below.

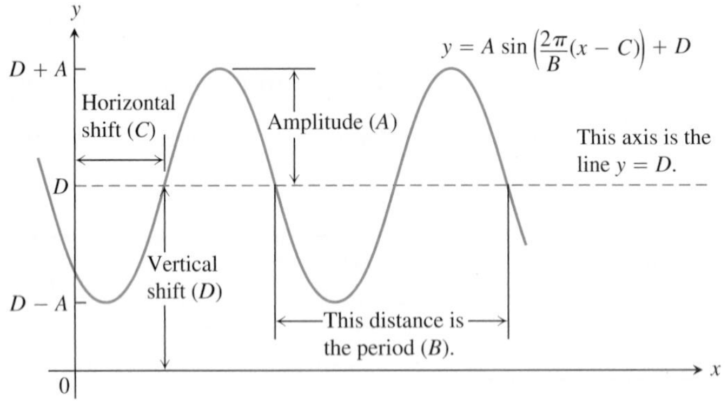

EXERCISES 1.3

1. On a circle of radius 10 m, how long is an arc that subtends a central angle of (**a**) $4\pi/5$ radians? (**b**) 110°?

2. A central angle in a circle of radius 8 is subtended by an arc of length 10π. Find the angle's radian and degree measures.

3. You want to make an 80° angle by marking an arc on the perimeter of a 12-in.-diameter disk and drawing lines from the ends of the arc to the disk's center. To the nearest tenth of an inch, how long should the arc be?

4. If you roll a 1-m-diameter wheel forward 30 cm over level ground, through what angle will the wheel turn? Answer in radians (to the nearest tenth) and degrees (to the nearest degree).

5. Copy and complete the following table of function values. If the function is undefined at a given angle, enter "UND." Do not use a calculator or tables.

$\boldsymbol{\theta}$	$-\pi$	$-2\pi/3$	0	$\pi/2$	$3\pi/4$
$\sin\theta$					
$\cos\theta$					
$\tan\theta$					
$\cot\theta$					
$\sec\theta$					
$\csc\theta$					

6. Copy and complete the following table of function values. If the function is undefined at a given angle, enter "UND." Do not use a calculator or tables.

$\boldsymbol{\theta}$	$-3\pi/2$	$-\pi/3$	$-\pi/6$	$\pi/4$	$5\pi/6$
$\sin\theta$					
$\cos\theta$					
$\tan\theta$					
$\cot\theta$					
$\sec\theta$					
$\csc\theta$					

In Exercises 7–12, one of $\sin x$, $\cos x$, and $\tan x$ is given. Find the other two if x lies in the specified interval.

7. $\sin x = \frac{3}{5}, \quad x \in \left[\frac{\pi}{2}, \pi\right]$

8. $\tan x = 2, \quad x \in \left[0, \frac{\pi}{2}\right]$

9. $\cos x = \frac{1}{3}, \quad x \in \left[-\frac{\pi}{2}, 0\right]$

10. $\cos x = -\frac{5}{13}, \quad x \in \left[\frac{\pi}{2}, \pi\right]$

11. $\tan x = \frac{1}{2}, \quad x \in \left[\pi, \frac{3\pi}{2}\right]$

12. $\sin x = -\frac{1}{2}, \quad x \in \left[\pi, \frac{3\pi}{2}\right]$

Graph the functions in Exercises 13–22. What is the period of each function?

13. $\sin 2x$

14. $\sin(x/2)$

15. $\cos \pi x$

16. $\cos \frac{\pi x}{2}$

17. $-\sin \frac{\pi x}{3}$

18. $-\cos 2\pi x$

19. $\cos\left(x - \frac{\pi}{2}\right)$

20. $\sin\left(x + \frac{\pi}{2}\right)$

21. $\sin\left(x - \frac{\pi}{4}\right) + 1$

22. $\cos\left(x + \frac{\pi}{4}\right) - 1$

Graph the functions in Exercises 23–26 in the *ts*-plane (*t*-axis horizontal, *s*-axis vertical). What is the period of each function? What symmetries do the graphs have?

23. $s = \cot 2t$

24. $s = -\tan \pi t$

25. $s = \sec\left(\frac{\pi t}{2}\right)$

26. $s = \csc\left(\frac{t}{2}\right)$

T **27. a.** Graph $y = \cos x$ and $y = \sec x$ together for $-3\pi/2 \le x \le 3\pi/2$. Comment on the behavior of $\sec x$ in relation to the signs and values of $\cos x$.

b. Graph $y = \sin x$ and $y = \csc x$ together for $-\pi \le x \le 2\pi$. Comment on the behavior of $\csc x$ in relation to the signs and values of $\sin x$.

T **28.** Graph $y = \tan x$ and $y = \cot x$ together for $-7 \le x \le 7$. Comment on the behavior of $\cot x$ in relation to the signs and values of $\tan x$.

29. Graph $y = \sin x$ and $y = \lfloor \sin x \rfloor$ together. What are the domain and range of $\lfloor \sin x \rfloor$?

30. Graph $y = \sin x$ and $y = \lceil \sin x \rceil$ together. What are the domain and range of $\lceil \sin x \rceil$?

Use the addition formulas to derive the identities in Exercises 31–36.

31. $\cos\left(x - \frac{\pi}{2}\right) = \sin x$

32. $\cos\left(x + \frac{\pi}{2}\right) = -\sin x$

33. $\sin\left(x + \frac{\pi}{2}\right) = \cos x$

34. $\sin\left(x - \frac{\pi}{2}\right) = -\cos x$

35. $\cos(A - B) = \cos A \cos B + \sin A \sin B$ (Exercise 53 provides a different derivation.)

36. $\sin(A - B) = \sin A \cos B - \cos A \sin B$

37. What happens if you take $B = A$ in the trigonometric identity $\cos(A - B) = \cos A \cos B + \sin A \sin B$? Does the result agree with something you already know?

38. What happens if you take $B = 2\pi$ in the addition formulas? Do the results agree with something you already know?

In Exercises 39–42, express the given quantity in terms of $\sin x$ and $\cos x$.

39. $\cos(\pi + x)$

40. $\sin(2\pi - x)$

41. $\sin\left(\frac{3\pi}{2} - x\right)$

42. $\cos\left(\frac{3\pi}{2} + x\right)$

43. Evaluate $\sin \frac{7\pi}{12}$ as $\sin\left(\frac{\pi}{4} + \frac{\pi}{3}\right)$.

44. Evaluate $\cos \frac{11\pi}{12}$ as $\cos\left(\frac{\pi}{4} + \frac{2\pi}{3}\right)$.

45. Evaluate $\cos \frac{\pi}{12}$.

46. Evaluate $\sin \frac{5\pi}{12}$.

Find the function values in Exercises 47–50.

47. $\cos^2 \frac{\pi}{8}$

48. $\cos^2 \frac{\pi}{12}$

49. $\sin^2 \frac{\pi}{12}$

50. $\sin^2 \frac{\pi}{8}$

51. The tangent sum formula The standard formula for the tangent of the sum of two angles is

$$\tan(A + B) = \frac{\tan A + \tan B}{1 - \tan A \tan B}.$$

Derive the formula.

52. (*Continuation of Exercise 51.*) Derive a formula for $\tan(A - B)$.

53. Apply the law of cosines to the triangle in the accompanying figure to derive the formula for $\cos(A - B)$.

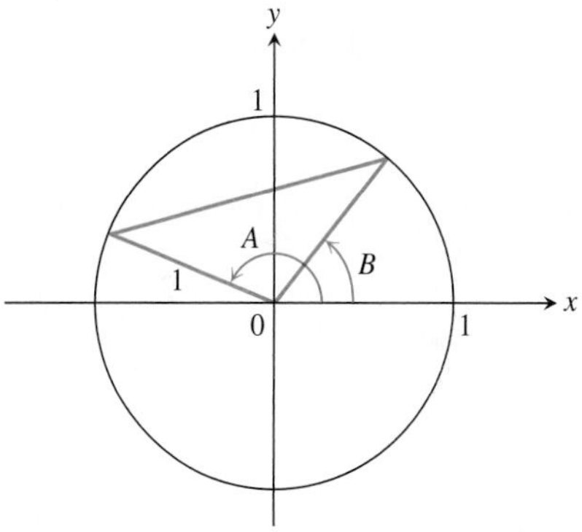

54. a. Apply the formula for $\cos(A - B)$ to the identity $\sin\theta = \cos\left(\frac{\pi}{2} - \theta\right)$ to obtain the addition formula for $\sin(A + B)$.

b. Derive the formula for $\cos(A + B)$ by substituting $-B$ for B in the formula for $\cos(A - B)$ from Exercise 35.

55. A triangle has sides $a = 2$ and $b = 3$ and angle $C = 60°$. Find the length of side c.

56. A triangle has sides $a = 2$ and $b = 3$ and angle $C = 40°$. Find the length of side c.

57. The law of sines *The law of sines* says that if a, b, and c are the sides opposite the angles A, B, and C in a triangle, then

$$\frac{\sin A}{a} = \frac{\sin B}{b} = \frac{\sin C}{c}.$$

Use the accompanying figures and the identity $\sin(\pi - \theta) = \sin\theta$, if required, to derive the law.

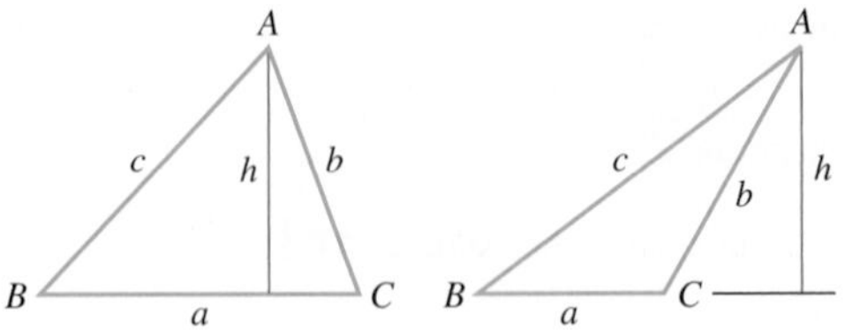

58. A triangle has sides $a = 2$ and $b = 3$ and angle $C = 60°$ (as in Exercise 55). Find the sine of angle B using the law of sines.

59. A triangle has side $c = 2$ and angles $A = \pi/4$ and $B = \pi/3$. Find the length a of the side opposite A.

T **60. The approximation $\sin x \approx x$** It is often useful to know that, when x is measured in radians, $\sin x \approx x$ for numerically small values of x. In Section 3.10, we will see why the approximation holds. The approximation error is less than 1 in 5000 if $|x| < 0.1$.

a. With your grapher in radian mode, graph $y = \sin x$ and $y = x$ together in a viewing window about the origin. What do you see happening as x nears the origin?

b. With your grapher in degree mode, graph $y = \sin x$ and $y = x$ together about the origin again. How is the picture different from the one obtained with radian mode?

c. A quick radian mode check Is your calculator in radian mode? Evaluate $\sin x$ at a value of x near the origin, say $x = 0.1$. If $\sin x \approx x$, the calculator is in radian mode; if not, it isn't. Try it.

For

$$f(x) = A \sin\left(\frac{2\pi}{B}(x - C)\right) + D,$$

identify A, B, C, and D for the sine functions in Exercises 61–64 and sketch their graphs.

61. $y = 2\sin(x + \pi) - 1$

62. $y = \frac{1}{2}\sin(\pi x - \pi) + \frac{1}{2}$

63. $y = -\frac{2}{\pi}\sin\left(\frac{\pi}{2}t\right) + \frac{1}{\pi}$

64. $y = \frac{L}{2\pi}\sin\frac{2\pi t}{L}, \quad L > 0$

COMPUTER EXPLORATIONS

In Exercises 65–68, you will explore graphically the general sine function

$$f(x) = A \sin\left(\frac{2\pi}{B}(x - C)\right) + D$$

as you change the values of the constants A, B, C, and D. Use a CAS or computer grapher to perform the steps in the exercises.

65. The period B Set the constants $A = 3$, $C = D = 0$.

a. Plot $f(x)$ for the values $B = 1, 3, 2\pi, 5\pi$ over the interval $-4\pi \le x \le 4\pi$. Describe what happens to the graph of the general sine function as the period increases.

b. What happens to the graph for negative values of B? Try it with $B = -3$ and $B = -2\pi$.

66. The horizontal shift C Set the constants $A = 3$, $B = 6$, $D = 0$.

a. Plot $f(x)$ for the values $C = 0, 1$, and 2 over the interval $-4\pi \le x \le 4\pi$. Describe what happens to the graph of the general sine function as C increases through positive values.

b. What happens to the graph for negative values of C?

c. What smallest positive value should be assigned to C so the graph exhibits no horizontal shift? Confirm your answer with a plot.

67. The vertical shift D Set the constants $A = 3$, $B = 6$, $C = 0$.

a. Plot $f(x)$ for the values $D = 0, 1$, and 3 over the interval $-4\pi \le x \le 4\pi$. Describe what happens to the graph of the general sine function as D increases through positive values.

b. What happens to the graph for negative values of D?

68. The amplitude A Set the constants $B = 6$, $C = D = 0$.

a. Describe what happens to the graph of the general sine function as A increases through positive values. Confirm your answer by plotting $f(x)$ for the values $A = 1, 5$, and 9.

b. What happens to the graph for negative values of A?

1.4 Exponential Functions

In this section we take an intuitive view of exponential functions to introduce their basic properties and uses. In Chapter 5 we give a more rigorous treatment based on important calculus ideas and results.

Exponential Behavior

When a positive quantity P doubles, it increases by a factor of 2 and the quantity becomes $2P$. If it doubles again, it becomes $2(2P) = 2^2P$, and a third doubling gives $2(2^2P) = 2^3P$. Continuing to double in this fashion leads us to the consideration of the function $f(x) = 2^x$. We call this an *exponential* function because the variable x appears in the exponent of 2^x. Functions such as $g(x) = 10^x$ and $h(x) = (1/2)^x$ are other examples of exponential functions. In general, if $a \neq 1$ is a positive constant, the function

$$f(x) = a^x$$

is the **exponential function with base *a*.**

EXAMPLE 1 In 2000, \$100 is invested in a savings account, where it grows by accruing interest that is compounded annually (once a year) at an interest rate of 5.5%. Assuming no additional funds are deposited to the account and no money is withdrawn, give a formula for a function describing the amount A in the account after x years have elapsed.

Solution If $P = 100$, at the end of the first year the amount in the account is the original amount plus the interest accrued, or

$$P + \left(\frac{5.5}{100}\right)P = (1 + 0.055)P = (1.055)P.$$

At the end of the second year the account earns interest again and grows to

$$(1 + 0.055)\cdot(1.055P) = (1.055)^2P = 100\cdot(1.055)^2. \qquad P = 100$$

Continuing this process, after x years the value of the account is

$$A = 100\cdot(1.055)^x.$$

This is a multiple of the exponential function with base 1.055. Table 1.4 shows the amounts accrued over the first four years. Notice that the amount in the account each year is always 1.055 times its value in the previous year.

TABLE 1.4 Savings account growth

Year	Amount (dollars)	Increase (dollars)
2000	100	
2001	$100(1.055) = 105.50$	5.50
2002	$100(1.055)^2 = 111.30$	5.80
2003	$100(1.055)^3 = 117.42$	6.12
2004	$100(1.055)^4 = 123.88$	6.46

In general, the amount after x years is given by $P(1 + r)^x$, where r is the interest rate (expressed as a decimal). ■

For integer and rational exponents, the value of an exponential function $f(x) = a^x$ is obtained arithmetically as follows. If $x = n$ is a positive integer, the number a^n is given by multiplying a by itself n times:

$$a^n = \underbrace{a\cdot a\cdot\cdots\cdot a}_{n \text{ factors}}.$$

If $x = 0$, then $a^0 = 1$, and if $x = -n$ for some positive integer n, then

$$a^{-n} = \frac{1}{a^n} = \left(\frac{1}{a}\right)^n.$$

If $x = 1/n$ for some positive integer n, then

$$a^{1/n} = \sqrt[n]{a},$$

which is the positive number that when multiplied by itself n times gives a. If $x = p/q$ is any rational number, then

$$a^{p/q} = \sqrt[q]{a^p} = \left(\sqrt[q]{a}\right)^p.$$

If x is *irrational*, the meaning of a^x is not so clear, but its value can be defined by considering values for rational numbers that get closer and closer to x. This informal approach is based on the graph of the exponential function. In Chapter 5 we define the meaning in a rigorous way.

We displayed the graphs of several exponential functions in Section 1.1, and show them again here in Figure 1.49. These graphs describe the values of the exponential functions for all real inputs x. The value at an irrational number x is chosen so that the graph of a^x has no "holes" or "jumps." Of course, these words are not mathematical terms, but they do convey the informal idea. We mean that the value of a^x, when x is irrational, is chosen so that the function $f(x) = a^x$ is *continuous*, a notion that will be carefully explored in the next chapter. This choice ensures the graph retains its increasing behavior when $a > 1$, or decreasing behavior when $0 < a < 1$ (see Figure 1.49).

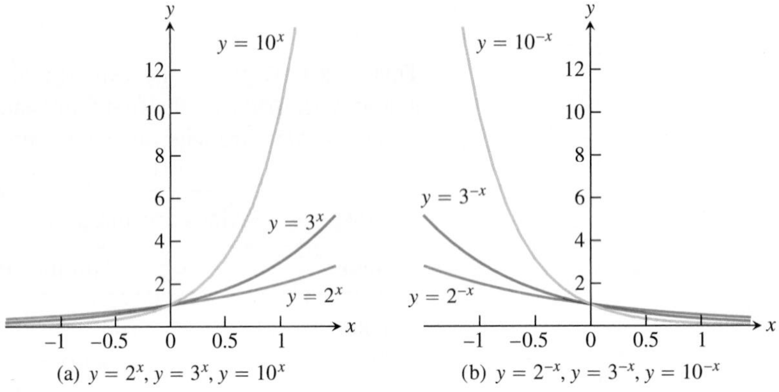

FIGURE 1.49 Graphs of exponential functions.

Exponential functions obey the familiar rules of exponents listed below. It is easy to check these rules using algebra when the exponents are integers or rational numbers. We prove them for all real exponents in Chapter 5.

Rules for Exponents

If $a > 0$ and $b > 0$, the following rules hold true for all real numbers x and y.

1. $a^x \cdot a^y = a^{x+y}$
2. $\dfrac{a^x}{a^y} = a^{x-y}$
3. $(a^x)^y = (a^y)^x = a^{xy}$
4. $a^x \cdot b^x = (ab)^x$
5. $\dfrac{a^x}{b^x} = \left(\dfrac{a}{b}\right)^x$

EXAMPLE 2

1. $3^{1.1} \cdot 3^{0.7} = 3^{1.1+0.7} = 3^{1.8}$

2. $\dfrac{(\sqrt{10})^3}{\sqrt{10}} = (\sqrt{10})^{3-1} = (\sqrt{10})^2 = 10$

3. $(5^{\sqrt{2}})^{\sqrt{2}} = 5^{\sqrt{2}\cdot\sqrt{2}} = 5^2 = 25$

4. $7^{\pi} \cdot 8^{\pi} = (56)^{\pi}$

5. $\left(\dfrac{4}{9}\right)^{1/2} = \dfrac{4^{1/2}}{9^{1/2}} = \dfrac{2}{3}$

■

The Natural Exponential Function e^x

The most important exponential function used for modeling natural, physical, and economic phenomena is the **natural exponential function**, whose base is the special number e. The number e is irrational, and its value is 2.718281828 to nine decimal places. It might seem strange that we would use this number for a base rather than a simple number like 2 or 10. The advantage in using e as a base is that it simplifies many of the calculations in calculus.

If you look at Figure 1.49a you can see that the graphs of the exponential functions $y = a^x$ get steeper as the base a gets larger. This idea of steepness is conveyed by the slope of the tangent line to the graph at a point. Tangent lines to graphs of functions are defined precisely in the next chapter, but intuitively the tangent line to the graph at a point is a line that just touches the graph at the point, like a tangent to a circle. Figure 1.50 shows the slope of the graph of $y = a^x$ as it crosses the y-axis for several values of a. Notice that the slope is exactly equal to 1 when a equals the number e. The slope is smaller than 1 if $a < e$, and larger than 1 if $a > e$. This is the property that makes the number e so useful in calculus: **The graph of $y = e^x$ has slope 1 when it crosses the y-axis.**

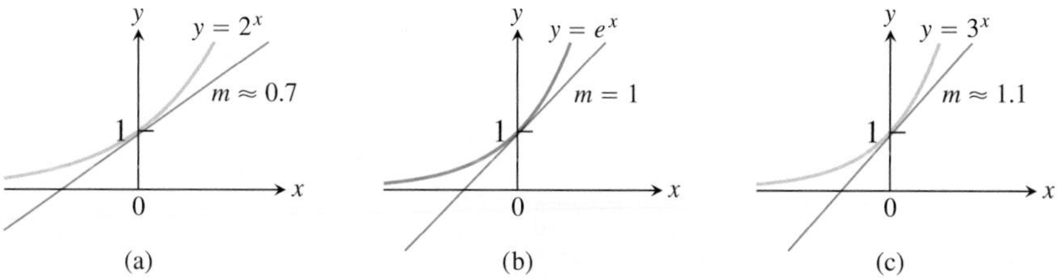

FIGURE 1.50 Among the exponential functions, the graph of $y = e^x$ has the property that the slope m of the tangent line to the graph is exactly 1 when it crosses the y-axis. The slope is smaller for a base less than e, such as 2^x, and larger for a base greater than e, such as 3^x.

In Chapter 3 we use that slope property to prove e is the number the quantity $(1 + 1/x)^x$ approaches as x becomes large without bound. That result provides one way to compute the value of e, at least approximately. The graph and table in Figure 1.51 show the behavior of this expression and how it gets closer and closer to the line $y = e \approx 2.718281828$ as x gets larger and larger. (This *limit* idea is made precise in the next chapter.) A rigorous discussion of e will be given in Chapter 5.

x	$(1 + 1/x)^x$
1000	2.7169
2000	2.7176
3000	2.7178
4000	2.7179
5000	2.7180
6000	2.7181
7000	2.7181

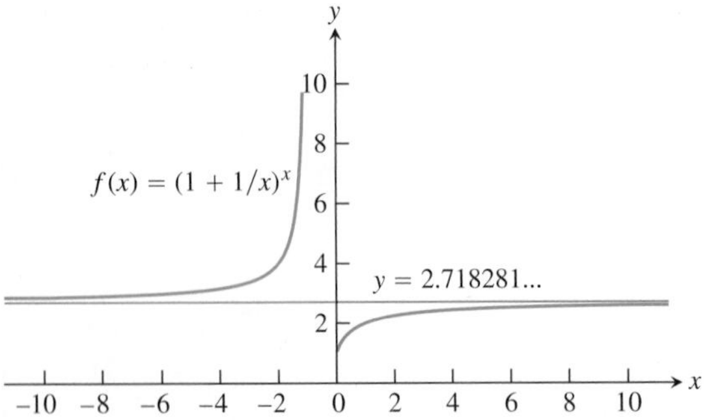

FIGURE 1.51 A graph and table of values for $f(x) = (1 + 1/x)^x$ both suggest that as x gets larger and larger, $f(x)$ gets closer and closer to $e \approx 2.7182818\ldots$.

Exponential Growth and Decay

The exponential functions $y = e^{kx}$, where k is a nonzero constant, are frequently used for modeling exponential growth or decay. The function $y = y_0 e^{kx}$ is a model for **exponential growth** if $k > 0$ and a model for **exponential decay** if $k < 0$. Here y_0 represents a constant. For an example of exponential growth, interest **compounded continuously** uses the model $y = P \cdot e^{rt}$, where P is the initial investment, r is the interest rate as a decimal, and t is time in units consistent with r. An example of exponential decay is the model $y = A \cdot e^{-1.2 \times 10^{-4} t}$, which represents how the radioactive element carbon-14 decays over time. Here A is the original amount of carbon-14 and t is the time in years. Carbon-14 decay is used to date the remains of dead organisms such as shells, seeds, and wooden artifacts. Figure 1.52 shows graphs of exponential growth and exponential decay.

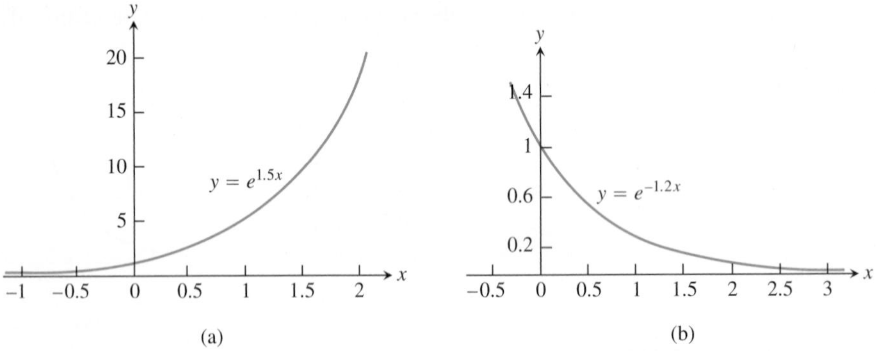

FIGURE 1.52 Graphs of (a) exponential growth, $k = 1.5 > 0$, and (b) exponential decay, $k = -1.2 < 0$.

EXAMPLE 3 Investment companies often use the model $y = Pe^{rt}$ in calculating the growth of an investment. Use this model to track the growth of \$100 invested in 2000 at an annual interest rate of 5.5%.

Solution Let $t = 0$ represent 2000, $t = 1$ represent 2001, and so on. Then the exponential growth model is $y(t) = Pe^{rt}$, where $P = 100$ (the initial investment), $r = 0.055$ (the annual interest rate expressed as a decimal), and t is time in years. To predict the amount in the account in 2004, after four years have elapsed, we take $t = 4$ and calculate

$$\begin{aligned} y(4) &= 100\, e^{0.055(4)} \\ &= 100\, e^{0.22} \\ &= 124.61. \qquad \text{Nearest cent using calculator} \end{aligned}$$

This compares with \$123.88 in the account when the interest is compounded annually from Example 1. ■

EXAMPLE 4 Laboratory experiments indicate that some atoms emit a part of their mass as radiation, with the remainder of the atom re-forming to make an atom of some new element. For example, radioactive carbon-14 decays into nitrogen; radium eventually decays into lead. If y_0 is the number of radioactive nuclei present at time zero, the number still present at any later time t will be

$$y = y_0\, e^{-rt}, \qquad r > 0.$$

The number r is called the **decay rate** of the radioactive substance. (We will see how this formula is obtained in Section 6.5.) For carbon-14, the decay rate has been determined experimentally to be about $r = 1.2 \times 10^{-4}$ when t is measured in years. Predict the percent of carbon-14 present after 866 years have elapsed.

Solution If we start with an amount y_0 of carbon-14 nuclei, after 866 years we are left with the amount

$$\begin{aligned} y(866) &= y_0\, e^{(-1.2\times 10^{-4})(866)} \\ &\approx (0.901)y_0. \qquad \text{Calculator evaluation} \end{aligned}$$

That is, after 866 years, we are left with about 90% of the original amount of carbon-14, so about 10% of the original nuclei have decayed. In Example 6 in the next section, you will see how to find the number of years required for half of the radioactive nuclei present in a sample to decay (called the *half-life* of the substance). ■

You may wonder why we use the family of functions $y = e^{kx}$ for different values of the constant k instead of the general exponential functions $y = a^x$. In the next section, we show that the exponential function a^x is equal to e^{kx} for an appropriate value of k. So the formula $y = e^{kx}$ covers the entire range of possibilities, and we will see that it is easier to use.

EXERCISES 1.4

In Exercises 1–6, sketch the given curves together in the appropriate coordinate plane and label each curve with its equation.

1. $y = 2^x, y = 4^x, y = 3^{-x}, y = (1/5)^x$
2. $y = 3^x, y = 8^x, y = 2^{-x}, y = (1/4)^x$
3. $y = 2^{-t}$ and $y = -2^t$
4. $y = 3^{-t}$ and $y = -3^t$
5. $y = e^x$ and $y = 1/e^x$
6. $y = -e^x$ and $y = -e^{-x}$

In each of Exercises 7–10, sketch the shifted exponential curves.

7. $y = 2^x - 1$ and $y = 2^{-x} - 1$
8. $y = 3^x + 2$ and $y = 3^{-x} + 2$
9. $y = 1 - e^x$ and $y = 1 - e^{-x}$
10. $y = -1 - e^x$ and $y = -1 - e^{-x}$

Use the laws of exponents to simplify the expressions in Exercises 11–20.

11. $16^2 \cdot 16^{-1.75}$

12. $9^{1/3} \cdot 9^{1/6}$

13. $\dfrac{4^{4.2}}{4^{3.7}}$

14. $\dfrac{3^{5/3}}{3^{2/3}}$

15. $\left(25^{1/8}\right)^4$

16. $\left(13^{\sqrt{2}}\right)^{\sqrt{2}/2}$

17. $2^{\sqrt{3}} \cdot 7^{\sqrt{3}}$

18. $\left(\sqrt{3}\right)^{1/2} \cdot \left(\sqrt{12}\right)^{1/2}$

19. $\left(\dfrac{2}{\sqrt{2}}\right)^4$

20. $\left(\dfrac{\sqrt{6}}{3}\right)^2$

Find the domain and range for each of the functions in Exercises 21–24.

21. $f(x) = \dfrac{1}{2 + e^x}$

22. $g(t) = \cos(e^{-t})$

23. $g(t) = \sqrt{1 + 3^{-t}}$

24. $f(x) = \dfrac{3}{1 - e^{2x}}$

T In Exercises 25–28, use graphs to find approximate solutions.

25. $2^x = 5$

26. $e^x = 4$

27. $3^x - 0.5 = 0$

28. $3 - 2^{-x} = 0$

T In Exercises 29–36, use an exponential model and a graphing calculator to estimate the answer in each problem.

29. Population growth The population of Knoxville is 500,000 and is increasing at the rate of 3.75% each year. Approximately when will the population reach 1 million?

30. Population growth The population of Silver Run in the year 1890 was 6250. Assume the population increased at a rate of 2.75% per year.

a. Estimate the population in 1915 and 1940.

b. Approximately when did the population reach 50,000?

31. Radioactive decay The half-life of phosphorus-32 is about 14 days. There are 6.6 grams present initially.

a. Express the amount of phosphorus-32 remaining as a function of time t.

b. When will there be 1 gram remaining?

32. If John invests \$2300 in a savings account with a 6% interest rate compounded annually, how long will it take until John's account has a balance of \$4150?

33. Doubling your money Determine how much time is required for an investment to double in value if interest is earned at the rate of 6.25% compounded annually.

34. Tripling your money Determine how much time is required for an investment to triple in value if interest is earned at the rate of 5.75% compounded continuously.

35. Cholera bacteria Suppose that a colony of bacteria starts with 1 bacterium and doubles in number every half hour. How many bacteria will the colony contain at the end of 24 hr?

36. Eliminating a disease Suppose that in any given year the number of cases of a disease is reduced by 20%. If there are 10,000 cases today, how many years will it take

a. to reduce the number of cases to 1000?

b. to eliminate the disease; that is, to reduce the number of cases to less than 1?

1.5 Inverse Functions and Logarithms

A function that undoes, or inverts, the effect of a function f is called the *inverse* of f. Many common functions, though not all, are paired with an inverse. In this section we present the natural logarithmic function $y = \ln x$ as the inverse of the exponential function $y = e^x$, and we also give examples of several inverse trigonometric functions.

One-to-One Functions

A function is a rule for which each value from its range is the output for at least one element in its domain. Some functions assign the same range value to more than one element in the domain. The function $f(x) = x^2$ assigns the same value, 1, to both of the numbers -1 and $+1$; the sines of $\pi/3$ and $2\pi/3$ are both $\sqrt{3}/2$. Other functions assume no value in their range more than once. The square roots and cubes of different numbers are always different. A function that has distinct values at distinct elements in its domain is called one-to-one. These functions take on any one value in their range exactly once.

DEFINITION A function $f(x)$ is **one-to-one** on a domain D if $f(x_1) \neq f(x_2)$ whenever $x_1 \neq x_2$ in D.

EXAMPLE 1

(a) $f(x) = \sqrt{x}$ is one-to-one on any domain of nonnegative numbers because $\sqrt{x_1} \neq \sqrt{x_2}$ whenever $x_1 \neq x_2$.

(b) $g(x) = \sin x$ is *not* one-to-one on the interval $[0, \pi]$ because $\sin(\pi/6) = \sin(5\pi/6)$. The sine function *is* one-to-one on $[0, \pi/2]$ however, because it is an increasing function on $[0, \pi/2]$ giving distinct outputs for distinct inputs. ■

The graph of a one-to-one function $y = f(x)$ can intersect a given horizontal line at most once. If it intersects the line more than once, it assumes the same y-value for at least two different x-values and is therefore not one-to-one (Figure 1.53b).

The Horizontal Line Test for One-to-One Functions
A function $y = f(x)$ is one-to-one if and only if its graph intersects each horizontal line at most once.

Inverse Functions

Since each output of a one-to-one function comes from just one input, the effect of the function can be inverted to send an output back to the input from which it came.

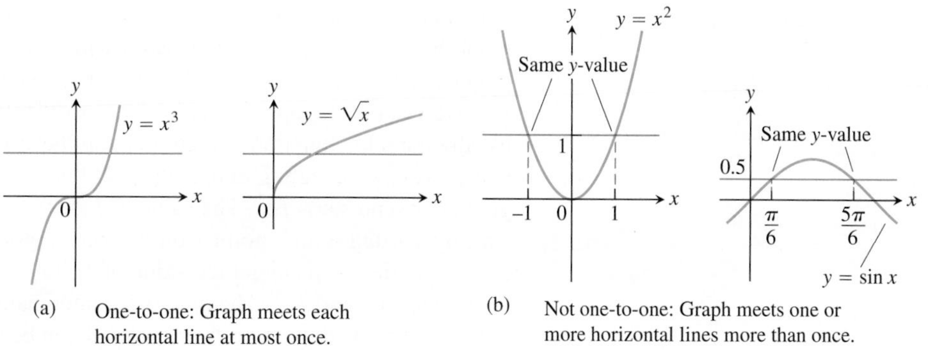

FIGURE 1.53 Using the horizontal line test, we see that (a) $y = x^3$ and $y = \sqrt{x}$ are one-to-one on their domains $(-\infty, \infty)$ and $[0, \infty)$, but (b) $y = x^2$ and $y = \sin x$ are not one-to-one on their domains $(-\infty, \infty)$.

DEFINITION Suppose that f is a one-to-one function on a domain D with range R. The **inverse funtion** f^{-1} is defined by

$$f^{-1}(a) = b \text{ if } f(b) = a.$$

The domain of f^{-1} is R and the range of f^{-1} is D.

The symbol f^{-1} for the inverse of f is read "f inverse." The "-1" in f^{-1} is *not* an exponent: $f^{-1}(x)$ does not mean $1/f(x)$. Notice that the domains and ranges of f and f^{-1} are interchanged.

If we apply f to send an input x to the output $f(x)$ and follow by applying f^{-1} to $f(x)$ we get right back to x, just where we started. Similarly, if we take some number y in the range of f, apply f^{-1} to it, and then apply f to the resulting value $f^{-1}(y)$, we get back the value y with which we began. Composing a function and its inverse has the same effect as doing nothing.

$$(f^{-1} \circ f)(x) = x, \qquad \text{for all } x \text{ in the domain of } f$$

$$(f \circ f^{-1})(y) = y, \qquad \text{for all } y \text{ in the domain of } f^{-1} \text{ (or range of } f)$$

Only a one-to-one function can have an inverse. The reason is that if $f(x_1) = y$ and $f(x_2) = y$ for two distinct inputs x_1 and x_2, then there is no way to assign a value to $f^{-1}(y)$ that satisfies both $f^{-1}(f(x_1)) = x_1$ and $f^{-1}(f(x_2)) = x_2$.

A function that is increasing on an interval, satisfying $f(x_2) > f(x_1)$ when $x_2 > x_1$, is one-to-one and has an inverse. Decreasing functions also have an inverse. Functions that are neither increasing nor decreasing may still be one-to-one and have an inverse, as with the function $f(x) = 1/x$ for $x \neq 0$ and $f(0) = 0$, defined on $(-\infty, \infty)$ and passing the horizontal line test.

Finding Inverses

The graphs of a function and its inverse are closely related. To read the value of a function from its graph, we start at a point x on the x-axis, go vertically to the graph, and then move horizontally to the y-axis to read the value of y. The inverse function can be read from the graph by reversing this process. Start with a point y on the y-axis, go horizontally to the graph, and then move vertically to the x-axis to read the value of $x = f^{-1}(y)$ (Figure 1.54).

We want to set up the graph of f^{-1} so that its input values lie along the x-axis, as is usually done for functions, rather than on the y-axis. To achieve this we interchange the x and y axes by reflecting across the 45° line $y = x$. After this reflection we have a new graph that represents f^{-1}. The value of $f^{-1}(x)$ can now be read from the graph in the usual way, by starting with a point x on the x-axis, going vertically to the graph and then horizontally to the y-axis to get the value of $f^{-1}(x)$. Figure 1.54 indicates the relation between the graphs of f and f^{-1}. The graphs are interchanged by reflection through the line $y = x$.

The process of passing from f to f^{-1} can be summarized as a two-step process.

1. Solve the equation $y = f(x)$ for x. This gives a formula $x = f^{-1}(y)$ where x is expressed as a function of y.
2. Interchange x and y, obtaining a formula $y = f^{-1}(x)$ where f^{-1} is expressed in the conventional format with x as the independent variable and y as the dependent variable.

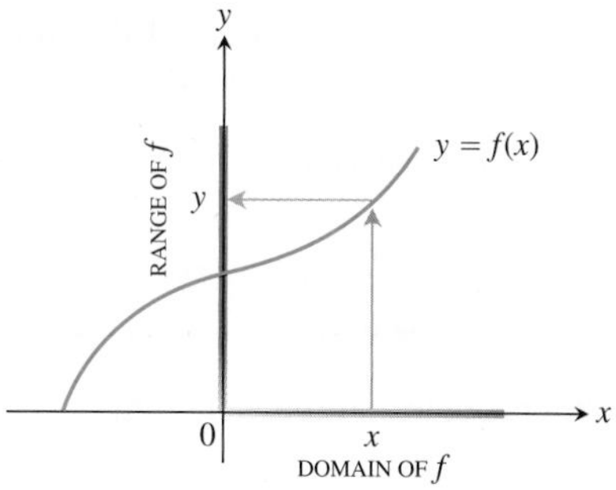

(a) To find the value of f at x, we start at x, go up to the curve, and then over to the y-axis.

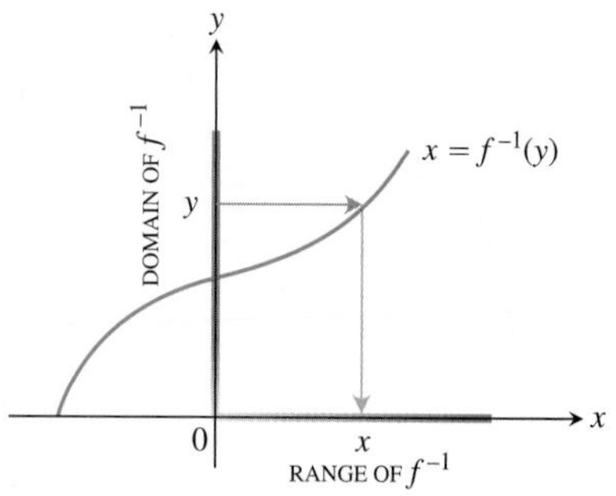

(b) The graph of f is already the graph of f^{-1}, but with x and y interchanged. To find the x that gave y, we start at y and go over to the curve and down to the x-axis. The domain of f^{-1} is the range of f. The range of f^{-1} is the domain of f.

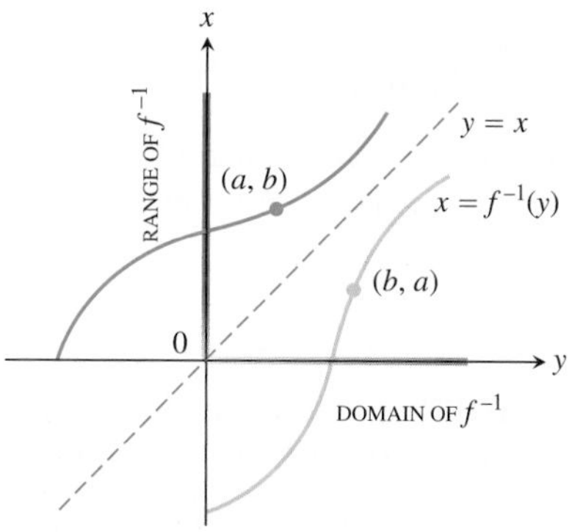

(c) To draw the graph of f^{-1} in the more usual way, we reflect the system in the line $y = x$.

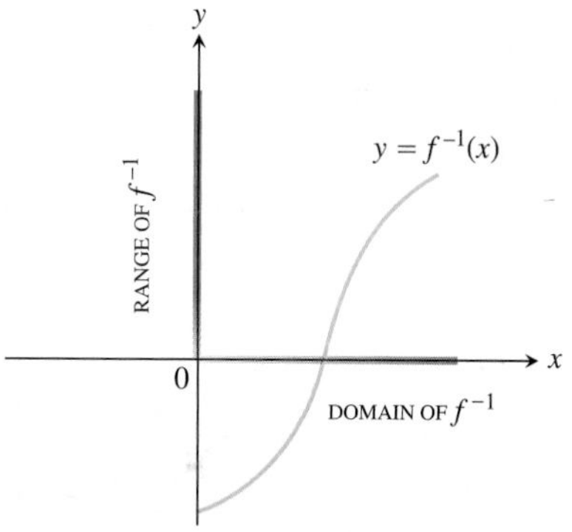

(d) Then we interchange the letters x and y. We now have a normal-looking graph of f^{-1} as a function of x.

FIGURE 1.54 Determining the graph of $y = f^{-1}(x)$ from the graph of $y = f(x)$.

EXAMPLE 2 Find the inverse of $y = \frac{1}{2}x + 1$, expressed as a function of x.

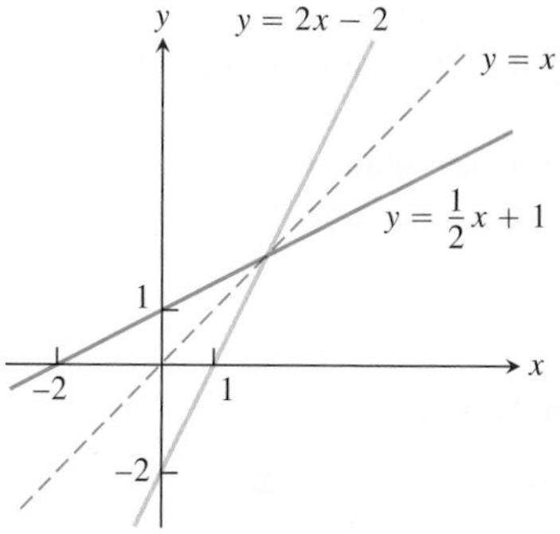

FIGURE 1.55 Graphing $f(x) = (1/2)x + 1$ and $f^{-1}(x) = 2x - 2$ together shows the graphs' symmetry with respect to the line $y = x$ (Example 2).

Solution

1. *Solve for x in terms of y:*
$$y = \frac{1}{2}x + 1$$
$$2y = x + 2$$
$$x = 2y - 2.$$

2. *Interchange x and y:* $y = 2x - 2$.

The inverse of the function $f(x) = (1/2)x + 1$ is the function $f^{-1}(x) = 2x - 2$. To check, we verify that both composites give the identity function:

$$f^{-1}(f(x)) = 2\left(\frac{1}{2}x + 1\right) - 2 = x + 2 - 2 = x$$

$$f(f^{-1}(x)) = \frac{1}{2}(2x - 2) + 1 = x - 1 + 1 = x.$$

See Figure 1.55. ■

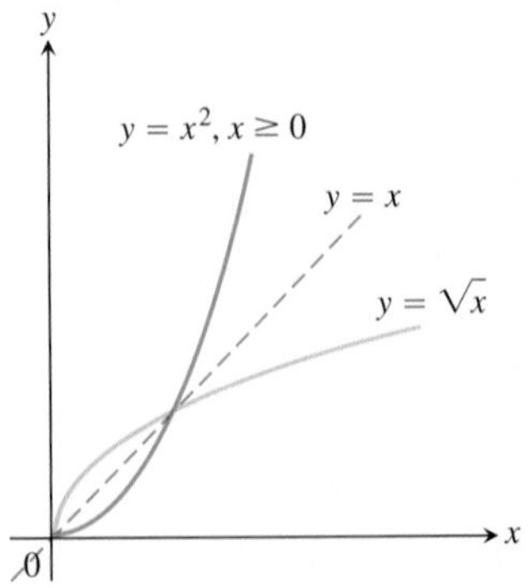

FIGURE 1.56 The functions $y = \sqrt{x}$ and $y = x^2, x \geq 0$, are inverses of one another (Example 3).

EXAMPLE 3 Find the inverse of the function $y = x^2, x \geq 0$, expressed as a function of x.

Solution We first solve for x in terms of y:

$$y = x^2$$

$$\sqrt{y} = \sqrt{x^2} = |x| = x \qquad |x| = x \text{ because } x \geq 0$$

We then interchange x and y, obtaining

$$y = \sqrt{x}.$$

The inverse of the function $y = x^2, x \geq 0$, is the function $y = \sqrt{x}$ (Figure 1.56).

Notice that the function $y = x^2, x \geq 0$, with domain *restricted* to the nonnegative real numbers, *is* one-to-one (Figure 1.53a) and has an inverse. On the other hand, the function $y = x^2$, with no domain restrictions, *is not* one-to-one (Figure 1.53b) and therefore has no inverse. ■

Logarithmic Functions

If a is any positive real number other than 1, the base a exponential function $f(x) = a^x$ is one-to-one. It therefore has an inverse. Its inverse is called the *logarithm function with base a*.

> **DEFINITION** The **logarithm function with base *a***, $y = \log_a x$, is the inverse of the base a exponential function $y = a^x$ $(a > 0, a \neq 1)$.

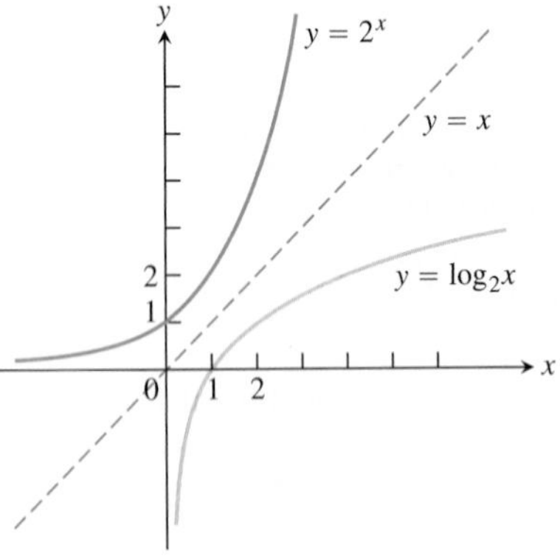

FIGURE 1.57 The graph of 2^x and its inverse, $\log_2 x$.

The domain of $\log_a x$ is $(0, \infty)$, the range of a^x. The range of $\log_a x$ is $(-\infty, \infty)$, the domain of a^x.

Figure 1.21 in Section 1.1 shows the graphs of four logarithmic functions with $a > 1$. Figure 1.57 shows the graph of $y = \log_2 x$. The graph of $y = a^x, a > 1$, increases rapidly for $x > 0$, so its inverse, $y = \log_a x$, increases slowly for $x > 1$.

Because we have no technique yet for solving the equation $y = a^x$ for x in terms of y, we do not have an explicit formula for computing the logarithm at a given value of x. Nevertheless, we can obtain the graph of $y = \log_a x$ by reflecting the graph of the exponential $y = a^x$ across the line $y = x$. Figure 1.57 shows the graph for $a = 2$.

Logarithms with base 2 are commonly used in computer science. Logarithms with base e and base 10 are so important in applications that calculators have special keys for them. They also have their own special notation and names:

$$\log_e x \quad \text{is written as} \quad \ln x.$$

$$\log_{10} x \quad \text{is written as} \quad \log x.$$

The function $y = \ln x$ is called the **natural logarithm function**, and $y = \log x$ is often called the **common logarithm function**. For the natural logarithm,

$$\ln x = y \iff e^y = x.$$

In particular, if we set $x = e$, we obtain

$$\ln e = 1$$

because $e^1 = e$.

Properties of Logarithms

Logarithms, invented by John Napier, were the single most important improvement in arithmetic calculation before the modern electronic computer. What made them so useful is that the properties of logarithms reduce multiplication of positive numbers to addition of their logarithms, division of positive numbers to subtraction of their logarithms, and exponentiation of a number to multiplying its logarithm by the exponent.

HISTORICAL BIOGRAPHY

John Napier
(1550–1617)

We summarize these properties as a series of rules that we prove in Chapter 4. Although here we state the Power Rule for all real powers r, the case when r is an irrational number cannot be dealt with properly until Chapter 5.

Algebraic Properties of the Natural Logarithm

For any numbers $b > 0$ and $x > 0$, the natural logarithm satisfies the following rules:

1. *Product Rule:* $\ln bx = \ln b + \ln x$
2. *Quotient Rule:* $\ln \frac{b}{x} = \ln b - \ln x$
3. *Reciprocal Rule:* $\ln \frac{1}{x} = -\ln x$ — Rule 2 with $b = 1$
4. *Power Rule:* $\ln x^r = r \ln x$

In Chapter 5 we will prove these algebraic properties are valid for logarithmic functions with any base a. We now illustrate how the rules apply.

EXAMPLE 4

(a) $\ln 4 + \ln \sin x = \ln (4 \sin x)$ — Product

(b) $\ln \frac{x + 1}{2x - 3} = \ln (x + 1) - \ln (2x - 3)$ — Quotient

(c) $\ln \frac{1}{8} = -\ln 8$ — Reciprocal

$= -\ln 2^3 = -3 \ln 2$ — Power ■

Because a^x and $\log_a x$ are inverses, composing them in either order gives the identity function.

Inverse Properties for a^x and $\log_a x$

1. Base a: $a^{\log_a x} = x, \quad \log_a a^x = x, \quad a > 0, a \neq 1, x > 0$
2. Base e: $e^{\ln x} = x, \quad \ln e^x = x, \quad x > 0$

Substituting a^x for x in the equation $x = e^{\ln x}$ enables us to rewrite a^x as a power of e:

$$\begin{aligned} a^x &= e^{\ln(a^x)} && \text{Substitute } a^x \text{ for } x \text{ in } x = e^{\ln x}. \\ &= e^{x \ln a} && \text{Power Rule for logs} \\ &= e^{(\ln a)x}. && \text{Exponent rearranged} \end{aligned}$$

Thus, the exponential function a^x is the same as e^{kx} for $k = \ln a$.

> Every exponential function is a power of the natural exponential function.
>
> $$a^x = e^{x \ln a}$$
>
> That is, a^x is the same as e^x raised to the power $\ln a$: $a^x = e^{kx}$ for $k = \ln a$.

For example,

$$2^x = e^{(\ln 2)x} = e^{x \ln 2}, \qquad \text{and} \qquad 5^{-3x} = e^{(\ln 5)(-3x)} = e^{-3x \ln 5}.$$

Returning once more to the properties of a^x and $\log_a x$, we have

$$\begin{aligned} \ln x &= \ln(a^{\log_a x}) && \text{Inverse Property for } a^x \text{ and } \log_a x \\ &= (\log_a x)(\ln a). && \text{Power Rule for logarithms, with } r = \log_a x \end{aligned}$$

Rewriting this equation as $\log_a x = (\ln x)/(\ln a)$ shows that every logarithmic function is a constant multiple of the natural logarithm $\ln x$. This allows us to extend the algebraic properties for $\ln x$ to $\log_a x$. For instance, $\log_a bx = \log_a b + \log_a x$.

> **Change of Base Formula**
> Every logarithmic function is a constant multiple of the natural logarithm.
>
> $$\log_a x = \frac{\ln x}{\ln a} \qquad (a > 0, a \neq 1)$$

Applications

In Section 1.4 we looked at examples of exponential growth and decay problems. Here we use properties of logarithms to answer more questions concerning such problems.

EXAMPLE 5 Sarah invests \$1000 in an account that earns 5.25% interest compounded annually. How long will it take the account to reach \$2500?

Solution From Example 1, Section 1.4 with $P = 1000$ and $r = 0.0525$, the amount in the account at any time t in years is $1000(1.0525)^t$, so we need to solve the equation

$$1000(1.0525)^t = 2500.$$

Thus we have

$$\begin{aligned} (1.0525)^t &= 2.5 && \text{Divide by 1000.} \\ \ln(1.0525)^t &= \ln 2.5 && \text{Take logarithms of both sides.} \end{aligned}$$

$$t \ln 1.0525 = \ln 2.5 \qquad \text{Power Rule}$$

$$t = \frac{\ln 2.5}{\ln 1.0525} \approx 17.9 \qquad \text{Values obtained by calculator}$$

The amount in Sarah's account will reach \$2500 in 18 years, when the annual interest payment is deposited for that year. ■

EXAMPLE 6 The **half-life** of a radioactive element is the time required for half of the radioactive nuclei present in a sample to decay. It is a remarkable fact that the half-life is a constant that does not depend on the number of radioactive nuclei initially present in the sample, but only on the radioactive substance.

To see why, let y_0 be the number of radioactive nuclei initially present in the sample. Then the number y present at any later time t will be $y = y_0 e^{-kt}$. We seek the value of t at which the number of radioactive nuclei present equals half the original number:

$$y_0 e^{-kt} = \frac{1}{2} y_0$$

$$e^{-kt} = \frac{1}{2}$$

$$-kt = \ln \frac{1}{2} = -\ln 2 \qquad \text{Reciprocal Rule for logarithms}$$

$$t = \frac{\ln 2}{k}. \qquad (1)$$

This value of t is the half-life of the element. It depends only on the value of k; the number y_0 does not have any effect.

The effective radioactive lifetime of polonium-210 is so short that we measure it in days rather than years. The number of radioactive atoms remaining after t days in a sample that starts with y_0 radioactive atoms is

$$y = y_0 e^{-5 \times 10^{-3} t}.$$

The element's half-life is

$$\text{Half-life} = \frac{\ln 2}{k} \qquad \text{Eq. (1)}$$

$$= \frac{\ln 2}{5 \times 10^{-3}} \qquad \text{The } k \text{ from polonium's decay equation}$$

$$\approx 139 \text{ days.}$$ ■

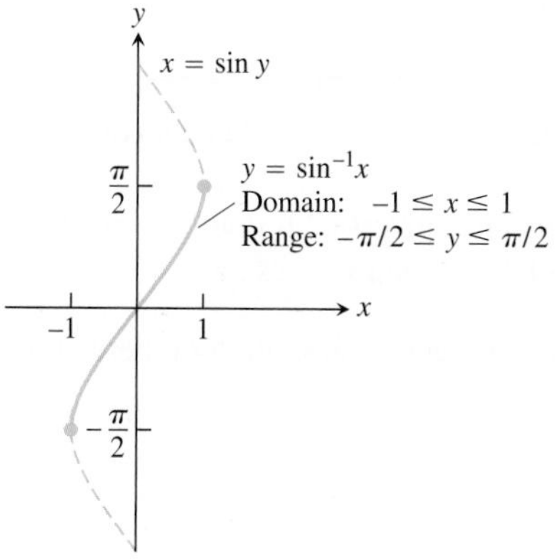

FIGURE 1.58 The graph of $y = \sin^{-1} x$.

Inverse Trigonometric Functions

The six basic trigonometric functions of a general radian angle x were reviewed in Section 1.3. These functions are not one-to-one (their values repeat periodically). However, we can restrict their domains to intervals on which they are one-to-one. The sine function increases from -1 at $x = -\pi/2$ to $+1$ at $x = \pi/2$. By restricting its domain to the interval $[-\pi/2, \pi/2]$ we make it one-to-one, so that it has an inverse $\sin^{-1} x$ (Figure 1.58). Similar domain restrictions can be applied to all six trigonometric functions.

Domain restrictions that make the trigonometric functions one-to-one

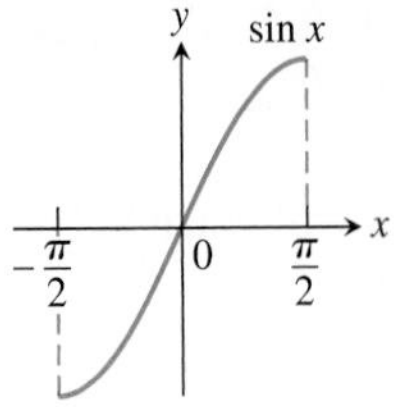

$y = \sin x$
Domain: $[-\pi/2, \pi/2]$
Range: $[-1, 1]$

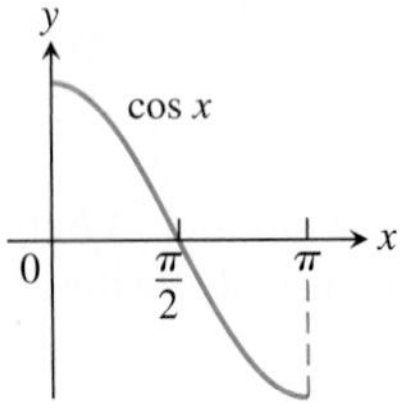

$y = \cos x$
Domain: $[0, \pi]$
Range: $[-1, 1]$

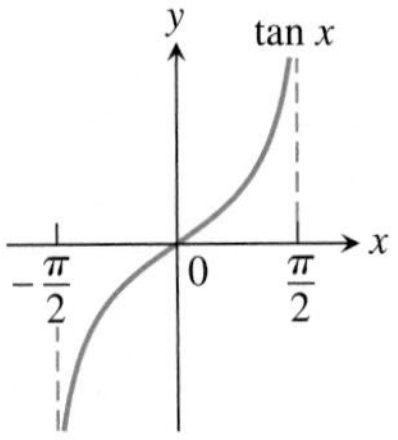

$y = \tan x$
Domain: $(-\pi/2, \pi/2)$
Range: $(-\infty, \infty)$

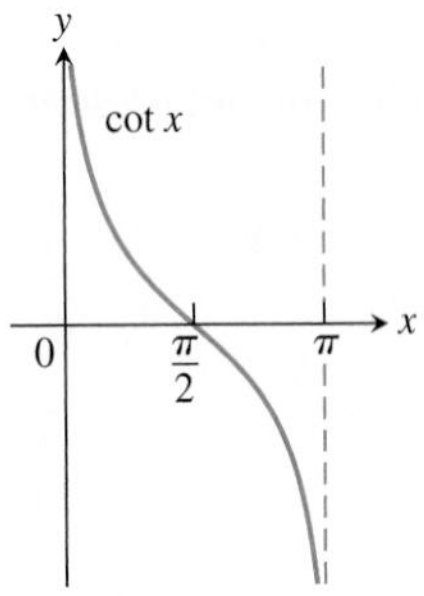

$y = \cot x$
Domain: $(0, \pi)$
Range: $(-\infty, \infty)$

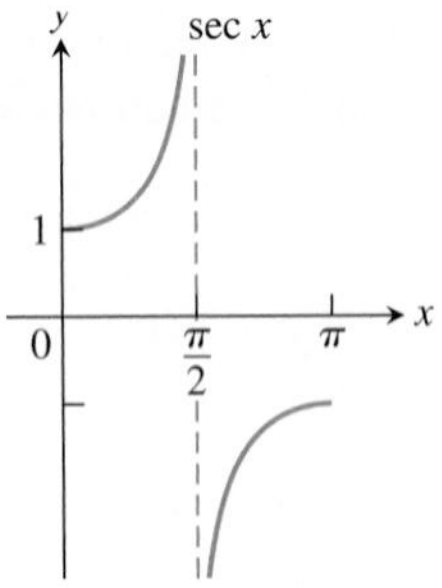

$y = \sec x$
Domain: $[0, \pi/2) \cup (\pi/2, \pi]$
Range: $(-\infty, -1] \cup [1, \infty)$

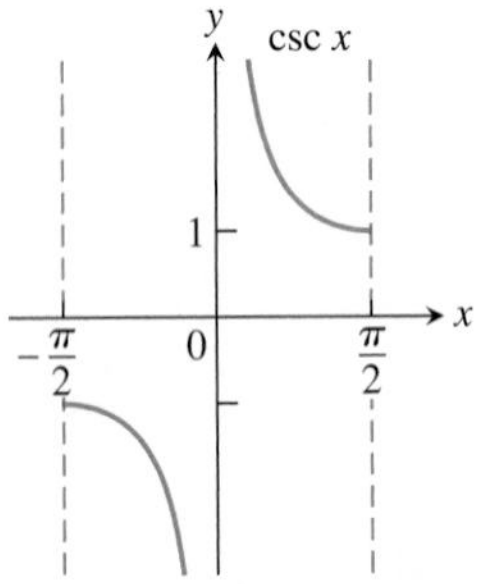

$y = \csc x$
Domain: $[-\pi/2, 0) \cup (0, \pi/2]$
Range: $(-\infty, -1] \cup [1, \infty)$

Since these restricted functions are now one-to-one, they have inverses, which we denote by

$$\begin{aligned}
y &= \sin^{-1} x \quad &\text{or}\quad y &= \arcsin x\\
y &= \cos^{-1} x \quad &\text{or}\quad y &= \arccos x\\
y &= \tan^{-1} x \quad &\text{or}\quad y &= \arctan x\\
y &= \cot^{-1} x \quad &\text{or}\quad y &= \operatorname{arccot} x\\
y &= \sec^{-1} x \quad &\text{or}\quad y &= \operatorname{arcsec} x\\
y &= \csc^{-1} x \quad &\text{or}\quad y &= \operatorname{arccsc} x
\end{aligned}$$

These equations are read "y equals the arcsine of x" or "y equals arcsin x" and so on.

Caution The -1 in the expressions for the inverse means "inverse." It does *not* mean reciprocal. For example, the *reciprocal* of $\sin x$ is $(\sin x)^{-1} = 1/\sin x = \csc x$.

We study the basic inverse trigonometric functions in Section 3.8, but look here at the arcsine and arccosine for illustrative purposes.

The Arcsine and Arccosine Functions

The arcsine of x is the radian angle in $[-\pi/2, \pi/2]$ whose sine is x. The arccosine is an angle in $[0, \pi]$ whose cosine is x.

DEFINITION

$y = \sin^{-1} x$ is the number in $[-\pi/2, \pi/2]$ for which $\sin y = x$.

$y = \cos^{-1} x$ is the number in $[0, \pi]$ for which $\cos y = x$.

The graph of $y = \sin^{-1} x$ (Figure 1.59b) is symmetric about the origin (it lies along the graph of $x = \sin y$). The arcsine is therefore an odd function:

$$\sin^{-1}(-x) = -\sin^{-1} x. \tag{2}$$

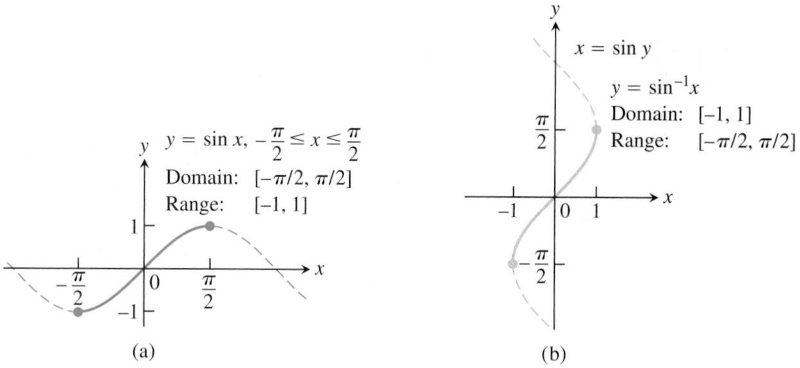

FIGURE 1.59 The graphs of (a) $y = \sin x$, $-\pi/2 \le x \le \pi/2$, and (b) its inverse, $y = \sin^{-1} x$. The graph of $\sin^{-1} x$, obtained by reflection across the line $y = x$, is a portion of the curve $x = \sin y$.

The graph of $y = \cos^{-1} x$ (Figure 1.60b) has no such symmetry.

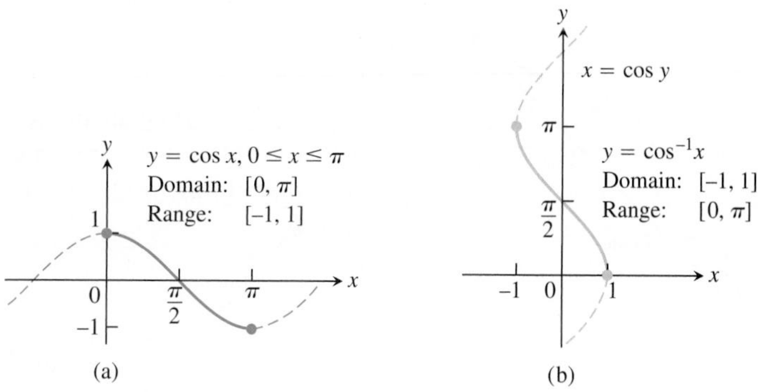

FIGURE 1.60 The graphs of (a) $y = \cos x$, $0 \le x \le \pi$, and (b) its inverse, $y = \cos^{-1} x$. The graph of $\cos^{-1} x$, obtained by reflection across the line $y = x$, is a portion of the curve $x = \cos y$.

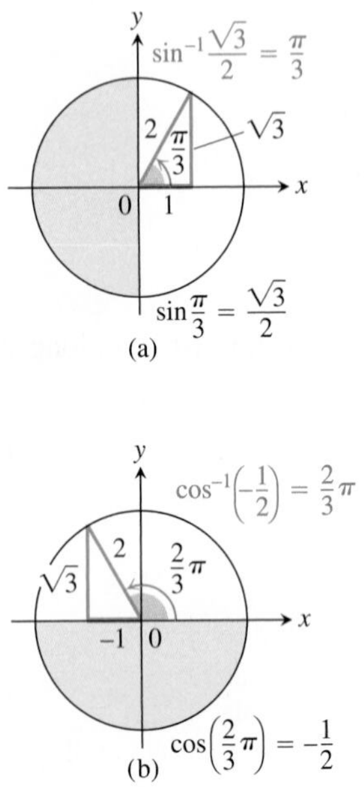

FIGURE 1.61 Values of the arcsine and arccosine functions (Example 7).

EXAMPLE 7 Evaluate **(a)** $\sin^{-1}\left(\frac{\sqrt{3}}{2}\right)$ and **(b)** $\cos^{-1}\left(-\frac{1}{2}\right)$.

Solution

(a) We see that

$$\sin^{-1}\left(\frac{\sqrt{3}}{2}\right) = \frac{\pi}{3}$$

because $\sin(\pi/3) = \sqrt{3}/2$ and $\pi/3$ belongs to the range $[-\pi/2, \pi/2]$ of the arcsine function. See Figure 1.61a.

(b) We have

$$\cos^{-1}\left(-\frac{1}{2}\right) = \frac{2\pi}{3}$$

because $\cos(2\pi/3) = -1/2$ and $2\pi/3$ belongs to the range $[0, \pi]$ of the arccosine function. See Figure 1.61b. ■

Using the same procedure illustrated in Example 7, we can create the following table of common values for the arcsine and arccosine functions.

x	$\sin^{-1} x$	$\cos^{-1} x$
$\sqrt{3}/2$	$\pi/3$	$\pi/6$
$\sqrt{2}/2$	$\pi/4$	$\pi/4$
$1/2$	$\pi/6$	$\pi/3$
$-1/2$	$-\pi/6$	$2\pi/3$
$-\sqrt{2}/2$	$-\pi/4$	$3\pi/4$
$-\sqrt{3}/2$	$-\pi/3$	$5\pi/6$

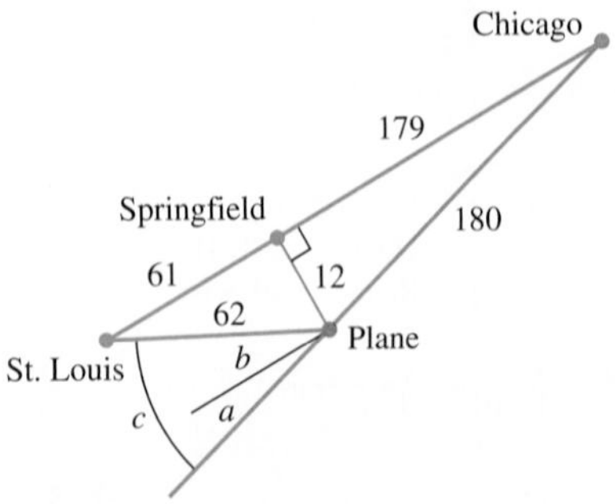

FIGURE 1.62 Diagram for drift correction (Example 8), with distances rounded to the nearest mile (drawing not to scale).

EXAMPLE 8 During an airplane flight from Chicago to St. Louis, the navigator determines that the plane is 12 mi off course, as shown in Figure 1.62. Find the angle a for a course parallel to the original correct course, the angle b, and the drift correction angle $c = a + b$.

Solution

$$a = \sin^{-1}\frac{12}{180} \approx 0.067 \text{ radian} \approx 3.8°$$

$$b = \sin^{-1}\frac{12}{62} \approx 0.195 \text{ radian} \approx 11.2°$$

$$c = a + b \approx 15°.$$

■

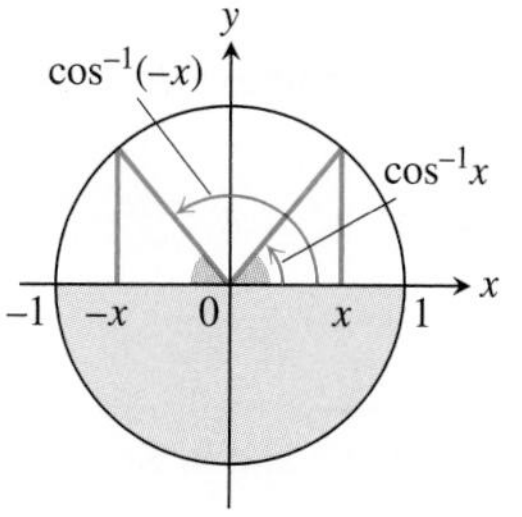

FIGURE 1.63 $\cos^{-1} x$ and $\cos^{-1}(-x)$ are supplementary angles (so their sum is π).

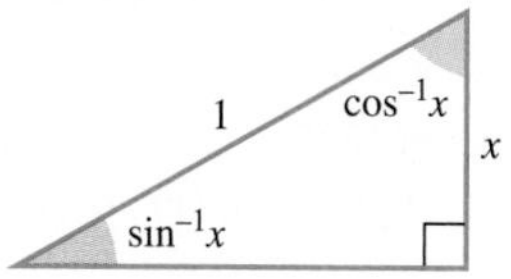

FIGURE 1.64 $\sin^{-1} x$ and $\cos^{-1} x$ are complementary angles (so their sum is $\pi/2$).

Identities Involving Arcsine and Arccosine

As we can see from Figure 1.63, the arccosine of x satisfies the identity

$$\cos^{-1} x + \cos^{-1}(-x) = \pi, \tag{3}$$

or

$$\cos^{-1}(-x) = \pi - \cos^{-1} x. \tag{4}$$

Also, we can see from the triangle in Figure 1.64 that for $x > 0$,

$$\sin^{-1} x + \cos^{-1} x = \pi/2. \tag{5}$$

Equation (5) holds for the other values of x in $[-1, 1]$ as well, but we cannot conclude this from the triangle in Figure 1.64. It is, however, a consequence of Equations (2) and (4) (Exercise 70).

The arctangent, arccotangent, arcsecant, and arccosecant functions are defined in Section 3.8. There we develop additional properties of the inverse trigonometric functions in a calculus setting using the identities discussed here.

EXERCISES 1.5

Which of the functions graphed in Exercises 1–6 are one-to-one, and which are not?

1.

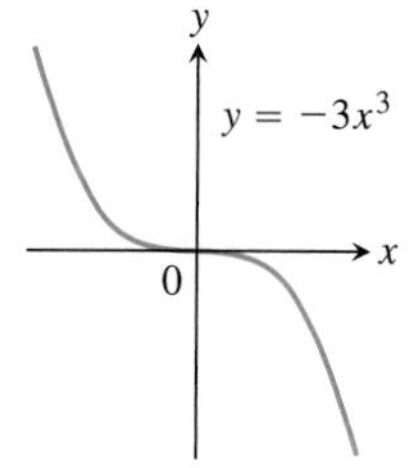

2.

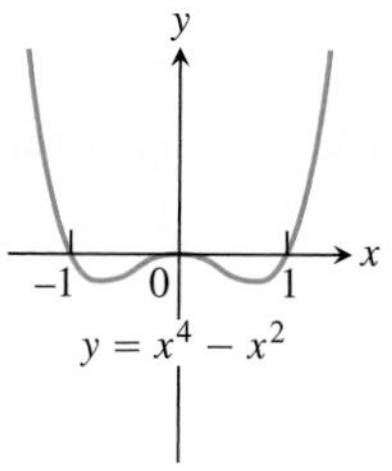

3.

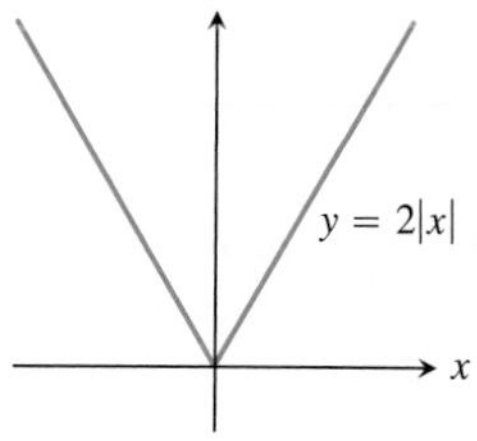

4.

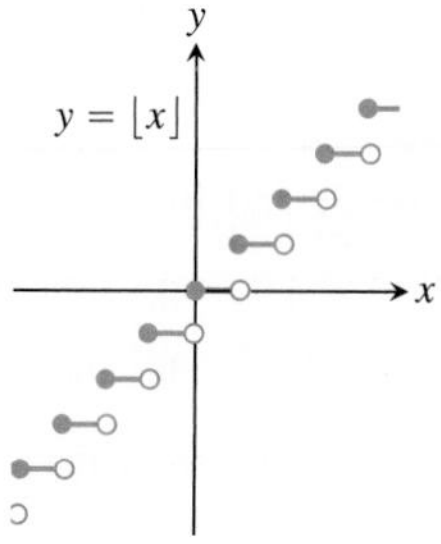

5.

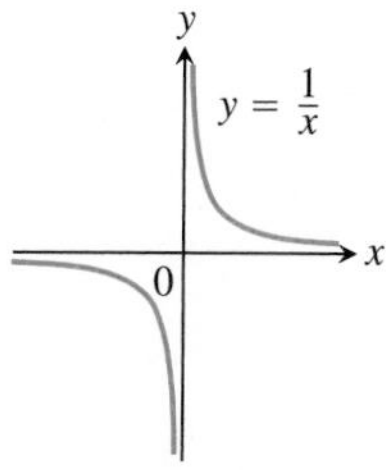

6.

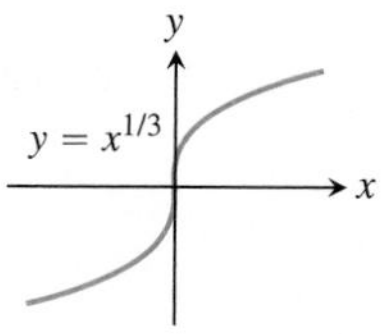

Each of Exercises 7–10 shows the graph of a function $y = f(x)$. Copy the graph and draw in the line $y = x$. Then use symmetry with respect to the line $y = x$ to add the graph of f^{-1} to your sketch. (It is not necessary to find a formula for f^{-1}.) Identify the domain and range of f^{-1}.

7.

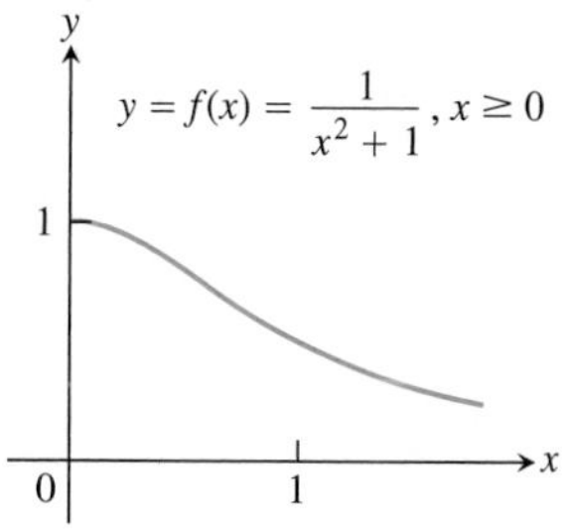

8.

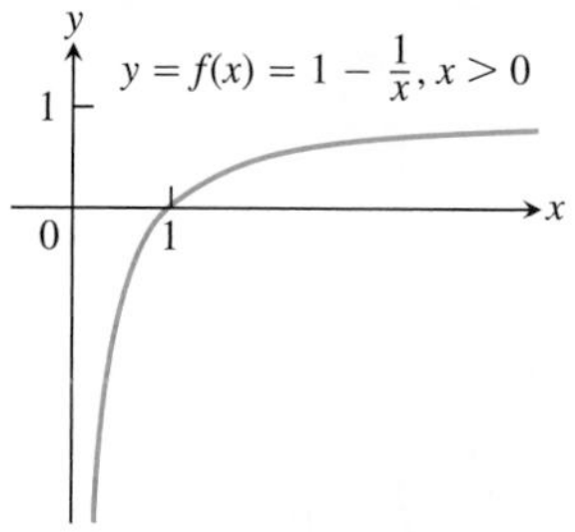

9.

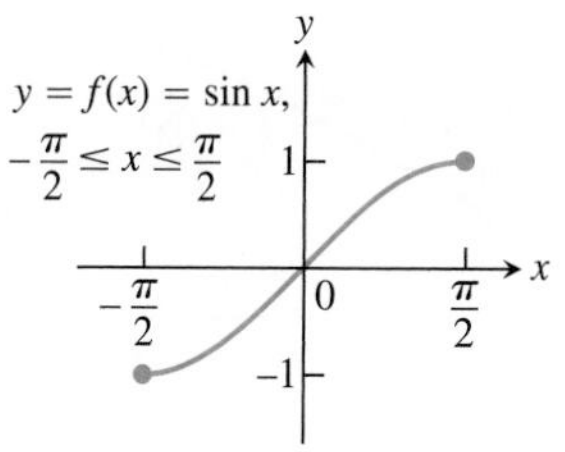

10.

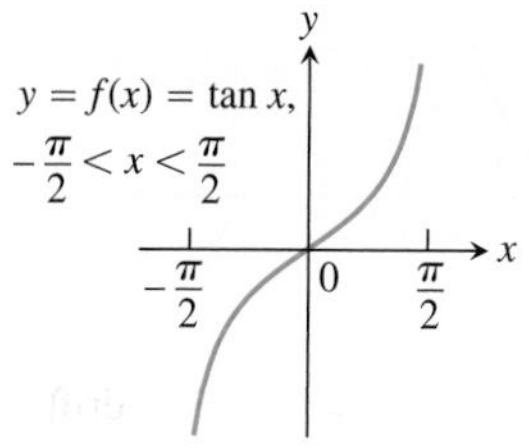

11. a. Graph the function $f(x) = \sqrt{1 - x^2}, 0 \le x \le 1$. What symmetry does the graph have?

b. Show that f is its own inverse. (Remember that $\sqrt{x^2} = x$ if $x \ge 0$.)

12. a. Graph the function $f(x) = 1/x$. What symmetry does the graph have?

b. Show that f is its own inverse.

Each of Exercises 13–18 gives a formula for a function $y = f(x)$ and shows the graphs of f and f^{-1}. Find a formula for f^{-1} in each case.

13. $f(x) = x^2 + 1, \quad x \ge 0$

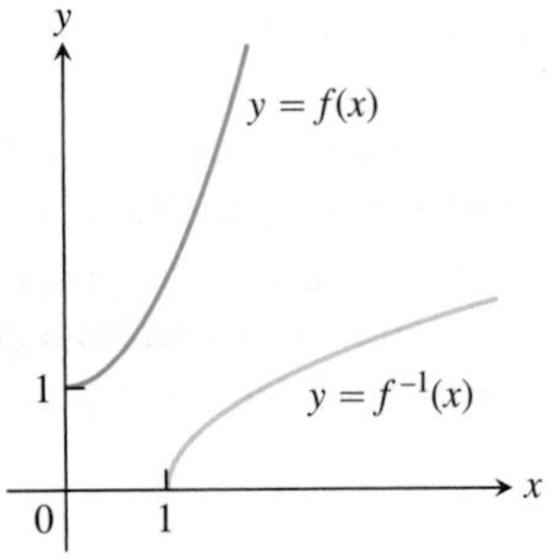

14. $f(x) = x^2, \quad x \le 0$

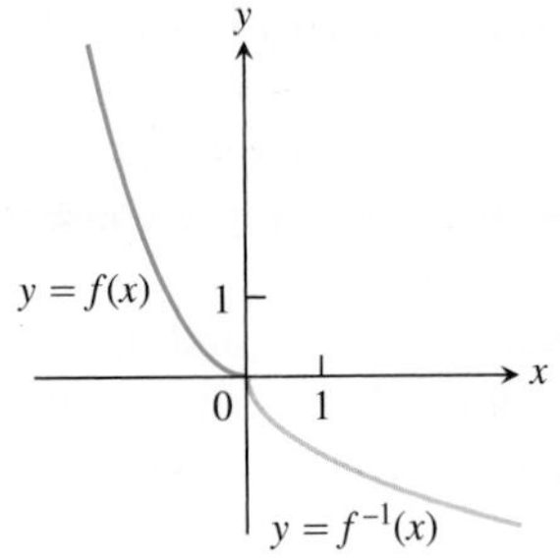

15. $f(x) = x^3 - 1$

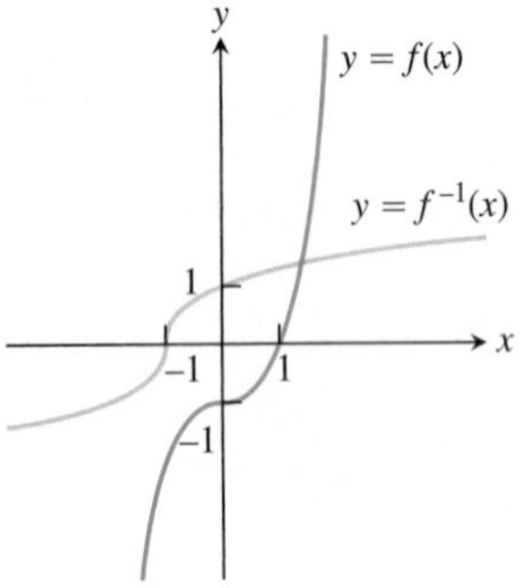

16. $f(x) = x^2 - 2x + 1, \quad x \ge 1$

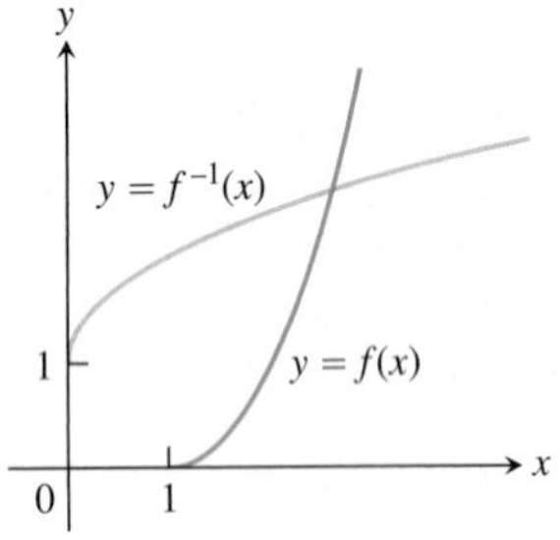

17. $f(x) = (x + 1)^2, \quad x \ge -1$

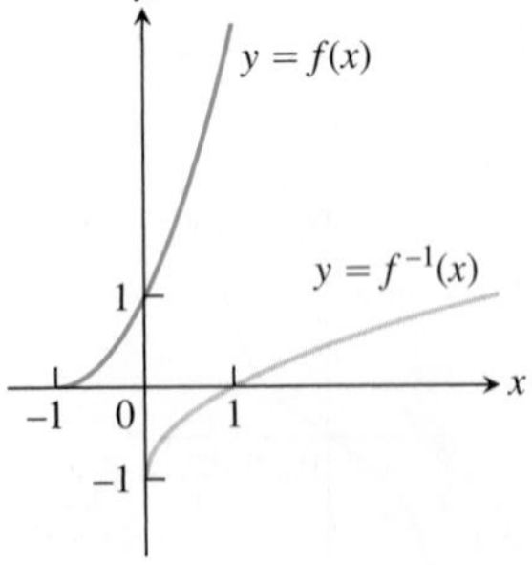

18. $f(x) = x^{2/3}, \quad x \ge 0$

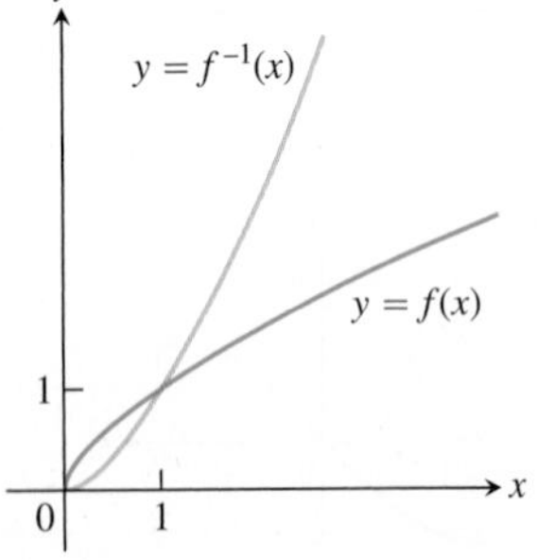

Each of Exercises 19–24 gives a formula for a function $y = f(x)$. In each case, find $f^{-1}(x)$ and identify the domain and range of f^{-1}. As a check, show that $f(f^{-1}(x)) = f^{-1}(f(x)) = x$.

19. $f(x) = x^5$

20. $f(x) = x^4, \quad x \ge 0$

21. $f(x) = x^3 + 1$

22. $f(x) = (1/2)x - 7/2$

23. $f(x) = 1/x^2, \quad x > 0$

24. $f(x) = 1/x^3, \quad x \ne 0$

25. Express the following logarithms in terms of ln 2 and ln 3.

a. $\ln 0.75$ **b.** $\ln (4/9)$

c. $\ln (1/2)$ **d.** $\ln \sqrt[3]{9}$

e. $\ln 3\sqrt{2}$ **f.** $\ln \sqrt{13.5}$

26. Express the following logarithms in terms of ln 5 and ln 7.

a. $\ln (1/125)$ **b.** $\ln 9.8$

c. $\ln 7\sqrt{7}$ **d.** $\ln 1225$

e. $\ln 0.056$ **f.** $(\ln 35 + \ln (1/7))/(\ln 25)$

Use the properties of logarithms to simplify the expressions in Exercises 27 and 28.

27. a. $\ln \sin \theta - \ln \left(\dfrac{\sin \theta}{5}\right)$ **b.** $\ln (3x^2 - 9x) + \ln \left(\dfrac{1}{3x}\right)$

c. $\dfrac{1}{2}\ln (4t^4) - \ln 2$

28. a. $\ln \sec \theta + \ln \cos \theta$ **b.** $\ln (8x + 4) - 2 \ln 2$

c. $3 \ln \sqrt[3]{t^2 - 1} - \ln (t + 1)$

Find simpler expressions for the quantities in Exercises 29–32.

29. a. $e^{\ln 7.2}$ **b.** $e^{-\ln x^2}$ **c.** $e^{\ln x - \ln y}$

30. a. $e^{\ln (x^2+y^2)}$ **b.** $e^{-\ln 0.3}$ **c.** $e^{\ln \pi x - \ln 2}$

31. a. $2 \ln \sqrt{e}$ **b.** $\ln (\ln e^e)$ **c.** $\ln (e^{-x^2-y^2})$

32. a. $\ln (e^{\sec \theta})$ **b.** $\ln (e^{(e^x)})$ **c.** $\ln (e^{2 \ln x})$

In Exercises 33–38, solve for y in terms of t or x, as appropriate.

33. $\ln y = 2t + 4$

34. $\ln y = -t + 5$

35. $\ln (y - 40) = 5t$

36. $\ln (1 - 2y) = t$

37. $\ln (y - 1) - \ln 2 = x + \ln x$

38. $\ln (y^2 - 1) - \ln (y + 1) = \ln (\sin x)$

In Exercises 39 and 40, solve for k.

39. a. $e^{2k} = 4$ **b.** $100e^{10k} = 200$ **c.** $e^{k/1000} = a$

40. a. $e^{5k} = \dfrac{1}{4}$ **b.** $80e^k = 1$ **c.** $e^{(\ln 0.8)k} = 0.8$

In Exercises 41–44, solve for t.

41. a. $e^{-0.3t} = 27$ **b.** $e^{kt} = \dfrac{1}{2}$ **c.** $e^{(\ln 0.2)t} = 0.4$

42. a. $e^{-0.01t} = 1000$ **b.** $e^{kt} = \dfrac{1}{10}$ **c.** $e^{(\ln 2)t} = \dfrac{1}{2}$

43. $e^{\sqrt{t}} = x^2$

44. $e^{(x^2)}e^{(2x+1)} = e^t$

Simplify the expressions in Exercises 45–48.

45. **a.** $5^{\log_5 7}$ **b.** $8^{\log_8 \sqrt{2}}$ **c.** $1.3^{\log_{1.3} 75}$

d. $\log_4 16$ **e.** $\log_3 \sqrt{3}$ **f.** $\log_4 \left(\frac{1}{4}\right)$

46. **a.** $2^{\log_2 3}$ **b.** $10^{\log_{10} (1/2)}$ **c.** $\pi^{\log_\pi 7}$

d. $\log_{11} 121$ **e.** $\log_{121} 11$ **f.** $\log_3 \left(\frac{1}{9}\right)$

47. **a.** $2^{\log_4 x}$ **b.** $9^{\log_3 x}$ **c.** $\log_2 (e^{(\ln 2)(\sin x)})$

48. **a.** $25^{\log_5 (3x^2)}$ **b.** $\log_e (e^x)$ **c.** $\log_4 (2^{e^x \sin x})$

Express the ratios in Exercises 49 and 50 as ratios of natural logarithms and simplify.

49. **a.** $\dfrac{\log_2 x}{\log_3 x}$ **b.** $\dfrac{\log_2 x}{\log_8 x}$ **c.** $\dfrac{\log_x a}{\log_{x^2} a}$

50. **a.** $\dfrac{\log_9 x}{\log_3 x}$ **b.** $\dfrac{\log_{\sqrt{10}} x}{\log_{\sqrt{2}} x}$ **c.** $\dfrac{\log_a b}{\log_b a}$

In Exercises 51–54, find the exact value of each expression.

51. **a.** $\sin^{-1}\left(\frac{-1}{2}\right)$ **b.** $\sin^{-1}\left(\frac{1}{\sqrt{2}}\right)$ **c.** $\sin^{-1}\left(\frac{-\sqrt{3}}{2}\right)$

52. **a.** $\cos^{-1}\left(\frac{1}{2}\right)$ **b.** $\cos^{-1}\left(\frac{-1}{\sqrt{2}}\right)$ **c.** $\cos^{-1}\left(\frac{\sqrt{3}}{2}\right)$

53. **a.** $\arccos(-1)$ **b.** $\arccos(0)$

54. **a.** $\arcsin(-1)$ **b.** $\arcsin\left(-\frac{1}{\sqrt{2}}\right)$

55. If $f(x)$ is one-to-one, can anything be said about $g(x) = -f(x)$? Is it also one-to-one? Give reasons for your answer.

56. If $f(x)$ is one-to-one and $f(x)$ is never zero, can anything be said about $h(x) = 1/f(x)$? Is it also one-to-one? Give reasons for your answer.

57. Suppose that the range of g lies in the domain of f so that the composite $f \circ g$ is defined. If f and g are one-to-one, can anything be said about $f \circ g$? Give reasons for your answer.

58. If a composite $f \circ g$ is one-to-one, must g be one-to-one? Give reasons for your answer.

59. Find a formula for the inverse function f^{-1} and verify that $(f \circ f^{-1})(x) = (f^{-1} \circ f)(x) = x$.

a. $f(x) = \dfrac{100}{1 + 2^{-x}}$ **b.** $f(x) = \dfrac{50}{1 + 1.1^{-x}}$

60. Inverse functions Let $y = f(x) = mx + b, m \neq 0$.

a. Give a convincing argument that f is a one-to-one function.

b. Find a formula for the inverse of f. How are the slopes of the graphs of f and f^{-1} related?

c. If the graphs of two functions are parallel lines with a nonzero slope, what can you say about the graphs of the inverses of the functions?

d. If the graphs of two functions are perpendicular lines with a nonzero slope, what can you say about the graphs of the inverses of the functions?

61. Radioactive decay The half-life of a certain radioactive substance is 12 hours. There are 8 grams present initially.

a. Express the amount of substance remaining as a function of time t.

b. When will there be 1 gram remaining?

62. Doubling your money Determine how much time is required for a \$500 investment to double in value if interest is earned at the rate of 4.75% compounded annually.

63. Population growth The population of Glenbrook is 375,000 and is increasing at the rate of 2.25% per year. Predict when the population will be 1 million.

64. Radon-222 The decay equation for radon-222 gas is known to be $y = y_0 e^{-0.18t}$, with t in days. About how long will it take the radon in a sealed sample of air to fall to 90% of its original value?

T **65.** The equation $x^2 = 2^x$ has three solutions: $x = 2, x = 4$, and one other. Estimate the third solution as accurately as you can by graphing.

T **66.** Could $x^{\ln 2}$ possibly be the same as $2^{\ln x}$ for $x > 0$? Graph the two functions and explain what you see.

67. Start with the graph of $y = \ln x$. Find an equation of the graph that results from

a. shifting down 3 units.

b. shifting right 1 unit.

c. shifting left 1, up 3 units.

d. shifting down 4, right 2 units.

e. reflecting about the y-axis.

f. reflecting about the line $y = x$.

68. Start with the graph of $y = \ln x$. Find an equation of the graph that results from

a. vertical stretching by a factor of 2.

b. horizontal stretching by a factor of 3.

c. vertical compression by a factor of 4.

d. horizontal compression by a factor of 2.

69. Prove that $\cos(\sin^{-1} x) = \sqrt{1 - x^2}$.

70. The identity $\sin^{-1} x + \cos^{-1} x = \pi/2$ Figure 1.64 establishes the identity for $0 < x < 1$. To establish it for the rest of $[-1, 1]$, verify by direct calculation that it holds for $x = 1$, 0, and -1. Then, for values of x in $(-1, 0)$, let $x = -a, a > 0$, and apply Eqs. (2) and (4) to the sum $\sin^{-1}(-a) + \cos^{-1}(-a)$.

1.6 Graphing with Calculators and Computers

A graphing calculator or a computer with graphing software enables us to graph very complicated functions with high precision. Many of these functions could not otherwise be easily graphed. However, care must be taken when using such devices for graphing purposes, and in this section we address some of the issues involved. In Chapter 4 we will see how calculus helps us determine that we are accurately viewing all the important features of a function's graph.

Graphing Windows

When using a graphing calculator or computer as a graphing tool, a portion of the graph is displayed in a rectangular **display** or **viewing window**. Often the default window gives an incomplete or misleading picture of the graph. We use the term *square window* when the units or scales on both axes are the same. This term does not mean that the display window itself is square (usually it is rectangular), but instead it means that the x-unit is the same as the y-unit.

When a graph is displayed in the default window, the x-unit may differ from the y-unit of scaling in order to fit the graph in the window. The viewing window is set by specifying an interval $[a, b]$ for the x-values and an interval $[c, d]$ for the y-values. The machine selects equally spaced x-values in $[a, b]$ and then plots the points $(x, f(x))$. A point is plotted if and only if x lies in the domain of the function and $f(x)$ lies within the interval $[c, d]$. A short line segment is then drawn between each plotted point and its next neighboring point. We now give illustrative examples of some common problems that may occur with this procedure.

EXAMPLE 1 Graph the function $f(x) = x^3 - 7x^2 + 28$ in each of the following display or viewing windows:

(a) $[-10, 10]$ by $[-10, 10]$ **(b)** $[-4, 4]$ by $[-50, 10]$ **(c)** $[-4, 10]$ by $[-60, 60]$

Solution

(a) We select $a = -10$, $b = 10$, $c = -10$, and $d = 10$ to specify the interval of x-values and the range of y-values for the window. The resulting graph is shown in Figure 1.65a. It appears that the window is cutting off the bottom part of the graph and that the interval of x-values is too large. Let's try the next window.

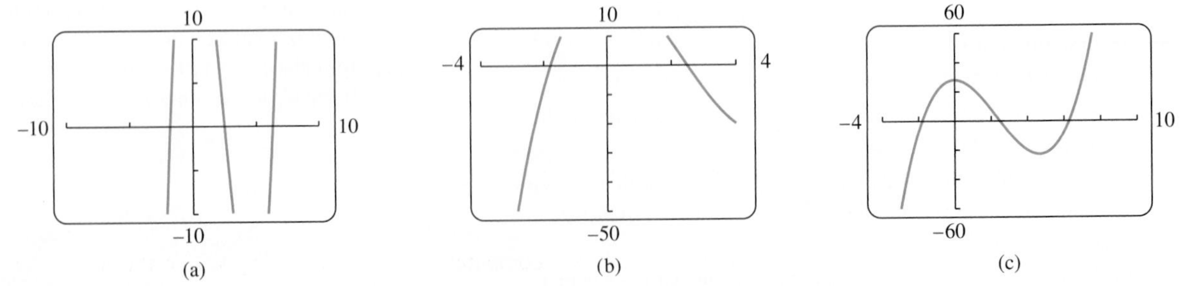

FIGURE 1.65 The graph of $f(x) = x^3 - 7x^2 + 28$ in different viewing windows. Selecting a window giving a clear picture of a graph is often a trial-and-error process (Example 1).

(b) Now we see more features of the graph (Figure 1.65b), but the top is missing and we need to view more to the right of $x = 4$ as well. The next window should help.

(c) Figure 1.65c shows the graph in this new viewing window. Observe that we get a more complete picture of the graph in this window and it is a reasonable graph of a third-degree polynomial. ■

EXAMPLE 2 When a graph is displayed, the x-unit may differ from the y-unit, as in the graphs shown in Figures 1.65b and 1.65c. The result is distortion in the picture, which may be misleading. The display window can be made square by compressing or stretching the units on one axis to match the scale on the other, giving the true graph. Many systems have built-in functions to make the window "square." If yours does not, you will have to do some calculations and set the window size manually to get a square window, or bring to your viewing some foreknowledge of the true picture.

Figure 1.66a shows the graphs of the perpendicular lines $y = x$ and $y = -x + 3\sqrt{2}$, together with the semicircle $y = \sqrt{9 - x^2}$, in a nonsquare $[-6, 6]$ by $[-6, 8]$ display window. Notice the distortion. The lines do not appear to be perpendicular, and the semicircle appears to be elliptical in shape.

Figure 1.66b shows the graphs of the same functions in a square window in which the x-units are scaled to be the same as the y-units. Notice that the $[-6, 6]$ by $[-4, 4]$ viewing window has the same x-axis in both figures, but the scaling on the x-axis has been compressed in Figure 1.66b to make the window square. Figure 1.66c gives an enlarged view with a square $[-3, 3]$ by $[0, 4]$ window. ■

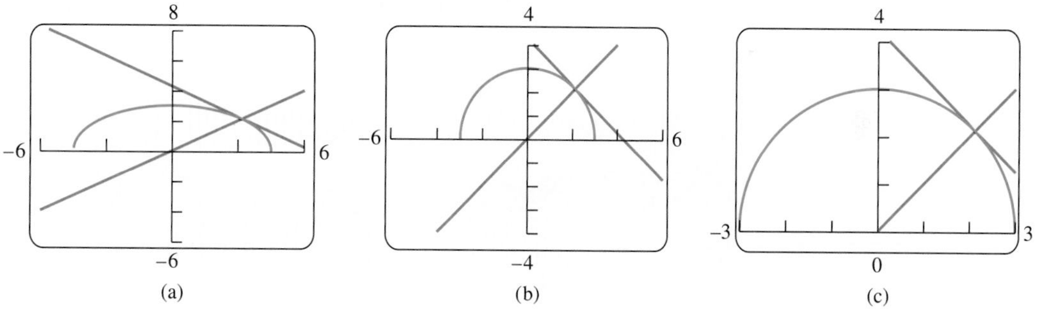

FIGURE 1.66 Graphs of the perpendicular lines $y = x$ and $y = -x + 3\sqrt{2}$, and the semicircle $y = \sqrt{9 - x^2}$ appear (a) distorted in a nonsquare window, but clear in (b) and (c) square windows (Example 2).

If the denominator of a rational function is zero at some x-value within the viewing window, a calculator or graphing computer software may produce a steep near-vertical line segment from the top to the bottom of the window. Here is an example.

EXAMPLE 3 Graph the function $y = \dfrac{1}{2 - x}$.

Solution Figure 1.67a shows the graph in the $[-10, 10]$ by $[-10, 10]$ default square window with our computer graphing software. Notice the near-vertical line segment at $x = 2$. It is not truly a part of the graph and $x = 2$ does not belong to the domain of the function. By trial and error we can eliminate the line by changing the viewing window to the smaller $[-6, 6]$ by $[-4, 4]$ view, revealing a better graph (Figure 1.67b). ■

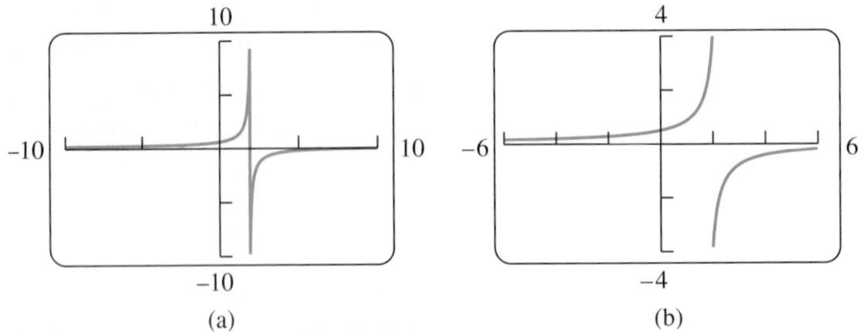

FIGURE 1.67 Graphs of the function $y = \dfrac{1}{2 - x}$. A vertical line may appear without a careful choice of the viewing window (Example 3).

Sometimes the graph of a trigonometric function oscillates very rapidly. When a calculator or computer software plots the points of the graph and connects them, many of the maximum and minimum points are actually missed. The resulting graph is then very misleading.

EXAMPLE 4 Graph the function $f(x) = \sin 100x$.

Solution Figure 1.68a shows the graph of f in the viewing window $[-12, 12]$ by $[-1, 1]$. We see that the graph looks very strange because the sine curve should oscillate periodically between -1 and 1. This behavior is not exhibited in Figure 1.68a. We might experiment with a smaller viewing window, say $[-6, 6]$ by $[-1, 1]$, but the graph is not better (Figure 1.68b). The difficulty is that the period of the trigonometric function

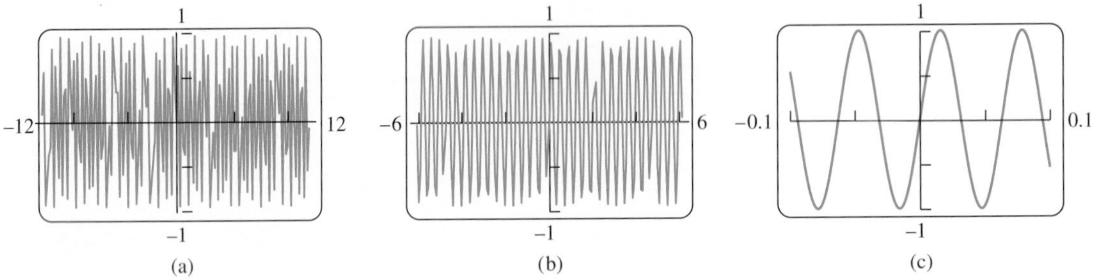

FIGURE 1.68 Graphs of the function $y = \sin 100x$ in three viewing windows. Because the period is $2\pi/100 \approx 0.063$, the smaller window in (c) best displays the true aspects of this rapidly oscillating function (Example 4).

$y = \sin 100x$ is very small $(2\pi/100 \approx 0.063)$. If we choose the much smaller viewing window $[-0.1, 0.1]$ by $[-1, 1]$ we get the graph shown in Figure 1.68c. This graph reveals the expected oscillations of a sine curve. ■

EXAMPLE 5 Graph the function $y = \cos x + \dfrac{1}{50}\sin 50x$.

Solution In the viewing window $[-6, 6]$ by $[-1, 1]$ the graph appears much like the cosine function with some small sharp wiggles on it (Figure 1.69a). We get a better look when we significantly reduce the window to $[-0.6, 0.6]$ by $[0.8, 1.02]$, obtaining the graph in Figure 1.69b. We now see the small but rapid oscillations of the second term, $1/50 \sin 50x$, added to the comparatively larger values of the cosine curve. ■

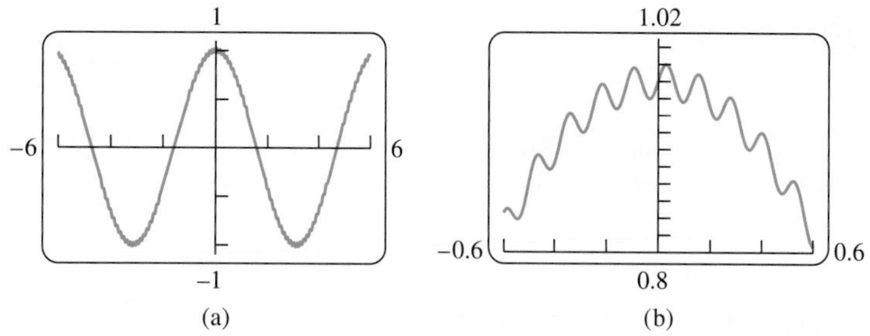

FIGURE 1.69 In (b) we see a close-up view of the function $y = \cos x + \frac{1}{50}\sin 50x$ graphed in (a). The term $\cos x$ clearly dominates the second term, $\frac{1}{50}\sin 50x$, which produces the rapid oscillations along the cosine curve. Both views are needed for a clear idea of the graph (Example 5).

EXAMPLE 6 Graph the function $y = x^{1/3}$.

Solution Some graphing devices display the graph shown in Figure 1.70a. When we compare it with the graph of $y = x^{1/3} = \sqrt[3]{x}$ in Figure 1.15, we see that the left branch for $x < 0$ is missing. The reason the graphs differ is that many calculators and computer software programs calculate $x^{1/3}$ as $e^{(1/3)\ln x}$. Since the logarithmic function is not defined for negative values of x, the computing device can only produce the right branch where $x > 0$.

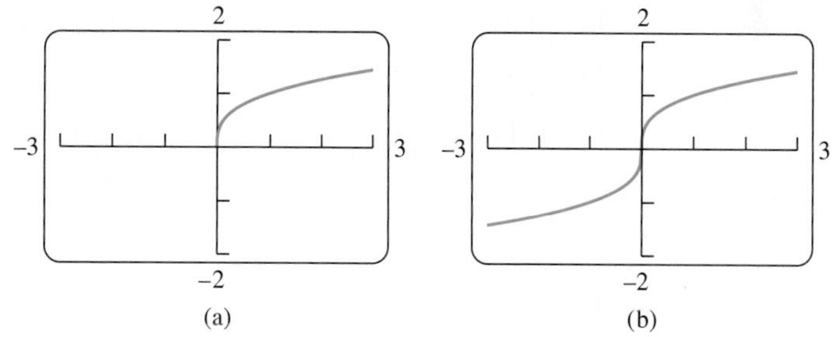

FIGURE 1.70 The graph of $y = x^{1/3}$ is missing the left branch in (a). In (b) we graph the function $f(x) = \frac{x}{|x|}\cdot|x|^{1/3}$ obtaining both branches. (See Example 6.).

To obtain the full picture showing both branches, we can graph the function

$$f(x) = \frac{x}{|x|}\cdot|x|^{1/3}.$$

This function equals $x^{1/3}$ except at $x = 0$ (where f is undefined, although $0^{1/3} = 0$). The graph of f is shown in Figure 1.70b. ■

EXERCISES 1.6

T In Exercises 1–4, use a graphing calculator or computer to determine which of the given viewing windows displays the most appropriate graph of the specified function.

1. $f(x) = x^4 - 7x^2 + 6x$
   a. $[-1, 1]$ by $[-1, 1]$ b. $[-2, 2]$ by $[-5, 5]$
   c. $[-10, 10]$ by $[-10, 10]$ d. $[-5, 5]$ by $[-25, 15]$
2. $f(x) = x^3 - 4x^2 - 4x + 16$
   a. $[-1, 1]$ by $[-5, 5]$ b. $[-3, 3]$ by $[-10, 10]$
   c. $[-5, 5]$ by $[-10, 20]$ d. $[-20, 20]$ by $[-100, 100]$
3. $f(x) = 5 + 12x - x^3$
   a. $[-1, 1]$ by $[-1, 1]$ b. $[-5, 5]$ by $[-10, 10]$
   c. $[-4, 4]$ by $[-20, 20]$ d. $[-4, 5]$ by $[-15, 25]$
4. $f(x) = \sqrt{5 + 4x - x^2}$
   a. $[-2, 2]$ by $[-2, 2]$ b. $[-2, 6]$ by $[-1, 4]$
   c. $[-3, 7]$ by $[0, 10]$ d. $[-10, 10]$ by $[-10, 10]$

T In Exercises 5–30, determine an appropriate viewing window for the given function and use it to display its graph.

5. $f(x) = x^4 - 4x^3 + 15$
6. $f(x) = \frac{x^3}{3} - \frac{x^2}{2} - 2x + 1$
7. $f(x) = x^5 - 5x^4 + 10$
8. $f(x) = 4x^3 - x^4$
9. $f(x) = x\sqrt{9 - x^2}$
10. $f(x) = x^2(6 - x^3)$
11. $y = 2x - 3x^{2/3}$
12. $y = x^{1/3}(x^2 - 8)$
13. $y = 5x^{2/5} - 2x$
14. $y = x^{2/3}(5 - x)$
15. $y = |x^2 - 1|$
16. $y = |x^2 - x|$
17. $y = \frac{x + 3}{x + 2}$
18. $y = 1 - \frac{1}{x + 3}$
19. $f(x) = \frac{x^2 + 2}{x^2 + 1}$
20. $f(x) = \frac{x^2 - 1}{x^2 + 1}$
21. $f(x) = \frac{x - 1}{x^2 - x - 6}$
22. $f(x) = \frac{8}{x^2 - 9}$
23. $f(x) = \frac{6x^2 - 15x + 6}{4x^2 - 10x}$
24. $f(x) = \frac{x^2 - 3}{x - 2}$
25. $y = \sin 250x$
26. $y = 3\cos 60x$
27. $y = \cos\left(\frac{x}{50}\right)$
28. $y = \frac{1}{10}\sin\left(\frac{x}{10}\right)$
29. $y = x + \frac{1}{10}\sin 30x$
30. $y = x^2 + \frac{1}{50}\cos 100x$
31. Graph the lower half of the circle defined by the equation $x^2 + 2x = 4 + 4y - y^2$.
32. Graph the upper branch of the hyperbola $y^2 - 16x^2 = 1$.
33. Graph four periods of the function $f(x) = -\tan 2x$.
34. Graph two periods of the function $f(x) = 3\cot\frac{x}{2} + 1$.
35. Graph the function $f(x) = \sin 2x + \cos 3x$.
36. Graph the function $f(x) = \sin^3 x$.

T Another way to avoid incorrect connections when using a graphing device is through the use of a "dot mode," which plots only the points. If your graphing utility allows that mode, use it to plot the functions in Exercises 37–40.

37. $y = \frac{1}{x - 3}$
38. $y = \sin\frac{1}{x}$
39. $y = x\lfloor x \rfloor$
40. $y = \frac{x^3 - 1}{x^2 - 1}$

T Use a graphing calculator or computer to graph the functions specified in Exercises 41–50.

41. $y = e^x + e^{-x}$
42. $y = e^x - e^{-x}$
43. $y = e^{-x}\sin x$
44. $y = e^{-2x}\cos\frac{x}{2}$
45. $y = e^{x^3 - x}$
46. $y = e^{\sin x}$
47. $y = \frac{e^x}{x^2}$
48. $y = xe^{-x}$
49. $y = x\ln x$
50. $y = \frac{\ln x}{\sqrt{x}}$

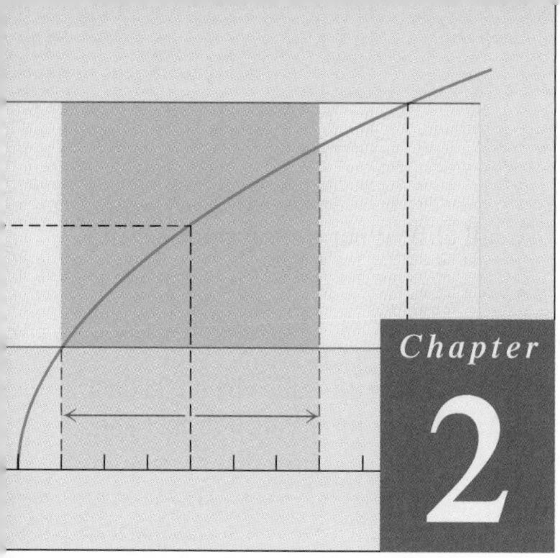

Chapter 2 LIMITS AND CONTINUITY

OVERVIEW The concept of a limit is fundamental to finding the velocity of a moving object and the tangent to a curve. In this chapter we develop the limit, first intuitively and then formally. Limits are used to describe the way a function varies. Some functions vary *continuously*; small changes in x produce only small changes in $f(x)$. Other functions can have values that jump, vary erratically, or tend to increase or decrease without bound. The notion of limit gives a precise way to distinguish between these behaviors.

2.1 Rates of Change and Tangents to Curves

In this section we look at average and instantaneous rates of change, ideas that are closely related to the slope of a curve at a point P on the curve. These concepts lead naturally to the main idea of this chapter, the limit. At the end of this chapter, we return to the topics of instantaneous rates of change and slopes of curves and see how limits enable us to calculate them.

Average and Instantaneous Speed

HISTORICAL BIOGRAPHY*

Galileo Galilei
(1564–1642)

In the late sixteenth century, Galileo discovered that a solid object dropped from rest (not moving), near the surface of the earth and allowed to fall freely, will fall a distance proportional to the square of the time it has been falling. This type of motion is called **free fall**. It assumes negligible air resistance to slow the object down, and that gravity is the only force acting on the falling body. If y denotes the distance fallen in feet after t seconds, then Galileo's law is

$$y = 16t^2,$$

where 16 is the constant of proportionality. (If y is measured in meters, the constant is 4.9.)

A moving body's **average speed** during an interval of time is found by dividing the distance covered by the time elapsed. The unit of measure is length per unit time: kilometers per hour, feet (or meters) per second, or whatever is appropriate to the problem at hand.

---

*To learn more about the historical figures and the development of the major elements and topics of calculus, visit **www.aw-bc.com/thomas**.

EXAMPLE 1 A rock breaks loose from the top of a tall cliff. What is its average speed

(a) during the first 2 sec of fall?

(b) during the 1-sec interval between second 1 and second 2?

Solution The average speed of the rock during a given time interval is the change in distance, Δy, divided by the length of the time interval, Δt. Measuring distance in feet and time in seconds, we have the following calculations:

(a) For the first 2 sec: $\dfrac{\Delta y}{\Delta t} = \dfrac{16(2)^2 - 16(0)^2}{2 - 0} = 32\,\dfrac{\text{ft}}{\text{sec}}$

(b) From sec 1 to sec 2: $\dfrac{\Delta y}{\Delta t} = \dfrac{16(2)^2 - 16(1)^2}{2 - 1} = 48\,\dfrac{\text{ft}}{\text{sec}}$ ■

The next example examines what happens when we look at the average speed of a falling object over shorter and shorter time intervals. Our discussion is informal here, but will be made precise in Chapter 3.

EXAMPLE 2 Find the speed of the falling rock at $t = 1$ and $t = 2$ sec.

Solution We can calculate the average speed of the rock over a time interval $[t_0, t_0 + h]$, having length $\Delta t = h$, as

$$\frac{\Delta y}{\Delta t} = \frac{16(t_0 + h)^2 - 16t_0^{\,2}}{h}. \tag{1}$$

We cannot use this formula to calculate the "instantaneous" speed at t_0 by substituting $h = 0$, because we cannot divide by zero. But we *can* use it to calculate average speeds over increasingly short time intervals starting at $t_0 = 1$ and $t_0 = 2$. When we do so, we see a pattern (Table 2.1).

TABLE 2.1 Average speeds over short time intervals

Average speed: $\dfrac{\Delta y}{\Delta t} = \dfrac{16(t_0 + h)^2 - 16t_0^{\,2}}{h}$

Length of time interval h	Average speed over interval of length h starting at $t_0 = 1$	Average speed over interval of length h starting at $t_0 = 2$
1	48	80
0.1	33.6	65.6
0.01	32.16	64.16
0.001	32.016	64.016
0.0001	32.0016	64.0016

The average speed on intervals starting at $t_0 = 1$ seems to approach a limiting value of 32 as the length of the interval decreases. This suggests that the rock is falling at a speed of 32 ft/sec at $t_0 = 1$ sec. Let's confirm this algebraically.

If we set $t_0 = 1$ and then expand the numerator in Equation (1) and simplify, we find that

$$\frac{\Delta y}{\Delta t} = \frac{16(1 + h)^2 - 16(1)^2}{h} = \frac{16(1 + 2h + h^2) - 16}{h}$$

$$= \frac{32h + 16h^2}{h} = 32 + 16h.$$

For values of h different from 0, the expressions on the right and left are equivalent and the average speed is $32 + 16h$ ft/sec. We can now see why the average speed has the limiting value $32 + 16(0) = 32$ ft/sec as h approaches 0.

Similarly, setting $t_0 = 2$ in Equation (1), the procedure yields

$$\frac{\Delta y}{\Delta t} = 64 + 16h$$

for values of h different from 0. As h gets closer and closer to 0, the average speed has the limiting value 64 ft/sec when $t_0 = 2$ sec. ■

Average Rates of Change and Secant Lines

Given an arbitrary function $y = f(x)$, we calculate the average rate of change of y with respect to x over the interval $[x_1, x_2]$ by dividing the change in the value of y, $\Delta y = f(x_2) - f(x_1)$, by the length $\Delta x = x_2 - x_1 = h$ of the interval over which the change occurs.

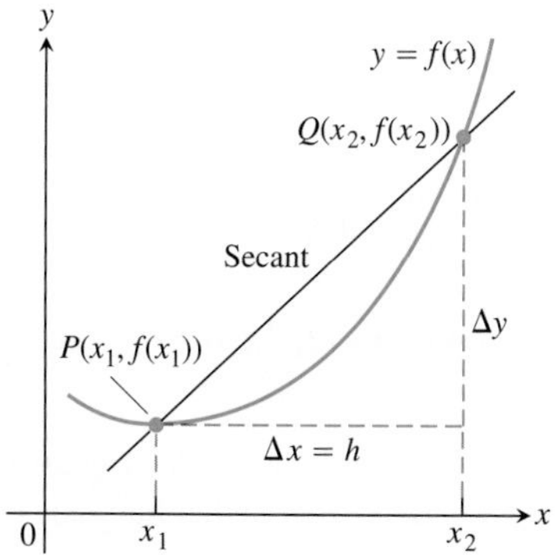

FIGURE 2.1 A secant to the graph $y = f(x)$. Its slope is $\Delta y/\Delta x$, the average rate of change of f over the interval $[x_1, x_2]$.

DEFINITION The **average rate of change** of $y = f(x)$ with respect to x over the interval $[x_1, x_2]$ is

$$\frac{\Delta y}{\Delta x} = \frac{f(x_2) - f(x_1)}{x_2 - x_1} = \frac{f(x_1 + h) - f(x_1)}{h}, \qquad h \neq 0.$$

Geometrically, the rate of change of f over $[x_1, x_2]$ is the slope of the line through the points $P(x_1, f(x_1))$ and $Q(x_2, f(x_2))$ (Figure 2.1). In geometry, a line joining two points of a curve is a **secant** to the curve. Thus, the average rate of change of f from x_1 to x_2 is identical with the slope of secant PQ. Let's consider what happens as the point Q approaches the point P along the curve, so the length h of the interval over which the change occurs approaches zero.

Slope of a Curve

We know what is meant by the slope of a straight line, which tells us the rate at which it rises or falls—its rate of change as the graph of a linear function. But what is meant by the *slope of a curve* at a point P on the curve? If there is a *tangent* line to the curve at P—a line that just touches the curve like the tangent to a circle—it would be reasonable to identify *the slope of the tangent* as the slope of the curve at P. So we need a precise meaning for the tangent at a point on a curve.

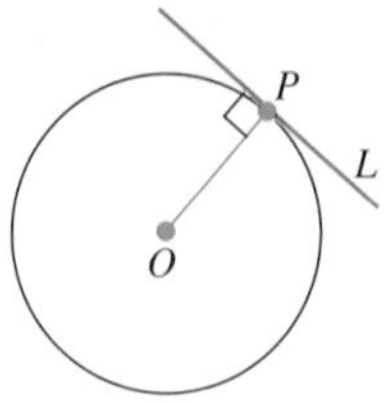

FIGURE 2.2 L is tangent to the circle at P if it passes through P perpendicular to radius OP.

HISTORICAL BIOGRAPHY

Pierre de Fermat
(1601–1665)

For circles, tangency is straightforward. A line L is tangent to a circle at a point P if L passes through P perpendicular to the radius at P (Figure 2.2). Such a line just *touches* the circle. But what does it mean to say that a line L is tangent to some other curve C at a point P?

To define tangency for general curves, we need an approach that takes into account the behavior of the secants through P and nearby points Q as Q moves toward P along the curve (Figure 2.3). It goes like this:

1. We start with what we *can* calculate, namely the slope of the secant PQ.
2. Investigate the limiting value of the secant slope as Q approaches P along the curve.
3. If the *limit* exists, take it to be the slope of the curve at P and define the tangent to the curve at P to be the line through P with this slope.

This procedure is what we were doing in the falling-rock problem discussed above. The next example illustrates the geometric idea.

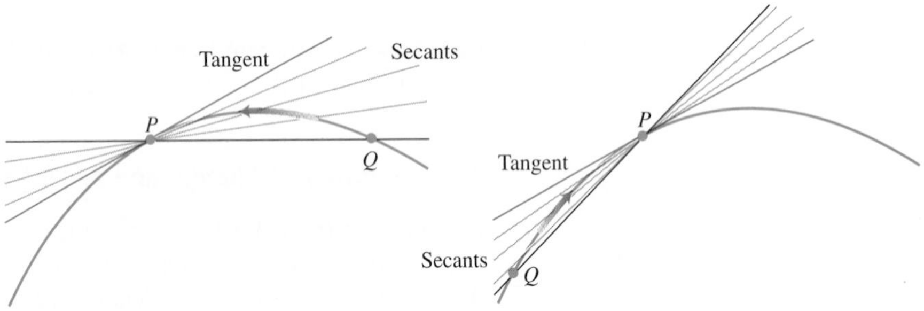

FIGURE 2.3 The tangent to the curve at P is the line through P whose slope is the limit of the secant slopes as $Q \to P$ from either side.

EXAMPLE 3 Find the slope of the parabola $y = x^2$ at the point $P(2, 4)$. Write an equation for the tangent to the parabola at this point.

Solution We begin with a secant line through $P(2, 4)$ and $Q(2 + h, (2 + h)^2)$ nearby. We then write an expression for the slope of the secant PQ and investigate what happens to the slope as Q approaches P along the curve:

$$\text{Secant slope} = \frac{\Delta y}{\Delta x} = \frac{(2 + h)^2 - 2^2}{h} = \frac{h^2 + 4h + 4 - 4}{h}$$

$$= \frac{h^2 + 4h}{h} = h + 4.$$

If $h > 0$, then Q lies above and to the right of P, as in Figure 2.4. If $h < 0$, then Q lies to the left of P (not shown). In either case, as Q approaches P along the curve, h approaches zero and the secant slope approaches 4:

As h approaches 0, the sum $(h + 4)$ approaches the limiting value 4.

We take 4 to be the parabola's slope at P.

The tangent to the parabola at P is the line through P with slope 4:

$$y = 4 + 4(x - 2) \qquad \text{Point-slope equation}$$

$$y = 4x - 4.$$

■

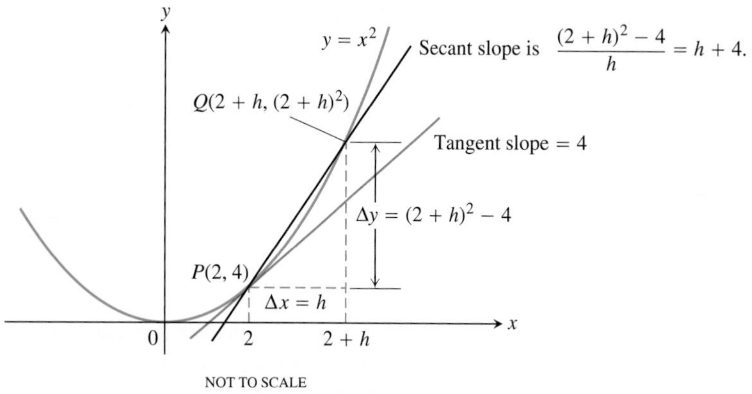

FIGURE 2.4 Finding the slope of the parabola $y = x^2$ at the point $P(2, 4)$ as the limit of secant slopes (Example 3).

Instantaneous Rates of Change

The rates at which the rock in Example 2 was falling at the instants $t = 1$ and $t = 2$ are called *instantaneous rates of change*. Instantaneous rates and slopes of tangent lines are intimately connected, as we will now see in the following examples.

EXAMPLE 4 Figure 2.5 shows how a population of fruit flies (*Drosophila*) grew in a 50-day experiment. The number of flies was counted at regular intervals, the counted values plotted with respect to time, and the points joined by a smooth curve (colored blue in Figure 2.5). Find the average growth rate from day 23 to day 45.

Solution There were 150 flies on day 23 and 340 flies on day 45. Thus the number of flies increased by $340 - 150 = 190$ in $45 - 23 = 22$ days. The average rate of change of the population from day 23 to day 45 was

$$\text{Average rate of change: } \frac{\Delta p}{\Delta t} = \frac{340 - 150}{45 - 23} = \frac{190}{22} \approx 8.6 \text{ flies/day}.$$

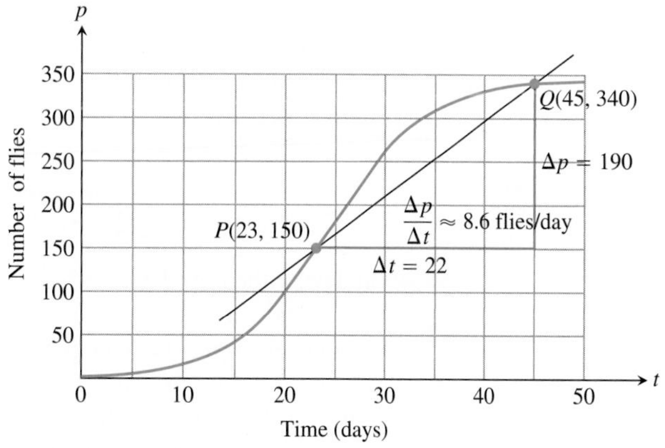

FIGURE 2.5 Growth of a fruit fly population in a controlled experiment. The average rate of change over 22 days is the slope $\Delta p/\Delta t$ of the secant line (Example 4).

This average is the slope of the secant through the points P and Q on the graph in Figure 2.5. ■

The average rate of change from day 23 to day 45 calculated in Example 4 does not tell us how fast the population was changing on day 23 itself. For that we need to examine time intervals closer to the day in question.

EXAMPLE 5 How fast was the number of flies in the population of Example 4 growing on day 23?

Solution To answer this question, we examine the average rates of change over increasingly short time intervals starting at day 23. In geometric terms, we find these rates by calculating the slopes of secants from P to Q, for a sequence of points Q approaching P along the curve (Figure 2.6).

Q	Slope of $PQ = \Delta p/\Delta t$ (flies/day)
(45, 340)	$\frac{340 - 150}{45 - 23} \approx 8.6$
(40, 330)	$\frac{330 - 150}{40 - 23} \approx 10.6$
(35, 310)	$\frac{310 - 150}{35 - 23} \approx 13.3$
(30, 265)	$\frac{265 - 150}{30 - 23} \approx 16.4$

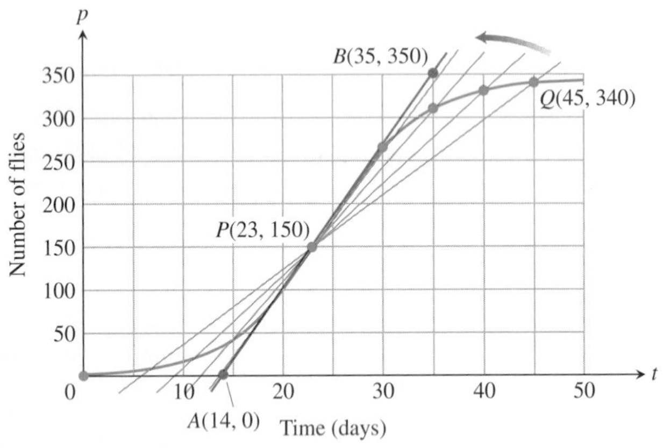

FIGURE 2.6 The positions and slopes of four secants through the point P on the fruit fly graph (Example 5).

The values in the table show that the secant slopes rise from 8.6 to 16.4 as the t-coordinate of Q decreases from 45 to 30, and we would expect the slopes to rise slightly higher as t continued on toward 23. Geometrically, the secants rotate about P and seem to approach the red tangent line in the figure. Since the line appears to pass through the points (14, 0) and (35, 350), it has slope

$$\frac{350 - 0}{35 - 14} = 16.7 \text{ flies/day (approximately).}$$

On day 23 the population was increasing at a rate of about 16.7 flies/day. ■

Our examples have suggested the limit idea. Instantaneous rates are limiting values of average rates; the slope of the tangent line to a curve at a point equals the limiting values of the slopes of the associated secant lines. Instantaneous rates and tangent lines appear in many other contexts. To talk about the two constructively, and to deepen our understanding of the connection between them, we need to investigate the process by which limiting values, or *limits*, are defined and determined. We begin their study in the next section.

EXERCISES 2.1

In Exercises 1–6, find the average rate of change of the function over the given interval or intervals.

1. $f(x) = x^3 + 1$;
   a. $[2, 3]$ b. $[-1, 1]$
2. $g(x) = x^2$;
   a. $[-1, 1]$ b. $[-2, 0]$
3. $h(t) = \cot t$;
   a. $[\pi/4, 3\pi/4]$ b. $[\pi/6, \pi/2]$
4. $g(t) = 2 + \cos t$;
   a. $[0, \pi]$ b. $[-\pi, \pi]$
5. $R(\theta) = \sqrt{4\theta + 1}$; $[0, 2]$
6. $P(\theta) = \theta^3 - 4\theta^2 + 5\theta$; $[1, 2]$
7. **Speed of a car** The accompanying figure shows the time-to-distance graph for a sports car accelerating from a standstill.

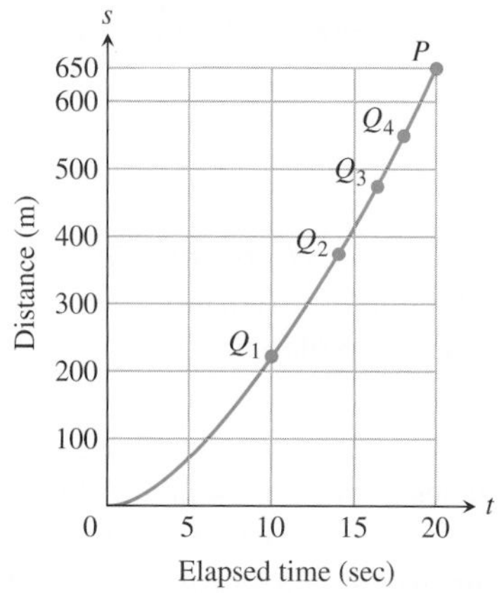

   a. Estimate the slopes of secants PQ_1, PQ_2, PQ_3, and PQ_4, arranging them in order in a table like the one in Figure 2.6. What are the appropriate units for these slopes?
   b. Then estimate the car's speed at time $t = 20$ sec.
8. The accompanying figure shows the plot of distance fallen versus time for an object that fell from the lunar landing module a distance 80 m to the surface of the moon.
   a. Estimate the slopes of the secants PQ_1, PQ_2, PQ_3, and PQ_4, arranging them in a table like the one in Figure 2.6.
   b. About how fast was the object going when it hit the surface?

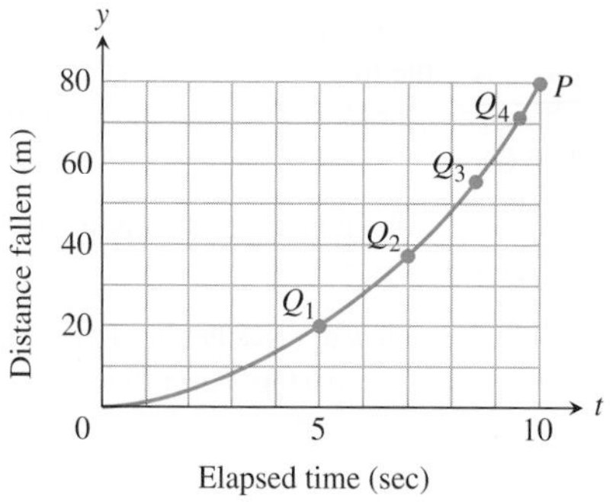

In Exercises 9–16, use the method in Example 3 to find **(a)** the slope of the curve at the given point P, and **(b)** an equation of the tangent line at P.

9. $y = x^2 - 3$, $P(2, 1)$
10. $y = 5 - x^2$, $P(1, 4)$
11. $y = x^2 - 2x - 3$, $P(2, -3)$
12. $y = x^2 - 4x$, $P(1, -3)$
13. $y = x^3$, $P(2, 8)$
14. $y = 2 - x^3$, $P(1, 1)$
15. $y = x^3 - 12x$, $P(1, -11)$
16. $y = x^3 - 3x^2 + 4$, $P(2, 0)$

T 17. The profits of a small company for each of the first five years of its operation are given in the following table:

Year	Profit in $1000s
2000	6
2001	27
2002	62
2003	111
2004	174

   a. Plot points representing the profit as a function of year, and join them by as smooth a curve as you can.
   b. What is the average rate of increase of the profits between 2002 and 2004?
   c. Use your graph to estimate the rate at which the profits were changing in 2002.

T 18. Make a table of values for the function $F(x) = (x + 2)/(x - 2)$ at the points $x = 1.2$, $x = 11/10$, $x = 101/100$, $x = 1001/1000$, $x = 10001/10000$, and $x = 1$.
   a. Find the average rate of change of $F(x)$ over the intervals $[1, x]$ for each $x \neq 1$ in your table.
   b. Extending the table if necessary, try to determine the rate of change of $F(x)$ at $x = 1$.

T **19.** Let $g(x) = \sqrt{x}$ for $x \geq 0$.

a. Find the average rate of change of $g(x)$ with respect to x over the intervals [1, 2], [1, 1.5] and $[1, 1 + h]$.

b. Make a table of values of the average rate of change of g with respect to x over the interval $[1, 1 + h]$ for some values of h approaching zero, say $h = 0.1, 0.01, 0.001, 0.0001, 0.00001$, and 0.000001.

c. What does your table indicate is the rate of change of $g(x)$ with respect to x at $x = 1$?

d. Calculate the limit as h approaches zero of the average rate of change of $g(x)$ with respect to x over the interval $[1, 1 + h]$.

T **20.** Let $f(t) = 1/t$ for $t \neq 0$.

a. Find the average rate of change of f with respect to t over the intervals (i) from $t = 2$ to $t = 3$, and (ii) from $t = 2$ to $t = T$.

b. Make a table of values of the average rate of change of f with respect to t over the interval $[2, T]$, for some values of T approaching 2, say $T = 2.1, 2.01, 2.001, 2.0001, 2.00001$, and 2.000001.

c. What does your table indicate is the rate of change of f with respect to t at $t = 2$?

d. Calculate the limit as T approaches 2 of the average rate of change of f with respect to t over the interval from 2 to T. You will have to do some algebra before you can substitute $T = 2$.

2.2 Limit of a Function and Limit Laws

In Section 2.1 we saw that limits arise when finding the instantaneous rate of change of a function or the tangent to a curve. Here we begin with an informal definition of *limit* and show how we can calculate the values of limits. A precise definition is presented in the next section.

HISTORICAL ESSAY*

Limits

Limits of Function Values

Let $f(x)$ be defined on an open interval about x_0, *except possibly at x_0 itself.* If $f(x)$ is arbitrarily close to L (as close to L as we like) for all x sufficiently close to x_0, we say that f approaches the **limit** L as x approaches x_0, and we write

$$\lim_{x \to x_0} f(x) = L,$$

which is read "the limit of $f(x)$ as x approaches x_0 is L." Essentially, the definition says that the values of $f(x)$ are close to the number L whenever x is close to x_0 (on either side of x_0). This definition is "informal" because phrases like *arbitrarily close* and *sufficiently close* are imprecise; their meaning depends on the context. To a machinist manufacturing a piston, *close* may mean *within a few thousandths of an inch*. To an astronomer studying distant galaxies, *close* may mean *within a few thousand light-years*. Nevertheless, the definition is clear enough to enable us to recognize and evaluate limits of specific functions. We will need the precise definition of Section 2.3, however, when we set out to prove theorems about limits.

EXAMPLE 1 How does the function

$$f(x) = \frac{x^2 - 1}{x - 1}$$

behave near $x = 1$?

*To learn more about the historical figures and the development of the major elements and topics of calculus, **visit www.aw-bc.com/thomas.**

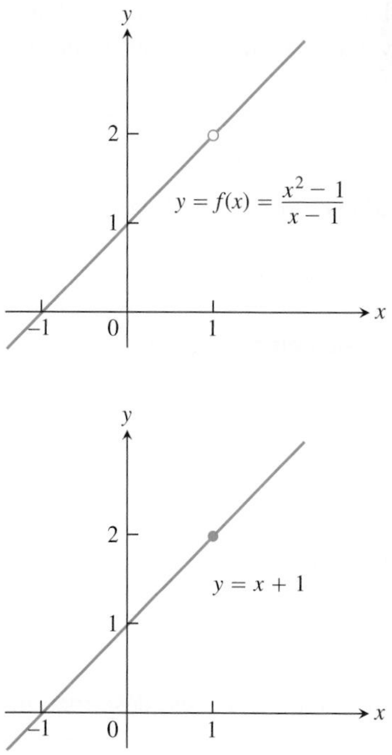

FIGURE 2.7 The graph of f is identical with the line $y = x + 1$ except at $x = 1$, where f is not defined (Example 1).

Solution The given formula defines f for all real numbers x except $x = 1$ (we cannot divide by zero). For any $x \neq 1$, we can simplify the formula by factoring the numerator and canceling common factors:

$$f(x) = \frac{(x - 1)(x + 1)}{x - 1} = x + 1 \qquad \text{for} \qquad x \neq 1.$$

The graph of f is thus the line $y = x + 1$ with the point $(1, 2)$ *removed.* This removed point is shown as a "hole" in Figure 2.7. Even though $f(1)$ is not defined, it is clear that we can make the value of $f(x)$ *as close as we want* to 2 by choosing x *close enough* to 1 (Table 2.2).

TABLE 2.2 The closer x gets to 1, the closer $f(x) = (x^2 - 1)/(x - 1)$ seems to get to 2

Values of x below and above 1	$f(x) = \frac{x^2 - 1}{x - 1} = x + 1, \quad x \neq 1$
0.9	1.9
1.1	2.1
0.99	1.99
1.01	2.01
0.999	1.999
1.001	2.001
0.999999	1.999999
1.000001	2.000001

We say that $f(x)$ approaches the *limit* 2 as x approaches 1, and write

$$\lim_{x \to 1} f(x) = 2, \qquad \text{or} \qquad \lim_{x \to 1} \frac{x^2 - 1}{x - 1} = 2.$$ ■

EXAMPLE 2 The function f in Figure 2.8 has limit 2 as $x \to 1$ even though f is not defined at $x = 1$. The function g has limit 2 as $x \to 1$ even though $2 \neq g(1)$. The function h

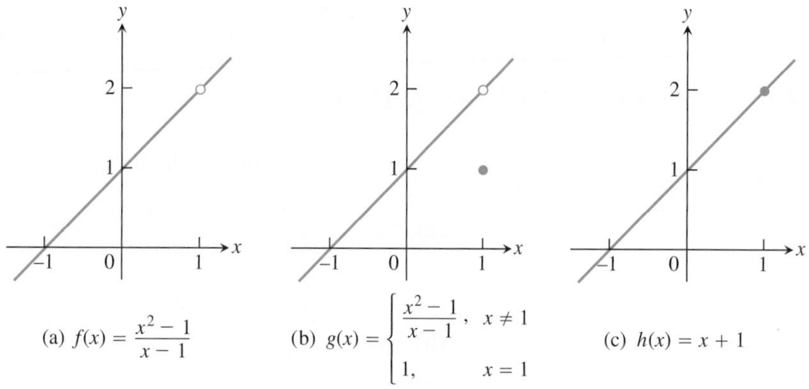

FIGURE 2.8 The limits of $f(x)$, $g(x)$, and $h(x)$ all equal 2 as x approaches 1. However, only $h(x)$ has the same function value as its limit at $x = 1$ (Example 2).

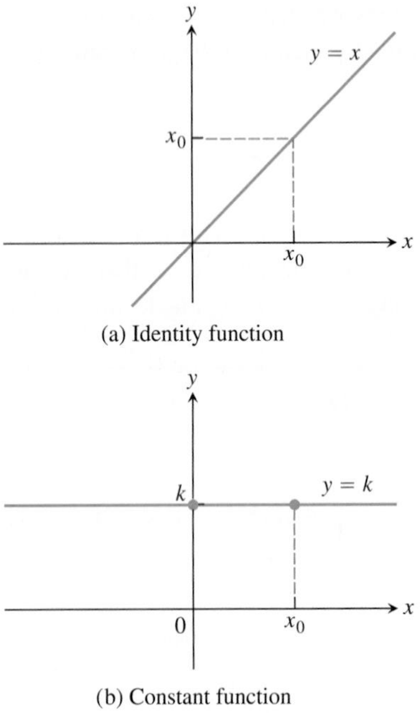

FIGURE 2.9 The functions in Example 3 have limits at all points x_0.

is the only one whose limit as $x \to 1$ equals its value at $x = 1$. For h, we have $\lim_{x\to 1} h(x) = h(1)$. This equality of limit and function value is special, and we return to it in Section 2.6. ■

EXAMPLE 3

(a) If f is the **identity function** $f(x) = x$, then for any value of x_0 (Figure 2.9a),

$$\lim_{x\to x_0} f(x) = \lim_{x\to x_0} x = x_0.$$

(b) If f is the **constant function** $f(x) = k$ (function with the constant value k), then for any value of x_0 (Figure 2.9b),

$$\lim_{x\to x_0} f(x) = \lim_{x\to x_0} k = k.$$

For instance,

$$\lim_{x\to 3} x = 3 \quad \text{and} \quad \lim_{x\to -7}(4) = \lim_{x\to 2}(4) = 4.$$

We prove these results in Example 3 in Section 2.3. ■

Some ways that limits can fail to exist are illustrated in Figure 2.10 and described in the next example.

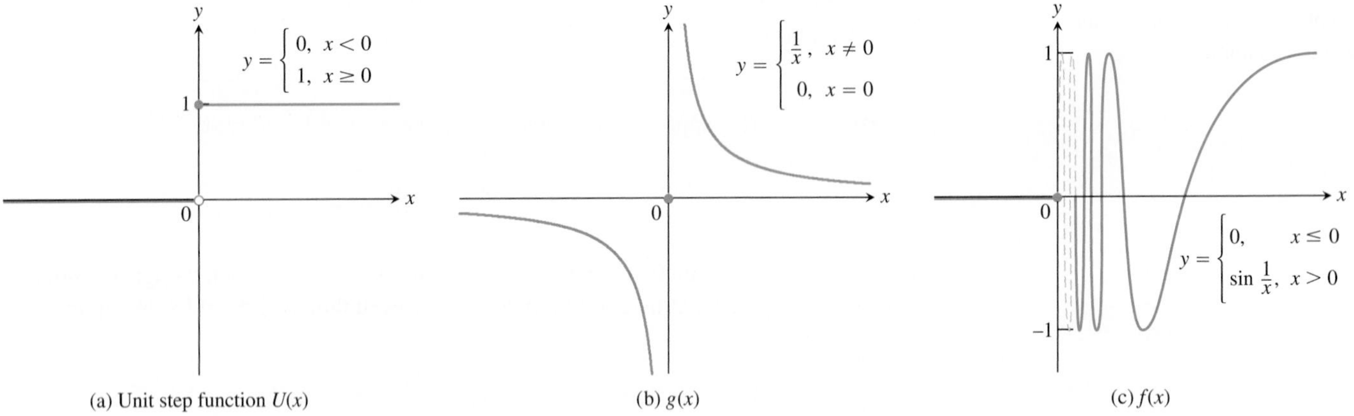

FIGURE 2.10 None of these functions has a limit as x approaches 0 (Example 4).

EXAMPLE 4 Discuss the behavior of the following functions as $x \to 0$.

(a) $U(x) = \begin{cases} 0, & x < 0 \\ 1, & x \ge 0 \end{cases}$

(b) $g(x) = \begin{cases} \dfrac{1}{x}, & x \ne 0 \\ 0, & x = 0 \end{cases}$

(c) $f(x) = \begin{cases} 0, & x \le 0 \\ \sin\dfrac{1}{x}, & x > 0 \end{cases}$

Solution

(a) It *jumps:* **The unit step function** $U(x)$ has no limit as $x \to 0$ because its values jump at $x = 0$. For negative values of x arbitrarily close to zero, $U(x) = 0$. For positive values of x arbitrarily close to zero, $U(x) = 1$. There is no *single* value L approached by $U(x)$ as $x \to 0$ (Figure 2.10a).

(b) It *grows too large to have a limit*: $g(x)$ has no limit as $x \to 0$ because the values of g grow arbitrarily large in absolute value as $x \to 0$ and do not stay close to *any* fixed real number (Figure 2.10b).

(c) It *oscillates too much to have a limit*: $f(x)$ has no limit as $x \to 0$ because the function's values oscillate between $+1$ and -1 in every open interval containing 0. The values do not stay close to any one number as $x \to 0$ (Figure 2.10c). ■

The Limit Laws

The following theorem tells how to calculate limits of functions that are arithmetic combinations of functions whose limits we already know.

THEOREM 1—Limit Laws If L, M, c and k are real numbers and

$$\lim_{x\to c} f(x) = L \quad \text{and} \quad \lim_{x\to c} g(x) = M, \quad \text{then}$$

1. *Sum Rule*: $$\lim_{x\to c}(f(x) + g(x)) = L + M$$

The limit of the sum of two functions is the sum of their limits.

2. *Difference Rule*: $$\lim_{x\to c}(f(x) - g(x)) = L - M$$

The limit of the difference of two functions is the difference of their limits.

3. *Product Rule*: $$\lim_{x\to c}(f(x)\cdot g(x)) = L\cdot M$$

The limit of a product of two functions is the product of their limits.

4. *Constant Multiple Rule:* $$\lim_{x\to c}(k\cdot f(x)) = k\cdot L$$

The limit of a constant times a function is the constant times the limit of the function.

5. *Quotient Rule*: $$\lim_{x\to c}\frac{f(x)}{g(x)} = \frac{L}{M}, \quad M \neq 0$$

The limit of a quotient of two functions is the quotient of their limits, provided the limit of the denominator is not zero.

6. *Power Rule*: If r and s are integers with no common factor and $s \neq 0$, then

$$\lim_{x\to c}(f(x))^{r/s} = L^{r/s}$$

provided that $L^{r/s}$ is a real number. (If s is even, we assume that $L > 0$.)

The limit of a rational power of a function is that power of the limit of the function, provided the limit power is a real number.

We can convince ourselves that the properties in Theorem 1 are true (although these intuitive arguments do not constitute proofs). If x is sufficiently close to c, then $f(x)$ is close to L and $g(x)$ is close to M, from our informal definition of a limit. It is then reasonable that $f(x) + g(x)$ is close to $L + M$; $f(x) - g(x)$ is close to $L - M$; $f(x)g(x)$ is close to LM; $kf(x)$ is close to kL; and that $f(x)/g(x)$ is close to L/M if M is not zero. We prove the Sum Rule in Section 2.3, based on a precise definition of limit. Rules 2–5 are proved in Appendix 5. Rule 6 is proved in more advanced texts.

EXAMPLE 5 Use the observations $\lim_{x\to c} k = k$ and $\lim_{x\to c} x = c$ (Example 3) and the properties of limits to find the following limits.

(a) $\lim\limits_{x\to c}(x^3 + 4x^2 - 3)$ **(b)** $\lim\limits_{x\to c}\dfrac{x^4 + x^2 - 1}{x^2 + 5}$ **(c)** $\lim\limits_{x\to -2}\sqrt{4x^2 - 3}$

Solution

(a)
$$\begin{aligned}\lim_{x\to c}(x^3 + 4x^2 - 3) &= \lim_{x\to c} x^3 + \lim_{x\to c} 4x^2 - \lim_{x\to c} 3 && \text{Sum and Difference Rules}\\ &= c^3 + 4c^2 - 3 && \text{Product and Multiple Rules}\end{aligned}$$

(b)
$$\begin{aligned}\lim_{x\to c}\frac{x^4 + x^2 - 1}{x^2 + 5} &= \frac{\lim\limits_{x\to c}(x^4 + x^2 - 1)}{\lim\limits_{x\to c}(x^2 + 5)} && \text{Quotient Rule}\\ &= \frac{\lim\limits_{x\to c} x^4 + \lim\limits_{x\to c} x^2 - \lim\limits_{x\to c} 1}{\lim\limits_{x\to c} x^2 + \lim\limits_{x\to c} 5} && \text{Sum and Difference Rules}\\ &= \frac{c^4 + c^2 - 1}{c^2 + 5} && \text{Power or Product Rule}\end{aligned}$$

(c)
$$\begin{aligned}\lim_{x\to -2}\sqrt{4x^2 - 3} &= \sqrt{\lim_{x\to -2}(4x^2 - 3)} && \text{Power Rule with } r/s = \tfrac{1}{2}\\ &= \sqrt{\lim_{x\to -2} 4x^2 - \lim_{x\to -2} 3} && \text{Difference Rule}\\ &= \sqrt{4(-2)^2 - 3} && \text{Product and Multiple Rules}\\ &= \sqrt{16 - 3}\\ &= \sqrt{13}\end{aligned}$$

■

Two consequences of Theorem 1 further simplify the task of calculating limits of polynomials and rational functions. To evaluate the limit of a polynomial function as x approaches c, merely substitute c for x in the formula for the function. To evaluate the limit of a rational function as x approaches a point c *at which the denominator is not zero*, substitute c for x in the formula for the function. (See Examples 5a and 5b.)

THEOREM 2—Limits of Polynomials

If $P(x) = a_n x^n + a_{n-1}x^{n-1} + \cdots + a_0$, then

$$\lim_{x\to c} P(x) = P(c) = a_n c^n + a_{n-1}c^{n-1} + \cdots + a_0.$$

THEOREM 3—Limits of Rational Functions
If $P(x)$ and $Q(x)$ are polynomials and $Q(c) \neq 0$, then

$$\lim_{x \to c} \frac{P(x)}{Q(x)} = \frac{P(c)}{Q(c)}.$$

EXAMPLE 6

$$\lim_{x \to -1} \frac{x^3 + 4x^2 - 3}{x^2 + 5} = \frac{(-1)^3 + 4(-1)^2 - 3}{(-1)^2 + 5} = \frac{0}{6} = 0$$ ∎

Identifying Common Factors
It can be shown that if $Q(x)$ is a polynomial and $Q(c) = 0$, then $(x - c)$ is a factor of $Q(x)$. Thus, if the numerator and denominator of a rational function of x are both zero at $x = c$, they have $(x - c)$ as a common factor.

Eliminating Zero Denominators Algebraically

Theorem 3 applies only if the denominator of the rational function is not zero at the limit point c. If the denominator is zero, canceling common factors in the numerator and denominator may reduce the fraction to one whose denominator is no longer zero at c. If this happens, we can find the limit by substitution in the simplified fraction.

EXAMPLE 7 Evaluate

$$\lim_{x \to 1} \frac{x^2 + x - 2}{x^2 - x}.$$

Solution We cannot substitute $x = 1$ because it makes the denominator zero. We test the numerator to see if it, too, is zero at $x = 1$. It is, so it has a factor of $(x - 1)$ in common with the denominator. Canceling the $(x - 1)$'s gives a simpler fraction with the same values as the original for $x \neq 1$:

$$\frac{x^2 + x - 2}{x^2 - x} = \frac{(x - 1)(x + 2)}{x(x - 1)} = \frac{x + 2}{x}, \qquad \text{if } x \neq 1.$$

Using the simpler fraction, we find the limit of these values as $x \to 1$ by substitution:

$$\lim_{x \to 1} \frac{x^2 + x - 2}{x^2 - x} = \lim_{x \to 1} \frac{x + 2}{x} = \frac{1 + 2}{1} = 3.$$

See Figure 2.11. ∎

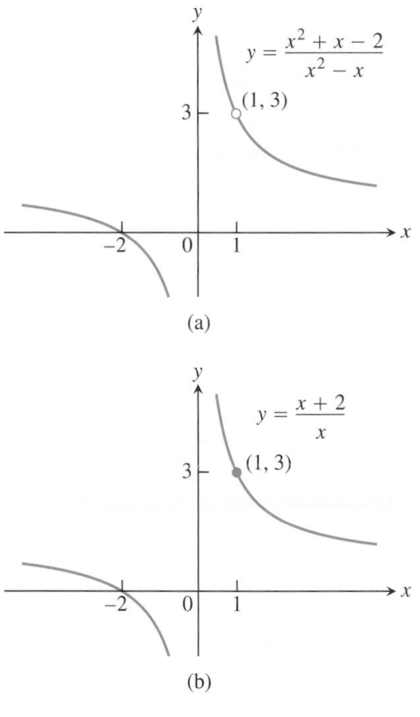

FIGURE 2.11 The graph of $f(x) = (x^2 + x - 2)/(x^2 - x)$ in part (a) is the same as the graph of $g(x) = (x + 2)/x$ in part (b) except at $x = 1$, where f is undefined. The functions have the same limit as $x \to 1$ (Example 7).

Using Calculators and Computers to Estimate Limits

When we cannot use the Quotient Rule in Theorem 1 because the limit of the denominator is zero, we can try using a calculator or computer to guess the limit numerically as x gets closer and closer to c. We used this approach in Example 1, but calculators and computers can give *false values and misleading impressions* for functions that are undefined at a point or fail to have a limit there, as we now illustrate.

EXAMPLE 8 Guess the value of $\displaystyle\lim_{x \to 0} \frac{\sqrt{x^2 + 100} - 10}{x^2}$.

Solution Table 2.3 lists values of the function for several values near $x = 0$. As x approaches 0 through the values ± 1, ± 0.5, ± 0.10, and ± 0.01, the function seems to approach the number 0.05.

As we take even smaller values of x, ± 0.0005, ± 0.0001, ± 0.00001, and ± 0.000001, the function appears to approach the value 0.

Is the answer 0.05 or 0, or some other value? We resolve this question in the next example.

TABLE 2.3 Computer values of $f(x) = \dfrac{\sqrt{x^2+100}-10}{x^2}$ near $x = 0$

x	$f(x)$	
± 1	0.049876	approaches 0.05?
± 0.5	0.049969	
± 0.1	0.049999	
± 0.01	0.050000	
± 0.0005	0.080000	approaches 0?
± 0.0001	0.000000	
± 0.00001	0.000000	
± 0.000001	0.000000	

■

Using a computer or calculator may give ambiguous results, as in the last example. We cannot substitute $x = 0$ in the problem, and the numerator and denominator have no obvious common factors (as in Example 7). Sometimes, however, we can create a common factor algebraically.

EXAMPLE 9 Evaluate

$$\lim_{x\to 0} \frac{\sqrt{x^2+100}-10}{x^2}.$$

Solution This is the limit we considered in Example 8. We can create a common factor by multiplying both numerator and denominator by the expression $\sqrt{x^2+100}+10$ (obtained by changing the sign after the square root). The preliminary algebra rationalizes the numerator:

$$\begin{aligned}
\frac{\sqrt{x^2+100}-10}{x^2} &= \frac{\sqrt{x^2+100}-10}{x^2} \cdot \frac{\sqrt{x^2+100}+10}{\sqrt{x^2+100}+10} \\
&= \frac{x^2+100-100}{x^2\left(\sqrt{x^2+100}+10\right)} \\
&= \frac{x^2}{x^2\left(\sqrt{x^2+100}+10\right)} && \text{Common factor } x^2 \\
&= \frac{1}{\sqrt{x^2+100}+10}. && \text{Cancel } x^2 \text{ for } x \neq 0
\end{aligned}$$

Therefore,

$$\lim_{x\to 0} \frac{\sqrt{x^2+100}-10}{x^2} = \lim_{x\to 0} \frac{1}{\sqrt{x^2+100}+10}$$

$$= \frac{1}{\sqrt{0^2+100}+10}$$ Denominator not 0 at $x = 0$; substitute

$$= \frac{1}{20} = 0.05.$$

This calculation provides the correct answer to the ambiguous computer results in Example 8. ■

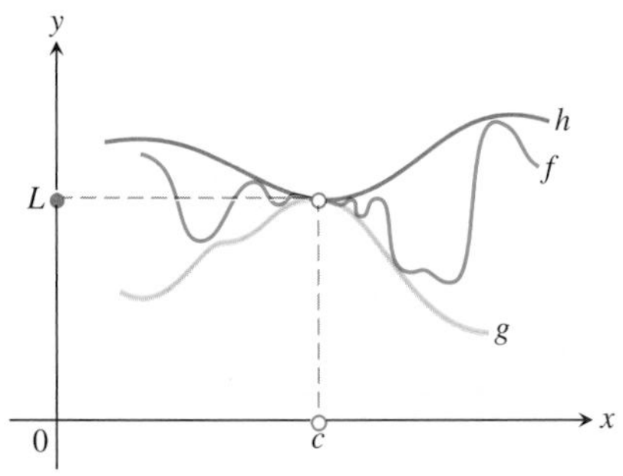

FIGURE 2.12 The graph of f is sandwiched between the graphs of g and h.

We cannot always algebraically resolve the problem of finding the limit of a quotient where the denominator becomes zero. In some cases the limit might then be found with the aid of some geometry applied to the problem (see the proof of Theorem 7 in Section 2.4), or through methods of calculus (illustrated in Sections 4.4 and 4.6). The next theorem is also useful.

The Sandwich Theorem

The following theorem enables us to calculate a variety of limits. It is called the Sandwich Theorem because it refers to a function f whose values are sandwiched between the values of two other functions g and h that have the same limit L at a point c. Being trapped between the values of two functions that approach L, the values of f must also approach L (Figure 2.12). You will find a proof in Appendix 5.

THEOREM 4—The Sandwich Theorem Suppose that $g(x) \le f(x) \le h(x)$ for all x in some open interval containing c, except possibly at $x = c$ itself. Suppose also that

$$\lim_{x\to c} g(x) = \lim_{x\to c} h(x) = L.$$

Then $\lim_{x\to c} f(x) = L$.

The Sandwich Theorem is also called the Squeeze Theorem or the Pinching Theorem.

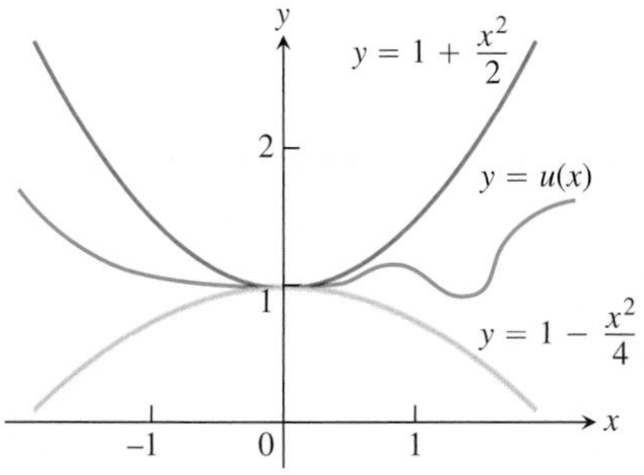

FIGURE 2.13 Any function $u(x)$ whose graph lies in the region between $y = 1 + (x^2/2)$ and $y = 1 - (x^2/4)$ has limit 1 as $x \to 0$ (Example 10).

EXAMPLE 10 Given that

$$1 - \frac{x^2}{4} \le u(x) \le 1 + \frac{x^2}{2} \quad \text{for all } x \ne 0,$$

find $\lim_{x\to 0} u(x)$, no matter how complicated u is.

Solution Since

$$\lim_{x\to 0}(1 - (x^2/4)) = 1 \quad \text{and} \quad \lim_{x\to 0}(1 + (x^2/2)) = 1,$$

the Sandwich Theorem implies that $\lim_{x\to 0} u(x) = 1$ (Figure 2.13). ■

EXAMPLE 11

(a) (See Figure 2.14a.) It follows from the definition of $\sin\theta$ (see Section 1.3) that $-|\theta| \le \sin\theta \le |\theta|$ for all θ. Since $\lim_{\theta\to 0}(-|\theta|) = \lim_{\theta\to 0}|\theta| = 0$, we have

$$\lim_{\theta\to 0} \sin\theta = 0.$$

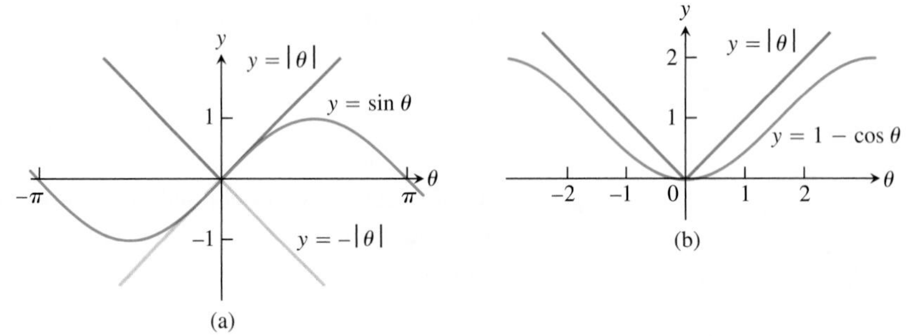

FIGURE 2.14 The Sandwich Theorem shows that (a) $\lim_{\theta\to 0}\sin\theta = 0$ and (b) $\lim_{\theta\to 0}(1 - \cos\theta) = 0$ (Example 11).

(b) (See Figure 2.14b.) From the definition of $\cos\theta$, $0 \le 1 - \cos\theta \le |\theta|$ for all θ, and we have $\lim_{\theta\to 0}(1 - \cos\theta) = 0$ or

$$\lim_{\theta\to 0} \cos\theta = 1.$$

(c) For any function $f(x)$, if $\lim_{x\to c}|f(x)| = 0$, then $\lim_{x\to c} f(x) = 0$. The argument: $-|f(x)| \le f(x) \le |f(x)|$ and $-|f(x)|$ and $|f(x)|$ have limit 0 as $x \to c$. ■

Another important property of limits is given by the next theorem. A proof is given in the next section.

THEOREM 5 If $f(x) \le g(x)$ for all x in some open interval containing c, except possibly at $x = c$ itself, and the limits of f and g both exist as x approaches c, then

$$\lim_{x\to c} f(x) \le \lim_{x\to c} g(x).$$

The assertion resulting from replacing the less than or equal to ($\le$) inequality by the strict less than ($<$) inequality in Theorem 5 is false. Figure 2.14a shows that for $\theta \ne 0$, $-|\theta| < \sin\theta < |\theta|$, but in the limit as $\theta \to 0$, equality holds.

EXERCISES 2.2

1. For the function $g(x)$ graphed here, find the following limits or explain why they do not exist.

a. $\lim_{x\to 1} g(x)$ **b.** $\lim_{x\to 2} g(x)$ **c.** $\lim_{x\to 3} g(x)$

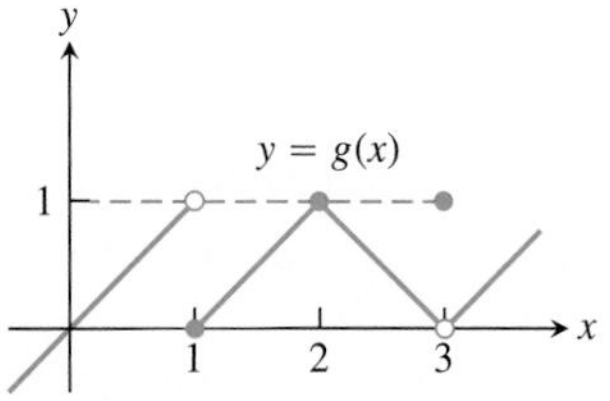

2. For the function $f(t)$ graphed here, find the following limits or explain why they do not exist.

a. $\lim_{t\to -2} f(t)$ **b.** $\lim_{t\to -1} f(t)$ **c.** $\lim_{t\to 0} f(t)$

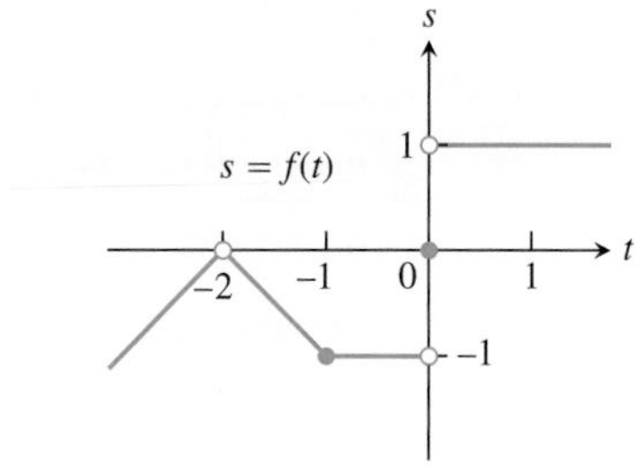

3. Which of the following statements about the function $y = f(x)$ graphed here are true, and which are false?

a. $\lim_{x\to 0} f(x)$ exists.
b. $\lim_{x\to 0} f(x) = 0$.
c. $\lim_{x\to 0} f(x) = 1$.
d. $\lim_{x\to 1} f(x) = 1$.
e. $\lim_{x\to 1} f(x) = 0$.
f. $\lim_{x\to x_0} f(x)$ exists at every point x_0 in $(-1, 1)$.

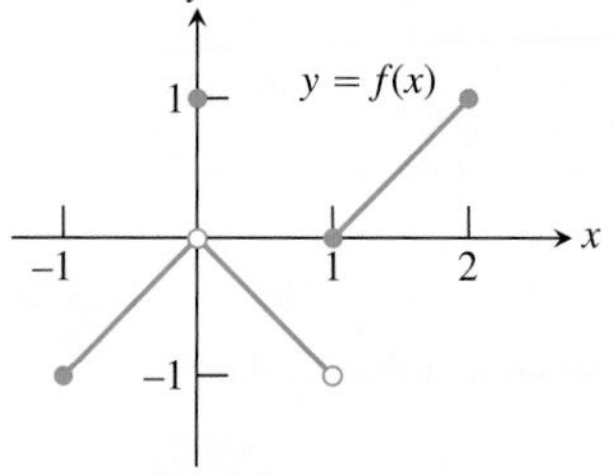

4. Which of the following statements about the function $y = f(x)$ graphed here are true, and which are false?

a. $\lim_{x\to 2} f(x)$ does not exist.
b. $\lim_{x\to 2} f(x) = 2$.
c. $\lim_{x\to 1} f(x)$ does not exist.
d. $\lim_{x\to x_0} f(x)$ exists at every point x_0 in $(-1, 1)$.
e. $\lim_{x\to x_0} f(x)$ exists at every point x_0 in $(1, 3)$.

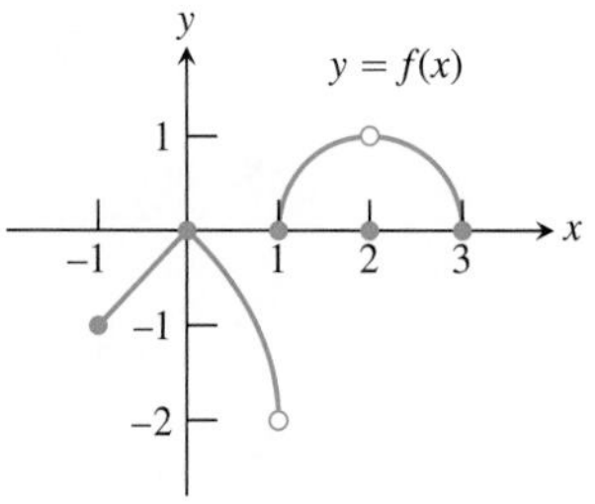

In Exercises 5 and 6, explain why the limits do not exist.

5. $\lim_{x\to 0} \dfrac{x}{|x|}$ **6.** $\lim_{x\to 1} \dfrac{1}{x-1}$

7. Suppose that a function $f(x)$ is defined for all real values of x except $x = x_0$. Can anything be said about the existence of $\lim_{x\to x_0} f(x)$? Give reasons for your answer.

8. Suppose that a function $f(x)$ is defined for all x in $[-1, 1]$. Can anything be said about the existence of $\lim_{x\to 0} f(x)$? Give reasons for your answer.

9. If $\lim_{x\to 1} f(x) = 5$, must f be defined at $x = 1$? If it is, must $f(1) = 5$? Can we conclude *anything* about the values of f at $x = 1$? Explain.

10. If $f(1) = 5$, must $\lim_{x\to 1} f(x)$ exist? If it does, then must $\lim_{x\to 1} f(x) = 5$? Can we conclude *anything* about $\lim_{x\to 1} f(x)$? Explain.

Find the limits in Exercises 11–28.

11. $\lim_{x\to -7} (2x + 5)$ **12.** $\lim_{x\to 12} (10 - 3x)$

13. $\lim_{x\to 2} (-x^2 + 5x - 2)$ **14.** $\lim_{x\to -2} (x^3 - 2x^2 + 4x + 8)$

15. $\lim_{t\to 6} 8(t - 5)(t - 7)$ **16.** $\lim_{s\to 2/3} 3s(2s - 1)$

17. $\lim_{x\to 2} \dfrac{x+3}{x+6}$ **18.** $\lim_{x\to 5} \dfrac{4}{x-7}$

19. $\lim_{y\to -5} \dfrac{y^2}{5-y}$ **20.** $\lim_{y\to 2} \dfrac{y+2}{y^2+5y+6}$

21. $\lim_{x\to -1} 3(2x - 1)^2$ **22.** $\lim_{x\to -4} (x + 3)^{1984}$

23. $\lim_{y\to -3} (5 - y)^{4/3}$ **24.** $\lim_{z\to 0} (2z - 8)^{1/3}$

25. $\lim_{h\to 0} \dfrac{3}{\sqrt{3h+1}+1}$ **26.** $\lim_{h\to 0} \dfrac{5}{\sqrt{5h+4}+2}$

27. $\lim_{h\to 0} \dfrac{\sqrt{3h+1}-1}{h}$ **28.** $\lim_{h\to 0} \dfrac{\sqrt{5h+4}-2}{h}$

Find the limits in Exercises 29–46.

29. $\lim_{x\to 5} \dfrac{x-5}{x^2-25}$

30. $\lim_{x\to -3} \dfrac{x+3}{x^2+4x+3}$

31. $\lim_{x\to -5} \dfrac{x^2+3x-10}{x+5}$

32. $\lim_{x\to 2} \dfrac{x^2-7x+10}{x-2}$

33. $\lim_{t\to 1} \dfrac{t^2+t-2}{t^2-1}$

34. $\lim_{t\to -1} \dfrac{t^2+3t+2}{t^2-t-2}$

35. $\lim_{x\to -2} \dfrac{-2x-4}{x^3+2x^2}$

36. $\lim_{y\to 0} \dfrac{5y^3+8y^2}{3y^4-16y^2}$

37. $\lim_{u\to 1} \dfrac{u^4-1}{u^3-1}$

38. $\lim_{v\to 2} \dfrac{v^3-8}{v^4-16}$

39. $\lim_{x\to 9} \dfrac{\sqrt{x}-3}{x-9}$

40. $\lim_{x\to 4} \dfrac{4x-x^2}{2-\sqrt{x}}$

41. $\lim_{x\to 1} \dfrac{x-1}{\sqrt{x+3}-2}$

42. $\lim_{x\to -1} \dfrac{\sqrt{x^2+8}-3}{x+1}$

43. $\lim_{x\to 2} \dfrac{\sqrt{x^2+12}-4}{x-2}$

44. $\lim_{x\to -2} \dfrac{x+2}{\sqrt{x^2+5}-3}$

45. $\lim_{x\to -3} \dfrac{2-\sqrt{x^2-5}}{x+3}$

46. $\lim_{x\to 4} \dfrac{4-x}{5-\sqrt{x^2+9}}$

Find the limits in Exercises 47–54.

47. $\lim_{x\to 0} (2\sin x - 1)$

48. $\lim_{x\to 0} \sin^2 x$

49. $\lim_{x\to 0} \sec x$

50. $\lim_{x\to 0} \tan x$

51. $\lim_{x\to 0} \dfrac{1+x+\sin x}{3\cos x}$

52. $\lim_{x\to 0} (x^2-1)(2-\cos x)$

53. $\lim_{x\to 0} \sqrt{x+1}\cos^{1/3} x$

54. $\lim_{x\to 0} \sqrt{1+\cos^2 x}$

55. Suppose $\lim_{x\to 0} f(x) = 1$ and $\lim_{x\to 0} g(x) = -5$. Name the rules in Theorem 1 that are used to accomplish steps (a), (b), and (c) of the following calculation.

$$\lim_{x\to 0} \frac{2f(x)-g(x)}{(f(x)+7)^{2/3}} = \frac{\lim_{x\to 0}(2f(x)-g(x))}{\lim_{x\to 0}(f(x)+7)^{2/3}} \qquad \text{(a)}$$

$$= \frac{\lim_{x\to 0} 2f(x) - \lim_{x\to 0} g(x)}{\left(\lim_{x\to 0}\left(f(x)+7\right)\right)^{2/3}} \qquad \text{(b)}$$

$$= \frac{2\lim_{x\to 0} f(x) - \lim_{x\to 0} g(x)}{\left(\lim_{x\to 0} f(x) + \lim_{x\to 0} 7\right)^{2/3}} \qquad \text{(c)}$$

$$= \frac{(2)(1)-(-5)}{(1+7)^{2/3}} = \frac{7}{4}$$

56. Let $\lim_{x\to 1} h(x) = 5$, $\lim_{x\to 1} p(x) = 1$, and $\lim_{x\to 1} r(x) = 2$. Name the rules in Theorem 1 that are used to accomplish steps (a), (b), and (c) of the following calculation.

$$\lim_{x\to 1} \frac{\sqrt{5h(x)}}{p(x)(4-r(x))} = \frac{\lim_{x\to 1}\sqrt{5h(x)}}{\lim_{x\to 1}(p(x)(4-r(x)))} \qquad \text{(a)}$$

$$= \frac{\sqrt{\lim_{x\to 1} 5h(x)}}{\left(\lim_{x\to 1} p(x)\right)\left(\lim_{x\to 1}\left(4-r(x)\right)\right)} \qquad \text{(b)}$$

$$= \frac{\sqrt{5\lim_{x\to 1} h(x)}}{\left(\lim_{x\to 1} p(x)\right)\left(\lim_{x\to 1} 4 - \lim_{x\to 1} r(x)\right)} \qquad \text{(c)}$$

$$= \frac{\sqrt{(5)(5)}}{(1)(4-2)} = \frac{5}{2}$$

57. Suppose $\lim_{x\to c} f(x) = 5$ and $\lim_{x\to c} g(x) = -2$. Find

a. $\lim_{x\to c} f(x)g(x)$

b. $\lim_{x\to c} 2f(x)g(x)$

c. $\lim_{x\to c} (f(x) + 3g(x))$

d. $\lim_{x\to c} \dfrac{f(x)}{f(x)-g(x)}$

58. Suppose $\lim_{x\to 4} f(x) = 0$ and $\lim_{x\to 4} g(x) = -3$. Find

a. $\lim_{x\to 4} (g(x) + 3)$

b. $\lim_{x\to 4} xf(x)$

c. $\lim_{x\to 4} (g(x))^2$

d. $\lim_{x\to 4} \dfrac{g(x)}{f(x)-1}$

59. Suppose $\lim_{x\to b} f(x) = 7$ and $\lim_{x\to b} g(x) = -3$. Find

a. $\lim_{x\to b} (f(x) + g(x))$

b. $\lim_{x\to b} f(x)\cdot g(x)$

c. $\lim_{x\to b} 4g(x)$

d. $\lim_{x\to b} f(x)/g(x)$

60. Suppose that $\lim_{x\to -2} p(x) = 4$, $\lim_{x\to -2} r(x) = 0$, and $\lim_{x\to -2} s(x) = -3$. Find

a. $\lim_{x\to -2} (p(x) + r(x) + s(x))$

b. $\lim_{x\to -2} p(x)\cdot r(x)\cdot s(x)$

c. $\lim_{x\to -2} (-4p(x) + 5r(x))/s(x)$

Because of their connection with secant lines, tangents, and instantaneous rates, limits of the form

$$\lim_{h\to 0} \frac{f(x+h)-f(x)}{h}$$

occur frequently in calculus. In Exercises 61–66, evaluate this limit for the given value of x and function f.

61. $f(x) = x^2, \quad x = 1$

62. $f(x) = x^2, \quad x = -2$

63. $f(x) = 3x - 4, \quad x = 2$

64. $f(x) = 1/x, \quad x = -2$

65. $f(x) = \sqrt{x}, \quad x = 7$

66. $f(x) = \sqrt{3x+1}, \quad x = 0$

67. If $\sqrt{5-2x^2} \le f(x) \le \sqrt{5-x^2}$ for $-1 \le x \le 1$, find $\lim_{x\to 0} f(x)$.

68. If $2 - x^2 \le g(x) \le 2\cos x$ for all x, find $\lim_{x\to 0} g(x)$.

69. a. It can be shown that the inequalities

$$1 - \frac{x^2}{6} < \frac{x\sin x}{2-2\cos x} < 1$$

hold for all values of x close to zero. What, if anything, does this tell you about

$$\lim_{x\to 0} \frac{x\sin x}{2-2\cos x}?$$

Give reasons for your answer.

T **b.** Graph $y = 1 - (x^2/6)$, $y = (x \sin x)/(2 - 2\cos x)$, and $y = 1$ together for $-2 \le x \le 2$. Comment on the behavior of the graphs as $x \to 0$.

70. a. Suppose that the inequalities

$$\frac{1}{2} - \frac{x^2}{24} < \frac{1 - \cos x}{x^2} < \frac{1}{2}$$

hold for values of x close to zero. (They do, as you will see in Section 8.9.) What, if anything, does this tell you about

$$\lim_{x \to 0} \frac{1 - \cos x}{x^2}?$$

Give reasons for your answer.

T **b.** Graph the equations $y = (1/2) - (x^2/24)$, $y = (1 - \cos x)/x^2$, and $y = 1/2$ together for $-2 \le x \le 2$. Comment on the behavior of the graphs as $x \to 0$.

T You will find a graphing calculator useful for Exercises 71–80.

71. Let $f(x) = (x^2 - 9)/(x + 3)$.

a. Make a table of the values of f at the points $x = -3.1$, -3.01, -3.001, and so on as far as your calculator can go. Then estimate $\lim_{x \to -3} f(x)$. What estimate do you arrive at if you evaluate f at $x = -2.9, -2.99, -2.999, \ldots$ instead?

b. Support your conclusions in part (a) by graphing f near $x_0 = -3$ and using Zoom and Trace to estimate y-values on the graph as $x \to -3$.

c. Find $\lim_{x \to -3} f(x)$ algebraically, as in Example 7.

72. Let $g(x) = (x^2 - 2)/(x - \sqrt{2})$.

a. Make a table of the values of g at the points $x = 1.4, 1.41, 1.414$, and so on through successive decimal approximations of $\sqrt{2}$. Estimate $\lim_{x \to \sqrt{2}} g(x)$.

b. Support your conclusion in part (a) by graphing g near $x_0 = \sqrt{2}$ and using Zoom and Trace to estimate y-values on the graph as $x \to \sqrt{2}$.

c. Find $\lim_{x \to \sqrt{2}} g(x)$ algebraically.

73. Let $G(x) = (x + 6)/(x^2 + 4x - 12)$.

a. Make a table of the values of G at $x = -5.9, -5.99, -5.999$, and so on. Then estimate $\lim_{x \to -6} G(x)$. What estimate do you arrive at if you evaluate G at $x = -6.1, -6.01, -6.001, \ldots$ instead?

b. Support your conclusions in part (a) by graphing G and using Zoom and Trace to estimate y-values on the graph as $x \to -6$.

c. Find $\lim_{x \to -6} G(x)$ algebraically.

74. Let $h(x) = (x^2 - 2x - 3)/(x^2 - 4x + 3)$.

a. Make a table of the values of h at $x = 2.9, 2.99, 2.999$, and so on. Then estimate $\lim_{x \to 3} h(x)$. What estimate do you arrive at if you evaluate h at $x = 3.1, 3.01, 3.001, \ldots$ instead?

b. Support your conclusions in part (a) by graphing h near $x_0 = 3$ and using Zoom and Trace to estimate y-values on the graph as $x \to 3$.

c. Find $\lim_{x \to 3} h(x)$ algebraically.

75. Let $f(x) = (x^2 - 1)/(|x| - 1)$.

a. Make tables of the values of f at values of x that approach $x_0 = -1$ from above and below. Then estimate $\lim_{x \to -1} f(x)$.

b. Support your conclusion in part (a) by graphing f near $x_0 = -1$ and using Zoom and Trace to estimate y-values on the graph as $x \to -1$.

c. Find $\lim_{x \to -1} f(x)$ algebraically.

76. Let $F(x) = (x^2 + 3x + 2)/(2 - |x|)$.

a. Make tables of values of F at values of x that approach $x_0 = -2$ from above and below. Then estimate $\lim_{x \to -2} F(x)$.

b. Support your conclusion in part (a) by graphing F near $x_0 = -2$ and using Zoom and Trace to estimate y-values on the graph as $x \to -2$.

c. Find $\lim_{x \to -2} F(x)$ algebraically.

77. Let $g(\theta) = (\sin \theta)/\theta$.

a. Make a table of the values of g at values of θ that approach $\theta_0 = 0$ from above and below. Then estimate $\lim_{\theta \to 0} g(\theta)$.

b. Support your conclusion in part (a) by graphing g near $\theta_0 = 0$.

78. Let $G(t) = (1 - \cos t)/t^2$.

a. Make tables of values of G at values of t that approach $t_0 = 0$ from above and below. Then estimate $\lim_{t \to 0} G(t)$.

b. Support your conclusion in part (a) by graphing G near $t_0 = 0$.

79. Let $f(x) = x^{1/(1-x)}$.

a. Make tables of values of f at values of x that approach $x_0 = 1$ from above and below. Does f appear to have a limit as $x \to 1$? If so, what is it? If not, why not?

b. Support your conclusions in part (a) by graphing f near $x_0 = 1$.

80. Let $f(x) = (3^x - 1)/x$.

a. Make tables of values of f at values of x that approach $x_0 = 0$ from above and below. Does f appear to have a limit as $x \to 0$? If so, what is it? If not, why not?

b. Support your conclusions in part (a) by graphing f near $x_0 = 0$.

81. If $x^4 \le f(x) \le x^2$ for x in $[-1, 1]$ and $x^2 \le f(x) \le x^4$ for $x < -1$ and $x > 1$, at what points c do you automatically know $\lim_{x \to c} f(x)$? What can you say about the value of the limit at these points?

82. Suppose that $g(x) \le f(x) \le h(x)$ for all $x \ne 2$ and suppose that

$$\lim_{x \to 2} g(x) = \lim_{x \to 2} h(x) = -5.$$

Can we conclude anything about the values of f, g, and h at $x = 2$? Could $f(2) = 0$? Could $\lim_{x \to 2} f(x) = 0$? Give reasons for your answers.

83. If $\lim_{x\to 4} \dfrac{f(x) - 5}{x - 2} = 1$, find $\lim_{x\to 4} f(x)$.

84. If $\lim_{x\to -2} \dfrac{f(x)}{x^2} = 1$, find

a. $\lim_{x\to -2} f(x)$ **b.** $\lim_{x\to -2} \dfrac{f(x)}{x}$

85. a. If $\lim_{x\to 2} \dfrac{f(x) - 5}{x - 2} = 3$, find $\lim_{x\to 2} f(x)$.

b. If $\lim_{x\to 2} \dfrac{f(x) - 5}{x - 2} = 4$, find $\lim_{x\to 2} f(x)$.

86. If $\lim_{x\to 0} \dfrac{f(x)}{x^2} = 1$, find

a. $\lim_{x\to 0} f(x)$ **b.** $\lim_{x\to 0} \dfrac{f(x)}{x}$

T **87. a.** Graph $g(x) = x \sin(1/x)$ to estimate $\lim_{x\to 0} g(x)$, zooming in on the origin as necessary.

b. Confirm your estimate in part (a) with a proof.

T **88. a.** Graph $h(x) = x^2 \cos(1/x^3)$ to estimate $\lim_{x\to 0} h(x)$, zooming in on the origin as necessary.

b. Confirm your estimate in part (a) with a proof.

COMPUTER EXPLORATIONS

In Exercises 89–94, use a CAS to perform the following steps:

a. Plot the function near the point x_0 being approached.

b. From your plot guess the value of the limit.

89. $\lim_{x\to 2} \dfrac{x^4 - 16}{x - 2}$ **90.** $\lim_{x\to -1} \dfrac{x^3 - x^2 - 5x - 3}{(x + 1)^2}$

91. $\lim_{x\to 0} \dfrac{\sqrt[3]{1 + x} - 1}{x}$ **92.** $\lim_{x\to 3} \dfrac{x^2 - 9}{\sqrt{x^2 + 7} - 4}$

93. $\lim_{x\to 0} \dfrac{1 - \cos x}{x \sin x}$ **94.** $\lim_{x\to 0} \dfrac{2x^2}{3 - 3\cos x}$

2.3 The Precise Definition of a Limit

We now turn our attention to the precise definition of a limit. We replace vague phrases like "gets arbitrarily close to" in the informal definition with specific conditions that can be applied to any particular example. With a precise definition, we can prove the limit properties given in the preceding section and establish many important limits.

To show that the limit of $f(x)$ as $x \to x_0$ equals the number L, we need to show that the gap between $f(x)$ and L can be made "as small as we choose" if x is kept "close enough" to x_0. Let us see what this would require if we specified the size of the gap between $f(x)$ and L.

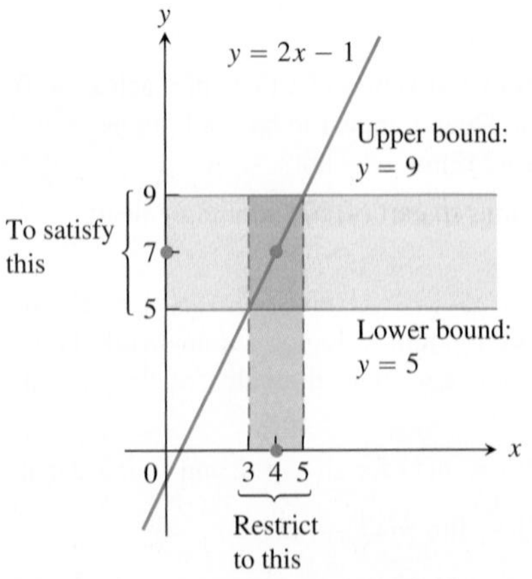

FIGURE 2.15 Keeping x within 1 unit of $x_0 = 4$ will keep y within 2 units of $y_0 = 7$ (Example 1).

EXAMPLE 1 Consider the function $y = 2x - 1$ near $x_0 = 4$. Intuitively it appears that y is close to 7 when x is close to 4, so $\lim_{x\to 4}(2x - 1) = 7$. However, how close to $x_0 = 4$ does x have to be so that $y = 2x - 1$ differs from 7 by, say, less than 2 units?

Solution We are asked: For what values of x is $|y - 7| < 2$? To find the answer we first express $|y - 7|$ in terms of x:

$$|y - 7| = |(2x - 1) - 7| = |2x - 8|.$$

The question then becomes: what values of x satisfy the inequality $|2x - 8| < 2$? To find out, we solve the inequality:

$$|2x - 8| < 2$$
$$-2 < 2x - 8 < 2$$
$$6 < 2x < 10$$
$$3 < x < 5$$
$$-1 < x - 4 < 1.$$

Keeping x within 1 unit of $x_0 = 4$ will keep y within 2 units of $y_0 = 7$ (Figure 2.15). ■

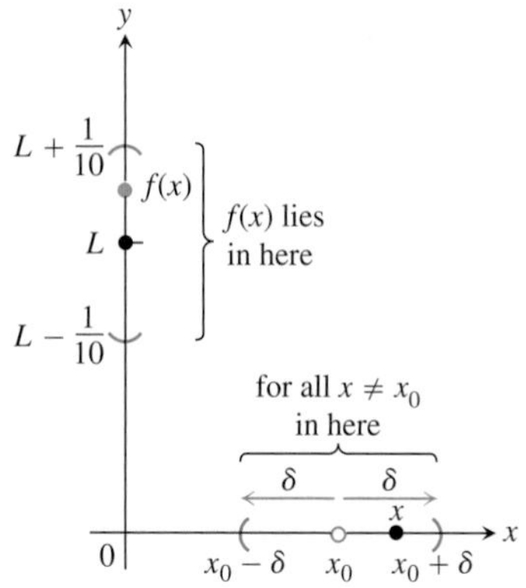

FIGURE 2.16 How should we define $\delta > 0$ so that keeping x within the interval $(x_0 - \delta, x_0 + \delta)$ will keep $f(x)$ within the interval $\left(L - \frac{1}{10}, L + \frac{1}{10}\right)$?

In the previous example we determined how close x must be to a particular value x_0 to ensure that the outputs $f(x)$ of some function lie within a prescribed interval about a limit value L. To show that the limit of $f(x)$ as $x \to x_0$ actually equals L, we must be able to show that the gap between $f(x)$ and L can be made less than *any prescribed error*, no matter how small, by holding x close enough to x_0.

Definition of Limit

Suppose we are watching the values of a function $f(x)$ as x approaches x_0 (without taking on the value of x_0 itself). Certainly we want to be able to say that $f(x)$ stays within one-tenth of a unit from L as soon as x stays within some distance δ of x_0 (Figure 2.16). But that in itself is not enough, because as x continues on its course toward x_0, what is to prevent $f(x)$ from jittering about within the interval from $L - (1/10)$ to $L + (1/10)$ without tending toward L?

We can be told that the error can be no more than $1/100$ or $1/1000$ or $1/100{,}000$. Each time, we find a new δ-interval about x_0 so that keeping x within that interval satisfies the new error tolerance. And each time the possibility exists that $f(x)$ jitters away from L at some stage.

The figures on the next page illustrate the problem. You can think of this as a quarrel between a skeptic and a scholar. The skeptic presents ϵ-challenges to prove that the limit does not exist or, more precisely, that there is room for doubt. The scholar answers every challenge with a δ-interval around x_0 that keeps the function values within ϵ of L.

How do we stop this seemingly endless series of challenges and responses? By proving that for every error tolerance ϵ that the challenger can produce, we can find, calculate, or conjure a matching distance δ that keeps x "close enough" to x_0 to keep $f(x)$ within that tolerance of L (Figure 2.17). This leads us to the precise definition of a limit.

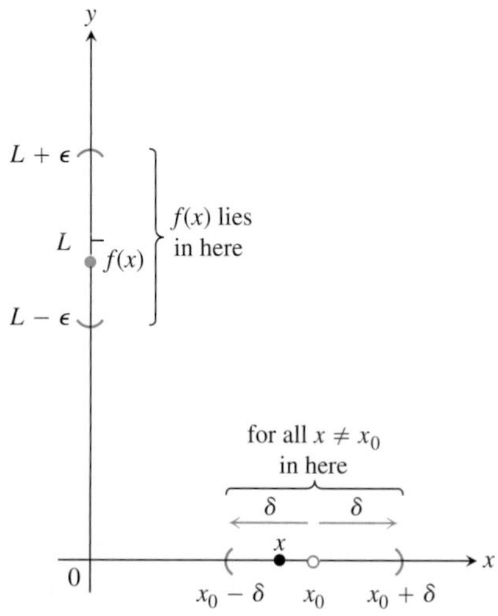

FIGURE 2.17 The relation of δ and ϵ in the definition of limit.

DEFINITION Let $f(x)$ be defined on an open interval about x_0, except possibly at x_0 itself. We say that the **limit of $f(x)$ as x approaches x_0 is the number L**, and write

$$\lim_{x \to x_0} f(x) = L,$$

if, for every number $\epsilon > 0$, there exists a corresponding number $\delta > 0$ such that for all x,

$$0 < |x - x_0| < \delta \quad \Rightarrow \quad |f(x) - L| < \epsilon.$$

One way to think about the definition is to suppose we are machining a generator shaft to a close tolerance. We may try for diameter L, but since nothing is perfect, we must be satisfied with a diameter $f(x)$ somewhere between $L - \epsilon$ and $L + \epsilon$. The δ is the measure of how accurate our control setting for x must be to guarantee this degree of accuracy in the diameter of the shaft. Notice that as the tolerance for error becomes stricter, we may have to adjust δ. That is, the value of δ, how tight our control setting must be, depends on the value of ϵ, the error tolerance.

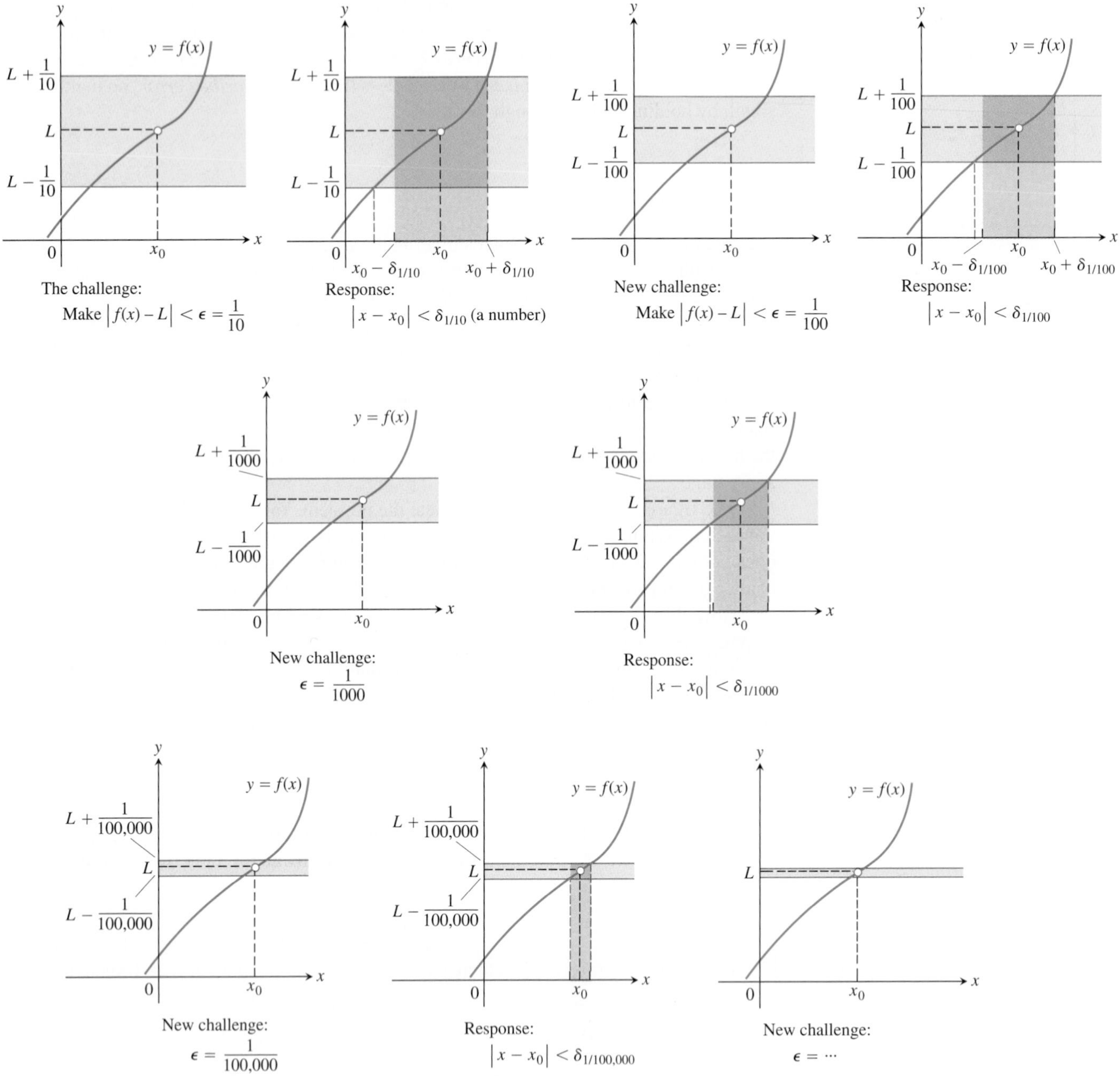

Examples: Testing the Definition

The formal definition of limit does not tell how to find the limit of a function, but it enables us to verify that a suspected limit is correct. The following examples show how the definition can be used to verify limit statements for specific functions. However, the real purpose of the definition is not to do calculations like this, but rather to prove general theorems so that the calculation of specific limits can be simplified.

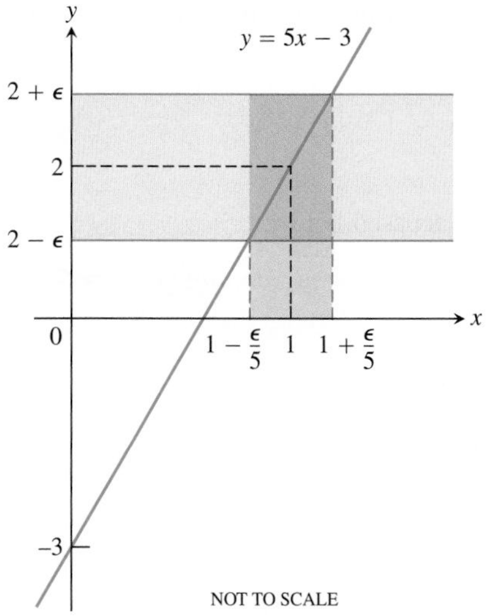

FIGURE 2.18 If $f(x) = 5x - 3$, then $0 < |x - 1| < \epsilon/5$ guarantees that $|f(x) - 2| < \epsilon$ (Example 2).

EXAMPLE 2 Show that

$$\lim_{x \to 1} (5x - 3) = 2.$$

Solution Set $x_0 = 1$, $f(x) = 5x - 3$, and $L = 2$ in the definition of limit. For any given $\epsilon > 0$, we have to find a suitable $\delta > 0$ so that if $x \neq 1$ and x is within distance δ of $x_0 = 1$, that is, whenever

$$0 < |x - 1| < \delta,$$

it is true that $f(x)$ is within distance ϵ of $L = 2$, so

$$|f(x) - 2| < \epsilon.$$

We find δ by working backward from the ϵ-inequality:

$$|(5x - 3) - 2| = |5x - 5| < \epsilon$$
$$5|x - 1| < \epsilon$$
$$|x - 1| < \epsilon/5.$$

Thus, we can take $\delta = \epsilon/5$ (Figure 2.18). If $0 < |x - 1| < \delta = \epsilon/5$, then

$$|(5x - 3) - 2| = |5x - 5| = 5|x - 1| < 5(\epsilon/5) = \epsilon,$$

which proves that $\lim_{x \to 1}(5x - 3) = 2$.

The value of $\delta = \epsilon/5$ is not the only value that will make $0 < |x - 1| < \delta$ imply $|5x - 5| < \epsilon$. Any smaller positive δ will do as well. The definition does not ask for a "best" positive δ, just one that will work. ■

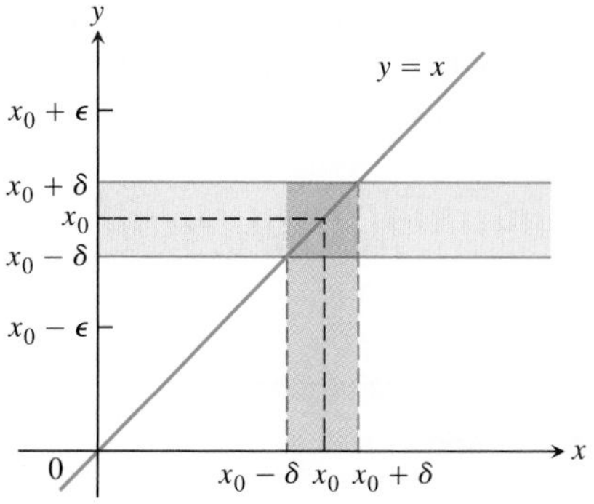

FIGURE 2.19 For the function $f(x) = x$, we find that $0 < |x - x_0| < \delta$ will guarantee $|f(x) - x_0| < \epsilon$ whenever $\delta \le \epsilon$ (Example 3a).

EXAMPLE 3 Prove:

(a) $\lim_{x \to x_0} x = x_0$ **(b)** $\lim_{x \to x_0} k = k$ (k constant).

Solution

(a) Let $\epsilon > 0$ be given. We must find $\delta > 0$ such that for all x

$$0 < |x - x_0| < \delta \quad \text{implies} \quad |x - x_0| < \epsilon.$$

The implication will hold if δ equals ϵ or any smaller positive number (Figure 2.19). This proves that $\lim_{x \to x_0} x = x_0$.

(b) Let $\epsilon > 0$ be given. We must find $\delta > 0$ such that for all x

$$0 < |x - x_0| < \delta \quad \text{implies} \quad |k - k| < \epsilon.$$

Since $k - k = 0$, we can use any positive number for δ and the implication will hold (Figure 2.20). This proves that $\lim_{x \to x_0} k = k$. ■

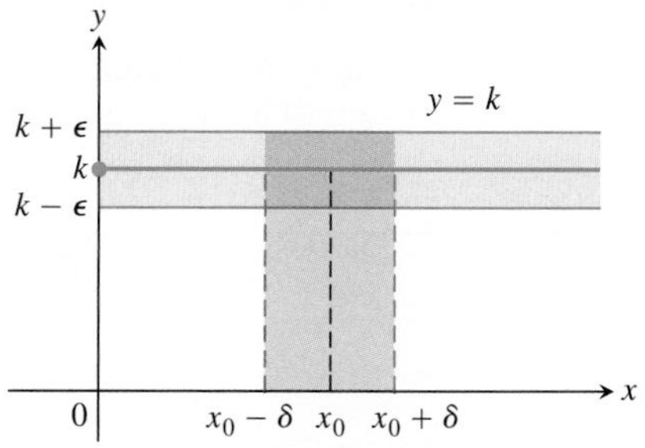

FIGURE 2.20 For the function $f(x) = k$, we find that $|f(x) - k| < \epsilon$ for any positive δ (Example 3b).

Finding Deltas Algebraically for Given Epsilons

In Examples 2 and 3, the interval of values about x_0 for which $|f(x) - L|$ was less than ϵ was symmetric about x_0 and we could take δ to be half the length of that interval. When such symmetry is absent, as it usually is, we can take δ to be the distance from x_0 to the interval's *nearer* endpoint.

EXAMPLE 4 For the limit $\lim_{x\to 5}\sqrt{x-1} = 2$, find a $\delta > 0$ that works for $\epsilon = 1$. That is, find a $\delta > 0$ such that for all x

$$0 < |x - 5| < \delta \quad \Rightarrow \quad |\sqrt{x-1} - 2| < 1.$$

Solution We organize the search into two steps, as discussed below.

1. *Solve the inequality* $|\sqrt{x-1} - 2| < 1$ *to find an interval containing* $x_0 = 5$ *on which the inequality holds for all* $x \neq x_0$.

$$\begin{aligned} |\sqrt{x-1} - 2| &< 1 \\ -1 < \sqrt{x-1} - 2 &< 1 \\ 1 < \sqrt{x-1} &< 3 \\ 1 < x - 1 &< 9 \\ 2 < x &< 10 \end{aligned}$$

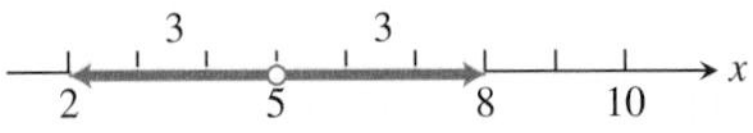

FIGURE 2.21 An open interval of radius 3 about $x_0 = 5$ will lie inside the open interval (2, 10).

The inequality holds for all x in the open interval (2, 10), so it holds for all $x \neq 5$ in this interval as well.

2. *Find a value of* $\delta > 0$ *to place the centered interval* $5 - \delta < x < 5 + \delta$ (centered at $x_0 = 5$) *inside the interval* (2, 10). The distance from 5 to the nearer endpoint of (2, 10) is 3 (Figure 2.21). If we take $\delta = 3$ or any smaller positive number, then the inequality $0 < |x - 5| < \delta$ will automatically place x between 2 and 10 to make $|\sqrt{x-1} - 2| < 1$ (Figure 2.22)

$$0 < |x - 5| < 3 \quad \Rightarrow \quad |\sqrt{x-1} - 2| < 1.$$

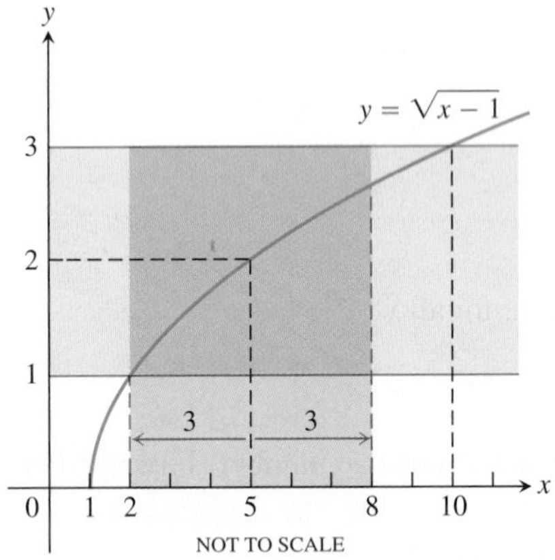

FIGURE 2.22 The function and intervals in Example 4.

How to Find Algebraically a δ for a Given f, L, x_0, and $\epsilon > 0$

The process of finding a $\delta > 0$ such that for all x

$$0 < |x - x_0| < \delta \quad \Rightarrow \quad |f(x) - L| < \epsilon$$

can be accomplished in two steps.

1. *Solve the inequality* $|f(x) - L| < \epsilon$ to find an open interval (a, b) containing x_0 on which the inequality holds for all $x \neq x_0$.
2. *Find a value of* $\delta > 0$ that places the open interval $(x_0 - \delta, x_0 + \delta)$ centered at x_0 inside the interval (a, b). The inequality $|f(x) - L| < \epsilon$ will hold for all $x \neq x_0$ in this δ-interval.

EXAMPLE 5 Prove that $\lim_{x\to 2} f(x) = 4$ if

$$f(x) = \begin{cases} x^2, & x \neq 2 \\ 1, & x = 2. \end{cases}$$

Solution Our task is to show that given $\epsilon > 0$ there exists a $\delta > 0$ such that for all x

$$0 < |x - 2| < \delta \quad \Rightarrow \quad |f(x) - 4| < \epsilon.$$

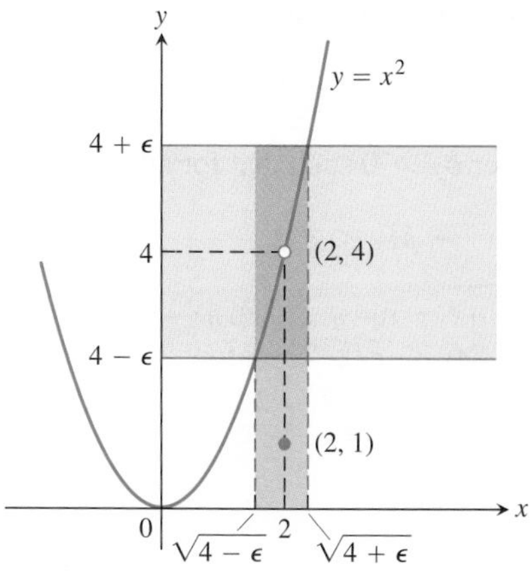

FIGURE 2.23 An interval containing $x = 2$ so that the function in Example 5 satisfies $|f(x) - 4| < \epsilon$.

1. *Solve the inequality $|f(x) - 4| < \epsilon$ to find an open interval containing $x_0 = 2$ on which the inequality holds for all $x \neq x_0$.*

For $x \neq x_0 = 2$, we have $f(x) = x^2$, and the inequality to solve is $|x^2 - 4| < \epsilon$:

$$|x^2 - 4| < \epsilon$$
$$-\epsilon < x^2 - 4 < \epsilon$$
$$4 - \epsilon < x^2 < 4 + \epsilon$$
$$\sqrt{4 - \epsilon} < |x| < \sqrt{4 + \epsilon} \qquad \text{Assumes } \epsilon < 4\text{; see below.}$$
$$\sqrt{4 - \epsilon} < x < \sqrt{4 + \epsilon}. \qquad \text{An open interval about } x_0 = 2 \text{ that solves the inequality}$$

The inequality $|f(x) - 4| < \epsilon$ holds for all $x \neq 2$ in the open interval $\left(\sqrt{4 - \epsilon}, \sqrt{4 + \epsilon}\right)$ (Figure 2.23).

2. *Find a value of $\delta > 0$ that places the centered interval $(2 - \delta, 2 + \delta)$ inside the interval $\left(\sqrt{4 - \epsilon}, \sqrt{4 + \epsilon}\right)$.*

Take δ to be the distance from $x_0 = 2$ to the nearer endpoint of $\left(\sqrt{4 - \epsilon}, \sqrt{4 + \epsilon}\right)$. In other words, take $\delta = \min\left\{2 - \sqrt{4 - \epsilon}, \sqrt{4 + \epsilon} - 2\right\}$, the *minimum* (the smaller) of the two numbers $2 - \sqrt{4 - \epsilon}$ and $\sqrt{4 + \epsilon} - 2$. If δ has this or any smaller positive value, the inequality $0 < |x - 2| < \delta$ will automatically place x between $\sqrt{4 - \epsilon}$ and $\sqrt{4 + \epsilon}$ to make $|f(x) - 4| < \epsilon$. For all x,

$$0 < |x - 2| < \delta \quad \Rightarrow \quad |f(x) - 4| < \epsilon.$$

This completes the proof for $\epsilon < 4$.

If $\epsilon \geq 4$, then we take δ to be the distance from $x_0 = 2$ to the nearer endpoint of the interval $\left(0, \sqrt{4 + \epsilon}\right)$. In other words, take $\delta = \min\left\{2, \sqrt{4 + \epsilon} - 2\right\}$. (See Figure 2.23) ■

Using the Definition to Prove Theorems

We do not usually rely on the formal definition of limit to verify specific limits such as those in the preceding examples. Rather we appeal to general theorems about limits, in particular the theorems of Section 2.2. The definition is used to prove these theorems (Appendix 5). As an example, we prove part 1 of Theorem 1, the Sum Rule.

EXAMPLE 6 Given that $\lim_{x \to c} f(x) = L$ and $\lim_{x \to c} g(x) = M$, prove that

$$\lim_{x \to c} (f(x) + g(x)) = L + M.$$

Solution Let $\epsilon > 0$ be given. We want to find a positive number δ such that for all x

$$0 < |x - c| < \delta \quad \Rightarrow \quad |f(x) + g(x) - (L + M)| < \epsilon.$$

Regrouping terms, we get

$$|f(x) + g(x) - (L + M)| = |(f(x) - L) + (g(x) - M)|$$
$$\leq |f(x) - L| + |g(x) - M|. \qquad \text{Triangle Inequality: } |a + b| \leq |a| + |b|$$

Since $\lim_{x\to c} f(x) = L$, there exists a number $\delta_1 > 0$ such that for all x

$$0 < |x - c| < \delta_1 \quad \Rightarrow \quad |f(x) - L| < \epsilon/2.$$

Similarly, since $\lim_{x\to c} g(x) = M$, there exists a number $\delta_2 > 0$ such that for all x

$$0 < |x - c| < \delta_2 \quad \Rightarrow \quad |g(x) - M| < \epsilon/2.$$

Let $\delta = \min\{\delta_1, \delta_2\}$, the smaller of δ_1 and δ_2. If $0 < |x - c| < \delta$ then $|x - c| < \delta_1$, so $|f(x) - L| < \epsilon/2$, and $|x - c| < \delta_2$, so $|g(x) - M| < \epsilon/2$. Therefore

$$|f(x) + g(x) - (L + M)| < \frac{\epsilon}{2} + \frac{\epsilon}{2} = \epsilon.$$

This shows that $\lim_{x\to c}(f(x) + g(x)) = L + M$. ■

Let's also prove Theorem 5 of Section 2.2.

EXAMPLE 7 Given that $\lim_{x\to c} f(x) = L$ and $\lim_{x\to c} g(x) = M$, and that $f(x) \le g(x)$ for all x in an open interval containing c (except possibly c itself), prove that $L \le M$.

Solution We use the method of proof by contradiction. Suppose, on the contrary, that $L > M$. Then by the limit of a difference property in Theorem 1,

$$\lim_{x\to c} (g(x) - f(x)) = M - L.$$

Therefore, for any $\epsilon > 0$, there exists $\delta > 0$ such that

$$|(g(x) - f(x)) - (M - L)| < \epsilon \qquad \text{whenever} \quad 0 < |x - c| < \delta.$$

Since $L - M > 0$ by hypothesis, we take $\epsilon = L - M$ in particular and we have a number $\delta > 0$ such that

$$|(g(x) - f(x)) - (M - L)| < L - M \qquad \text{whenever} \quad 0 < |x - c| < \delta.$$

Since $a \le |a|$ for any number a, we have

$$(g(x) - f(x)) - (M - L) < L - M \qquad \text{whenever} \quad 0 < |x - c| < \delta$$

which simplifies to

$$g(x) < f(x) \qquad \text{whenever} \quad 0 < |x - c| < \delta.$$

But this contradicts $f(x) \le g(x)$. Thus the inequality $L > M$ must be false. Therefore $L \le M$. ■

EXERCISES 2.3

In Exercises 1–6, sketch the interval (a, b) on the x-axis with the point x_0 inside. Then find a value of $\delta > 0$ such that for all x, $0 < |x - x_0| < \delta \Rightarrow a < x < b$.

1. $a = 1, \quad b = 7, \quad x_0 = 5$
2. $a = 1, \quad b = 7, \quad x_0 = 2$
3. $a = -7/2, \quad b = -1/2, \quad x_0 = -3$
4. $a = -7/2, \quad b = -1/2, \quad x_0 = -3/2$
5. $a = 4/9, \quad b = 4/7, \quad x_0 = 1/2$
6. $a = 2.7591, \quad b = 3.2391, \quad x_0 = 3$

In Exercises 7–14, use the graphs to find a $\delta > 0$ such that for all x

$$0 < |x - x_0| < \delta \quad \Rightarrow \quad |f(x) - L| < \epsilon.$$

7.

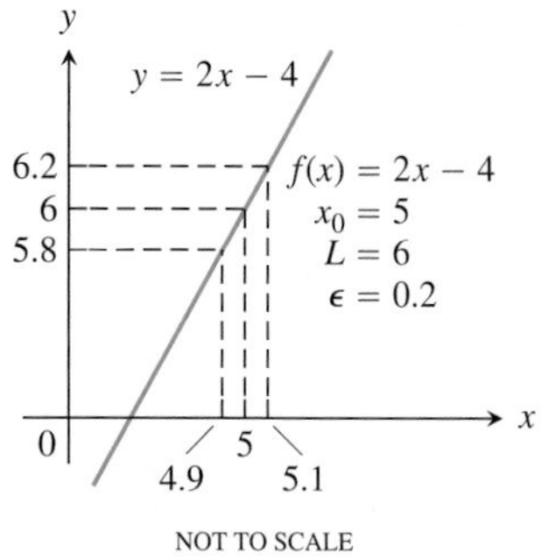

8.

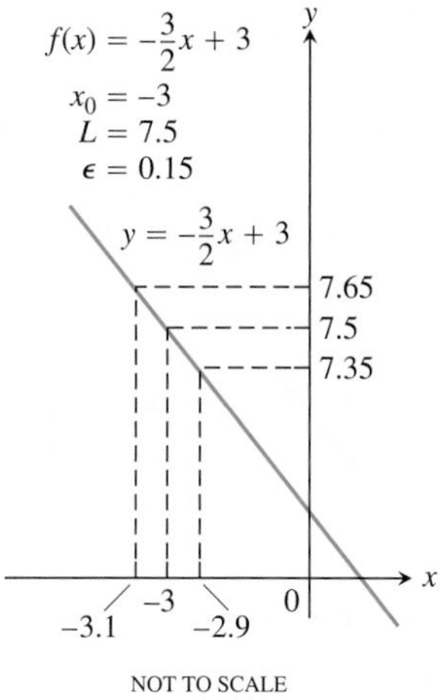

9.

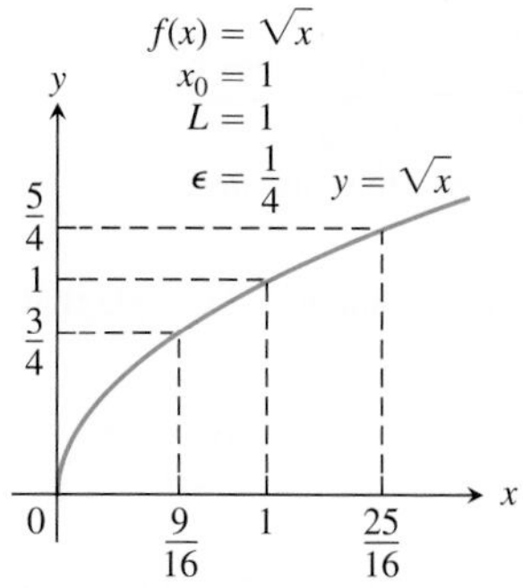

10.

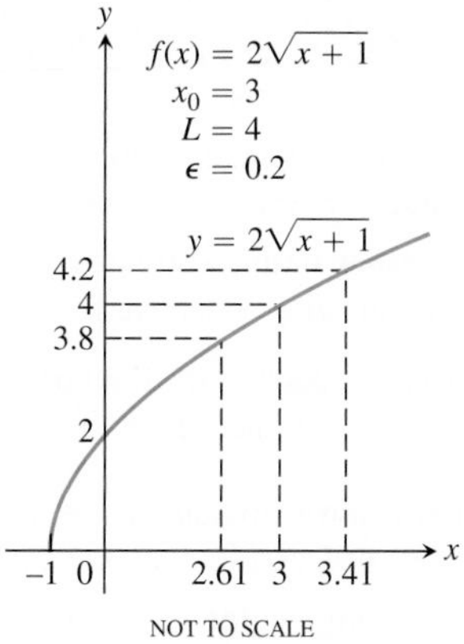

11.

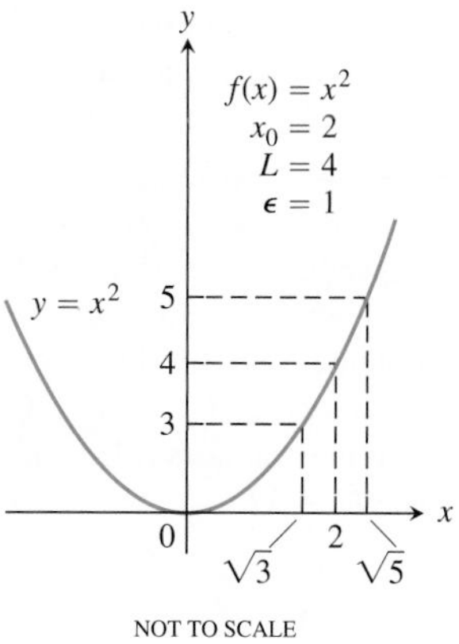

12.

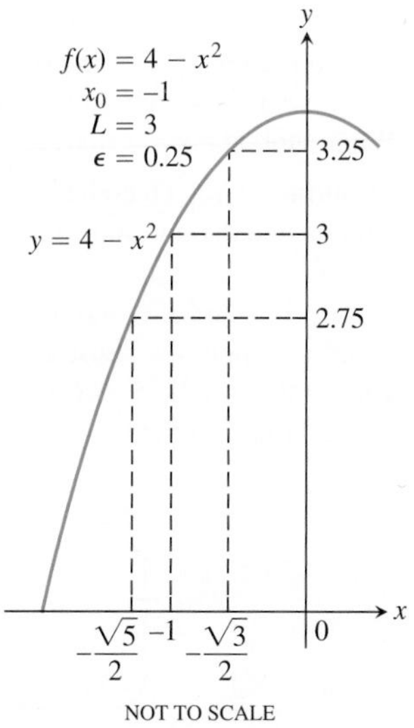

13.

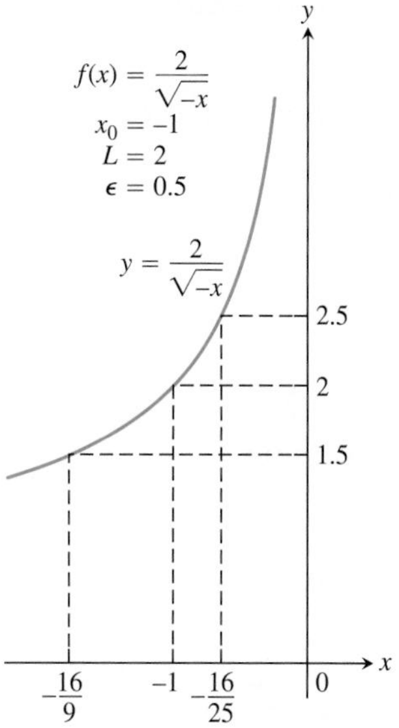

14.

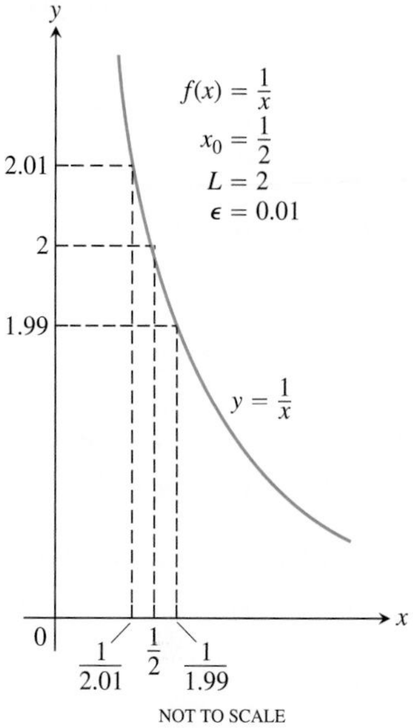

Each of Exercises 15–30 gives a function $f(x)$ and numbers L, x_0 and $\epsilon > 0$. In each case, find an open interval about x_0 on which the inequality $|f(x) - L| < \epsilon$ holds. Then give a value for $\delta > 0$ such that for all x satisfying $0 < |x - x_0| < \delta$ the inequality $|f(x) - L| < \epsilon$ holds.

15. $f(x) = x + 1, \quad L = 5, \quad x_0 = 4, \quad \epsilon = 0.01$

16. $f(x) = 2x - 2, \quad L = -6, \quad x_0 = -2, \quad \epsilon = 0.02$

17. $f(x) = \sqrt{x + 1}, \quad L = 1, \quad x_0 = 0, \quad \epsilon = 0.1$

18. $f(x) = \sqrt{x}, \quad L = 1/2, \quad x_0 = 1/4, \quad \epsilon = 0.1$

19. $f(x) = \sqrt{19 - x}, \quad L = 3, \quad x_0 = 10, \quad \epsilon = 1$

20. $f(x) = \sqrt{x - 7}, \quad L = 4, \quad x_0 = 23, \quad \epsilon = 1$

21. $f(x) = 1/x, \quad L = 1/4, \quad x_0 = 4, \quad \epsilon = 0.05$

22. $f(x) = x^2, \quad L = 3, \quad x_0 = \sqrt{3}, \quad \epsilon = 0.1$

23. $f(x) = x^2, \quad L = 4, \quad x_0 = -2, \quad \epsilon = 0.5$

24. $f(x) = 1/x, \quad L = -1, \quad x_0 = -1, \quad \epsilon = 0.1$

25. $f(x) = x^2 - 5, \quad L = 11, \quad x_0 = 4, \quad \epsilon = 1$

26. $f(x) = 120/x, \quad L = 5, \quad x_0 = 24, \quad \epsilon = 1$

27. $f(x) = mx, \quad m > 0, \quad L = 2m, \quad x_0 = 2, \quad \epsilon = 0.03$

28. $f(x) = mx, \quad m > 0, \quad L = 3m, \quad x_0 = 3, \quad \epsilon = c > 0$

29. $f(x) = mx + b, \quad m > 0, \quad L = (m/2) + b,$
$x_0 = 1/2, \quad \epsilon = c > 0$

30. $f(x) = mx + b, \quad m > 0, \quad L = m + b, \quad x_0 = 1,$
$\epsilon = 0.05$

Each of Exercises 31–36 gives a function $f(x)$, a point x_0, and a positive number ϵ. Find $L = \lim_{x \to x_0} f(x)$. Then find a number $\delta > 0$ such that for all x

$$0 < |x - x_0| < \delta \quad \Rightarrow \quad |f(x) - L| < \epsilon.$$

31. $f(x) = 3 - 2x, \quad x_0 = 3, \quad \epsilon = 0.02$

32. $f(x) = -3x - 2, \quad x_0 = -1, \quad \epsilon = 0.03$

33. $f(x) = \dfrac{x^2 - 4}{x - 2}, \quad x_0 = 2, \quad \epsilon = 0.05$

34. $f(x) = \dfrac{x^2 + 6x + 5}{x + 5}, \quad x_0 = -5, \quad \epsilon = 0.05$

35. $f(x) = \sqrt{1 - 5x}, \quad x_0 = -3, \quad \epsilon = 0.5$

36. $f(x) = 4/x, \quad x_0 = 2, \quad \epsilon = 0.4$

Prove the limit statements in Exercises 37–50.

37. $\lim_{x \to 4} (9 - x) = 5$

38. $\lim_{x \to 3} (3x - 7) = 2$

39. $\lim_{x \to 9} \sqrt{x - 5} = 2$

40. $\lim_{x \to 0} \sqrt{4 - x} = 2$

41. $\lim_{x \to 1} f(x) = 1$ if $f(x) = \begin{cases} x^2, & x \neq 1 \\ 2, & x = 1 \end{cases}$

42. $\lim_{x \to -2} f(x) = 4$ if $f(x) = \begin{cases} x^2, & x \neq -2 \\ 1, & x = -2 \end{cases}$

43. $\lim_{x \to 1} \dfrac{1}{x} = 1$

44. $\lim_{x \to \sqrt{3}} \dfrac{1}{x^2} = \dfrac{1}{3}$

45. $\lim_{x \to -3} \dfrac{x^2 - 9}{x + 3} = -6$

46. $\lim_{x \to 1} \dfrac{x^2 - 1}{x - 1} = 2$

47. $\lim_{x \to 1} f(x) = 2$ if $f(x) = \begin{cases} 4 - 2x, & x < 1 \\ 6x - 4, & x \geq 1 \end{cases}$

48. $\lim_{x \to 0} f(x) = 0$ if $f(x) = \begin{cases} 2x, & x < 0 \\ x/2, & x \geq 0 \end{cases}$

49. $\lim_{x \to 0} x \sin \dfrac{1}{x} = 0$

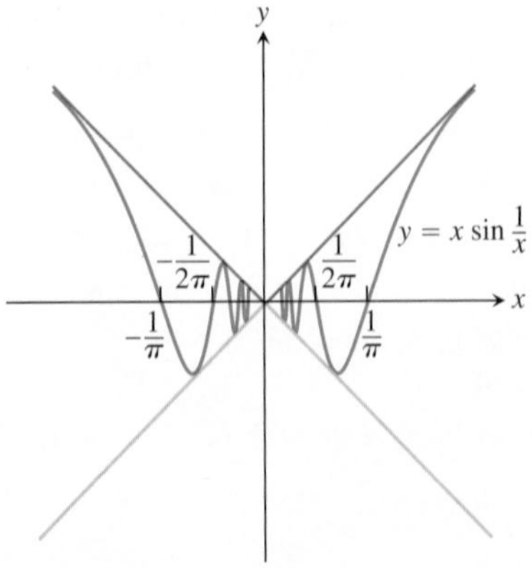

50. $\lim_{x \to 0} x^2 \sin \dfrac{1}{x} = 0$

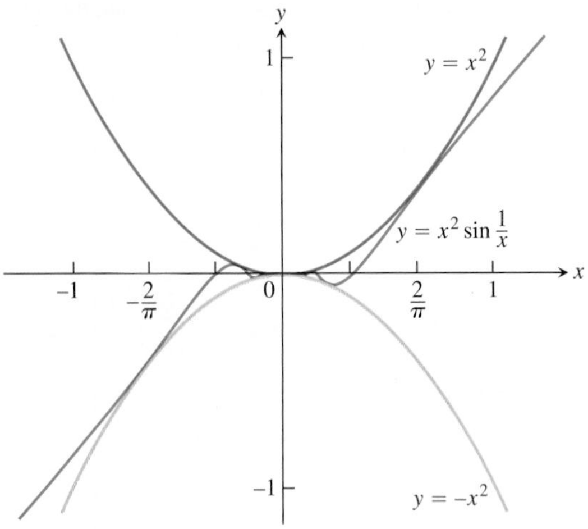

51. Define what it means to say that $\lim_{x \to 0} g(x) = k$.

52. Prove that $\lim_{x \to c} f(x) = L$ if and only if $\lim_{h \to 0} f(h + c) = L$.

53. A wrong statement about limits Show by example that the following statement is wrong.

> The number L is the limit of $f(x)$ as x approaches x_0 if $f(x)$ gets closer to L as x approaches x_0.

Explain why the function in your example does not have the given value of L as a limit as $x \to x_0$.

54. Another wrong statement about limits Show by example that the following statement is wrong.

> The number L is the limit of $f(x)$ as x approaches x_0 if, given any $\epsilon > 0$, there exists a value of x for which $|f(x) - L| < \epsilon$.

Explain why the function in your example does not have the given value of L as a limit as $x \to x_0$.

T **55. Grinding engine cylinders** Before contracting to grind engine cylinders to a cross-sectional area of 9 in^2, you need to know how much deviation from the ideal cylinder diameter of $x_0 = 3.385$ in. you can allow and still have the area come within 0.01 in^2 of the required 9 in^2. To find out, you let $A = \pi(x/2)^2$ and look for the interval in which you must hold x to make $|A - 9| \leq 0.01$. What interval do you find?

56. Manufacturing electrical resistors Ohm's law for electrical circuits like the one shown in the accompanying figure states that $V = RI$. In this equation, V is a constant voltage, I is the current in amperes, and R is the resistance in ohms. Your firm has been asked to supply the resistors for a circuit in which V will be 120 volts and I is to be 5 ± 0.1 amp. In what interval does R have to lie for I to be within 0.1 amp of the value $I_0 = 5$?

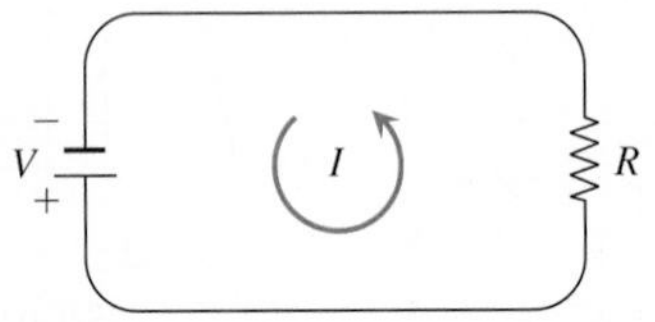

Showing L is not a limit We can prove that $\lim_{x \to x_0} f(x) \neq L$ by providing an $\epsilon > 0$ such that no possible $\delta > 0$ satisfies the condition

$$\text{For all } x, \quad 0 < |x - x_0| < \delta \quad \Rightarrow \quad |f(x) - L| < \epsilon.$$

We accomplish this for our candidate ϵ by showing that for each $\delta > 0$ there exists a value of x such that

$$0 < |x - x_0| < \delta \quad \text{and} \quad |f(x) - L| \geq \epsilon.$$

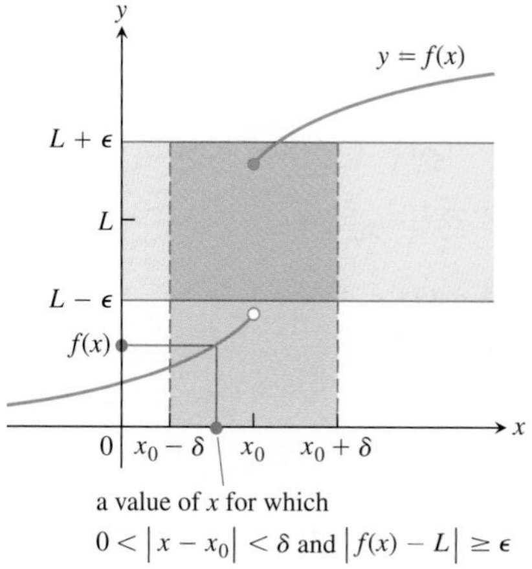

57. Let $f(x) = \begin{cases} x, & x < 1 \\ x + 1, & x > 1. \end{cases}$

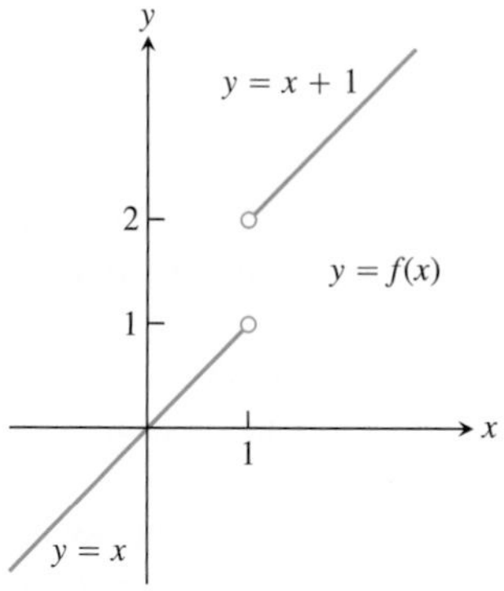

a. Let $\epsilon = 1/2$. Show that no possible $\delta > 0$ satisfies the following condition:

$$\text{For all } x, \quad 0 < |x - 1| < \delta \quad \Rightarrow \quad |f(x) - 2| < 1/2.$$

That is, for each $\delta > 0$ show that there is a value of x such that

$$0 < |x - 1| < \delta \quad \text{and} \quad |f(x) - 2| \geq 1/2.$$

This will show that $\lim_{x \to 1} f(x) \neq 2$.

b. Show that $\lim_{x \to 1} f(x) \neq 1$.

c. Show that $\lim_{x \to 1} f(x) \neq 1.5$.

58. Let $h(x) = \begin{cases} x^2, & x < 2 \\ 3, & x = 2 \\ 2, & x > 2. \end{cases}$

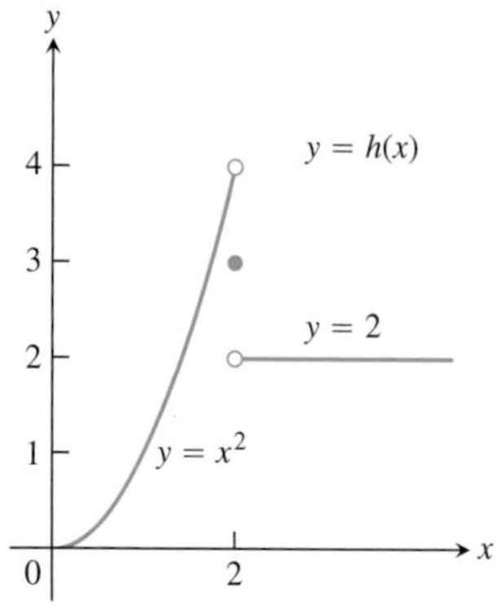

Show that

a. $\lim_{x \to 2} h(x) \neq 4$

b. $\lim_{x \to 2} h(x) \neq 3$

c. $\lim_{x \to 2} h(x) \neq 2$

59. For the function graphed here, explain why

a. $\lim_{x \to 3} f(x) \neq 4$

b. $\lim_{x \to 3} f(x) \neq 4.8$

c. $\lim_{x \to 3} f(x) \neq 3$

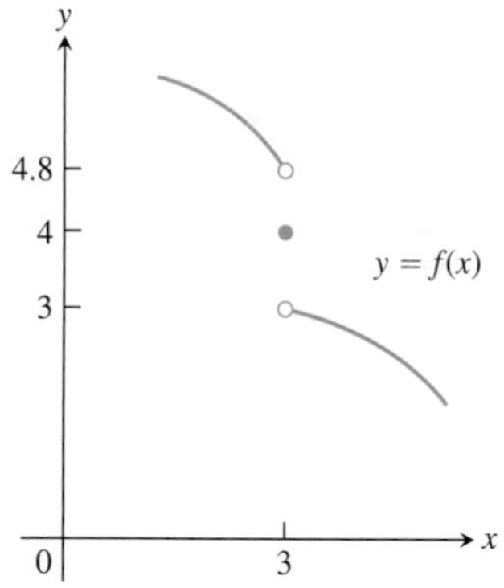

60. a. For the function graphed here, show that $\lim_{x \to -1} g(x) \neq 2$.

b. Does $\lim_{x \to -1} g(x)$ appear to exist? If so, what is the value of the limit? If not, why not?

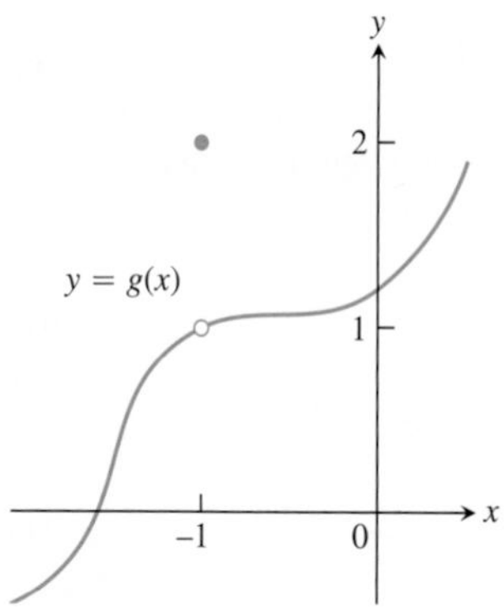

COMPUTER EXPLORATIONS

In Exercises 61–66, you will further explore finding deltas graphically. Use a CAS to perform the following steps:

a. Plot the function $y = f(x)$ near the point x_0 being approached.

b. Guess the value of the limit L and then evaluate the limit symbolically to see if you guessed correctly.

c. Using the value $\epsilon = 0.2$, graph the banding lines $y_1 = L - \epsilon$ and $y_2 = L + \epsilon$ together with the function f near x_0.

d. From your graph in part (c), estimate a $\delta > 0$ such that for all x

$$0 < |x - x_0| < \delta \quad \Rightarrow \quad |f(x) - L| < \epsilon.$$

Test your estimate by plotting f, y_1, and y_2 over the interval $0 < |x - x_0| < \delta$. For your viewing window use $x_0 - 2\delta \le x \le x_0 + 2\delta$ and $L - 2\epsilon \le y \le L + 2\epsilon$. If any function values lie outside the interval $[L - \epsilon, L + \epsilon]$, your choice of δ was too large. Try again with a smaller estimate.

e. Repeat parts (c) and (d) successively for $\epsilon = 0.1, 0.05$, and 0.001.

61. $f(x) = \dfrac{x^4 - 81}{x - 3}$, $x_0 = 3$

62. $f(x) = \dfrac{5x^3 + 9x^2}{2x^5 + 3x^2}$, $x_0 = 0$

63. $f(x) = \dfrac{\sin 2x}{3x}$, $x_0 = 0$

64. $f(x) = \dfrac{x(1 - \cos x)}{x - \sin x}$, $x_0 = 0$

65. $f(x) = \dfrac{\sqrt[3]{x} - 1}{x - 1}$, $x_0 = 1$

66. $f(x) = \dfrac{3x^2 - (7x + 1)\sqrt{x} + 5}{x - 1}$, $x_0 = 1$

2.4 One-Sided Limits and Limits at Infinity

In this section we extend the limit concept to *one-sided limits*, which are limits as x approaches the number x_0 from the left-hand side (where $x < x_0$) or the right-hand side ($x > x_0$) only. We also analyze the graphs of certain rational functions as well as other functions with limit behavior as $x \to \pm\infty$.

One-Sided Limits

To have a limit L as x approaches c, a function f must be defined on *both sides* of c and its values $f(x)$ must approach L as x approaches c from either side. Because of this, ordinary limits are called **two-sided**.

If f fails to have a two-sided limit at c, it may still have a one-sided limit, that is, a limit if the approach is only from one side. If the approach is from the right, the limit is a **right-hand limit**. From the left, it is a **left-hand limit**.

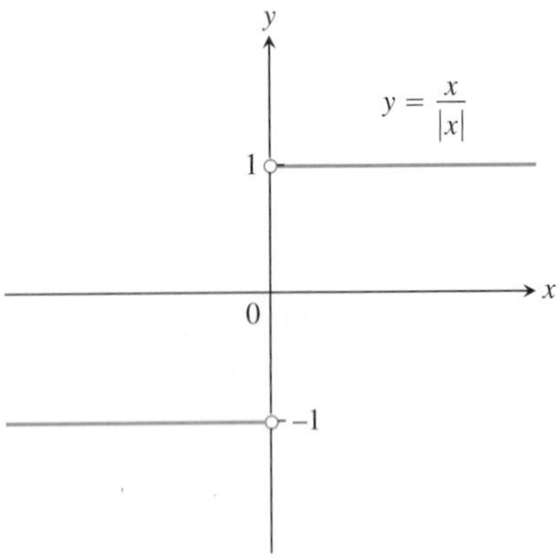

FIGURE 2.24 Different right-hand and left-hand limits at the origin.

The function $f(x) = x/|x|$ (Figure 2.24) has limit 1 as x approaches 0 from the right, and limit -1 as x approaches 0 from the left. Since these one-sided limit values are not the same, there is no single number that $f(x)$ approaches as x approaches 0. So $f(x)$ does not have a (two-sided) limit at 0.

Intuitively, if $f(x)$ is defined on an interval (c, b), where $c < b$, and approaches arbitrarily close to L as x approaches c from within that interval, then f has **right-hand limit** L at c. We write

$$\lim_{x \to c^+} f(x) = L.$$

The symbol "$x \to c^+$" means that we consider only values of x greater than c.

Similarly, if $f(x)$ is defined on an interval (a, c), where $a < c$ and approaches arbitrarily close to M as x approaches c from within that interval, then f has **left-hand limit** M at c. We write

$$\lim_{x \to c^-} f(x) = M.$$

The symbol "$x \to c^-$" means that we consider only x values less than c.

These informal definitions are illustrated in Figure 2.25. For the function $f(x) = x/|x|$ in Figure 2.24 we have

$$\lim_{x \to 0^+} f(x) = 1 \qquad \text{and} \qquad \lim_{x \to 0^-} f(x) = -1.$$

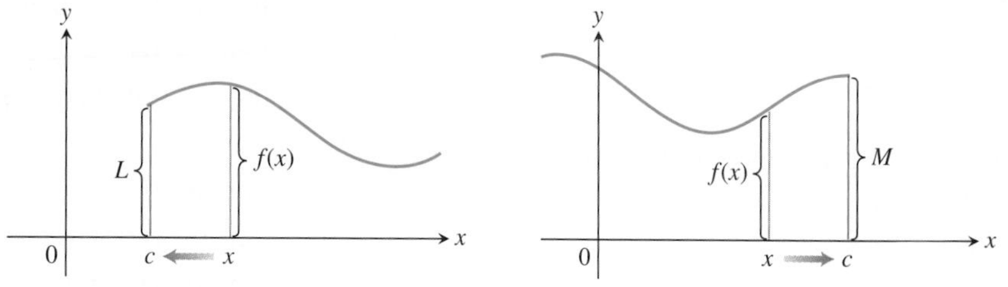

(a) $\lim_{x \to c^+} f(x) = L$ (b) $\lim_{x \to c^-} f(x) = M$

FIGURE 2.25 (a) Right-hand limit as x approaches c. (b) Left-hand limit as x approaches c.

EXAMPLE 1 The domain of $f(x) = \sqrt{4 - x^2}$ is $[-2, 2]$; its graph is the semicircle in Figure 2.26. We have

$$\lim_{x \to -2^+} \sqrt{4 - x^2} = 0 \qquad \text{and} \qquad \lim_{x \to 2^-} \sqrt{4 - x^2} = 0.$$

The function does not have a left-hand limit at $x = -2$ or a right-hand limit at $x = 2$. It does not have ordinary two-sided limits at either -2 or 2. ■

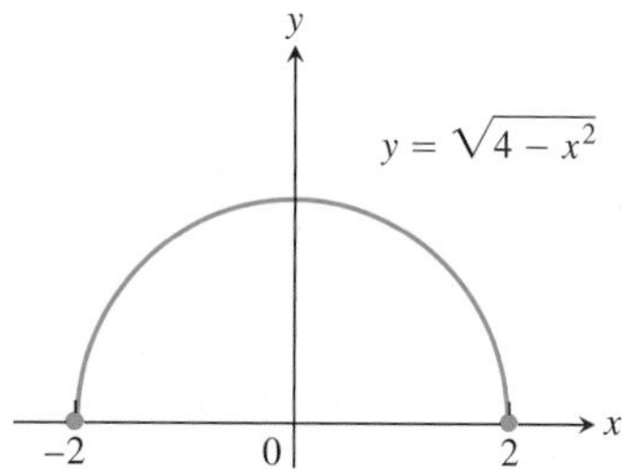

FIGURE 2.26 $\lim_{x \to 2^-} \sqrt{4 - x^2} = 0$ and $\lim_{x \to -2^+} \sqrt{4 - x^2} = 0$ (Example 1).

One-sided limits have all the properties listed in Theorem 1 in Section 2.2. The right-hand limit of the sum of two functions is the sum of their right-hand limits, and so on. The theorems for limits of polynomials and rational functions hold with one-sided limits, as does the Sandwich Theorem and Theorem 5. One-sided limits are related to limits in the following way.

THEOREM 6 A function $f(x)$ has a limit as x approaches c if and only if it has left-hand and right-hand limits there and these one-sided limits are equal:

$$\lim_{x \to c} f(x) = L \quad \Leftrightarrow \quad \lim_{x \to c^-} f(x) = L \quad \text{and} \quad \lim_{x \to c^+} f(x) = L.$$

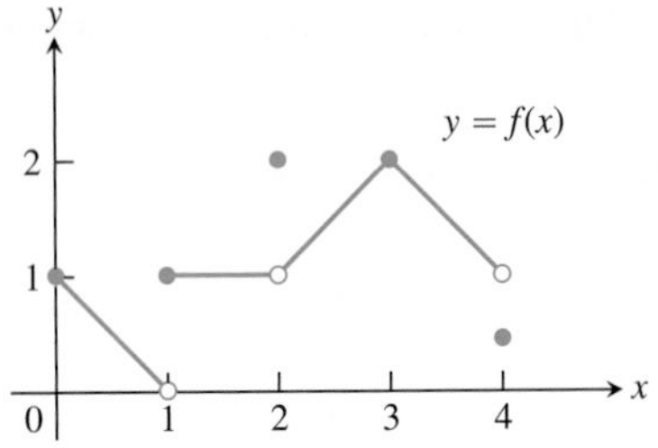

FIGURE 2.27 Graph of the function in Example 2.

EXAMPLE 2 For the function graphed in Figure 2.27,

At $x = 0$: $\lim_{x\to 0^+} f(x) = 1$,

$\lim_{x\to 0^-} f(x)$ and $\lim_{x\to 0} f(x)$ do not exist. The function is not defined to the left of $x = 0$.

At $x = 1$: $\lim_{x\to 1^-} f(x) = 0$ even though $f(1) = 1$,

$\lim_{x\to 1^+} f(x) = 1$,

$\lim_{x\to 1} f(x)$ does not exist. The right- and left-hand limits are not equal.

At $x = 2$: $\lim_{x\to 2^-} f(x) = 1$,

$\lim_{x\to 2^+} f(x) = 1$,

$\lim_{x\to 2} f(x) = 1$ even though $f(2) = 2$.

At $x = 3$: $\lim_{x\to 3^-} f(x) = \lim_{x\to 3^+} f(x) = \lim_{x\to 3} f(x) = f(3) = 2$.

At $x = 4$: $\lim_{x\to 4^-} f(x) = 1$ even though $f(4) \neq 1$,

$\lim_{x\to 4^+} f(x)$ and $\lim_{x\to 4} f(x)$ do not exist. The function is not defined to the right of $x = 4$.

At every other point c in [0, 4], $f(x)$ has limit $f(c)$. ■

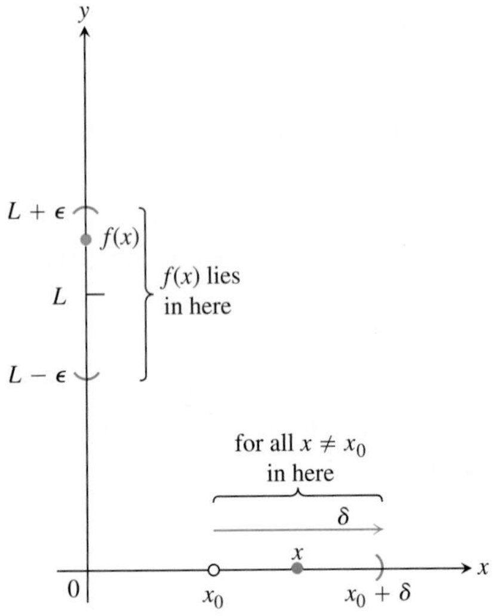

FIGURE 2.28 Intervals associated with the definition of right-hand limit.

Precise Definitions of One-Sided Limits

The formal definition of the limit in Section 2.3 is readily modified for one-sided limits.

DEFINITIONS We say that $f(x)$ has **right-hand limit L at x_0**, and write

$$\lim_{x\to x_0^+} f(x) = L \qquad \text{(See Figure 2.28)}$$

if for every number $\epsilon > 0$ there exists a corresponding number $\delta > 0$ such that for all x

$$x_0 < x < x_0 + \delta \qquad \Rightarrow \qquad |f(x) - L| < \epsilon.$$

We say that f has **left-hand limit L at x_0**, and write

$$\lim_{x\to x_0^-} f(x) = L \qquad \text{(See Figure 2.29)}$$

if for every number $\epsilon > 0$ there exists a corresponding number $\delta > 0$ such that for all x

$$x_0 - \delta < x < x_0 \qquad \Rightarrow \qquad |f(x) - L| < \epsilon.$$

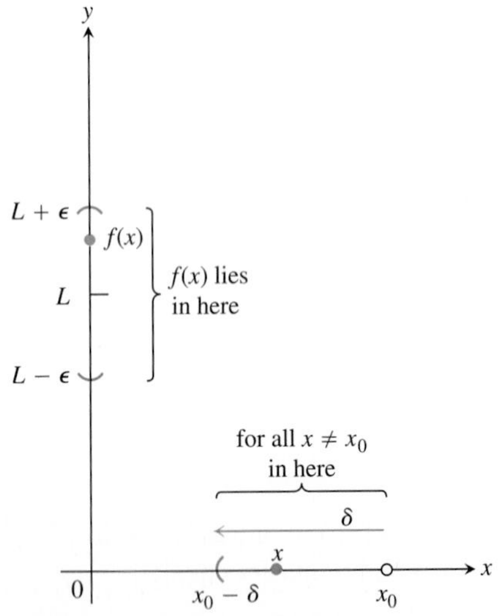

FIGURE 2.29 Intervals associated with the definition of left-hand limit.

EXAMPLE 3 Prove that

$$\lim_{x\to 0^+} \sqrt{x} = 0.$$

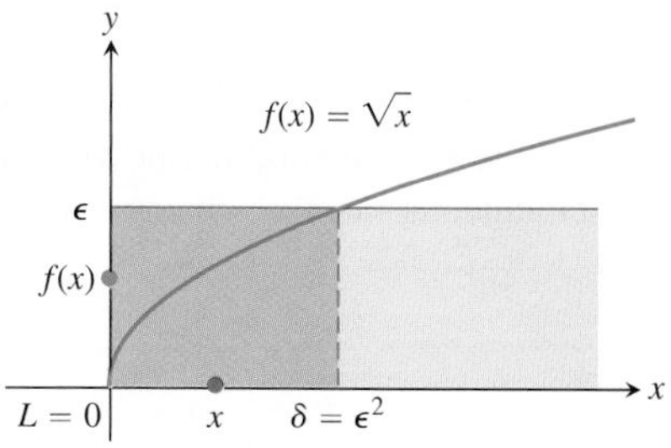

FIGURE 2.30 $\lim_{x\to 0^+} \sqrt{x} = 0$ in Example 3.

Solution Let $\epsilon > 0$ be given. Here $x_0 = 0$ and $L = 0$, so we want to find a $\delta > 0$ such that for all x

$$0 < x < \delta \quad \Rightarrow \quad |\sqrt{x} - 0| < \epsilon,$$

or

$$0 < x < \delta \quad \Rightarrow \quad \sqrt{x} < \epsilon.$$

Squaring both sides of this last inequality gives

$$x < \epsilon^2 \quad \text{if} \quad 0 < x < \delta.$$

If we choose $\delta = \epsilon^2$ we have

$$0 < x < \delta = \epsilon^2 \quad \Rightarrow \quad \sqrt{x} < \epsilon,$$

or

$$0 < x < \epsilon^2 \quad \Rightarrow \quad |\sqrt{x} - 0| < \epsilon.$$

According to the definition, this shows that $\lim_{x\to 0^+} \sqrt{x} = 0$ (Figure 2.30). ■

The functions examined so far have had some kind of limit at each point of interest. In general, that need not be the case.

EXAMPLE 4 Show that $y = \sin(1/x)$ has no limit as x approaches zero from either side (Figure 2.31).

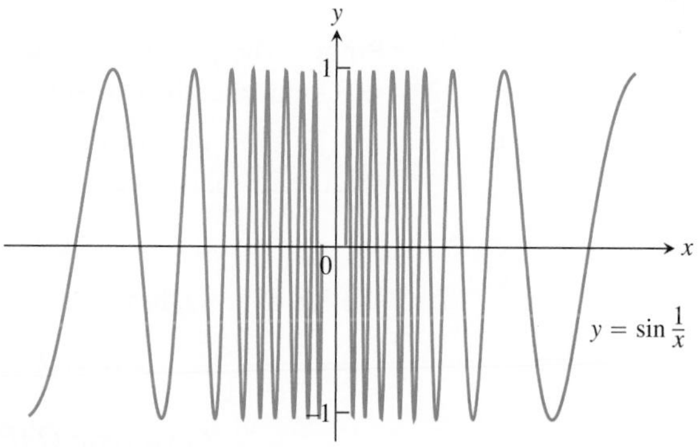

FIGURE 2.31 The function $y = \sin(1/x)$ has neither a right-hand nor a left-hand limit as x approaches zero (Example 4).

Solution As x approaches zero, its reciprocal, $1/x$, grows without bound and the values of $\sin(1/x)$ cycle repeatedly from -1 to 1. There is no single number L that the function's values stay increasingly close to as x approaches zero. This is true even if we restrict x to positive values or to negative values. The function has neither a right-hand limit nor a left-hand limit at $x = 0$. ■

Limits Involving $(\sin \theta)/\theta$

A central fact about $(\sin \theta)/\theta$ is that in radian measure its limit as $\theta \to 0$ is 1. We can see this in Figure 2.32 and confirm it algebraically using the Sandwich Theorem. You will see the importance of this limit in Section 3.4, where instantaneous rates of change of the trigonometric functions are studied.

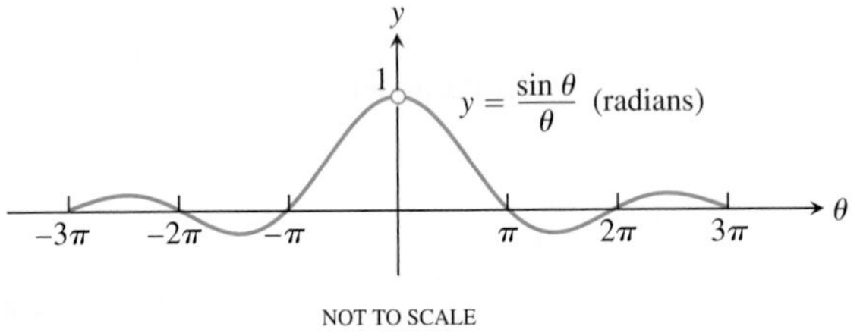

FIGURE 2.32 The graph of $f(\theta) = (\sin \theta)/\theta$ shows that the right- and left-hand limits as θ approaches 0 are both 1.

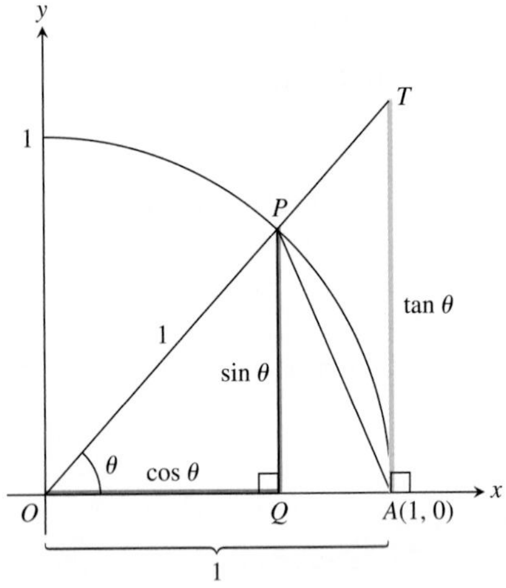

FIGURE 2.33 The figure for the proof of Theorem 7. $TA/OA = \tan\theta$, but $OA = 1$, so $TA = \tan\theta$.

THEOREM 7

$$\lim_{\theta \to 0} \frac{\sin \theta}{\theta} = 1 \qquad (\theta \text{ in radians}) \qquad (1)$$

Proof The plan is to show that the right-hand and left-hand limits are both 1. Then we will know that the two-sided limit is 1 as well.

To show that the right-hand limit is 1, we begin with positive values of θ less than $\pi/2$ (Figure 2.33). Notice that

$$\text{Area } \Delta OAP < \text{ area sector } OAP < \text{ area } \Delta OAT.$$

We can express these areas in terms of θ as follows:

$$\text{Area } \Delta OAP = \frac{1}{2}\text{base} \times \text{height} = \frac{1}{2}(1)(\sin\theta) = \frac{1}{2}\sin\theta$$

$$\text{Area sector } OAP = \frac{1}{2}r^2\theta = \frac{1}{2}(1)^2\theta = \frac{\theta}{2} \qquad (2)$$

$$\text{Area } \Delta OAT = \frac{1}{2}\text{base} \times \text{height} = \frac{1}{2}(1)(\tan\theta) = \frac{1}{2}\tan\theta.$$

Thus,

$$\frac{1}{2}\sin\theta < \frac{1}{2}\theta < \frac{1}{2}\tan\theta.$$

This last inequality goes the same way if we divide all three terms by the number $(1/2)\sin\theta$, which is positive since $0 < \theta < \pi/2$:

$$1 < \frac{\theta}{\sin\theta} < \frac{1}{\cos\theta}.$$

Equation (2) is where radian measure comes in: The area of sector OAP is $\theta/2$ only if θ is measured in radians.

Taking reciprocals reverses the inequalities:

$$1 > \frac{\sin\theta}{\theta} > \cos\theta.$$

Since $\lim_{\theta\to 0^+}\cos\theta = 1$ (Example 11b, Section 2.2), the Sandwich Theorem gives

$$\lim_{\theta\to 0^+}\frac{\sin\theta}{\theta} = 1.$$

Recall that $\sin\theta$ and θ are both *odd functions* (Section 1.1). Therefore, $f(\theta) = (\sin\theta)/\theta$ is an *even function*, with a graph symmetric about the y-axis (see Figure 2.32). This symmetry implies that the left-hand limit at 0 exists and has the same value as the right-hand limit:

$$\lim_{\theta\to 0^-}\frac{\sin\theta}{\theta} = 1 = \lim_{\theta\to 0^+}\frac{\sin\theta}{\theta},$$

so $\lim_{\theta\to 0}(\sin\theta)/\theta = 1$ by Theorem 6. ■

EXAMPLE 5 Show that **(a)** $\lim_{h\to 0}\dfrac{\cos h - 1}{h} = 0$ and **(b)** $\lim_{x\to 0}\dfrac{\sin 2x}{5x} = \dfrac{2}{5}$.

Solution

(a) Using the half-angle formula $\cos h = 1 - 2\sin^2(h/2)$, we calculate

$$\begin{aligned}\lim_{h\to 0}\frac{\cos h - 1}{h} &= \lim_{h\to 0} -\frac{2\sin^2(h/2)}{h}\\ &= -\lim_{\theta\to 0}\frac{\sin\theta}{\theta}\sin\theta \qquad \text{Let } \theta = h/2.\\ &= -(1)(0) = 0.\end{aligned}$$

(b) Equation (1) does not apply to the original fraction. We need a $2x$ in the denominator, not a $5x$. We produce it by multiplying numerator and denominator by $2/5$:

$$\begin{aligned}\lim_{x\to 0}\frac{\sin 2x}{5x} &= \lim_{x\to 0}\frac{(2/5)\cdot\sin 2x}{(2/5)\cdot 5x}\\ &= \frac{2}{5}\lim_{x\to 0}\frac{\sin 2x}{2x} \qquad \text{Now, Eq. (1) applies with } \theta = 2x.\\ &= \frac{2}{5}(1) = \frac{2}{5}\end{aligned}$$

■

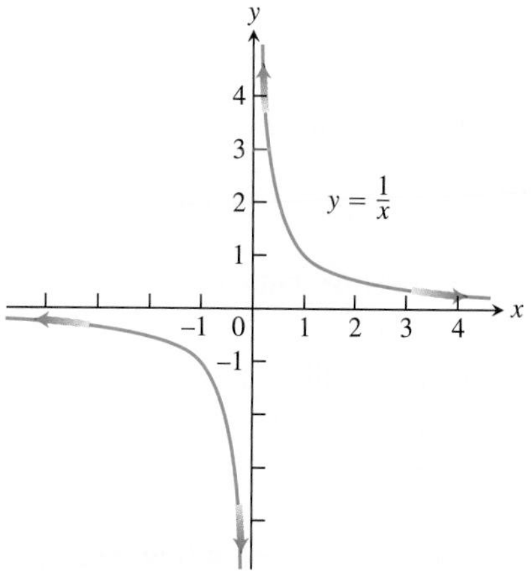

FIGURE 2.34 The graph of $y = 1/x$ approaches 0 as $x \to \infty$ or $x \to -\infty$.

Finite Limits as $x \to \pm\infty$

The symbol for infinity (∞) does not represent a real number. We use ∞ to describe the behavior of a function when the values in its domain or range outgrow all finite bounds. For example, the function $f(x) = 1/x$ is defined for all $x \neq 0$ (Figure 2.34). When x is positive and becomes increasingly large, $1/x$ becomes increasingly small. When x is negative and its magnitude becomes increasingly large, $1/x$ again becomes small. We summarize these observations by saying that $f(x) = 1/x$ has limit 0 as $x \to \pm\infty$ or that 0 is a *limit of* $f(x) = 1/x$ *at infinity and negative infinity*. Here is a precise definition.

DEFINITIONS

1. We say that $f(x)$ has the **limit L as x approaches infinity** and write
$$\lim_{x\to\infty} f(x) = L$$
if, for every number $\epsilon > 0$, there exists a corresponding number M such that for all x
$$x > M \quad\Rightarrow\quad |f(x) - L| < \epsilon.$$

2. We say that $f(x)$ has the **limit L as x approaches minus infinity** and write
$$\lim_{x\to-\infty} f(x) = L$$
if, for every number $\epsilon > 0$, there exists a corresponding number N such that for all x
$$x < N \quad\Rightarrow\quad |f(x) - L| < \epsilon.$$

Intuitively, $\lim_{x\to\infty} f(x) = L$ if, as x moves increasingly far from the origin in the positive direction, $f(x)$ gets arbitrarily close to L. Similarly, $\lim_{x\to-\infty} f(x) = L$ if, as x moves increasingly far from the origin in the negative direction, $f(x)$ gets arbitrarily close to L.

The strategy for calculating limits of functions as $x \to \pm\infty$ is similar to the one for finite limits in Section 2.2. There we first found the limits of the constant and identity functions $y = k$ and $y = x$. We then extended these results to other functions by applying a theorem about limits of algebraic combinations. Here we do the same thing, except that the starting functions are $y = k$ and $y = 1/x$ instead of $y = k$ and $y = x$.

The basic facts to be verified by applying the formal definition are
$$\lim_{x\to\pm\infty} k = k \qquad \text{and} \qquad \lim_{x\to\pm\infty} \frac{1}{x} = 0. \tag{3}$$

We prove the latter and leave the former to Exercises 75 and 76.

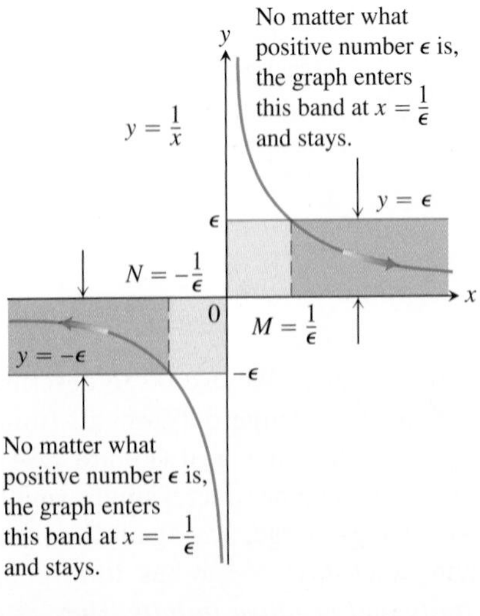

FIGURE 2.35 The geometry behind the argument in Example 6.

EXAMPLE 6 Show that

(a) $\lim_{x\to\infty} \frac{1}{x} = 0$ **(b)** $\lim_{x\to-\infty} \frac{1}{x} = 0.$

Solution

(a) Let $\epsilon > 0$ be given. We must find a number M such that for all x
$$x > M \quad\Rightarrow\quad \left|\frac{1}{x} - 0\right| = \left|\frac{1}{x}\right| < \epsilon.$$
The implication will hold if $M = 1/\epsilon$ or any larger positive number (Figure 2.35). This proves $\lim_{x\to\infty} (1/x) = 0$.

(b) Let $\epsilon > 0$ be given. We must find a number N such that for all x
$$x < N \quad\Rightarrow\quad \left|\frac{1}{x} - 0\right| = \left|\frac{1}{x}\right| < \epsilon.$$
The implication will hold if $N = -1/\epsilon$ or any number less than $-1/\epsilon$ (Figure 2.35). This proves $\lim_{x\to-\infty} (1/x) = 0$. ■

Limits at infinity have properties similar to those of finite limits.

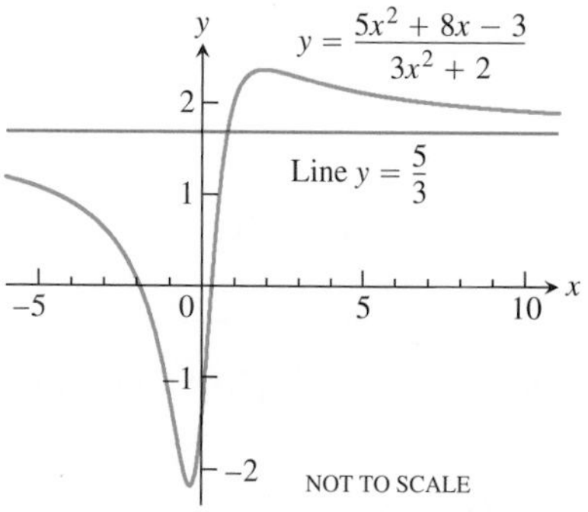

FIGURE 2.36 The graph of the function in Example 8. The graph approaches the line $y = 5/3$ as $|x|$ increases.

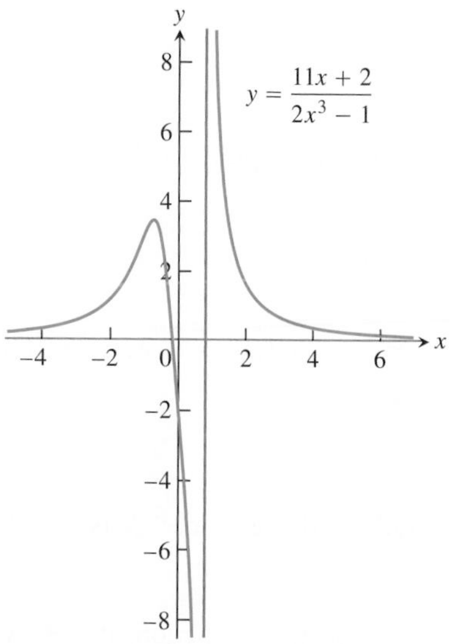

FIGURE 2.37 The graph of the function in Example 9. The graph approaches the x-axis as $|x|$ increases.

THEOREM 8—Limit Laws as $x \to \pm\infty$ If L, M, and k, are real numbers and

$$\lim_{x\to\pm\infty} f(x) = L \quad \text{and} \quad \lim_{x\to\pm\infty} g(x) = M, \quad \text{then}$$

1. *Sum Rule:* $\lim_{x\to\pm\infty}(f(x) + g(x)) = L + M$
2. *Difference Rule:* $\lim_{x\to\pm\infty}(f(x) - g(x)) = L - M$
3. *Product Rule:* $\lim_{x\to\pm\infty}(f(x)\cdot g(x)) = L\cdot M$
4. *Constant Multiple Rule:* $\lim_{x\to\pm\infty}(k\cdot f(x)) = k\cdot L$
5. *Quotient Rule:* $\lim_{x\to\pm\infty}\frac{f(x)}{g(x)} = \frac{L}{M}, \quad M \neq 0$
6. *Power Rule:* If r and s are integers with no common factors, $s \neq 0$, then $$\lim_{x\to\pm\infty}(f(x))^{r/s} = L^{r/s}$$ provided that $L^{r/s}$ is a real number. (If s is even, we assume that $L > 0$.)

These properties are just like the properties in Theorem 1, Section 2.2, and we use them the same way.

EXAMPLE 7

(a) $$\lim_{x\to\infty}\left(5 + \frac{1}{x}\right) = \lim_{x\to\infty} 5 + \lim_{x\to\infty}\frac{1}{x} \qquad \text{Sum Rule}$$
$$= 5 + 0 = 5 \qquad \text{Known limits}$$

(b) $$\lim_{x\to-\infty}\frac{\pi\sqrt{3}}{x^2} = \lim_{x\to-\infty}\pi\sqrt{3}\cdot\frac{1}{x}\cdot\frac{1}{x}$$
$$= \lim_{x\to-\infty}\pi\sqrt{3}\cdot\lim_{x\to-\infty}\frac{1}{x}\cdot\lim_{x\to-\infty}\frac{1}{x} \qquad \text{Product rule}$$
$$= \pi\sqrt{3}\cdot 0\cdot 0 = 0 \qquad \text{Known limits}$$ ■

Limits at Infinity of Rational Functions

To determine the limit of a rational function as $x \to \pm\infty$, we can divide the numerator and denominator by the highest power of x in the denominator. What happens then depends on the degrees of the polynomials involved.

EXAMPLE 8

$$\lim_{x\to\infty}\frac{5x^2 + 8x - 3}{3x^2 + 2} = \lim_{x\to\infty}\frac{5 + (8/x) - (3/x^2)}{3 + (2/x^2)} \qquad \text{Divide numerator and denominator by } x^2.$$
$$= \frac{5 + 0 - 0}{3 + 0} = \frac{5}{3} \qquad \text{See Fig. 2.36}$$ ■

EXAMPLE 9

$$\lim_{x\to-\infty}\frac{11x + 2}{2x^3 - 1} = \lim_{x\to-\infty}\frac{(11/x^2) + (2/x^3)}{2 - (1/x^3)} \qquad \text{Divide numerator and denominator by } x^3.$$
$$= \frac{0 + 0}{2 - 0} = 0 \qquad \text{See Fig. 2.37.}$$ ■

We give an example of the case when the degree of the numerator is greater than the degree of the denominator in the next section (Example 9, Section 2.5).

Horizontal Asymptotes

If the distance between the graph of a function and some fixed line approaches zero as a point on the graph moves increasingly far from the origin, we say that the graph approaches the line asymptotically and that the line is an *asymptote* of the graph.

Looking at $f(x) = 1/x$ (see Figure 2.34), we observe that the x-axis is an asymptote of the curve on the right because

$$\lim_{x\to\infty} \frac{1}{x} = 0$$

and on the left because

$$\lim_{x\to-\infty} \frac{1}{x} = 0.$$

We say that the x-axis is a *horizontal asymptote* of the graph of $f(x) = 1/x$.

DEFINITION A line $y = b$ is a **horizontal asymptote** of the graph of a function $y = f(x)$ if either

$$\lim_{x\to\infty} f(x) = b \quad \text{or} \quad \lim_{x\to-\infty} f(x) = b.$$

The curve

$$f(x) = \frac{5x^2 + 8x - 3}{3x^2 + 2}$$

sketched in Figure 2.36 (Example 8) has the line $y = 5/3$ as a horizontal asymptote on both the right and the left because

$$\lim_{x\to\infty} f(x) = \frac{5}{3} \quad \text{and} \quad \lim_{x\to-\infty} f(x) = \frac{5}{3}.$$

EXAMPLE 10 The x-axis (the line $y = 0$) is a horizontal asymptote of the graph of $y = e^x$ because

$$\lim_{x\to-\infty} e^x = 0.$$

To see this, we use the definition of a limit as x approaches $-\infty$. So let $\epsilon > 0$ be given, but arbitrary. We must find a constant N such that for all x,

$$x < N \quad \Rightarrow \quad \left|e^x - 0\right| < \epsilon.$$

Now $\left|e^x - 0\right| = e^x$, so the condition that needs to be satisfied whenever $x < N$ is

$$e^x < \epsilon.$$

Let $x = N$ be the number where $e^x = \epsilon$. Since e^x is an increasing function, if $x < N$, then $e^x < \epsilon$. We find N by taking the natural logarithm of both sides of the equation $e^N = \epsilon$, so $N = \ln \epsilon$ (see Figure 2.38). With this value of N the condition is satisfied, and we conclude that $\lim_{x\to-\infty} e^x = 0$. ■

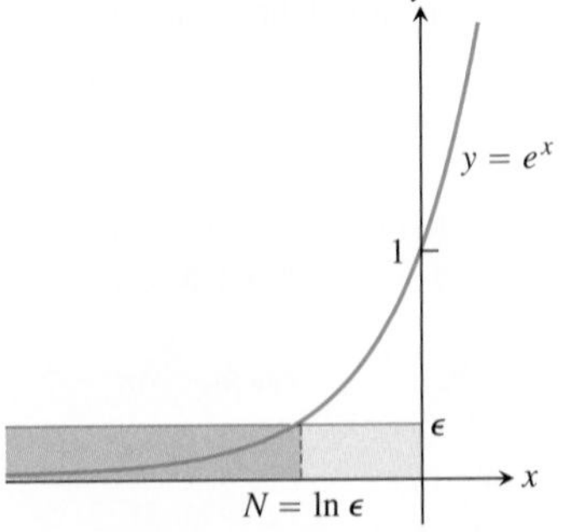

FIGURE 2.38 The graph of $y = e^x$ approaches the x-axis as $x \to -\infty$ (Example 10).

EXAMPLE 11 Find $\lim_{x\to\infty} \sin(1/x)$.

Solution We introduce the new variable $t = 1/x$. From Example 6, we know that $t \to 0^+$ as $x \to \infty$ (see Figure 2.34). Therefore,

$$\lim_{x\to\infty} \sin\frac{1}{x} = \lim_{t\to 0^+} \sin t = 0.$$

■

Likewise, we can investigate the behavior of $y = f(1/x)$ as $x \to 0$ by investigating $y = f(t)$ as $t \to \pm\infty$, where $t = 1/x$.

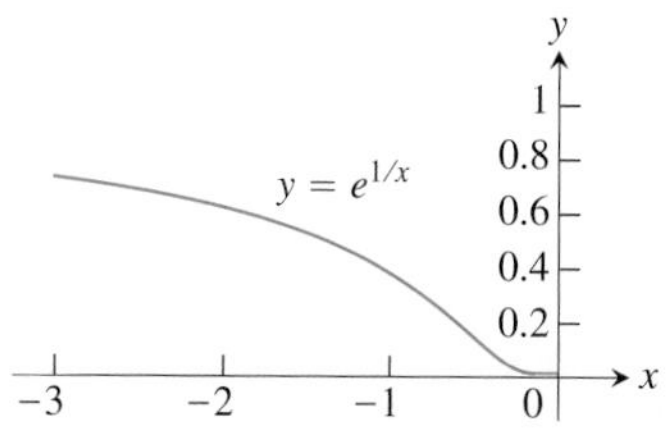

FIGURE 2.39 The graph of $y = e^{1/x}$ for $x < 0$ shows $\lim_{x\to 0^-} e^{1/x} = 0$ (Example 12).

EXAMPLE 12 Find $\lim_{x\to 0^-} e^{1/x}$.

Solution We let $t = 1/x$. From Figure 2.34, we know that $t \to -\infty$ as $x \to 0^-$. Therefore,

$$\lim_{x\to 0^-} e^{1/x} = \lim_{t\to -\infty} e^t = 0 \qquad \text{Example 10}$$

(Figure 2.39). ■

The Sandwich Theorem Revisited

The Sandwich Theorem also holds for limits as $x \to \pm\infty$.

EXAMPLE 13 Using the Sandwich Theorem, find the horizontal asymptote of the curve

$$y = 2 + \frac{\sin x}{x}.$$

Solution We are interested in the behavior as $x \to \pm\infty$. Since

$$0 \le \left|\frac{\sin x}{x}\right| \le \left|\frac{1}{x}\right|$$

and $\lim_{x\to\pm\infty} |1/x| = 0$, we have $\lim_{x\to\pm\infty} (\sin x)/x = 0$ by the Sandwich Theorem. Hence,

$$\lim_{x\to\pm\infty} \left(2 + \frac{\sin x}{x}\right) = 2 + 0 = 2,$$

and the line $y = 2$ is a horizontal asymptote of the curve on both left and right (Figure 2.40).

This example illustrates that a curve may cross one of its horizontal asymptotes, perhaps many times. ■

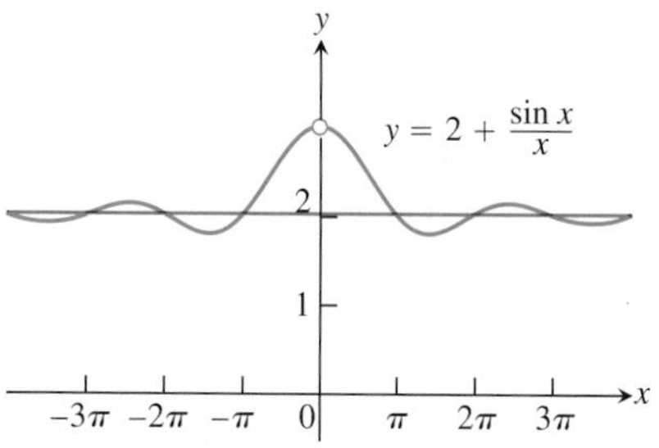

FIGURE 2.40 A curve may cross one of its asymptotes infinitely often (Example 13).

The graph of a function may have more than one horizontal asymptote. For example, the graph of the arctangent function discussed further on (Section 3.8) has two horizontal asymptotes.

Oblique Asymptotes

If the degree of the numerator of a rational function is one greater than the degree of the denominator, the graph has an **oblique (slanted) asymptote**. We find an equation for the asymptote by dividing numerator by denominator to express f as a linear function plus a remainder that goes to zero as $x \to \pm\infty$. Here's an example.

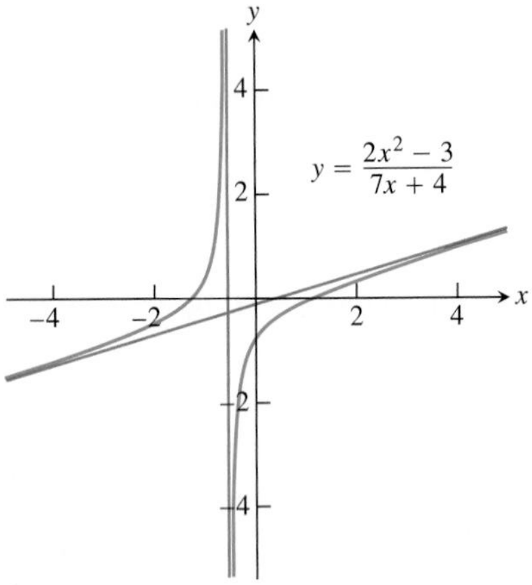

FIGURE 2.41 The function in Example 14 has an oblique asymptote.

EXAMPLE 14 Find the oblique asymptote for the graph of

$$f(x) = \frac{2x^2 - 3}{7x + 4}.$$

Solution By long division, we find

$$f(x) = \frac{2x^2 - 3}{7x + 4}$$

$$= \underbrace{\left(\frac{2}{7}x - \frac{8}{49}\right)}_{\text{linear function } g(x)} + \underbrace{\frac{-115}{49(7x + 4)}}_{\text{remainder}}$$

As $x \to \pm\infty$, the remainder, whose magnitude gives the vertical distance between the graphs of f and g, goes to zero, making the (slanted) line

$$g(x) = \frac{2}{7}x - \frac{8}{49}$$

an asymptote of the graph of f (Figure 2.41). The line $y = g(x)$ is an asymptote both to the right and to the left. In the next section you will see that the function $f(x)$ grows arbitrarily large in absolute value as x approaches $-4/7$, where the denominator becomes zero (Figure 2.41). ■

EXERCISES 2.4

1. Which of the following statements about the function $y = f(x)$ graphed here are true, and which are false?

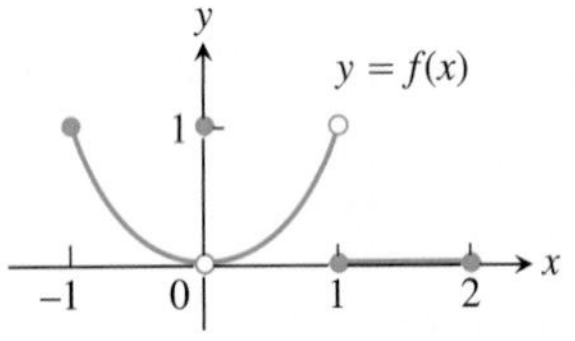

a. $\lim_{x\to -1^+} f(x) = 1$ **b.** $\lim_{x\to 0^-} f(x) = 0$

c. $\lim_{x\to 0^-} f(x) = 1$ **d.** $\lim_{x\to 0^-} f(x) = \lim_{x\to 0^+} f(x)$

e. $\lim_{x\to 0} f(x)$ exists **f.** $\lim_{x\to 0} f(x) = 0$

g. $\lim_{x\to 0} f(x) = 1$ **h.** $\lim_{x\to 1} f(x) = 1$

i. $\lim_{x\to 1} f(x) = 0$ **j.** $\lim_{x\to 2^-} f(x) = 2$

k. $\lim_{x\to -1^-} f(x)$ does not exist. **l.** $\lim_{x\to 2^+} f(x) = 0$

2. Which of the following statements about the function $y = f(x)$ graphed here are true, and which are false?

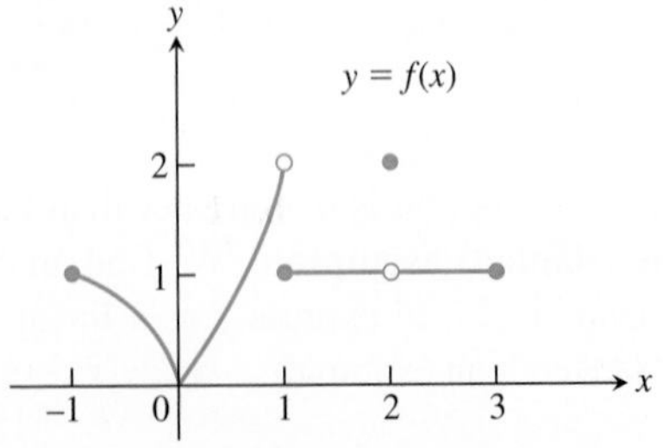

a. $\lim_{x\to -1^+} f(x) = 1$ **b.** $\lim_{x\to 2} f(x)$ does not exist.

c. $\lim_{x\to 2} f(x) = 2$ **d.** $\lim_{x\to 1^-} f(x) = 2$

e. $\lim_{x\to 1^+} f(x) = 1$ **f.** $\lim_{x\to 1} f(x)$ does not exist.

g. $\lim_{x\to 0^+} f(x) = \lim_{x\to 0^-} f(x)$

h. $\lim_{x\to c} f(x)$ exists at every c in the open interval $(-1, 1)$.

i. $\lim_{x\to c} f(x)$ exists at every c in the open interval $(1, 3)$.

j. $\lim_{x\to -1^-} f(x) = 0$ **k.** $\lim_{x\to 3^+} f(x)$ does not exist.

3. Let $f(x) = \begin{cases} 3 - x, & x < 2 \\ \frac{x}{2} + 1, & x > 2. \end{cases}$

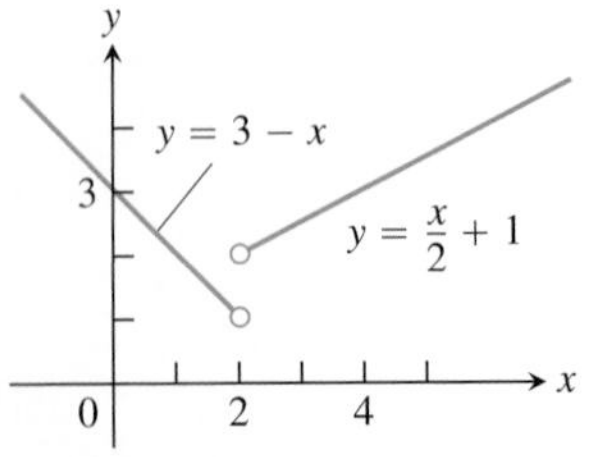

a. Find $\lim_{x\to 2^+} f(x)$ and $\lim_{x\to 2^-} f(x)$.

b. Does $\lim_{x\to 2} f(x)$ exist? If so, what is it? If not, why not?

c. Find $\lim_{x\to 4^-} f(x)$ and $\lim_{x\to 4^+} f(x)$.

d. Does $\lim_{x\to 4} f(x)$ exist? If so, what is it? If not, why not?

4. Let $f(x) = \begin{cases} 3 - x, & x < 2 \\ 2, & x = 2 \\ \frac{x}{2}, & x > 2. \end{cases}$

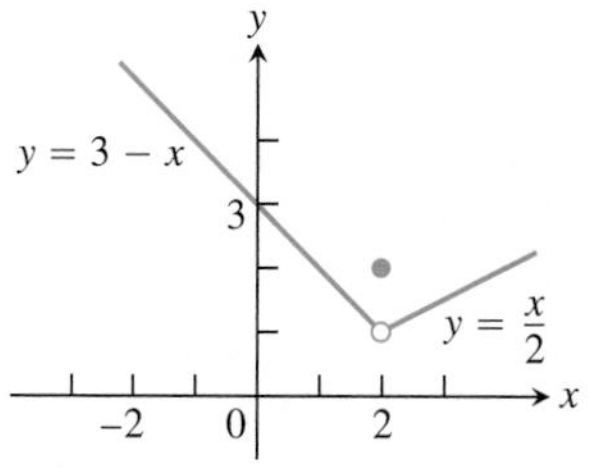

a. Find $\lim_{x\to 2^+} f(x)$, $\lim_{x\to 2^-} f(x)$, and $f(2)$.

b. Does $\lim_{x\to 2} f(x)$ exist? If so, what is it? If not, why not?

c. Find $\lim_{x\to -1^-} f(x)$ and $\lim_{x\to -1^+} f(x)$.

d. Does $\lim_{x\to -1} f(x)$ exist? If so, what is it? If not, why not?

5. Let $f(x) = \begin{cases} 0, & x \le 0 \\ \sin\frac{1}{x}, & x > 0. \end{cases}$

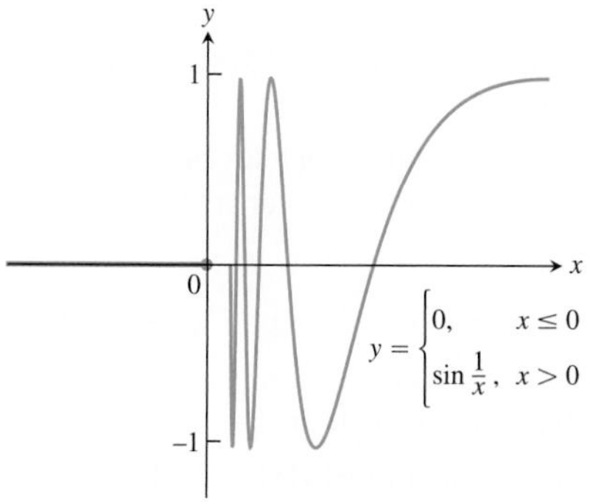

a. Does $\lim_{x\to 0^+} f(x)$ exist? If so, what is it? If not, why not?

b. Does $\lim_{x\to 0^-} f(x)$ exist? If so, what is it? If not, why not?

c. Does $\lim_{x\to 0} f(x)$ exist? If so, what is it? If not, why not?

6. Let $g(x) = \sqrt{x}\sin(1/x)$.

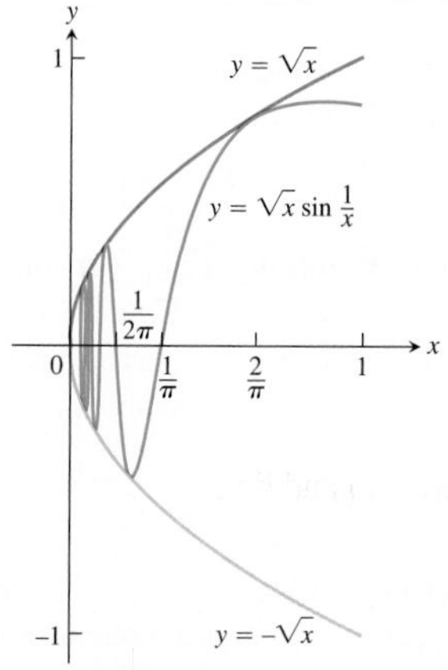

a. Does $\lim_{x\to 0^+} g(x)$ exist? If so, what is it? If not, why not?

b. Does $\lim_{x\to 0^-} g(x)$ exist? If so, what is it? If not, why not?

c. Does $\lim_{x\to 0} g(x)$ exist? If so, what is it? If not, why not?

7. a. Graph $f(x) = \begin{cases} x^3, & x \ne 1 \\ 0, & x = 1. \end{cases}$

b. Find $\lim_{x\to 1^-} f(x)$ and $\lim_{x\to 1^+} f(x)$.

c. Does $\lim_{x\to 1} f(x)$ exist? If so, what is it? If not, why not?

8. a. Graph $f(x) = \begin{cases} 1 - x^2, & x \ne 1 \\ 2, & x = 1. \end{cases}$

b. Find $\lim_{x\to 1^+} f(x)$ and $\lim_{x\to 1^-} f(x)$.

c. Does $\lim_{x\to 1} f(x)$ exist? If so, what is it? If not, why not?

Graph the functions in Exercises 9 and 10. Then answer these questions.

a. What are the domain and range of f?

b. At what points c, if any, does $\lim_{x\to c} f(x)$ exist?

c. At what points does only the left-hand limit exist?

d. At what points does only the right-hand limit exist?

9. $f(x) = \begin{cases} \sqrt{1 - x^2}, & 0 \le x < 1 \\ 1, & 1 \le x < 2 \\ 2, & x = 2 \end{cases}$

10. $f(x) = \begin{cases} x, & -1 \le x < 0, \text{ or } 0 < x \le 1 \\ 1, & x = 0 \\ 0, & x < -1 \text{ or } x > 1 \end{cases}$

Find the limits in Exercises 11–18.

11. $\displaystyle\lim_{x\to -0.5^-} \sqrt{\frac{x + 2}{x + 1}}$

12. $\displaystyle\lim_{x\to 1^+} \sqrt{\frac{x - 1}{x + 2}}$

13. $\displaystyle\lim_{x\to -2^+} \left(\frac{x}{x + 1}\right)\left(\frac{2x + 5}{x^2 + x}\right)$

14. $\displaystyle\lim_{x\to 1^-} \left(\frac{1}{x + 1}\right)\left(\frac{x + 6}{x}\right)\left(\frac{3 - x}{7}\right)$

15. $\displaystyle\lim_{h\to 0^+} \frac{\sqrt{h^2 + 4h + 5} - \sqrt{5}}{h}$

16. $\displaystyle\lim_{h\to 0^-} \frac{\sqrt{6} - \sqrt{5h^2 + 11h + 6}}{h}$

17. a. $\displaystyle\lim_{x\to -2^+} (x + 3)\frac{|x + 2|}{x + 2}$ **b.** $\displaystyle\lim_{x\to -2^-} (x + 3)\frac{|x + 2|}{x + 2}$

18. a. $\displaystyle\lim_{x\to 1^+} \frac{\sqrt{2x}\,(x - 1)}{|x - 1|}$ **b.** $\displaystyle\lim_{x\to 1^-} \frac{\sqrt{2x}\,(x - 1)}{|x - 1|}$

Use the graph of the greatest integer function $y = \lfloor x \rfloor$, Figure 1.9 in Section 1.1, to help you find the limits in Exercises 19 and 20.

19. a. $\displaystyle\lim_{\theta\to 3^+} \frac{\lfloor \theta \rfloor}{\theta}$ **b.** $\displaystyle\lim_{\theta\to 3^-} \frac{\lfloor \theta \rfloor}{\theta}$

20. a. $\displaystyle\lim_{t\to 4^+} (t - \lfloor t \rfloor)$ **b.** $\displaystyle\lim_{t\to 4^-} (t - \lfloor t \rfloor)$

Find the limits in Exercises 21–36.

21. $\displaystyle\lim_{\theta\to 0} \frac{\sin\sqrt{2}\theta}{\sqrt{2}\theta}$

22. $\displaystyle\lim_{t\to 0} \frac{\sin kt}{t}$ (k constant)

23. $\lim_{y\to 0} \frac{\sin 3y}{4y}$

24. $\lim_{h\to 0^-} \frac{h}{\sin 3h}$

25. $\lim_{x\to 0} \frac{\tan 2x}{x}$

26. $\lim_{t\to 0} \frac{2t}{\tan t}$

27. $\lim_{x\to 0} \frac{x \csc 2x}{\cos 5x}$

28. $\lim_{x\to 0} 6x^2(\cot x)(\csc 2x)$

29. $\lim_{x\to 0} \frac{x + x\cos x}{\sin x \cos x}$

30. $\lim_{x\to 0} \frac{x^2 - x + \sin x}{2x}$

31. $\lim_{t\to 0} \frac{\sin(1-\cos t)}{1-\cos t}$

32. $\lim_{h\to 0} \frac{\sin(\sin h)}{\sin h}$

33. $\lim_{\theta\to 0} \frac{\sin\theta}{\sin 2\theta}$

34. $\lim_{x\to 0} \frac{\sin 5x}{\sin 4x}$

35. $\lim_{x\to 0} \frac{\tan 3x}{\sin 8x}$

36. $\lim_{y\to 0} \frac{\sin 3y \cot 5y}{y \cot 4y}$

In Exercises 37–42, find the limit of each function **(a)** as $x \to \infty$ and **(b)** as $x \to -\infty$. (You may wish to visualize your answer with a graphing calculator or computer.)

37. $f(x) = \frac{2}{x} - 3$

38. $f(x) = \pi - \frac{2}{x^2}$

39. $g(x) = \frac{1}{2 + (1/x)}$

40. $g(x) = \frac{1}{8 - (5/x^2)}$

41. $h(x) = \frac{-5 + (7/x)}{3 - (1/x^2)}$

42. $h(x) = \frac{3 - (2/x)}{4 + (\sqrt{2}/x^2)}$

Find the limits in Exercises 43–50.

43. $\lim_{x\to\infty} \frac{\sin 2x}{x}$

44. $\lim_{\theta\to -\infty} \frac{\cos\theta}{3\theta}$

45. $\lim_{t\to -\infty} \frac{2 - t + \sin t}{t + \cos t}$

46. $\lim_{r\to\infty} \frac{r + \sin r}{2r + 7 - 5\sin r}$

47. $\lim_{x\to\infty} e^{-x}\sin x$

48. $\lim_{x\to -\infty} e^x \cos^{-1}\left(\frac{1}{x}\right)$

49. $\lim_{x\to -\infty} \frac{e^x - e^{-x}}{e^x + e^{-x}}$

50. $\lim_{x\to\infty} \frac{3x^2 + e^{-x}}{\sin(1/x) - 2x^2}$

In Exercises 51–60, find the limit of each rational function **(a)** as $x \to \infty$ and **(b)** as $x \to -\infty$.

51. $f(x) = \frac{2x + 3}{5x + 7}$

52. $f(x) = \frac{2x^3 + 7}{x^3 - x^2 + x + 7}$

53. $f(x) = \frac{x + 1}{x^2 + 3}$

54. $f(x) = \frac{3x + 7}{x^2 - 2}$

55. $h(x) = \frac{7x^3}{x^3 - 3x^2 + 6x}$

56. $g(x) = \frac{1}{x^3 - 4x + 1}$

57. $g(x) = \frac{10x^5 + x^4 + 31}{x^6}$

58. $h(x) = \frac{9x^4 + x}{2x^4 + 5x^2 - x + 6}$

59. $h(x) = \frac{-2x^3 - 2x + 3}{3x^3 + 3x^2 - 5x}$

60. $h(x) = \frac{-x^4}{x^4 - 7x^3 + 7x^2 + 9}$

The process by which we determine limits of rational functions applies equally well to ratios containing noninteger or negative powers of x: divide numerator and denominator by the highest power of x in the denominator and proceed from there. Find the limits in Exercises 61–66.

61. $\lim_{x\to\infty} \frac{2\sqrt{x} + x^{-1}}{3x - 7}$

62. $\lim_{x\to\infty} \frac{2 + \sqrt{x}}{2 - \sqrt{x}}$

63. $\lim_{x\to -\infty} \frac{\sqrt[3]{x} - \sqrt[5]{x}}{\sqrt[3]{x} + \sqrt[5]{x}}$

64. $\lim_{x\to\infty} \frac{x^{-1} + x^{-4}}{x^{-2} - x^{-3}}$

65. $\lim_{x\to\infty} \frac{2x^{5/3} - x^{1/3} + 7}{x^{8/5} + 3x + \sqrt{x}}$

66. $\lim_{x\to -\infty} \frac{\sqrt[3]{x} - 5x + 3}{2x + x^{2/3} - 4}$

67. Once you know $\lim_{x\to a^+} f(x)$ and $\lim_{x\to a^-} f(x)$ at an interior point of the domain of f, do you then know $\lim_{x\to a} f(x)$? Give reasons for your answer.

68. If you know that $\lim_{x\to c} f(x)$ exists, can you find its value by calculating $\lim_{x\to c^+} f(x)$? Give reasons for your answer.

69. Suppose that f is an odd function of x. Does knowing that $\lim_{x\to 0^+} f(x) = 3$ tell you anything about $\lim_{x\to 0^-} f(x)$? Give reasons for your answer.

70. Suppose that f is an even function of x. Does knowing that $\lim_{x\to 2^-} f(x) = 7$ tell you anything about either $\lim_{x\to -2^-} f(x)$ or $\lim_{x\to -2^+} f(x)$? Give reasons for your answer.

71. Suppose that $f(x)$ and $g(x)$ are polynomials in x and that $\lim_{x\to\infty}(f(x)/g(x)) = 2$. Can you conclude anything about $\lim_{x\to -\infty}(f(x)/g(x))$? Give reasons for your answer.

72. Suppose that $f(x)$ and $g(x)$ are polynomials in x. Can the graph of $f(x)/g(x)$ have an asymptote if $g(x)$ is never zero? Give reasons for your answer.

73. How many horizontal asymptotes can the graph of a given rational function have? Give reasons for your answer.

74. Find $\lim_{x\to\infty}\left(\sqrt{x^2 + x} - \sqrt{x^2 - x}\right)$.

Use the formal definitions of limits as $x \to \pm\infty$ to establish the limits in Exercises 75 and 76.

75. If f has the constant value $f(x) = k$, then $\lim_{x\to\infty} f(x) = k$.

76. If f has the constant value $f(x) = k$, then $\lim_{x\to -\infty} f(x) = k$.

77. Given $\epsilon > 0$, find an interval $I = (5, 5 + \delta)$, $\delta > 0$, such that if x lies in I, then $\sqrt{x - 5} < \epsilon$. What limit is being verified and what is its value?

78. Given $\epsilon > 0$, find an interval $I = (4 - \delta, 4)$, $\delta > 0$, such that if x lies in I, then $\sqrt{4 - x} < \epsilon$. What limit is being verified and what is its value?

Use the definitions of right-hand and left-hand limits to prove the limit statements in Exercises 79 and 80.

79. $\lim_{x\to 0^-} \frac{x}{|x|} = -1$

80. $\lim_{x\to 2^+} \frac{x - 2}{|x - 2|} = 1$

81. **Greatest integer function** Find **(a)** $\lim_{x\to 400^+} \lfloor x \rfloor$ and **(b)** $\lim_{x\to 400^-} \lfloor x \rfloor$; then use limit definitions to verify your findings. **(c)** Based on your conclusions in parts (a) and (b), can anything be said about $\lim_{x\to 400} \lfloor x \rfloor$? Give reasons for your answers.

82. **One-sided limits** Let $f(x) = \begin{cases} x^2 \sin(1/x), & x < 0 \\ \sqrt{x}, & x > 0. \end{cases}$

Find **(a)** $\lim_{x\to 0^+} f(x)$ and **(b)** $\lim_{x\to 0^-} f(x)$; then use limit definitions to verify your findings. **(c)** Based on your conclusions in parts (a) and (b), can anything be said about $\lim_{x\to 0} f(x)$? Give reasons for your answer.

T Sometimes a change of variable can change an unfamiliar expression into one whose limit we know how to find, such as in Example 11, where we substituted $t = 1/x$ when finding a limit as $x \to \infty$. This suggests a creative way to "see" limits at infinity. Describe the procedure and use it to picture and determine limits in Exercises 83–88.

83. $\lim_{x\to\pm\infty} x \sin\frac{1}{x}$

84. $\lim_{x\to-\infty} \frac{\cos(1/x)}{1 + (1/x)}$

85. $\lim_{x\to\pm\infty} \frac{3x + 4}{2x - 5}$

86. $\lim_{x\to\infty} \left(\frac{1}{x}\right)^{1/x}$

87. $\lim_{x\to\pm\infty} \left(3 + \frac{2}{x}\right)\left(\cos\frac{1}{x}\right)$

88. $\lim_{x\to\infty} \left(\frac{3}{x^2} - \cos\frac{1}{x}\right)\left(1 + \sin\frac{1}{x}\right)$

2.5 Infinite Limits and Vertical Asymptotes

In this section we extend the concept of limit to *infinite limits*, which are not limits as before, but rather an entirely new use of the term limit. Infinite limits provide useful symbols and language for describing the behavior of functions whose values become arbitrarily large. We continue our analysis of graphs of rational functions from the last section and introduce vertical asymptotes.

Infinite Limits

Let us look again at the function $f(x) = 1/x$. As $x \to 0^+$, the values of f grow without bound, eventually reaching and surpassing every positive real number. That is, given any positive real number B, however large, the values of f become larger still (Figure 2.42). Thus, f has no limit as $x \to 0^+$. It is nevertheless convenient to describe the behavior of f by saying that $f(x)$ approaches ∞ as $x \to 0^+$. We write

$$\lim_{x\to 0^+} f(x) = \lim_{x\to 0^+} \frac{1}{x} = \infty.$$

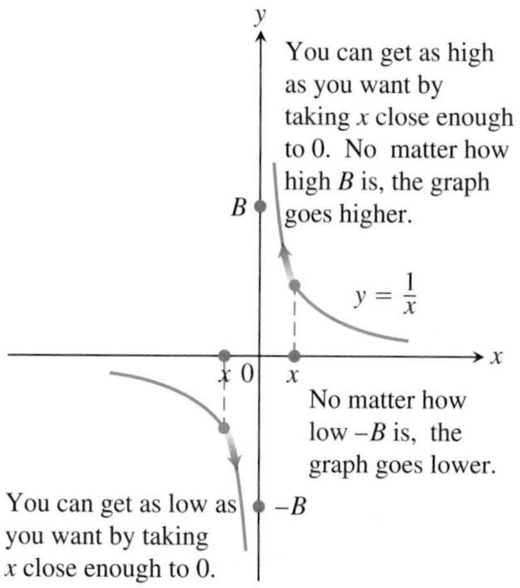

FIGURE 2.42 One-sided infinite limits: $\lim_{x\to 0^+} \frac{1}{x} = \infty$ and $\lim_{x\to 0^-} \frac{1}{x} = -\infty$

In writing this, we are *not* saying that the limit exists. Nor are we saying that there is a real number ∞, for there is no such number. Rather, we are saying that $\lim_{x\to 0^+} (1/x)$ *does not exist because* $1/x$ *becomes arbitrarily large and positive as* $x \to 0^+$.

As $x \to 0^-$, the values of $f(x) = 1/x$ become arbitrarily large and negative. Given any negative real number $-B$, the values of f eventually lie below $-B$. (See Figure 2.42.) We write

$$\lim_{x\to 0^-} f(x) = \lim_{x\to 0^-} \frac{1}{x} = -\infty.$$

Again, we are not saying that the limit exists and equals the number $-\infty$. There *is* no real number $-\infty$. We are describing the behavior of a function whose limit as $x \to 0^-$ *does not exist because its values become arbitrarily large and negative.*

EXAMPLE 1 Find $\lim_{x\to 1^+} \frac{1}{x - 1}$ and $\lim_{x\to 1^-} \frac{1}{x - 1}$.

Geometric Solution The graph of $y = 1/(x - 1)$ is the graph of $y = 1/x$ shifted 1 unit to the right (Figure 2.43). Therefore, $y = 1/(x - 1)$ behaves near 1 exactly the way $y = 1/x$ behaves near 0:

$$\lim_{x\to 1^+} \frac{1}{x - 1} = \infty \quad \text{and} \quad \lim_{x\to 1^-} \frac{1}{x - 1} = -\infty.$$

FIGURE 2.43 Near $x = 1$, the function $y = 1/(x - 1)$ behaves the way the function $y = 1/x$ behaves near $x = 0$. Its graph is the graph of $y = 1/x$ shifted 1 unit to the right (Example 1).

Analytic Solution Think about the number $x - 1$ and its reciprocal. As $x \to 1^+$, we have $(x - 1) \to 0^+$ and $1/(x - 1) \to \infty$. As $x \to 1^-$, we have $(x - 1) \to 0^-$ and $1/(x - 1) \to -\infty$. ■

EXAMPLE 2 Discuss the behavior of

$$f(x) = \frac{1}{x^2} \quad \text{near} \quad x = 0.$$

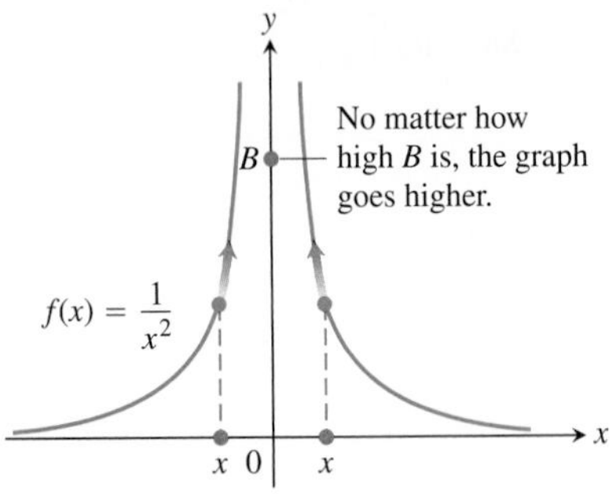

FIGURE 2.44 The graph of $f(x)$ in Example 2 approaches infinity as $x \to 0$.

Solution As x approaches zero from either side, the values of $1/x^2$ are positive and become arbitrarily large (Figure 2.44):

$$\lim_{x \to 0} f(x) = \lim_{x \to 0} \frac{1}{x^2} = \infty .$$

The function $y = 1/x$ shows no consistent behavior as $x \to 0$. We have $1/x \to \infty$ if $x \to 0^+$, but $1/x \to -\infty$ if $x \to 0^-$. All we can say about $\lim_{x \to 0} (1/x)$ is that it does not exist. The function $y = 1/x^2$ is different. Its values approach infinity as x approaches zero from either side, so we can say that $\lim_{x \to 0} (1/x^2) = \infty$.

EXAMPLE 3

(a) $$\lim_{x \to 2} \frac{(x-2)^2}{x^2 - 4} = \lim_{x \to 2} \frac{(x-2)^2}{(x-2)(x+2)} = \lim_{x \to 2} \frac{x-2}{x+2} = 0$$

(b) $$\lim_{x \to 2} \frac{x-2}{x^2-4} = \lim_{x \to 2} \frac{x-2}{(x-2)(x+2)} = \lim_{x \to 2} \frac{1}{x+2} = \frac{1}{4}$$

(c) $$\lim_{x \to 2^+} \frac{x-3}{x^2-4} = \lim_{x \to 2^+} \frac{x-3}{(x-2)(x+2)} = -\infty$$ The values are negative for $x > 2$, x near 2.

(d) $$\lim_{x \to 2^-} \frac{x-3}{x^2-4} = \lim_{x \to 2^-} \frac{x-3}{(x-2)(x+2)} = \infty$$ The values are positive for $x < 2$, x near 2.

(e) $$\lim_{x \to 2} \frac{x-3}{x^2-4} = \lim_{x \to 2} \frac{x-3}{(x-2)(x+2)} \text{ does not exist.}$$ See parts (c) and (d).

(f) $$\lim_{x \to 2} \frac{2-x}{(x-2)^3} = \lim_{x \to 2} \frac{-(x-2)}{(x-2)^3} = \lim_{x \to 2} \frac{-1}{(x-2)^2} = -\infty$$

In parts (a) and (b) the effect of the zero in the denominator at $x = 2$ is canceled because the numerator is zero there also. Thus a finite limit exists. This is not true in part (f), where cancellation still leaves a zero factor in the denominator.

Precise Definitions of Infinite Limits

Instead of requiring $f(x)$ to lie arbitrarily close to a finite number L for all x sufficiently close to x_0, the definitions of infinite limits require $f(x)$ to lie arbitrarily far from zero. Except for this change, the language is identical with what we have seen before. Figures 2.45 and 2.46 accompany these definitions.

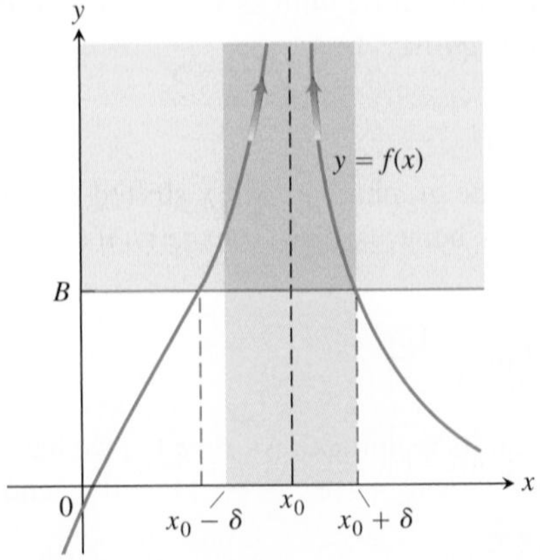

FIGURE 2.45 For $x_0 - \delta < x < x_0 + \delta$, the graph of $f(x)$ lies above the line $y = B$.

DEFINITIONS

1. We say that ***f*(*x*) approaches infinity as *x* approaches x_0**, and write
$$\lim_{x \to x_0} f(x) = \infty,$$
if for every positive real number B there exists a corresponding $\delta > 0$ such that for all x
$$0 < |x - x_0| < \delta \quad \Rightarrow \quad f(x) > B.$$

2. We say that ***f*(*x*) approaches negative infinity as *x* approaches x_0**, and write
$$\lim_{x \to x_0} f(x) = -\infty,$$
if for every negative real number $-B$ there exists a corresponding $\delta > 0$ such that for all x
$$0 < |x - x_0| < \delta \quad \Rightarrow \quad f(x) < -B.$$

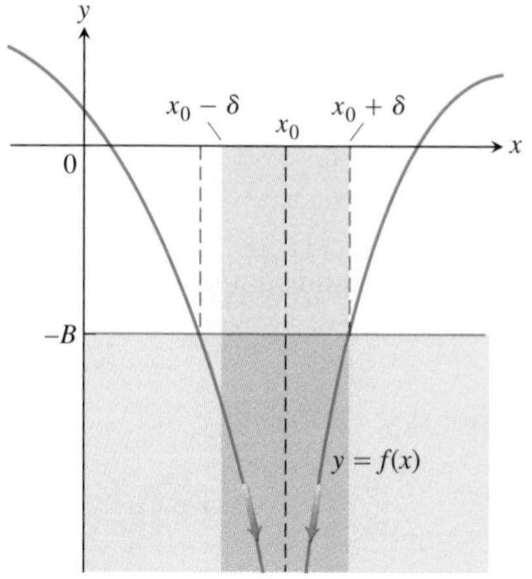

FIGURE 2.46 For $x_0 - \delta < x < x_0 + \delta$, the graph of $f(x)$ lies below the line $y = -B$.

The precise definitions of one-sided infinite limits at x_0 are similar and are stated in the exercises.

EXAMPLE 4 Prove that $\lim_{x\to 0} \frac{1}{x^2} = \infty$.

Solution Given $B > 0$, we want to find $\delta > 0$ such that

$$0 < |x - 0| < \delta \quad \text{implies} \quad \frac{1}{x^2} > B.$$

Now,

$$\frac{1}{x^2} > B \qquad \text{if and only if } x^2 < \frac{1}{B}$$

or, equivalently,

$$|x| < \frac{1}{\sqrt{B}}.$$

Thus, choosing $\delta = 1/\sqrt{B}$ (or any smaller positive number), we see that

$$|x| < \delta \quad \text{implies} \quad \frac{1}{x^2} > \frac{1}{\delta^2} \geq B.$$

Therefore, by definition,

$$\lim_{x\to 0} \frac{1}{x^2} = \infty.$$

■

Vertical Asymptotes

Notice that the distance between a point on the graph of $y = 1/x$ and the y-axis approaches zero as the point moves vertically along the graph and away from the origin (Figure 2.47). This behavior occurs because

$$\lim_{x\to 0^+} \frac{1}{x} = \infty \qquad \text{and} \qquad \lim_{x\to 0^-} \frac{1}{x} = -\infty.$$

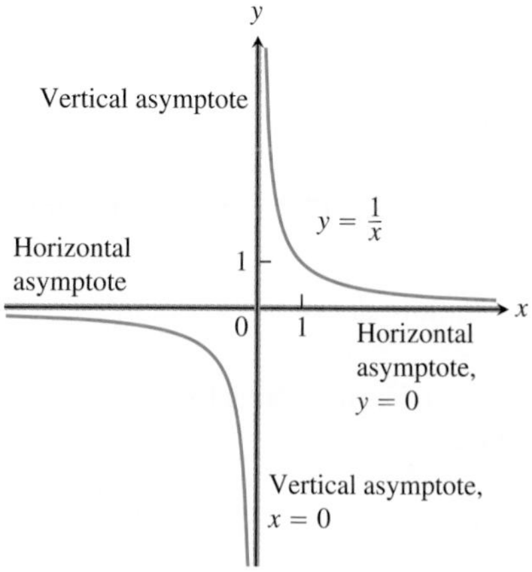

FIGURE 2.47 The coordinate axes are asymptotes of both branches of the hyperbola $y = 1/x$.

We say that the line $x = 0$ (the y-axis) is a *vertical asymptote* of the graph of $y = 1/x$. Observe that the denominator is zero at $x = 0$ and the function is undefined there.

DEFINITION A line $x = a$ is a **vertical asymptote** of the graph of a function $y = f(x)$ if either

$$\lim_{x\to a^+} f(x) = \pm\infty \qquad \text{or} \qquad \lim_{x\to a^-} f(x) = \pm\infty.$$

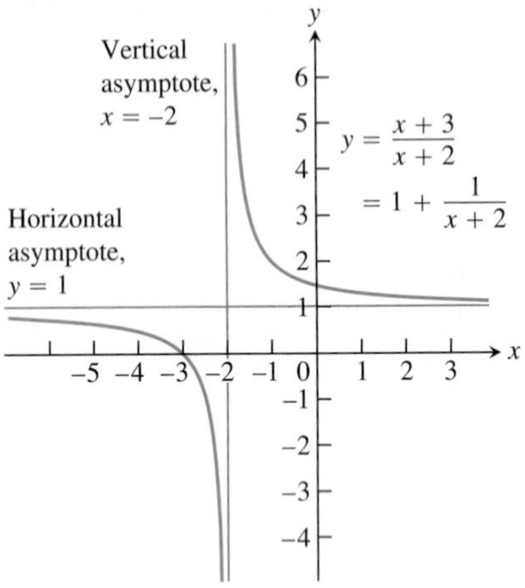

FIGURE 2.48 The lines $y = 1$ and $x = -2$ are asymptotes of the curve $y = (x + 3)/(x + 2)$ (Example 5).

EXAMPLE 5 Find the horizontal and vertical asymptotes of the curve

$$y = \frac{x + 3}{x + 2}.$$

Solution We are interested in the behavior as $x \to \pm\infty$ and as $x \to -2$, where the denominator is zero.

The asymptotes are quickly revealed if we recast the rational function as a polynomial with a remainder, by dividing $(x + 2)$ into $(x + 3)$.

$$\begin{array}{r} 1 \\ x + 2 \overline{)\, x + 3} \\ \underline{x + 2} \\ 1 \end{array}$$

This result enables us to rewrite y:

$$y = 1 + \frac{1}{x + 2}.$$

We now see that the curve in question is the graph of $y = 1/x$ shifted 1 unit up and 2 units left (Figure 2.48). The asymptotes, instead of being the coordinate axes, are now the lines $y = 1$ and $x = -2$. ■

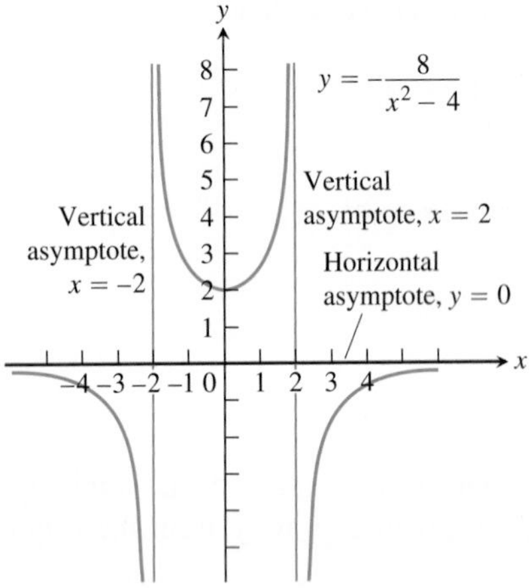

FIGURE 2.49 Graph of $y = -8/(x^2 - 4)$. Notice that the curve approaches the x-axis from only one side. Asymptotes do not have to be two-sided (Example 6).

EXAMPLE 6 Find the horizontal and vertical asymptotes of the graph of

$$f(x) = -\frac{8}{x^2 - 4}.$$

Solution We are interested in the behavior as $x \to \pm\infty$ and as $x \to \pm 2$, where the denominator is zero. Notice that f is an even function of x, so its graph is symmetric with respect to the y-axis.

(a) *The behavior as* $x \to \pm\infty$. Since $\lim_{x\to\infty} f(x) = 0$, the line $y = 0$ is a horizontal asymptote of the graph to the right. By symmetry it is an asymptote to the left as well (Figure 2.49). Notice that the curve approaches the x-axis from only the negative side (or from below).

(b) *The behavior as* $x \to \pm 2$. Since

$$\lim_{x\to 2^+} f(x) = -\infty \qquad \text{and} \qquad \lim_{x\to 2^-} f(x) = \infty,$$

the line $x = 2$ is a vertical asymptote both from the right and from the left. By symmetry, the same holds for the line $x = -2$.

There are no other asymptotes because f has a finite limit at every other point. ■

EXAMPLE 7 The graph of the natural logarithm function has the y-axis (the line $x = 0$) as a vertical asymptote. We see this from the graph sketched in Figure 2.50 (which is the reflection of the graph of the natural exponential function across the line $y = x$) and the fact that the x-axis is a horizontal asymptote of $y = e^x$ (Example 10, Section 2.4). Thus,

$$\lim_{x\to 0^+} \ln x = -\infty.$$

The same result is true for $y = \log_a x$ whenever $a > 1$. ■

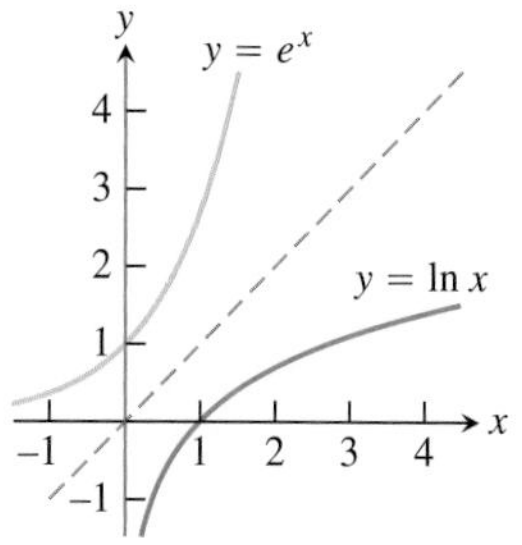

FIGURE 2.50 The line $x = 0$ is a vertical asymptote of the natural logarithm function (Example 7).

EXAMPLE 8 The curves

$$y = \sec x = \frac{1}{\cos x} \qquad \text{and} \qquad y = \tan x = \frac{\sin x}{\cos x}$$

both have vertical asymptotes at odd-integer multiples of $\pi/2$, where $\cos x = 0$ (Figure 2.51).

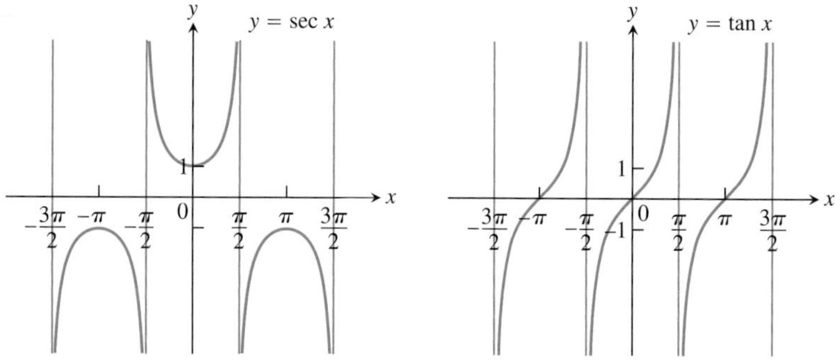

FIGURE 2.51 The graphs of sec x and tan x have infinitely many vertical asymptotes (Example 8). ■

EXAMPLE 9 Find the asymptotes of the graph of

$$f(x) = \frac{x^2 - 3}{2x - 4}.$$

Solution We are interested in the behavior as $x \to \pm\infty$ and also as $x \to 2$, where the denominator is zero. We divide $(2x - 4)$ into $(x^2 - 3)$:

$$\begin{array}{r} \frac{x}{2} + 1 \\ 2x - 4 \overline{\big) x^2 - 3} \\ \underline{x^2 - 2x} \\ 2x - 3 \\ \underline{2x - 4} \\ 1 \end{array}$$

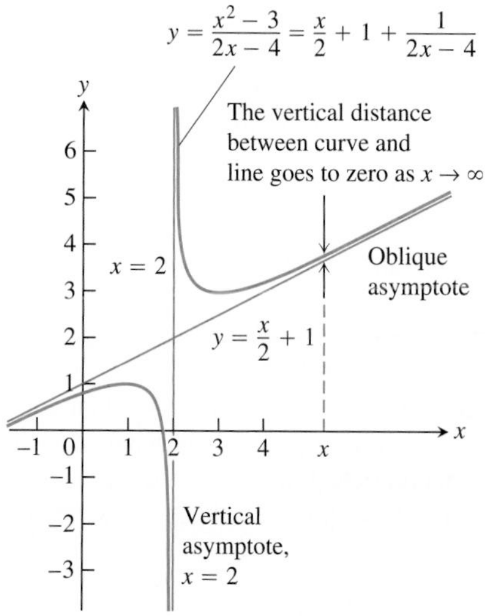

FIGURE 2.52 The graph of $f(x) = (x^2 - 3)/(2x - 4)$ has a vertical asymptote and an oblique asymptote (Example 9).

This tells us that

$$f(x) = \frac{x^2 - 3}{2x - 4} = \underbrace{\frac{x}{2} + 1}_{\text{linear}} + \underbrace{\frac{1}{2x - 4}}_{\text{remainder}}.$$

Since $\lim_{x\to 2^+} f(x) = \infty$ and $\lim_{x\to 2^-} f(x) = -\infty$, the line $x = 2$ is a two-sided vertical asymptote. As $x \to \pm\infty$, the remainder approaches 0 and $f(x) \to (x/2) + 1$. The line $y = (x/2) + 1$ is an oblique asymptote both to the right and to the left (Figure 2.52). ■

Notice in Example 9, that if the degree of the numerator in a rational function is greater than the degree of the denominator, then the limit is $+\infty$ or $-\infty$, depending on the signs assumed by the numerator and denominator as $|x|$ becomes large.

EXERCISES 2.5

Find the limits in Exercises 1–12.

1. $\lim_{x\to 0^+} \frac{1}{3x}$

2. $\lim_{x\to 0^-} \frac{5}{2x}$

3. $\lim_{x\to 2^-} \frac{3}{x-2}$

4. $\lim_{x\to 3^+} \frac{1}{x-3}$

5. $\lim_{x\to -8^+} \frac{2x}{x+8}$

6. $\lim_{x\to -5^-} \frac{3x}{2x+10}$

7. $\lim_{x\to 7} \frac{4}{(x-7)^2}$

8. $\lim_{x\to 0} \frac{-1}{x^2(x+1)}$

9. **a.** $\lim_{x\to 0^+} \frac{2}{3x^{1/3}}$ **b.** $\lim_{x\to 0^-} \frac{2}{3x^{1/3}}$

10. **a.** $\lim_{x\to 0^+} \frac{2}{x^{1/5}}$ **b.** $\lim_{x\to 0^-} \frac{2}{x^{1/5}}$

11. $\lim_{x\to 0} \frac{4}{x^{2/5}}$

12. $\lim_{x\to 0} \frac{1}{x^{2/3}}$

Find the limits in Exercises 13–16.

13. $\lim_{x\to(\pi/2)^-} \tan x$

14. $\lim_{x\to(-\pi/2)^+} \sec x$

15. $\lim_{\theta\to 0^-} (1+\csc\theta)$

16. $\lim_{\theta\to 0} (2-\cot\theta)$

Find the limits in Exercises 17–22.

17. $\lim \frac{1}{x^2-4}$ as

a. $x\to 2^+$ **b.** $x\to 2^-$

c. $x\to -2^+$ **d.** $x\to -2^-$

18. $\lim \frac{x}{x^2-1}$ as

a. $x\to 1^+$ **b.** $x\to 1^-$

c. $x\to -1^+$ **d.** $x\to -1^-$

19. $\lim \left(\frac{x^2}{2}-\frac{1}{x}\right)$ as

a. $x\to 0^+$ **b.** $x\to 0^-$

c. $x\to \sqrt[3]{2}$ **d.** $x\to -1$

20. $\lim \frac{x^2-1}{2x+4}$ as

a. $x\to -2^+$ **b.** $x\to -2^-$

c. $x\to 1^+$ **d.** $x\to 0^-$

21. $\lim \frac{x^2-3x+2}{x^3-2x^2}$ as

a. $x\to 0^+$ **b.** $x\to 2^+$

c. $x\to 2^-$ **d.** $x\to 2$

e. What, if anything, can be said about the limit as $x\to 0$?

22. $\lim \frac{x^2-3x+2}{x^3-4x}$ as

a. $x\to 2^+$ **b.** $x\to -2^+$

c. $x\to 0^-$ **d.** $x\to 1^+$

e. What, if anything, can be said about the limit as $x\to 0$?

Find the limits in Exercises 23–26.

23. $\lim \left(2-\frac{3}{t^{1/3}}\right)$ as

a. $t\to 0^+$ **b.** $t\to 0^-$

24. $\lim \left(\frac{1}{t^{3/5}}+7\right)$ as

a. $t\to 0^+$ **b.** $t\to 0^-$

25. $\lim \left(\frac{1}{x^{2/3}}+\frac{2}{(x-1)^{2/3}}\right)$ as

a. $x\to 0^+$ **b.** $x\to 0^-$

c. $x\to 1^+$ **d.** $x\to 1^-$

26. $\lim \left(\frac{1}{x^{1/3}}-\frac{1}{(x-1)^{4/3}}\right)$ as

a. $x\to 0^+$ **b.** $x\to 0^-$

c. $x\to 1^+$ **d.** $x\to 1^-$

Graph the rational functions in Exercises 27–38. Include the graphs and equations of the asymptotes.

27. $y=\frac{1}{x-1}$

28. $y=\frac{1}{x+1}$

29. $y=\frac{1}{2x+4}$

30. $y=\frac{-3}{x-3}$

31. $y=\frac{x+3}{x+2}$

32. $y=\frac{2x}{x+1}$

33. $y=\frac{x^2}{x-1}$

34. $y=\frac{x^2+1}{x-1}$

35. $y=\frac{x^2-4}{x-1}$

36. $y=\frac{x^2-1}{2x+4}$

37. $y=\frac{x^2-1}{x}$

38. $y=\frac{x^3+1}{x^2}$

In Exercises 39–42, sketch the graph of a function $y=f(x)$ that satisfies the given conditions. No formulas are required—just label the coordinate axes and sketch an appropriate graph. (The answers are not unique, so your graphs may not be exactly like those in the answer section.)

39. $f(0)=0$, $f(1)=2$, $f(-1)=-2$, $\lim_{x\to-\infty} f(x)=-1$, and $\lim_{x\to\infty} f(x)=1$

40. $f(0)=0$, $\lim_{x\to\pm\infty} f(x)=0$, $\lim_{x\to 0^+} f(x)=2$, and $\lim_{x\to 0^-} f(x)=-2$

41. $f(0) = 0, \lim_{x \to \pm\infty} f(x) = 0, \lim_{x \to 1^-} f(x) = \lim_{x \to -1^+} f(x) = \infty,$
$\lim_{x \to 1^+} f(x) = -\infty$, and $\lim_{x \to -1^-} f(x) = -\infty$

42. $f(2) = 1, f(-1) = 0, \lim_{x \to \infty} f(x) = 0, \lim_{x \to 0^+} f(x) = \infty,$
$\lim_{x \to 0^-} f(x) = -\infty$, and $\lim_{x \to -\infty} f(x) = 1$

In Exercises 43–46, find a function that satisfies the given conditions and sketch its graph. (The answers here are not unique. Any function that satisfies the conditions is acceptable. Feel free to use formulas defined in pieces if that will help.)

43. $\lim_{x \to \pm\infty} f(x) = 0, \lim_{x \to 2^-} f(x) = \infty$, and $\lim_{x \to 2^+} f(x) = \infty$

44. $\lim_{x \to \pm\infty} g(x) = 0, \lim_{x \to 3^-} g(x) = -\infty$, and $\lim_{x \to 3^+} g(x) = \infty$

45. $\lim_{x \to -\infty} h(x) = -1, \lim_{x \to \infty} h(x) = 1, \lim_{x \to 0^-} h(x) = -1$, and
$\lim_{x \to 0^+} h(x) = 1$

46. $\lim_{x \to \pm\infty} k(x) = 1, \lim_{x \to 1^-} k(x) = \infty$, and $\lim_{x \to 1^+} k(x) = -\infty$

Use formal definitions to prove the limit statements in Exercises 47–50.

47. $\lim_{x \to 0} \frac{-1}{x^2} = -\infty$

48. $\lim_{x \to 0} \frac{1}{|x|} = \infty$

49. $\lim_{x \to 3} \frac{-2}{(x-3)^2} = -\infty$

50. $\lim_{x \to -5} \frac{1}{(x+5)^2} = \infty$

51. Here is the definition of **infinite right-hand limit**.

> We say that $f(x)$ approaches infinity as x approaches x_0 from the right, and write
>
> $$\lim_{x \to x_0^+} f(x) = \infty,$$
>
> if, for every positive real number B, there exists a corresponding number $\delta > 0$ such that for all x
>
> $$x_0 < x < x_0 + \delta \quad \Rightarrow \quad f(x) > B.$$

Modify the definition to cover the following cases.

a. $\lim_{x \to x_0^-} f(x) = \infty$

b. $\lim_{x \to x_0^+} f(x) = -\infty$

c. $\lim_{x \to x_0^-} f(x) = -\infty$

Use the formal definitions from Exercise 51 to prove the limit statements in Exercises 52–56.

52. $\lim_{x \to 0^+} \frac{1}{x} = \infty$

53. $\lim_{x \to 0^-} \frac{1}{x} = -\infty$

54. $\lim_{x \to 2^-} \frac{1}{x-2} = -\infty$

55. $\lim_{x \to 2^+} \frac{1}{x-2} = \infty$

56. $\lim_{x \to 1^-} \frac{1}{1-x^2} = \infty$

Each of the functions in Exercises 57–60 is given as the sum or difference of two terms. First graph the terms (with the same set of axes). Then, using these graphs as guides, sketch in the graph of the function.

57. $y = \sec x + \frac{1}{x}, \quad -\frac{\pi}{2} < x < \frac{\pi}{2}$

58. $y = \sec x - \frac{1}{x^2}, \quad -\frac{\pi}{2} < x < \frac{\pi}{2}$

59. $y = \tan x + \frac{1}{x^2}, \quad -\frac{\pi}{2} < x < \frac{\pi}{2}$

60. $y = \frac{1}{x} - \tan x, \quad -\frac{\pi}{2} < x < \frac{\pi}{2}$

T Graph the curves in Exercises 61–64. Explain the relation between the curve's formula and what you see.

61. $y = \frac{x}{\sqrt{4 - x^2}}$

62. $y = \frac{-1}{\sqrt{4 - x^2}}$

63. $y = x^{2/3} + \frac{1}{x^{1/3}}$

64. $y = \sin\left(\frac{\pi}{x^2 + 1}\right)$

T In Exercises 65–68, use the graph of $y = f(1/x)$ to find $\lim_{x \to \infty} f(x)$ and $\lim_{x \to -\infty} f(x)$.

65. $f(x) = xe^x$

66. $f(x) = x^2 e^{-x}$

67. $f(x) = \frac{\ln |x|}{x}$

68. $f(x) = \frac{e^{1/x}}{\ln |x|}$

T Graph the functions in Exercises 69 and 70. Then answer the following questions.

a. How does the graph behave as $x \to 0^+$?

b. How does the graph behave as $x \to \pm\infty$?

c. How does the graph behave at $x = 1$ and $x = -1$?

Give reasons for your answers.

69. $y = \frac{3}{2}\left(x - \frac{1}{x}\right)^{2/3}$

70. $y = \frac{3}{2}\left(\frac{x}{x-1}\right)^{2/3}$

2.6 Continuity

When we plot function values generated in a laboratory or collected in the field, we often connect the plotted points with an unbroken curve to show what the function's values are likely to have been at the times we did not measure (Figure 2.53). In doing so, we are

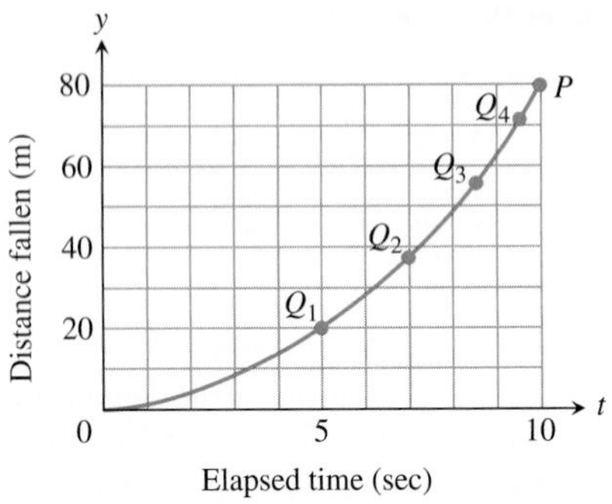

FIGURE 2.53 Connecting plotted points by an unbroken curve from experimental data $Q_1, Q_2, Q_3, \ldots$ for a falling object.

assuming that we are working with a *continuous function*, so its outputs vary continuously with the inputs and do not jump from one value to another without taking on the values in between. The limit of a continuous function as x approaches c can be found simply by calculating the value of the function at c. (We found this to be true for polynomials in Section 2.2.)

Intuitively, any function $y = f(x)$ whose graph can be sketched over its domain in one continuous motion without lifting the pencil is an example of a continuous function. In this section we investigate more precisely what it means for a function to be continuous. We also study the properties of continuous functions, and see that many of the function types presented in Section 1.1 are continuous.

Continuity at a Point

To understand continuity, it helps to consider a function like the one in Figure 2.54 whose limits we investigated in Example 2, Section 2.4.

EXAMPLE 1 Find the points at which the function f in Figure 2.54 is continuous and the points at which f is discontinuous.

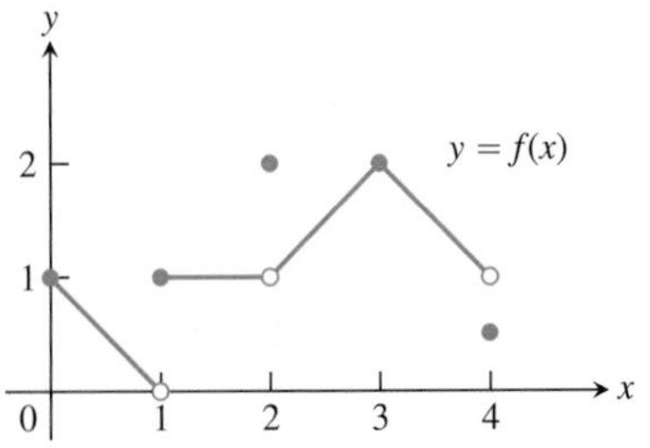

FIGURE 2.54 The function is continuous on $[0, 4]$ except at $x = 1, x = 2$, and $x = 4$ (Example 1).

Solution The function f is continuous at every point in its domain [0,4] except at $x = 1, x = 2$, and $x = 4$. At these points, there are breaks in the graph. Note the relationship between the limit of f and the value of f at each point of the function's domain.

Points at which f is continuous:

At $x = 0$,	$\lim_{x\to 0^+} f(x) = f(0)$.
At $x = 3$,	$\lim_{x\to 3} f(x) = f(3)$.
At $0 < c < 4, c \neq 1, 2$,	$\lim_{x\to c} f(x) = f(c)$.

Points at which f is discontinuous:

At $x = 1$,	$\lim_{x\to 1} f(x)$ does not exist.
At $x = 2$,	$\lim_{x\to 2} f(x) = 1$, but $1 \neq f(2)$.
At $x = 4$,	$\lim_{x\to 4^-} f(x) = 1$, but $1 \neq f(4)$.
At $c < 0, c > 4$,	these points are not in the domain of f. ■

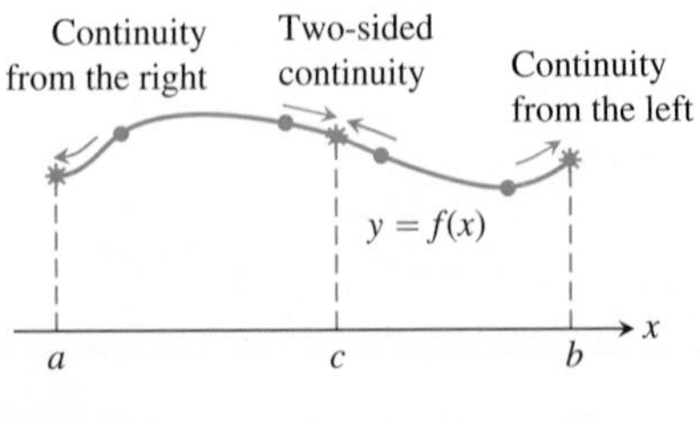

FIGURE 2.55 Continuity at points a, b, and c.

To define continuity at a point in a function's domain, we need to define continuity at an interior point (which involves a two-sided limit) and continuity at an endpoint (which involves a one-sided limit) (Figure 2.55).

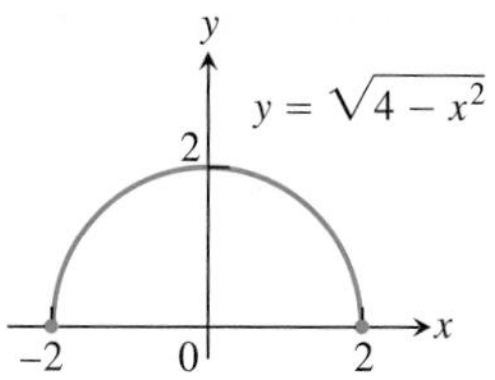

FIGURE 2.56 A function that is continuous at every domain point (Example 2).

DEFINITION

Interior point: A function $y = f(x)$ is **continuous at an interior point c** of its domain if

$$\lim_{x \to c} f(x) = f(c).$$

Endpoint: A function $y = f(x)$ is **continuous at a left endpoint a** or is **continuous at a right endpoint b** of its domain if

$$\lim_{x \to a^+} f(x) = f(a) \quad \text{or} \quad \lim_{x \to b^-} f(x) = f(b), \quad \text{respectively.}$$

If a function f is not continuous at a point c, we say that f is **discontinuous** at c and c is a **point of discontinuity** of f. Note that c need not be in the domain of f.

A function f is **right-continuous (continuous from the right)** at a point $x = c$ in its domain if $\lim_{x \to c^+} f(x) = f(c)$. It is **left-continuous (continuous from the left)** at c if $\lim_{x \to c^-} f(x) = f(c)$. Thus, a function is continuous at a left endpoint a of its domain if it is right-continuous at a and continuous at a right endpoint b of its domain if it is left-continuous at b. A function is continuous at an interior point c of its domain if and only if it is both right-continuous and left-continuous at c (Figure 2.55).

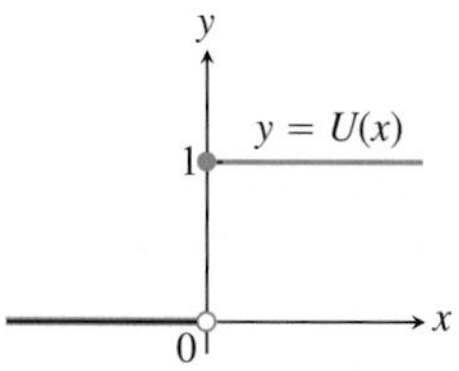

FIGURE 2.57 A function that is right-continuous, but not left-continuous, at the origin. It has a jump discontinuity there (Example 3).

EXAMPLE 2 The function $f(x) = \sqrt{4 - x^2}$ is continuous at every point of its domain $[-2, 2]$ (Figure 2.56), including $x = -2$, where f is right-continuous, and $x = 2$, where f is left-continuous. ■

EXAMPLE 3 The unit step function $U(x)$, graphed in Figure 2.57, is right-continuous at $x = 0$, but is neither left-continuous nor continuous there. It has a jump discontinuity at $x = 0$. ■

We summarize continuity at a point in the form of a test.

Continuity Test

A function $f(x)$ is continuous at an interior point $x = c$ of its domain if and only if it meets the following three conditions.

1. $f(c)$ exists — (c lies in the domain of f)
2. $\lim_{x \to c} f(x)$ exists — (f has a limit as $x \to c$)
3. $\lim_{x \to c} f(x) = f(c)$ — (the limit equals the function value)

For one-sided continuity and continuity at an endpoint, the limits in parts 2 and 3 of the test should be replaced by the appropriate one-sided limits.

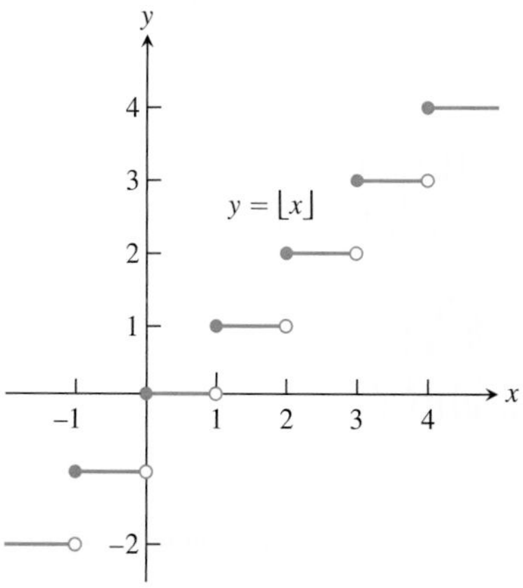

FIGURE 2.58 The greatest integer function is continuous at every noninteger point. It is right-continuous, but not left-continuous, at every integer point (Example 4).

EXAMPLE 4 The function $y = \lfloor x \rfloor$ introduced in Section 1.1 is graphed in Figure 2.58. It is discontinuous at every integer because the left-hand and right-hand limits are not equal as $x \to n$:

$$\lim_{x \to n^-} \lfloor x \rfloor = n - 1 \quad \text{and} \quad \lim_{x \to n^+} \lfloor x \rfloor = n.$$

Since $\lfloor n \rfloor = n$, the greatest integer function is right-continuous at every integer n (but not left-continuous).

The greatest integer function is continuous at every real number other than the integers. For example,

$$\lim_{x \to 1.5} \lfloor x \rfloor = 1 = \lfloor 1.5 \rfloor .$$

In general, if $n - 1 < c < n$, n an integer, then

$$\lim_{x \to c} \lfloor x \rfloor = n - 1 = \lfloor c \rfloor .$$

■

Figure 2.59 is a catalog of discontinuity types. The function in Figure 2.59a is continuous at $x = 0$. The function in Figure 2.59b would be continuous if it had $f(0) = 1$. The function in Figure 2.59c would be continuous if $f(0)$ were 1 instead of 2. The discontinuities in Figure 2.59b and c are **removable**. Each function has a limit as $x \to 0$, and we can remove the discontinuity by setting $f(0)$ equal to this limit.

The discontinuities in Figure 2.59d through f are more serious: $\lim_{x \to 0} f(x)$ does not exist, and there is no way to improve the situation by changing f at 0. The step function in Figure 2.59d has a **jump discontinuity**: The one-sided limits exist but have different values. The function $f(x) = 1/x^2$ in Figure 2.59e has an **infinite discontinuity**. The function in Figure 2.59f has an **oscillating discontinuity**: It oscillates too much to have a limit as $x \to 0$.

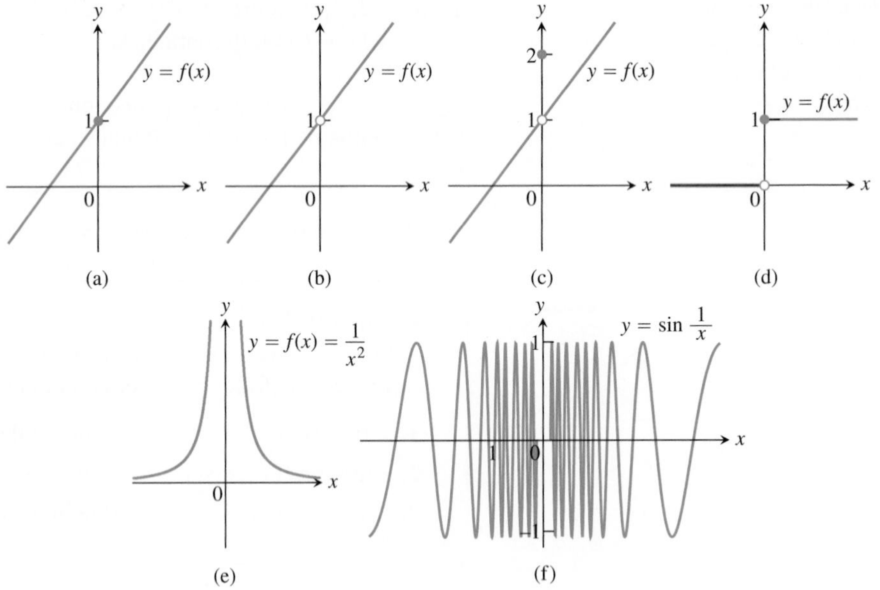

FIGURE 2.59 The function in (a) is continuous at $x = 0$; the functions in (b) through (f) are not.

Continuous Functions

A function is **continuous on an interval** if and only if it is continuous at every point of the interval. For example, the semicircle function graphed in Figure 2.56 is continuous on the interval $[-2, 2]$, which is its domain. A **continuous function** is one that is continuous at every point of its domain. A continuous function need not be continuous on every interval.

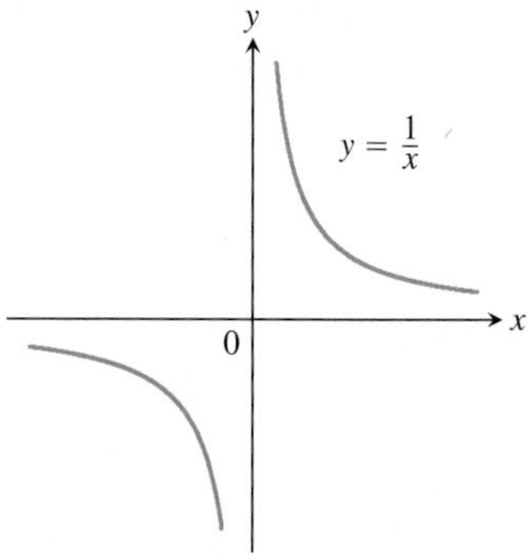

FIGURE 2.60 The function $y = 1/x$ is continuous at every value of x except $x = 0$. It has a point of discontinuity at $x = 0$ (Example 5).

EXAMPLE 5

(a) The function $y = 1/x$ (Figure 2.60) is a continuous function because it is continuous at every point of its domain. It has a point of discontinuity at $x = 0$, however, because it is not defined there; that is, it is discontinuous on any interval containing $x = 0$.

(b) The identity function $f(x) = x$ and constant functions are continuous everywhere by Example 3, Section 2.3. ∎

Algebraic combinations of continuous functions are continuous wherever they are defined.

THEOREM 9—Properties of Continuous Functions If the functions f and g are continuous at $x = c$, then the following combinations are continuous at $x = c$.

1. *Sums:* $f + g$
2. *Differences:* $f - g$
3. *Products:* $f \cdot g$
4. *Constant multiples:* $k \cdot f$, for any number k
5. *Quotients:* f/g, provided $g(c) \neq 0$
6. *Powers:* $f^{r/s}$, provided it is defined on an open interval containing c, where r and s are integers

Most of the results in Theorem 9 follow from the limit rules in Theorem 1, Section 2.2. For instance, to prove the sum property we have

$$\begin{aligned}
\lim_{x \to c}(f + g)(x) &= \lim_{x \to c}(f(x) + g(x)) \\
&= \lim_{x \to c} f(x) + \lim_{x \to c} g(x), && \text{Sum Rule, Theorem 1} \\
&= f(c) + g(c) && \text{Continuity of } f, g \text{ at } c \\
&= (f + g)(c).
\end{aligned}$$

This shows that $f + g$ is continuous.

EXAMPLE 6

(a) Every polynomial $P(x) = a_n x^n + a_{n-1}x^{n-1} + \cdots + a_0$ is continuous because $\lim_{x \to c} P(x) = P(c)$ by Theorem 2, Section 2.2.

(b) If $P(x)$ and $Q(x)$ are polynomials, then the rational function $P(x)/Q(x)$ is continuous wherever it is defined ($Q(c) \neq 0$) by the Quotient Rule in Theorem 9.

EXAMPLE 7 The function $f(x) = |x|$ is continuous at every value of x. If $x > 0$, we have $f(x) = x$, a polynomial. If $x < 0$, we have $f(x) = -x$, another polynomial. Finally, at the origin, $\lim_{x \to 0}|x| = 0 = |0|$. ∎

The functions $y = \sin x$ and $y = \cos x$ are continuous at $x = 0$ by Example 11 of Section 2.2. Both functions are, in fact, continuous everywhere (see Exercise 62). It follows from Theorem 9 that all six trigonometric functions are then continuous wherever they are defined. For example, $y = \tan x$ is continuous on $\cdots \cup (-\pi/2, \pi/2) \cup (\pi/2, 3\pi/2) \cup \cdots$.

Inverse Functions and Continuity

The inverse function of any continuous function is continuous over its domain. This result is suggested from the observation that the graph of f^{-1}, being the reflection of the graph of f across the line $y = x$, cannot have any breaks in it when the graph of f has no breaks. A rigorous proof that f^{-1} is continuous whenever f is continuous is given in more advanced texts. It follows that the inverse trigonometric functions are all continuous over their domains.

We defined the exponential function $y = a^x$ in Section 1.4 informally by its graph. Recall that the graph was obtained from the graph of $y = a^x$ for x a rational number by filling in the holes at the irrational points x, so the function $y = a^x$ was defined to be continuous over the entire real line. The inverse function $y = \log_a x$ is also continuous. In particular, the natural exponential function $y = e^x$, and the natural logarithm function $y = \ln x$, are both continuous over their domains.

Composites

All composites of continuous functions are continuous. The idea is that if $f(x)$ is continuous at $x = c$ and $g(x)$ is continuous at $x = f(c)$, then $g \circ f$ is continuous at $x = c$ (Figure 2.61). In this case, the limit as $x \to c$ is $g(f(c))$.

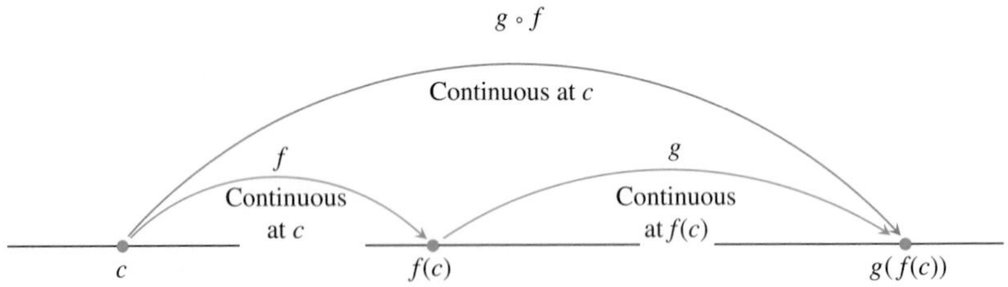

FIGURE 2.61 Composites of continuous functions are continuous.

> **THEOREM 10—Composite of Continuous Functions** If f is continuous at c and g is continuous at $f(c)$, then the composite $g \circ f$ is continuous at c.

Intuitively, Theorem 10 is reasonable because if x is close to c, then $f(x)$ is close to $f(c)$, and since g is continuous at $f(c)$, it follows that $g(f(x))$ is close to $g(f(c))$.

The continuity of composites holds for any finite number of functions. The only requirement is that each function be continuous where it is applied. For an outline of the proof of Theorem 10, see Exercise 6 in Appendix 5.

EXAMPLE 8 Show that the following functions are continuous everywhere on their respective domains.

(a) $y = \sqrt{x^2 - 2x - 5}$ **(b)** $y = \dfrac{x^{2/3}}{1 + x^4}$

(c) $y = \left|\dfrac{x - 2}{x^2 - 2}\right|$ **(d)** $y = \left|\dfrac{x \sin x}{x^2 + 2}\right|$

Solution

(a) The square root function is continuous on $[0, \infty)$ because it is a rational power of the continuous identity function $f(x) = x$ (Part 6, Theorem 9). The given function is then the composite of the polynomial $f(x) = x^2 - 2x - 5$ with the square root function $g(t) = \sqrt{t}$.

(b) The numerator is a rational power of the identity function; the denominator is an everywhere-positive polynomial. Therefore, the quotient is continuous.

(c) The quotient $(x - 2)/(x^2 - 2)$ is continuous for all $x \neq \pm\sqrt{2}$, and the function is the composition of this quotient with the continuous absolute value function (Example 7).

(d) Because the sine function is everywhere-continuous (Exercise 62), the numerator term $x \sin x$ is the product of continuous functions, and the denominator term $x^2 + 2$ is an everywhere-positive polynomial. The given function is the composite of a quotient of continuous functions with the continuous absolute value function (Figure 2.62). ■

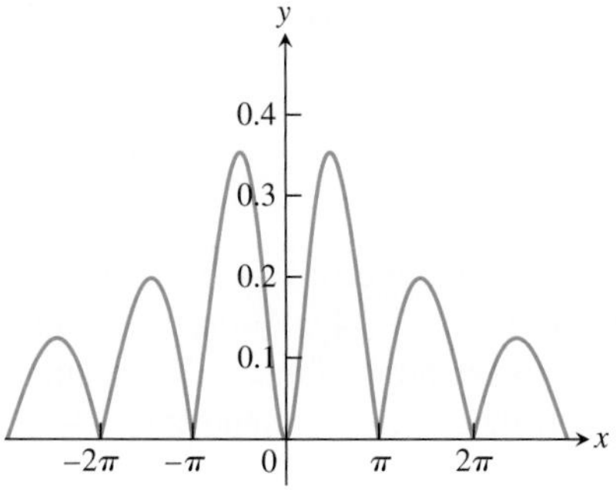

FIGURE 2.62 The graph suggests that $y = |(x \sin x)/(x^2 + 2)|$ is continuous (Example 8d).

Theorem 10 is actually a consequence of a more general result which we now state and prove.

> **THEOREM 11—Limits of Continuous Functions** If g is continuous at the point b and $\lim_{x\to c} f(x) = b$, then
>
> $$\lim_{x\to c} g(f(x)) = g(b) = g(\lim_{x\to c} (f(x))).$$

Proof Let $\epsilon > 0$ be given. Since g is continuous at b, there exists a number $\delta_1 > 0$ such that

$$|g(y) - g(b)| < \epsilon \quad \text{whenever} \quad 0 < |y - b| < \delta_1.$$

Since $\lim_{x\to c} f(x) = b$, there exists a $\delta > 0$ such that

$$|f(x) - b| < \delta_1 \quad \text{whenever} \quad 0 < |x - c| < \delta.$$

If we let $y = f(x)$, we then have that

$$|y - b| < \delta_1 \quad \text{whenever} \quad 0 < |x - c| < \delta$$

which implies from the first statement that $|g(y) - g(b)| = |g(f(x)) - g(b)| < \epsilon$ whenever $0 < |x - c| < \delta$. From the definition of limit, this proves that $\lim_{x\to c} g(f(x)) = g(b)$. ■

EXAMPLE 9

(a) $$\lim_{x\to 1}\sin^{-1}\left(\frac{1-x}{1-x^2}\right) = \sin^{-1}\left(\lim_{x\to 1}\frac{1-x}{1-x^2}\right)$$ Arcsine is continuous.

$$= \sin^{-1}\left(\lim_{x\to 1}\frac{1}{1+x}\right)$$ Cancel common factor $(1-x)$.

$$= \sin^{-1}\frac{1}{2} = \frac{\pi}{6}$$

(b) $$\lim_{x\to 0}\sqrt{x+1}\,e^{\tan x} = \lim_{x\to 0}\sqrt{x+1}\cdot\exp\left(\lim_{x\to 0}\tan x\right)$$ Exponential is continuous.

$$= 1\cdot e^0 = 1$$ ■

Continuous Extension to a Point

The function $y = f(x) = (\sin x)/x$ is continuous at every point except $x = 0$. In this it is like the function $y = 1/x$. But $y = (\sin x)/x$ is different from $y = 1/x$ in that it has a finite limit as $x \to 0$ (Theorem 7). It is therefore possible to extend the function's domain to include the point $x = 0$ in such a way that the extended function is continuous at $x = 0$. We define a new function

$$F(x) = \begin{cases} \dfrac{\sin x}{x}, & x \neq 0 \\ 1, & x = 0. \end{cases}$$

The function $F(x)$ is continuous at $x = 0$ because

$$\lim_{x\to 0}\frac{\sin x}{x} = F(0)$$

(Figure 2.63).

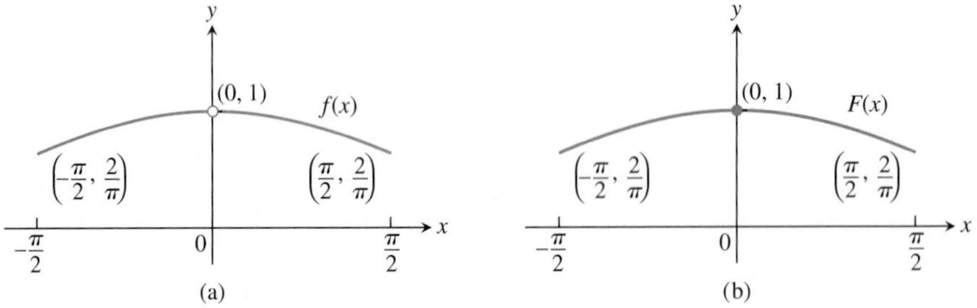

FIGURE 2.63 The graph (a) of $f(x) = (\sin x)/x$ for $-\pi/2 \leq x \leq \pi/2$ does not include the point (0, 1) because the function is not defined at $x = 0$. (b) We can remove the discontinuity from the graph by defining the new function $F(x)$ with $F(0) = 1$ and $F(x) = f(x)$ everywhere else. Note that $F(0) = \lim_{x\to 0} f(x)$.

More generally, a function (such as a rational function) may have a limit even at a point where it is not defined. If $f(c)$ is not defined, but $\lim_{x\to c} f(x) = L$ exists, we can define a new function $F(x)$ by the rule

$$F(x) = \begin{cases} f(x), & \text{if } x \text{ is in the domain of } f \\ L, & \text{if } x = c. \end{cases}$$

The function F is continuous at $x = c$. It is called the **continuous extension** of f to $x = c$. For rational functions f, continuous extensions are usually found by canceling common factors.

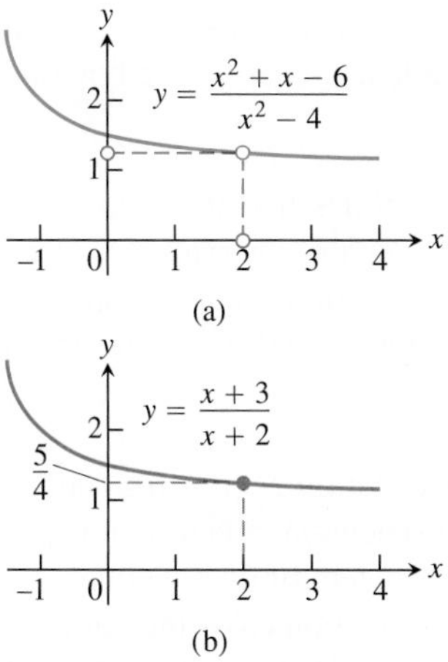

FIGURE 2.64 (a) The graph of $f(x)$ and (b) the graph of its continuous extension $F(x)$ (Example 10).

EXAMPLE 10 Show that

$$f(x) = \frac{x^2 + x - 6}{x^2 - 4}, \quad x \neq 2$$

has a continuous extension to $x = 2$, and find that extension.

Solution Although $f(2)$ is not defined, if $x \neq 2$ we have

$$f(x) = \frac{x^2 + x - 6}{x^2 - 4} = \frac{(x - 2)(x + 3)}{(x - 2)(x + 2)} = \frac{x + 3}{x + 2}.$$

The new function

$$F(x) = \frac{x + 3}{x + 2}$$

is equal to $f(x)$ for $x \neq 2$, but is continuous at $x = 2$, having there the value of $5/4$. Thus F is the continuous extension of f to $x = 2$, and

$$\lim_{x \to 2} \frac{x^2 + x - 6}{x^2 - 4} = \lim_{x \to 2} f(x) = \frac{5}{4}.$$

The graph of f is shown in Figure 2.64. The continuous extension F has the same graph except with no hole at $(2, 5/4)$. Effectively, F is the function f with its point of discontinuity at $x = 2$ removed. ■

Intermediate Value Theorem for Continuous Functions

Functions that are continuous on intervals have properties that make them particularly useful in mathematics and its applications. One of these is the *Intermediate Value Property*. A function is said to have the **Intermediate Value Property** if whenever it takes on two values, it also takes on all the values in between.

THEOREM 12—The Intermediate Value Theorem for Continuous Functions
A function $y = f(x)$ that is continuous on a closed interval $[a, b]$ takes on every value between $f(a)$ and $f(b)$. In other words, if y_0 is any value between $f(a)$ and $f(b)$, then $y_0 = f(c)$ for some c in $[a, b]$.

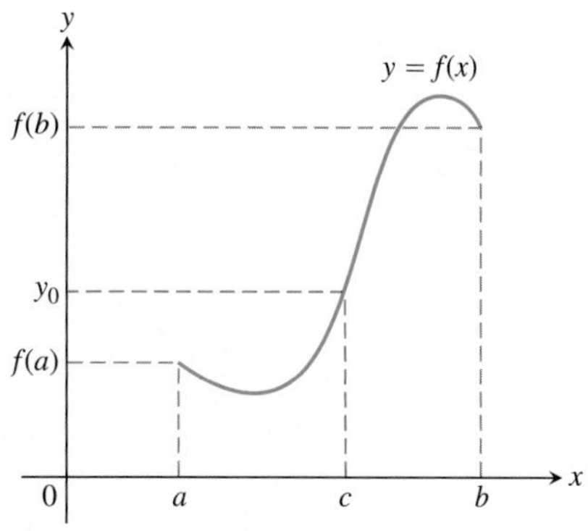

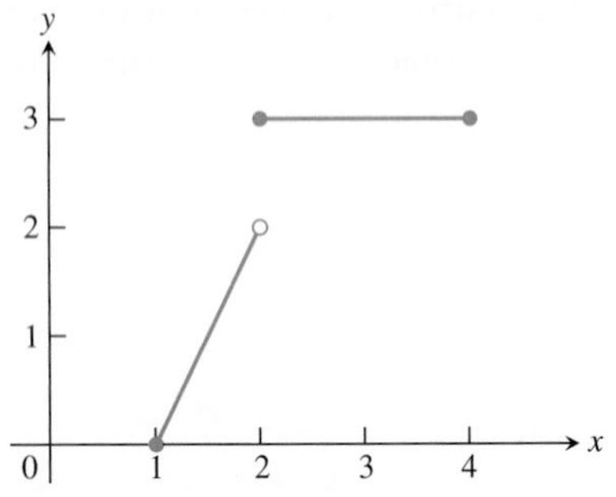

FIGURE 2.65 The function
$$f(x) = \begin{cases} 2x - 2, & 1 \le x < 2 \\ 3, & 2 \le x \le 4 \end{cases}$$
does not take on all values between $f(1) = 0$ and $f(4) = 3$; it misses all the values between 2 and 3.

Geometrically, the Intermediate Value Theorem says that any horizontal line $y = y_0$ crossing the y-axis between the numbers $f(a)$ and $f(b)$ will cross the curve $y = f(x)$ at least once over the interval $[a, b]$.

The proof of the Intermediate Value Theorem depends on the completeness property of the real number system and can be found in more advanced texts.

The continuity of f on the interval is essential to Theorem 12. If f is discontinuous at even one point of the interval, the theorem's conclusion may fail, as it does for the function graphed in Figure 2.65.

A Consequence for Graphing: Connectivity Theorem 12 implies that the graph of a function continuous on an interval cannot have any breaks over the interval. It will be **connected**—a single, unbroken curve, like the graph of sin x. It will not have jumps like the graph of the greatest integer function (Figure 2.58), or separate branches like the graph of $1/x$ (Figure 2.60).

A Consequence for Root Finding We call a solution of the equation $f(x) = 0$ a **root** of the equation or **zero** of the function f. The Intermediate Value Theorem tells us that if f is continuous, then any interval on which f changes sign contains a zero of the function.

In practical terms, when we see the graph of a continuous function cross the horizontal axis on a computer screen, we know it is not stepping across. There really is a point where the function's value is zero. This consequence leads to a procedure for estimating the zeros of any continuous function we can graph:

1. Graph the function over a large interval to see roughly where the zeros are.
2. Zoom in on each zero to estimate its x-coordinate value.

You can practice this procedure on your graphing calculator or computer in some of the exercises. Figure 2.66 shows a typical sequence of steps in a graphical solution of the equation $x^3 - x - 1 = 0$.

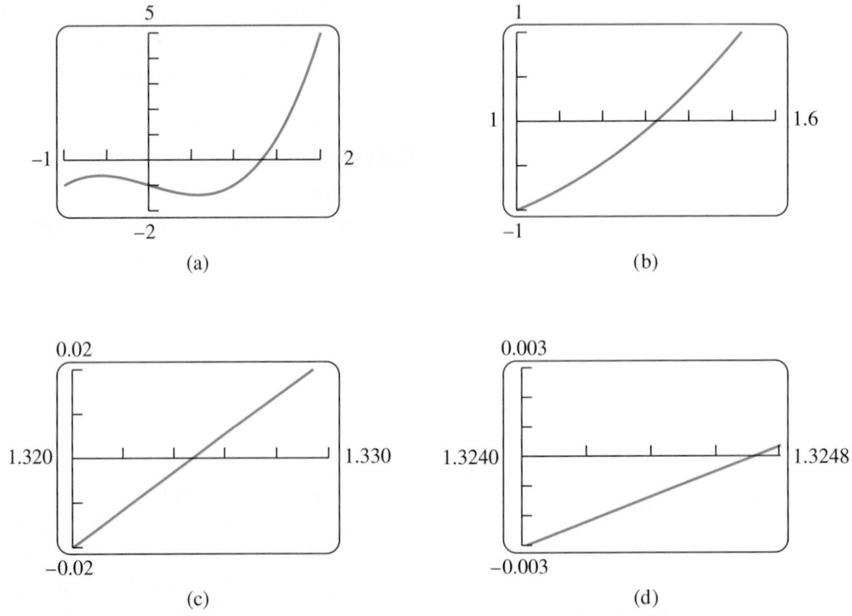

FIGURE 2.66 Zooming in on a zero of the function $f(x) = x^3 - x - 1$. The zero is near $x = 1.3247$.

EXERCISES 2.6

In Exercises 1–4, say whether the function graphed is continuous on $[-1, 3]$. If not, where does it fail to be continuous and why?

1.

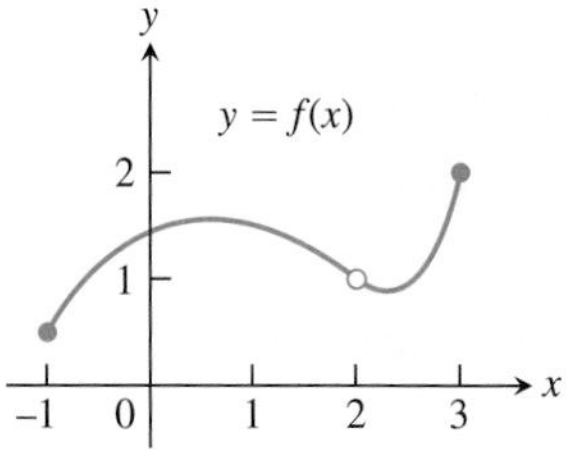

2.

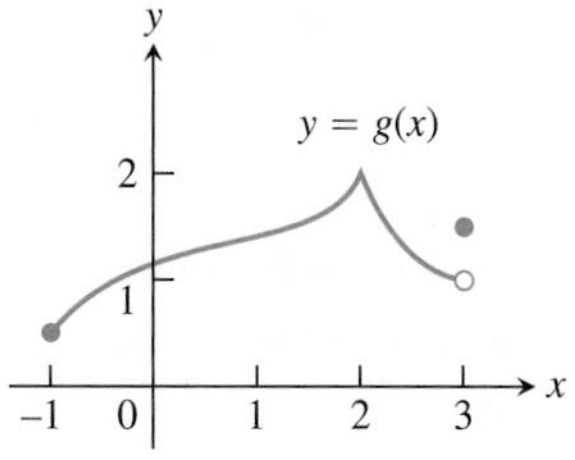

3.

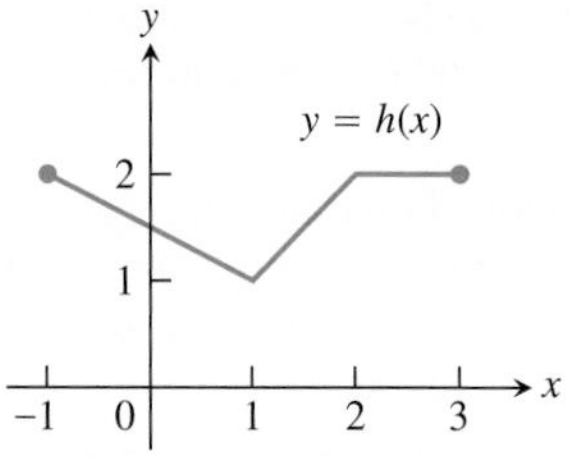

4.

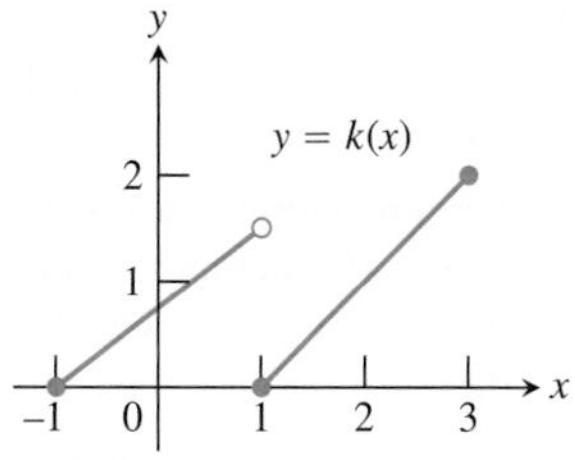

Exercises 5–10 are about the function

$$f(x) = \begin{cases} x^2 - 1, & -1 \le x < 0 \\ 2x, & 0 < x < 1 \\ 1, & x = 1 \\ -2x + 4, & 1 < x < 2 \\ 0, & 2 < x < 3 \end{cases}$$

graphed in the accompanying figure.

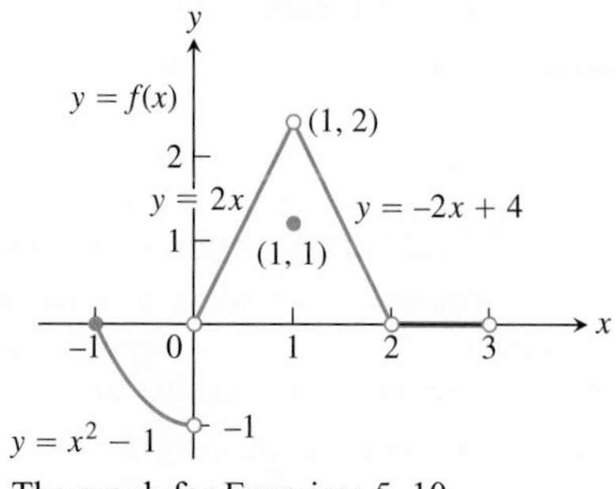

The graph for Exercises 5–10.

5. a. Does $f(-1)$ exist?

b. Does $\lim_{x\to -1^+} f(x)$ exist?

c. Does $\lim_{x\to -1^+} f(x) = f(-1)$?

d. Is f continuous at $x = -1$?

6. a. Does $f(1)$ exist?

b. Does $\lim_{x\to 1} f(x)$ exist?

c. Does $\lim_{x\to 1} f(x) = f(1)$?

d. Is f continuous at $x = 1$?

7. a. Is f defined at $x = 2$? (Look at the definition of f.)

b. Is f continuous at $x = 2$?

8. At what values of x is f continuous?

9. What value should be assigned to $f(2)$ to make the extended function continuous at $x = 2$?

10. To what new value should $f(1)$ be changed to remove the discontinuity?

At which points do the functions in Exercises 11 and 12 fail to be continuous? At which points, if any, are the discontinuities removable? Not removable? Give reasons for your answers.

11. Exercise 1, Section 2.4

12. Exercise 2, Section 2.4

At what points are the functions in Exercises 13–28 continuous?

13. $y = \dfrac{1}{x-2} - 3x$

14. $y = \dfrac{1}{(x+2)^2} + 4$

15. $y = \dfrac{x+1}{x^2 - 4x + 3}$

16. $y = \dfrac{x+3}{x^2 - 3x - 10}$

17. $y = |x - 1| + \sin x$

18. $y = \dfrac{1}{|x| + 1} - \dfrac{x^2}{2}$

19. $y = \dfrac{\cos x}{x}$

20. $y = \dfrac{x+2}{\cos x}$

21. $y = \csc 2x$

22. $y = \tan \dfrac{\pi x}{2}$

23. $y = \dfrac{x \tan x}{x^2 + 1}$

24. $y = \dfrac{\sqrt{x^4 + 1}}{1 + \sin^2 x}$

25. $y = \sqrt{2x + 3}$

26. $y = \sqrt[4]{3x - 1}$

27. $y = (2x - 1)^{1/3}$

28. $y = (2 - x)^{1/5}$

Find the limits in Exercises 29–34. Are the functions continuous at the point being approached?

29. $\lim\limits_{x\to\pi} \sin(x - \sin x)$

30. $\lim\limits_{t\to 0} \sin\left(\dfrac{\pi}{2}\cos(\tan t)\right)$

31. $\lim\limits_{y\to 1} \sec(y \sec^2 y - \tan^2 y - 1)$

32. $\lim\limits_{x\to 0} \tan\left(\dfrac{\pi}{4}\cos(\sin x^{1/3})\right)$

33. $\lim\limits_{x\to 0^+} \sin\left(\dfrac{\pi}{2}e^{\sqrt{x}}\right)$

34. $\lim\limits_{x\to 1} \cos^{-1}(\ln\sqrt{x})$

35. Define $g(3)$ in a way that extends $g(x) = (x^2 - 9)/(x - 3)$ to be continuous at $x = 3$.

36. Define $h(2)$ in a way that extends $h(t) = (t^2 + 3t - 10)/(t - 2)$ to be continuous at $t = 2$.

37. Define $f(1)$ in a way that extends $f(s) = (s^3 - 1)/(s^2 - 1)$ to be continuous at $s = 1$.

38. Define $g(4)$ in a way that extends

$$g(x) = (x^2 - 16)/(x^2 - 3x - 4)$$

to be continuous at $x = 4$.

39. For what value of a is

$$f(x) = \begin{cases} x^2 - 1, & x < 3 \\ 2ax, & x \geq 3 \end{cases}$$

continuous at every x?

40. For what value of b is

$$g(x) = \begin{cases} x, & x < -2 \\ bx^2, & x \geq -2 \end{cases}$$

continuous at every x?

T In Exercises 41–44, graph the function f to see whether it appears to have a continuous extension to the origin. If it does, use Trace and Zoom to find a good candidate for the extended function's value at $x = 0$. If the function does not appear to have a continuous extension, can it be extended to be continuous at the origin from the right or from the left? If so, what do you think the extended function's value(s) should be?

41. $f(x) = \dfrac{10^x - 1}{x}$ **42.** $f(x) = \dfrac{10^{|x|} - 1}{x}$

43. $f(x) = \dfrac{\sin x}{|x|}$ **44.** $f(x) = (1 + 2x)^{1/x}$

45. A continuous function $y = f(x)$ is known to be negative at $x = 0$ and positive at $x = 1$. Why does the equation $f(x) = 0$ have at least one solution between $x = 0$ and $x = 1$? Illustrate with a sketch.

46. Explain why the equation $\cos x = x$ has at least one solution.

47. Roots of a cubic Show that the equation $x^3 - 15x + 1 = 0$ has three solutions in the interval $[-4, 4]$.

48. A function value Show that the function $F(x) = (x - a)^2 \cdot (x - b)^2 + x$ takes on the value $(a + b)/2$ for some value of x.

49. Solving an equation If $f(x) = x^3 - 8x + 10$, show that there are values c for which $f(c)$ equals **(a)** π; **(b)** $-\sqrt{3}$; **(c)** 5,000,000.

50. Explain why the following five statements ask for the same information.

a. Find the roots of $f(x) = x^3 - 3x - 1$.

b. Find the x-coordinates of the points where the curve $y = x^3$ crosses the line $y = 3x + 1$.

c. Find all the values of x for which $x^3 - 3x = 1$.

d. Find the x-coordinates of the points where the cubic curve $y = x^3 - 3x$ crosses the line $y = 1$.

e. Solve the equation $x^3 - 3x - 1 = 0$.

51. Removable discontinuity Give an example of a function $f(x)$ that is continuous for all values of x except $x = 2$, where it has a removable discontinuity. Explain how you know that f is discontinuous at $x = 2$, and how you know the discontinuity is removable.

52. Nonremovable discontinuity Give an example of a function $g(x)$ that is continuous for all values of x except $x = -1$, where it has a nonremovable discontinuity. Explain how you know that g is discontinuous there and why the discontinuity is not removable.

53. A function discontinuous at every point

a. Use the fact that every nonempty interval of real numbers contains both rational and irrational numbers to show that the function

$$f(x) = \begin{cases} 1, & \text{if } x \text{ is rational} \\ 0, & \text{if } x \text{ is irrational} \end{cases}$$

is discontinuous at every point.

b. Is f right-continuous or left-continuous at any point?

54. If functions $f(x)$ and $g(x)$ are continuous for $0 \leq x \leq 1$, could $f(x)/g(x)$ possibly be discontinuous at a point of $[0, 1]$? Give reasons for your answer.

55. If the product function $h(x) = f(x) \cdot g(x)$ is continuous at $x = 0$, must $f(x)$ and $g(x)$ be continuous at $x = 0$? Give reasons for your answer.

56. Discontinuous composite of continuous functions Give an example of functions f and g, both continuous at $x = 0$, for which the composite $f \circ g$ is discontinuous at $x = 0$. Does this contradict Theorem 10? Give reasons for your answer.

57. Never-zero continuous functions Is it true that a continuous function that is never zero on an interval never changes sign on that interval? Give reasons for your answer.

58. Stretching a rubber band Is it true that if you stretch a rubber band by moving one end to the right and the other to the left, some point of the band will end up in its original position? Give reasons for your answer.

59. A fixed point theorem Suppose that a function f is continuous on the closed interval $[0, 1]$ and that $0 \leq f(x) \leq 1$ for every x in $[0, 1]$. Show that there must exist a number c in $[0, 1]$ such that $f(c) = c$ (c is called a **fixed point** of f).

60. The sign-preserving property of continuous functions Let f be defined on an interval (a, b) and suppose that $f(c) \neq 0$ at some c where f is continuous. Show that there is an interval $(c - \delta, c + \delta)$ about c where f has the same sign as $f(c)$. Notice how remarkable this conclusion is. Although f is defined throughout (a, b), it is not required to be continuous at any point except c. That and the condition $f(c) \neq 0$ are enough to make f different from zero (positive or negative) throughout an entire interval.

61. Prove that f is continuous at c if and only if

$$\lim_{h \to 0} f(c + h) = f(c).$$

62. Use Exercise 61 together with the identities

$$\sin(h + c) = \sin h \cos c + \cos h \sin c,$$

$$\cos(h + c) = \cos h \cos c - \sin h \sin c$$

to prove that $f(x) = \sin x$ and $g(x) = \cos x$ are continuous at every point $x = c$.

T Use a graphing calculator or computer grapher to solve the equations in Exercises 63–70.

63. $x^3 - 3x - 1 = 0$

64. $2x^3 - 2x^2 - 2x + 1 = 0$

65. $x(x - 1)^2 = 1$ (one root)

66. $x^x = 2$

67. $\sqrt{x} + \sqrt{1 + x} = 4$

68. $x^3 - 15x + 1 = 0$ (three roots)

69. $\cos x = x$ (one root). Make sure you are using radian mode.

70. $2 \sin x = x$ (three roots). Make sure you are using radian mode.

2.7 Tangents and Derivatives at a Point

This section makes precise our discussion in Section 2.1 of slopes and tangent lines to a curve. We saw how these notions are related to the instantaneous rate of change of a function, which is an interpretation of the *derivative* of the function. We define the derivative here.

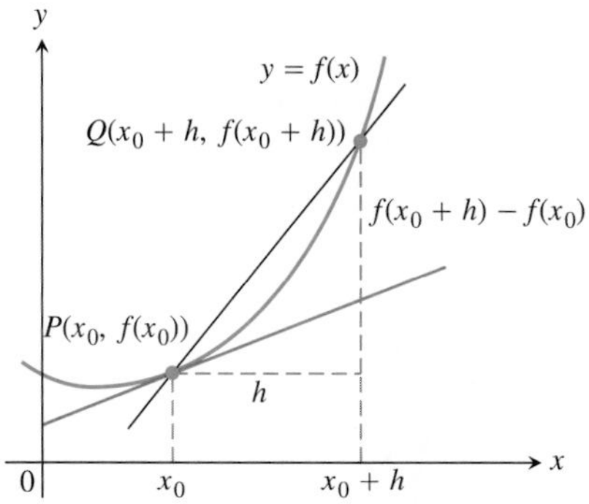

FIGURE 2.67 The slope of the tangent line at P is $\lim_{h \to 0} \frac{f(x_0 + h) - f(x_0)}{h}$.

Finding a Tangent to the Graph of a Function

To find a tangent to an arbitrary curve $y = f(x)$ at a point $P(x_0, f(x_0))$, we use the procedure introduced in Section 2.1. We calculate the slope of the secant through P and a nearby point $Q(x_0 + h, f(x_0 + h))$. We then investigate the limit of the slope as $h \to 0$ (Figure 2.67). If the limit exists, we call it the slope of the curve at P and define the tangent at P to be the line through P having this slope.

DEFINITIONS The **slope of the curve** $y = f(x)$ at the point $P(x_0, f(x_0))$ is the number

$$m = \lim_{h \to 0} \frac{f(x_0 + h) - f(x_0)}{h} \quad \text{(provided the limit exists).}$$

The **tangent line** to the curve at P is the line through P with this slope.

In Section 2.1, Example 3, we applied these definitions to find the slope of the parabola $f(x) = x^2$ at the point $P(2, 4)$ and the tangent line to the parabola at P. Let's look at another example.

EXAMPLE 1

(a) Find the slope of the curve $y = 1/x$ at $x = a \neq 0$.

(b) Where does the slope equal $-1/4$?

(c) What happens to the tangent to the curve at the point $(a, 1/a)$ as a changes?

Solution

(a) Here $f(x) = 1/x$. The slope at $(a, 1/a)$ is

$$\lim_{h \to 0} \frac{f(a + h) - f(a)}{h} = \lim_{h \to 0} \frac{\frac{1}{a + h} - \frac{1}{a}}{h} = \lim_{h \to 0} \frac{1}{h} \frac{a - (a + h)}{a(a + h)}$$

$$= \lim_{h \to 0} \frac{-h}{ha(a + h)} = \lim_{h \to 0} \frac{-1}{a(a + h)} = -\frac{1}{a^2}.$$

Notice how we had to keep writing "$\lim_{h \to 0}$" before each fraction until the stage where we could evaluate the limit by substituting $h = 0$. The number a may be positive or negative, but not 0.

(b) The slope of $y = 1/x$ at the point where $x = a$ is $-1/a^2$. It will be $-1/4$ provided that

$$-\frac{1}{a^2} = -\frac{1}{4}.$$

This equation is equivalent to $a^2 = 4$, so $a = 2$ or $a = -2$. The curve has slope $-1/4$ at the two points $(2, 1/2)$ and $(-2, -1/2)$ (Figure 2.68).

(c) The slope $-1/a^2$ is always negative if $a \neq 0$. As $a \to 0^+$, the slope approaches $-\infty$ and the tangent becomes increasingly steep (Figure 2.69). We see this situation again as $a \to 0^-$. As a moves away from the origin in either direction, the slope approaches 0 and the tangent levels off to become horizontal. ■

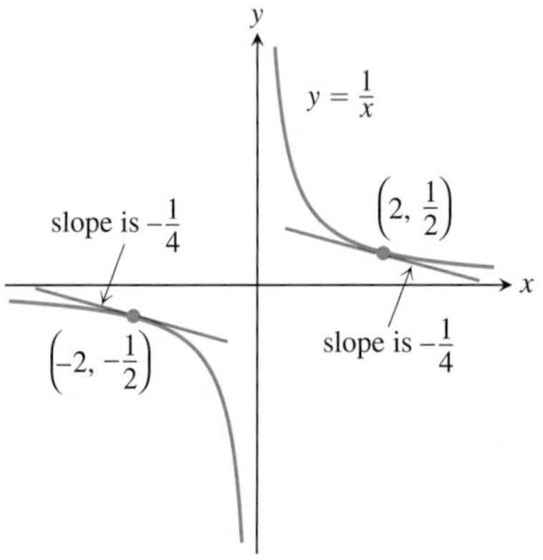

FIGURE 2.68 The two tangent lines to $y = 1/x$ having slope $-1/4$ (Example 1).

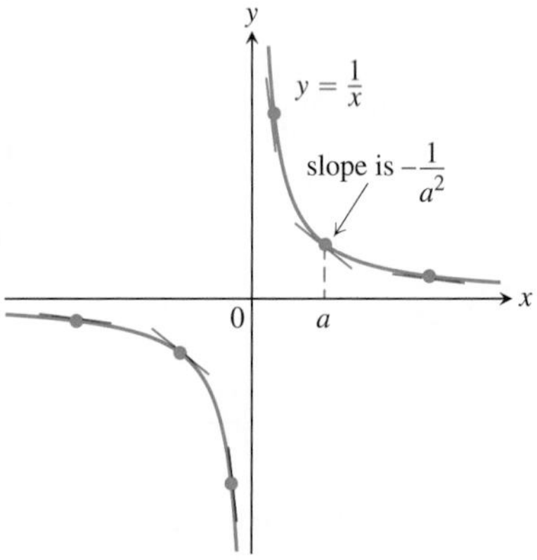

FIGURE 2.69 The tangent slopes, steep near the origin, become more gradual as the point tangency moves away.

Rates of Change: Derivative at a Point

The expression

$$\frac{f(x_0 + h) - f(x_0)}{h}$$

is called the **difference quotient of f at x_0 with increment h**. If the difference quotient has a limit as h approaches zero, that limit is given a special name and notation.

DEFINITION The **derivative of a function f at a point x_0**, denoted $f'(x_0)$, is

$$f'(x_0) = \lim_{h \to 0} \frac{f(x_0 + h) - f(x_0)}{h}$$

provided this limit exists.

If we interpret the difference quotient as the slope of a secant line, then the derivative gives the slope of the curve $y = f(x)$ at the point $P(x_0, f(x_0))$. Exercise 31 shows that the derivative of the linear function $f(x) = mx + b$ at any point x_0 is simply the slope of the line,

$$f'(x_0) = m,$$

as it should be.

If we interpret the difference quotient as an average rate of change (Section 2.1), the derivative gives the function's instantaneous rate of change with respect to x at the point $x = x_0$.

EXAMPLE 2 In Examples 1 and 2 in Section 2.1, we studied the speed of a rock falling freely from rest near the surface of the earth. We knew that the rock fell $y = 16t^2$ feet during the first t sec, and we used a sequence of average rates over increasingly short intervals to estimate the rock's speed at the instant $t = 1$. Exactly what *was* the rock's speed at this time?

Solution We let $f(t) = 16t^2$. The average speed of the rock over the interval between $t = 1$ and $t = 1 + h$ seconds was

$$\frac{f(1 + h) - f(1)}{h} = \frac{16(1 + h)^2 - 16(1)^2}{h} = \frac{16(h^2 + 2h)}{h} = 16(h + 2).$$

The rock's speed at the instant $t = 1$ was

$$\lim_{h \to 0} 16(h + 2) = 16(0 + 2) = 32 \text{ ft/sec}.$$

Our original estimate of 32 ft/ sec was right. ■

Summary

We have been discussing slopes of curves, lines tangent to a curve, the rate of change of a function, the limit of the difference quotient, and the derivative of a function at a point. All of these ideas refer to the same thing, summarized here:

1. The slope of $y = f(x)$ at $x = x_0$
2. The slope of the tangent to the curve $y = f(x)$ at $x = x_0$
3. The rate of change of $f(x)$ with respect to x at $x = x_0$
4. The derivative $f'(x_0)$ at a point
5. The limit of the difference quotient, $\lim_{h \to 0} \dfrac{f(x_0 + h) - f(x_0)}{h}$

The derivative is one of the two most important mathematical concepts in calculus. We begin a thorough study of it in Chapter 3. The other important concept is the *integral*, and we initiate its study in Chapter 5.

EXERCISES 2.7

In Exercises 1–4, use the grid and a straight edge to make a rough estimate of the slope of the curve (in y-units per x-unit) at the points P_1 and P_2. Graphs can shift during a press run, so your estimates may be somewhat different from those in the back of the book.

1.

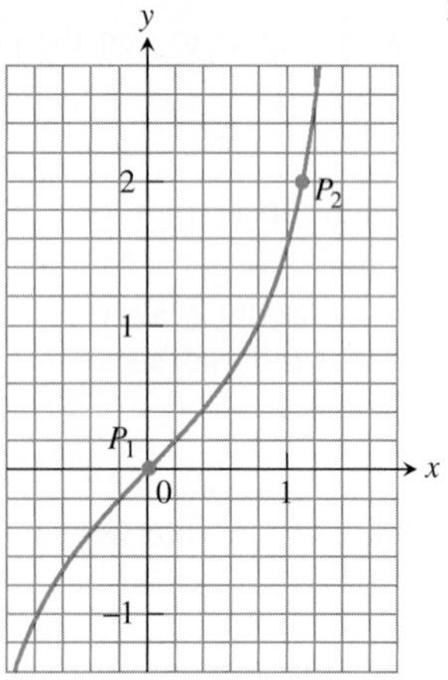

2.

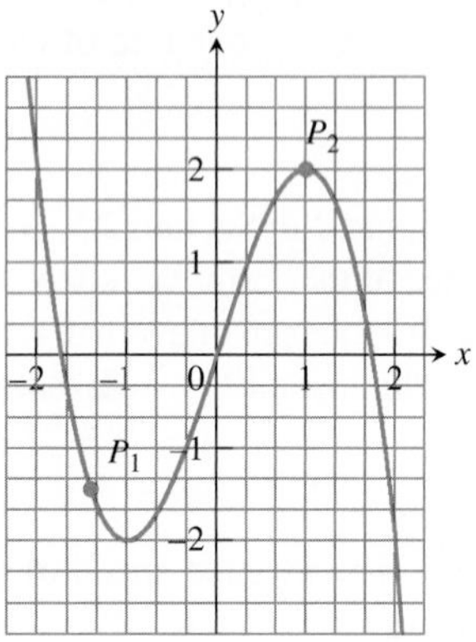

3.

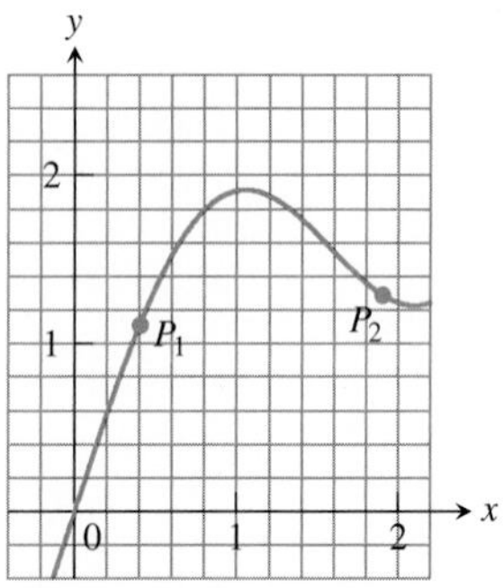

4.

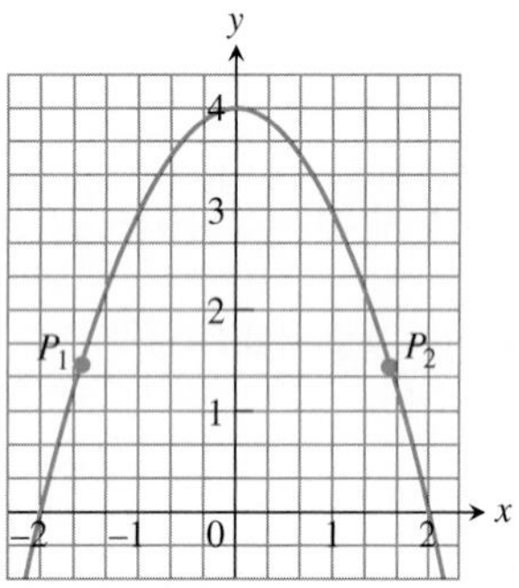

In Exercises 5–10, find an equation for the tangent to the curve at the given point. Then sketch the curve and tangent together.

5. $y = 3 - x^2,\quad (-1, 2)$

6. $y = (x - 1)^2 + 1,\quad (1, 1)$

7. $y = 2\sqrt{x},\quad (1, 2)$

8. $y = \dfrac{1}{x^2},\quad (-1, 1)$

9. $y = x^3 + 1,\quad (-2, -7)$

10. $y = \dfrac{1}{x^3},\quad \left(-2, -\dfrac{1}{8}\right)$

In Exercises 11–18, find the slope of the function's graph at the given point. Then find an equation for the line tangent to the graph there.

11. $f(x) = x^2 + 1,\quad (2, 5)$

12. $f(x) = x - 2x^2,\quad (1, -1)$

13. $g(x) = \dfrac{x}{x - 2},\quad (3, 3)$

14. $g(x) = \dfrac{8}{x^2},\quad (2, 2)$

15. $h(t) = t^3 - t,\quad (2, 6)$

16. $h(t) = t^3 + 3t,\quad (1, 4)$

17. $f(x) = \sqrt{x},\quad (4, 2)$

18. $f(x) = \sqrt{x + 1},\quad (8, 3)$

In Exercises 19–22, find the slope of the curve at the point indicated.

19. $y = 5x^2,\quad x = -1$

20. $y = 1 - x^2,\quad x = 2$

21. $y = \dfrac{1}{x - 1},\quad x = 3$

22. $y = \dfrac{x - 1}{x + 1},\quad x = 0$

At what points do the graphs of the functions in Exercises 23 and 24 have horizontal tangents?

23. $f(x) = x^2 + 4x - 1$

24. $g(x) = x^3 - 3x$

25. Find equations of all lines having slope -1 that are tangent to the curve $y = 1/(x - 1)$.

26. Find an equation of the straight line having slope $1/4$ that is tangent to the curve $y = \sqrt{x}$.

27. Object dropped from a tower An object is dropped from the top of a 100-m-high tower. Its height above ground after t sec is $100 - 4.9t^2$ m. How fast is it falling 2 sec after it is dropped?

28. Speed of a rocket At t sec after liftoff, the height of a rocket is $3t^2$ ft. How fast is the rocket climbing 10 sec after liftoff?

29. Circle's changing area What is the rate of change of the area of a circle ($A = \pi r^2$) with respect to the radius when the radius is $r = 3$?

30. Ball's changing volume What is the rate of change of the volume of a ball ($V = (4/3)\pi r^3$) with respect to the radius when the radius is $r = 2$?

31. Show that the line $y = mx + b$ is its own tangent at any point $(x_0, mx_0 + b)$.

32. Find the slope of the tangent to the curve $y = 1/\sqrt{x}$ at the point where $x = 4$.

33. Does the graph of

$$f(x) = \begin{cases} x^2 \sin(1/x), & x \neq 0 \\ 0, & x = 0 \end{cases}$$

have a tangent at the origin? Give reasons for your answer.

34. Does the graph of

$$g(x) = \begin{cases} x \sin(1/x), & x \neq 0 \\ 0, & x = 0 \end{cases}$$

have a tangent at the origin? Give reasons for your answer.

Vertical Tangents We say that the curve $y = f(x)$ has a **vertical tangent** at the point where $x = x_0$ if $\lim_{h\to 0} (f(x_0 + h) - f(x_0))/h = \infty$ or $-\infty$. Vertical tangent at $x = 0$ (see accompanying figure):

$$\lim_{h\to 0} \frac{f(0 + h) - f(0)}{h} = \lim_{h\to 0} \frac{h^{1/3} - 0}{h} = \lim_{h\to 0} \frac{1}{h^{2/3}} = \infty$$

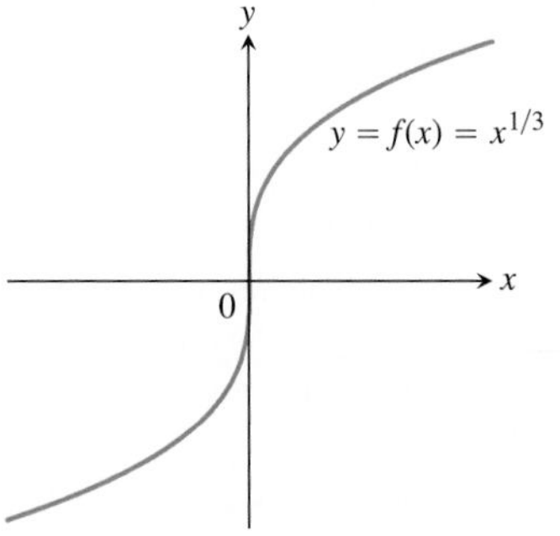

VERTICAL TANGENT AT ORIGIN

No vertical tangent at $x = 0$ (see next figure):

$$\lim_{h \to 0} \frac{g(0 + h) - g(0)}{h} = \lim_{h \to 0} \frac{h^{2/3} - 0}{h}$$
$$= \lim_{h \to 0} \frac{1}{h^{1/3}}$$

does not exist, because the limit is ∞ from the right and $-\infty$ from the left.

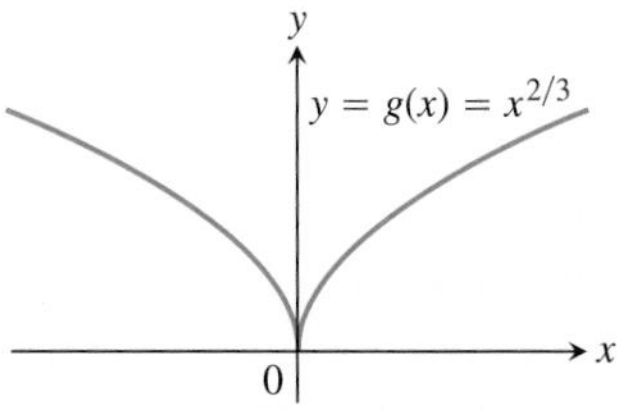

NO VERTICAL TANGENT AT ORIGIN

35. Does the graph of

$$f(x) = \begin{cases} -1, & x < 0 \\ 0, & x = 0 \\ 1, & x > 0 \end{cases}$$

have a vertical tangent at the origin? Give reasons for your answer.

36. Does the graph of

$$U(x) = \begin{cases} 0, & x < 0 \\ 1, & x \geq 0 \end{cases}$$

have a vertical tangent at the point (0, 1)? Give reasons for your answer.

T **a.** Graph the curves in Exercises 37–46. Where do the graphs appear to have vertical tangents?

b. Confirm your findings in part (a) with limit calculations. But before you do, read the introduction to Exercises 35 and 36.

37. $y = x^{2/5}$

38. $y = x^{4/5}$

39. $y = x^{1/5}$

40. $y = x^{3/5}$

41. $y = 4x^{2/5} - 2x$

42. $y = x^{5/3} - 5x^{2/3}$

43. $y = x^{2/3} - (x - 1)^{1/3}$

44. $y = x^{1/3} + (x - 1)^{1/3}$

45. $y = \begin{cases} -\sqrt{|x|}, & x \leq 0 \\ \sqrt{x}, & x > 0 \end{cases}$

46. $y = \sqrt{|4 - x|}$

COMPUTER EXPLORATIONS

Use a CAS to perform the following steps for the functions in Exercises 47–50.

a. Plot $y = f(x)$ over the interval $(x_0 - 1/2) \leq x \leq (x_0 + 3)$.

b. Holding x_0 fixed, the difference quotient

$$q(h) = \frac{f(x_0 + h) - f(x_0)}{h}$$

at x_0 becomes a function of the step size h. Enter this function into your CAS workspace.

c. Find the limit of q as $h \to 0$.

d. Define the secant lines $y = f(x_0) + q \cdot (x - x_0)$ for $h = 3, 2,$ and 1. Graph them together with f and the tangent line over the interval in part (a).

47. $f(x) = x^3 + 2x, \quad x_0 = 0$

48. $f(x) = x + \frac{5}{x}, \quad x_0 = 1$

49. $f(x) = x + \sin(2x), \quad x_0 = \pi/2$

50. $f(x) = \cos x + 4\sin(2x), \quad x_0 = \pi$

Chapter 2 Questions to Guide Your Review

1. What is the average rate of change of the function $g(t)$ over the interval from $t = a$ to $t = b$? How is it related to a secant line?
2. What limit must be calculated to find the rate of change or slope of a function $g(t)$ at $t = t_0$?
3. What is an informal or intuitive definition of the limit

$$\lim_{x \to x_0} f(x) = L?$$

Why is the definition "informal"? Give examples.

4. Does the existence and value of the limit of a function $f(x)$ as x approaches x_0 ever depend on what happens at $x = x_0$? Explain and give examples.
5. What function behaviors might occur for which the limit may fail to exist? Give examples.
6. What theorems are available for calculating limits? Give examples of how the theorems are used.

7. How are one-sided limits related to limits? How can this relationship sometimes be used to calculate a limit or prove it does not exist? Give examples.

8. What is the value of $\lim_{\theta \to 0}((\sin\theta)/\theta)$? Does it matter whether θ is measured in degrees or radians? Explain.

9. What exactly does $\lim_{x \to x_0} f(x) = L$ mean? Give an example in which you find a $\delta > 0$ for a given f, L, x_0, and $\epsilon > 0$ in the precise definition of limit.

10. Give precise definitions of the following statements.

 a. $\lim_{x \to 2^-} f(x) = 5$ **b.** $\lim_{x \to 2^+} f(x) = 5$

 c. $\lim_{x \to 2} f(x) = \infty$ **d.** $\lim_{x \to 2} f(x) = -\infty$

11. What exactly do $\lim_{x \to \infty} f(x) = L$ and $\lim_{x \to -\infty} f(x) = L$ mean? Give examples.

12. What are $\lim_{x \to \pm\infty} k$ (k a constant) and $\lim_{x \to \pm\infty}(1/x)$? How do you extend these results to other functions? Give examples.

13. How do you find the limit of a rational function as $x \to \pm\infty$? Give examples.

14. What are horizontal and vertical asymptotes? Give examples.

15. What conditions must be satisfied by a function if it is to be continuous at an interior point of its domain? At an endpoint?

16. How can looking at the graph of a function help you tell where the function is continuous?

17. What does it mean for a function to be right-continuous at a point? Left-continuous? How are continuity and one-sided continuity related?

18. What can be said about the continuity of polynomials? Of rational functions? Of trigonometric functions? Of rational powers and algebraic combinations of functions? Of exponential and logarithm functions? Of inverse functions? Of composites of functions? Of absolute values of functions?

19. Under what circumstances can you extend a function $f(x)$ to be continuous at a point $x = c$? Give an example.

20. What does it mean for a function to be continuous on an interval?

21. What does it mean for a function to be continuous? Give examples to illustrate the fact that a function that is not continuous on its entire domain may still be continuous on selected intervals within the domain.

22. What are the basic types of discontinuity? Give an example of each. What is a removable discontinuity? Give an example.

23. What does it mean for a function to have the Intermediate Value Property? What conditions guarantee that a function has this property over an interval? What are the consequences for graphing and solving the equation $f(x) = 0$?

24. It is often said that a function is continuous if you can draw its graph without having to lift your pen from the paper. Why is that?

25. What does it mean for a line to be tangent to a curve C at a point P?

26. What is the significance of the formula

$$\lim_{h \to 0} \frac{f(x_0 + h) - f(x_0)}{h}?$$

Interpret the formula geometrically and physically.

27. How do you find the tangent to the curve $y = f(x)$ at a point $P(x_0, f(x_0))$ on the curve?

28. How does the slope of the curve $y = f(x)$ at $x = x_0$ relate to the function's rate of change with respect to x at $x = x_0$? To the derivative of f at x_0?

Chapter 2 Practice Exercises

1. Graph the function

$$f(x) = \begin{cases} 1, & x \le -1 \\ -x, & -1 < x < 0 \\ 1, & x = 0 \\ -x, & 0 < x < 1 \\ 1, & x \ge 1. \end{cases}$$

Then discuss, in detail, limits, one-sided limits, continuity, and one-sided continuity of f at $x = -1, 0$, and 1. Are any of the discontinuities removable? Explain.

2. Repeat the instructions of Exercise 1 for

$$f(x) = \begin{cases} 0, & x \le -1 \\ 1/x, & 0 < |x| < 1 \\ 0, & x = 1 \\ 1, & x > 1. \end{cases}$$

3. Suppose that $f(t)$ and $g(t)$ are defined for all t and that $\lim_{t \to t_0} f(t) = -7$ and $\lim_{t \to t_0} g(t) = 0$. Find the limit as $t \to t_0$ of the following functions.

 a. $3f(t)$ **b.** $(f(t))^2$

 c. $f(t) \cdot g(t)$ **d.** $\dfrac{f(t)}{g(t) - 7}$

 e. $\cos(g(t))$ **f.** $|f(t)|$

 g. $f(t) + g(t)$ **h.** $1/f(t)$

4. Suppose that $f(x)$ and $g(x)$ are defined for all x and that $\lim_{x \to 0} f(x) = 1/2$ and $\lim_{x \to 0} g(x) = \sqrt{2}$. Find the limits as $x \to 0$ of the following functions.

 a. $-g(x)$ **b.** $g(x) \cdot f(x)$

 c. $f(x) + g(x)$ **d.** $1/f(x)$

 e. $x + f(x)$ **f.** $\dfrac{f(x) \cdot \cos x}{x - 1}$

In Exercises 5 and 6, find the value that $\lim_{x\to 0} g(x)$ must have if the given limit statements hold.

5. $\lim_{x\to 0}\left(\frac{4-g(x)}{x}\right)=1$ **6.** $\lim_{x\to -4}\left(x\lim_{x\to 0} g(x)\right)=2$

7. On what intervals are the following functions continuous?

a. $f(x)=x^{1/3}$ **b.** $g(x)=x^{3/4}$

c. $h(x)=x^{-2/3}$ **d.** $k(x)=x^{-1/6}$

8. On what intervals are the following functions continuous?

a. $f(x)=\tan x$ **b.** $g(x)=\csc x$

c. $h(x)=\frac{\cos x}{x-\pi}$ **d.** $k(x)=\frac{\sin x}{x}$

In Exercises 9–24, find the limit or explain why it does not exist.

9. $\lim \frac{x^2-4x+4}{x^3+5x^2-14x}$

a. as $x\to 0$ **b.** as $x\to 2$

10. $\lim \frac{x^2+x}{x^5+2x^4+x^3}$

a. as $x\to 0$ **b.** as $x\to -1$

11. $\lim_{x\to 1}\frac{1-\sqrt{x}}{1-x}$ **12.** $\lim_{x\to a}\frac{x^2-a^2}{x^4-a^4}$

13. $\lim_{h\to 0}\frac{(x+h)^2-x^2}{h}$ **14.** $\lim_{x\to 0}\frac{(x+h)^2-x^2}{h}$

15. $\lim_{x\to 0}\frac{\frac{1}{2+x}-\frac{1}{2}}{x}$ **16.** $\lim_{x\to 0}\frac{(2+x)^3-8}{x}$

17. $\lim_{x\to 0}\frac{\tan(2x)}{\tan(\pi x)}$ **18.** $\lim_{x\to\pi^-}\csc x$

19. $\lim_{x\to\pi}\sin\left(\frac{x}{2}+\sin x\right)$ **20.** $\lim_{x\to 1} e^{(x^2+x-2)}$

21. $\lim_{t\to 3^+}\ln(t-3)$ **22.** $\lim_{t\to 1} t^2\ln\left(2-\sqrt{t}\right)$

23. $\lim_{\theta\to 0^+}\sqrt{\theta}\,e^{\cos(\pi/\theta)}$ **24.** $\lim_{z\to 0^+}\frac{2e^{1/z}}{e^{1/z}+1}$

In Exercises 25–28, find the limit of $g(x)$ as x approaches the indicated value.

25. $\lim_{x\to 0^+}(4g(x))^{1/3}=2$ **26.** $\lim_{x\to\sqrt{5}}\frac{1}{x+g(x)}=2$

27. $\lim_{x\to 1}\frac{3x^2+1}{g(x)}=\infty$ **28.** $\lim_{x\to -2}\frac{5-x^2}{\sqrt{g(x)}}=0$

Find the limits in Exercises 29–42.

29. $\lim_{x\to\infty}\frac{2x+3}{5x+7}$ **30.** $\lim_{x\to -\infty}\frac{2x^2+3}{5x^2+7}$

31. $\lim_{x\to -\infty}\frac{x^2-4x+8}{3x^3}$ **32.** $\lim_{x\to\infty}\frac{1}{x^2-7x+1}$

33. $\lim_{x\to -\infty}\frac{x^2-7x}{x+1}$ **34.** $\lim_{x\to\infty}\frac{x^4+x^3}{12x^3+128}$

35. $\lim_{x\to\infty}\frac{\sin x}{\lfloor x\rfloor}$ (If you have a grapher, try graphing the function for $-5\le x\le 5$.)

36. $\lim_{\theta\to\infty}\frac{\cos\theta-1}{\theta}$ (If you have a grapher, try graphing $f(x)=x(\cos(1/x)-1)$ near the origin to "see" the limit at infinity.)

37. $\lim_{x\to\infty}\frac{x+\sin x+2\sqrt{x}}{x+\sin x}$ **38.** $\lim_{x\to\infty}\frac{x^{2/3}+x^{-1}}{x^{2/3}+\cos^2 x}$

39. $\lim_{x\to\infty} e^{1/x}\cos\frac{1}{x}$ **40.** $\lim_{t\to\infty}\ln\left(1+\frac{1}{t}\right)$

41. $\lim_{x\to -\infty}\tan^{-1}x$ **42.** $\lim_{t\to -\infty} e^{3t}\sin^{-1}\frac{1}{t}$

43. Can $f(x)=x(x^2-1)/|x^2-1|$ be extended to be continuous at $x=1$ or -1? Give reasons for your answers. (Graph the function—you will find the graph interesting.)

44. Explain why the function $f(x)=\sin(1/x)$ has no continuous extension to $x=0$.

T In Exercises 45–48, graph the function to see whether it appears to have a continuous extension to the given point a. If it does, use Trace and Zoom to find a good candidate for the extended function's value at a. If the function does not appear to have a continuous extension, can it be extended to be continuous from the right or left? If so, what do you think the extended function's value should be?

45. $f(x)=\frac{x-1}{x-\sqrt[4]{x}}$, $a=1$ **46.** $g(\theta)=\frac{5\cos\theta}{4\theta-2\pi}$, $a=\pi/2$

47. $h(t)=(1+|t|)^{1/t}$, $a=0$ **48.** $k(x)=\frac{x}{1-2^{|x|}}$, $a=0$

T **49.** Let $f(x)=x^3-x-1$.

a. Show that f has a zero between -1 and 2.

b. Solve the equation $f(x)=0$ graphically with an error of magnitude at most 10^{-8}.

c. It can be shown that the exact value of the solution in part (b) is

$$\left(\frac{1}{2}+\frac{\sqrt{69}}{18}\right)^{1/3}+\left(\frac{1}{2}-\frac{\sqrt{69}}{18}\right)^{1/3}.$$

Evaluate this exact answer and compare it with the value you found in part (b).

T **50.** Let $f(\theta)=\theta^3-2\theta+2$.

a. Show that f has a zero between -2 and 0.

b. Solve the equation $f(\theta)=0$ graphically with an error of magnitude at most 10^{-4}.

c. It can be shown that the exact value of the solution in part (b) is

$$\left(\sqrt{\frac{19}{27}}-1\right)^{1/3}-\left(\sqrt{\frac{19}{27}}+1\right)^{1/3}.$$

Evaluate this exact answer and compare it with the value you found in part (b).

Chapter 2 Additional and Advanced Exercises

T **1. Assigning a value to 0^0** The laws of exponents tell us that $a^0 = 1$ if a is any number different from zero. They also tell us that $0^n = 0$ if n is any positive number.

If we tried to extend these rules to include the case 0^0, we would get conflicting results. The first rule would say $0^0 = 1$, whereas the second would say $0^0 = 0$.

We are not dealing with a question of right or wrong here. Neither rule applies as it stands, so there is no contradiction. We could, in fact, define 0^0 to have any value we wanted as long as we could persuade others to agree.

What value would you like 0^0 to have? Here is an example that might help you to decide. (See Exercise 2 below for another example.)

a. Calculate x^x for $x = 0.1, 0.01, 0.001$, and so on as far as your calculator can go. Record the values you get. What pattern do you see?

b. Graph the function $y = x^x$ for $0 < x \leq 1$. Even though the function is not defined for $x \leq 0$, the graph will approach the y-axis from the right. Toward what y-value does it seem to be headed? Zoom in to further support your idea.

T **2. A reason you might want 0^0 to be something other than 0 or 1** As the number x increases through positive values, the numbers $1/x$ and $1/(\ln x)$ both approach zero. What happens to the number

$$f(x) = \left(\frac{1}{x}\right)^{1/(\ln x)}$$

as x increases? Here are two ways to find out.

a. Evaluate f for $x = 10, 100, 1000$, and so on as far as your calculator can reasonably go. What pattern do you see?

b. Graph f in a variety of graphing windows, including windows that contain the origin. What do you see? Trace the y-values along the graph. What do you find?

3. Lorentz contraction In relativity theory, the length of an object, say a rocket, appears to an observer to depend on the speed at which the object is traveling with respect to the observer. If the observer measures the rocket's length as L_0 at rest, then at speed v the length will appear to be

$$L = L_0\sqrt{1 - \frac{v^2}{c^2}}.$$

This equation is the Lorentz contraction formula. Here, c is the speed of light in a vacuum, about 3×10^8 m/sec. What happens to L as v increases? Find $\lim_{v \to c^-} L$. Why was the left-hand limit needed?

4. Controlling the flow from a draining tank Torricelli's law says that if you drain a tank like the one in the figure shown, the rate y at which water runs out is a constant times the square root of the water's depth x. The constant depends on the size and shape of the exit valve.

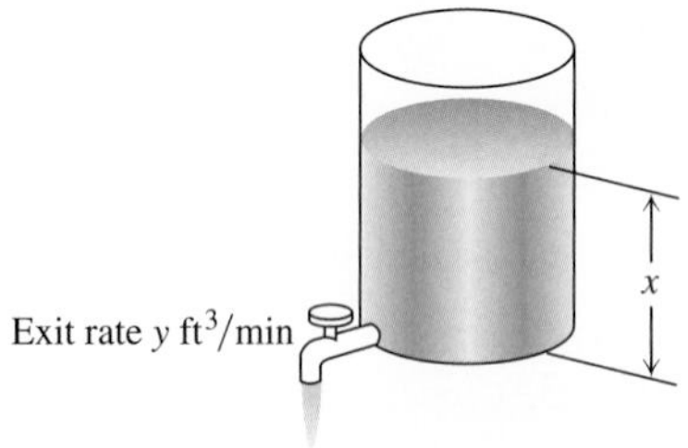

Suppose that $y = \sqrt{x}/2$ for a certain tank. You are trying to maintain a fairly constant exit rate by adding water to the tank with a hose from time to time. How deep must you keep the water if you want to maintain the exit rate

a. within 0.2 ft^3/min of the rate $y_0 = 1\ \text{ft}^3/\text{min}$?

b. within 0.1 ft^3/min of the rate $y_0 = 1\ \text{ft}^3/\text{min}$?

5. Thermal expansion in precise equipment As you may know, most metals expand when heated and contract when cooled. The dimensions of a piece of laboratory equipment are sometimes so critical that the shop where the equipment is made must be held at the same temperature as the laboratory where the equipment is to be used. A typical aluminum bar that is 10 cm wide at 70°F will be

$$y = 10 + (t - 70) \times 10^{-4}$$

centimeters wide at a nearby temperature t. Suppose that you are using a bar like this in a gravity wave detector, where its width must stay within 0.0005 cm of the ideal 10 cm. How close to $t_0 = 70°\text{F}$ must you maintain the temperature to ensure that this tolerance is not exceeded?

6. Stripes on a measuring cup The interior of a typical 1-L measuring cup is a right circular cylinder of radius 6 cm (see accompanying figure). The volume of water we put in the cup is therefore a function of the level h to which the cup is filled, the formula being

$$V = \pi 6^2 h = 36\pi h.$$

How closely must we measure h to measure out 1 L of water ($1000\ \text{cm}^3$) with an error of no more than 1% ($10\ \text{cm}^3$)?

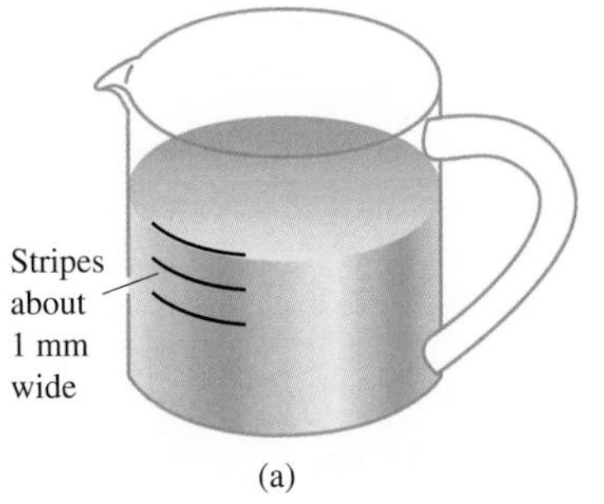

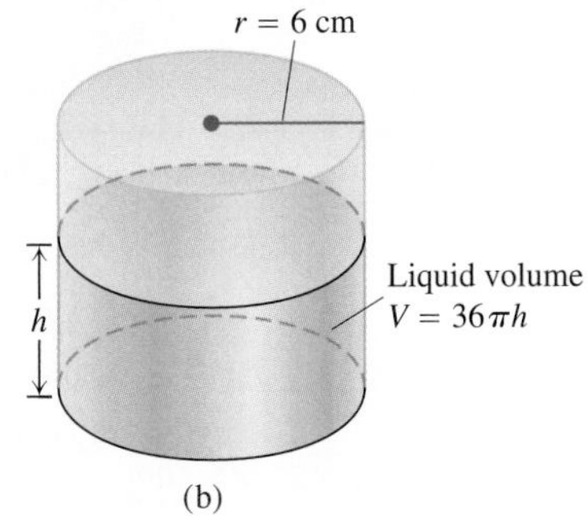

A 1-L measuring cup (a), modeled as a right circular cylinder (b) of radius $r = 6$ cm

In Exercises 7–10, use the formal definition of limit to prove that the function is continuous at x_0.

7. $f(x) = x^2 - 7, \quad x_0 = 1$ **8.** $g(x) = 1/(2x), \quad x_0 = 1/4$

9. $h(x) = \sqrt{2x - 3}, \quad x_0 = 2$ **10.** $F(x) = \sqrt{9 - x}, \quad x_0 = 5$

11. Uniqueness of limits Show that a function cannot have two different limits at the same point. That is, if $\lim_{x \to x_0} f(x) = L_1$ and $\lim_{x \to x_0} f(x) = L_2$, then $L_1 = L_2$.

12. Prove the limit Constant Multiple Rule:
$\lim_{x \to c} kf(x) = k \lim_{x \to c} f(x)$ for any constant k.

13. One-sided limits If $\lim_{x \to 0^+} f(x) = A$ and $\lim_{x \to 0^-} f(x) = B$, find

a. $\lim_{x \to 0^+} f(x^3 - x)$ **b.** $\lim_{x \to 0^-} f(x^3 - x)$

c. $\lim_{x \to 0^+} f(x^2 - x^4)$ **d.** $\lim_{x \to 0^-} f(x^2 - x^4)$

14. Limits and continuity Which of the following statements are true, and which are false? If true, say why; if false, give a counterexample (that is, an example confirming the falsehood).

a. If $\lim_{x \to a} f(x)$ exists but $\lim_{x \to a} g(x)$ does not exist, then $\lim_{x \to a}(f(x) + g(x))$ does not exist.

b. If neither $\lim_{x \to a} f(x)$ nor $\lim_{x \to a} g(x)$ exists, then $\lim_{x \to a} (f(x) + g(x))$ does not exist.

c. If f is continuous at x, then so is $|f|$.

d. If $|f|$ is continuous at a, then so is f.

In Exercises 15 and 16, use the formal definition of limit to prove that the function has a continuous extension to the given value of x.

15. $f(x) = \dfrac{x^2 - 1}{x + 1}, \quad x = -1$ **16.** $g(x) = \dfrac{x^2 - 2x - 3}{2x - 6}, \quad x = 3$

17. A function continuous at only one point Let

$$f(x) = \begin{cases} x, & \text{if } x \text{ is rational} \\ 0, & \text{if } x \text{ is irrational.} \end{cases}$$

a. Show that f is continuous at $x = 0$.

b. Use the fact that every nonempty open interval of real numbers contains both rational and irrational numbers to show that f is not continuous at any nonzero value of x.

18. The Dirichlet ruler function If x is a rational number, then x can be written in a unique way as a quotient of integers m/n where $n > 0$ and m and n have no common factors greater than 1. (We say that such a fraction is in *lowest terms*. For example, 6/4 written in lowest terms is 3/2.) Let $f(x)$ be defined for all x in the interval [0, 1] by

$$f(x) = \begin{cases} 1/n, & \text{if } x = m/n \text{ is a rational number in lowest terms} \\ 0, & \text{if } x \text{ is irrational.} \end{cases}$$

For instance, $f(0) = f(1) = 1, f(1/2) = 1/2, f(1/3) = f(2/3) = 1/3, f(1/4) = f(3/4) = 1/4$, and so on.

a. Show that f is discontinuous at every rational number in [0, 1].

b. Show that f is continuous at every irrational number in [0, 1]. (*Hint*: If ϵ is a given positive number, show that there are only finitely many rational numbers r in [0, 1] such that $f(r) \geq \epsilon$.)

c. Sketch the graph of f. Why do you think f is called the "ruler function"?

19. Antipodal points Is there any reason to believe that there is always a pair of antipodal (diametrically opposite) points on Earth's equator where the temperatures are the same? Explain.

20. If $\lim_{x \to c} (f(x) + g(x)) = 3$ and $\lim_{x \to c} (f(x) - g(x)) = -1$, find $\lim_{x \to c} f(x)g(x)$.

21. Roots of a quadratic equation that is almost linear The equation $ax^2 + 2x - 1 = 0$, where a is a constant, has two roots if $a > -1$ and $a \neq 0$, one positive and one negative:

$$r_+(a) = \frac{-1 + \sqrt{1 + a}}{a}, \qquad r_-(a) = \frac{-1 - \sqrt{1 + a}}{a}.$$

a. What happens to $r_+(a)$ as $a \to 0$? As $a \to -1^+$?

b. What happens to $r_-(a)$ as $a \to 0$? As $a \to -1^+$?

c. Support your conclusions by graphing $r_+(a)$ and $r_-(a)$ as functions of a. Describe what you see.

d. For added support, graph $f(x) = ax^2 + 2x - 1$ simultaneously for $a = 1, 0.5, 0.2, 0.1$, and 0.05.

22. Root of an equation Show that the equation $x + 2\cos x = 0$ has at least one solution.

23. Bounded functions A real-valued function f is **bounded from above** on a set D if there exists a number N such that $f(x) \le N$ for all x in D. We call N, when it exists, an **upper bound** for f on D and say that f is bounded from above by N. In a similar manner, we say that f is **bounded from below** on D if there exists a number M such that $f(x) \ge M$ for all x in D. We call M, when it exists, a **lower bound** for f on D and say that f is bounded from below by M. We say that f is **bounded** on D if it is bounded from both above and below.

a. Show that f is bounded on D if and only if there exists a number B such that $|f(x)| \le B$ for all x in D.

b. Suppose that f is bounded from above by N. Show that if $\lim_{x\to x_0} f(x) = L$, then $L \le N$.

c. Suppose that f is bounded from below by M. Show that if $\lim_{x\to x_0} f(x) = L$, then $L \ge M$.

24. *Max $\{a, b\}$ and min $\{a, b\}$*

a. Show that the expression

$$\max\{a, b\} = \frac{a+b}{2} + \frac{|a-b|}{2}$$

equals a if $a \ge b$ and equals b if $b \ge a$. In other words, $\max\{a, b\}$ gives the larger of the two numbers a and b.

b. Find a similar expression for $\min\{a, b\}$, the smaller of a and b.

Generalized Limits Involving $\sin\theta/\theta$ The formula $\lim_{\theta\to 0}(\sin\theta)/\theta = 1$ can be generalized. If $\lim_{x\to c} f(x) = 0$ and $f(x)$ is never zero in an open interval containing the point $x = c$, except possibly c itself, then

$$\lim_{x\to c}\frac{\sin f(x)}{f(x)} = 1.$$

Here are several examples.

a. $\displaystyle\lim_{x\to 0}\frac{\sin x^2}{x^2} = 1.$

b. $\displaystyle\lim_{x\to 0}\frac{\sin x^2}{x} = \lim_{x\to 0}\frac{\sin x^2}{x^2}\lim_{x\to 0}\frac{x^2}{x} = 1\cdot 0 = 0.$

c. $\displaystyle\lim_{x\to -1}\frac{\sin(x^2-x-2)}{x+1} = \lim_{x\to -1}\frac{\sin(x^2-x-2)}{(x^2-x-2)}\cdot$

$\displaystyle\lim_{x\to -1}\frac{(x^2-x-2)}{x+1} = 1\cdot\lim_{x\to -1}\frac{(x+1)(x-2)}{x+1} = -3.$

d. $\displaystyle\lim_{x\to 1}\frac{\sin\left(1-\sqrt{x}\right)}{x-1} = \lim_{x\to 1}\frac{\sin\left(1-\sqrt{x}\right)}{1-\sqrt{x}}\frac{1-\sqrt{x}}{x-1} =$

$\displaystyle 1\cdot\lim_{x\to 1}\frac{\left(1-\sqrt{x}\right)\left(1+\sqrt{x}\right)}{(x-1)\left(1+\sqrt{x}\right)} = \lim_{x\to 1}\frac{1-x}{(x-1)\left(1+\sqrt{x}\right)} = -\frac{1}{2}.$

Find the limits in Exercises 25–30.

25. $\displaystyle\lim_{x\to 0}\frac{\sin(1-\cos x)}{x}$

26. $\displaystyle\lim_{x\to 0^+}\frac{\sin x}{\sin\sqrt{x}}$

27. $\displaystyle\lim_{x\to 0}\frac{\sin(\sin x)}{x}$

28. $\displaystyle\lim_{x\to 0}\frac{\sin(x^2+x)}{x}$

29. $\displaystyle\lim_{x\to 2}\frac{\sin(x^2-4)}{x-2}$

30. $\displaystyle\lim_{x\to 9}\frac{\sin\left(\sqrt{x}-3\right)}{x-9}$

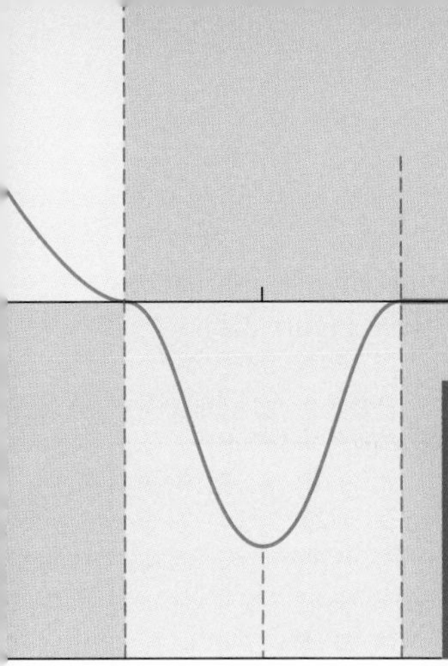

Chapter 3 DIFFERENTIATION

OVERVIEW In Chapter 2 we introduced the derivative of a function at a point. The derivative measures the rate at which a function changes and gives the slope of its graph. In this chapter we develop rules for finding the derivative function easily, without having to calculate any limits directly. The rules are used in problems involving rates of change, and also to approximate complicated functions.

3.1 The Derivative as a Function

HISTORICAL ESSAY

The Derivative

In Section 2.7 we defined the derivative of $y = f(x)$ at the point $x = x_0$ to be the limit

$$f'(x_0) = \lim_{h \to 0} \frac{f(x_0 + h) - f(x_0)}{h}.$$

We now investigate the derivative as a *function* derived from f by considering the limit at each point x in the domain of f.

DEFINITION The **derivative** of the function $f(x)$ with respect to the variable x is the function f' whose value at x is

$$f'(x) = \lim_{h \to 0} \frac{f(x + h) - f(x)}{h},$$

provided the limit exists.

We use the notation $f(x)$ in the definition to emphasize the independent variable x with respect to which the derivative function $f'(x)$ is being defined. The domain of f' is the set of points in the domain of f for which the limit exists, and the domain may be the same or smaller than the domain of f. If f' exists at a particular x, we say that f is **differentiable (has a derivative) at x**. If f' exists at every point in the domain of f, we call f **differentiable**.

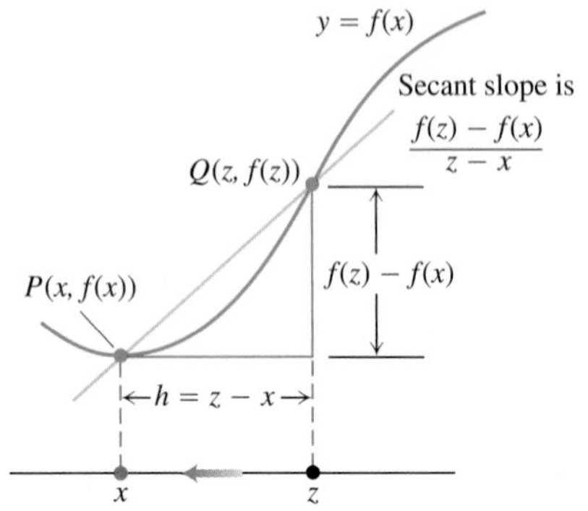

Derivative of f at x is

$$f'(x) = \lim_{h\to 0} \frac{f(x+h)-f(x)}{h}$$

$$= \lim_{z\to x} \frac{f(z)-f(x)}{z-x}$$

FIGURE 3.1 Two forms for the difference quotient.

If we write $z = x + h$, then $h = z - x$ and h approaches 0 if and only if z approaches x. Therefore, an equivalent definition of the derivative is as follows (see Figure 3.1).

Alternative Formula for the Derivative

$$f'(x) = \lim_{z\to x} \frac{f(z)-f(x)}{z-x}.$$

Calculating Derivatives from the Definition

The process of calculating a derivative is called **differentiation**. To emphasize the idea that differentiation is an operation performed on a function $y = f(x)$, we use the notation

$$\frac{d}{dx} f(x)$$

as another way to denote the derivative $f'(x)$. Example 1 of Section 2.7 illustrated the differentiation process for the function $y = 1/x$ when $x = a$. For x representing any point in the domain, we get the formula

$$\frac{d}{dx}\left(\frac{1}{x}\right) = -\frac{1}{x^2}.$$

Here are two more examples in which we allow x to be any point in the domain of f.

EXAMPLE 1 Differentiate $f(x) = \dfrac{x}{x-1}$.

Solution Here we have $f(x) = \dfrac{x}{x-1}$ and $f(x+h) = \dfrac{(x+h)}{(x+h)-1}$, so

$$f'(x) = \lim_{h\to 0} \frac{f(x+h)-f(x)}{h} \qquad \text{Definition}$$

$$= \lim_{h\to 0} \frac{\dfrac{x+h}{x+h-1} - \dfrac{x}{x-1}}{h}$$

$$= \lim_{h\to 0} \frac{1}{h} \cdot \frac{(x+h)(x-1) - x(x+h-1)}{(x+h-1)(x-1)} \qquad \frac{a}{b} - \frac{c}{d} = \frac{ad-cb}{bd}$$

$$= \lim_{h\to 0} \frac{1}{h} \cdot \frac{-h}{(x+h-1)(x-1)} \qquad \text{Simplify}$$

$$= \lim_{h\to 0} \frac{-1}{(x+h-1)(x-1)} = \frac{-1}{(x-1)^2}. \qquad \text{Cancel } h \neq 0$$

■

EXAMPLE 2 Find the derivative of $y = \sqrt{x}$ for $x > 0$.

You will often need to know the derivative of $\sqrt{x}$ for $x > 0$:

$$\frac{d}{dx}\sqrt{x} = \frac{1}{2\sqrt{x}}$$

Solution We use the alternative form to calculate f':

$$\begin{aligned} f'(x) &= \lim_{z\to x}\frac{f(z)-f(x)}{z-x} \\ &= \lim_{z\to x}\frac{\sqrt{z}-\sqrt{x}}{z-x} \\ &= \lim_{z\to x}\frac{\sqrt{z}-\sqrt{x}}{\left(\sqrt{z}-\sqrt{x}\right)\left(\sqrt{z}+\sqrt{x}\right)} \\ &= \lim_{z\to x}\frac{1}{\sqrt{z}+\sqrt{x}} = \frac{1}{2\sqrt{x}}. \end{aligned}$$

■

Notations

There are many ways to denote the derivative of a function $y = f(x)$, where the independent variable is x and the dependent variable is y. Some common alternative notations for the derivative are

$$f'(x) = y' = \frac{dy}{dx} = \frac{df}{dx} = \frac{d}{dx}f(x) = D(f)(x) = D_x f(x).$$

The symbols d/dx and D indicate the operation of differentiation. We read dy/dx as "the derivative of y with respect to x," and df/dx and $(d/dx)f(x)$ as "the derivative of f with respect to x." The "prime" notations y' and f' come from notations that Newton used for derivatives. The d/dx notations are similar to those used by Leibniz. The symbol dy/dx should not be regarded as a ratio (until we introduce the idea of "differentials" in Section 3.10).

To indicate the value of a derivative at a specified number $x = a$, we use the notation

$$f'(a) = \left.\frac{dy}{dx}\right|_{x=a} = \left.\frac{df}{dx}\right|_{x=a} = \left.\frac{d}{dx}f(x)\right|_{x=a}.$$

For instance, in Example 2

$$f'(4) = \left.\frac{d}{dx}\sqrt{x}\right|_{x=4} = \left.\frac{1}{2\sqrt{x}}\right|_{x=4} = \frac{1}{2\sqrt{4}} = \frac{1}{4}.$$

Graphing the Derivative

We can often make a reasonable plot of the derivative of $y = f(x)$ by estimating the slopes on the graph of f. That is, we plot the points $(x, f'(x))$ in the xy-plane and connect them with a smooth curve, which represents $y = f'(x)$.

EXAMPLE 3 Graph the derivative of the function $y = f(x)$ in Figure 3.2a.

Solution We sketch the tangents to the graph of f at frequent intervals and use their slopes to estimate the values of $f'(x)$ at these points. We plot the corresponding $(x, f'(x))$ pairs and connect them with a smooth curve as sketched in Figure 3.2b (on page 128). ■

What can we learn from the graph of $y = f'(x)$? At a glance we can see

1. where the rate of change of f is positive, negative, or zero;
2. the rough size of the growth rate at any x and its size in relation to the size of $f(x)$;
3. where the rate of change itself is increasing or decreasing.

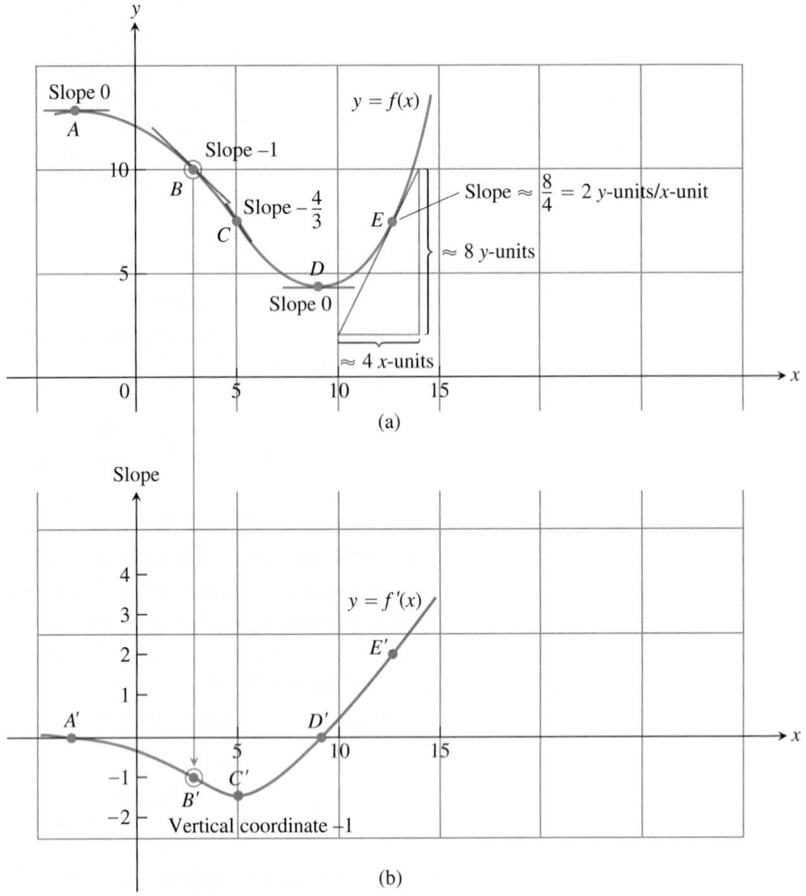

FIGURE 3.2 We made the graph of $y = f'(x)$ in (b) by plotting slopes from the graph of $y = f(x)$ in (a). The vertical coordinate of B' is the slope at B and so on. The graph of f' is a visual record of how the slope of f changes with x.

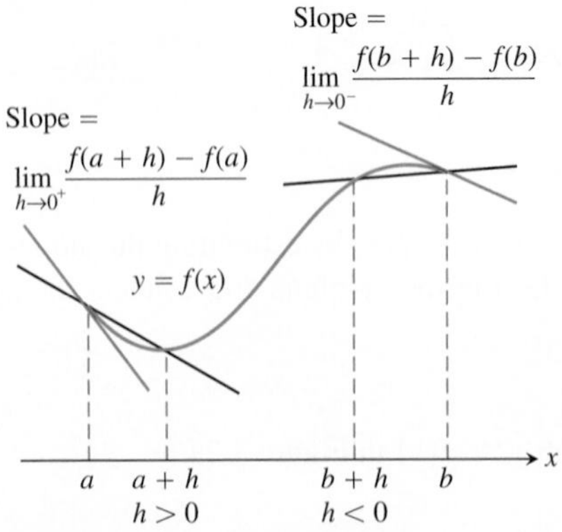

FIGURE 3.3 Derivatives at endpoints are one-sided limits.

Differentiable on an Interval; One-Sided Derivatives

A function $y = f(x)$ is **differentiable on an open interval** (finite or infinite) if it has a derivative at each point of the interval. It is differentiable on a closed interval $[a, b]$ if it is differentiable on the interior (a, b) and if the limits

$$\lim_{h \to 0^+} \frac{f(a + h) - f(a)}{h} \qquad \textbf{Right-hand derivative at } \boldsymbol{a}$$

$$\lim_{h \to 0^-} \frac{f(b + h) - f(b)}{h} \qquad \textbf{Left-hand derivative at } \boldsymbol{b}$$

exist at the endpoints (Figure 3.3).

Right-hand and left-hand derivatives may be defined at any point of a function's domain. The usual relation between one-sided and two-sided limits holds for these derivatives. Because of Theorem 6, Section 2.4, a function has a derivative at a point if and only if it has left-hand and right-hand derivatives there, and these one-sided derivatives are equal.

EXAMPLE 4 Show that the function $y = |x|$ is differentiable on $(-\infty, 0)$ and $(0, \infty)$ but has no derivative at $x = 0$.

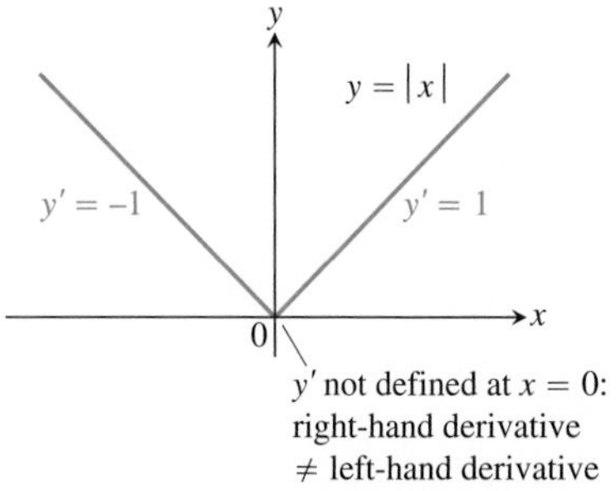

FIGURE 3.4 The function $y = |x|$ is not differentiable at the origin where the graph has a "corner."

Solution From Section 2.7, the derivative of $y = mx + b$ is the slope m. Thus, to the right of the origin,

$$\frac{d}{dx}(|x|) = \frac{d}{dx}(x) = \frac{d}{dx}(1 \cdot x) = 1. \qquad \frac{d}{dx}(mx + b) = m,\ |x| = x$$

To the left,

$$\frac{d}{dx}(|x|) = \frac{d}{dx}(-x) = \frac{d}{dx}(-1 \cdot x) = -1 \qquad |x| = -x$$

(Figure 3.4). There can be no derivative at the origin because the one-sided derivatives differ there:

$$\begin{aligned}
\text{Right-hand derivative of } |x| \text{ at zero} &= \lim_{h \to 0^+} \frac{|0 + h| - |0|}{h} = \lim_{h \to 0^+} \frac{|h|}{h} \\
&= \lim_{h \to 0^+} \frac{h}{h} \qquad |h| = h \text{ when } h > 0 \\
&= \lim_{h \to 0^+} 1 = 1 \\
\text{Left-hand derivative of } |x| \text{ at zero} &= \lim_{h \to 0^-} \frac{|0 + h| - |0|}{h} = \lim_{h \to 0^-} \frac{|h|}{h} \\
&= \lim_{h \to 0^-} \frac{-h}{h} \qquad |h| = -h \text{ when } h < 0 \\
&= \lim_{h \to 0^-} -1 = -1.
\end{aligned}$$

■

EXAMPLE 5 In Example 2 we found that for $x > 0$,

$$\frac{d}{dx}\sqrt{x} = \frac{1}{2\sqrt{x}}.$$

We apply the definition to examine if the derivative exists at $x = 0$:

$$\lim_{h \to 0^+} \frac{\sqrt{0 + h} - \sqrt{0}}{h} = \lim_{h \to 0^+} \frac{1}{\sqrt{h}} = \infty.$$

Since the (right-hand) limit is not finite, there is no derivative at $x = 0$. Since the slopes of the secant lines joining the origin to the points $(h, \sqrt{h})$ on a graph of $y = \sqrt{x}$ approach ∞, the graph has a *vertical tangent* at the origin. (See Figure 1.15 on page 7). ■

When Does a Function *Not* Have a Derivative at a Point?

A function has a derivative at a point x_0 if the slopes of the secant lines through $P(x_0, f(x_0))$ and a nearby point Q on the graph approach a finite limit as Q approaches P. Whenever the secants fail to take up a limiting position or become vertical as Q approaches P, the derivative does not exist. Thus differentiability is a "smoothness" condition on the graph of f. A function can fail to have a derivative at a point for several reasons, such as at points where the graph has

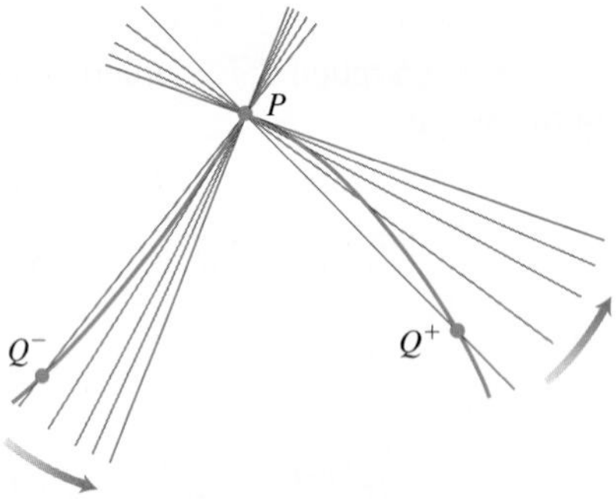

1. a *corner*, where the one-sided derivatives differ.

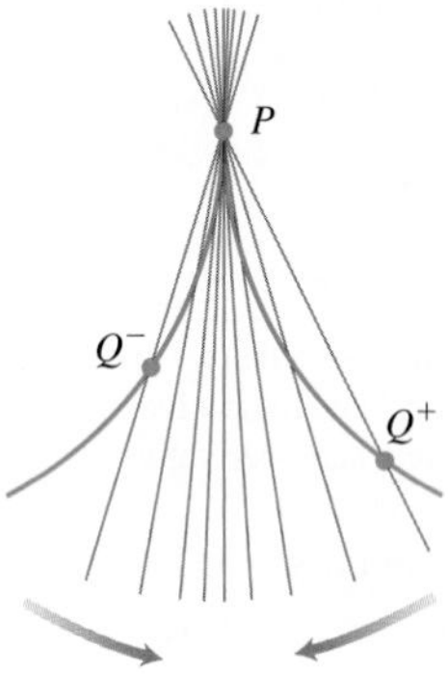

2. a *cusp*, where the slope of PQ approaches ∞ from one side and $-\infty$ from the other.

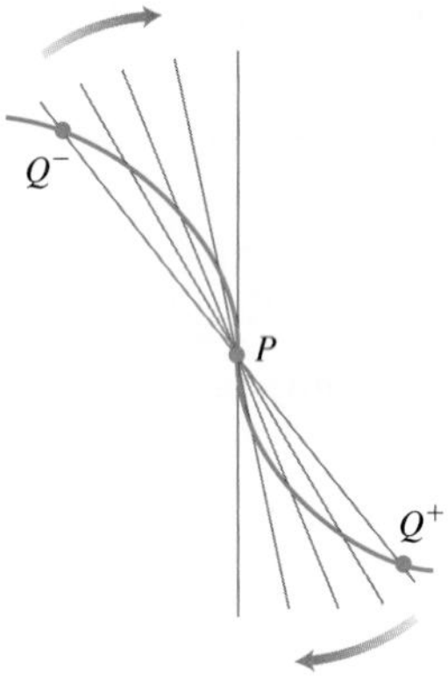

3. a *vertical tangent*, where the slope of PQ approaches ∞ from both sides or approaches $-\infty$ from both sides (here, $-\infty$).

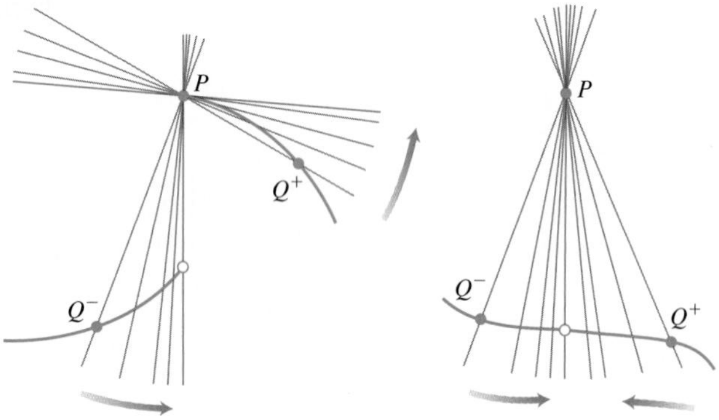

4. a *discontinuity* (two examples shown).

Differentiable Functions Are Continuous

A function is continuous at every point where it has a derivative.

THEOREM 1—Differentiability Implies Continuity If f has a derivative at $x = c$, then f is continuous at $x = c$.

Proof Given that $f'(c)$ exists, we must show that $\lim_{x\to c} f(x) = f(c)$, or equivalently, that $\lim_{h\to 0} f(c+h) = f(c)$. If $h \neq 0$, then

$$\begin{aligned} f(c+h) &= f(c) + (f(c+h) - f(c)) \\ &= f(c) + \frac{f(c+h) - f(c)}{h} \cdot h. \end{aligned}$$

Now take limits as $h \to 0$. By Theorem 1 of Section 2.2,

$$\begin{aligned} \lim_{h\to 0} f(c+h) &= \lim_{h\to 0} f(c) + \lim_{h\to 0} \frac{f(c+h) - f(c)}{h} \cdot \lim_{h\to 0} h \\ &= f(c) + f'(c) \cdot 0 \\ &= f(c) + 0 \\ &= f(c). \end{aligned}$$

■

Similar arguments with one-sided limits show that if f has a derivative from one side (right or left) at $x = c$ then f is continuous from that side at $x = c$.

Theorem 1 says that if a function has a discontinuity at a point (for instance, a jump discontinuity), then it cannot be differentiable there. The greatest integer function $y = \lfloor x \rfloor$ fails to be differentiable at every integer $x = n$ (Example 4, Section 2.6).

Caution The converse of Theorem 1 is false. A function need not have a derivative at a point where it is continuous, as we saw in Example 4.

The Intermediate Value Property of Derivatives (Darboux's Theorem)

Not every function can be some function's derivative, as we see from the following theorem, first proved in 1875 by the French mathematician Jean Gaston Darboux (1842–1917).

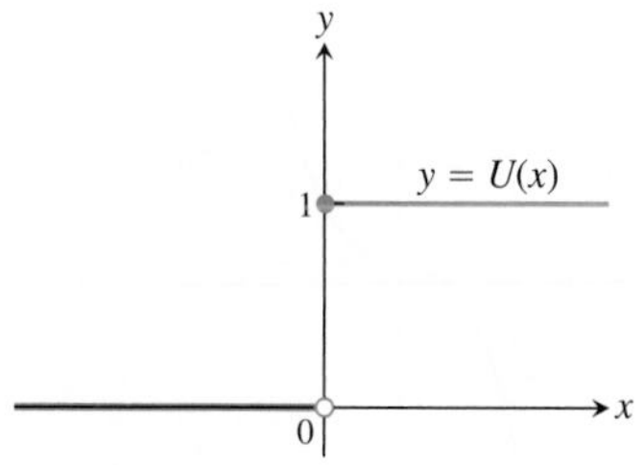

FIGURE 3.5 The unit step function does not have the Intermediate Value Property and cannot be the derivative of a function on the real line.

THEOREM 2—Darboux's Theorem If a and b are any two points in an interval on which f is differentiable, then f' takes on every value between $f'(a)$ and $f'(b)$.

Theorem 2 (which we will not prove) says that a function cannot *be* a derivative on an interval unless it has the Intermediate Value Property there. For example, the unit step function in Figure 3.5 cannot be the derivative of any real-valued function on the real line. In Chapter 5 we will see that every continuous function is a derivative of some function.

In Section 4.4, we invoke Theorem 2 to analyze what happens at a point on the graph of a twice-differentiable function where it changes its "bending" behavior.

EXERCISES 3.1

Using the definition, calculate the derivatives of the functions in Exercises 1–6. Then find the values of the derivatives as specified.

1. $f(x) = 4 - x^2;\quad f'(-3), f'(0), f'(1)$
2. $F(x) = (x - 1)^2 + 1;\quad F'(-1), F'(0), F'(2)$
3. $g(t) = \dfrac{1}{t^2};\quad g'(-1), g'(2), g'\left(\sqrt{3}\right)$
4. $k(z) = \dfrac{1 - z}{2z};\quad k'(-1), k'(1), k'\left(\sqrt{2}\right)$
5. $p(\theta) = \sqrt{3\theta};\quad p'(1), p'(3), p'(2/3)$
6. $r(s) = \sqrt{2s + 1};\quad r'(0), r'(1), r'(1/2)$

In Exercises 7–12, find the indicated derivatives.

7. $\dfrac{dy}{dx}$ if $y = 2x^3$
8. $\dfrac{dr}{ds}$ if $r = \dfrac{s^3}{2} + 1$
9. $\dfrac{ds}{dt}$ if $s = \dfrac{t}{2t + 1}$
10. $\dfrac{dv}{dt}$ if $v = t - \dfrac{1}{t}$
11. $\dfrac{dp}{dq}$ if $p = \dfrac{1}{\sqrt{q + 1}}$
12. $\dfrac{dz}{dw}$ if $z = \dfrac{1}{\sqrt{3w - 2}}$

In Exercises 13–16, differentiate the functions and find the slope of the tangent line at the given value of the independent variable.

13. $f(x) = x + \dfrac{9}{x},\quad x = -3$
14. $k(x) = \dfrac{1}{2 + x},\quad x = 2$
15. $s = t^3 - t^2,\quad t = -1$
16. $y = (x + 1)^3,\quad x = -2$

In Exercises 17–18, differentiate the functions. Then find an equation of the tangent line at the indicated point on the graph of the function.

17. $y = f(x) = \dfrac{8}{\sqrt{x - 2}},\quad (x, y) = (6, 4)$
18. $w = g(z) = 1 + \sqrt{4 - z},\quad (z, w) = (3, 2)$

In Exercises 19–22, find the values of the derivatives.

19. $\left.\dfrac{ds}{dt}\right|_{t=-1}$ if $s = 1 - 3t^2$
20. $\left.\dfrac{dy}{dx}\right|_{x=\sqrt{3}}$ if $y = 1 - \dfrac{1}{x}$
21. $\left.\dfrac{dr}{d\theta}\right|_{\theta=0}$ if $r = \dfrac{2}{\sqrt{4 - \theta}}$
22. $\left.\dfrac{dw}{dz}\right|_{z=4}$ if $w = z + \sqrt{z}$

Use the formula

$$f'(x) = \lim_{z \to x} \frac{f(z) - f(x)}{z - x}$$

to find the derivative of the functions in Exercises 23–26.

23. $f(x) = \dfrac{1}{x + 2}$
24. $f(x) = \dfrac{1}{(x - 1)^2}$
25. $g(x) = \dfrac{x}{x - 1}$
26. $g(x) = 1 + \sqrt{x}$

Match the functions graphed in Exercises 27–30 with the derivatives graphed in the accompanying figures (a)–(d).

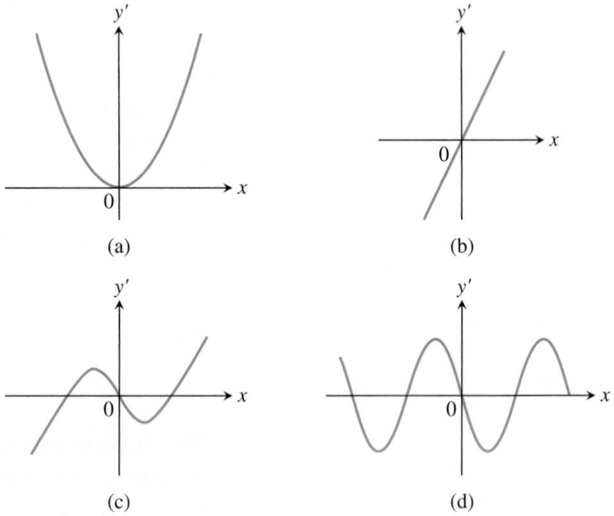

27.

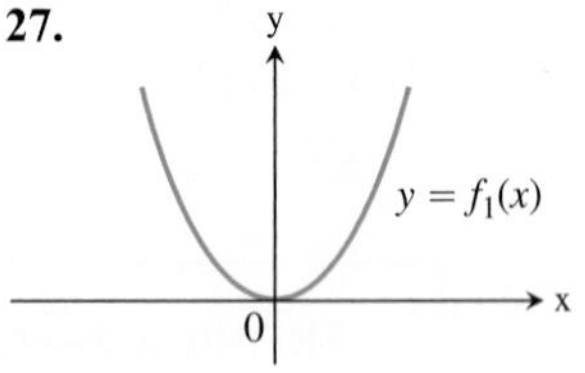

28.

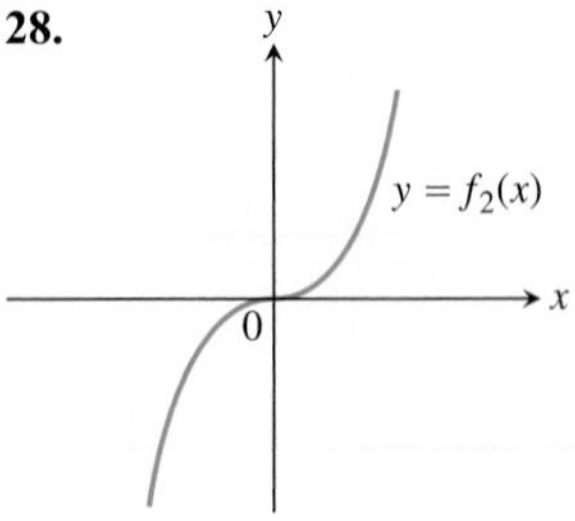

29.

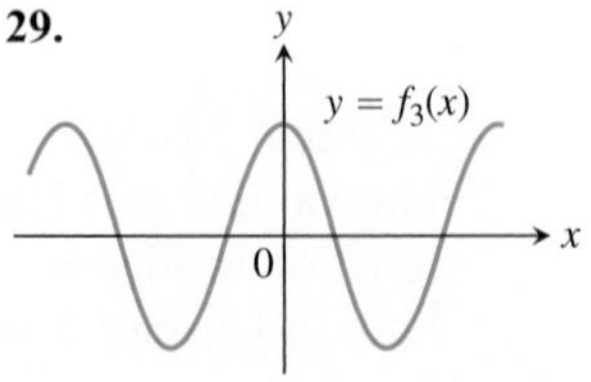

30.

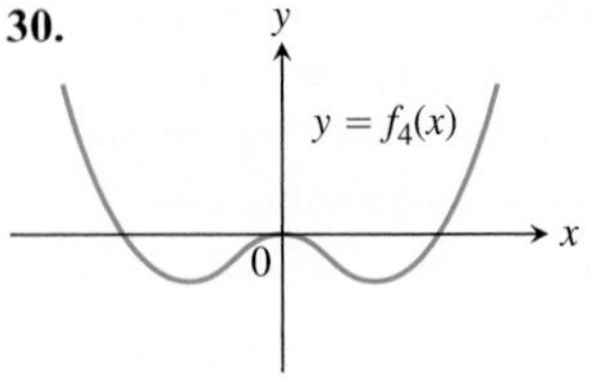

31. a. The graph in the accompanying figure is made of line segments joined end to end. At which points of the interval $[-4, 6]$ is f' not defined? Give reasons for your answer.

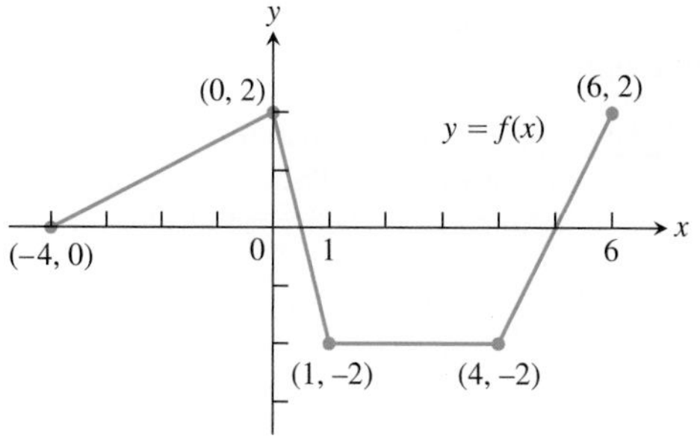

b. Graph the derivative of f.
The graph should show a step function.

32. Growth in the economy The graph in the accompanying figure shows the average annual percentage change $y = f(t)$ in the U.S. gross national product (GNP) for the years 1983–1988. Graph dy/dt (where defined). (*Source*: *Statistical Abstracts of the United States*, 110th Edition, U.S. Department of Commerce, p. 427.)

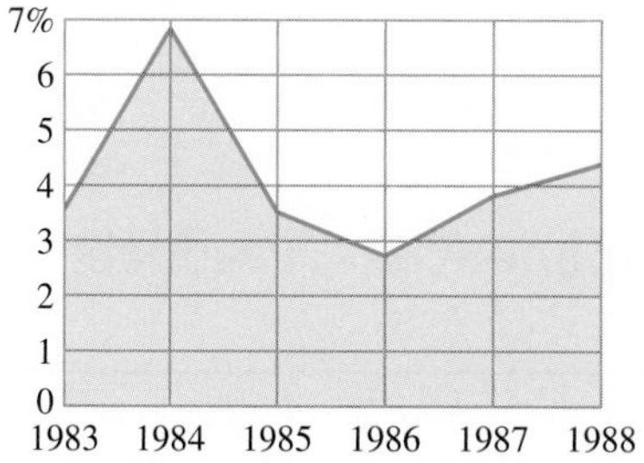

Compare the right-hand and left-hand derivatives to show that the functions in Exercises 33–36 are not differentiable at the point P.

33.

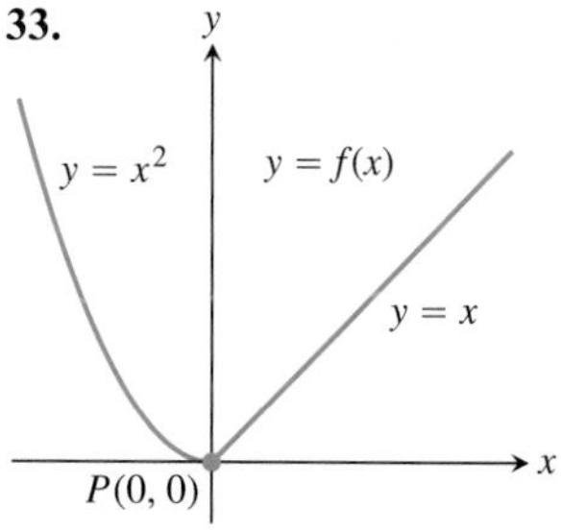

34.

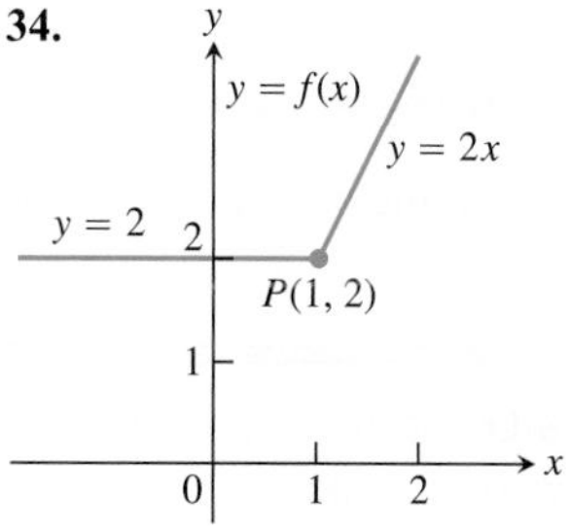

35.

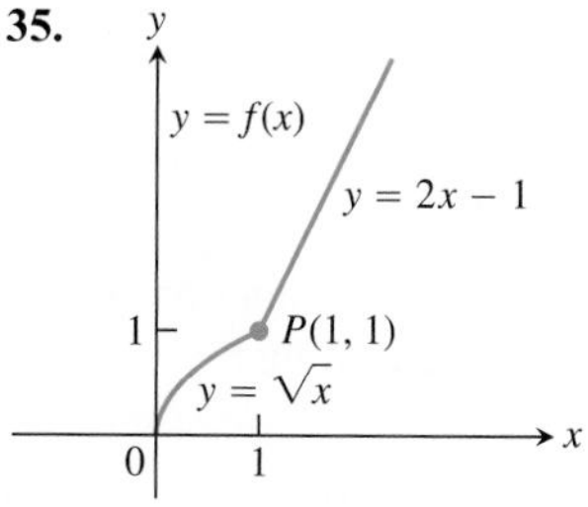

36.

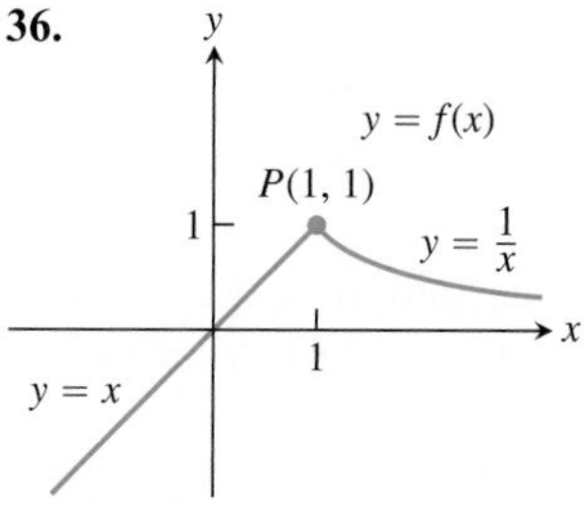

Each figure in Exercises 37–42 shows the graph of a function over a closed interval D. At what domain points does the function appear to be

a. differentiable?

b. continuous but not differentiable?

c. neither continuous nor differentiable?

Give reasons for your answers.

37.

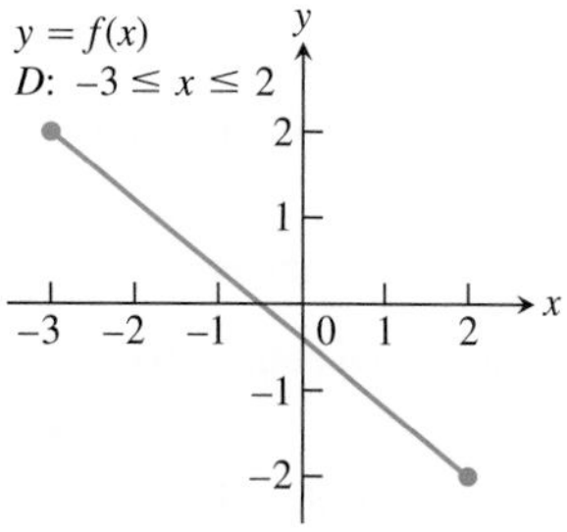

38.

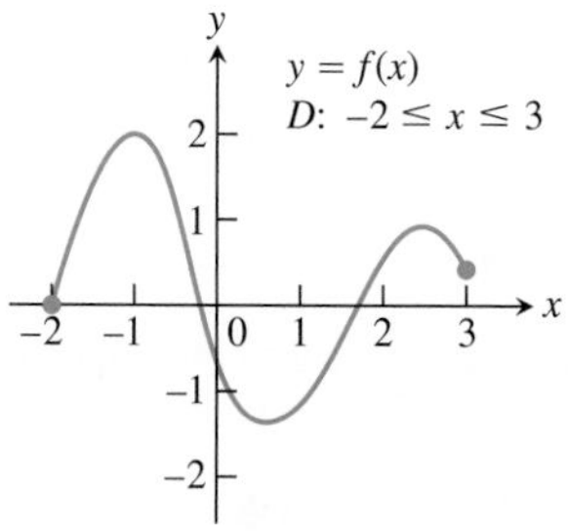

39.

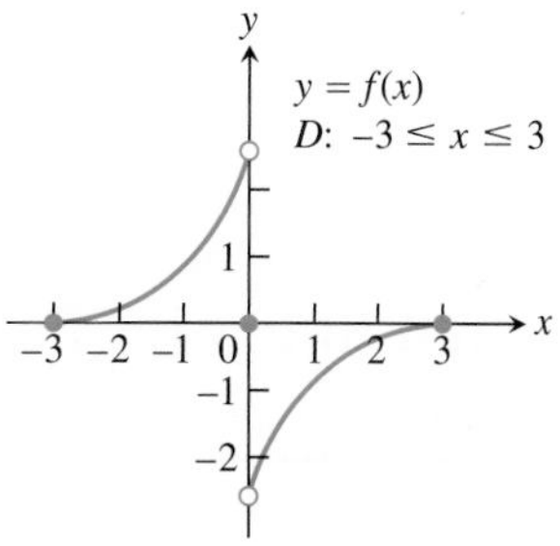

40.

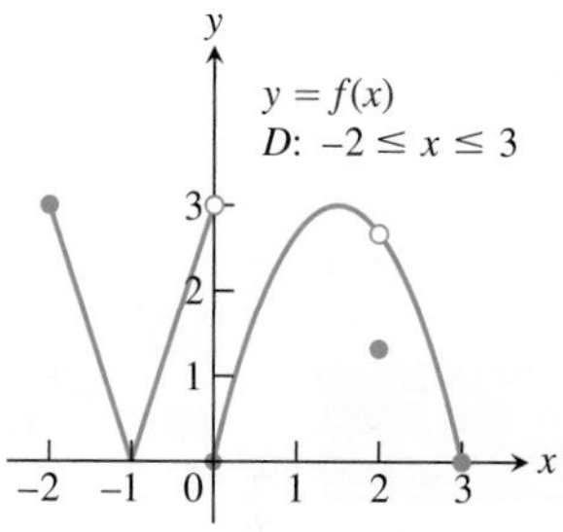

41.

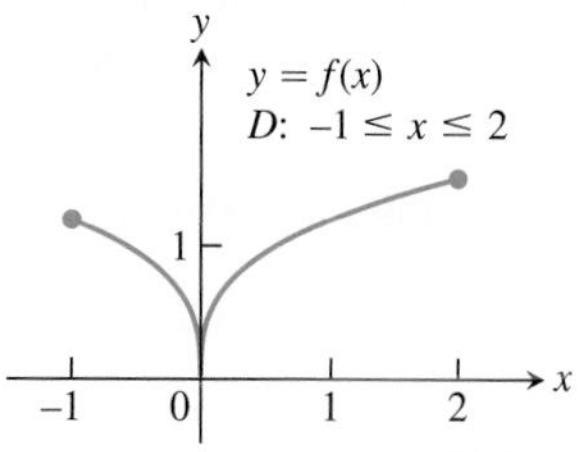

42.

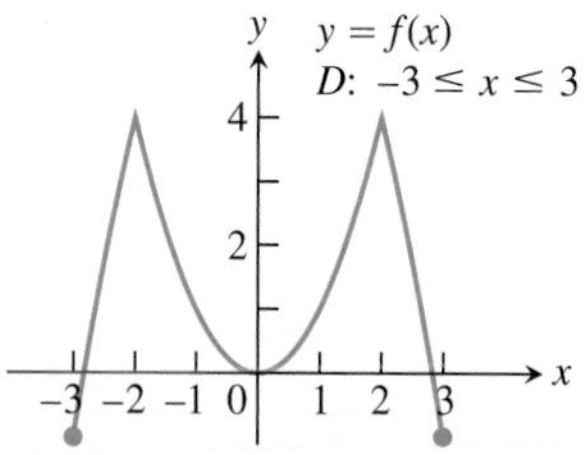

43. Tangent to a parabola Does the parabola $y = 2x^2 - 13x + 5$ have a tangent whose slope is -1? If so, find an equation for the line and the point of tangency. If not, why not?

44. Tangent to $y = \sqrt{x}$ Does any tangent to the curve $y = \sqrt{x}$ cross the x-axis at $x = -1$? If so, find an equation for the line and the point of tangency. If not, why not?

45. a. Let $f(x)$ be a function satisfying $|f(x)| \le x^2$ for $-1 \le x \le 1$. Show that f is differentiable at $x = 0$ and find $f'(0)$.

b. Show that

$$f(x) = \begin{cases} x^2 \sin \dfrac{1}{x}, & x \neq 0 \\ 0, & x = 0 \end{cases}$$

is differentiable at $x = 0$ and find $f'(0)$.

T **46. Weierstrass's nowhere differentiable continuous function** The sum of the first eight terms of the Weierstrass function $f(x) = \sum_{n=0}^{\infty} (2/3)^n \cos(9^n \pi x)$ is

$$g(x) = \cos(\pi x) + (2/3)^1 \cos(9\pi x) + (2/3)^2 \cos(9^2 \pi x) + (2/3)^3 \cos(9^3 \pi x) + \cdots + (2/3)^7 \cos(9^7 \pi x).$$

Graph this sum. Zoom in several times. How wiggly and bumpy is this graph? Specify a viewing window in which the displayed portion of the graph is smooth.

COMPUTER EXPLORATIONS

Use a CAS to perform the following steps for the functions in Exercises 47–52.

a. Plot $y = f(x)$ to see that function's global behavior.

b. Define the difference quotient q at a general point x, with general step size h.

c. Take the limit as $h \to 0$. What formula does this give?

d. Substitute the value $x = x_0$ and plot the function $y = f(x)$ together with its tangent line at that point.

e. Substitute various values for x larger and smaller than x_0 into the formula obtained in part (c). Do the numbers make sense with your picture?

f. Graph the formula obtained in part (c). What does it mean when its values are negative? Zero? Positive? Does this make sense with your plot from part (a)? Give reasons for your answer.

47. $f(x) = x^3 + x^2 - x, \quad x_0 = 1$

48. $f(x) = x^{1/3} + x^{2/3}, \quad x_0 = 1$

49. $f(x) = \dfrac{4x}{x^2 + 1}, \quad x_0 = 2$

50. $f(x) = \dfrac{x - 1}{3x^2 + 1}, \quad x_0 = -1$

51. $f(x) = \sin 2x, \quad x_0 = \pi/2$

52. $f(x) = x^2 \cos x, \quad x_0 = \pi/4$

3.2 Differentiation Rules for Polynomials, Exponentials, Products, and Quotients

This section introduces several rules that allow us to differentiate constant functions, power functions, polynomials, exponential functions, rational functions, and certain combinations of them.

Powers, Multiples, Sums, and Differences

The first rule of differentiation is that the derivative of every constant function is zero.

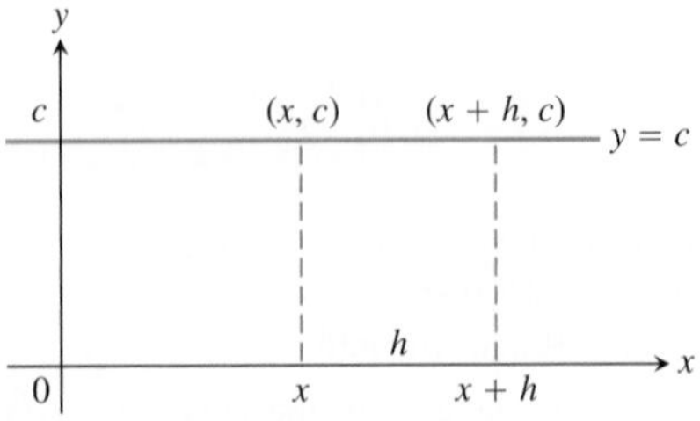

FIGURE 3.6 The rule $(d/dx)(c) = 0$ is another way to say that the values of constant functions never change and that the slope of a horizontal line is zero at every point.

> **RULE 1 Derivative of a Constant Function**
> If f has the constant value $f(x) = c$, then
> $$\frac{df}{dx} = \frac{d}{dx}(c) = 0.$$

Proof of Rule 1 We apply the definition of derivative to $f(x) = c$, the function whose outputs have the constant value c (Figure 3.6). At every value of x, we find that

$$f'(x) = \lim_{h \to 0} \frac{f(x + h) - f(x)}{h} = \lim_{h \to 0} \frac{c - c}{h} = \lim_{h \to 0} 0 = 0. \quad \blacksquare$$

From Section 2.7, we know that

$$\frac{d}{dx}(x) = \frac{d}{dx}(1 \cdot x) = 1 \qquad \frac{d}{dx}(mx + b) = m = 1$$

and

$$\frac{d}{dx}\left(\frac{1}{x}\right) = -\frac{1}{x^2}, \quad \text{or} \quad \frac{d}{dx}\left(x^{-1}\right) = -x^{-2}$$

From Example 2, Section 3.1, we also know that

$$\frac{d}{dx}\left(\sqrt{x}\right) = \frac{1}{2\sqrt{x}}, \quad \text{or} \quad \frac{d}{dx}\left(x^{1/2}\right) = \frac{1}{2}x^{-1/2}.$$

These three examples illustrate a general rule for differentiating a power x^n. We first prove the rule when n is a positive integer.

> **Power Rule for Positive Integers:**
> If n is a positive integer, then
>
> $$\frac{d}{dx}x^n = nx^{n-1}.$$

HISTORICAL BIOGRAPHY

Richard Courant
(1888–1972)

Proof of the Positive Integer Power Rule The formula

$$z^n - x^n = (z - x)(z^{n-1} + z^{n-2}x + \cdots + zx^{n-2} + x^{n-1})$$

can be verified by multiplying out the right-hand side. Then from the alternative form for the definition of the derivative,

$$\begin{aligned} f'(x) &= \lim_{z \to x} \frac{f(z) - f(x)}{z - x} = \lim_{z \to x} \frac{z^n - x^n}{z - x} \\ &= \lim_{z \to x}(z^{n-1} + z^{n-2}x + \cdots + zx^{n-2} + x^{n-1}) \qquad n \text{ terms} \\ &= nx^{n-1}. \end{aligned}$$

■

The Power Rule is actually valid for all real numbers n. We have seen examples for a negative integer and fractional power, but n could be an irrational number as well. To apply the Power Rule, we subtract 1 from the original exponent n and multiply the result by n. Here we state the general version of the rule, but postpone its proof until Section 3.7.

> **RULE 2 Power Rule (General Version)**
> If n is any real number, then
>
> $$\frac{d}{dx}x^n = nx^{n-1},$$
>
> for all x where the powers x^n and x^{n-1} are defined.

EXAMPLE 1 Differentiate the following powers of x.

(a) x^3 **(b)** $x^{2/3}$ **(c)** $x^{\sqrt{2}}$ **(d)** $\frac{1}{x^4}$ **(e)** $x^{-4/3}$ **(f)** $\sqrt{x^{2+\pi}}$

Solution

(a) $\frac{d}{dx}(x^3) = 3x^{3-1} = 3x^2$ **(b)** $\frac{d}{dx}(x^{2/3}) = \frac{2}{3}x^{(2/3)-1} = \frac{2}{3}x^{-1/3}$

(c) $\frac{d}{dx}\left(x^{\sqrt{2}}\right) = \sqrt{2}x^{\sqrt{2}-1}$ **(d)** $\frac{d}{dx}\left(\frac{1}{x^4}\right) = \frac{d}{dx}(x^{-4}) = -4x^{-4-1} = -4x^{-5} = -\frac{4}{x^5}$

(e) $\frac{d}{dx}(x^{-4/3}) = -\frac{4}{3}x^{-(4/3)-1} = -\frac{4}{3}x^{-7/3}$

(f) $\frac{d}{dx}\left(\sqrt{x^{2+\pi}}\right) = \frac{d}{dx}\left(x^{1+(\pi/2)}\right) = \left(1 + \frac{\pi}{2}\right)x^{1+(\pi/2)-1} = \frac{1}{2}(2 + \pi)\sqrt{x^{\pi}}$ ■

The third rule says that when a differentiable function is multiplied by a constant, its derivative is multiplied by the same constant.

RULE 3 Constant Multiple Rule
If u is a differentiable function of x, and c is a constant, then

$$\frac{d}{dx}(cu) = c\frac{du}{dx}.$$

In particular, if n is any real number, then

$$\frac{d}{dx}(cx^n) = cnx^{n-1}.$$

Proof of Rule 3

$$\frac{d}{dx}cu = \lim_{h\to 0}\frac{cu(x+h) - cu(x)}{h} \quad \text{Derivative definition with } f(x) = cu(x)$$

$$= c\lim_{h\to 0}\frac{u(x+h) - u(x)}{h} \quad \text{Limit property}$$

$$= c\frac{du}{dx} \quad u \text{ is differentiable.}$$ ■

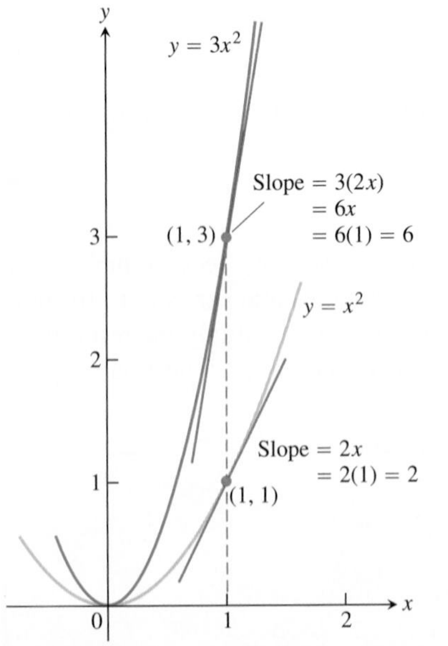

FIGURE 3.7 The graphs of $y = x^2$ and $y = 3x^2$. Tripling the y-coordinates triples the slope (Example 2).

EXAMPLE 2

(a) The derivative formula

$$\frac{d}{dx}(3x^2) = 3 \cdot 2x = 6x$$

says that if we rescale the graph of $y = x^2$ by multiplying each y-coordinate by 3, then we multiply the slope at each point by 3 (Figure 3.7).

(b) Negative of a function

The derivative of the negative of a differentiable function u is the negative of the function's derivative. Rule 3 with $c = -1$ gives

$$\frac{d}{dx}(-u) = \frac{d}{dx}(-1 \cdot u) = -1 \cdot \frac{d}{dx}(u) = -\frac{du}{dx}. \qquad \blacksquare$$

The next rule says that the derivative of the sum of two differentiable functions is the sum of their derivatives.

Denoting Functions by *u* and *v*
The functions we are working with when we need a differentiation formula are likely to be denoted by letters like f and g. When we apply the formula, we do not want to have it using these same letters in some other way. To guard against this problem, we denote the functions in differentiation rules by letters like u and v that are not likely to be already in use.

RULE 4 Derivative Sum Rule

If u and v are differentiable functions of x, then their sum $u + v$ is differentiable at every point where u and v are both differentiable. At such points,

$$\frac{d}{dx}(u + v) = \frac{du}{dx} + \frac{dv}{dx}.$$

For example, if $y = x^4 + 12x$, then y is the sum of $u(x) = x^4$ and $v(x) = 12x$. We then have

$$\frac{dy}{dx} = \frac{d}{dx}(x^4) + \frac{d}{dx}(12x) = 4x^3 + 12.$$

Proof of Rule 4 We apply the definition of derivative to $f(x) = u(x) + v(x)$:

$$\begin{aligned}\frac{d}{dx}[u(x) + v(x)] &= \lim_{h\to 0} \frac{[u(x+h) + v(x+h)] - [u(x) + v(x)]}{h} \\ &= \lim_{h\to 0}\left[\frac{u(x+h) - u(x)}{h} + \frac{v(x+h) - v(x)}{h}\right] \\ &= \lim_{h\to 0}\frac{u(x+h) - u(x)}{h} + \lim_{h\to 0}\frac{v(x+h) - v(x)}{h} = \frac{du}{dx} + \frac{dv}{dx}. \qquad \blacksquare\end{aligned}$$

Combining the Sum Rule with the Constant Multiple Rule gives the **Difference Rule,** which says that the derivative of a *difference* of differentiable functions is the difference of their derivatives.

$$\frac{d}{dx}(u - v) = \frac{d}{dx}[u + (-1)v] = \frac{du}{dx} + (-1)\frac{dv}{dx} = \frac{du}{dx} - \frac{dv}{dx}$$

The Sum Rule also extends to finite sums of more than two functions. If $u_1, u_2, \ldots, u_n$ are differentiable at x, then so is $u_1 + u_2 + \cdots + u_n$, and

$$\frac{d}{dx}(u_1 + u_2 + \cdots + u_n) = \frac{du_1}{dx} + \frac{du_2}{dx} + \cdots + \frac{du_n}{dx}.$$

EXAMPLE 3

$$y = x^3 + \frac{4}{3}x^2 - 5x + 1$$

$$\begin{aligned}\frac{dy}{dx} &= \frac{d}{dx}x^3 + \frac{d}{dx}\left(\frac{4}{3}x^2\right) - \frac{d}{dx}(5x) + \frac{d}{dx}(1) \\ &= 3x^2 + \frac{4}{3} \cdot 2x - 5 + 0 = 3x^2 + \frac{8}{3}x - 5 \qquad \blacksquare\end{aligned}$$

We can differentiate any polynomial term by term, the way we differentiated the polynomial in Example 3. All polynomials are differentiable everywhere.

Proof of the Sum Rule for Sums of More Than Two Functions We prove the statement

$$\frac{d}{dx}(u_1 + u_2 + \cdots + u_n) = \frac{du_1}{dx} + \frac{du_2}{dx} + \cdots + \frac{du_n}{dx}$$

by mathematical induction (see Appendix 2). The statement is true for $n = 2$, as was just proved. This is Step 1 of the induction proof.

Step 2 is to show that if the statement is true for any positive integer $n = k$, where $k \geq n_0 = 2$, then it is also true for $n = k + 1$. So suppose that

$$\frac{d}{dx}(u_1 + u_2 + \cdots + u_k) = \frac{du_1}{dx} + \frac{du_2}{dx} + \cdots + \frac{du_k}{dx}. \tag{1}$$

Then

$$\frac{d}{dx}(\underbrace{u_1 + u_2 + \cdots + u_k}_{\text{Call the function defined by this sum } u.} + \underbrace{u_{k+1}}_{\text{Call this function } v.})$$

$$= \frac{d}{dx}(u_1 + u_2 + \cdots + u_k) + \frac{du_{k+1}}{dx} \qquad \text{Rule 4 for } \frac{d}{dx}(u + v)$$

$$= \frac{du_1}{dx} + \frac{du_2}{dx} + \cdots + \frac{du_k}{dx} + \frac{du_{k+1}}{dx}. \qquad \text{Eq. (1)}$$

With these steps verified, the mathematical induction principle now guarantees the Sum Rule for every integer $n \geq 2$. ■

EXAMPLE 4 Does the curve $y = x^4 - 2x^2 + 2$ have any horizontal tangents? If so, where?

Solution The horizontal tangents, if any, occur where the slope dy/dx is zero. We have,

$$\frac{dy}{dx} = \frac{d}{dx}(x^4 - 2x^2 + 2) = 4x^3 - 4x.$$

Now solve the equation $\dfrac{dy}{dx} = 0$ for x:

$$\begin{aligned} 4x^3 - 4x &= 0 \\ 4x(x^2 - 1) &= 0 \\ x &= 0, 1, -1. \end{aligned}$$

The curve $y = x^4 - 2x^2 + 2$ has horizontal tangents at $x = 0, 1$, and -1. The corresponding points on the curve are $(0, 2)$, $(1, 1)$ and $(-1, 1)$. See Figure 3.8. ■

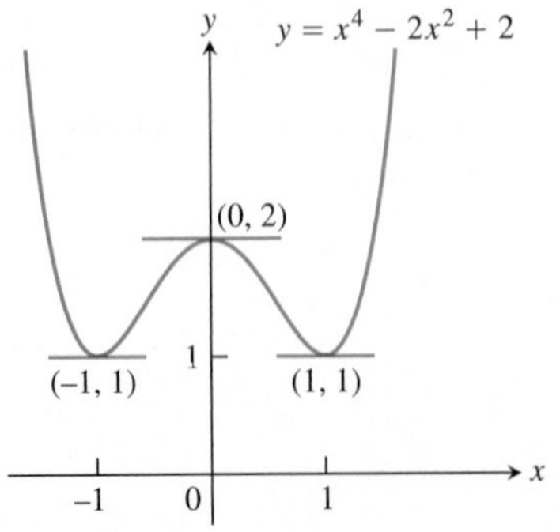

FIGURE 3.8 The curve $y = x^4 - 2x^2 + 2$ and its horizontal tangents (Example 4).

Derivatives of Exponential Functions

We briefly reviewed exponential functions in Section 1.4. When we apply the definition of the derivative to $f(x) = a^x$, we get

$$\begin{aligned}
\frac{d}{dx}(a^x) &= \lim_{h\to 0}\frac{a^{x+h} - a^x}{h} && \text{Derivative definition}\\
&= \lim_{h\to 0}\frac{a^x \cdot a^h - a^x}{h} && a^{x+h} = a^x \cdot a^h\\
&= \lim_{h\to 0} a^x \cdot \frac{a^h - 1}{h} && \text{Factoring out } a^x\\
&= a^x \cdot \lim_{h\to 0}\frac{a^h - 1}{h} && a^x \text{ is constant as } h \to 0.\\
&= \underbrace{\left(\lim_{h\to 0}\frac{a^h - 1}{h}\right)}_{\text{a fixed number } L} \cdot a^x. && (2)
\end{aligned}$$

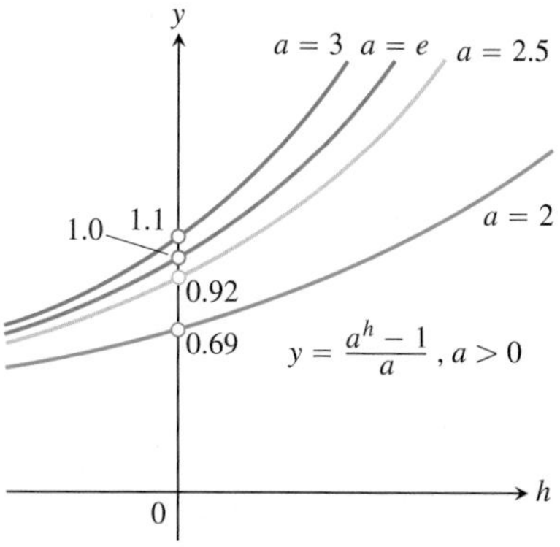

FIGURE 3.9 The position of the curve $y = (a^h - 1)/h$, $a > 0$, varies continuously with a.

Thus we see that the derivative of a^x is a constant multiple L of a^x. The constant L is a limit unlike any we have encountered before. Note, however, that it equals the derivative of $f(x) = a^x$ at $x = 0$:

$$f'(0) = \lim_{h\to 0}\frac{a^h - a^0}{h} = \lim_{h\to 0}\frac{a^h - 1}{h} = L.$$

The limit L is therefore the slope of the graph of $f(x) = a^x$ where it crosses the y-axis. In Chapter 5, where we carefully develop the logarithmic and exponential functions, we prove that the limit L exists and has the value $\ln a$. For now we investigate values of L by graphing the function $y = (a^h - 1)/h$ and studying its behavior as h approaches 0.

Figure 3.9 shows the graphs of $y = (a^h - 1)/h$ for four different values of a. The limit L is approximately 0.69 if $a = 2$, about 0.92 if $a = 2.5$, and about 1.1 if $a = 3$. It appears that the value of L is 1 at some number a chosen between 2.5 and 3. That number is given by $a = e \approx 2.718281828$. With this choice of base we obtain the natural exponential function $f(x) = e^x$ as in Section 1.4, and see that it satisfies the property

$$f'(0) = \lim_{h\to 0}\frac{e^h - 1}{h} = 1. \qquad (3)$$

That the limit is 1 implies an important relationship between the natural exponential function e^x and its derivative:

$$\begin{aligned}
\frac{d}{dx}(e^x) &= \lim_{h\to 0}\left(\frac{e^h - 1}{h}\right)\cdot e^x && \text{Eq. (2) with } a = e\\
&= 1 \cdot e^x = e^x. && \text{Eq. (3)}
\end{aligned}$$

Therefore the natural exponential function is its own derivative.

Derivative of the Natural Exponential Function

$$\frac{d}{dx}(e^x) = e^x$$

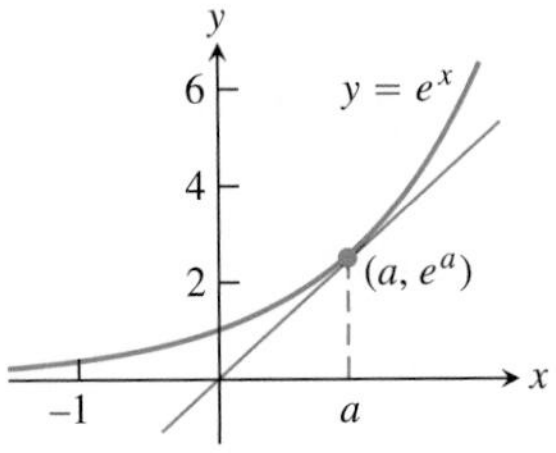

FIGURE 3.10 The line through the origin is tangent to the graph of $y = e^x$ when $a = 1$ (Example 5).

EXAMPLE 5 Find an equation for a line that is tangent to the graph of $y = e^x$ and goes through the origin.

Solution Since the line passes through the origin, its equation is of the form $y = mx$, where m is the slope. If it is tangent to the graph at the point (a, e^a), the slope is $m = (e^a - 0)/(a - 0)$. The slope of the natural exponential at $x = a$ is e^a. Because these slopes are the same, we then have that $e^a = e^a/a$. It follows that $a = 1$ and $m = e$, so the equation of the tangent line is $y = ex$. See Figure 3.10. ■

We might ask if there are functions *other* than the natural exponential function that are their own derivatives. The answer is that the only functions that satisfy the property that $f'(x) = f(x)$ are functions that are constant multiples of the natural exponential function, $f(x) = c \cdot e^x$, c any constant. We prove this fact in Section 6.4. Note from the Constant Multiple Rule that indeed

$$\frac{d}{dx}(c \cdot e^x) = c \cdot \frac{d}{dx}(e^x) = c \cdot e^x.$$

Products and Quotients

While the derivative of the sum of two functions is the sum of their derivatives, the derivative of the product of two functions is *not* the product of their derivatives. For instance,

$$\frac{d}{dx}(x \cdot x) = \frac{d}{dx}(x^2) = 2x, \qquad \text{while} \qquad \frac{d}{dx}(x) \cdot \frac{d}{dx}(x) = 1 \cdot 1 = 1.$$

The derivative of a product of two functions is the sum of *two* products, as we now explain.

RULE 5 Derivative Product Rule
If u and v are differentiable at x, then so is their product uv, and

$$\frac{d}{dx}(uv) = u\frac{dv}{dx} + v\frac{du}{dx}.$$

The derivative of the product uv is u times the derivative of v plus v times the derivative of u. In prime notation, $(uv)' = uv' + vu'$. In function notation,

$$\frac{d}{dx}[f(x)g(x)] = f(x)g'(x) + g(x)f'(x).$$

EXAMPLE 6 Find the derivative of

$$y = \frac{1}{x}\left(x^2 + e^x\right).$$

Solution We apply the Product Rule with $u = 1/x$ and $v = x^2 + e^x$:

$$\begin{aligned}\frac{d}{dx}\left[\frac{1}{x}\left(x^2 + e^x\right)\right] &= \frac{1}{x}\left(2x + e^x\right) + \left(x^2 + e^x\right)\left(-\frac{1}{x^2}\right) \\ &= 2 + \frac{e^x}{x} - 1 - \frac{e^x}{x^2} \\ &= 1 + (x - 1)\frac{e^x}{x^2}.\end{aligned}$$

$\frac{d}{dx}(uv) = u\frac{dv}{dx} + v\frac{du}{dx}$, and $\frac{d}{dx}\left(\frac{1}{x}\right) = -\frac{1}{x^2}$

■

Proof of the Product Rule

$$\frac{d}{dx}(uv) = \lim_{h \to 0} \frac{u(x + h)v(x + h) - u(x)v(x)}{h}$$

To change this fraction into an equivalent one that contains difference quotients for the derivatives of u and v, we subtract and add $u(x + h)v(x)$ in the numerator:

$$\begin{aligned}\frac{d}{dx}(uv) &= \lim_{h \to 0} \frac{u(x + h)v(x + h) - u(x + h)v(x) + u(x + h)v(x) - u(x)v(x)}{h} \\ &= \lim_{h \to 0}\left[u(x + h)\frac{v(x + h) - v(x)}{h} + v(x)\frac{u(x + h) - u(x)}{h}\right] \\ &= \lim_{h \to 0} u(x + h) \cdot \lim_{h \to 0} \frac{v(x + h) - v(x)}{h} + v(x) \cdot \lim_{h \to 0} \frac{u(x + h) - u(x)}{h}.\end{aligned}$$

As h approaches zero, $u(x + h)$ approaches $u(x)$ because u, being differentiable at x, is continuous at x. The two fractions approach the values of dv/dx at x and du/dx at x. In short,

$$\frac{d}{dx}(uv) = u\frac{dv}{dx} + v\frac{du}{dx}.$$

■

Picturing the Product Rule

Suppose $u(x)$ and $v(x)$ are positive and increase when x increases, and $h > 0$.

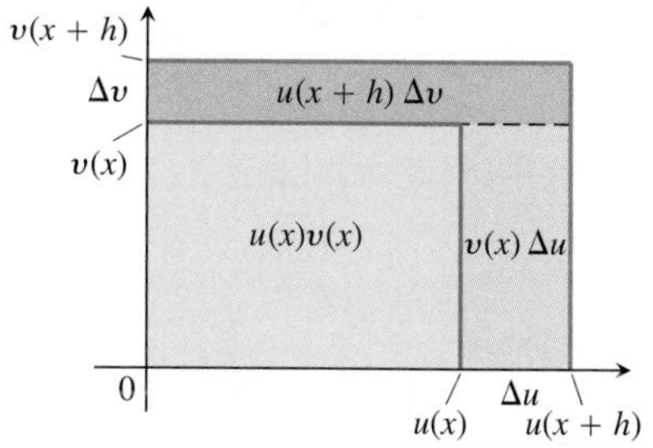

Then the change in the product uv is the difference in areas of the larger and smaller "squares," which is the sum of the upper and righthand reddish-shaded rectangles. That is,

$$\begin{aligned}\Delta(uv) &= u(x + h)v(x + h) - u(x)v(x) \\ &= u(x + h)\Delta v + v(x)\Delta u.\end{aligned}$$

Division by h gives

$$\frac{\Delta(uv)}{h} = u(x + h)\frac{\Delta v}{h} + v(x)\frac{\Delta u}{h}.$$

The limit as $h \to 0^+$ gives the Product Rule.

EXAMPLE 7 Find the derivative of $y = (x^2 + 1)(x^3 + 3)$.

Solution

(a) From the Product Rule with $u = x^2 + 1$ and $v = x^3 + 3$, we find

$$\begin{aligned}\frac{d}{dx}\left[(x^2 + 1)(x^3 + 3)\right] &= (x^2 + 1)(3x^2) + (x^3 + 3)(2x) \\ &= 3x^4 + 3x^2 + 2x^4 + 6x \\ &= 5x^4 + 3x^2 + 6x.\end{aligned}$$

(b) This particular product can be differentiated as well (perhaps better) by multiplying out the original expression for y and differentiating the resulting polynomial:

$$y = (x^2 + 1)(x^3 + 3) = x^5 + x^3 + 3x^2 + 3$$

$$\frac{dy}{dx} = 5x^4 + 3x^2 + 6x.$$

This is in agreement with our first calculation. ■

Just as the derivative of the product of two differentiable functions is not the product of their derivatives, the derivative of the quotient of two functions is not the quotient of their derivatives. What happens instead is the Quotient Rule.

RULE 6 Derivative Quotient Rule
If u and v are differentiable at x and if $v(x) \neq 0$, then the quotient u/v is differentiable at x, and

$$\frac{d}{dx}\left(\frac{u}{v}\right) = \frac{v\dfrac{du}{dx} - u\dfrac{dv}{dx}}{v^2}.$$

In function notation,

$$\frac{d}{dx}\left[\frac{f(x)}{g(x)}\right] = \frac{g(x)f'(x) - f(x)g'(x)}{g^2(x)}.$$

EXAMPLE 8 Find the derivative of

(a) $y = \dfrac{t^2 - 1}{t^2 + 1}$, **(b)** $y = e^{-x}$.

Solution

(a) We apply the Quotient Rule with $u = t^2 - 1$ and $v = t^2 + 1$:

$$\frac{dy}{dt} = \frac{(t^2 + 1) \cdot 2t - (t^2 - 1) \cdot 2t}{(t^2 + 1)^2} \qquad \frac{d}{dt}\left(\frac{u}{v}\right) = \frac{v(du/dt) - u(dv/dt)}{v^2}$$

$$= \frac{2t^3 + 2t - 2t^3 + 2t}{(t^2 + 1)^2}$$

$$= \frac{4t}{(t^2 + 1)^2}.$$

(b) $$\frac{d}{dx}(e^{-x}) = \frac{d}{dx}\left(\frac{1}{e^x}\right) = \frac{e^x \cdot 0 - 1 \cdot e^x}{(e^x)^2} = \frac{-1}{e^x} = -e^{-x}$$ ■

Proof of the Quotient Rule

$$\frac{d}{dx}\left(\frac{u}{v}\right) = \lim_{h\to 0}\frac{\dfrac{u(x+h)}{v(x+h)} - \dfrac{u(x)}{v(x)}}{h}$$
$$= \lim_{h\to 0}\frac{v(x)u(x+h) - u(x)v(x+h)}{hv(x+h)v(x)}$$

To change the last fraction into an equivalent one that contains the difference quotients for the derivatives of u and v, we subtract and add $v(x)u(x)$ in the numerator. We then get

$$\frac{d}{dx}\left(\frac{u}{v}\right) = \lim_{h\to 0}\frac{v(x)u(x+h) - v(x)u(x) + v(x)u(x) - u(x)v(x+h)}{hv(x+h)v(x)}$$
$$= \lim_{h\to 0}\frac{v(x)\dfrac{u(x+h)-u(x)}{h} - u(x)\dfrac{v(x+h)-v(x)}{h}}{v(x+h)v(x)}.$$

Taking the limits in the numerator and denominator now gives the Quotient Rule. ■

The choice of which rules to use in solving a differentiation problem can make a difference in how much work you have to do. Here is an example.

EXAMPLE 9 Rather than using the Quotient Rule to find the derivative of

$$y = \frac{(x-1)(x^2-2x)}{x^4},$$

expand the numerator and divide by x^4:

$$y = \frac{(x-1)(x^2-2x)}{x^4} = \frac{x^3 - 3x^2 + 2x}{x^4} = x^{-1} - 3x^{-2} + 2x^{-3}.$$

Then use the Sum and Power Rules:

$$\frac{dy}{dx} = -x^{-2} - 3(-2)x^{-3} + 2(-3)x^{-4}$$
$$= -\frac{1}{x^2} + \frac{6}{x^3} - \frac{6}{x^4}.$$

■

Second- and Higher-Order Derivatives

If $y = f(x)$ is a differentiable function, then its derivative $f'(x)$ is also a function. If f' is also differentiable, then we can differentiate f' to get a new function of x denoted by f''. So $f'' = (f')'$. The function f'' is called the **second derivative** of f because it is the derivative of the first derivative. It is written in several ways:

$$f''(x) = \frac{d^2y}{dx^2} = \frac{d}{dx}\left(\frac{dy}{dx}\right) = \frac{dy'}{dx} = y'' = D^2(f)(x) = D_x^2 f(x).$$

The symbol D^2 means the operation of differentiation is performed twice.

If $y = x^6$, then $y' = 6x^5$ and we have

$$y'' = \frac{dy'}{dx} = \frac{d}{dx}(6x^5) = 30x^4.$$

Thus $D^2(x^6) = 30x^4$.

If y'' is differentiable, its derivative, $y''' = dy''/dx = d^3y/dx^3$ is the **third derivative** of y with respect to x. The names continue as you imagine, with

$$y^{(n)} = \frac{d}{dx}y^{(n-1)} = \frac{d^ny}{dx^n} = D^ny$$

denoting the ***n*th derivative** of y with respect to x for any positive integer n.

We can interpret the second derivative as the rate of change of the slope of the tangent to the graph of $y = f(x)$ at each point. You will see in the next chapter that the second derivative reveals whether the graph bends upward or downward from the tangent line as we move off the point of tangency. In the next section, we interpret both the second and third derivatives in terms of motion along a straight line.

How to Read the Symbols for Derivatives

y'	"y prime"
y''	"y double prime"
$\frac{d^2y}{dx^2}$	"d squared y dx squared"
y'''	"y triple prime"
$y^{(n)}$	"y super n"
$\frac{d^ny}{dx^n}$	"d to the n of y by dx to the n"
D^n	"D to the n"

EXAMPLE 10 The first four derivatives of $y = x^3 - 3x^2 + 2$ are

First derivative: $y' = 3x^2 - 6x$

Second derivative: $y'' = 6x - 6$

Third derivative: $y''' = 6$

Fourth derivative: $y^{(4)} = 0$.

The function has derivatives of all orders, the fifth and later derivatives all being zero. ■

EXERCISES 3.2

In Exercises 1–12, find the first and second derivatives.

1. $y = -x^2 + 3$
2. $y = x^2 + x + 8$
3. $s = 5t^3 - 3t^5$
4. $w = 3z^7 - 7z^3 + 21z^2$
5. $y = \frac{4x^3}{3} - x + 2e^x$
6. $y = \frac{x^3}{3} + \frac{x^2}{2} + \frac{x}{4}$
7. $w = 3z^{-2} - \frac{1}{z}$
8. $s = -2t^{-1} + \frac{4}{t^2}$
9. $y = 6x^2 - 10x - 5x^{-2}$
10. $y = 4 - 2x - x^{-3}$
11. $r = \frac{1}{3s^2} - \frac{5}{2s}$
12. $r = \frac{12}{\theta} - \frac{4}{\theta^3} + \frac{1}{\theta^4}$

In Exercises 13–16, find y' **(a)** by applying the Product Rule and **(b)** by multiplying the factors to produce a sum of simpler terms to differentiate.

13. $y = (3 - x^2)(x^3 - x + 1)$
14. $y = (x - 1)(x^2 + x + 1)$
15. $y = (x^2 + 1)\left(x + 5 + \frac{1}{x}\right)$
16. $y = \left(x + \frac{1}{x}\right)\left(x - \frac{1}{x} + 1\right)$

Find the derivatives of the functions in Exercises 17–36.

17. $y = \frac{2x + 5}{3x - 2}$
18. $z = \frac{2x + 1}{x^2 - 1}$
19. $g(x) = \frac{x^2 - 4}{x + 0.5}$
20. $f(t) = \frac{t^2 - 1}{t^2 + t - 2}$
21. $v = (1 - t)(1 + t^2)^{-1}$
22. $w = (2x - 7)^{-1}(x + 5)$
23. $y = 2e^{-x}$
24. $y = \frac{x^2 + 3e^x}{2e^x - x}$
25. $v = \frac{1 + x - 4\sqrt{x}}{x}$
26. $r = 2\left(\frac{1}{\sqrt{\theta}} + \sqrt{\theta}\right)$
27. $y = x^3e^x$
28. $w = re^{-r}$
29. $y = x^{9/4}$
30. $y = x^{-3/5} + \pi^{3/2}$

31. $s = 2t^{3/2} + 3e^2$

32. $w = \dfrac{1}{z^{1.4}} + \dfrac{\pi}{\sqrt{z}}$

33. $y = \sqrt[7]{x^2} - x^e$

34. $y = \sqrt[3]{x^{9.6}} + 2e^{1.3}$

35. $r = \dfrac{e^s}{s}$

36. $r = e^\theta\left(\dfrac{1}{\theta^2} + \theta^{-\pi/2}\right)$

Find the derivatives of all orders of the functions in Exercises 37 and 38.

37. $y = \dfrac{x^4}{2} - \dfrac{3}{2}x^2 - x$

38. $y = \dfrac{x^5}{120}$

Find the first and second derivatives of the functions in Exercises 39–46.

39. $y = \dfrac{x^3 + 7}{x}$

40. $s = \dfrac{t^2 + 5t - 1}{t^2}$

41. $r = \dfrac{(\theta - 1)(\theta^2 + \theta + 1)}{\theta^3}$

42. $u = \dfrac{(x^2 + x)(x^2 - x + 1)}{x^4}$

43. $w = 3z^2e^z$

44. $w = e^z(z - 1)(z^2 + 1)$

45. $p = \left(\dfrac{q^2 + 3}{12q}\right)\left(\dfrac{q^4 - 1}{q^3}\right)$

46. $p = \dfrac{q^2 + 3}{(q - 1)^3 + (q + 1)^3}$

47. Suppose u and v are functions of x that are differentiable at $x = 0$ and that

$$u(0) = 5, \quad u'(0) = -3, \quad v(0) = -1, \quad v'(0) = 2.$$

Find the values of the following derivatives at $x = 0$.

a. $\dfrac{d}{dx}(uv)$ **b.** $\dfrac{d}{dx}\left(\dfrac{u}{v}\right)$ **c.** $\dfrac{d}{dx}\left(\dfrac{v}{u}\right)$ **d.** $\dfrac{d}{dx}(7v - 2u)$

48. Suppose u and v are differentiable functions of x and that

$$u(1) = 2, \quad u'(1) = 0, \quad v(1) = 5, \quad v'(1) = -1.$$

Find the values of the following derivatives at $x = 1$.

a. $\dfrac{d}{dx}(uv)$ **b.** $\dfrac{d}{dx}\left(\dfrac{u}{v}\right)$ **c.** $\dfrac{d}{dx}\left(\dfrac{v}{u}\right)$ **d.** $\dfrac{d}{dx}(7v - 2u)$

49. a. Normal to a curve Find an equation for the line perpendicular to the tangent to the curve $y = x^3 - 4x + 1$ at the point $(2, 1)$.

b. Smallest slope What is the smallest slope on the curve? At what point on the curve does the curve have this slope?

c. Tangents having specified slope Find equations for the tangents to the curve at the points where the slope of the curve is 8.

50. a. Horizontal tangents Find equations for the horizontal tangents to the curve $y = x^3 - 3x - 2$. Also find equations for the lines that are perpendicular to these tangents at the points of tangency.

b. Smallest slope What is the smallest slope on the curve? At what point on the curve does the curve have this slope? Find an equation for the line that is perpendicular to the curve's tangent at this point.

51. Find the tangents to *Newton's serpentine* (graphed here) at the origin and the point $(1, 2)$.

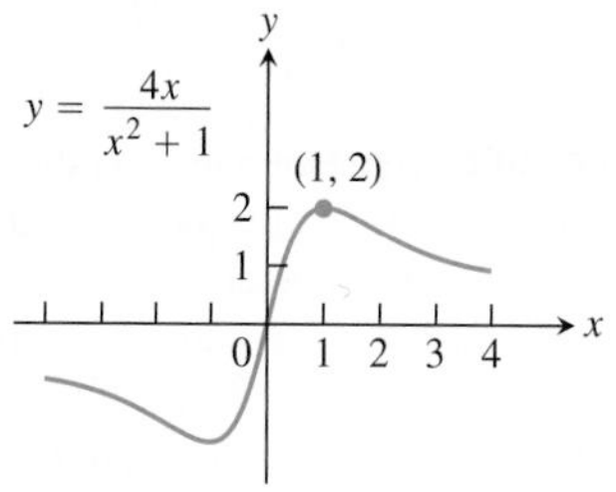

52. Find the tangent to the *Witch of Agnesi* (graphed here) at the point $(2, 1)$.

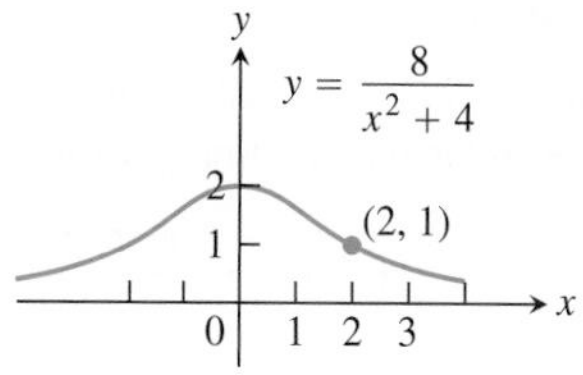

53. Quadratic tangent to identity function The curve $y = ax^2 + bx + c$ passes through the point $(1, 2)$ and is tangent to the line $y = x$ at the origin. Find a, b, and c.

54. Quadratics having a common tangent The curves $y = x^2 + ax + b$ and $y = cx - x^2$ have a common tangent line at the point $(1, 0)$. Find a, b, and c.

55. a. Find an equation for the line that is tangent to the curve $y = x^3 - x$ at the point $(-1, 0)$.

T **b.** Graph the curve and tangent line together. The tangent intersects the curve at another point. Use Zoom and Trace to estimate the point's coordinates.

T **c.** Confirm your estimates of the coordinates of the second intersection point by solving the equations for the curve and tangent simultaneously (Solver key).

56. a. Find an equation for the line that is tangent to the curve $y = x^3 - 6x^2 + 5x$ at the origin.

T **b.** Graph the curve and tangent together. The tangent intersects the curve at another point. Use Zoom and Trace to estimate the point's coordinates.

T **c.** Confirm your estimates of the coordinates of the second intersection point by solving the equations for the curve and tangent simultaneously (Solver key).

57. The general polynomial of degree n has the form

$$P(x) = a_nx^n + a_{n-1}x^{n-1} + \cdots + a_2x^2 + a_1x + a_0$$

where $a_n \neq 0$. Find $P'(x)$.

58. **The body's reaction to medicine** The reaction of the body to a dose of medicine can sometimes be represented by an equation of the form

$$R = M^2\left(\frac{C}{2} - \frac{M}{3}\right),$$

where C is a positive constant and M is the amount of medicine absorbed in the blood. If the reaction is a change in blood pressure, R is measured in millimeters of mercury. If the reaction is a change in temperature, R is measured in degrees, and so on.

Find dR/dM. This derivative, as a function of M, is called the sensitivity of the body to the medicine. In Section 4.5, we will see how to find the amount of medicine to which the body is most sensitive.

59. Suppose that the function v in the Product Rule has a constant value c. What does the Product Rule then say? What does this say about the Constant Multiple Rule?

60. **The Reciprocal Rule**

a. The *Reciprocal Rule* says that at any point where the function $v(x)$ is differentiable and different from zero,

$$\frac{d}{dx}\left(\frac{1}{v}\right) = -\frac{1}{v^2}\frac{dv}{dx}.$$

Show that the Reciprocal Rule is a special case of the Quotient Rule.

b. Show that the Reciprocal Rule and the Product Rule together imply the Quotient Rule.

61. **Generalizing the Product Rule** The Product Rule gives the formula

$$\frac{d}{dx}(uv) = u\frac{dv}{dx} + v\frac{du}{dx}$$

for the derivative of the product uv of two differentiable functions of x.

a. What is the analogous formula for the derivative of the product uvw of *three* differentiable functions of x?

b. What is the formula for the derivative of the product $u_1u_2u_3u_4$ of *four* differentiable functions of x?

c. What is the formula for the derivative of a product $u_1u_2u_3\cdots u_n$ of a finite number n of differentiable functions of x?

62. **Power Rule for negative integers** Use the Quotient Rule to prove the Power Rule for negative integers, that is,

$$\frac{d}{dx}(x^{-m}) = -mx^{-m-1}$$

where m is a positive integer.

63. **Cylinder pressure** If gas in a cylinder is maintained at a constant temperature T, the pressure P is related to the volume V by a formula of the form

$$P = \frac{nRT}{V - nb} - \frac{an^2}{V^2},$$

in which a, b, n, and R are constants. Find dP/dV. (See accompanying figure.)

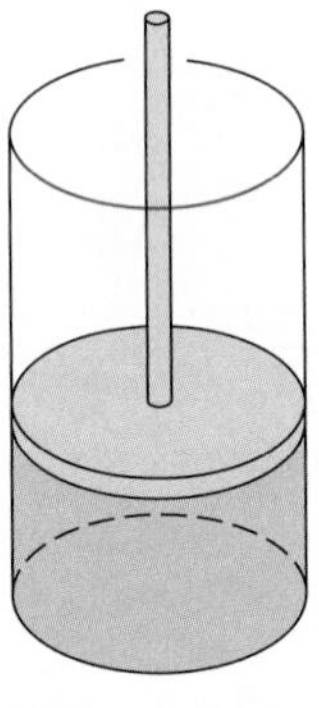

64. **The best quantity to order** One of the formulas for inventory management says that the average weekly cost of ordering, paying for, and holding merchandise is

$$A(q) = \frac{km}{q} + cm + \frac{hq}{2},$$

where q is the quantity you order when things run low (shoes, radios, brooms, or whatever the item might be); k is the cost of placing an order (the same, no matter how often you order); c is the cost of one item (a constant); m is the number of items sold each week (a constant); and h is the weekly holding cost per item (a constant that takes into account things such as space, utilities, insurance, and security). Find dA/dq and d^2A/dq^2.

3.3 The Derivative as a Rate of Change

In Section 2.1 we introduced average and instantaneous rates of change. In this section we study further applications in which derivatives model the rates at which things change. It is natural to think of a quantity changing with respect to time, but other variables can be treated in the same way. For example, an economist may want to study how the cost of producing steel varies with the number of tons produced.

Instantaneous Rates of Change

If we interpret the difference quotient $(f(x+h)-f(x))/h$ as the average rate of change in f over the interval from x to $x+h$, we can interpret its limit as $h \to 0$ as the rate at which f is changing at the point x.

DEFINITION The **instantaneous rate of change** of f with respect to x at x_0 is the derivative

$$f'(x_0) = \lim_{h \to 0} \frac{f(x_0+h)-f(x_0)}{h},$$

provided the limit exists.

Thus, instantaneous rates are limits of average rates.

It is conventional to use the word *instantaneous* even when x does not represent time. The word is, however, frequently omitted. When we say *rate of change*, we mean *instantaneous rate of change*.

EXAMPLE 1 The area A of a circle is related to its diameter by the equation

$$A = \frac{\pi}{4}D^2.$$

How fast does the area change with respect to the diameter when the diameter is 10 m?

Solution The rate of change of the area with respect to the diameter is

$$\frac{dA}{dD} = \frac{\pi}{4} \cdot 2D = \frac{\pi D}{2}.$$

When $D = 10$ m, the area is changing with respect to diameter at the rate $(\pi/2)10 = 5\pi\ \text{m}^2/\text{m}$. ■

Motion Along a Line: Displacement, Velocity, Speed, Acceleration, and Jerk

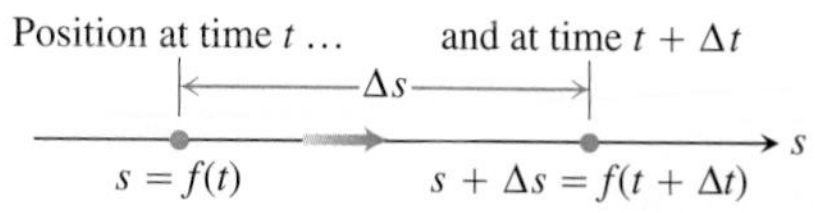

FIGURE 3.11 The positions of a body moving along a coordinate line at time t and shortly later at time $t + \Delta t$.

Suppose that an object is moving along a coordinate line (say an s-axis) so that we know its position s on that line as a function of time t:

$$s = f(t).$$

The **displacement** of the object over the time interval from t to $t + \Delta t$ (Figure 3.11) is

$$\Delta s = f(t + \Delta t) - f(t),$$

and the **average velocity** of the object over that time interval is

$$v_{av} = \frac{\text{displacement}}{\text{travel time}} = \frac{\Delta s}{\Delta t} = \frac{f(t+\Delta t)-f(t)}{\Delta t}.$$

To find the body's velocity at the exact instant t, we take the limit of the average velocity over the interval from t to $t + \Delta t$ as Δt shrinks to zero. This limit is the derivative of f with respect to t.

DEFINITION **Velocity (instantaneous velocity)** is the derivative of position with respect to time. If a body's position at time t is $s = f(t)$, then the body's velocity at time t is

$$v(t) = \frac{ds}{dt} = \lim_{\Delta t \to 0} \frac{f(t + \Delta t) - f(t)}{\Delta t}.$$

Besides telling how fast an object is moving, its velocity tells the direction of motion. When the object is moving forward (s increasing), the velocity is positive; when the body is moving backward (s decreasing), the velocity is negative (Figure 3.12).

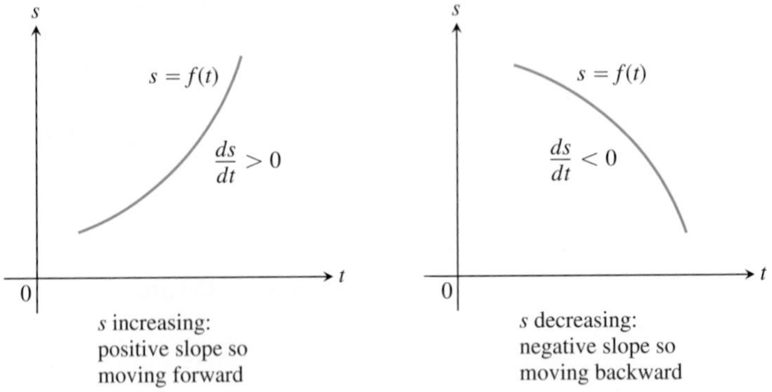

FIGURE 3.12 For motion $s = f(t)$ along a straight line, $v = ds/dt$ is positive when s increases and negative when s decreases.

If we drive to a friend's house and back at 30 mph, say, the speedometer will show 30 on the way over but it will not show -30 on the way back, even though our distance from home is decreasing. The speedometer always shows *speed*, which is the absolute value of velocity. Speed measures the rate of progress regardless of direction.

DEFINITION **Speed** is the absolute value of velocity.

$$\text{Speed} = |v(t)| = \left|\frac{ds}{dt}\right|$$

EXAMPLE 2 Figure 3.13 shows the velocity $v = f'(t)$ of a particle moving on a coordinate line. The particle moves forward for the first 3 sec, moves backward for the next 2 sec, stands still for a second, and moves forward again. The particle achieves its greatest speed at time $t = 4$, while moving backward. ■

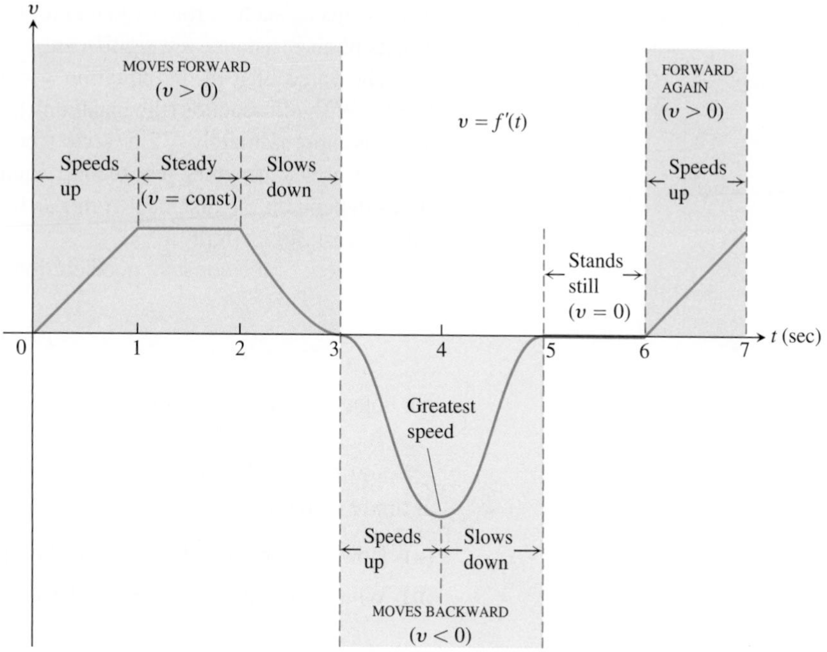

FIGURE 3.13 The velocity graph for Example 2.

HISTORICAL BIOGRAPHY

Bernard Bolzano
(1781–1848)

The rate at which a body's velocity changes is the body's *acceleration*. The acceleration measures how quickly the body picks up or loses speed.

A sudden change in acceleration is called a *jerk*. When a ride in a car or a bus is jerky, it is not that the accelerations involved are necessarily large but that the changes in acceleration are abrupt.

DEFINITIONS **Acceleration** is the derivative of velocity with respect to time. If a body's position at time t is $s = f(t)$, then the body's acceleration at time t is

$$a(t) = \frac{dv}{dt} = \frac{d^2s}{dt^2}.$$

Jerk is the derivative of acceleration with respect to time:

$$j(t) = \frac{da}{dt} = \frac{d^3s}{dt^3}.$$

Near the surface of the Earth all bodies fall with the same constant acceleration. Galileo's experiments with free fall (Example 1, Section 2.1) lead to the equation

$$s = \frac{1}{2}gt^2,$$

where s is the distance fallen and g is the acceleration due to Earth's gravity. This equation holds in a vacuum, where there is no air resistance, and closely models the fall of dense, heavy objects, such as rocks or steel tools, for the first few seconds of their fall, before the effects of air resistance are significant.

The value of g in the equation $s = (1/2)gt^2$ depends on the units used to measure t and s. With t in seconds (the usual unit), the value of g determined by measurement at sea level is approximately 32 ft/sec^2 (feet per second squared) in English units, and $g = 9.8 \text{ m/sec}^2$ (meters per second squared) in metric units. (These gravitational constants depend on the distance from Earth's center of mass, and are slightly lower on top of Mt. Everest, for example.)

The jerk of the constant acceleration of gravity ($g = 32 \text{ ft/sec}^2$) is zero:

$$j = \frac{d}{dt}(g) = 0.$$

An object does not exhibit jerkiness during free fall.

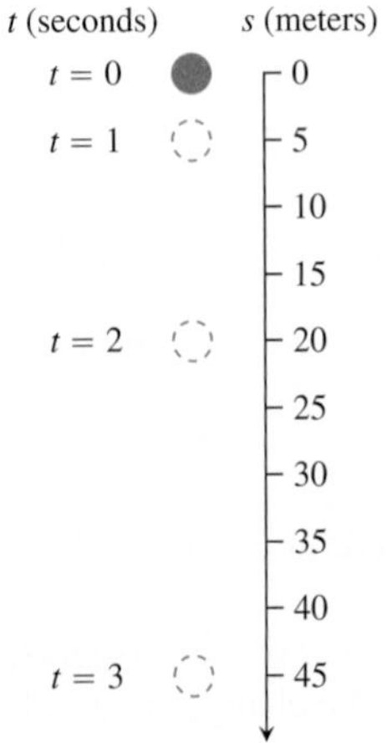

FIGURE 3.14 A ball bearing falling from rest (Example 3).

EXAMPLE 3 Figure 3.14 shows the free fall of a heavy ball bearing released from rest at time $t = 0$ sec.

(a) How many meters does the ball fall in the first 2 sec?

(b) What is its velocity, speed, and acceleration when $t = 2$?

Solution

(a) The metric free-fall equation is $s = 4.9t^2$. During the first 2 sec, the ball falls

$$s(2) = 4.9(2)^2 = 19.6 \text{ m}.$$

(b) At any time t, *velocity* is the derivative of position:

$$v(t) = s'(t) = \frac{d}{dt}(4.9t^2) = 9.8t.$$

At $t = 2$, the velocity is

$$v(2) = 19.6 \text{ m/sec}$$

in the downward (increasing s) direction. The *speed* at $t = 2$ is

$$\text{Speed} = |v(2)| = 19.6 \text{ m/sec}.$$

The *acceleration* at any time t is

$$a(t) = v'(t) = s''(t) = 9.8 \text{ m/sec}^2.$$

At $t = 2$, the acceleration is 9.8 m/sec^2. ■

EXAMPLE 4 A dynamite blast blows a heavy rock straight up with a launch velocity of 160 ft/sec (about 109 mph) (Figure 3.15a). It reaches a height of $s = 160t - 16t^2$ ft after t sec.

(a) How high does the rock go?

(b) What are the velocity and speed of the rock when it is 256 ft above the ground on the way up? On the way down?

(c) What is the acceleration of the rock at any time t during its flight (after the blast)?

(d) When does the rock hit the ground again?

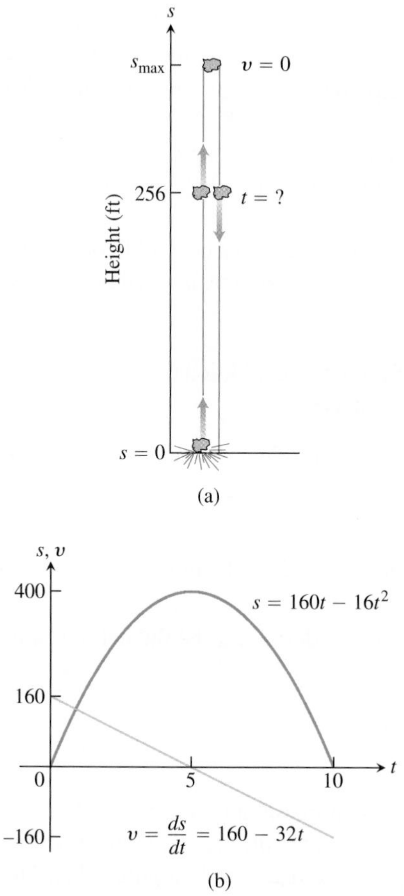

FIGURE 3.15 (a) The rock in Example 4. (b) The graphs of s and v as functions of time; s is largest when $v = ds/dt = 0$. The graph of s is *not* the path of the rock: It is a plot of height versus time. The slope of the plot is the rock's velocity, graphed here as a straight line.

Solution

(a) In the coordinate system we have chosen, s measures height from the ground up, so the velocity is positive on the way up and negative on the way down. The instant the rock is at its highest point is the one instant during the flight when the velocity is 0. To find the maximum height, all we need to do is to find when $v = 0$ and evaluate s at this time.

At any time t, the velocity is

$$v = \frac{ds}{dt} = \frac{d}{dt}(160t - 16t^2) = 160 - 32t \text{ ft/sec}.$$

The velocity is zero when

$$160 - 32t = 0 \quad \text{or} \quad t = 5 \text{ sec}.$$

The rock's height at $t = 5$ sec is

$$s_{max} = s(5) = 160(5) - 16(5)^2 = 800 - 400 = 400 \text{ ft}.$$

See Figure 3.15b.

(b) To find the rock's velocity at 256 ft on the way up and again on the way down, we first find the two values of t for which

$$s(t) = 160t - 16t^2 = 256.$$

To solve this equation, we write

$$\begin{aligned} 16t^2 - 160t + 256 &= 0 \\ 16(t^2 - 10t + 16) &= 0 \\ (t - 2)(t - 8) &= 0 \\ t = 2 \text{ sec}, t &= 8 \text{ sec}. \end{aligned}$$

The rock is 256 ft above the ground 2 sec after the explosion and again 8 sec after the explosion. The rock's velocities at these times are

$$\begin{aligned} v(2) &= 160 - 32(2) = 160 - 64 = 96 \text{ ft/sec}. \\ v(8) &= 160 - 32(8) = 160 - 256 = -96 \text{ ft/sec}. \end{aligned}$$

At both instants, the rock's speed is 96 ft/sec. Since $v(2) > 0$, the rock is moving upward (s is increasing) at $t = 2$ sec; it is moving downward (s is decreasing) at $t = 8$ because $v(8) < 0$.

(c) At any time during its flight following the explosion, the rock's acceleration is a constant

$$a = \frac{dv}{dt} = \frac{d}{dt}(160 - 32t) = -32 \text{ ft/sec}^2.$$

The acceleration is always downward. As the rock rises, it slows down; as it falls, it speeds up.

(d) The rock hits the ground at the positive time t for which $s = 0$. The equation $160t - 16t^2 = 0$ factors to give $16t(10 - t) = 0$, so it has solutions $t = 0$ and $t = 10$. At $t = 0$, the blast occurred and the rock was thrown upward. It returned to the ground 10 sec later. ■

Derivatives in Economics

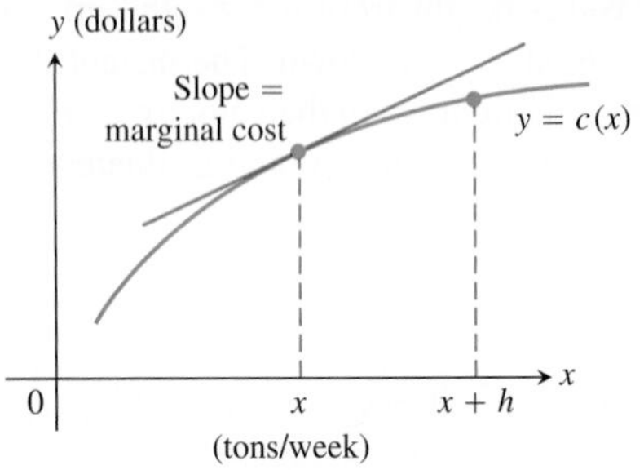

FIGURE 3.16 Weekly steel production: $c(x)$ is the cost of producing x tons per week. The cost of producing an additional h tons is $c(x+h) - c(x)$.

Engineers use the terms *velocity* and *acceleration* to refer to the derivatives of functions describing motion. Economists, too, have a specialized vocabulary for rates of change and derivatives. They call them *marginals*.

In a manufacturing operation, the *cost of production* $c(x)$ is a function of x, the number of units produced. The **marginal cost of production** is the rate of change of cost with respect to level of production, so it is dc/dx.

Suppose that $c(x)$ represents the dollars needed to produce x tons of steel in one week. It costs more to produce $x + h$ units per week, and the cost difference, divided by h, is the average cost of producing each additional ton:

$$\frac{c(x+h) - c(x)}{h} = \begin{array}{l}\text{average cost of each of the additional} \\ h \text{ tons of steel produced.}\end{array}$$

The limit of this ratio as $h \to 0$ is the *marginal cost* of producing more steel per week when the current weekly production is x tons (Figure 3.16):

$$\frac{dc}{dx} = \lim_{h \to 0} \frac{c(x+h) - c(x)}{h} = \text{marginal cost of production.}$$

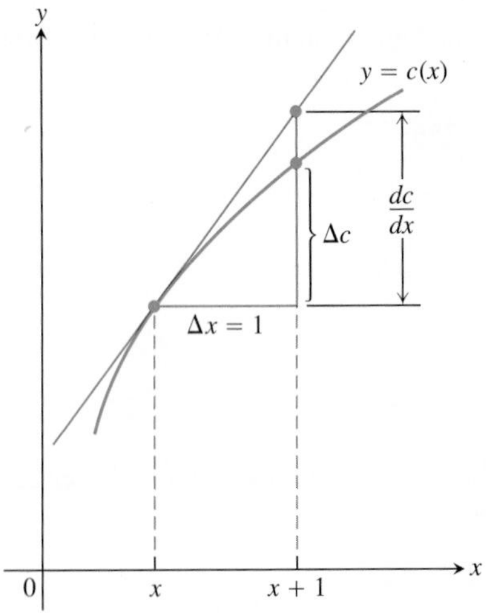

FIGURE 3.17 The marginal cost dc/dx is approximately the extra cost Δc of producing $\Delta x = 1$ more unit.

Sometimes the marginal cost of production is loosely defined to be the extra cost of producing one additional unit:

$$\frac{\Delta c}{\Delta x} = \frac{c(x+1) - c(x)}{1},$$

which is approximated by the value of dc/dx at x. This approximation is acceptable if the slope of the graph of c does not change quickly near x. Then the difference quotient will be close to its limit dc/dx, which is the rise in the tangent line if $\Delta x = 1$ (Figure 3.17). The approximation works best for large values of x.

Economists often represent a total cost function by a cubic polynomial

$$c(x) = \alpha x^3 + \beta x^2 + \gamma x + \delta$$

where δ represents *fixed costs* such as rent, heat, equipment capitalization, and management costs. The other terms represent *variable costs* such as the costs of raw materials, taxes, and labor. Fixed costs are independent of the number of units produced, whereas variable costs depend on the quantity produced. A cubic polynomial is usually adequate to capture the cost behavior on a relevant quantity interval.

EXAMPLE 5 Suppose that it costs

$$c(x) = x^3 - 6x^2 + 15x$$

dollars to produce x radiators when 8 to 30 radiators are produced and that

$$r(x) = x^3 - 3x^2 + 12x$$

gives the dollar revenue from selling x radiators. Your shop currently produces 10 radiators a day. About how much extra will it cost to produce one more radiator a day, and what is your estimated increase in revenue for selling 11 radiators a day?

Solution The cost of producing one more radiator a day when 10 are produced is about $c'(10)$:

$$c'(x) = \frac{d}{dx}\left(x^3 - 6x^2 + 15x\right) = 3x^2 - 12x + 15$$

$$c'(10) = 3(100) - 12(10) + 15 = 195.$$

The additional cost will be about \$195. The marginal revenue is

$$r'(x) = \frac{d}{dx}(x^3 - 3x^2 + 12x) = 3x^2 - 6x + 12.$$

The marginal revenue function estimates the increase in revenue that will result from selling one additional unit. If you currently sell 10 radiators a day, you can expect your revenue to increase by about

$$r'(10) = 3(100) - 6(10) + 12 = \$252$$

if you increase sales to 11 radiators a day. ■

EXAMPLE 6 To get some feel for the language of marginal rates, consider marginal tax rates. If your marginal income tax rate is 28% and your income increases by \$1000, you can expect to pay an extra \$280 in taxes. This does not mean that you pay 28% of your entire income in taxes. It just means that at your current income level I, the rate of increase of taxes T with respect to income is $dT/dI = 0.28$. You will pay \$0.28 out of every extra dollar you earn in taxes. Of course, if you earn a lot more, you may land in a higher tax bracket and your marginal rate will increase. ■

EXERCISES 3.3

Exercises 1–6 give the positions $s = f(t)$ of a body moving on a coordinate line, with s in meters and t in seconds.

a. Find the body's displacement and average velocity for the given time interval.

b. Find the body's speed and acceleration at the endpoints of the interval.

c. When, if ever, during the interval does the body change direction?

1. $s = t^2 - 3t + 2, \quad 0 \le t \le 2$

2. $s = 6t - t^2, \quad 0 \le t \le 6$

3. $s = -t^3 + 3t^2 - 3t, \quad 0 \le t \le 3$

4. $s = (t^4/4) - t^3 + t^2, \quad 0 \le t \le 3$

5. $s = \frac{25}{t^2} - \frac{5}{t}, \quad 1 \le t \le 5$

6. $s = \frac{25}{t + 5}, \quad -4 \le t \le 0$

7. Particle motion At time t, the position of a body moving along the s-axis is $s = t^3 - 6t^2 + 9t$ m.

a. Find the body's acceleration each time the velocity is zero.

b. Find the body's speed each time the acceleration is zero.

c. Find the total distance traveled by the body from $t = 0$ to $t = 2$.

8. Particle motion At time $t \ge 0$, the velocity of a body moving along the s-axis is $v = t^2 - 4t + 3$.

a. Find the body's acceleration each time the velocity is zero.

b. When is the body moving forward? Backward?

c. When is the body's velocity increasing? Decreasing?

9. Free fall on Mars and Jupiter The equations for free fall at the surfaces of Mars and Jupiter (s in meters, t in seconds) are $s = 1.86t^2$ on Mars and $s = 11.44t^2$ on Jupiter. How long does it take a rock falling from rest to reach a velocity of 27.8 m/sec (about 100 km/h) on each planet?

10. Lunar projectile motion A rock thrown vertically upward from the surface of the moon at a velocity of 24 m/sec (about 86 km/h) reaches a height of $s = 24t - 0.8t^2$ meters in t sec.

a. Find the rock's velocity and acceleration at time t. (The acceleration in this case is the acceleration of gravity on the moon.)

b. How long does it take the rock to reach its highest point?

c. How high does the rock go?

d. How long does it take the rock to reach half its maximum height?

e. How long is the rock aloft?

11. Finding g on a small airless planet Explorers on a small airless planet used a spring gun to launch a ball bearing vertically upward from the surface at a launch velocity of 15 m/sec. Because the acceleration of gravity at the planet's surface was g_s m/sec^2, the explorers expected the ball bearing to reach a height of $s = 15t - (1/2)g_s t^2$ meters t sec later. The ball bearing reached its maximum height 20 sec after being launched. What was the value of g_s?

12. Speeding bullet A 45-caliber bullet fired straight up from the surface of the moon would reach a height of $s = 832t - 2.6t^2$ feet after t sec. On Earth, in the absence of air, its height would be $s = 832t - 16t^2$ ft after t sec. How long will the bullet be aloft in each case? How high will the bullet go?

13. Free fall from the Tower of Pisa Had Galileo dropped a cannonball from the Tower of Pisa, 179 ft above the ground, the ball's height above the ground t sec into the fall would have been $s = 179 - 16t^2$.

a. What would have been the ball's velocity, speed, and acceleration at time t?

b. About how long would it have taken the ball to hit the ground?

c. What would have been the ball's velocity at the moment of impact?

14. Galileo's free-fall formula Galileo developed a formula for a body's velocity during free fall by rolling balls from rest down increasingly steep inclined planks and looking for a limiting formula that would predict a ball's behavior when the plank was vertical and the ball fell freely; see part (a) of the accompanying figure. He found that, for any given angle of the plank, the ball's velocity t sec into motion was a constant multiple of t. That is, the velocity was given by a formula of the form $v = kt$. The value of the constant k depended on the inclination of the plank.

In modern notation—part (b) of the figure—with distance in meters and time in seconds, what Galileo determined by experiment was that, for any given angle θ, the ball's velocity t sec into the roll was

$$v = 9.8(\sin\theta)t \text{ m/sec}.$$

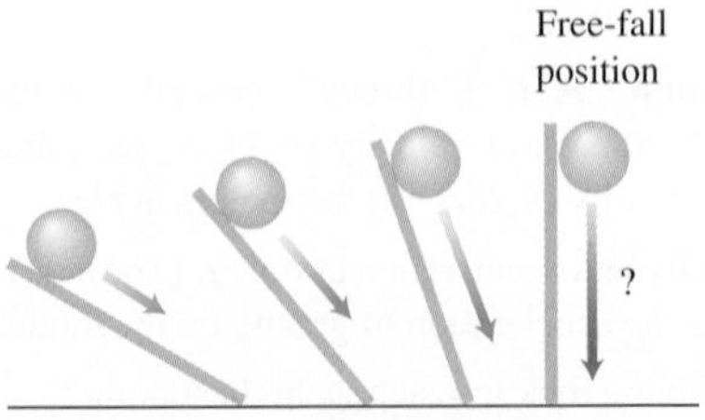

(a)

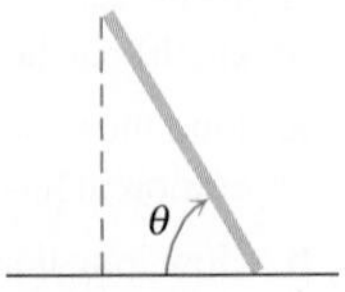

(b)

a. What is the equation for the ball's velocity during free fall?

b. Building on your work in part (a), what constant acceleration does a freely falling body experience near the surface of Earth?

15. The accompanying figure shows the velocity $v = ds/dt = f(t)$ (m/sec) of a body moving along a coordinate line.

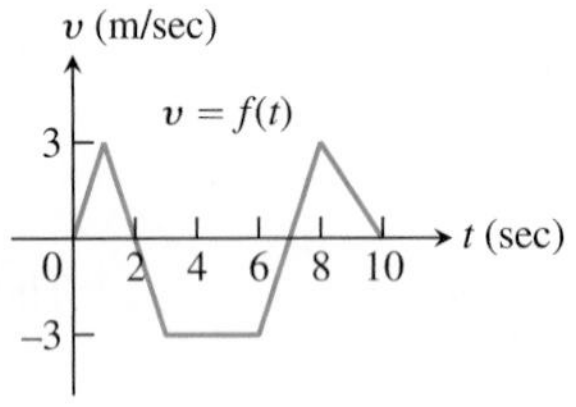

a. When does the body reverse direction?

b. When (approximately) is the body moving at a constant speed?

c. Graph the body's speed for $0 \le t \le 10$.

d. Graph the acceleration, where defined.

16. A particle P moves on the number line shown in part (a) of the accompanying figure. Part (b) shows the position of P as a function of time t.

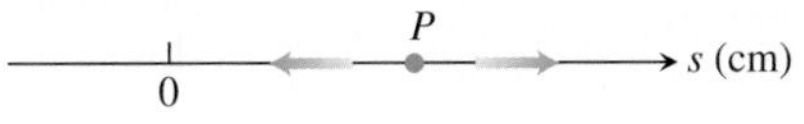

(a)

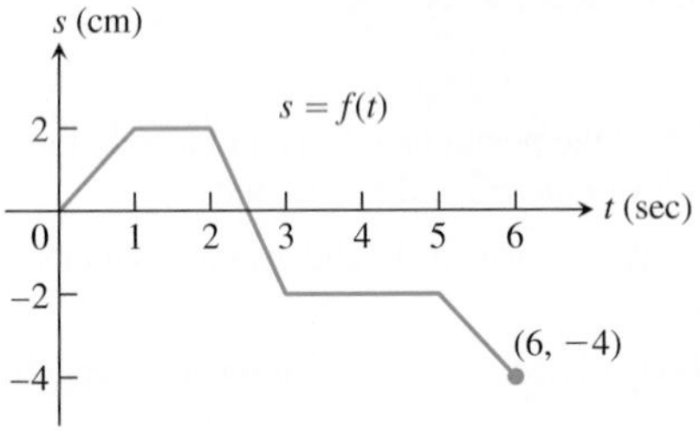

(b)

a. When is P moving to the left? Moving to the right? Standing still?

b. Graph the particle's velocity and speed (where defined).

17. Launching a rocket When a model rocket is launched, the propellant burns for a few seconds, accelerating the rocket upward. After burnout, the rocket coasts upward for a while and then begins to fall. A small explosive charge pops out a parachute shortly after the rocket starts down. The parachute slows the rocket to keep it from breaking when it lands.

The figure here shows velocity data from the flight of the model rocket. Use the data to answer the following.

a. How fast was the rocket climbing when the engine stopped?

b. For how many seconds did the engine burn?

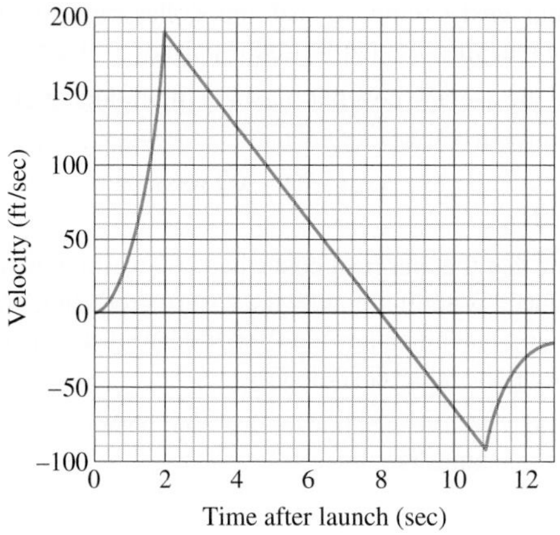

c. When did the rocket reach its highest point? What was its velocity then?

d. When did the parachute pop out? How fast was the rocket falling then?

e. How long did the rocket fall before the parachute opened?

f. When was the rocket's acceleration greatest?

g. When was the acceleration constant? What was its value then (to the nearest integer)?

18. The accompanying figure shows the velocity $v = f(t)$ of a particle moving on a coordinate line.

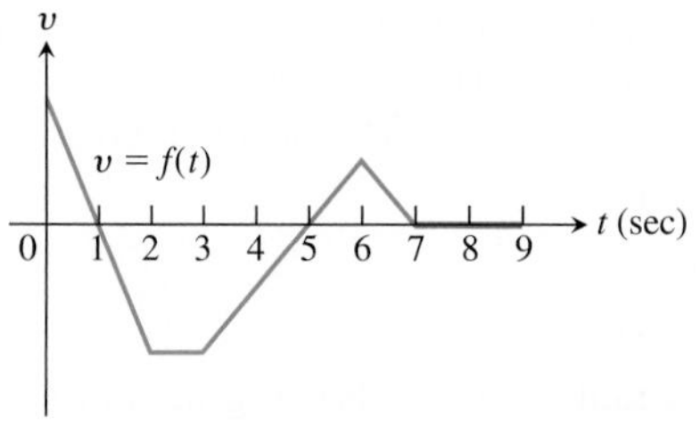

a. When does the particle move forward? Move backward? Speed up? Slow down?

b. When is the particle's acceleration positive? Negative? Zero?

c. When does the particle move at its greatest speed?

d. When does the particle stand still for more than an instant?

19. Two falling balls The multiflash photograph in the accompanying figure shows two balls falling from rest. The vertical rulers are marked in centimeters. Use the equation $s = 490t^2$ (the free-fall equation for s in centimeters and t in seconds) to answer the following questions.

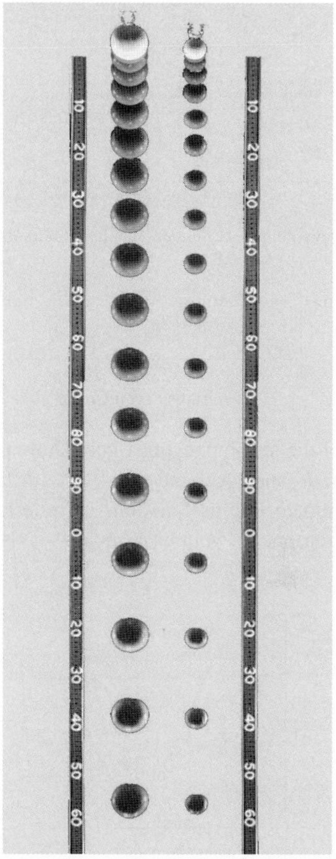

a. How long did it take the balls to fall the first 160 cm? What was their average velocity for the period?

b. How fast were the balls falling when they reached the 160-cm mark? What was their acceleration then?

c. About how fast was the light flashing (flashes per second)?

20. A traveling truck The graph on page 156 shows the position s of a truck traveling on a highway. The truck starts at $t = 0$ and returns 15 h later at $t = 15$.

a. Use the technique described in Section 3.1, Example 3, to graph the truck's velocity $v = ds/dt$ for $0 \leq t \leq 15$. Then repeat the process, with the velocity curve, to graph the truck's acceleration dv/dt.

b. Suppose that $s = 15t^2 - t^3$. Graph ds/dt and d^2s/dt^2 and compare your graphs with those in part (a).

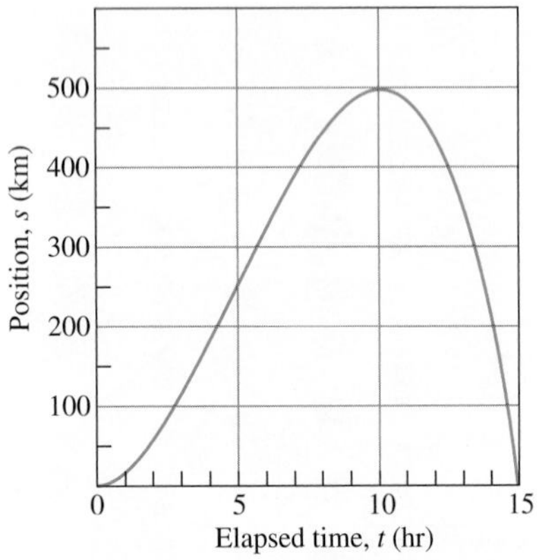

21. The graphs in the accompanying figure show the position s, velocity $v = ds/dt$, and acceleration $a = d^2s/dt^2$ of a body moving along a coordinate line as functions of time t. Which graph is which? Give reasons for your answers.

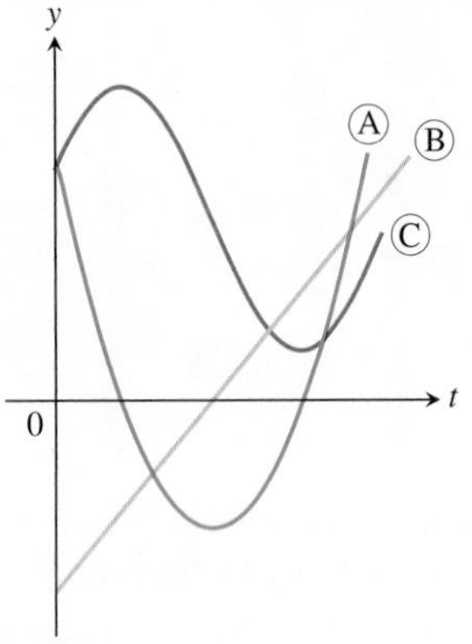

22. The graphs in Figure 3.18 show the position s, the velocity $v = ds/dt$, and the acceleration $a = d^2s/dt^2$ of a body moving along the coordinate line as functions of time t. Which graph is which? Give reasons for your answers.

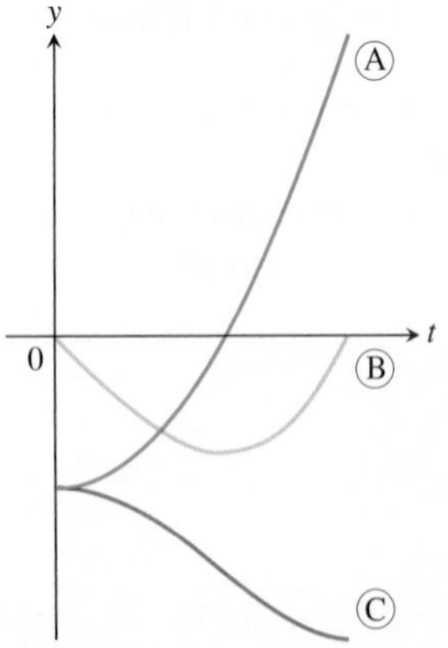

FIGURE 3.18 The graphs for Exercise 22.

23. Marginal cost Suppose that the dollar cost of producing x washing machines is $c(x) = 2000 + 100x - 0.1x^2$.

a. Find the average cost per machine of producing the first 100 washing machines.

b. Find the marginal cost when 100 washing machines are produced.

c. Show that the marginal cost when 100 washing machines are produced is approximately the cost of producing one more washing machine after the first 100 have been made, by calculating the latter cost directly.

24. Marginal revenue Suppose that the revenue from selling x washing machines is

$$r(x) = 20{,}000\left(1 - \frac{1}{x}\right)$$

dollars.

a. Find the marginal revenue when 100 machines are produced.

b. Use the function $r'(x)$ to estimate the increase in revenue that will result from increasing production from 100 machines a week to 101 machines a week.

c. Find the limit of $r'(x)$ as $x \to \infty$. How would you interpret this number?

25. Bacterium population When a bactericide was added to a nutrient broth in which bacteria were growing, the bacterium population continued to grow for a while, but then stopped growing and began to decline. The size of the population at time t (hours) was $b = 10^6 + 10^4t - 10^3t^2$. Find the growth rates at

a. $t = 0$ hours.

b. $t = 5$ hours.

c. $t = 10$ hours.

26. Draining a tank The number of gallons of water in a tank t minutes after the tank has started to drain is $Q(t) = 200(30 - t)^2$. How fast is the water running out at the end of 10 min? What is the average rate at which the water flows out during the first 10 min?

T **27. Draining a tank** It takes 12 hours to drain a storage tank by opening the valve at the bottom. The depth y of fluid in the tank t hours after the valve is opened is given by the formula

$$y = 6\left(1 - \frac{t}{12}\right)^2 \text{ m}.$$

a. Find the rate dy/dt (m/h) at which the tank is draining at time t.

b. When is the fluid level in the tank falling fastest? Slowest? What are the values of dy/dt at these times?

c. Graph y and dy/dt together and discuss the behavior of y in relation to the signs and values of dy/dt.

28. Inflating a balloon The volume $V = (4/3)\pi r^3$ of a spherical balloon changes with the radius.

a. At what rate (ft^3/ft) does the volume change with respect to the radius when $r = 2$ ft?

b. By approximately how much does the volume increase when the radius changes from 2 to 2.2 ft?

29. Airplane takeoff Suppose that the distance an aircraft travels along a runway before takeoff is given by $D = (10/9)t^2$, where D is measured in meters from the starting point and t is measured in seconds from the time the brakes are released. The aircraft will become airborne when its speed reaches 200 km/h. How long will it take to become airborne, and what distance will it travel in that time?

30. Volcanic lava fountains Although the November 1959 Kilauea Iki eruption on the island of Hawaii began with a line of fountains along the wall of the crater, activity was later confined to a single vent in the crater's floor, which at one point shot lava 1900 ft straight into the air (a world record). What was the lava's exit velocity in feet per second? In miles per hour? (*Hint*: If v_0 is the exit velocity of a particle of lava, its height t sec later will be $s = v_0t - 16t^2$ ft. Begin by finding the time at which $ds/dt = 0$. Neglect air resistance.)

T Exercises 31–34 give the position function $s = f(t)$ of a body moving along the s-axis as a function of time t. Graph f together with the velocity function $v(t) = ds/dt = f'(t)$ and the acceleration function $a(t) = d^2s/dt^2 = f''(t)$. Comment on the body's behavior in relation to the signs and values of v and a. Include in your commentary such topics as the following:

a. When is the body momentarily at rest?

b. When does it move to the left (down) or to the right (up)?

c. When does it change direction?

d. When does it speed up and slow down?

e. When is it moving fastest (highest speed)? Slowest?

f. When is it farthest from the axis origin?

31. $s = 200t - 16t^2, \quad 0 \le t \le 12.5$ (a heavy object fired straight up from Earth's surface at 200 ft/sec)

32. $s = t^2 - 3t + 2, \quad 0 \le t \le 5$

33. $s = t^3 - 6t^2 + 7t, \quad 0 \le t \le 4$

34. $s = 4 - 7t + 6t^2 - t^3, \quad 0 \le t \le 4$

3.4 Derivatives of Trigonometric Functions

Many of the phenomena of nature we want information about are approximately periodic (electromagnetic fields, heart rhythms, tides, weather). The derivatives of sines and cosines play a key role in describing periodic changes. This section shows how to differentiate the six basic trigonometric functions.

Derivative of the Sine Function

To calculate the derivative of $f(x) = \sin x$, for x measured in radians, we combine the limits in Example 5a and Theorem 7 in Section 2.4 with the angle sum identity for the sine:

$$\sin(x + h) = \sin x \cos h + \cos x \sin h.$$

If $f(x) = \sin x$, then

$$\begin{aligned}
f'(x) &= \lim_{h\to 0}\frac{f(x+h)-f(x)}{h} = \lim_{h\to 0}\frac{\sin(x+h)-\sin x}{h} && \text{Derivative definition}\\
&= \lim_{h\to 0}\frac{(\sin x\cos h + \cos x \sin h) - \sin x}{h} = \lim_{h\to 0}\frac{\sin x(\cos h - 1) + \cos x \sin h}{h}\\
&= \lim_{h\to 0}\left(\sin x\cdot\frac{\cos h - 1}{h}\right) + \lim_{h\to 0}\left(\cos x\cdot\frac{\sin h}{h}\right)\\
&= \sin x\cdot\lim_{h\to 0}\frac{\cos h - 1}{h} + \cos x\cdot\lim_{h\to 0}\frac{\sin h}{h} = \sin x\cdot 0 + \cos x\cdot 1 = \cos x.
\end{aligned}$$

Example 5a and Theorem 7, Section 2.4

The derivative of the sine function is the cosine function:

$$\frac{d}{dx}(\sin x) = \cos x.$$

EXAMPLE 1

(a) $y = x^2 - \sin x$:

$$\frac{dy}{dx} = 2x - \frac{d}{dx}(\sin x) \qquad \text{Difference Rule}$$

$$= 2x - \cos x.$$

(b) $y = e^x \sin x$:

$$\frac{dy}{dx} = e^x \frac{d}{dx}(\sin x) + \frac{d}{dx}(e^x)\sin x \qquad \text{Product Rule}$$

$$= e^x \cos x + e^x \sin x$$

$$= e^x(\cos x + \sin x).$$

(c) $y = \dfrac{\sin x}{x}$:

$$\frac{dy}{dx} = \frac{x \cdot \dfrac{d}{dx}(\sin x) - \sin x \cdot 1}{x^2} \qquad \text{Quotient Rule}$$

$$= \frac{x\cos x - \sin x}{x^2}.$$

■

Derivative of the Cosine Function

With the help of the angle sum formula for the cosine,

$$\cos(x + h) = \cos x \cos h - \sin x \sin h,$$

we have

$$\frac{d}{dx}(\cos x) = \lim_{h \to 0} \frac{\cos(x+h) - \cos x}{h} \qquad \text{Derivative definition}$$

$$= \lim_{h \to 0} \frac{(\cos x \cos h - \sin x \sin h) - \cos x}{h} \qquad \text{Cosine angle sum identity}$$

$$= \lim_{h \to 0} \frac{\cos x(\cos h - 1) - \sin x \sin h}{h}$$

$$= \lim_{h\to 0} \cos x \cdot \frac{\cos h - 1}{h} - \lim_{h\to 0} \sin x \cdot \frac{\sin h}{h}$$

$$= \cos x \cdot \lim_{h\to 0} \frac{\cos h - 1}{h} - \sin x \cdot \lim_{h\to 0} \frac{\sin h}{h}$$

$$= \cos x \cdot 0 - \sin x \cdot 1 \qquad \text{Example 5a and Theorem 7, Section 2.4}$$

$$= -\sin x.$$

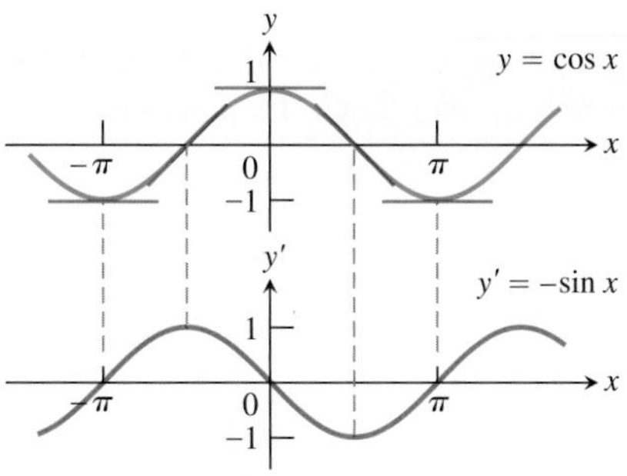

FIGURE 3.19 The curve $y' = -\sin x$ as the graph of the slopes of the tangents to the curve $y = \cos x$.

The derivative of the cosine function is the negative of the sine function:

$$\frac{d}{dx}(\cos x) = -\sin x.$$

Figure 3.19 shows a way to visualize this result.

EXAMPLE 2

(a) $y = 5e^x + \cos x$:

$$\frac{dy}{dx} = \frac{d}{dx}(5e^x) + \frac{d}{dx}(\cos x) \qquad \text{Sum Rule}$$

$$= 5e^x - \sin x.$$

(b) $y = \sin x \cos x$:

$$\frac{dy}{dx} = \sin x \frac{d}{dx}(\cos x) + \cos x \frac{d}{dx}(\sin x) \qquad \text{Product Rule}$$

$$= \sin x(-\sin x) + \cos x(\cos x)$$

$$= \cos^2 x - \sin^2 x.$$

(c) $y = \dfrac{\cos x}{1 - \sin x}$:

$$\frac{dy}{dx} = \frac{(1 - \sin x)\frac{d}{dx}(\cos x) - \cos x \frac{d}{dx}(1 - \sin x)}{(1 - \sin x)^2} \qquad \text{Quotient Rule}$$

$$= \frac{(1 - \sin x)(-\sin x) - \cos x(0 - \cos x)}{(1 - \sin x)^2}$$

$$= \frac{1 - \sin x}{(1 - \sin x)^2} \qquad \sin^2 x + \cos^2 x = 1$$

$$= \frac{1}{1 - \sin x}.$$

■

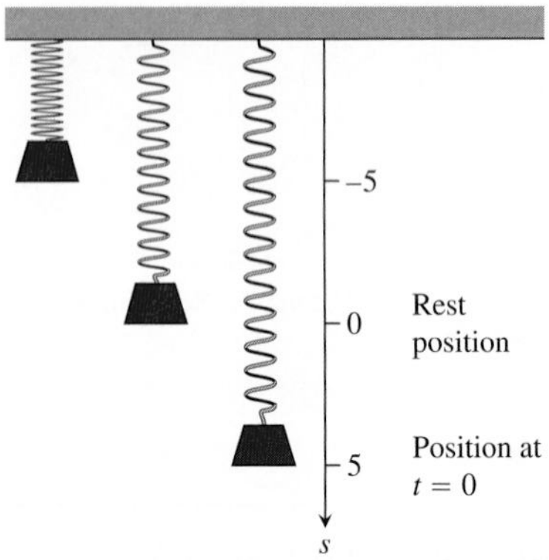

FIGURE 3.20 A body hanging from a vertical spring and then displaced oscillates above and below its rest position. Its motion is described by trigonometric functions (Example 3).

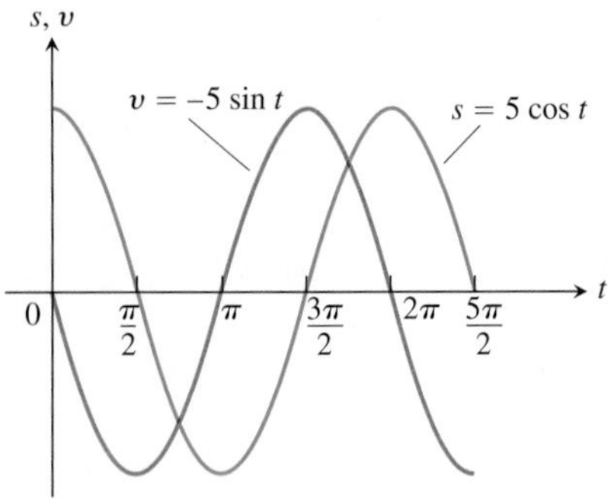

FIGURE 3.21 The graphs of the position and velocity of the body in Example 3.

Simple Harmonic Motion

The motion of a body bobbing freely up and down with no resistance on the end of a spring or bungee cord is an example of *simple harmonic motion*. The next example describes a case in which there are no opposing forces such as friction or buoyancy to slow the motion.

EXAMPLE 3 A body hanging from a spring (Figure 3.20) is stretched down 5 units beyond its rest position and released at time $t = 0$ to bob up and down. Its position at any later time t is

$$s = 5 \cos t.$$

What are its velocity and acceleration at time t?

Solution We have

Position: $s = 5 \cos t$

Velocity: $v = \frac{ds}{dt} = \frac{d}{dt}(5 \cos t) = -5 \sin t$

Acceleration: $a = \frac{dv}{dt} = \frac{d}{dt}(-5 \sin t) = -5 \cos t.$

Notice how much we can learn from these equations:

1. As time passes, the weight moves down and up between $s = -5$ and $s = 5$ on the s-axis. The amplitude of the motion is 5. The period of the motion is 2π.
2. The velocity $v = -5 \sin t$ attains its greatest magnitude, 5, when $\cos t = 0$, as the graphs show in Figure 3.21. Hence, the speed of the weight, $|v| = 5|\sin t|$, is greatest when $\cos t = 0$, that is, when $s = 0$ (the rest position). The speed of the weight is zero when $\sin t = 0$. This occurs when $s = 5 \cos t = \pm 5$, at the endpoints of the interval of motion.
3. The acceleration value is always the exact opposite of the position value. When the weight is above the rest position, gravity is pulling it back down; when the weight is below the rest position, the spring is pulling it back up.
4. The acceleration, $a = -5 \cos t$, is zero only at the rest position, where $\cos t = 0$ and the force of gravity and the force from the spring balance each other. When the weight is anywhere else, the two forces are unequal and acceleration is nonzero. The acceleration is greatest in magnitude at the points farthest from the rest position, where $\cos t = \pm 1$. ■

EXAMPLE 4 The jerk of the simple harmonic motion in Example 3 is

$$j = \frac{da}{dt} = \frac{d}{dt}(-5 \cos t) = 5 \sin t.$$

It has its greatest magnitude when $\sin t = \pm 1$, not at the extremes of the displacement but at the rest position, where the acceleration changes direction and sign. ■

Derivatives of the Other Basic Trigonometric Functions

Because $\sin x$ and $\cos x$ are differentiable functions of x, the related functions

$$\tan x = \frac{\sin x}{\cos x}, \qquad \cot x = \frac{\cos x}{\sin x}, \qquad \sec x = \frac{1}{\cos x}, \qquad \text{and} \qquad \csc x = \frac{1}{\sin x}$$

are differentiable at every value of x at which they are defined. Their derivatives, calculated from the Quotient Rule, are given by the following formulas. Notice the negative signs in the derivative formulas for the cofunctions.

Derivatives of the Other Trigonometric Functions

$$\frac{d}{dx}(\tan x) = \sec^2 x \qquad \frac{d}{dx}(\cot x) = -\csc^2 x$$

$$\frac{d}{dx}(\sec x) = \sec x \tan x \qquad \frac{d}{dx}(\csc x) = -\csc x \cot x$$

To show a typical calculation, we find the derivative of the tangent function. The other derivations are left to Exercise 50.

EXAMPLE 5 Find $d(\tan x)/dx$.

Solution

$$\frac{d}{dx}\left(\tan x\right) = \frac{d}{dx}\left(\frac{\sin x}{\cos x}\right) = \frac{\cos x \frac{d}{dx}\left(\sin x\right) - \sin x \frac{d}{dx}\left(\cos x\right)}{\cos^2 x} \qquad \text{Quotient Rule}$$

$$= \frac{\cos x \cos x - \sin x(-\sin x)}{\cos^2 x}$$

$$= \frac{\cos^2 x + \sin^2 x}{\cos^2 x}$$

$$= \frac{1}{\cos^2 x} = \sec^2 x$$

■

EXAMPLE 6 Find y'' if $y = \sec x$.

Solution

$$y = \sec x$$

$$y' = \sec x \tan x$$

$$y'' = \frac{d}{dx}(\sec x \tan x)$$

$$= \sec x \frac{d}{dx}(\tan x) + \tan x \frac{d}{dx}(\sec x) \qquad \text{Product Rule}$$

$$= \sec x(\sec^2 x) + \tan x(\sec x \tan x)$$

$$= \sec^3 x + \sec x \tan^2 x$$

■

The differentiability of the trigonometric functions throughout their domains gives another proof of their continuity at every point in their domains (Theorem 1, Section 3.1). So we can calculate limits of algebraic combinations and composites of trigonometric functions by direct substitution.

EXAMPLE 7

$$\lim_{x\to 0}\frac{\sqrt{2+\sec x}}{\cos(\pi-\tan x)}=\frac{\sqrt{2+\sec 0}}{\cos(\pi-\tan 0)}=\frac{\sqrt{2+1}}{\cos(\pi-0)}=\frac{\sqrt{3}}{-1}=-\sqrt{3}$$ ■

EXERCISES 3.4

In Exercises 1–12, find dy/dx.

1. $y=-10x+3\cos x$

2. $y=\dfrac{3}{x}+5\sin x$

3. $y=\csc x-4\sqrt{x}+7$

4. $y=x^2\cot x-\dfrac{1}{x^2}$

5. $y=(\sec x+\tan x)(\sec x-\tan x)$

6. $y=(\sin x+\cos x)\sec x$

7. $y=\dfrac{\cot x}{1+\cot x}$

8. $y=\dfrac{\cos x}{1+\sin x}$

9. $y=\dfrac{4}{\cos x}+\dfrac{1}{\tan x}$

10. $y=\dfrac{\cos x}{x}+\dfrac{x}{\cos x}$

11. $y=x^2\sin x+2x\cos x-2\sin x$

12. $y=x^2\cos x-2x\sin x-2\cos x$

In Exercises 13–16, find ds/dt.

13. $s=\tan t-e^{-t}$

14. $s=t^2-\sec t+5e^t$

15. $s=\dfrac{1+\csc t}{1-\csc t}$

16. $s=\dfrac{\sin t}{1-\cos t}$

In Exercises 17–20, find $dr/d\theta$.

17. $r=4-\theta^2\sin\theta$

18. $r=\theta\sin\theta+\cos\theta$

19. $r=\sec\theta\csc\theta$

20. $r=(1+\sec\theta)\sin\theta$

In Exercises 21–24, find dp/dq.

21. $p=5+\dfrac{1}{\cot q}$

22. $p=(1+\csc q)\cos q$

23. $p=\dfrac{\sin q+\cos q}{\cos q}$

24. $p=\dfrac{\tan q}{1+\tan q}$

25. Find y'' if

a. $y=\csc x$.

b. $y=\sec x$.

26. Find $y^{(4)}=d^4y/dx^4$ if

a. $y=-2\sin x$.

b. $y=9\cos x$.

In Exercises 27–30, graph the curves over the given intervals, together with their tangents at the given values of x. Label each curve and tangent with its equation.

27. $y=\sin x,\quad -3\pi/2\le x\le 2\pi$
$x=-\pi,\ 0,\ 3\pi/2$

28. $y=\tan x,\quad -\pi/2<x<\pi/2$
$x=-\pi/3,\ 0,\ \pi/3$

29. $y=\sec x,\quad -\pi/2<x<\pi/2$
$x=-\pi/3,\ \pi/4$

30. $y=1+\cos x,\quad -3\pi/2\le x\le 2\pi$
$x=-\pi/3,\ 3\pi/2$

T Do the graphs of the functions in Exercises 31–34 have any horizontal tangents in the interval $0\le x\le 2\pi$? If so, where? If not, why not? Visualize your findings by graphing the functions with a grapher.

31. $y=x+\sin x$

32. $y=2x+\sin x$

33. $y=x-\cot x$

34. $y=x+2\cos x$

35. Find all points on the curve $y=\tan x$, $-\pi/2<x<\pi/2$, where the tangent line is parallel to the line $y=2x$. Sketch the curve and tangent(s) together, labeling each with its equation.

36. Find all points on the curve $y=\cot x$, $0<x<\pi$, where the tangent line is parallel to the line $y=-x$. Sketch the curve and tangent(s) together, labeling each with its equation.

In Exercises 37 and 38, find an equation for **(a)** the tangent to the curve at P and **(b)** the horizontal tangent to the curve at Q.

37.

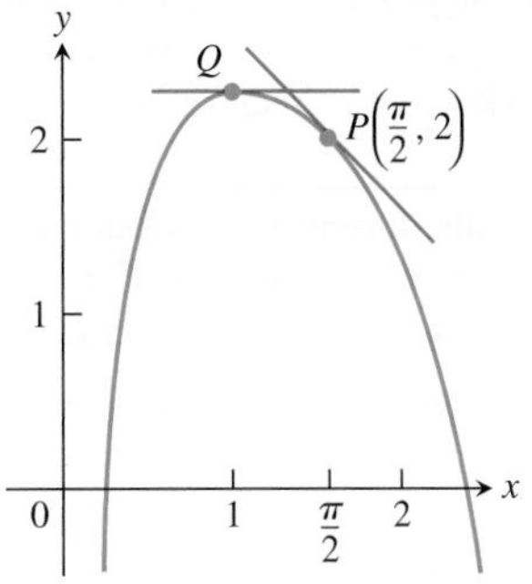

$y = 4 + \cot x - 2\csc x$

38.

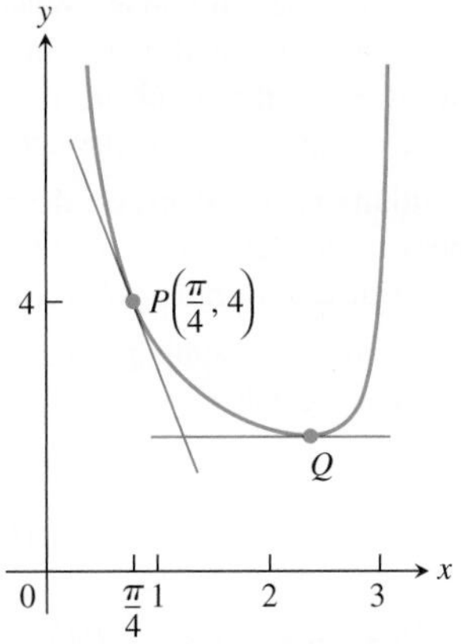

$y = 1 + \sqrt{2}\csc x + \cot x$

Find the limits in Exercises 39–44.

39. $\lim_{x\to 2} \sin\left(\frac{1}{x} - \frac{1}{2}\right)$

40. $\lim_{x\to -\pi/6} \sqrt{1 + \cos(\pi \csc x)}$

41. $\lim_{x\to 0} \sec\left[e^x + \pi \tan\left(\frac{\pi}{4\sec x}\right) - 1\right]$

42. $\lim_{x\to 0} \sin\left(\frac{\pi + \tan x}{\tan x - 2\sec x}\right)$

43. $\lim_{t\to 0} \tan\left(1 - \frac{\sin t}{t}\right)$

44. $\lim_{\theta\to 0} \cos\left(\frac{\pi\theta}{\sin\theta}\right)$

The equations in Exercises 45 and 46 give the position $s = f(t)$ of a body moving on a coordinate line (s in meters, t in seconds). Find the body's velocity, speed, acceleration, and jerk at time $t = \pi/4$ sec.

45. $s = 2 - 2\sin t$

46. $s = \sin t + \cos t$

47. Is there a value of c that will make

$$f(x) = \begin{cases} \dfrac{\sin^2 3x}{x^2}, & x \neq 0 \\ c, & x = 0 \end{cases}$$

continuous at $x = 0$? Give reasons for your answer.

48. Is there a value of b that will make

$$g(x) = \begin{cases} x + b, & x < 0 \\ \cos x, & x \geq 0 \end{cases}$$

continuous at $x = 0$? Differentiable at $x = 0$? Give reasons for your answers.

49. Find $d^{999}/dx^{999}(\cos x)$.

50. Derive the formula for the derivative with respect to x of

a. $\sec x$. **b.** $\csc x$. **c.** $\cot x$.

T **51.** Graph $y = \cos x$ for $-\pi \leq x \leq 2\pi$. On the same screen, graph

$$y = \frac{\sin(x + h) - \sin x}{h}$$

for $h = 1, 0.5, 0.3$, and 0.1. Then, in a new window, try $h = -1, -0.5$, and -0.3. What happens as $h \to 0^+$? As $h \to 0^-$? What phenomenon is being illustrated here?

T **52.** Graph $y = -\sin x$ for $-\pi \leq x \leq 2\pi$. On the same screen, graph

$$y = \frac{\cos(x + h) - \cos x}{h}$$

for $h = 1, 0.5, 0.3$, and 0.1. Then, in a new window, try $h = -1, -0.5$, and -0.3. What happens as $h \to 0^+$? As $h \to 0^-$? What phenomenon is being illustrated here?

T **53. Centered difference quotients** The *centered difference quotient*

$$\frac{f(x + h) - f(x - h)}{2h}$$

is used to approximate $f'(x)$ in numerical work because (1) its limit as $h \to 0$ equals $f'(x)$ when $f'(x)$ exists, and (2) it usually gives a better approximation of $f'(x)$ for a given value of h than the difference quotient

$$\frac{f(x + h) - f(x)}{h}.$$

See the accompanying figure.

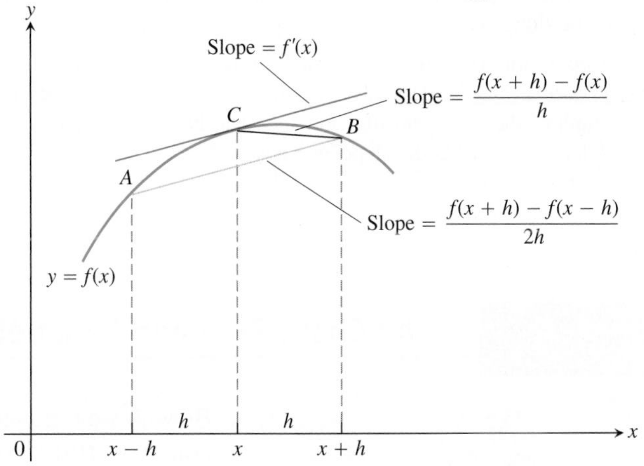

a. To see how rapidly the centered difference quotient for $f(x) = \sin x$ converges to $f'(x) = \cos x$, graph $y = \cos x$ together with

$$y = \frac{\sin(x + h) - \sin(x - h)}{2h}$$

over the interval $[-\pi, 2\pi]$ for $h = 1, 0.5$, and 0.3. Compare the results with those obtained in Exercise 51 for the same values of h.

b. To see how rapidly the centered difference quotient for $f(x) = \cos x$ converges to $f'(x) = -\sin x$, graph $y = -\sin x$ together with

$$y = \frac{\cos(x + h) - \cos(x - h)}{2h}$$

over the interval $[-\pi, 2\pi]$ for $h = 1, 0.5$, and 0.3. Compare the results with those obtained in Exercise 52 for the same values of h.

54. A caution about centered difference quotients (*Continuation of Exercise 53.*) The quotient

$$\frac{f(x + h) - f(x - h)}{2h}$$

may have a limit as $h \to 0$ when f has no derivative at x. As a case in point, take $f(x) = |x|$ and calculate

$$\lim_{h \to 0} \frac{|0 + h| - |0 - h|}{2h}.$$

As you will see, the limit exists even though $f(x) = |x|$ has no derivative at $x = 0$. *Moral:* Before using a centered difference quotient, be sure the derivative exists.

T **55. Slopes on the graph of the tangent function** Graph $y = \tan x$ and its derivative together on $(-\pi/2, \pi/2)$. Does the graph of the tangent function appear to have a smallest slope? A largest slope? Is the slope ever negative? Give reasons for your answers.

T **56. Slopes on the graph of the cotangent function** Graph $y = \cot x$ and its derivative together for $0 < x < \pi$. Does the graph of the cotangent function appear to have a smallest slope? A largest slope? Is the slope ever positive? Give reasons for your answers.

T **57. Exploring $(\sin kx)/x$** Graph $y = (\sin x)/x$, $y = (\sin 2x)/x$, and $y = (\sin 4x)/x$ together over the interval $-2 \le x \le 2$. Where does each graph appear to cross the y-axis? Do the graphs really intersect the axis? What would you expect the graphs of $y = (\sin 5x)/x$ and $y = (\sin(-3x))/x$ to do as $x \to 0$? Why? What about the graph of $y = (\sin kx)/x$ for other values of k? Give reasons for your answers.

T **58. Radians versus degrees: degree mode derivatives** What happens to the derivatives of $\sin x$ and $\cos x$ if x is measured in degrees instead of radians? To find out, take the following steps.

a. With your graphing calculator or computer grapher in *degree mode*, graph

$$f(h) = \frac{\sin h}{h}$$

and estimate $\lim_{h\to 0} f(h)$. Compare your estimate with $\pi/180$. Is there any reason to believe the limit *should* be $\pi/180$?

b. With your grapher still in degree mode, estimate

$$\lim_{h \to 0} \frac{\cos h - 1}{h}.$$

c. Now go back to the derivation of the formula for the derivative of $\sin x$ in the text and carry out the steps of the derivation using degree-mode limits. What formula do you obtain for the derivative?

d. Work through the derivation of the formula for the derivative of $\cos x$ using degree-mode limits. What formula do you obtain for the derivative?

e. The disadvantages of the degree-mode formulas become apparent as you start taking derivatives of higher order. Try it. What are the second and third degree-mode derivatives of $\sin x$ and $\cos x$?

3.5 The Chain Rule and Parametric Equations

How do we differentiate $F(x) = \sin(x^2 - 4)$, which is the composite $f \circ g$ of the functions $y = f(u) = \sin u$ and $u = g(x) = x^2 - 4$? The answer, given by the *Chain Rule*, says that the derivative is the product of the derivatives of f and g. We will learn the rule in this section and apply it to curves in the plane defined by *parametric equations*.

Derivative of a Composite Function

The function $y = \frac{3}{2}x = \frac{1}{2}(3x)$ is the composite of the functions $y = \frac{1}{2}u$ and $u = 3x$.

FIGURE 3.22 When gear A makes x turns, gear B makes u turns and gear C makes y turns. By comparing circumferences or counting teeth, we see that $y = u/2$ (C turns one-half turn for each B turn) and $u = 3x$ (B turns three times for A's one), so $y = 3x/2$. Thus, $dy/dx = 3/2 = (1/2)(3) = (dy/du)(du/dx)$.

We have

$$\frac{dy}{dx} = \frac{3}{2}, \qquad \frac{dy}{du} = \frac{1}{2}, \qquad \text{and} \qquad \frac{du}{dx} = 3.$$

Since $\frac{3}{2} = \frac{1}{2} \cdot 3$, we see in this case that

$$\frac{dy}{dx} = \frac{dy}{du} \cdot \frac{du}{dx}.$$

If we think of the derivative as a rate of change, our intuition allows us to see that this relationship is reasonable. If $y = f(u)$ changes half as fast as u and $u = g(x)$ changes three times as fast as x, then we expect y to change $3/2$ times as fast as x. This effect is much like that of a multiple gear train (Figure 3.22). Let's look at another example.

EXAMPLE 1 The function

$$y = (3x^2 + 1)^2$$

is the composite of $y = f(u) = u^2$ and $u = g(x) = 3x^2 + 1$. Calculating derivatives, we see that

$$\begin{aligned}
\frac{dy}{du} \cdot \frac{du}{dx} &= 2u \cdot 6x \\
&= 2(3x^2 + 1) \cdot 6x \\
&= 36x^3 + 12x.
\end{aligned}$$

Calculating the derivative from the expanded formula $(3x^2 + 1)^2 = 9x^4 + 6x^2 + 1$ gives the same result:

$$\begin{aligned}
\frac{dy}{dx} &= \frac{d}{dx}(9x^4 + 6x^2 + 1) \\
&= 36x^3 + 12x.
\end{aligned}$$

■

The derivative of the composite function $f(g(x))$ at x is the derivative of f at $g(x)$ times the derivative of g at x. This is known as the Chain Rule (Figure 3.23).

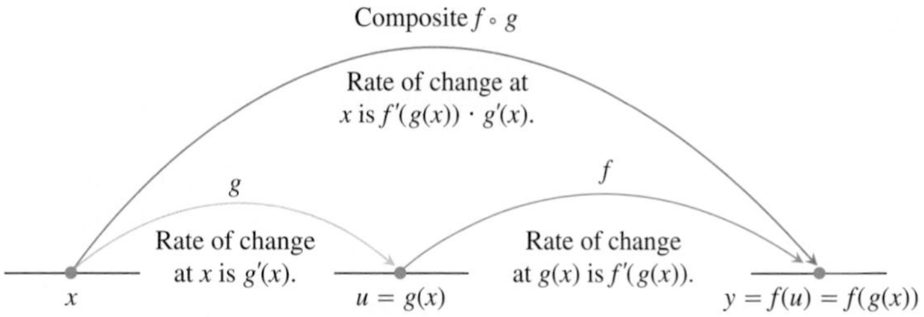

FIGURE 3.23 Rates of change multiply: The derivative of $f \circ g$ at x is the derivative of f at $g(x)$ times the derivative of g at x.

THEOREM 3—The Chain Rule If $f(u)$ is differentiable at the point $u = g(x)$ and $g(x)$ is differentiable at x, then the composite function $(f \circ g)(x) = f(g(x))$ is differentiable at x, and

$$(f \circ g)'(x) = f'(g(x)) \cdot g'(x).$$

In Leibniz's notation, if $y = f(u)$ and $u = g(x)$, then

$$\frac{dy}{dx} = \frac{dy}{du} \cdot \frac{du}{dx},$$

where dy/du is evaluated at $u = g(x)$.

Intuitive "Proof" of the Chain Rule:

Let Δu be the change in u corresponding to a change of Δx in x, that is

$$\Delta u = g(x + \Delta x) - g(x)$$

Then the corresponding change in y is

$$\Delta y = f(u + \Delta u) - f(u).$$

It would be tempting to write

$$\frac{\Delta y}{\Delta x} = \frac{\Delta y}{\Delta u} \cdot \frac{\Delta u}{\Delta x} \tag{1}$$

and take the limit as $\Delta x \to 0$:

$$\begin{aligned} \frac{dy}{dx} &= \lim_{\Delta x \to 0} \frac{\Delta y}{\Delta x} \\ &= \lim_{\Delta x \to 0} \frac{\Delta y}{\Delta u} \cdot \frac{\Delta u}{\Delta x} \\ &= \lim_{\Delta x \to 0} \frac{\Delta y}{\Delta u} \cdot \lim_{\Delta x \to 0} \frac{\Delta u}{\Delta x} \\ &= \lim_{\Delta u \to 0} \frac{\Delta y}{\Delta u} \cdot \lim_{\Delta x \to 0} \frac{\Delta u}{\Delta x} \\ &= \frac{dy}{du} \frac{du}{dx}. \end{aligned}$$

(Note that $\Delta u \to 0$ as $\Delta x \to 0$ since g is continuous.)

The only flaw in this reasoning is that in Equation (1) it might happen that $\Delta u = 0$ (even when $\Delta x \neq 0$) and, of course, we can't divide by 0. The proof requires a different approach to overcome this flaw, and we give a precise proof in Section 3.10. ■

EXAMPLE 2 An object moves along the x-axis so that its position at any time $t \geq 0$ is given by $x(t) = \cos(t^2 + 1)$. Find the velocity of the object as a function of t.

Solution We know that the velocity is dx/dt. In this instance, x is a composite function: $x = \cos(u)$ and $u = t^2 + 1$. We have

$$\frac{dx}{du} = -\sin(u) \qquad x = \cos(u)$$

$$\frac{du}{dt} = 2t. \qquad u = t^2 + 1$$

By the Chain Rule,

$$\begin{aligned}\frac{dx}{dt} &= \frac{dx}{du}\cdot\frac{du}{dt}\\ &= -\sin(u)\cdot 2t \qquad \frac{dx}{du} \text{ evaluated at } u\\ &= -\sin(t^2+1)\cdot 2t\\ &= -2t\sin(t^2+1).\end{aligned}$$

■

"Outside-Inside" Rule

A difficulty with the Leibniz notation is that it doesn't state specifically where the derivatives in the Chain Rule are supposed to be evaluated. So it sometimes helps to think about the Chain Rule using functional notation. If $y = f(g(x))$, then

$$\frac{dy}{dx} = f'(g(x))\cdot g'(x).$$

In words, differentiate the "outside" function f and evaluate it at the "inside" function $g(x)$ left alone; then multiply by the derivative of the "inside function."

EXAMPLE 3 Differentiate $\sin(x^2 + e^x)$ with respect to x.

Solution

$$\frac{d}{dx}\sin\underbrace{(x^2+e^x)}_{\text{inside}} = \cos\underbrace{(x^2+e^x)}_{\substack{\text{inside}\\ \text{left alone}}}\cdot\underbrace{(2x+e^x)}_{\substack{\text{derivative of}\\ \text{the inside}}}$$

■

EXAMPLE 4 Differentiate $y = e^{\cos x}$.

Solution Here the inside function is $u = g(x) = \cos x$ and the outside function is the exponential function $f(x) = e^x$. Applying the Chain Rule, we get

$$\frac{dy}{dx} = \frac{d}{dx}(e^{\cos x}) = e^{\cos x}\frac{d}{dx}(\cos x) = e^{\cos x}(-\sin x) = -e^{\cos x}\sin x.$$

■

Generalizing Example 4, we see that the Chain Rule gives the formula

$$\frac{d}{dx}e^u = e^u\frac{du}{dx}.$$

Thus, for example,

$$\frac{d}{dx}(e^{kx}) = e^{kx}\cdot\frac{d}{dx}(kx) = ke^{kx}, \quad \text{for any constant } k$$

and

$$\frac{d}{dx}\left(e^{x^2}\right) = e^{x^2}\cdot\frac{d}{dx}(x^2) = 2xe^{x^2}.$$

Repeated Use of the Chain Rule

We sometimes have to use the Chain Rule two or more times to find a derivative.

HISTORICAL BIOGRAPHY

Johann Bernoulli
(1667–1748)

EXAMPLE 5 Find the derivative of $g(t) = \tan(5 - \sin 2t)$.

Solution Notice here that the tangent is a function of $5 - \sin 2t$, whereas the sine is a function of $2t$, which is itself a function of t. Therefore, by the Chain Rule,

$$\begin{aligned} g'(t) &= \frac{d}{dt}(\tan(5 - \sin 2t)) && \text{Derivative of } \tan u \text{ with } u = 5 - \sin 2t \\ &= \sec^2(5 - \sin 2t) \cdot \frac{d}{dt}(5 - \sin 2t) && \text{Derivative of } 5 - \sin u \text{ with } u = 2t \\ &= \sec^2(5 - \sin 2t) \cdot \left(0 - \cos 2t \cdot \frac{d}{dt}(2t)\right) \\ &= \sec^2(5 - \sin 2t) \cdot (-\cos 2t) \cdot 2 \\ &= -2(\cos 2t)\sec^2(5 - \sin 2t). \end{aligned}$$

■

The Chain Rule with Powers of a Function

If f is a differentiable function of u and if u is a differentiable function of x, then substituting $y = f(u)$ into the Chain Rule formula

$$\frac{dy}{dx} = \frac{dy}{du} \cdot \frac{du}{dx}$$

leads to the formula

$$\frac{d}{dx} f(u) = f'(u)\frac{du}{dx}.$$

Here's an example of how it works: If n is any real number and $f(u) = u^n$, the Power Rule (Rule 2) tells us that $f'(u) = nu^{n-1}$. If u is a differentiable function of x, then we can use the Chain Rule to extend this to the **Power Chain Rule**:

$$\frac{d}{dx}u^n = nu^{n-1}\frac{du}{dx}. \qquad \frac{d}{du}(u^n) = nu^{n-1}$$

EXAMPLE 6

(a)
$$\begin{aligned} \frac{d}{dx}(5x^3 - x^4)^7 &= 7(5x^3 - x^4)^6 \frac{d}{dx}(5x^3 - x^4) && \text{Power Chain Rule with } u = 5x^3 - x^4, n = 7 \\ &= 7(5x^3 - x^4)^6(5 \cdot 3x^2 - 4x^3) \\ &= 7(5x^3 - x^4)^6(15x^2 - 4x^3) \end{aligned}$$

(b)
$$\begin{aligned} \frac{d}{dx}\left(\frac{1}{3x - 2}\right) &= \frac{d}{dx}(3x - 2)^{-1} \\ &= -1(3x - 2)^{-2}\frac{d}{dx}(3x - 2) && \text{Power Chain Rule with } u = 3x - 2, n = -1 \\ &= -1(3x - 2)^{-2}(3) \\ &= -\frac{3}{(3x - 2)^2} \end{aligned}$$

In part (b) we could also find the derivative with the Quotient Rule.

$\sin^n x$ means $(\sin x)^n$, $n \neq -1$.

(c) $$\frac{d}{dx}(\sin^5 x) = 5\sin^4 x \cdot \frac{d}{dx}\sin x \qquad \text{Power Chain Rule with } u = \sin x,\ n = 5$$
$$= 5\sin^4 x \cos x$$

(d) $$\frac{d}{dx}\left(e^{\sqrt{3x+1}}\right) = e^{\sqrt{3x+1}} \cdot \frac{d}{dx}\left(\sqrt{3x+1}\right)$$
$$= e^{\sqrt{3x+1}} \cdot \frac{1}{2}(3x+1)^{-1/2} \cdot 3$$
$$= \frac{3}{2\sqrt{3x+1}}e^{\sqrt{3x+1}}$$ ■

EXAMPLE 7 In Section 3.1, we saw that the absolute value function $y = |x|$ is not differentiable at $x = 0$. However, the function *is* differentiable at all other real numbers as we now show. Since $|x| = \sqrt{x^2}$, we can derive the following useful formula:

$$\frac{d}{dx}(|x|) = \frac{d}{dx}\sqrt{x^2}$$
$$= \frac{1}{2\sqrt{x^2}} \cdot \frac{d}{dx}(x^2) \qquad \text{Power Chain Rule with } u = x^2,\ n = 1/2,\ x \neq 0$$
$$= \frac{1}{2|x|} \cdot 2x \qquad \sqrt{x^2} = |x|$$
$$= \frac{x}{|x|}, \quad x \neq 0.$$ ■

EXAMPLE 8 The formulas for the derivatives of both $\sin x$ and $\cos x$ were obtained under the assumption that x is measured in radians, *not* degrees. The Chain Rule gives us new insight into the difference between the two. Since $180° = \pi$ radians, $x° = \pi x/180$ radians where $x°$ means the angle x measured in degrees.

By the Chain Rule,

$$\frac{d}{dx}\sin(x°) = \frac{d}{dx}\sin\left(\frac{\pi x}{180}\right) = \frac{\pi}{180}\cos\left(\frac{\pi x}{180}\right) = \frac{\pi}{180}\cos(x°).$$

See Figure 3.24. Similarly, the derivative of $\cos(x°)$ is $-(\pi/180)\sin(x°)$.

The factor $\pi/180$, annoying in the first derivative, would compound with repeated differentiation. We see at a glance a compelling reason for the use of radian measure. ■

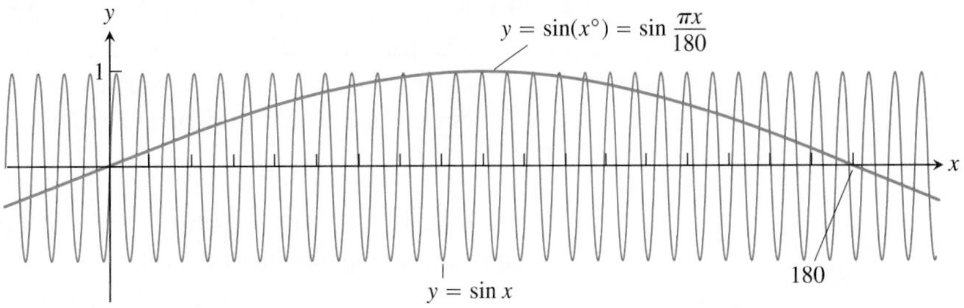

FIGURE 3.24 $\operatorname{Sin}(x°)$ oscillates only $\pi/180$ times as often as $\sin x$ oscillates. Its maximum slope is $\pi/180$ at $x = 0$ (Example 8).

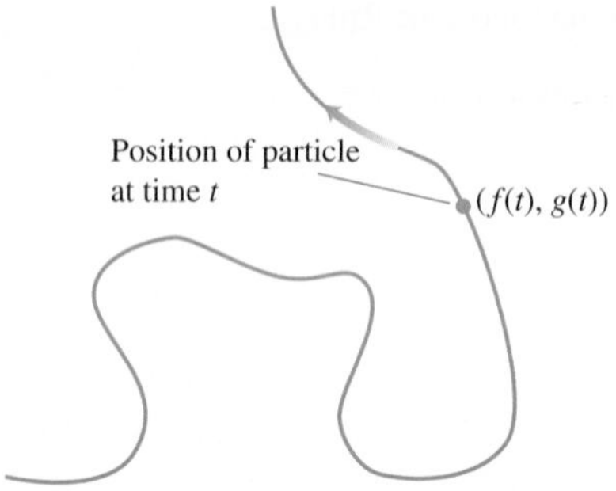

FIGURE 3.25 The path traced by a particle moving in the xy-plane is not always the graph of a function of x or a function of y.

Parametric Equations

Instead of describing a curve by expressing the y-coordinate of a point $P(x, y)$ on the curve as a function of x, it is sometimes more convenient to describe the curve by expressing *both* coordinates as functions of a third variable t. Figure 3.25 shows the path of a moving particle described by a pair of equations, $x = f(t)$ and $y = g(t)$. For studying motion, t usually denotes time. Equations like these have advantages over a Cartesian formula because they tell us the particle's position $(x, y) = (f(t), g(t))$ at any time t. They can also model paths that are not graphs of functions and fail the vertical line test like the path in Figure 3.25.

DEFINITION If x and y are given as functions

$$x = f(t), \qquad y = g(t)$$

over an interval of t-values, then the set of points $(x, y) = (f(t), g(t))$ defined by these equations is a **parametric curve**. The equations are **parametric equations** for the curve.

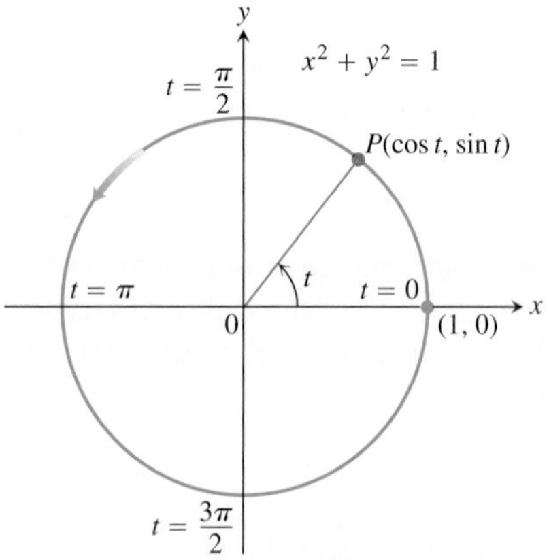

FIGURE 3.26 The equations $x = \cos t$ and $y = \sin t$ describe motion on the circle $x^2 + y^2 = 1$. The arrow shows the direction of increasing t (Example 9).

The variable t is a **parameter** for the curve, and its domain I is the **parameter interval**. If I is a closed interval, $a \le t \le b$, the point $(f(a), g(a))$ is the **initial point** of the curve. The point $(f(b), g(b))$ is the **terminal point**. When we give parametric equations and a parameter interval for a curve, we say that we have **parametrized** the curve. The equations and interval together constitute a **parametrization** of the curve. A given curve can be represented by different sets of parametric equations. (See Exercises 93 and 94.)

EXAMPLE 9 Graph the parametric curves

(a) $x = \cos t, \qquad y = \sin t, \qquad 0 \le t \le 2\pi.$

(b) $x = a\cos t, \qquad y = a\sin t, \qquad 0 \le t \le 2\pi.$

Solution

(a) Since $x^2 + y^2 = \cos^2 t + \sin^2 t = 1$, the parametric curve lies along the unit circle $x^2 + y^2 = 1$. As t increases from 0 to 2π, the point $(x, y) = (\cos t, \sin t)$ starts at $(1, 0)$ and traces the entire circle once counterclockwise (Figure 3.26).

(b) For $x = a\cos t$, $y = a\sin t$, $0 \le t \le 2\pi$, we have $x^2 + y^2 = a^2\cos^2 t + a^2\sin^2 t = a^2$. The parametrization describes a motion that begins at the point $(a, 0)$ and traverses the circle $x^2 + y^2 = a^2$ once counterclockwise, returning to $(a, 0)$ at $t = 2\pi$. The graph is a circle centered at the origin with radius $r = a$ and coordinate points $(a\cos t, a\sin t)$. ■

EXAMPLE 10 The position $P(x, y)$ of a particle moving in the xy-plane is given by the equations and parameter interval

$$x = \sqrt{t}, \qquad y = t, \qquad t \ge 0.$$

Identify the path traced by the particle and describe the motion.

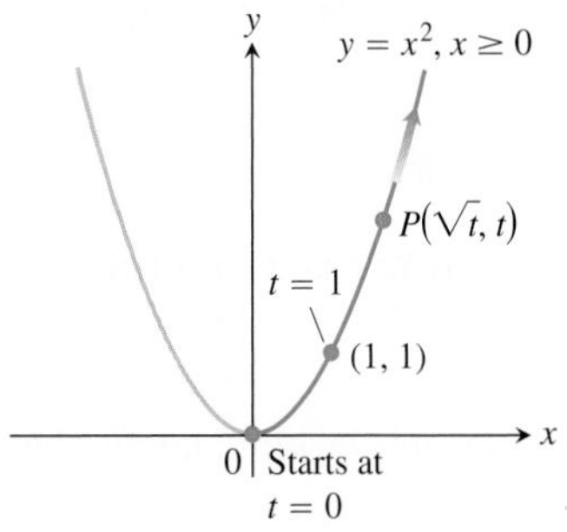

FIGURE 3.27 The equations $x = \sqrt{t}$ and $y = t$ and the interval $t \geq 0$ describe the motion of a particle that traces the right-hand half of the parabola $y = x^2$ (Example 10).

Solution We try to identify the path by eliminating t between the equations $x = \sqrt{t}$ and $y = t$. With any luck, this will produce a recognizable algebraic relation between x and y. We find that

$$y = t = \left(\sqrt{t}\right)^2 = x^2.$$

Thus, the particle's position coordinates satisfy the equation $y = x^2$, so the particle moves along the parabola $y = x^2$.

It would be a mistake, however, to conclude that the particle's path is the entire parabola $y = x^2$; it is only half the parabola. The particle's x-coordinate is never negative. The particle starts at (0, 0) when $t = 0$ and rises into the first quadrant as t increases (Figure 3.27). The parameter interval is $[0, \infty)$ and there is no terminal point. ■

EXAMPLE 11 Find a parametrization for the line segment with endpoints $(-2, 1)$ and (3, 5).

Solution Using $(-2, 1)$ we create the parametric equations

$$x = -2 + at, \qquad y = 1 + bt.$$

These represent a line, as we can see by solving each equation for t and equating to obtain

$$\frac{x + 2}{a} = \frac{y - 1}{b}.$$

This line goes through the point $(-2, 1)$ when $t = 0$. We determine a and b so that the line goes through (3, 5) when $t = 1$.

$$3 = -2 + a \quad \Rightarrow \quad a = 5 \qquad x = 3 \text{ when } t = 1.$$
$$5 = 1 + b \quad \Rightarrow \quad b = 4 \qquad y = 5 \text{ when } t = 1.$$

Therefore,

$$x = -2 + 5t, \qquad y = 1 + 4t, \qquad 0 \leq t \leq 1$$

is a parametrization of the line segment with initial point $(-2, 1)$ and terminal point (3, 5). ■

Slopes of Parametrized Curves

A parametrized curve $x = f(t)$ and $y = g(t)$ is **differentiable** at t if f and g are differentiable at t. At a point on a differentiable parametrized curve where y is also a differentiable function of x, the derivatives dy/dt, dx/dt, and dy/dx are related by the Chain Rule:

$$\frac{dy}{dt} = \frac{dy}{dx} \cdot \frac{dx}{dt}.$$

If $dx/dt \neq 0$, we may divide both sides of this equation by dx/dt to solve for dy/dx.

Parametric Formula for dy/dx

If all three derivatives exist and $dx/dt \neq 0$,

$$\frac{dy}{dx} = \frac{dy/dt}{dx/dt}. \tag{2}$$

EXAMPLE 12 Describe the motion of a particle whose position $P(x, y)$ at time t is given by

$$x = a \cos t, \qquad y = b \sin t, \qquad 0 \le t \le 2\pi .$$

Find the line tangent to the curve at the point $(a/\sqrt{2}, b/\sqrt{2})$, where $t = \pi/4$. (The constants a and b are both positive.)

Solution We find a Cartesian equation for the particle's coordinates by eliminating t between the equations

$$\cos t = \frac{x}{a}, \qquad \sin t = \frac{y}{b}.$$

The identity $\cos^2 t + \sin^2 t = 1$ yields

$$\left(\frac{x}{a}\right)^2 + \left(\frac{y}{b}\right)^2 = 1, \qquad \text{or} \qquad \frac{x^2}{a^2} + \frac{y^2}{b^2} = 1.$$

The particle's coordinates (x, y) satisfy the equation $(x^2/a^2) + (y^2/b^2) = 1$, so the particle moves along this ellipse. When $t = 0$, the particle's coordinates are

$$x = a \cos(0) = a, \qquad y = b \sin(0) = 0,$$

so the motion starts at $(a, 0)$. As t increases, the particle rises and moves toward the left, moving counterclockwise. It traverses the ellipse once, returning to its starting position $(a, 0)$ at $t = 2\pi$.

The slope of the tangent line to the ellipse when $t = \pi/4$ is

$$\begin{aligned} \left.\frac{dy}{dx}\right|_{t=\pi/4} &= \left.\frac{dy/dt}{dx/dt}\right|_{t=\pi/4} && \text{Eq. (2)} \\ &= \left.\frac{b \cos t}{-a \sin t}\right|_{t=\pi/4} \\ &= \frac{b/\sqrt{2}}{-a/\sqrt{2}} = -\frac{b}{a}. \end{aligned}$$

The tangent line is

$$\begin{aligned} y - \frac{b}{\sqrt{2}} &= -\frac{b}{a}\left(x - \frac{a}{\sqrt{2}}\right) \\ y &= \frac{b}{\sqrt{2}} - \frac{b}{a}\left(x - \frac{a}{\sqrt{2}}\right) \end{aligned}$$

or

$$y = -\frac{b}{a}x + \sqrt{2}b. \qquad \blacksquare$$

If parametric equations define y as a twice-differentiable function of x, we can apply Equation (2) to the function $dy/dx = y'$ to calculate d^2y/dx^2 as a function of t:

$$\frac{d^2y}{dx^2} = \frac{d}{dx}(y') = \frac{dy'/dt}{dx/dt}. \qquad \text{Eq. (2) with } y' \text{ in place of } y$$

Parametric Formula for d^2y/dx^2

If the equations $x = f(t)$, $y = g(t)$ define y as a twice-differentiable function of x, then at any point where $dx/dt \neq 0$ and $y' = dy/dx$,

$$\frac{d^2y}{dx^2} = \frac{dy'/dt}{dx/dt}. \tag{3}$$

EXAMPLE 13 Find d^2y/dx^2 as a function of t if $x = t - t^2$, $y = t - t^3$.

Finding d^2y/dx^2 in Terms of t

1. Express $y' = dy/dx$ in terms of t.
2. Find dy'/dt.
3. Divide dy'/dt by dx/dt.

Solution

1. Express $y' = dy/dx$ in terms of t.

$$y' = \frac{dy}{dx} = \frac{dy/dt}{dx/dt} = \frac{1 - 3t^2}{1 - 2t}$$

2. Differentiate y' with respect to t.

$$\frac{dy'}{dt} = \frac{d}{dt}\left(\frac{1 - 3t^2}{1 - 2t}\right) = \frac{2 - 6t + 6t^2}{(1 - 2t)^2} \qquad \text{Quotient Rule}$$

3. Divide dy'/dt by dx/dt.

$$\frac{d^2y}{dx^2} = \frac{dy'/dt}{dx/dt} = \frac{(2 - 6t + 6t^2)/(1 - 2t)^2}{1 - 2t} = \frac{2 - 6t + 6t^2}{(1 - 2t)^3} \qquad \text{Eq. (3)}$$ ■

EXERCISES 3.5

In Exercises 1–8, given $y = f(u)$ and $u = g(x)$, find $dy/dx = f'(g(x))g'(x)$.

1. $y = 6u - 9, \quad u = (1/2)x^4$
2. $y = 2u^3, \quad u = 8x - 1$
3. $y = \sin u, \quad u = 3x + 1$
4. $y = \cos u, \quad u = -x/3$
5. $y = \cos u, \quad u = \sin x$
6. $y = \sin u, \quad u = x - \cos x$
7. $y = \tan u, \quad u = 10x - 5$
8. $y = -\sec u, \quad u = x^2 + 7x$

In Exercises 9–22, write the function in the form $y = f(u)$ and $u = g(x)$. Then find dy/dx as a function of x.

9. $y = (2x + 1)^5$
10. $y = \sqrt[3]{2x}$
11. $y = \left(1 - \frac{x}{7}\right)^{-7}$
12. $y = \left(\frac{x}{2} - 1\right)^{-10}$
13. $y = (1 - 6x)^{2/3}$
14. $y = \left(\frac{x}{5} + \frac{1}{5x}\right)^5$
15. $y = \sec(\tan x)$
16. $y = \cot\left(\pi - \frac{1}{x}\right)$
17. $y = \sin^3 x$
18. $y = 5\cos^{-4} x$
19. $y = e^{-5x}$
20. $y = e^{2x/3}$
21. $y = e^{5-7x}$
22. $y = e^{\left(4\sqrt{x}+x^2\right)}$

Find the derivatives of the functions in Exercises 23–48.

23. $p = \sqrt{3 - t}$
24. $y = x(x^2 + 1)^{1/2}$
25. $s = \frac{4}{3\pi}\sin 3t + \frac{4}{5\pi}\cos 5t$
26. $y = \sin[(2t + 5)^{-2/3}]$
27. $r = (\csc\theta + \cot\theta)^{-1}$
28. $r = -(\sec\theta + \tan\theta)^{-1}$
29. $y = x^2\sin^4 x + x\cos^{-2} x$
30. $z = \cos[(1 - 6t)^{2/3}]$
31. $y = \frac{1}{21}(3x - 2)^7 + \left(4 - \frac{1}{2x^2}\right)^{-1}$
32. $g(x) = 2(2x^{-1/2} + 1)^{-1/3}$
33. $y = (4x + 3)^4(x + 1)^{-3}$
34. $y = x(x^2 + 1)^{-1/2}$
35. $y = xe^{-x} + e^{3x}$
36. $y = (1 + 2x)e^{-2x}$
37. $y = (x^2 - 2x + 2)e^{5x/2}$
38. $y = (9x^2 - 6x + 2)e^{x^3}$
39. $h(x) = x\tan\left(2\sqrt{x}\right) + 7$
40. $k(x) = x^2\sec\left(\frac{1}{x}\right)$
41. $f(\theta) = \left(\frac{\sin\theta}{1 + \cos\theta}\right)^2$
42. $g(t) = \left(\frac{1 + \cos t}{\sin t}\right)^{-1}$
43. $h(\theta) = \sqrt[3]{1 + \cos 2\theta}$
44. $r = \sec\sqrt{\theta}\tan\left(\frac{1}{\theta}\right)$

45. $q = \sin\left(\frac{t}{\sqrt{t+1}}\right)$

46. $q = \cot\left(\frac{\sin t}{t}\right)$

47. $y = \cos\left(e^{-\theta^2}\right)$

48. $y = \theta^3 e^{-2\theta} \cos 5\theta$

In Exercises 49–60, find dy/dt.

49. $y = \sin^2(\pi t - 2)$

50. $y = \sec^2 \pi t$

51. $y = (1 + \cos 2t)^{-4}$

52. $y = (1 + \cot(t/2))^{-2}$

53. $y = e^{\cos^2(\pi t - 1)}$

54. $y = \left(e^{\sin(t/2)}\right)^3$

55. $y = \sin(\cos(2t - 5))$

56. $y = \cos\left(5 \sin\left(\frac{t}{3}\right)\right)$

57. $y = \left(1 + \tan^4\left(\frac{t}{12}\right)\right)^3$

58. $y = \frac{1}{6}(1 + \cos^2(7t))^3$

59. $y = \sqrt{1 + \cos(t^2)}$

60. $y = 4 \sin \sqrt{1 + \sqrt{t}}$

Find y'' in Exercises 61–66.

61. $y = \left(1 + \frac{1}{x}\right)^3$

62. $y = \left(1 - \sqrt{x}\right)^{-1}$

63. $y = \frac{1}{9}\cot(3x - 1)$

64. $y = 9 \tan\left(\frac{x}{3}\right)$

65. $y = e^{x^2} + 5x$

66. $y = \sin(x^2 e^x)$

In Exercises 67–72, find the value of $(f \circ g)'$ at the given value of x.

67. $f(u) = u^5 + 1, \quad u = g(x) = \sqrt{x}, \quad x = 1$

68. $f(u) = 1 - \frac{1}{u}, \quad u = g(x) = \frac{1}{1 - x}, \quad x = -1$

69. $f(u) = \cot\frac{\pi u}{10}, \quad u = g(x) = 5\sqrt{x}, \quad x = 1$

70. $f(u) = u + \frac{1}{\cos^2 u}, \quad u = g(x) = \pi x, \quad x = 1/4$

71. $f(u) = \frac{2u}{u^2 + 1}, \quad u = g(x) = 10x^2 + x + 1, \quad x = 0$

72. $f(u) = \left(\frac{u - 1}{u + 1}\right)^2, \quad u = g(x) = \frac{1}{x^2} - 1, \quad x = -1$

73. Suppose that functions f and g and their derivatives with respect to x have the following values at $x = 2$ and $x = 3$.

x	$f(x)$	$g(x)$	$f'(x)$	$g'(x)$
2	8	2	1/3	−3
3	3	−4	2π	5

Find the derivatives with respect to x of the following combinations at the given value of x.

a. $2f(x), \quad x = 2$

b. $f(x) + g(x), \quad x = 3$

c. $f(x) \cdot g(x), \quad x = 3$

d. $f(x)/g(x), \quad x = 2$

e. $f(g(x)), \quad x = 2$

f. $\sqrt{f(x)}, \quad x = 2$

g. $1/g^2(x), \quad x = 3$

h. $\sqrt{f^2(x) + g^2(x)}, \quad x = 2$

74. Suppose that the functions f and g and their derivatives with respect to x have the following values at $x = 0$ and $x = 1$.

x	$f(x)$	$g(x)$	$f'(x)$	$g'(x)$
0	1	1	5	1/3
1	3	−4	−1/3	−8/3

Find the derivatives with respect to x of the following combinations at the given value of x,

a. $5f(x) - g(x), \quad x = 1$

b. $f(x)g^3(x), \quad x = 0$

c. $\frac{f(x)}{g(x) + 1}, \quad x = 1$

d. $f(g(x)), \quad x = 0$

e. $g(f(x)), \quad x = 0$

f. $(x^{11} + f(x))^{-2}, \quad x = 1$

g. $f(x + g(x)), \quad x = 0$

75. Find ds/dt when $\theta = 3\pi/2$ if $s = \cos\theta$ and $d\theta/dt = 5$.

76. Find dy/dt when $x = 1$ if $y = x^2 + 7x - 5$ and $dx/dt = 1/3$.

What happens if you can write a function as a composite in different ways? Do you get the same derivative each time? The Chain Rule says you should. Try it with the functions in Exercises 77 and 78.

77. Find dy/dx if $y = x$ by using the Chain Rule with y as a composite of

a. $y = (u/5) + 7 \quad$ and $\quad u = 5x - 35$

b. $y = 1 + (1/u) \quad$ and $\quad u = 1/(x - 1)$.

78. Find dy/dx if $y = x^{3/2}$ by using the Chain Rule with y as a composite of

a. $y = u^3 \quad$ and $\quad u = \sqrt{x}$

b. $y = \sqrt{u} \quad$ and $\quad u = x^3$.

79. **a.** Find the tangent to the curve $y = 2\tan(\pi x/4)$ at $x = 1$.

b. Slopes on a tangent curve What is the smallest value the slope of the curve can ever have on the interval $-2 < x < 2$? Give reasons for your answer.

80. **Slopes on sine curves**

a. Find equations for the tangents to the curves $y = \sin 2x$ and $y = -\sin(x/2)$ at the origin. Is there anything special about how the tangents are related? Give reasons for your answer.

b. Can anything be said about the tangents to the curves $y = \sin mx$ and $y = -\sin(x/m)$ at the origin (m a constant $\neq 0$)? Give reasons for your answer.

c. For a given m, what are the largest values the slopes of the curves $y = \sin mx$ and $y = -\sin(x/m)$ can ever have? Give reasons for your answer.

d. The function $y = \sin x$ completes one period on the interval $[0, 2\pi]$, the function $y = \sin 2x$ completes two periods, the function $y = \sin(x/2)$ completes half a period, and so on. Is there any relation between the number of periods $y = \sin mx$ completes on $[0, 2\pi]$ and the slope of the curve $y = \sin mx$ at the origin? Give reasons for your answer.

Exercises 81–92 give parametric equations and parameter intervals for the motion of a particle in the xy-plane. Identify the particle's path by finding a Cartesian equation for it. Graph the Cartesian equation. (The graphs will vary with the equation used.) Indicate the portion of the graph traced by the particle and the direction of motion.

81. $x = \cos 2t, \quad y = \sin 2t, \quad 0 \le t \le \pi$

82. $x = \cos(\pi - t), \quad y = \sin(\pi - t), \quad 0 \le t \le \pi$

83. $x = 4\cos t, \quad y = 2\sin t, \quad 0 \le t \le 2\pi$

84. $x = 4\sin t, \quad y = 5\cos t, \quad 0 \le t \le 2\pi$

85. $x = 3t, \quad y = 9t^2, \quad -\infty < t < \infty$

86. $x = -\sqrt{t}, \quad y = t, \quad t \ge 0$

87. $x = 2t - 5, \quad y = 4t - 7, \quad -\infty < t < \infty$

88. $x = 3 - 3t, \quad y = 2t, \quad 0 \le t \le 1$

89. $x = t, \quad y = \sqrt{1 - t^2}, \quad -1 \le t \le 0$

90. $x = \sqrt{t + 1}, \quad y = \sqrt{t}, \quad t \ge 0$

91. $x = \sec^2 t - 1, \quad y = \tan t, \quad -\pi/2 < t < \pi/2$

92. $x = -\sec t, \quad y = \tan t, \quad -\pi/2 < t < \pi/2$

93. Find parametric equations and a parameter interval for the motion of a particle that starts at $(a, 0)$ and traces the circle $x^2 + y^2 = a^2$

a. once clockwise. **b.** once counterclockwise.

c. twice clockwise. **d.** twice counterclockwise.

(There are many ways to do these, so your answers may not be the same as the ones in the back of the book.)

94. Find parametric equations and a parameter interval for the motion of a particle that starts at $(a, 0)$ and traces the ellipse $(x^2/a^2) + (y^2/b^2) = 1$

a. once clockwise. **b.** once counterclockwise.

c. twice clockwise. **d.** twice counterclockwise.

(As in Exercise 93, there are many correct answers.)

In Exercises 95–100, find a parametrization for the curve.

95. the line segment with endpoints $(-1, -3)$ and $(4, 1)$

96. the line segment with endpoints $(-1, 3)$ and $(3, -2)$

97. the lower half of the parabola $x - 1 = y^2$

98. the left half of the parabola $y = x^2 + 2x$

99. the ray (half line) with initial point $(2, 3)$ that passes through the point $(-1, -1)$

100. the ray (half line) with initial point $(-1, 2)$ that passes through the point $(0, 0)$

In Exercises 101–108, find an equation for the line tangent to the curve at the point defined by the given value of t. Also, find the value of d^2y/dx^2 at this point.

101. $x = 2\cos t, \quad y = 2\sin t, \quad t = \pi/4$

102. $x = \cos t, \quad y = \sqrt{3}\cos t, \quad t = 2\pi/3$

103. $x = t, \quad y = \sqrt{t}, \quad t = 1/4$

104. $x = -\sqrt{t + 1}, \quad y = \sqrt{3t}, \quad t = 3$

105. $x = 2t^2 + 3, \quad y = t^4, \quad t = -1$

106. $x = t - \sin t, \quad y = 1 - \cos t, \quad t = \pi/3$

107. $x = \cos t, \quad y = 1 + \sin t, \quad t = \pi/2$

108. $x = \sec^2 t - 1, \quad y = \tan t, \quad t = -\pi/4$

109. Running machinery too fast Suppose that a piston is moving straight up and down and that its position at time t sec is

$$s = A\cos(2\pi bt),$$

with A and b positive. The value of A is the amplitude of the motion, and b is the frequency (number of times the piston moves up and down each second). What effect does doubling the frequency have on the piston's velocity, acceleration, and jerk? (Once you find out, you will know why some machinery breaks when you run it too fast.)

110. Temperatures in Fairbanks, Alaska The graph in Figure 3.28 shows the average Fahrenheit temperature in Fairbanks, Alaska, during a typical 365-day year. The equation that approximates the temperature on day x is

$$y = 37\sin\left[\frac{2\pi}{365}(x - 101)\right] + 25.$$

a. On what day is the temperature increasing the fastest?

b. About how many degrees per day is the temperature increasing when it is increasing at its fastest?

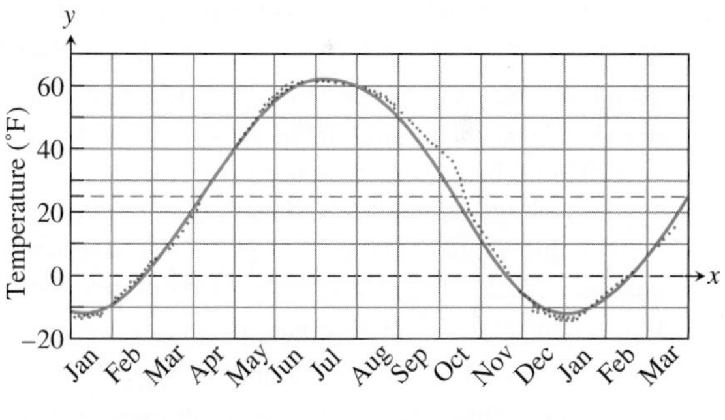

FIGURE 3.28 Normal mean air temperatures at Fairbanks, Alaska, plotted as data points, and the approximating sine function (Exercise 110).

111. Particle motion The position of a particle moving along a coordinate line is $s = \sqrt{1 + 4t}$, with s in meters and t in seconds. Find the particle's velocity and acceleration at $t = 6$ sec.

112. Constant acceleration Suppose that the velocity of a falling body is $v = k\sqrt{s}$ m/sec (k a constant) at the instant the body has fallen s m from its starting point. Show that the body's acceleration is constant.

113. Falling meteorite The velocity of a heavy meteorite entering Earth's atmosphere is inversely proportional to $\sqrt{s}$ when it is s km from Earth's center. Show that the meteorite's acceleration is inversely proportional to s^2.

114. Particle acceleration A particle moves along the x-axis with velocity $dx/dt = f(x)$. Show that the particle's acceleration is $f(x)f'(x)$.

115. Temperature and the period of a pendulum For oscillations of small amplitude (short swings), we may safely model the relationship between the period T and the length L of a simple pendulum with the equation

$$T = 2\pi\sqrt{\frac{L}{g}},$$

where g is the constant acceleration of gravity at the pendulum's location. If we measure g in centimeters per second squared, we measure L in centimeters and T in seconds. If the pendulum is made of metal, its length will vary with temperature, either increasing or decreasing at a rate that is roughly proportional to L. In symbols, with u being temperature and k the proportionality constant,

$$\frac{dL}{du} = kL.$$

Assuming this to be the case, show that the rate at which the period changes with respect to temperature is $kT/2$.

116. Chain Rule Suppose that $f(x) = x^2$ and $g(x) = |x|$. Then the composites

$$(f \circ g)(x) = |x|^2 = x^2 \quad \text{and} \quad (g \circ f)(x) = |x^2| = x^2$$

are both differentiable at $x = 0$ even though g itself is not differentiable at $x = 0$. Does this contradict the Chain Rule? Explain.

117. Tangents Suppose that $u = g(x)$ is differentiable at $x = 1$ and that $y = f(u)$ is differentiable at $u = g(1)$. If the graph of $y = f(g(x))$ has a horizontal tangent at $x = 1$, can we conclude anything about the tangent to the graph of g at $x = 1$ or the tangent to the graph of f at $u = g(1)$? Give reasons for your answer.

118. Suppose that $u = g(x)$ is differentiable at $x = -5$, $y = f(u)$ is differentiable at $u = g(-5)$, and $(f \circ g)'(-5)$ is negative. What, if anything, can be said about the values of $g'(-5)$ and $f'(g(-5))$?

T **119. The derivative of sin 2x** Graph the function $y = 2\cos 2x$ for $-2 \le x \le 3.5$. Then, on the same screen, graph

$$y = \frac{\sin 2(x + h) - \sin 2x}{h}$$

for $h = 1.0, 0.5$, and 0.2. Experiment with other values of h, including negative values. What do you see happening as $h \to 0$? Explain this behavior.

T **120. The derivative of cos (x^2)** Graph $y = -2x\sin(x^2)$ for $-2 \le x \le 3$. Then, on the same screen, graph

$$y = \frac{\cos((x + h)^2) - \cos(x^2)}{h}$$

for $h = 1.0, 0.7$, and 0.3. Experiment with other values of h. What do you see happening as $h \to 0$? Explain this behavior.

T The curves in Exercises 121 and 122 are called *Bowditch curves* or *Lissajous figures*. In each case, find the point in the interior of the first quadrant where the tangent to the curve is horizontal, and find the equations of the two tangents at the origin.

121.

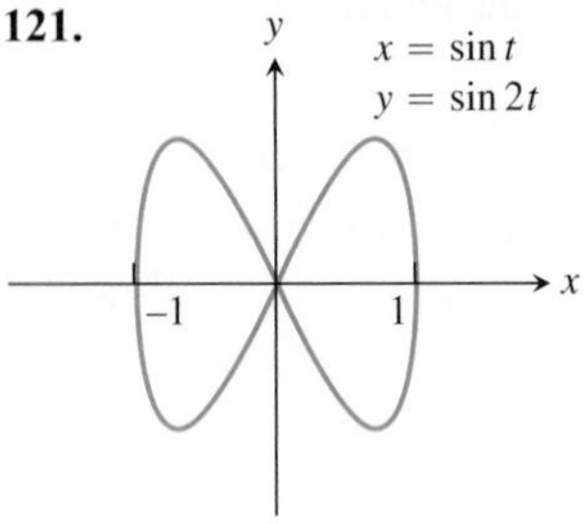

122.

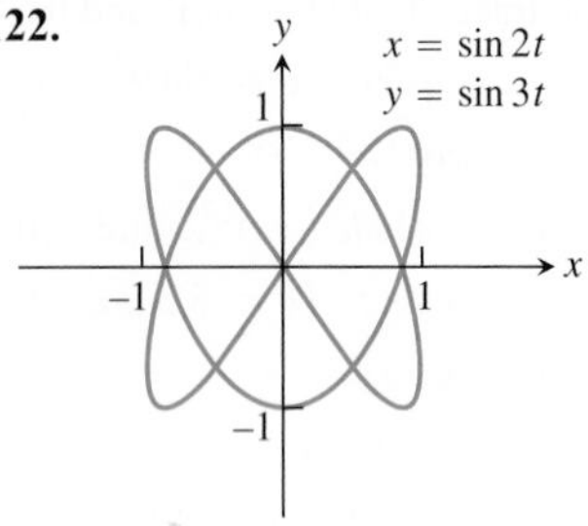

Using the Chain Rule, show that the Power Rule $(d/dx)x^n = nx^{n-1}$ holds for the functions x^n in Exercises 123 and 124.

123. $x^{1/4} = \sqrt{\sqrt{x}}$

124. $x^{3/4} = \sqrt{x\sqrt{x}}$

COMPUTER EXPLORATIONS

125. As Figure 3.29 shows, the trigonometric "polynomial"

$$s = f(t) = 0.78540 - 0.63662\cos 2t - 0.07074\cos 6t$$
$$-0.02546\cos 10t - 0.01299\cos 14t$$

gives a good approximation of the sawtooth function $s = g(t)$ on the interval $[-\pi, \pi]$. How well does the derivative of f approximate the derivative of g at the points where dg/dt is defined? To find out, carry out the following steps.

a. Graph dg/dt (where defined) over $[-\pi, \pi]$.

b. Find df/dt.

c. Graph df/dt. Where does the approximation of dg/dt by df/dt seem to be best? Least good? Approximations by trigonometric polynomials are important in the theories of heat and oscillation, but we must not expect too much of them, as we see in the next exercise.

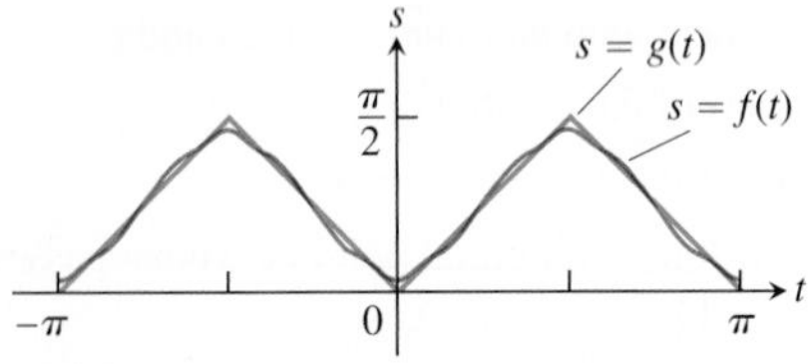

FIGURE 3.29 The approximation of a sawtooth function by a trigonometric "polynomial" (Exercise 125).

126. (*Continuation of Exercise 125.*) In Exercise 125, the trigonometric polynomial $f(t)$ that approximated the sawtooth function $g(t)$ on $[-\pi, \pi]$ had a derivative that approximated the derivative of the sawtooth function. It is possible, however, for a trigonometric polynomial to approximate a function in a reasonable way without its derivative approximating the function's derivative at all well. As a case in point, the "polynomial"

$$s = h(t) = 1.2732 \sin 2t + 0.4244 \sin 6t + 0.25465 \sin 10t + 0.18189 \sin 14t + 0.14147 \sin 18t$$

graphed in Figure 3.30 approximates the step function $s = k(t)$ shown there. Yet the derivative of h is nothing like the derivative of k.

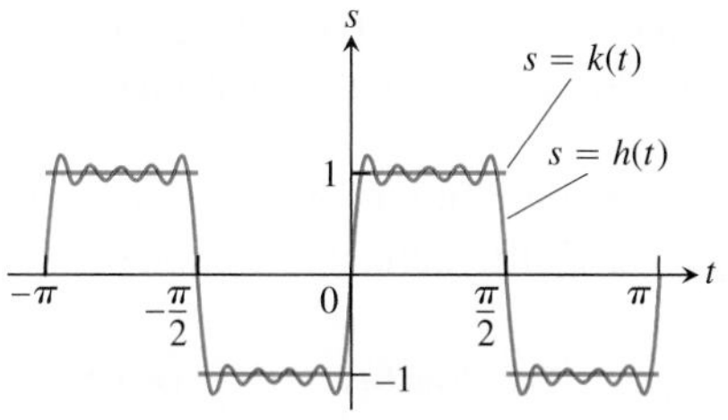

FIGURE 3.30 The approximation of a step function by a trigonometric "polynomial" (Exercise 126).

a. Graph dk/dt (where defined) over $[-\pi, \pi]$.

b. Find dh/dt.

c. Graph dh/dt to see how badly the graph fits the graph of dk/dt. Comment on what you see.

Use a CAS to perform the following steps on the parametrized curves in Exercises 127–130.

a. Plot the curve for the given interval of t values.

b. Find dy/dx and d^2y/dx^2 at the point t_0.

c. Find an equation for the tangent line to the curve at the point defined by the given value t_0. Plot the curve together with the tangent line on a single graph.

127. $x = \frac{1}{3}t^3, \quad y = \frac{1}{2}t^2, \quad 0 \le t \le 1, \quad t_0 = 1/2$

128. $x = 2t^3 - 16t^2 + 25t + 5, \quad y = t^2 + t - 3, \quad 0 \le t \le 6, \quad t_0 = 3/2$

129. $x = t - \cos t, \quad y = 1 + \sin t, \quad -\pi \le t \le \pi, \quad t_0 = \pi/4$

130. $x = e^t \cos t, \quad y = e^t \sin t, \quad 0 \le t \le \pi, \quad t_0 = \pi/2$

3.6 Implicit Differentiation

Most of the functions we have dealt with so far have been described by an equation of the form $y = f(x)$ that expresses y explicitly in terms of the variable x. We have learned rules for differentiating functions defined in this way. In Section 3.5 we also learned how to find the derivative dy/dx when a curve is defined parametrically by equations $x = x(t)$ and $y = y(t)$.

A third situation occurs when we encounter equations like

$$x^2 + y^2 - 25 = 0, \qquad y^2 - x = 0, \qquad \text{or} \quad x^3 + y^3 - 9xy = 0.$$

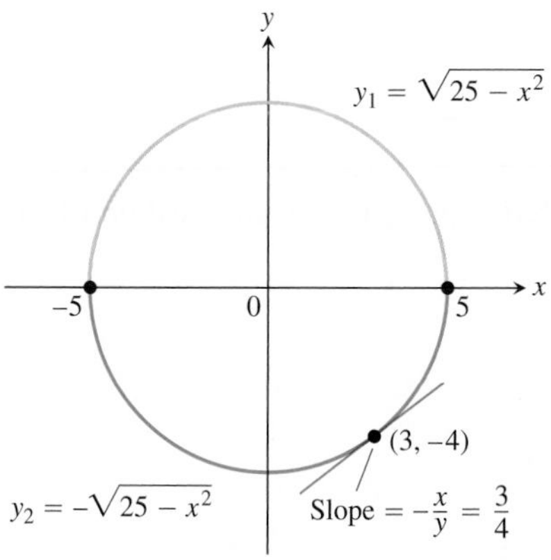

FIGURE 3.31 The circle combines the graphs of two functions. The graph of y_2 is the lower semicircle and passes through $(3, -4)$.

(See Figures 3.31, 3.32, and 3.33.) These equations define an *implicit* relation between the variables x and y. In some cases we may be able to solve such an equation for y as an explicit function (or even several functions) of x. When we cannot put an equation $F(x, y) = 0$ in the form $y = f(x)$ to differentiate it in the usual way, we may still be able to find dy/dx by *implicit differentiation*. This section describes the technique.

Implicitly Defined Functions

We begin with examples involving familiar equations for which we can solve for y as a function of x to calculate dy/dx in the usual way. Then we differentiate the equations implicitly, and find the derivative to provide a comparison of the two methods. Following the examples, we summarize the steps involved in the new method. In the examples and exercises, it is always assumed that the given equation determines y implicitly as a differentiable function of x so that dy/dx exists.

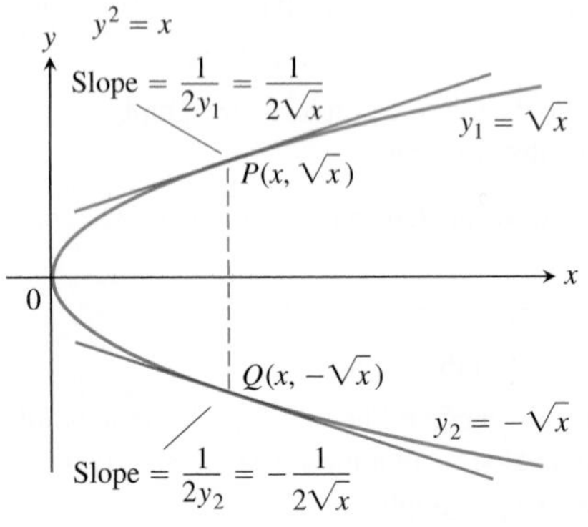

FIGURE 3.32 The equation $y^2 - x = 0$, or $y^2 = x$ as it is usually written, defines two differentiable functions of x on the interval $x \geq 0$. Example 1 shows how to find the derivatives of these functions without solving the equation $y^2 = x$ for y.

EXAMPLE 1 Find dy/dx if $y^2 = x$.

Solution The equation $y^2 = x$ defines two differentiable functions of x that we can actually find, namely $y_1 = \sqrt{x}$ and $y_2 = -\sqrt{x}$ (Figure 3.32). We know how to calculate the derivative of each of these for $x > 0$:

$$\frac{dy_1}{dx} = \frac{1}{2\sqrt{x}} \quad \text{and} \quad \frac{dy_2}{dx} = -\frac{1}{2\sqrt{x}}.$$

But suppose that we knew only that the equation $y^2 = x$ defined y as one or more differentiable functions of x for $x > 0$ without knowing exactly what these functions were. Could we still find dy/dx?

The answer is yes. To find dy/dx, we simply differentiate both sides of the equation $y^2 = x$ with respect to x, treating $y = f(x)$ as a differentiable function of x:

$$y^2 = x$$

$$2y\frac{dy}{dx} = 1 \qquad \text{The Chain Rule gives } \frac{d}{dx}(y^2) = \frac{d}{dx}[f(x)]^2 = 2f(x)f'(x) = 2y\frac{dy}{dx}.$$

$$\frac{dy}{dx} = \frac{1}{2y}.$$

This one formula gives the derivatives we calculated for *both* explicit solutions $y_1 = \sqrt{x}$ and $y_2 = -\sqrt{x}$:

$$\frac{dy_1}{dx} = \frac{1}{2y_1} = \frac{1}{2\sqrt{x}} \quad \text{and} \quad \frac{dy_2}{dx} = \frac{1}{2y_2} = \frac{1}{2\left(-\sqrt{x}\right)} = -\frac{1}{2\sqrt{x}}.$$ ■

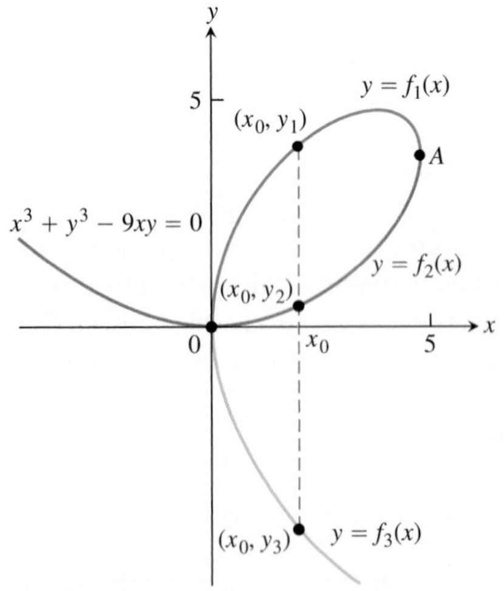

FIGURE 3.33 The curve $x^3 + y^3 - 9xy = 0$ is not the graph of any one function of x. The curve can, however, be divided into separate arcs that *are* the graphs of functions of x. This particular curve, called a *folium*, dates to Descartes in 1638.

EXAMPLE 2 Find the slope of the circle $x^2 + y^2 = 25$ at the point $(3, -4)$.

Solution The circle is not the graph of a single function of x. Rather it is the combined graphs of two differentiable functions, $y_1 = \sqrt{25 - x^2}$ and $y_2 = -\sqrt{25 - x^2}$ (Figure 3.31). The point $(3, -4)$ lies on the graph of y_2, so we can find the slope by calculating explicitly:

$$\left.\frac{dy_2}{dx}\right|_{x=3} = -\left.\frac{-2x}{2\sqrt{25 - x^2}}\right|_{x=3} = -\frac{-6}{2\sqrt{25 - 9}} = \frac{3}{4}.$$

We can solve this problem more easily by differentiating the given equation of the circle implicitly with respect to x:

$$\frac{d}{dx}(x^2) + \frac{d}{dx}(y^2) = \frac{d}{dx}(25)$$

$$2x + 2y\frac{dy}{dx} = 0$$

$$\frac{dy}{dx} = -\frac{x}{y}.$$

The slope at $(3, -4)$ is $\left.-\frac{x}{y}\right|_{(3,-4)} = -\frac{3}{-4} = \frac{3}{4}.$

Notice that unlike the slope formula for dy_2/dx, which applies only to points below the x-axis, the formula $dy/dx = -x/y$ applies everywhere the circle has a slope. Notice also that the derivative involves *both* variables x and y, not just the independent variable x. ■

To calculate the derivatives of other implicitly defined functions, we proceed as in Examples 1 and 2: We treat y as a differentiable implicit function of x and apply the usual rules to differentiate both sides of the defining equation.

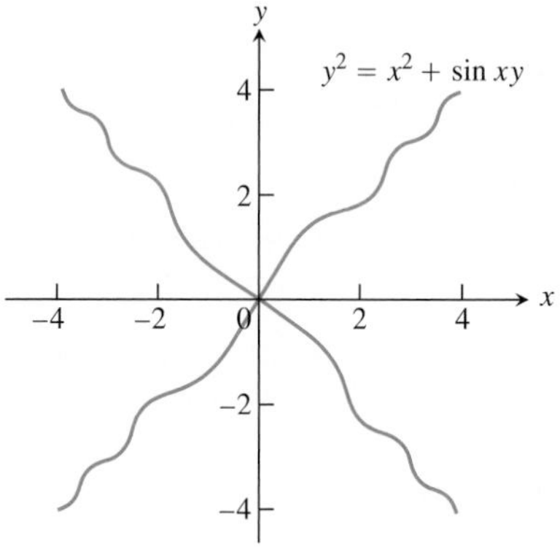

FIGURE 3.34 The graph of $y^2 = x^2 + \sin xy$ in Example 3. The example shows how to find slopes on this implicitly defined curve.

EXAMPLE 3 Find dy/dx if $y^2 = x^2 + \sin xy$ (Figure 3.34).

Solution

$$y^2 = x^2 + \sin xy$$

$$\frac{d}{dx}(y^2) = \frac{d}{dx}(x^2) + \frac{d}{dx}(\sin xy) \qquad \text{Differentiate both sides with respect to } x \ldots$$

$$2y\frac{dy}{dx} = 2x + (\cos xy)\frac{d}{dx}(xy) \qquad \ldots \text{treating } y \text{ as a function of } x \text{ and using the Chain Rule.}$$

$$2y\frac{dy}{dx} = 2x + (\cos xy)\left(y + x\frac{dy}{dx}\right) \qquad \text{Treat } xy \text{ as a product.}$$

$$2y\frac{dy}{dx} - (\cos xy)\left(x\frac{dy}{dx}\right) = 2x + (\cos xy)y \qquad \text{Collect terms with } dy/dx \ldots$$

$$(2y - x\cos xy)\frac{dy}{dx} = 2x + y\cos xy \qquad \ldots \text{and factor out } dy/dx.$$

$$\frac{dy}{dx} = \frac{2x + y\cos xy}{2y - x\cos xy} \qquad \text{Solve for } dy/dx \text{ by dividing.}$$

Notice that the formula for dy/dx applies everywhere that the implicitly defined curve has a slope. Notice again that the derivative involves *both* variables x and y, not just the independent variable x. ■

Implicit Differentiation

1. Differentiate both sides of the equation with respect to x, treating y as a differentiable function of x.
2. Collect the terms with dy/dx on one side of the equation.
3. Solve for dy/dx.

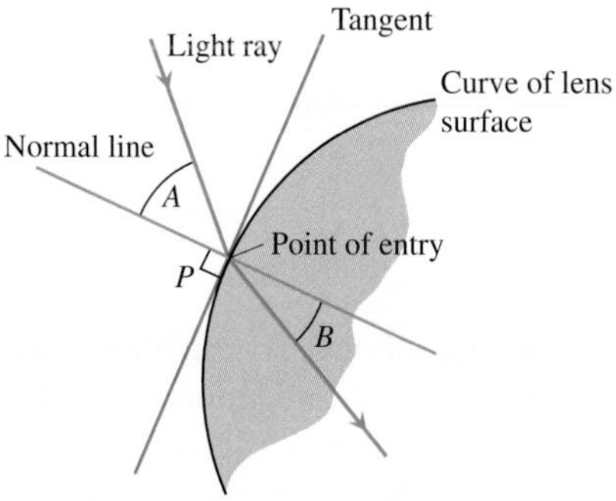

FIGURE 3.35 The profile of a lens, showing the bending (refraction) of a ray of light as it passes through the lens surface.

Lenses, Tangents, and Normal Lines

In the law that describes how light changes direction as it enters a lens, the important angles are the angles the light makes with the line perpendicular to the surface of the lens at the point of entry (angles A and B in Figure 3.35). This line is called the *normal* to the surface at the point of entry. In a profile view of a lens like the one in Figure 3.35, the **normal** is the line perpendicular to the tangent of the profile curve at the point of entry.

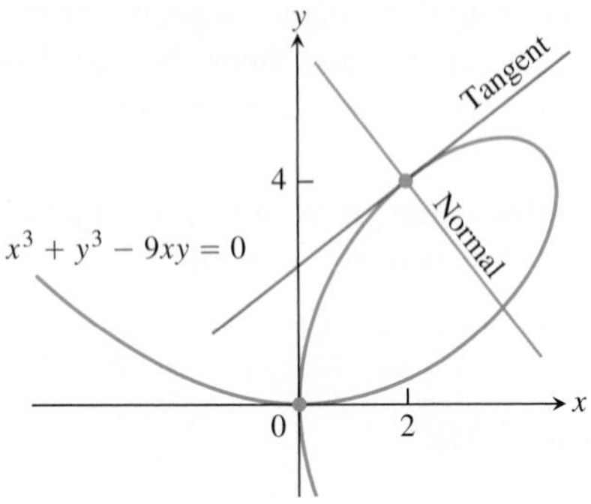

FIGURE 3.36 Example 4 shows how to find equations for the tangent and normal to the folium of Descartes at (2, 4).

EXAMPLE 4 Show that the point (2, 4) lies on the curve $x^3 + y^3 - 9xy = 0$. Then find the tangent and normal to the curve there (Figure 3.36).

Solution The point (2, 4) lies on the curve because its coordinates satisfy the equation given for the curve: $2^3 + 4^3 - 9(2)(4) = 8 + 64 - 72 = 0$.

To find the slope of the curve at (2, 4), we first use implicit differentiation to find a formula for dy/dx:

$$x^3 + y^3 - 9xy = 0$$

$$\frac{d}{dx}(x^3) + \frac{d}{dx}(y^3) - \frac{d}{dx}(9xy) = \frac{d}{dx}(0)$$

$$3x^2 + 3y^2\frac{dy}{dx} - 9\left(x\frac{dy}{dx} + y\frac{dx}{dx}\right) = 0 \qquad \text{Differentiate both sides with respect to } x.$$

$$(3y^2 - 9x)\frac{dy}{dx} + 3x^2 - 9y = 0 \qquad \text{Treat } xy \text{ as a product and } y \text{ as a function of } x.$$

$$3(y^2 - 3x)\frac{dy}{dx} = 9y - 3x^2$$

$$\frac{dy}{dx} = \frac{3y - x^2}{y^2 - 3x}. \qquad \text{Solve for } dy/dx.$$

We then evaluate the derivative at $(x, y) = (2, 4)$:

$$\left.\frac{dy}{dx}\right|_{(2,4)} = \left.\frac{3y - x^2}{y^2 - 3x}\right|_{(2,4)} = \frac{3(4) - 2^2}{4^2 - 3(2)} = \frac{8}{10} = \frac{4}{5}.$$

The tangent at (2, 4) is the line through (2, 4) with slope 4/5:

$$y = 4 + \frac{4}{5}(x - 2)$$

$$y = \frac{4}{5}x + \frac{12}{5}.$$

The normal to the curve at (2, 4) is the line perpendicular to the tangent there, the line through (2, 4) with slope $-5/4$:

$$y = 4 - \frac{5}{4}(x - 2)$$

$$y = -\frac{5}{4}x + \frac{13}{2}.$$

■

The quadratic formula enables us to solve a second-degree equation like $y^2 - 2xy + 3x^2 = 0$ for y in terms of x. There is a formula for the three roots of a cubic equation that is like the quadratic formula but much more complicated. If this formula is used to solve the equation $x^3 + y^3 = 9xy$ for y in terms of x, then three functions determined by the equation are

$$y = f(x) = \sqrt[3]{-\frac{x^3}{2} + \sqrt{\frac{x^6}{4} - 27x^3}} + \sqrt[3]{-\frac{x^3}{2} - \sqrt{\frac{x^6}{4} - 27x^3}}$$

and

$$y = \frac{1}{2}\left[-f(x) \pm \sqrt{-3}\left(\sqrt[3]{-\frac{x^3}{2} + \sqrt{\frac{x^6}{4} - 27x^3}} - \sqrt[3]{-\frac{x^3}{2} - \sqrt{\frac{x^6}{4} - 27x^3}}\right)\right].$$

Using implicit differentiation in Example 4 was much simpler than calculating dy/dx directly from any of the above formulas. Finding slopes on curves defined by higher-degree equations usually requires implicit differentiation because we cannot find an explicit formula for y.

Derivatives of Higher Order

Implicit differentiation can also be used to find higher derivatives. Here is an example.

EXAMPLE 5 Find d^2y/dx^2 if $2x^3 - 3y^2 = 8$.

Solution To start, we differentiate both sides of the equation with respect to x in order to find $y' = dy/dx$.

$$\frac{d}{dx}(2x^3 - 3y^2) = \frac{d}{dx}(8)$$

$$6x^2 - 6yy' = 0 \qquad \text{Treat } y \text{ as a function of } x.$$

$$y' = \frac{x^2}{y}, \quad \text{when } y \neq 0 \qquad \text{Solve for } y'.$$

We now apply the Quotient Rule to find y''.

$$y'' = \frac{d}{dx}\left(\frac{x^2}{y}\right) = \frac{2xy - x^2y'}{y^2} = \frac{2x}{y} - \frac{x^2}{y^2}\cdot y'$$

Finally, we substitute $y' = x^2/y$ to express y'' in terms of x and y.

$$y'' = \frac{2x}{y} - \frac{x^2}{y^2}\left(\frac{x^2}{y}\right) = \frac{2x}{y} - \frac{x^4}{y^3}, \quad \text{when } y \neq 0$$

■

EXERCISE 3.6

Use implicit differentiation to find dy/dx in Exercises 1–14.

1. $x^2y + xy^2 = 6$
2. $x^3 + y^3 = 18xy$
3. $2xy + y^2 = x + y$
4. $x^3 - xy + y^3 = 1$
5. $x^2(x - y)^2 = x^2 - y^2$
6. $(3xy + 7)^2 = 6y$
7. $y^2 = \frac{x - 1}{x + 1}$
8. $x^2 = \frac{x - y}{x + y}$
9. $x = \tan y$
10. $xy = \cot(xy)$
11. $e^{2x} = \sin(x + 3y)$
12. $x + \sin y = xy$
13. $y \sin\left(\frac{1}{y}\right) = 1 - xy$
14. $e^{x^2y} = 2x + 2y$

Find $dr/d\theta$ in Exercises 15–18.

15. $\theta^{1/2} + r^{1/2} = 1$
16. $r - 2\sqrt{\theta} = \frac{3}{2}\theta^{2/3} + \frac{4}{3}\theta^{3/4}$
17. $\sin(r\theta) = \frac{1}{2}$
18. $\cos r + \cot\theta = e^{r\theta}$

In Exercises 19–26, use implicit differentiation to find dy/dx and then d^2y/dx^2.

19. $x^2 + y^2 = 1$
20. $x^{2/3} + y^{2/3} = 1$
21. $y^2 = e^{x^2} + 2x$
22. $y^2 - 2x = 1 - 2y$
23. $2\sqrt{y} = x - y$
24. $xy + y^2 = 1$

25. If $x^3 + y^3 = 16$, find the value of d^2y/dx^2 at the point (2, 2).

26. If $xy + y^2 = 1$, find the value of d^2y/dx^2 at the point $(0, -1)$.

In Exercises 27 and 28, find the slope of the curve at the given points.

27. $y^2 + x^2 = y^4 - 2x$ at $(-2, 1)$ and $(-2, -1)$

28. $(x^2 + y^2)^2 = (x - y)^2$ at $(1, 0)$ and $(1, -1)$

In Exercises 29–38, verify that the given point is on the curve and find the lines that are **(a)** tangent and **(b)** normal to the curve at the given point.

29. $x^2 + xy - y^2 = 1, \quad (2, 3)$

30. $x^2 + y^2 = 25, \quad (3, -4)$

31. $x^2y^2 = 9, \quad (-1, 3)$

32. $y^2 - 2x - 4y - 1 = 0, \quad (-2, 1)$

33. $6x^2 + 3xy + 2y^2 + 17y - 6 = 0, \quad (-1, 0)$

34. $x^2 - \sqrt{3}xy + 2y^2 = 5, \quad (\sqrt{3}, 2)$

35. $2xy + \pi \sin y = 2\pi, \quad (1, \pi/2)$

36. $x \sin 2y = y \cos 2x, \quad (\pi/4, \pi/2)$

37. $y = 2 \sin(\pi x - y), \quad (1, 0)$

38. $x^2 \cos^2 y - \sin y = 0, \quad (0, \pi)$

39. **Parallel tangents** Find the two points where the curve $x^2 + xy + y^2 = 7$ crosses the x-axis, and show that the tangents to the curve at these points are parallel. What is the common slope of these tangents?

40. **Power rule for rational exponents** Let p and q be integers with $q > 0$. If $y = x^{p/q}$, differentiate the equivalent equation $y^q = x^p$ implicitly and show that, for $y \neq 0$,

$$\frac{d}{dx}x^{p/q} = \frac{p}{q}x^{(p/q)-1}.$$

41. **The eight curve** Find the slopes of the curve $y^4 = y^2 - x^2$ at the two points shown here.

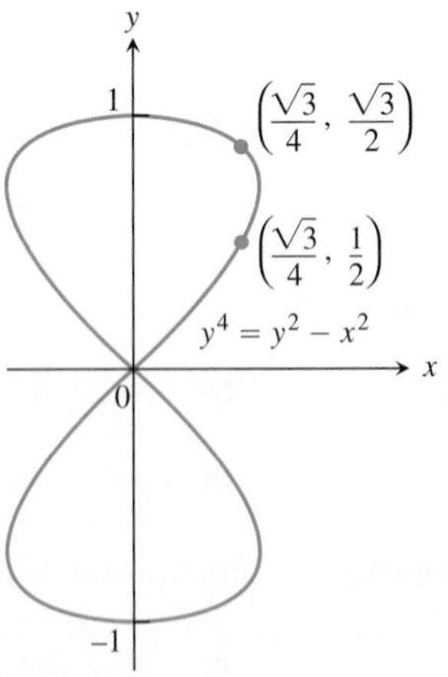

42. **The cissoid of Diocles (from about 200 B.C.)** Find equations for the tangent and normal to the cissoid of Diocles $y^2(2 - x) = x^3$ at (1, 1).

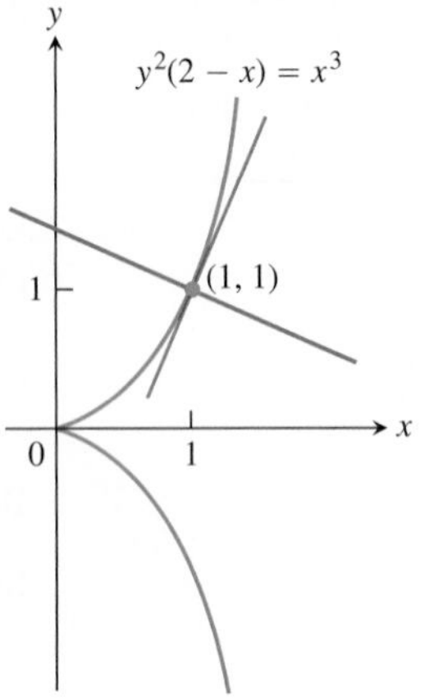

43. **The devil's curve (Gabriel Cramer, 1750)** Find the slopes of the devil's curve $y^4 - 4y^2 = x^4 - 9x^2$ at the four indicated points.

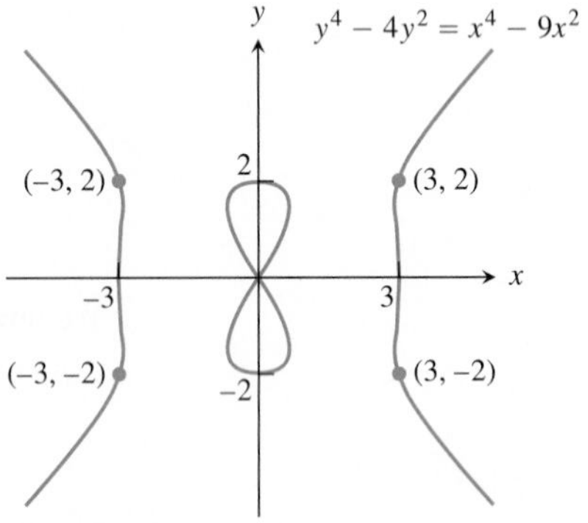

44. **The folium of Descartes** (See Figure 3.33.)

a. Find the slope of the folium of Descartes $x^3 + y^3 - 9xy = 0$ at the points (4, 2) and (2, 4).

b. At what point other than the origin does the folium have a horizontal tangent?

c. Find the coordinates of the point A in Figure 3.33, where the folium has a vertical tangent.

Assuming that the equations in Exercises 45–48 define x and y implicitly as differentiable functions $x = f(t)$, $y = g(t)$, find the slope of the curve $x = f(t)$, $y = g(t)$ at the given value of t.

45. $x^3 + 2t^2 = 9, \quad 2y^3 - 3t^2 = 4, \quad t = 2$

46. $x = \sqrt{5 - \sqrt{t}}, \quad y(t - 1) = \sqrt{t}, \quad t = 4$

47. $x + 2x^{3/2} = t^2 + t, \quad y\sqrt{t + 1} + 2t\sqrt{y} = 4, \quad t = 0$

48. $x \sin t + 2x = t, \quad t \sin t - 2t = y, \quad t = \pi$

49. **Intersecting normal** The line that is normal to the curve $x^2 + 2xy - 3y^2 = 0$ at (1, 1) intersects the curve at what other point?

50. **Normals parallel to a line** Find the normals to the curve $xy + 2x - y = 0$ that are parallel to the line $2x + y = 0$.

51. Normals to a parabola Show that if it is possible to draw three normals from the point $(a, 0)$ to the parabola $x = y^2$ shown here, then a must be greater than $1/2$. One of the normals is the x-axis. For what value of a are the other two normals perpendicular?

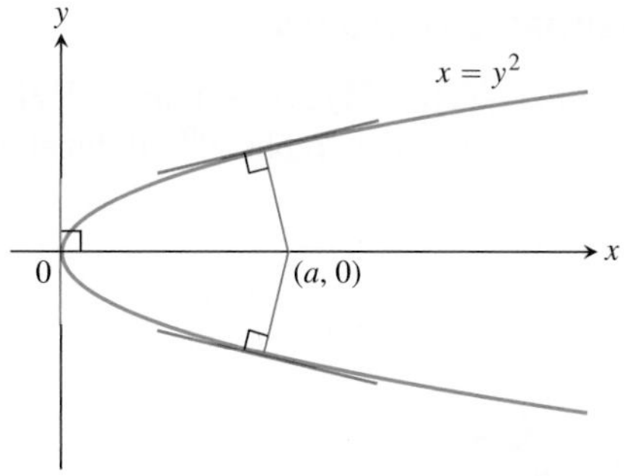

52. Is there anything special about the tangents to the curves $y^2 = x^3$ and $2x^2 + 3y^2 = 5$ at the points $(1, \pm 1)$? Give reasons for your answer.

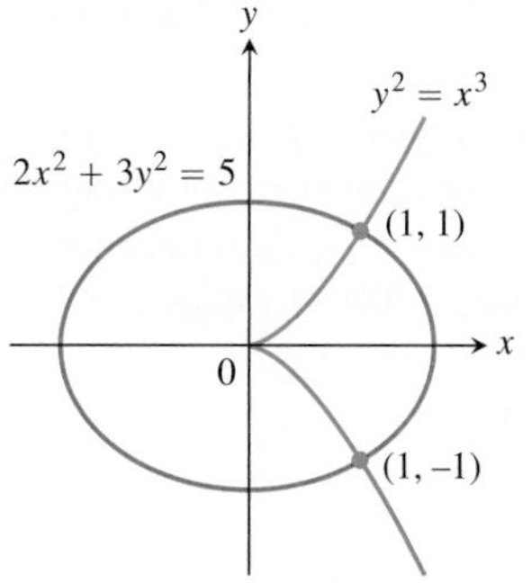

T In Exercises 53 and 54, find both dy/dx (treating y as a differentiable function of x) and dx/dy (treating x as a differentiable function of y). How do dy/dx and dx/dy seem to be related? Explain the relationship geometrically in terms of the graphs.

53. $xy^3 + x^2y = 6$

54. $x^3 + y^2 = \sin^2 y$

COMPUTER EXPLORATIONS

55. a. Given that $x^4 + 4y^2 = 1$, find dy/dx two ways: (1) by solving for y and differentiating the resulting functions in the usual way and (2) by implicit differentiation. Do you get the same result each way?

b. Solve the equation $x^4 + 4y^2 = 1$ for y and graph the resulting functions together to produce a complete graph of the equation $x^4 + 4y^2 = 1$. Then add the graphs of the first derivatives of these functions to your display. Could you have predicted the general behavior of the derivative graphs from looking at the graph of $x^4 + 4y^2 = 1$? Could you have predicted the general behavior of the graph of $x^4 + 4y^2 = 1$ by looking at the derivative graphs? Give reasons for your answers.

56. a. Given that $(x - 2)^2 + y^2 = 4$ find dy/dx two ways: (1) by solving for y and differentiating the resulting functions with respect to x and (2) by implicit differentiation. Do you get the same result each way?

b. Solve the equation $(x - 2)^2 + y^2 = 4$ for y and graph the resulting functions together to produce a complete graph of the equation $(x - 2)^2 + y^2 = 4$. Then add the graphs of the functions' first derivatives to your picture. Could you have predicted the general behavior of the derivative graphs from looking at the graph of $(x - 2)^2 + y^2 = 4$? Could you have predicted the general behavior of the graph of $(x - 2)^2 + y^2 = 4$ by looking at the derivative graphs? Give reasons for your answers.

Use a CAS to perform the following steps in Exercises 57–64.

a. Plot the equation with the implicit plotter of a CAS. Check to see that the given point P satisfies the equation.

b. Using implicit differentiation, find a formula for the derivative dy/dx and evaluate it at the given point P.

c. Use the slope found in part (b) to find an equation for the tangent line to the curve at P. Then plot the implicit curve and tangent line together on a single graph.

57. $x^3 - xy + y^3 = 7, \quad P(2, 1)$

58. $x^5 + y^3x + yx^2 + y^4 = 4, \quad P(1, 1)$

59. $y^2 + y = \dfrac{2 + x}{1 - x}, \quad P(0, 1)$

60. $y^3 + \cos xy = x^2, \quad P(1, 0)$

61. $x + \tan\left(\dfrac{y}{x}\right) = 2, \quad P\left(1, \dfrac{\pi}{4}\right)$

62. $xy^3 + \tan(x + y) = 1, \quad P\left(\dfrac{\pi}{4}, 0\right)$

63. $2y^2 + (xy)^{1/3} = x^2 + 2, \quad P(1, 1)$

64. $x\sqrt{1 + 2y} + y = x^2, \quad P(1, 0)$

3.7 Derivatives of Inverse Functions and Logarithms

In Section 1.5 we saw how the inverse of a function undoes, or inverts, the effect of that function. We defined there the natural logarithm function $f^{-1}(x) = \ln x$ as the inverse of the natural exponential function $f(x) = e^x$. This is one of the most important function-

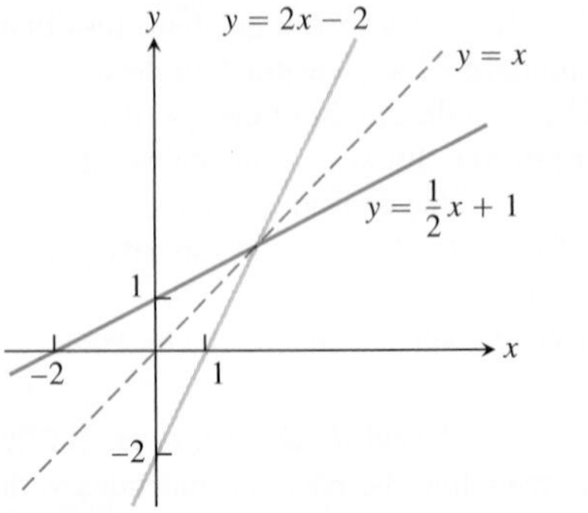

FIGURE 3.37 Graphing a line and its inverse together shows the graphs' symmetry with respect to the line $y = x$. The slopes are reciprocals of each other.

inverse pairs in mathematics and science. We learned how to differentiate the exponential function in Section 3.2. Here we learn a rule for differentiating the inverse of a differentiable function and we apply the rule to find the derivative of the natural logarithm function.

Derivatives of Inverses of Differentiable Functions

We calculated the inverse of the function $f(x) = (1/2)x + 1$ as $f^{-1}(x) = 2x - 2$ in Example 2 of Section 1.5. Figure 3.37 shows again the graphs of both functions. If we calculate their derivatives, we see that

$$\frac{d}{dx} f(x) = \frac{d}{dx}\left(\frac{1}{2}x + 1\right) = \frac{1}{2}$$

$$\frac{d}{dx} f^{-1}(x) = \frac{d}{dx}(2x - 2) = 2.$$

The derivatives are reciprocals of one another, so the slope of one line is the reciprocal of the slope of its inverse line. (See Figure 3.37.)

This is not a special case. Reflecting any nonhorizontal or nonvertical line across the line $y = x$ always inverts the line's slope. If the original line has slope $m \neq 0$, the reflected line has slope $1/m$.

The reciprocal relationship between the slopes of f and f^{-1} holds for other functions as well, but we must be careful to compare slopes at corresponding points. If the slope of $y = f(x)$ at the point $(a, f(a))$ is $f'(a)$ and $f'(a) \neq 0$, then the slope of $y = f^{-1}(x)$ at the point $(f(a), a)$ is the reciprocal $1/f'(a)$ (Figure 3.38). If we set $b = f(a)$, then

$$(f^{-1})'(b) = \frac{1}{f'(a)} = \frac{1}{f'(f^{-1}(b))}.$$

If $y = f(x)$ has a horizontal tangent line at $(a, f(a))$ then the inverse function f^{-1} has a vertical tangent line at $(f(a), a)$, and this infinite slope implies that f^{-1} is not differentiable at $f(a)$. Theorem 4 gives the conditions under which f^{-1} is differentiable in its domain, which is the same as the range of f.

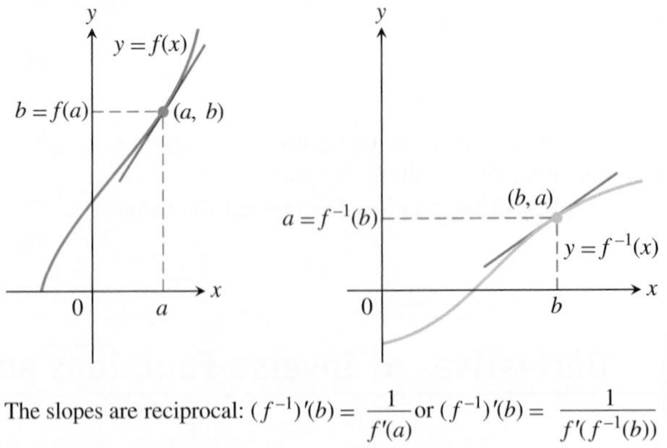

FIGURE 3.38 The graphs of inverse functions have reciprocal slopes at corresponding points.

THEOREM 4—The Derivative Rule for Inverses If f has an interval I as domain and $f'(x)$ exists and is never zero on I, then f^{-1} is differentiable at every point in its domain. The value of $(f^{-1})'$ at a point b in the domain of f^{-1} is the reciprocal of the value of f' at the point $a = f^{-1}(b)$:

$$(f^{-1})'(b) = \frac{1}{f'(f^{-1}(b))}$$

or

$$\left.\frac{df^{-1}}{dx}\right|_{x=b} = \frac{1}{\left.\dfrac{df}{dx}\right|_{x=f^{-1}(b)}} \tag{1}$$

The proof of Theorem 4 is omitted. Evidence for the result can be seen in the following way. When $y = f(x)$ is differentiable at $x = a$ and we change x by a small amount Δx, the corresponding change in y is approximately

$$\Delta y \approx f'(a)\,\Delta x. \qquad \frac{\Delta y}{\Delta x} \approx f'(a)$$

This means that y changes about $f'(a)$ times as fast as x when $x = a$ and that x changes about $1/f'(a)$ times as fast as y when $y = b$. It is reasonable that the derivative of f^{-1} at b is the reciprocal of the derivative of f at a.

EXAMPLE 1 The function $f(x) = x^2, x \geq 0$ and its inverse $f^{-1}(x) = \sqrt{x}$ have derivatives $f'(x) = 2x$ and $(f^{-1})'(x) = 1/(2\sqrt{x})$.

Theorem 4 predicts that the derivative of $f^{-1}(x)$ is

$$\begin{aligned}(f^{-1})'(x) &= \frac{1}{f'(f^{-1}(x))} \\ &= \frac{1}{2(f^{-1}(x))} \qquad f'(x) = 2x \text{ with } x \text{ replaced by } f^{-1}(x) \\ &= \frac{1}{2(\sqrt{x})}.\end{aligned}$$

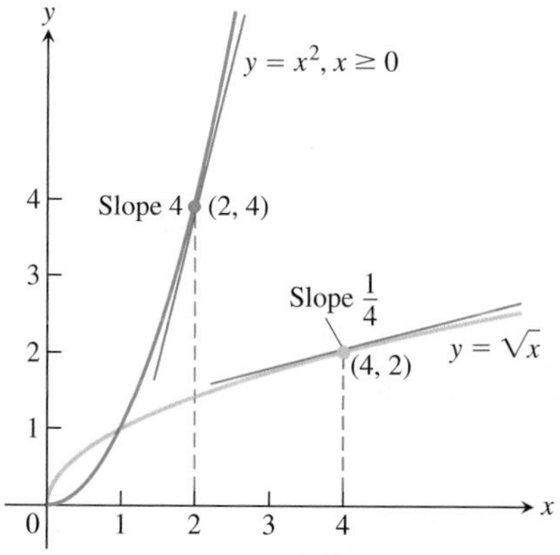

FIGURE 3.39 The derivative of $f^{-1}(x) = \sqrt{x}$ at the point (4, 2) is the reciprocal of the derivative of $f(x) = x^2$ at (2, 4) (Example 1).

Theorem 4 gives a derivative that agrees with our calculation using the Power Rule for the derivative of the square root function.

Let's examine Theorem 4 at a specific point. We pick $x = 2$ (the number a) and $f(2) = 4$ (the value b). Theorem 4 says that the derivative of f at 2, $f'(2) = 4$, and the derivative of f^{-1} at $f(2)$, $(f^{-1})'(4)$, are reciprocals. It states that

$$(f^{-1})'(4) = \frac{1}{f'(f^{-1}(4))} = \frac{1}{f'(2)} = \left.\frac{1}{2x}\right|_{x=2} = \frac{1}{4}.$$

See Figure 3.39. ■

Equation (1) sometimes enables us to find specific values of df^{-1}/dx without knowing a formula for f^{-1}.

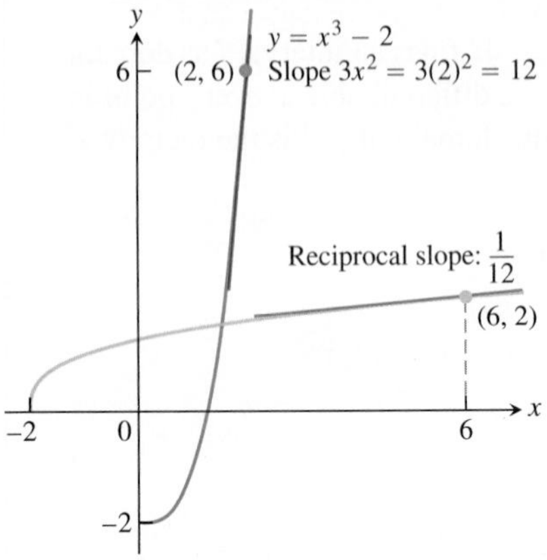

FIGURE 3.40 The derivative of $f(x) = x^3 - 2$ at $x = 2$ tells us the derivative of f^{-1} at $x = 6$ (Example 2).

EXAMPLE 2 Let $f(x) = x^3 - 2$. Find the value of df^{-1}/dx at $x = 6 = f(2)$ without finding a formula for $f^{-1}(x)$.

Solution

$$\left.\frac{df}{dx}\right|_{x=2} = \left.3x^2\right|_{x=2} = 12$$

$$\left.\frac{df^{-1}}{dx}\right|_{x=f(2)} = \frac{1}{\left.\frac{df}{dx}\right|_{x=2}} = \frac{1}{12} \qquad \text{Eq. (1)}$$

See Figure 3.40. ■

Parametrizing Inverse Functions

We can graph or represent any function $y = f(x)$ parametrically as

$$x = t \quad \text{and} \quad y = f(t).$$

Interchanging t and $f(t)$ produces parametric equations for the inverse:

$$x = f(t) \quad \text{and} \quad y = t$$

(see Section 3.5).

For example, to graph the one-to-one function $f(x) = x^2, x \geq 0$, on a graphing device together with its inverse and the line $y = x, x \geq 0$, use the parametric graphing option with

$$\begin{aligned} &\text{Graph of } f: && x_1 = t, && y_1 = t^2, && t \geq 0 \\ &\text{Graph of } f^{-1}: && x_2 = t^2, && y_2 = t \\ &\text{Graph of } y = x: && x_3 = t, && y_3 = t \end{aligned}$$

Derivative of the Natural Logarithm Function

Since we know the exponential function $f(x) = e^x$ is differentiable everywhere, we can apply Theorem 4 to find the derivative of its inverse $f^{-1}(x) = \ln x$:

$$\begin{aligned} (f^{-1})'(x) &= \frac{1}{f'(f^{-1}(x))} && \text{Theorem 4} \\ &= \frac{1}{e^{f^{-1}(x)}} && f'(u) = e^u \\ &= \frac{1}{e^{\ln x}} \\ &= \frac{1}{x} && \text{Inverse function relationship} \end{aligned}$$

Alternate Derivation Instead of applying Theorem 4 directly, we can find the derivative of $y = \ln x$ using implicit differentiation, as follows:

$$\begin{aligned} y &= \ln x \\ e^y &= x && \text{Inverse function relationship} \\ \frac{d}{dx}(e^y) &= \frac{d}{dx}(x) && \text{Differentiate implicitly} \\ e^y \frac{dy}{dx} &= 1 && \text{Chain Rule} \\ \frac{dy}{dx} &= \frac{1}{e^y} = \frac{1}{x} && e^y = x \end{aligned}$$

No matter which derivation we use, the derivative of $y = \ln x$ with respect to x is

$$\frac{d}{dx}(\ln x) = \frac{1}{x}, \quad x > 0.$$

If u is a differentiable function of x with $u > 0$, we apply the Chain Rule to get

$$\frac{d}{dx}(\ln u) = \frac{1}{u}\frac{du}{dx}, \qquad u > 0 \tag{2}$$

EXAMPLE 3

(a) $\dfrac{d}{dx}\ln 2x = \dfrac{1}{2x}\dfrac{d}{dx}(2x) = \dfrac{1}{2x}(2) = \dfrac{1}{x}$

(b) Equation (2) with $u = x^2 + 3$ gives

$$\frac{d}{dx}\ln(x^2+3) = \frac{1}{x^2+3}\cdot\frac{d}{dx}(x^2+3) = \frac{1}{x^2+3}\cdot 2x = \frac{2x}{x^2+3}.$$ ■

Notice the remarkable occurrence in Example 3(a). The function $y = \ln 2x$ has the same derivative as the function $y = \ln x$. This is true of $y = \ln bx$ for any constant b, provided that $bx > 0$:

$$\frac{d}{dx}\ln bx = \frac{1}{bx}\cdot\frac{d}{dx}(bx) = \frac{1}{bx}(b) = \frac{1}{x}. \tag{3}$$

If $x < 0$ and $b < 0$, then $bx > 0$ and Equation (3) still applies. In particular, if $x < 0$ and $b = -1$ we get

$$\frac{d}{dx}\ln(-x) = \frac{1}{x} \qquad \text{for } x < 0.$$

Since $|x| = x$ when $x > 0$ and $|x| = -x$ when $x < 0$, we have the important result

$$\frac{d}{dx}\ln|x| = \frac{1}{x}, \quad x \neq 0 \tag{4}$$

The Derivatives of a^u and $\log_a u$

We start with the equation $a^x = e^{\ln(a^x)} = e^{x \ln a}$:

$$\frac{d}{dx}a^x = \frac{d}{dx}e^{x\ln a} = e^{x\ln a}\cdot\frac{d}{dx}(x\ln a) \qquad \frac{d}{dx}e^u = e^u\frac{du}{dx}$$
$$= a^x \ln a.$$

If $a > 0$, then

$$\frac{d}{dx}a^x = a^x \ln a.$$

This equation shows why e^x is the exponential function preferred in calculus. If $a = e$, then $\ln a = 1$ and the derivative of a^x simplifies to

$$\frac{d}{dx}e^x = e^x \ln e = e^x.$$

With the Chain Rule, we get a more general form for the derivative of an exponential function.

> If $a > 0$ and u is a differentiable function of x, then a^u is a differentiable function of x and
>
> $$\frac{d}{dx}a^u = a^u \ln a \frac{du}{dx}. \qquad (5)$$

In Section 3.2 we looked at the derivative $f'(0)$ for the exponential functions $f(x) = a^x$ at various values of the base a. The number $f'(0)$ is the limit, $\lim_{h\to 0}(a^h - 1)/h$, and gives the slope of the graph of a^x when it crosses the y-axis at the point (0, 1). We now see that the value of this slope is

$$\lim_{h\to 0}\frac{a^h - 1}{h} = \ln a. \qquad (6)$$

In particular, when $a = e$ we obtain

$$\lim_{h\to 0}\frac{e^h - 1}{h} = \ln e = 1.$$

However, we have not fully justified that these limits actually exist. While all of the arguments given in deriving the derivatives of the exponential and logarithmic functions are correct, they do assume the existence of these limits. In Chapter 5 we will give another development of the theory of logarithmic and exponential functions which fully justifies that both limits do in fact exist and have the values derived above.

To find the derivative of $\log_a u$ for an arbitrary base ($a > 0$, $a \neq 1$), we start with the change-of-base formula for logarithms (reviewed in Section 1.5) and express $\log_a u$ in terms of natural logarithms,

$$\log_a x = \frac{\ln x}{\ln a}.$$

Taking derivatives, we have

$$\begin{aligned}\frac{d}{dx}\log_a x &= \frac{d}{dx}\left(\frac{\ln x}{\ln a}\right)\\ &= \frac{1}{\ln a}\cdot\frac{d}{dx}\ln x \qquad \text{ln } a \text{ is a constant}\\ &= \frac{1}{\ln a}\cdot\frac{1}{x}\\ &= \frac{1}{x\ln a}.\end{aligned}$$

If u is a differentiable function of x and $u > 0$, the Chain Rule gives the following formula.

For $a > 0$ and $a \neq 1$,

$$\frac{d}{dx}\log_a u = \frac{1}{u\ln a}\frac{du}{dx}. \qquad (7)$$

Logarithmic Differentiation

The derivatives of positive functions given by formulas that involve products, quotients, and powers can often be found more quickly if we take the natural logarithm of both sides before differentiating. This enables us to use the laws of logarithms to simplify the formulas before differentiating. The process, called **logarithmic differentiation**, is illustrated in the next example.

EXAMPLE 4 Find dy/dx if

$$y = \frac{(x^2+1)(x+3)^{1/2}}{x-1}, \qquad x > 1.$$

Solution We take the natural logarithm of both sides and simplify the result with the algebraic properties of logarithms in Section 1.5:

$$\begin{aligned}\ln y &= \ln\frac{(x^2+1)(x+3)^{1/2}}{x-1}\\ &= \ln\left((x^2+1)(x+3)^{1/2}\right) - \ln(x-1) \qquad \text{Rule 2}\\ &= \ln(x^2+1) + \ln(x+3)^{1/2} - \ln(x-1) \qquad \text{Rule 1}\\ &= \ln(x^2+1) + \frac{1}{2}\ln(x+3) - \ln(x-1). \qquad \text{Rule 3}\end{aligned}$$

We then take derivatives of both sides with respect to x, using Equation (2) on the left:

$$\frac{1}{y}\frac{dy}{dx} = \frac{1}{x^2+1}\cdot 2x + \frac{1}{2}\cdot\frac{1}{x+3} - \frac{1}{x-1}.$$

Next we solve for dy/dx:

$$\frac{dy}{dx} = y\left(\frac{2x}{x^2 + 1} + \frac{1}{2x + 6} - \frac{1}{x - 1}\right).$$

Finally, we substitute for y:

$$\frac{dy}{dx} = \frac{(x^2 + 1)(x + 3)^{1/2}}{x - 1}\left(\frac{2x}{x^2 + 1} + \frac{1}{2x + 6} - \frac{1}{x - 1}\right).$$

■

Proof of the Power Rule (General Version)

We can now define x^n for any $x > 0$ and any real number n as $x^n = e^{n \ln x}$. Therefore, the n in the equation $\ln x^n = n \ln x$ no longer needs to be rational—it can be any fixed number as long as $x > 0$:

$$\ln x^n = \ln (e^{n \ln x}) = n \ln x \qquad \ln e^u = u, \text{ any } u$$

Together, the law $a^x/a^y = a^{x-y}$ and the definition $x^n = e^{n \ln x}$ enable us to establish the Power Rule for differentiation for any real number n. Differentiating x^n with respect to x gives

$$\begin{aligned}
\frac{d}{dx}x^n &= \frac{d}{dx}e^{n \ln x} && \text{Definition of } x^n, x > 0 \\
&= e^{n \ln x} \cdot \frac{d}{dx}(n \ln x) && \text{Chain Rule for } e^u \\
&= x^n \cdot \frac{n}{x} && \text{The definition again} \\
&= nx^{n-1}.
\end{aligned}$$

In short, as long as $x > 0$,

$$\frac{d}{dx}x^n = nx^{n-1}.$$

If $y = x^n$, y', and x^{n-1} all exist for $x < 0$, then

$$\ln|y| = \ln|x|^n = n \ln|x|.$$

Using logarithmic differentiation and Equation (4) we have

$$\frac{y'}{y} = \frac{n}{x}.$$

Solving for the derivative,

$$y' = n\frac{y}{x} = n\frac{x^n}{x} = nx^{n-1}.$$

(Notice in this case the need to *assume* the existence of the derivative y'.)

It can also be shown directly from the definition of the derivative that the derivative equals 0 when $x = 0$ and $n \neq 0$. This completes the proof of the general version of the Power Rule for all values of x. ■

EXAMPLE 5 Differentiate $f(x) = x^x, x > 0$.

Solution We note that $f(x) = x^x = e^{x \ln x}$, so differentiation gives

$$\begin{aligned} f'(x) &= \frac{d}{dx}(e^{x \ln x}) \\ &= e^{x \ln x}\frac{d}{dx}(x \ln x) && \tfrac{d}{dx}e^u,\ u = x \ln x \\ &= e^{x \ln x}\left(\ln x + x \cdot \frac{1}{x}\right) \\ &= x^x(\ln x + 1) && x > 0 \end{aligned}$$

■

The Number e Expressed as a Limit

In Section 1.4 we defined the number e as the base value for which the exponential function $y = a^x$ has slope 1 when it crosses the y-axis at $(0, 1)$. Thus e is the constant that satisfies the equation

$$\lim_{h \to 0} \frac{e^h - 1}{h} = \ln e = 1. \qquad \text{slope equals } \ln e \text{ from Eq. (6)}$$

We also stated that e could be calculated as $\lim_{y \to \infty}(1 + 1/y)^y$, or by substituting $y = 1/x$, as $\lim_{x \to 0}(1 + x)^{1/x}$. We now prove this result.

> **THEOREM 5—The Number e as a Limit** The number e can be calculated as the limit
>
> $$e = \lim_{x \to 0}(1 + x)^{1/x}.$$

Proof If $f(x) = \ln x$, then $f'(x) = 1/x$, so $f'(1) = 1$. But, by the definition of derivative,

$$\begin{aligned} f'(1) &= \lim_{h \to 0}\frac{f(1 + h) - f(1)}{h} = \lim_{x \to 0}\frac{f(1 + x) - f(1)}{x} \\ &= \lim_{x \to 0}\frac{\ln(1 + x) - \ln 1}{x} = \lim_{x \to 0}\frac{1}{x}\ln(1 + x) && \ln 1 = 0 \\ &= \lim_{x \to 0}\ln(1 + x)^{1/x} = \ln\left[\lim_{x \to 0}(1 + x)^{1/x}\right] && \text{ln is continuous, Theorem 11 in Chapter 2} \end{aligned}$$

Because $f'(1) = 1$, we have

$$\ln\left[\lim_{x \to 0}(1 + x)^{1/x}\right] = 1$$

Therefore, exponentiating both sides we get

$$\lim_{x \to 0}(1 + x)^{1/x} = e.$$

■

Approximating the limit in Theorem 5 by taking x very small gives approximations to e. Its value is $e \approx 2.718281828459045$ to 15 decimal places.

EXERCISES 3.7

In Exercises 1–4:

a. Find $f^{-1}(x)$.

b. Graph f and f^{-1} together.

c. Evaluate df/dx at $x = a$ and df^{-1}/dx at $x = f(a)$ to show that at these points $df^{-1}/dx = 1/(df/dx)$.

1. $f(x) = 2x + 3, \quad a = -1$

2. $f(x) = (1/5)x + 7, \quad a = -1$

3. $f(x) = 5 - 4x, \quad a = 1/2$

4. $f(x) = 2x^2, \quad x \geq 0, \quad a = 5$

5. a. Show that $f(x) = x^3$ and $g(x) = \sqrt[3]{x}$ are inverses of one another.

b. Graph f and g over an x-interval large enough to show the graphs intersecting at $(1, 1)$ and $(-1, -1)$. Be sure the picture shows the required symmetry about the line $y = x$.

c. Find the slopes of the tangents to the graphs of f and g at $(1, 1)$ and $(-1, -1)$ (four tangents in all).

d. What lines are tangent to the curves at the origin?

6. a. Show that $h(x) = x^3/4$ and $k(x) = (4x)^{1/3}$ are inverses of one another.

b. Graph h and k over an x-interval large enough to show the graphs intersecting at $(2, 2)$ and $(-2, -2)$. Be sure the picture shows the required symmetry about the line $y = x$.

c. Find the slopes of the tangents to the graphs at h and k at $(2, 2)$ and $(-2, -2)$.

d. What lines are tangent to the curves at the origin?

7. Let $f(x) = x^3 - 3x^2 - 1, x \geq 2$. Find the value of df^{-1}/dx at the point $x = -1 = f(3)$.

8. Let $f(x) = x^2 - 4x - 5, x > 2$. Find the value of df^{-1}/dx at the point $x = 0 = f(5)$.

9. Suppose that the differentiable function $y = f(x)$ has an inverse and that the graph of f passes through the point $(2, 4)$ and has a slope of $1/3$ there. Find the value of df^{-1}/dx at $x = 4$.

10. Suppose that the differentiable function $y = g(x)$ has an inverse and that the graph of g passes through the origin with slope 2. Find the slope of the graph of g^{-1} at the origin.

In Exercises 11–40, find the derivative of y with respect to x, t, or θ, as appropriate.

11. $y = \ln 3x$

12. $y = \ln kx$, k constant

13. $y = \ln (t^2)$

14. $y = \ln (t^{3/2})$

15. $y = \ln \dfrac{3}{x}$

16. $y = \ln \dfrac{10}{x}$

17. $y = \ln (\theta + 1)$

18. $y = \ln (2\theta + 2)$

19. $y = \ln x^3$

20. $y = (\ln x)^3$

21. $y = t(\ln t)^2$

22. $y = t\sqrt{\ln t}$

23. $y = \dfrac{x^4}{4}\ln x - \dfrac{x^4}{16}$

24. $y = \dfrac{x^3}{3}\ln x - \dfrac{x^3}{9}$

25. $y = \dfrac{\ln t}{t}$

26. $y = \dfrac{1 + \ln t}{t}$

27. $y = \dfrac{\ln x}{1 + \ln x}$

28. $y = \dfrac{x \ln x}{1 + \ln x}$

29. $y = \ln (\ln x)$

30. $y = \ln (\ln (\ln x))$

31. $y = \theta(\sin (\ln \theta) + \cos (\ln \theta))$

32. $y = \ln (\sec \theta + \tan \theta)$

33. $y = \ln \dfrac{1}{x\sqrt{x + 1}}$

34. $y = \dfrac{1}{2}\ln \dfrac{1 + x}{1 - x}$

35. $y = \dfrac{1 + \ln t}{1 - \ln t}$

36. $y = \sqrt{\ln \sqrt{t}}$

37. $y = \ln (\sec (\ln \theta))$

38. $y = \ln \left(\dfrac{\sqrt{\sin \theta \cos \theta}}{1 + 2\ln \theta}\right)$

39. $y = \ln \left(\dfrac{(x^2 + 1)^5}{\sqrt{1 - x}}\right)$

40. $y = \ln \sqrt{\dfrac{(x + 1)^5}{(x + 2)^{20}}}$

In Exercises 41–54, use logarithmic differentiation to find the derivative of y with respect to the given independent variable.

41. $y = \sqrt{x(x + 1)}$

42. $y = \sqrt{(x^2 + 1)(x - 1)^2}$

43. $y = \sqrt{\dfrac{t}{t + 1}}$

44. $y = \sqrt{\dfrac{1}{t(t + 1)}}$

45. $y = \sqrt{\theta + 3}\sin \theta$

46. $y = (\tan \theta)\sqrt{2\theta + 1}$

47. $y = t(t + 1)(t + 2)$

48. $y = \dfrac{1}{t(t + 1)(t + 2)}$

49. $y = \dfrac{\theta + 5}{\theta \cos \theta}$

50. $y = \dfrac{\theta \sin \theta}{\sqrt{\sec \theta}}$

51. $y = \dfrac{x\sqrt{x^2 + 1}}{(x + 1)^{2/3}}$

52. $y = \sqrt{\dfrac{(x + 1)^{10}}{(2x + 1)^5}}$

53. $y = \sqrt[3]{\dfrac{x(x - 2)}{x^2 + 1}}$

54. $y = \sqrt[3]{\dfrac{x(x + 1)(x - 2)}{(x^2 + 1)(2x + 3)}}$

In Exercises 55–62, find the derivative of y with respect to x, t, or θ, as appropriate.

55. $y = \ln (\cos^2 \theta)$

56. $y = \ln (3\theta e^{-\theta})$

57. $y = \ln (3te^{-t})$

58. $y = \ln (2e^{-t}\sin t)$

59. $y = \ln \left(\dfrac{e^\theta}{1 + e^\theta}\right)$

60. $y = \ln \left(\dfrac{\sqrt{\theta}}{1 + \sqrt{\theta}}\right)$

61. $y = e^{(\cos t + \ln t)}$

62. $y = e^{\sin t}(\ln t^2 + 1)$

In Exercises 63–66, find dy/dx.

63. $\ln y = e^y \sin x$

64. $\ln xy = e^{x+y}$

65. $x^y = y^x$

66. $\tan y = e^x + \ln x$

In Exercises 67–88, find the derivative of y with respect to the given independent variable.

67. $y = 2^x$

68. $y = 3^{-x}$

69. $y = 5^{\sqrt{s}}$

70. $y = 2^{(s^2)}$

71. $y = x^{\pi}$

72. $y = t^{1-e}$

73. $y = \log_2 5\theta$

74. $y = \log_3(1 + \theta \ln 3)$

75. $y = \log_4 x + \log_4 x^2$

76. $y = \log_{25} e^x - \log_5 \sqrt{x}$

77. $y = \log_2 r \cdot \log_4 r$

78. $y = \log_3 r \cdot \log_9 r$

79. $y = \log_3\left(\left(\frac{x+1}{x-1}\right)^{\ln 3}\right)$

80. $y = \log_5\sqrt{\left(\frac{7x}{3x+2}\right)^{\ln 5}}$

81. $y = \theta \sin(\log_7 \theta)$

82. $y = \log_7\left(\frac{\sin\theta\cos\theta}{e^{\theta}\,2^{\theta}}\right)$

83. $y = \log_5 e^x$

84. $y = \log_2\left(\frac{x^2e^2}{2\sqrt{x+1}}\right)$

85. $y = 3^{\log_2 t}$

86. $y = 3\log_8(\log_2 t)$

87. $y = \log_2(8t^{\ln 2})$

88. $y = t\log_3\left(e^{(\sin t)(\ln 3)}\right)$

In Exercises 89–96, use logarithmic differentiation to find the derivative of y with respect to the given independent variable.

89. $y = (x+1)^x$

90. $y = x^{(x+1)}$

91. $y = (\sqrt{t})^t$

92. $y = t^{\sqrt{t}}$

93. $y = (\sin x)^x$

94. $y = x^{\sin x}$

95. $y = x^{\ln x}$

96. $y = (\ln x)^{\ln x}$

97. If we write $g(x)$ for $f^{-1}(x)$, Equation (1) can be written as

$$g'(f(a)) = \frac{1}{f'(a)}, \quad \text{or} \quad g'(f(a)) \cdot f'(a) = 1.$$

If we then write x for a, we get

$$g'(f(x)) \cdot f'(x) = 1.$$

The latter equation may remind you of the Chain Rule, and indeed there is a connection.

Assume that f and g are differentiable functions that are inverses of one another, so that $(g \circ f)(x) = x$. Differentiate both sides of this equation with respect to x, using the Chain Rule to express $(g \circ f)'(x)$ as a product of derivatives of g and f. What do you find? (This is not a proof of Theorem 4 because we assume here the theorem's conclusion that $g = f^{-1}$ is differentiable.)

98. Show that $\lim_{n\to\infty}\left(1 + \frac{x}{n}\right)^n = e^x$ for any $x > 0$.

99. If $y = A\sin(\ln x) + B\cos(\ln x)$, where A and B are constants, show that

$$x^2y'' + xy' + y = 0.$$

100. Using mathematical induction, show that

$$\frac{d^n}{dx^n}\ln x = (-1)^{n-1}\frac{(n-1)!}{x^n}.$$

COMPUTER EXPLORATIONS

In Exercises 101–108, you will explore some functions and their inverses together with their derivatives and tangent line approximations at specified points. Perform the following steps using your CAS:

a. Plot the function $y = f(x)$ together with its derivative over the given interval. Explain why you know that f is one-to-one over the interval.

b. Solve the equation $y = f(x)$ for x as a function of y, and name the resulting inverse function g.

c. Find the equation for the tangent line to f at the specified point $(x_0, f(x_0))$.

d. Find the equation for the tangent line to g at the point $(f(x_0), x_0)$ located symmetrically across the 45° line $y = x$ (which is the graph of the identity function). Use Theorem 4 to find the slope of this tangent line.

e. Plot the functions f and g, the identity, the two tangent lines, and the line segment joining the points $(x_0, f(x_0))$ and $(f(x_0), x_0)$. Discuss the symmetries you see across the main diagonal.

101. $y = \sqrt{3x-2}, \quad \frac{2}{3} \le x \le 4, \quad x_0 = 3$

102. $y = \frac{3x+2}{2x-11}, \quad -2 \le x \le 2, \quad x_0 = 1/2$

103. $y = \frac{4x}{x^2+1}, \quad -1 \le x \le 1, \quad x_0 = 1/2$

104. $y = \frac{x^3}{x^2+1}, \quad -1 \le x \le 1, \quad x_0 = 1/2$

105. $y = x^3 - 3x^2 - 1, \quad 2 \le x \le 5, \quad x_0 = \frac{27}{10}$

106. $y = 2 - x - x^3, \quad -2 \le x \le 2, \quad x_0 = \frac{3}{2}$

107. $y = e^x, \quad -3 \le x \le 5, \quad x_0 = 1$

108. $y = \sin x, \quad -\frac{\pi}{2} \le x \le \frac{\pi}{2}, \quad x_0 = 1$

In Exercises 109 and 110, repeat the steps above to solve for the functions $y = f(x)$ and $x = f^{-1}(y)$ defined implicitly by the given equations over the interval.

109. $y^{1/3} - 1 = (x+2)^3, \quad -5 \le x \le 5, \quad x_0 = -3/2$

110. $\cos y = x^{1/5}, \quad 0 \le x \le 1, \quad x_0 = 1/2$

3.8 Inverse Trigonometric Functions

We introduced the six basic inverse trigonometric functions in Section 1.5, but focused there on the arcsine and arccosine functions. Here we complete the study of how all six inverse trigonometric functions are defined, graphed, and evaluated, and how their derivatives are computed.

Inverses of tan *x*, cot *x*, sec *x*, and csc *x*

The graphs of all six basic inverse trigonometric functions are shown in Figure 3.41. We obtain these graphs by reflecting the graphs of the restricted trigonometric functions (as discussed in Section 1.5) through the line $y = x$. Let's take a closer look at the arctangent, arccotangent, arcsecant, and arccosecant functions.

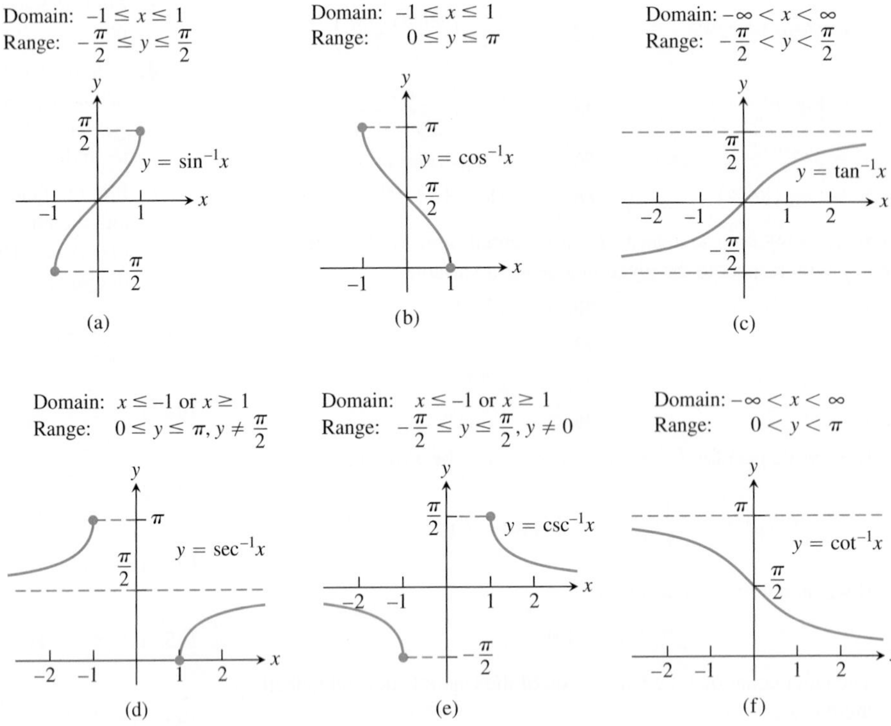

FIGURE 3.41 Graphs of the six basic inverse trigonometric functions.

The arctangent of x is a radian angle whose tangent is x. The arccotangent of x is an angle whose cotangent is x.

DEFINITION

$y = \tan^{-1} x$ is the number in $(-\pi/2, \pi/2)$ for which $\tan y = x$.

$y = \cot^{-1} x$ is the number in $(0, \pi)$ for which $\cot y = x$.

We use open intervals to avoid values where the tangent and cotangent are undefined.

The graph of $y = \tan^{-1} x$ is symmetric about the origin because it is a branch of the graph $x = \tan y$ that is symmetric about the origin (Figure 3.41c). Algebraically this means that

$$\tan^{-1}(-x) = -\tan^{-1} x;$$

the arctangent is an odd function. The graph of $y = \cot^{-1} x$ has no such symmetry (Figure 3.41f). Notice from Figure 3.41c that the graph of the arctangent function has two horizontal asymptotes; one at $y = \pi/2$ and the other at $y = -\pi/2$.

The inverses of the restricted forms of $\sec x$ and $\csc x$ are chosen to be the functions graphed in Figures 3.41d and 3.41e.

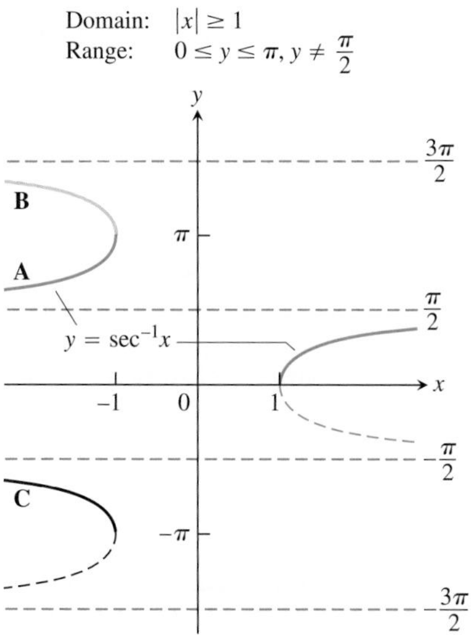

FIGURE 3.42 There are several logical choices for the left-hand branch of $y = \sec^{-1} x$. With choice **A**, $\sec^{-1} x = \cos^{-1}(1/x)$, a useful identity employed by many calculators.

Caution There is no general agreement about how to define $\sec^{-1} x$ for negative values of x. We chose angles in the second quadrant between $\pi/2$ and π. This choice makes $\sec^{-1} x = \cos^{-1}(1/x)$. It also makes $\sec^{-1} x$ an increasing function on each interval of its domain. Some tables choose $\sec^{-1} x$ to lie in $[-\pi, -\pi/2)$ for $x < 0$ and some texts choose it to lie in $[\pi, 3\pi/2)$ (Figure 3.42). These choices simplify the formula for the derivative (our formula needs absolute value signs) but fail to satisfy the computational equation $\sec^{-1} x = \cos^{-1}(1/x)$. From this, we can derive the identity

$$\sec^{-1} x = \cos^{-1}\left(\frac{1}{x}\right) = \frac{\pi}{2} - \sin^{-1}\left(\frac{1}{x}\right) \tag{1}$$

by applying Equation (5) in Section 1.5.

EXAMPLE 1 The accompanying figures show two values of $\tan^{-1} x$.

x	$\tan^{-1} x$
$\sqrt{3}$	$\pi/3$
1	$\pi/4$
$\sqrt{3}/3$	$\pi/6$
$-\sqrt{3}/3$	$-\pi/6$
-1	$-\pi/4$
$-\sqrt{3}$	$-\pi/3$

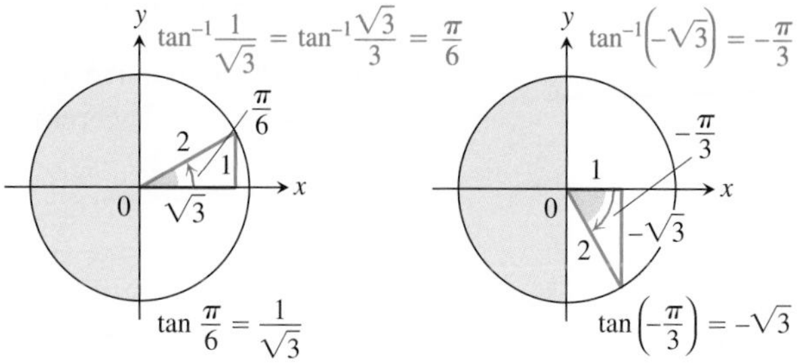

The angles come from the first and fourth quadrants because the range of $\tan^{-1} x$ is $(-\pi/2, \pi/2)$. ■

The Derivative of $y = \sin^{-1} u$

We know that the function $x = \sin y$ is differentiable in the interval $-\pi/2 < y < \pi/2$ and that its derivative, the cosine, is positive there. Theorem 4 in Section 3.7 therefore assures us that the inverse function $y = \sin^{-1} x$ is differentiable throughout the interval $-1 < x < 1$. We cannot expect it to be differentiable at $x = 1$ or $x = -1$ because the tangents to the graph are vertical at these points (see Figure 3.43 on the next page).

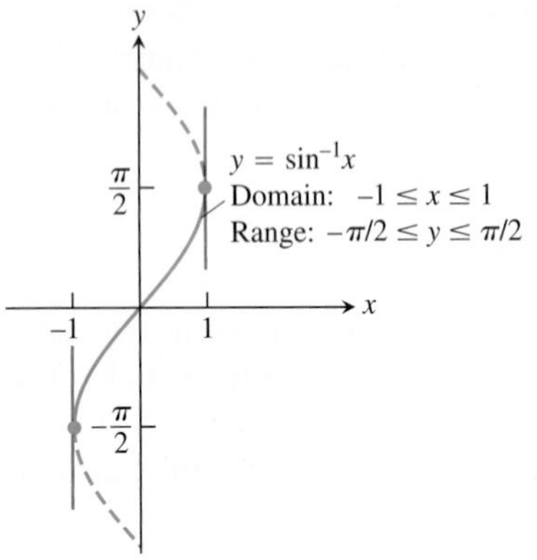

FIGURE 3.43 The graph of $y = \sin^{-1} x$ has vertical tangents at $x = -1$ and $x = 1$.

We find the derivative of $y = \sin^{-1} x$ by applying Theorem 4 with $f(x) = \sin x$ and $f^{-1}(x) = \sin^{-1} x$:

$$\begin{aligned}
(f^{-1})'(x) &= \frac{1}{f'(f^{-1}(x))} && \text{Theorem 4} \\
&= \frac{1}{\cos(\sin^{-1} x)} && f'(u) = \cos u \\
&= \frac{1}{\sqrt{1 - \sin^2(\sin^{-1} x)}} && \cos u = \sqrt{1 - \sin^2 u} \\
&= \frac{1}{\sqrt{1 - x^2}} && \sin(\sin^{-1} x) = x
\end{aligned}$$

If u is a differentiable function of x with $|u| < 1$, we apply the Chain Rule to get

$$\frac{d}{dx}(\sin^{-1} u) = \frac{1}{\sqrt{1 - u^2}} \frac{du}{dx}, \qquad |u| < 1.$$

EXAMPLE 2

$$\frac{d}{dx}(\sin^{-1} x^2) = \frac{1}{\sqrt{1 - (x^2)^2}} \cdot \frac{d}{dx}(x^2) = \frac{2x}{\sqrt{1 - x^4}}$$ ■

The Derivative of $y = \tan^{-1} u$

We find the derivative of $y = \tan^{-1} x$ by applying Theorem 4 with $f(x) = \tan x$ and $f^{-1}(x) = \tan^{-1} x$. Theorem 4 can be applied because the derivative of $\tan x$ is positive for $-\pi/2 < x < \pi/2$:

$$\begin{aligned}
(f^{-1})'(x) &= \frac{1}{f'(f^{-1}(x))} && \text{Theorem 4} \\
&= \frac{1}{\sec^2(\tan^{-1} x)} && f'(u) = \sec^2 u \\
&= \frac{1}{1 + \tan^2(\tan^{-1} x)} && \sec^2 u = 1 + \tan^2 u \\
&= \frac{1}{1 + x^2} && \tan(\tan^{-1} x) = x
\end{aligned}$$

The derivative is defined for all real numbers. If u is a differentiable function of x, we get the Chain Rule form:

$$\frac{d}{dx}(\tan^{-1} u) = \frac{1}{1 + u^2}\frac{du}{dx}.$$

The Derivative of $y = \sec^{-1} u$

Since the derivative of sec x is positive for $0 < x < \pi/2$ and $\pi/2 < x < \pi$, Theorem 4 says that the inverse function $y = \sec^{-1} x$ is differentiable. Instead of applying the formula in Theorem 4 directly, we find the derivative of $y = \sec^{-1} x$, $|x| > 1$, using implicit differentiation and the Chain Rule as follows:

$$y = \sec^{-1} x$$

$$\sec y = x \qquad \text{Inverse function relationship}$$

$$\frac{d}{dx}(\sec y) = \frac{d}{dx}x \qquad \text{Differentiate both sides.}$$

$$\sec y \tan y \frac{dy}{dx} = 1 \qquad \text{Chain Rule}$$

$$\frac{dy}{dx} = \frac{1}{\sec y \tan y} \qquad \text{Since } |x| > 1, y \text{ lies in } (0, \pi/2) \cup (\pi/2, \pi) \text{ and } \sec y \tan y \neq 0.$$

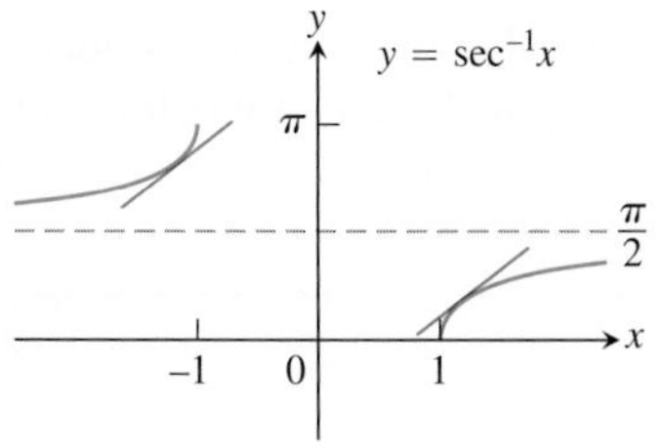

FIGURE 3.44 The slope of the curve $y = \sec^{-1} x$ is positive for both $x < -1$ and $x > 1$.

To express the result in terms of x, we use the relationships

$$\sec y = x \qquad \text{and} \qquad \tan y = \pm\sqrt{\sec^2 y - 1} = \pm\sqrt{x^2 - 1}$$

to get

$$\frac{dy}{dx} = \pm\frac{1}{x\sqrt{x^2 - 1}}.$$

Can we do anything about the $\pm$ sign? A glance at Figure 3.44 shows that the slope of the graph $y = \sec^{-1} x$ is always positive. Thus,

$$\frac{d}{dx}\sec^{-1} x = \begin{cases} +\dfrac{1}{x\sqrt{x^2 - 1}} & \text{if } x > 1 \\ -\dfrac{1}{x\sqrt{x^2 - 1}} & \text{if } x < -1. \end{cases}$$

With the absolute value symbol, we can write a single expression that eliminates the "$\pm$" ambiguity:

$$\frac{d}{dx}\sec^{-1} x = \frac{1}{|x|\sqrt{x^2 - 1}}.$$

If u is a differentiable function of x with $|u| > 1$, we have the formula

$$\frac{d}{dx}(\sec^{-1} u) = \frac{1}{|u|\sqrt{u^2 - 1}}\frac{du}{dx}, \qquad |u| > 1.$$

EXAMPLE 3

$$\begin{aligned}\frac{d}{dx}\sec^{-1}(5x^4) &= \frac{1}{|5x^4|\sqrt{(5x^4)^2 - 1}}\frac{d}{dx}(5x^4) \\ &= \frac{1}{5x^4\sqrt{25x^8 - 1}}(20x^3) && 5x^4 > 1 > 0 \\ &= \frac{4}{x\sqrt{25x^8 - 1}}\end{aligned}$$

■

Derivatives of the Other Three

We could use the same techniques to find the derivatives of the other three inverse trigonometric functions—arccosine, arccotangent, and arccosecant—but there is a much easier way, thanks to the following identities.

Inverse Function–Inverse Cofunction Identities

$$\cos^{-1} x = \pi/2 - \sin^{-1} x$$

$$\cot^{-1} x = \pi/2 - \tan^{-1} x$$

$$\csc^{-1} x = \pi/2 - \sec^{-1} x$$

We saw the first of these identities in Equation (5) of Section 1.5. The others are derived in a similar way. It follows easily that the derivatives of the inverse cofunctions are the negatives of the derivatives of the corresponding inverse functions. For example, the derivative of $\cos^{-1} x$ is calculated as follows:

$$\begin{aligned}\frac{d}{dx}(\cos^{-1} x) &= \frac{d}{dx}\left(\frac{\pi}{2} - \sin^{-1} x\right) && \text{Identity} \\ &= -\frac{d}{dx}(\sin^{-1} x) \\ &= -\frac{1}{\sqrt{1 - x^2}} && \text{Derivative of arcsine}\end{aligned}$$

TABLE 3.1 Derivatives of the inverse trigonometric functions

1. $\dfrac{d(\sin^{-1} u)}{dx} = \dfrac{du/dx}{\sqrt{1-u^2}}, \quad |u| < 1$

2. $\dfrac{d(\cos^{-1} u)}{dx} = -\dfrac{du/dx}{\sqrt{1-u^2}}, \quad |u| < 1$

3. $\dfrac{d(\tan^{-1} u)}{dx} = \dfrac{du/dx}{1+u^2}$

4. $\dfrac{d(\cot^{-1} u)}{dx} = -\dfrac{du/dx}{1+u^2}$

5. $\dfrac{d(\sec^{-1} u)}{dx} = \dfrac{du/dx}{|u|\sqrt{u^2-1}}, \quad |u| > 1$

6. $\dfrac{d(\csc^{-1} u)}{dx} = \dfrac{-du/dx}{|u|\sqrt{u^2-1}}, \quad |u| > 1$

EXERCISES 3.8

Use reference triangles like that in Example 1 to find the angles in Exercises 1–12.

1. a. $\tan^{-1} 1$ b. $\tan^{-1}(-\sqrt{3})$ c. $\tan^{-1}\left(\dfrac{1}{\sqrt{3}}\right)$

2. a. $\tan^{-1}(-1)$ b. $\tan^{-1}\sqrt{3}$ c. $\tan^{-1}\left(\dfrac{-1}{\sqrt{3}}\right)$

3. a. $\sin^{-1}\left(\dfrac{-1}{2}\right)$ b. $\sin^{-1}\left(\dfrac{1}{\sqrt{2}}\right)$ c. $\sin^{-1}\left(\dfrac{-\sqrt{3}}{2}\right)$

4. a. $\sin^{-1}\left(\dfrac{1}{2}\right)$ b. $\sin^{-1}\left(\dfrac{-1}{\sqrt{2}}\right)$ c. $\sin^{-1}\left(\dfrac{\sqrt{3}}{2}\right)$

5. a. $\cos^{-1}\left(\dfrac{1}{2}\right)$ b. $\cos^{-1}\left(\dfrac{-1}{\sqrt{2}}\right)$ c. $\cos^{-1}\left(\dfrac{\sqrt{3}}{2}\right)$

6. a. $\cos^{-1}\left(\dfrac{-1}{2}\right)$ b. $\cos^{-1}\left(\dfrac{1}{\sqrt{2}}\right)$ c. $\cos^{-1}\left(\dfrac{-\sqrt{3}}{2}\right)$

7. a. $\sec^{-1}(-\sqrt{2})$ b. $\sec^{-1}\left(\dfrac{2}{\sqrt{3}}\right)$ c. $\sec^{-1}(-2)$

8. a. $\sec^{-1}\sqrt{2}$ b. $\sec^{-1}\left(\dfrac{-2}{\sqrt{3}}\right)$ c. $\sec^{-1} 2$

9. a. $\csc^{-1}\sqrt{2}$ b. $\csc^{-1}\left(\dfrac{-2}{\sqrt{3}}\right)$ c. $\csc^{-1} 2$

10. a. $\csc^{-1}(-\sqrt{2})$ b. $\csc^{-1}\left(\dfrac{2}{\sqrt{3}}\right)$ c. $\csc^{-1}(-2)$

11. a. $\cot^{-1}(-1)$ b. $\cot^{-1}(\sqrt{3})$ c. $\cot^{-1}\left(\dfrac{-1}{\sqrt{3}}\right)$

12. a. $\cot^{-1}(1)$ b. $\cot^{-1}(-\sqrt{3})$ c. $\cot^{-1}\left(\dfrac{1}{\sqrt{3}}\right)$

Find the limits in Exercises 13–20. (If in doubt, look at the function's graph.)

13. $\lim\limits_{x\to 1^-} \sin^{-1} x$

14. $\lim\limits_{x\to -1^+} \cos^{-1} x$

15. $\lim\limits_{x\to \infty} \tan^{-1} x$

16. $\lim\limits_{x\to -\infty} \tan^{-1} x$

17. $\lim\limits_{x\to \infty} \sec^{-1} x$

18. $\lim\limits_{x\to -\infty} \sec^{-1} x$

19. $\lim\limits_{x\to \infty} \csc^{-1} x$

20. $\lim\limits_{x\to -\infty} \csc^{-1} x$

In Exercises 21–42, find the derivative of y with respect to the appropriate variable.

21. $y = \cos^{-1}(x^2)$

22. $y = \cos^{-1}(1/x)$

23. $y = \sin^{-1}\sqrt{2}\, t$

24. $y = \sin^{-1}(1 - t)$

25. $y = \sec^{-1}(2s + 1)$

26. $y = \sec^{-1} 5s$

27. $y = \csc^{-1}(x^2 + 1), \quad x > 0$

28. $y = \csc^{-1}\dfrac{x}{2}$

29. $y = \sec^{-1}\dfrac{1}{t}, \quad 0 < t < 1$

30. $y = \sin^{-1}\dfrac{3}{t^2}$

31. $y = \cot^{-1}\sqrt{t}$

32. $y = \cot^{-1}\sqrt{t-1}$

33. $y = \ln(\tan^{-1}x)$

34. $y = \tan^{-1}(\ln x)$

35. $y = \csc^{-1}(e^t)$

36. $y = \cos^{-1}(e^{-t})$

37. $y = s\sqrt{1-s^2} + \cos^{-1}s$

38. $y = \sqrt{s^2-1} - \sec^{-1}s$

39. $y = \tan^{-1}\sqrt{x^2-1} + \csc^{-1}x, \quad x > 1$

40. $y = \cot^{-1}\dfrac{1}{x} - \tan^{-1}x$

41. $y = x\sin^{-1}x + \sqrt{1-x^2}$

42. $y = \ln(x^2+4) - x\tan^{-1}\left(\dfrac{x}{2}\right)$

43. You are sitting in a classroom next to the wall looking at the blackboard at the front of the room. The blackboard is 12 ft long and starts 3 ft from the wall you are sitting next to. Show that your viewing angle is

$$\alpha = \cot^{-1}\frac{x}{15} - \cot^{-1}\frac{x}{3}$$

if you are x ft from the front wall.

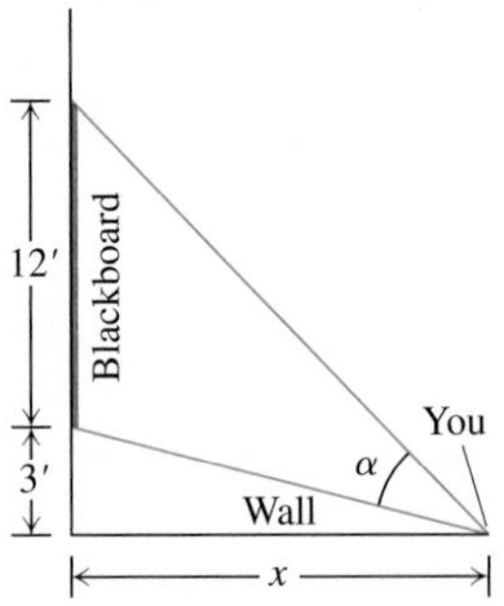

44. Find the angle α.

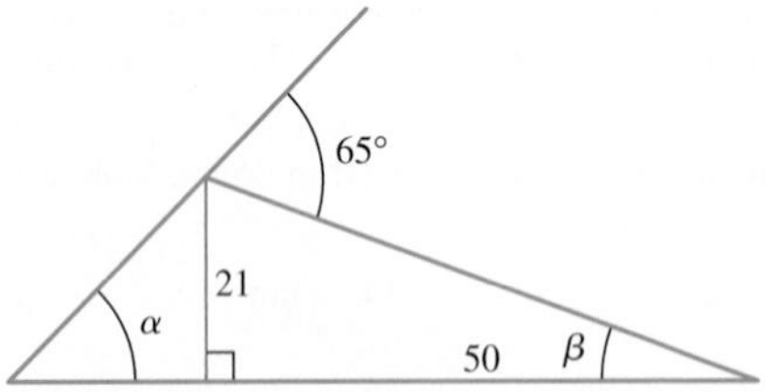

45. Here is an informal proof that $\tan^{-1}1 + \tan^{-1}2 + \tan^{-1}3 = \pi$. Explain what is going on.

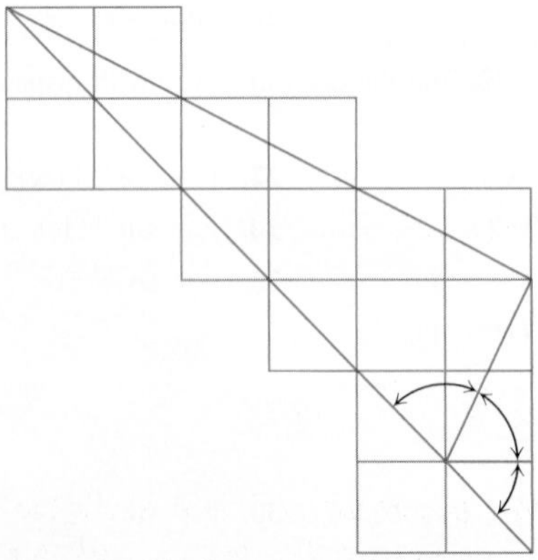

46. Two derivations of the identity $\sec^{-1}(-x) = \pi - \sec^{-1}x$

a. (*Geometric*) Here is a pictorial proof that $\sec^{-1}(-x) = \pi - \sec^{-1}x$. See if you can tell what is going on.

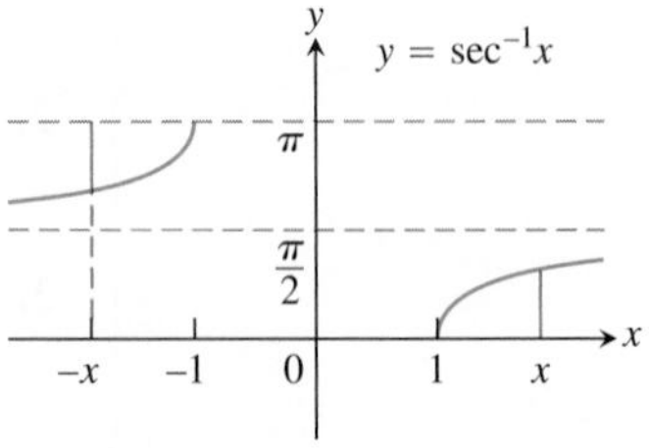

b. (*Algebraic*) Derive the identity $\sec^{-1}(-x) = \pi - \sec^{-1}x$ by combining the following two equations from the text:

$$\cos^{-1}(-x) = \pi - \cos^{-1}x \qquad \text{Eq. (3), Section 1.5}$$

$$\sec^{-1}x = \cos^{-1}(1/x) \qquad \text{Eq. (1)}$$

47. The identity $\sin^{-1}x + \cos^{-1}x = \pi/2$ Figure 1.65 establishes the identity for $0 < x < 1$. To establish it for the rest of $[-1, 1]$, verify by direct calculation that it holds for $x = 1, 0$, and -1. Then, for values of x in $(-1, 0)$, let $x = -a, a > 0$, and apply Eqs. (1) and (3) to the sum $\sin^{-1}(-a) + \cos^{-1}(-a)$.

48. Show that the sum $\tan^{-1}x + \tan^{-1}(1/x)$ is constant.

Which of the expressions in Exercises 49–52 are defined, and which are not? Give reasons for your answers.

49. **a.** $\tan^{-1}2$ **b.** $\cos^{-1}2$

50. **a.** $\csc^{-1}(1/2)$ **b.** $\csc^{-1}2$

51. **a.** $\sec^{-1}0$ **b.** $\sin^{-1}\sqrt{2}$

52. **a.** $\cot^{-1}(-1/2)$ **b.** $\cos^{-1}(-5)$

53. Use the identity

$$\csc^{-1}u = \frac{\pi}{2} - \sec^{-1}u$$

to derive the formula for the derivative of $\csc^{-1}u$ in Table 3.1 from the formula for the derivative of $\sec^{-1}u$.

54. Derive the formula

$$\frac{dy}{dx} = \frac{1}{1+x^2}$$

for the derivative of $y = \tan^{-1}x$ by differentiating both sides of the equivalent equation $\tan y = x$.

55. Use the Derivative Rule in Section 3.7, Theorem 4, to derive

$$\frac{d}{dx}\sec^{-1}x = \frac{1}{|x|\sqrt{x^2-1}}, \quad |x| > 1.$$

56. Use the identity

$$\cot^{-1}u = \frac{\pi}{2} - \tan^{-1}u$$

to derive the formula for the derivative of $\cot^{-1} u$ in Table 3.1 from the formula for the derivative of $\tan^{-1} u$.

57. What is special about the functions

$$f(x) = \sin^{-1}\frac{x-1}{x+1}, \quad x \geq 0, \quad \text{and} \quad g(x) = 2\tan^{-1}\sqrt{x}?$$

Explain.

58. What is special about the functions

$$f(x) = \sin^{-1}\frac{1}{\sqrt{x^2+1}} \quad \text{and} \quad g(x) = \tan^{-1}\frac{1}{x}?$$

Explain.

T **59.** Find the values of

a. $\sec^{-1} 1.5$ **b.** $\csc^{-1}(-1.5)$ **c.** $\cot^{-1} 2$

T **60.** Find the values of

a. $\sec^{-1}(-3)$ **b.** $\csc^{-1} 1.7$ **c.** $\cot^{-1}(-2)$

T In Exercises 61–63, find the domain and range of each composite function. Then graph the composites on separate screens. Do the graphs make sense in each case? Give reasons for your answers. Comment on any differences you see.

61. **a.** $y = \tan^{-1}(\tan x)$ **b.** $y = \tan(\tan^{-1} x)$

62. **a.** $y = \sin^{-1}(\sin x)$ **b.** $y = \sin(\sin^{-1} x)$

63. **a.** $y = \cos^{-1}(\cos x)$ **b.** $y = \cos(\cos^{-1} x)$

T Use your graphing utility for Exercises 64–68.

64. Graph $y = \sec(\sec^{-1} x) = \sec(\cos^{-1}(1/x))$. Explain what you see.

65. Newton's serpentine Graph Newton's serpentine, $y = 4x/(x^2+1)$. Then graph $y = 2\sin(2\tan^{-1} x)$ in the same graphing window. What do you see? Explain.

66. Graph the rational function $y = (2 - x^2)/x^2$. Then graph $y = \cos(2\sec^{-1} x)$ in the same graphing window. What do you see? Explain.

67. Graph $f(x) = \sin^{-1} x$ together with its first two derivatives. Comment on the behavior of f and the shape of its graph in relation to the signs and values of f' and f''.

68. Graph $f(x) = \tan^{-1} x$ together with its first two derivatives. Comment on the behavior of f and the shape of its graph in relation to the signs and values of f' and f''.

3.9 Related Rates

In this section we look at problems that ask for the rate at which some variable changes when it is known how the rate of some other related variable (or perhaps several variables) changes. The problem of finding a rate of change from other known rates of change is called a *related rates problem*.

Related Rates Equations

Suppose we are pumping air into a spherical balloon. Both the volume and radius of the balloon are increasing over time. If V is the volume and r is the radius of the balloon at an instant of time, then

$$V = \frac{4}{3}\pi r^3.$$

Using the Chain Rule, we differentiate both sides with respect to t to find an equation relating the rates of change of V and v,

$$\frac{dV}{dt} = \frac{dV}{dr}\frac{dr}{dt} = 4\pi r^2 \frac{dr}{dt}.$$

So if we know the radius r of the balloon and the rate dV/dt at which the volume is increasing at a given instant of time, then we can solve this last equation for dr/dt to find how fast the radius is increasing at that instant. Note that it is easier to directly measure the rate of increase of the volume (the rate at which air is being pumped into the balloon) than it is to measure the increase in the radius. The related rates equation allows us to calculate dr/dt from dV/dt.

Very often the key to relating the variables in a related rates problem is drawing a picture that shows the geometric relations between them, as illustrated in the following example.

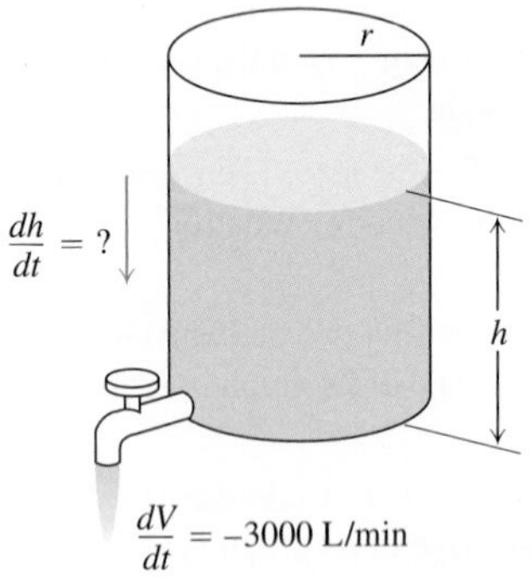

FIGURE 3.45 The rate of change of fluid volume in a cylindrical tank is related to the rate of change of fluid level in the tank (Example 1).

EXAMPLE 1 How rapidly will the fluid level inside a vertical cylindrical tank drop if we pump the fluid out at the rate of 3000 L/min?

Solution We draw a picture of a partially filled vertical cylindrical tank, calling its radius r and the height of the fluid h (Figure 3.45). Call the volume of the fluid V.

As time passes, the radius remains constant, but V and h change. We think of V and h as differentiable functions of time and use t to represent time. We are told that

$$\frac{dV}{dt} = -3000. \qquad \text{We pump out at the rate of 3000 L/min. The rate is negative because the volume is decreasing.}$$

We are asked to find

$$\frac{dh}{dt}. \qquad \text{How fast will the fluid level drop?}$$

To find dh/dt, we first write an equation that relates h to V. The equation depends on the units chosen for V, r, and h. With V in liters and r and h in meters, the appropriate equation for the cylinder's volume is

$$V = 1000\pi r^2 h$$

because a cubic meter contains 1000 L.

Since V and h are differentiable functions of t, we can differentiate both sides of the equation $V = 1000\pi r^2 h$ with respect to t to get an equation that relates dh/dt to dV/dt:

$$\frac{dV}{dt} = 1000\pi r^2 \frac{dh}{dt}. \qquad r \text{ is a constant.}$$

We substitute the known value $dV/dt = -3000$ and solve for dh/dt:

$$\frac{dh}{dt} = \frac{-3000}{1000\pi r^2} = -\frac{3}{\pi r^2}.$$

The fluid level will drop at the rate of $3/(\pi r^2)$ m/min.

The equation $dh/dt = -3/\pi r^2$ shows how the rate at which the fluid level drops depends on the tank's radius. If r is small, dh/dt will be large; if r is large, dh/dt will be small.

$$\text{If } r = 1 \text{ m:} \quad \frac{dh}{dt} = -\frac{3}{\pi} \approx -0.95 \text{ m/min} = -95 \text{ cm/min}.$$

$$\text{If } r = 10 \text{ m:} \quad \frac{dh}{dt} = -\frac{3}{100\pi} \approx -0.0095 \text{ m/min} = -0.95 \text{ cm/min}.$$

■

Related Rates Problem Strategy

1. *Draw a picture and name the variables and constants.* Use t for time. Assume that all variables are differentiable functions of t.
2. *Write down the numerical information* (in terms of the symbols you have chosen).
3. *Write down what you are asked to find* (usually a rate, expressed as a derivative).
4. *Write an equation that relates the variables.* You may have to combine two or more equations to get a single equation that relates the variable whose rate you want to the variables whose rates you know.
5. *Differentiate with respect to t.* Then express the rate you want in terms of the rate and variables whose values you know.
6. *Evaluate.* Use known values to find the unknown rate.

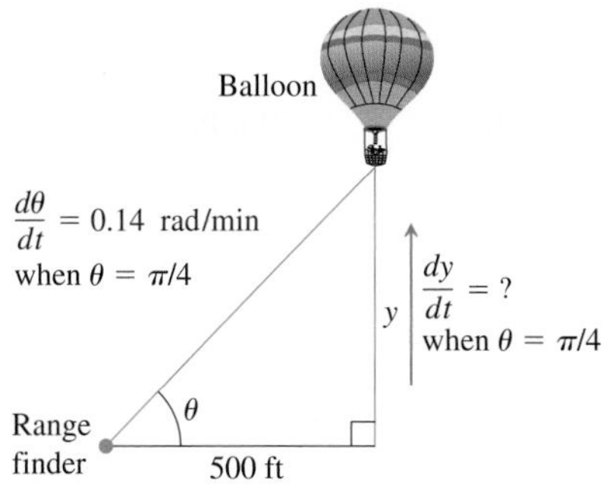

FIGURE 3.46 The rate of change of the balloon's height is related to the rate of change of the angle the range finder makes with the ground (Example 2).

EXAMPLE 2 A hot air balloon rising straight up from a level field is tracked by a range finder 500 ft from the liftoff point. At the moment the range finder's elevation angle is $\pi/4$, the angle is increasing at the rate of 0.14 rad/min. How fast is the balloon rising at that moment?

Solution We answer the question in six steps.

1. *Draw a picture and name the variables and constants* (Figure 3.46). The variables in the picture are

   θ = the angle in radians the range finder makes with the ground.

   y = the height in feet of the balloon.

We let t represent time in minutes and assume that θ and y are differentiable functions of t.

The one constant in the picture is the distance from the range finder to the liftoff point (500 ft). There is no need to give it a special symbol.

2. *Write down the additional numerical information.*

$$\frac{d\theta}{dt} = 0.14 \text{ rad/min} \qquad \text{when} \qquad \theta = \frac{\pi}{4}$$

3. *Write down what we are to find.* We want dy/dt when $\theta = \pi/4$.
4. *Write an equation that relates the variables y and θ.*

$$\frac{y}{500} = \tan\theta \qquad \text{or} \qquad y = 500\tan\theta$$

5. *Differentiate with respect to t using the Chain Rule.* The result tells how dy/dt (which we want) is related to $d\theta/dt$ (which we know).

$$\frac{dy}{dt} = 500\,(\sec^2\theta)\,\frac{d\theta}{dt}$$

6. *Evaluate with $\theta = \pi/4$ and $d\theta/dt = 0.14$ to find dy/dt.*

$$\frac{dy}{dt} = 500\left(\sqrt{2}\right)^2(0.14) = 140 \qquad \sec\frac{\pi}{4} = \sqrt{2}$$

At the moment in question, the balloon is rising at the rate of 140 ft/min. ∎

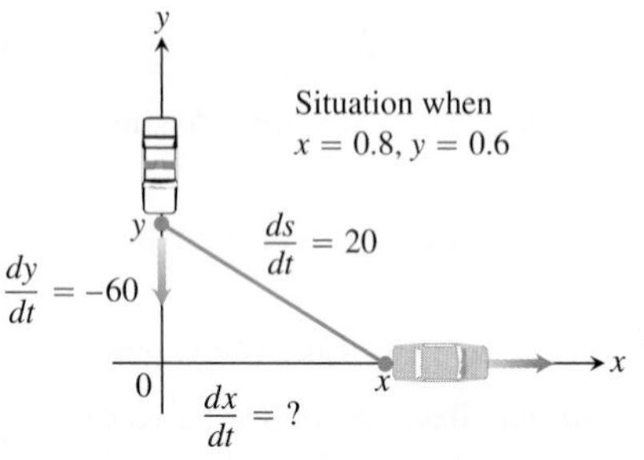

FIGURE 3.47 The speed of the car is related to the speed of the police cruiser and the rate of change of the distance between them (Example 3).

EXAMPLE 3 A police cruiser, approaching a right-angled intersection from the north, is chasing a speeding car that has turned the corner and is now moving straight east. When the cruiser is 0.6 mi north of the intersection and the car is 0.8 mi to the east, the police determine with radar that the distance between them and the car is increasing at 20 mph. If the cruiser is moving at 60 mph at the instant of measurement, what is the speed of the car?

Solution We picture the car and cruiser in the coordinate plane, using the positive x-axis as the eastbound highway and the positive y-axis as the southbound highway (Figure 3.47). We let t represent time and set

$$x = \text{position of car at time } t$$

$$y = \text{position of cruiser at time } t$$

$$s = \text{distance between car and cruiser at time } t.$$

We assume that x, y, and s are differentiable functions of t.

We want to find dx/dt when

$$x = 0.8 \text{ mi}, \qquad y = 0.6 \text{ mi}, \qquad \frac{dy}{dt} = -60 \text{ mph}, \qquad \frac{ds}{dt} = 20 \text{ mph}.$$

Note that dy/dt is negative because y is decreasing.

We differentiate the distance equation

$$s^2 = x^2 + y^2$$

(we could also use $s = \sqrt{x^2 + y^2}$), and obtain

$$2s\frac{ds}{dt} = 2x\frac{dx}{dt} + 2y\frac{dy}{dt}$$

$$\frac{ds}{dt} = \frac{1}{s}\left(x\frac{dx}{dt} + y\frac{dy}{dt}\right)$$

$$= \frac{1}{\sqrt{x^2 + y^2}}\left(x\frac{dx}{dt} + y\frac{dy}{dt}\right).$$

Finally, use $x = 0.8$, $y = 0.6$, $dy/dt = -60$, $ds/dt = 20$, and solve for dx/dt.

$$20 = \frac{1}{\sqrt{(0.8)^2 + (0.6)^2}}\left(0.8\frac{dx}{dt} + (0.6)(-60)\right)$$

$$\frac{dx}{dt} = \frac{20\sqrt{(0.8)^2 + (0.6)^2} + (0.6)(60)}{0.8} = 70$$

At the moment in question, the car's speed is 70 mph. ■

EXAMPLE 4 Water runs into a conical tank at the rate of 9 ft^3/min. The tank stands point down and has a height of 10 ft and a base radius of 5 ft. How fast is the water level rising when the water is 6 ft deep?

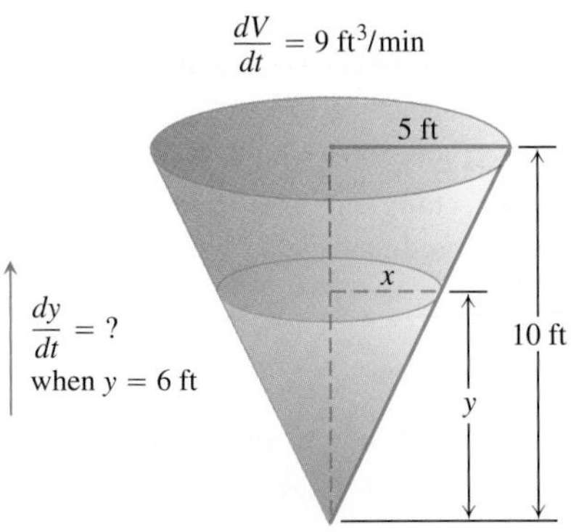

FIGURE 3.48 The geometry of the conical tank and the rate at which water fills the tank determine how fast the water level rises (Example 4).

Solution Figure 3.48 shows a partially filled conical tank. The variables in the problem are

V = volume (ft^3) of the water in the tank at time t (min)

x = radius (ft) of the surface of the water at time t

y = depth (ft) of water in tank at time t.

We assume that V, x, and y are differentiable functions of t. The constants are the dimensions of the tank. We are asked for dy/dt when

$$y = 6\ \text{ft} \quad \text{and} \quad \frac{dV}{dt} = 9\ \text{ft}^3/\text{min}.$$

The water forms a cone with volume

$$V = \frac{1}{3}\pi x^2 y.$$

This equation involves x as well as V and y. Because no information is given about x and dx/dt at the time in question, we need to eliminate x. The similar triangles in Figure 3.48 give us a way to express x in terms of y:

$$\frac{x}{y} = \frac{5}{10} \quad \text{or} \quad x = \frac{y}{2}.$$

Therefore,

$$V = \frac{1}{3}\pi\left(\frac{y}{2}\right)^2 y = \frac{\pi}{12}y^3$$

to give the derivative

$$\frac{dV}{dt} = \frac{\pi}{12}\cdot 3y^2\frac{dy}{dt} = \frac{\pi}{4}y^2\frac{dy}{dt}.$$

Finally, use $y = 6$ and $dV/dt = 9$ to solve for dy/dt.

$$9 = \frac{\pi}{4}(6)^2\frac{dy}{dt}$$

$$\frac{dy}{dt} = \frac{1}{\pi} \approx 0.32$$

At the moment in question, the water level is rising at about 0.32 ft/min. ■

EXERCISES 3.9

1. **Area** Suppose that the radius r and area $A = \pi r^2$ of a circle are differentiable functions of t. Write an equation that relates dA/dt to dr/dt.

2. **Surface area** Suppose that the radius r and surface area $S = 4\pi r^2$ of a sphere are differentiable functions of t. Write an equation that relates dS/dt to dr/dt.

3. **Volume** The radius r and height h of a right circular cylinder are related to the cylinder's volume V by the formula $V = \pi r^2 h$.
   a. How is dV/dt related to dh/dt if r is constant?
   b. How is dV/dt related to dr/dt if h is constant?
   c. How is dV/dt related to dr/dt and dh/dt if neither r nor h is constant?

4. **Volume** The radius r and height h of a right circular cone are related to the cone's volume V by the equation $V = (1/3)\pi r^2 h$.
   a. How is dV/dt related to dh/dt if r is constant?
   b. How is dV/dt related to dr/dt if h is constant?
   c. How is dV/dt related to dr/dt and dh/dt if neither r nor h is constant?

5. **Changing voltage** The voltage V (volts), current I (amperes), and resistance R (ohms) of an electric circuit like the one shown here are related by the equation $V = IR$. Suppose that V is increasing at the rate of 1 volt/sec while I is decreasing at the rate of 1/3 amp/sec. Let t denote time in seconds.

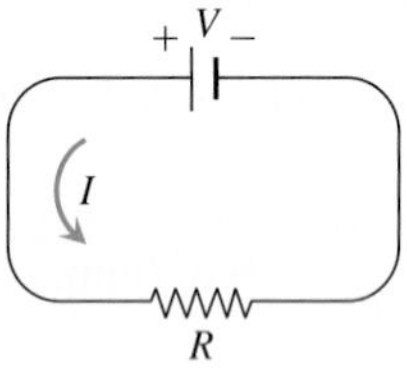

   a. What is the value of dV/dt?
   b. What is the value of dI/dt?
   c. What equation relates dR/dt to dV/dt and dI/dt?
   d. Find the rate at which R is changing when $V = 12$ volts and $I = 2$ amp. Is R increasing, or decreasing?

6. **Electrical power** The power P (watts) of an electric circuit is related to the circuit's resistance R (ohms) and current I (amperes) by the equation $P = RI^2$.
   a. How are dP/dt, dR/dt, and dI/dt related if none of P, R, and I are constant?
   b. How is dR/dt related to dI/dt if P is constant?

7. **Distance** Let x and y be differentiable functions of t and let $s = \sqrt{x^2 + y^2}$ be the distance between the points $(x, 0)$ and $(0, y)$ in the xy-plane.
   a. How is ds/dt related to dx/dt if y is constant?
   b. How is ds/dt related to dx/dt and dy/dt if neither x nor y is constant?
   c. How is dx/dt related to dy/dt if s is constant?

8. **Diagonals** If x, y, and z are lengths of the edges of a rectangular box, the common length of the box's diagonals is $s = \sqrt{x^2 + y^2 + z^2}$.
   a. Assuming that x, y, and z are differentiable functions of t, how is ds/dt related to dx/dt, dy/dt, and dz/dt?
   b. How is ds/dt related to dy/dt and dz/dt if x is constant?
   c. How are dx/dt, dy/dt, and dz/dt related if s is constant?

9. **Area** The area A of a triangle with sides of lengths a and b enclosing an angle of measure θ is

$$A = \frac{1}{2}ab \sin \theta.$$

   a. How is dA/dt related to $d\theta/dt$ if a and b are constant?
   b. How is dA/dt related to $d\theta/dt$ and da/dt if only b is constant?
   c. How is dA/dt related to $d\theta/dt$, da/dt, and db/dt if none of a, b, and θ are constant?

10. **Heating a plate** When a circular plate of metal is heated in an oven, its radius increases at the rate of 0.01 cm/min. At what rate is the plate's area increasing when the radius is 50 cm?

11. **Changing dimensions in a rectangle** The length l of a rectangle is decreasing at the rate of 2 cm/sec while the width w is increasing at the rate of 2 cm/sec. When $l = 12$ cm and $w = 5$ cm, find the rates of change of **(a)** the area, **(b)** the perimeter, and **(c)** the lengths of the diagonals of the rectangle. Which of these quantities are decreasing, and which are increasing?

12. **Changing dimensions in a rectangular box** Suppose that the edge lengths x, y, and z of a closed rectangular box are changing at the following rates:

$$\frac{dx}{dt} = 1 \text{ m/sec}, \quad \frac{dy}{dt} = -2 \text{ m/sec}, \quad \frac{dz}{dt} = 1 \text{ m/sec}.$$

Find the rates at which the box's **(a)** volume, **(b)** surface area, and **(c)** diagonal length $s = \sqrt{x^2 + y^2 + z^2}$ are changing at the instant when $x = 4$, $y = 3$, and $z = 2$.

13. **A sliding ladder** A 13-ft ladder is leaning against a house when its base starts to slide away. By the time the base is 12 ft from the house, the base is moving at the rate of 5 ft/sec.
   a. How fast is the top of the ladder sliding down the wall then?
   b. At what rate is the area of the triangle formed by the ladder, wall, and ground changing then?
   c. At what rate is the angle θ between the ladder and the ground changing then?

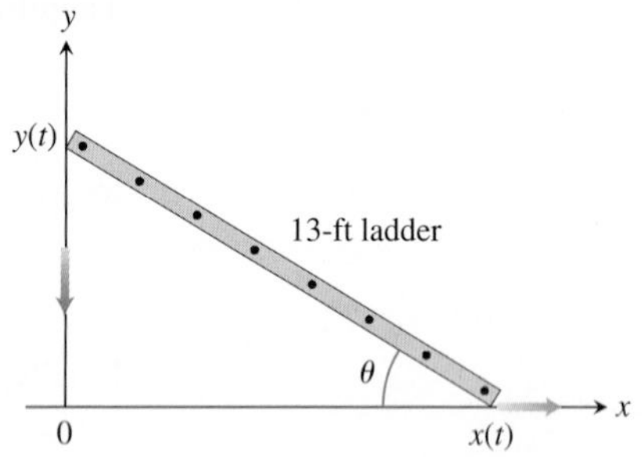

14. **Commercial air traffic** Two commercial airplanes are flying at 40,000 ft along straight-line courses that intersect at right angles. Plane A is approaching the intersection point at a speed of 442 knots (nautical miles per hour; a nautical mile is 2000 yd). Plane B is approaching the intersection at 481 knots. At what rate is the distance between the planes changing when A is 5 nautical miles from the intersection point and B is 12 nautical miles from the intersection point?

15. **Flying a kite** A girl flies a kite at a height of 300 ft, the wind carrying the kite horizontally away from her at a rate of 25 ft/sec. How fast must she let out the string when the kite is 500 ft away from her?

16. **Boring a cylinder** The mechanics at Lincoln Automotive are reboring a 6-in.-deep cylinder to fit a new piston. The machine they are using increases the cylinder's radius one-thousandth of an inch every 3 min. How rapidly is the cylinder volume increasing when the bore (diameter) is 3.800 in.?

17. **A growing sand pile** Sand falls from a conveyor belt at the rate of 10 m^3/min onto the top of a conical pile. The height of the pile is always three-eighths of the base diameter. How fast are the **(a)** height and **(b)** radius changing when the pile is 4 m high? Answer in centimeters per minute.

18. A draining conical reservoir Water is flowing at the rate of $50\ \text{m}^3/\text{min}$ from a shallow concrete conical reservoir (vertex down) of base radius 45 m and height 6 m.

a. How fast (centimeters per minute) is the water level falling when the water is 5 m deep?

b. How fast is the radius of the water's surface changing then? Answer in centimeters per minute.

19. A draining hemispherical reservoir Water is flowing at the rate of $6\ \text{m}^3/\text{min}$ from a reservoir shaped like a hemispherical bowl of radius 13 m, shown here in profile. Answer the following questions, given that the volume of water in a hemispherical bowl of radius R is $V = (\pi/3)y^2(3R - y)$ when the water is y meters deep.

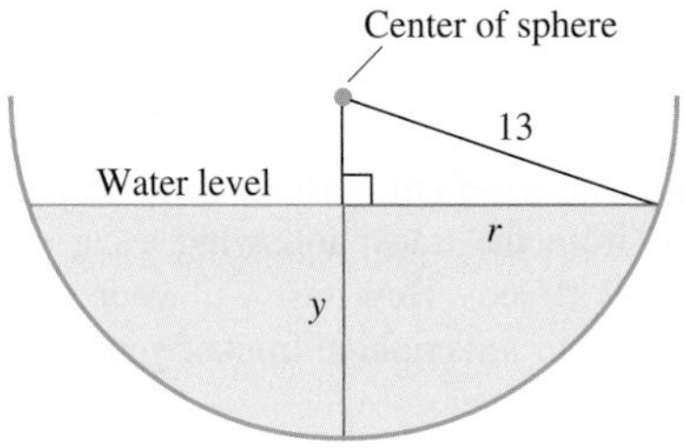

a. At what rate is the water level changing when the water is 8 m deep?

b. What is the radius r of the water's surface when the water is y m deep?

c. At what rate is the radius r changing when the water is 8 m deep?

20. A growing raindrop Suppose that a drop of mist is a perfect sphere and that, through condensation, the drop picks up moisture at a rate proportional to its surface area. Show that under these circumstances the drop's radius increases at a constant rate.

21. The radius of an inflating balloon A spherical balloon is inflated with helium at the rate of $100\pi\ \text{ft}^3/\text{min}$. How fast is the balloon's radius increasing at the instant the radius is 5 ft? How fast is the surface area increasing?

22. Hauling in a dinghy A dinghy is pulled toward a dock by a rope from the bow through a ring on the dock 6 ft above the bow. The rope is hauled in at the rate of 2 ft/sec.

a. How fast is the boat approaching the dock when 10 ft of rope are out?

b. At what rate is the angle θ changing then (see the figure)?

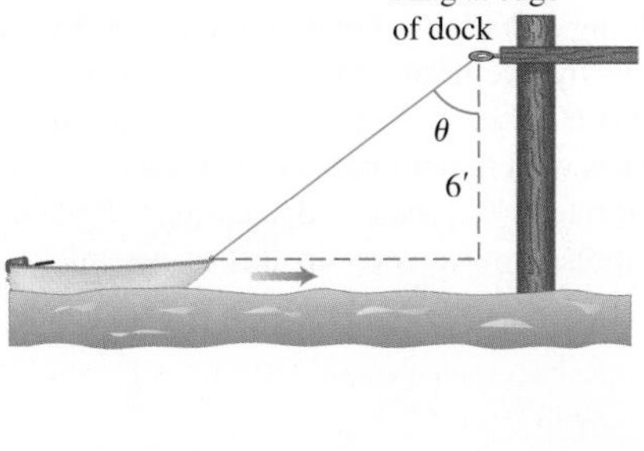

23. A balloon and a bicycle A balloon is rising vertically above a level, straight road at a constant rate of 1 ft/sec. Just when the balloon is 65 ft above the ground, a bicycle moving at a constant rate of 17 ft/sec passes under it. How fast is the distance $s(t)$ between the bicycle and balloon increasing 3 sec later?

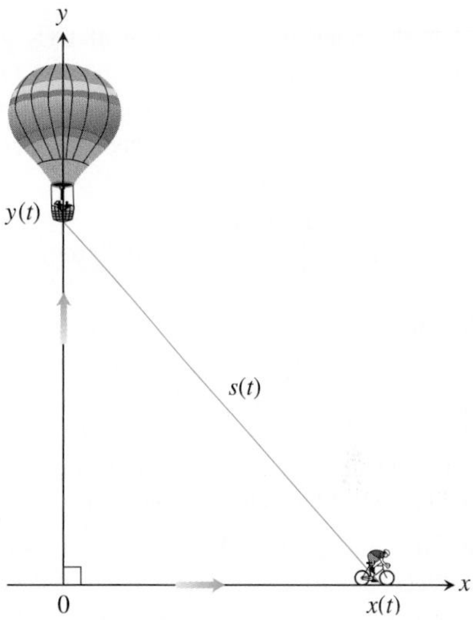

24. Making coffee Coffee is draining from a conical filter into a cylindrical coffeepot at the rate of $10\ \text{in}^3/\text{min}$.

a. How fast is the level in the pot rising when the coffee in the cone is 5 in. deep?

b. How fast is the level in the cone falling then?

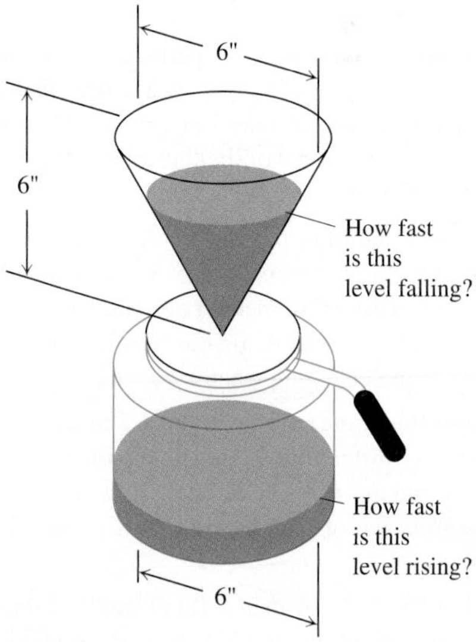

25. Cardiac output In the late 1860s, Adolf Fick, a professor of physiology in the Faculty of Medicine in Würzberg, Germany, developed one of the methods we use today for measuring how much blood your heart pumps in a minute. Your cardiac output as you read this sentence is probably about 7 L/min. At rest it is likely to be a bit under 6 L/min. If you are a trained marathon runner running a marathon, your cardiac output can be as high as 30 L/min.

Your cardiac output can be calculated with the formula

$$y = \frac{Q}{D},$$

where Q is the number of milliliters of CO_2 you exhale in a minute and D is the difference between the CO_2 concentration (ml/L) in the blood pumped to the lungs and the CO_2 concentration in the blood returning from the lungs. With $Q = 233$ ml/min and $D = 97 - 56 = 41$ ml/L,

$$y = \frac{233 \text{ ml/min}}{41 \text{ ml/L}} \approx 5.68 \text{ L/min},$$

fairly close to the 6 L/min that most people have at basal (resting) conditions. (Data courtesy of J. Kenneth Herd, M.D., Quillan College of Medicine, East Tennessee State University.)

Suppose that when $Q = 233$ and $D = 41$, we also know that D is decreasing at the rate of 2 units a minute but that Q remains unchanged. What is happening to the cardiac output?

26. **Cost, revenue, and profit** A company can manufacture x items at a cost of $c(x)$ thousand dollars, a sales revenue of $r(x)$ thousand dollars, and a profit of $p(x) = r(x) - c(x)$ thousand dollars. Find dc/dt, dr/dt, and dp/dt for the following values of x and dx/dt.

    a. $r(x) = 9x$, $c(x) = x^3 - 6x^2 + 15x$, and $dx/dt = 0.1$ when $x = 2$

    b. $r(x) = 70x$, $c(x) = x^3 - 6x^2 + 45/x$, and $dx/dt = 0.05$ when $x = 1.5$

27. **Moving along a parabola** A particle moves along the parabola $y = x^2$ in the first quadrant in such a way that its x-coordinate (measured in meters) increases at a steady 10 m/sec. How fast is the angle of inclination θ of the line joining the particle to the origin changing when $x = 3$ m?

28. **Moving along another parabola** A particle moves from right to left along the parabolic curve $y = \sqrt{-x}$ in such a way that its x-coordinate (measured in meters) decreases at the rate of 8 m/sec. How fast is the angle of inclination θ of the line joining the particle to the origin changing when $x = -4$?

29. **Motion in the plane** The coordinates of a particle in the metric xy-plane are differentiable functions of time t with $dx/dt = -1$ m/sec and $dy/dt = -5$ m/sec. How fast is the particle's distance from the origin changing as it passes through the point (5, 12)?

30. **A moving shadow** A man 6 ft tall walks at the rate of 5 ft/sec toward a streetlight that is 16 ft above the ground. At what rate is the tip of his shadow moving? At what rate is the length of his shadow changing when he is 10 ft from the base of the light?

31. **Another moving shadow** A light shines from the top of a pole 50 ft high. A ball is dropped from the same height from a point 30 ft away from the light. (See accompanying figure.) How fast is the shadow of the ball moving along the ground 1/2 sec later? (Assume the ball falls a distance $s = 16t^2$ ft in t sec.)

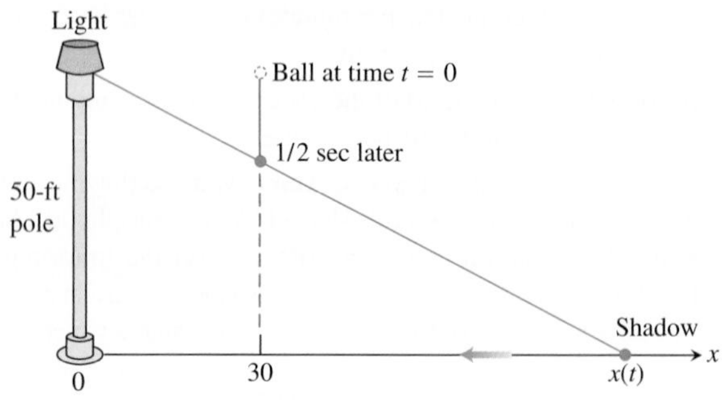

32. **Videotaping a moving car** You are videotaping a race from a stand 132 ft from the track, following a car that is moving at 180 mi/h (264 ft/sec). How fast will your camera angle θ be changing when the car is right in front of you? A half second later?

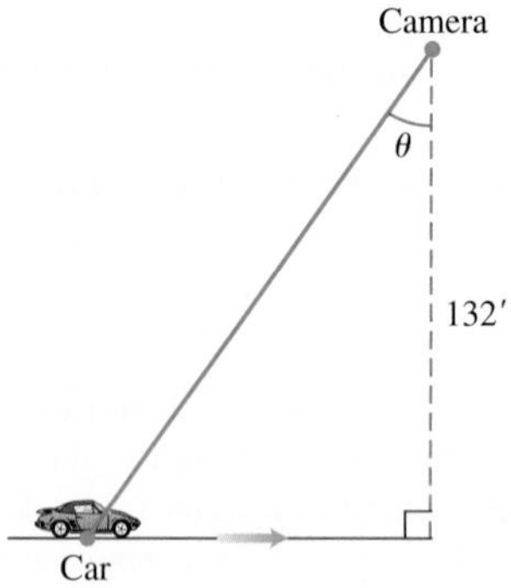

33. **A melting ice layer** A spherical iron ball 8 in. in diameter is coated with a layer of ice of uniform thickness. If the ice melts at the rate of 10 in^3/min, how fast is the thickness of the ice decreasing when it is 2 in. thick? How fast is the outer surface area of ice decreasing?

34. **Highway patrol** A highway patrol plane flies 3 mi above a level, straight road at a steady 120 mi/h. The pilot sees an oncoming car and with radar determines that at the instant the line-of-sight distance from plane to car is 5 mi, the line-of-sight distance is decreasing at the rate of 160 mi/h. Find the car's speed along the highway.

35. **A building's shadow** On a morning of a day when the sun will pass directly overhead, the shadow of an 80-ft building on level ground is 60 ft long. At the moment in question, the angle θ the sun makes with the ground is increasing at the rate of 0.27°/min. At what rate is the shadow decreasing? (Remember to use radians. Express your answer in inches per minute, to the nearest tenth.)

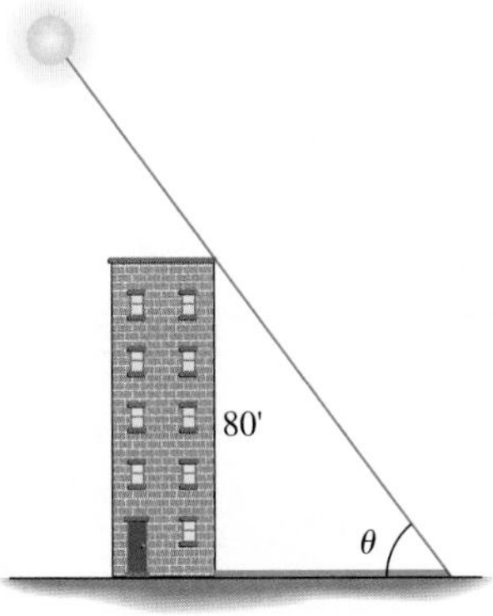

36. Walkers A and B are walking on straight streets that meet at right angles. A approaches the intersection at 2 m/sec; B moves away from the intersection at 1 m/sec. At what rate is the angle θ changing when A is 10 m from the intersection and B is 20 m from the intersection? Express your answer in degrees per second to the nearest degree.

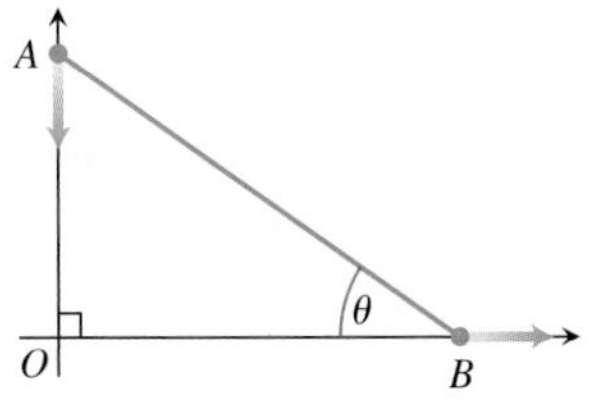

37. Baseball players A baseball diamond is a square 90 ft on a side. A player runs from first base to second at a rate of 16 ft/sec.

a. At what rate is the player's distance from third base changing when the player is 30 ft from first base?

b. At what rates are angles θ_1 and θ_2 (see the figure) changing at that time?

c. The player slides into second base at the rate of 15 ft/sec. At what rates are angles θ_1 and θ_2 changing as the player touches base?

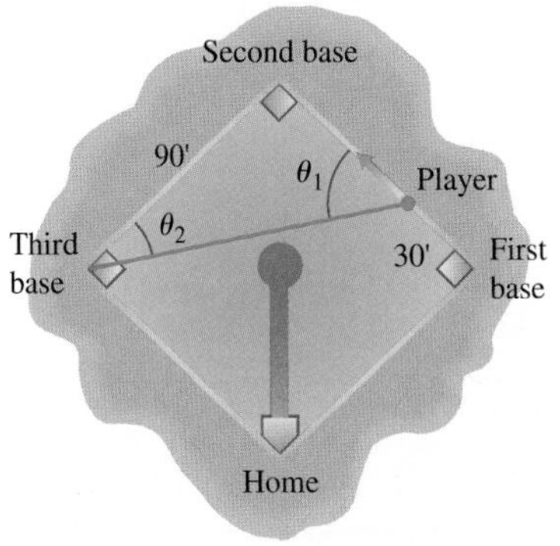

38. Ships Two ships are steaming straight away from a point O along routes that make a 120° angle. Ship A moves at 14 knots (nautical miles per hour; a nautical mile is 2000 yd). Ship B moves at 21 knots. How fast are the ships moving apart when $OA = 5$ and $OB = 3$ nautical miles?

3.10 Linearization and Differentials

Sometimes we can approximate complicated functions with simpler ones that give the accuracy we want for specific applications and are easier to work with. The approximating functions discussed in this section are called *linearizations*, and they are based on tangent lines. Other approximating functions, such as polynomials, are discussed in Chapter 8.

We introduce new variables dx and dy, called *differentials*, and define them in a way that makes Leibniz's notation for the derivative dy/dx a true ratio. We use dy to estimate error in measurement, which then provides for a precise proof of the Chain Rule (Section 3.5).

Linearization

As you can see in Figure 3.49 on the next page, the tangent to the curve $y = x^2$ lies close to the curve near the point of tangency. For a brief interval to either side, the y-values along the tangent line give good approximations to the y-values on the curve. We observe this phenomenon by zooming in on the two graphs at the point of tangency or by looking at tables of values for the difference between $f(x)$ and its tangent line near the x-coordinate of the point of tangency. The phenomenon is true not just for parabolas; every differentiable curve behaves locally like its tangent line.

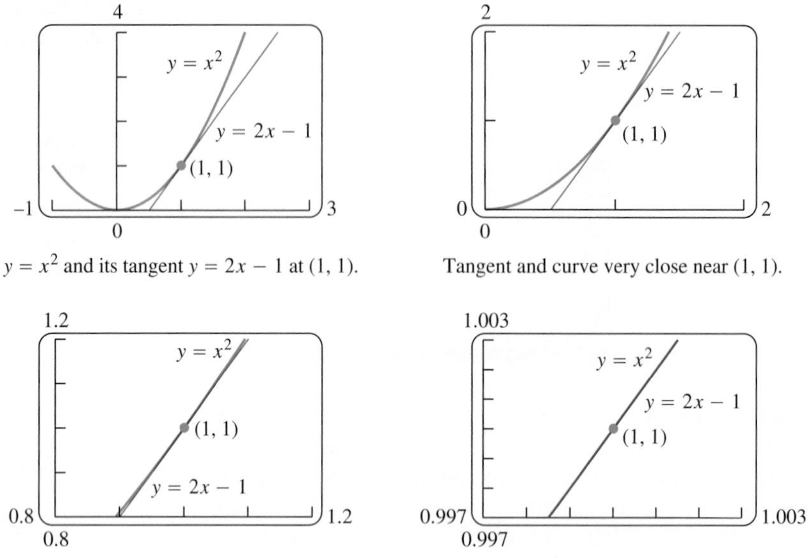

$y = x^2$ and its tangent $y = 2x - 1$ at (1, 1).

Tangent and curve very close near (1, 1).

Tangent and curve very close throughout entire x-interval shown.

Tangent and curve closer still. Computer screen cannot distinguish tangent from curve on this x-interval.

FIGURE 3.49 The more we magnify the graph of a function near a point where the function is differentiable, the flatter the graph becomes and the more it resembles its tangent.

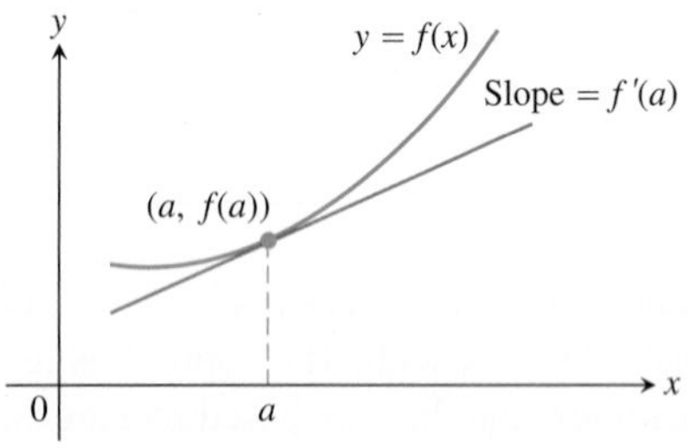

FIGURE 3.50 The tangent to the curve $y = f(x)$ at $x = a$ is the line $L(x) = f(a) + f'(a)(x - a)$.

In general, the tangent to $y = f(x)$ at a point $x = a$, where f is differentiable (Figure 3.50), passes through the point $(a, f(a))$, so its point-slope equation is

$$y = f(a) + f'(a)(x - a).$$

Thus, this tangent line is the graph of the linear function

$$L(x) = f(a) + f'(a)(x - a).$$

For as long as this line remains close to the graph of f, $L(x)$ gives a good approximation to $f(x)$.

DEFINITIONS If f is differentiable at $x = a$, then the approximating function

$$L(x) = f(a) + f'(a)(x - a)$$

is the **linearization** of f at a. The approximation

$$f(x) \approx L(x)$$

of f by L is the **standard linear approximation** of f at a. The point $x = a$ is the **center** of the approximation.

EXAMPLE 1 Find the linearization of $f(x) = \sqrt{1 + x}$ at $x = 0$ (Figure 3.51).

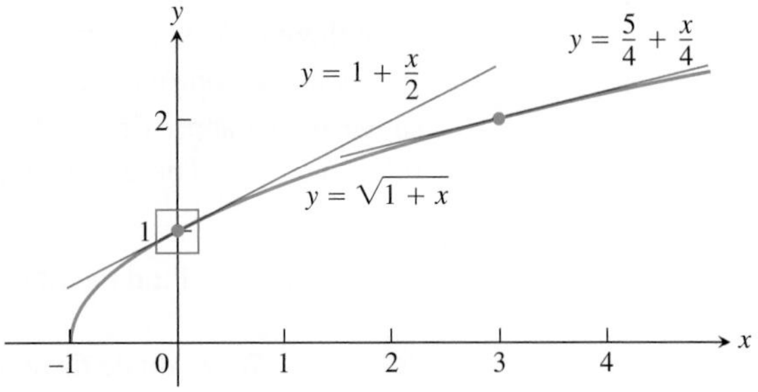

FIGURE 3.51 The graph of $y = \sqrt{1 + x}$ and its linearizations at $x = 0$ and $x = 3$. Figure 3.52 shows a magnified view of the small window about 1 on the y-axis.

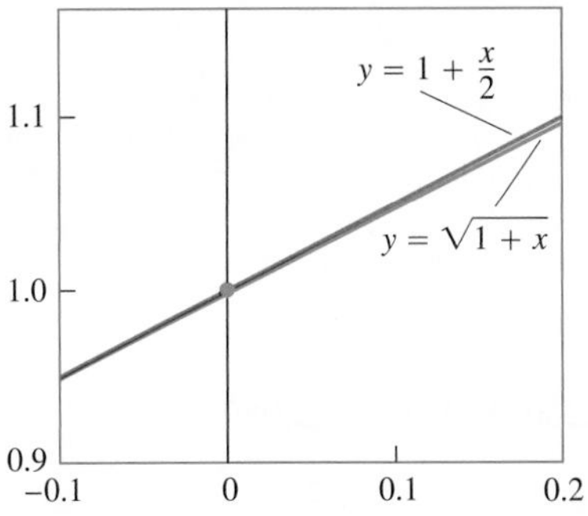

FIGURE 3.52 Magnified view of the window in Figure 3.51.

Solution Since

$$f'(x) = \frac{1}{2}\left(1 + x\right)^{-1/2},$$

we have $f(0) = 1$ and $f'(0) = 1/2$, giving the linearization

$$L(x) = f(a) + f'(a)(x - a) = 1 + \frac{1}{2}\left(x - 0\right) = 1 + \frac{x}{2}.$$

See Figure 3.52. ■

The table below shows how accurate the approximation $\sqrt{1 + x} \approx 1 + (x/2)$ from Example 1 is for some values of x near 0. As we move away from zero, we lose accuracy. For example, for $x = 2$, the linearization gives 2 as the approximation for $\sqrt{3}$, which is not even accurate to one decimal place.

Approximation	True value	|True value − approximation|
$\sqrt{1.2} \approx 1 + \frac{0.2}{2} = 1.10$	1.095445	$<10^{-2}$
$\sqrt{1.05} \approx 1 + \frac{0.05}{2} = 1.025$	1.024695	$<10^{-3}$
$\sqrt{1.005} \approx 1 + \frac{0.005}{2} = 1.00250$	1.002497	$<10^{-5}$

Do not be misled by the preceding calculations into thinking that whatever we do with a linearization is better done with a calculator. In practice, we would never use a linearization to find a particular square root. The utility of a linearization is its ability to replace a complicated formula by a simpler one over an entire interval of values. If we have to work with $\sqrt{1+x}$ for x close to 0 and can tolerate the small amount of error involved, we can work with $1 + (x/2)$ instead. Of course, we then need to know how much error there is. We have more to say on the estimation of error in Chapter 8.

A linear approximation normally loses accuracy away from its center. As Figure 3.51 suggests, the approximation $\sqrt{1+x} \approx 1 + (x/2)$ will probably be too crude to be useful near $x = 3$. There, we need the linearization at $x = 3$.

EXAMPLE 2 Find the linearization of $f(x) = \sqrt{1+x}$ at $x = 3$.

Solution We evaluate the equation defining $L(x)$ at $a = 3$. With

$$f(3) = 2, \qquad f'(3) = \frac{1}{2}\left(1+x\right)^{-1/2}\bigg|_{x=3} = \frac{1}{4},$$

we have

$$L(x) = 2 + \frac{1}{4}(x-3) = \frac{5}{4} + \frac{x}{4}.$$

At $x = 3.2$, the linearization in Example 2 gives

$$\sqrt{1+x} = \sqrt{1+3.2} \approx \frac{5}{4} + \frac{3.2}{4} = 1.250 + 0.800 = 2.050,$$

which differs from the true value $\sqrt{4.2} \approx 2.04939$ by less than one one-thousandth. The linearization in Example 1 gives

$$\sqrt{1+x} = \sqrt{1+3.2} \approx 1 + \frac{3.2}{2} = 1 + 1.6 = 2.6,$$

a result that is off by more than 25%.

EXAMPLE 3 Find the linearization of $f(x) = \cos x$ at $x = \pi/2$ (Figure 3.53).

Solution Since $f(\pi/2) = \cos(\pi/2) = 0$, $f'(x) = -\sin x$, and $f'(\pi/2) = -\sin(\pi/2) = -1$, we have

$$\begin{aligned} L(x) &= f(a) + f'(a)(x-a) \\ &= 0 + (-1)\left(x - \frac{\pi}{2}\right) \\ &= -x + \frac{\pi}{2}. \end{aligned}$$

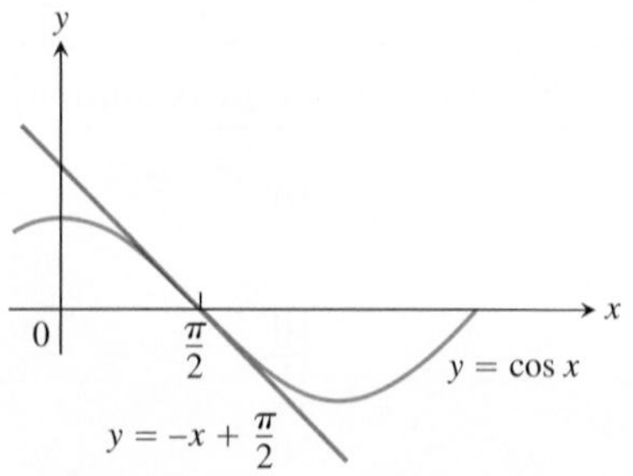

FIGURE 3.53 The graph of $f(x) = \cos x$ and its linearization at $x = \pi/2$. Near $x = \pi/2$, $\cos x \approx -x + (\pi/2)$ (Example 3).

An important linear approximation for roots and powers is

$$(1+x)^k \approx 1 + kx \qquad (x \text{ near } 0;\ \text{any number } k)$$

(Exercise 15). This approximation, good for values of x sufficiently close to zero, has broad application. For example, when x is small,

$$\sqrt{1+x} \approx 1 + \frac{1}{2}x \qquad k = 1/2$$

$$\frac{1}{1-x} = (1-x)^{-1} \approx 1 + (-1)(-x) = 1 + x \qquad k = -1;\ \text{replace } x \text{ by } -x.$$

$$\sqrt[3]{1+5x^4} = (1+5x^4)^{1/3} \approx 1 + \frac{1}{3}(5x^4) = 1 + \frac{5}{3}x^4 \qquad k = 1/3;\ \text{replace } x \text{ by } 5x^4.$$

$$\frac{1}{\sqrt{1-x^2}} = (1-x^2)^{-1/2} \approx 1 + \left(-\frac{1}{2}\right)(-x^2) = 1 + \frac{1}{2}x^2 \qquad k = -1/2;\ \text{replace } x \text{ by } -x^2.$$

Differentials

We sometimes use the Leibniz notation dy/dx to represent the derivative of y with respect to x. Contrary to its appearance, it is not a ratio. We now introduce two new variables dx and dy with the property that if their ratio exists, it will be equal to the derivative.

DEFINITION Let $y = f(x)$ be a differentiable function. The **differential dx** is an independent variable. The **differential dy** is

$$dy = f'(x)\,dx.$$

Unlike the independent variable dx, the variable dy is always a dependent variable. It depends on both x and dx. If dx is given a specific value and x is a particular number in the domain of the function f, then these values determine the numerical value of dy.

EXAMPLE 4

(a) Find dy if $y = x^5 + 37x$.

(b) Find the value of dy when $x = 1$ and $dx = 0.2$.

Solution

(a) $dy = (5x^4 + 37)\,dx$

(b) Substituting $x = 1$ and $dx = 0.2$ in the expression for dy, we have

$$dy = (5 \cdot 1^4 + 37)0.2 = 8.4.$$

■

The geometric meaning of differentials is shown in Figure 3.54 on the next page. Let $x = a$ and set $dx = \Delta x$. The corresponding change in $y = f(x)$ is

$$\Delta y = f(a + dx) - f(a).$$

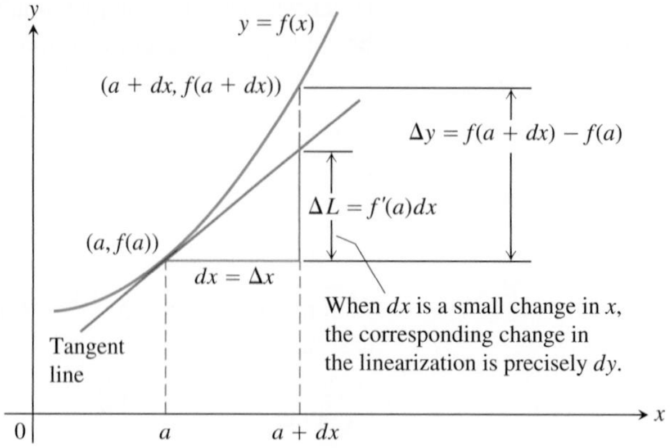

FIGURE 3.54 Geometrically, the differential dy is the change ΔL in the linearization of f when $x = a$ changes by an amount $dx = \Delta x$.

The corresponding change in the tangent line L is

$$\begin{aligned}\Delta L &= L(a + dx) - L(a)\\ &= \underbrace{f(a) + f'(a)[(a + dx) - a]}_{L(a+dx)} - \underbrace{f(a)}_{L(a)}\\ &= f'(a)\,dx.\end{aligned}$$

That is, the change in the linearization of f is precisely the value of the differential dy when $x = a$ and $dx = \Delta x$. Therefore, dy represents the amount the tangent line rises or falls when x changes by an amount $dx = \Delta x$.

If $dx \neq 0$, then the quotient of the differential dy by the differential dx is equal to the derivative $f'(x)$ because

$$dy \div dx = \frac{f'(x)\,dx}{dx} = f'(x) = \frac{dy}{dx}.$$

We sometimes write

$$df = f'(x)\,dx$$

in place of $dy = f'(x)\,dx$, calling df the **differential of f**. For instance, if $f(x) = 3x^2 - 6$, then

$$df = d(3x^2 - 6) = 6x\,dx.$$

Every differentiation formula like

$$\frac{d(u + v)}{dx} = \frac{du}{dx} + \frac{dv}{dx} \quad \text{or} \quad \frac{d(\sin u)}{dx} = \cos u\,\frac{du}{dx}$$

has a corresponding differential form like

$$d(u + v) = du + dv \quad \text{or} \quad d(\sin u) = \cos u\,du.$$

EXAMPLE 5

(a) $d(\tan 2x) = \sec^2(2x)\, d(2x) = 2\sec^2 2x\, dx$

(b) $d\left(\frac{x}{x+1}\right) = \frac{(x+1)\,dx - x\,d(x+1)}{(x+1)^2} = \frac{x\,dx + dx - x\,dx}{(x+1)^2} = \frac{dx}{(x+1)^2}$ ■

Estimating with Differentials

Suppose we know the value of a differentiable function $f(x)$ at a point a and want to predict how much this value will change if we move to a nearby point $a + dx$. If $dx = \Delta x$ is small, then we can see from Figure 3.54 that Δy is approximately equal to the differential dy. Since

$$f(a + dx) = f(a) + \Delta y,$$

the differential approximation gives

$$f(a + dx) \approx f(a) + dy$$

where $dx = \Delta x$. Thus the approximation $\Delta y \approx dy$ can be used to calculate $f(a + dx)$ when $f(a)$ is known and dx is small.

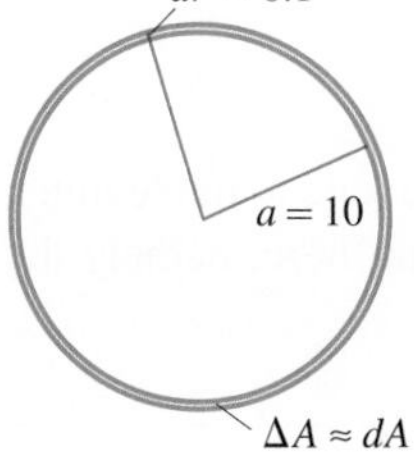

FIGURE 3.55 When dr is small compared with a, as it is when $dr = 0.1$ and $a = 10$, the differential $dA = 2\pi a\, dr$ gives a way to estimate the area of the circle with radius $r = a + dr$ (Example 6).

EXAMPLE 6 The radius r of a circle increases from $a = 10$ m to 10.1 m (Figure 3.55). Use dA to estimate the increase in the circle's area A. Estimate the area of the enlarged circle and compare your estimate to the true area.

Solution Since $A = \pi r^2$, the estimated increase is

$$dA = A'(a)\, dr = 2\pi a\, dr = 2\pi(10)(0.1) = 2\pi \text{ m}^2.$$

Thus,

$$\begin{aligned} A(10 + 0.1) &\approx A(10) + 2\pi \\ &= \pi(10)^2 + 2\pi = 102\pi. \end{aligned}$$

The area of a circle of radius 10.1 m is approximately 102π m^2.

The true area is

$$\begin{aligned} A(10.1) &= \pi(10.1)^2 \\ &= 102.01\pi \text{ m}^2. \end{aligned}$$

The error in our estimate is 0.01π m^2, which is the difference $\Delta A - dA$. ■

Error in Differential Approximation

Let $f(x)$ be differentiable at $x = a$ and suppose that $dx = \Delta x$ is an increment of x. We have two ways to describe the change in f as x changes from a to $a + \Delta x$:

The true change:	$\Delta f = f(a + \Delta x) - f(a)$
The differential estimate:	$df = f'(a)\,\Delta x.$

How well does df approximate Δf?

We measure the approximation error by subtracting df from Δf:

$$\begin{aligned}\text{Approximation error} &= \Delta f - df \\ &= \Delta f - f'(a)\Delta x \\ &= \underbrace{f(a + \Delta x) - f(a)}_{\Delta f} - f'(a)\Delta x \\ &= \underbrace{\left(\frac{f(a + \Delta x) - f(a)}{\Delta x} - f'(a)\right)}_{\text{Call this part } \epsilon} \cdot \Delta x \\ &= \epsilon \cdot \Delta x.\end{aligned}$$

As $\Delta x \to 0$, the difference quotient

$$\frac{f(a + \Delta x) - f(a)}{\Delta x}$$

approaches $f'(a)$ (remember the definition of $f'(a)$), so the quantity in parentheses becomes a very small number (which is why we called it ϵ). In fact, $\epsilon \to 0$ as $\Delta x \to 0$. When Δx is small, the approximation error $\epsilon\ \Delta x$ is smaller still.

$$\underbrace{\Delta f}_{\substack{\text{true}\\ \text{change}}} = \underbrace{f'(a)\Delta x}_{\substack{\text{estimated}\\ \text{change}}} + \underbrace{\epsilon\ \Delta x}_{\text{error}}$$

Although we do not know exactly how small the error is and will not be able to make much progress on this front until Chapter 8, there is something worth noting here, namely the *form* taken by the equation.

> **Change in $y = f(x)$ near $x = a$**
>
> If $y = f(x)$ is differentiable at $x = a$ and x changes from a to $a + \Delta x$, the change Δy in f is given by an equation of the form
>
> $$\Delta y = f'(a)\ \Delta x + \epsilon\ \Delta x \qquad (1)$$
>
> in which $\epsilon \to 0$ as $\Delta x \to 0$.

In Example 6 we found that

$$\Delta A = \pi(10.1)^2 - \pi(10)^2 = (102.01 - 100)\pi = (\underbrace{2\pi}_{dA} + \underbrace{0.01\pi}_{\text{error}})\ \text{m}^2$$

so the approximation error is $\Delta A - dA = \epsilon\ \Delta r = 0.01\pi$ and $\epsilon = 0.01\pi/\Delta r = 0.01\pi/0.1 = 0.1\pi$ m.

Equation (1) enables us to prove the Chain Rule correctly.

Proof of the Chain Rule

Our goal is to show that if $f(u)$ is a differentiable function of u and $u = g(x)$ is a differentiable function of x, then the composite $y = f(g(x))$ is a differentiable function of x. More precisely, if g is differentiable at x_0 and f is differentiable at $g(x_0)$, then the composite is differentiable at x_0 and

$$\left.\frac{dy}{dx}\right|_{x=x_0} = f'(g(x_0)) \cdot g'(x_0).$$

Let Δx be an increment in x and let Δu and Δy be the corresponding increments in u and y. Applying Equation (1) we have,

$$\Delta u = g'(x_0)\Delta x + \epsilon_1 \Delta x = (g'(x_0) + \epsilon_1)\Delta x,$$

where $\epsilon_1 \to 0$ as $\Delta x \to 0$. Similarly,

$$\Delta y = f'(u_0)\Delta u + \epsilon_2 \Delta u = (f'(u_0) + \epsilon_2)\Delta u,$$

where $\epsilon_2 \to 0$ as $\Delta u \to 0$. Notice also that $\Delta u \to 0$ as $\Delta x \to 0$. Combining the equations for Δu and Δy gives

$$\Delta y = (f'(u_0) + \epsilon_2)(g'(x_0) + \epsilon_1)\Delta x,$$

so

$$\frac{\Delta y}{\Delta x} = f'(u_0)g'(x_0) + \epsilon_2 g'(x_0) + f'(u_0)\epsilon_1 + \epsilon_2\epsilon_1.$$

Since ϵ_1 and ϵ_2 go to zero as Δx goes to zero, three of the four terms on the right vanish in the limit, leaving

$$\left.\frac{dy}{dx}\right|_{x=x_0} = \lim_{\Delta x \to 0} \frac{\Delta y}{\Delta x} = f'(u_0)g'(x_0) = f'(g(x_0)) \cdot g'(x_0).$$ ■

Sensitivity to Change

The equation $df = f'(x)\,dx$ tells how *sensitive* the output of f is to a change in input at different values of x. The larger the value of f' at x, the greater the effect of a given change dx. As we move from a to a nearby point $a + dx$, we can describe the change in f in three ways:

	True	**Estimated**
Absolute change	$\Delta f = f(a + dx) - f(a)$	$df = f'(a)\,dx$
Relative change	$\dfrac{\Delta f}{f(a)}$	$\dfrac{df}{f(a)}$
Percentage change	$\dfrac{\Delta f}{f(a)} \times 100$	$\dfrac{df}{f(a)} \times 100$

EXERCISES 3.10

In Exercises 1–5, find the linearization $L(x)$ of $f(x)$ at $x = a$.

1. $f(x) = x^3 - 2x + 3, \quad a = 2$
2. $f(x) = \sqrt{x^2 + 9}, \quad a = -4$
3. $f(x) = x + \dfrac{1}{x}, \quad a = 1$
4. $f(x) = \sqrt[3]{x}, \quad a = -8$
5. $f(x) = \tan x, \quad a = \pi$
6. **Common linear approximations at $x = 0$** Find the linearizations of the following functions at $x = 0$.
   (a) $\sin x$ **(b)** $\cos x$ **(c)** $\tan x$
   (d) e^x **(e)** $\ln(1 + x)$

You want linearizations that will replace the functions in Exercises 7–14 over intervals that include the given points x_0. To make your subsequent work as simple as possible, you want to center each linearization not at x_0 but at a nearby integer $x = a$ at which the given function and its derivative are easy to evaluate. What linearization do you use in each case?

7. $f(x) = x^2 + 2x, \quad x_0 = 0.1$
8. $f(x) = x^{-1}, \quad x_0 = 0.9$
9. $f(x) = 2x^2 + 4x - 3, \quad x_0 = -0.9$
10. $f(x) = 1 + x, \quad x_0 = 8.1$
11. $f(x) = \sqrt[3]{x}, \quad x_0 = 8.5$
12. $f(x) = \dfrac{x}{x + 1}, \quad x_0 = 1.3$
13. $f(x) = e^{-x}, \quad x_0 = -0.1$
14. $f(x) = \sin^{-1} x, \quad x_0 = \pi/12$
15. Show that the linearization of $f(x) = (1 + x)^k$ at $x = 0$ is $L(x) = 1 + kx$.
16. Use the linear approximation $(1 + x)^k \approx 1 + kx$ to find an approximation for the function $f(x)$ for values of x near zero.
   a. $f(x) = (1 - x)^6$ **b.** $f(x) = \dfrac{2}{1 - x}$
   c. $f(x) = \dfrac{1}{\sqrt{1 + x}}$ **d.** $f(x) = \sqrt{2 + x^2}$
   e. $f(x) = (4 + 3x)^{1/3}$ **f.** $f(x) = \sqrt[3]{\left(1 - \dfrac{1}{2 + x}\right)^2}$
17. **Faster than a calculator** Use the approximation $(1 + x)^k \approx 1 + kx$ to estimate the following.
   a. $(1.0002)^{50}$ **b.** $\sqrt[3]{1.009}$
18. Find the linearization of $f(x) = \sqrt{x + 1} + \sin x$ at $x = 0$. How is it related to the individual linearizations of $\sqrt{x + 1}$ and $\sin x$ at $x = 0$?

In Exercises 19–38, find dy.

19. $y = x^3 - 3\sqrt{x}$
20. $y = x\sqrt{1 - x^2}$
21. $y = \dfrac{2x}{1 + x^2}$
22. $y = \dfrac{2\sqrt{x}}{3(1 + \sqrt{x})}$
23. $2y^{3/2} + xy - x = 0$
24. $xy^2 - 4x^{3/2} - y = 0$
25. $y = \sin(5\sqrt{x})$
26. $y = \cos(x^2)$
27. $y = 4\tan(x^3/3)$
28. $y = \sec(x^2 - 1)$
29. $y = 3\csc(1 - 2\sqrt{x})$
30. $y = 2\cot\left(\dfrac{1}{\sqrt{x}}\right)$
31. $y = e^{\sqrt{x}}$
32. $y = xe^{-x}$
33. $y = \ln(1 + x^2)$
34. $y = \ln\left(\dfrac{x + 1}{\sqrt{x - 1}}\right)$
35. $y = \tan^{-1}(e^{x^2})$
36. $y = \cot^{-1}\left(\dfrac{1}{x^2}\right) + \cos^{-1} 2x$
37. $y = \sec^{-1}(e^{-x})$
38. $y = e^{\tan^{-1}\sqrt{x^2+1}}$

In Exercises 39–44, each function $f(x)$ changes value when x changes from x_0 to $x_0 + dx$. Find

a. the change $\Delta f = f(x_0 + dx) - f(x_0)$;
b. the value of the estimate $df = f'(x_0)\,dx$; and
c. the approximation error $|\Delta f - df|$.

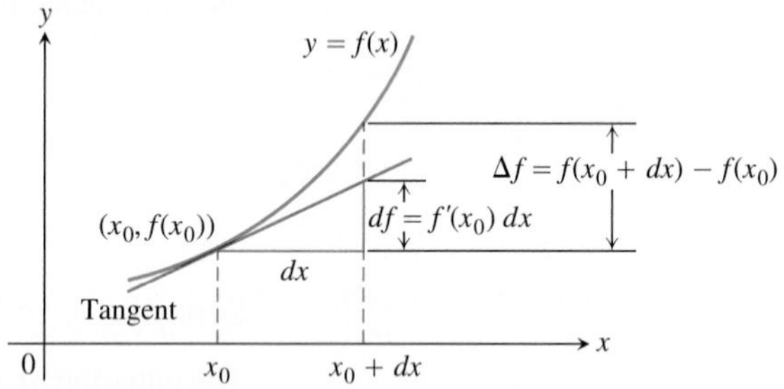

39. $f(x) = x^2 + 2x, \quad x_0 = 1, \quad dx = 0.1$
40. $f(x) = 2x^2 + 4x - 3, \quad x_0 = -1, \quad dx = 0.1$
41. $f(x) = x^3 - x, \quad x_0 = 1, \quad dx = 0.1$
42. $f(x) = x^4, \quad x_0 = 1, \quad dx = 0.1$
43. $f(x) = x^{-1}, \quad x_0 = 0.5, \quad dx = 0.1$
44. $f(x) = x^3 - 2x + 3, \quad x_0 = 2, \quad dx = 0.1$

In Exercises 45–50, write a differential formula that estimates the given change in volume or surface area.

45. The change in the volume $V = (4/3)\pi r^3$ of a sphere when the radius changes from r_0 to $r_0 + dr$
46. The change in the volume $V = x^3$ of a cube when the edge lengths change from x_0 to $x_0 + dx$

47. The change in the surface area $S = 6x^2$ of a cube when the edge lengths change from x_0 to $x_0 + dx$

48. The change in the lateral surface area $S = \pi r\sqrt{r^2 + h^2}$ of a right circular cone when the radius changes from r_0 to $r_0 + dr$ and the height does not change

49. The change in the volume $V = \pi r^2 h$ of a right circular cylinder when the radius changes from r_0 to $r_0 + dr$ and the height does not change

50. The change in the lateral surface area $S = 2\pi rh$ of a right circular cylinder when the height changes from h_0 to $h_0 + dh$ and the radius does not change

51. The radius of a circle is increased from 2.00 to 2.02 m.

a. Estimate the resulting change in area.

b. Express the estimate as a percentage of the circle's original area.

52. The diameter of a tree was 10 in. During the following year, the circumference increased 2 in. About how much did the tree's diameter increase? The tree's cross-section area?

53. Estimating volume Estimate the volume of material in a cylindrical shell with height 30 in., radius 6 in., and shell thickness 0.5 in.

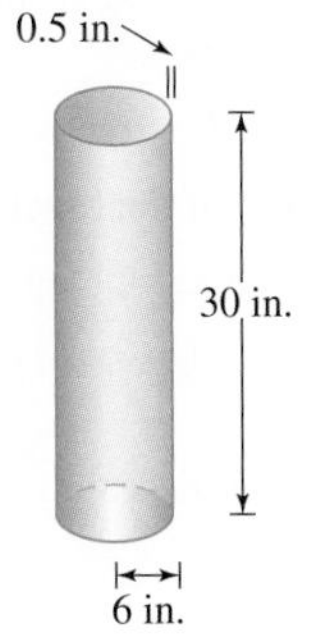

54. Estimating height of a building A surveyor, standing 30 ft from the base of a building, measures the angle of elevation to the top of the building to be 75°. How accurately must the angle be measured for the percentage error in estimating the height of the building to be less than 4%?

55. Tolerance The height and radius of a right circular cylinder are equal, so the cylinder's volume is $V = \pi h^3$. The volume is to be calculated with an error of no more than 1% of the true value. Find approximately the greatest error that can be tolerated in the measurement of h, expressed as a percentage of h.

56. Tolerance

a. About how accurately must the interior diameter of a 10-m-high cylindrical storage tank be measured to calculate the tank's volume to within 1% of its true value?

b. About how accurately must the tank's exterior diameter be measured to calculate the amount of paint it will take to paint the side of the tank to within 5% of the true amount?

57. Minting coins A manufacturer contracts to mint coins for the federal government. How much variation dr in the radius of the coins can be tolerated if the coins are to weigh within $1/1000$ of their ideal weight? Assume that the thickness does not vary.

58. Profit The profit P for a certain manufacturer selling x items is

$$P(x) = 200xe^{-x/400}.$$

Estimate the change and percent change in P as sales change from $x = 145$ to $x = 150$ items.

59. The effect of flight maneuvers on the heart The amount of work done by the heart's main pumping chamber, the left ventricle, is given by the equation

$$W = PV + \frac{V\delta v^2}{2g},$$

where W is the work per unit time, P is the average blood pressure, V is the volume of blood pumped out during the unit of time, δ ("delta") is the weight density of the blood, v is the average velocity of the exiting blood, and g is the acceleration of gravity.

When P, V, δ, and v remain constant, W becomes a function of g, and the equation takes the simplified form

$$W = a + \frac{b}{g} \ (a, b \text{ constant}).$$

As a member of NASA's medical team, you want to know how sensitive W is to apparent changes in g caused by flight maneuvers, and this depends on the initial value of g. As part of your investigation, you decide to compare the effect on W of a given change dg on the moon, where $g = 5.2$ ft/sec^2, with the effect the same change dg would have on Earth, where $g = 32$ ft/sec^2. Use the simplified equation above to find the ratio of dW_{moon} to dW_{Earth}.

60. Measuring acceleration of gravity When the length L of a clock pendulum is held constant by controlling its temperature, the pendulum's period T depends on the acceleration of gravity g. The period will therefore vary slightly as the clock is moved from place to place on the earth's surface, depending on the change in g. By keeping track of ΔT, we can estimate the variation in g from the equation $T = 2\pi(L/g)^{1/2}$ that relates T, g, and L.

a. With L held constant and g as the independent variable, calculate dT and use it to answer parts (b) and (c).

b. If g increases, will T increase or decrease? Will a pendulum clock speed up or slow down? Explain.

c. A clock with a 100-cm pendulum is moved from a location where $g = 980$ cm/sec^2 to a new location. This increases the period by $dT = 0.001$ sec. Find dg and estimate the value of g at the new location.

61. The edge of a cube is measured as 10 cm with an error of 1%. The cube's volume is to be calculated from this measurement. Estimate the percentage error in the volume calculation.

62. About how accurately should you measure the side of a square to be sure of calculating the area within 2% of its true value?

63. The diameter of a sphere is measured as 100 ± 1 cm and the volume is calculated from this measurement. Estimate the percentage error in the volume calculation.

64. Estimate the allowable percentage error in measuring the diameter D of a sphere if the volume is to be calculated correctly to within 3%.

65. The linearization is the best linear approximation (This is why we use the linearization.) Suppose that $y = f(x)$ is differentiable at $x = a$ and that $g(x) = m(x - a) + c$ is a linear function in which m and c are constants. If the error $E(x) = f(x) - g(x)$ were small enough near $x = a$, we might think of using g as a linear approximation of f instead of the linearization $L(x) = f(a) + f'(a)(x - a)$. Show that if we impose on g the conditions

1. $E(a) = 0$ The approximation error is zero at $x = a$.

2. $\lim_{x \to a} \frac{E(x)}{x - a} = 0$ The error is negligible when compared with $x - a$.

then $g(x) = f(a) + f'(a)(x - a)$. Thus, the linearization $L(x)$ gives the only linear approximation whose error is both zero at $x = a$ and negligible in comparison with $x - a$.

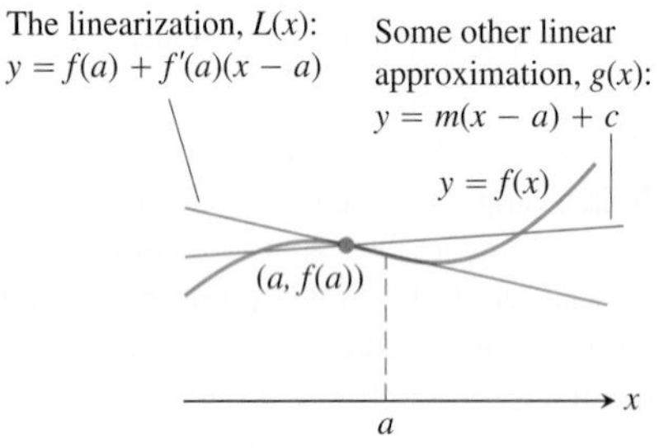

66. Quadratic approximations

a. Let $Q(x) = b_0 + b_1(x - a) + b_2(x - a)^2$ be a quadratic approximation to $f(x)$ at $x = a$ with the properties:

i. $Q(a) = f(a)$

ii. $Q'(a) = f'(a)$

iii. $Q''(a) = f''(a)$

Determine the coefficients b_0, b_1, and b_2.

b. Find the quadratic approximation to $f(x) = 1/(1 - x)$ at $x = 0$.

T **c.** Graph $f(x) = 1/(1 - x)$ and its quadratic approximation at $x = 0$. Then zoom in on the two graphs at the point (0, 1). Comment on what you see.

T **d.** Find the quadratic approximation to $g(x) = 1/x$ at $x = 1$. Graph g and its quadratic approximation together. Comment on what you see.

T **e.** Find the quadratic approximation to $h(x) = \sqrt{1 + x}$ at $x = 0$. Graph h and its quadratic approximation together. Comment on what you see.

f. What are the linearizations of f, g, and h at the respective points in parts (b), (d), and (e)?

67. The linearization of 2^x

a. Find the linearization of $f(x) = 2^x$ at $x = 0$. Then round its coefficients to two decimal places.

T **b.** Graph the linearization and function together for $-3 \le x \le 3$ and $-1 \le x \le 1$.

68. The linearization of $\log_3 x$

a. Find the linearization of $f(x) = \log_3 x$ at $x = 3$. Then round its coefficients to two decimal places.

T **b.** Graph the linearization and function together in the window $0 \le x \le 8$ and $2 \le x \le 4$.

COMPUTER EXPLORATIONS

In Exercises 69–74, use a CAS to estimate the magnitude of the error in using the linearization in place of the function over a specified interval I. Perform the following steps:

a. Plot the function f over I.

b. Find the linearization L of the function at the point a.

c. Plot f and L together on a single graph.

d. Plot the absolute error $|f(x) - L(x)|$ over I and find its maximum value.

e. From your graph in part (d), estimate as large a $\delta > 0$ as you can, satisfying

$$|x - a| < \delta \quad \Rightarrow \quad |f(x) - L(x)| < \epsilon$$

for $\epsilon = 0.5, 0.1$, and 0.01. Then check graphically to see if your δ-estimate holds true.

69. $f(x) = x^3 + x^2 - 2x, \quad [-1, 2], \quad a = 1$

70. $f(x) = \dfrac{x - 1}{4x^2 + 1}, \quad \left[-\dfrac{3}{4}, 1\right], \quad a = \dfrac{1}{2}$

71. $f(x) = x^{2/3}(x - 2), \quad [-2, 3], \quad a = 2$

72. $f(x) = \sqrt{x} - \sin x, \quad [0, 2\pi], \quad a = 2$

73. $f(x) = x2^x, \quad [0, 2], \quad a = 1$

74. $f(x) = \sqrt{x}\sin^{-1} x, \quad [0, 1], \quad a = \dfrac{1}{2}$

3.11 Hyperbolic Functions

The hyperbolic functions are formed by taking combinations of the two exponential functions e^x and e^{-x}. The hyperbolic functions simplify many mathematical expressions and occur frequently in mathematical applications. For instance, they are used to compute the tension in a cable suspended by its two ends, as in an electric transmission line. In this section we give a brief introduction to hyperbolic functions, their graphs, and their derivatives.

Definitions and Identities

The hyperbolic cosine and hyperbolic sine functions are defined by the first two equations in Table 3.2. The table also lists the definitions of the hyperbolic tangent, cotangent, secant, and cosecant. As we will see, the hyperbolic functions bear a number of similarities to the trigonometric functions after which they are named.

The notation $\cosh x$ is often read "kosh x," rhyming with "gosh x," and $\sinh x$ is pronounced as if spelled "cinch x," rhyming with "pinch x."

TABLE 3.2 The six basic hyperbolic functions

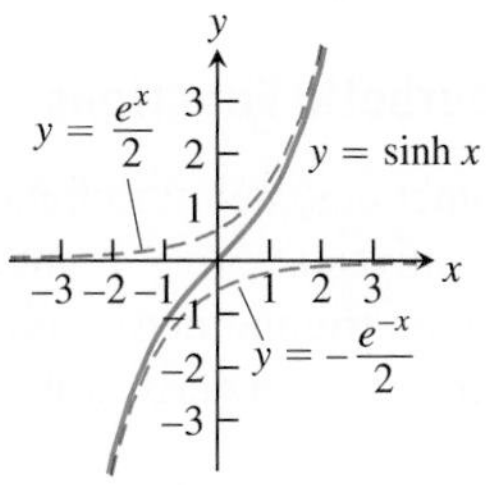

(a)

Hyperbolic sine:

$$\sinh x = \frac{e^x - e^{-x}}{2}$$

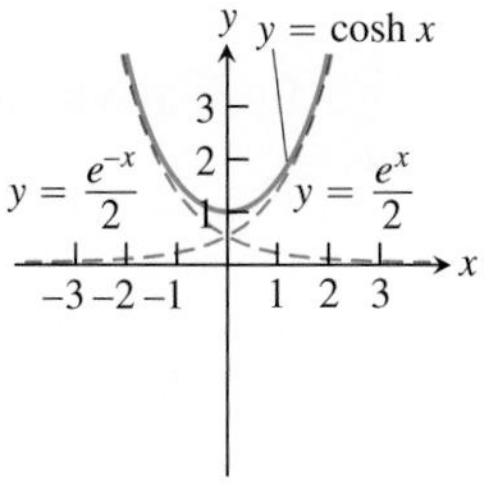

(b)

Hyperbolic cosine:

$$\cosh x = \frac{e^x + e^{-x}}{2}$$

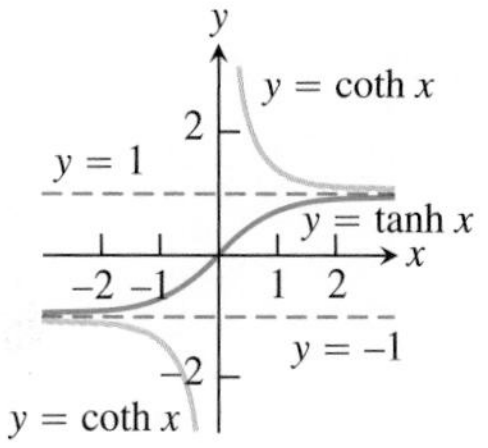

(c)

Hyperbolic tangent:

$$\tanh x = \frac{\sinh x}{\cosh x} = \frac{e^x - e^{-x}}{e^x + e^{-x}}$$

Hyperbolic cotangent:

$$\coth x = \frac{\cosh x}{\sinh x} = \frac{e^x + e^{-x}}{e^x - e^{-x}}$$

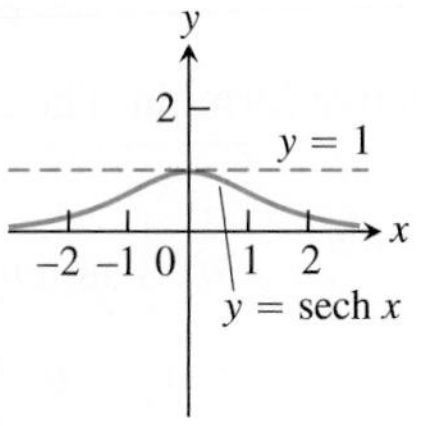

(d)

Hyperbolic secant:

$$\operatorname{sech} x = \frac{1}{\cosh x} = \frac{2}{e^x + e^{-x}}$$

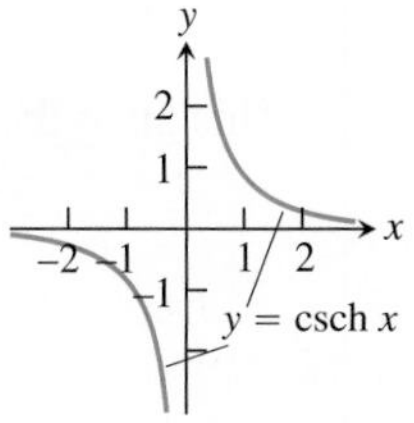

(e)

Hyperbolic cosecant:

$$\operatorname{csch} x = \frac{1}{\sinh x} = \frac{2}{e^x - e^{-x}}$$

TABLE 3.3 Identities for hyperbolic functions

$$\cosh^2 x - \sinh^2 x = 1$$
$$\sinh 2x = 2 \sinh x \cosh x$$
$$\cosh 2x = \cosh^2 x + \sinh^2 x$$
$$\cosh^2 x = \frac{\cosh 2x + 1}{2}$$
$$\sinh^2 x = \frac{\cosh 2x - 1}{2}$$
$$\tanh^2 x = 1 - \operatorname{sech}^2 x$$
$$\coth^2 x = 1 + \operatorname{csch}^2 x$$

Hyperbolic functions satisfy the identities in Table 3.3. Except for differences in sign, these resemble identities we know for the trigonometric functions. The identities are proved directly from the definitions, as we show here for the second one:

$$\begin{aligned} 2 \sinh x \cosh x &= 2\left(\frac{e^x - e^{-x}}{2}\right)\left(\frac{e^x + e^{-x}}{2}\right) \\ &= \frac{e^{2x} - e^{-2x}}{2} \\ &= \sinh 2x. \end{aligned}$$

The other identities are obtained similarly, by substituting in the definitions of the hyperbolic functions and using algebra. Like many standard functions, hyperbolic functions and their inverses are easily evaluated with calculators, which have special keys or keystroke sequences for that purpose.

For any real number u, we know the point with coordinates $(\cos u, \sin u)$ lies on the unit circle $x^2 + y^2 = 1$. So the trigonometric functions are sometimes called the *circular* functions. Because of the first identity

$$\cosh^2 u - \sinh^2 u = 1,$$

with u substituted for x in Table 3.3, the point having coordinates $(\cosh u, \sinh u)$ lies on the right-hand branch of the hyperbola $x^2 - y^2 = 1$. This is where the *hyperbolic* functions get their name.

Derivatives of Hyperbolic Functions

The six hyperbolic functions, being rational combinations of the differentiable functions e^x and e^{-x}, have derivatives at every point at which they are defined (Table 3.4). Again, there are similarities with trigonometric functions.

The derivative formulas are derived from the derivative of e^u:

$$\begin{aligned} \frac{d}{dx}(\sinh u) &= \frac{d}{dx}\left(\frac{e^u - e^{-u}}{2}\right) && \text{Definition of } \sinh u \\ &= \frac{e^u\, du/dx + e^{-u}\, du/dx}{2} && \text{Derivative of } e^u \\ &= \cosh u \frac{du}{dx} && \text{Definition of } \cosh u \end{aligned}$$

This gives the first derivative formula. The calculation

$$\begin{aligned} \frac{d}{dx}(\operatorname{csch} u) &= \frac{d}{dx}\left(\frac{1}{\sinh u}\right) && \text{Definition of } \operatorname{csch} u \\ &= -\frac{\cosh u}{\sinh^2 u}\frac{du}{dx} && \text{Quotient Rule} \\ &= -\frac{1}{\sinh u}\frac{\cosh u}{\sinh u}\frac{du}{dx} && \text{Rearrange terms.} \\ &= -\operatorname{csch} u \coth u \frac{du}{dx} && \text{Definitions of } \operatorname{csch} u \text{ and } \coth u \end{aligned}$$

gives the last formula. The others are obtained similarly.

TABLE 3.4 Derivatives of hyperbolic functions

$$\frac{d}{dx}(\sinh u) = \cosh u \frac{du}{dx}$$
$$\frac{d}{dx}(\cosh u) = \sinh u \frac{du}{dx}$$
$$\frac{d}{dx}(\tanh u) = \operatorname{sech}^2 u \frac{du}{dx}$$
$$\frac{d}{dx}(\coth u) = -\operatorname{csch}^2 u \frac{du}{dx}$$
$$\frac{d}{dx}(\operatorname{sech} u) = -\operatorname{sech} u \tanh u \frac{du}{dx}$$
$$\frac{d}{dx}(\operatorname{csch} u) = -\operatorname{csch} u \coth u \frac{du}{dx}$$

EXAMPLE 1 From Table 3.4, we find the derivative

$$\frac{d}{dt}\left(\tanh\sqrt{1+t^2}\right) = \operatorname{sech}^2\sqrt{1+t^2}\cdot\frac{d}{dt}\left(\sqrt{1+t^2}\right)$$
$$= \frac{t}{\sqrt{1+t^2}}\operatorname{sech}^2\sqrt{1+t^2}$$ ■

Inverse Hyperbolic Functions

The inverses of the six basic hyperbolic functions are very useful in integration (see Chapter 7). Since $d(\sinh x)/dx = \cosh x > 0$, the hyperbolic sine is an increasing function of x. We denote its inverse by

$$y = \sinh^{-1} x.$$

For every value of x in the interval $-\infty < x < \infty$, the value of $y = \sinh^{-1} x$ is the number whose hyperbolic sine is x. The graphs of $y = \sinh x$ and $y = \sinh^{-1} x$ are shown in Figure 3.56a.

The function $y = \cosh x$ is not one-to-one, as we can see from its graph in Table 3.2. The restricted function $y = \cosh x, x \geq 0$, however, is one-to-one and therefore has an inverse, denoted by

$$y = \cosh^{-1} x.$$

For every value of $x \geq 1$, $y = \cosh^{-1} x$ is the number in the interval $0 \leq y < \infty$ whose hyperbolic cosine is x. The graphs of $y = \cosh x, x \geq 0$, and $y = \cosh^{-1} x$ are shown in Figure 3.56b.

Like $y = \cosh x$, the function $y = \operatorname{sech} x = 1/\cosh x$ fails to be one-to-one, but its restriction to nonnegative values of x does have an inverse, denoted by

$$y = \operatorname{sech}^{-1} x.$$

For every value of x in the interval $(0, 1]$, $y = \operatorname{sech}^{-1} x$ is the nonnegative number whose hyperbolic secant is x. The graphs of $y = \operatorname{sech} x, x \geq 0$, and $y = \operatorname{sech}^{-1} x$ are shown in Figure 3.56c.

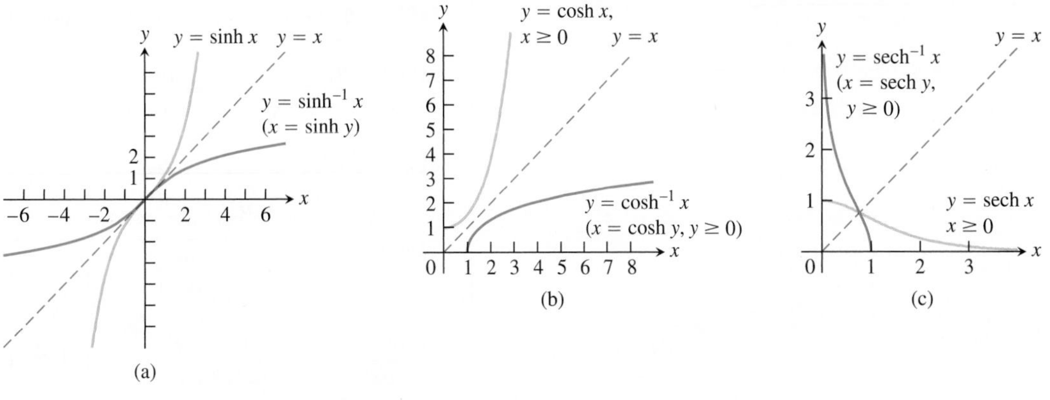

FIGURE 3.56 The graphs of the inverse hyperbolic sine, cosine, and secant of x. Notice the symmetries about the line $y = x$.

The hyperbolic tangent, cotangent, and cosecant are one-to-one on their domains and therefore have inverses, denoted by

$$y = \tanh^{-1} x, \qquad y = \coth^{-1} x, \qquad y = \operatorname{csch}^{-1} x.$$

These functions are graphed in Figure 3.57.

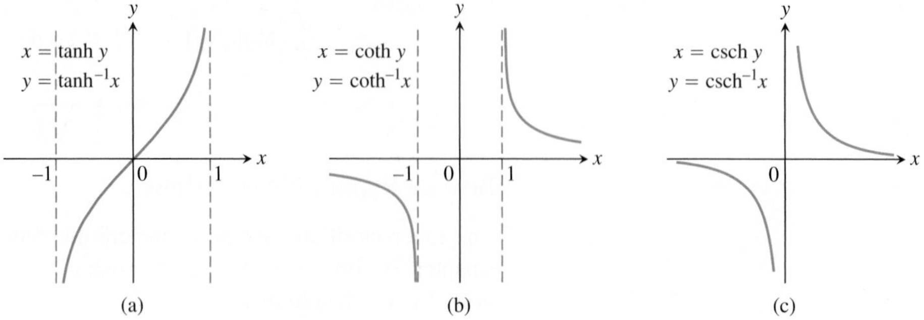

FIGURE 3.57 The graphs of the inverse hyperbolic tangent, cotangent, and cosecant of x.

Useful Identities

TABLE 3.5 Identities for inverse hyperbolic functions

$$\operatorname{sech}^{-1} x = \cosh^{-1}\frac{1}{x}$$

$$\operatorname{csch}^{-1} x = \sinh^{-1}\frac{1}{x}$$

$$\coth^{-1} x = \tanh^{-1}\frac{1}{x}$$

We use the identities in Table 3.5 to calculate the values of $\operatorname{sech}^{-1} x$, $\operatorname{csch}^{-1} x$, and $\coth^{-1} x$ on calculators that give only $\cosh^{-1} x$, $\sinh^{-1} x$, and $\tanh^{-1} x$. These identities are direct consequences of the definitions. For example, if $0 < x \le 1$, then

$$\operatorname{sech}\left(\cosh^{-1}\left(\frac{1}{x}\right)\right) = \frac{1}{\cosh\left(\cosh^{-1}\left(\frac{1}{x}\right)\right)} = \frac{1}{\left(\frac{1}{x}\right)} = x$$

so

$$\cosh^{-1}\left(\frac{1}{x}\right) = \operatorname{sech}^{-1} x$$

since the hyperbolic secant is one-to-one on $(0, 1]$.

Derivatives of Inverse Hyperbolic Functions

We will see that the chief use of inverse hyperbolic functions lies in integrations that reverse the derivative formulas in Table 3.6.

TABLE 3.6 Derivatives of inverse hyperbolic functions

$$\frac{d(\sinh^{-1} u)}{dx} = \frac{1}{\sqrt{1+u^2}}\frac{du}{dx}$$

$$\frac{d(\cosh^{-1} u)}{dx} = \frac{1}{\sqrt{u^2-1}}\frac{du}{dx}, \qquad u > 1$$

$$\frac{d(\tanh^{-1} u)}{dx} = \frac{1}{1-u^2}\frac{du}{dx}, \qquad |u| < 1$$

$$\frac{d(\coth^{-1} u)}{dx} = \frac{1}{1-u^2}\frac{du}{dx}, \qquad |u| > 1$$

$$\frac{d(\operatorname{sech}^{-1} u)}{dx} = \frac{-du/dx}{u\sqrt{1-u^2}}, \qquad 0 < u < 1$$

$$\frac{d(\operatorname{csch}^{-1} u)}{dx} = \frac{-du/dx}{|u|\sqrt{1+u^2}}, \qquad u \ne 0$$

The restrictions $|u| < 1$ and $|u| > 1$ on the derivative formulas for $\tanh^{-1} u$ and $\coth^{-1} u$ come from the natural restrictions on the values of these functions. (See Figure 3.57a and b.) The distinction between $|u| < 1$ and $|u| > 1$ becomes important when we convert the derivative formulas into integral formulas in Chapter 5, Table 5.7.

We illustrate how the derivatives of the inverse hyperbolic functions are found in Example 2, where we calculate $d(\cosh^{-1} u)/dx$. The other derivatives are obtained by similar calculations.

EXAMPLE 2 Show that if u is a differentiable function of x whose values are greater than 1, then

$$\frac{d}{dx}(\cosh^{-1} u) = \frac{1}{\sqrt{u^2 - 1}}\frac{du}{dx}.$$

Solution First we find the derivative of $y = \cosh^{-1} x$ for $x > 1$ by applying Theorem 4 with $f(x) = \cosh x$ and $f^{-1}(x) = \cosh^{-1} x$. Theorem 4 can be applied because the derivative of $\cosh x$ is positive for $0 < x$.

$$\begin{aligned}(f^{-1})'(x) &= \frac{1}{f'(f^{-1}(x))} && \text{Theorem 4}\\ &= \frac{1}{\sinh(\cosh^{-1} x)} && f'(u) = \sinh u\\ &= \frac{1}{\sqrt{\cosh^2(\cosh^{-1} x) - 1}} && \cosh^2 u - \sinh^2 u = 1,\ \sinh u = \sqrt{\cosh^2 u - 1}\\ &= \frac{1}{\sqrt{x^2 - 1}} && \cosh(\cosh^{-1} x) = x\end{aligned}$$

HISTORICAL BIOGRAPHY

Sonya Kovalevsky
(1850–1891)

The Chain Rule gives the final result:

$$\frac{d}{dx}(\cosh^{-1} u) = \frac{1}{\sqrt{u^2 - 1}}\frac{du}{dx}.$$

■

EXERCISES 3.11

Each of Exercises 1–4 gives a value of $\sinh x$ or $\cosh x$. Use the definitions and the identity $\cosh^2 x - \sinh^2 x = 1$ to find the values of the remaining five hyperbolic functions.

1. $\sinh x = -\frac{3}{4}$

2. $\sinh x = \frac{4}{3}$

3. $\cosh x = \frac{17}{15}, \quad x > 0$

4. $\cosh x = \frac{13}{5}, \quad x > 0$

Rewrite the expressions in Exercises 5–10 in terms of exponentials and simplify the results as much as you can.

5. $2\cosh(\ln x)$

6. $\sinh(2\ln x)$

7. $\cosh 5x + \sinh 5x$

8. $\cosh 3x - \sinh 3x$

9. $(\sinh x + \cosh x)^4$

10. $\ln(\cosh x + \sinh x) + \ln(\cosh x - \sinh x)$

11. Use the identities

$$\sinh(x + y) = \sinh x \cosh y + \cosh x \sinh y$$
$$\cosh(x + y) = \cosh x \cosh y + \sinh x \sinh y$$

to show that

a. $\sinh 2x = 2\sinh x \cosh x$

b. $\cosh 2x = \cosh^2 x + \sinh^2 x.$

12. Use the definitions of $\cosh x$ and $\sinh x$ to show that

$$\cosh^2 x - \sinh^2 x = 1.$$

In Exercises 13–24, find the derivative of y with respect to the appropriate variable.

13. $y = 6\sinh\frac{x}{3}$ **14.** $y = \frac{1}{2}\sinh(2x+1)$

15. $y = 2\sqrt{t}\tanh\sqrt{t}$ **16.** $y = t^2\tanh\frac{1}{t}$

17. $y = \ln(\sinh z)$ **18.** $y = \ln(\cosh z)$

19. $y = \operatorname{sech}\theta(1 - \ln\operatorname{sech}\theta)$ **20.** $y = \operatorname{csch}\theta(1 - \ln\operatorname{csch}\theta)$

21. $y = \ln\cosh v - \frac{1}{2}\tanh^2 v$ **22.** $y = \ln\sinh v - \frac{1}{2}\coth^2 v$

23. $y = (x^2+1)\operatorname{sech}(\ln x)$

(*Hint:* Before differentiating, express in terms of exponentials and simplify.)

24. $y = (4x^2 - 1)\operatorname{csch}(\ln 2x)$

In Exercises 25–36, find the derivative of y with respect to the appropriate variable.

25. $y = \sinh^{-1}\sqrt{x}$ **26.** $y = \cosh^{-1}2\sqrt{x+1}$

27. $y = (1-\theta)\tanh^{-1}\theta$ **28.** $y = (\theta^2 + 2\theta)\tanh^{-1}(\theta+1)$

29. $y = (1-t)\coth^{-1}\sqrt{t}$ **30.** $y = (1-t^2)\coth^{-1}t$

31. $y = \cos^{-1}x - x\operatorname{sech}^{-1}x$ **32.** $y = \ln x + \sqrt{1-x^2}\operatorname{sech}^{-1}x$

33. $y = \operatorname{csch}^{-1}\left(\frac{1}{2}\right)^{\theta}$ **34.** $y = \operatorname{csch}^{-1}2^{\theta}$

35. $y = \sinh^{-1}(\tan x)$

36. $y = \cosh^{-1}(\sec x),\quad 0 < x < \pi/2$

When hyperbolic function keys are not available on a calculator, it is still possible to evaluate the inverse hyperbolic functions by expressing them as logarithms, as shown here.

$$\sinh^{-1}x = \ln\left(x + \sqrt{x^2+1}\right), \qquad -\infty < x < \infty$$
$$\cosh^{-1}x = \ln\left(x + \sqrt{x^2-1}\right), \qquad x \ge 1$$
$$\tanh^{-1}x = \frac{1}{2}\ln\frac{1+x}{1-x}, \qquad |x| < 1$$
$$\operatorname{sech}^{-1}x = \ln\left(\frac{1+\sqrt{1-x^2}}{x}\right), \qquad 0 < x \le 1$$
$$\operatorname{csch}^{-1}x = \ln\left(\frac{1}{x} + \frac{\sqrt{1+x^2}}{|x|}\right), \qquad x \ne 0$$
$$\coth^{-1}x = \frac{1}{2}\ln\frac{x+1}{x-1}, \qquad |x| > 1$$

Use the formulas in the box here to express the numbers in Exercises 37–42 in terms of natural logarithms.

37. $\sinh^{-1}(-5/12)$ **38.** $\cosh^{-1}(5/3)$

39. $\tanh^{-1}(-1/2)$ **40.** $\coth^{-1}(5/4)$

41. $\operatorname{sech}^{-1}(3/5)$ **42.** $\operatorname{csch}^{-1}(-1/\sqrt{3})$

43. Show that if a function f is defined on an interval symmetric about the origin (so that f is defined at $-x$ whenever it is defined at x), then

$$f(x) = \frac{f(x) + f(-x)}{2} + \frac{f(x) - f(-x)}{2}.$$

Then show that $(f(x) + f(-x))/2$ is even and that $(f(x) - f(-x))/2$ is odd. How does the equation relate e^x to $\sinh x$ and $\cosh x$?

44. Derive the formula $\sinh^{-1}x = \ln\left(x + \sqrt{x^2+1}\right)$, $-\infty < x < \infty$. Explain in your derivation why the plus sign is used with the square root instead of the minus sign.

45. Skydiving If a body of mass m falling from rest under the action of gravity encounters an air resistance proportional to the square of the velocity, then the body's velocity t sec into the fall satisfies the *differential equation*

$$m\frac{dv}{dt} = mg - kv^2,$$

where k is a constant that depends on the body's aerodynamic properties and the density of the air. (We assume that the fall is short enough so that the variation in the air's density will not affect the outcome significantly.)

a. Show that

$$v = \sqrt{\frac{mg}{k}}\tanh\left(\sqrt{\frac{gk}{m}}\,t\right)$$

satisfies the differential equation and the initial condition that $v = 0$ when $t = 0$.

b. Find the body's *limiting velocity*, $\lim_{t\to\infty} v$.

c. For a 160-lb skydiver ($mg = 160$), with time in seconds and distance in feet, a typical value for k is 0.005. What is the diver's limiting velocity?

46. Accelerations whose magnitudes are proportional to displacement Suppose that the position of a body moving along a coordinate line at time t is

a. $s = a\cos kt + b\sin kt$

b. $s = a\cosh kt + b\sinh kt.$

Show in both cases that the acceleration d^2s/dt^2 is proportional to s but that in the first case it is directed toward the origin, whereas in the second case it is directed away from the origin.

47. Use the definitions of the hyperbolic functions to find each of the following limits

(a) $\lim_{x\to\infty}\tanh x$ **(b)** $\lim_{x\to-\infty}\tanh x$

(c) $\lim_{x\to\infty}\sinh x$ **(d)** $\lim_{x\to-\infty}\sinh x$

(e) $\lim_{x\to\infty}\operatorname{sech} x$ **(f)** $\lim_{x\to\infty}\coth x$

(g) $\lim_{x\to 0^+}\coth x$ **(h)** $\lim_{x\to 0^-}\coth x$

(i) $\lim_{x\to-\infty}\operatorname{csch} x$

48. Instead of using Theorem 4, as in Example 2, find the derivative of $y = \cosh^{-1} x$, $x > 1$, using implicit differentiation and the Chain Rule.

49. **Hanging cables** Imagine a cable, like a telephone line or TV cable, strung from one support to another and hanging freely. The cable's weight per unit length is a constant w and the horizontal tension at its lowest point is a *vector* of length H. If we choose a coordinate system for the plane of the cable in which the x-axis is horizontal, the force of gravity is straight down, the positive y-axis points straight up, and the lowest point of the cable lies at the point $y = H/w$ on the y-axis (see accompanying figure), then it can be shown that the cable lies along the graph of the hyperbolic cosine

$$y = \frac{H}{w} \cosh \frac{w}{H} x.$$

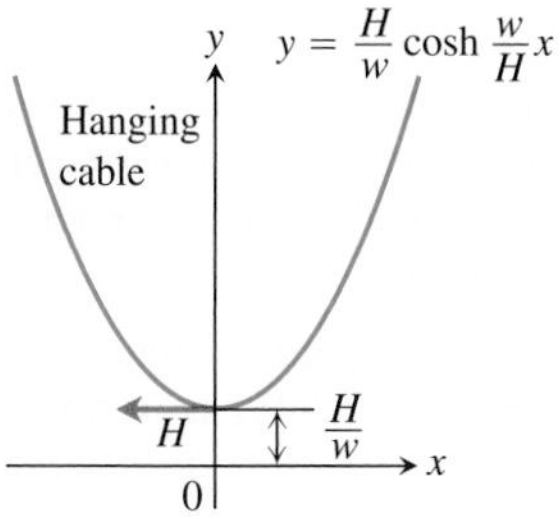

Such a curve is sometimes called a **chain curve** or a **catenary**, the latter deriving from the Latin *catena*, meaning "chain."

a. Let $P(x, y)$ denote an arbitrary point on the cable. The next accompanying figure displays the tension at P as a vector of length (magnitude) T, as well as the tension H at the lowest point A. Show that the cable's slope at P is

$$\tan \phi = \frac{dy}{dx} = \sinh \frac{w}{H} x.$$

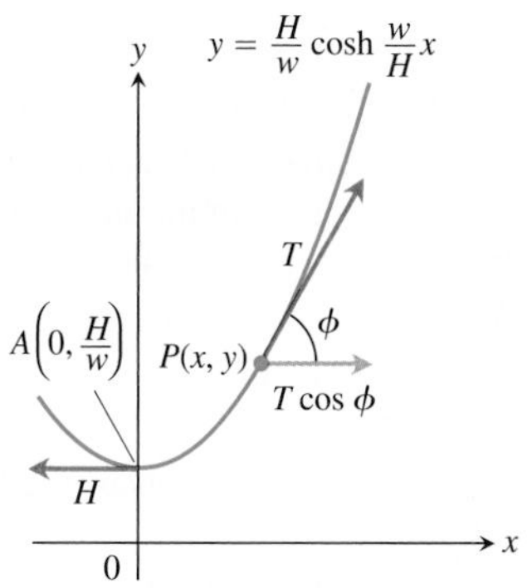

b. Using the result from part (a) and the fact that the horizontal tension at P must equal H (the cable is not moving), show that $T = wy$. Hence, the magnitude of the tension at $P(x, y)$ is exactly equal to the weight of y units of cable.

50. (*Continuation of Exercise 49.*) The length of arc AP in the Exercise 49 figure is $s = (1/a) \sinh ax$, where $a = w/H$. Show that the coordinates of P may be expressed in terms of s as

$$x = \frac{1}{a} \sinh^{-1} as, \qquad y = \sqrt{s^2 + \frac{1}{a^2}}.$$

Chapter 3 Questions to Guide Your Review

1. What is the derivative of a function f? How is its domain related to the domain of f? Give examples.

2. What role does the derivative play in defining slopes, tangents, and rates of change?

3. How can you sometimes graph the derivative of a function when all you have is a table of the function's values?

4. What does it mean for a function to be differentiable on an open interval? On a closed interval?

5. How are derivatives and one-sided derivatives related?

6. Describe geometrically when a function typically does *not* have a derivative at a point.

7. How is a function's differentiability at a point related to its continuity there, if at all?

8. Could the unit step function

$$U(x) = \begin{cases} 0, & x < 0 \\ 1, & x \geq 0 \end{cases}$$

possibly be the derivative of some other function on $[-1, 1]$? Explain.

9. What rules do you know for calculating derivatives? Give some examples.

10. Explain how the three formulas

a. $\frac{d}{dx}(x^n) = nx^{n-1}$

b. $\frac{d}{dx}(cu) = c\frac{du}{dx}$

c. $\frac{d}{dx}(u_1 + u_2 + \cdots + u_n) = \frac{du_1}{dx} + \frac{du_2}{dx} + \cdots + \frac{du_n}{dx}$

enable us to differentiate any polynomial.

11. What formula do we need, in addition to the three listed in Question 10, to differentiate rational functions?

12. What is a second derivative? A third derivative? How many derivatives do the functions you know have? Give examples.

13. What is the derivative of the exponential function e^x? How does the domain of the derivative compare with the domain of the function?

14. What is the relationship between a function's average and instantaneous rates of change? Give an example.

15. How do derivatives arise in the study of motion? What can you learn about a body's motion along a line by examining the derivatives of the body's position function? Give examples.

16. How can derivatives arise in economics?

17. Give examples of still other applications of derivatives.

18. What do the limits $\lim_{h\to 0}((\sin h)/h)$ and $\lim_{h\to 0}((\cos h - 1)/h)$ have to do with the derivatives of the sine and cosine functions? What *are* the derivatives of these functions?

19. Once you know the derivatives of $\sin x$ and $\cos x$, how can you find the derivatives of $\tan x$, $\cot x$, $\sec x$, and $\csc x$? What *are* the derivatives of these functions?

20. At what points are the six basic trigonometric functions continuous? How do you know?

21. What is the rule for calculating the derivative of a composite of two differentiable functions? How is such a derivative evaluated? Give examples.

22. What is the formula for the slope dy/dx of a parametrized curve $x = f(t), y = g(t)$? When does the formula apply? When can you expect to be able to find d^2y/dx^2 as well? Give examples.

23. If u is a differentiable function of x, how do you find $(d/dx)(u^n)$ if n is an integer? If n is a real number? Give examples.

24. What is implicit differentiation? When do you need it? Give examples.

25. What is the derivative of the natural logarithm function $\ln x$? How does the domain of the derivative compare with the domain of the function?

26. What is the derivative of the exponential function a^x, $a > 0$ and $a \neq 1$? What is the geometric significance of the limit of $(a^h - 1)/h$ as $h \to 0$? What is the limit when a is the number e?

27. What is the derivative of $\log_a x$? Are there any restrictions on a?

28. What is logarithmic differentiation? Give an example.

29. How can you write any real power of x as a power of e? Are there any restrictions on x? How does this lead to the Power Rule for differentiating arbitrary real powers?

30. What is one way of expressing the special number e as a limit? What is an approximate numerical value of e correct to 7 decimal places?

31. What are the derivatives of the inverse trigonometric functions? How do the domains of the derivatives compare with the domains of the functions?

32. How do related rates problems arise? Give examples.

33. Outline a strategy for solving related rates problems. Illustrate with an example.

34. What is the linearization $L(x)$ of a function $f(x)$ at a point $x = a$? What is required of f at a for the linearization to exist? How are linearizations used? Give examples.

35. If x moves from a to a nearby value $a + dx$, how do you estimate the corresponding change in the value of a differentiable function $f(x)$? How do you estimate the relative change? The percentage change? Give an example.

36. What are the six basic hyperbolic functions? Comment on their domains, ranges, and graphs. What are some of the identities relating them?

37. What are the derivatives of the six basic hyperbolic functions? What similarities do you see here with the six basic trigonometric functions?

38. How are the inverse hyperbolic functions defined? Comment on their domains, ranges, and graphs. How can you find values of $\operatorname{sech}^{-1}x$, $\operatorname{csch}^{-1}x$, and $\coth^{-1}x$ using a calculator's keys for $\cosh^{-1}x$, $\sinh^{-1}x$, and $\tanh^{-1}x$?

Chapter 3 Practice Exercises

Find the derivatives of the functions in Exercises 1–64.

1. $y = x^5 - 0.125x^2 + 0.25x$
2. $y = 3 - 0.7x^3 + 0.3x^7$
3. $y = x^3 - 3(x^2 + \pi^2)$
4. $y = x^7 + \sqrt{7x} - \dfrac{1}{\pi + 1}$
5. $y = (x + 1)^2(x^2 + 2x)$
6. $y = (2x - 5)(4 - x)^{-1}$
7. $y = (\theta^2 + \sec\theta + 1)^3$
8. $y = \left(-1 - \dfrac{\csc\theta}{2} - \dfrac{\theta^2}{4}\right)^2$
9. $s = \dfrac{\sqrt{t}}{1 + \sqrt{t}}$
10. $s = \dfrac{1}{\sqrt{t} - 1}$
11. $y = 2\tan^2 x - \sec^2 x$
12. $y = \dfrac{1}{\sin^2 x} - \dfrac{2}{\sin x}$
13. $s = \cos^4(1 - 2t)$
14. $s = \cot^3\left(\dfrac{2}{t}\right)$
15. $s = (\sec t + \tan t)^5$
16. $s = \csc^5(1 - t + 3t^2)$
17. $r = \sqrt{2\theta\sin\theta}$
18. $r = 2\theta\sqrt{\cos\theta}$
19. $r = \sin\sqrt{2\theta}$
20. $r = \sin\left(\theta + \sqrt{\theta + 1}\right)$
21. $y = \dfrac{1}{2}x^2\csc\dfrac{2}{x}$
22. $y = 2\sqrt{x}\sin\sqrt{x}$
23. $y = x^{-1/2}\sec(2x)^2$
24. $y = \sqrt{x}\csc(x + 1)^3$

25. $y = 5\cot x^2$

26. $y = x^2 \cot 5x$

27. $y = x^2 \sin^2(2x^2)$

28. $y = x^{-2}\sin^2(x^3)$

29. $s = \left(\frac{4t}{t+1}\right)^{-2}$

30. $s = \frac{-1}{15(15t-1)^3}$

31. $y = \left(\frac{\sqrt{x}}{1+x}\right)^2$

32. $y = \left(\frac{2\sqrt{x}}{2\sqrt{x}+1}\right)^2$

33. $y = \sqrt{\frac{x^2+x}{x^2}}$

34. $y = 4x\sqrt{x+\sqrt{x}}$

35. $r = \left(\frac{\sin\theta}{\cos\theta - 1}\right)^2$

36. $r = \left(\frac{1+\sin\theta}{1-\cos\theta}\right)^2$

37. $y = (2x+1)\sqrt{2x+1}$

38. $y = 20(3x-4)^{1/4}(3x-4)^{-1/5}$

39. $y = \frac{3}{(5x^2 + \sin 2x)^{3/2}}$

40. $y = (3 + \cos^3 3x)^{-1/3}$

41. $y = 10e^{-x/5}$

42. $y = \sqrt{2}e^{\sqrt{2}x}$

43. $y = \frac{1}{4}xe^{4x} - \frac{1}{16}e^{4x}$

44. $y = x^2 e^{-2/x}$

45. $y = \ln(\sin^2\theta)$

46. $y = \ln(\sec^2\theta)$

47. $y = \log_2(x^2/2)$

48. $y = \log_5(3x-7)$

49. $y = 8^{-t}$

50. $y = 9^{2t}$

51. $y = 5x^{3.6}$

52. $y = \sqrt{2}x^{-\sqrt{2}}$

53. $y = (x+2)^{x+2}$

54. $y = 2(\ln x)^{x/2}$

55. $y = \sin^{-1}\sqrt{1-u^2}, \quad 0 < u < 1$

56. $y = \sin^{-1}\left(\frac{1}{\sqrt{v}}\right), \quad v > 1$

57. $y = \ln \cos^{-1} x$

58. $y = z\cos^{-1} z - \sqrt{1-z^2}$

59. $y = t\tan^{-1} t - \frac{1}{2}\ln t$

60. $y = (1+t^2)\cot^{-1} 2t$

61. $y = z\sec^{-1} z - \sqrt{z^2-1}, \quad z > 1$

62. $y = 2\sqrt{x-1}\,\sec^{-1}\sqrt{x}$

63. $y = \csc^{-1}(\sec\theta), \quad 0 < \theta < \pi/2$

64. $y = (1+x^2)e^{\tan^{-1} x}$

In Exercises 65–78, find dy/dx by implicit differentiation.

65. $xy + 2x + 3y = 1$

66. $x^2 + xy + y^2 - 5x = 2$

67. $x^3 + 4xy - 3y^{4/3} = 2x$

68. $5x^{4/5} + 10y^{6/5} = 15$

69. $\sqrt{xy} = 1$

70. $x^2y^2 = 1$

71. $y^2 = \frac{x}{x+1}$

72. $y^2 = \sqrt{\frac{1+x}{1-x}}$

73. $e^{x+2y} = 1$

74. $y^2 = 2e^{-1/x}$

75. $\ln(x/y) = 1$

76. $x\sin^{-1} y = 1 + x^2$

77. $ye^{\tan^{-1} x} = 2$

78. $x^y = \sqrt{2}$

In Exercises 79 and 80, find dp/dq.

79. $p^3 + 4pq - 3q^2 = 2$

80. $q = (5p^2 + 2p)^{-3/2}$

In Exercises 81 and 82, find dr/ds.

81. $r\cos 2s + \sin^2 s = \pi$

82. $2rs - r - s + s^2 = -3$

83. Find d^2y/dx^2 by implicit differentiation:

a. $x^3 + y^3 = 1$ **b.** $y^2 = 1 - \frac{2}{x}$

84. a. By differentiating $x^2 - y^2 = 1$ implicitly, show that $dy/dx = x/y$.

b. Then show that $d^2y/dx^2 = -1/y^3$.

85. Suppose that functions $f(x)$ and $g(x)$ and their first derivatives have the following values at $x = 0$ and $x = 1$.

x	$f(x)$	$g(x)$	$f'(x)$	$g'(x)$
0	1	1	-3	$1/2$
1	3	5	$1/2$	-4

Find the first derivatives of the following combinations at the given value of x.

a. $6f(x) - g(x), \quad x = 1$ **b.** $f(x)g^2(x), \quad x = 0$

c. $\frac{f(x)}{g(x)+1}, \quad x = 1$ **d.** $f(g(x)), \quad x = 0$

e. $g(f(x)), \quad x = 0$ **f.** $(x + f(x))^{3/2}, \quad x = 1$

g. $f(x + g(x)), \quad x = 0$

86. Suppose that the function $f(x)$ and its first derivative have the following values at $x = 0$ and $x = 1$.

x	$f(x)$	$f'(x)$
0	9	-2
1	-3	$1/5$

Find the first derivatives of the following combinations at the given value of x.

a. $\sqrt{x}\,f(x), \quad x = 1$ **b.** $\sqrt{f(x)}, \quad x = 0$

c. $f(\sqrt{x}), \quad x = 1$ **d.** $f(1 - 5\tan x), \quad x = 0$

e. $\frac{f(x)}{2+\cos x}, \quad x = 0$ **f.** $10\sin\left(\frac{\pi x}{2}\right)f^2(x), \quad x = 1$

87. Find the value of dy/dt at $t = 0$ if $y = 3\sin 2x$ and $x = t^2 + \pi$.

88. Find the value of ds/du at $u = 2$ if $s = t^2 + 5t$ and $t = (u^2 + 2u)^{1/3}$.

89. Find the value of dw/ds at $s = 0$ if $w = \sin\left(e^{\sqrt{r}}\right)$ and $r = 3\sin(s + \pi/6)$.

90. Find the value of dr/dt at $t = 0$ if $r = (\theta^2 + 7)^{1/3}$ and $\theta^2 e^t + \theta = 1$.

91. If $y^3 + y = 2\cos x$, find the value of d^2y/dx^2 at the point $(0, 1)$.

92. If $x^{1/3} + y^{1/3} = 4$, find d^2y/dx^2 at the point $(8, 8)$.

In Exercises 93 and 94, find the derivative using the definition.

93. $f(t) = \dfrac{1}{2t + 1}$ **94.** $g(x) = 2x^2 + 1$

95. a. Graph the function

$$f(x) = \begin{cases} x^2, & -1 \le x < 0 \\ -x^2, & 0 \le x \le 1. \end{cases}$$

b. Is f continuous at $x = 0$?

c. Is f differentiable at $x = 0$?

Give reasons for your answers.

96. a. Graph the function

$$f(x) = \begin{cases} x, & -1 \le x < 0 \\ \tan x, & 0 \le x \le \pi/4. \end{cases}$$

b. Is f continuous at $x = 0$?

c. Is f differentiable at $x = 0$?

Give reasons for your answers.

97. a. Graph the function

$$f(x) = \begin{cases} x, & 0 \le x \le 1 \\ 2 - x, & 1 < x \le 2. \end{cases}$$

b. Is f continuous at $x = 1$?

c. Is f differentiable at $x = 1$?

Give reasons for your answers.

98. For what value or values of the constant m, if any, is

$$f(x) = \begin{cases} \sin 2x, & x \le 0 \\ mx, & x > 0 \end{cases}$$

a. continuous at $x = 0$?

b. differentiable at $x = 0$?

Give reasons for your answers.

99. Tangents with specified slope Are there any points on the curve $y = (x/2) + 1/(2x - 4)$ where the slope is $-3/2$? If so, find them.

100. Tangents with specified slope Are there any points on the curve $y = x - e^{-x}$ where the slope is 2? If so, find them.

101. Horizontal tangents Find the points on the curve $y = 2x^3 - 3x^2 - 12x + 20$ where the tangent is parallel to the x-axis.

102. Tangent intercepts Find the x- and y-intercepts of the line that is tangent to the curve $y = x^3$ at the point $(-2, -8)$.

103. Tangents perpendicular or parallel to lines Find the points on the curve $y = 2x^3 - 3x^2 - 12x + 20$ where the tangent is

a. perpendicular to the line $y = 1 - (x/24)$.

b. parallel to the line $y = \sqrt{2} - 12x$.

104. Intersecting tangents Show that the tangents to the curve $y = (\pi \sin x)/x$ at $x = \pi$ and $x = -\pi$ intersect at right angles.

105. Normals parallel to a line Find the points on the curve $y = \tan x$, $-\pi/2 < x < \pi/2$, where the normal is parallel to the line $y = -x/2$. Sketch the curve and normals together, labeling each with its equation.

106. Tangent and normal lines Find equations for the tangent and normal to the curve $y = 1 + \cos x$ at the point $(\pi/2, 1)$. Sketch the curve, tangent, and normal together, labeling each with its equation.

107. Tangent parabola The parabola $y = x^2 + C$ is to be tangent to the line $y = x$. Find C.

108. Slope of tangent Show that the tangent to the curve $y = x^3$ at any point (a, a^3) meets the curve again at a point where the slope is four times the slope at (a, a^3).

109. Tangent curve For what value of c is the curve $y = c/(x + 1)$ tangent to the line through the points $(0, 3)$ and $(5, -2)$?

110. Normal to a circle Show that the normal line at any point of the circle $x^2 + y^2 = a^2$ passes through the origin.

In Exercises 111–116, find equations for the lines that are tangent and normal to the curve at the given point.

111. $x^2 + 2y^2 = 9, \quad (1, 2)$

112. $e^x + y^2 = 2, \quad (0, 1)$

113. $xy + 2x - 5y = 2, \quad (3, 2)$

114. $(y - x)^2 = 2x + 4, \quad (6, 2)$

115. $x + \sqrt{xy} = 6, \quad (4, 1)$

116. $x^{3/2} + 2y^{3/2} = 17, \quad (1, 4)$

117. Find the slope of the curve $x^3y^3 + y^2 = x + y$ at the points $(1, 1)$ and $(1, -1)$.

118. The graph shown suggests that the curve $y = \sin(x - \sin x)$ might have horizontal tangents at the x-axis. Does it? Give reasons for your answer.

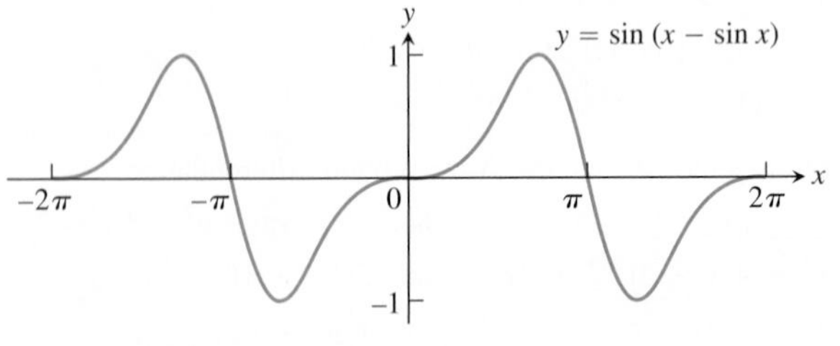

In Exercises 119 and 120, find an equation for the line in the xy-plane that is tangent to the curve at the point corresponding to the given value of t. Also, find the value of d^2y/dx^2 at this point.

119. $x = (1/2)\tan t, \quad y = (1/2)\sec t, \quad t = \pi/3$

120. $x = 1 + 1/t^2, \quad y = 1 - 3/t, \quad t = 2$

Each of the figures in Exercises 121 and 122 shows two graphs, the graph of a function $y = f(x)$ together with the graph of its derivative $f'(x)$. Which graph is which? How do you know?

121.

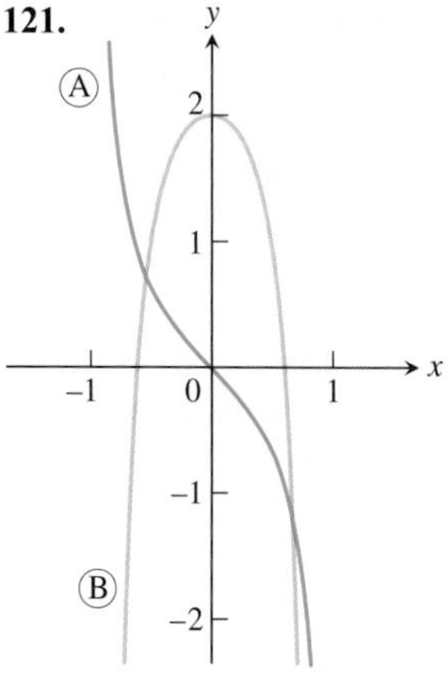

122.

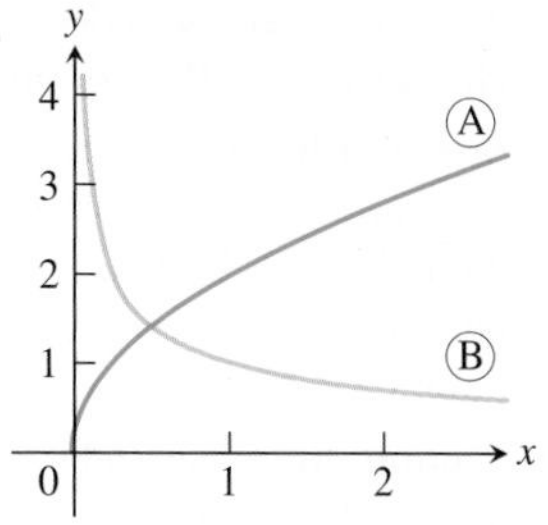

123. Use the following information to graph the function $y = f(x)$ for $-1 \le x \le 6$.

i. The graph of f is made of line segments joined end to end.

ii. The graph starts at the point $(-1, 2)$.

iii. The derivative of f, where defined, agrees with the step function shown here.

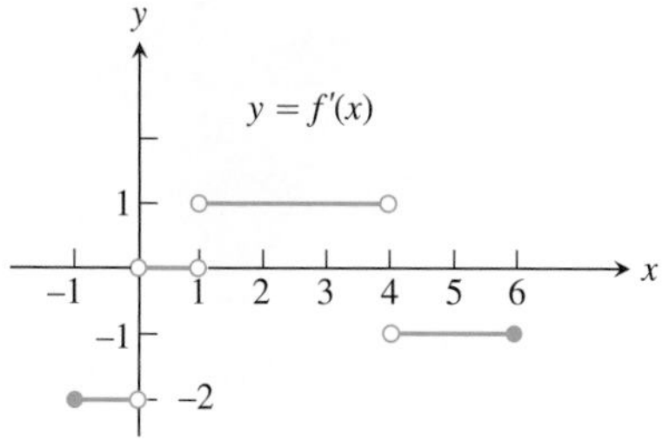

124. Repeat Exercise 123, supposing that the graph starts at $(-1, 0)$ instead of $(-1, 2)$.

Exercises 125 and 126 are about the graphs in Figure 3.58 (right-hand column). The graphs in part (a) show the numbers of rabbits and foxes in a small arctic population. The number of rabbits increases at first, as the rabbits reproduce. But the foxes prey on rabbits and, as the number of foxes increases, the rabbit population levels off and then drops. Figure 3.58b shows the graph of the derivative of the rabbit population.

125. a. What is the value of the derivative of the rabbit population in Figure 3.58 when the number of rabbits is largest? Smallest?

b. What is the size of the rabbit population in Figure 3.58 when its derivative is largest? Smallest (negative value)?

126. In what units should the slopes of the rabbit and fox population curves be measured?

Find the limits in Exercises 127–134.

127. $\lim_{x\to 0} \dfrac{\sin x}{2x^2 - x}$

128. $\lim_{x\to 0} \dfrac{3x - \tan 7x}{2x}$

129. $\lim_{r\to 0} \dfrac{\sin r}{\tan 2r}$

130. $\lim_{\theta\to 0} \dfrac{\sin(\sin\theta)}{\theta}$

131. $\lim_{\theta\to(\pi/2)^-} \dfrac{4\tan^2\theta + \tan\theta + 1}{\tan^2\theta + 5}$

132. $\lim_{\theta\to 0^+} \dfrac{1 - 2\cot^2\theta}{5\cot^2\theta - 7\cot\theta - 8}$

133. $\lim_{x\to 0} \dfrac{x\sin x}{2 - 2\cos x}$

134. $\lim_{\theta\to 0} \dfrac{1 - \cos\theta}{\theta^2}$

Show how to extend the functions in Exercises 135 and 136 to be continuous at the origin.

135. $g(x) = \dfrac{\tan(\tan x)}{\tan x}$

136. $f(x) = \dfrac{\tan(\tan x)}{\sin(\sin x)}$

In Exercises 137–142, use logarithmic differentiation to find the derivative of y with respect to the appropriate variable.

137. $y = \dfrac{2(x^2 + 1)}{\sqrt{\cos 2x}}$

138. $y = \sqrt[10]{\dfrac{3x + 4}{2x - 4}}$

139. $y = \left(\dfrac{(t + 1)(t - 1)}{(t - 2)(t + 3)}\right)^5, \quad t > 2$

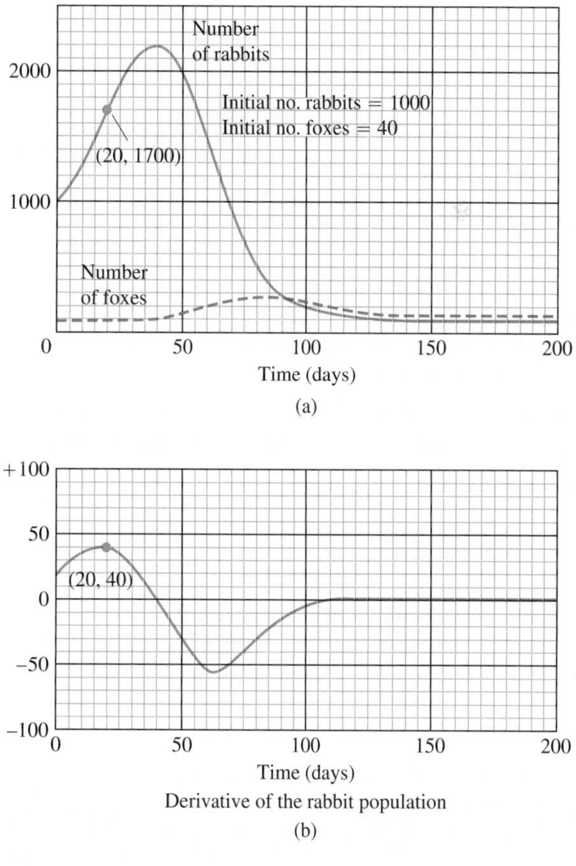

FIGURE 3.58 Rabbits and foxes in an arctic predator-prey food chain.

140. $y = \dfrac{2u2^u}{\sqrt{u^2 + 1}}$

141. $y = (\sin \theta)^{\sqrt{\theta}}$ **142.** $y = (\ln x)^{1/(\ln x)}$

In Exercises 143–152, find dy/dx.

143. $y = \sinh^2 3x$ **144.** $\tan x = \tanh^2 y$

145. $\sin^{-1} x = \operatorname{sech} y$ **146.** $\sinh y = \sec x$

147. $\tan^{-1} y = \tanh^{-1} x$ **148.** $y = \tanh (\ln x)$

149. $x = \cosh (\ln y)$ **150.** $y = \sinh (\tan^{-1} e^{3x})$

151. $y = \sinh^{-1} (\tan x)$

152. $y^2 + x \cosh y + \sinh^2 x = 50$

153. Right circular cylinder The total surface area S of a right circular cylinder is related to the base radius r and height h by the equation $S = 2\pi r^2 + 2\pi rh$.

a. How is dS/dt related to dr/dt if h is constant?

b. How is dS/dt related to dh/dt if r is constant?

c. How is dS/dt related to dr/dt and dh/dt if neither r nor h is constant?

d. How is dr/dt related to dh/dt if S is constant?

154. Right circular cone The lateral surface area S of a right circular cone is related to the base radius r and height h by the equation $S = \pi r\sqrt{r^2 + h^2}$.

a. How is dS/dt related to dr/dt if h is constant?

b. How is dS/dt related to dh/dt if r is constant?

c. How is dS/dt related to dr/dt and dh/dt if neither r nor h is constant?

155. Circle's changing area The radius of a circle is changing at the rate of $-2/\pi$ m/sec. At what rate is the circle's area changing when $r = 10$ m?

156. Cube's changing edges The volume of a cube is increasing at the rate of 1200 cm^3/min at the instant its edges are 20 cm long. At what rate are the lengths of the edges changing at that instant?

157. Resistors connected in parallel If two resistors of R_1 and R_2 ohms are connected in parallel in an electric circuit to make an R-ohm resistor, the value of R can be found from the equation

$$\frac{1}{R} = \frac{1}{R_1} + \frac{1}{R_2}.$$

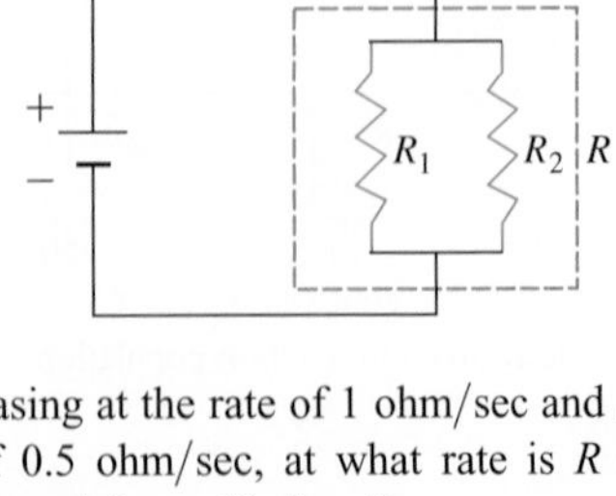

If R_1 is decreasing at the rate of 1 ohm/sec and R_2 is increasing at the rate of 0.5 ohm/sec, at what rate is R changing when $R_1 = 75$ ohms and $R_2 = 50$ ohms?

158. Impedance in a series circuit The impedance Z (ohms) in a series circuit is related to the resistance R (ohms) and reactance X (ohms) by the equation $Z = \sqrt{R^2 + X^2}$. If R is increasing at 3 ohms/sec and X is decreasing at 2 ohms/sec, at what rate is Z changing when $R = 10$ ohms and $X = 20$ ohms?

159. Speed of moving particle The coordinates of a particle moving in the metric xy-plane are differentiable functions of time t with $dx/dt = 10$ m/sec and $dy/dt = 5$ m/sec. How fast is the particle moving away from the origin as it passes through the point $(3, -4)$?

160. Motion of a particle A particle moves along the curve $y = x^{3/2}$ in the first quadrant in such a way that its distance from the origin increases at the rate of 11 units per second. Find dx/dt when $x = 3$.

161. Draining a tank Water drains from the conical tank shown in the accompanying figure at the rate of 5 ft^3/min.

a. What is the relation between the variables h and r in the figure?

b. How fast is the water level dropping when $h = 6$ ft?

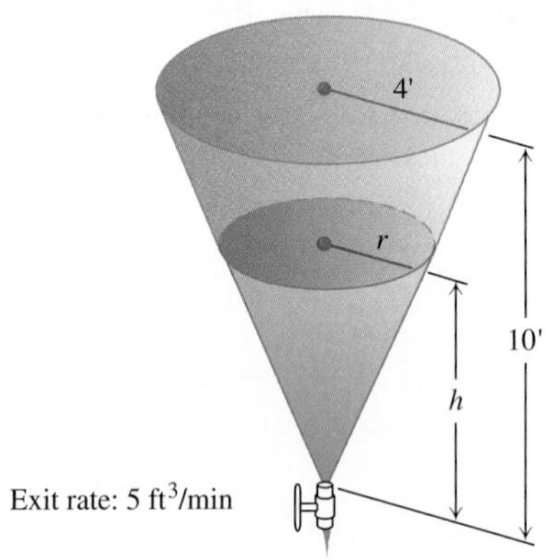

162. Rotating spool As television cable is pulled from a large spool to be strung from the telephone poles along a street, it unwinds from the spool in layers of constant radius (see accompanying figure). If the truck pulling the cable moves at a steady 6 ft/sec (a touch over 4 mph), use the equation $s = r\theta$ to find how fast (radians per second) the spool is turning when the layer of radius 1.2 ft is being unwound.

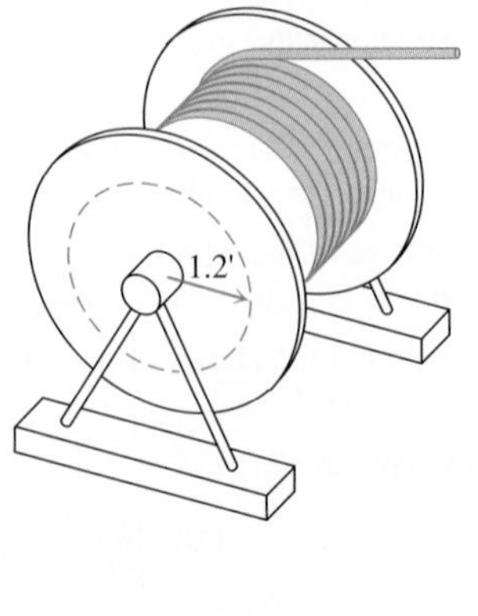

163. Moving searchlight beam The figure shows a boat 1 km offshore, sweeping the shore with a searchlight. The light turns at a constant rate, $d\theta/dt = -0.6$ rad/sec.

a. How fast is the light moving along the shore when it reaches point A?

b. How many revolutions per minute is 0.6 rad/sec?

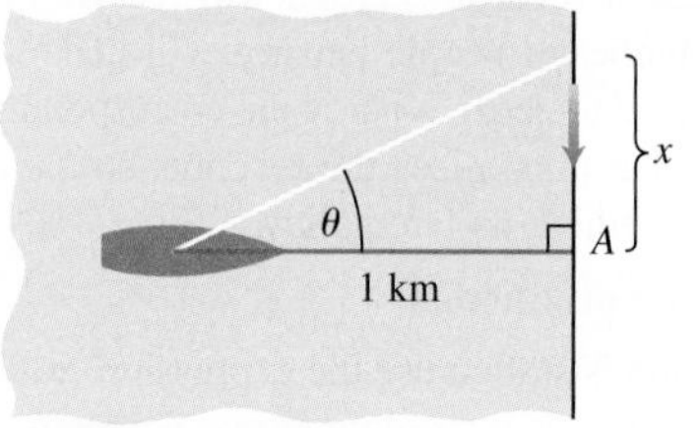

164. Points moving on coordinate axes Points A and B move along the x- and y-axes, respectively, in such a way that the distance r (meters) along the perpendicular from the origin to the line AB remains constant. How fast is OA changing, and is it increasing, or decreasing, when $OB = 2r$ and B is moving toward O at the rate of $0.3r$ m/sec?

165. Find the linearizations of

a. $\tan x$ at $x = -\pi/4$ **b.** $\sec x$ at $x = -\pi/4$.

Graph the curves and linearizations together.

166. We can obtain a useful linear approximation of the function $f(x) = 1/(1 + \tan x)$ at $x = 0$ by combining the approximations

$$\frac{1}{1+x} \approx 1 - x \quad \text{and} \quad \tan x \approx x$$

to get

$$\frac{1}{1 + \tan x} \approx 1 - x.$$

Show that this result is the standard linear approximation of $1/(1 + \tan x)$ at $x = 0$.

167. Find the linearization of $f(x) = \sqrt{1 + x} + \sin x - 0.5$ at $x = 0$.

168. Find the linearization of $f(x) = 2/(1 - x) + \sqrt{1 + x} - 3.1$ at $x = 0$.

169. Surface area of a cone Write a formula that estimates the change that occurs in the lateral surface area of a right circular cone when the height changes from h_0 to $h_0 + dh$ and the radius does not change.

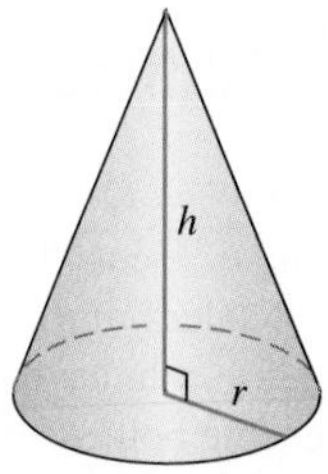

$V = \frac{1}{3}\pi r^2 h$

$S = \pi r\sqrt{r^2 + h^2}$

(Lateral surface area)

170. Controlling error

a. How accurately should you measure the edge of a cube to be reasonably sure of calculating the cube's surface area with an error of no more than 2%?

b. Suppose that the edge is measured with the accuracy required in part (a). About how accurately can the cube's volume be calculated from the edge measurement? To find out, estimate the percentage error in the volume calculation that might result from using the edge measurement.

171. Compounding error The circumference of the equator of a sphere is measured as 10 cm with a possible error of 0.4 cm. This measurement is then used to calculate the radius. The radius is then used to calculate the surface area and volume of the sphere. Estimate the percentage errors in the calculated values of

a. the radius.

b. the surface area.

c. the volume.

172. Finding height To find the height of a lamppost (see accompanying figure), you stand a 6 ft pole 20 ft from the lamp and measure the length a of its shadow, finding it to be 15 ft, give or take an inch. Calculate the height of the lamppost using the value $a = 15$ and estimate the possible error in the result.

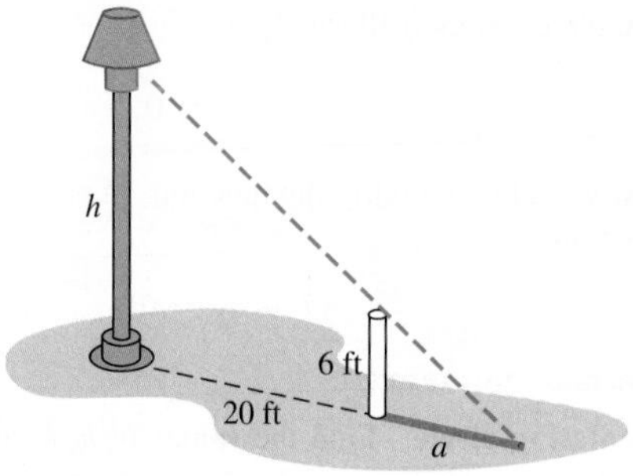

Chapter 3 Additional and Advanced Exercises

1. An equation like $\sin^2\theta + \cos^2\theta = 1$ is called an **identity** because it holds for all values of θ. An equation like $\sin\theta = 0.5$ is not an identity because it holds only for selected values of θ, not all. If you differentiate both sides of a trigonometric identity in θ with respect to θ, the resulting new equation will also be an identity.

   Differentiate the following to show that the resulting equations hold for all θ.

   a. $\sin 2\theta = 2\sin\theta\cos\theta$

   b. $\cos 2\theta = \cos^2\theta - \sin^2\theta$

2. If the identity $\sin(x + a) = \sin x\cos a + \cos x\sin a$ is differentiated with respect to x, is the resulting equation also an identity? Does this principle apply to the equation $x^2 - 2x - 8 = 0$? Explain.

3. **a.** Find values for the constants a, b, and c that will make

   $$f(x) = \cos x \quad \text{and} \quad g(x) = a + bx + cx^2$$

   satisfy the conditions

   $$f(0) = g(0), \quad f'(0) = g'(0), \quad \text{and} \quad f''(0) = g''(0).$$

   b. Find values for b and c that will make

   $$f(x) = \sin(x + a) \quad \text{and} \quad g(x) = b\sin x + c\cos x$$

   satisfy the conditions

   $$f(0) = g(0) \quad \text{and} \quad f'(0) = g'(0).$$

   c. For the determined values of a, b, and c, what happens for the third and fourth derivatives of f and g in each of parts (a) and (b)?

4. **Solutions to differential equations**

   a. Show that $y = \sin x$, $y = \cos x$, and $y = a\cos x + b\sin x$ (a and b constants) all satisfy the equation

   $$y'' + y = 0.$$

   b. How would you modify the functions in part (a) to satisfy the equation

   $$y'' + 4y = 0?$$

   Generalize this result.

5. **An osculating circle** Find the values of h, k, and a that make the circle $(x - h)^2 + (y - k)^2 = a^2$ tangent to the parabola $y = x^2 + 1$ at the point $(1, 2)$ and that also make the second derivatives d^2y/dx^2 have the same value on both curves there. Circles like this one that are tangent to a curve and have the same second derivative as the curve at the point of tangency are called *osculating circles* (from the Latin *osculari*, meaning "to kiss"). We encounter them again in Chapter 11.

6. **Marginal revenue** A bus will hold 60 people. The number x of people per trip who use the bus is related to the fare charged (p dollars) by the law $p = [3 - (x/40)]^2$. Write an expression for the total revenue $r(x)$ per trip received by the bus company. What number of people per trip will make the marginal revenue dr/dx equal to zero? What is the corresponding fare? (This fare is the one that maximizes the revenue, so the bus company should probably rethink its fare policy.)

7. **Industrial production**

   a. Economists often use the expression "rate of growth" in relative rather than absolute terms. For example, let $u = f(t)$ be the number of people in the labor force at time t in a given industry. (We treat this function as though it were differentiable even though it is an integer-valued step function.)

   Let $v = g(t)$ be the average production per person in the labor force at time t. The total production is then $y = uv$. If the labor force is growing at the rate of 4% per year ($du/dt = 0.04u$) and the production per worker is growing at the rate of 5% per year ($dv/dt = 0.05v$), find the rate of growth of the total production, y.

   b. Suppose that the labor force in part (a) is decreasing at the rate of 2% per year while the production per person is increasing at the rate of 3% per year. Is the total production increasing, or is it decreasing, and at what rate?

8. **Designing a gondola** The designer of a 30-ft-diameter spherical hot air balloon wants to suspend the gondola 8 ft below the bottom of the balloon with cables tangent to the surface of the balloon, as shown. Two of the cables are shown running from the top edges of the gondola to their points of tangency, $(-12, -9)$ and $(12, -9)$. How wide should the gondola be?

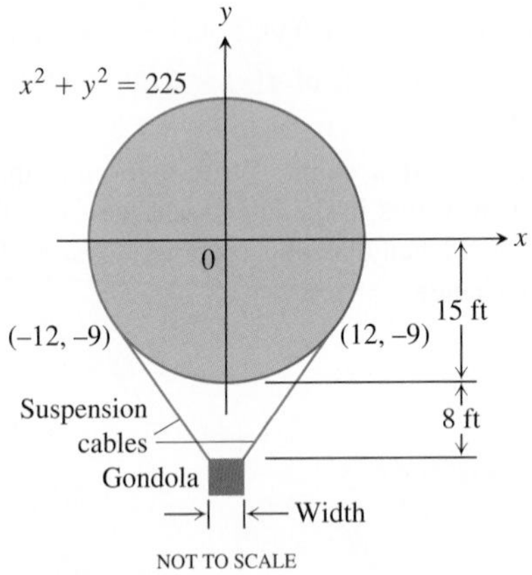

9. **Pisa by parachute** On August 5, 1988, Mike McCarthy of London jumped from the top of the Tower of Pisa. He then

opened his parachute in what he said was a world record low-level parachute jump of 179 ft. Make a rough sketch to show the shape of the graph of his speed during the jump. (*Source: Boston Globe*, Aug. 6, 1988.)

10. **Motion of a particle** The position at time $t \geq 0$ of a particle moving along a coordinate line is
$$s = 10\cos(t + \pi/4).$$
   a. What is the particle's starting position $(t = 0)$?
   b. What are the points farthest to the left and right of the origin reached by the particle?
   c. Find the particle's velocity and acceleration at the points in part (b).
   d. When does the particle first reach the origin? What are its velocity, speed, and acceleration then?

11. **Shooting a paper clip** On Earth, you can easily shoot a paper clip 64 ft straight up into the air with a rubber band. In t sec after firing, the paper clip is $s = 64t - 16t^2$ ft above your hand.
   a. How long does it take the paper clip to reach its maximum height? With what velocity does it leave your hand?
   b. On the moon, the same acceleration will send the paper clip to a height of $s = 64t - 2.6t^2$ ft in t sec. About how long will it take the paper clip to reach its maximum height, and how high will it go?

12. **Velocities of two particles** At time t sec, the positions of two particles on a coordinate line are $s_1 = 3t^3 - 12t^2 + 18t + 5$ m and $s_2 = -t^3 + 9t^2 - 12t$ m. When do the particles have the same velocities?

13. **Velocity of a particle** A particle of constant mass m moves along the x-axis. Its velocity v and position x satisfy the equation
$$\frac{1}{2}m(v^2 - v_0{}^2) = \frac{1}{2}k(x_0{}^2 - x^2),$$
where k, v_0, and x_0 are constants. Show that whenever $v \neq 0$,
$$m\frac{dv}{dt} = -kx.$$

14. **Average and instantaneous velocity**
   a. Show that if the position x of a moving point is given by a quadratic function of t, $x = At^2 + Bt + C$, then the average velocity over any time interval $[t_1, t_2]$ is equal to the instantaneous velocity at the midpoint of the time interval.
   b. What is the geometric significance of the result in part (a)?

15. Find all values of the constants m and b for which the function
$$y = \begin{cases} \sin x, & x < \pi \\ mx + b, & x \geq \pi \end{cases}$$
is
   a. continuous at $x = \pi$.
   b. differentiable at $x = \pi$.

16. Does the function
$$f(x) = \begin{cases} \dfrac{1 - \cos x}{x}, & x \neq 0 \\ 0, & x = 0 \end{cases}$$
have a derivative at $x = 0$? Explain.

17. a. For what values of a and b will
$$f(x) = \begin{cases} ax, & x < 2 \\ ax^2 - bx + 3, & x \geq 2 \end{cases}$$
be differentiable for all values of x?
   b. Discuss the geometry of the resulting graph of f.

18. a. For what values of a and b will
$$g(x) = \begin{cases} ax + b, & x \leq -1 \\ ax^3 + x + 2b, & x > -1 \end{cases}$$
be differentiable for all values of x?
   b. Discuss the geometry of the resulting graph of g.

19. **Odd differentiable functions** Is there anything special about the derivative of an odd differentiable function of x? Give reasons for your answer.

20. **Even differentiable functions** Is there anything special about the derivative of an even differentiable function of x? Give reasons for your answer.

21. Suppose that the functions f and g are defined throughout an open interval containing the point x_0, that f is differentiable at x_0, that $f(x_0) = 0$, and that g is continuous at x_0. Show that the product fg is differentiable at x_0. This process shows, for example, that although $|x|$ is not differentiable at $x = 0$, the product $x|x|$ *is* differentiable at $x = 0$.

22. *(Continuation of Exercise 21.)* Use the result of Exercise 21 to show that the following functions are differentiable at $x = 0$.
   a. $|x|\sin x$ b. $x^{2/3}\sin x$ c. $\sqrt[3]{x}(1 - \cos x)$
   d. $h(x) = \begin{cases} x^2\sin(1/x), & x \neq 0 \\ 0, & x = 0 \end{cases}$

23. Is the derivative of
$$h(x) = \begin{cases} x^2\sin(1/x), & x \neq 0 \\ 0, & x = 0 \end{cases}$$
continuous at $x = 0$? How about the derivative of $k(x) = xh(x)$? Give reasons for your answers.

24. Suppose that a function f satisfies the following conditions for all real values of x and y:
   i. $f(x + y) = f(x)\cdot f(y)$.
   ii. $f(x) = 1 + xg(x)$, where $\lim_{x\to 0} g(x) = 1$.
   Show that the derivative $f'(x)$ exists at every value of x and that $f'(x) = f(x)$.

25. The generalized product rule Use mathematical induction to prove that if $y = u_1 u_2 \cdots u_n$ is a finite product of differentiable functions, then y is differentiable on their common domain and

$$\frac{dy}{dx} = \frac{du_1}{dx} u_2 \cdots u_n + u_1 \frac{du_2}{dx} \cdots u_n + \cdots + u_1 u_2 \cdots u_{n-1} \frac{du_n}{dx}.$$

26. Leibniz's rule for higher-order derivatives of products Leibniz's rule for higher-order derivatives of products of differentiable functions says that

a. $$\frac{d^2(uv)}{dx^2} = \frac{d^2u}{dx^2} v + 2 \frac{du}{dx}\frac{dv}{dx} + u \frac{d^2v}{dx^2}$$

b. $$\frac{d^3(uv)}{dx^3} = \frac{d^3u}{dx^3} v + 3 \frac{d^2u}{dx^2}\frac{dv}{dx} + 3 \frac{du}{dx}\frac{d^2v}{dx^2} + u \frac{d^3v}{dx^3}$$

c. $$\frac{d^n(uv)}{dx^n} = \frac{d^nu}{dx^n} v + n \frac{d^{n-1}u}{dx^{n-1}}\frac{dv}{dx} + \cdots + \frac{n(n-1)\cdots(n-k+1)}{k!} \frac{d^{n-k}u}{dx^{n-k}}\frac{d^kv}{dx^k} + \cdots + u \frac{d^nv}{dx^n}.$$

The equations in parts (a) and (b) are special cases of the equation in part (c). Derive the equation in part (c) by mathematical induction, using

$$\binom{m}{k} + \binom{m}{k+1} = \frac{m!}{k!(m-k)!} + \frac{m!}{(k+1)!(m-k-1)!}.$$

27. The period of a clock pendulum The period T of a clock pendulum (time for one full swing and back) is given by the formula $T^2 = 4\pi^2 L/g$, where T is measured in seconds, $g = 32.2$ ft/sec^2, and L, the length of the pendulum, is measured in feet. Find approximately

a. the length of a clock pendulum whose period is $T = 1$ sec.

b. the change dT in T if the pendulum in part (a) is lengthened 0.01 ft.

c. the amount the clock gains or loses in a day as a result of the period's changing by the amount dT found in part (b).

28. The melting ice cube Assume an ice cube retains its cubical shape as it melts. If we call its edge length s, its volume is $V = s^3$ and its surface area is $6s^2$. We assume that V and s are differentiable functions of time t. We assume also that the cube's volume decreases at a rate that is proportional to its surface area. (This latter assumption seems reasonable enough when we think that the melting takes place at the surface: Changing the amount of surface changes the amount of ice exposed to melt.) In mathematical terms,

$$\frac{dV}{dt} = -k(6s^2), \qquad k > 0.$$

The minus sign indicates that the volume is decreasing. We assume that the proportionality factor k is constant. (It probably depends on many things, such as the relative humidity of the surrounding air, the air temperature, and the incidence or absence of sunlight, to name only a few.) Assume a particular set of conditions in which the cube lost 1/4 of its volume during the first hour, and that the volume is V_0 when $t = 0$. How long will it take the ice cube to melt?

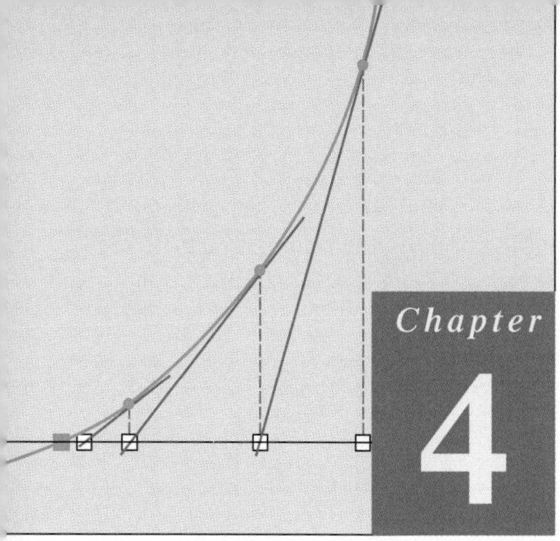

APPLICATIONS OF DERIVATIVES

OVERVIEW In this chapter we use derivatives to find extreme values of functions, to determine and analyze the shapes of graphs, to calculate limits of fractions whose numerators and denominators both approach zero or infinity, and to find numerically where a function equals zero. We also introduce the idea of recovering a function from its derivative. The key to many of these applications is the Mean Value Theorem, whose corollaries pave the way to integral calculus in Chapter 5.

4.1 Extreme Values of Functions

This section shows how to locate and identify extreme (maximum or minimum) values of a continuous function from its derivative. Once we can do this, we can solve a variety of problems in which we find the optimal (best) way to do something in a given situation (see Section 4.5).

DEFINITIONS Let f be a function with domain D. Then f has an **absolute** (or **global**) **maximum** value on D at a point c if

$$f(x) \le f(c) \qquad \text{for all } x \text{ in } D$$

and an **absolute** (or **global**) **minimum** value on D at c if

$$f(x) \ge f(c) \qquad \text{for all } x \text{ in } D.$$

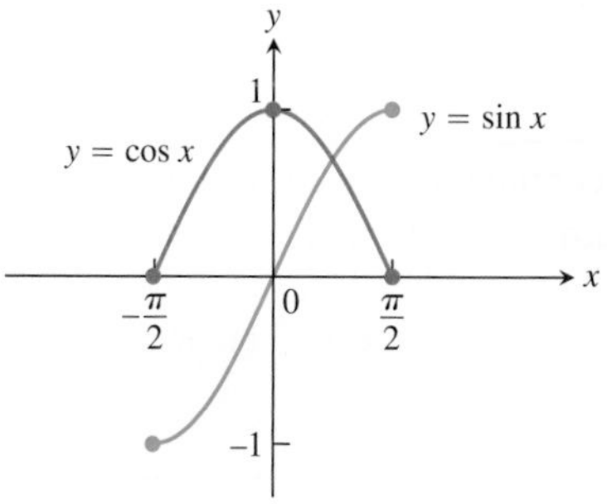

FIGURE 4.1 Absolute extrema for the sine and cosine functions on $[-\pi/2, \pi/2]$. These values can depend on the domain of a function.

For example, on the closed interval $[-\pi/2, \pi/2]$ the function $f(x) = \cos x$ takes on an absolute maximum value of 1 (once) and an absolute minimum value of 0 (twice). On the same interval, the function $g(x) = \sin x$ takes on a maximum value of 1 and a minimum value of -1 (Figure 4.1).

Functions with the same defining rule can have different extrema (maximum or minimum values), depending on the domain. We see this in the following example.

EXAMPLE 1 The absolute extrema of the following functions on their domains can be seen in Figure 4.2.

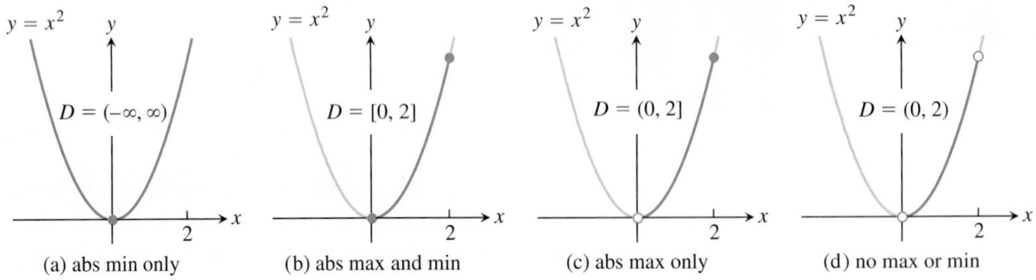

FIGURE 4.2 Graphs for Example 1.

Function rule	Domain D	Absolute extrema on D
(a) $y = x^2$	$(-\infty, \infty)$	No absolute maximum. Absolute minimum of 0 at $x = 0$.
(b) $y = x^2$	$[0, 2]$	Absolute maximum of 4 at $x = 2$. Absolute minimum of 0 at $x = 0$.
(c) $y = x^2$	$(0, 2]$	Absolute maximum of 4 at $x = 2$. No absolute minimum.
(d) $y = x^2$	$(0, 2)$	No absolute extrema.

HISTORICAL BIOGRAPHY

Daniel Bernoulli
(1700–1789)

The following theorem asserts that a function which is continuous at every point of a closed interval $[a, b]$ has an absolute maximum and an absolute minimum value on the interval. We look for these values when we graph a function. (See Figure 4.3.)

THEOREM 1—The Extreme Value Theorem If f is continuous on a closed interval $[a, b]$, then f attains both an absolute maximum value M and an absolute minimum value m in $[a, b]$. That is, there are numbers x_1 and x_2 in $[a, b]$ with $f(x_1) = m$, $f(x_2) = M$, and $m \le f(x) \le M$ for every other x in $[a, b]$.

The proof of the Extreme Value Theorem requires a detailed knowledge of the real number system (see Appendix 7) and we will not give it here. Figure 4.3 illustrates possible locations for the absolute extrema of a continuous function on a closed interval $[a, b]$.

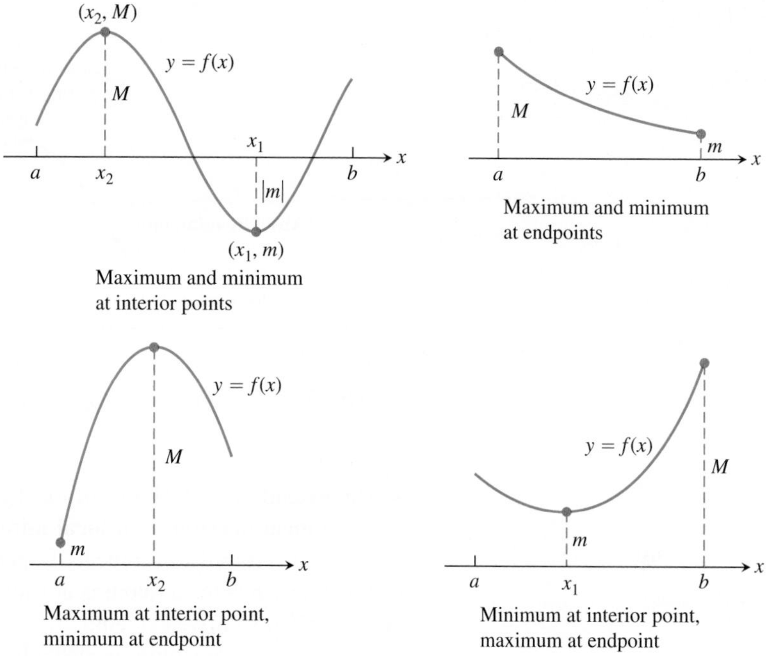

FIGURE 4.3 Some possibilities for a continuous function's maximum and minimum on a closed interval $[a, b]$.

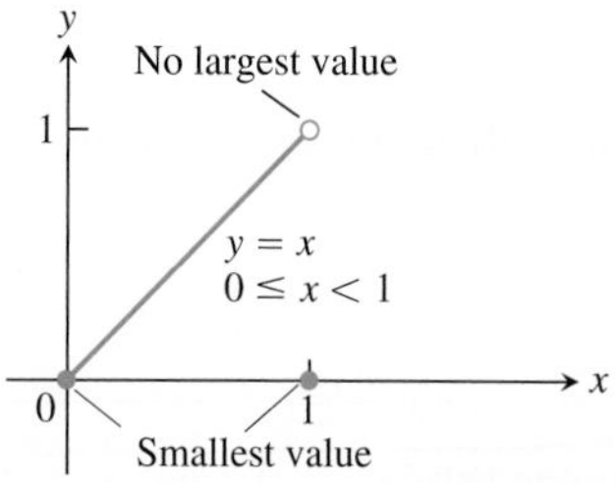

FIGURE 4.4 Even a single point of discontinuity can keep a function from having either a maximum or minimum value on a closed interval. The function

$$y = \begin{cases} x, & 0 \leq x < 1 \\ 0, & x = 1 \end{cases}$$

is continuous at every point of $[0, 1]$ except $x = 1$, yet its graph over $[0, 1]$ does not have a highest point.

As we observed for the function $y = \cos x$, it is possible that an absolute minimum (or absolute maximum) may occur at two or more different points of the interval.

The requirements in Theorem 1 that the interval be closed and finite, and that the function be continuous, are key ingredients. Without them, the conclusion of the theorem need not hold. Example 1 shows that an absolute extreme value may not exist if the interval fails to be both closed and finite. Figure 4.4 shows that the continuity requirement cannot be omitted.

Local (Relative) Extreme Values

Figure 4.5 shows a graph with five points where a function has extreme values on its domain $[a, b]$. The function's absolute minimum occurs at a even though at e the function's value is smaller than at any other point *nearby*. The curve rises to the left and falls to the right around c, making $f(c)$ a maximum locally. The function attains its absolute maximum at d.

DEFINITIONS A function f has a **local maximum** value at an interior point c of its domain if

$$f(x) \leq f(c) \qquad \text{for all } x \text{ in some open interval containing } c.$$

A function f has a **local minimum** value at an interior point c of its domain if

$$f(x) \geq f(c) \qquad \text{for all } x \text{ in some open interval containing } c.$$

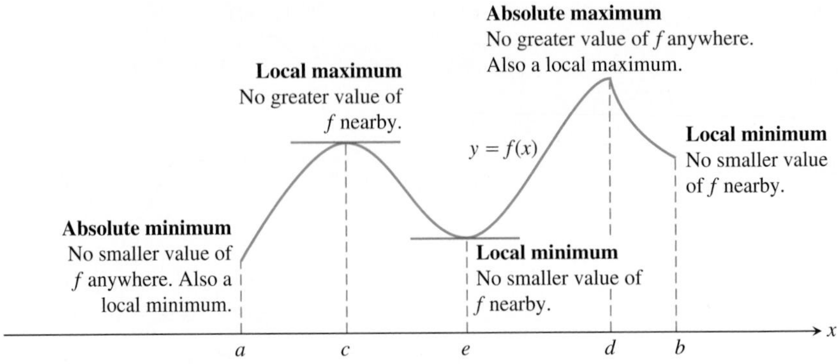

FIGURE 4.5 How to classify maxima and minima.

We can extend the definitions of local extrema to the endpoints of intervals by defining f to have a **local maximum** or **local minimum** value *at an endpoint* c if the appropriate inequality holds for all x in some half-open interval in its domain containing c. In Figure 4.5, the function f has local maxima at c and d and local minima at a, e, and b. Local extrema are also called **relative extrema**.

An absolute maximum is also a local maximum. Being the largest value overall, it is also the largest value in its immediate neighborhood. Hence, *a list of all local maxima will automatically include the absolute maximum if there is one*. Similarly, *a list of all local minima will include the absolute minimum if there is one*.

Finding Extrema

The next theorem explains why we usually need to investigate only a few values to find a function's extrema.

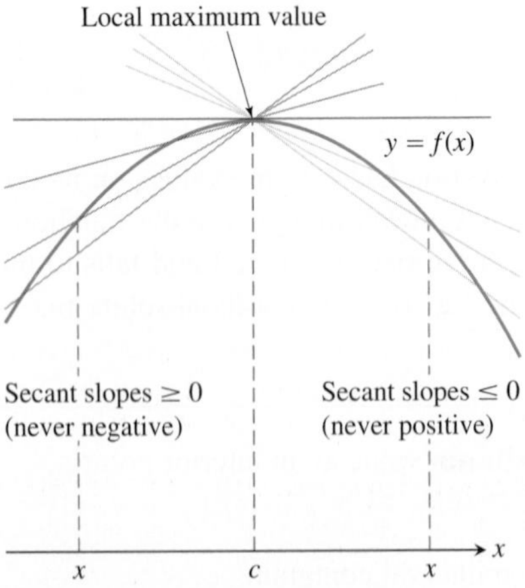

FIGURE 4.6 A curve with a local maximum value. The slope at c, simultaneously the limit of nonpositive numbers and nonnegative numbers, is zero.

THEOREM 2—The First Derivative Theorem for Local Extreme Values If f has a local maximum or minimum value at an interior point c of its domain, and if f' is defined at c, then

$$f'(c) = 0.$$

Proof To prove that $f'(c)$ is zero at a local extremum, we show first that $f'(c)$ cannot be positive and second that $f'(c)$ cannot be negative. The only number that is neither positive nor negative is zero, so that is what $f'(c)$ must be.

To begin, suppose that f has a local maximum value at $x = c$ (Figure 4.6) so that $f(x) - f(c) \leq 0$ for all values of x near enough to c. Since c is an interior point of f's domain, $f'(c)$ is defined by the two-sided limit

$$\lim_{x \to c} \frac{f(x) - f(c)}{x - c}.$$

This means that the right-hand and left-hand limits both exist at $x = c$ and equal $f'(c)$. When we examine these limits separately, we find that

$$f'(c) = \lim_{x \to c^+} \frac{f(x) - f(c)}{x - c} \leq 0. \qquad \text{Because } (x - c) > 0 \text{ and } f(x) \leq f(c) \qquad (1)$$

Similarly,

$$f'(c) = \lim_{x \to c^-} \frac{f(x) - f(c)}{x - c} \geq 0. \qquad \text{Because } (x - c) < 0 \text{ and } f(x) \leq f(c) \qquad (2)$$

Together, Equations (1) and (2) imply $f'(c) = 0$.

This proves the theorem for local maximum values. To prove it for local minimum values, we simply use $f(x) \geq f(c)$, which reverses the inequalities in Equations (1) and (2). ■

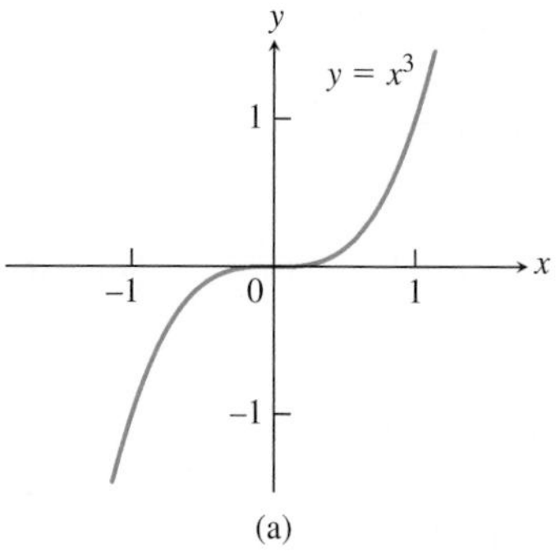

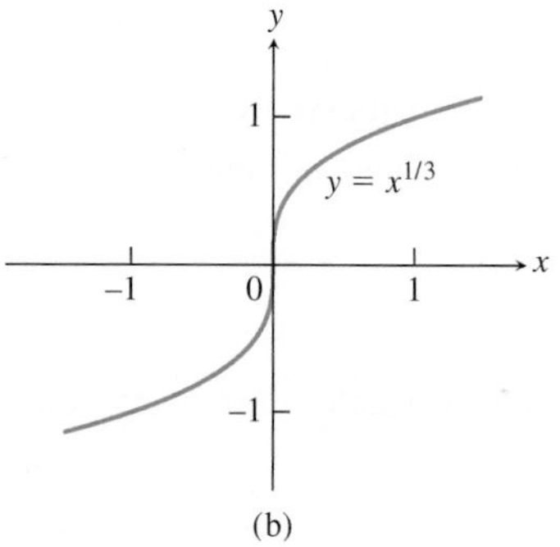

FIGURE 4.7 Critical points without extreme values. (a) $y' = 3x^2$ is 0 at $x = 0$, but $y = x^3$ has no extremum there. (b) $y' = (1/3)x^{-2/3}$ is undefined at $x = 0$, but $y = x^{1/3}$ has no extremum there.

Theorem 2 says that a function's first derivative is always zero at an interior point where the function has a local extreme value and the derivative is defined. Hence the only places where a function f can possibly have an extreme value (local or global) are

1. interior points where $f' = 0$,
2. interior points where f' is undefined,
3. endpoints of the domain of f.

The following definition helps us to summarize.

> **DEFINITION** An interior point of the domain of a function f where f' is zero or undefined is a **critical point** of f.

Thus the only domain points where a function can assume extreme values are critical points and endpoints. However, be careful not to misinterpret what is being said here. A function may have a critical point at $x = c$ without having a local extreme value there. For instance, both of the functions $y = x^3$ and $y = x^{1/3}$ have critical points at the origin and a zero value there, but each function is positive to the right of the origin and negative to the left. So neither function has a local extreme value at the origin. Instead, each function has a *point of inflection* there (see Figure 4.7). Inflection points are defined and explored further in Section 4.4.

Most problems that ask for extreme values call for finding the absolute extrema of a continuous function on a closed and finite interval. Theorem 1 assures us that such values exist; Theorem 2 tells us that they are taken on only at critical points and endpoints. Often we can simply list these points and calculate the corresponding function values to find what the largest and smallest values are, and where they are located.

> **How to Find the Absolute Extrema of a Continuous Function f on a Finite Closed Interval**
>
> 1. Evaluate f at all critical points and endpoints.
> 2. Take the largest and smallest of these values.

EXAMPLE 2 Find the absolute maximum and minimum values of $f(x) = 10x(2 - \ln x)$ on the interval $[1, e^2]$.

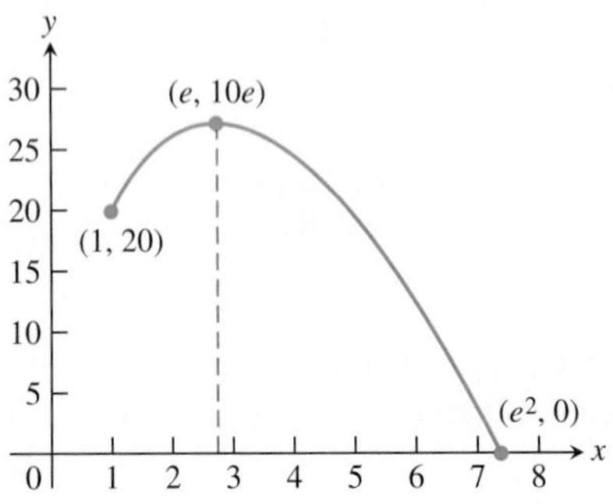

FIGURE 4.8 The extreme values of $f(x) = 10x(2 - \ln x)$ on $[1, e^2]$ occur at $x = e$ and $x = e^2$ (Example 2).

Solution Figure 4.8 suggests that f has its absolute maximum value near $x = 3$ and its absolute minimum value of 0 at $x = e^2$. Let's check this observation.

We evaluate the function at the critical points and endpoints and take the largest and smallest of the resulting values.

The first derivative is

$$f'(x) = 10(2 - \ln x) - 10x\left(\frac{1}{x}\right) = 10(1 - \ln x).$$

The only critical point in the domain $[1, e^2]$ is the point $x = e$, where $\ln x = 1$. The values of f at this one critical point and at the endpoints are

Critical point value:	$f(e) = 10e$
Endpoint values:	$f(1) = 10(2 - \ln 1) = 20$
	$f(e^2) = 10e^2(2 - 2\ln e) = 0.$

We can see from this list that the function's absolute maximum value is $10e \approx 27.2$; it occurs at the critical interior point $x = e$. The absolute minimum value is 0 and occurs at the right endpoint $x = e^2$. ■

EXAMPLE 3 Find the absolute maximum and minimum values of $f(x) = x^{2/3}$ on the interval $[-2, 3]$.

Solution We evaluate the function at the critical points and endpoints and take the largest and smallest of the resulting values.

The first derivative

$$f'(x) = \frac{2}{3}x^{-1/3} = \frac{2}{3\sqrt[3]{x}}$$

has no zeros but is undefined at the interior point $x = 0$. The values of f at this one critical point and at the endpoints are

Critical point value:	$f(0) = 0$
Endpoint values:	$f(-2) = (-2)^{2/3} = \sqrt[3]{4}$
	$f(3) = (3)^{2/3} = \sqrt[3]{9}.$

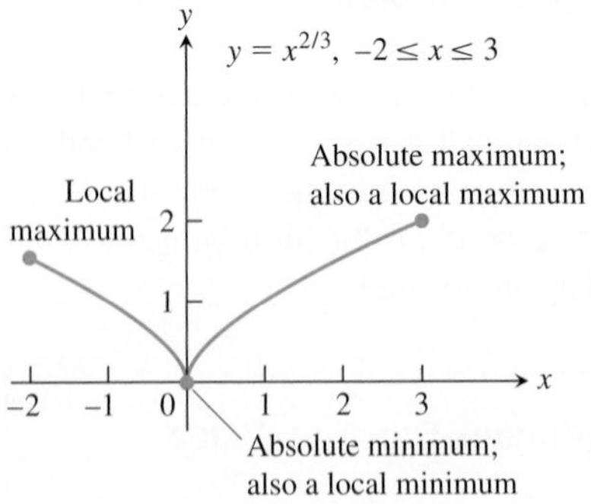

FIGURE 4.9 The extreme values of $f(x) = x^{2/3}$ on $[-2, 3]$ occur at $x = 0$ and $x = 3$ (Example 3).

We can see from this list that the function's absolute maximum value is $\sqrt[3]{9} \approx 2.08$, and it occurs at the right endpoint $x = 3$. The absolute minimum value is 0, and it occurs at the interior point $x = 0$ where the graph has a cusp (Figure 4.9). ■

EXERCISES 4.1

In Exercises 1–6, determine from the graph whether the function has any absolute extreme values on $[a, b]$. Then explain how your answer is consistent with Theorem 1.

1.

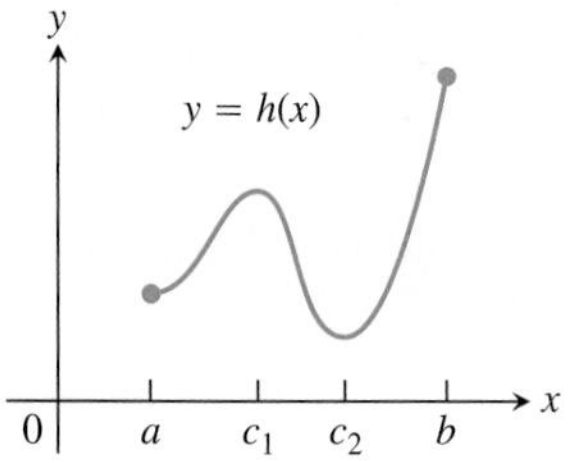

2.

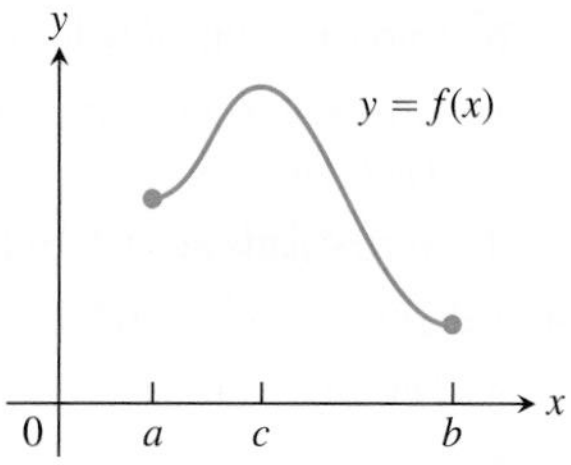

3.

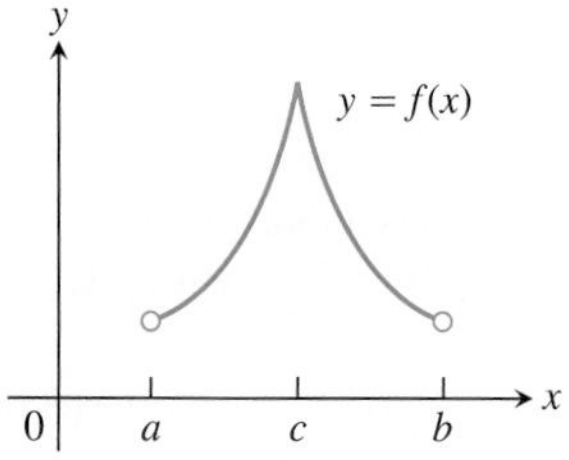

4.

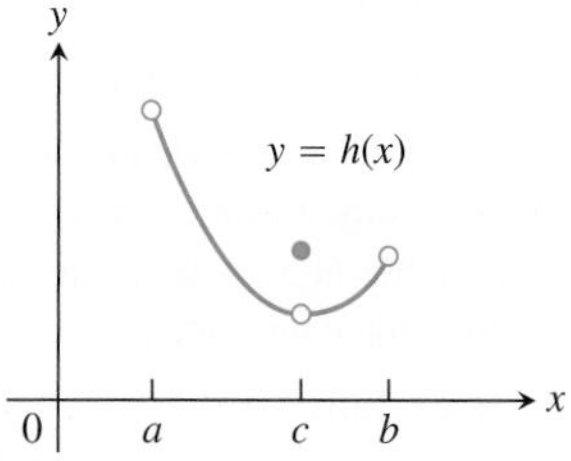

5.

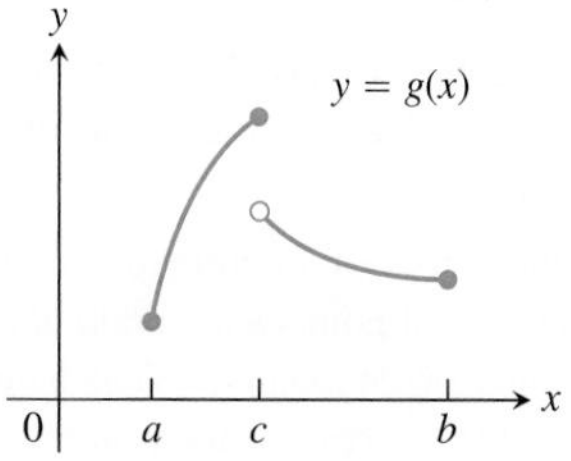

6.

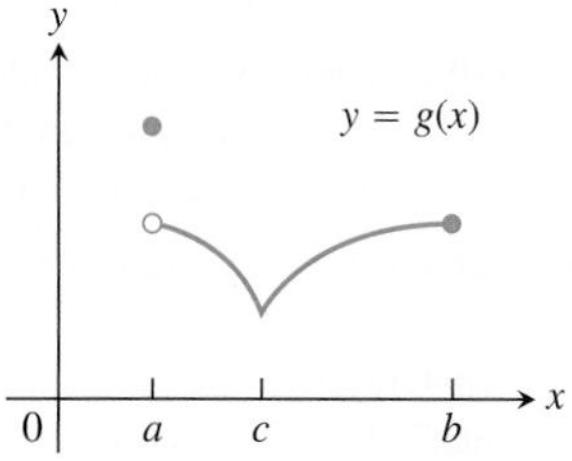

In Exercises 7–10, find the extreme values and where they occur.

7.

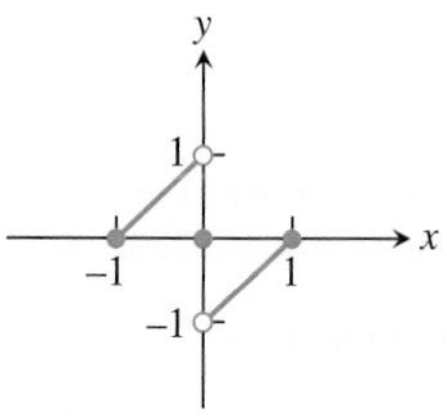

8.

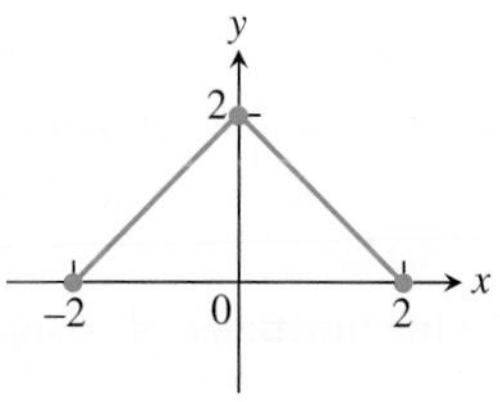

9.

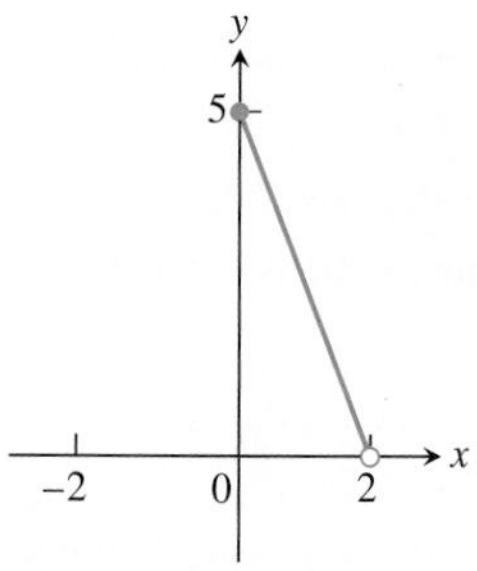

10.

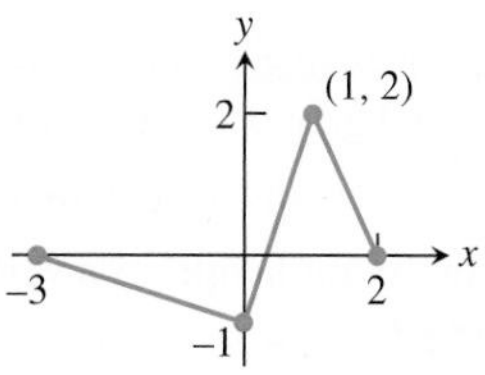

In Exercises 11–14, match the table with a graph.

11.

x	$f'(x)$
a	0
b	0
c	5

12.

x	$f'(x)$
a	0
b	0
c	-5

13.

x	$f'(x)$
a	does not exist
b	0
c	-2

14.

x	$f'(x)$
a	does not exist
b	does not exist
c	-1.7

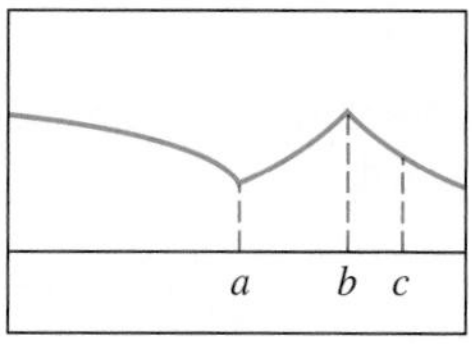

(a)

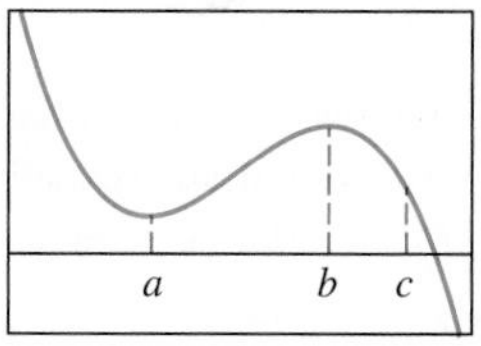

(b)

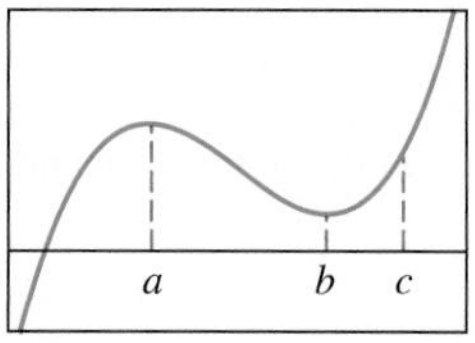

(c)

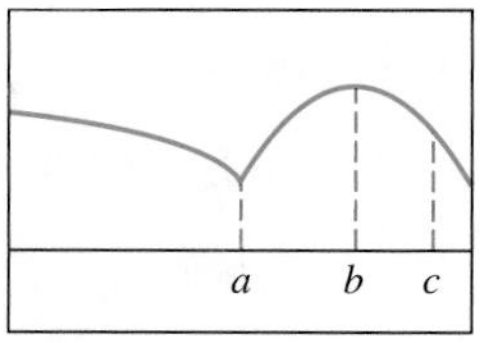

(d)

In Exercises 15–34, find the absolute maximum and minimum values of each function on the given interval. Then graph the function. Identify the points on the graph where the absolute extrema occur, and include their coordinates.

15. $f(x) = \frac{2}{3}x - 5, \quad -2 \le x \le 3$

16. $f(x) = -x - 4, \quad -4 \le x \le 1$

17. $f(x) = x^2 - 1, \quad -1 \le x \le 2$

18. $f(x) = 4 - x^2, \quad -3 \le x \le 1$

19. $F(x) = -\frac{1}{x^2}, \quad 0.5 \le x \le 2$

20. $F(x) = -\frac{1}{x}, \quad -2 \le x \le -1$

21. $h(x) = \sqrt[3]{x}, \quad -1 \le x \le 8$

22. $h(x) = -3x^{2/3}, \quad -1 \le x \le 1$

23. $g(x) = \sqrt{4 - x^2}, \quad -2 \le x \le 1$

24. $g(x) = -\sqrt{5 - x^2}, \quad -\sqrt{5} \le x \le 0$

25. $f(\theta) = \sin\theta, \quad -\frac{\pi}{2} \le \theta \le \frac{5\pi}{6}$

26. $f(\theta) = \tan\theta, \quad -\frac{\pi}{3} \le \theta \le \frac{\pi}{4}$

27. $g(x) = \csc x, \quad \frac{\pi}{3} \le x \le \frac{2\pi}{3}$

28. $g(x) = \sec x, \quad -\frac{\pi}{3} \le x \le \frac{\pi}{6}$

29. $f(t) = 2 - |t|, \quad -1 \le t \le 3$

30. $f(t) = |t - 5|, \quad 4 \le t \le 7$

31. $g(x) = xe^{-x}, \quad -1 \le x \le 1$

32. $h(x) = \ln(x + 1), \quad 0 \le x \le 3$

33. $f(x) = \frac{1}{x} + \ln x, \quad 0.5 \le x \le 4$

34. $g(x) = e^{-x^2}, \quad -2 \le x \le 1$

In Exercises 35–38, find the function's absolute maximum and minimum values and say where they are assumed.

35. $f(x) = x^{4/3}, \quad -1 \le x \le 8$

36. $f(x) = x^{5/3}, \quad -1 \le x \le 8$

37. $g(\theta) = \theta^{3/5}, \quad -32 \le \theta \le 1$

38. $h(\theta) = 3\theta^{2/3}, \quad -27 \le \theta \le 8$

In Exercises 39–54, find the extreme values of the function and where they occur.

39. $y = 2x^2 - 8x + 9$

40. $y = x^3 - 2x + 4$

41. $y = x^3 + x^2 - 8x + 5$

42. $y = x^3 - 3x^2 + 3x - 2$

43. $y = \sqrt{x^2 - 1}$

44. $y = \dfrac{1}{\sqrt{1 - x^2}}$

45. $y = \dfrac{1}{\sqrt[3]{1 - x^2}}$

46. $y = \sqrt{3 + 2x - x^2}$

47. $y = \dfrac{x}{x^2 + 1}$

48. $y = \dfrac{x + 1}{x^2 + 2x + 2}$

49. $y = e^x + e^{-x}$

50. $y = e^x - e^{-x}$

51. $y = x \ln x$

52. $y = x^2 \ln x$

53. $y = \cos^{-1}(x^2)$

54. $y = \sin^{-1}(e^x)$

In Exercises 55–62, find the derivative at each critical point and determine the local extreme values.

55. $y = x^{2/3}(x + 2)$

56. $y = x^{2/3}(x^2 - 4)$

57. $y = x\sqrt{4 - x^2}$

58. $y = x^2\sqrt{3 - x}$

59. $y = \begin{cases} 4 - 2x, & x \le 1 \\ x + 1, & x > 1 \end{cases}$

60. $y = \begin{cases} 3 - x, & x < 0 \\ 3 + 2x - x^2, & x \ge 0 \end{cases}$

61. $y = \begin{cases} -x^2 - 2x + 4, & x \le 1 \\ -x^2 + 6x - 4, & x > 1 \end{cases}$

62. $y = \begin{cases} -\frac{1}{4}x^2 - \frac{1}{2}x + \frac{15}{4}, & x \le 1 \\ x^3 - 6x^2 + 8x, & x > 1 \end{cases}$

In Exercises 63 and 64, give reasons for your answers.

63. Let $f(x) = (x - 2)^{2/3}$.

a. Does $f'(2)$ exist?

b. Show that the only local extreme value of f occurs at $x = 2$.

c. Does the result in part (b) contradict the Extreme Value Theorem?

d. Repeat parts (a) and (b) for $f(x) = (x - a)^{2/3}$, replacing 2 by a.

64. Let $f(x) = |x^3 - 9x|$.

a. Does $f'(0)$ exist?

b. Does $f'(3)$ exist?

c. Does $f'(-3)$ exist?

d. Determine all extrema of f.

65. A minimum with no derivative The function $f(x) = |x|$ has an absolute minimum value at $x = 0$ even though f is not differentiable at $x = 0$. Is this consistent with Theorem 2? Give reasons for your answer.

66. Even functions If an even function $f(x)$ has a local maximum value at $x = c$, can anything be said about the value of f at $x = -c$? Give reasons for your answer.

67. Odd functions If an odd function $g(x)$ has a local minimum value at $x = c$, can anything be said about the value of g at $x = -c$? Give reasons for your answer.

68. We know how to find the extreme values of a continuous function $f(x)$ by investigating its values at critical points and endpoints. But what if there *are* no critical points or endpoints? What happens then? Do such functions really exist? Give reasons for your answers.

69. The function

$$V(x) = x(10 - 2x)(16 - 2x), \qquad 0 < x < 5,$$

models the volume of a box.

a. Find the extreme values of V.

b. Interpret any values found in part (a) in terms of volume of the box.

70. Cubic functions Consider the cubic function

$$f(x) = ax^3 + bx^2 + cx + d.$$

a. Show that f can have 0, 1, or 2 critical points. Give examples and graphs to support your argument.

b. How many local extreme values can f have?

71. Maximum height of a vertically moving body The height of a body moving vertically is given by

$$s = -\frac{1}{2}gt^2 + v_0 t + s_0, \qquad g > 0,$$

with s in meters and t in seconds. Find the body's maximum height.

72. Peak alternating current Suppose that at any given time t (in seconds) the current i (in amperes) in an alternating current circuit is $i = 2\cos t + 2\sin t$. What is the peak current for this circuit (largest magnitude)?

T Graph the functions in Exercises 73–76. Then find the extreme values of the function on the interval and say where they occur.

73. $f(x) = |x - 2| + |x + 3|, \quad -5 \le x \le 5$

74. $g(x) = |x - 1| - |x - 5|, \quad -2 \le x \le 7$

75. $h(x) = |x + 2| - |x - 3|, \quad -\infty < x < \infty$

76. $k(x) = |x + 1| + |x - 3|, \quad -\infty < x < \infty$

COMPUTER EXPLORATIONS

In Exercises 77–84, you will use a CAS to help find the absolute extrema of the given function over the specified closed interval. Perform the following steps.

a. Plot the function over the interval to see its general behavior there.

b. Find the interior points where $f' = 0$. (In some exercises, you may have to use the numerical equation solver to approximate a solution.) You may want to plot f' as well.

c. Find the interior points where f' does not exist.

d. Evaluate the function at all points found in parts (b) and (c) and at the endpoints of the interval.

e. Find the function's absolute extreme values on the interval and identify where they occur.

77. $f(x) = x^4 - 8x^2 + 4x + 2, \quad [-20/25, 64/25]$

78. $f(x) = -x^4 + 4x^3 - 4x + 1, \quad [-3/4, 3]$

79. $f(x) = x^{2/3}(3 - x), \quad [-2, 2]$

80. $f(x) = 2 + 2x - 3x^{2/3}, \quad [-1, 10/3]$

81. $f(x) = \sqrt{x} + \cos x, \quad [0, 2\pi]$

82. $f(x) = x^{3/4} - \sin x + \dfrac{1}{2}, \quad [0, 2\pi]$

83. $f(x) = \pi x^2 e^{-3x/2}, \quad [0, 5]$

84. $f(x) = \ln(2x + x\sin x), \quad [1, 15]$

4.2 The Mean Value Theorem

We know that constant functions have zero derivatives, but could there be a more complicated function whose derivative is always zero? If two functions have identical derivatives over an interval, how are the functions related? We answer these and other questions in this chapter by applying the Mean Value Theorem. First we introduce a special case, known as Rolle's Theorem, which is used to prove the Mean Value Theorem.

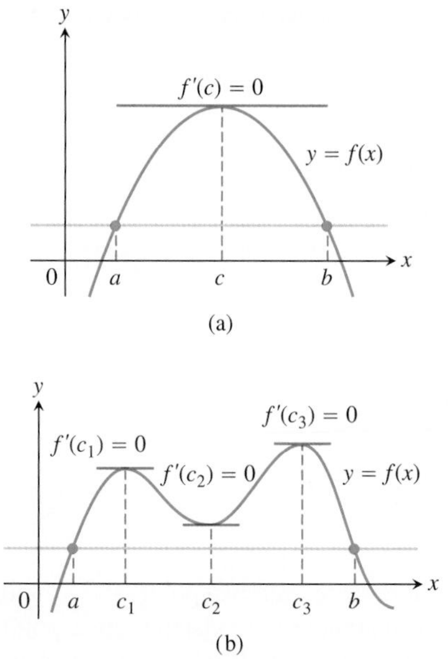

FIGURE 4.10 Rolle's Theorem says that a differentiable curve has at least one horizontal tangent between any two points where it crosses a horizontal line. It may have just one (a), or it may have more (b).

Rolle's Theorem

As suggested by its graph, if a differentiable function crosses a horizontal line at two different points, there is at least one point between them where the tangent to the graph is horizontal and the derivative is zero (Figure 4.10). We now state and prove this result.

> **THEOREM 3—Rolle's Theorem** Suppose that $y = f(x)$ is continuous at every point of the closed interval $[a, b]$ and differentiable at every point of its interior (a, b). If $f(a) = f(b)$, then there is at least one number c in (a, b) at which $f'(c) = 0$.

Proof Being continuous, f assumes absolute maximum and minimum values on $[a, b]$ by Theorem 1. These can occur only

1. at interior points where f' is zero,
2. at interior points where f' does not exist,
3. at the endpoints of the function's domain, in this case a and b.

HISTORICAL BIOGRAPHY

Michel Rolle
(1652–1719)

By hypothesis, f has a derivative at every interior point. That rules out possibility (2), leaving us with interior points where $f' = 0$ and with the two endpoints a and b.

If either the maximum or the minimum occurs at a point c between a and b, then $f'(c) = 0$ by Theorem 2 in Section 4.1, and we have found a point for Rolle's Theorem.

If both the absolute maximum and the absolute minimum occur at the endpoints, then because $f(a) = f(b)$ it must be the case that f is a constant function with $f(x) = f(a) = f(b)$ for every $x \in [a, b]$. Therefore $f'(x) = 0$ and the point c can be taken anywhere in the interior (a, b). ■

The hypotheses of Theorem 3 are essential. If they fail at even one point, the graph may not have a horizontal tangent (Figure 4.11).

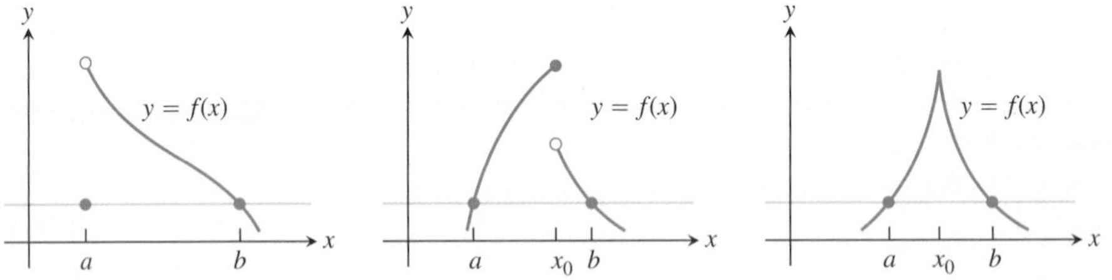

(a) Discontinuous at an endpoint of $[a, b]$

(b) Discontinuous at an interior point of $[a, b]$

(c) Continuous on $[a, b]$ but not differentiable at an interior point

FIGURE 4.11 There may be no horizontal tangent if the hypotheses of Rolle's Theorem do not hold.

Rolle's Theorem may be combined with the Intermediate Value Theorem to show when there is only one real solution of an equation $f(x) = 0$ between two points where the values of differentiable function f have opposite signs.

EXAMPLE 1 Show that the equation

$$x^3 + 3x + 1 = 0$$

has exactly one real solution.

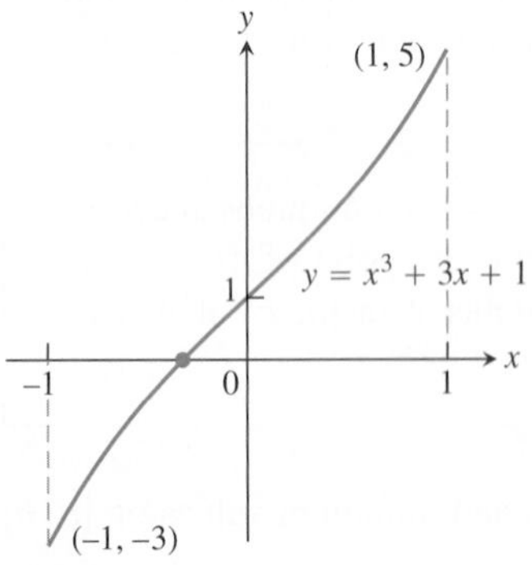

FIGURE 4.12 The only real zero of the polynomial $y = x^3 + 3x + 1$ is the one shown here where the curve crosses the x-axis between -1 and 0 (Example 1).

Solution Let

$$y = f(x) = x^3 + 3x + 1.$$

Then the derivative

$$f'(x) = 3x^2 + 3$$

is never zero (because it is always positive). Now, if there were even two points $x = a$ and $x = b$ where $f(x)$ was zero, Rolle's Theorem would guarantee the existence of a point $x = c$ in between them where f' was zero. Therefore, f has no more than one zero. It does in fact have one zero, because the Intermediate Value Theorem tells us that the graph of $y = f(x)$ crosses the x-axis somewhere between $x = -1$ (where $y = -3$) and $x = 0$ (where $y = 1$). (See Figure 4.12.) ■

Our main use of Rolle's Theorem is in proving the Mean Value Theorem.

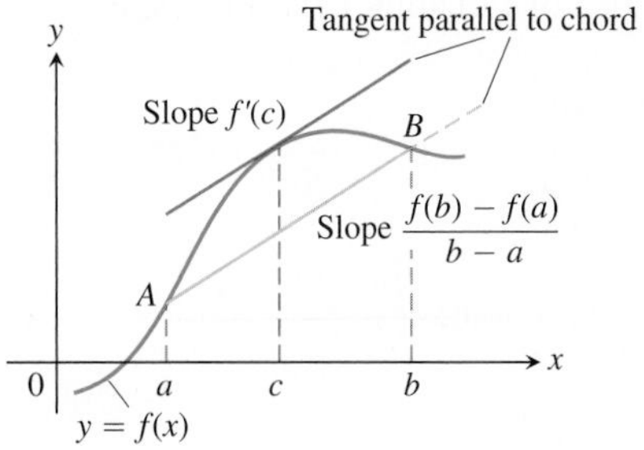

FIGURE 4.13 Geometrically, the Mean Value Theorem says that somewhere between A and B the curve has at least one tangent parallel to chord AB.

The Mean Value Theorem

The Mean Value Theorem, which was first stated by Joseph-Louis Lagrange, is a slanted version of Rolle's Theorem (Figure 4.13). The Mean Value Theorem guarantees that there is a point where the tangent line is parallel to the chord AB.

HISTORICAL BIOGRAPHY

Joseph-Louis Lagrange
(1736–1813)

> **THEOREM 4—The Mean Value Theorem** Suppose $y = f(x)$ is continuous on a closed interval $[a, b]$ and differentiable on the interval's interior (a, b). Then there is at least one point c in (a, b) at which
>
> $$\frac{f(b) - f(a)}{b - a} = f'(c). \tag{1}$$

Proof We picture the graph of f and draw a line through the points $A(a, f(a))$ and $B(b, f(b))$ (see Figure 4.14). The line is the graph of the function

$$g(x) = f(a) + \frac{f(b) - f(a)}{b - a}(x - a) \tag{2}$$

(point-slope equation). The vertical difference between the graphs of f and g at x is

$$\begin{aligned} h(x) &= f(x) - g(x) \\ &= f(x) - f(a) - \frac{f(b) - f(a)}{b - a}(x - a). \end{aligned} \tag{3}$$

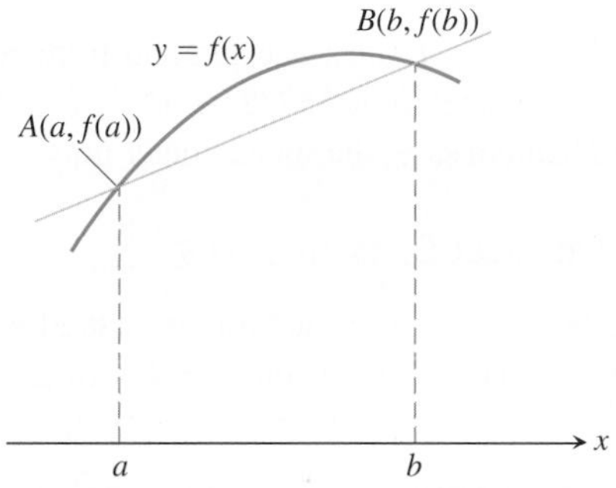

FIGURE 4.14 The graph of f and the chord AB over the interval $[a, b]$.

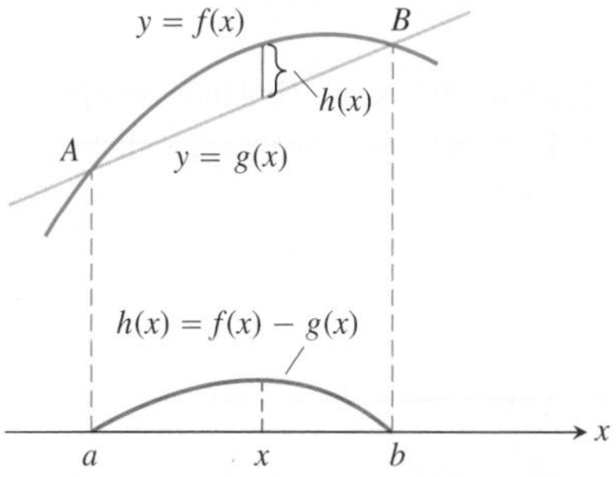

FIGURE 4.15 The chord AB is the graph of the function $g(x)$. The function $h(x) = f(x) - g(x)$ gives the vertical distance between the graphs of f and g at x.

Figure 4.15 shows the graphs of f, g, and h together.

The function h satisfies the hypotheses of Rolle's Theorem on $[a, b]$. It is continuous on $[a, b]$ and differentiable on (a, b) because both f and g are. Also, $h(a) = h(b) = 0$ because the graphs of f and g both pass through A and B. Therefore $h'(c) = 0$ at some point $c \in (a, b)$. This is the point we want for Equation (1).

To verify Equation (1), we differentiate both sides of Equation (3) with respect to x and then set $x = c$:

$$h'(x) = f'(x) - \frac{f(b) - f(a)}{b - a} \qquad \text{Derivative of Eq. (3) . . .}$$

$$h'(c) = f'(c) - \frac{f(b) - f(a)}{b - a} \qquad \text{. . . with } x = c$$

$$0 = f'(c) - \frac{f(b) - f(a)}{b - a} \qquad h'(c) = 0$$

$$f'(c) = \frac{f(b) - f(a)}{b - a}, \qquad \text{Rearranged}$$

which is what we set out to prove. ■

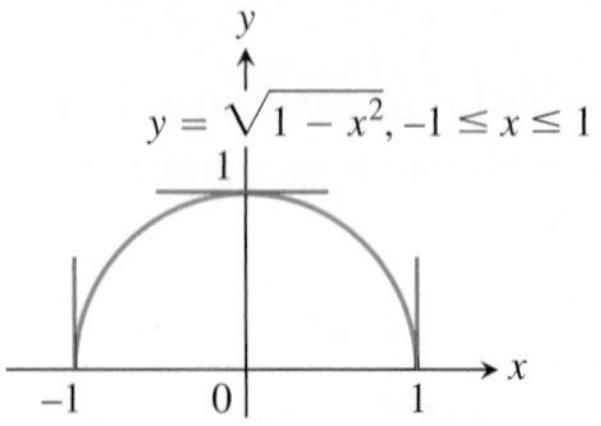

FIGURE 4.16 The function $f(x) = \sqrt{1 - x^2}$ satisfies the hypotheses (and conclusion) of the Mean Value Theorem on $[-1, 1]$ even though f is not differentiable at -1 and 1.

The hypotheses of the Mean Value Theorem do not require f to be differentiable at either a or b. Continuity at a and b is enough (Figure 4.16).

EXAMPLE 2 The function $f(x) = x^2$ (Figure 4.17) is continuous for $0 \le x \le 2$ and differentiable for $0 < x < 2$. Since $f(0) = 0$ and $f(2) = 4$, the Mean Value Theorem says that at some point c in the interval, the derivative $f'(x) = 2x$ must have the value $(4 - 0)/(2 - 0) = 2$. In this (exceptional) case we can identify c by solving the equation $2c = 2$ to get $c = 1$. ■

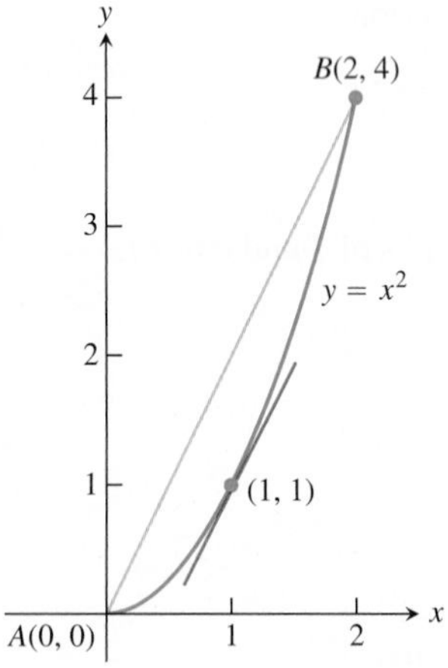

FIGURE 4.17 As we find in Example 2, $c = 1$ is where the tangent is parallel to the chord.

A Physical Interpretation

Think of the number $(f(b) - f(a))/(b - a)$ as the average change in f over $[a, b]$ and $f'(c)$ as an instantaneous change. Then the Mean Value Theorem says that at some interior point the instantaneous change must equal the average change over the entire interval.

EXAMPLE 3 If a car accelerating from zero takes 8 sec to go 352 ft, its average velocity for the 8-sec interval is $352/8 = 44$ ft/sec. At some point during the acceleration, the Mean Value Theorem says, the speedometer must read exactly 30 mph (44 ft/sec) (Figure 4.18). ■

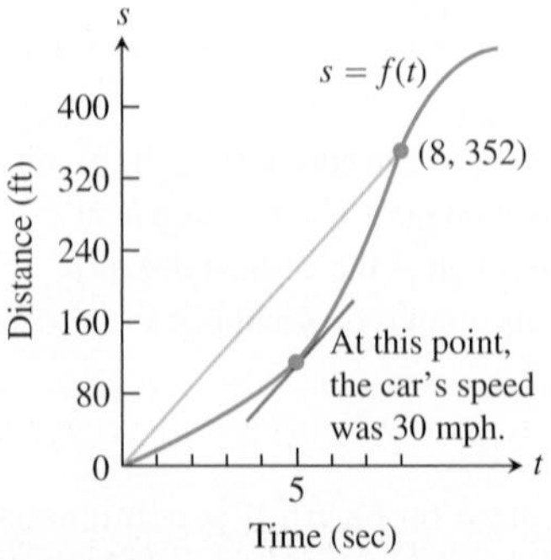

FIGURE 4.18 Distance versus elapsed time for the car in Example 3.

Mathematical Consequences

At the beginning of the section, we asked what kind of function has a zero derivative over an interval. The first corollary of the Mean Value Theorem provides the answer.

> **COROLLARY 1** If $f'(x) = 0$ at each point x of an open interval (a, b), then $f(x) = C$ for all $x \in (a, b)$, where C is a constant.

Proof We want to show that f has a constant value on the interval (a, b). We do so by showing that if x_1 and x_2 are any two points in (a, b), then $f(x_1) = f(x_2)$. Numbering x_1 and x_2 from left to right, we have $x_1 < x_2$. Then f satisfies the hypotheses of the Mean Value Theorem on $[x_1, x_2]$: It is differentiable at every point of $[x_1, x_2]$ and hence continuous at every point as well. Therefore,

$$\frac{f(x_2) - f(x_1)}{x_2 - x_1} = f'(c)$$

at some point c between x_1 and x_2. Since $f' = 0$ throughout (a, b), this equation translates successively into

$$\frac{f(x_2) - f(x_1)}{x_2 - x_1} = 0, \qquad f(x_2) - f(x_1) = 0, \qquad \text{and} \qquad f(x_1) = f(x_2). \qquad \blacksquare$$

At the beginning of this section, we also asked about the relationship between two functions that have identical derivatives over an interval. The next corollary tells us that their values on the interval have a constant difference.

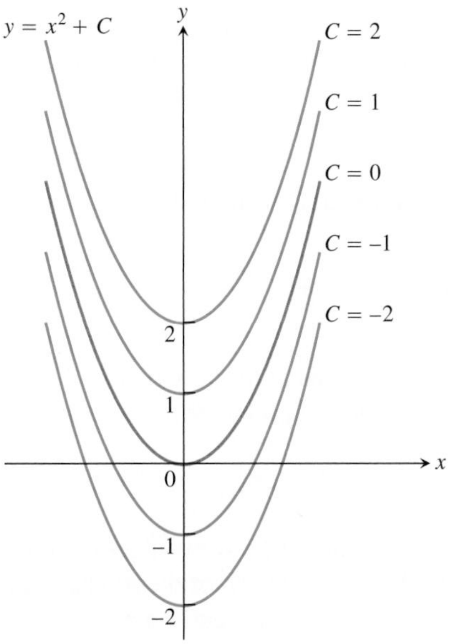

FIGURE 4.19 From a geometric point of view, Corollary 2 of the Mean Value Theorem says that the graphs of functions with identical derivatives on an interval can differ only by a vertical shift there. The graphs of the functions with derivative $2x$ are the parabolas $y = x^2 + C$, shown here for selected values of C.

> **COROLLARY 2** If $f'(x) = g'(x)$ at each point x in an open interval (a, b), then there exists a constant C such that $f(x) = g(x) + C$ for all $x \in (a, b)$. That is, $f - g$ is a constant on (a, b).

Proof At each point $x \in (a, b)$ the derivative of the difference function $h = f - g$ is

$$h'(x) = f'(x) - g'(x) = 0.$$

Thus, $h(x) = C$ on (a, b) by Corollary 1. That is, $f(x) - g(x) = C$ on (a, b), so $f(x) = g(x) + C$. $\blacksquare$

Corollaries 1 and 2 are also true if the open interval (a, b) fails to be finite. That is, they remain true if the interval is (a, ∞), $(-\infty, b)$, or $(-\infty, \infty)$.

Corollary 2 plays an important role when we discuss antiderivatives in Section 4.8. It tells us, for instance, that since the derivative of $f(x) = x^2$ on $(-\infty, \infty)$ is $2x$, any other function with derivative $2x$ on $(-\infty, \infty)$ must have the formula $x^2 + C$ for some value of C (Figure 4.19).

EXAMPLE 4 Find the function $f(x)$ whose derivative is $\sin x$ and whose graph passes through the point $(0, 2)$.

Solution Since $f(x)$ has the same derivative as $g(x) = -\cos x$, we know that $f(x) = -\cos x + C$ for some constant C. The value of C can be determined from the condition that $f(0) = 2$ (the graph of f passes through $(0, 2)$):

$$f(0) = -\cos(0) + C = 2, \qquad \text{so} \qquad C = 3.$$

The function is $f(x) = -\cos x + 3$. $\blacksquare$

Finding Velocity and Position from Acceleration

Corollary 2 helps us find the velocity and displacement functions of a body falling freely from rest with acceleration 9.8 m/sec^2.

We know that $v(t)$ is some function whose derivative is 9.8. We also know that the derivative of $g(t) = 9.8t$ is 9.8. By Corollary 2,

$$v(t) = 9.8t + C$$

for some constant C. Since the body falls from rest, $v(0) = 0$. Thus

$$9.8(0) + C = 0, \quad \text{and} \quad C = 0.$$

The velocity function must be $v(t) = 9.8t$. What about the position function $s(t)$?

We know that $s(t)$ is some function whose derivative is $9.8t$. We also know that the derivative of $f(t) = 4.9t^2$ is $9.8t$. By Corollary 2,

$$s(t) = 4.9t^2 + C$$

for some constant C. If the initial height is $s(0) = h$, measured positive downward from the rest position, then

$$4.9(0)^2 + C = h, \quad \text{and} \quad C = h.$$

The position function must be $s(t) = 4.9t^2 + h$.

The ability to find functions from their rates of change is one of the very powerful tools of calculus. As we will see, it lies at the heart of the mathematical developments in Chapter 5.

Proofs of the Laws of Logarithms

The algebraic properties of logarithms were stated in Section 1.5. We can prove those properties by applying Corollary 2 of the Mean Value Theorem to each of them. The steps in the proofs are similar to those used in solving problems involving logarithms.

Proof that $\ln bx = \ln b + \ln x$ The argument starts by observing that $\ln bx$ and $\ln x$ have the same derivative:

$$\frac{d}{dx}\ln(bx) = \frac{b}{bx} = \frac{1}{x} = \frac{d}{dx}\ln x.$$

According to Corollary 2 of the Mean Value Theorem, then, the functions must differ by a constant, which means that

$$\ln bx = \ln x + C$$

for some C.

Since this last equation holds for all positive values of x, it must hold for $x = 1$. Hence,

$$\begin{aligned} \ln(b \cdot 1) &= \ln 1 + C \\ \ln b &= 0 + C && \ln 1 = 0 \\ C &= \ln b. \end{aligned}$$

By substituting we conclude,

$$\ln bx = \ln b + \ln x. \qquad \blacksquare$$

Proof that $\ln x^r = r \ln x$ We use the same-derivative argument again. For all positive values of x,

$$\begin{aligned} \frac{d}{dx}\ln x^r &= \frac{1}{x^r}\frac{d}{dx}(x^r) && \text{Chain Rule} \\ &= \frac{1}{x^r} r x^{r-1} && \text{Derivative Power Rule} \\ &= r \cdot \frac{1}{x} = \frac{d}{dx}(r \ln x). \end{aligned}$$

Since $\ln x^r$ and $r \ln x$ have the same derivative,

$$\ln x^r = r \ln x + C$$

for some constant C. Taking x to be 1 identifies C as zero, and we're done. ■

You are asked to prove the Quotient Rule for logarithms,

$$\ln\left(\frac{b}{x}\right) = \ln b - \ln x,$$

in Exercise 65. The Reciprocal Rule, $\ln(1/x) = -\ln x$, is a special case of the Quotient Rule, obtained by taking $b = 1$ and noting that $\ln 1 = 0$.

Laws of Exponents

The laws of exponents for the natural exponential e^x are consequences of the algebraic properties of $\ln x$. They follow from the inverse relationship between these functions.

> **Laws of Exponents for e^x**
>
> For all numbers x, x_1, and x_2, the natural exponential e^x obeys the following laws:
>
> **1.** $e^{x_1} \cdot e^{x_2} = e^{x_1 + x_2}$
>
> **2.** $e^{-x} = \dfrac{1}{e^x}$
>
> **3.** $\dfrac{e^{x_1}}{e^{x_2}} = e^{x_1 - x_2}$
>
> **4.** $(e^{x_1})^{x_2} = e^{x_1 x_2} = (e^{x_2})^{x_1}$

Proof of Law 1 Let

$$y_1 = e^{x_1} \quad \text{and} \quad y_2 = e^{x_2}. \tag{4}$$

Then

$$\begin{aligned}
x_1 &= \ln y_1 \quad \text{and} \quad x_2 = \ln y_2 && \text{Take logs of both sides of Eqs. (4).} \\
x_1 + x_2 &= \ln y_1 + \ln y_2 \\
&= \ln y_1 y_2 && \text{Product Rule for logarithms} \\
e^{x_1 + x_2} &= e^{\ln y_1 y_2} && \text{Exponentiate.} \\
&= y_1 y_2 && e^{\ln u} = u \\
&= e^{x_1} e^{x_2}.
\end{aligned}$$

■

The proof of Law 4 is similar. Laws 2 and 3 follow from Law 1 (Exercises 67 and 68).

EXERCISES 4.2

Find the value or values of c that satisfy the equation

$$\frac{f(b) - f(a)}{b - a} = f'(c)$$

in the conclusion of the Mean Value Theorem for the functions and intervals in Exercises 1–4.

1. $f(x) = x^2 + 2x - 1, \quad [0, 1]$

2. $f(x) = x^{2/3}, \quad [0, 1]$

3. $f(x) = \sin^{-1} x, \quad [-1, 1]$

4. $f(x) = \ln(x - 1), \quad [2, 4]$

Which of the functions in Exercises 5–8 satisfy the hypotheses of the Mean Value Theorem on the given interval, and which do not? Give reasons for your answers.

5. $f(x) = x^{2/3}, \quad [-1, 8]$

6. $f(x) = x^{4/5}, \quad [0, 1]$

7. $f(x) = \sqrt{x(1-x)}, \quad [0, 1]$

8. $f(x) = \begin{cases} \dfrac{\sin x}{x}, & -\pi \le x < 0 \\ 0, & x = 0 \end{cases}$

9. The function

$$f(x) = \begin{cases} x, & 0 \le x < 1 \\ 0, & x = 1 \end{cases}$$

is zero at $x = 0$ and $x = 1$ and differentiable on $(0, 1)$, but its derivative on $(0, 1)$ is never zero. How can this be? Doesn't Rolle's Theorem say the derivative has to be zero somewhere in $(0, 1)$? Give reasons for your answer.

10. For what values of a, m and b does the function

$$f(x) = \begin{cases} 3, & x = 0 \\ -x^2 + 3x + a, & 0 < x < 1 \\ mx + b, & 1 \le x \le 2 \end{cases}$$

satisfy the hypotheses of the Mean Value Theorem on the interval $[0, 2]$?

11. a. Plot the zeros of each polynomial on a line together with the zeros of its first derivative.

i) $y = x^2 - 4$

ii) $y = x^2 + 8x + 15$

iii) $y = x^3 - 3x^2 + 4 = (x + 1)(x - 2)^2$

iv) $y = x^3 - 33x^2 + 216x = x(x - 9)(x - 24)$

b. Use Rolle's Theorem to prove that between every two zeros of $x^n + a_{n-1}x^{n-1} + \cdots + a_1x + a_0$ there lies a zero of

$$nx^{n-1} + (n-1)a_{n-1}x^{n-2} + \cdots + a_1.$$

12. Suppose that f'' is continuous on $[a, b]$ and that f has three zeros in the interval. Show that f'' has at least one zero in (a, b). Generalize this result.

13. Show that if $f'' > 0$ throughout an interval $[a, b]$, then f' has at most one zero in $[a, b]$. What if $f'' < 0$ throughout $[a, b]$ instead?

14. Show that a cubic polynomial can have at most three real zeros.

Show that the functions in Exercises 15–22 have exactly one zero in the given interval.

15. $f(x) = x^4 + 3x + 1, \quad [-2, -1]$

16. $f(x) = x^3 + \dfrac{4}{x^2} + 7, \quad (-\infty, 0)$

17. $g(t) = \sqrt{t} + \sqrt{1+t} - 4, \quad (0, \infty)$

18. $g(t) = \dfrac{1}{1-t} + \sqrt{1+t} - 3.1, \quad (-1, 1)$

19. $r(\theta) = \theta + \sin^2\left(\dfrac{\theta}{3}\right) - 8, \quad (-\infty, \infty)$

20. $r(\theta) = 2\theta - \cos^2\theta + \sqrt{2}, \quad (-\infty, \infty)$

21. $r(\theta) = \sec\theta - \dfrac{1}{\theta^3} + 5, \quad (0, \pi/2)$

22. $r(\theta) = \tan\theta - \cot\theta - \theta, \quad (0, \pi/2)$

23. Suppose that $f(-1) = 3$ and that $f'(x) = 0$ for all x. Must $f(x) = 3$ for all x? Give reasons for your answer.

24. Suppose that $f(0) = 5$ and that $f'(x) = 2$ for all x. Must $f(x) = 2x + 5$ for all x? Give reasons for your answer.

25. Suppose that $f'(x) = 2x$ for all x. Find $f(2)$ if

a. $f(0) = 0$ **b.** $f(1) = 0$ **c.** $f(-2) = 3$.

26. What can be said about functions whose derivatives are constant? Give reasons for your answer.

In Exercises 27–32, find all possible functions with the given derivative.

27. a. $y' = x$ **b.** $y' = x^2$ **c.** $y' = x^3$

28. a. $y' = 2x$ **b.** $y' = 2x - 1$ **c.** $y' = 3x^2 + 2x - 1$

29. a. $y' = -\dfrac{1}{x^2}$ **b.** $y' = 1 - \dfrac{1}{x^2}$ **c.** $y' = 5 + \dfrac{1}{x^2}$

30. a. $y' = \dfrac{1}{2\sqrt{x}}$ **b.** $y' = \dfrac{1}{\sqrt{x}}$ **c.** $y' = 4x - \dfrac{1}{\sqrt{x}}$

31. a. $y' = \sin 2t$ **b.** $y' = \cos\dfrac{t}{2}$ **c.** $y' = \sin 2t + \cos\dfrac{t}{2}$

32. a. $y' = \sec^2\theta$ **b.** $y' = \sqrt{\theta}$ **c.** $y' = \sqrt{\theta} - \sec^2\theta$

In Exercises 33–36, find the function with the given derivative whose graph passes through the point P.

33. $f'(x) = 2x - 1, \quad P(0, 0)$

34. $g'(x) = \dfrac{1}{x^2} + 2x, \quad P(1, -1)$

35. $f'(x) = e^{2x}, \quad P\left(0, \dfrac{3}{2}\right)$

36. $r'(t) = \sec t \tan t - 1, \quad P(0, 0)$

Exercises 37–40 give the velocity $v = ds/dt$ and initial position of a body moving along a coordinate line. Find the body's position at time t.

37. $v = 9.8t + 5, \quad s(0) = 10$

38. $v = 32t - 2, \quad s(0.5) = 4$

39. $v = \sin \pi t, \quad s(0) = 0$

40. $v = \dfrac{2}{\pi}\cos\dfrac{2t}{\pi}, \quad s(\pi^2) = 1$

Exercises 41–44 give the acceleration $a = d^2s/dt^2$, initial velocity, and initial position of a body moving on a coordinate line. Find the body's position at time t.

41. $a = e^t, \quad v(0) = 20, \quad s(0) = 5$

42. $a = 9.8, \quad v(0) = -3, \quad s(0) = 0$

43. $a = -4 \sin 2t, \quad v(0) = 2, \quad s(0) = -3$

44. $a = \dfrac{9}{\pi^2} \cos \dfrac{3t}{\pi}, \quad v(0) = 0, \quad s(0) = -1$

45. Temperature change It took 14 sec for a mercury thermometer to rise from $-19°C$ to $100°C$ when it was taken from a freezer and placed in boiling water. Show that somewhere along the way the mercury was rising at the rate of $8.5°C/\text{sec}$.

46. A trucker handed in a ticket at a toll booth showing that in 2 hours she had covered 159 mi on a toll road with speed limit 65 mph. The trucker was cited for speeding. Why?

47. Classical accounts tell us that a 170-oar trireme (ancient Greek or Roman warship) once covered 184 sea miles in 24 hours. Explain why at some point during this feat the trireme's speed exceeded 7.5 knots (sea miles per hour).

48. A marathoner ran the 26.2-mi New York City Marathon in 2.2 hours. Show that at least twice the marathoner was running at exactly 11 mph.

49. Show that at some instant during a 2-hour automobile trip the car's speedometer reading will equal the average speed for the trip.

50. Free fall on the moon On our moon, the acceleration of gravity is $1.6\ \text{m/sec}^2$. If a rock is dropped into a crevasse, how fast will it be going just before it hits bottom 30 sec later?

51. The geometric mean of *a* and *b* The *geometric mean* of two positive numbers a and b is the number $\sqrt{ab}$. Show that the value of c in the conclusion of the Mean Value Theorem for $f(x) = 1/x$ on an interval of positive numbers $[a, b]$ is $c = \sqrt{ab}$.

52. The arithmetic mean of *a* and *b* The *arithmetic mean* of two numbers a and b is the number $(a + b)/2$. Show that the value of c in the conclusion of the Mean Value Theorem for $f(x) = x^2$ on any interval $[a, b]$ is $c = (a + b)/2$.

T **53.** Graph the function

$$f(x) = \sin x \sin (x + 2) - \sin^2 (x + 1).$$

What does the graph do? Why does the function behave this way? Give reasons for your answers.

54. Rolle's Theorem

a. Construct a polynomial $f(x)$ that has zeros at $x = -2, -1, 0, 1,$ and 2.

b. Graph f and its derivative f' together. How is what you see related to Rolle's Theorem?

c. Do $g(x) = \sin x$ and its derivative g' illustrate the same phenomenon?

55. Unique solution Assume that f is continuous on $[a, b]$ and differentiable on (a, b). Also assume that $f(a)$ and $f(b)$ have opposite signs and that $f' \neq 0$ between a and b. Show that $f(x) = 0$ exactly once between a and b.

56. Parallel tangents Assume that f and g are differentiable on $[a, b]$ and that $f(a) = g(a)$ and $f(b) = g(b)$. Show that there is at least one point between a and b where the tangents to the graphs of f and g are parallel or the same line. Illustrate with a sketch.

57. If the graphs of two differentiable functions $f(x)$ and $g(x)$ start at the same point in the plane and the functions have the same rate of change at every point, do the graphs have to be identical? Give reasons for your answer.

58. Show that for any numbers a and b, the sine inequality $|\sin b - \sin a| \leq |b - a|$ is true.

59. Assume that f is differentiable on $a \leq x \leq b$ and that $f(b) < f(a)$. Show that f' is negative at some point between a and b.

60. Let f be a function defined on an interval $[a, b]$. What conditions could you place on f to guarantee that

$$\min f' \leq \frac{f(b) - f(a)}{b - a} \leq \max f',$$

where $\min f'$ and $\max f'$ refer to the minimum and maximum values of f' on $[a, b]$? Give reasons for your answers.

T **61.** Use the inequalities in Exercise 60 to estimate $f(0.1)$ if $f'(x) = 1/(1 + x^4 \cos x)$ for $0 \leq x \leq 0.1$ and $f(0) = 1$.

T **62.** Use the inequalities in Exercise 60 to estimate $f(0.1)$ if $f'(x) = 1/(1 - x^4)$ for $0 \leq x \leq 0.1$ and $f(0) = 2$.

63. Let f be differentiable at every value of x and suppose that $f(1) = 1$, that $f' < 0$ on $(-\infty, 1)$, and that $f' > 0$ on $(1, \infty)$.

a. Show that $f(x) \geq 1$ for all x.

b. Must $f'(1) = 0$? Explain.

64. Let $f(x) = px^2 + qx + r$ be a quadratic function defined on a closed interval $[a, b]$. Show that there is exactly one point c in (a, b) at which f satisfies the conclusion of the Mean Value Theorem.

65. Use the same-derivative argument, as was done to prove the Product and Power Rules for logarithms, to prove the Quotient Rule property.

66. Use the same-derivative argument to prove the identities

a. $\tan^{-1} x + \cot^{-1} x = \dfrac{\pi}{2}$

b. $\sec^{-1} x + \csc^{-1} x = \dfrac{\pi}{2}$

67. Starting with the equation $e^{x_1}e^{x_2} = e^{x_1 + x_2}$, derived in the text, show that $e^{-x} = 1/e^x$ for any real number x. Then show that $e^{x_1}/e^{x_2} = e^{x_1 - x_2}$ for any numbers x_1 and x_2.

68. Show that $(e^{x_1})^{x_2} = e^{x_1 x_2} = (e^{x_2})^{x_1}$ for any numbers x_1 and x_2.

4.3 Monotonic Functions and the First Derivative Test

In sketching the graph of a differentiable function it is useful to know where it increases (rises from left to right) and where it decreases (falls from left to right) over an interval. This section defines precisely what it means for a function to be increasing or decreasing over an interval, and gives a test to determine where it increases and where it decreases. We also show how to test the critical points of a function to identify whether local extreme values are present.

Increasing Functions and Decreasing Functions

We show that the only functions with positive derivatives are increasing functions; the only functions with negative derivatives are decreasing functions.

DEFINITIONS Let f be a function defined on an interval I and let x_1 and x_2 be any two points in I.

1. If $f(x_2) > f(x_1)$ whenever $x_1 < x_2$, then f is said to be **increasing** on I.
2. If $f(x_2) < f(x_1)$ whenever $x_1 < x_2$, then f is said to be **decreasing** on I.

A function that is increasing or decreasing on I is called **monotonic** on I.

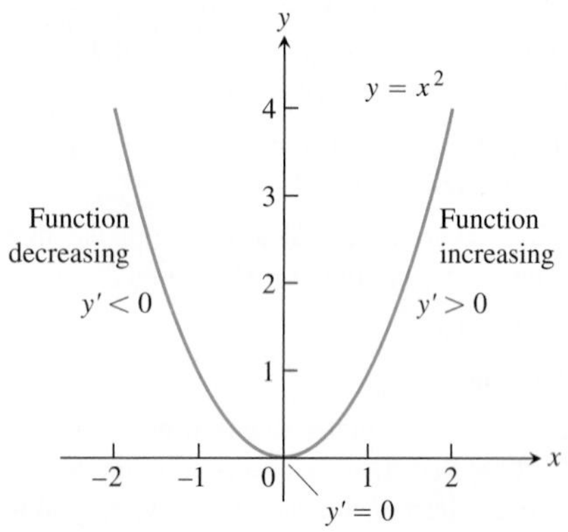

FIGURE 4.20 The function $f(x) = x^2$ is monotonic on the intervals $(-\infty, 0]$ and $[0, \infty)$, but it is not monotonic on $(-\infty, \infty)$.

It is important to realize that the definitions of increasing and decreasing functions must be satisfied for *every* pair of points x_1 and x_2 in I with $x_1 < x_2$. Because of the inequality $<$ comparing the function values, and not $\leq$, it is sometimes said that f is *strictly* increasing or decreasing on I. The interval I may be finite or infinite.

The function $f(x) = x^2$ decreases on $(-\infty, 0]$ and increases on $[0, \infty)$ as can be seen from its graph (Figure 4.20). The function f is monotonic on $(-\infty, 0]$ and $[0, \infty)$, but it is not monotonic on $(-\infty, \infty)$. Notice that on the interval $(-\infty, 0)$ the tangents have negative slopes, so the first derivative is always negative there; for $(0, \infty)$ the tangents have positive slopes and the first derivative is positive. The following result confirms these observations.

COROLLARY 3 Suppose that f is continuous on $[a, b]$ and differentiable on (a, b).

If $f'(x) > 0$ at each point $x \in (a, b)$, then f is increasing on $[a, b]$.
If $f'(x) < 0$ at each point $x \in (a, b)$, then f is decreasing on $[a, b]$.

Proof Let x_1 and x_2 be any two points in $[a, b]$ with $x_1 < x_2$. The Mean Value Theorem applied to f on $[x_1, x_2]$ says that

$$f(x_2) - f(x_1) = f'(c)(x_2 - x_1)$$

for some c between x_1 and x_2. The sign of the right-hand side of this equation is the same as the sign of $f'(c)$ because $x_2 - x_1$ is positive. Therefore, $f(x_2) > f(x_1)$ if f' is positive on (a, b) and $f(x_2) < f(x_1)$ if f' is negative on (a, b). ■

Here is how to apply the First Derivative Test to find where a function is increasing and decreasing. If $a < b$ are two critical points for a function f, and if f' exists but is not zero on the interval (a, b), then f' must be positive on (a, b) or negative there (Theorem 2, Section 3.1). One way we can determine the sign of f' on the interval is simply by evaluating f' for some point x in (a, b). Then we apply Corollary 3. Corollary 3 is valid for infinite as well as finite intervals, and we use this fact in our analysis in the next example.

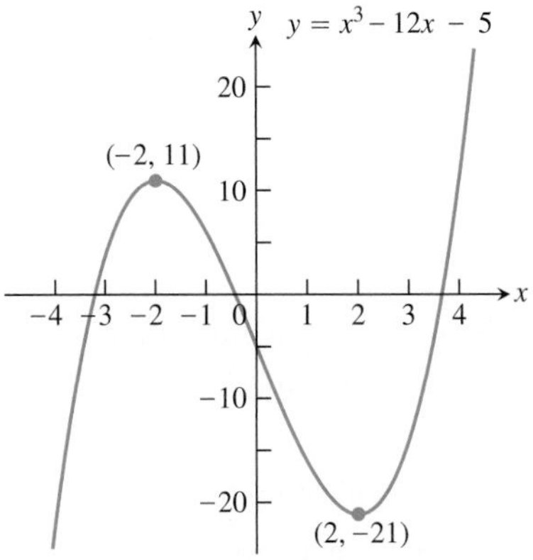

FIGURE 4.21 The function $f(x) = x^3 - 12x - 5$ is monotonic on three separate intervals (Example 1).

EXAMPLE 1 Find the critical points of $f(x) = x^3 - 12x - 5$ and identify the intervals on which f is increasing and on which f is decreasing.

Solution The function f is everywhere continuous and differentiable. The first derivative

$$\begin{aligned} f'(x) &= 3x^2 - 12 = 3(x^2 - 4) \\ &= 3(x + 2)(x - 2) \end{aligned}$$

is zero at $x = -2$ and $x = 2$. These critical points subdivide the domain of f into intervals $(-\infty, -2)$, $(-2, 2)$, and $(2, \infty)$ on which f' is either positive or negative. We determine the sign of f' by evaluating f at a convenient point in each subinterval. The behavior of f is determined by then applying Corollary 3 to each subinterval. The results are summarized in the following table, and the graph of f is given in Figure 4.21.

Interval	$-\infty < x < -2$	$-2 < x < 2$	$2 < x < \infty$
f' Evaluated	$f'(-3) = 15$	$f'(0) = -12$	$f'(3) = 15$
Sign of f'	$+$	$-$	$+$
Behavior of f	increasing	decreasing	increasing

■

Knowing where a function increases and decreases also tells us how to test for the nature of local extreme values.

HISTORICAL BIOGRAPHY

Edmund Halley
(1656–1742)

First Derivative Test for Local Extrema

In Figure 4.22, at the points where f has a minimum value, $f' < 0$ immediately to the left and $f' > 0$ immediately to the right. (If the point is an endpoint, there is only one side to consider.) Thus, the function is decreasing on the left of the minimum value and it is increasing on its right. Similarly, at the points where f has a maximum value, $f' > 0$ immediately to the left and $f' < 0$ immediately to the right. Thus, the function is increasing on the left of the maximum value and decreasing on its right. In summary, at a local extreme point, the sign of $f'(x)$ changes.

These observations lead to a test for the presence and nature of local extreme values of differentiable functions.

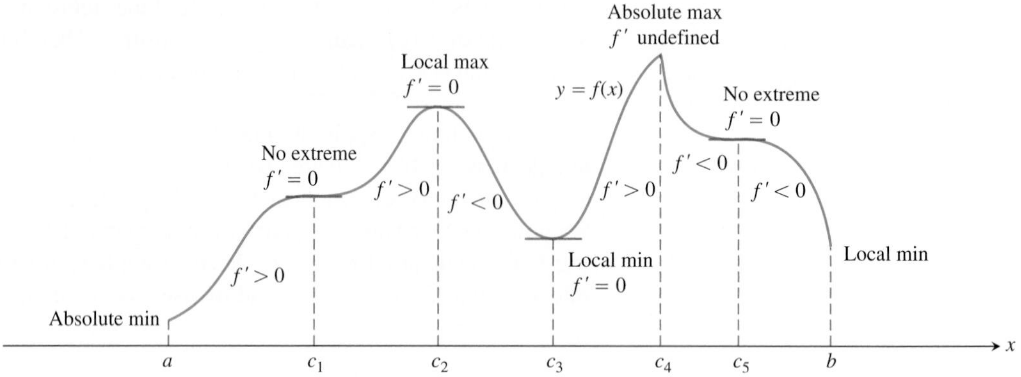

FIGURE 4.22 A function's first derivative tells how the graph rises and falls.

> **First Derivative Test for Local Extrema**
>
> Suppose that c is a critical point of a continuous function f, and that f is differentiable at every point in some interval containing c except possibly at c itself. Moving across c from left to right,
>
> 1. if f' changes from negative to positive at c, then f has a local minimum at c;
> 2. if f' changes from positive to negative at c, then f has a local maximum at c;
> 3. if f' does not change sign at c (that is, f' is positive on both sides of c or negative on both sides), then f has no local extremum at c.

The test for local extrema at endpoints is similar, but there is only one side to consider.

Proof Part (1). Since the sign of f' changes from negative to positive at c, there are numbers a and b such that $f' < 0$ on (a, c) and $f' > 0$ on (c, b). If $x \in (a, c)$, then $f(c) < f(x)$ because $f' < 0$ implies that f is decreasing on $[a, c]$. If $x \in (c, b)$, then $f(c) < f(x)$ because $f' > 0$ implies that f is increasing on $[c, b]$. Therefore, $f(x) \geq f(c)$ for every $x \in (a, b)$. By definition, f has a local minimum at c.

Parts (2) and (3) are proved similarly. ■

EXAMPLE 2 Find the critical points of

$$f(x) = (x^2 - 3)e^x.$$

Identify the intervals on which f is increasing and decreasing. Find the function's local and absolute extreme values.

Solution The function f is continuous and differentiable for all real numbers, so the critical points occur only at the zeros of f'.

Using the Product Rule, we find the derivative

$$\begin{aligned} f'(x) &= (x^2 - 3) \cdot \frac{d}{dx} e^x + \frac{d}{dx}(x^2 - 3) \cdot e^x \\ &= (x^2 - 3) \cdot e^x + (2x) \cdot e^x \\ &= (x^2 + 2x - 3)e^x. \end{aligned}$$

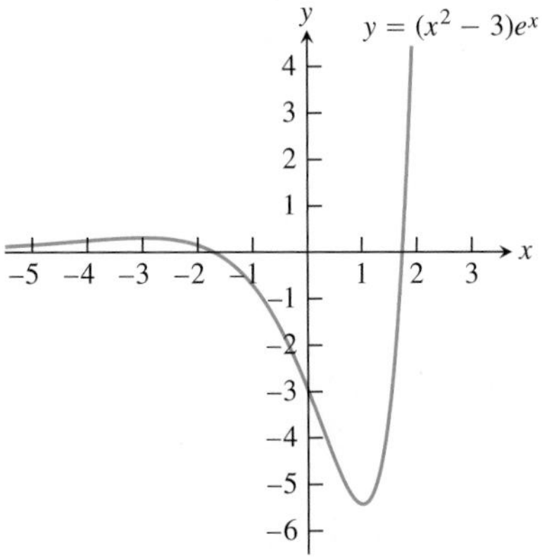

FIGURE 4.23 The graph of $f(x) = (x^2 - 3)e^x$. (Example 2)

Since e^x is never zero, the first derivative is zero if and only if

$$x^2 + 2x - 3 = 0$$

$$(x + 3)(x - 1) = 0.$$

The zeros $x = -3$ and $x = 1$ partition the x-axis into intervals as follows.

Interval	$x < -3$	$-3 < x < 1$	$1 < x$
Sign of f'	$+$	$-$	$+$
Behavior of f	increasing	decreasing	increasing

We can see from the table that there is a local maximum (about 0.299) at $x = -3$ and a local minimum (about -5.437) at $x = 1$. The local minimum value is also an absolute minimum because $f(x) > 0$ for $|x| > \sqrt{3}$. There is no absolute maximum. The function increases on $(-\infty, -3)$ and $(1, \infty)$ and decreases on $(-3, 1)$. Figure 4.23 shows the graph. ■

EXAMPLE 3 Find the critical points of

$$f(x) = x^{1/3}(x - 4) = x^{4/3} - 4x^{1/3}.$$

Identify the intervals on which f is increasing and decreasing. Find the function's local and absolute extreme values.

Solution The function f is continuous at all x since it is the product of two continuous functions, $x^{1/3}$ and $(x - 4)$. The first derivative

$$\begin{aligned} f'(x) &= \frac{d}{dx}\left(x^{4/3} - 4x^{1/3}\right) = \frac{4}{3}x^{1/3} - \frac{4}{3}x^{-2/3} \\ &= \frac{4}{3}x^{-2/3}\left(x - 1\right) = \frac{4(x - 1)}{3x^{2/3}} \end{aligned}$$

is zero at $x = 1$ and undefined at $x = 0$. There are no endpoints in the domain, so the critical points $x = 0$ and $x = 1$ are the only places where f might have an extreme value.

The critical points partition the x-axis into intervals on which f' is either positive or negative. The sign pattern of f' reveals the behavior of f between and at the critical points. We can display the information in a table like the following:

Interval	$x < 0$	$0 < x < 1$	$x > 1$
Sign of f'	$-$	$-$	$+$
Behavior of f	decreasing	decreasing	increasing

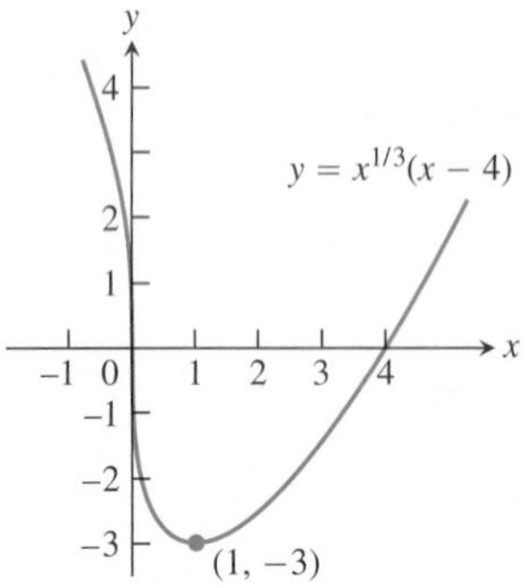

FIGURE 4.24 The function $f(x) = x^{1/3}(x - 4)$ decreases when $x < 1$ and increases when $x > 1$ (Example 3).

Corollary 3 to the Mean Value Theorem tells us that f decreases on $(-\infty, 0)$, decreases on $(0, 1)$, and increases on $(1, \infty)$. The First Derivative Test for Local Extrema tells us that f does not have an extreme value at $x = 0$ (f' does not change sign) and that f has a local minimum at $x = 1$ (f' changes from negative to positive).

The value of the local minimum is $f(1) = 1^{1/3}(1 - 4) = -3$. This is also an absolute minimum. Figure 4.24 shows this value in relation to the function's graph.

Note that $\lim_{x \to 0} f'(x) = -\infty$, so the graph of f has a vertical tangent at the origin. ■

EXERCISES 4.3

Answer the following questions about the functions whose derivatives are given in Exercises 1–8:

a. What are the critical points of f?

b. On what intervals is f increasing or decreasing?

c. At what points, if any, does f assume local maximum and minimum values?

1. $f'(x) = x(x - 1)$

2. $f'(x) = (x - 1)(x + 2)$

3. $f'(x) = (x - 1)^2(x + 2)$

4. $f'(x) = (x - 1)^2(x + 2)^2$

5. $f'(x) = (x - 1)e^{-x}$

6. $f'(x) = (x - 7)(x + 1)(x + 5)$

7. $f'(x) = x^{-1/3}(x + 2)$

8. $f'(x) = x^{-1/2}(x - 3)$

In Exercises 9–32:

a. Find the intervals on which the function is increasing and decreasing.

b. Then identify the function's local extreme values, if any, saying where they are taken on.

c. Which, if any, of the extreme values are absolute?

T **d.** Support your findings with a graphing calculator or computer grapher.

9. $g(t) = -t^2 - 3t + 3$

10. $g(t) = -3t^2 + 9t + 5$

11. $h(x) = -x^3 + 2x^2$

12. $h(x) = 2x^3 - 18x$

13. $f(\theta) = 3\theta^2 - 4\theta^3$

14. $f(\theta) = 6\theta - \theta^3$

15. $f(r) = 3r^3 + 16r$

16. $h(r) = (r + 7)^3$

17. $f(x) = x^4 - 8x^2 + 16$

18. $g(x) = x^4 - 4x^3 + 4x^2$

19. $H(t) = \frac{3}{2}t^4 - t^6$

20. $K(t) = 15t^3 - t^5$

21. $g(x) = x\sqrt{8 - x^2}$

22. $g(x) = x^2\sqrt{5 - x}$

23. $f(x) = \frac{x^2 - 3}{x - 2}, \quad x \neq 2$

24. $f(x) = \frac{x^3}{3x^2 + 1}$

25. $f(x) = x^{1/3}(x + 8)$

26. $g(x) = x^{2/3}(x + 5)$

27. $h(x) = x^{1/3}(x^2 - 4)$

28. $k(x) = x^{2/3}(x^2 - 4)$

29. $f(x) = e^{2x} + e^{-x}$

30. $f(x) = e^{\sqrt{x}}$

31. $f(x) = x \ln x$

32. $f(x) = x^2 \ln x$

In Exercises 33–40:

a. Identify the function's local extreme values in the given domain, and say where they are assumed.

b. Which of the extreme values, if any, are absolute?

T **c.** Support your findings with a graphing calculator or computer grapher.

33. $f(x) = 2x - x^2, \quad -\infty < x \leq 2$

34. $f(x) = (x + 1)^2, \quad -\infty < x \leq 0$

35. $g(x) = x^2 - 4x + 4, \quad 1 \leq x < \infty$

36. $g(x) = -x^2 - 6x - 9, \quad -4 \leq x < \infty$

37. $f(t) = 12t - t^3, \quad -3 \leq t < \infty$

38. $f(t) = t^3 - 3t^2, \quad -\infty < t \leq 3$

39. $h(x) = \frac{x^3}{3} - 2x^2 + 4x, \quad 0 \leq x < \infty$

40. $k(x) = x^3 + 3x^2 + 3x + 1, \quad -\infty < x \leq 0$

In Exercises 41–44:

a. Find the local extrema of each function on the given interval, and say where they are assumed.

T **b.** Graph the function and its derivative together. Comment on the behavior of f in relation to the signs and values of f'.

41. $f(x) = \dfrac{x}{2} - 2\sin\dfrac{x}{2}, \quad 0 \le x \le 2\pi$

42. $f(x) = -2\cos x - \cos^2 x, \quad -\pi \le x \le \pi$

43. $f(x) = \csc^2 x - 2\cot x, \quad 0 < x < \pi$

44. $f(x) = \sec^2 x - 2\tan x, \quad \dfrac{-\pi}{2} < x < \dfrac{\pi}{2}$

Show that the functions in Exercises 45 and 46 have local extreme values at the given values of θ, and say which kind of local extreme the function has.

45. $h(\theta) = 3\cos\dfrac{\theta}{2}, \quad 0 \le \theta \le 2\pi, \quad$ at $\theta = 0$ and $\theta = 2\pi$

46. $h(\theta) = 5\sin\dfrac{\theta}{2}, \quad 0 \le \theta \le \pi, \quad$ at $\theta = 0$ and $\theta = \pi$

47. Sketch the graph of a differentiable function $y = f(x)$ through the point $(1, 1)$ if $f'(1) = 0$ and

a. $f'(x) > 0$ for $x < 1$ and $f'(x) < 0$ for $x > 1$;

b. $f'(x) < 0$ for $x < 1$ and $f'(x) > 0$ for $x > 1$;

c. $f'(x) > 0$ for $x \ne 1$;

d. $f'(x) < 0$ for $x \ne 1$.

48. Sketch the graph of a differentiable function $y = f(x)$ that has

a. a local minimum at $(1, 1)$ and a local maximum at $(3, 3)$;

b. a local maximum at $(1, 1)$ and a local minimum at $(3, 3)$;

c. local maxima at $(1, 1)$ and $(3, 3)$;

d. local minima at $(1, 1)$ and $(3, 3)$.

49. Sketch the graph of a continuous function $y = g(x)$ such that

a. $g(2) = 2$, $0 < g' < 1$ for $x < 2$, $g'(x) \to 1^-$ as $x \to 2^-$, $-1 < g' < 0$ for $x > 2$, and $g'(x) \to -1^+$ as $x \to 2^+$;

b. $g(2) = 2$, $g' < 0$ for $x < 2$, $g'(x) \to -\infty$ as $x \to 2^-$, $g' > 0$ for $x > 2$, and $g'(x) \to \infty$ as $x \to 2^+$.

50. Sketch the graph of a continuous function $y = h(x)$ such that

a. $h(0) = 0$, $-2 \le h(x) \le 2$ for all x, $h'(x) \to \infty$ as $x \to 0^-$, and $h'(x) \to \infty$ as $x \to 0^+$;

b. $h(0) = 0$, $-2 \le h(x) \le 0$ for all x, $h'(x) \to \infty$ as $x \to 0^-$, and $h'(x) \to -\infty$ as $x \to 0^+$.

51. Locate and identify the absolute extreme values of

a. $\ln(\cos x)$ on $[-\pi/4, \pi/3]$,

b. $\cos(\ln x)$ on $[1/2, 2]$.

52. a. Prove that $f(x) = x - \ln x$ is increasing for $x > 1$.

b. Using part (a), show that $\ln x < x$ if $x > 1$.

53. Find the absolute maximum and minimum values of $f(x) = e^x - 2x$ on $[0, 1]$.

54. Where does the periodic function $f(x) = 2e^{\sin(x/2)}$ take on its extreme values and what are these values?

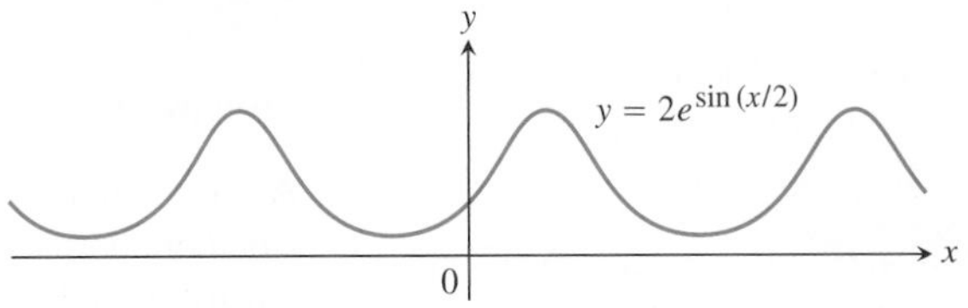

55. Find the absolute maximum value of $f(x) = x^2 \ln(1/x)$ and say where it is assumed.

56. Find the intervals on which the function $f(x) = ax^2 + bx + c$, $a \ne 0$, is increasing and decreasing. Describe the reasoning behind your answer.

57. As x moves from left to right through the point $c = 2$, is the graph of $f(x) = x^3 - 3x + 2$ rising, or is it falling? Give reasons for your answer.

58. a. Prove that $e^x \ge 1 + x$ if $x \ge 0$.

b. Use the result in part (a) to show that

$$e^x \ge 1 + x + \frac{1}{2}x^2.$$

59. Show that increasing functions and decreasing functions are one-to-one. That is, show that for any x_1 and x_2 in I, $x_2 \ne x_1$ implies $f(x_2) \ne f(x_1)$.

Use the results of Exercise 59 to show that the functions in Exercises 60–64 have inverses over their domains. Find a formula for df^{-1}/dx using Theorem 4, Section 3.7.

60. $f(x) = (1/3)x + (5/6)$

61. $f(x) = 27x^3$

62. $f(x) = 1 - 8x^3$

63. $f(x) = (1 - x)^3$

64. $f(x) = x^{5/3}$

4.4 Concavity and Curve Sketching

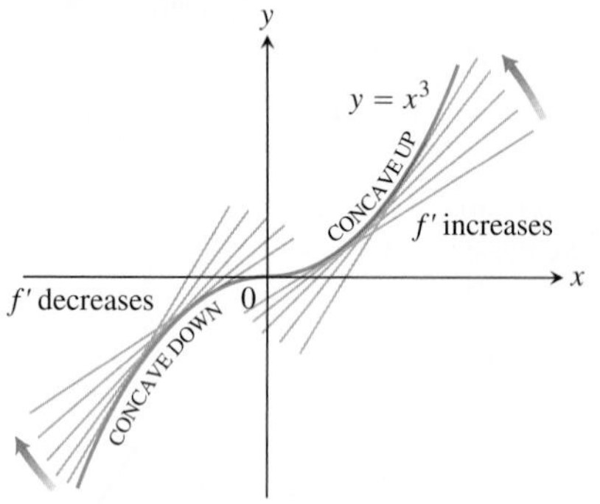

FIGURE 4.25 The graph of $f(x) = x^3$ is concave down on $(-\infty, 0)$ and concave up on $(0, \infty)$ (Example 1a).

In Section 4.3 we saw how the first derivative tells us where a function is increasing and where it is decreasing. At a critical point of a differentiable function, the First Derivative Test tells us whether there is a local maximum or a local minimum, or whether the graph just continues to rise or fall there.

In this section we see how the second derivative gives information about the way the graph of a differentiable function bends or turns. This additional information reveals key aspects of the behavior of a function, so we can present these features in a sketch of the graph.

Concavity

As you can see in Figure 4.25, the curve $y = x^3$ rises as x increases, but the portions defined on the intervals $(-\infty, 0)$ and $(0, \infty)$ turn in different ways. As we approach the origin from the left along the curve, the curve turns to our right and falls below its tangents. The slopes of the tangents are decreasing on the interval $(-\infty, 0)$. As we move away from the origin along the curve to the right, the curve turns to our left and rises above its tangents. The slopes of the tangents are increasing on the interval $(0, \infty)$. This turning or bending behavior defines the *concavity* of the curve.

DEFINITION The graph of a differentiable function $y = f(x)$ is

(a) **concave up** on an open interval I if f' is increasing on I

(b) **concave down** on an open interval I if f' is decreasing on I.

If $y = f(x)$ has a second derivative, we can apply Corollary 3 of the Mean Value Theorem to conclude that f' increases if $f'' > 0$ on I, and decreases if $f'' < 0$.

The Second Derivative Test for Concavity

Let $y = f(x)$ be twice-differentiable on an interval I.

1. If $f'' > 0$ on I, the graph of f over I is concave up.
2. If $f'' < 0$ on I, the graph of f over I is concave down.

If $y = f(x)$ is twice-differentiable, we will use the notations f'' and y'' interchangeably when denoting the second derivative.

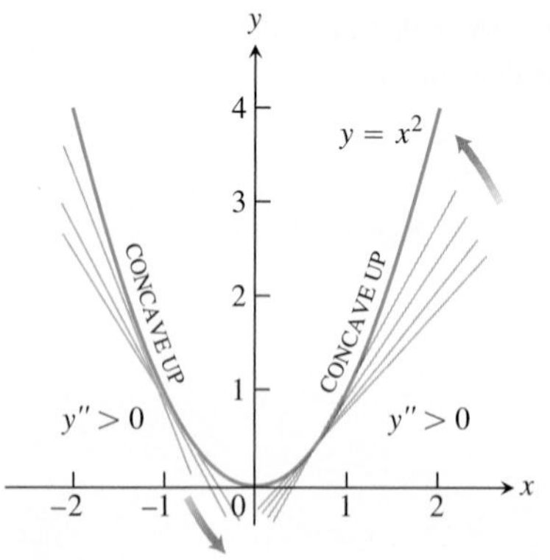

FIGURE 4.26 The graph of $f(x) = x^2$ is concave up on every interval (Example 1b).

EXAMPLE 1

(a) The curve $y = x^3$ (Figure 4.25) is concave down on $(-\infty, 0)$ where $y'' = 6x < 0$ and concave up on $(0, \infty)$ where $y'' = 6x > 0$.

(b) The curve $y = x^2$ (Figure 4.26) is concave up on $(-\infty, \infty)$ because its second derivative $y'' = 2$ is always positive. ■

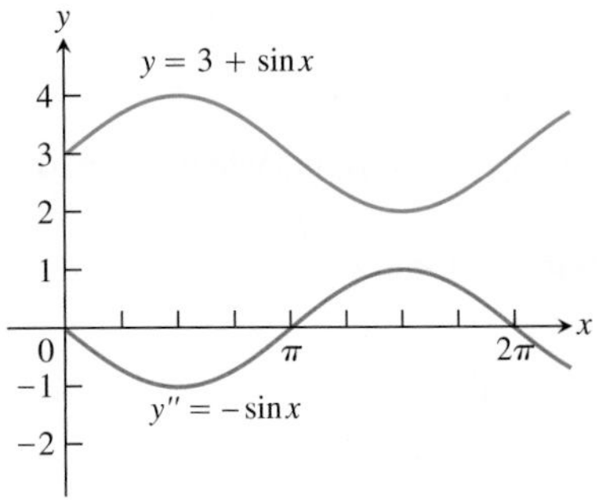

FIGURE 4.27 Using the graph of y'' to determine the concavity of y (Example 2).

EXAMPLE 2 Determine the concavity of $y = 3 + \sin x$ on $[0, 2\pi]$.

Solution The graph of $y = 3 + \sin x$ is concave down on $(0, \pi)$, where $y'' = -\sin x$ is negative. It is concave up on $(\pi, 2\pi)$, where $y'' = -\sin x$ is positive (Figure 4.27). ■

Points of Inflection

The curve $y = 3 + \sin x$ in Example 2 changes concavity at the point $(\pi, 3)$. We call $(\pi, 3)$ a *point of inflection* of the curve.

> **DEFINITION** A point where the graph of a function has a tangent line and where the concavity changes is a **point of inflection**.

A point on a curve where y'' is positive on one side and negative on the other is a point of inflection. At such a point, y'' is either zero (because derivatives have the Intermediate Value Property) or undefined. If y is a twice-differentiable function, $y'' = 0$ at a point of inflection and y' has a local maximum or minimum. However, the next example shows an inflection point may not exist where $y'' = 0$.

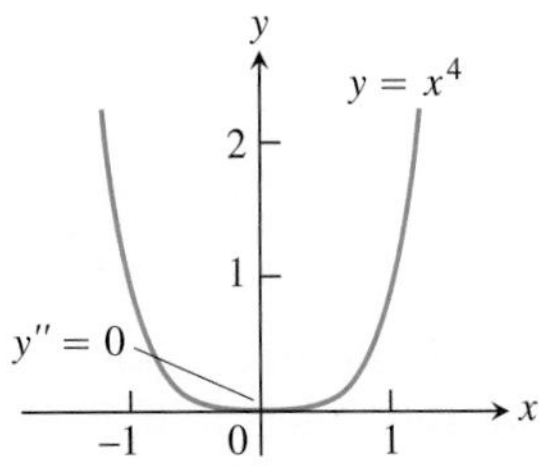

FIGURE 4.28 The graph of $y = x^4$ has no inflection point at the origin, even though $y'' = 0$ there (Example 3).

EXAMPLE 3 The curve $y = x^4$ has no inflection point at $x = 0$ (Figure 4.28). Even though $y'' = 12x^2$ is zero there, it does not change sign. ■

EXAMPLE 4 The curve $y = x^{1/3}$ has a point of inflection at $x = 0$ (Figure 4.29), but y'' does not exist there.

$$y'' = \frac{d^2}{dx^2}\left(x^{1/3}\right) = \frac{d}{dx}\left(\frac{1}{3}x^{-2/3}\right) = -\frac{2}{9}x^{-5/3}.$$ ■

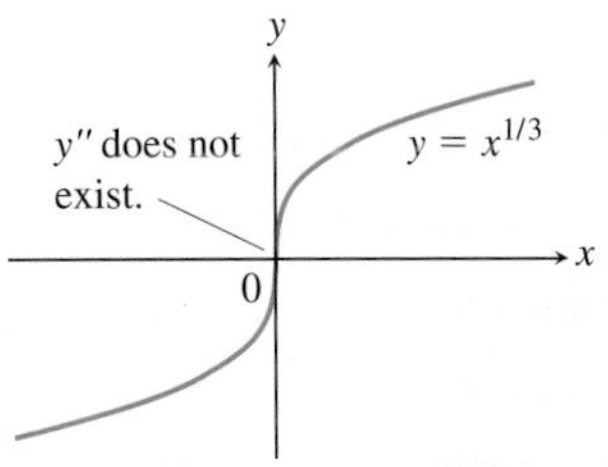

FIGURE 4.29 A point where y'' fails to exist can be a point of inflection (Example 4).

We see from Example 3 that a zero second derivative does not always produce a point of inflection. From Example 4, we see that inflection points can also occur where there *is* no second derivative.

To study the motion of a body moving along a line as a function of time, we often are interested in knowing when the body's acceleration, given by the second derivative, is positive or negative. The points of inflection on the graph of the body's position function reveal where the acceleration changes sign.

EXAMPLE 5 A particle is moving along a horizontal line with position function

$$s(t) = 2t^3 - 14t^2 + 22t - 5, \qquad t \ge 0.$$

Find the velocity and acceleration, and describe the motion of the particle.

Solution The velocity is

$$v(t) = s'(t) = 6t^2 - 28t + 22 = 2(t - 1)(3t - 11),$$

and the acceleration is

$$a(t) = v'(t) = s''(t) = 12t - 28 = 4(3t - 7).$$

When the function $s(t)$ is increasing, the particle is moving to the right; when $s(t)$ is decreasing, the particle is moving to the left.

Notice that the first derivative ($v = s'$) is zero when $t = 1$ and $t = 11/3$.

Interval	$0 < t < 1$	$1 < t < 11/3$	$11/3 < t$
Sign of $v = s'$	$+$	$-$	$+$
Behavior of *s*	increasing	decreasing	increasing
Particle motion	right	left	right

The particle is moving to the right in the time intervals $[0, 1)$ and $(11/3, \infty)$, and moving to the left in $(1, 11/3)$. It is momentarily stationary (at rest), at $t = 1$ and $t = 11/3$.

The acceleration $a(t) = s''(t) = 4(3t - 7)$ is zero when $t = 7/3$.

Interval	$0 < t < 7/3$	$7/3 < t$
Sign of $a = s''$	$-$	$+$
Graph of *s*	concave down	concave up

The body starts out moving to the right while slowing down and then begins moving to the left at $t = 1$ under the influence of the leftward acceleration over the time interval $[0, 7/3]$. The acceleration then changes direction at $t = 7/3$ but the body continues moving leftward, slowing down under the rightward acceleration. At $t = 11/3$ the body reverses direction again: moving to the right in the same direction as the acceleration. ■

Second Derivative Test for Local Extrema

Instead of looking for sign changes in f' at critical points, we can sometimes use the following test to determine the presence and character of local extrema.

THEOREM 5—Second Derivative Test for Local Extrema Suppose f'' is continuous on an open interval that contains $x = c$.

1. If $f'(c) = 0$ and $f''(c) < 0$, then f has a local maximum at $x = c$.
2. If $f'(c) = 0$ and $f''(c) > 0$, then f has a local minimum at $x = c$.
3. If $f'(c) = 0$ and $f''(c) = 0$, then the test fails. The function f may have a local maximum, a local minimum, or neither.

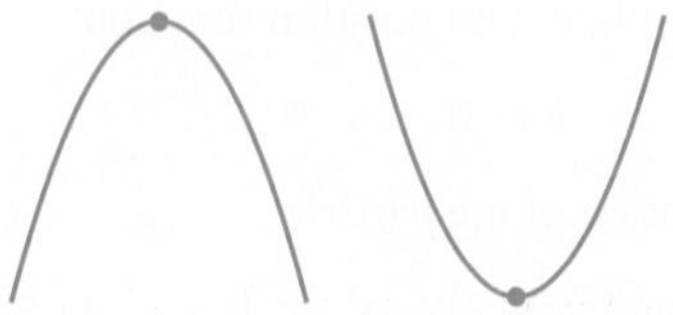

$f' = 0, f'' < 0$
$\Rightarrow$ local max

$f' = 0, f'' > 0$
$\Rightarrow$ local min

Proof Part (1). If $f''(c) < 0$, then $f''(x) < 0$ on some open interval I containing the point c, since f'' is continuous. Therefore, f' is decreasing on I. Since $f'(c) = 0$, the sign of f' changes from positive to negative at c so f has a local maximum at c by the First Derivative Test.

The proof of Part (2) is similar.

For Part (3), consider the three functions $y = x^4$, $y = -x^4$, and $y = x^3$. For each function, the first and second derivatives are zero at $x = 0$. Yet the function $y = x^4$ has a local minimum there, $y = -x^4$ has a local maximum, and $y = x^3$ is increasing in any open interval containing $x = 0$ (having neither a maximum nor a minimum there). Thus the test fails. ■

This test requires us to know f'' *only at c itself* and not in an interval about c. This makes the test easy to apply. That's the good news. The bad news is that the test is inconclusive if $f'' = 0$ or if f'' does not exist at $x = c$. When this happens, use the First Derivative Test for local extreme values.

Together f' and f'' tell us the shape of the function's graph, that is, where the critical points are located and what happens at a critical point, where the function is increasing and where it is decreasing, and how the curve is turning or bending as defined by its concavity. We use this information to sketch a graph of the function that captures its key features.

EXAMPLE 6 Sketch a graph of the function

$$f(x) = x^4 - 4x^3 + 10$$

using the following steps.

(a) Identify where the extrema of f occur.

(b) Find the intervals on which f is increasing and the intervals on which f is decreasing.

(c) Find where the graph of f is concave up and where it is concave down.

(d) Sketch the general shape of the graph for f.

(e) Plot some specific points, such as local maximum and minimum points, points of inflection, and intercepts. Then sketch the curve.

Solution f is continuous since $f'(x) = 4x^3 - 12x^2$ exists. The domain of f is $(-\infty, \infty)$, and the domain of f' is also $(-\infty, \infty)$. Thus, the critical points of f occur only at the zeros of f'. Since

$$f'(x) = 4x^3 - 12x^2 = 4x^2(x - 3)$$

the first derivative is zero at $x = 0$ and $x = 3$.

Interval	$x < 0$	$0 < x < 3$	$3 < x$
Sign of f'	$-$	$-$	$+$
Behavior of f	decreasing	decreasing	increasing

(a) Using the First Derivative Test for local extrema and the table above, we see that there is no extremum at $x = 0$ and a local minimum at $x = 3$.

(b) Using the table above, we see that f is decreasing on $(-\infty, 0]$ and $[0, 3]$, and increasing on $[3, \infty)$.

(c) $f''(x) = 12x^2 - 24x = 12x(x - 2)$ is zero at $x = 0$ and $x = 2$.

Interval	$x < 0$	$0 < x < 2$	$2 < x$
Sign of f''	$+$	$-$	$+$
Behavior of f	concave up	concave down	concave up

We see that f is concave up on the intervals $(-\infty, 0)$ and $(2, \infty)$, and concave down on $(0, 2)$.

(d) Summarizing the information in the two tables above, we obtain

$x < 0$	$0 < x < 2$	$2 < x < 3$	$3 < x$
decreasing	decreasing	decreasing	increasing
concave up	concave down	concave up	concave up

The general shape of the curve is

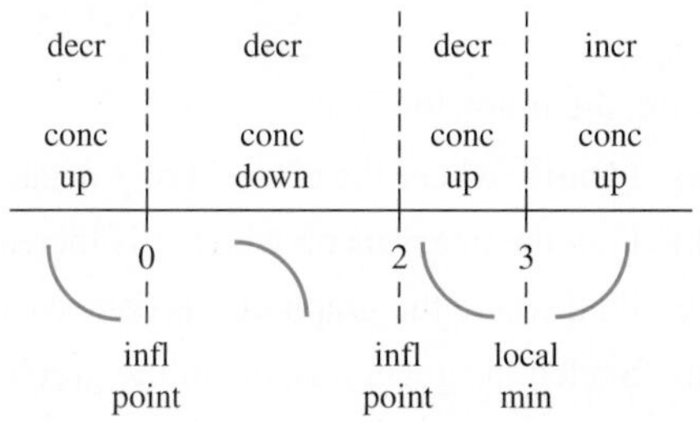

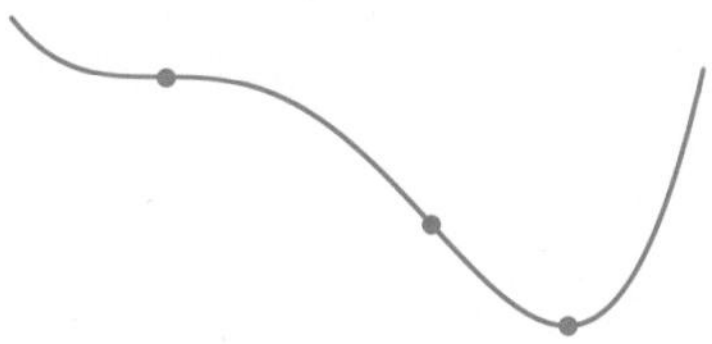

General shape.

(e) Plot the curve's intercepts (if possible) and the points where y' and y'' are zero. Indicate any local extreme values and inflection points. Use the general shape as a guide to sketch the curve. (Plot additional points as needed.) Figure 4.30 shows the graph of f. ■

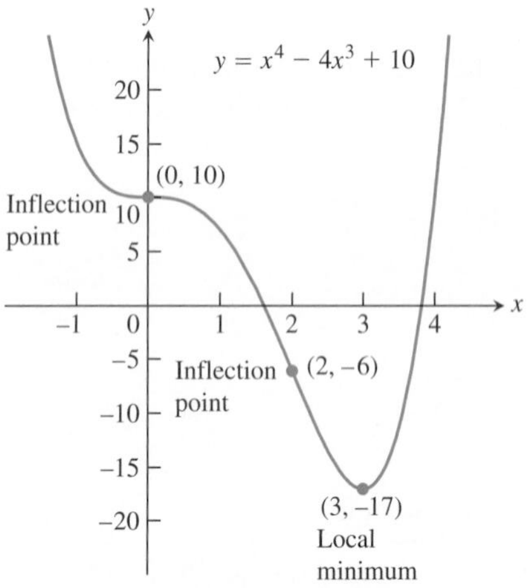

FIGURE 4.30 The graph of $f(x) = x^4 - 4x^3 + 10$ (Example 6).

The steps in Example 6 give a procedure for graphing the key features of a function.

Strategy for Graphing $y = f(x)$

1. Identify the domain of f and any symmetries the curve may have.
2. Find y' and y''.
3. Find the critical points of f, if any, and identify the function's behavior at each one.
4. Find where the curve is increasing and where it is decreasing.
5. Find the points of inflection, if any occur, and determine the concavity of the curve.
6. Identify any asymptotes.
7. Plot key points, such as the intercepts and the points found in Steps 3–5, and sketch the curve.

EXAMPLE 7 Sketch the graph of $f(x) = \dfrac{(x+1)^2}{1+x^2}$.

Solution

1. The domain of f is $(-\infty, \infty)$ and there are no symmetries about either axis or the origin (Section 1.1).
2. *Find f' and f''.*

$$f(x) = \frac{(x+1)^2}{1+x^2}$$

x-intercept at $x = -1$, y-intercept ($y = 1$) at $x = 0$

$$f'(x) = \frac{(1+x^2)\cdot 2(x+1) - (x+1)^2 \cdot 2x}{(1+x^2)^2}$$

$$= \frac{2(1-x^2)}{(1+x^2)^2}$$

Critical points: $x = -1, x = 1$

$$f''(x) = \frac{(1+x^2)^2 \cdot 2(-2x) - 2(1-x^2)[2(1+x^2)\cdot 2x]}{(1+x^2)^4}$$

$$= \frac{4x(x^2-3)}{(1+x^2)^3}$$

After some algebra

3. *Behavior at critical points.* The critical points occur only at $x = \pm 1$ where $f'(x) = 0$ (Step 2) since f' exists everywhere over the domain of f. At $x = -1$, $f''(-1) = 1 > 0$ yielding a relative minimum by the Second Derivative Test. At $x = 1$, $f''(1) = -1 < 0$ yielding a relative maximum by the Second Derivative test.
4. *Increasing and decreasing.* We see that on the interval $(-\infty, -1)$ the derivative $f'(x) < 0$, and the curve is decreasing. On the interval $(-1, 1)$, $f'(x) > 0$ and the curve is increasing; it is decreasing on $(1, \infty)$ where $f'(x) < 0$ again.
5. *Inflection points.* Notice that the denominator of the second derivative (Step 2) is always positive. The second derivative f'' is zero when $x = -\sqrt{3}, 0$, and $\sqrt{3}$. The second derivative changes sign at each of these points: negative on $\left(-\infty, -\sqrt{3}\right)$, positive on $\left(-\sqrt{3}, 0\right)$, negative on $\left(0, \sqrt{3}\right)$, and positive again on $\left(\sqrt{3}, \infty\right)$. Thus each point is a point of inflection. The curve is concave down on the interval $\left(-\infty, -\sqrt{3}\right)$, concave up on $\left(-\sqrt{3}, 0\right)$, concave down on $\left(0, \sqrt{3}\right)$, and concave up again on $\left(\sqrt{3}, \infty\right)$.
6. *Asymptotes.* Expanding the numerator of $f(x)$ and then dividing both numerator and denominator by x^2 gives

$$f(x) = \frac{(x+1)^2}{1+x^2} = \frac{x^2+2x+1}{1+x^2}$$

Expanding numerator

$$= \frac{1 + (2/x) + (1/x^2)}{(1/x^2) + 1}.$$

Dividing by x^2

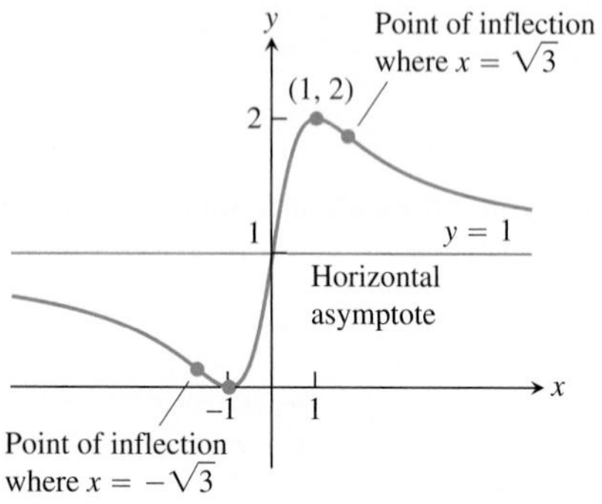

FIGURE 4.31 The graph of $y = \dfrac{(x+1)^2}{1+x^2}$ (Example 7).

We see that $f(x) \to 1^+$ as $x \to \infty$ and that $f(x) \to 1^-$ as $x \to -\infty$. Thus, the line $y = 1$ is a horizontal asymptote.

Since f decreases on $(-\infty, -1)$ and then increases on $(-1, 1)$, we know that $f(-1) = 0$ is a local minimum. Although f decreases on $(1, \infty)$, it never crosses the horizontal asymptote $y = 1$ on that interval (it approaches the asymptote from above). So the graph never becomes negative, and $f(-1) = 0$ is an absolute minimum as well. Likewise, $f(1) = 2$ is an absolute maximum because the graph never crosses the asymptote $y = 1$ on the interval $(-\infty, -1)$, approaching it from below. Therefore, there are no vertical asymptotes (the range of f is $0 \le y \le 2$).

7. The graph of f is sketched in Figure 4.31. Notice how the graph is concave down as it approaches the horizontal asymptote $y = 1$ as $x \to -\infty$, and concave up in its approach to $y = 1$ as $x \to \infty$. ■

EXAMPLE 8 Sketch the graph of $f(x) = e^{2/x}$.

Solution The domain of f is $(-\infty, 0) \cup (0, \infty)$ and there are no symmetries about either axis or the origin. The derivatives of f are

$$f'(x) = e^{2/x}\left(-\frac{2}{x^2}\right) = -\frac{2e^{2/x}}{x^2}$$

and

$$f''(x) = \frac{x^2(2e^{2/x})(-2/x^2) - 2e^{2/x}(2x)}{x^4} = \frac{4e^{2/x}(1+x)}{x^4}.$$

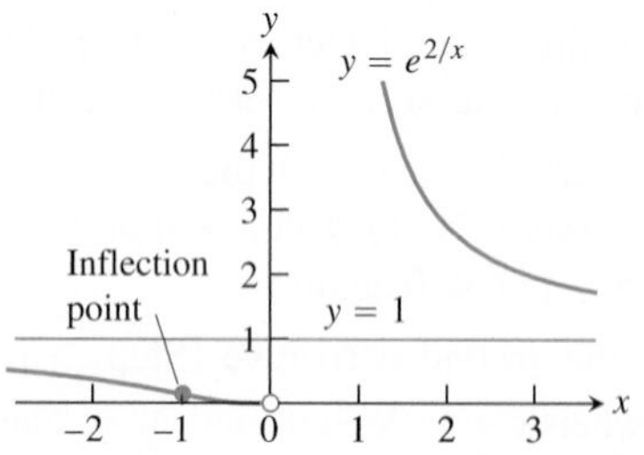

FIGURE 4.32 The graph of $y = e^{2/x}$ has a point of inflection at $(-1, e^{-2})$. The line $y = 1$ is a horizontal asymptote and $x = 0$ is a vertical asymptote (Example 8).

Both derivatives exist everywhere over the domain of f. Moreover, since $e^{2/x}$ and x^2 are both positive for all $x \neq 0$, we see that $f' < 0$ everywhere over the domain and the graph is everywhere decreasing. Examining the second derivative, we see that $f''(x) = 0$ at $x = -1$. Since $e^{2/x} > 0$ and $x^4 > 0$, we have $f'' < 0$ for $x < -1$ and $f'' > 0$ for $x > -1, x \neq 0$. Therefore, the point $(-1, e^{-2})$ is a point of inflection. The curve is concave down on the interval $(-\infty, -1)$ and concave up over $(-1, 0) \cup (0, \infty)$.

From Example 12, Section 2.4, we see that $\lim_{x \to 0^-} f(x) = 0$. As $x \to 0^+$, we see that $2/x \to \infty$, so $\lim_{x \to 0^+} f(x) = \infty$ and the y-axis is a vertical asymptote. Also, as $x \to -\infty$, $2/x \to 0^-$ and so $\lim_{x \to -\infty} f(x) = e^0 = 1$. Therefore, $y = 1$ is a horizontal asymptote. There are no absolute extrema since f never takes on the value 0. The graph of f is sketched in Figure 4.32. ■

Graphical Behavior of Functions from Derivatives

As we saw in Examples 6 through 8, we can learn much about a twice-differentiable function $y = f(x)$ by examining its first derivative. We can find where the function's graph rises and falls and where any local extrema are located. We can differentiate y' to learn how the graph bends as it passes over the intervals of rise and fall. We can determine the shape of the function's graph. Information we cannot get from the derivative is how to place the graph in the xy-plane. But, as we discovered in Section 4.2, the only additional information we need to position the graph is the value of f at one point. Information about the asymptotes is found using limits (Sections 2.4 and 2.5).

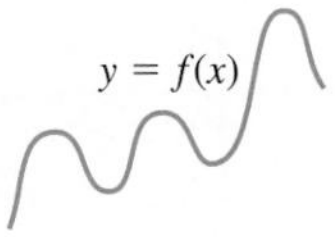 Differentiable $\Rightarrow$ smooth, connected; graph may rise and fall	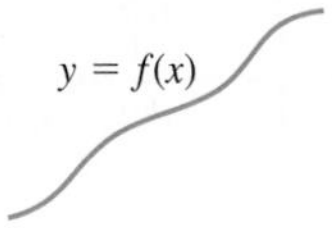 $y' > 0 \Rightarrow$ rises from left to right; may be wavy	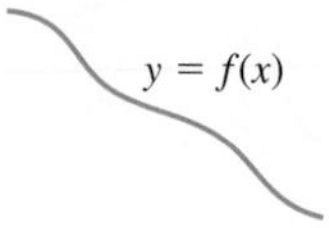 $y' < 0 \Rightarrow$ falls from left to right; may be wavy
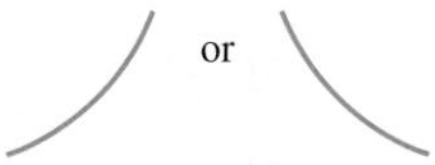 $y'' > 0 \Rightarrow$ concave up throughout; no waves; graph may rise or fall	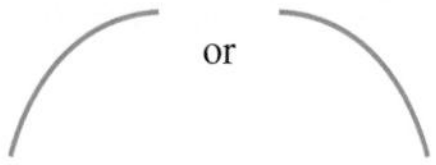 $y'' < 0 \Rightarrow$ concave down throughout; no waves; graph may rise or fall	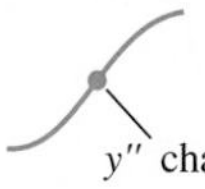 Inflection point
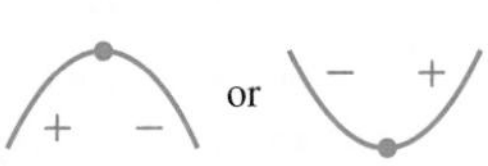 y' changes sign $\Rightarrow$ graph has local maximum or local minimum	 $y' = 0$ and $y'' < 0$ at a point; graph has local maximum	 $y' = 0$ and $y'' > 0$ at a point; graph has local minimum

EXERCISES 4.4

Identify the inflection points and local maxima and minima of the functions graphed in Exercises 1–8. Identify the intervals on which the functions are concave up and concave down.

1. $y = \frac{x^3}{3} - \frac{x^2}{2} - 2x + \frac{1}{3}$

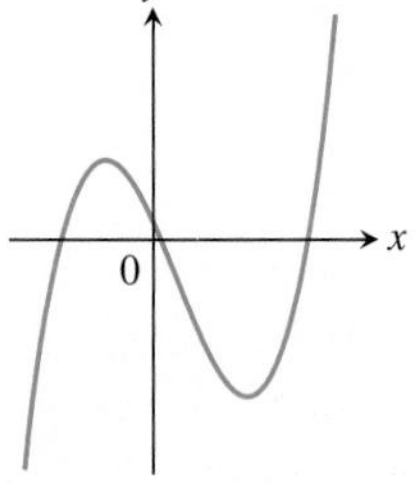

2. $y = \frac{x^4}{4} - 2x^2 + 4$

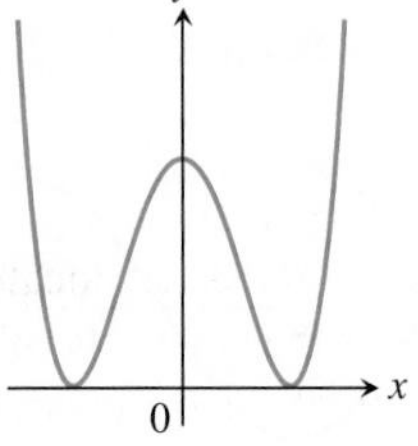

3. $y = \frac{3}{4}(x^2 - 1)^{2/3}$

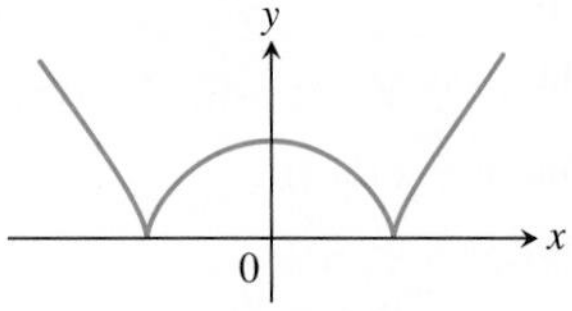

4. $y = \frac{9}{14}x^{1/3}(x^2 - 7)$

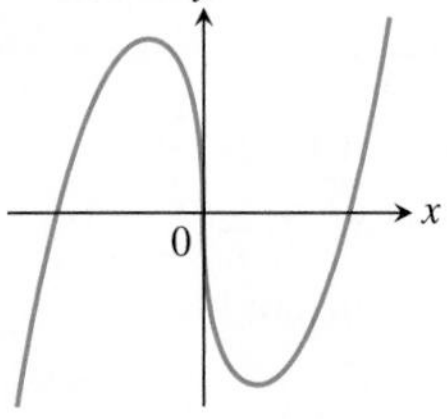

5. $y = x + \sin 2x, -\frac{2\pi}{3} \le x \le \frac{2\pi}{3}$

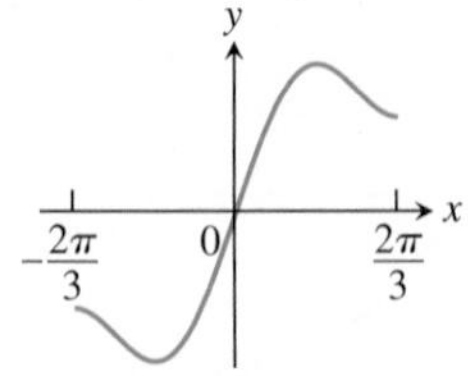

6. $y = \tan x - 4x, -\frac{\pi}{2} < x < \frac{\pi}{2}$

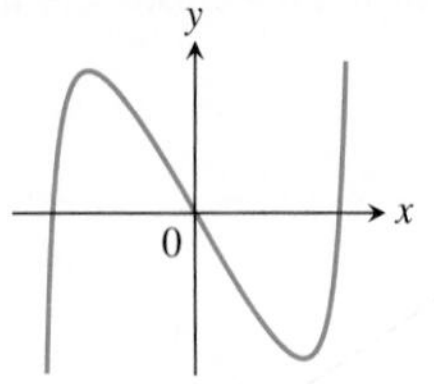

7. $y = \sin|x|, -2\pi \le x \le 2\pi$

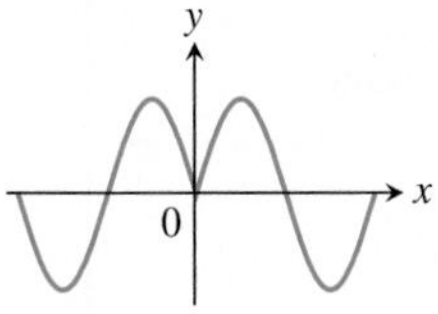

NOT TO SCALE

8. $y = 2\cos x - \sqrt{2}x, -\pi \le x \le \frac{3\pi}{2}$

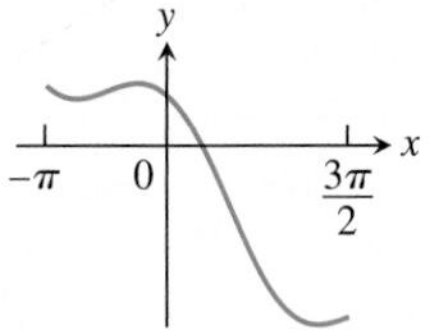

Use the steps of the graphing procedure on page 264 to graph the equations in Exercises 9–42. Include the coordinates of any local extreme points and inflection points.

9. $y = x^2 - 4x + 3$

10. $y = 6 - 2x - x^2$

11. $y = x^3 - 3x + 3$

12. $y = x(6 - 2x)^2$

13. $y = -2x^3 + 6x^2 - 3$

14. $y = (x - 2)^3 + 1$

15. $y = x^4 - 2x^2 = x^2(x^2 - 2)$

16. $y = -x^4 + 6x^2 - 4 = x^2(6 - x^2) - 4$

17. $y = 4x^3 - x^4 = x^3(4 - x)$

18. $y = x^4 + 2x^3 = x^3(x + 2)$

19. $y = x^5 - 5x^4 = x^4(x - 5)$

20. $y = x\left(\frac{x}{2} - 5\right)^4$

21. $y = x + \sin x, \quad 0 \le x \le 2\pi$

22. $y = x - \sin x, \quad 0 \le x \le 2\pi$

23. $y = x^{1/5}$

24. $y = x^{2/5}$

25. $y = 2x - 3x^{2/3}$

26. $y = x^{2/3}\left(\frac{5}{2} - x\right)$

27. $y = x\sqrt{8 - x^2}$

28. $y = (2 - x^2)^{3/2}$

29. $y = \frac{x^2 - 3}{x - 2}, \quad x \ne 2$

30. $y = \frac{x^3}{3x^2 + 1}$

31. $y = |x^2 - 1|$

32. $y = \sqrt{|x|} = \begin{cases} \sqrt{-x}, & x < 0 \\ \sqrt{x}, & x \ge 0 \end{cases}$

33. $y = xe^{1/x}$

34. $y = \frac{e^x}{x}$

35. $y = \ln(3 - x^2)$

36. $y = x(\ln x)^2$

37. $y = e^x - 2e^{-x} - 3x$

38. $y = xe^{-x}$

39. $y = \ln(\cos x)$

40. $y = \frac{\ln x}{\sqrt{x}}$

41. $y = \frac{1}{1 + e^{-x}}$

42. $y = \frac{e^x}{1 + e^x}$

Each of Exercises 43–62 gives the first derivative of a continuous function $y = f(x)$. Find y'' and then use steps 2–4 of the graphing procedure on page 264 to sketch the general shape of the graph of f.

43. $y' = 2 + x - x^2$

44. $y' = x^2 - x - 6$

45. $y' = x(x - 3)^2$

46. $y' = x^2(2 - x)$

47. $y' = x(x^2 - 12)$

48. $y' = (x^2 - 2x)(x - 5)^2$

49. $y' = \sec^2 x, \quad -\frac{\pi}{2} < x < \frac{\pi}{2}$

50. $y' = \tan x, \quad -\frac{\pi}{2} < x < \frac{\pi}{2}$

51. $y' = \cot\frac{\theta}{2}, \quad 0 < \theta < 2\pi$

52. $y' = \csc^2\frac{\theta}{2}, \quad 0 < \theta < 2\pi$

53. $y' = \tan^2\theta - 1, \quad -\frac{\pi}{2} < \theta < \frac{\pi}{2}$

54. $y' = 1 - \cot^2\theta, \quad 0 < \theta < \pi$

55. $y' = \cos t, \quad 0 \le t \le 2\pi$

56. $y' = \sin t, \quad 0 \le t \le 2\pi$

57. $y' = (x + 1)^{-2/3}$

58. $y' = (x - 2)^{-1/3}$

59. $y' = x^{-2/3}(x - 1)$

60. $y' = x^{-4/5}(x + 1)$

61. $y' = 2|x| = \begin{cases} -2x, & x \le 0 \\ 2x, & x > 0 \end{cases}$

62. $y' = \begin{cases} -x^2, & x \le 0 \\ x^2, & x > 0 \end{cases}$

Each of Exercises 63–66 shows the graphs of the first and second derivatives of a function $y = f(x)$. Copy the picture and add to it a sketch of the approximate graph of f, given that the graph passes through the point P.

63.

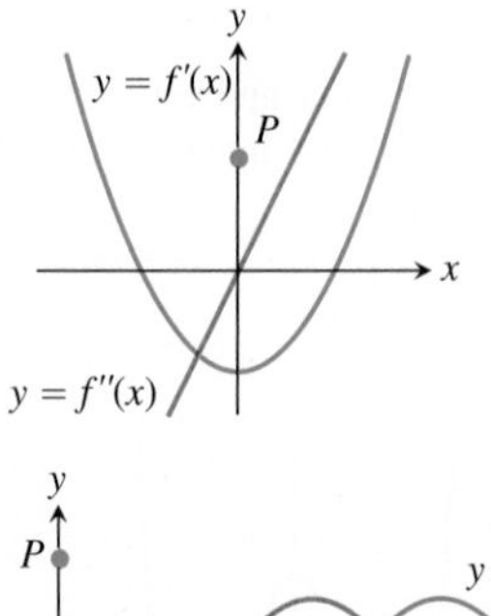

64.

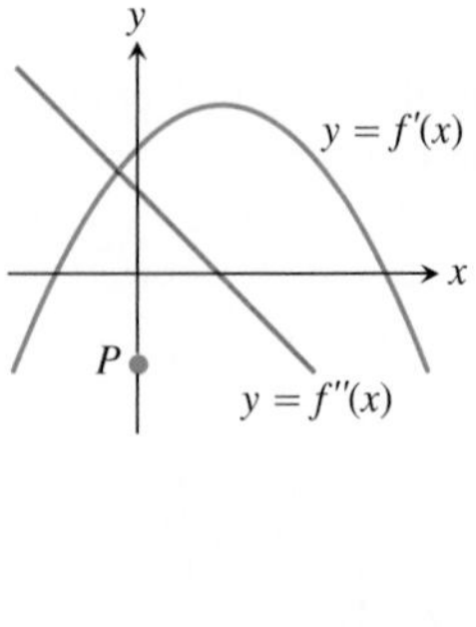

65.

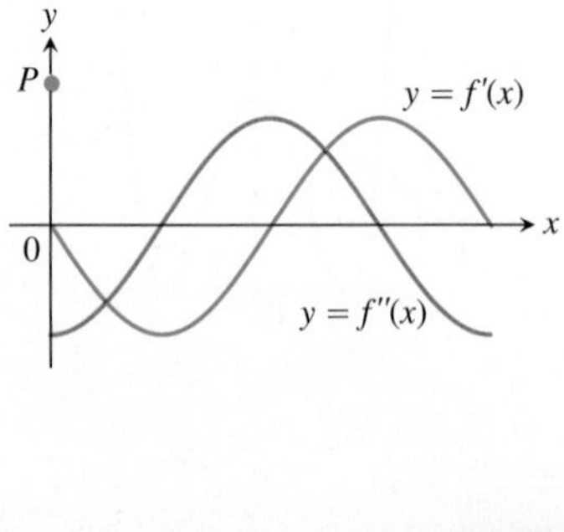

66.

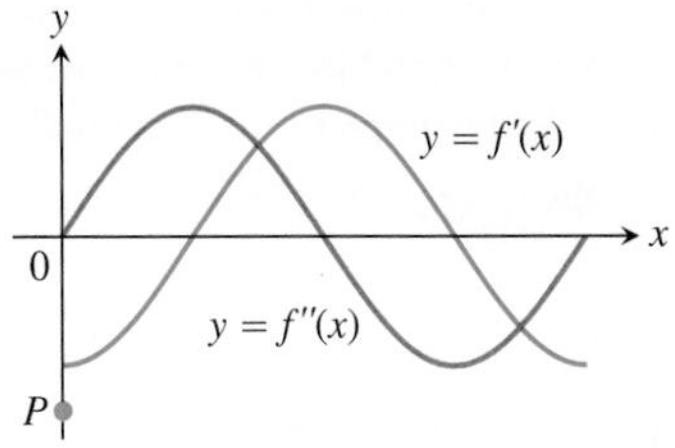

67. The accompanying figure shows a portion of the graph of a twice-differentiable function $y = f(x)$. At each of the five labeled points, classify y' and y'' as positive, negative, or zero.

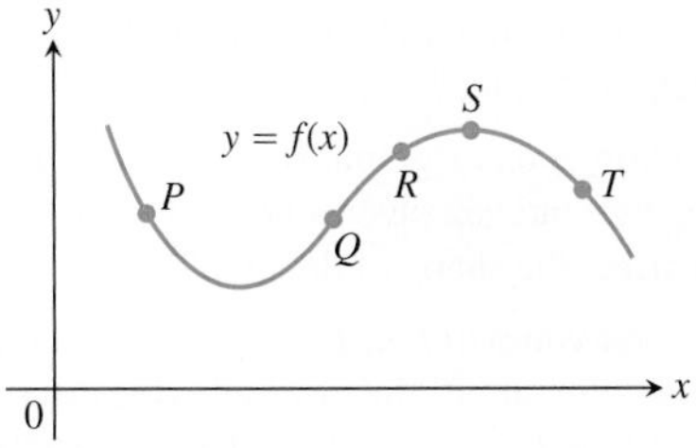

68. Sketch a smooth connected curve $y = f(x)$ with

$f(-2) = 8,$ $\quad f'(2) = f'(-2) = 0,$

$f(0) = 4,$ $\quad f'(x) < 0 \quad \text{for} \quad |x| < 2,$

$f(2) = 0,$ $\quad f''(x) < 0 \quad \text{for} \quad x < 0,$

$f'(x) > 0 \quad \text{for} \quad |x| > 2,$ $\quad f''(x) > 0 \quad \text{for} \quad x > 0.$

69. Sketch the graph of a twice-differentiable function $y = f(x)$ with the following properties. Label coordinates where possible.

x	y	**Derivatives**
$x < 2$		$y' < 0, \quad y'' > 0$
2	1	$y' = 0, \quad y'' > 0$
$2 < x < 4$		$y' > 0, \quad y'' > 0$
4	4	$y' > 0, \quad y'' = 0$
$4 < x < 6$		$y' > 0, \quad y'' < 0$
6	7	$y' = 0, \quad y'' < 0$
$x > 6$		$y' < 0, \quad y'' < 0$

70. Sketch the graph of a twice-differentiable function $y = f(x)$ that passes through the points $(-2, 2), (-1, 1), (0, 0), (1, 1)$ and $(2, 2)$ and whose first two derivatives have the following sign patterns:

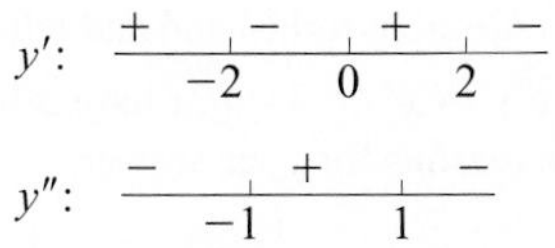

Motion Along a Line The graphs in Exercises 71 and 72 show the position $s = f(t)$ of a body moving back and forth on a coordinate line. **(a)** When is the body moving away from the origin? Toward the origin? At approximately what times is the **(b)** velocity equal to zero? **(c)** Acceleration equal to zero? **(d)** When is the acceleration positive? Negative?

71.

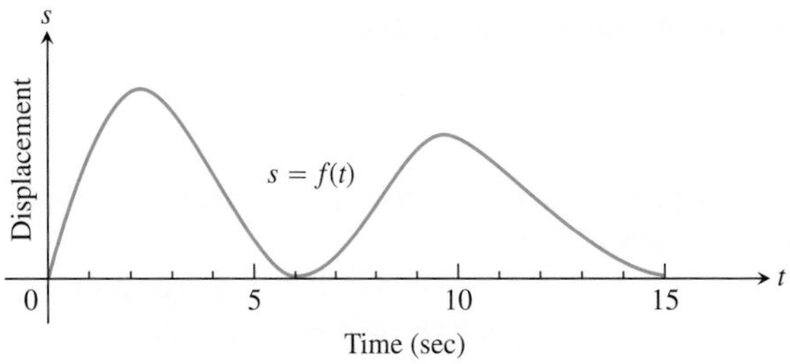

72.

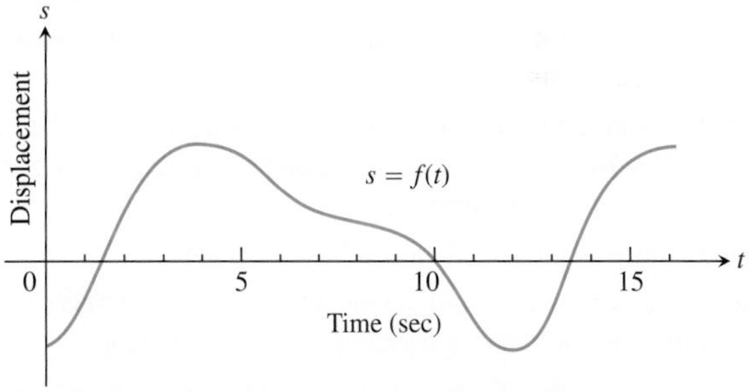

73. Marginal cost The accompanying graph shows the hypothetical cost $c = f(x)$ of manufacturing x items. At approximately what production level does the marginal cost change from decreasing to increasing?

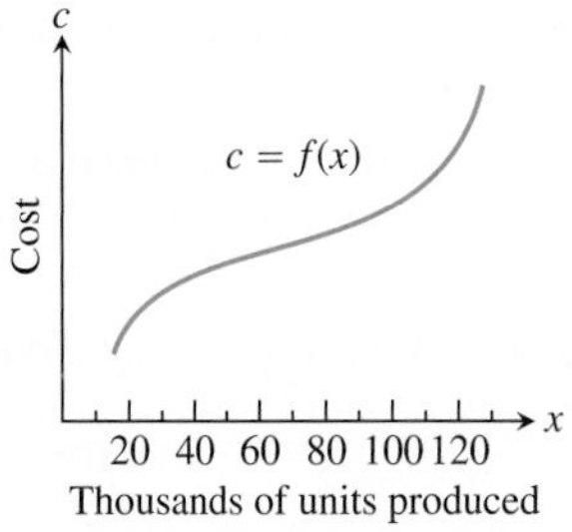

74. The accompanying graph shows the monthly revenue of the Widget Corporation for the last 12 years. During approximately what time intervals was the marginal revenue increasing? Decreasing?

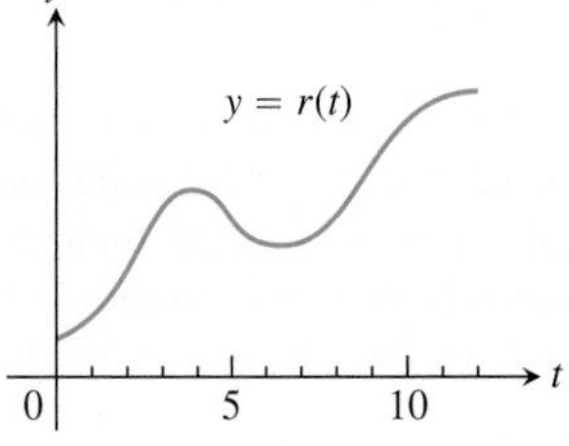

75. Suppose the derivative of the function $y = f(x)$ is

$$y' = (x-1)^2(x-2).$$

At what points, if any, does the graph of f have a local minimum, local maximum, or point of inflection? (Hint: Draw the sign pattern for y'.)

76. Suppose the derivative of the function $y = f(x)$ is

$$y' = (x-1)^2(x-2)(x-4).$$

At what points, if any, does the graph of f have a local minimum, local maximum, or point of inflection?

77. For $x > 0$, sketch a curve $y = f(x)$ that has $f(1) = 0$ and $f'(x) = 1/x$. Can anything be said about the concavity of such a curve? Give reasons for your answer.

78. Can anything be said about the graph of a function $y = f(x)$ that has a continuous second derivative that is never zero? Give reasons for your answer.

79. If b, c, and d are constants, for what value of b will the curve $y = x^3 + bx^2 + cx + d$ have a point of inflection at $x = 1$? Give reasons for your answer.

80. Horizontal tangents True, or false? Explain.

a. The graph of every polynomial of even degree (largest exponent even) has at least one horizontal tangent.

b. The graph of every polynomial of odd degree (largest exponent odd) has at least one horizontal tangent.

81. Parabolas

a. Find the coordinates of the vertex of the parabola $y = ax^2 + bx + c$, $a \neq 0$.

b. When is the parabola concave up? Concave down? Give reasons for your answers.

82. Is it true that the concavity of the graph of a twice-differentiable function $y = f(x)$ changes every time $f''(x) = 0$? Give reasons for your answer.

83. Quadratic curves What can you say about the inflection points of a quadratic curve $y = ax^2 + bx + c$, $a \neq 0$? Give reasons for your answer.

84. Cubic curves What can you say about the inflection points of a cubic curve $y = ax^3 + bx^2 + cx + d$, $a \neq 0$? Give reasons for your answer.

COMPUTER EXPLORATIONS

In Exercises 85–88, find the inflection points (if any) on the graph of the function and the coordinates of the points on the graph where the function has a local maximum or local minimum value. Then graph the function in a region large enough to show all these points simultaneously. Add to your picture the graphs of the function's first and second derivatives. How are the values at which these graphs intersect the x-axis related to the graph of the function? In what other ways are the graphs of the derivatives related to the graph of the function?

85. $y = x^5 - 5x^4 - 240$

86. $y = x^3 - 12x^2$

87. $y = \frac{4}{5}x^5 + 16x^2 - 25$

88. $y = \frac{x^4}{4} - \frac{x^3}{3} - 4x^2 + 12x + 20$

89. Graph $f(x) = 2x^4 - 4x^2 + 1$ and its first two derivatives together. Comment on the behavior of f in relation to the signs and values of f' and f''.

90. Graph $f(x) = x \cos x$ and its second derivative together for $0 \le x \le 2\pi$. Comment on the behavior of the graph of f in relation to the signs and values of f''.

91. a. On a common screen, graph $f(x) = x^3 + kx$ for $k = 0$ and nearby positive and negative values of k. How does the value of k seem to affect the shape of the graph?

b. Find $f'(x)$. As you will see, $f'(x)$ is a quadratic function of x. Find the discriminant of the quadratic (the discriminant of $ax^2 + bx + c$ is $b^2 - 4ac$). For what values of k is the discriminant positive? Zero? Negative? For what values of k does f' have two zeros? One or no zeros? Now explain what the value of k has to do with the shape of the graph of f.

c. Experiment with other values of k. What appears to happen as $k \to -\infty$? As $k \to \infty$?

92. a. On a common screen, graph $f(x) = x^4 + kx^3 + 6x^2$, $-2 \le x \le 2$ for $k = -4$, and some nearby integer values of k. How does the value of k seem to affect the shape of the graph?

b. Find $f''(x)$. As you will see, $f''(x)$ is a quadratic function of x. What is the discriminant of this quadratic (see Exercise 91(b))? For what values of k is the discriminant positive? Zero? Negative? For what values of k does $f''(x)$ have two zeros? One or no zeros? Now explain what the value of k has to do with the shape of the graph of f.

93. a. Graph $y = x^{2/3}(x^2 - 2)$ for $-3 \le x \le 3$. Then use calculus to confirm what the screen shows about concavity, rise, and fall. (Depending on your grapher, you may have to enter $x^{2/3}$ as $(x^2)^{1/3}$ to obtain a plot for negative values of x.)

b. Does the curve have a cusp at $x = 0$, or does it just have a corner with different right-hand and left-hand derivatives?

94. a. Graph $y = 9x^{2/3}(x-1)$ for $-0.5 \le x \le 1.5$. Then use calculus to confirm what the screen shows about concavity, rise, and fall. What concavity does the curve have to the left of the origin? (Depending on your grapher, you may have to enter $x^{2/3}$ as $(x^2)^{1/3}$ to obtain a plot for negative values of x.)

b. Does the curve have a cusp at $x = 0$, or does it just have a corner with different right-hand and left-hand derivatives?

95. Does the curve $y = x^2 + 3 \sin 2x$ have a horizontal tangent near $x = -3$? Give reasons for your answer.

4.5 Applied Optimization

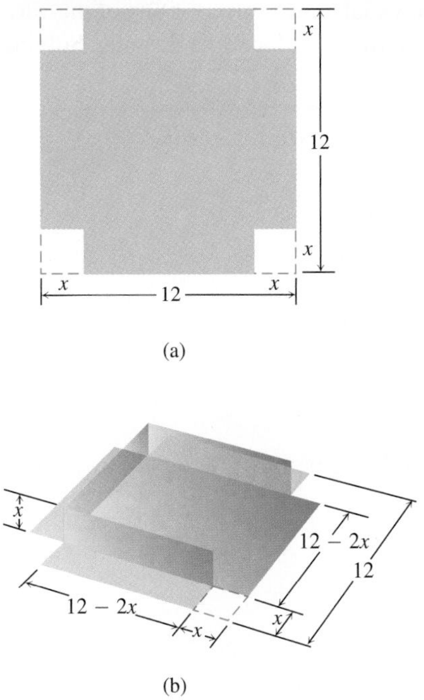

FIGURE 4.33 An open box made by cutting the corners from a square sheet of tin. What size corners maximize the box's volume (Example 1)?

To optimize something often means to maximize or minimize some aspect of it. For example, what are the dimensions of a rectangle with fixed perimeter having *maximum area*? What are the dimensions for the *least expensive* cylindrical can of a given volume? How many items should be produced for the *most profitable* production run? In this section we use derivatives to solve a variety of optimization problems in business, mathematics, physics, and economics.

Examples from Business and Industry

EXAMPLE 1 An open-top box is to be made by cutting small congruent squares from the corners of a 12-in.-by-12-in. sheet of tin and bending up the sides. How large should the squares cut from the corners be to make the box hold as much as possible?

Solution We start with a picture (Figure 4.33). In the figure, the corner squares are x in. on a side. The volume of the box is a function of this variable:

$$V(x) = x(12 - 2x)^2 = 144x - 48x^2 + 4x^3. \qquad V = hlw$$

Since the sides of the sheet of tin are only 12 in. long, $x \le 6$ and the domain of V is the interval $0 \le x \le 6$.

A graph of V (Figure 4.34) suggests a minimum value of 0 at $x = 0$ and $x = 6$ and a maximum near $x = 2$. To learn more, we examine the first derivative of V with respect to x:

$$\frac{dV}{dx} = 144 - 96x + 12x^2 = 12(12 - 8x + x^2) = 12(2 - x)(6 - x).$$

Of the two zeros, $x = 2$ and $x = 6$, only $x = 2$ lies in the interior of the function's domain and makes the critical-point list. The values of V at this one critical point and two endpoints are

Critical-point value: $V(2) = 128$

Endpoint values: $V(0) = 0, \qquad V(6) = 0.$

The maximum volume is 128 in.^{3}. The cutout squares should be 2 in. on a side. ■

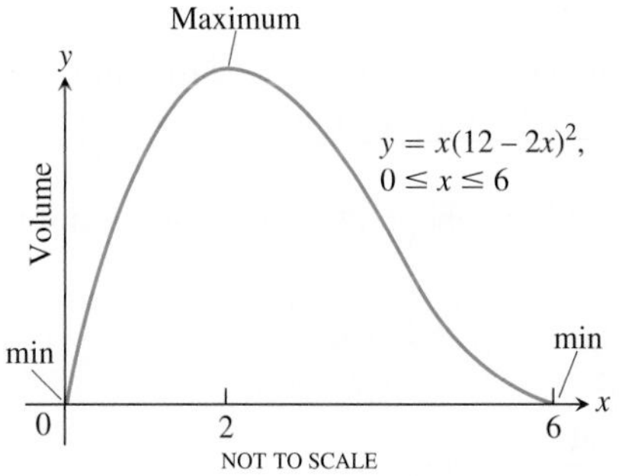

FIGURE 4.34 The volume of the box in Figure 4.33 graphed as a function of x.

EXAMPLE 2 You have been asked to design a 1-liter can shaped like a right circular cylinder (Figure 4.35). What dimensions will use the least material?

Solution *Volume of can:* If r and h are measured in centimeters, then the volume of the can in cubic centimeters is

$$\pi r^2 h = 1000. \qquad 1 \text{ liter} = 1000 \text{ cm}^3$$

Surface area of can: $A = \underbrace{2\pi r^2}_{\text{circular ends}} + \underbrace{2\pi rh}_{\text{cylindrical wall}}$

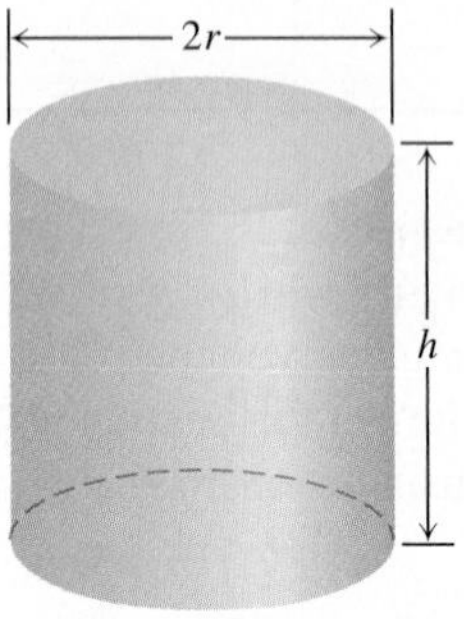

FIGURE 4.35 This 1-L can uses the least material when $h = 2r$ (Example 2).

How can we interpret the phrase "least material"? First, it is customary to ignore the thickness of the material and the waste in manufacturing. Then we ask for dimensions r and h that make the total surface area as small as possible while satisfying the constraint $\pi r^2 h = 1000$.

To express the surface area as a function of one variable, we solve for one of the variables in $\pi r^2 h = 1000$ and substitute that expression into the surface area formula. Solving for h is easier:

$$h = \frac{1000}{\pi r^2}.$$

Thus,

$$\begin{aligned} A &= 2\pi r^2 + 2\pi r h \\ &= 2\pi r^2 + 2\pi r\left(\frac{1000}{\pi r^2}\right) \\ &= 2\pi r^2 + \frac{2000}{r}. \end{aligned}$$

Our goal is to find a value of $r > 0$ that minimizes the value of A. Figure 4.36 suggests that such a value exists.

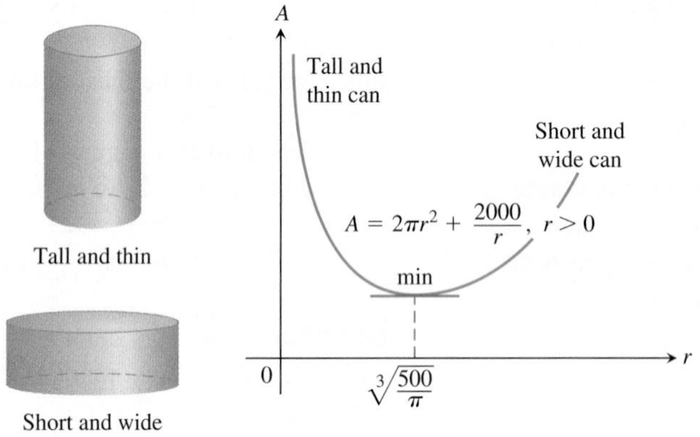

FIGURE 4.36 The graph of $A = 2\pi r^2 + 2000/r$ is concave up.

Notice from the graph that for small r (a tall thin container, like a piece of pipe), the term $2000/r$ dominates and A is large. For large r (a short wide container, like a pizza pan), the term $2\pi r^2$ dominates and A again is large.

Since A is differentiable on $r > 0$, an interval with no endpoints, it can have a minimum value only where its first derivative is zero.

$$\begin{aligned} \frac{dA}{dr} &= 4\pi r - \frac{2000}{r^2} \\ 0 &= 4\pi r - \frac{2000}{r^2} && \text{Set } dA/dr = 0. \\ 4\pi r^3 &= 2000 && \text{Multiply by } r^2. \\ r &= \sqrt[3]{\frac{500}{\pi}} \approx 5.42 && \text{Solve for } r. \end{aligned}$$

What happens at $r = \sqrt[3]{500/\pi}$?

The second derivative

$$\frac{d^2A}{dr^2} = 4\pi + \frac{4000}{r^3}$$

is positive throughout the domain of A. The graph is therefore everywhere concave up and the value of A at $r = \sqrt[3]{500/\pi}$ an absolute minimum.

The corresponding value of h (after a little algebra) is

$$h = \frac{1000}{\pi r^2} = 2\sqrt[3]{\frac{500}{\pi}} = 2r.$$

The 1-L can that uses the least material has height equal to the diameter, here with $r \approx 5.42$ cm and $h \approx 10.84$ cm. ■

Examples from Mathematics and Physics

EXAMPLE 3 A rectangle is to be inscribed in a semicircle of radius 2. What is the largest area the rectangle can have, and what are its dimensions?

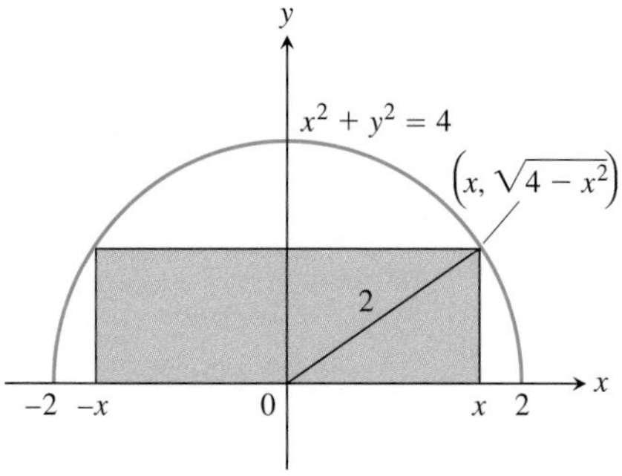

FIGURE 4.37 The rectangle inscribed in the semicircle in Example 3.

Solution Let $(x, \sqrt{4 - x^2})$ be the coordinates of the corner of the rectangle obtained by placing the circle and rectangle in the coordinate plane (Figure 4.37). The length, height, and area of the rectangle can then be expressed in terms of the position x of the lower right-hand corner:

$$\text{Length: } 2x, \qquad \text{Height: } \sqrt{4 - x^2}, \qquad \text{Area: } 2x \cdot \sqrt{4 - x^2}.$$

Notice that the values of x are to be found in the interval $0 \le x \le 2$, where the selected corner of the rectangle lies.

Our goal is to find the absolute maximum value of the function

$$A(x) = 2x\sqrt{4 - x^2}$$

on the domain $[0, 2]$.

The derivative

$$\frac{dA}{dx} = \frac{-2x^2}{\sqrt{4 - x^2}} + 2\sqrt{4 - x^2}$$

is not defined when $x = 2$ and is equal to zero when

$$\begin{aligned} \frac{-2x^2}{\sqrt{4 - x^2}} + 2\sqrt{4 - x^2} &= 0 \\ -2x^2 + 2(4 - x^2) &= 0 \\ 8 - 4x^2 &= 0 \\ x^2 = 2 \text{ or } x &= \pm\sqrt{2}. \end{aligned}$$

Of the two zeros, $x = \sqrt{2}$ and $x = -\sqrt{2}$, only $x = \sqrt{2}$ lies in the interior of A's domain and makes the critical-point list. The values of A at the endpoints and at this one critical point are

$$\begin{aligned} &\text{Critical-point value:} \quad A\left(\sqrt{2}\right) = 2\sqrt{2}\sqrt{4 - 2} = 4 \\ &\text{Endpoint values:} \quad A(0) = 0, \quad A(2) = 0. \end{aligned}$$

The area has a maximum value of 4 when the rectangle is $\sqrt{4 - x^2} = \sqrt{2}$ units high and $2x = 2\sqrt{2}$ unit long. ■

HISTORICAL BIOGRAPHY

Willebrord Snell van Royen
(1580–1626)

EXAMPLE 4 The speed of light depends on the medium through which it travels, and is generally slower in denser media.

Fermat's principle in optics states that light travels from one point to another along a path for which the time of travel is a minimum. Find the path that a ray of light will follow in going from a point A in a medium where the speed of light is c_1 to a point B in a second medium where its speed is c_2.

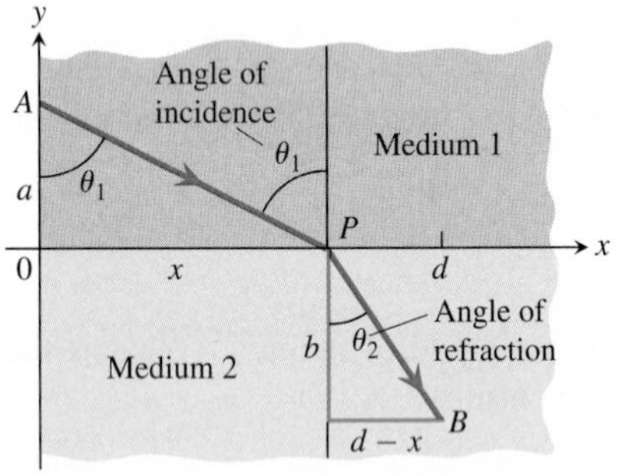

FIGURE 4.38 A light ray refracted (deflected from its path) as it passes from one medium to a denser medium (Example 4).

Solution Since light traveling from A to B follows the quickest route, we look for a path that will minimize the travel time. We assume that A and B lie in the xy-plane and that the line separating the two media is the x-axis (Figure 4.38).

In a uniform medium, where the speed of light remains constant, "shortest time" means "shortest path," and the ray of light will follow a straight line. Thus the path from A to B will consist of a line segment from A to a boundary point P, followed by another line segment from P to B. Distance equals rate times time, so

$$\text{Time} = \frac{\text{distance}}{\text{rate}}.$$

The time required for light to travel from A to P is

$$t_1 = \frac{AP}{c_1} = \frac{\sqrt{a^2 + x^2}}{c_1}.$$

From P to B, the time is

$$t_2 = \frac{PB}{c_2} = \frac{\sqrt{b^2 + (d - x)^2}}{c_2}.$$

The time from A to B is the sum of these:

$$t = t_1 + t_2 = \frac{\sqrt{a^2 + x^2}}{c_1} + \frac{\sqrt{b^2 + (d - x)^2}}{c_2}.$$

This equation expresses t as a differentiable function of x whose domain is $[0, d]$. We want to find the absolute minimum value of t on this closed interval. We find the derivative

$$\frac{dt}{dx} = \frac{x}{c_1\sqrt{a^2 + x^2}} - \frac{d - x}{c_2\sqrt{b^2 + (d - x)^2}}.$$

In terms of the angles θ_1 and θ_2 in Figure 4.38,

$$\frac{dt}{dx} = \frac{\sin\theta_1}{c_1} - \frac{\sin\theta_2}{c_2}.$$

If we restrict x to the interval $0 \le x \le d$, then t has a negative derivative at $x = 0$ and a positive derivative at $x = d$. By the Intermediate Value Theorem for Derivatives (Section 3.1), there is a point $x_0 \in [0, d]$ where $dt/dx = 0$ (Figure 4.39). There is only one such point because dt/dx is an increasing function of x (Exercise 52). At this point

$$\frac{\sin\theta_1}{c_1} = \frac{\sin\theta_2}{c_2}.$$

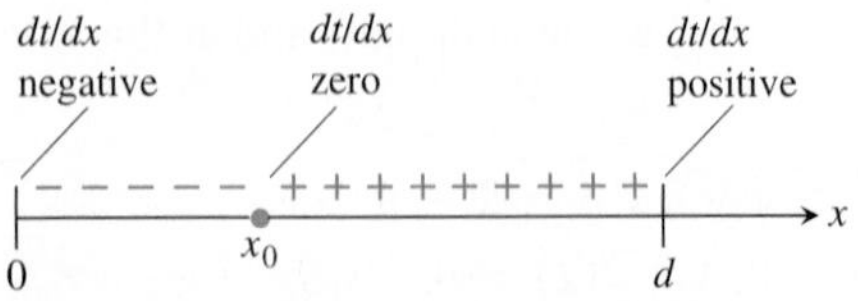

FIGURE 4.39 The sign pattern of dt/dx in Example 4.

This equation is **Snell's Law** or the **Law of Refraction**, and is an important principle in the theory of optics. It describes the path the ray of light follows. ∎

Examples from Economics

Suppose that

$$r(x) = \text{the revenue from selling } x \text{ items}$$
$$c(x) = \text{the cost of producing the } x \text{ items}$$
$$p(x) = r(x) - c(x) = \text{the profit from producing and selling } x \text{ items}.$$

The **marginal revenue, marginal cost**, and **marginal profit** when producing and selling x items are the derivatives

$$\frac{dr}{dx} = \text{marginal revenue},$$
$$\frac{dc}{dx} = \text{marginal cost},$$
$$\frac{dp}{dx} = \text{marginal profit}.$$

Let's consider the relationship of p to these derivatives.

If $r(x)$ and $c(x)$ are differentiable for all $x > 0$, and if $p(x) = r(x) - c(x)$ has a maximum value, it occurs at a production level at which $p'(x) = 0$. Since $p'(x) = r'(x) - c'(x)$, $p'(x) = 0$ implies that

$$r'(x) - c'(x) = 0 \qquad \text{or} \qquad r'(x) = c'(x).$$

Therefore

At a production level yielding maximum profit, marginal revenue equals marginal cost (Figure 4.40).

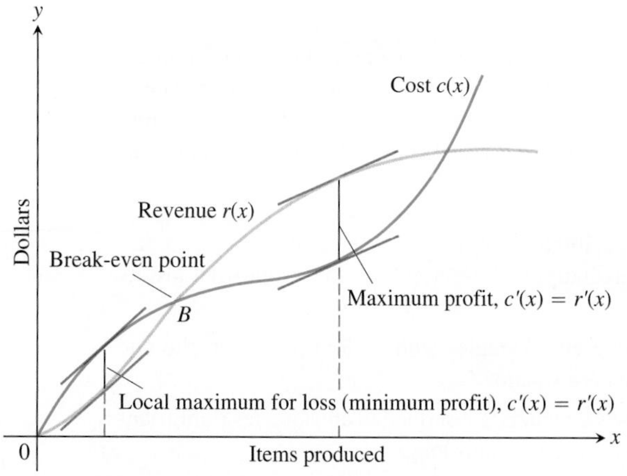

FIGURE 4.40 The graph of a typical cost function starts concave down and later turns concave up. It crosses the revenue curve at the break-even point B. To the left of B, the company operates at a loss. To the right, the company operates at a profit, with the maximum profit occurring where $c'(x) = r'(x)$. Farther to the right, cost exceeds revenue (perhaps because of a combination of rising labor and material costs and market saturation) and production levels become unprofitable again.

EXAMPLE 5 Suppose that $r(x) = 9x$ and $c(x) = x^3 - 6x^2 + 15x$, where x represents thousands of units. Is there a production level that maximizes profit? If so, what is it?

Solution Notice that $r'(x) = 9$ and $c'(x) = 3x^2 - 12x + 15$.

$$3x^2 - 12x + 15 = 9 \qquad \text{Set } c'(x) = r'(x).$$

$$3x^2 - 12x + 6 = 0$$

The two solutions of the quadratic equation are

$$x_1 = \frac{12 - \sqrt{72}}{6} = 2 - \sqrt{2} \approx 0.586 \quad \text{and}$$

$$x_2 = \frac{12 + \sqrt{72}}{6} = 2 + \sqrt{2} \approx 3.414.$$

The possible production levels for maximum profit are $x \approx 0.586$ thousand units or $x \approx 3.414$ thousand units. The second derivative of $p(x) = r(x) - c(x)$ is $p''(x) = -c''(x)$ since $r''(x)$ is everywhere zero. Thus, $p''(x) = 6(2 - x)$, which is negative at $x = 2 + \sqrt{2}$ and positive at $x = 2 - \sqrt{2}$. By the Second Derivative Test, a maximum profit occurs at about $x = 3.414$ (where revenue exceeds costs) and maximum loss occurs at about $x = 0.586$. The graphs of $r(x)$ and $c(x)$ are shown in Figure 4.41. ■

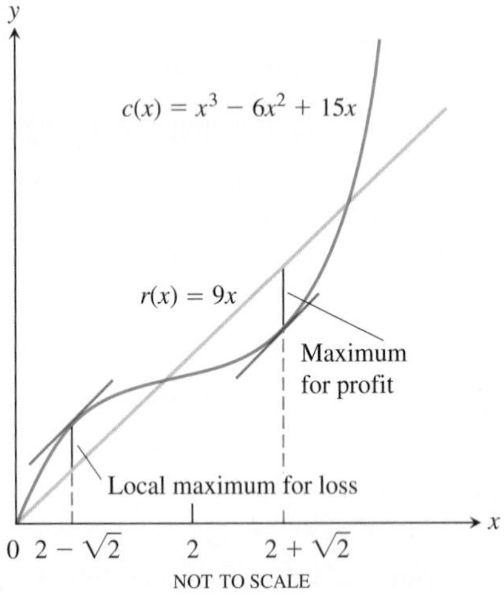

FIGURE 4.41 The cost and revenue curves for Example 5.

EXERCISES 4.5

Whenever you are maximizing or minimizing a function of a single variable, we urge you to graph it over the domain that is appropriate to the problem you are solving. The graph will provide insight before you calculate and will furnish a visual context for understanding your answer.

1. **Minimizing perimeter** What is the smallest perimeter possible for a rectangle whose area is 16 in.^{2}, and what are its dimensions?
2. Show that among all rectangles with an 8-m perimeter, the one with largest area is a square.
3. The figure shows a rectangle inscribed in an isosceles right triangle whose hypotenuse is 2 units long.
   a. Express the y-coordinate of P in terms of x. (*Hint:* Write an equation for the line AB.)
   b. Express the area of the rectangle in terms of x.
   c. What is the largest area the rectangle can have, and what are its dimensions?

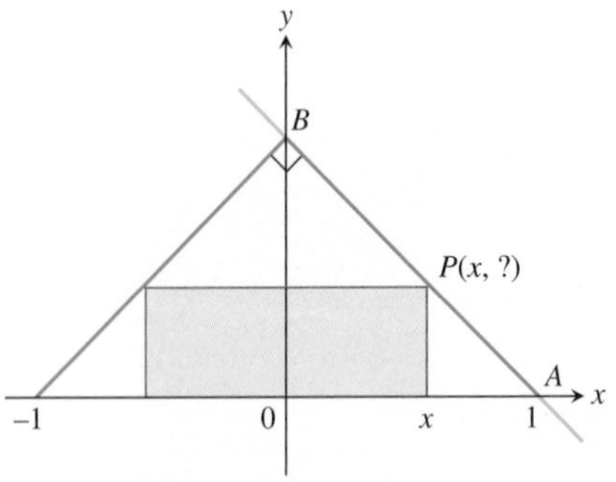

4. A rectangle has its base on the x-axis and its upper two vertices on the parabola $y = 12 - x^2$. What is the largest area the rectangle can have, and what are its dimensions?
5. You are planning to make an open rectangular box from an 8-in.-by-15-in. piece of cardboard by cutting congruent squares from the corners and folding up the sides. What are the dimensions of the box of largest volume you can make this way, and what is its volume?

6. You are planning to close off a corner of the first quadrant with a line segment 20 units long running from $(a, 0)$ to $(0, b)$. Show that the area of the triangle enclosed by the segment is largest when $a = b$.

7. **The best fencing plan** A rectangular plot of farmland will be bounded on one side by a river and on the other three sides by a single-strand electric fence. With 800 m of wire at your disposal, what is the largest area you can enclose, and what are its dimensions?

8. **The shortest fence** A 216 m^2 rectangular pea patch is to be enclosed by a fence and divided into two equal parts by another fence parallel to one of the sides. What dimensions for the outer rectangle will require the smallest total length of fence? How much fence will be needed?

9. **Designing a tank** Your iron works has contracted to design and build a 500 ft^3, square-based, open-top, rectangular steel holding tank for a paper company. The tank is to be made by welding thin stainless steel plates together along their edges. As the production engineer, your job is to find dimensions for the base and height that will make the tank weigh as little as possible.
   a. What dimensions do you tell the shop to use?
   b. Briefly describe how you took weight into account.

10. **Catching rainwater** A 1125 ft^3 open-top rectangular tank with a square base x ft on a side and y ft deep is to be built with its top flush with the ground to catch runoff water. The costs associated with the tank involve not only the material from which the tank is made but also an excavation charge proportional to the product xy.
   a. If the total cost is
   $$c = 5(x^2 + 4xy) + 10xy,$$
   what values of x and y will minimize it?
   b. Give a possible scenario for the cost function in part (a).

11. **Designing a poster** You are designing a rectangular poster to contain 50 in.^2 of printing with a 4-in. margin at the top and bottom and a 2-in. margin at each side. What overall dimensions will minimize the amount of paper used?

12. Find the volume of the largest right circular cone that can be inscribed in a sphere of radius 3.

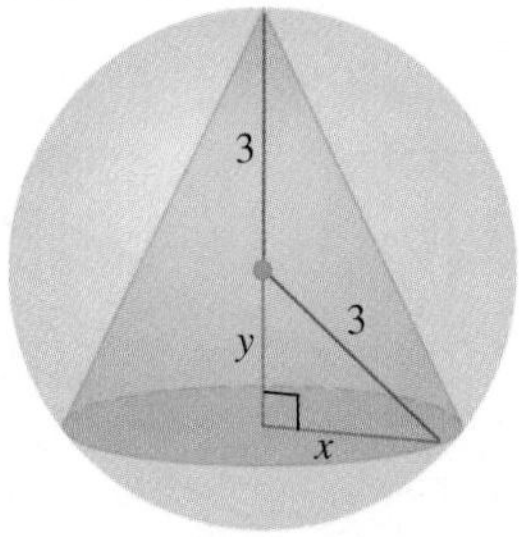

13. Two sides of a triangle have lengths a and b, and the angle between them is θ. What value of θ will maximize the triangle's area? (*Hint:* $A = (1/2)ab \sin\theta$.)

14. **Designing a can** What are the dimensions of the lightest open-top right circular cylindrical can that will hold a volume of 1000 cm^3? Compare the result here with the result in Example 2.

15. **Designing a can** You are designing a 1000 cm^3 right circular cylindrical can whose manufacture will take waste into account. There is no waste in cutting the aluminum for the side, but the top and bottom of radius r will be cut from squares that measure $2r$ units on a side. The total amount of aluminum used up by the can will therefore be
$$A = 8r^2 + 2\pi rh$$
rather than the $A = 2\pi r^2 + 2\pi rh$ in Example 2. In Example 2, the ratio of h to r for the most economical can was 2 to 1. What is the ratio now?

T 16. **Designing a box with a lid** A piece of cardboard measures 10 in. by 15 in. Two equal squares are removed from the corners of a 10-in. side as shown in the figure. Two equal rectangles are removed from the other corners so that the tabs can be folded to form a rectangular box with lid.

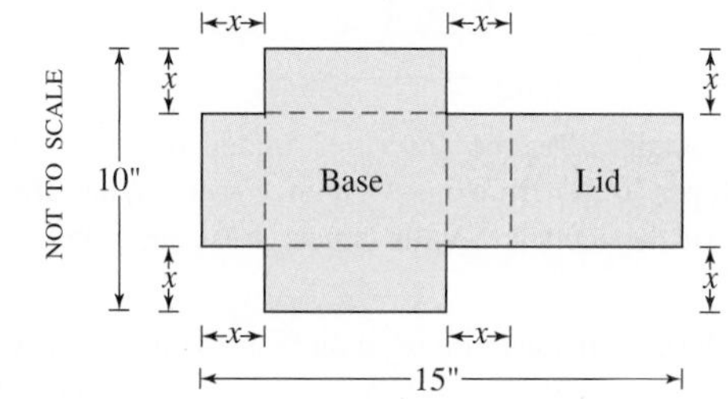

   a. Write a formula $V(x)$ for the volume of the box.
   b. Find the domain of V for the problem situation and graph V over this domain.
   c. Use a graphical method to find the maximum volume and the value of x that gives it.
   d. Confirm your result in part (c) analytically.

T 17. **Designing a suitcase** A 24-in.-by-36-in. sheet of cardboard is folded in half to form a 24-in.-by-18-in. rectangle as shown on the next page. Then four congruent squares of side length x are cut from the corners of the folded rectangle. The sheet is unfolded, and the six tabs are folded up to form a box with sides and a lid.

a. Write a formula $V(x)$ for the volume of the box.

b. Find the domain of V for the problem situation and graph V over this domain.

c. Use a graphical method to find the maximum volume and the value of x that gives it.

d. Confirm your result in part (c) analytically.

e. Find a value of x that yields a volume of 1120 in.^{3}.

f. Write a paragraph describing the issues that arise in part (b).

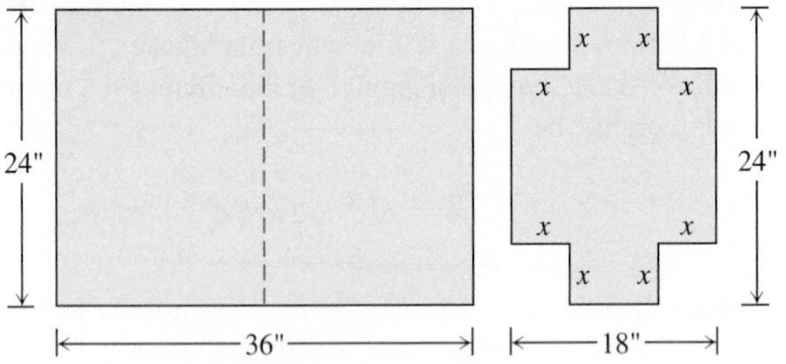

The sheet is then unfolded.

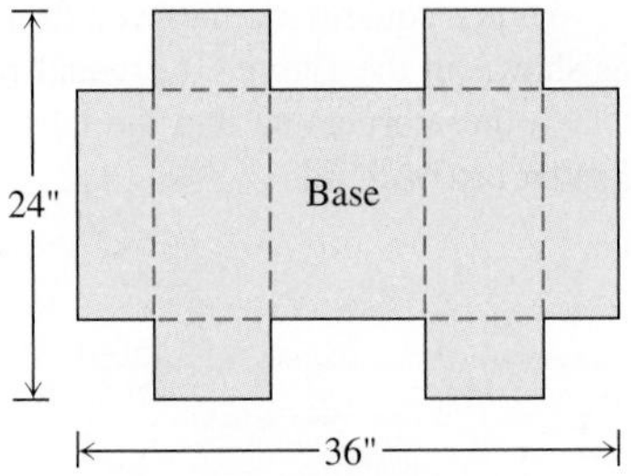

18. A rectangle is to be inscribed under the arch of the curve $y = 4\cos(0.5x)$ from $x = -\pi$ to $x = \pi$. What are the dimensions of the rectangle with largest area, and what is the largest area?

19. Find the dimensions of a right circular cylinder of maximum volume that can be inscribed in a sphere of radius 10 cm. What is the maximum volume?

20. **a.** The U.S. Postal Service will accept a box for domestic shipment only if the sum of its length and girth (distance around) does not exceed 108 in. What dimensions will give a box with a square end the largest possible volume?

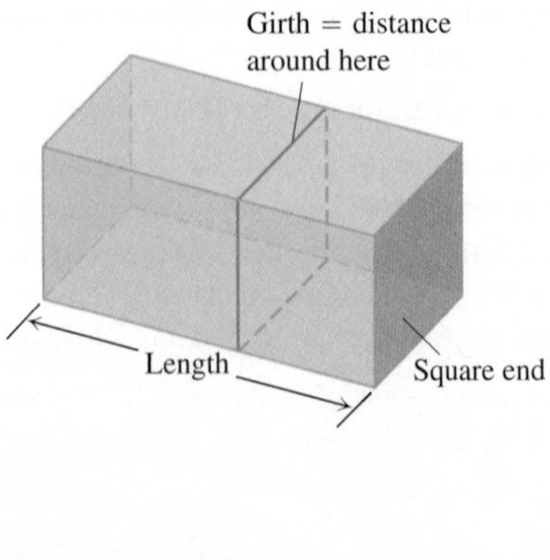

T **b.** Graph the volume of a 108-in. box (length plus girth equals 108 in.) as a function of its length and compare what you see with your answer in part (a).

21. (*Continuation of Exercise 20.*)

a. Suppose that instead of having a box with square ends you have a box with square sides so that its dimensions are h by h by w and the girth is $2h + 2w$. What dimensions will give the box its largest volume now?

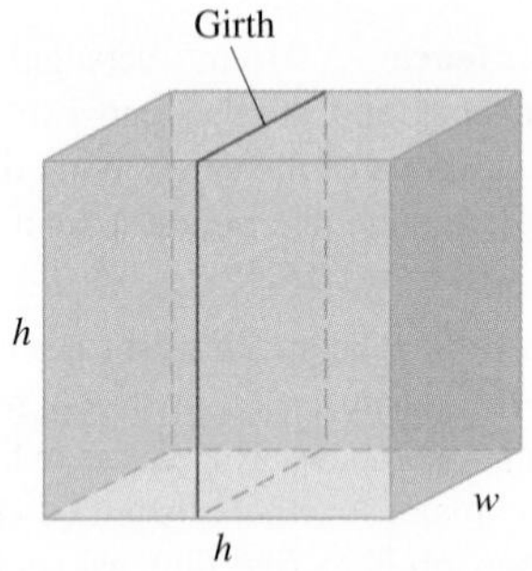

T **b.** Graph the volume as a function of h and compare what you see with your answer in part (a).

22. A window is in the form of a rectangle surmounted by a semicircle. The rectangle is of clear glass, whereas the semicircle is of tinted glass that transmits only half as much light per unit area as clear glass does. The total perimeter is fixed. Find the proportions of the window that will admit the most light. Neglect the thickness of the frame.

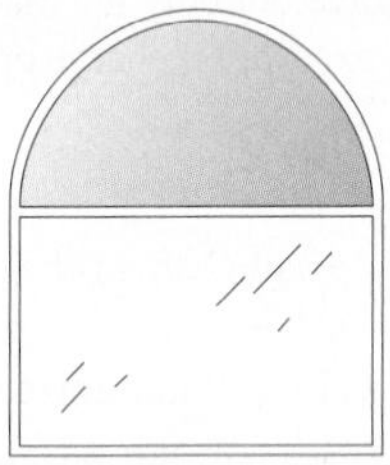

23. A silo (base not included) is to be constructed in the form of a cylinder surmounted by a hemisphere. The cost of construction per square unit of surface area is twice as great for the hemisphere as it is for the cylindrical sidewall. Determine the dimensions to be used if the volume is fixed and the cost of construction is to be kept to a minimum. Neglect the thickness of the silo and waste in construction.

24. The trough in the figure is to be made to the dimensions shown. Only the angle θ can be varied. What value of θ will maximize the trough's volume?

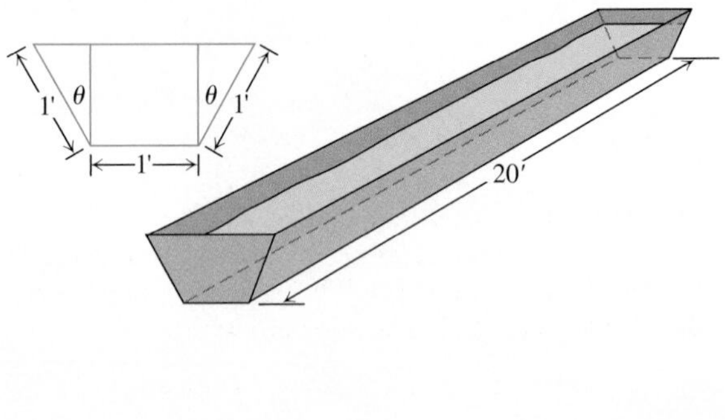

25. **Paper folding** A rectangular sheet of 8.5-in.-by-11-in. paper is placed on a flat surface. One of the corners is placed on the opposite longer edge, as shown in the figure, and held there as the paper is smoothed flat. The problem is to make the length of the crease as small as possible. Call the length L. Try it with paper.

a. Show that $L^2 = 2x^3/(2x - 8.5)$.

b. What value of x minimizes L^2?

c. What is the minimum value of L?

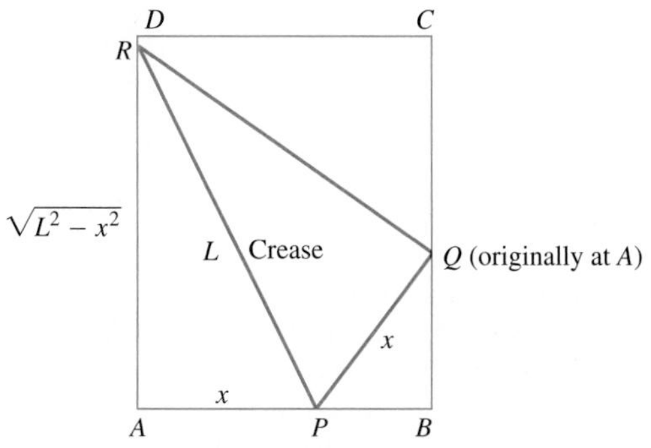

26. **Constructing cylinders** Compare the answers to the following two construction problems.

a. A rectangular sheet of perimeter 36 cm and dimensions x cm by y cm to be rolled into a cylinder as shown in part (a) of the figure. What values of x and y give the largest volume?

b. The same sheet is to be revolved about one of the sides of length y to sweep out the cylinder as shown in part (b) of the figure. What values of x and y give the largest volume?

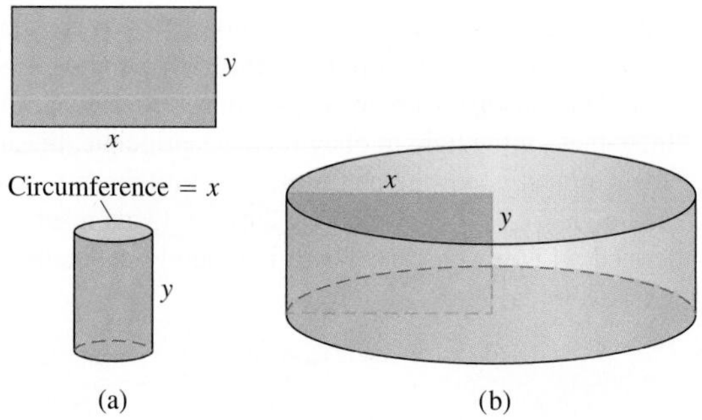

27. **Constructing cones** A right triangle whose hypotenuse is $\sqrt{3}$ m long is revolved about one of its legs to generate a right circular cone. Find the radius, height, and volume of the cone of greatest volume that can be made this way.

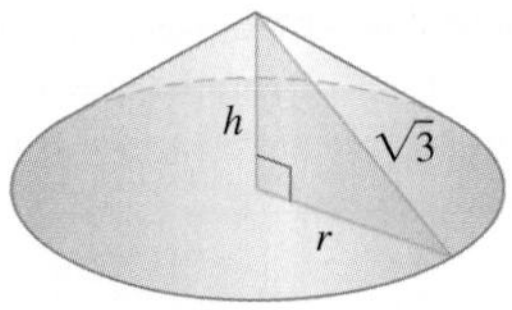

28. What value of a makes $f(x) = x^2 + (a/x)$ have

a. local minimum at $x = 2$?

b. a point of inflection at $x = 1$?

29. Show that $f(x) = x^2 + (a/x)$ cannot have a local maximum for any value of a.

30. What values of a and b make $f(x) = x^3 + ax^2 + bx$ have

a. a local maximum at $x = -1$ and a local minimum at $x = 3$?

b. a local minimum at $x = 4$ and a point of inflection at $x = 1$?

31. **Vertical motion** The height of an object moving vertically is given by

$$s = -16t^2 + 96t + 112,$$

with s in feet and t in seconds. Find

a. the object's velocity when $t = 0$

b. its maximum height and when it occurs

c. its velocity when $s = 0$.

32. **Quickest route** Jane is 2 mi offshore in a boat and wishes to reach a coastal village 6 mi down a straight shoreline from the point nearest the boat. She can row 2 mph and can walk 5 mph. Where should she land her boat to reach the village in the least amount of time?

33. **Shortest beam** The 8-ft wall shown here stands 27 ft from the building. Find the length of the shortest straight beam that will reach to the side of the building from the ground outside the wall.

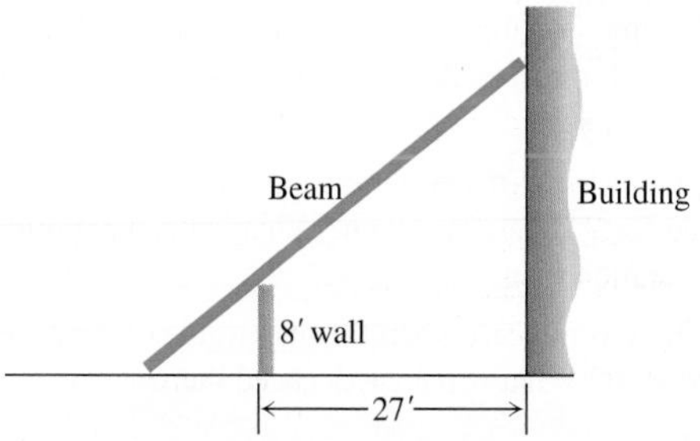

T 34. **Strength of a beam** The strength S of a rectangular wooden beam is proportional to its width times the square of its depth. (See the figure on the next page.)

a. Find the dimensions of the strongest beam that can be cut from a 12-in.-diameter cylindrical log.

b. Graph S as a function of the beam's width w, assuming the proportionality constant to be $k = 1$. Reconcile what you see with your answer in part (a).

c. On the same screen, graph S as a function of the beam's depth d, again taking $k = 1$. Compare the graphs with one another and with your answer in part (a). What would be the effect of changing to some other value of k? Try it.

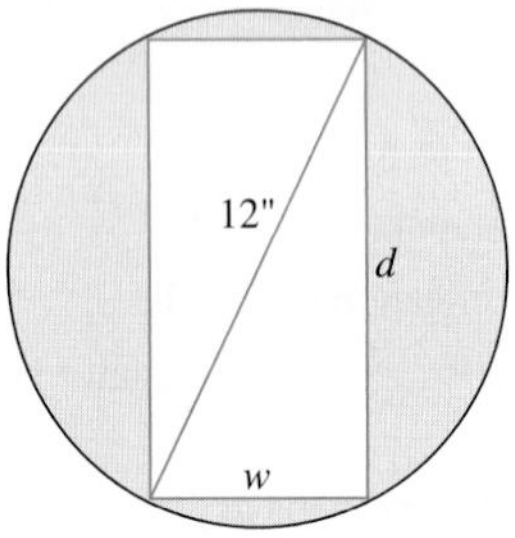

T **35. Stiffness of a beam** The stiffness S of a rectangular beam is proportional to its width times the cube of its depth.

a. Find the dimensions of the stiffest beam that can be cut from a 12-in.-diameter cylindrical log.

b. Graph S as a function of the beam's width w, assuming the proportionality constant to be $k = 1$. Reconcile what you see with your answer in part (a).

c. On the same screen, graph S as a function of the beam's depth d, again taking $k = 1$. Compare the graphs with one another and with your answer in part (a). What would be the effect of changing to some other value of k? Try it.

36. Motion on a line The positions of two particles on the s-axis are $s_1 = \sin t$ and $s_2 = \sin(t + \pi/3)$, with s_1 and s_2 in meters and t in seconds.

a. At what time(s) in the interval $0 \le t \le 2\pi$ do the particles meet?

b. What is the farthest apart that the particles ever get?

c. When in the interval $0 \le t \le 2\pi$ is the distance between the particles changing the fastest?

37. Frictionless cart A small frictionless cart, attached to the wall by a spring, is pulled 10 cm from its rest position and released at time $t = 0$ to roll back and forth for 4 sec. Its position at time t is $s = 10 \cos \pi t$.

a. What is the cart's maximum speed? When is the cart moving that fast? Where is it then? What is the magnitude of the acceleration then?

b. Where is the cart when the magnitude of the acceleration is greatest? What is the cart's speed then?

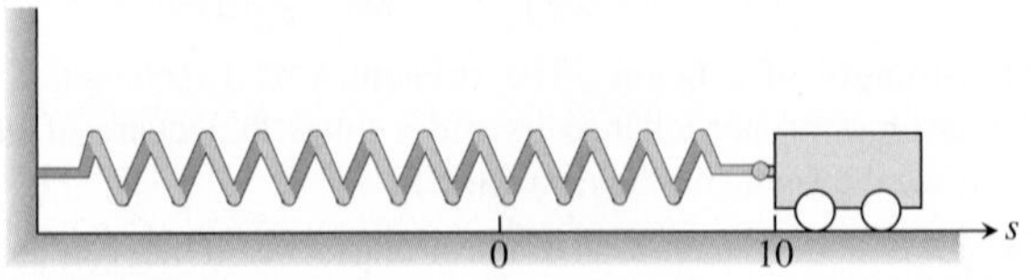

38. Two masses hanging side by side from springs have positions $s_1 = 2 \sin t$ and $s_2 = \sin 2t$, respectively.

a. At what times in the interval $0 < t$ do the masses pass each other? (*Hint:* $\sin 2t = 2 \sin t \cos t$.)

b. When in the interval $0 \le t \le 2\pi$ is the vertical distance between the masses the greatest? What is this distance? (*Hint:* $\cos 2t = 2\cos^2 t - 1$.)

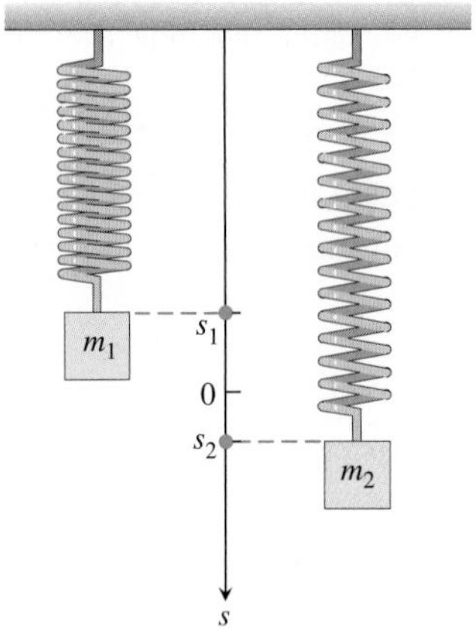

39. Locating a solar station You are under contract to build a solar station at ground level on the east–west line between the two buildings shown here. How far from the taller building should you place the station to maximize the number of hours it will be in the sun on a day when the sun passes directly overhead? Begin by observing that

$$\theta = \pi - \cot^{-1}\frac{x}{60} - \cot^{-1}\frac{50 - x}{30}.$$

Then find the value of x that maximizes θ.

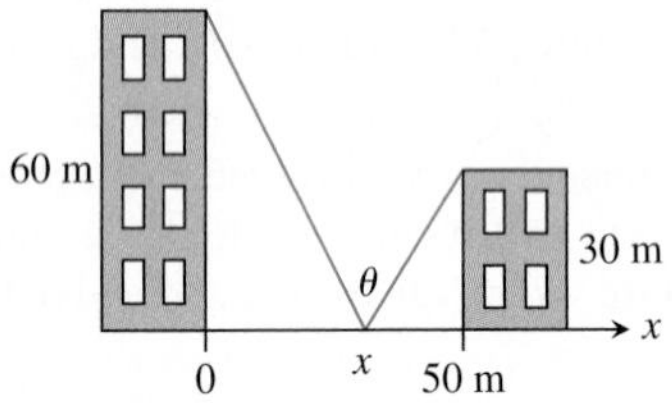

40. Fermat's principle in optics Fermat's principle in optics states that light always travels from one point to another along a path that minimizes the travel time. Light from a source A is reflected by a plane mirror to a receiver at point B, as shown in the figure. Show that for the light to obey Fermat's principle, the angle of incidence must equal the angle of reflection, both measured from the line normal to the reflecting surface. (This result can also be derived without calculus. There is a purely geometric argument, which you may prefer.)

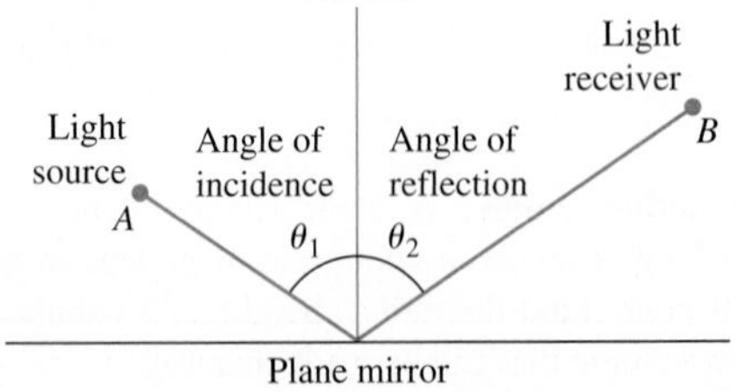

41. Tin pest When metallic tin is kept below 13.2°C, it slowly becomes brittle and crumbles to a gray powder. Tin objects eventually crumble to this gray powder spontaneously if kept in a cold climate for years. The Europeans who saw tin organ pipes in their churches crumble away years ago called the change *tin pest* because it seemed to be contagious, and indeed it was, for the gray powder is a catalyst for its own formation.

A *catalyst* for a chemical reaction is a substance that controls the rate of reaction without undergoing any permanent change in itself. An *autocatalytic reaction* is one whose product is a catalyst for its own formation. Such a reaction may proceed slowly at first if the amount of catalyst present is small and slowly again at the end, when most of the original substance is used up. But in between, when both the substance and its catalyst product are abundant, the reaction proceeds at a faster pace.

In some cases, it is reasonable to assume that the rate $v = dx/dt$ of the reaction is proportional both to the amount of the original substance present and to the amount of product. That is, v may be considered to be a function of x alone, and

$$v = kx(a - x) = kax - kx^2,$$

where

$x =$ the amount of product

$a =$ the amount of substance at the beginning

$k =$ a positive constant.

At what value of x does the rate v have a maximum? What is the maximum value of v?

42. Airplane landing path An airplane is flying at altitude H when it begins its descent to an airport runway that is at horizontal ground distance L from the airplane, as shown in the figure. Assume that the landing path of the airplane is the graph of a cubic polynomial function $y = ax^3 + bx^2 + cx + d$, where $y(-L) = H$ and $y(0) = 0$.

a. What is dy/dx at $x = 0$?

b. What is dy/dx at $x = -L$?

c. Use the values for dy/dx at $x = 0$ and $x = -L$ together with $y(0) = 0$ and $y(-L) = H$ to show that

$$y(x) = H\left[2\left(\frac{x}{L}\right)^3 + 3\left(\frac{x}{L}\right)^2\right].$$

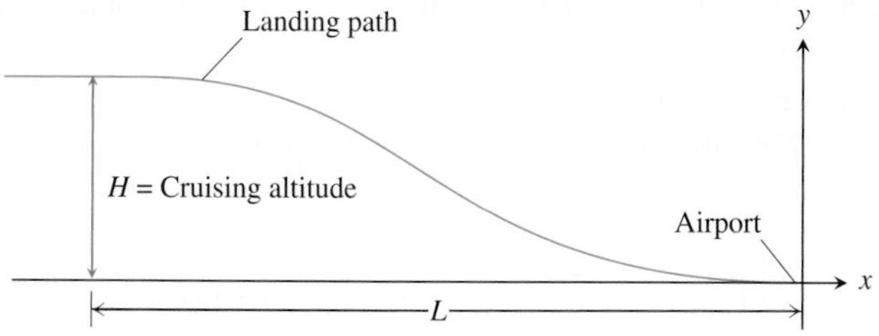

43. It costs you c dollars each to manufacture and distribute backpacks. If the backpacks sell at x dollars each, the number sold is given by

$$n = \frac{a}{x - c} + b(100 - x),$$

where a and b are positive constants. What selling price will bring a maximum profit?

44. You operate a tour service that offers the following rates:

$200 per person if 50 people (the minimum number to book the tour) go on the tour.

For each additional person, up to a maximum of 80 people total, the rate per person is reduced by $2.

It costs $6000 (a fixed cost) plus $32 per person to conduct the tour. How many people does it take to maximize your profit?

45. Wilson lot size formula One of the formulas for inventory management says that the average weekly cost of ordering, paying for, and holding merchandise is

$$A(q) = \frac{km}{q} + cm + \frac{hq}{2},$$

where q is the quantity you order when things run low (shoes, radios, brooms, or whatever the item might be), k is the cost of placing an order (the same, no matter how often you order), c is the cost of one item (a constant), m is the number of items sold each week (a constant), and h is the weekly holding cost per item (a constant that takes into account things such as space, utilities, insurance, and security).

a. Your job, as the inventory manager for your store, is to find the quantity that will minimize $A(q)$. What is it? (The formula you get for the answer is called the *Wilson lot size formula*.)

b. Shipping costs sometimes depend on order size. When they do, it is more realistic to replace k by $k + bq$, the sum of k and a constant multiple of q. What is the most economical quantity to order now?

46. Production level Prove that the production level (if any) at which average cost is smallest is a level at which the average cost equals marginal cost.

47. Show that if $r(x) = 6x$ and $c(x) = x^3 - 6x^2 + 15x$ are your revenue and cost functions, then the best you can do is break even (have revenue equal cost).

48. Production level Suppose that $c(x) = x^3 - 20x^2 + 20{,}000x$ is the cost of manufacturing x items. Find a production level that will minimize the average cost of making x items.

49. Sensitivity to medicine (*Continuation of Exercise 58, Section 3.2.*) Find the amount of medicine to which the body is most sensitive by finding the value of M that maximizes the derivative dR/dM, where

$$R = M^2\left(\frac{C}{2} - \frac{M}{3}\right)$$

and C is a constant.

50. How we cough

a. When we cough, the trachea (windpipe) contracts to increase the velocity of the air going out. This raises the questions of how much it should contract to maximize the velocity and whether it really contracts that much when we cough.

Under reasonable assumptions about the elasticity of the tracheal wall and about how the air near the wall is slowed by friction, the average flow velocity v can be modeled by the equation

$$v = c(r_0 - r)r^2 \text{ cm/sec}, \qquad \frac{r_0}{2} \le r \le r_0,$$

where r_0 is the rest radius of the trachea in centimeters and c is a positive constant whose value depends in part on the length of the trachea.

Show that v is greatest when $r = (2/3)r_0$, that is, when the trachea is about 33% contracted. The remarkable fact is that X-ray photographs confirm that the trachea contracts about this much during a cough.

T **b.** Take r_0 to be 0.5 and c to be 1 and graph v over the interval $0 \le r \le 0.5$. Compare what you see with the claim that v is at a maximum when $r = (2/3)r_0$.

51. An inequality for positive integers Show that if a, b, c, and d are positive integers, then

$$\frac{(a^2 + 1)(b^2 + 1)(c^2 + 1)(d^2 + 1)}{abcd} \ge 16.$$

52. The derivative dt/dx in Example 4

a. Show that

$$f(x) = \frac{x}{\sqrt{a^2 + x^2}}$$

is an increasing function of x.

b. Show that

$$g(x) = \frac{d - x}{\sqrt{b^2 + (d - x)^2}}$$

is a decreasing function of x.

c. Show that

$$\frac{dt}{dx} = \frac{x}{c_1\sqrt{a^2 + x^2}} - \frac{d - x}{c_2\sqrt{b^2 + (d - x)^2}}$$

is an increasing function of x.

53. Let $f(x)$ and $g(x)$ be the differentiable functions graphed here. Point c is the point where the vertical distance between the curves is the greatest. Is there anything special about the tangents to the two curves at c? Give reasons for your answer.

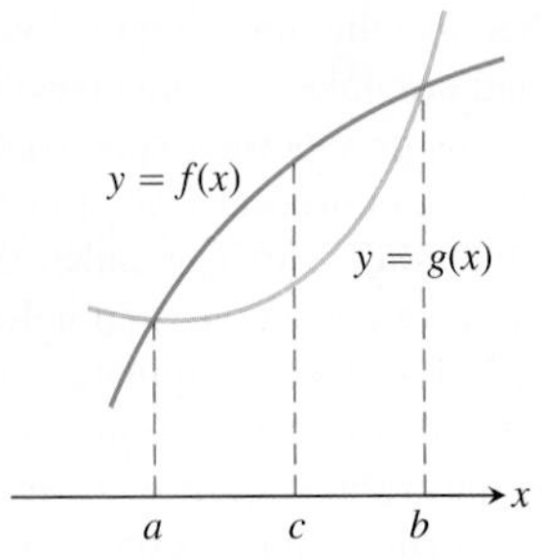

54. You have been asked to determine whether the function $f(x) = 3 + 4\cos x + \cos 2x$ is ever negative.

a. Explain why you need to consider values of x only in the interval $[0, 2\pi]$.

b. Is f ever negative? Explain.

55. a. The function $y = \cot x - \sqrt{2}\csc x$ has an absolute maximum value on the interval $0 < x < \pi$. Find it.

T **b.** Graph the function and compare what you see with your answer in part (a).

56. a. The function $y = \tan x + 3\cot x$ has an absolute minimum value on the interval $0 < x < \pi/2$. Find it.

T **b.** Graph the function and compare what you see with your answer in part (a).

57. a. How close does the curve $y = \sqrt{x}$ come to the point $(3/2, 0)$? (*Hint*: If you minimize the *square* of the distance, you can avoid square roots.)

T **b.** Graph the distance function and $y = \sqrt{x}$ together and reconcile what you see with your answer in part (a).

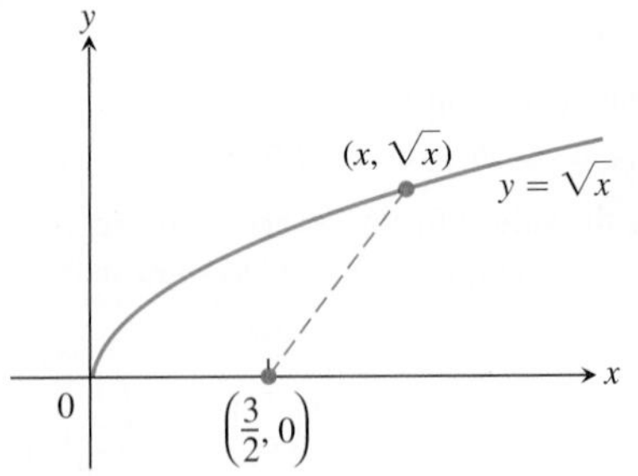

58. a. How close does the semicircle $y = \sqrt{16 - x^2}$ come to the point $(1, \sqrt{3})$?

T **b.** Graph the distance function and $y = \sqrt{16 - x^2}$ together and reconcile what you see with your answer in part (a).

4.6 Indeterminate Forms and L'Hôpital's Rule

HISTORICAL BIOGRAPHY

Guillaume François Antoine de l'Hôpital (1661–1704)
Johann Bernoulli (1667–1748)

John (Johann) Bernoulli discovered a rule using derivatives to calculate limits of fractions whose numerators and denominators both approach zero or $+\infty$. The rule is known today as **l'Hôpital's Rule**, after Guillaume de l'Hôpital. He was a French nobleman who wrote the first introductory differential calculus text, where the rule first appeared in print.

Indeterminate Form 0/0

If the continuous functions $f(x)$ and $g(x)$ are both zero at $x = a$, then

$$\lim_{x \to a} \frac{f(x)}{g(x)}$$

cannot be found by substituting $x = a$. The substitution produces $0/0$, a meaningless expression, which we cannot evaluate. We use $0/0$ as a notation for an expression known as an **indeterminate form**. Sometimes, but not always, limits that lead to indeterminate forms may be found by cancellation, rearrangement of terms, or other algebraic manipulations. This was our experience in Chapter 2. It took considerable analysis in Section 2.4 to find $\lim_{x \to 0} (\sin x)/x$. But we have had success with the limit

$$f'(a) = \lim_{x \to a} \frac{f(x) - f(a)}{x - a},$$

from which we calculate derivatives and which always produces the equivalent of $0/0$ when we substitute $x = a$. L'Hôpital's Rule enables us to draw on our success with derivatives to evaluate limits that otherwise lead to indeterminate forms.

THEOREM 6— L'Hôpital's Rule Suppose that $f(a) = g(a) = 0$, that f and g are differentiable on an open interval I containing a, and that $g'(x) \neq 0$ on I if $x \neq a$. Then

$$\lim_{x \to a} \frac{f(x)}{g(x)} = \lim_{x \to a} \frac{f'(x)}{g'(x)},$$

assuming that the limit on the right side of this equation exists.

We give a proof of Theorem 6 at the end of this section.

Caution
To apply l'Hôpital's Rule to f/g, divide the derivative of f by the derivative of g. Do not fall into the trap of taking the derivative of f/g. The quotient to use is f'/g', not $(f/g)'$.

EXAMPLE 1

(a) $$\lim_{x \to 0} \frac{3x - \sin x}{x} = \lim_{x \to 0} \frac{3 - \cos x}{1} = \left. \frac{3 - \cos x}{1} \right|_{x=0} = 2$$

(b) $$\lim_{x \to 0} \frac{\sqrt{1 + x} - 1}{x} = \lim_{x \to 0} \frac{\dfrac{1}{2\sqrt{1 + x}}}{1} = \frac{1}{2}$$

(c) $\lim_{x\to 0} \frac{\sqrt{1+x} - 1 - x/2}{x^2}$ $\qquad \frac{0}{0}$

$$= \lim_{x\to 0} \frac{(1/2)(1+x)^{-1/2} - 1/2}{2x} \qquad \text{Still } \tfrac{0}{0}\text{; differentiate again.}$$

$$= \lim_{x\to 0} \frac{-(1/4)(1+x)^{-3/2}}{2} = -\frac{1}{8} \qquad \text{Not } \tfrac{0}{0}\text{; limit is found.}$$

(d) $\lim_{x\to 0} \frac{x - \sin x}{x^3}$ $\qquad \frac{0}{0}$

$$= \lim_{x\to 0} \frac{1 - \cos x}{3x^2} \qquad \text{Still } \tfrac{0}{0}$$

$$= \lim_{x\to 0} \frac{\sin x}{6x} \qquad \text{Still } \tfrac{0}{0}$$

$$= \lim_{x\to 0} \frac{\cos x}{6} = \frac{1}{6} \qquad \text{Not } \tfrac{0}{0}\text{; limit is found.}$$

■

Here is a summary of the procedure we followed in Example 1.

Using L'Hôpital's Rule
To find

$$\lim_{x\to a} \frac{f(x)}{g(x)}$$

by l'Hôpital's Rule, continue to differentiate f and g, so long as we still get the form $0/0$ at $x = a$. But as soon as one or the other of these derivatives is different from zero at $x = a$ we stop differentiating. L'Hôpital's Rule does not apply when either the numerator or denominator has a finite nonzero limit.

EXAMPLE 2 Be careful to apply l'Hôpital's Rule correctly:

$$\lim_{x\to 0} \frac{1 - \cos x}{x + x^2} \qquad \frac{0}{0}$$

$$= \lim_{x\to 0} \frac{\sin x}{1 + 2x} = \frac{0}{1} = 0. \qquad \text{Not } \tfrac{0}{0}\text{; limit is found.}$$

Up to now the calculation is correct, but if we continue to differentiate in an attempt to apply l'Hôpital's Rule once more, we get

$$\lim_{x\to 0} \frac{1 - \cos x}{x + x^2} = \lim_{x\to 0} \frac{\sin x}{1 + 2x} = \lim_{x\to 0} \frac{\cos x}{2} = \frac{1}{2},$$

which is wrong. L'Hôpital's Rule can only be applied to limits which give indeterminate forms, and $0/1$ is not an indeterminate form. ■

L'Hôpital's Rule applies to one-sided limits as well.

EXAMPLE 3

Recall that ∞ and $+\infty$ mean the same thing.

(a) $\lim_{x\to 0^+} \frac{\sin x}{x^2}$ $\quad \frac{0}{0}$

$= \lim_{x\to 0^+} \frac{\cos x}{2x} = \infty$ $\quad$ Positive for $x > 0$.

(b) $\lim_{x\to 0^-} \frac{\sin x}{x^2}$ $\quad \frac{0}{0}$

$= \lim_{x\to 0^-} \frac{\cos x}{2x} = -\infty$ $\quad$ Negative for $x < 0$. ■

Indeterminate Forms ∞/∞, $\infty \cdot 0$, $\infty - \infty$

Sometimes when we try to evaluate a limit as $x \to a$ by substituting $x = a$ we get an ambiguous expression like ∞/∞, $\infty \cdot 0$, or $\infty - \infty$, instead of $0/0$. We first consider the form ∞/∞.

In more advanced books it is proved that l'Hôpital's Rule applies to the indeterminate form ∞/∞ as well as to $0/0$. If $f(x) \to \pm\infty$ and $g(x) \to \pm\infty$ as $x \to a$, then

$$\lim_{x\to a} \frac{f(x)}{g(x)} = \lim_{x\to a} \frac{f'(x)}{g'(x)}$$

provided the limit on the right exists. In the notation $x \to a$, a may be either finite or infinite. Moreover $x \to a$ may be replaced by the one-sided limits $x \to a^+$ or $x \to a^-$.

EXAMPLE 4 Find

(a) $\lim_{x\to \pi/2} \frac{\sec x}{1 + \tan x}$ **(b)** $\lim_{x\to\infty} \frac{\ln x}{2\sqrt{x}}$ **(c)** $\lim_{x\to\infty} \frac{e^x}{x^2}$.

Solution

(a) The numerator and denominator are discontinuous at $x = \pi/2$, so we investigate the one-sided limits there. To apply l'Hôpital's Rule, we can choose I to be any open interval with $x = \pi/2$ as an endpoint.

$\lim_{x\to(\pi/2)^-} \frac{\sec x}{1 + \tan x}$ $\quad \frac{\infty}{\infty}$ from the left

$$= \lim_{x\to(\pi/2)^-} \frac{\sec x \tan x}{\sec^2 x} = \lim_{x\to(\pi/2)^-} \sin x = 1$$

The right-hand limit is 1 also, with $(-\infty)/(-\infty)$ as the indeterminate form. Therefore, the two-sided limit is equal to 1.

(b) $\lim_{x\to\infty} \frac{\ln x}{2\sqrt{x}} = \lim_{x\to\infty} \frac{1/x}{1/\sqrt{x}} = \lim_{x\to\infty} \frac{1}{\sqrt{x}} = 0$

(c) $\lim_{x\to\infty} \frac{e^x}{x^2} = \lim_{x\to\infty} \frac{e^x}{2x} = \lim_{x\to\infty} \frac{e^x}{2} = \infty$ ■

Next we turn our attention to the indeterminate forms $\infty \cdot 0$ and $\infty - \infty$. Sometimes these forms can be handled by using algebra to convert them to a $0/0$ or ∞/∞ form. Here again we do not mean to suggest that $\infty \cdot 0$ or $\infty - \infty$ is a number. They are only notations for functional behaviors when considering limits. Here are examples of how we might work with these indeterminate forms.

EXAMPLE 5 Find

(a) $\lim_{x\to\infty}\left(x \sin \frac{1}{x}\right)$ **(b)** $\lim_{x\to 0^+} \sqrt{x} \ln x$

Solution

(a) $$\lim_{x\to\infty}\left(x \sin \frac{1}{x}\right) \qquad \infty \cdot 0$$

$$= \lim_{h\to 0^+}\left(\frac{1}{h} \sin h\right) = 1 \qquad \text{Let } h = 1/x.$$

(b) $$\lim_{x\to 0^+} \sqrt{x} \ln x = \lim_{x\to 0^+} \frac{\ln x}{1/\sqrt{x}} \qquad \infty/\infty$$

$$= \lim_{x\to 0^+} \frac{1/x}{-1/2x^{3/2}} = \lim_{x\to 0^+}\left(-2\sqrt{x}\right) = 0$$ ■

EXAMPLE 6 Find

$$\lim_{x\to 0}\left(\frac{1}{\sin x} - \frac{1}{x}\right).$$

Solution If $x \to 0^+$, then $\sin x \to 0^+$ and

$$\frac{1}{\sin x} - \frac{1}{x} \to \infty - \infty.$$

Similarly, if $x \to 0^-$, then $\sin x \to 0^-$ and

$$\frac{1}{\sin x} - \frac{1}{x} \to -\infty - (-\infty) = -\infty + \infty.$$

Neither form reveals what happens in the limit. To find out, we first combine the fractions:

$$\frac{1}{\sin x} - \frac{1}{x} = \frac{x - \sin x}{x \sin x} \qquad \text{Common denominator is } x \sin x.$$

Then apply l'Hôpital's Rule to the result:

$$\lim_{x\to 0}\left(\frac{1}{\sin x} - \frac{1}{x}\right) = \lim_{x\to 0} \frac{x - \sin x}{x \sin x} \qquad \frac{0}{0}$$

$$= \lim_{x\to 0} \frac{1 - \cos x}{\sin x + x \cos x} \qquad \text{Still } \frac{0}{0}$$

$$= \lim_{x\to 0} \frac{\sin x}{2 \cos x - x \sin x} = \frac{0}{2} = 0.$$ ■

Indeterminate Powers

Limits that lead to the indeterminate forms 1^∞, 0^0, and ∞^0 can sometimes be handled by first taking the logarithm of the function. We use l'Hôpital's Rule to find the limit of the logarithm expression and then exponentiate the result to find the original function limit. This procedure is justified by the continuity of the exponential function and Theorem 11 in Section 2.6, and it is formulated as follows.

> If $\lim_{x\to a} \ln f(x) = L$, then
>
> $$\lim_{x\to a} f(x) = \lim_{x\to a} e^{\ln f(x)} = e^L.$$
>
> Here a may be either finite or infinite.

EXAMPLE 7 Apply l'Hôpital's Rule to show that $\lim_{x\to 0^+} (1 + x)^{1/x} = e$.

Solution The limit leads to the indeterminate form 1^∞. We let $f(x) = (1 + x)^{1/x}$ and find $\lim_{x\to 0^+} \ln f(x)$. Since

$$\ln f(x) = \ln (1 + x)^{1/x} = \frac{1}{x} \ln (1 + x),$$

l' Hôpital's Rule now applies to give

$$\begin{aligned} \lim_{x\to 0^+} \ln f(x) &= \lim_{x\to 0^+} \frac{\ln (1 + x)}{x} \qquad \frac{0}{0} \\ &= \lim_{x\to 0^+} \frac{\frac{1}{1 + x}}{1} \\ &= \frac{1}{1} = 1. \end{aligned}$$

Therefore, $\lim_{x\to 0^+} (1 + x)^{1/x} = \lim_{x\to 0^+} f(x) = \lim_{x\to 0^+} e^{\ln f(x)} = e^1 = e.$ ■

EXAMPLE 8 Find $\lim_{x\to\infty} x^{1/x}$.

Solution The limit leads to the indeterminate form ∞^0. We let $f(x) = x^{1/x}$ and find $\lim_{x\to\infty} \ln f(x)$. Since

$$\ln f(x) = \ln x^{1/x} = \frac{\ln x}{x},$$

l'Hôpital's Rule gives

$$\begin{aligned} \lim_{x\to\infty} \ln f(x) &= \lim_{x\to\infty} \frac{\ln x}{x} \qquad \frac{\infty}{\infty} \\ &= \lim_{x\to\infty} \frac{1/x}{1} \\ &= \frac{0}{1} = 0. \end{aligned}$$

Therefore, $\lim_{x\to\infty} x^{1/x} = \lim_{x\to\infty} f(x) = \lim_{x\to\infty} e^{\ln f(x)} = e^0 = 1.$ ■

Proof of L'Hôpital's Rule

The proof of l'Hôpital's Rule is based on Cauchy's Mean Value Theorem, a Mean Value Theorem that involves two functions instead of one. We prove Cauchy's Theorem first and then show how it leads to l'Hôpital's Rule.

HISTORICAL BIOGRAPHY

Augustin-Louis Cauchy (1789–1857)

THEOREM 7—Cauchy's Mean Value Theorem Suppose functions f and g are continuous on $[a, b]$ and differentiable throughout (a, b) and also suppose $g'(x) \neq 0$ throughout (a, b). Then there exists a number c in (a, b) at which

$$\frac{f'(c)}{g'(c)} = \frac{f(b) - f(a)}{g(b) - g(a)}.$$

Proof We apply the Mean Value Theorem of Section 4.2 twice. First we use it to show that $g(a) \neq g(b)$. For if $g(b)$ did equal $g(a)$, then the Mean Value Theorem would give

$$g'(c) = \frac{g(b) - g(a)}{b - a} = 0$$

for some c between a and b, which cannot happen because $g'(x) \neq 0$ in (a, b).

We next apply the Mean Value Theorem to the function

$$F(x) = f(x) - f(a) - \frac{f(b) - f(a)}{g(b) - g(a)}[g(x) - g(a)].$$

This function is continuous and differentiable where f and g are, and $F(b) = F(a) = 0$. Therefore, there is a number c between a and b for which $F'(c) = 0$. When expressed in terms of f and g, this equation becomes

$$F'(c) = f'(c) - \frac{f(b) - f(a)}{g(b) - g(a)}[g'(c)] = 0$$

or

$$\frac{f'(c)}{g'(c)} = \frac{f(b) - f(a)}{g(b) - g(a)}.$$ ■

Notice that the Mean Value Theorem in Section 4.2 is Theorem 7 with $g(x) = x$.

Cauchy's Mean Value Theorem has a geometric interpretation for a curve C defined by the parametric equations $x = g(t)$ and $y = f(t)$. From Equation (2) in Section 3.5, the slope of the parametric curve at t is given by

$$\frac{dy/dt}{dx/dt} = \frac{f'(t)}{g'(t)},$$

so $f'(c)/g'(c)$ is the slope of the tangent to the curve when $t = c$. The secant line joining the two points $(g(a), f(a))$ and $(g(b), f(b))$ on C has slope

$$\frac{f(b) - f(a)}{g(b) - g(a)}.$$

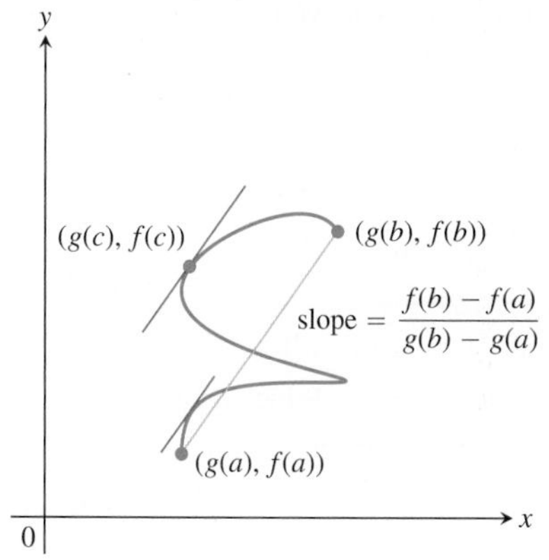

FIGURE 4.42 There is at least one value of the parameter $t = c$, $a < c < b$, for which the slope of the tangent to the curve at $(g(c), f(c))$ is the same as the slope of the secant line joining the points $(g(a), f(a))$ and $(g(b), f(b))$.

Theorem 7 says that there is a parameter value c in the interval (a, b) for which the slope of the tangent to the curve at the point $(g(c), f(c))$ is the same as the slope of the secant line joining the points $(g(a), f(a))$ and $(g(b), f(b))$. This geometric result is shown in Figure 4.42. Note that more than one such value c of the parameter may exist.

We now prove l'Hôpital's Rule.

Proof of l'Hôpital's Rule We first establish the limit equation for the case $x \to a^+$. The method needs almost no change to apply to $x \to a^-$, and the combination of these two cases establishes the result.

Suppose that x lies to the right of a. Then $g'(x) \neq 0$, and we can apply Cauchy's Mean Value Theorem to the closed interval from a to x. This step produces a number c between a and x such that

$$\frac{f'(c)}{g'(c)} = \frac{f(x) - f(a)}{g(x) - g(a)}.$$

But $f(a) = g(a) = 0$, so

$$\frac{f'(c)}{g'(c)} = \frac{f(x)}{g(x)}.$$

As x approaches a, c approaches a because it always lies between a and x. Therefore,

$$\lim_{x\to a^+} \frac{f(x)}{g(x)} = \lim_{c\to a^+} \frac{f'(c)}{g'(c)} = \lim_{x\to a^+} \frac{f'(x)}{g'(x)},$$

which establishes l'Hôpital's Rule for the case where x approaches a from above. The case where x approaches a from below is proved by applying Cauchy's Mean Value Theorem to the closed interval $[x, a]$, $x < a$. ■

EXERCISES 4.6

In Exercises 1–6, use l'Hôpital's Rule to evaluate the limit. Then evaluate the limit using a method studied in Chapter 2.

1. $\lim_{x\to 2} \frac{x - 2}{x^2 - 4}$
2. $\lim_{x\to 0} \frac{\sin 5x}{x}$
3. $\lim_{x\to\infty} \frac{5x^2 - 3x}{7x^2 + 1}$
4. $\lim_{x\to 1} \frac{x^3 - 1}{4x^3 - x - 3}$
5. $\lim_{x\to 0} \frac{1 - \cos x}{x^2}$
6. $\lim_{x\to\infty} \frac{2x^2 + 3x}{x^3 + x + 1}$

Use l'Hôpital's rule to find the limits in Exercises 7–46.

7. $\lim_{x\to 2} \frac{x - 2}{x^2 - 4}$
8. $\lim_{x\to -5} \frac{x^2 - 25}{x + 5}$
9. $\lim_{t\to -3} \frac{t^3 - 4t + 15}{t^2 - t - 12}$
10. $\lim_{t\to 1} \frac{t^3 - 1}{4t^3 - t - 3}$
11. $\lim_{x\to\infty} \frac{5x^3 - 2x}{7x^3 + 3}$
12. $\lim_{x\to\infty} \frac{x - 8x^2}{12x^2 + 5x}$
13. $\lim_{t\to 0} \frac{\sin t^2}{t}$
14. $\lim_{t\to 0} \frac{\sin 5t}{2t}$
15. $\lim_{x\to 0} \frac{8x^2}{\cos x - 1}$
16. $\lim_{x\to 0} \frac{\sin x - x}{x^3}$
17. $\lim_{\theta\to\pi/2} \frac{2\theta - \pi}{\cos(2\pi - \theta)}$
18. $\lim_{\theta\to-\pi/3} \frac{3\theta + \pi}{\sin(\theta + (\pi/3))}$
19. $\lim_{\theta\to\pi/2} \frac{1 - \sin\theta}{1 + \cos 2\theta}$
20. $\lim_{x\to 1} \frac{x - 1}{\ln x - \sin \pi x}$
21. $\lim_{x\to 0} \frac{x^2}{\ln(\sec x)}$
22. $\lim_{x\to\pi/2} \frac{\ln(\csc x)}{(x - (\pi/2))^2}$

23. $\lim_{t\to 0} \frac{t(1-\cos t)}{t-\sin t}$

24. $\lim_{t\to 0} \frac{t\sin t}{1-\cos t}$

25. $\lim_{x\to(\pi/2)^-} \left(x-\frac{\pi}{2}\right)\sec x$

26. $\lim_{x\to(\pi/2)^-} \left(\frac{\pi}{2}-x\right)\tan x$

27. $\lim_{\theta\to 0} \frac{3^{\sin\theta}-1}{\theta}$

28. $\lim_{\theta\to 0} \frac{(1/2)^{\theta}-1}{\theta}$

29. $\lim_{x\to 0} \frac{x2^x}{2^x-1}$

30. $\lim_{x\to 0} \frac{3^x-1}{2^x-1}$

31. $\lim_{x\to\infty} \frac{\ln(x+1)}{\log_2 x}$

32. $\lim_{x\to\infty} \frac{\log_2 x}{\log_3(x+3)}$

33. $\lim_{x\to 0^+} \frac{\ln(x^2+2x)}{\ln x}$

34. $\lim_{x\to 0^+} \frac{\ln(e^x-1)}{\ln x}$

35. $\lim_{y\to 0} \frac{\sqrt{5y+25}-5}{y}$

36. $\lim_{y\to 0} \frac{\sqrt{ay+a^2}-a}{y}, \quad a>0$

37. $\lim_{x\to\infty} (\ln 2x - \ln(x+1))$

38. $\lim_{x\to 0^+} (\ln x - \ln\sin x)$

39. $\lim_{h\to 0} \frac{\sin(a+h)-\sin a}{h}$

40. $\lim_{x\to 0^+} \left(\frac{3x+1}{x}-\frac{1}{\sin x}\right)$

41. $\lim_{x\to 1^+} \left(\frac{1}{x-1}-\frac{1}{\ln x}\right)$

42. $\lim_{x\to 0^+} (\csc x - \cot x + \cos x)$

43. $\lim_{\theta\to 0} \frac{\cos\theta - 1}{e^\theta - \theta - 1}$

44. $\lim_{h\to 0} \frac{e^h-(1+h)}{h^2}$

45. $\lim_{t\to\infty} \frac{e^t+t^2}{e^t-t}$

46. $\lim_{x\to\infty} x^2e^{-x}$

Find the limits in Exercise 47–56.

47. $\lim_{x\to 1^+} x^{1/(1-x)}$

48. $\lim_{x\to 1^+} x^{1/(x-1)}$

49. $\lim_{x\to\infty} (\ln x)^{1/x}$

50. $\lim_{x\to e^+} (\ln x)^{1/(x-e)}$

51. $\lim_{x\to 0^+} x^{-1/\ln x}$

52. $\lim_{x\to\infty} x^{1/\ln x}$

53. $\lim_{x\to\infty} (1+2x)^{1/(2\ln x)}$

54. $\lim_{x\to 0} (e^x+x)^{1/x}$

55. $\lim_{x\to 0^+} x^x$

56. $\lim_{x\to 0^+} \left(1+\frac{1}{x}\right)^x$

L'Hôpital's Rule does not help with the limits in Exercises 57–60. Try it—you just keep on cycling. Find the limits some other way.

57. $\lim_{x\to\infty} \frac{\sqrt{9x+1}}{\sqrt{x+1}}$

58. $\lim_{x\to 0^+} \frac{\sqrt{x}}{\sqrt{\sin x}}$

59. $\lim_{x\to(\pi/2)^-} \frac{\sec x}{\tan x}$

60. $\lim_{x\to 0^+} \frac{\cot x}{\csc x}$

61. Which one is correct, and which one is wrong? Give reasons for your answers.

a. $\lim_{x\to 3} \frac{x-3}{x^2-3} = \lim_{x\to 3} \frac{1}{2x} = \frac{1}{6}$

b. $\lim_{x\to 3} \frac{x-3}{x^2-3} = \frac{0}{6} = 0$

62. Which one is correct, and which one is wrong? Give reasons for your answers.

a. $\lim_{x\to 0} \frac{x^2-2x}{x^2-\sin x} = \lim_{x\to 0} \frac{2x-2}{2x-\cos x}$

$$= \lim_{x\to 0} \frac{2}{2+\sin x} = \frac{2}{2+0} = 1$$

b. $\lim_{x\to 0} \frac{x^2-2x}{x^2-\sin x} = \lim_{x\to 0} \frac{2x-2}{2x-\cos x} = \frac{-2}{0-1} = 2$

63. Only one of these calculations is correct. Which one? Why are the others wrong? Give reasons for your answers.

a. $\lim_{x\to 0^+} x\ln x = 0\cdot(-\infty) = 0$

b. $\lim_{x\to 0^+} x\ln x = 0\cdot(-\infty) = -\infty$

c. $\lim_{x\to 0^+} x\ln x = \lim_{x\to 0^+} \frac{\ln x}{(1/x)} = \frac{-\infty}{\infty} = -1$

d. $\lim_{x\to 0^+} x\ln x = \lim_{x\to 0^+} \frac{\ln x}{(1/x)}$

$$= \lim_{x\to 0^+} \frac{(1/x)}{(-1/x^2)} = \lim_{x\to 0^+} (-x) = 0$$

64. Find all values of c that satisfy the conclusion of Cauchy's Mean Value Theorem for the given functions and interval.

a. $f(x) = x, \quad g(x) = x^2, \quad (a,b) = (-2,0)$

b. $f(x) = x, \quad g(x) = x^2, \quad (a,b)$ arbitrary

c. $f(x) = x^3/3 - 4x, \quad g(x) = x^2, \quad (a,b) = (0,3)$

65. **Continuous extension** Find a value of c that makes the function

$$f(x) = \begin{cases} \dfrac{9x-3\sin 3x}{5x^3}, & x \neq 0 \\ c, & x = 0 \end{cases}$$

continuous at $x = 0$. Explain why your value of c works.

T 66. **$\infty - \infty$ Form**

a. Estimate the value of

$$\lim_{x\to\infty} \left(x - \sqrt{x^2+x}\right)$$

by graphing $f(x) = x - \sqrt{x^2+x}$ over a suitably large interval of x-values.

b. Now confirm your estimate by finding the limit with l'Hôpital's Rule. As the first step, multiply $f(x)$ by the fraction $(x+\sqrt{x^2+x})/(x+\sqrt{x^2+x})$ and simplify the new numerator.

T 67. **0/0 Form** Estimate the value of

$$\lim_{x\to 1} \frac{2x^2-(3x+1)\sqrt{x}+2}{x-1}$$

by graphing. Then confirm your estimate with l'Hôpital's Rule.

68. This exercise explores the difference between the limit

$$\lim_{x\to\infty} \left(1+\frac{1}{x^2}\right)^x$$

and the limit

$$\lim_{x\to\infty}\left(1+\frac{1}{x}\right)^x = e.$$

a. Use l'Hôpital's Rule to show that

$$\lim_{x\to\infty}\left(1+\frac{1}{x}\right)^x = e.$$

T **b.** Graph

$$f(x) = \left(1+\frac{1}{x^2}\right)^x \quad \text{and} \quad g(x) = \left(1+\frac{1}{x}\right)^x$$

together for $x \geq 0$. How does the behavior of f compare with that of g? Estimate the value of $\lim_{x\to\infty} f(x)$.

c. Confirm your estimate of $\lim_{x\to\infty} f(x)$ by calculating it with l'Hôpital's Rule.

69. Show that

$$\lim_{k\to\infty}\left(1+\frac{r}{k}\right)^k = e^r.$$

70. Given that $x > 0$, find the maximum value, if any, of

a. $x^{1/x}$

b. x^{1/x^2}

c. x^{1/x^n} (n a positive integer)

d. Show that $\lim_{x\to\infty} x^{1/x^n} = 1$ for every positive integer n.

T **71. The continuous extension of $(\sin x)^x$ to $[0, \pi]$**

a. Graph $f(x) = (\sin x)^x$ on the interval $0 \leq x \leq \pi$. What value would you assign to f to make it continuous at $x = 0$?

b. Verify your conclusion in (a) by finding $\lim_{x\to 0^+} f(x)$ with l'Hôpital's Rule.

c. Returning to the graph, estimate the maximum value of f on $[0, \pi]$. About where is max f taken on?

d. Sharpen your estimate in (c) by graphing f' in the same window to see where its graph crosses the x-axis. To simplify your work, you might want to delete the exponential factor from the expression for f' and graph just the factor that has a zero.

T **72. The function $(\sin x)^{\tan x}$** *(Continuation of Exercise 71.)*

a. Graph $f(x) = (\sin x)^{\tan x}$ on the interval $-7 \leq x \leq 7$. How do you account for the gaps in the graph? How wide are the gaps?

b. Now graph f on the interval $0 \leq x \leq \pi$. The function is not defined at $x = \pi/2$, but the graph has no break at this point. What is going on? What value does the graph appear to give for f at $x = \pi/2$? (*Hint:* Use l'Hôpital's Rule to find lim f as $x \to (\pi/2)^-$ and $x \to (\pi/2)^+$.)

c. Continuing with the graphs in (b), find max f and min f as accurately as you can and estimate the values of x at which they are taken on.

4.7 Newton's Method

In this section we study a numerical method, called *Newton's method* or the *Newton–Raphson method*, which is a technique to approximate the solution to an equation $f(x) = 0$. Essentially it uses tangent lines in place of the graph of $y = f(x)$ near the points where f is zero. (A value of x where f is zero is a *root* of the function f and a *solution* of the equation $f(x) = 0$.)

Procedure for Newton's Method

The goal of Newton's method for estimating a solution of an equation $f(x) = 0$ is to produce a sequence of approximations that approach the solution. We pick the first number x_0 of the sequence. Then, under favorable circumstances, the method does the rest by moving step by step toward a point where the graph of f crosses the x-axis (Figure 4.43). At each step the method approximates a zero of f with a zero of one of its linearizations. Here is how it works.

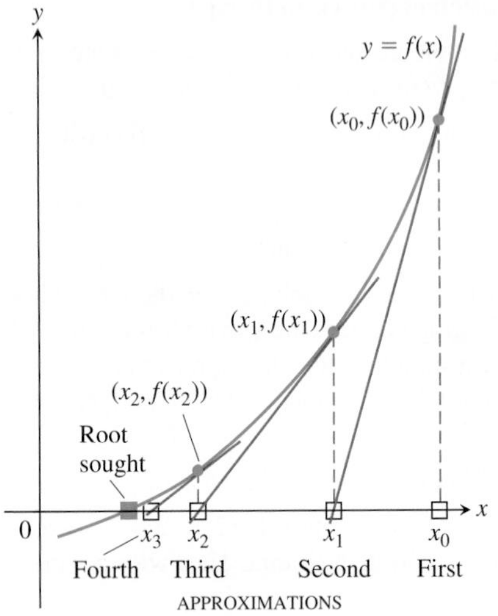

FIGURE 4.43 Newton's method starts with an initial guess x_0 and (under favorable circumstances) improves the guess one step at a time.

The initial estimate, x_0, may be found by graphing or just plain guessing. The method then uses the tangent to the curve $y = f(x)$ at $(x_0, f(x_0))$ to approximate the curve, calling the point x_1 where the tangent meets the x-axis (Figure 4.43). The number x_1 is usually a better approximation to the solution than is x_0. The point x_2 where the tangent to the curve at $(x_1, f(x_1))$ crosses the x-axis is the next approximation in the sequence. We continue on, using each approximation to generate the next, until we are close enough to the root to stop.

We can derive a formula for generating the successive approximations in the following way. Given the approximation x_n, the point-slope equation for the tangent to the curve at $(x_n, f(x_n))$ is

$$y = f(x_n) + f'(x_n)(x - x_n).$$

We can find where it crosses the x-axis by setting $y = 0$ (Figure 4.44).

$$0 = f(x_n) + f'(x_n)(x - x_n)$$

$$-\frac{f(x_n)}{f'(x_n)} = x - x_n$$

$$x = x_n - \frac{f(x_n)}{f'(x_n)} \qquad \text{If } f'(x_n) \neq 0$$

This value of x is the next approximation x_{n+1}. Here is a summary of Newton's method.

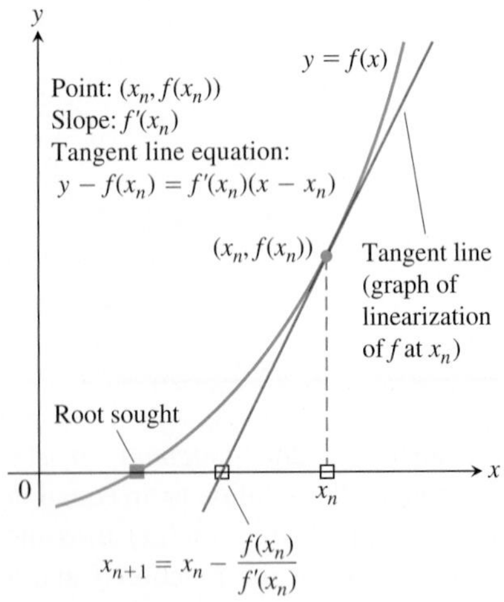

FIGURE 4.44 The geometry of the successive steps of Newton's method. From x_n we go up to the curve and follow the tangent line down to find x_{n+1}.

Procedure for Newton's Method

1. Guess a first approximation to a solution of the equation $f(x) = 0$. A graph of $y = f(x)$ may help.
2. Use the first approximation to get a second, the second to get a third, and so on, using the formula

$$x_{n+1} = x_n - \frac{f(x_n)}{f'(x_n)}, \qquad \text{if } f'(x_n) \neq 0 \tag{1}$$

Applying Newton's Method

Applications of Newton's method generally involve many numerical computations, making them well suited for computers or calculators. Nevertheless, even when the calculations are done by hand (which may be very tedious), they give a powerful way to find solutions of equations.

EXAMPLE 1 Find the x-coordinate of the point where the curve $y = x^3 - x$ crosses the horizontal line $y = 1$.

Solution The curve crosses the line when $x^3 - x = 1$ or $x^3 - x - 1 = 0$. When does $f(x) = x^3 - x - 1$ equal zero? Since $f(1) = -1$ and $f(2) = 5$, we know by the Intermediate Value Theorem there is a root in the interval $(1, 2)$ (Figure 4.45).

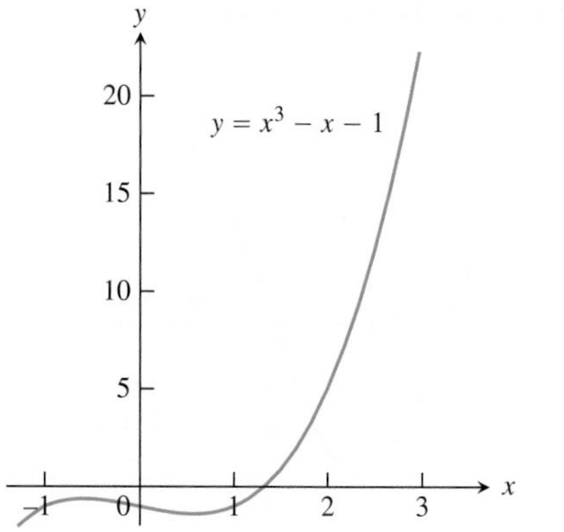

FIGURE 4.45 The graph of $f(x) = x^3 - x - 1$ crosses the x-axis once; this is the root we want to find (Example 1).

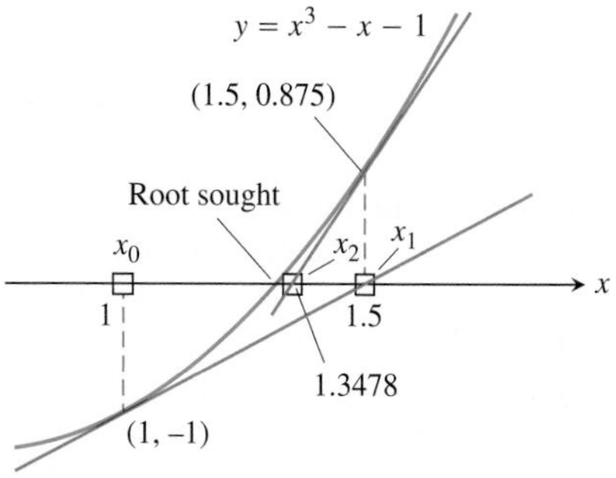

FIGURE 4.46 The first three x-values in Table 4.1 (four decimal places).

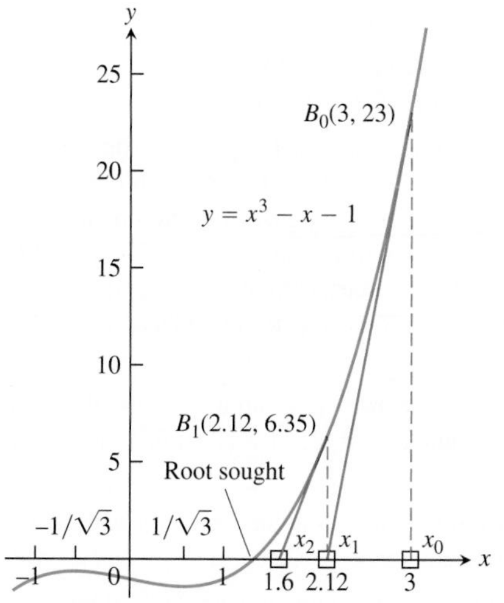

FIGURE 4.47 Any starting value x_0 to the right of $x = 1/\sqrt{3}$ will lead to the root.

We apply Newton's method to f with the starting value $x_0 = 1$. The results are displayed in Table 4.1 and Figure 4.46.

At $n = 5$, we come to the result $x_6 = x_5 = 1.3247\,17957$. When $x_{n+1} = x_n$, Equation (1) shows that $f(x_n) = 0$. We have found a solution of $f(x) = 0$ to nine decimals. ■

TABLE 4.1 The result of applying Newton's method to $f(x) = x^3 - x - 1$ with $x_0 = 1$

n	x_n	$f(x_n)$	$f'(x_n)$	$x_{n+1} = x_n - \dfrac{f(x_n)}{f'(x_n)}$
0	1	−1	2	1.5
1	1.5	0.875	5.75	1.3478 26087
2	1.3478 26087	0.1006 82173	4.4499 05482	1.3252 00399
3	1.3252 00399	0.0020 58362	4.2684 68292	1.3247 18174
4	1.3247 18174	0.0000 00924	4.2646 34722	1.3247 17957
5	1.3247 17957	−1.8672E-13	4.2646 32999	1.3247 17957

In Figure 4.47 we have indicated that the process in Example 1 might have started at the point $B_0(3, 23)$ on the curve, with $x_0 = 3$. Point B_0 is quite far from the x-axis, but the tangent at B_0 crosses the x-axis at about (2.12, 0), so x_1 is still an improvement over x_0. If we use Equation (1) repeatedly as before, with $f(x) = x^3 - x - 1$ and $f'(x) = 3x^2 - 1$, we obtain the nine-place solution $x_7 = x_6 = 1.3247\,17957$ in seven steps.

Convergence of the Approximations

In Chapter 8 we define precisely the idea of *convergence* for the approximations x_n in Newton's method. Intuitively, we mean that as the number n of approximations increases without bound, the values x_n get arbitrarily close to the desired root r. (This notion is similar to the idea of the limit of a function $g(t)$ as t approaches infinity, as defined in Section 2.4.)

In practice, Newton's method usually gives convergence with impressive speed, but this is not guaranteed. One way to test convergence is to begin by graphing the function to estimate a good starting value for x_0. You can test that you are getting closer to a zero of the function by evaluating $|f(x_n)|$ and check that the approximations are converging by evaluating $|x_n - x_{n+1}|$.

Newton's method does not always converge. For instance, if

$$f(x) = \begin{cases} -\sqrt{r - x}, & x < r \\ \sqrt{x - r}, & x \geq r, \end{cases}$$

the graph will be like the one in Figure 4.48. If we begin with $x_0 = r - h$, we get $x_1 = r + h$, and successive approximations go back and forth between these two values. No amount of iteration brings us closer to the root than our first guess.

If Newton's method does converge, it converges to a root. Be careful, however. There are situations in which the method appears to converge but there is no root there. Fortunately, such situations are rare.

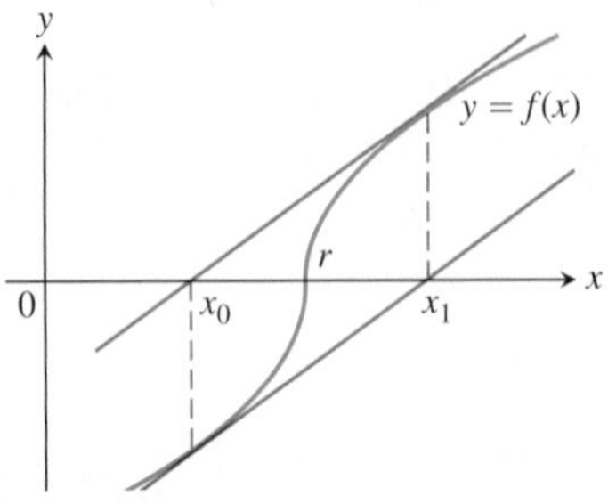

FIGURE 4.48 Newton's method fails to converge. You go from x_0 to x_1 and back to x_0, never getting any closer to r.

When Newton's method converges to a root, it may not be the root you have in mind. Figure 4.49 shows two ways this can happen.

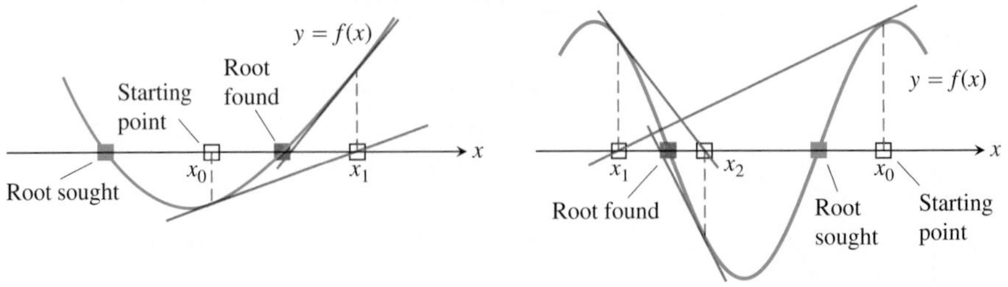

FIGURE 4.49 If you start too far away, Newton's method may miss the root you want.

EXERCISES 4.7

1. Use Newton's method to estimate the solutions of the equation $x^2 + x - 1 = 0$. Start with $x_0 = -1$ for the left-hand solution and with $x_0 = 1$ for the solution on the right. Then, in each case, find x_2.

2. Use Newton's method to estimate the one real solution of $x^3 + 3x + 1 = 0$. Start with $x_0 = 0$ and then find x_2.

3. Use Newton's method to estimate the two zeros of the function $f(x) = x^4 + x - 3$. Start with $x_0 = -1$ for the left-hand zero and with $x_0 = 1$ for the zero on the right. Then, in each case, find x_2.

4. Use Newton's method to estimate the two zeros of the function $f(x) = 2x - x^2 + 1$. Start with $x_0 = 0$ for the left-hand zero and with $x_0 = 2$ for the zero on the right. Then, in each case, find x_2.

In Exercises 5 and 6, use Newton's method to find all roots of the equation correct to six decimal places.

5. $e^{-x} = 2x + 1$

6. $\tan^{-1} x = 1 - 2x$

7. **Guessing a root** Suppose that your first guess is lucky, in the sense that x_0 is a root of $f(x) = 0$. Assuming that $f'(x_0)$ is defined and not 0, what happens to x_1 and later approximations?

8. **Estimating pi** You plan to estimate $\pi/2$ to five decimal places by using Newton's method to solve the equation $\cos x = 0$. Does it matter what your starting value is? Give reasons for your answer.

9. **Oscillation** Show that if $h > 0$, applying Newton's method to

$$f(x) = \begin{cases} \sqrt{x}, & x \geq 0 \\ \sqrt{-x}, & x < 0 \end{cases}$$

leads to $x_1 = -h$ if $x_0 = h$ and to $x_1 = h$ if $x_0 = -h$. Draw a picture that shows what is going on.

10. **Approximations that get worse and worse** Apply Newton's method to $f(x) = x^{1/3}$ with $x_0 = 1$ and calculate x_1, x_2, x_3, and x_4. Find a formula for $|x_n|$. What happens to $|x_n|$ as $n \to \infty$? Draw a picture that shows what is going on.

11. Explain why the following four statements ask for the same information:

 i) Find the roots of $f(x) = x^3 - 3x - 1$.

 ii) Find the x-coordinates of the intersections of the curve $y = x^3$ with the line $y = 3x + 1$.

 iii) Find the x-coordinates of the points where the curve $y = x^3 - 3x$ crosses the horizontal line $y = 1$.

 iv) Find the values of x where the derivative of $g(x) = (1/4)x^4 - (3/2)x^2 - x + 5$ equals zero.

12. **Locating a planet** To calculate a planet's space coordinates, we have to solve equations like $x = 1 + 0.5 \sin x$. Graphing the function $f(x) = x - 1 - 0.5 \sin x$ suggests that the function has a root near $x = 1.5$. Use one application of Newton's method to improve this estimate. That is, start with $x_0 = 1.5$ and find x_1. (The value of the root is 1.49870 to five decimal places.) Remember to use radians.

T 13. **Intersecting curves** The curve $y = \tan x$ crosses the line $y = 2x$ between $x = 0$ and $x = \pi/2$. Use Newton's method to find where.

T 14. **Real solutions of a quartic** Use Newton's method to find the two real solutions of the equation $x^4 - 2x^3 - x^2 - 2x + 2 = 0$.

T 15. **a.** How many solutions does the equation $\sin 3x = 0.99 - x^2$ have?

 b. Use Newton's method to find them.

16. **Intersection of curves**

  a. Does $\cos 3x$ ever equal x? Give reasons for your answer.

  b. Use Newton's method to find where.

17. Find the four real zeros of the function $f(x) = 2x^4 - 4x^2 + 1$.

T 18. **Estimating pi** Estimate π to as many decimal places as your calculator will display by using Newton's method to solve the equation $\tan x = 0$ with $x_0 = 3$.

19. **Intersection of curves** At what value(s) of x does $e^{-x^2} = x^2 - x + 1$?

20. **Intersection of curves** At what value(s) of x does $\ln(1 - x^2) = x - 1$?

21. Use the Intermediate Value Theorem from Section 2.6 to show that $f(x) = x^3 + 2x - 4$ has a root between $x = 1$ and $x = 2$. Then find the root to five decimal places.

22. **Factoring a quartic** Find the approximate values of r_1 through r_4 in the factorization

$$8x^4 - 14x^3 - 9x^2 + 11x - 1 = 8(x - r_1)(x - r_2)(x - r_3)(x - r_4).$$

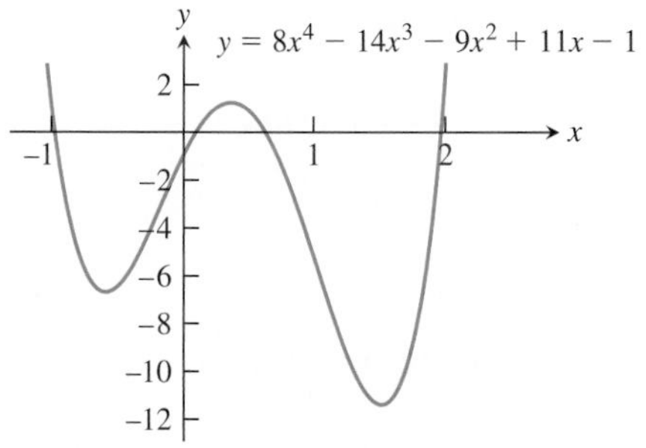

T 23. **Converging to different zeros** Use Newton's method to find the zeros of $f(x) = 4x^4 - 4x^2$ using the given starting values.

  a. $x_0 = -2$ and $x_0 = -0.8$, lying in $\left(-\infty, -\sqrt{2}/2\right)$

  b. $x_0 = -0.5$ and $x_0 = 0.25$, lying in $\left(-\sqrt{21}/7, \sqrt{21}/7\right)$

  c. $x_0 = 0.8$ and $x_0 = 2$, lying in $\left(\sqrt{2}/2, \infty\right)$

  d. $x_0 = -\sqrt{21}/7$ and $x_0 = \sqrt{21}/7$

24. **The sonobuoy problem** In submarine location problems, it is often necessary to find a submarine's closest point of approach (CPA) to a sonobuoy (sound detector) in the water. Suppose that the submarine travels on the parabolic path $y = x^2$ and that the buoy is located at the point $(2, -1/2)$.

  a. Show that the value of x that minimizes the distance between the submarine and the buoy is a solution of the equation $x = 1/(x^2 + 1)$.

  b. Solve the equation $x = 1/(x^2 + 1)$ with Newton's method.

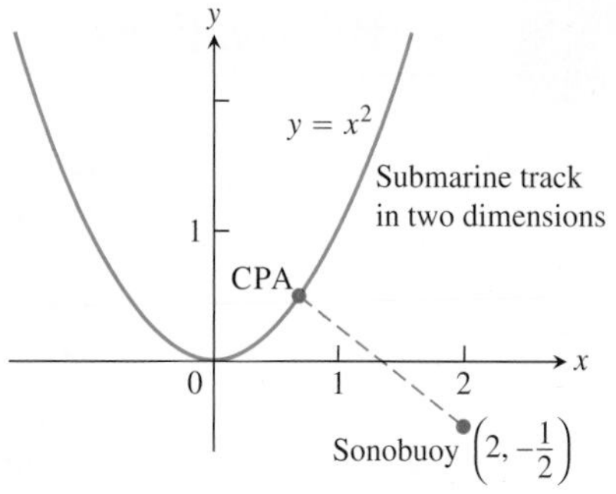

25. **Curves that are nearly flat at the root** Some curves are so flat that, in practice, Newton's method stops too far from the root to give a useful estimate. Try Newton's method on $f(x) = (x - 1)^{40}$ with a starting value of $x_0 = 2$ to see how close your machine comes to the root $x = 1$.

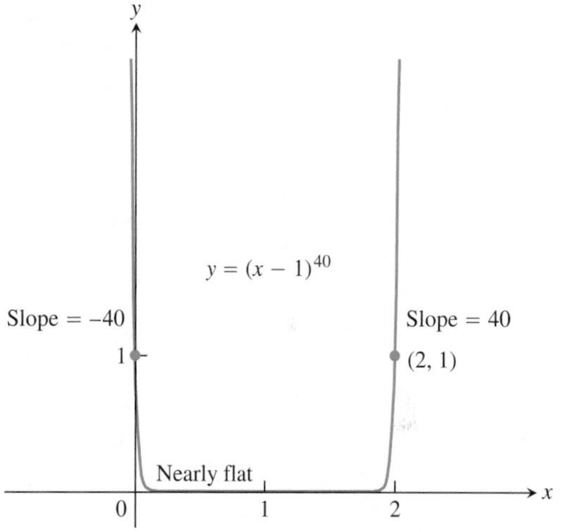

26. **Finding an ion concentration** While trying to find the acidity of a saturated solution of magnesium hydroxide in hydrochloric acid, you derive the equation

$$\frac{3.64 \times 10^{-11}}{[H_3O^+]^2} = [H_3O^+] + 3.6 \times 10^{-4}$$

for the hydronium ion concentration $[H_3O^+]$. To find the value of $[H_3O^+]$, you set $x = 10^4[H_3O^+]$ and convert the equation to

$$x^3 + 3.6x^2 - 36.4 = 0.$$

You then solve this by Newton's method. What do you get for x? (Make it good to two decimal places.) For $[H_3O^+]$?

4.8 Antiderivatives

We have studied how to find the derivative of a function. However, many problems require that we recover a function from its known derivative (from its known rate of change). For instance, we may know the velocity function of an object falling from an initial height and need to know its height at any time. More generally, we want to find a function F from its derivative f. If such a function F exists, it is called an *antiderivative* of f.

Finding Antiderivatives

DEFINITION A function F is an **antiderivative** of f on an interval I if $F'(x) = f(x)$ for all x in I.

The process of recovering a function $F(x)$ from its derivative $f(x)$ is called *antidifferentiation*. We use capital letters such as F to represent an antiderivative of a function f, G to represent an antiderivative of g, and so forth.

EXAMPLE 1 Find an antiderivative for each of the following functions.

(a) $f(x) = 2x$ **(b)** $g(x) = \cos x$ **(c)** $h(x) = \frac{1}{x} + 2e^{2x}$

Solution

(a) $F(x) = x^2$ **(b)** $G(x) = \sin x$ **(c)** $H(x) = \ln|x| + e^{2x}$

Each answer can be checked by differentiating. The derivative of $F(x) = x^2$ is $2x$. The derivative of $G(x) = \sin x$ is $\cos x$ and the derivative of $H(x) = \ln|x| + e^{2x}$ is $(1/x) + 2e^{2x}$. ■

The function $F(x) = x^2$ is not the only function whose derivative is $2x$. The function $x^2 + 1$ has the same derivative. So does $x^2 + C$ for any constant C. Are there others?

Corollary 2 of the Mean Value Theorem in Section 4.2 gives the answer: Any two antiderivatives of a function differ by a constant. So the functions $x^2 + C$, where C is an **arbitrary constant**, form *all* the antiderivatives of $f(x) = 2x$. More generally, we have the following result.

THEOREM 8 If F is an antiderivative of f on an interval I, then the most general antiderivative of f on I is

$$F(x) + C$$

where C is an arbitrary constant.

Thus the most general antiderivative of f on I is a *family* of functions $F(x) + C$ whose graphs are vertical translates of one another. We can select a particular antiderivative from this family by assigning a specific value to C. Here is an example showing how such an assignment might be made.

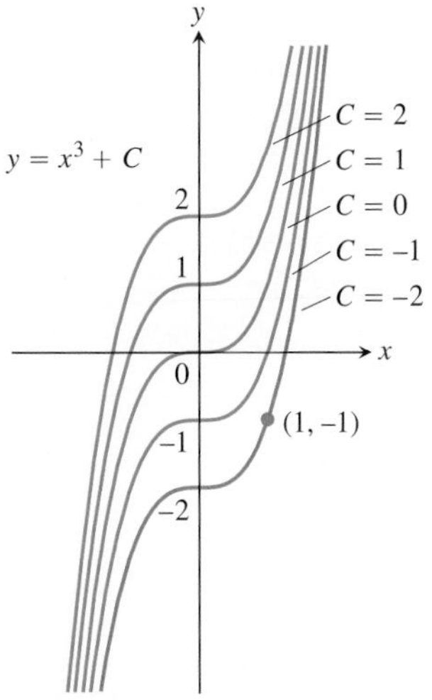

FIGURE 4.50 The curves $y = x^3 + C$ fill the coordinate plane without overlapping. In Example 2, we identify the curve $y = x^3 - 2$ as the one that passes through the given point $(1, -1)$.

EXAMPLE 2 Find an antiderivative of $f(x) = 3x^2$ that satisfies $F(1) = -1$.

Solution Since the derivative of x^3 is $3x^2$, the general antiderivative

$$F(x) = x^3 + C$$

gives all the antiderivatives of $f(x)$. The condition $F(1) = -1$ determines a specific value for C. Substituting $x = 1$ into $F(x) = x^3 + C$ gives

$$F(1) = (1)^3 + C = 1 + C.$$

Since $F(1) = -1$, solving for C gives $C = -2$. So

$$F(x) = x^3 - 2$$

is the antiderivative satisfying $F(1) = -1$. Notice that this assignment for C selects the particular curve from the family of curves $y = x^3 + C$ that passes through the point $(1, -1)$ in the plane (Figure 4.50). ■

By working backward from assorted differentiation rules, we can derive formulas and rules for antiderivatives. In each case there is an arbitrary constant C in the general expression representing all antiderivatives of a given function. Table 4.2 gives antiderivative formulas for a number of important functions.

The rules in Table 4.2 are easily verified by differentiating the general antiderivative formula to obtain the function to its left. For example, the derivative of $(\tan kx)/k + C$ is $\sec^2 kx$, whatever the value of the constants C or $k \neq 0$, and this establishes the formula for the most general antiderivative of $\sec^2 kx$.

TABLE 4.2 Antiderivative formulas, k a nonzero constant

	Function	General antiderivative		Function	General antiderivative
1.	x^n	$\frac{1}{n+1}x^{n+1} + C, \quad n \neq -1$	**8.**	e^{kx}	$\frac{1}{k}e^{kx} + C$
2.	$\sin kx$	$-\frac{1}{k}\cos kx + C$	**9.**	$\frac{1}{x}$	$\ln\lvert x\rvert + C, \quad x \neq 0$
3.	$\cos kx$	$\frac{1}{k}\sin kx + C$	**10.**	$\frac{1}{\sqrt{1 - k^2x^2}}$	$\frac{1}{k}\sin^{-1} kx + C$
4.	$\sec^2 kx$	$\frac{1}{k}\tan kx + C$	**11.**	$\frac{1}{1 + k^2x^2}$	$\frac{1}{k}\tan^{-1} kx + C$
5.	$\csc^2 kx$	$-\frac{1}{k}\cot kx + C$	**12.**	$\frac{1}{x\sqrt{k^2x^2 - 1}}$	$\sec^{-1} kx + C, \quad kx > 1$
6.	$\sec kx \tan kx$	$\frac{1}{k}\sec kx + C$	**13.**	a^{kx}	$\left(\frac{1}{k \ln a}\right)a^{kx} + C, \quad a > 0, \ a \neq 1$
7.	$\csc kx \cot kx$	$-\frac{1}{k}\csc kx + C$			

EXAMPLE 3 Find the general antiderivative of each of the following functions.

(a) $f(x) = x^5$ **(b)** $g(x) = \frac{1}{\sqrt{x}}$ **(c)** $h(x) = \sin 2x$

(d) $i(x) = \cos \frac{x}{2}$ **(e)** $j(x) = e^{-3x}$ **(f)** $k(x) = 2^x$

Solution

(a) $F(x) = \dfrac{x^6}{6} + C$ — Formula 1 with $n = 5$

(b) $g(x) = x^{-1/2}$, so

$$G(x) = \frac{x^{1/2}}{1/2} + C = 2\sqrt{x} + C$$ Formula 1 with $n = -1/2$

(c) $H(x) = \dfrac{-\cos 2x}{2} + C$ — Formula 2 with $k = 2$

(d) $I(x) = \dfrac{\sin(x/2)}{1/2} + C = 2\sin\dfrac{x}{2} + C$ — Formula 3 with $k = 1/2$

(e) $J(x) = -\dfrac{1}{3}e^{-3x} + C$ — Formula 8 with $k = -3$

(f) $K(x) = \left(\dfrac{1}{\ln 2}\right)2^x + C$ — Formula 13 with $a = 2$, $k = 1$ ■

Other derivative rules also lead to corresponding antiderivative rules. We can add and subtract antiderivatives, and multiply them by constants.

TABLE 4.3 Antiderivative linearity rules

		Function	General antiderivative
1.	*Constant Multiple Rule:*	$kf(x)$	$kF(x) + C$, k a constant
2.	*Negative Rule:*	$-f(x)$	$-F(x) + C$
3.	*Sum or Difference Rule:*	$f(x) \pm g(x)$	$F(x) \pm G(x) + C$

The formulas in Table 4.3 are easily proved by differentiating the antiderivatives and verifying that the result agrees with the original function. Formula 2 is the special case $k = -1$ in Formula 1.

EXAMPLE 4 Find the general antiderivative of

$$f(x) = \frac{3}{\sqrt{x}} + \sin 2x.$$

Solution We have that $f(x) = 3g(x) + h(x)$ for the functions g and h in Example 3. Since $G(x) = 2\sqrt{x}$ is an antiderivative of $g(x)$ from Example 3b, it follows from the Constant Multiple Rule for antiderivatives that $3G(x) = 3 \cdot 2\sqrt{x} = 6\sqrt{x}$ is an antiderivative of $3g(x) = 3/\sqrt{x}$. Likewise, from Example 3c we know that $H(x) = (-1/2)\cos 2x$ is an antiderivative of $h(x) = \sin 2x$. From the Sum Rule for antiderivatives, we then get that

$$\begin{aligned} F(x) &= 3G(x) + H(x) + C \\ &= 6\sqrt{x} - \frac{1}{2}\cos 2x + C \end{aligned}$$

is the general antiderivative formula for $f(x)$, where C is an arbitrary constant. ■

Antiderivatives play several important roles, and methods and techniques for finding them are a major part of calculus. (This is the subject of Chapter 7.)

Initial Value Problems and Differential Equations

Finding an antiderivative for a function $f(x)$ is the same problem as finding a function $y(x)$ that satisfies the equation

$$\frac{dy}{dx} = f(x).$$

This is called a **differential equation**, since it is an equation involving an unknown function y that is being differentiated. To solve it, we need a function $y(x)$ that satisfies the equation. This function is found by taking the antiderivative of $f(x)$. We fix the arbitrary constant arising in the antidifferentiation process by specifying an initial condition

$$y(x_0) = y_0.$$

This condition means the function $y(x)$ has the value y_0 when $x = x_0$. The combination of a differential equation and an initial condition is called an **initial value problem**. Such problems play important roles in all branches of science.

The most general antiderivative $F(x) + C$ (which is $x^3 + C$ in Example 2) of the function $f(x)$ gives the **general solution** $y = F(x) + C$ of the differential equation $dy/dx = f(x)$. The general solution gives *all* the solutions of the equation (there are infinitely many, one for each value of C). We **solve** the differential equation by finding its general solution. We then solve the initial value problem by finding the **particular solution** that satisfies the initial condition $y(x_0) = y_0$. In Example 2, the function $y = x^3 - 2$ is the particular solution of the differential equation $dy/dx = 3x^2$ satisfying the initial condition $y(1) = -1$.

Antiderivatives and Motion

We have seen that the derivative of the position of an object gives its velocity, and the derivative of its velocity gives its acceleration. If we know an object's acceleration, then by finding an antiderivative we can recover the velocity, and from an antiderivative of the velocity we can recover its position function. This procedure was used as an application of Corollary 2 in Section 4.2. Now that we have a terminology and conceptual framework in terms of antiderivatives, we revisit the problem from the point of view of differential equations.

EXAMPLE 5 A balloon ascending at the rate of 12 ft/sec is at a height 80 ft above the ground when a package is dropped. How long does it take the package to reach the ground?

Solution Let $v(t)$ denote the velocity of the package at time t, and let $s(t)$ denote its height above the ground. The acceleration of gravity near the surface of the earth is $32\ \text{ft/sec}^2$. Assuming no other forces act on the dropped package, we have

$$\frac{dv}{dt} = -32. \qquad \text{Negative because gravity acts in the direction of decreasing } s.$$

This leads to the following initial value problem.

Differential equation: $\dfrac{dv}{dt} = -32$

Initial condition: $v(0) = 12$ Balloon initially rising

This is our mathematical model for the package's motion. We solve the initial value problem to obtain the velocity of the package.

1. *Solve the differential equation*: The general formula for an antiderivative of -32 is

$$v = -32t + C.$$

Having found the general solution of the differential equation, we use the initial condition to find the particular solution that solves our problem.

2. *Evaluate C*:

$$\begin{aligned} 12 &= -32(0) + C \qquad \text{Initial condition } v(0) = 12 \\ C &= 12. \end{aligned}$$

The solution of the initial value problem is

$$v = -32t + 12.$$

Since velocity is the derivative of height and the height of the package is 80 ft at the time $t = 0$ when it is dropped, we now have a second initial value problem.

$$\begin{aligned} &\textit{Differential equation:} \quad \frac{ds}{dt} = -32t + 12 \qquad \text{Set } v = ds/dt \text{ in the last equation.} \\ &\textit{Initial condition:} \quad s(0) = 80 \end{aligned}$$

We solve this initial value problem to find the height as a function of t.

1. *Solve the differential equation*: Finding the general antiderivative of $-32t + 12$ gives

$$s = -16t^2 + 12t + C.$$

2. *Evaluate C*:

$$\begin{aligned} 80 &= -16(0)^2 + 12(0) + C \qquad \text{Initial condition } s(0) = 80 \\ C &= 80. \end{aligned}$$

The package's height above ground at time t is

$$s = -16t^2 + 12t + 80.$$

Use the solution: To find how long it takes the package to reach the ground, we set s equal to 0 and solve for t:

$$\begin{aligned} -16t^2 + 12t + 80 &= 0 \\ -4t^2 + 3t + 20 &= 0 \\ t &= \frac{-3 \pm \sqrt{329}}{-8} \qquad \text{Quadratic formula} \\ t \approx -1.89, &\qquad t \approx 2.64. \end{aligned}$$

The package hits the ground about 2.64 sec after it is dropped from the balloon. (The negative root has no physical meaning.) ■

Indefinite Integrals

A special symbol is used to denote the collection of all antiderivatives of a function f.

> **DEFINITION** The collection of all antiderivatives of f represents the **indefinite integral** of f with respect to x, and is denoted by
>
> $$\int f(x)\,dx.$$
>
> The symbol $\int$ is an **integral sign**. The function f is the **integrand** of the integral, and x is the **variable of integration**.

Using this notation, we restate the solutions of Example 1, as follows:

$$\int 2x\,dx = x^2 + C,$$

$$\int \cos x\,dx = \sin x + C,$$

$$\int \left(\frac{1}{x} + 2e^{2x}\right) dx = \ln|x| + e^{2x} + C.$$

This notation is related to the main application of antiderivatives, which will be explored in Chapter 5. Antiderivatives play a key role in computing limits of certain infinite sums, an unexpected and wonderfully useful role that is described in a central result of Chapter 5, called the Fundamental Theorem of Calculus.

EXAMPLE 6 Evaluate

$$\int (x^2 - 2x + 5)\,dx.$$

Solution If we recognize that $(x^3/3) - x^2 + 5x$ is an antiderivative of $x^2 - 2x + 5$, we can evaluate the integral as

$$\int (x^2 - 2x + 5)\,dx = \overbrace{\frac{x^3}{3} - x^2 + 5x}^{\text{antiderivative}} + \underbrace{C.}_{\text{arbitrary constant}}$$

If we do not recognize the antiderivative right away, we can generate it term-by-term with the Sum, Difference, and Constant Multiple Rules:

$$\begin{aligned}\int (x^2 - 2x + 5)\,dx &= \int x^2\,dx - \int 2x\,dx + \int 5\,dx \\ &= \int x^2\,dx - 2\int x\,dx + 5\int 1\,dx \\ &= \left(\frac{x^3}{3} + C_1\right) - 2\left(\frac{x^2}{2} + C_2\right) + 5(x + C_3) \\ &= \frac{x^3}{3} + C_1 - x^2 - 2C_2 + 5x + 5C_3.\end{aligned}$$

This formula is more complicated than it needs to be. If we combine C_1, $-2C_2$, and $5C_3$ into a single arbitrary constant $C = C_1 - 2C_2 + 5C_3$, the formula simplifies to

$$\frac{x^3}{3} - x^2 + 5x + C$$

and *still* gives all the antiderivatives there are. For this reason, we recommend that you go right to the final form even if you elect to integrate term-by-term. Write

$$\int (x^2 - 2x + 5)\,dx = \int x^2\,dx - \int 2x\,dx + \int 5\,dx$$
$$= \frac{x^3}{3} - x^2 + 5x + C.$$

Find the simplest antiderivative you can for each part and add the arbitrary constant of integration at the end. ■

EXERCISES 4.8

In Exercises 1–24, find an antiderivative for each function. Do as many as you can mentally. Check your answers by differentiation.

1. a. $2x$ **b.** x^2 **c.** $x^2 - 2x + 1$

2. a. $6x$ **b.** x^7 **c.** $x^7 - 6x + 8$

3. a. $-3x^{-4}$ **b.** x^{-4} **c.** $x^{-4} + 2x + 3$

4. a. $2x^{-3}$ **b.** $\frac{x^{-3}}{2} + x^2$ **c.** $-x^{-3} + x - 1$

5. a. $\frac{1}{x^2}$ **b.** $\frac{5}{x^2}$ **c.** $2 - \frac{5}{x^2}$

6. a. $-\frac{2}{x^3}$ **b.** $\frac{1}{2x^3}$ **c.** $x^3 - \frac{1}{x^3}$

7. a. $\frac{3}{2}\sqrt{x}$ **b.** $\frac{1}{2\sqrt{x}}$ **c.** $\sqrt{x} + \frac{1}{\sqrt{x}}$

8. a. $\frac{4}{3}\sqrt[3]{x}$ **b.** $\frac{1}{3\sqrt[3]{x}}$ **c.** $\sqrt[3]{x} + \frac{1}{\sqrt[3]{x}}$

9. a. $\frac{2}{3}x^{-1/3}$ **b.** $\frac{1}{3}x^{-2/3}$ **c.** $-\frac{1}{3}x^{-4/3}$

10. a. $\frac{1}{2}x^{-1/2}$ **b.** $-\frac{1}{2}x^{-3/2}$ **c.** $-\frac{3}{2}x^{-5/2}$

11. a. $\frac{1}{x}$ **b.** $\frac{7}{x}$ **c.** $1 - \frac{5}{x}$

12. a. $\frac{1}{3x}$ **b.** $\frac{2}{5x}$ **c.** $1 + \frac{4}{3x} - \frac{1}{x^2}$

13. a. $-\pi \sin \pi x$ **b.** $3 \sin x$ **c.** $\sin \pi x - 3 \sin 3x$

14. a. $\pi \cos \pi x$ **b.** $\frac{\pi}{2}\cos\frac{\pi x}{2}$ **c.** $\cos\frac{\pi x}{2} + \pi \cos x$

15. a. $\sec^2 x$ **b.** $\frac{2}{3}\sec^2\frac{x}{3}$ **c.** $-\sec^2\frac{3x}{2}$

16. a. $\csc^2 x$ **b.** $-\frac{3}{2}\csc^2\frac{3x}{2}$ **c.** $1 - 8\csc^2 2x$

17. a. $\csc x \cot x$ **b.** $-\csc 5x \cot 5x$ **c.** $-\pi \csc\frac{\pi x}{2}\cot\frac{\pi x}{2}$

18. a. $\sec x \tan x$ **b.** $4 \sec 3x \tan 3x$ **c.** $\sec\frac{\pi x}{2}\tan\frac{\pi x}{2}$

19. a. e^{3x} **b.** e^{-x} **c.** $e^{x/2}$

20. a. e^{-2x} **b.** $e^{4x/3}$ **c.** $e^{-x/5}$

21. a. 3^x **b.** 2^{-x} **c.** $\left(\frac{5}{3}\right)^x$

22. a. $x^{\sqrt{3}}$ **b.** x^{π} **c.** $x^{\sqrt{2}-1}$

23. a. $\frac{2}{\sqrt{1 - x^2}}$ **b.** $\frac{1}{2(x^2 + 1)}$ **c.** $\frac{1}{1 + 4x^2}$

24. a. $x - \left(\frac{1}{2}\right)^x$ **b.** $x^2 + 2^x$ **c.** $\pi^x - x^{-1}$

In Exercises 25–70, find the most general antiderivative or indefinite integral. Check your answers by differentiation.

25. $\int (x + 1)\,dx$ **26.** $\int (5 - 6x)\,dx$

27. $\int \left(3t^2 + \frac{t}{2}\right)dt$ **28.** $\int \left(\frac{t^2}{2} + 4t^3\right)dt$

29. $\int (2x^3 - 5x + 7)\,dx$ **30.** $\int (1 - x^2 - 3x^5)\,dx$

31. $\int \left(\frac{1}{x^2} - x^2 - \frac{1}{3}\right) dx$

32. $\int \left(\frac{1}{5} - \frac{2}{x^3} + 2x\right) dx$

33. $\int x^{-1/3}\, dx$

34. $\int x^{-5/4}\, dx$

35. $\int \left(\sqrt{x} + \sqrt[3]{x}\right) dx$

36. $\int \left(\frac{\sqrt{x}}{2} + \frac{2}{\sqrt{x}}\right) dx$

37. $\int \left(8y - \frac{2}{y^{1/4}}\right) dy$

38. $\int \left(\frac{1}{7} - \frac{1}{y^{5/4}}\right) dy$

39. $\int 2x(1 - x^{-3})\, dx$

40. $\int x^{-3}(x + 1)\, dx$

41. $\int \frac{t\sqrt{t} + \sqrt{t}}{t^2}\, dt$

42. $\int \frac{4 + \sqrt{t}}{t^3}\, dt$

43. $\int (-2 \cos t)\, dt$

44. $\int (-5 \sin t)\, dt$

45. $\int 7 \sin \frac{\theta}{3}\, d\theta$

46. $\int 3 \cos 5\theta\, d\theta$

47. $\int (-3 \csc^2 x)\, dx$

48. $\int \left(-\frac{\sec^2 x}{3}\right) dx$

49. $\int \frac{\csc \theta \cot \theta}{2}\, d\theta$

50. $\int \frac{2}{5} \sec \theta \tan \theta\, d\theta$

51. $\int (e^{3x} + 5e^{-x})\, dx$

52. $\int (2e^x - 3e^{-2x})\, dx$

53. $\int (e^{-x} + 4^x)\, dx$

54. $\int (1.3)^x\, dx$

55. $\int (4 \sec x \tan x - 2 \sec^2 x)\, dx$

56. $\int \frac{1}{2}(\csc^2 x - \csc x \cot x)\, dx$

57. $\int (\sin 2x - \csc^2 x)\, dx$

58. $\int (2 \cos 2x - 3 \sin 3x)\, dx$

59. $\int \frac{1 + \cos 4t}{2}\, dt$

60. $\int \frac{1 - \cos 6t}{2}\, dt$

61. $\int \left(\frac{1}{x} - \frac{5}{x^2 + 1}\right) dx$

62. $\int \left(\frac{2}{\sqrt{1 - y^2}} - \frac{1}{y^{1/4}}\right) dy$

63. $\int 3x^{\sqrt{3}}\, dx$

64. $\int x^{\sqrt{2}-1}\, dx$

65. $\int (1 + \tan^2 \theta)\, d\theta$
(*Hint:* $1 + \tan^2 \theta = \sec^2 \theta$)

66. $\int (2 + \tan^2 \theta)\, d\theta$

67. $\int \cot^2 x\, dx$
(*Hint:* $1 + \cot^2 x = \csc^2 x$)

68. $\int (1 - \cot^2 x)\, dx$

69. $\int \cos \theta (\tan \theta + \sec \theta)\, d\theta$

70. $\int \frac{\csc \theta}{\csc \theta - \sin \theta}\, d\theta$

Verify the formulas in Exercises 71–82 by differentiation.

71. $\int (7x - 2)^3\, dx = \frac{(7x - 2)^4}{28} + C$

72. $\int (3x + 5)^{-2}\, dx = -\frac{(3x + 5)^{-1}}{3} + C$

73. $\int \sec^2 (5x - 1)\, dx = \frac{1}{5} \tan (5x - 1) + C$

74. $\int \csc^2 \left(\frac{x - 1}{3}\right) dx = -3 \cot \left(\frac{x - 1}{3}\right) + C$

75. $\int \frac{1}{(x + 1)^2}\, dx = -\frac{1}{x + 1} + C$

76. $\int \frac{1}{(x + 1)^2}\, dx = \frac{x}{x + 1} + C$

77. $\int \frac{1}{x + 1}\, dx = \ln (x + 1) + C, \quad x > -1$

78. $\int xe^x\, dx = xe^x - e^x + C$

79. $\int \frac{dx}{a^2 + x^2} = \frac{1}{a} \tan^{-1} \left(\frac{x}{a}\right) + C$

80. $\int \frac{dx}{\sqrt{a^2 - x^2}} = \sin^{-1} \left(\frac{x}{a}\right) + C$

81. $\int \frac{\tan^{-1} x}{x^2}\, dx = \ln x - \frac{1}{2} \ln (1 + x^2) - \frac{\tan^{-1} x}{x} + C$

82. $\int (\sin^{-1} x)^2\, dx = x(\sin^{-1} x)^2 - 2x + 2\sqrt{1 - x^2} \sin^{-1} x + C$

83. Right, or wrong? Say which for each formula and give a brief reason for each answer.

a. $\int x \sin x\, dx = \frac{x^2}{2} \sin x + C$

b. $\int x \sin x\, dx = -x \cos x + C$

c. $\int x \sin x\, dx = -x \cos x + \sin x + C$

84. Right, or wrong? Say which for each formula and give a brief reason for each answer.

a. $\int \tan \theta \sec^2 \theta\, d\theta = \frac{\sec^3 \theta}{3} + C$

b. $\int \tan \theta \sec^2 \theta\, d\theta = \frac{1}{2} \tan^2 \theta + C$

c. $\int \tan \theta \sec^2 \theta\, d\theta = \frac{1}{2} \sec^2 \theta + C$

85. Right, or wrong? Say which for each formula and give a brief reason for each answer.

a. $\int (2x + 1)^2\, dx = \frac{(2x + 1)^3}{3} + C$

b. $\int 3(2x+1)^2\,dx = (2x+1)^3 + C$

c. $\int 6(2x+1)^2\,dx = (2x+1)^3 + C$

86. Right, or wrong? Say which for each formula and give a brief reason for each answer.

a. $\int \sqrt{2x+1}\,dx = \sqrt{x^2+x+C}$

b. $\int \sqrt{2x+1}\,dx = \sqrt{x^2+x}+C$

c. $\int \sqrt{2x+1}\,dx = \frac{1}{3}\left(\sqrt{2x+1}\right)^3 + C$

87. Which of the following graphs shows the solution of the initial value problem

$$\frac{dy}{dx} = 2x, \quad y = 4 \text{ when } x = 1?$$

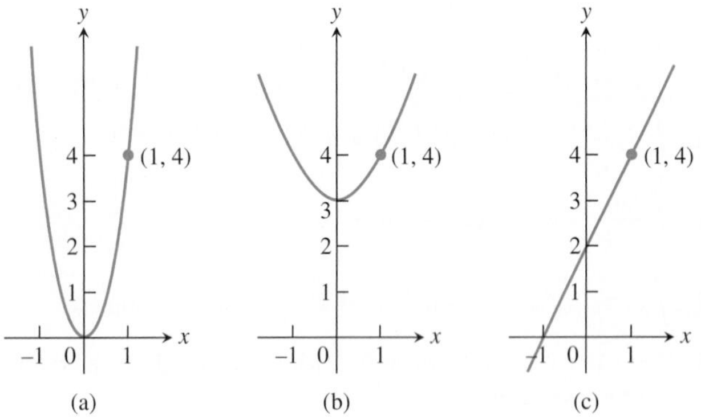

Give reasons for your answer.

88. Which of the following graphs shows the solution of the initial value problem

$$\frac{dy}{dx} = -x, \quad y = 1 \text{ when } x = -1?$$

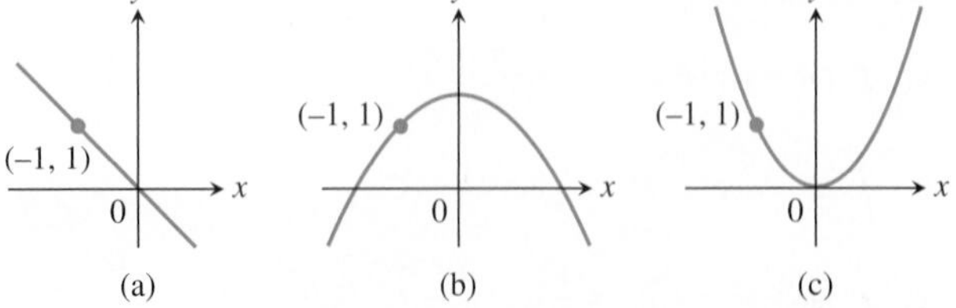

Give reasons for your answer.

Solve the initial value problems in Exercises 89–110.

89. $\frac{dy}{dx} = 2x - 7, \quad y(2) = 0$

90. $\frac{dy}{dx} = 10 - x, \quad y(0) = -1$

91. $\frac{dy}{dx} = \frac{1}{x^2} + x, \quad x > 0; \quad y(2) = 1$

92. $\frac{dy}{dx} = 9x^2 - 4x + 5, \quad y(-1) = 0$

93. $\frac{dy}{dx} = 3x^{-2/3}, \quad y(-1) = -5$

94. $\frac{dy}{dx} = \frac{1}{2\sqrt{x}}, \quad y(4) = 0$

95. $\frac{ds}{dt} = 1 + \cos t, \quad s(0) = 4$

96. $\frac{ds}{dt} = \cos t + \sin t, \quad s(\pi) = 1$

97. $\frac{dr}{d\theta} = -\pi \sin \pi\theta, \quad r(0) = 0$

98. $\frac{dr}{d\theta} = \cos \pi\theta, \quad r(0) = 1$

99. $\frac{dv}{dt} = \frac{1}{2}\sec t \tan t, \quad v(0) = 1$

100. $\frac{dv}{dt} = 8t + \csc^2 t, \quad v\left(\frac{\pi}{2}\right) = -7$

101. $\frac{dv}{dt} = \frac{3}{t\sqrt{t^2-1}}, \quad t > 1, v(2) = 0$

102. $\frac{dv}{dt} = \frac{8}{1+t^2} + \sec^2 t, \quad v(0) = 1$

103. $\frac{d^2y}{dx^2} = 2 - 6x; \quad y'(0) = 4, \quad y(0) = 1$

104. $\frac{d^2y}{dx^2} = 0; \quad y'(0) = 2, \quad y(0) = 0$

105. $\frac{d^2r}{dt^2} = \frac{2}{t^3}; \quad \left.\frac{dr}{dt}\right|_{t=1} = 1, \quad r(1) = 1$

106. $\frac{d^2s}{dt^2} = \frac{3t}{8}; \quad \left.\frac{ds}{dt}\right|_{t=4} = 3, \quad s(4) = 4$

107. $\frac{d^3y}{dx^3} = 6; \quad y''(0) = -8, \quad y'(0) = 0, \quad y(0) = 5$

108. $\frac{d^3\theta}{dt^3} = 0; \quad \theta''(0) = -2, \quad \theta'(0) = -\frac{1}{2}, \quad \theta(0) = \sqrt{2}$

109. $y^{(4)} = -\sin t + \cos t;$

$y'''(0) = 7, \quad y''(0) = y'(0) = -1, \quad y(0) = 0$

110. $y^{(4)} = -\cos x + 8\sin 2x;$

$y'''(0) = 0, \quad y''(0) = y'(0) = 1, \quad y(0) = 3$

111. Find the curve $y = f(x)$ in the xy-plane that passes through the point $(9, 4)$ and whose slope at each point is $3\sqrt{x}$.

112. a. Find a curve $y = f(x)$ with the following properties:

i) $\dfrac{d^2y}{dx^2} = 6x$

ii) Its graph passes through the point (0, 1), and has a horizontal tangent there.

b. How many curves like this are there? How do you know?

Exercises 113–116 show solution curves of differential equations. In each exercise, find an equation for the curve through the labeled point.

113.

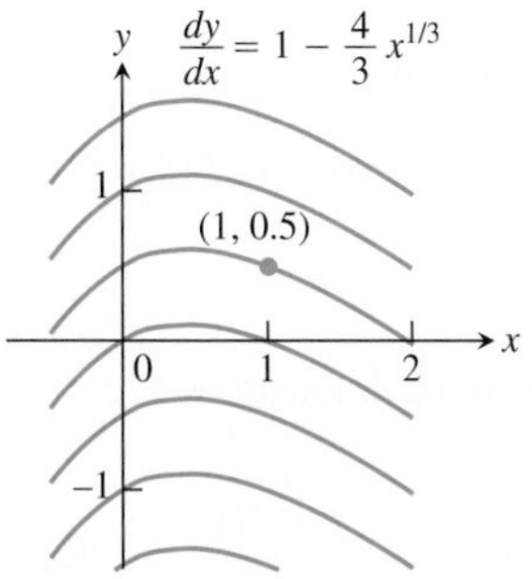

114.

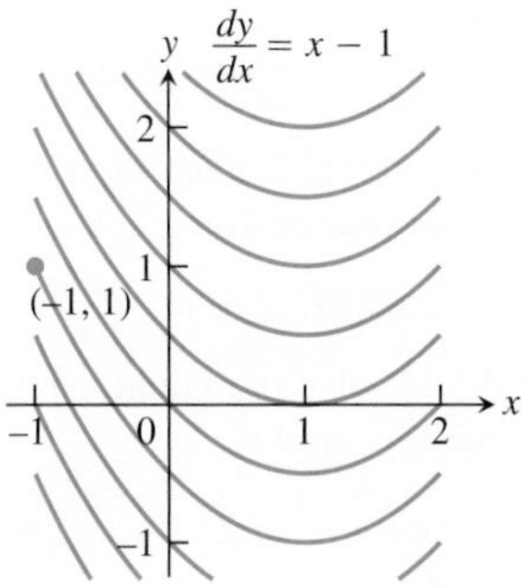

115.

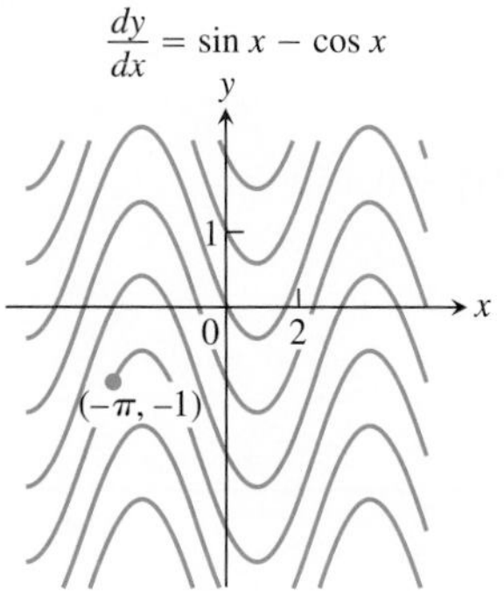

116.

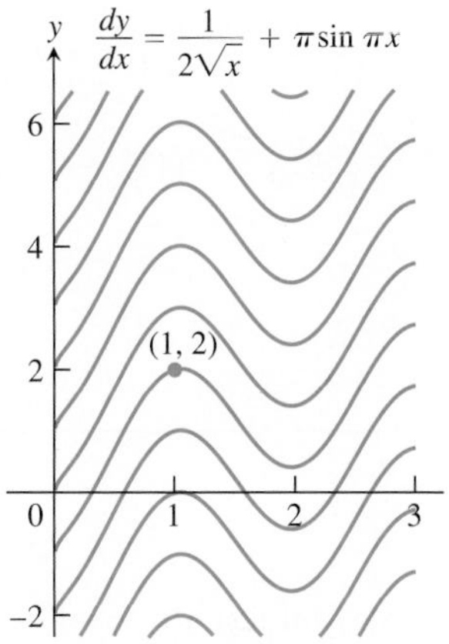

117. Finding displacement from an antiderivative of velocity

a. Suppose that the velocity of a body moving along the s-axis is

$$\frac{ds}{dt} = v = 9.8t - 3.$$

i) Find the body's displacement over the time interval from $t = 1$ to $t = 3$ given that $s = 5$ when $t = 0$.

ii) Find the body's displacement from $t = 1$ to $t = 3$ given that $s = -2$ when $t = 0$.

iii) Now find the body's displacement from $t = 1$ to $t = 3$ given that $s = s_0$ when $t = 0$.

b. Suppose that the position s of a body moving along a coordinate line is a differentiable function of time t. Is it true that once you know an antiderivative of the velocity function ds/dt you can find the body's displacement from $t = a$ to $t = b$ even if you do not know the body's exact position at either of those times? Give reasons for your answer.

118. Liftoff from Earth A rocket lifts off the surface of Earth with a constant acceleration of $20\ \text{m/sec}^2$. How fast will the rocket be going 1 min later?

119. Stopping a car in time You are driving along a highway at a steady 60 mph (88 ft/sec) when you see an accident ahead and slam on the brakes. What constant deceleration is required to stop your car in 242 ft? To find out, carry out the following steps.

1. Solve the initial value problem

Differential equation: $\dfrac{d^2s}{dt^2} = -k \quad$ (k constant)

Initial conditions: $\dfrac{ds}{dt} = 88$ and $s = 0$ when $t = 0$.

Measuring time and distance from when the brakes are applied.

2. Find the value of t that makes $ds/dt = 0$. (The answer will involve k.)

3. Find the value of k that makes $s = 242$ for the value of t you found in Step 2.

120. Stopping a motorcycle The State of Illinois Cycle Rider Safety Program requires motorcycle riders to be able to brake from 30 mph (44 ft/sec) to 0 in 45 ft. What constant deceleration does it take to do that?

121. Motion along a coordinate line A particle moves on a coordinate line with acceleration $a = d^2s/dt^2 = 15\sqrt{t} - \left(3/\sqrt{t}\right)$, subject to the conditions that $ds/dt = 4$ and $s = 0$ when $t = 1$. Find

a. the velocity $v = ds/dt$ in terms of t

b. the position s in terms of t.

T **122. The hammer and the feather** When *Apollo 15* astronaut David Scott dropped a hammer and a feather on the moon to demonstrate that in a vacuum all bodies fall with the same (constant) acceleration, he dropped them from about 4 ft above the ground. The television footage of the event shows the hammer and the feather falling more slowly than on Earth, where, in a vacuum, they would have taken only half a second to fall the 4 ft. How long did it take the hammer and feather to fall 4 ft on the moon? To find out, solve the following initial value problem for s as a function of t. Then find the value of t that makes s equal to 0.

Differential equation: $\dfrac{d^2s}{dt^2} = -5.2\ \text{ft/sec}^2$

Initial conditions: $\dfrac{ds}{dt} = 0$ and $s = 4$ when $t = 0$

123. Motion with constant acceleration The standard equation for the position s of a body moving with a constant acceleration a along a coordinate line is

$$s = \frac{a}{2}t^2 + v_0 t + s_0, \qquad (1)$$

where v_0 and s_0 are the body's velocity and position at time $t = 0$. Derive this equation by solving the initial value problem

Differential equation: $\dfrac{d^2s}{dt^2} = a$

Initial conditions: $\dfrac{ds}{dt} = v_0$ and $s = s_0$ when $t = 0$.

124. Free fall near the surface of a planet For free fall near the surface of a planet where the acceleration due to gravity has a constant magnitude of g length-units/sec^2, Equation (1) in Exercise 123 takes the form

$$s = -\frac{1}{2}gt^2 + v_0 t + s_0, \tag{2}$$

where s is the body's height above the surface. The equation has a minus sign because the acceleration acts downward, in the direction of decreasing s. The velocity v_0 is positive if the object is rising at time $t = 0$ and negative if the object is falling.

Instead of using the result of Exercise 123, you can derive Equation (2) directly by solving an appropriate initial value problem. What initial value problem? Solve it to be sure you have the right one, explaining the solution steps as you go along.

125. Suppose that

$$f(x) = \frac{d}{dx}\left(1 - \sqrt{x}\right) \quad \text{and} \quad g(x) = \frac{d}{dx}(x + 2).$$

Find:

a. $\displaystyle\int f(x)\,dx$ **b.** $\displaystyle\int g(x)\,dx$

c. $\displaystyle\int [-f(x)]\,dx$ **d.** $\displaystyle\int [-g(x)]\,dx$

e. $\displaystyle\int [f(x) + g(x)]\,dx$ **f.** $\displaystyle\int [f(x) - g(x)]\,dx$

126. Uniqueness of solutions If differentiable functions $y = F(x)$ and $y = G(x)$ both solve the initial value problem

$$\frac{dy}{dx} = f(x), \qquad y(x_0) = y_0,$$

on an interval I, must $F(x) = G(x)$ for every x in I? Give reasons for your answer.

COMPUTER EXPLORATIONS

Use a CAS to solve the initial value problems in Exercises 127–130. Plot the solution curves.

127. $y' = \cos^2 x + \sin x, \quad y(\pi) = 1$

128. $y' = \dfrac{1}{x} + x, \quad y(1) = -1$

129. $y' = \dfrac{1}{\sqrt{4 - x^2}}, \quad y(0) = 2$

130. $y'' = \dfrac{2}{x} + \sqrt{x}, \quad y(1) = 0, \quad y'(1) = 0$

Chapter 4 Questions to Guide Your Review

1. What can be said about the extreme values of a function that is continuous on a closed interval?
2. What does it mean for a function to have a local extreme value on its domain? An absolute extreme value? How are local and absolute extreme values related, if at all? Give examples.
3. How do you find the absolute extrema of a continuous function on a closed interval? Give examples.
4. What are the hypotheses and conclusion of Rolle's Theorem? Are the hypotheses really necessary? Explain.
5. What are the hypotheses and conclusion of the Mean Value Theorem? What physical interpretations might the theorem have?
6. State the Mean Value Theorem's three corollaries.
7. How can you sometimes identify a function $f(x)$ by knowing f' and knowing the value of f at a point $x = x_0$? Give an example.
8. What is the First Derivative Test for Local Extreme Values? Give examples of how it is applied.
9. How do you test a twice-differentiable function to determine where its graph is concave up or concave down? Give examples.
10. What is an inflection point? Give an example. What physical significance do inflection points sometimes have?
11. What is the Second Derivative Test for Local Extreme Values? Give examples of how it is applied.
12. What do the derivatives of a function tell you about the shape of its graph?
13. List the steps you would take to graph a polynomial function. Illustrate with an example.
14. What is a cusp? Give examples.
15. List the steps you would take to graph a rational function. Illustrate with an example.
16. Outline a general strategy for solving max-min problems. Give examples.

17. Describe l'Hôpital's Rule. How do you know when to use the rule and when to stop? Give an example.

18. How can you sometimes handle limits that lead to indeterminate forms ∞/∞, $\infty \cdot 0$, and $\infty - \infty$? Give examples.

19. How can you sometimes handle limits that lead to indeterminate forms 1^∞, 0^0, and ∞^∞? Give examples.

20. Describe Newton's method for solving equations. Give an example. What is the theory behind the method? What are some of the things to watch out for when you use the method?

21. Can a function have more than one antiderivative? If so, how are the antiderivatives related? Explain.

22. What is an indefinite integral? How do you evaluate one? What general formulas do you know for finding indefinite integrals?

23. How can you sometimes solve a differential equation of the form $dy/dx = f(x)$?

24. What is an initial value problem? How do you solve one? Give an example.

25. If you know the acceleration of a body moving along a coordinate line as a function of time, what more do you need to know to find the body's position function? Give an example.

Chapter 4 Practice Exercises

1. Does $f(x) = x^3 + 2x + \tan x$ have any local maximum or minimum values? Give reasons for your answer.

2. Does $g(x) = \csc x + 2 \cot x$ have any local maximum values? Give reasons for your answer.

3. Does $f(x) = (7 + x)(11 - 3x)^{1/3}$ have an absolute minimum value? An absolute maximum? If so, find them or give reasons why they fail to exist. List all critical points of f.

4. Find values of a and b such that the function

$$f(x) = \frac{ax + b}{x^2 - 1}$$

has a local extreme value of 1 at $x = 3$. Is this extreme value a local maximum, or a local minimum? Give reasons for your answer.

5. Does $g(x) = e^x - x$ have an absolute minimum value? An absolute maximum? If so, find them or give reasons why they fail to exist. List all critical points of g.

6. Does $f(x) = 2e^x/(1 + x^2)$ have an absolute minimum value? An absolute maximum? If so, find them or give reasons why they fail to exist. List all critical points of f.

In Exercises 7 and 8, find the absolute maximum and absolute minimum values of f over the interval.

7. $f(x) = x - 2 \ln x, \quad 1 \le x \le 3$

8. $f(x) = (4/x) + \ln x^2, \quad 1 \le x \le 4$

9. The greatest integer function $f(x) = \lfloor x \rfloor$, defined for all values of x, assumes a local maximum value of 0 at each point of $[0, 1)$. Could any of these local maximum values also be local minimum values of f? Give reasons for your answer.

10. **a.** Give an example of a differentiable function f whose first derivative is zero at some point c even though f has neither a local maximum nor a local minimum at c.

    b. How is this consistent with Theorem 2 in Section 4.1? Give reasons for your answer.

11. The function $y = 1/x$ does not take on either a maximum or a minimum on the interval $0 < x < 1$ even though the function is continuous on this interval. Does this contradict the Extreme Value Theorem for continuous functions? Why?

12. What are the maximum and minimum values of the function $y = |x|$ on the interval $-1 \le x < 1$? Notice that the interval is not closed. Is this consistent with the Extreme Value Theorem for continuous functions? Why?

T 13. A graph that is large enough to show a function's global behavior may fail to reveal important local features. The graph of $f(x) = (x^8/8) - (x^6/2) - x^5 + 5x^3$ is a case in point.

   a. Graph f over the interval $-2.5 \le x \le 2.5$. Where does the graph appear to have local extreme values or points of inflection?

   b. Now factor $f'(x)$ and show that f has a local maximum at $x = \sqrt[3]{5} \approx 1.70998$ and local minima at $x = \pm\sqrt{3} \approx \pm 1.73205$.

   c. Zoom in on the graph to find a viewing window that shows the presence of the extreme values at $x = \sqrt[3]{5}$ and $x = \sqrt{3}$.

   The moral here is that without calculus the existence of two of the three extreme values would probably have gone unnoticed. On any normal graph of the function, the values would lie close enough together to fall within the dimensions of a single pixel on the screen.

   (*Source*: *Uses of Technology in the Mathematics Curriculum*, by Benny Evans and Jerry Johnson, Oklahoma State University, published in 1990 under National Science Foundation Grant USE-8950044.)

T 14. (*Continuation of Exercise 13.*)

   a. Graph $f(x) = (x^8/8) - (2/5)x^5 - 5x - (5/x^2) + 11$ over the interval $-2 \le x \le 2$. Where does the graph appear to have local extreme values or points of inflection?

   b. Show that f has a local maximum value at $x = \sqrt[7]{5} \approx 1.2585$ and a local minimum value at $x = \sqrt[3]{2} \approx 1.2599$.

c. Zoom in to find a viewing window that shows the presence of the extreme values at $x = \sqrt[7]{5}$ and $x = \sqrt[3]{2}$.

15. a. Show that $g(t) = \sin^2 t - 3t$ decreases on every interval in its domain.

b. How many solutions does the equation $\sin^2 t - 3t = 5$ have? Give reasons for your answer.

16. a. Show that $y = \tan\theta$ increases on every interval in its domain.

b. If the conclusion in part (a) is really correct, how do you explain the fact that $\tan\pi = 0$ is less than $\tan(\pi/4) = 1$?

17. a. Show that the equation $x^4 + 2x^2 - 2 = 0$ has exactly one solution on $[0, 1]$.

T **b.** Find the solution to as many decimal places as you can.

18. a. Show that $f(x) = x/(x + 1)$ increases on every interval in its domain.

b. Show that $f(x) = x^3 + 2x$ has no local maximum or minimum values.

19. Water in a reservoir As a result of a heavy rain, the volume of water in a reservoir increased by 1400 acre-ft in 24 hours. Show that at some instant during that period the reservoir's volume was increasing at a rate in excess of 225,000 gal/min. (An acre-foot is $43{,}560\ \text{ft}^3$, the volume that would cover 1 acre to the depth of 1 ft. A cubic foot holds 7.48 gal.)

20. The formula $F(x) = 3x + C$ gives a different function for each value of C. All of these functions, however, have the same derivative with respect to x, namely $F'(x) = 3$. Are these the only differentiable functions whose derivative is 3? Could there be any others? Give reasons for your answers.

21. Show that

$$\frac{d}{dx}\left(\frac{x}{x+1}\right) = \frac{d}{dx}\left(-\frac{1}{x+1}\right)$$

even though

$$\frac{x}{x+1} \neq -\frac{1}{x+1}.$$

Doesn't this contradict Corollary 2 of the Mean Value Theorem? Give reasons for your answer.

22. Calculate the first derivatives of $f(x) = x^2/(x^2 + 1)$ and $g(x) = -1/(x^2 + 1)$. What can you conclude about the graphs of these functions?

In Exercises 23 and 24, use the graph to answer the questions.

23. Identify any global extreme values of f and the values of x at which they occur.

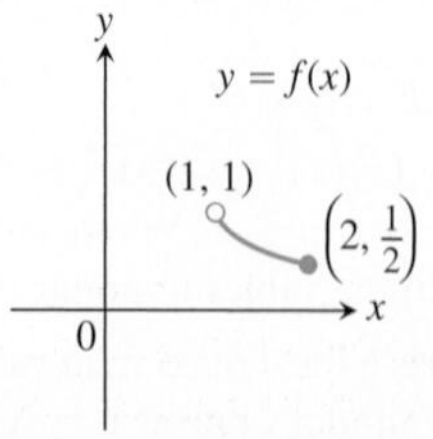

24. Estimate the intervals on which the function $y = f(x)$ is

a. increasing.

b. decreasing.

c. Use the given graph of f' to indicate where any local extreme values of the function occur, and whether each extreme is a relative maximum or minimum.

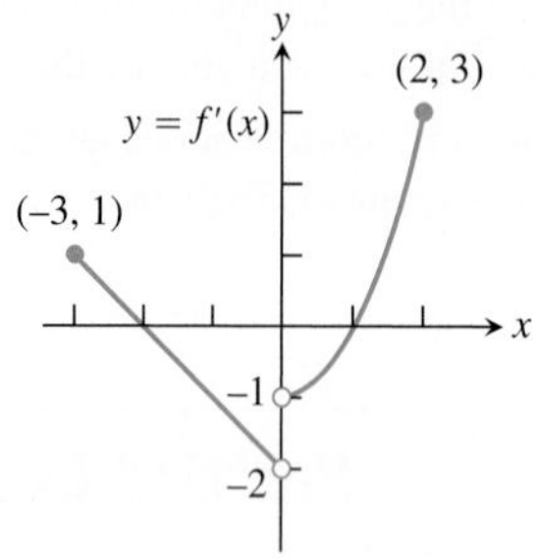

Each of the graphs in Exercises 25 and 26 is the graph of the position function $s = f(t)$ of a body moving on a coordinate line (t represents time). At approximately what times (if any) is each body's **(a)** velocity equal to zero? **(b)** Acceleration equal to zero? During approximately what time intervals does the body move **(c)** forward? **(d)** Backward?

25.

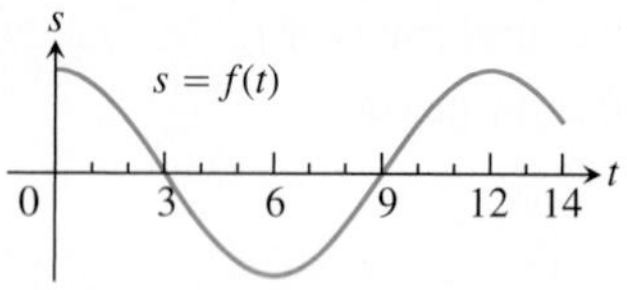

26.

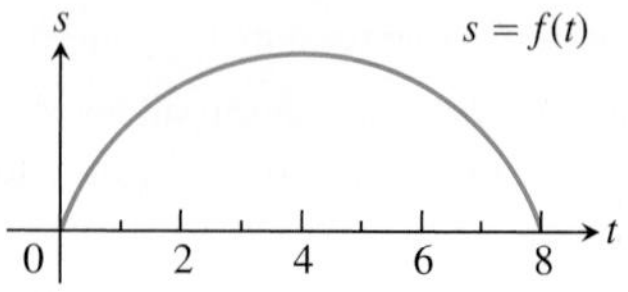

Graph the curves in Exercises 27–42.

27. $y = x^2 - (x^3/6)$

28. $y = x^3 - 3x^2 + 3$

29. $y = -x^3 + 6x^2 - 9x + 3$

30. $y = (1/8)(x^3 + 3x^2 - 9x - 27)$

31. $y = x^3(8 - x)$

32. $y = x^2(2x^2 - 9)$

33. $y = x - 3x^{2/3}$

34. $y = x^{1/3}(x - 4)$

35. $y = x\sqrt{3 - x}$

36. $y = x\sqrt{4 - x^2}$

37. $y = (x - 3)^2 e^x$

38. $y = xe^{-x^2}$

39. $y = \ln(x^2 - 4x + 3)$

40. $y = \ln(\sin x)$

41. $y = \sin^{-1}\left(\frac{1}{x}\right)$

42. $y = \tan^{-1}\left(\frac{1}{x}\right)$

Each of Exercises 43–48 gives the first derivative of a function $y = f(x)$. **(a)** At what points, if any, does the graph of f have a local maximum, local minimum, or inflection point? **(b)** Sketch the general shape of the graph.

43. $y' = 16 - x^2$

44. $y' = x^2 - x - 6$

45. $y' = 6x(x + 1)(x - 2)$

46. $y' = x^2(6 - 4x)$

47. $y' = x^4 - 2x^2$

48. $y' = 4x^2 - x^4$

In Exercises 49–52, graph each function. Then use the function's first derivative to explain what you see.

49. $y = x^{2/3} + (x - 1)^{1/3}$

50. $y = x^{2/3} + (x - 1)^{2/3}$

51. $y = x^{1/3} + (x - 1)^{1/3}$

52. $y = x^{2/3} - (x - 1)^{1/3}$

Sketch the graphs of the functions in Exercises 53–60.

53. $y = \dfrac{x + 1}{x - 3}$

54. $y = \dfrac{2x}{x + 5}$

55. $y = \dfrac{x^2 + 1}{x}$

56. $y = \dfrac{x^2 - x + 1}{x}$

57. $y = \dfrac{x^3 + 2}{2x}$

58. $y = \dfrac{x^4 - 1}{x^2}$

59. $y = \dfrac{x^2 - 4}{x^2 - 3}$

60. $y = \dfrac{x^2}{x^2 - 4}$

Use l'Hôpital's Rule to find the limits in Exercises 61–72.

61. $\lim_{x\to 1} \dfrac{x^2 + 3x - 4}{x - 1}$

62. $\lim_{x\to 1} \dfrac{x^a - 1}{x^b - 1}$

63. $\lim_{x\to \pi} \dfrac{\tan x}{x}$

64. $\lim_{x\to 0} \dfrac{\tan x}{x + \sin x}$

65. $\lim_{x\to 0} \dfrac{\sin^2 x}{\tan (x^2)}$

66. $\lim_{x\to 0} \dfrac{\sin mx}{\sin nx}$

67. $\lim_{x\to \pi/2^-} \sec 7x \cos 3x$

68. $\lim_{x\to 0^+} \sqrt{x} \sec x$

69. $\lim_{x\to 0} (\csc x - \cot x)$

70. $\lim_{x\to 0} \left(\dfrac{1}{x^4} - \dfrac{1}{x^2}\right)$

71. $\lim_{x\to \infty} \left(\sqrt{x^2 + x + 1} - \sqrt{x^2 - x}\right)$

72. $\lim_{x\to \infty} \left(\dfrac{x^3}{x^2 - 1} - \dfrac{x^3}{x^2 + 1}\right)$

Find the limits in Exercises 73–84.

73. $\lim_{x\to 0} \dfrac{10^x - 1}{x}$

74. $\lim_{\theta\to 0} \dfrac{3^\theta - 1}{\theta}$

75. $\lim_{x\to 0} \dfrac{2^{\sin x} - 1}{e^x - 1}$

76. $\lim_{x\to 0} \dfrac{2^{-\sin x} - 1}{e^x - 1}$

77. $\lim_{x\to 0} \dfrac{5 - 5 \cos x}{e^x - x - 1}$

78. $\lim_{x\to 0} \dfrac{4 - 4e^x}{xe^x}$

79. $\lim_{t\to 0^+} \dfrac{t - \ln (1 + 2t)}{t^2}$

80. $\lim_{x\to 4} \dfrac{\sin^2 (\pi x)}{e^{x-4} + 3 - x}$

81. $\lim_{t\to 0^+} \left(\dfrac{e^t}{t} - \dfrac{1}{t}\right)$

82. $\lim_{y\to 0^+} e^{-1/y} \ln y$

83. $\lim_{x\to \infty} \left(1 + \dfrac{b}{x}\right)^{kx}$

84. $\lim_{x\to \infty} \left(1 + \dfrac{2}{x} + \dfrac{7}{x^2}\right)$

85. The sum of two nonnegative numbers is 36. Find the numbers if

a. the difference of their square roots is to be as large as possible.

b. the sum of their square roots is to be as large as possible.

86. The sum of two nonnegative numbers is 20. Find the numbers

a. if the product of one number and the square root of the other is to be as large as possible.

b. if one number plus the square root of the other is to be as large as possible.

87. An isosceles triangle has its vertex at the origin and its base parallel to the x-axis with the vertices above the axis on the curve $y = 27 - x^2$. Find the largest area the triangle can have.

88. A customer has asked you to design an open-top rectangular stainless steel vat. It is to have a square base and a volume of 32 ft^3, to be welded from quarter-inch plate, and to weigh no more than necessary. What dimensions do you recommend?

89. Find the height and radius of the largest right circular cylinder that can be put in a sphere of radius $\sqrt{3}$.

90. The figure here shows two right circular cones, one upside down inside the other. The two bases are parallel, and the vertex of the smaller cone lies at the center of the larger cone's base. What values of r and h will give the smaller cone the largest possible volume?

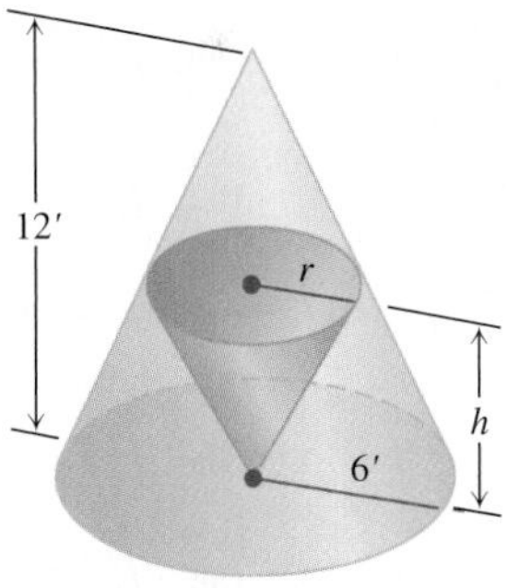

91. Manufacturing tires Your company can manufacture x hundred grade A tires and y hundred grade B tires a day, where $0 \le x \le 4$ and

$$y = \frac{40 - 10x}{5 - x}.$$

Your profit on a grade A tire is twice your profit on a grade B tire. What is the most profitable number of each kind to make?

92. Particle motion The positions of two particles on the s-axis are $s_1 = \cos t$ and $s_2 = \cos (t + \pi/4)$.

a. What is the farthest apart the particles ever get?

b. When do the particles collide?

T **93. Open-top box** An open-top rectangular box is constructed from a 10-in.-by-16-in. piece of cardboard by cutting squares of equal side length from the corners and folding up the sides. Find analytically the dimensions of the box of largest volume and the maximum volume. Support your answers graphically.

94. The ladder problem What is the approximate length (in feet) of the longest ladder you can carry horizontally around the corner of the corridor shown here? Round your answer down to the nearest foot.

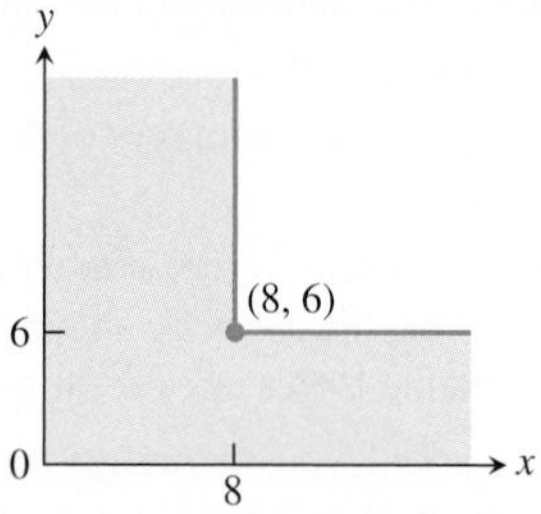

95. Let $f(x) = 3x - x^3$. Show that the equation $f(x) = -4$ has a solution in the interval [2, 3] and use Newton's method to find it.

96. Let $f(x) = x^4 - x^3$. Show that the equation $f(x) = 75$ has a solution in the interval [3, 4] and use Newton's method to find it.

Find the indefinite integrals (most general antiderivatives) in Exercises 97–120. Check your answers by differentiation.

97. $\int (x^3 + 5x - 7)\, dx$

98. $\int \left(8t^3 - \frac{t^2}{2} + t\right) dt$

99. $\int \left(3\sqrt{t} + \frac{4}{t^2}\right) dt$

100. $\int \left(\frac{1}{2\sqrt{t}} - \frac{3}{t^4}\right) dt$

101. $\int \frac{dr}{(r+5)^2}$

102. $\int \frac{6\, dr}{\left(r - \sqrt{2}\right)^3}$

103. $\int 3\theta\sqrt{\theta^2 + 1}\, d\theta$

104. $\int \frac{\theta}{\sqrt{7 + \theta^2}}\, d\theta$

105. $\int x^3(1 + x^4)^{-1/4}\, dx$

106. $\int (2 - x)^{3/5}\, dx$

107. $\int \sec^2 \frac{s}{10}\, ds$

108. $\int \csc^2 \pi s\, ds$

109. $\int \csc\sqrt{2}\theta \cot\sqrt{2}\theta\, d\theta$

110. $\int \sec\frac{\theta}{3}\tan\frac{\theta}{3}\, d\theta$

111. $\int \sin^2 \frac{x}{4}\, dx$ $\left(\textit{Hint: } \sin^2\theta = \frac{1 - \cos 2\theta}{2}\right)$

112. $\int \cos^2 \frac{x}{2}\, dx$

113. $\int \left(\frac{3}{x} - x\right) dx$

114. $\int \left(\frac{5}{x^2} + \frac{2}{x^2 + 1}\right) dx$

115. $\int \left(\frac{1}{2}e^t - e^{-t}\right) dt$

116. $\int (5^s + s^5)\, ds$

117. $\int \theta^{1-\pi}\, d\theta$

118. $\int 2^{\pi + r}\, dr$

119. $\int \frac{3}{2x\sqrt{x^2 - 1}}\, dx$

120. $\int \frac{d\theta}{\sqrt{16 - \theta^2}}$

Solve the initial value problems in Exercises 121–124.

121. $\frac{dy}{dx} = \frac{x^2 + 1}{x^2}, \quad y(1) = -1$

122. $\frac{dy}{dx} = \left(x + \frac{1}{x}\right)^2, \quad y(1) = 1$

123. $\frac{d^2r}{dt^2} = 15\sqrt{t} + \frac{3}{\sqrt{t}}; \quad r'(1) = 8, \quad r(1) = 0$

124. $\frac{d^3r}{dt^3} = -\cos t; \quad r''(0) = r'(0) = 0, \quad r(0) = -1$

125. Can the integrations in (a) and (b) both be correct? Explain.

a. $\int \frac{dx}{\sqrt{1 - x^2}} = \sin^{-1} x + C$

b. $\int \frac{dx}{\sqrt{1 - x^2}} = -\int -\frac{dx}{\sqrt{1 - x^2}} = -\cos^{-1} x + C$

126. Can the integrations in (a) and (b) both be correct? Explain.

a. $\int \frac{dx}{\sqrt{1 - x^2}} = -\int -\frac{dx}{\sqrt{1 - x^2}} = -\cos^{-1} x + C$

b. $\int \frac{dx}{\sqrt{1 - x^2}} = \int \frac{-du}{\sqrt{1 - (-u)^2}}$ $\quad x = -u,\ dx = -du$

$= \int \frac{-du}{\sqrt{1 - u^2}}$

$= \cos^{-1} u + C$

$= \cos^{-1}(-x) + C$ $\quad u = -x$

127. The rectangle shown here has one side on the positive y-axis, one side on the positive x-axis, and its upper right-hand vertex on the curve $y = e^{-x^2}$. What dimensions give the rectangle its largest area, and what is that area?

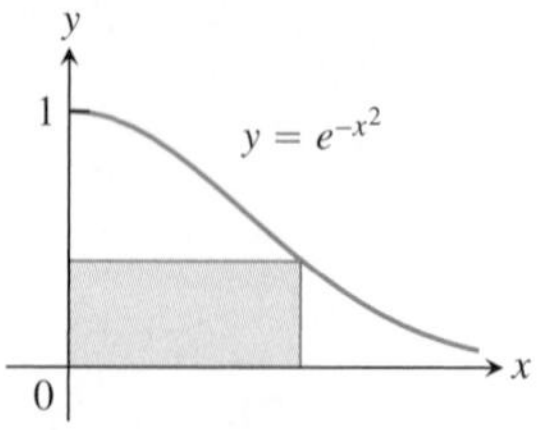

128. The rectangle shown here has one side on the positive y-axis, one side on the positive x-axis, and its upper right-hand vertex on the curve $y = (\ln x)/x^2$. What dimensions give the rectangle its largest area, and what is that area?

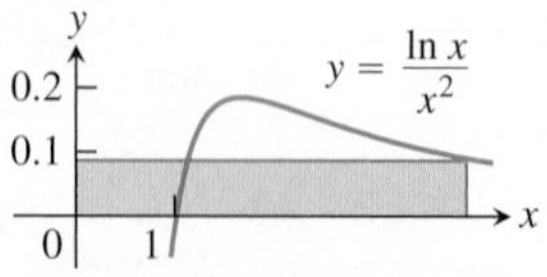

In Exercises 129 and 130, find the absolute maximum and minimum values of each function on the given interval.

129. $y = x \ln 2x - x, \quad \left[\frac{1}{2e}, \frac{e}{2}\right]$

130. $y = 10x(2 - \ln x), \quad (0, e^2]$

In Exercises 131 and 132, find the absolute maxima and minima of the functions and say where they are assumed.

131. $f(x) = e^{x/\sqrt{x^4+1}}$

132. $g(x) = e^{\sqrt{3-2x-x^2}}$

T **133.** Graph the following functions and use what you see to locate and estimate the extreme values, identify the coordinates of the inflection points, and identify the intervals on which the graphs are concave up and concave down. Then confirm your estimates by working with the functions' derivatives.

a. $y = (\ln x)/\sqrt{x}$ **b.** $y = e^{-x^2}$

c. $y = (1 + x)e^{-x}$

T **134.** Graph $f(x) = x \ln x$. Does the function appear to have an absolute minimum value? Confirm your answer with calculus.

T **135.** Graph $f(x) = (\sin x)^{\sin x}$ over $[0, 3\pi]$. Explain what you see.

136. A round underwater transmission cable consists of a core of copper wires surrounded by nonconducting insulation. If x denotes the ratio of the radius of the core to the thickness of the insulation, it is known that the speed of the transmission signal is given by the equation $v = x^2 \ln(1/x)$. If the radius of the core is 1 cm, what insulation thickness h will allow the greatest transmission speed?

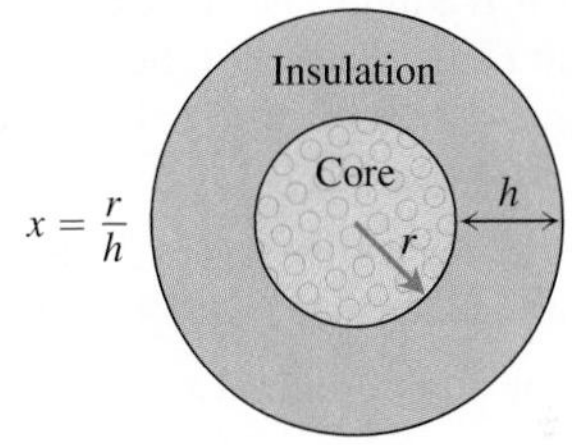

Chapter 4 Additional and Advanced Exercises

1. What can you say about a function whose maximum and minimum values on an interval are equal? Give reasons for your answer.

2. Is it true that a discontinuous function cannot have both an absolute maximum and an absolute minimum value on a closed interval? Give reasons for your answer.

3. Can you conclude anything about the extreme values of a continuous function on an open interval? On a half-open interval? Give reasons for your answer.

4. Local extrema Use the sign pattern for the derivative

$$\frac{df}{dx} = 6(x - 1)(x - 2)^2(x - 3)^3(x - 4)^4$$

to identify the points where f has local maximum and minimum values.

5. Local extrema

a. Suppose that the first derivative of $y = f(x)$ is

$$y' = 6(x + 1)(x - 2)^2.$$

At what points, if any, does the graph of f have a local maximum, local minimum, or point of inflection?

b. Suppose that the first derivative of $y = f(x)$ is

$$y' = 6x(x + 1)(x - 2).$$

At what points, if any, does the graph of f have a local maximum, local minimum, or point of inflection?

6. If $f'(x) \le 2$ for all x, what is the most the values of f can increase on $[0, 6]$? Give reasons for your answer.

7. Bounding a function Suppose that f is continuous on $[a, b]$ and that c is an interior point of the interval. Show that if $f'(x) \le 0$ on $[a, c)$ and $f'(x) \ge 0$ on $(c, b]$, then $f(x)$ is never less than $f(c)$ on $[a, b]$.

8. An inequality

a. Show that $-1/2 \le x/(1 + x^2) \le 1/2$ for every value of x.

b. Suppose that f is a function whose derivative is $f'(x) = x/(1 + x^2)$. Use the result in part (a) to show that

$$|f(b) - f(a)| \le \frac{1}{2}|b - a|$$

for any a and b.

9. The derivative of $f(x) = x^2$ is zero at $x = 0$, but f is not a constant function. Doesn't this contradict the corollary of the Mean Value Theorem that says that functions with zero derivatives are constant? Give reasons for your answer.

10. Extrema and inflection points Let $h = fg$ be the product of two differentiable functions of x.

a. If f and g are positive, with local maxima at $x = a$, and if f' and g' change sign at a, does h have a local maximum at a?

b. If the graphs of f and g have inflection points at $x = a$, does the graph of h have an inflection point at a?

In either case, if the answer is yes, give a proof. If the answer is · give a counterexample.

11. **Finding a function** Use the following information to find the values of a, b, and c in the formula $f(x) = (x + a)/(bx^2 + cx + 2)$.
    i) The values of a, b, and c are either 0 or 1.
    ii) The graph of f passes through the point $(-1, 0)$.
    iii) The line $y = 1$ is an asymptote of the graph of f.

12. **Horizontal tangent** For what value or values of the constant k will the curve $y = x^3 + kx^2 + 3x - 4$ have exactly one horizontal tangent?

13. **Largest inscribed triangle** Points A and B lie at the ends of a diameter of a unit circle and point C lies on the circumference. Is it true that the area of triangle ABC is largest when the triangle is isosceles? How do you know?

14. **Proving the second derivative test** The Second Derivative Test for Local Maxima and Minima (Section 4.4) says:
    a. f has a local maximum value at $x = c$ if $f'(c) = 0$ and $f''(c) < 0$
    b. f has a local minimum value at $x = c$ if $f'(c) = 0$ and $f''(c) > 0$.

    To prove statement (a), let $\epsilon = (1/2)|f''(c)|$. Then use the fact that
    $$f''(c) = \lim_{h \to 0} \frac{f'(c + h) - f'(c)}{h} = \lim_{h \to 0} \frac{f'(c + h)}{h}$$
    to conclude that for some $\delta > 0$,
    $$0 < |h| < \delta \quad \Rightarrow \quad \frac{f'(c + h)}{h} < f''(c) + \epsilon < 0.$$
    Thus, $f'(c + h)$ is positive for $-\delta < h < 0$ and negative for $0 < h < \delta$. Prove statement (b) in a similar way.

15. **Hole in a water tank** You want to bore a hole in the side of the tank shown here at a height that will make the stream of water coming out hit the ground as far from the tank as possible. If you drill the hole near the top, where the pressure is low, the water will exit slowly but spend a relatively long time in the air. If you drill the hole near the bottom, the water will exit at a higher velocity but have only a short time to fall. Where is the best place, if any, for the hole? (*Hint:* How long will it take an exiting particle of water to fall from height y to the ground?)

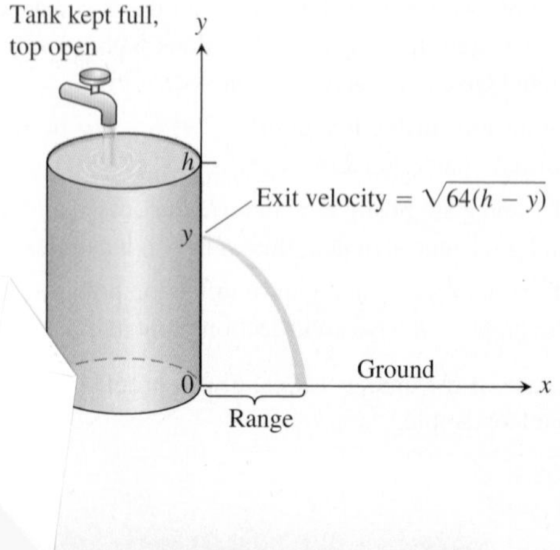

16. **Kicking a field goal** An American football player wants to kick a field goal with the ball being on a right hash mark. Assume that the goal posts are b feet apart and that the hash mark line is a distance $a > 0$ feet from the right goal post. (See the accompanying figure.) Find the distance h from the goal post line that gives the kicker his largest angle β. Assume that the football field is flat.

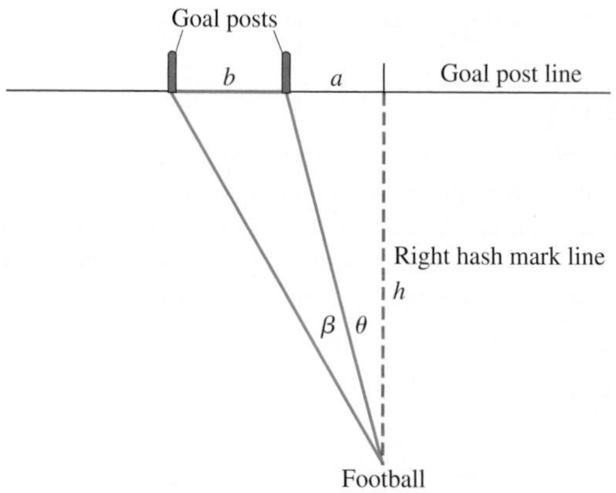

17. **A max-min problem with a variable answer** Sometimes the solution of a max-min problem depends on the proportions of the shapes involved. As a case in point, suppose that a right circular cylinder of radius r and height h is inscribed in a right circular cone of radius R and height H, as shown here. Find the value of r (in terms of R and H) that maximizes the total surface area of the cylinder (including top and bottom). As you will see, the solution depends on whether $H \le 2R$ or $H > 2R$.

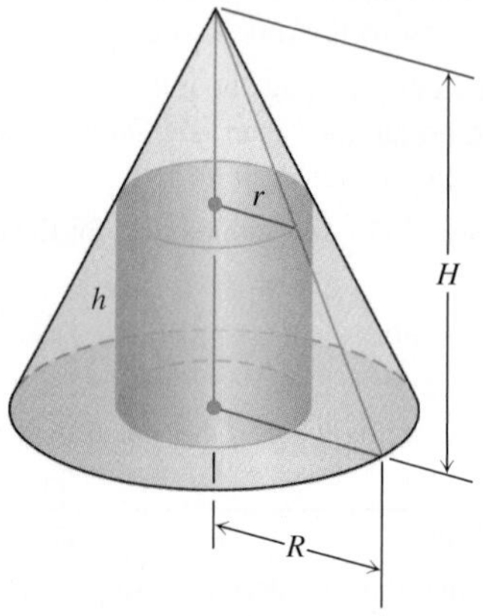

18. **Minimizing a parameter** Find the smallest value of the positive constant m that will make $mx - 1 + (1/x)$ greater than or equal to zero for all positive values of x.

19. Evaluate the following limits.
    a. $\lim_{x \to 0} \dfrac{2 \sin 5x}{3x}$ **b.** $\lim_{x \to 0} \sin 5x \cot 3x$
    c. $\lim_{x \to 0} x \csc^2 \sqrt{2x}$ **d.** $\lim_{x \to \pi/2} (\sec x - \tan x)$

e. $\lim_{x \to 0} \frac{x - \sin x}{x - \tan x}$ **f.** $\lim_{x \to 0} \frac{\sin x^2}{x \sin x}$

g. $\lim_{x \to 0} \frac{\sec x - 1}{x^2}$ **h.** $\lim_{x \to 2} \frac{x^3 - 8}{x^2 - 4}$

20. L'Hôpital's Rule does not help with the following limits. Find them some other way.

a. $\lim_{x \to \infty} \frac{\sqrt{x + 5}}{\sqrt{x + 5}}$ **b.** $\lim_{x \to \infty} \frac{2x}{x + 7\sqrt{x}}$

21. Suppose that it costs a company $y = a + bx$ dollars to produce x units per week. It can sell x units per week at a price of $P = c - ex$ dollars per unit. Each of a, b, c, and e represents a positive constant. **(a)** What production level maximizes the profit? **(b)** What is the corresponding price? **(c)** What is the weekly profit at this level of production? **(d)** At what price should each item be sold to maximize profits if the government imposes a tax of t dollars per item sold? Comment on the difference between this price and the price before the tax.

22. Estimating reciprocals without division You can estimate the value of the reciprocal of a number a without ever dividing by a if you apply Newton's method to the function $f(x) = (1/x) - a$. For example, if $a = 3$, the function involved is $f(x) = (1/x) - 3$.

a. Graph $y = (1/x) - 3$. Where does the graph cross the x-axis?

b. Show that the recursion formula in this case is

$$x_{n+1} = x_n(2 - 3x_n),$$

so there is no need for division.

23. To find $x = \sqrt[q]{a}$, we apply Newton's method to $f(x) = x^q - a$. Here we assume that a is a positive real number and q is a positive integer. Show that x_1 is a "weighted average" of x_0 and a/x_0^{q-1}, and find the coefficients m_0, m_1 such that

$$x_1 = m_0 x_0 + m_1\left(\frac{a}{x_0^{q-1}}\right), \qquad \begin{matrix} m_0 > 0, m_1 > 0, \\ m_0 + m_1 = 1. \end{matrix}$$

What conclusion would you reach if x_0 and a/x_0^{q-1} were equal? What would be the value of x_1 in that case?

24. The family of straight lines $y = ax + b$ (a, b arbitrary constants) can be characterized by the relation $y'' = 0$. Find a similar relation satisfied by the family of all circles

$$(x - h)^2 + (y - h)^2 = r^2,$$

where h and r are arbitrary constants. (*Hint:* Eliminate h and r from the set of three equations including the given one and two obtained by successive differentiation.)

25. Free fall in the fourteenth century In the middle of the fourteenth century, Albert of Saxony (1316–1390) proposed a model of free fall that assumed that the velocity of a falling body was proportional to the distance fallen. It seemed reasonable to think that a body that had fallen 20 ft might be moving twice as fast as a body that had fallen 10 ft. And besides, none of the instruments in use at the time were accurate enough to prove otherwise. Today we can see just how far off Albert of Saxony's model was by solving the initial value problem implicit in his model. Solve the problem and compare your solution graphically with the equation $s = 16t^2$. You will see that it describes a motion that starts too slowly at first and then becomes too fast too soon to be realistic.

T **26. Group blood testing** During World War II it was necessary to administer blood tests to large numbers of recruits. There are two standard ways to administer a blood test to N people. In method 1, each person is tested separately. In method 2, the blood samples of x people are pooled and tested as one large sample. If the test is negative, this one test is enough for all x people. If the test is positive, then each of the x people is tested separately, requiring a total of $x + 1$ tests. Using the second method and some probability theory it can be shown that, on the average, the total number of tests y will be

$$y = N\left(1 - q^x + \frac{1}{x}\right).$$

With $q = 0.99$ and $N = 1000$, find the integer value of x that minimizes y. Also find the integer value of x that maximizes y. (This second result is not important to the real-life situation.) The group testing method was used in World War II with a savings of 80% over the individual testing method, but not with the given value of q.

27. Assume that the brakes of an automobile produce a constant deceleration of k ft/sec^2. **(a)** Determine what k must be to bring an automobile traveling 60 mi/hr (88 ft/sec) to rest in a distance of 100 ft from the point where the brakes are applied. **(b)** With the same k, how far would a car traveling 30 mi/hr travel before being brought to a stop?

28. Let $f(x)$, $g(x)$ be two continuously differentiable functions satisfying the relationships $f'(x) = g(x)$ and $f''(x) = -f(x)$. Let $h(x) = f^2(x) + g^2(x)$. If $h(0) = 5$, find $h(10)$.

29. Can there be a curve satisfying the following conditions? d^2y/dx^2 is everywhere equal to zero and, when $x = 0$, $y = 0$ and $dy/dx = 1$. Give a reason for your answer.

30. Find the equation for the curve in the xy-plane that passes through the point $(1, -1)$ if its slope at x is always $3x^2 + 2$.

31. A particle moves along the x-axis. Its acceleration is $a = -t^2$. At $t = 0$, the particle is at the origin. In the course of its motion, it reaches the point $x = b$, where $b > 0$, but no point beyond b. Determine its velocity at $t = 0$.

32. A particle moves with acceleration $a = \sqrt{t} - (1/\sqrt{t})$. Assuming that the velocity $v = 4/3$ and the position $s = -4/15$ when $t = 0$, find

a. the velocity v in terms of t.

b. the position s in terms of t.

33. Given $f(x) = ax^2 + 2bx + c$ with $a > 0$. By considering the minimum, prove that $f(x) \geq 0$ for all real x if and only if $b^2 - ac \leq 0$.

34. Schwarz's inequality

a. In Exercise 33, let

$$f(x) = (a_1x + b_1)^2 + (a_2x + b_2)^2 + \cdots + (a_nx + b_n)^2,$$

and deduce Schwarz's inequality:

$$(a_1b_1 + a_2b_2 + \cdots + a_nb_n)^2$$
$$\le \left(a_1{}^2 + a_2{}^2 + \cdots + a_n{}^2\right)\left(b_1{}^2 + b_2{}^2 + \cdots + b_n{}^2\right).$$

b. Show that equality holds in Schwarz's inequality only if there exists a real number x that makes a_ix equal $-b_i$ for every value of i from 1 to n.

35. The best branching angles for blood vessels and pipes When a smaller pipe branches off from a larger one in a flow system, we may want it to run off at an angle that is best from some energy-saving point of view. We might require, for instance, that energy loss due to friction be minimized along the section AOB shown in the accompanying figure. In this diagram, B is a given point to be reached by the smaller pipe, A is a point in the larger pipe upstream from B, and O is the point where the branching occurs. A law due to Poiseuille states that the loss of energy due to friction in nonturbulent flow is proportional to the length of the path and inversely proportional to the fourth power of the radius. Thus, the loss along AO is $(kd_1)/R^4$ and along OB is $(kd_2)/r^4$, where k is a constant, d_1 is the length of AO, d_2 is the length of OB, R is the radius of the larger pipe, and r is the radius of the smaller pipe. The angle θ is to be chosen to minimize the sum of these two losses:

$$L = k\frac{d_1}{R^4} + k\frac{d_2}{r^4}.$$

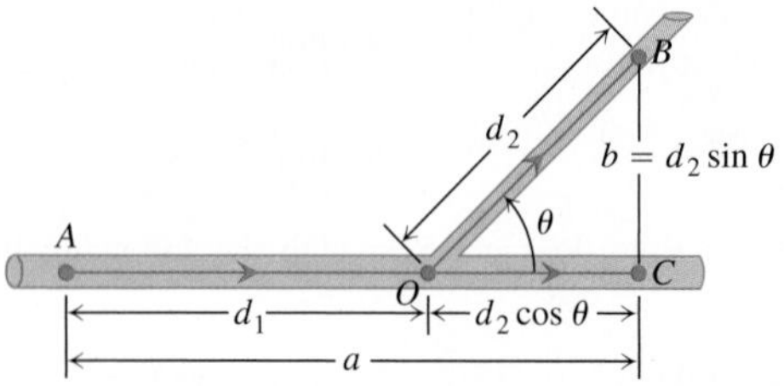

In our model, we assume that $AC = a$ and $BC = b$ are fixed. Thus we have the relations

$$d_1 + d_2\cos\theta = a \qquad d_2\sin\theta = b,$$

so that

$$d_2 = b\csc\theta,$$
$$d_1 = a - d_2\cos\theta = a - b\cot\theta.$$

We can express the total loss L as a function of θ:

$$L = k\left(\frac{a - b\cot\theta}{R^4} + \frac{b\csc\theta}{r^4}\right).$$

a. Show that the critical value of θ for which $dL/d\theta$ equals zero is

$$\theta_c = \cos^{-1}\frac{r^4}{R^4}.$$

b. If the ratio of the pipe radii is $r/R = 5/6$, estimate to the nearest degree the optimal branching angle given in part (a).

INTEGRATION

OVERVIEW One of the great achievements of classical geometry was to obtain formulas for the areas and volumes of triangles, spheres, and cones. In this chapter we study a method to calculate the areas and volumes of these and other more general shapes. The method we develop, called *integration*, is a tool for calculating much more than areas and volumes. The *integral* is of fundamental importance in statistics, the sciences, and engineering. It allows us to calculate quantities ranging from probabilities and averages to energy consumption and the forces against a dam's floodgates.

5.1 Estimating with Finite Sums

This section shows how area, average values, and the distance traveled by an object over time can all be approximated by finite sums. In Section 5.3 we will see that finite sums are the basis for defining the integral.

Area

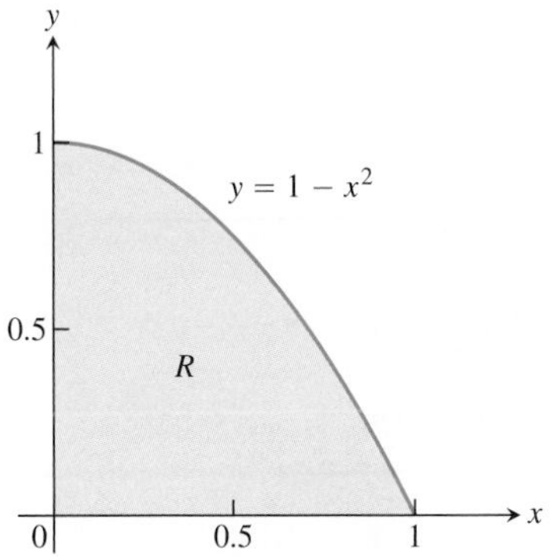

FIGURE 5.1 The area of the region R cannot be found by a simple formula.

The area of a region with a curved boundary can be approximated by summing the areas of a collection of rectangles. Using more rectangles increases the accuracy of the approximation.

Suppose, for instance, we want to find the area of the shaded region R that lies above the x-axis, below the graph of $y = 1 - x^2$, and between the vertical lines $x = 0$ and $x = 1$ (Figure 5.1). Unfortunately, there is no simple geometric formula for calculating the areas of general shapes having curved boundaries like the region R.

While we do not yet have a method for determining the exact area of R, we can approximate it in a simple way. Figure 5.2a shows two rectangles that together contain the region R. Each rectangle has width $1/2$ and they have heights 1 and $3/4$, moving from left to right. The height of each rectangle is the maximum value of the function f, obtained by evaluating f at the left endpoint of the subinterval of $[0, 1]$ forming the base of the rectangle. The total area of the two rectangles approximates the area A of the region R,

$$A \approx 1 \cdot \frac{1}{2} + \frac{3}{4} \cdot \frac{1}{2} = \frac{7}{8} = 0.875.$$

This estimate is larger than the true area A, since the two rectangles contain R. We say that 0.875 is an **upper sum** because it is obtained by taking the height of each rectangle

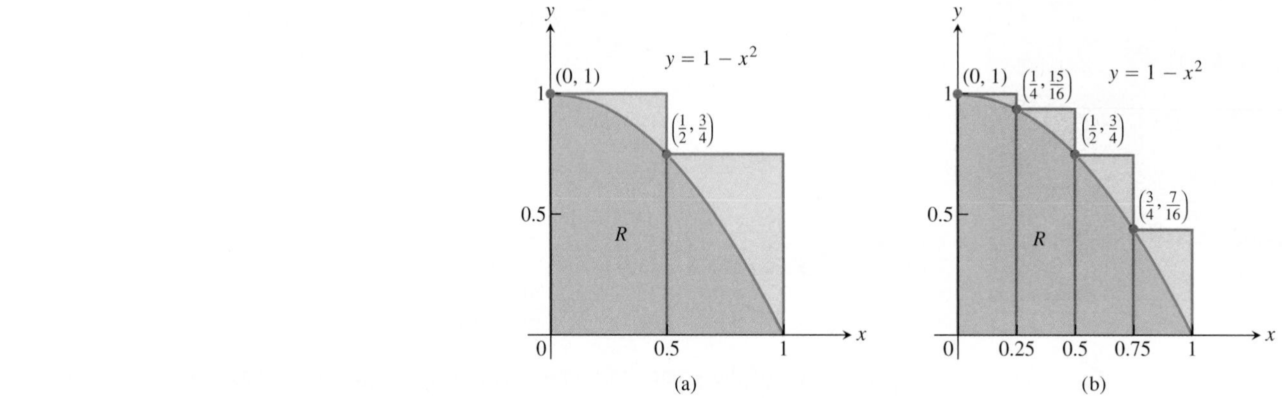

FIGURE 5.2 (a) We get an upper estimate of the area of R by using two rectangles containing R. (b) Four rectangles give a better upper estimate. Both estimates overshoot the true value for the area.

as the maximum (uppermost) value of $f(x)$ for x a point in the base interval of the rectangle. In Figure 5.2b, we improve our estimate by using four thinner rectangles, each of width $1/4$, which taken together contain the region R. These four rectangles give the approximation

$$A \approx 1 \cdot \frac{1}{4} + \frac{15}{16} \cdot \frac{1}{4} + \frac{3}{4} \cdot \frac{1}{4} + \frac{7}{16} \cdot \frac{1}{4} = \frac{25}{32} = 0.78125,$$

which is still greater than A since the four rectangles contain R.

Suppose instead we use four rectangles contained *inside* the region R to estimate the area, as in Figure 5.3a. Each rectangle has width $1/4$ as before, but the rectangles are shorter and lie entirely beneath the graph of f. The function $f(x) = 1 - x^2$ is decreasing

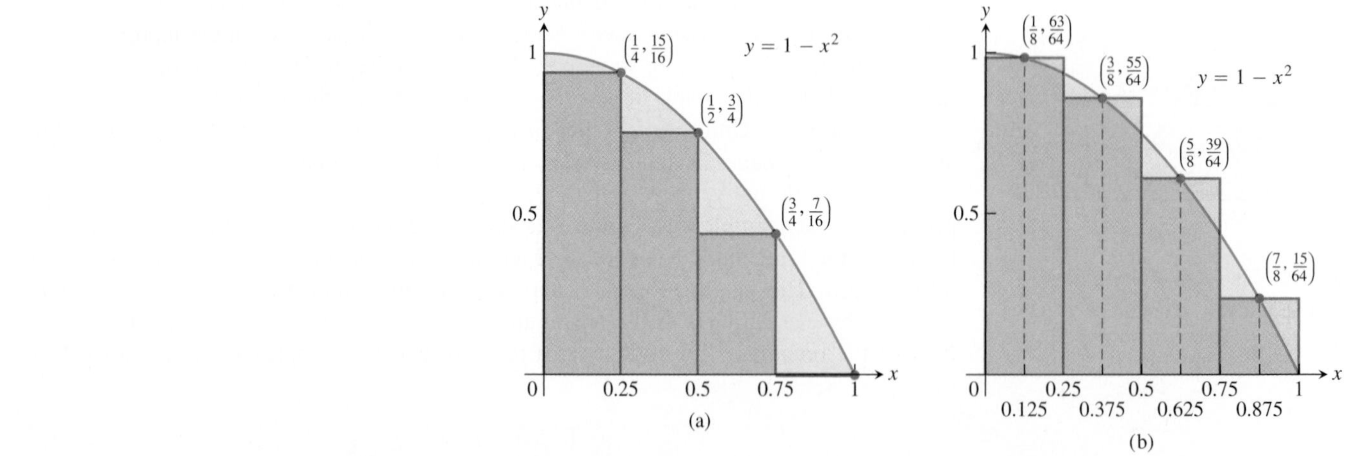

FIGURE 5.3 (a) Rectangles contained in R give an estimate for the area that undershoots the true value. (b) The midpoint rule uses rectangles whose height is the value of $y = f(x)$ at the midpoints of their bases.

on [0,1], so the height of each of these rectangles is given by the value of f at the right endpoint of the subinterval forming its base. The fourth rectangle has zero height and therefore contributes no area. Summing these rectangles with heights equal to the minimum value of $f(x)$ for x a point in each base subinterval, gives a **lower sum** approximation to the area,

$$A \approx \frac{15}{16}\cdot\frac{1}{4}+\frac{3}{4}\cdot\frac{1}{4}+\frac{7}{16}\cdot\frac{1}{4}+0\cdot\frac{1}{4}=\frac{17}{32}=0.53125.$$

This estimate is smaller than the area A since the rectangles all lie inside of the region R. The true value of A lies somewhere between these lower and upper sums:

$$0.53125 < A < 0.78125.$$

By considering both lower and upper sum approximations we get not only estimates for the area, but also a bound on the size of the possible error in these estimates since the true value of the area lies somewhere between them. Here the error cannot be greater than the difference $0.78125 - 0.53125 = 0.25$.

Yet another estimate can be obtained by using rectangles whose heights are the values of f at the midpoints of their bases (Figure 5.3b). This method of estimation is called the **midpoint rule** for approximating the area. The midpoint rule gives an estimate that is between a lower sum and an upper sum, but it is not quite so clear whether it overestimates or underestimates the true area. With four rectangles of width $1/4$ as before, the midpoint rule estimates the area of R to be

$$A \approx \frac{63}{64}\cdot\frac{1}{4}+\frac{55}{64}\cdot\frac{1}{4}+\frac{39}{64}\cdot\frac{1}{4}+\frac{15}{64}\cdot\frac{1}{4}=\frac{172}{64}\cdot\frac{1}{4}=0.671875.$$

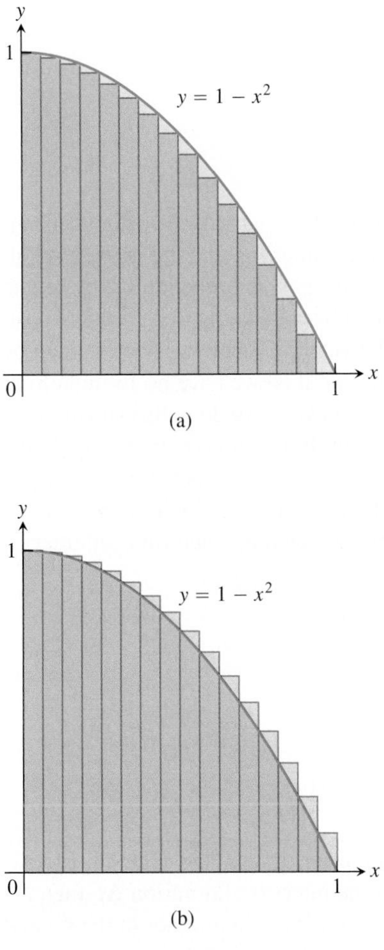

FIGURE 5.4 (a) A lower sum using 16 rectangles of equal width $\Delta x = 1/16$. (b) An upper sum using 16 rectangles.

In each of our computed sums, the interval $[a, b]$ over which the function f is defined was subdivided into n subintervals of equal width (also called length) $\Delta x = (b - a)/n$, and f was evaluated at a point in each subinterval: c_1 in the first subinterval, c_2 in the second subinterval, and so on. The finite sums then all take the form

$$f(c_1)\,\Delta x + f(c_2)\,\Delta x + f(c_3)\,\Delta x + \cdots + f(c_n)\,\Delta x.$$

By taking more and more rectangles, with each rectangle thinner than before, it appears that these finite sums give better and better approximations to the true area of the region R.

Figure 5.4a shows a lower sum approximation for the area of R using 16 rectangles of equal width. The sum of their areas is 0.634765625, which appears close to the true area, but is still smaller since the rectangles lie inside R.

Figure 5.4b shows an upper sum approximation using 16 rectangles of equal width. The sum of their areas is 0.697265625, which is somewhat larger than the true area because the rectangles taken together contain R. The midpoint rule for 16 rectangles gives a total area approximation of 0.6669921875, but it is not immediately clear whether this estimate is larger or smaller than the true area.

EXAMPLE 1 Table 5.1 shows the values of upper and lower sum approximations to the area of R using up to 1000 rectangles. In Section 5.2 we will see how to get an exact value of the areas of regions such as R by taking a limit as the base width of each rectangle goes to zero and the number of rectangles goes to infinity. With the techniques developed there, we will be able to show that the area of R is exactly $2/3$. ■

TABLE 5.1 Finite approximations for the area of R

Number of subintervals	Lower sum	Midpoint rule	Upper sum
2	.375	.6875	.875
4	.53125	.671875	.78125
16	.634765625	.6669921875	.697265625
50	.6566	.6667	.6766
100	.66165	.666675	.67165
1000	.6661665	.66666675	.6671665

Distance Traveled

Suppose we know the velocity function $v(t)$ of a car moving down a highway, without changing direction, and want to know how far it traveled between times $t = a$ and $t = b$. If we already know an antiderivative $F(t)$ of $v(t)$ we can find the car's position function $s(t)$ by setting $s(t) = F(t) + C$. The distance traveled can then be found by calculating the change in position, $s(b) - s(a)$ (see Exercise 117, Section 4.8). If the velocity function is determined by recording a speedometer reading at various times on the car, then we have no formula from which to obtain an antiderivative function for velocity. So what do we do in this situation?

When we don't know an antiderivative for the velocity function $v(t)$, we can apply the same principal of approximating the distance traveled with finite sums as before. We subdivide the interval $[a, b]$ into short time intervals on each of which the velocity is considered to be fairly constant. Then we approximate the distance traveled on each time subinterval with the usual distance formula

$$\text{distance} = \text{velocity} \times \text{time}$$

and add the results across $[a, b]$.

Suppose the subdivided interval looks like

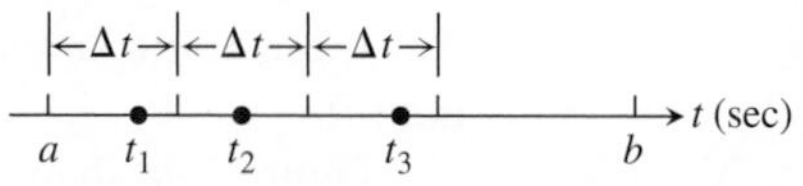

with the subintervals all of equal length Δt. Pick a number t_1 in the first interval. If Δt is so small that the velocity barely changes over a short time interval of duration Δt, then the distance traveled in the first time interval is about $v(t_1)\,\Delta t$. If t_2 is a number in the second interval, the distance traveled in the second time interval is about $v(t_2)\,\Delta t$. The sum of the distances traveled over all the time intervals is

$$D \approx v(t_1)\,\Delta t + v(t_2)\,\Delta t + \cdots + v(t_n)\,\Delta t,$$

where n is the total number of subintervals.

EXAMPLE 2 The velocity function of a projectile fired straight into the air is $f(t) = 160 - 9.8t$ m/sec. Use the summation technique just described to estimate how far the projectile rises during the first 3 sec. How close do the sums come to the exact value of 435.9 m?

Solution We explore the results for different numbers of intervals and different choices of evaluation points. Notice that $f(t)$ is decreasing, so choosing left endpoints gives an upper sum estimate; choosing right endpoints gives a lower sum estimate.

(a) *Three subintervals of length* 1, *with f evaluated at left endpoints giving an upper sum*:

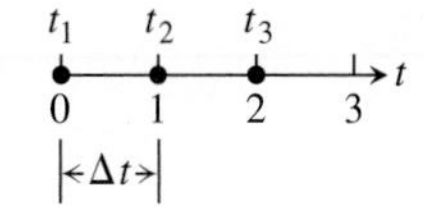

With f evaluated at $t = 0, 1$, and 2, we have

$$\begin{aligned} D &\approx f(t_1)\,\Delta t + f(t_2)\,\Delta t + f(t_3)\,\Delta t \\ &= [160 - 9.8(0)](1) + [160 - 9.8(1)](1) + [160 - 9.8(2)](1) \\ &= 450.6. \end{aligned}$$

(b) *Three subintervals of length* 1, *with f evaluated at right endpoints giving a lower sum*:

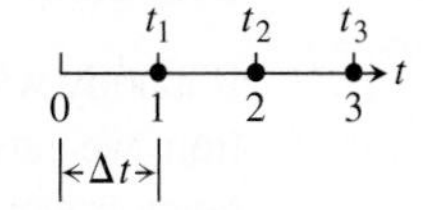

With f evaluated at $t = 1, 2$, and 3, we have

$$\begin{aligned} D &\approx f(t_1)\,\Delta t + f(t_2)\,\Delta t + f(t_3)\,\Delta t \\ &= [160 - 9.8(1)](1) + [160 - 9.8(2)](1) + [160 - 9.8(3)](1) \\ &= 421.2. \end{aligned}$$

(c) *With six subintervals of length* $1/2$, *we get*

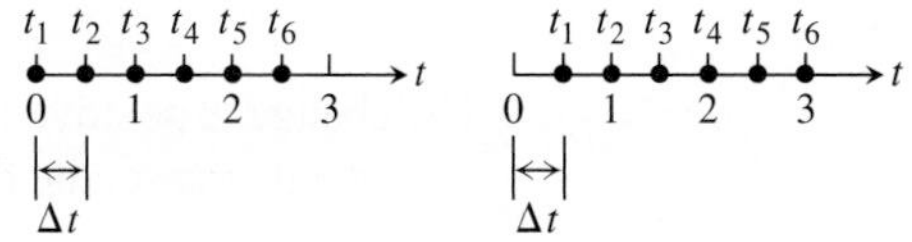

An upper sum using left endpoints: $D \approx 443.25$; a lower sum using right endpoints: $D \approx 428.55$.

These six-interval estimates are somewhat closer than the three-interval estimates. The results improve as the subintervals get shorter.

As we can see in Table 5.2, the left-endpoint upper sums approach the true value 435.9 from above, whereas the right-endpoint lower sums approach it from below. The true value lies between these upper and lower sums. The magnitude of the error in the closest entries is 0.23, a small percentage of the true value.

$$\begin{aligned} \text{Error magnitude} &= |\text{true value} - \text{calculated value}| \\ &= |435.9 - 435.67| = 0.23. \end{aligned}$$

$$\text{Error percentage} = \frac{0.23}{435.9} \approx 0.05\%.$$

It would be reasonable to conclude from the table's last entries that the projectile rose about 436 m during its first 3 sec of flight. ■

TABLE 5.2 Travel-distance estimates

Number of subintervals	Length of each subinterval	Upper sum	Lower sum
3	1	450.6	421.2
6	1/2	443.25	428.55
12	1/4	439.57	432.22
24	1/8	437.74	434.06
48	1/16	436.82	434.98
96	1/32	436.36	435.44
192	1/64	436.13	435.67

Displacement Versus Distance Traveled

If a body with position function $s(t)$ moves along a coordinate line without changing direction, we can calculate the total distance it travels from $t = a$ to $t = b$ by summing the distance traveled over small intervals, as in Example 2. If the body reverses direction one or more times during the trip, then we need to use the body's *speed* $|v(t)|$, which is the absolute value of its velocity function, $v(t)$, to find the total distance traveled. Using the velocity itself, as in Example 2, only gives an estimate to the body's **displacement**, $s(b) - s(a)$, the difference between its initial and final positions.

To see why, partition the time interval $[a, b]$ into small enough equal subintervals Δt so that the body's velocity does not change very much from time t_{k-1} to t_k. Then $v(t_k)$ gives a good approximation of the velocity throughout the interval. Accordingly, the change in the body's position coordinate during the time interval is about

$$v(t_k)\,\Delta t.$$

The change is positive if $v(t_k)$ is positive and negative if $v(t_k)$ is negative.

In either case, the distance traveled during the subinterval is about

$$|v(t_k)|\,\Delta t.$$

The **total distance traveled** is approximately the sum

$$|v(t_1)|\,\Delta t + |v(t_2)|\,\Delta t + \cdots + |v(t_n)|\,\Delta t.$$

Average Value of a Nonnegative Function

The average value of a collection of n numbers $x_1, x_2, \ldots, x_n$ is obtained by adding them together and dividing by n. But what is the average value of a continuous function f on an interval $[a, b]$? Such a function can assume infinitely many values. For example, the temperature at a certain location in a town is a continuous function that goes up and down each day. What does it mean to say that the average temperature in the town over the course of a day is 73 degrees?

When a function is constant, this question is easy to answer. A function with constant value c on an interval $[a, b]$ has average value c. When c is positive, its graph over $[a, b]$ gives a rectangle of height c. The average value of the function can then be interpreted geometrically as the area of this rectangle divided by its width $b - a$ (Figure 5.5a).

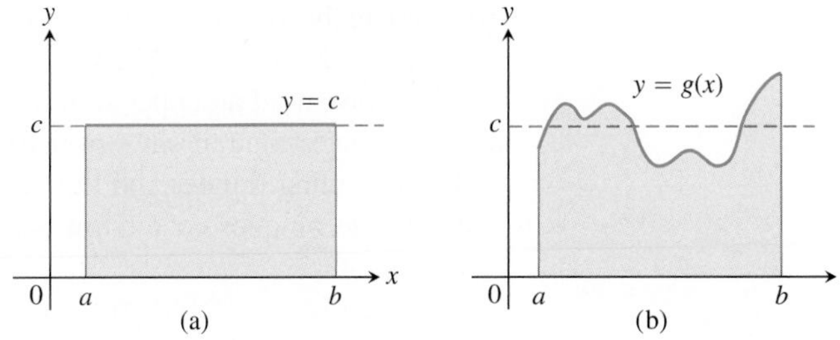

FIGURE 5.5 (a) The average value of $f(x) = c$ on $[a, b]$ is the area of the rectangle divided by $b - a$. (b) The average value of $g(x)$ on $[a, b]$ is the area beneath its graph divided by $b - a$.

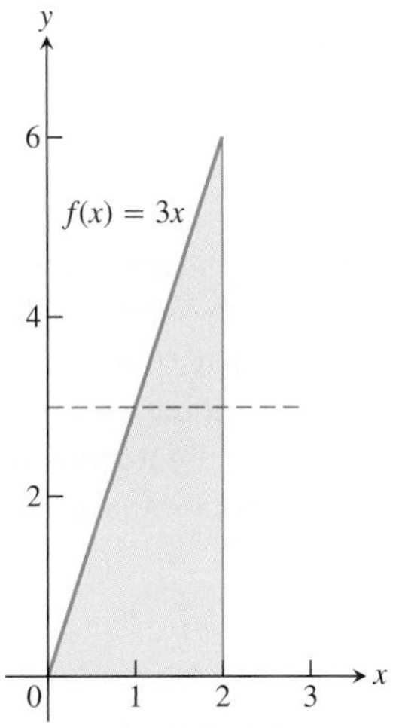

FIGURE 5.6 The average value of $f(x) = 3x$ over $[0, 2]$ is 3 (Example 3).

What if we want to find the average value of a nonconstant function, such as the function g in Figure 5.5b? We can think of this graph as a snapshot of the height of some water that is sloshing around in a tank, between enclosing walls at $x = a$ and $x = b$. As the water moves, its height over each point changes, but its average height remains the same. To get the average height of the water, we let it settle down until it is level and its height is constant. The resulting height c equals the area under the graph of g divided by $b - a$. We are led to *define* the average value of a nonnegative function on an interval $[a, b]$ to be the area under its graph divided by $b - a$. For this definition to be valid, we need a precise understanding of what is meant by the area under a graph. This will be obtained in Section 5.3, but for now we look at two simple examples.

EXAMPLE 3 What is the average value of the function $f(x) = 3x$ on the interval [0,2]?

Solution The average equals the area under the graph divided by the width of the interval. In this case we do not need finite approximation to estimate the area of the region under the graph: a triangle of height 6 and base 2 has area 6 (Figure 5.6). The width of the interval is $b - a = 2 - 0 = 2$. The average value of the function is $6/2 = 3$. ■

EXAMPLE 4 Estimate the average value of the function $f(x) = \sin x$ on the interval $[0, \pi]$.

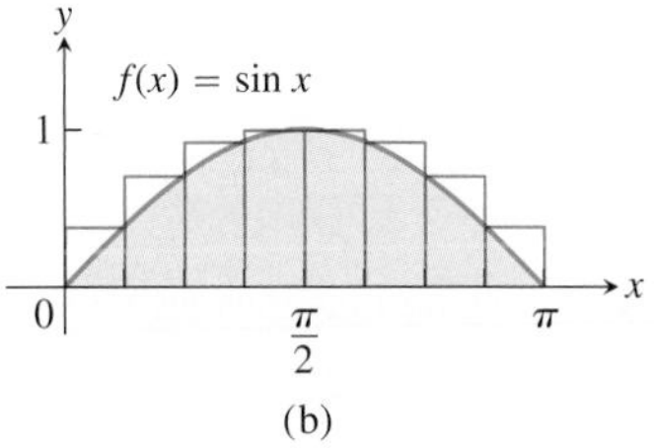

FIGURE 5.7 Approximating the area under $f(x) = \sin x$ between 0 and π to compute the average value of $\sin x$ over $[0, \pi]$, using eight rectangles (Example 4).

Solution Looking at the graph of $\sin x$ between 0 and π in Figure 5.7, we can see that its average height is somewhere between 0 and 1. To find the average we need to calculate the area A under the graph and then divide this area by the length of the interval, $\pi - 0 = \pi$.

We do not have a simple way to determine the area, so we approximate it with finite sums. To get an upper sum approximation, we add the areas of eight rectangles of equal width $\pi/8$ that together contain the region beneath the graph of $y = \sin x$ and above the x-axis on $[0, \pi]$. We choose the heights of the rectangles to be the largest value of $\sin x$ on each subinterval. Over a particular subinterval, this largest value may occur at the left endpoint, the right endpoint, or somewhere between them. We evaluate $\sin x$ at this point to get the height of the rectangle for an upper sum. The sum of the rectangle areas then estimates the total area (Figure 5.7):

$$A \approx \left(\sin\frac{\pi}{8} + \sin\frac{\pi}{4} + \sin\frac{3\pi}{8} + \sin\frac{\pi}{2} + \sin\frac{\pi}{2} + \sin\frac{5\pi}{8} + \sin\frac{3\pi}{4} + \sin\frac{7\pi}{8}\right)\cdot\frac{\pi}{8}$$

$$\approx (.38 + .71 + .92 + 1 + 1 + .92 + .71 + .38)\cdot\frac{\pi}{8} = (6.02)\cdot\frac{\pi}{8} \approx 2.365.$$

To estimate the average value of $\sin x$ we divide the estimated area by π and obtain the approximation $2.365/\pi \approx 0.753$.

Since we used an upper sum to approximate the area, this estimate is greater than the actual average value of $\sin x$ over $[0, \pi]$. If we use more and more rectangles, with each rectangle getting thinner and thinner, we get closer and closer to the true average value. Using the techniques covered in Section 5.3, we will show that the true average value is $2/\pi \approx 0.64$.

As before, we could just as well have used rectangles lying under the graph of $y = \sin x$ and calculated a lower sum approximation, or we could have used the midpoint rule. In Section 5.3 we will see that in each case, the approximations are close to the true area if all the rectangles are sufficiently thin. ■

Summary

The area under the graph of a positive function, the distance traveled by a moving object that doesn't change direction, and the average value of a nonnegative function over an interval can all be approximated by finite sums. First we subdivide the interval into subintervals, treating the appropriate function f as if it were constant over each particular subinterval. Then we multiply the width of each subinterval by the value of f at some point within it, and add these products together. If the interval $[a, b]$ is subdivided into n subintervals of equal widths $\Delta x = (b - a)/n$, and if $f(c_k)$ is the value of f at the chosen point c_k in the kth subinterval, this process gives a finite sum of the form

$$f(c_1)\,\Delta x + f(c_2)\,\Delta x + f(c_3)\,\Delta x + \cdots + f(c_n)\,\Delta x.$$

The choices for the c_k could maximize or minimize the value of f in the kth subinterval, or give some value in between. The true value lies somewhere between the approximations given by upper sums and lower sums. The finite sum approximations we looked at improved as we took more subintervals of thinner width.

EXERCISES 5.1

In Exercises 1–4 use finite approximations to estimate the area under the graph of the function using

a. a lower sum with two rectangles of equal width.

b. a lower sum with four rectangles of equal width.

c. an upper sum with two rectangles of equal width.

d. an upper sum with four rectangles of equal width.

1. $f(x) = x^2$ between $x = 0$ and $x = 1$.

2. $f(x) = x^3$ between $x = 0$ and $x = 1$.

3. $f(x) = 1/x$ between $x = 1$ and $x = 5$.

4. $f(x) = 4 - x^2$ between $x = -2$ and $x = 2$.

Using rectangles whose height is given by the value of the function at the midpoint of the rectangle's base (*the midpoint rule*) estimate the area under the graphs of the following functions, using first two and then four rectangles.

5. $f(x) = x^2$ between $x = 0$ and $x = 1$.

6. $f(x) = x^3$ between $x = 0$ and $x = 1$.

7. $f(x) = 1/x$ between $x = 1$ and $x = 5$.

8. $f(x) = 4 - x^2$ between $x = -2$ and $x = 2$.

9. Distance traveled The accompanying table shows the velocity of a model train engine moving along a track for 10 sec. Estimate the distance traveled by the engine using 10 subintervals of length 1 with

a. left-endpoint values.

b. right-endpoint values.

Time (sec)	Velocity (in./sec)	Time (sec)	Velocity (in./sec)
0	0	6	11
1	12	7	6
2	22	8	2
3	10	9	6
4	5	10	0
5	13		

10. Distance traveled upstream You are sitting on the bank of a tidal river watching the incoming tide carry a bottle upstream. You record the velocity of the flow every 5 minutes for an hour, with the results shown in the accompanying table. About how far upstream did the bottle travel during that hour? Find an estimate using 12 subintervals of length 5 with

a. left-endpoint values.

b. right-endpoint values.

Time (min)	Velocity (m/sec)	Time (min)	Velocity (m/sec)
0	1	35	1.2
5	1.2	40	1.0
10	1.7	45	1.8
15	2.0	50	1.5
20	1.8	55	1.2
25	1.6	60	0
30	1.4		

11. Length of a road You and a companion are about to drive a twisty stretch of dirt road in a car whose speedometer works but whose odometer (mileage counter) is broken. To find out how long this particular stretch of road is, you record the car's velocity at 10-sec intervals, with the results shown in the accompanying table. Estimate the length of the road using

a. left-endpoint values.

b. right-endpoint values.

Time (sec)	Velocity (converted to ft/sec) (30 mi/h = 44 ft/sec)	Time (sec)	Velocity (converted to ft/sec) (30 mi/h = 44 ft/sec)
0	0	70	15
10	44	80	22
20	15	90	35
30	35	100	44
40	30	110	30
50	44	120	35
60	35		

12. Distance from velocity data The accompanying table gives data for the velocity of a vintage sports car accelerating from 0 to 142 mi/h in 36 sec (10 thousandths of an hour).

Time (h)	Velocity (mi/h)	Time (h)	Velocity (mi/h)
0.0	0	0.006	116
0.001	40	0.007	125
0.002	62	0.008	132
0.003	82	0.009	137
0.004	96	0.010	142
0.005	108		

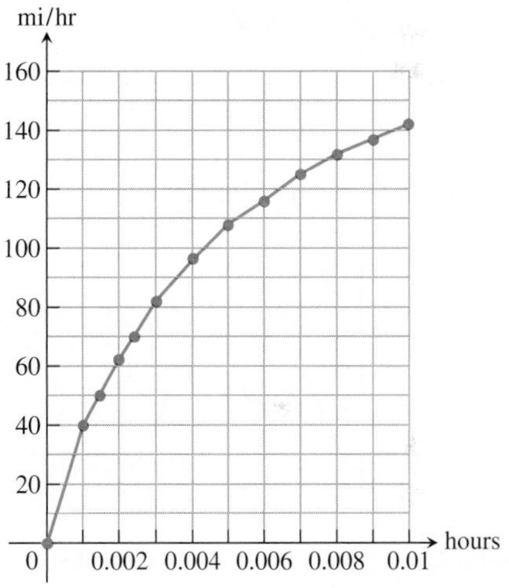

a. Use rectangles to estimate how far the car traveled during the 36 sec it took to reach 142 mi/h.

b. Roughly how many seconds did it take the car to reach the halfway point? About how fast was the car going then?

13. Free fall with air resistance An object is dropped straight down from a helicopter. The object falls faster and faster but its acceleration (rate of change of its velocity) decreases over time because of air resistance. The acceleration is measured in ft/sec^2 and recorded every second after the drop for 5 sec, as shown:

t	0	1	2	3	4	5
a	32.00	19.41	11.77	7.14	4.33	2.63

a. Find an upper estimate for the speed when $t = 5$.

b. Find a lower estimate for the speed when $t = 5$.

c. Find an upper estimate for the distance fallen when $t = 3$.

14. **Distance traveled by a projectile** An object is shot straight upward from sea level with an initial velocity of 400 ft/sec.

 a. Assuming that gravity is the only force acting on the object, give an upper estimate for its velocity after 5 sec have elapsed. Use $g = 32$ ft/sec^2 for the gravitational acceleration.

 b. Find a lower estimate for the height attained after 5 sec.

In Exercises 15–18, use a finite sum to estimate the average value of f on the given interval by partitioning the interval into four subintervals of equal length and evaluating f at the subinterval midpoints.

15. $f(x) = x^3$ on $[0, 2]$ **16.** $f(x) = 1/x$ on $[1, 9]$

17. $f(t) = (1/2) + \sin^2 \pi t$ on $[0, 2]$

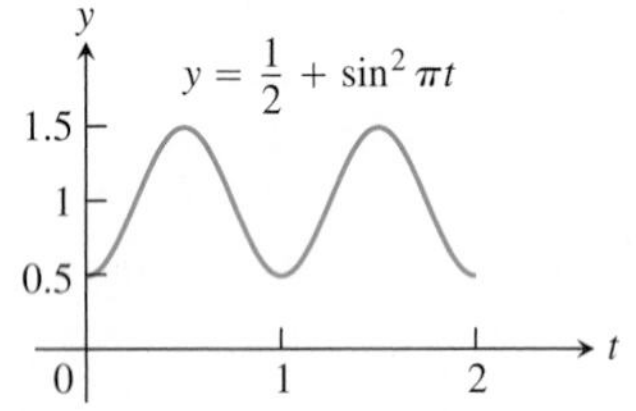

18. $f(t) = 1 - \left(\cos \frac{\pi t}{4}\right)^4$ on $[0, 4]$

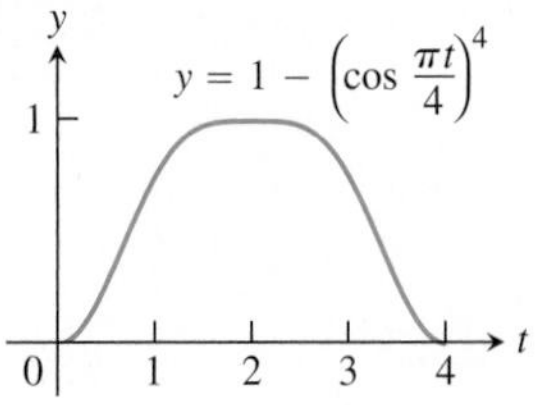

19. **Water pollution** Oil is leaking out of a tanker damaged at sea. The damage to the tanker is worsening as evidenced by the increased leakage each hour, recorded in the following table.

Time (h)	0	1	2	3	4
Leakage (gal/h)	50	70	97	136	190

Time (h)	5	6	7	8
Leakage (gal/h)	265	369	516	720

 a. Give an upper and a lower estimate of the total quantity of oil that has escaped after 5 hours.

 b. Repeat part (a) for the quantity of oil that has escaped after 8 hours.

 c. The tanker continues to leak 720 gal/h after the first 8 hours. If the tanker originally contained 25,000 gal of oil, approximately how many more hours will elapse in the worst case before all the oil has spilled? In the best case?

20. **Air pollution** A power plant generates electricity by burning oil. Pollutants produced as a result of the burning process are removed by scrubbers in the smokestacks. Over time, the scrubbers become less efficient and eventually they must be replaced when the amount of pollution released exceeds government standards. Measurements are taken at the end of each month determining the rate at which pollutants are released into the atmosphere, recorded as follows.

Month	Jan	Feb	Mar	Apr	May	Jun
Pollutant release rate (tons/day)	0.20	0.25	0.27	0.34	0.45	0.52

Month	Jul	Aug	Sep	Oct	Nov	Dec
Pollutant release rate (tons/day)	0.63	0.70	0.81	0.85	0.89	0.95

 a. Assuming a 30-day month and that new scrubbers allow only 0.05 ton/day released, give an upper estimate of the total tonnage of pollutants released by the end of June. What is a lower estimate?

 b. In the best case, approximately when will a total of 125 tons of pollutants have been released into the atmosphere?

21. Inscribe a regular n-sided polygon inside a circle of radius 1 and compute the area of the polygon for the following values of n:

 a. 4 (square) **b.** 8 (octagon) **c.** 16

 d. Compare the areas in parts (a), (b), and (c) with the area of the circle.

22. *(Continuation of Exercise 21.)*

 a. Inscribe a regular n-sided polygon inside a circle of radius 1 and compute the area of one of the n congruent triangles formed by drawing radii to the vertices of the polygon.

 b. Compute the limit of the area of the inscribed polygon as $n \to \infty$.

 c. Repeat the computations in parts (a) and (b) for a circle of radius r.

COMPUTER EXPLORATIONS

In Exercises 23–26, use a CAS to perform the following steps.

 a. Plot the functions over the given interval.

 b. Subdivide the interval into $n = 100, 200$, and 1000 subintervals of equal length and evaluate the function at the midpoint of each subinterval.

 c. Compute the average value of the function values generated in part (b).

 d. Solve the equation $f(x) =$ (average value) for x using the average value calculated in part (c) for the $n = 1000$ partitioning.

23. $f(x) = \sin x$ on $[0, \pi]$ **24.** $f(x) = \sin^2 x$ on $[0, \pi]$

25. $f(x) = x \sin \frac{1}{x}$ on $\left[\frac{\pi}{4}, \pi\right]$ **26.** $f(x) = x \sin^2 \frac{1}{x}$ on $\left[\frac{\pi}{4}, \pi\right]$

5.2 Sigma Notation and Limits of Finite Sums

In estimating with finite sums in Section 5.1, we encountered sums with many terms (up to 1000 in Table 5.1, for instance). In this section we introduce a more convenient notation for sums with a large number of terms. After describing the notation and stating several of its properties, we look at what happens to a finite sum approximation as the number of terms approaches infinity.

Finite Sums and Sigma Notation

Sigma notation enables us to write a sum with many terms in the compact form

$$\sum_{k=1}^{n} a_k = a_1 + a_2 + a_3 + \cdots + a_{n-1} + a_n.$$

The Greek letter Σ (capital sigma, corresponding to our letter S), stands for "sum." The **index of summation** k tells us where the sum begins (at the number below the Σ symbol) and where it ends (at the number above Σ). Any letter can be used to denote the index, but the letters i, j, and k are customary.

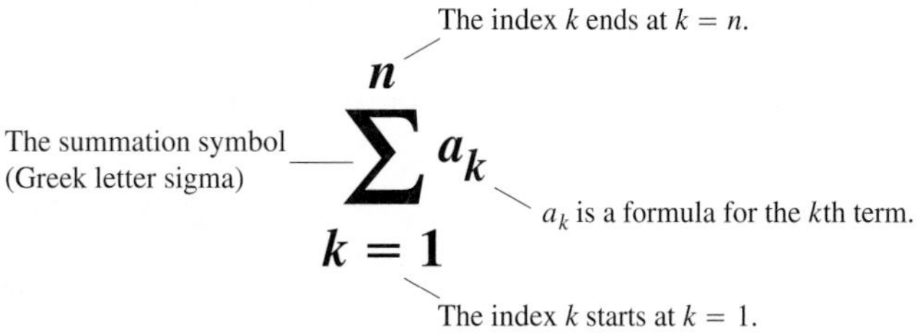

Thus we can write

$$1^2 + 2^2 + 3^2 + 4^2 + 5^2 + 6^2 + 7^2 + 8^2 + 9^2 + 10^2 + 11^2 = \sum_{k=1}^{11} k^2,$$

and

$$f(1) + f(2) + f(3) + \cdots + f(100) = \sum_{i=1}^{100} f(i).$$

EXAMPLE 1

The sum in sigma notation	**The sum written out, one term for each value of *k***	**The value of the sum**
$\sum_{k=1}^{5} k$	$1 + 2 + 3 + 4 + 5$	15
$\sum_{k=1}^{3} (-1)^k k$	$(-1)^1(1) + (-1)^2(2) + (-1)^3(3)$	$-1 + 2 - 3 = -2$
$\sum_{k=1}^{2} \frac{k}{k+1}$	$\frac{1}{1+1} + \frac{2}{2+1}$	$\frac{1}{2} + \frac{2}{3} = \frac{7}{6}$
$\sum_{k=4}^{5} \frac{k^2}{k-1}$	$\frac{4^2}{4-1} + \frac{5^2}{5-1}$	$\frac{16}{3} + \frac{25}{4} = \frac{139}{12}$

■

The lower limit of summation does not have to be 1; it can be any integer.

EXAMPLE 2 Express the sum $1 + 3 + 5 + 7 + 9$ in sigma notation.

Solution The formula generating the terms changes with the lower limit of summation, but the terms generated remain the same. It is often simplest to start with $k = 0$ or $k = 1$.

Starting with $k = 0$: $$1 + 3 + 5 + 7 + 9 = \sum_{k=0}^{4}(2k + 1)$$

Starting with $k = 1$: $$1 + 3 + 5 + 7 + 9 = \sum_{k=1}^{5}(2k - 1)$$

Starting with $k = 2$: $$1 + 3 + 5 + 7 + 9 = \sum_{k=2}^{6}(2k - 3)$$

Starting with $k = -3$: $$1 + 3 + 5 + 7 + 9 = \sum_{k=-3}^{1}(2k + 7)$$ ■

When we have a sum such as

$$\sum_{k=1}^{3}(k + k^2)$$

we can rearrange its terms,

$$\begin{aligned}\sum_{k=1}^{3}(k + k^2) &= (1 + 1^2) + (2 + 2^2) + (3 + 3^2) \\ &= (1 + 2 + 3) + (1^2 + 2^2 + 3^2) \qquad \text{Regroup terms.} \\ &= \sum_{k=1}^{3} k + \sum_{k=1}^{3} k^2\end{aligned}$$

This illustrates a general rule for finite sums:

$$\sum_{k=1}^{n}(a_k + b_k) = \sum_{k=1}^{n} a_k + \sum_{k=1}^{n} b_k$$

Four such rules are given below. A proof that they are valid can be obtained using mathematical induction (see Appendix 2).

Algebra Rules for Finite Sums

1. *Sum Rule*: $$\sum_{k=1}^{n}(a_k + b_k) = \sum_{k=1}^{n} a_k + \sum_{k=1}^{n} b_k$$
2. *Difference Rule*: $$\sum_{k=1}^{n}(a_k - b_k) = \sum_{k=1}^{n} a_k - \sum_{k=1}^{n} b_k$$
3. *Constant Multiple Rule*: $$\sum_{k=1}^{n} ca_k = c \cdot \sum_{k=1}^{n} a_k \qquad \text{(Any number } c\text{)}$$
4. *Constant Value Rule*: $$\sum_{k=1}^{n} c = n \cdot c \qquad (c \text{ is any constant value.})$$

EXAMPLE 3

(a) $\sum_{k=1}^{n}(3k - k^2) = 3\sum_{k=1}^{n} k - \sum_{k=1}^{n} k^2$ — Difference Rule and Constant Multiple Rule

(b) $\sum_{k=1}^{n}(-a_k) = \sum_{k=1}^{n}(-1)\cdot a_k = -1\cdot\sum_{k=1}^{n} a_k = -\sum_{k=1}^{n} a_k$ — Constant Multiple Rule

(c) $\sum_{k=1}^{3}(k + 4) = \sum_{k=1}^{3} k + \sum_{k=1}^{3} 4$ — Sum Rule

$= (1 + 2 + 3) + (3\cdot 4)$ — Constant Value Rule

$= 6 + 12 = 18$

(d) $\sum_{k=1}^{n}\frac{1}{n} = n\cdot\frac{1}{n} = 1$ — Constant Value Rule ($1/n$ is constant) ■

HISTORICAL BIOGRAPHY

Carl Friedrich Gauss (1777–1855)

Over the years people have discovered a variety of formulas for the values of finite sums. The most famous of these are the formula for the sum of the first n integers (Gauss is said to have discovered it at age 8) and the formulas for the sums of the squares and cubes of the first n integers.

EXAMPLE 4 Show that the sum of the first n integers is

$$\sum_{k=1}^{n} k = \frac{n(n + 1)}{2}.$$

Solution: The formula tells us that the sum of the first 4 integers is

$$\frac{(4)(5)}{2} = 10.$$

Addition verifies this prediction:

$$1 + 2 + 3 + 4 = 10.$$

To prove the formula in general, we write out the terms in the sum twice, once forward and once backward.

$$\begin{array}{ccccccccc} 1 & + & 2 & + & 3 & + & \cdots & + & n \\ n & + & (n-1) & + & (n-2) & + & \cdots & + & 1 \end{array}$$

If we add the two terms in the first column we get $1 + n = n + 1$. Similarly, if we add the two terms in the second column we get $2 + (n - 1) = n + 1$. The two terms in any column sum to $n + 1$. When we add the n columns together we get n terms, each equal to $n + 1$, for a total of $n(n + 1)$. Since this is twice the desired quantity, the sum of the first n integers is $(n)(n + 1)/2$. ■

Formulas for the sums of the squares and cubes of the first n integers are proved using mathematical induction (see Appendix 2). We state them here.

The first n squares: $\sum_{k=1}^{n} k^2 = \frac{n(n + 1)(2n + 1)}{6}$

The first n cubes: $\sum_{k=1}^{n} k^3 = \left(\frac{n(n + 1)}{2}\right)^2$

Limits of Finite Sums

The finite sum approximations we considered in Section 5.1 got more accurate as the number of terms increased and the subinterval widths (lengths) became thinner. The next example shows how to calculate a limiting value as the widths of the subintervals go to zero and their number grows to infinity.

EXAMPLE 5 Find the limiting value of lower sum approximations to the area of the region R below the graph of $y = 1 - x^2$ and above the interval [0, 1] on the x-axis using equal width rectangles whose widths approach zero and whose number approaches infinity. (See Figure 5.4a.)

Solution We compute a lower sum approximation using n rectangles of equal width $\Delta x = (1 - 0)/n$, and then we see what happens as $n \to \infty$. We start by subdividing [0, 1] into n equal width subintervals

$$\left[0, \frac{1}{n}\right], \left[\frac{1}{n}, \frac{2}{n}\right], \ldots, \left[\frac{n-1}{n}, \frac{n}{n}\right].$$

Each subinterval has width $1/n$. The function $1 - x^2$ is decreasing on [0, 1], and its smallest value in a subinterval occurs at the subinterval's right endpoint. So a lower sum is constructed with rectangles whose height over the subinterval $[(k-1)/n, k/n]$ is $f(k/n) = 1 - (k/n)^2$, giving the sum

$$f\left(\frac{1}{n}\right)\left(\frac{1}{n}\right) + f\left(\frac{2}{n}\right)\left(\frac{1}{n}\right) + \cdots + f\left(\frac{k}{n}\right)\left(\frac{1}{n}\right) + \cdots + f\left(\frac{n}{n}\right)\left(\frac{1}{n}\right).$$

We write this in sigma notation and simplify,

$$\begin{aligned}
\sum_{k=1}^{n} f\left(\frac{k}{n}\right)\left(\frac{1}{n}\right) &= \sum_{k=1}^{n}\left(1 - \left(\frac{k}{n}\right)^2\right)\left(\frac{1}{n}\right) \\
&= \sum_{k=1}^{n}\left(\frac{1}{n} - \frac{k^2}{n^3}\right) \\
&= \sum_{k=1}^{n}\frac{1}{n} - \sum_{k=1}^{n}\frac{k^2}{n^3} && \text{Difference Rule} \\
&= n \cdot \frac{1}{n} - \frac{1}{n^3}\sum_{k=1}^{n} k^2 && \text{Constant Value and Constant Multiple Rules} \\
&= 1 - \left(\frac{1}{n^3}\right)\frac{(n)(n+1)(2n+1)}{6} && \text{Sum of the First } n \text{ Squares} \\
&= 1 - \frac{2n^3 + 3n^2 + n}{6n^3}. && \text{Numerator expanded}
\end{aligned}$$

We have obtained an expression for the lower sum that holds for any n. Taking the limit of this expression as $n \to \infty$, we see that the lower sums converge as the number of subintervals increases and the subinterval widths approach zero:

$$\lim_{n \to \infty}\left(1 - \frac{2n^3 + 3n^2 + n}{6n^3}\right) = 1 - \frac{2}{6} = \frac{2}{3}.$$

The lower sum approximations converge to $2/3$. A similar calculation shows that the upper sum approximations also converge to $2/3$ (Exercise 35). Any finite sum approximation,

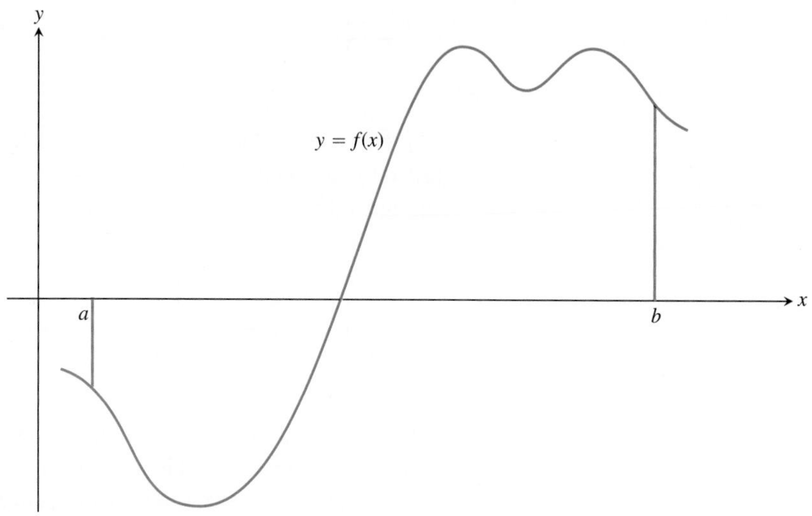

FIGURE 5.8 A typical continuous function $y = f(x)$ over a closed interval $[a, b]$.

in the sense of our summary at the end of Section 5.1, also converges to the same value, 2/3. This is because it is possible to show that any finite sum approximation is trapped between the lower and upper sum approximations. For this reason we are led to *define* the area of the region R as this limiting value. In Section 5.3 we study the limits of such finite approximations in a general setting. ■

Riemann Sums

HISTORICAL BIOGRAPHY

Georg Friedrich Bernhard Riemann (1826–1866)

The theory of limits of finite approximations was made precise by the German mathematician Bernhard Riemann. We now introduce the notion of a *Riemann sum*, which underlies the theory of the definite integral studied in the next section.

We begin with an arbitrary function f defined on a closed interval $[a, b]$. Like the function pictured in Figure 5.8, f may have negative as well as positive values. We subdivide the interval $[a, b]$ into subintervals, not necessarily of equal widths (or lengths), and form sums in the same way as for the finite approximations in Section 5.1. To do so, we choose $n - 1$ points $\{x_1, x_2, x_3, \ldots, x_{n-1}\}$ between a and b and satisfying

$$a < x_1 < x_2 < \cdots < x_{n-1} < b.$$

To make the notation consistent, we denote a by x_0 and b by x_n, so that

$$a = x_0 < x_1 < x_2 < \cdots < x_{n-1} < x_n = b.$$

The set

$$P = \{x_0, x_1, x_2, \ldots, x_{n-1}, x_n\}$$

is called a **partition** of $[a, b]$.

The partition P divides $[a, b]$ into n closed subintervals

$$[x_0, x_1], [x_1, x_2], \ldots, [x_{n-1}, x_n].$$

The first of these subintervals is $[x_0, x_1]$, the second is $[x_1, x_2]$, and the ***k*th subinterval of** P is $[x_{k-1}, x_k]$, for k an integer between 1 and n.

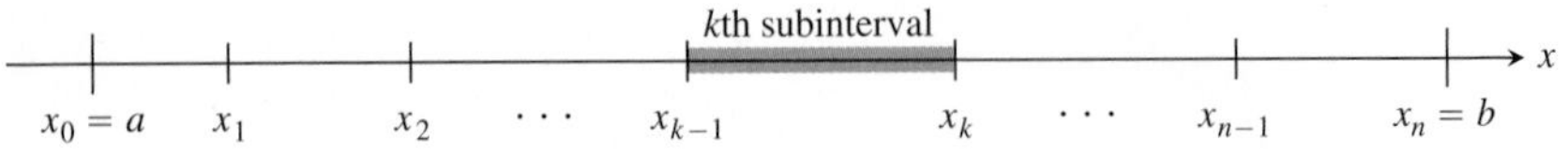

The width of the first subinterval $[x_0, x_1]$ is denoted Δx_1, the width of the second $[x_1, x_2]$ is denoted Δx_2, and the width of the kth subinterval is $\Delta x_k = x_k - x_{k-1}$. If all n subintervals have equal width, then the common width Δx is equal to $(b - a)/n$.

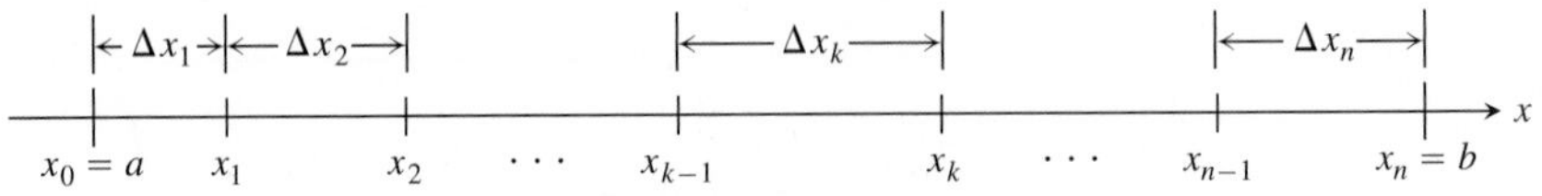

In each subinterval we select some point. The point chosen in the kth subinterval $[x_{k-1}, x_k]$ is called c_k. Then on each subinterval we stand a vertical rectangle that stretches from the x-axis to touch the curve at $(c_k, f(c_k))$. These rectangles can be above or below the x-axis, depending on whether $f(c_k)$ is positive or negative, or on it if $f(c_k) = 0$ (Figure 5.9).

On each subinterval we form the product $f(c_k) \cdot \Delta x_k$. This product is positive, negative, or zero, depending on the sign of $f(c_k)$. When $f(c_k) > 0$, the product $f(c_k) \cdot \Delta x_k$ is the area of a rectangle with height $f(c_k)$ and width Δx_k. When $f(c_k) < 0$, the product $f(c_k) \cdot \Delta x_k$ is a negative number, the negative of the area of a rectangle of width Δx_k that drops from the x-axis to the negative number $f(c_k)$.

Finally we sum all these products to get

$$S_P = \sum_{k=1}^{n} f(c_k)\, \Delta x_k .$$

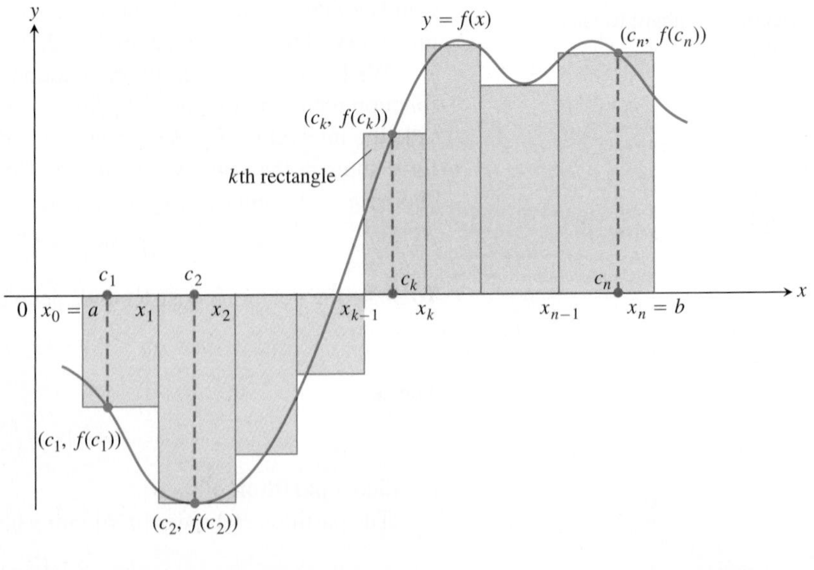

FIGURE 5.9 The rectangles approximate the region between the graph of the function $y = f(x)$ and the x-axis.

The sum S_P is called a **Riemann sum for f on the interval $[a, b]$**. There are many such sums, depending on the partition P we choose, and the choices of the points c_k in the subintervals.

In Example 5, where the subintervals all had equal widths $\Delta x = 1/n$, we could make them thinner by simply increasing their number n. When a partition has subintervals of varying widths, we can ensure they are all thin by controlling the width of a widest (longest) subinterval. We define the **norm** of a partition P, written $\|P\|$, to be the largest of all the subinterval widths. If $\|P\|$ is a small number, then all of the subintervals in the partition P have a small width. Let's look at an example of these ideas.

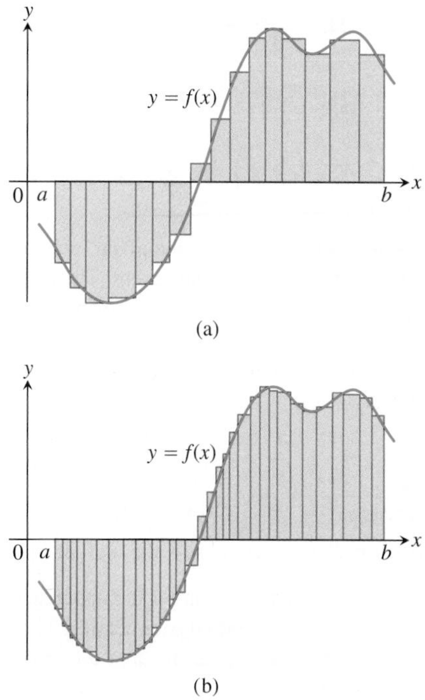

FIGURE 5.10 The curve of Figure 5.9 with rectangles from finer partitions of $[a, b]$. Finer partitions create collections of rectangles with thinner bases that approximate the region between the graph of f and the x-axis with increasing accuracy.

EXAMPLE 6 The set $P = \{0, 0.2, 0.6, 1, 1.5, 2\}$ is a partition of $[0, 2]$. There are five subintervals of P: $[0, 0.2]$, $[0.2, 0.6]$, $[0.6, 1]$, $[1, 1.5]$, and $[1.5, 2]$:

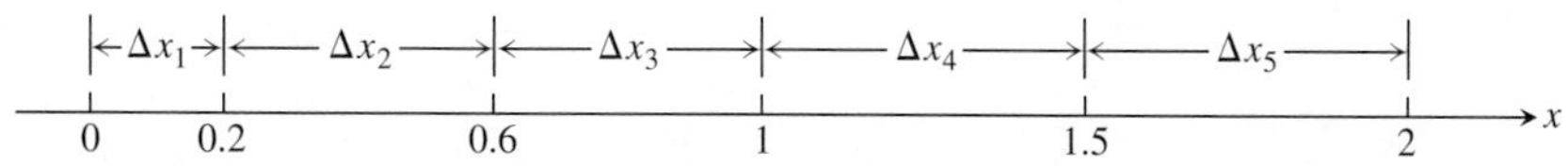

The lengths of the subintervals are $\Delta x_1 = 0.2$, $\Delta x_2 = 0.4$, $\Delta x_3 = 0.4$, $\Delta x_4 = 0.5$, and $\Delta x_5 = 0.5$. The longest subinterval length is 0.5, so the norm of the partition is $\|P\| = 0.5$. In this example, there are two subintervals of this length. ■

Any Riemann sum associated with a partition of a closed interval $[a, b]$ defines rectangles that approximate the region between the graph of a continuous function f and the x-axis. Partitions with norm approaching zero lead to collections of rectangles that approximate this region with increasing accuracy, as suggested by Figure 5.10. We will see in the next section that if the function f is continuous over the closed interval $[a, b]$, then no matter how we choose the partition P and the points c_k in its subintervals to construct a Riemann sum, a single limiting value is approached as the subinterval widths, controlled by the norm of the partition, approach zero.

EXERCISES 5.2

Write the sums in Exercises 1–6 without sigma notation. Then evaluate them.

1. $\displaystyle\sum_{k=1}^{2} \frac{6k}{k+1}$ **2.** $\displaystyle\sum_{k=1}^{3} \frac{k-1}{k}$

3. $\displaystyle\sum_{k=1}^{4} \cos k\pi$ **4.** $\displaystyle\sum_{k=1}^{5} \sin k\pi$

5. $\displaystyle\sum_{k=1}^{3} (-1)^{k+1} \sin \frac{\pi}{k}$ **6.** $\displaystyle\sum_{k=1}^{4} (-1)^{k} \cos k\pi$

7. Which of the following express $1 + 2 + 4 + 8 + 16 + 32$ in sigma notation?

a. $\displaystyle\sum_{k=1}^{6} 2^{k-1}$ **b.** $\displaystyle\sum_{k=0}^{5} 2^{k}$ **c.** $\displaystyle\sum_{k=-1}^{4} 2^{k+1}$

8. Which of the following express $1 - 2 + 4 - 8 + 16 - 32$ in sigma notation?

a. $\displaystyle\sum_{k=1}^{6} (-2)^{k-1}$ **b.** $\displaystyle\sum_{k=0}^{5} (-1)^{k} 2^{k}$ **c.** $\displaystyle\sum_{k=-2}^{3} (-1)^{k+1} 2^{k+2}$

9. Which formula is not equivalent to the other two?

a. $\displaystyle\sum_{k=2}^{4} \frac{(-1)^{k-1}}{k-1}$ **b.** $\displaystyle\sum_{k=0}^{2} \frac{(-1)^{k}}{k+1}$ **c.** $\displaystyle\sum_{k=-1}^{1} \frac{(-1)^{k}}{k+2}$

10. Which formula is not equivalent to the other two?

a. $\displaystyle\sum_{k=1}^{4} (k-1)^{2}$ **b.** $\displaystyle\sum_{k=-1}^{3} (k+1)^{2}$ **c.** $\displaystyle\sum_{k=-3}^{-1} k^{2}$

Express the sums in Exercises 11–16 in sigma notation. The form of your answer will depend on your choice of the lower limit of summation.

11. $1 + 2 + 3 + 4 + 5 + 6$ **12.** $1 + 4 + 9 + 16$

13. $\frac{1}{2} + \frac{1}{4} + \frac{1}{8} + \frac{1}{16}$ **14.** $2 + 4 + 6 + 8 + 10$

15. $1 - \frac{1}{2} + \frac{1}{3} - \frac{1}{4} + \frac{1}{5}$ **16.** $-\frac{1}{5} + \frac{2}{5} - \frac{3}{5} + \frac{4}{5} - \frac{5}{5}$

17. Suppose that $\sum_{k=1}^{n} a_k = -5$ and $\sum_{k=1}^{n} b_k = 6$. Find the values of

a. $\sum_{k=1}^{n} 3a_k$ **b.** $\sum_{k=1}^{n} \frac{b_k}{6}$ **c.** $\sum_{k=1}^{n} (a_k + b_k)$

d. $\sum_{k=1}^{n} (a_k - b_k)$ **e.** $\sum_{k=1}^{n} (b_k - 2a_k)$

18. Suppose that $\sum_{k=1}^{n} a_k = 0$ and $\sum_{k=1}^{n} b_k = 1$. Find the values of

a. $\sum_{k=1}^{n} 8a_k$ **b.** $\sum_{k=1}^{n} 250b_k$

c. $\sum_{k=1}^{n} (a_k + 1)$ **d.** $\sum_{k=1}^{n} (b_k - 1)$

Evaluate the sums in Exercises 19–28.

19. a. $\sum_{k=1}^{10} k$ **b.** $\sum_{k=1}^{10} k^2$ **c.** $\sum_{k=1}^{10} k^3$

20. a. $\sum_{k=1}^{13} k$ **b.** $\sum_{k=1}^{13} k^2$ **c.** $\sum_{k=1}^{13} k^3$

21. $\sum_{k=1}^{7} (-2k)$ **22.** $\sum_{k=1}^{5} \frac{\pi k}{15}$

23. $\sum_{k=1}^{6} (3 - k^2)$ **24.** $\sum_{k=1}^{6} (k^2 - 5)$

25. $\sum_{k=1}^{5} k(3k + 5)$ **26.** $\sum_{k=1}^{7} k(2k + 1)$

27. $\sum_{k=1}^{5} \frac{k^3}{225} + \left(\sum_{k=1}^{5} k\right)^3$ **28.** $\left(\sum_{k=1}^{7} k\right)^2 - \sum_{k=1}^{7} \frac{k^3}{4}$

In Exercises 29–32, graph each function $f(x)$ over the given interval. Partition the interval into four subintervals of equal length. Then add to your sketch the rectangles associated with the Riemann sum $\Sigma_{k=1}^{4} f(c_k)\,\Delta x_k$, given that c_k is the (a) left-hand endpoint, (b) right-hand endpoint, (c) midpoint of the kth subinterval. (Make a separate sketch for each set of rectangles.)

29. $f(x) = x^2 - 1, \quad [0, 2]$ **30.** $f(x) = -x^2, \quad [0, 1]$

31. $f(x) = \sin x, \quad [-\pi, \pi]$ **32.** $f(x) = \sin x + 1, \quad [-\pi, \pi]$

33. Find the norm of the partition $P = \{0, 1.2, 1.5, 2.3, 2.6, 3\}$.

34. Find the norm of the partition $P = \{-2, -1.6, -0.5, 0, 0.8, 1\}$.

For the functions in Exercises 35–40 find a formula for the upper sum obtained by dividing the interval $[a, b]$ into n equal subintervals. Then take a limit of these sums as $n \to \infty$ to calculate the area under the curve over $[a, b]$.

35. $f(x) = 1 - x^2$ over the interval $[0, 1]$.

36. $f(x) = 2x$ over the interval $[0, 3]$.

37. $f(x) = x^2 + 1$ over the interval $[0, 3]$.

38. $f(x) = 3x^2$ over the interval $[0, 1]$.

39. $f(x) = x + x^2$ over the interval $[0, 1]$.

40. $f(x) = 3x + 2x^2$ over the interval $[0, 1]$.

5.3 The Definite Integral

In Section 5.2 we investigated the limit of a finite sum for a function defined over a closed interval $[a, b]$ using n subintervals of equal width (or length), $(b - a)/n$. In this section we consider the limit of more general Riemann sums as the norm of the partitions of $[a, b]$ approaches zero. For general Riemann sums the subintervals of the partitions need not have equal widths. The limiting process then leads to the definition of the *definite integral* of a function over a closed interval $[a, b]$.

Limits of Riemann Sums

The definition of the definite integral is based on the idea that for certain functions, as the norm of the partitions of $[a, b]$ approaches zero, the values of the corresponding Riemann sums approach a limiting value I. What we mean by this converging idea is that a Riemann sum will be close to the number I provided that the norm of its partition is sufficiently small (so that all of its subintervals have thin enough widths). We introduce the symbol ϵ as a small positive number that specifies how close to I the Riemann sum must be, and the symbol δ as a second small positive number that specifies how small the norm of a partition must be in order for convergence to happen. Here is a precise formulation.

DEFINITION Let $f(x)$ be a function defined on a closed interval $[a, b]$. We say that a number I is the **definite integral of f over $[a, b]$** and that I is the limit of the Riemann sums $\sum_{k=1}^{n} f(c_k)\,\Delta x_k$ if the following condition is satisfied:

Given any number $\epsilon > 0$ there is a corresponding number $\delta > 0$ such that for every partition $P = \{x_0, x_1, \ldots, x_n\}$ of $[a, b]$ with $\|P\| < \delta$ and any choice of c_k in $[x_{k-1}, x_k]$, we have

$$\left| \sum_{k=1}^{n} f(c_k)\,\Delta x_k - I \right| < \epsilon.$$

Leibniz introduced a notation for the definite integral that captures its construction as a limit of Riemann sums. He envisioned the finite sums $\sum_{k=1}^{n} f(c_k)\,\Delta x_k$ becoming an infinite sum of function values $f(x)$ multiplied by "infinitesimal" subinterval widths dx. The sum symbol $\sum$ is replaced in the limit by the integral symbol $\int$, whose origin is in the letter "S." The function values $f(c_k)$ are replaced by a continuous selection of function values $f(x)$. The subinterval widths Δx_k become the differential dx. It is as if we are summing all products of the form $f(x) \cdot dx$ as x goes from a to b. While this notation captures the process of constructing an integral, it is Riemann's definition that gives a precise meaning to the definite integral.

Notation and Existence of the Definite Integral

The symbol for the number I in the definition of the definite integral is

$$\int_a^b f(x)\,dx$$

which is read as "the integral from a to b of f of x dee x" or sometimes as "the integral from a to b of f of x with respect to x." The component parts in the integral symbol also have names:

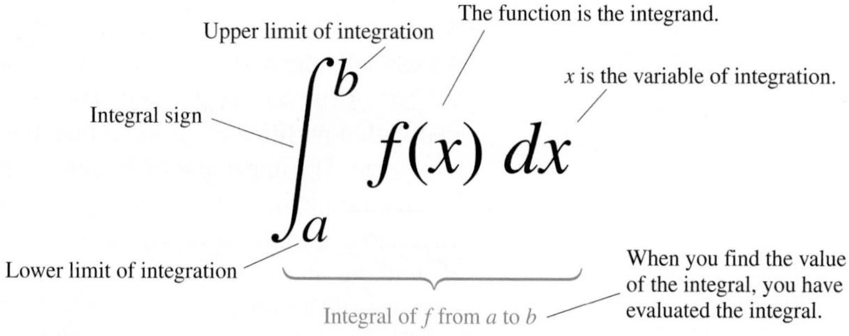

When the definition is satisfied, we say the Riemann sums of f on $[a, b]$ **converge** to the definite integral $I = \int_a^b f(x)\,dx$ and that f is **integrable** over $[a, b]$. We have many choices for a partition P with norm going to zero, and many choices of points c_k for each partition. The definite integral exists when we always get the same limit I, no matter what choices are made. When the limit exists we write it as the definite integral

$$\lim_{\|P\|\to 0} \sum_{k=1}^{n} f(c_k)\,\Delta x_k = I = \int_a^b f(x)\,dx.$$

When each partition has n equal subintervals, each of width $\Delta x = (b - a)/n$, we will also write

$$\lim_{n\to\infty} \sum_{k=1}^{n} f(c_k)\,\Delta x = I = \int_a^b f(x)\,dx.$$

The limit of any Riemann sum is always taken as the norm of the partitions approaches zero and the number of subintervals goes to infinity.

The value of the definite integral of a function over any particular interval depends on the function, not on the letter we choose to represent its independent variable. If we decide to use t or u instead of x, we simply write the integral as

$$\int_a^b f(t)\,dt \qquad \text{or} \qquad \int_a^b f(u)\,du \qquad \text{instead of} \qquad \int_a^b f(x)\,dx.$$

No matter how we write the integral, it is still the same number, defined as a limit of Riemann sums. Since it does not matter what letter we use, the variable of integration is called a **dummy variable**.

Since there are so many choices to be made in taking a limit of Riemann sums, it might seem difficult to show that such a limit exists. It turns out, however, that no matter what choices are made, the Riemann sums associated with a *continuous* function converge to the same limit.

THEOREM 1—The Existence of Definite Integrals A continuous function is integrable. That is, if a function f is continuous on an interval $[a, b]$, then its definite integral over $[a, b]$ exists.

By the Extreme Value Theorem (Theorem 1, Section 4.1), when f is continuous we can choose c_k so that $f(c_k)$ gives the maximum value of f on $[x_{k-1}, x_k]$, giving an upper sum. We can choose c_k to give the minimum value of f on $[x_{k-1}, x_k]$, giving a lower sum. We can pick c_k to be the midpoint of $[x_{k-1}, x_k]$, the rightmost point x_k, or a random point. We can take the partitions of equal or varying widths. In each case we get the same limit for $\sum_{k=1}^{n} f(c_k)\,\Delta x_k$ as $\|P\| \to 0$. The idea behind Theorem 1 is that a Riemann sum associated with a partition is no more than the upper sum of that partition and no less than the lower sum. The upper and lower sums converge to the same value when $\|P\| \to 0$. All other Riemann sums lie between the upper and lower sums and have the same limit. A proof of Theorem 1 involves a careful analysis of functions, partitions, and limits along this line of thinking and is left to a more advanced text. An indication of this proof is given in Exercises 80 and 81.

Theorem 1 says nothing about how to *calculate* definite integrals. A method of calculation will be developed in Section 5.4, through a connection to the process of taking antiderivatives.

Integrable and Nonintegrable Functions

Theorem 1 tells us that functions continuous over the interval $[a, b]$ are integrable there. Functions that are not continuous may or may not be integrable. Discontinuous functions that are integrable include those that are increasing on $[a, b]$, and the *piecewise-continuous functions* defined in Additional Exercises 11–18 at the end of this chapter. (The latter are continuous except at a finite number of points in $[a, b]$.) For integrability to fail, a function needs to be sufficiently discontinuous so that the region between its graph and the x-axis cannot be approximated well by increasingly thin rectangles. Here is an example of a function that is not integrable.

EXAMPLE 1 The function

$$f(x) = \begin{cases} 1, & \text{if } x \text{ is rational} \\ 0, & \text{if } x \text{ is irrational} \end{cases}$$

has no Riemann integral over $[0, 1]$. Underlying this is the fact that between any two numbers there is both a rational number and an irrational number. Thus the function jumps up and down too erratically over $[0, 1]$ to allow the region beneath its graph and above the x-axis to be approximated by rectangles, no matter how thin they are. We show, in fact, that upper sum approximations and lower sum approximations converge to different limiting values.

If we pick a partition P of $[0, 1]$ and choose c_k to be the point giving the maximum value for f on $[x_{k-1}, x_k]$ then the corresponding Riemann sum is

$$U = \sum_{k=1}^{n} f(c_k)\,\Delta x_k = \sum_{k=1}^{n} (1)\,\Delta x_k = 1,$$

since each subinterval $[x_{k-1}, x_k]$ contains a rational number where $f(c_k) = 1$. Note that the lengths of the intervals in the partition sum to 1, $\sum_{k=1}^{n} \Delta x_k = 1$. So each such Riemann sum equals 1, and a limit of Riemann sums using these choices equals 1.

On the other hand, if we pick c_k to be the point giving the minimum value for f on $[x_{k-1}, x_k]$, then the Riemann sum is

$$L = \sum_{k=1}^{n} f(c_k)\,\Delta x_k = \sum_{k=1}^{n} (0)\,\Delta x_k = 0,$$

since each subinterval $[x_{k-1}, x_k]$ contains an irrational number c_k where $f(c_k) = 0$. The limit of Riemann sums using these choices equals zero. Since the limit depends on the choices of c_k, the function f is not integrable. ■

Properties of Definite Integrals

In defining $\int_a^b f(x)\,dx$ as a limit of sums $\sum_{k=1}^{n} f(c_k)\,\Delta x_k$, we moved from left to right across the interval $[a, b]$. What would happen if we instead move right to left, starting with $x_0 = b$ and ending at $x_n = a$? Each Δx_k in the Riemann sum would change its sign, with $x_k - x_{k-1}$ now negative instead of positive. With the same choices of c_k in each subinterval, the sign of any Riemann sum would change, as would the sign of the limit, the integral $\int_b^a f(x)\,dx$. Since we have not previously given a meaning to integrating backward, we are led to define

$$\int_b^a f(x)\,dx = -\int_a^b f(x)\,dx.$$

Another extension of the integral is to an interval of zero width, when $a = b$. Since $f(c_k)\,\Delta x_k$ is zero when the interval width $\Delta x_k = 0$, whenever $f(a)$ exists we define

$$\int_a^a f(x)\,dx = 0.$$

Theorem 2 states seven properties of integrals, given as rules that they satisfy, including the two above. These rules become very useful in the process of computing integrals. We will refer to them repeatedly to simplify our calculations.

Rules 2 through 7 have geometric interpretations, shown in Figure 5.11. The graphs in these figures are of positive functions, but the rules apply to general integrable functions.

THEOREM 2 When f and g are integrable, the definite integral satisfies Rules 1 to 7 in Table 5.3.

TABLE 5.3 Rules satisfied by definite integrals

1. *Order of Integration:*	$\int_b^a f(x)\,dx = -\int_a^b f(x)\,dx$	A Definition
2. *Zero Width Interval:*	$\int_a^a f(x)\,dx = 0$	A Definition when $f(a)$ exists
3. *Constant Multiple:*	$\int_a^b kf(x)\,dx = k\int_a^b f(x)\,dx$	Any Number k
	$\int_a^b -f(x)\,dx = -\int_a^b f(x)\,dx$	$k = -1$
4. *Sum and Difference:*	$\int_a^b (f(x) \pm g(x))\,dx = \int_a^b f(x)\,dx \pm \int_a^b g(x)\,dx$	
5. *Additivity:*	$\int_a^b f(x)\,dx + \int_b^c f(x)\,dx = \int_a^c f(x)\,dx$	
6. *Max-Min Inequality:*	If f has maximum value max f and minimum value min f on $[a, b]$, then $\min f \cdot (b - a) \le \int_a^b f(x)\,dx \le \max f \cdot (b - a).$	
7. *Domination:*	$f(x) \ge g(x)$ on $[a, b] \Rightarrow \int_a^b f(x)\,dx \ge \int_a^b g(x)\,dx$	
	$f(x) \ge 0$ on $[a, b] \Rightarrow \int_a^b f(x)\,dx \ge 0$	(Special Case)

While Rules 1 and 2 are definitions, Rules 3 to 7 of Table 5.3 must be proved. The following is a proof of one of these rules. Similar proofs can be given to verify the other properties in Table 5.3.

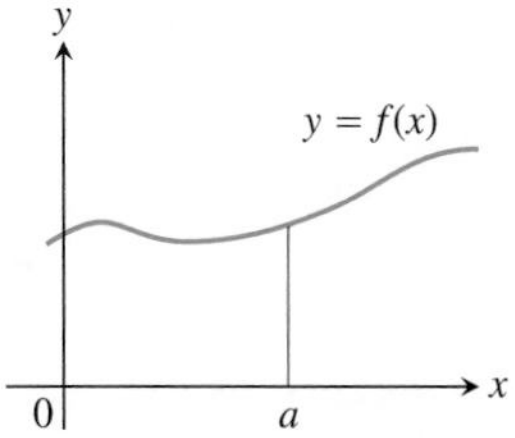

(a) *Zero Width Interval:*

$$\int_a^a f(x)\,dx = 0.$$

(The area under a point is 0.)

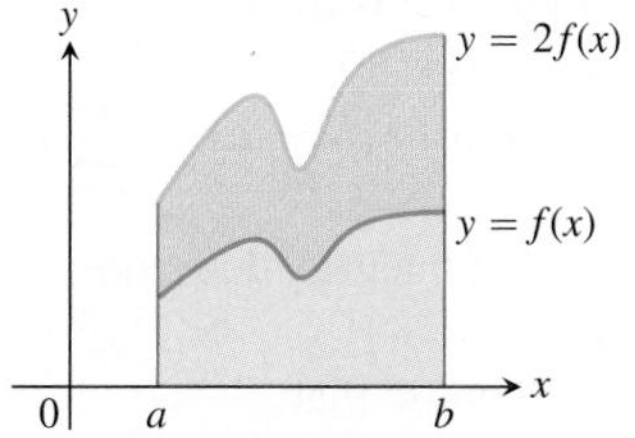

(b) *Constant Multiple:*

$$\int_a^b kf(x)\,dx = k\int_a^b f(x)\,dx.$$

(Shown for $k = 2$.)

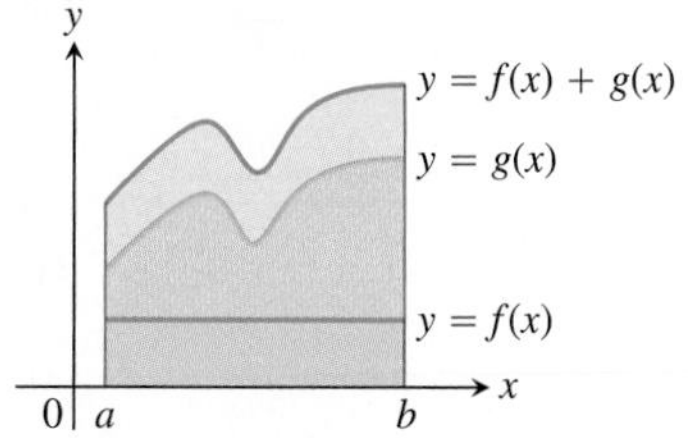

(c) *Sum:*

$$\int_a^b (f(x) + g(x))\,dx = \int_a^b f(x)\,dx + \int_a^b g(x)\,dx$$

(Areas add)

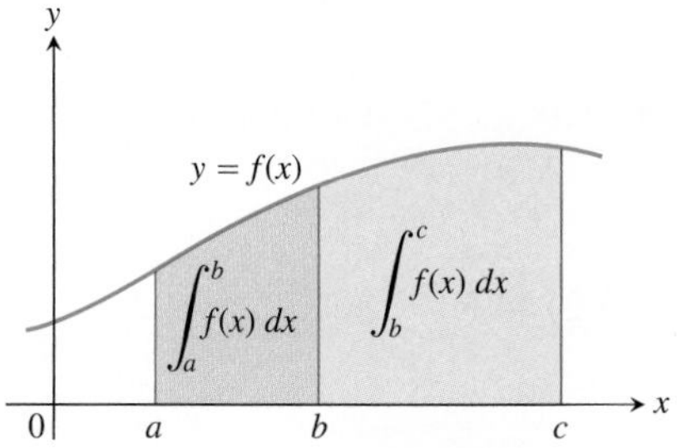

(d) *Additivity for definite integrals:*

$$\int_a^b f(x)\,dx + \int_b^c f(x)\,dx = \int_a^c f(x)\,dx$$

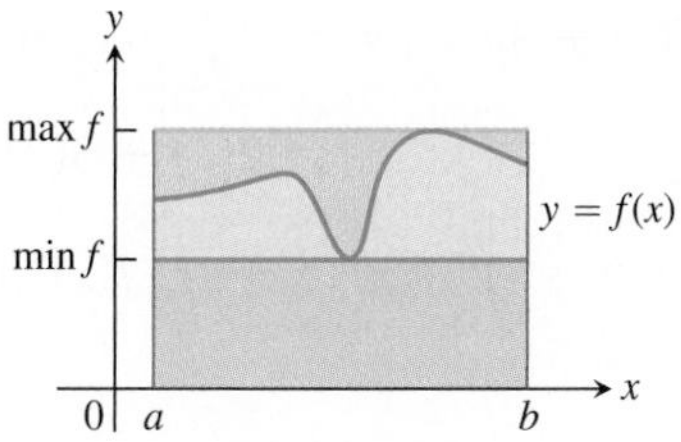

(e) *Max-Min Inequality:*

$$\min f\cdot(b-a) \le \int_a^b f(x)\,dx$$
$$\le \max f\cdot(b-a)$$

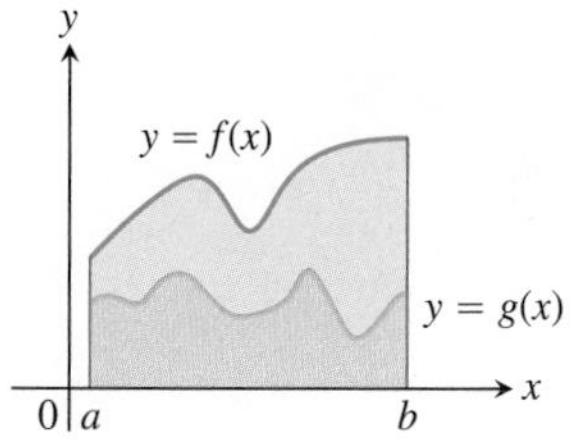

(f) *Domination:*

$f(x) \ge g(x)$ on $[a, b]$

$$\Rightarrow \int_a^b f(x)\,dx \ge \int_a^b g(x)\,dx$$

FIGURE 5.11 Geometric interpretations of Rules 2–7 in Table 5.3.

Proof of Rule 6 Rule 6 says that the integral of f over $[a, b]$ is never smaller than the minimum value of f times the length of the interval and never larger than the maximum value of f times the length of the interval. The reason is that for every partition of $[a, b]$ and for every choice of the points c_k,

$$\begin{aligned}
\min f\cdot(b-a) &= \min f\cdot\sum_{k=1}^{n}\Delta x_k && \sum_{k=1}^{n}\Delta x_k = b-a \\
&= \sum_{k=1}^{n}\min f\cdot\Delta x_k && \text{Constant Multiple Rule} \\
&\le \sum_{k=1}^{n} f(c_k)\,\Delta x_k && \min f \le f(c_k) \\
&\le \sum_{k=1}^{n}\max f\cdot\Delta x_k && f(c_k) \le \max f \\
&= \max f\cdot\sum_{k=1}^{n}\Delta x_k && \text{Constant Multiple Rule} \\
&= \max f\cdot(b-a).
\end{aligned}$$

In short, all Riemann sums for f on $[a, b]$ satisfy the inequality

$$\min f \cdot (b - a) \leq \sum_{k=1}^{n} f(c_k)\,\Delta x_k \leq \max f \cdot (b - a).$$

Hence their limit, the integral, does too. ■

EXAMPLE 2 Suppose that

$$\int_{-1}^{1} f(x)\,dx = 5, \qquad \int_{1}^{4} f(x)\,dx = -2, \qquad \int_{-1}^{1} h(x)\,dx = 7.$$

Then

1. $\displaystyle\int_{4}^{1} f(x)\,dx = -\int_{1}^{4} f(x)\,dx = -(-2) = 2$ Rule 1

2. $\displaystyle\int_{-1}^{1} [2f(x) + 3h(x)]\,dx = 2\int_{-1}^{1} f(x)\,dx + 3\int_{-1}^{1} h(x)\,dx$ Rules 3 and 4
$\displaystyle\qquad = 2(5) + 3(7) = 31$

3. $\displaystyle\int_{-1}^{4} f(x)\,dx = \int_{-1}^{1} f(x)\,dx + \int_{1}^{4} f(x)\,dx = 5 + (-2) = 3$ Rule 5 ■

EXAMPLE 3 Show that the value of $\int_0^1 \sqrt{1 + \cos x}\,dx$ is less than or equal to $\sqrt{2}$.

Solution The Max-Min Inequality for definite integrals (Rule 6) says that $\min f \cdot (b - a)$ is a *lower bound* for the value of $\int_a^b f(x)\,dx$ and that $\max f \cdot (b - a)$ is an *upper bound*. The maximum value of $\sqrt{1 + \cos x}$ on $[0, 1]$ is $\sqrt{1 + 1} = \sqrt{2}$, so

$$\int_0^1 \sqrt{1 + \cos x}\,dx \leq \sqrt{2} \cdot (1 - 0) = \sqrt{2}.$$ ■

Area Under the Graph of a Nonnegative Function

We now make precise the notion of the area of a region with curved boundary, capturing the idea of approximating a region by increasingly many rectangles. The area under the graph of a nonnegative continuous function is defined to be a definite integral.

> **DEFINITION** If $y = f(x)$ is nonnegative and integrable over a closed interval $[a, b]$, then the **area under the curve $y = f(x)$ over $[a, b]$** is the integral of f from a to b,
>
> $$A = \int_a^b f(x)\,dx.$$

For the first time we have a rigorous definition for the area of a region whose boundary is the graph of any continuous function. We now apply this to a simple example, the area under a straight line, where we can verify that our new definition agrees with our previous notion of area.

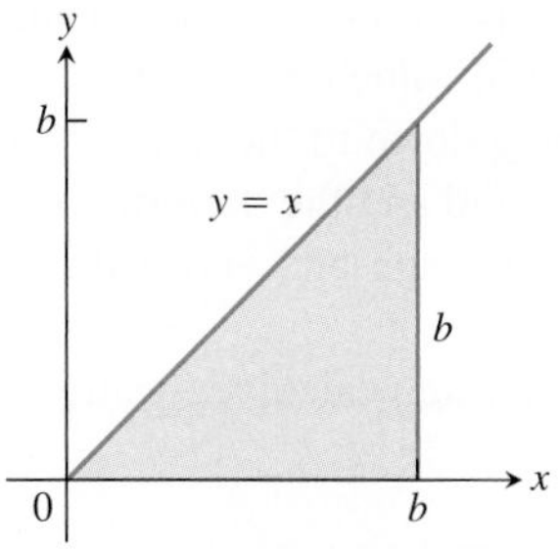

FIGURE 5.12 The region in Example 4 is a triangle.

EXAMPLE 4 Compute $\int_0^b x\,dx$ and find the area A under $y = x$ over the interval $[0, b]$, $b > 0$.

Solution The region of interest is a triangle (Figure 5.12). We compute the area in two ways.

(a) To compute the definite integral as the limit of Riemann sums, we calculate $\lim_{\|P\|\to 0} \sum_{k=1}^{n} f(c_k)\,\Delta x_k$ for partitions whose norms go to zero. Theorem 1 tells us that it does not matter how we choose the partitions or the points c_k as long as the norms approach zero. All choices give the exact same limit. So we consider the partition P that subdivides the interval $[0, b]$ into n subintervals of equal width $\Delta x = (b - 0)/n = b/n$, and we choose c_k to be the right endpoint in each subinterval. The partition is $P = \left\{0, \frac{b}{n}, \frac{2b}{n}, \frac{3b}{n}, \ldots, \frac{nb}{n}\right\}$ and $c_k = \frac{kb}{n}$. So

$$\begin{aligned}\sum_{k=1}^{n} f(c_k)\,\Delta x &= \sum_{k=1}^{n} \frac{kb}{n} \cdot \frac{b}{n} && f(c_k) = c_k\\ &= \sum_{k=1}^{n} \frac{kb^2}{n^2}\\ &= \frac{b^2}{n^2} \sum_{k=1}^{n} k && \text{Constant Multiple Rule}\\ &= \frac{b^2}{n^2} \cdot \frac{n(n+1)}{2} && \text{Sum of First } n \text{ Integers}\\ &= \frac{b^2}{2}\left(1 + \frac{1}{n}\right)\end{aligned}$$

As $n \to \infty$ and $\|P\| \to 0$, this last expression on the right has the limit $b^2/2$. Therefore,

$$\int_0^b x\,dx = \frac{b^2}{2}.$$

(b) Since the area equals the definite integral for a nonnegative function, we can quickly derive the definite integral by using the formula for the area of a triangle having base length b and height $y = b$. The area is $A = (1/2)\,b \cdot b = b^2/2$. Again we conclude that $\int_0^b x\,dx = b^2/2$. ■

Example 4 can be generalized to integrate $f(x) = x$ over any closed interval $[a, b]$, $0 < a < b$.

$$\begin{aligned}\int_a^b x\,dx &= \int_a^0 x\,dx + \int_0^b x\,dx && \text{Rule 5}\\ &= -\int_0^a x\,dx + \int_0^b x\,dx && \text{Rule 1}\\ &= -\frac{a^2}{2} + \frac{b^2}{2}. && \text{Example 4}\end{aligned}$$

In conclusion, we have the following rule for integrating $f(x) = x$:

$$\int_a^b x\,dx = \frac{b^2}{2} - \frac{a^2}{2}, \qquad a < b \tag{1}$$

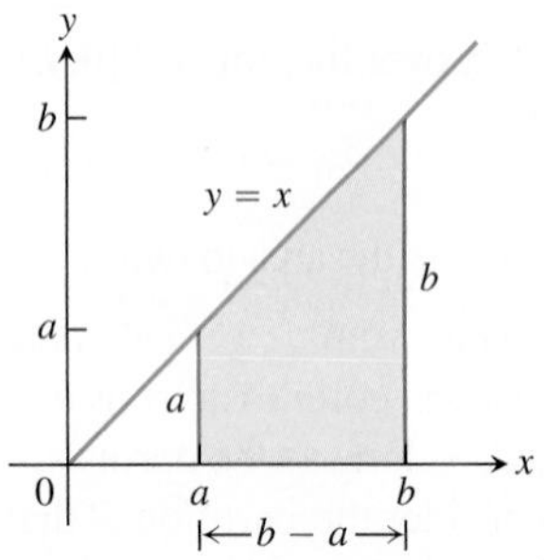

FIGURE 5.13 The area of this trapezoidal region is $A = (b^2 - a^2)/2$.

This computation gives the area of a trapezoid (Figure 5.13). Equation (1) remains valid when a and b are negative. When $a < b < 0$, the definite integral value $(b^2 - a^2)/2$ is a negative number, the negative of the area of a trapezoid dropping down to the line $y = x$ below the x-axis. When $a < 0$ and $b > 0$, Equation (1) is still valid and the definite integral gives the difference between two areas, the area under the graph and above $[0, b]$ minus the area below $[a, 0]$ and over the graph.

The following results can also be established using a Riemann sum calculation similar to that in Example 4 (Exercises 75 and 76).

$$\int_a^b c\,dx = c(b - a), \qquad c \text{ any constant} \tag{2}$$

$$\int_a^b x^2\,dx = \frac{b^3}{3} - \frac{a^3}{3}, \qquad a < b \tag{3}$$

Average Value of a Continuous Function Revisited

In Section 5.1 we introduced informally the average value of a nonnegative continuous function f over an interval $[a, b]$, leading us to define this average as the area under the graph of $y = f(x)$ divided by $b - a$. In integral notation we write this as

$$\text{Average} = \frac{1}{b - a}\int_a^b f(x)\,dx.$$

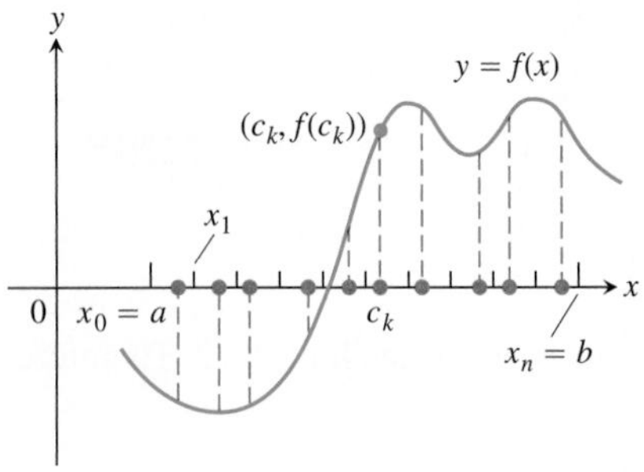

FIGURE 5.14 A sample of values of a function on an interval $[a, b]$.

We can use this formula to give a precise definition of the average value of any continuous (or integrable) function, whether positive, negative or both.

Alternately, we can use the following reasoning. We start with the idea from arithmetic that the average of n numbers is their sum divided by n. A continuous function f on $[a, b]$ may have infinitely many values, but we can still sample them in an orderly way. We divide $[a, b]$ into n subintervals of equal width $\Delta x = (b - a)/n$ and evaluate f at a point c_k in each (Figure 5.14). The average of the n sampled values is

$$\begin{aligned}
\frac{f(c_1) + f(c_2) + \cdots + f(c_n)}{n} &= \frac{1}{n}\sum_{k=1}^{n} f(c_k) \\
&= \frac{\Delta x}{b - a}\sum_{k=1}^{n} f(c_k) \qquad \Delta x = \frac{b-a}{n},\ \text{so}\ \frac{1}{n} = \frac{\Delta x}{b-a} \\
&= \frac{1}{b - a}\sum_{k=1}^{n} f(c_k)\,\Delta x
\end{aligned}$$

The average is obtained by dividing a Riemann sum for f on $[a, b]$ by $(b - a)$. As we increase the size of the sample and let the norm of the partition approach zero, the average approaches $(1/(b - a))\int_a^b f(x)\,dx$. Both points of view lead us to the following definition.

DEFINITION If f is integrable on $[a, b]$, then its **average value on** $[a, b]$, also called its **mean value**, is

$$\text{av}(f) = \frac{1}{b - a}\int_a^b f(x)\,dx.$$

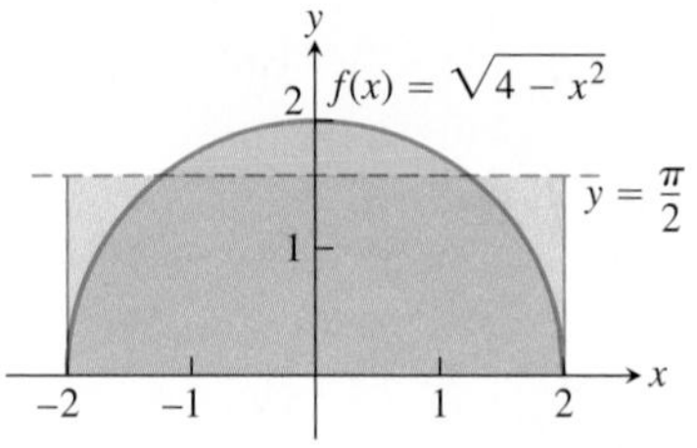

FIGURE 5.15 The average value of $f(x) = \sqrt{4 - x^2}$ on $[-2, 2]$ is $\pi/2$ (Example 5).

EXAMPLE 5 Find the average value of $f(x) = \sqrt{4 - x^2}$ on $[-2, 2]$.

Solution We recognize $f(x) = \sqrt{4 - x^2}$ as a function whose graph is the upper semicircle of radius 2 centered at the origin (Figure 5.15).

The area between the semicircle and the x-axis from -2 to 2 can be computed using the geometry formula

$$\text{Area} = \frac{1}{2} \cdot \pi r^2 = \frac{1}{2} \cdot \pi(2)^2 = 2\pi.$$

Because f is nonnegative, the area is also the value of the integral of f from -2 to 2,

$$\int_{-2}^{2} \sqrt{4 - x^2}\, dx = 2\pi.$$

Therefore, the average value of f is

$$\text{av}(f) = \frac{1}{2 - (-2)} \int_{-2}^{2} \sqrt{4 - x^2}\, dx = \frac{1}{4}(2\pi) = \frac{\pi}{2}.$$ ■

EXERCISES 5.3

Express the limits in Exercises 1–8 as definite integrals.

1. $\lim_{\|P\| \to 0} \sum_{k=1}^{n} c_k^2\, \Delta x_k$, where P is a partition of $[0, 2]$

2. $\lim_{\|P\| \to 0} \sum_{k=1}^{n} 2c_k^3\, \Delta x_k$, where P is a partition of $[-1, 0]$

3. $\lim_{\|P\| \to 0} \sum_{k=1}^{n} (c_k^2 - 3c_k)\, \Delta x_k$, where P is a partition of $[-7, 5]$

4. $\lim_{\|P\| \to 0} \sum_{k=1}^{n} \left(\frac{1}{c_k}\right) \Delta x_k$, where P is a partition of $[1, 4]$

5. $\lim_{\|P\| \to 0} \sum_{k=1}^{n} \frac{1}{1 - c_k}\, \Delta x_k$, where P is a partition of $[2, 3]$

6. $\lim_{\|P\| \to 0} \sum_{k=1}^{n} \sqrt{4 - c_k^2}\, \Delta x_k$, where P is a partition of $[0, 1]$

7. $\lim_{\|P\| \to 0} \sum_{k=1}^{n} (\sec c_k)\, \Delta x_k$, where P is a partition of $[-\pi/4, 0]$

8. $\lim_{\|P\| \to 0} \sum_{k=1}^{n} (\tan c_k)\, \Delta x_k$, where P is a partition of $[0, \pi/4]$

9. Suppose that f and g are integrable and that

$$\int_1^2 f(x)\, dx = -4, \quad \int_1^5 f(x)\, dx = 6, \quad \int_1^5 g(x)\, dx = 8.$$

Use the rules in Table 5.3 to find

a. $\int_2^2 g(x)\, dx$ **b.** $\int_5^1 g(x)\, dx$

c. $\int_1^2 3f(x)\, dx$ **d.** $\int_2^5 f(x)\, dx$

e. $\int_1^5 [f(x) - g(x)]\, dx$ **f.** $\int_1^5 [4f(x) - g(x)]\, dx$

10. Suppose that f and h are integrable and that

$$\int_1^9 f(x)\, dx = -1, \quad \int_7^9 f(x)\, dx = 5, \quad \int_7^9 h(x)\, dx = 4.$$

Use the rules in Table 5.3 to find

a. $\int_1^9 -2f(x)\, dx$ **b.** $\int_7^9 [f(x) + h(x)]\, dx$

c. $\int_7^9 [2f(x) - 3h(x)]\, dx$ **d.** $\int_9^1 f(x)\, dx$

e. $\int_1^7 f(x)\, dx$ **f.** $\int_9^7 [h(x) - f(x)]\, dx$

11. Suppose that $\int_1^2 f(x)\, dx = 5$. Find

a. $\int_1^2 f(u)\, du$ **b.** $\int_1^2 \sqrt{3} f(z)\, dz$

c. $\int_2^1 f(t)\, dt$ **d.** $\int_1^2 [-f(x)]\, dx$

12. Suppose that $\int_{-3}^{0} g(t)\,dt = \sqrt{2}$. Find

a. $\int_{0}^{-3} g(t)\,dt$ **b.** $\int_{-3}^{0} g(u)\,du$

c. $\int_{-3}^{0} [-g(x)]\,dx$ **d.** $\int_{-3}^{0} \frac{g(r)}{\sqrt{2}}\,dr$

13. Suppose that f is integrable and that $\int_0^3 f(z)\,dz = 3$ and $\int_0^4 f(z)\,dz = 7$. Find

a. $\int_3^4 f(z)\,dz$ **b.** $\int_4^3 f(t)\,dt$

14. Suppose that h is integrable and that $\int_{-1}^{1} h(r)\,dr = 0$ and $\int_{-1}^{3} h(r)\,dr = 6$. Find

a. $\int_1^3 h(r)\,dr$ **b.** $-\int_3^1 h(u)\,du$

In Exercises 15–22, graph the integrands and use areas to evaluate the integrals.

15. $\int_{-2}^{4}\left(\frac{x}{2}+3\right)dx$ **16.** $\int_{1/2}^{3/2}(-2x+4)\,dx$

17. $\int_{-3}^{3}\sqrt{9-x^2}\,dx$ **18.** $\int_{-4}^{0}\sqrt{16-x^2}\,dx$

19. $\int_{-2}^{1}|x|\,dx$ **20.** $\int_{-1}^{1}(1-|x|)\,dx$

21. $\int_{-1}^{1}(2-|x|)\,dx$ **22.** $\int_{-1}^{1}\left(1+\sqrt{1-x^2}\right)dx$

Use areas to evaluate the integrals in Exercises 23–26.

23. $\int_0^b \frac{x}{2}\,dx,\quad b>0$ **24.** $\int_0^b 4x\,dx,\quad b>0$

25. $\int_a^b 2s\,ds,\quad 0<a<b$ **26.** $\int_a^b 3t\,dt,\quad 0<a<b$

Use the results of Equations (1) and (3) to evaluate the integrals in Exercises 27–38.

27. $\int_1^{\sqrt{2}} x\,dx$ **28.** $\int_{0.5}^{2.5} x\,dx$ **29.** $\int_{\pi}^{2\pi} \theta\,d\theta$

30. $\int_{\sqrt{2}}^{5\sqrt{2}} r\,dr$ **31.** $\int_0^{\sqrt[3]{7}} x^2\,dx$ **32.** $\int_0^{0.3} s^2\,ds$

33. $\int_0^{1/2} t^2\,dt$ **34.** $\int_0^{\pi/2} \theta^2\,d\theta$ **35.** $\int_a^{2a} x\,dx$

36. $\int_a^{\sqrt{3}a} x\,dx$ **37.** $\int_0^{\sqrt[3]{b}} x^2\,dx$ **38.** $\int_0^{3b} x^2\,dx$

Use the rules in Table 5.3 and Equations (1)–(3) to evaluate the integrals in Exercises 39–50.

39. $\int_3^1 7\,dx$ **40.** $\int_0^{-2} \sqrt{2}\,dx$

41. $\int_0^2 5x\,dx$ **42.** $\int_3^5 \frac{x}{8}\,dx$

43. $\int_0^2 (2t-3)\,dt$ **44.** $\int_0^{\sqrt{2}} \left(t-\sqrt{2}\right)dt$

45. $\int_2^1 \left(1+\frac{z}{2}\right)dz$ **46.** $\int_3^0 (2z-3)\,dz$

47. $\int_1^2 3u^2\,du$ **48.** $\int_{1/2}^1 24u^2\,du$

49. $\int_0^2 (3x^2+x-5)\,dx$ **50.** $\int_1^0 (3x^2+x-5)\,dx$

In Exercises 51–54 use a definite integral to find the area of the region between the given curve and the x-axis on the interval $[0, b]$.

51. $y = 3x^2$ **52.** $y = \pi x^2$

53. $y = 2x$ **54.** $y = \frac{x}{2} + 1$

In Exercises 55–62, graph the function and find its average value over the given interval.

55. $f(x) = x^2 - 1$ on $\left[0, \sqrt{3}\right]$

56. $f(x) = -\frac{x^2}{2}$ on $[0, 3]$ **57.** $f(x) = -3x^2 - 1$ on $[0, 1]$

58. $f(x) = 3x^2 - 3$ on $[0, 1]$

59. $f(t) = (t-1)^2$ on $[0, 3]$

60. $f(t) = t^2 - t$ on $[-2, 1]$

61. $g(x) = |x| - 1$ on **a.** $[-1, 1]$, **b.** $[1, 3]$, and **c.** $[-1, 3]$

62. $h(x) = -|x|$ on **a.** $[-1, 0]$, **b.** $[0, 1]$, and **c.** $[-1, 1]$

63. What values of a and b maximize the value of

$$\int_a^b (x - x^2)\,dx?$$

(*Hint:* Where is the integrand positive?)

64. What values of a and b minimize the value of

$$\int_a^b (x^4 - 2x^2)\,dx?$$

65. Use the Max-Min Inequality to find upper and lower bounds for the value of

$$\int_0^1 \frac{1}{1+x^2}\,dx.$$

66. (*Continuation of Exercise 65.*) Use the Max-Min Inequality to find upper and lower bounds for

$$\int_0^{0.5} \frac{1}{1+x^2}\,dx \quad \text{and} \quad \int_{0.5}^1 \frac{1}{1+x^2}\,dx.$$

Add these to arrive at an improved estimate of

$$\int_0^1 \frac{1}{1+x^2}\,dx.$$

67. Show that the value of $\int_0^1 \sin(x^2)\,dx$ cannot possibly be 2.

68. Show that the value of $\int_0^1 \sqrt{x+8}\,dx$ lies between $2\sqrt{2} \approx 2.8$ and 3.

69. Integrals of nonnegative functions Use the Max-Min Inequality to show that if f is integrable then

$$f(x) \geq 0 \quad \text{on} \quad [a, b] \quad \Rightarrow \quad \int_a^b f(x)\,dx \geq 0.$$

70. Integrals of nonpositive functions Show that if f is integrable then

$$f(x) \leq 0 \quad \text{on} \quad [a, b] \quad \Rightarrow \quad \int_a^b f(x)\,dx \leq 0.$$

71. Use the inequality $\sin x \leq x$, which holds for $x \geq 0$, to find an upper bound for the value of $\int_0^1 \sin x\,dx$.

72. The inequality $\sec x \geq 1 + (x^2/2)$ holds on $(-\pi/2, \pi/2)$. Use it to find a lower bound for the value of $\int_0^1 \sec x\,dx$.

73. If $\text{av}(f)$ really is a typical value of the integrable function $f(x)$ on $[a, b]$, then the constant function $\text{av}(f)$ should have the same integral over $[a, b]$ as f. Does it? That is, does

$$\int_a^b \text{av}(f)\,dx = \int_a^b f(x)\,dx?$$

Give reasons for your answer.

74. It would be nice if average values of integrable functions obeyed the following rules on an interval $[a, b]$.

a. $\text{av}(f+g) = \text{av}(f) + \text{av}(g)$

b. $\text{av}(kf) = k\,\text{av}(f)$ (any number k)

c. $\text{av}(f) \leq \text{av}(g)$ if $f(x) \leq g(x)$ on $[a, b]$.

Do these rules ever hold? Give reasons for your answers.

75. Use limits of Riemann sums as in Example 4a to establish Equation (2).

76. Use limits of Riemann sums as in Example 4a to establish Equation (3).

77. Upper and lower sums for increasing functions

a. Suppose the graph of a continuous function $f(x)$ rises steadily as x moves from left to right across an interval $[a, b]$. Let P be a partition of $[a, b]$ into n subintervals of length $\Delta x = (b-a)/n$. Show by referring to the accompanying figure that the difference between the upper and lower sums for f on this partition can be represented graphically as the area of a rectangle R whose dimensions are $[f(b) - f(a)]$ by Δx. (*Hint*: The difference $U - L$ is the sum of areas of rectangles whose diagonals $Q_0Q_1, Q_1Q_2, \ldots, Q_{n-1}Q_n$ lie along the curve. There is no overlapping when these rectangles are shifted horizontally onto R.)

b. Suppose that instead of being equal, the lengths Δx_k of the subintervals of the partition of $[a, b]$ vary in size. Show that

$$U - L \leq |f(b) - f(a)|\,\Delta x_{\max},$$

where $\Delta x_{\max}$ is the norm of P, and hence that $\lim_{\|P\|\to 0} (U - L) = 0$.

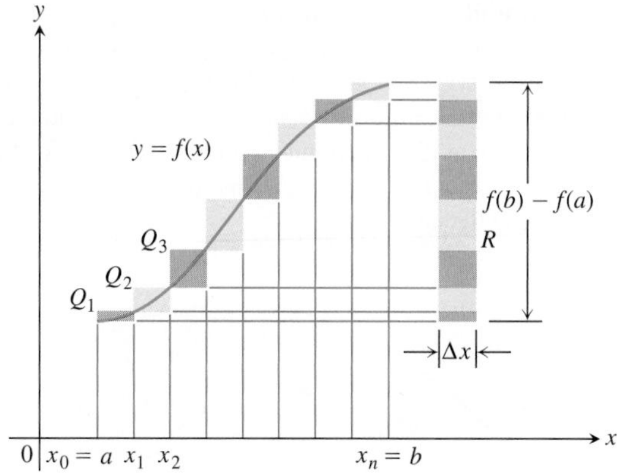

78. Upper and lower sums for decreasing functions (*Continuation of Exercise 77.*)

a. Draw a figure like the one in Exercise 77 for a continuous function $f(x)$ whose values decrease steadily as x moves from left to right across the interval $[a, b]$. Let P be a partition of $[a, b]$ into subintervals of equal length. Find an expression for $U - L$ that is analogous to the one you found for $U - L$ in Exercise 77a.

b. Suppose that instead of being equal, the lengths Δx_k of the subintervals of P vary in size. Show that the inequality

$$U - L \leq |f(b) - f(a)|\,\Delta x_{\max}$$

of Exercise 77b still holds and hence that $\lim_{\|P\|\to 0} (U - L) = 0$.

79. Use the formula

$$\sin h + \sin 2h + \sin 3h + \cdots + \sin mh = \frac{\cos(h/2) - \cos((m + (1/2))h)}{2\sin(h/2)}$$

to find the area under the curve $y = \sin x$ from $x = 0$ to $x = \pi/2$ in two steps:

a. Partition the interval $[0, \pi/2]$ into n subintervals of equal length and calculate the corresponding upper sum U; then

b. Find the limit of U as $n \to \infty$ and $\Delta x = (b - a)/n \to 0$.

80. Suppose that f is continuous and nonnegative over $[a, b]$, as in the figure on the next page. By inserting points

$$x_1, x_2, \ldots, x_{k-1}, x_k, \ldots, x_{n-1}$$

as shown, divide $[a, b]$ into n subintervals of lengths $\Delta x_1 = x_1 - a$, $\Delta x_2 = x_2 - x_1, \ldots, \Delta x_n = b - x_{n-1}$, which need not be equal.

a. If $m_k = \min\{f(x) \text{ for } x \text{ in the } k\text{th subinterval}\}$, explain the connection between the *lower sum*

$$L = m_1\,\Delta x_1 + m_2\,\Delta x_2 + \cdots + m_n\,\Delta x_n$$

and the shaded region in the first part of the figure.

b. If $M_k = \max\{f(x) \text{ for } x \text{ in the } k\text{th subinterval}\}$, explain the connection between the *upper sum*

$$U = M_1\,\Delta x_1 + M_2\,\Delta x_2 + \cdots + M_n\,\Delta x_n$$

and the shaded region in the second part of the figure.

c. Explain the connection between $U - L$ and the shaded regions along the curve in the third part of the figure.

81. We say f is **uniformly continuous** on $[a, b]$ if given any $\epsilon > 0$ there is a $\delta > 0$ such that if x_1, x_2 are in $[a, b]$ and $|x_1 - x_2| < \delta$ then $|f(x_1) - f(x_2)| < \epsilon$. It can be shown that a continuous function on $[a, b]$ is uniformly continuous. Use this and the figure below to show that if f is continuous and $\epsilon > 0$ is given, it is possible to make $U - L \le \epsilon \cdot (b - a)$ by making the largest of the Δx_k's sufficiently small.

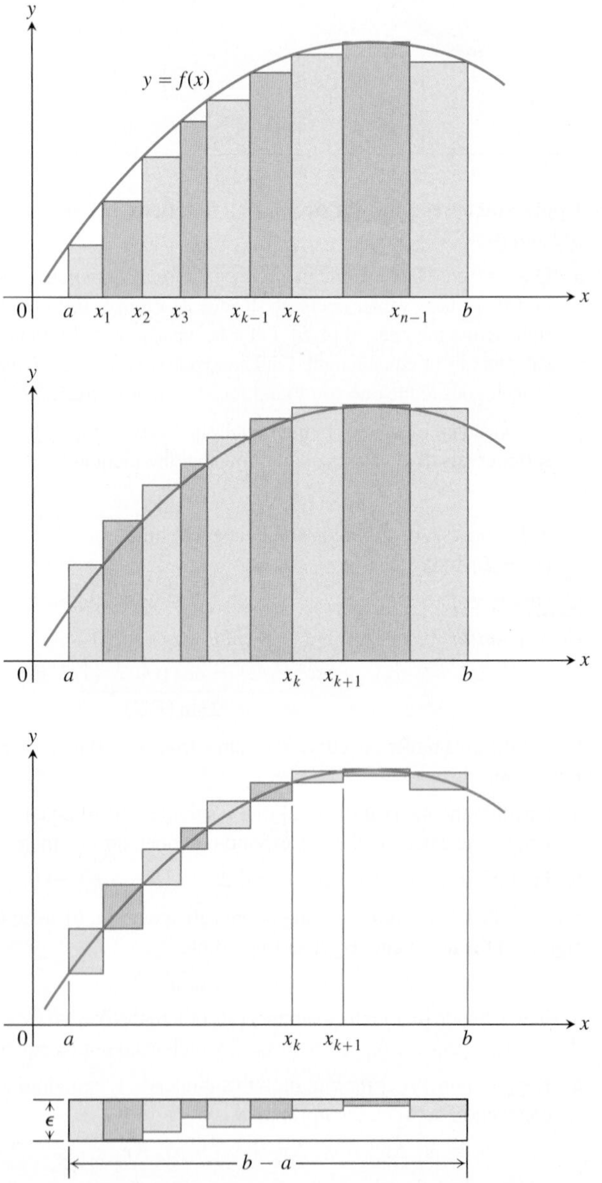

82. If you average 30 mi/h on a 150-mi trip and then return over the same 150 mi at the rate of 50 mi/h, what is your average speed for the trip? Give reasons for your answer. (*Source:* David H. Pleacher, *The Mathematics Teacher*, Vol. 85, No. 6, pp. 445–446, September 1992.)

COMPUTER EXPLORATIONS

If your CAS can draw rectangles associated with Riemann sums, use it to draw rectangles associated with Riemann sums that converge to the integrals in Exercises 83–88. Use $n = 4$, 10, 20, and 50 subintervals of equal length in each case.

83. $\int_0^1 (1 - x)\, dx = \frac{1}{2}$

84. $\int_0^1 (x^2 + 1)\, dx = \frac{4}{3}$

85. $\int_{-\pi}^{\pi} \cos x\, dx = 0$

86. $\int_0^{\pi/4} \sec^2 x\, dx = 1$

87. $\int_{-1}^{1} |x|\, dx = 1$

88. $\int_1^2 \frac{1}{x}\, dx$ (The integral's value is about 0.693.)

In Exercises 89–96, use a CAS to perform the following steps:

a. Plot the functions over the given interval.

b. Partition the interval into $n = 100, 200$, and 1000 subintervals of equal length, and evaluate the function at the midpoint of each subinterval.

c. Compute the average value of the function values generated in part (b).

d. Solve the equation $f(x) = $ (average value) for x using the average value calculated in part (c) for the $n = 1000$ partitioning.

89. $f(x) = \sin x$ on $[0, \pi]$

90. $f(x) = \sin^2 x$ on $[0, \pi]$

91. $f(x) = x \sin \frac{1}{x}$ on $\left[\frac{\pi}{4}, \pi\right]$

92. $f(x) = x \sin^2 \frac{1}{x}$ on $\left[\frac{\pi}{4}, \pi\right]$

93. $f(x) = xe^{-x}$ on $[0, 1]$

94. $f(x) = e^{-x^2}$ on $[0, 1]$

95. $f(x) = \frac{\ln x}{x}$ on $[2, 5]$

96. $f(x) = \frac{1}{\sqrt{1 - x^2}}$ on $\left[0, \frac{1}{2}\right]$

5.4 The Fundamental Theorem of Calculus

HISTORICAL BIOGRAPHY

Sir Isaac Newton
(1642–1727)

In this section we present the Fundamental Theorem of Calculus, which is the central theorem of integral calculus. It connects integration and differentiation, enabling us to compute integrals using an antiderivative of the integrand function rather than by taking limits of Riemann sums as we did in Section 5.3. Leibniz and Newton exploited this relationship and started mathematical developments that fueled the scientific revolution for the next 200 years.

Along the way, we present an integral version of the Mean Value Theorem, which is another important theorem of integral calculus and used to prove the Fundamental Theorem.

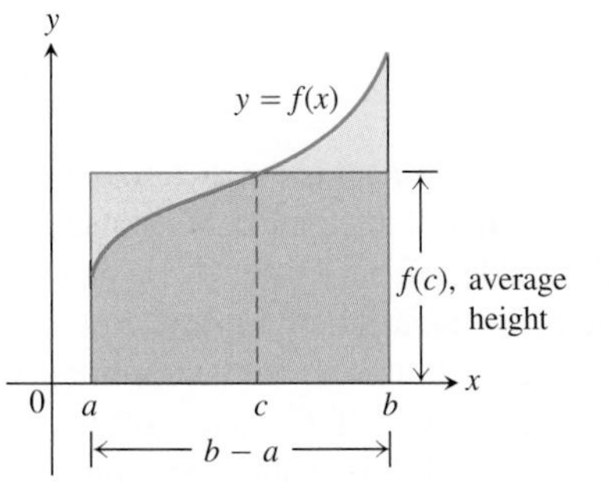

FIGURE 5.16 The value $f(c)$ in the Mean Value Theorem is, in a sense, the average (or *mean*) height of f on $[a, b]$. When $f \geq 0$, the area of the rectangle is the area under the graph of f from a to b,

$$f(c)(b - a) = \int_a^b f(x)\,dx.$$

Mean Value Theorem for Definite Integrals

In the previous section, we defined the average value of a continuous function over a closed interval $[a, b]$ as the definite integral $\int_a^b f(x)\,dx$ divided by the length or width $b - a$ of the interval. The Mean Value Theorem for Definite Integrals asserts that this average value is *always* taken on at least once by the function f in the interval.

The graph in Figure 5.16 shows a *positive* continuous function $y = f(x)$ defined over the interval $[a, b]$. Geometrically, the Mean Value Theorem says that there is a number c in $[a, b]$ such that the rectangle with height equal to the average value $f(c)$ of the function and base width $b - a$ has exactly the same area as the region beneath the graph of f from a to b.

THEOREM 3—The Mean Value Theorem for Definite Integrals If f is continuous on $[a, b]$, then at some point c in $[a, b]$,

$$f(c) = \frac{1}{b - a}\int_a^b f(x)\,dx.$$

Proof If we divide both sides of the Max-Min Inequality (Table 5.3, Rule 6) by $(b - a)$, we obtain

$$\min f \leq \frac{1}{b - a}\int_a^b f(x)\,dx \leq \max f.$$

Since f is continuous, the Intermediate Value Theorem for Continuous Functions (Section 2.6) says that f must assume every value between $\min f$ and $\max f$. It must therefore assume the value $(1/(b - a))\int_a^b f(x)\,dx$ at some point c in $[a, b]$. ■

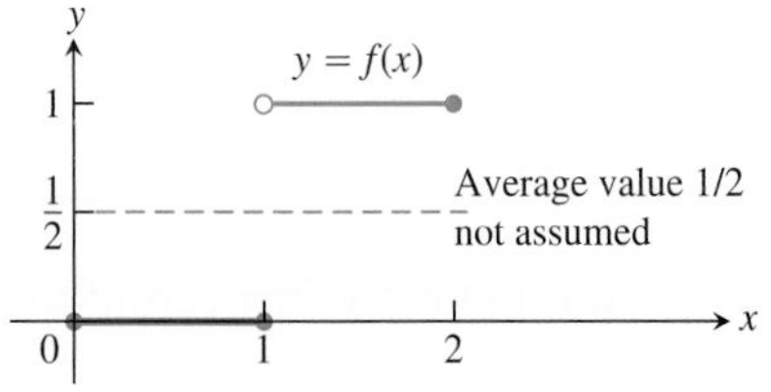

FIGURE 5.17 A discontinuous function need not assume its average value.

The continuity of f is important here. It is possible that a discontinuous function never equals its average value (Figure 5.17).

EXAMPLE 1 Show that if f is continuous on $[a, b]$, $a \neq b$, and if

$$\int_a^b f(x)\,dx = 0,$$

then $f(x) = 0$ at least once in $[a, b]$.

Solution The average value of f on $[a, b]$ is

$$\text{av}(f) = \frac{1}{b-a}\int_a^b f(x)\,dx = \frac{1}{b-a}\cdot 0 = 0.$$

By the Mean Value Theorem, f assumes this value at some point $c \in [a, b]$. ■

Fundamental Theorem, Part 1

If $f(t)$ is an integrable function over a finite interval I, then the integral from any fixed number $a \in I$ to another number $x \in I$ defines a new function F whose value at x is

$$F(x) = \int_a^x f(t)\,dt. \tag{1}$$

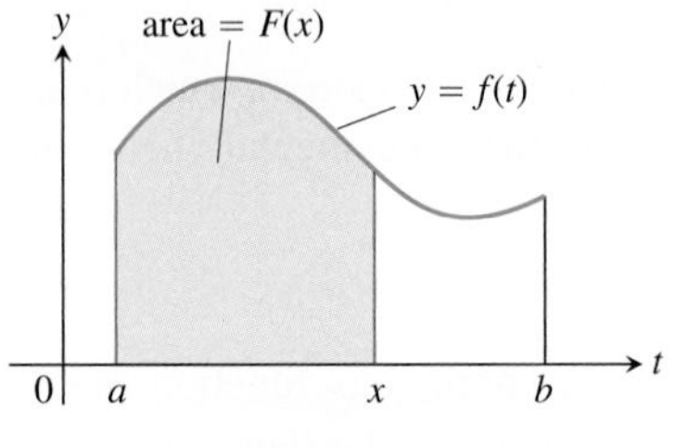

FIGURE 5.18 The function $F(x)$ defined by Equation (1) gives the area under the graph of f from a to x when f is nonnegative and $x > a$.

For example, if f is nonnegative and x lies to the right of a, then $F(x)$ is the area under the graph from a to x (Figure 5.18). The variable x is the upper limit of integration of an integral, but F is just like any other real-valued function of a real variable. For each value of the input x, there is a well-defined numerical output, in this case the definite integral of f from a to x.

Equation (1) gives a way to define new functions (see Section 5.7), but its importance now is the connection it makes between integrals and derivatives. If f is any continuous function, then the Fundamental Theorem asserts that F is a differentiable function of x whose derivative is f itself. At every value of x, it asserts that

$$\frac{d}{dx}F(x) = f(x).$$

To gain some insight into why this result holds, we look at the geometry behind it.

If $f \geq 0$ on $[a, b]$, then the computation of $F'(x)$ from the definition of the derivative means taking the limit as $h \to 0$ of the difference quotient

$$\frac{F(x+h) - F(x)}{h}.$$

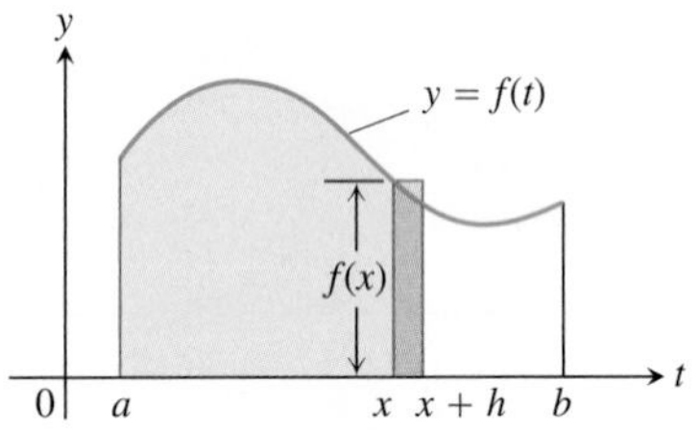

FIGURE 5.19 In Equation (1), $F(x)$ is the area to the left of x. Also, $F(x+h)$ is the area to the left of $x+h$. The difference quotient $[F(x+h) - F(x)]/h$ is then approximately equal to $f(x)$, the height of the rectangle shown here.

For $h > 0$, the numerator is obtained by subtracting two areas, so it is the area under the graph of f from x to $x + h$ (Figure 5.19). If h is small, this area is approximately equal to the area of the rectangle of height $f(x)$ and width h, which can be seen from Figure 5.19. That is,

$$F(x+h) - F(x) \approx hf(x).$$

Dividing both sides of this approximation by h and letting $h \to 0$, it is reasonable to expect that

$$F'(x) = \lim_{h\to 0}\frac{F(x+h) - F(x)}{h} = f(x).$$

This result is true even if the function f is not positive, and it forms the first part of the Fundamental Theorem of Calculus.

THEOREM 4—The Fundamental Theorem of Calculus, Part 1 If f is continuous on $[a, b]$ then $F(x) = \int_a^x f(t)\,dt$ is continuous on $[a, b]$ and differentiable on (a, b) and its derivative is $f(x)$;

$$F'(x) = \frac{d}{dx}\int_a^x f(t)\,dt = f(x). \tag{2}$$

Before proving Theorem 4, we look at several examples to gain a better understanding of what it says.

EXAMPLE 2 Use the Fundamental Theorem to find dy/dx if

(a) $y = \int_a^x \cos t\, dt$ **(b)** $y = \int_x^5 3t \sin t\, dt$ **(c)** $y = \int_1^{x^2} \cos t\, dt$

Solution

(a) $\dfrac{dy}{dx} = \dfrac{d}{dx}\displaystyle\int_a^x \cos t\, dt = \cos x$ Eq. (2) with $f(t) = \cos t$

(b) $\dfrac{dy}{dx} = \dfrac{d}{dx}\displaystyle\int_x^5 3t \sin t\, dt = \dfrac{d}{dx}\left(-\int_5^x 3t \sin t\, dt\right)$ Table 5.3, Rule 1

$$= -\frac{d}{dx}\int_5^x 3t \sin t\, dt$$

$= -3x \sin x$ Eq. (2) with $f(t) = 3t \sin t$

(c) The upper limit of integration is not x but x^2. This makes y a composite of the two functions,

$$y = \int_1^u \cos t\, dt \quad \text{and} \quad u = x^2.$$

We must therefore apply the Chain Rule when finding dy/dx.

$$\begin{aligned}
\frac{dy}{dx} &= \frac{dy}{du} \cdot \frac{du}{dx} \\
&= \left(\frac{d}{du}\int_1^u \cos t\, dt\right) \cdot \frac{du}{dx} \\
&= \cos u \cdot \frac{du}{dx} \\
&= \cos(x^2) \cdot 2x \\
&= 2x \cos x^2
\end{aligned}$$

■

Proof of Theorem 4 We prove the Fundamental Theorem by applying the definition of the derivative directly to the function $F(x)$, when x and $x + h$ are in (a, b). This means writing out the difference quotient

$$\frac{F(x + h) - F(x)}{h} \tag{3}$$

and showing that its limit as $h \to 0$ is the number $f(x)$ for each x in (a, b). Thus,

$$\begin{aligned}
F'(x) &= \lim_{h \to 0} \frac{F(x + h) - F(x)}{h} \\
&= \lim_{h \to 0} \frac{1}{h}\left[\int_a^{x+h} f(t)\, dt - \int_a^x f(t)\, dt\right] \\
&= \lim_{h \to 0} \frac{1}{h}\int_x^{x+h} f(t)\, dt
\end{aligned}$$

Table 5.3, Rule 5

According to the Mean Value Theorem for Definite Integrals, the value before taking the limit in the last expression is one of the values taken on by f in the interval between x and $x + h$. That is, for some number c in this interval,

$$\frac{1}{h}\int_{x}^{x+h} f(t)\,dt = f(c). \tag{4}$$

As $h \to 0$, $x + h$ approaches x, forcing c to approach x also (because c is trapped between x and $x + h$). Since f is continuous at x, $f(c)$ approaches $f(x)$:

$$\lim_{h\to 0} f(c) = f(x). \tag{5}$$

In conclusion, we have

$$\begin{aligned} F'(x) &= \lim_{h\to 0}\frac{1}{h}\int_{x}^{x+h} f(t)\,dt \\ &= \lim_{h\to 0} f(c) && \text{Eq. (4)} \\ &= f(x). && \text{Eq. (5)} \end{aligned}$$

If $x = a$ or b, then the limit of Equation (3) is interpreted as a one-sided limit with $h \to 0^+$ or $h \to 0^-$, respectively. Then Theorem 1 in Section 3.1 shows that F is continuous for every point of $[a, b]$. This concludes the proof. ■

Fundamental Theorem, Part 2 (The Evaluation Theorem)

We now come to the second part of the Fundamental Theorem of Calculus. This part describes how to evaluate definite integrals without having to calculate limits of Riemann sums. Instead we find and evaluate an antiderivative at the upper and lower limits of integration.

THEOREM 4 (Continued)—The Fundamental Theorem of Calculus, Part 2 If f is continuous at every point of $[a, b]$ and F is any antiderivative of f on $[a, b]$, then

$$\int_{a}^{b} f(x)\,dx = F(b) - F(a).$$

Proof Part 1 of the Fundamental Theorem tells us that an antiderivative of f exists, namely

$$G(x) = \int_{a}^{x} f(t)\,dt.$$

Thus, if F is *any* antiderivative of f, then $F(x) = G(x) + C$ for some constant C for $a < x < b$ (by Corollary 2 of the Mean Value Theorem for Derivatives, Section 4.2). Since both F and G are continuous on $[a, b]$, we see that $F(x) = G(x) + C$ also holds when $x = a$ and $x = b$ by taking one-sided limits (as $x \to a^+$ and $x \to b^-$).

Evaluating $F(b) - F(a)$, we have

$$\begin{aligned} F(b) - F(a) &= [G(b) + C] - [G(a) + C] \\ &= G(b) - G(a) \\ &= \int_a^b f(t)\,dt - \int_a^a f(t)\,dt \\ &= \int_a^b f(t)\,dt - 0 \\ &= \int_a^b f(t)\,dt. \end{aligned}$$

■

The theorem says that to calculate the definite integral of f over $[a, b]$ all we need to do is:

1. Find an antiderivative F of f, and
2. Calculate the number $\int_a^b f(x)\,dx = F(b) - F(a)$.

The usual notation for $F(b) - F(a)$ is

$$F(x)\Big]_a^b \quad \text{or} \quad \Big[F(x)\Big]_a^b,$$

depending on whether F has one or more terms.

EXAMPLE 3

(a) $\displaystyle\int_0^{\pi} \cos x\,dx = \sin x\Big]_0^{\pi} = \sin\pi - \sin 0 = 0 - 0 = 0$

(b) $\displaystyle\int_0^{1/2} \frac{dx}{\sqrt{1 - x^2}} = \sin^{-1}x\Big]_0^{1/2} = \sin^{-1}\frac{1}{2} - \sin^{-1}0 = \frac{\pi}{6} - 0 = \frac{\pi}{6}$

(c) $\displaystyle\int_1^4 \left(\frac{3}{2}\sqrt{x} - \frac{2}{x}\right)dx = \Big[x^{3/2} - 2\ln x\Big]_1^4 = [4^{3/2} - 2\ln 4] - [1^{3/2} - 2\ln 1]$

$\displaystyle = [8 - \ln 16] - [1 - 0] = 7 - \ln 16.$ ■

The process used in Example 3 was much easier than a Riemann sum computation.

The conclusions of the Fundamental Theorem tell us several things. Equation (2) can be rewritten as

$$\frac{d}{dx}\int_a^x f(t)\,dt = \frac{dF}{dx} = f(x),$$

which says that if you first integrate the function f and then differentiate the result, you get the function f back again. Likewise, the equation

$$\int_a^x \frac{dF}{dt}\,dt = \int_a^x f(t)\,dt = F(x) - F(a)$$

says that if you first differentiate the function F and then integrate the result, you get the function F back (adjusted by an integration constant). In a sense, the processes of integration and differentiation are "inverses" of each other. The Fundamental Theorem also says that every continuous function f has an antiderivative F. And it says that the differential equation $dy/dx = f(x)$ has a solution (namely, any of the functions $y = F(x) + C$) for every continuous function f.

Total Area

The Riemann sum contains terms such as $f(c_k)\,\Delta_k$ which give the area of a rectangle when $f(c_k)$ is positive. When $f(c_k)$ is negative, then the product $f(c_k)\,\Delta_k$ is the negative of the rectangle's area. When we add up such terms for a negative function we get the negative of the area between the curve and the x-axis. If we then take the absolute value, we obtain the correct positive area.

To compute the area of the region bounded by the graph of a function $y = f(x)$ and the x-axis when the function takes on both positive and negative values, we must be careful to break up the interval $[a, b]$ into subintervals on which the function doesn't change sign. Otherwise we might get cancellation between positive and negative signed areas, leading to an incorrect total. The correct total area is obtained by adding the absolute value of the definite integral over each subinterval where $f(x)$ does not change sign. The term "area" will be taken to mean *total area*.

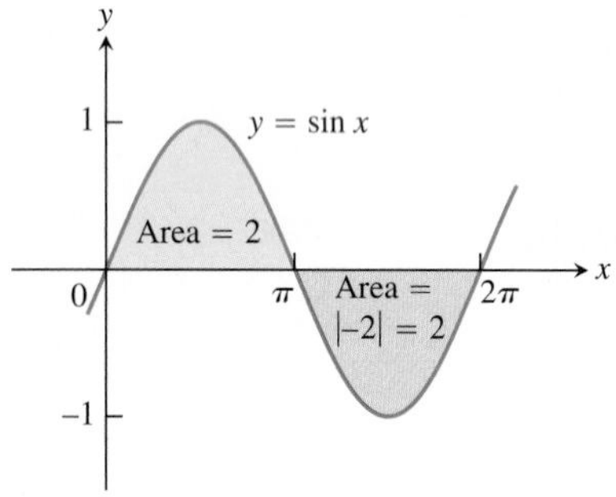

FIGURE 5.20 The total area between $y = \sin x$ and the x-axis for $0 \le x \le 2\pi$ is the sum of the absolute values of two integrals (Example 4).

EXAMPLE 4 Figure 5.20 shows the graph of the function $f(x) = \sin x$ between $x = 0$ and $x = 2\pi$. Compute

(a) the definite integral of $f(x)$ over $[0, 2\pi]$.

(b) the area between the graph of $f(x)$ and the x-axis over $[0, 2\pi]$.

Solution The definite integral for $f(x) = \sin x$ is given by

$$\int_0^{2\pi} \sin x\,dx = -\cos x\Big]_0^{2\pi} = -[\cos 2\pi - \cos 0] = -[1 - 1] = 0.$$

The definite integral is zero because the portions of the graph above and below the x-axis make canceling contributions.

The area between the graph of $f(x)$ and the x-axis over $[0, 2\pi]$ is calculated by breaking up the domain of $\sin x$ into two pieces: the interval $[0, \pi]$ over which it is nonnegative and the interval $[\pi, 2\pi]$ over which it is nonpositive.

$$\int_0^{\pi} \sin x\,dx = -\cos x\Big]_0^{\pi} = -[\cos \pi - \cos 0] = -[-1 - 1] = 2.$$

$$\int_{\pi}^{2\pi} \sin x\,dx = -\cos x\Big]_{\pi}^{2\pi} = -[\cos 2\pi - \cos \pi] = -[1 - (-1)] = -2.$$

The second integral gives a negative value. The area between the graph and the axis is obtained by adding the absolute values

$$\text{Area} = |2| + |-2| = 4.$$

■

Summary:

To find the area between the graph of $y = f(x)$ and the x-axis over the interval $[a, b]$:

1. Subdivide $[a, b]$ at the zeros of f.
2. Integrate f over each subinterval.
3. Add the absolute values of the integrals.

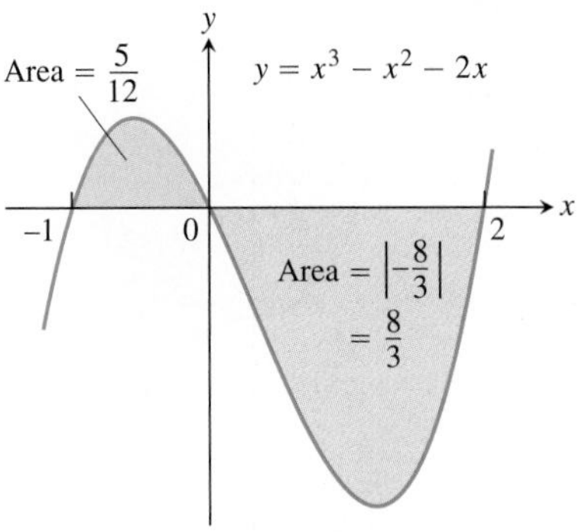

FIGURE 5.21 The region between the curve $y = x^3 - x^2 - 2x$ and the x-axis (Example 5).

EXAMPLE 5 Find the area of the region between the x-axis and the graph of $f(x) = x^3 - x^2 - 2x$, $-1 \le x \le 2$.

Solution First find the zeros of f. Since

$$f(x) = x^3 - x^2 - 2x = x(x^2 - x - 2) = x(x + 1)(x - 2),$$

the zeros are $x = 0$, -1, and 2 (Figure 5.21). The zeros subdivide $[-1, 2]$ into two subintervals: $[-1, 0]$, on which $f \ge 0$, and $[0, 2]$, on which $f \le 0$. We integrate f over each subinterval and add the absolute values of the calculated integrals.

$$\int_{-1}^{0} (x^3 - x^2 - 2x)\,dx = \left[\frac{x^4}{4} - \frac{x^3}{3} - x^2\right]_{-1}^{0} = 0 - \left[\frac{1}{4} + \frac{1}{3} - 1\right] = \frac{5}{12}$$

$$\int_{0}^{2} (x^3 - x^2 - 2x)\,dx = \left[\frac{x^4}{4} - \frac{x^3}{3} - x^2\right]_{0}^{2} = \left[4 - \frac{8}{3} - 4\right] - 0 = -\frac{8}{3}$$

The total enclosed area is obtained by adding the absolute values of the calculated integrals,

$$\text{Total enclosed area} = \frac{5}{12} + \left|-\frac{8}{3}\right| = \frac{37}{12}.$$ ■

EXERCISES 5.4

Evaluate the integrals in Exercises 1–32.

1. $\int_{-2}^{0} (2x + 5)\,dx$

2. $\int_{-3}^{4} \left(5 - \frac{x}{2}\right) dx$

3. $\int_{0}^{4} \left(3x - \frac{x^3}{4}\right) dx$

4. $\int_{-2}^{2} (x^3 - 2x + 3)\,dx$

5. $\int_{0}^{1} \left(x^2 + \sqrt{x}\right) dx$

6. $\int_{0}^{5} x^{3/2}\,dx$

7. $\int_{1}^{32} x^{-6/5}\,dx$

8. $\int_{-2}^{-1} \frac{2}{x^2}\,dx$

9. $\int_{0}^{\pi} \sin x\,dx$

10. $\int_{0}^{\pi} (1 + \cos x)\,dx$

11. $\int_{0}^{\pi/3} 2\sec^2 x\,dx$

12. $\int_{\pi/6}^{5\pi/6} \csc^2 x\,dx$

13. $\int_{\pi/4}^{3\pi/4} \csc\theta\cot\theta\,d\theta$

14. $\int_{0}^{\pi/3} 4\sec u\tan u\,du$

15. $\int_{\pi/2}^{0} \frac{1 + \cos 2t}{2}\,dt$

16. $\int_{-\pi/3}^{\pi/3} \frac{1 - \cos 2t}{2}\,dt$

17. $\int_{-\pi/2}^{\pi/2} (8y^2 + \sin y)\,dy$

18. $\int_{-\pi/3}^{-\pi/4} \left(4\sec^2 t + \frac{\pi}{t^2}\right) dt$

19. $\int_{1}^{-1} (r + 1)^2\,dr$

20. $\int_{-\sqrt{3}}^{\sqrt{3}} (t + 1)(t^2 + 4)\,dt$

21. $\int_{\sqrt{2}}^{1} \left(\frac{u^7}{2} - \frac{1}{u^5}\right) du$

22. $\int_{1/2}^{1} \left(\frac{1}{v^3} - \frac{1}{v^4}\right) dv$

23. $\int_{1}^{\sqrt{2}} \frac{s^2 + \sqrt{s}}{s^2}\,ds$

24. $\int_{9}^{4} \frac{1 - \sqrt{u}}{\sqrt{u}}\,du$

25. $\int_{-4}^{4} |x|\,dx$

26. $\int_{0}^{\pi} \frac{1}{2}(\cos x + |\cos x|)\,dx$

27. $\int_{0}^{\ln 2} e^{3x}\,dx$

28. $\int_{1}^{2} \left(\frac{1}{x} - e^{-x}\right) dx$

29. $\int_{0}^{1} \frac{4}{1 + x^2}\,dx$

30. $\int_{2}^{5} \frac{x\,dx}{\sqrt{1 + x^2}}$

31. $\int_{2}^{4} x^{\pi - 1}\,dx$

32. $\int_{-1}^{0} \pi^{x-1}\,dx$

In Exercises 33 and 34, guess an antiderivative for the integrand function. Validate your guess by differentiation and then evaluate the given definite integral. (*Hint:* Keep in mind the Chain Rule in guessing an antiderivative. You will learn how to find such antiderivatives in the next section.)

33. $\int_{0}^{1} xe^{x^2}\,dx$

34. $\int_{1}^{2} \frac{\ln x}{x}\,dx$

Find the derivatives in Exercises 35–40.

a. by evaluating the integral and differentiating the result.

b. by differentiating the integral directly.

35. $\frac{d}{dx}\int_0^{\sqrt{x}} \cos t\, dt$

36. $\frac{d}{dx}\int_1^{\sin x} 3t^2\, dt$

37. $\frac{d}{dt}\int_0^{t^4} \sqrt{u}\, du$

38. $\frac{d}{d\theta}\int_0^{\tan\theta} \sec^2 y\, dy$

39. $\frac{d}{dx}\int_0^{x^3} e^{-t}\, dt$

40. $\frac{d}{dt}\int_0^{\sqrt{t}} \left(x^4 + \frac{3}{\sqrt{1-x^2}}\right) dx$

Find dy/dx in Exercises 41–50.

41. $y = \int_0^x \sqrt{1+t^2}\, dt$

42. $y = \int_1^x \frac{1}{t}\, dt, \quad x > 0$

43. $y = \int_{\sqrt{x}}^0 \sin(t^2)\, dt$

44. $y = \int_0^{x^2} \cos\sqrt{t}\, dt$

45. $y = \int_0^{\sin x} \frac{dt}{\sqrt{1-t^2}}, \quad |x| < \frac{\pi}{2}$

46. $y = \int_{\tan x}^0 \frac{dt}{1+t^2}$

47. $y = \int_0^{e^{x^2}} \frac{1}{\sqrt{t}}\, dt$

48. $y = \int_{2^x}^1 \sqrt[3]{t}\, dt$

49. $y = \int_0^{\sin^{-1} x} \cos t\, dt$

50. $y = \int_{-1}^{x^{1/\pi}} \sin^{-1} t\, dt$

In Exercises 51–56, find the total area between the region and the x-axis.

51. $y = -x^2 - 2x, \quad -3 \le x \le 2$

52. $y = 3x^2 - 3, \quad -2 \le x \le 2$

53. $y = x^3 - 3x^2 + 2x, \quad 0 \le x \le 2$

54. $y = x^3 - 4x, \quad -2 \le x \le 2$

55. $y = x^{1/3}, \quad -1 \le x \le 8$

56. $y = x^{1/3} - x, \quad -1 \le x \le 8$

Find the areas of the shaded regions in Exercises 57–60.

57.

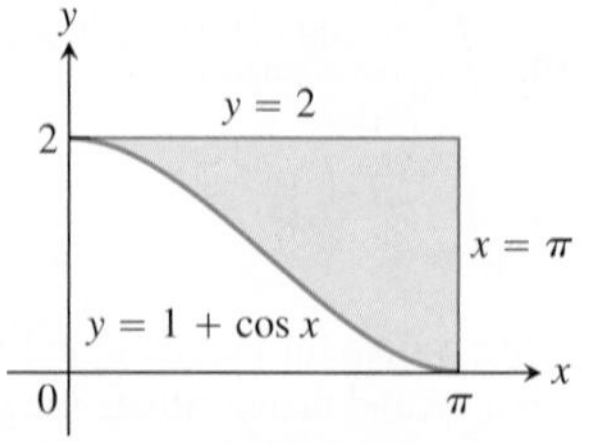

58.

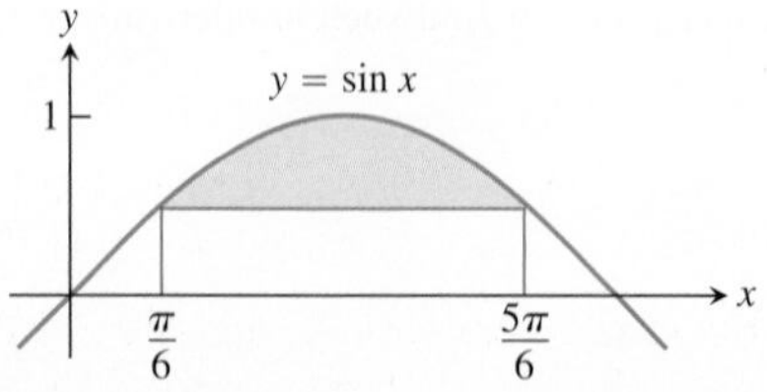

59.

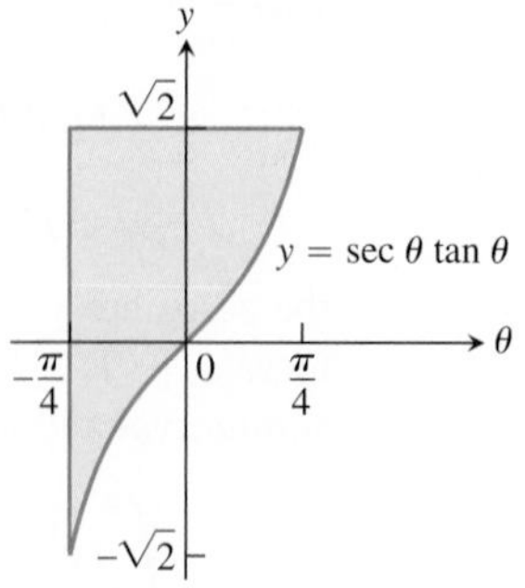

60.

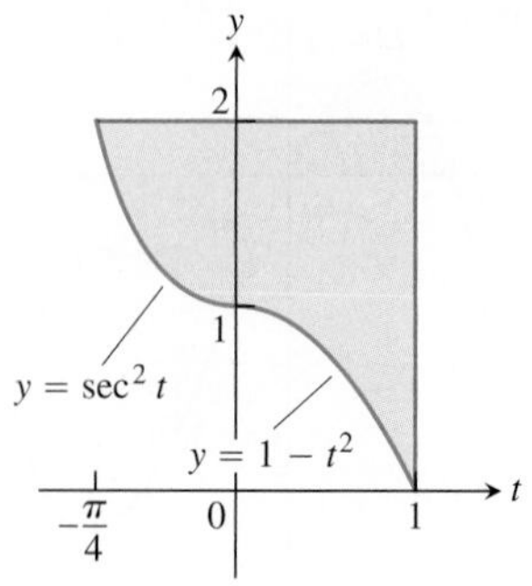

Each of the following functions solves one of the initial value problems in Exercises 61–64. Which function solves which problem? Give brief reasons for your answers.

a. $y = \int_1^x \frac{1}{t}\, dt - 3$

b. $y = \int_0^x \sec t\, dt + 4$

c. $y = \int_{-1}^x \sec t\, dt + 4$

d. $y = \int_\pi^x \frac{1}{t}\, dt - 3$

61. $\frac{dy}{dx} = \frac{1}{x}, \quad y(\pi) = -3$

62. $y' = \sec x, \quad y(-1) = 4$

63. $y' = \sec x, \quad y(0) = 4$

64. $y' = \frac{1}{x}, \quad y(1) = -3$

Express the solutions of the initial value problems in Exercises 65–68 in terms of integrals.

65. $\frac{dy}{dx} = \sec x, \quad y(2) = 3$

66. $\frac{dy}{dx} = \sqrt{1+x^2}, \quad y(1) = -2$

67. $\frac{ds}{dt} = f(t), \quad s(t_0) = s_0$

68. $\frac{dv}{dt} = g(t), \quad v(t_0) = v_0$

69. Archimedes' area formula for parabolas Archimedes (287–212 B.C.), inventor, military engineer, physicist, and the greatest mathematician of classical times in the Western world, discovered that the area under a parabolic arch is two-thirds the base times the height. Sketch the parabolic arch $y = h - (4h/b^2)x^2$, $-b/2 \le x \le b/2$, assuming that h and b are positive. Then use calculus to find the area of the region enclosed between the arch and the x-axis.

70. Revenue from marginal revenue Suppose that a company's marginal revenue from the manufacture and sale of egg beaters is

$$\frac{dr}{dx} = 2 - 2/(x+1)^2,$$

where r is measured in thousands of dollars and x in thousands of units. How much money should the company expect from a production run of $x = 3$ thousand egg beaters? To find out, integrate the marginal revenue from $x = 0$ to $x = 3$.

71. Cost from marginal cost The marginal cost of printing a poster when x posters have been printed is

$$\frac{dc}{dx} = \frac{1}{2\sqrt{x}}$$

dollars. Find $c(100) - c(1)$, the cost of printing posters 2–100.

72. (*Continuation of Exercise 71.*) Find $c(400) - c(100)$, the cost of printing posters 101–400.

73. Show that if k is a positive constant, then the area between the x-axis and one arch of the curve $y = \sin kx$ is $2/k$.

74. Find

$$\lim_{x \to 0} \frac{1}{x^3} \int_0^x \frac{t^2}{t^4 + 1}\, dt.$$

75. Suppose $\int_1^x f(t)\, dt = x^2 - 2x + 1$. Find $f(x)$.

76. Find $f(4)$ if $\int_0^x f(t)\, dt = x \cos \pi x$.

77. Find the linearization of

$$f(x) = 2 - \int_2^{x+1} \frac{9}{1 + t}\, dt$$

at $x = 1$.

78. Find the linearization of

$$g(x) = 3 + \int_1^{x^2} \sec(t - 1)\, dt$$

at $x = -1$.

79. Suppose that f has a positive derivative for all values of x and that $f(1) = 0$. Which of the following statements must be true of the function

$$g(x) = \int_0^x f(t)\, dt?$$

Give reasons for your answers.

a. g is a differentiable function of x.

b. g is a continuous function of x.

c. The graph of g has a horizontal tangent at $x = 1$.

d. g has a local maximum at $x = 1$.

e. g has a local minimum at $x = 1$.

f. The graph of g has an inflection point at $x = 1$.

g. The graph of dg/dx crosses the x-axis at $x = 1$.

80. Another proof of The Evaluation Theorem

a. Let $a = x_0 < x_1 < x_2 \cdots < x_n = b$ be any partition of $[a, b]$, and let F be any antiderivative of f. Show that

$$F(b) - F(a) = \sum_{i=1}^{n} [F(x_i) - F(x_{i-1})].$$

b. Apply the Mean Value Theorem to each term to show $F(x_i) - F(x_{i-1}) = f(c_i)(x_i - x_{i-1})$ for some c_i in the interval (x_{i-1}, x_i). Then show that $F(b) - F(a)$ is a Riemann sum for f on $[a, b]$.

c. From part b and the definition of the definite integral, show that

$$F(b) - F(a) = \int_a^b f(x)\, dx.$$

COMPUTER EXPLORATIONS

In Exercises 81–84, let $F(x) = \int_a^x f(t)\, dt$ for the specified function f and interval $[a, b]$. Use a CAS to perform the following steps and answer the questions posed.

a. Plot the functions f and F together over $[a, b]$.

b. Solve the equation $F'(x) = 0$. What can you see to be true about the graphs of f and F at points where $F'(x) = 0$? Is your observation borne out by Part 1 of the Fundamental Theorem coupled with information provided by the first derivative? Explain your answer.

c. Over what intervals (approximately) is the function F increasing and decreasing? What is true about f over those intervals?

d. Calculate the derivative f' and plot it together with F. What can you see to be true about the graph of F at points where $f'(x) = 0$? Is your observation borne out by Part 1 of the Fundamental Theorem? Explain your answer.

81. $f(x) = x^3 - 4x^2 + 3x, \quad [0, 4]$

82. $f(x) = 2x^4 - 17x^3 + 46x^2 - 43x + 12, \quad \left[0, \frac{9}{2}\right]$

83. $f(x) = \sin 2x \cos \frac{x}{3}, \quad [0, 2\pi]$

84. $f(x) = x \cos \pi x, \quad [0, 2\pi]$

In Exercises 85–88, let $F(x) = \int_a^{u(x)} f(t)\, dt$ for the specified a, u, and f. Use a CAS to perform the following steps and answer the questions posed.

a. Find the domain of F.

b. Calculate $F'(x)$ and determine its zeros. For what points in its domain is F increasing? Decreasing?

c. Calculate $F''(x)$ and determine its zero. Identify the local extrema and the points of inflection of F.

d. Using the information from parts (a)–(c), draw a rough hand-sketch of $y = F(x)$ over its domain. Then graph $F(x)$ on your CAS to support your sketch.

85. $a = 1, \quad u(x) = x^2, \quad f(x) = \sqrt{1 - x^2}$

86. $a = 0, \quad u(x) = x^2, \quad f(x) = \sqrt{1 - x^2}$

87. $a = 0, \quad u(x) = 1 - x, \quad f(x) = x^2 - 2x - 3$

88. $a = 0, \quad u(x) = 1 - x^2, \quad f(x) = x^2 - 2x - 3$

In Exercises 89 and 90, assume that f is continuous and $u(x)$ is twice-differentiable.

89. Calculate $\frac{d}{dx}\int_a^{u(x)} f(t)\, dt$ and check your answer using a CAS.

90. Calculate $\frac{d^2}{dx^2}\int_a^{u(x)} f(t)\, dt$ and check your answer using a CAS.

5.5 Indefinite Integrals and the Substitution Rule

The Fundamental Theorem of Calculus says that a definite integral of a continuous function can be computed directly if we can find an antiderivative of the function. In Section 4.8 we defined the **indefinite integral** of the function f with respect to x as the set of *all* antiderivatives of f, symbolized by

$$\int f(x)\,dx.$$

The connection between antiderivatives and the definite integral stated in the Fundamental Theorem now explains this notation. When finding the indefinite integral of a function f, remember that it always includes an arbitrary constant C.

We must distinguish carefully between definite and indefinite integrals. A definite integral $\int_a^b f(x)\,dx$ is a *number*. An indefinite integral $\int f(x)\,dx$ is a *function* plus an arbitrary constant C.

So far, we have only been able to find antiderivatives of functions that are clearly recognizable as derivatives. In this section we begin to develop more general techniques for finding antiderivatives.

Substitution: Running the Chain Rule Backwards

If u is a differentiable function of x and n is any number different from -1, the Chain Rule tells us that

$$\frac{d}{dx}\left(\frac{u^{n+1}}{n+1}\right) = u^n\frac{du}{dx}.$$

From another point of view, this same equation says that $u^{n+1}/(n+1)$ is one of the antiderivatives of the function $u^n(du/dx)$. Therefore,

$$\int\left(u^n\frac{du}{dx}\right)dx = \frac{u^{n+1}}{n+1} + C.$$

The integral on the left-hand side of this equation is usually written in the simpler "differential" form, giving

$$\int u^n\,du = \frac{u^{n+1}}{n+1} + C \qquad (n \neq -1,\ n \text{ any number}).$$

In deriving this equation, we assumed u to be a differentiable function of the variable x, but the name of the variable does not matter and does not appear in the final formula. We could have represented the variable with θ, t, y, or any other letter.

EXAMPLE 1 Find

$$\int \sqrt{2x+1}\,dx$$

Solution The integral does not fit the formula

$$\int u^n\,du$$

with $u = 2x + 1$ and $n = 1/2$, because

$$du = \frac{du}{dx} \cdot dx = 2\,dx$$

is not precisely dx. The constant factor 2 is missing from the integral. However, we can introduce this factor after the integral sign if we compensate for it by a factor of $1/2$ in front of the integral sign. So we write

$$\begin{aligned}
\int \sqrt{2x+1}\,dx &= \frac{1}{2}\int \sqrt{2x+1}\cdot 2\,dx \\
&= \frac{1}{2}\int u^{1/2}\,du && \text{Let } u = 2x+1,\quad du = 2\,dx \\
&= \frac{1}{2}\frac{u^{3/2}}{3/2} + C \\
&= \frac{1}{3}(2x+1)^{3/2} + C && \text{Substitute } 2x+1 \text{ for } u.
\end{aligned}$$

■

The substitution in Example 1 is an instance of the following general rule.

THEOREM 5—The Substitution Rule If $u = g(x)$ is a differentiable function whose range is an interval I and f is continuous on I, then

$$\int f(g(x))g'(x)\,dx = \int f(u)\,du.$$

Proof The rule is true because, by the Chain Rule, $F(g(x))$ is an antiderivative of $f(g(x)) \cdot g'(x)$ whenever F is an antiderivative of f:

$$\begin{aligned}
\frac{d}{dx}F(g(x)) &= F'(g(x))\cdot g'(x) && \text{Chain Rule} \\
&= f(g(x))\cdot g'(x). && \text{Because } F' = f
\end{aligned}$$

If we make the substitution $u = g(x)$ then

$$\begin{aligned}
\int f(g(x))g'(x)\,dx &= \int \frac{d}{dx}F(g(x))\,dx \\
&= F(g(x)) + C && \text{Fundamental Theorem} \\
&= F(u) + C && u = g(x) \\
&= \int F'(u)\,du && \text{Fundamental Theorem} \\
&= \int f(u)\,du && F' = f
\end{aligned}$$

■

The Substitution Rule provides the following method to evaluate the integral

$$\int f(g(x))g'(x)\,dx,$$

when f and g' are continuous functions:

1. Substitute $u = g(x)$ and $du = g'(x)\,dx$ to obtain the integral
$$\int f(u)\,du.$$
2. Integrate with respect to u.
3. Replace u by $g(x)$ in the result.

EXAMPLE 2
$$\begin{aligned}
\int \cos(7\theta + 5)\,d\theta &= \int \cos u \cdot \frac{1}{7}\,du && \text{Let } u = 7\theta + 5,\ du = 7\,d\theta,\ (1/7)\,du = d\theta. \\
&= \frac{1}{7}\int \cos u\,du && \text{With the } (1/7) \text{ out front, the integral is now in standard form.} \\
&= \frac{1}{7}\sin u + C && \text{Integrate with respect to } u, \text{ Table 4.2.} \\
&= \frac{1}{7}\sin(7\theta + 5) + C && \text{Replace } u \text{ by } 7\theta + 5.
\end{aligned}$$

We can verify this solution by differentiating and checking that we obtain the original function $\cos(7\theta + 5)$. ■

EXAMPLE 3
$$\begin{aligned}
\int x^2 e^{x^3}\,dx &= \int e^{x^3} \cdot x^2\,dx \\
&= \int e^u \cdot \frac{1}{3}\,du && \text{Let } u = x^3,\ du = 3x^2\,dx,\ (1/3)\,du = x^2\,dx. \\
&= \frac{1}{3}\int e^u\,du \\
&= \frac{1}{3}e^u + C && \text{Integrate with respect to } u. \\
&= \frac{1}{3}e^{x^3} + C && \text{Replace } u \text{ by } x^3 + 1.
\end{aligned}$$
■

An integrand may require some algebraic manipulation before the substitution method can be applied. The next example gives an important integral obtained by multiplying the integrand by an algebraic form equal to 1, leading to an appropriate substitution.

HISTORICAL BIOGRAPHY

George David Birkhoff
(1884–1944)

EXAMPLE 4
$$\begin{aligned}
\int \sec x\,dx &= \int (\sec x)(1)\,dx = \int \sec x \cdot \frac{\sec x + \tan x}{\sec x + \tan x}\,dx && \frac{\sec x + \tan x}{\sec x + \tan x} \text{ is a form of 1} \\
&= \int \frac{\sec^2 x + \sec x \tan x}{\sec x + \tan x}\,dx \\
&= \int \frac{du}{u} && u = \tan x + \sec x,\ du = (\sec^2 x + \sec x \tan x)\,dx \\
&= \ln|u| + C = \ln|\sec x + \tan x| + C.
\end{aligned}$$
■

EXAMPLE 5

$$\int \frac{\ln x^2}{x}\,dx = \int \frac{2\ln x}{x}\,dx \qquad \text{Power Rule for logarithms}$$

$$= \int 2\ln x \cdot \frac{1}{x}\,dx$$

$$= \int 2u\,du \qquad \text{Let } u = \ln x,\ du = (1/x)\,dx.$$

$$= u^2 + C \qquad \text{Integrate with respect to } u.$$

$$= (\ln x)^2 + C \qquad \text{Replace } u \text{ by } \ln x.$$

■

EXAMPLE 6

$$\int \frac{1}{\cos^2 2x}\,dx = \int \sec^2 2x\,dx \qquad \frac{1}{\cos 2x} = \sec 2x$$

$$= \int \sec^2 u \cdot \frac{1}{2}\,du \qquad u = 2x,\ du = 2\,dx,\ dx = (1/2)\,du$$

$$= \frac{1}{2}\int \sec^2 u\,du$$

$$= \frac{1}{2}\tan u + C \qquad \frac{d}{du}\tan u = \sec^2 u$$

$$= \frac{1}{2}\tan 2x + C \qquad u = 2x$$

■

The success of the substitution method depends on finding a substitution that changes an integral we cannot evaluate directly into one that we can. If the first substitution fails, try to simplify the integrand further with additional substitutions (see Exercises 55 and 56).

EXAMPLE 7 Evaluate

$$\int \frac{2z\,dz}{\sqrt[3]{z^2+1}}.$$

Solution We can use the substitution method of integration as an exploratory tool: Substitute for the most troublesome part of the integrand and see how things work out. For the integral here, we might try $u = z^2 + 1$ or we might even press our luck and take u to be the entire cube root. Here is what happens in each case.

Solution 1: Substitute $u = z^2 + 1$.

$$\int \frac{2z\,dz}{\sqrt[3]{z^2+1}} = \int \frac{du}{u^{1/3}} \qquad \text{Let } u = z^2 + 1,\ du = 2z\,dz.$$

$$= \int u^{-1/3}\,du \qquad \text{In the form } \int u^n\,du$$

$$= \frac{u^{2/3}}{2/3} + C \qquad \text{Integrate with respect to } u.$$

$$= \frac{3}{2}u^{2/3} + C$$

$$= \frac{3}{2}(z^2+1)^{2/3} + C \qquad \text{Replace } u \text{ by } z^2 + 1.$$

Solution 2: Substitute $u = \sqrt[3]{z^2 + 1}$ instead.

$$\int \frac{2z\,dz}{\sqrt[3]{z^2+1}} = \int \frac{3u^2\,du}{u} \qquad \text{Let } u = \sqrt[3]{z^2+1},\ u^3 = z^2 + 1,\ 3u^2\,du = 2z\,dz.$$

$$= 3\int u\,du$$

$$= 3 \cdot \frac{u^2}{2} + C \qquad \text{Integrate with respect to } u.$$

$$= \frac{3}{2}(z^2 + 1)^{2/3} + C \qquad \text{Replace } u \text{ by } (z^2+1)^{1/3}.$$

The Integrals of $\sin^2 x$ and $\cos^2 x$

Sometimes we can use trigonometric identities to transform integrals we do not know how to evaluate into ones we can evaluate using the substitution rule.

EXAMPLE 8

(a) $$\int \sin^2 x\,dx = \int \frac{1 - \cos 2x}{2}\,dx \qquad \sin^2 x = \frac{1-\cos 2x}{2}$$

$$= \frac{1}{2}\int (1 - \cos 2x)\,dx = \frac{1}{2}\int dx - \frac{1}{2}\int \cos 2x\,dx$$

$$= \frac{1}{2}x - \frac{1}{2}\frac{\sin 2x}{2} + C = \frac{x}{2} - \frac{\sin 2x}{4} + C$$

(b) $$\int \cos^2 x\,dx = \int \frac{1 + \cos 2x}{2}\,dx \qquad \cos^2 x = \frac{1+\cos 2x}{2}$$

$$= \frac{x}{2} + \frac{\sin 2x}{4} + C$$

EXERCISES 5.5

Evaluate the indefinite integrals in Exercises 1–12 by using the given substitutions to reduce the integrals to standard form.

1. $\int \sin 3x\,dx,\quad u = 3x$

2. $\int x \sin(2x^2)\,dx,\quad u = 2x^2$

3. $\int \sec 2t \tan 2t\,dt,\quad u = 2t$

4. $\int \left(1 - \cos\frac{t}{2}\right)^2 \sin\frac{t}{2}\,dt,\quad u = 1 - \cos\frac{t}{2}$

5. $\int 28(7x - 2)^{-5}\,dx,\quad u = 7x - 2$

6. $\int x^3(x^4 - 1)^2\,dx,\quad u = x^4 - 1$

7. $\int \frac{9r^2\,dr}{\sqrt{1 - r^3}},\quad u = 1 - r^3$

8. $\int 12(y^4 + 4y^2 + 1)^2(y^3 + 2y)\,dy,\quad u = y^4 + 4y^2 + 1$

9. $\int \sqrt{x}\sin^2(x^{3/2} - 1)\,dx,\quad u = x^{3/2} - 1$

10. $\int \frac{1}{x^2}\cos^2\left(\frac{1}{x}\right)dx,\quad u = -\frac{1}{x}$

11. $\int \csc^2 2\theta \cot 2\theta\,d\theta$

a. Using $u = \cot 2\theta$ **b.** Using $u = \csc 2\theta$

12. $\int \frac{dx}{\sqrt{5x + 8}}$

a. Using $u = 5x + 8$ **b.** Using $u = \sqrt{5x + 8}$

Evaluate the integrals in Exercises 13–54.

13. $\int \sqrt{3-2s}\,ds$

14. $\int (2x+1)^3\,dx$

15. $\int \frac{1}{\sqrt{5s+4}}\,ds$

16. $\int \frac{3\,dx}{(2-x)^2}$

17. $\int \theta\sqrt[4]{1-\theta^2}\,d\theta$

18. $\int \frac{4y\,dy}{\sqrt{2y^2+1}}$

19. $\int \frac{1}{\sqrt{x}\,(1+\sqrt{x})^2}\,dx$

20. $\int \frac{(1+\sqrt{x})^3}{\sqrt{x}}\,dx$

21. $\int \cos(3z+4)\,dz$

22. $\int \tan^2 x \sec^2 x\,dx$

23. $\int \tan x\,dx$

24. $\int \tan^7 \frac{x}{2} \sec^2 \frac{x}{2}\,dx$

25. $\int r^2\left(\frac{r^3}{18}-1\right)^5 dr$

26. $\int r^4\left(7-\frac{r^5}{10}\right)^3 dr$

27. $\int x^{1/2}\sin(x^{3/2}+1)\,dx$

28. $\int x^{1/3}\sin(x^{4/3}-8)\,dx$

29. $\int \frac{\sin(2t+1)}{\cos^2(2t+1)}\,dt$

30. $\int \frac{6\cos t}{(2+\sin t)^3}\,dt$

31. $\int \frac{1}{\theta^2}\sin\frac{1}{\theta}\cos\frac{1}{\theta}\,d\theta$

32. $\int \frac{\sec z \tan z}{\sqrt{\sec z}}\,dz$

33. $\int \frac{1}{t^2}\cos\left(\frac{1}{t}-1\right)dt$

34. $\int \frac{\cos\sqrt{\theta}}{\sqrt{\theta}\sin^2\sqrt{\theta}}\,d\theta$

35. $\int (s^3+2s^2-5s+5)(3s^2+4s-5)\,ds$

36. $\int t^3(1+t^4)^3\,dt$

37. $\int \sqrt{\frac{x-1}{x^5}}\,dx$

38. $\int x^3\sqrt{x^2+1}\,dx$

39. $\int (\cos x)\,e^{\sin x}\,dx$

40. $\int (\sin 2\theta)\,e^{\sin^2\theta}\,d\theta$

41. $\int \frac{1}{\sqrt{xe^{-\sqrt{x}}}}\sec^2(e^{\sqrt{x}}+1)\,dx$

42. $\int \frac{1}{x^2}e^{1/x}\sec(1+e^{1/x})\tan(1+e^{1/x})\,dx$

43. $\int \frac{dx}{x\ln x}$

44. $\int \frac{\ln\sqrt{t}}{t}\,dt$

45. $\int \frac{dz}{1+e^z}$

46. $\int \frac{dx}{x\sqrt{x^4-1}}$

47. $\int \frac{5}{9+4r^2}\,dr$

48. $\int \frac{1}{\sqrt{e^{2\theta}-1}}\,d\theta$

49. $\int \frac{e^{\sin^{-1}x}\,dx}{\sqrt{1-x^2}}$

50. $\int \frac{e^{\cos^{-1}x}\,dx}{\sqrt{1-x^2}}$

51. $\int \frac{(\sin^{-1}x)^2\,dx}{\sqrt{1-x^2}}$

52. $\int \frac{\sqrt{\tan^{-1}x}\,dx}{1+x^2}$

53. $\int \frac{dy}{(\tan^{-1}y)(1+y^2)}$

54. $\int \frac{dy}{(\sin^{-1}y)\sqrt{1-y^2}}$

If you do not know what substitution to make, try reducing the integral step by step, using a trial substitution to simplify the integral a bit and then another to simplify it some more. You will see what we mean if you try the sequences of substitutions in Exercises 55 and 56.

55. $\int \frac{18\tan^2 x\sec^2 x}{(2+\tan^3 x)^2}\,dx$

a. $u=\tan x$, followed by $v=u^3$, then by $w=2+v$

b. $u=\tan^3 x$, followed by $v=2+u$

c. $u=2+\tan^3 x$

56. $\int \sqrt{1+\sin^2(x-1)}\,\sin(x-1)\cos(x-1)\,dx$

a. $u=x-1$, followed by $v=\sin u$, then by $w=1+v^2$

b. $u=\sin(x-1)$, followed by $v=1+u^2$

c. $u=1+\sin^2(x-1)$

Evaluate the integrals in Exercises 57 and 58.

57. $\int \frac{(2r-1)\cos\sqrt{3(2r-1)^2+6}}{\sqrt{3(2r-1)^2+6}}\,dr$

58. $\int \frac{\sin\sqrt{\theta}}{\sqrt{\theta}\cos^3\sqrt{\theta}}\,d\theta$

Solve the initial value problems in Exercises 59–64.

59. $\frac{ds}{dt}=12t(3t^2-1)^3, \quad s(1)=3$

60. $\frac{dy}{dx}=4x(x^2+8)^{-1/3}, \quad y(0)=0$

61. $\frac{ds}{dt}=8\sin^2\left(t+\frac{\pi}{12}\right), \quad s(0)=8$

62. $\frac{dr}{d\theta}=3\cos^2\left(\frac{\pi}{4}-\theta\right), \quad r(0)=\frac{\pi}{8}$

63. $\frac{d^2s}{dt^2}=-4\sin\left(2t-\frac{\pi}{2}\right), \quad s'(0)=100, \quad s(0)=0$

64. $\frac{d^2y}{dx^2}=4\sec^2 2x\tan 2x, \quad y'(0)=4, \quad y(0)=-1$

65. The velocity of a particle moving back and forth on a line is $v=ds/dt=6\sin 2t$ m/sec for all t. If $s=0$ when $t=0$, find the value of s when $t=\pi/2$ sec.

66. The acceleration of a particle moving back and forth on a line is $a=d^2s/dt^2=\pi^2\cos\pi t$ m/sec² for all t. If $s=0$ and $v=8$ m/sec when $t=0$, find s when $t=1$ sec.

67. It looks as if we can integrate $2 \sin x \cos x$ with respect to x in three different ways:

a. $\int 2 \sin x \cos x \, dx = \int 2u \, du$ $\quad u = \sin x,$

$= u^2 + C_1 = \sin^2 x + C_1$

b. $\int 2 \sin x \cos x \, dx = \int -2u \, du$ $\quad u = \cos x,$

$= -u^2 + C_2 = -\cos^2 x + C_2$

c. $\int 2 \sin x \cos x \, dx = \int \sin 2x \, dx$ $\quad 2 \sin x \cos x = \sin 2x$

$= -\dfrac{\cos 2x}{2} + C_3.$

Can all three integrations be correct? Give reasons for your answer.

68. The substitution $u = \tan x$ gives

$$\int \sec^2 x \tan x \, dx = \int u \, du = \frac{u^2}{2} + C = \frac{\tan^2 x}{2} + C.$$

The substitution $u = \sec x$ gives

$$\int \sec^2 x \tan x \, dx = \int u \, du = \frac{u^2}{2} + C = \frac{\sec^2 x}{2} + C.$$

Can both integrations be correct? Give reasons for your answer.

5.6 Substitution and Area Between Curves

There are two methods for evaluating a definite integral by substitution. The first method is to find an antiderivative using substitution, and then to evaluate the definite integral by applying the Fundamental Theorem. The second method extends the process of substitution directly to *definite* integrals by changing the limits of integration. We apply the new formula introduced here to the problem of computing the area between two curves.

Substitution Formula

The following formula shows how the limits of integration change when the variable of integration is changed by substitution.

THEOREM 6—Substitution in Definite Integrals If g' is continuous on the interval $[a, b]$ and f is continuous on the range of g, then

$$\int_a^b f(g(x)) \cdot g'(x) \, dx = \int_{g(a)}^{g(b)} f(u) \, du$$

Proof Let F denote any antiderivative of f. Then,

$$\begin{aligned} \int_a^b f(g(x)) \cdot g'(x) \, dx &= F(g(x)) \Big]_{x=a}^{x=b} && \frac{d}{dx} F(g(x)) = F'(g(x))g'(x) = f(g(x))g'(x) \\ &= F(g(b)) - F(g(a)) \\ &= F(u) \Big]_{u=g(a)}^{u=g(b)} \\ &= \int_{g(a)}^{g(b)} f(u) \, du. && \text{Fundamental Theorem, Part 2} \end{aligned}$$

■

To use the formula, make the same u-substitution $u = g(x)$ and $du = g'(x) \, dx$ you would use to evaluate the corresponding indefinite integral. Then integrate the transformed integral with respect to u from the value $g(a)$ (the value of u at $x = a$) to the value $g(b)$ (the value of u at $x = b$).

EXAMPLE 1 Evaluate $\int_{-1}^{1} 3x^2\sqrt{x^3+1}\,dx$.

Solution We have two choices.

Method 1: Transform the integral and evaluate the transformed integral with the transformed limits given in Theorem 6.

$$\int_{-1}^{1} 3x^2\sqrt{x^3+1}\,dx \qquad \begin{array}{l}\text{Let } u = x^3+1,\ du = 3x^2\,dx.\\ \text{When } x=-1,\ u=(-1)^3+1=0.\\ \text{When } x=1,\ u=(1)^3+1=2.\end{array}$$

$$= \int_0^2 \sqrt{u}\,du$$

$$= \frac{2}{3}u^{3/2}\Big]_0^2 \qquad \text{Evaluate the new definite integral.}$$

$$= \frac{2}{3}\left[2^{3/2}-0^{3/2}\right] = \frac{2}{3}\left[2\sqrt{2}\right] = \frac{4\sqrt{2}}{3}$$

Method 2: Transform the integral as an indefinite integral, integrate, change back to x, and use the original x-limits.

$$\int 3x^2\sqrt{x^3+1}\,dx = \int \sqrt{u}\,du \qquad \text{Let } u = x^3+1,\ du = 3x^2\,dx.$$

$$= \frac{2}{3}u^{3/2}+C \qquad \text{Integrate with respect to } u.$$

$$= \frac{2}{3}(x^3+1)^{3/2}+C \qquad \text{Replace } u \text{ by } x^3+1.$$

$$\int_{-1}^{1} 3x^2\sqrt{x^3+1}\,dx = \frac{2}{3}(x^3+1)^{3/2}\Big]_{-1}^{1} \qquad \text{Use the integral just found, with limits of integration for } x.$$

$$= \frac{2}{3}\left[((1)^3+1)^{3/2}-((-1)^3+1)^{3/2}\right]$$

$$= \frac{2}{3}\left[2^{3/2}-0^{3/2}\right] = \frac{2}{3}\left[2\sqrt{2}\right] = \frac{4\sqrt{2}}{3}$$

■

Which method is better—evaluating the transformed definite integral with transformed limits using Theorem 6, or transforming the integral, integrating, and transforming back to use the original limits of integration? In Example 1, the first method seems easier, but that is not always the case. Generally, it is best to know both methods and to use whichever one seems better at the time.

EXAMPLE 2

(a) $$\int_0^{\ln 2} e^{3x}\,dx = \int_0^{\ln 8} e^u\cdot\frac{1}{3}\,du \qquad \begin{array}{l}u=3x,\ \frac{1}{3}\,du = dx,\ u(0)=0,\\ u(\ln 2) = 3\ln 2 = \ln 2^3 = \ln 8\end{array}$$

$$= \frac{1}{3}\int_0^{\ln 8} e^u\,du$$

$$= \frac{1}{3}e^u\Big]_0^{\ln 8}$$

$$= \frac{1}{3}[8-1] = \frac{7}{3}$$

$$\textbf{(b)} \int_{-\pi/4}^{\pi/4} \tan x\, dx = \int_{-\pi/4}^{\pi/4} \frac{\sin x}{\cos x}\, dx$$

$$= -\int_{\sqrt{2}/2}^{\sqrt{2}/2} \frac{du}{u}$$

$u = \cos x$, $du = -\sin x\, dx$
When $x = -\pi/4$, $u = \sqrt{2}/2$,
When $x = \pi/4$, $u = \sqrt{2}/2$

$$= -\ln |u| \Big]_{\sqrt{2}/2}^{\sqrt{2}/2} = 0$$

Integrate, zero width interval ■

Definite Integrals of Symmetric Functions

The Substitution Formula in Theorem 6 simplifies the calculation of definite integrals of even and odd functions (Section 1.1) over a symmetric interval $[-a, a]$ (Figure 5.22). The following theorem explains the zero integral in Example 2b.

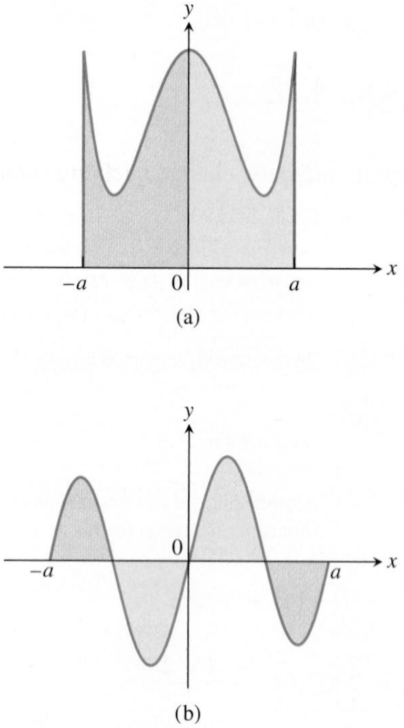

FIGURE 5.22 (a) f even, $\int_{-a}^{a} f(x)\, dx = 2\int_{0}^{a} f(x)\, dx$
(b) f odd, $\int_{-a}^{a} f(x)\, dx = 0$

THEOREM 7 Let f be continuous on the symmetric interval $[-a, a]$.

(a) If f is even, then $\displaystyle\int_{-a}^{a} f(x)\, dx = 2\int_{0}^{a} f(x)\, dx$.

(b) If f is odd, then $\displaystyle\int_{-a}^{a} f(x)\, dx = 0$.

Proof of Part (a)

$$\int_{-a}^{a} f(x)\, dx = \int_{-a}^{0} f(x)\, dx + \int_{0}^{a} f(x)\, dx$$

Additivity Rule for Definite Integrals

$$= -\int_{0}^{-a} f(x)\, dx + \int_{0}^{a} f(x)\, dx$$

Order of Integration Rule

$$= -\int_{0}^{a} f(-u)(-du) + \int_{0}^{a} f(x)\, dx$$

Let $u = -x$, $du = -dx$.
When $x = 0$, $u = 0$.
When $x = -a$, $u = a$.

$$= \int_{0}^{a} f(-u)\, du + \int_{0}^{a} f(x)\, dx$$

$$= \int_{0}^{a} f(u)\, du + \int_{0}^{a} f(x)\, dx$$

f is even, so $f(-u) = f(u)$.

$$= 2\int_{0}^{a} f(x)\, dx$$

The proof of part (b) is entirely similar and you are asked to give it in Exercise 114. ■

The assertions of Theorem 7 remain true when f is an integrable function (rather than having the stronger property of being continuous), but the proof is more difficult and best left to a more advanced course.

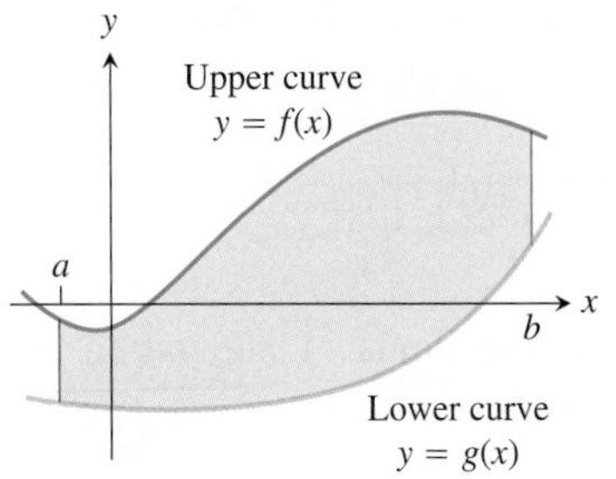

FIGURE 5.23 The region between the curves $y = f(x)$ and $y = g(x)$ and the lines $x = a$ and $x = b$.

EXAMPLE 3 Evaluate $\int_{-2}^{2} (x^4 - 4x^2 + 6)\, dx$.

Solution Since $f(x) = x^4 - 4x^2 + 6$ satisfies $f(-x) = f(x)$, it is even on the symmetric interval $[-2, 2]$, so

$$\begin{aligned}\int_{-2}^{2} (x^4 - 4x^2 + 6)\, dx &= 2\int_{0}^{2} (x^4 - 4x^2 + 6)\, dx\\ &= 2\left[\frac{x^5}{5} - \frac{4}{3}x^3 + 6x\right]_0^2\\ &= 2\left(\frac{32}{5} - \frac{32}{3} + 12\right) = \frac{232}{15}.\end{aligned}$$ ■

Areas Between Curves

Suppose we want to find the area of a region that is bounded above by the curve $y = f(x)$, below by the curve $y = g(x)$, and on the left and right by the lines $x = a$ and $x = b$ (Figure 5.23). The region might accidentally have a shape whose area we could find with geometry, but if f and g are arbitrary continuous functions, we usually have to find the area with an integral.

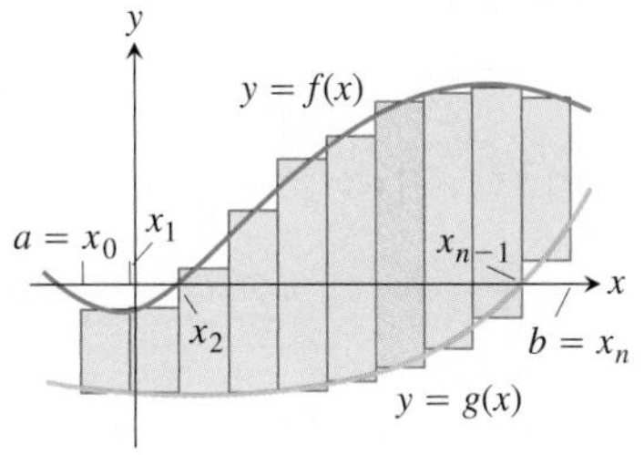

FIGURE 5.24 We approximate the region with rectangles perpendicular to the x-axis.

To see what the integral should be, we first approximate the region with n vertical rectangles based on a partition $P = \{x_0, x_1, \ldots, x_n\}$ of $[a, b]$ (Figure 5.24). The area of the kth rectangle (Figure 5.25) is

$$\Delta A_k = \text{height} \times \text{width} = [f(c_k) - g(c_k)]\, \Delta x_k.$$

We then approximate the area of the region by adding the areas of the n rectangles:

$$A \approx \sum_{k=1}^{n} \Delta A_k = \sum_{k=1}^{n} [f(c_k) - g(c_k)]\, \Delta x_k. \qquad \text{Riemann sum}$$

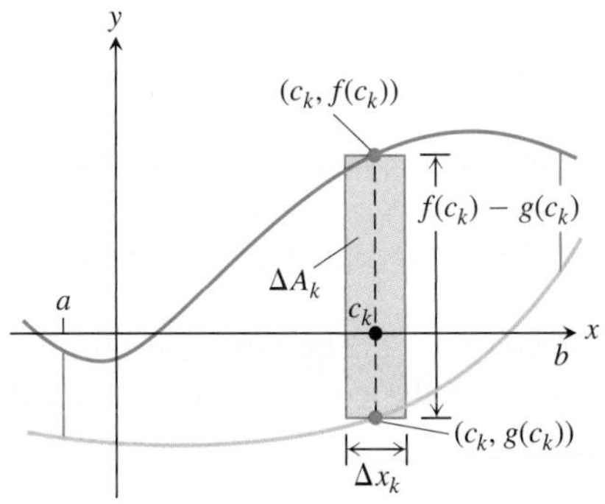

FIGURE 5.25 The area ΔA_k of the kth rectangle is the product of its height, $f(c_k) - g(c_k)$, and its width, Δx_k.

As $\|P\| \to 0$, the sums on the right approach the limit $\int_a^b [f(x) - g(x)]\, dx$ because f and g are continuous. We take the area of the region to be the value of this integral. That is,

$$A = \lim_{\|P\|\to 0} \sum_{k=1}^{n} [f(c_k) - g(c_k)]\, \Delta x_k = \int_a^b [f(x) - g(x)]\, dx.$$

DEFINITION If f and g are continuous with $f(x) \geq g(x)$ throughout $[a, b]$, then the **area of the region between the curves $y = f(x)$ and $y = g(x)$ from a to b** is the integral of $(f - g)$ from a to b:

$$A = \int_a^b [f(x) - g(x)]\, dx.$$

When applying this definition it is helpful to graph the curves. The graph reveals which curve is the upper curve f and which is the lower curve g. It also helps you find the limits of integration if they are not given. You may need to find where the curves intersect to determine the limits of integration, and this may involve solving the equation $f(x) = g(x)$

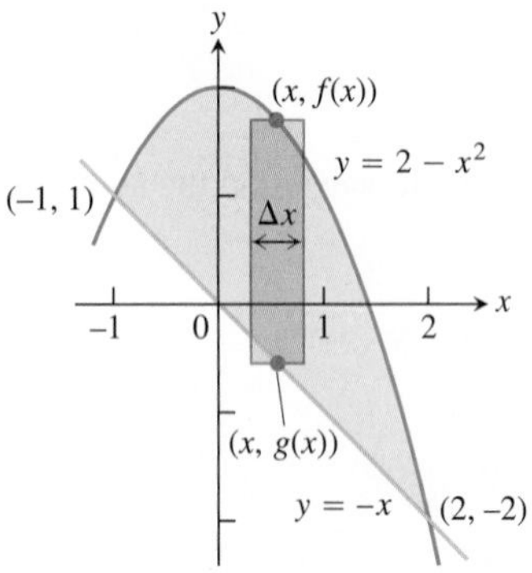

FIGURE 5.26 The region in Example 4 with a typical approximating rectangle.

for values of x. Then you can integrate the function $f - g$ for the area between the intersections.

EXAMPLE 4 Find the area of the region enclosed by the parabola $y = 2 - x^2$ and the line $y = -x$.

Solution First we sketch the two curves (Figure 5.26). The limits of integration are found by solving $y = 2 - x^2$ and $y = -x$ simultaneously for x.

$$\begin{aligned} 2 - x^2 &= -x && \text{Equate } f(x) \text{ and } g(x). \\ x^2 - x - 2 &= 0 && \text{Rewrite.} \\ (x + 1)(x - 2) &= 0 && \text{Factor.} \\ x = -1, \quad x &= 2. && \text{Solve.} \end{aligned}$$

The region runs from $x = -1$ to $x = 2$. The limits of integration are $a = -1, b = 2$.

The area between the curves is

$$\begin{aligned} A &= \int_a^b [f(x) - g(x)]\,dx = \int_{-1}^{2} [(2 - x^2) - (-x)]\,dx \\ &= \int_{-1}^{2} (2 + x - x^2)\,dx = \left[2x + \frac{x^2}{2} - \frac{x^3}{3}\right]_{-1}^{2} \\ &= \left(4 + \frac{4}{2} - \frac{8}{3}\right) - \left(-2 + \frac{1}{2} + \frac{1}{3}\right) = \frac{9}{2} \end{aligned}$$

■

If the formula for a bounding curve changes at one or more points, we subdivide the region into subregions that correspond to the formula changes and apply the formula for the area between curves to each subregion.

HISTORICAL BIOGRAPHY

Richard Dedekind
(1831–1916)

EXAMPLE 5 Find the area of the region in the first quadrant that is bounded above by $y = \sqrt{x}$ and below by the x-axis and the line $y = x - 2$.

Solution The sketch (Figure 5.27) shows that the region's upper boundary is the graph of $f(x) = \sqrt{x}$. The lower boundary changes from $g(x) = 0$ for $0 \le x \le 2$ to $g(x) = x - 2$ for $2 \le x \le 4$ (both formulas agree at $x = 2$). We subdivide the region at $x = 2$ into subregions A and B, shown in Figure 5.27.

The limits of integration for region A are $a = 0$ and $b = 2$. The left-hand limit for region B is $a = 2$. To find the right-hand limit, we solve the equations $y = \sqrt{x}$ and $y = x - 2$ simultaneously for x:

$$\begin{aligned} \sqrt{x} &= x - 2 && \text{Equate } f(x) \text{ and } g(x). \\ x &= (x - 2)^2 = x^2 - 4x + 4 && \text{Square both sides.} \\ x^2 - 5x + 4 &= 0 && \text{Rewrite.} \\ (x - 1)(x - 4) &= 0 && \text{Factor.} \\ x = 1, \quad x &= 4. && \text{Solve.} \end{aligned}$$

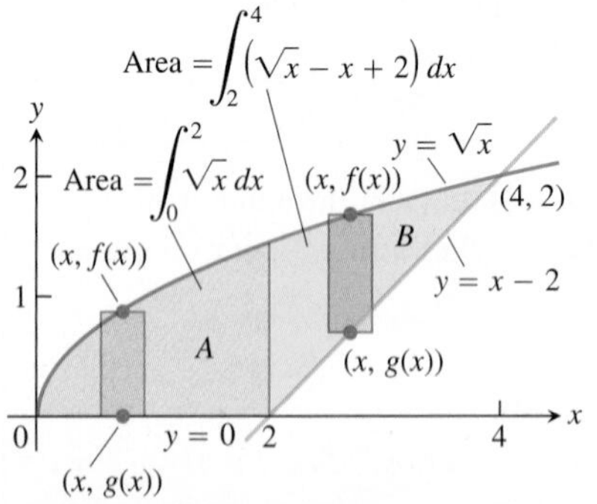

FIGURE 5.27 When the formula for a bounding curve changes, the area integral changes to become the sum of integrals to match, one integral for each of the shaded regions shown here for Example 5.

Only the value $x = 4$ satisfies the equation $\sqrt{x} = x - 2$. The value $x = 1$ is an extraneous root introduced by squaring. The right-hand limit is $b = 4$.

$$\begin{aligned} &\text{For } 0 \le x \le 2: && f(x) - g(x) = \sqrt{x} - 0 = \sqrt{x} \\ &\text{For } 2 \le x \le 4: && f(x) - g(x) = \sqrt{x} - (x - 2) = \sqrt{x} - x + 2 \end{aligned}$$

We add the area of subregions A and B to find the total area:

$$\text{Total area} = \underbrace{\int_0^2 \sqrt{x}\,dx}_{\text{area of } A} + \underbrace{\int_2^4 (\sqrt{x} - x + 2)\,dx}_{\text{area of } B}$$

$$= \left[\frac{2}{3}x^{3/2}\right]_0^2 + \left[\frac{2}{3}x^{3/2} - \frac{x^2}{2} + 2x\right]_2^4$$

$$= \frac{2}{3}(2)^{3/2} - 0 + \left(\frac{2}{3}(4)^{3/2} - 8 + 8\right) - \left(\frac{2}{3}(2)^{3/2} - 2 + 4\right)$$

$$= \frac{2}{3}(8) - 2 = \frac{10}{3}.$$

■

Integration with Respect to *y*

If a region's bounding curves are described by functions of y, the approximating rectangles are horizontal instead of vertical and the basic formula has y in place of x.

For regions like these

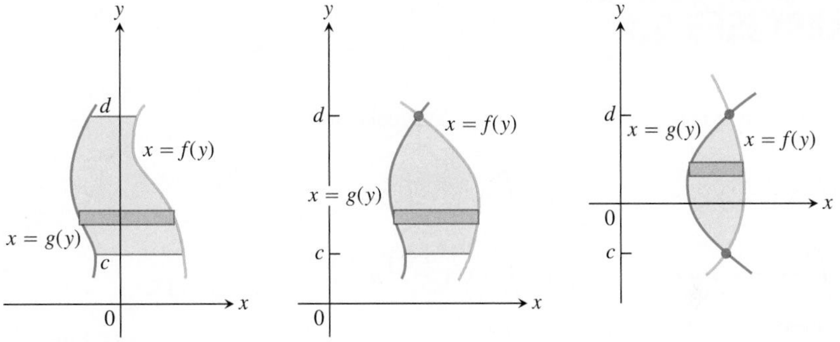

use the formula

$$A = \int_c^d [f(y) - g(y)]\,dy.$$

In this equation f always denotes the right-hand curve and g the left-hand curve, so $f(y) - g(y)$ is nonnegative.

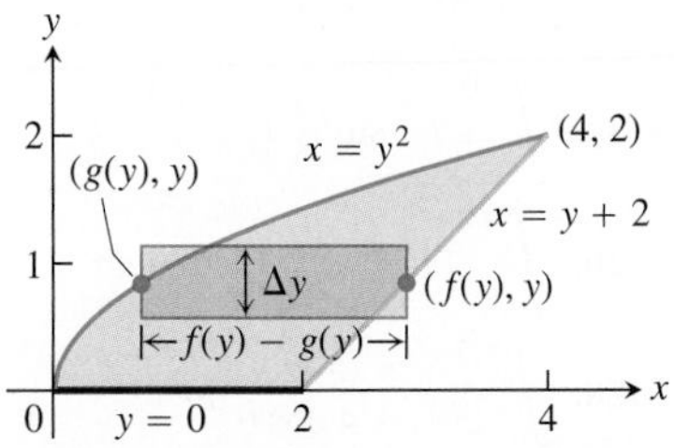

FIGURE 5.28 It takes two integrations to find the area of this region if we integrate with respect to x. It takes only one if we integrate with respect to y (Example 6).

EXAMPLE 6 Find the area of the region in Example 5 by integrating with respect to y.

Solution We first sketch the region and a typical *horizontal* rectangle based on a partition of an interval of y-values (Figure 5.28). The region's right-hand boundary is the line $x = y + 2$, so $f(y) = y + 2$. The left-hand boundary is the curve $x = y^2$, so $g(y) = y^2$. The lower limit of integration is $y = 0$. We find the upper limit by solving $x = y + 2$ and $x = y^2$ simultaneously for y:

$y + 2 = y^2$	Equate $f(y) = y + 2$ and $g(y) = y^2$.
$y^2 - y - 2 = 0$	Rewrite.
$(y + 1)(y - 2) = 0$	Factor.
$y = -1, \quad y = 2$	Solve.

The upper limit of integration is $b = 2$. (The value $y = -1$ gives a point of intersection *below* the x-axis.)

The area of the region is

$$A = \int_a^b [f(y) - g(y)]\,dy = \int_0^2 [y + 2 - y^2]\,dy$$
$$= \int_0^2 [2 + y - y^2]\,dy$$
$$= \left[2y + \frac{y^2}{2} - \frac{y^3}{3}\right]_0^2$$
$$= 4 + \frac{4}{2} - \frac{8}{3} = \frac{10}{3}.$$

This is the result of Example 5, found with less work. ■

EXERCISES 5.6

Use the Substitution Formula in Theorem 6 to evaluate the integrals in Exercises 1–46.

1. a. $\int_0^3 \sqrt{y+1}\,dy$ b. $\int_{-1}^0 \sqrt{y+1}\,dy$
2. a. $\int_0^1 r\sqrt{1-r^2}\,dr$ b. $\int_{-1}^1 r\sqrt{1-r^2}\,dr$
3. a. $\int_0^{\pi/4} \tan x \sec^2 x\,dx$ b. $\int_{-\pi/4}^0 \tan x \sec^2 x\,dx$
4. a. $\int_0^{\pi} 3\cos^2 x \sin x\,dx$ b. $\int_{2\pi}^{3\pi} 3\cos^2 x \sin x\,dx$
5. a. $\int_0^1 t^3(1+t^4)^3\,dt$ b. $\int_{-1}^1 t^3(1+t^4)^3\,dt$
6. a. $\int_0^{\sqrt{7}} t(t^2+1)^{1/3}\,dt$ b. $\int_{-\sqrt{7}}^0 t(t^2+1)^{1/3}\,dt$
7. a. $\int_{-1}^1 \frac{5r}{(4+r^2)^2}\,dr$ b. $\int_0^1 \frac{5r}{(4+r^2)^2}\,dr$
8. a. $\int_0^1 \frac{10\sqrt{v}}{(1+v^{3/2})^2}\,dv$ b. $\int_1^4 \frac{10\sqrt{v}}{(1+v^{3/2})^2}\,dv$
9. a. $\int_0^{\sqrt{3}} \frac{4x}{\sqrt{x^2+1}}\,dx$ b. $\int_{-\sqrt{3}}^{\sqrt{3}} \frac{4x}{\sqrt{x^2+1}}\,dx$
10. a. $\int_0^1 \frac{x^3}{\sqrt{x^4+9}}\,dx$ b. $\int_{-1}^0 \frac{x^3}{\sqrt{x^4+9}}\,dx$
11. a. $\int_0^{\pi/6} (1-\cos 3t)\sin 3t\,dt$ b. $\int_{\pi/6}^{\pi/3} (1-\cos 3t)\sin 3t\,dt$
12. a. $\int_{-\pi/2}^0 \left(2+\tan\frac{t}{2}\right)\sec^2\frac{t}{2}\,dt$ b. $\int_{-\pi/2}^{\pi/2} \left(2+\tan\frac{t}{2}\right)\sec^2\frac{t}{2}\,dt$
13. a. $\int_0^{2\pi} \frac{\cos z}{\sqrt{4+3\sin z}}\,dz$ b. $\int_{-\pi}^{\pi} \frac{\cos z}{\sqrt{4+3\sin z}}\,dz$
14. a. $\int_{-\pi/2}^0 \frac{\sin w}{(3+2\cos w)^2}\,dw$ b. $\int_0^{\pi/2} \frac{\sin w}{(3+2\cos w)^2}\,dw$
15. $\int_0^1 \sqrt{t^5+2t}\,(5t^4+2)\,dt$
16. $\int_1^4 \frac{dy}{2\sqrt{y}\,(1+\sqrt{y})^2}$
17. $\int_0^{\pi/6} \cos^{-3} 2\theta \sin 2\theta\,d\theta$
18. $\int_{\pi}^{3\pi/2} \cot^5\left(\frac{\theta}{6}\right)\sec^2\left(\frac{\theta}{6}\right)d\theta$
19. $\int_0^{\pi} 5(5-4\cos t)^{1/4}\sin t\,dt$
20. $\int_0^{\pi/4} (1-\sin 2t)^{3/2}\cos 2t\,dt$
21. $\int_0^1 (4y-y^2+4y^3+1)^{-2/3}(12y^2-2y+4)\,dy$
22. $\int_0^1 (y^3+6y^2-12y+9)^{-1/2}(y^2+4y-4)\,dy$
23. $\int_0^{\sqrt[3]{\pi^2}} \sqrt{\theta}\cos^2(\theta^{3/2})\,d\theta$
24. $\int_{-1}^{-1/2} t^{-2}\sin^2\left(1+\frac{1}{t}\right)dt$
25. $\int_0^{\pi/4} (1+e^{\tan\theta})\sec^2\theta\,d\theta$
26. $\int_{\pi/4}^{\pi/2} (1+e^{\cot\theta})\csc^2\theta\,d\theta$
27. $\int_0^{\pi} \frac{\sin t}{2-\cos t}\,dt$
28. $\int_0^{\pi/3} \frac{4\sin\theta}{1-4\cos\theta}\,d\theta$
29. $\int_1^2 \frac{2\ln x}{x}\,dx$
30. $\int_2^4 \frac{dx}{x\ln x}$
31. $\int_2^4 \frac{dx}{x(\ln x)^2}$
32. $\int_2^{16} \frac{dx}{2x\sqrt{\ln x}}$
33. $\int_0^{\pi/2} \tan\frac{x}{2}\,dx$
34. $\int_{\pi/4}^{\pi/2} \cot t\,dt$

35. $\int_{\pi/2}^{\pi} 2 \cot \frac{\theta}{3}\, d\theta$

36. $\int_{0}^{\pi/12} 6 \tan 3x\, dx$

37. $\int_{-\pi/2}^{\pi/2} \frac{2 \cos \theta\, d\theta}{1 + (\sin \theta)^2}$

38. $\int_{\pi/6}^{\pi/4} \frac{\csc^2 x\, dx}{1 + (\cot x)^2}$

39. $\int_{0}^{\ln \sqrt{3}} \frac{e^x\, dx}{1 + e^{2x}}$

40. $\int_{1}^{e^{\pi/4}} \frac{4\, dt}{t(1 + \ln^2 t)}$

41. $\int_{0}^{1} \frac{4\, ds}{\sqrt{4 - s^2}}$

42. $\int_{0}^{3\sqrt{2}/4} \frac{ds}{\sqrt{9 - 4s^2}}$

43. $\int_{\sqrt{2}}^{2} \frac{\sec^2 (\sec^{-1} x)\, dx}{x\sqrt{x^2 - 1}}$

44. $\int_{2/\sqrt{3}}^{2} \frac{\cos (\sec^{-1} x)\, dx}{x\sqrt{x^2 - 1}}$

45. $\int_{-1}^{-\sqrt{2}/2} \frac{dy}{y\sqrt{4y^2 - 1}}$

46. $\int_{-2/3}^{-\sqrt{2}/3} \frac{dy}{y\sqrt{9y^2 - 1}}$

Find the total areas of the shaded regions in Exercises 47–62.

47.

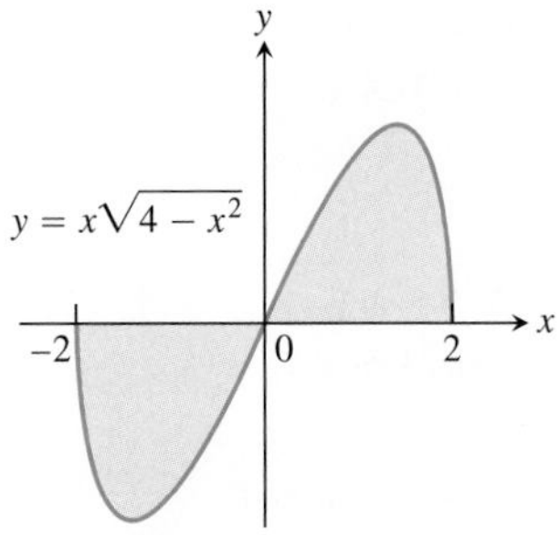

48.

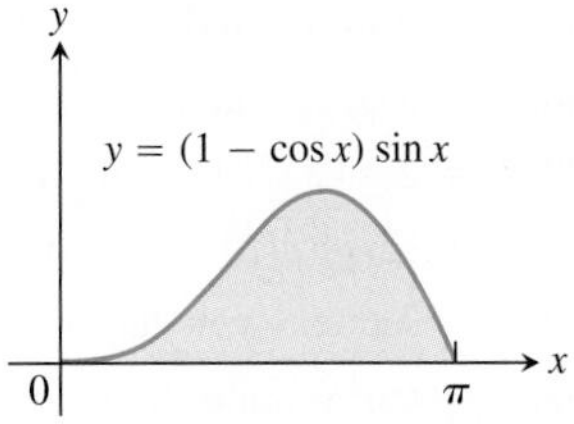

49.

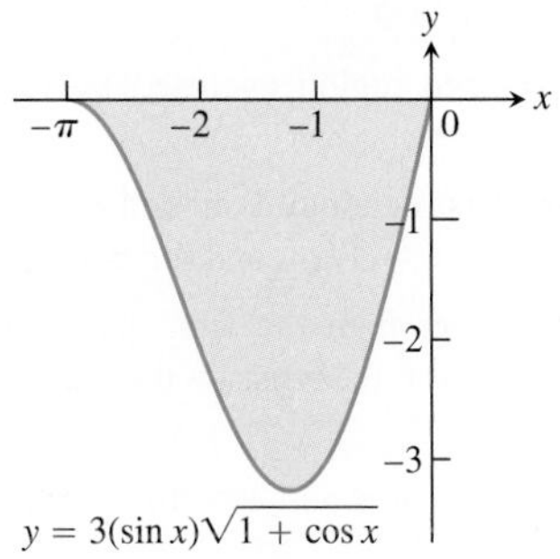

50.

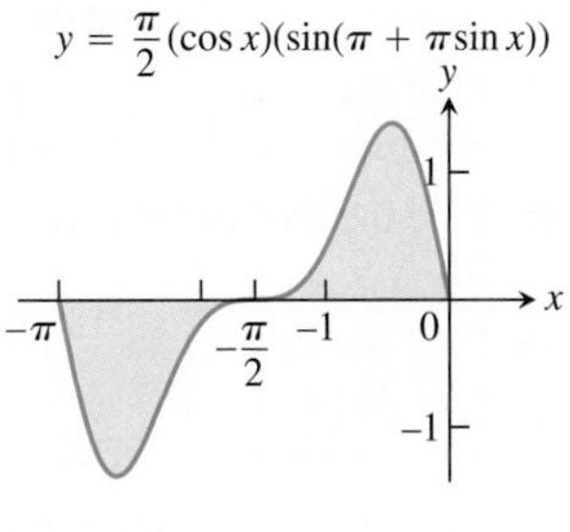

51.

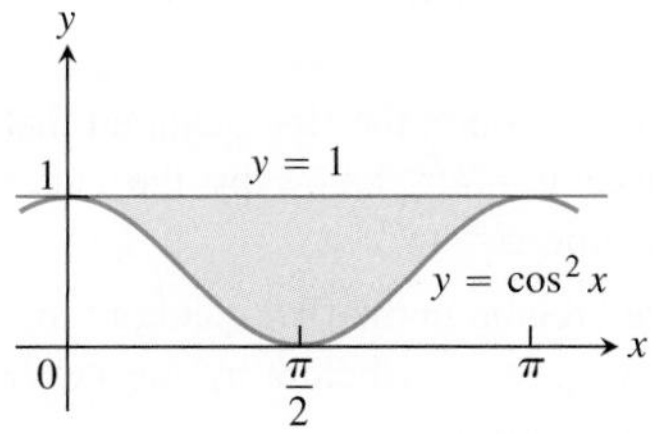

52.

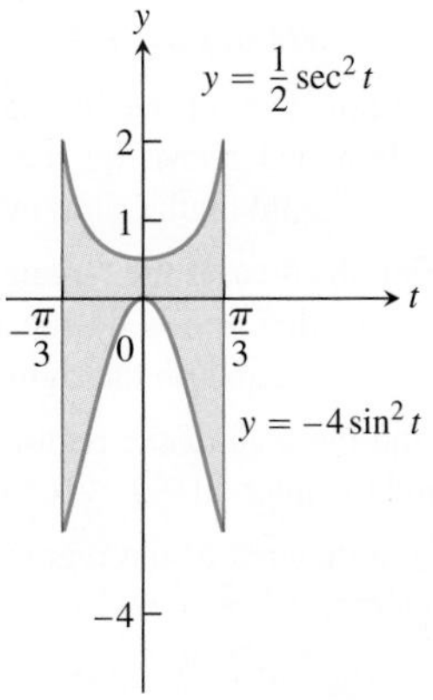

53.

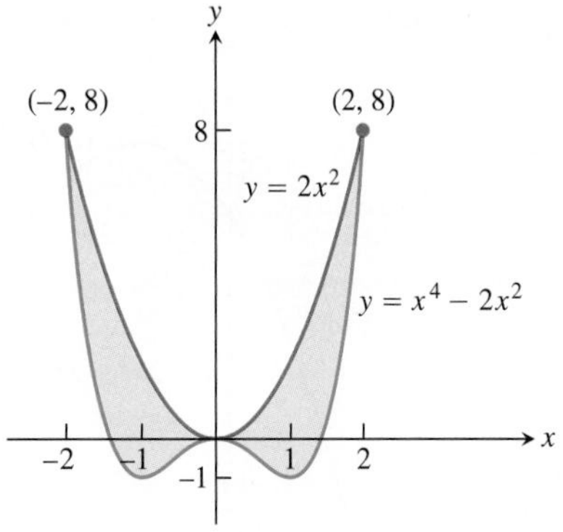

NOT TO SCALE

54.

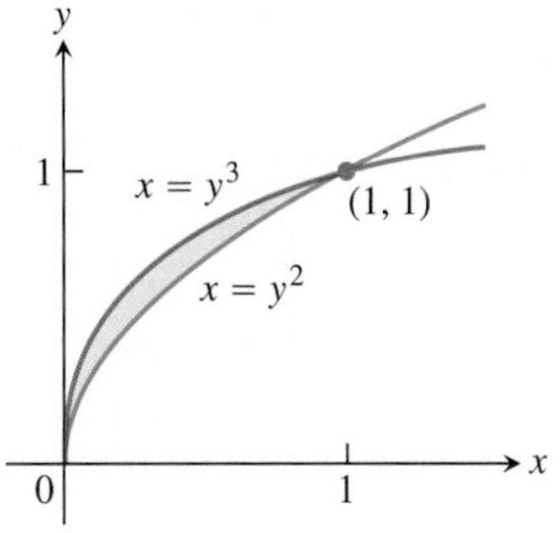

55.

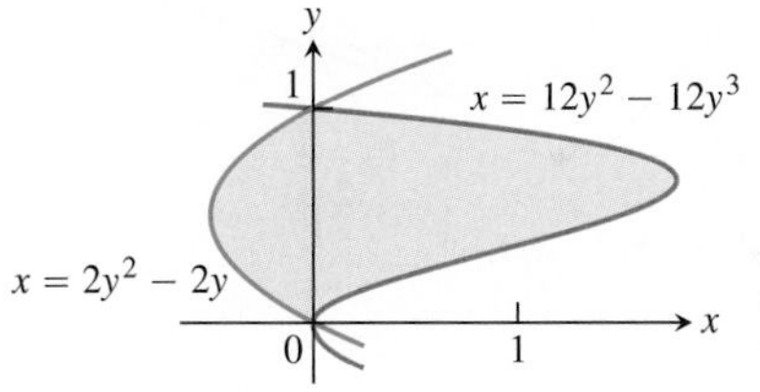

56.

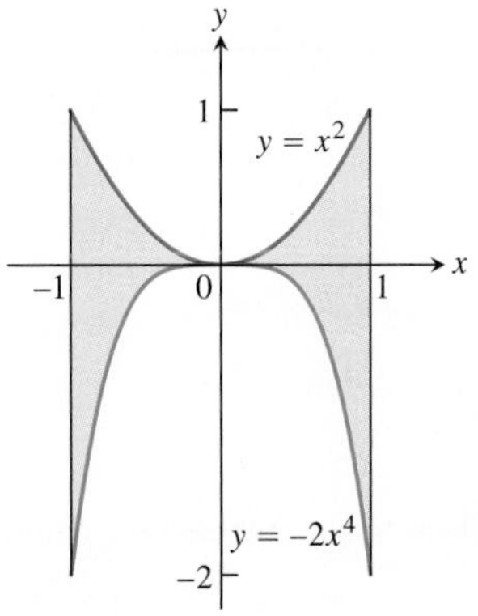

57.

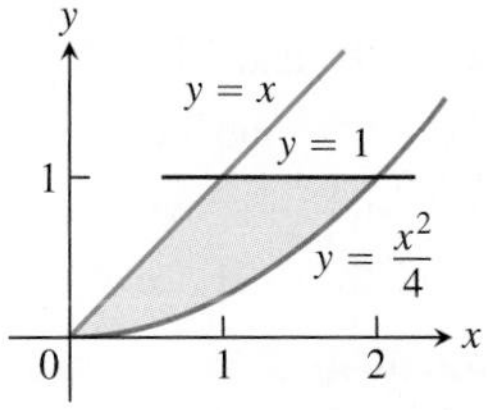

58.

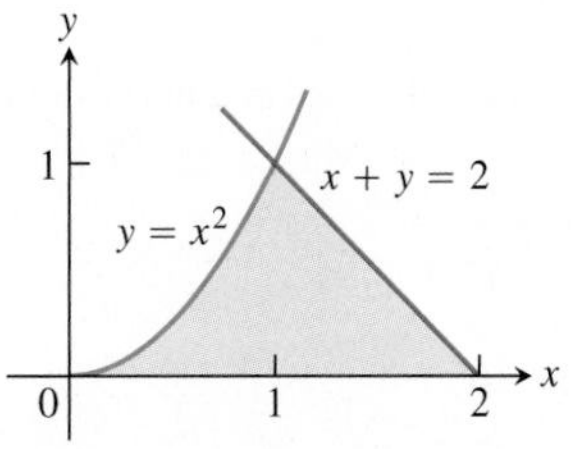

59.

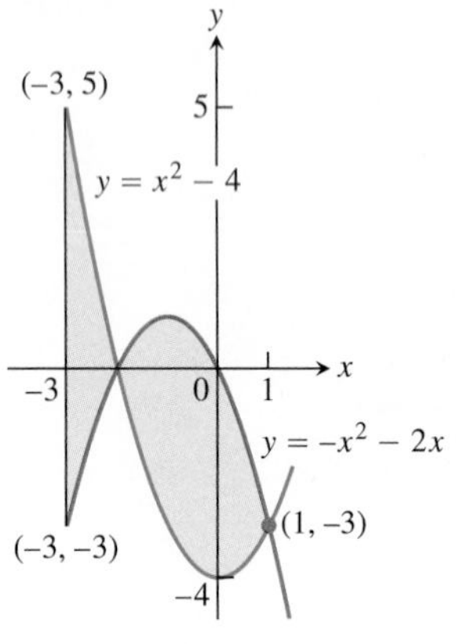

60.

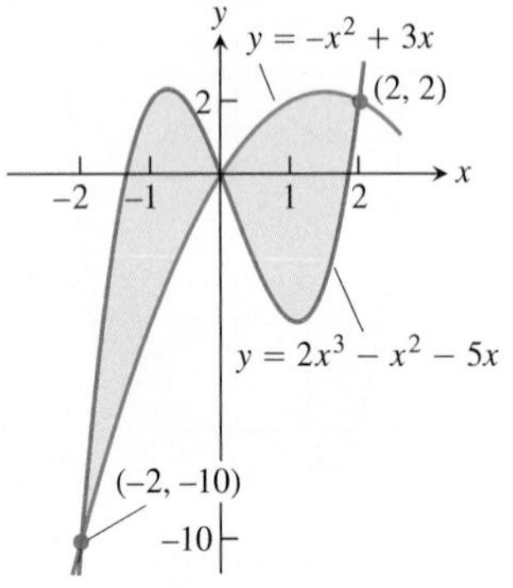

61.

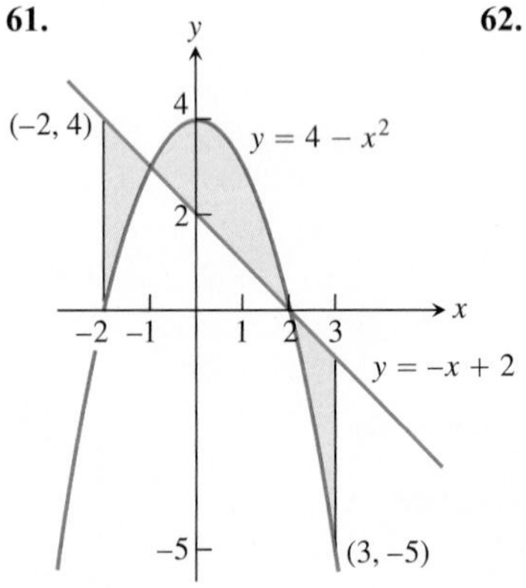

62.

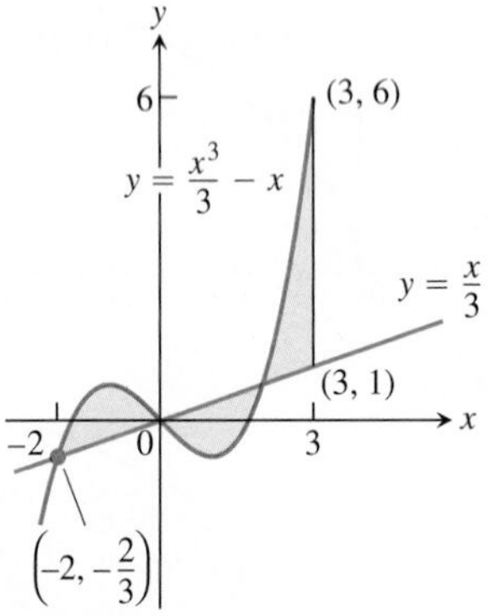

Find the areas of the regions enclosed by the lines and curves in Exercises 63–72.

63. $y = x^2 - 2$ and $y = 2$

64. $y = 2x - x^2$ and $y = -3$

65. $y = x^4$ and $y = 8x$

66. $y = x^2 - 2x$ and $y = x$

67. $y = x^2$ and $y = -x^2 + 4x$

68. $y = 7 - 2x^2$ and $y = x^2 + 4$

69. $y = x^4 - 4x^2 + 4$ and $y = x^2$

70. $y = x\sqrt{a^2 - x^2}$, $a > 0$, and $y = 0$

71. $y = \sqrt{|x|}$ and $5y = x + 6$ (How many intersection points are there?)

72. $y = |x^2 - 4|$ and $y = (x^2/2) + 4$

Find the areas of the regions enclosed by the lines and curves in Exercises 73–80.

73. $x = 2y^2$, $x = 0$, and $y = 3$

74. $x = y^2$ and $x = y + 2$

75. $y^2 - 4x = 4$ and $4x - y = 16$

76. $x - y^2 = 0$ and $x + 2y^2 = 3$

77. $x + y^2 = 0$ and $x + 3y^2 = 2$

78. $x - y^{2/3} = 0$ and $x + y^4 = 2$

79. $x = y^2 - 1$ and $x = |y|\sqrt{1 - y^2}$

80. $x = y^3 - y^2$ and $x = 2y$

Find the areas of the regions enclosed by the curves in Exercises 81–84.

81. $4x^2 + y = 4$ and $x^4 - y = 1$

82. $x^3 - y = 0$ and $3x^2 - y = 4$

83. $x + 4y^2 = 4$ and $x + y^4 = 1$, for $x \geq 0$

84. $x + y^2 = 3$ and $4x + y^2 = 0$

Find the areas of the regions enclosed by the lines and curves in Exercises 85–92.

85. $y = 2\sin x$ and $y = \sin 2x$, $0 \leq x \leq \pi$

86. $y = 8\cos x$ and $y = \sec^2 x$, $-\pi/3 \leq x \leq \pi/3$

87. $y = \cos(\pi x/2)$ and $y = 1 - x^2$

88. $y = \sin(\pi x/2)$ and $y = x$

89. $y = \sec^2 x$, $y = \tan^2 x$, $x = -\pi/4$, and $x = \pi/4$

90. $x = \tan^2 y$ and $x = -\tan^2 y$, $-\pi/4 \leq y \leq \pi/4$

91. $x = 3\sin y\sqrt{\cos y}$ and $x = 0$, $0 \leq y \leq \pi/2$

92. $y = \sec^2(\pi x/3)$ and $y = x^{1/3}$, $-1 \leq x \leq 1$

93. Find the area of the propeller-shaped region enclosed by the curve $x - y^3 = 0$ and the line $x - y = 0$.

94. Find the area of the propeller-shaped region enclosed by the curves $x - y^{1/3} = 0$ and $x - y^{1/5} = 0$.

95. Find the area of the region in the first quadrant bounded by the line $y = x$, the line $x = 2$, the curve $y = 1/x^2$, and the x-axis.

96. Find the area of the "triangular" region in the first quadrant bounded on the left by the y-axis and on the right by the curves $y = \sin x$ and $y = \cos x$.

97. Find the area between the curves $y = \ln x$ and $y = \ln 2x$ from $x = 1$ to $x = 5$.

98. Find the area between the curve $y = \tan x$ and the x-axis from $x = -\pi/4$ to $x = \pi/3$.

99. Find the area of the "triangular" region in the first quadrant that is bounded above by the curve $y = e^{2x}$, below by the curve $y = e^x$, and on the right by the line $x = \ln 3$.

100. Find the area of the "triangular" region in the first quadrant that is bounded above by the curve $y = e^{x/2}$, below by the curve $y = e^{-x/2}$, and on the right by the line $x = 2\ln 2$.

101. Find the area of the region between the curve $y = 2x/(1 + x^2)$ and the interval $-2 \leq x \leq 2$ of the x-axis.

102. Find the area of the region between the curve $y = 2^{1-x}$ and the interval $-1 \leq x \leq 1$ of the x-axis.

103. The region bounded below by the parabola $y = x^2$ and above by the line $y = 4$ is to be partitioned into two subsections of equal area by cutting across it with the horizontal line $y = c$.

a. Sketch the region and draw a line $y = c$ across it that looks about right. In terms of c, what are the coordinates of the points where the line and parabola intersect? Add them to your figure.

b. Find c by integrating with respect to y. (This puts c in the limits of integration.)

c. Find c by integrating with respect to x. (This puts c into the integrand as well.)

104. Find the area of the region between the curve $y = 3 - x^2$ and the line $y = -1$ by integrating with respect to **a.** x, **b.** y.

105. Find the area of the region in the first quadrant bounded on the left by the y-axis, below by the line $y = x/4$, above left by the curve $y = 1 + \sqrt{x}$, and above right by the curve $y = 2/\sqrt{x}$.

106. Find the area of the region in the first quadrant bounded on the left by the y-axis, below by the curve $x = 2\sqrt{y}$, above left by the curve $x = (y - 1)^2$, and above right by the line $x = 3 - y$.

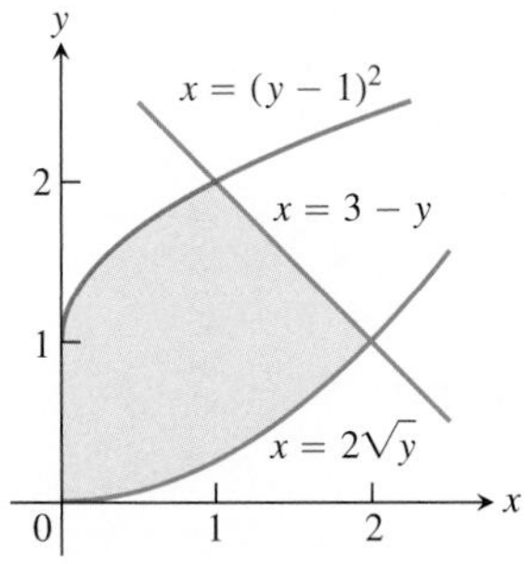

107. The figure here shows triangle AOC inscribed in the region cut from the parabola $y = x^2$ by the line $y = a^2$. Find the limit of the ratio of the area of the triangle to the area of the parabolic region as a approaches zero.

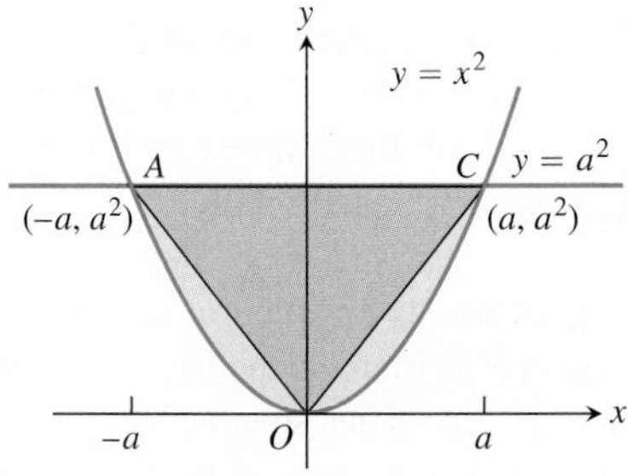

108. Suppose the area of the region between the graph of a positive continuous function f and the x-axis from $x = a$ to $x = b$ is 4 square units. Find the area between the curves $y = f(x)$ and $y = 2f(x)$ from $x = a$ to $x = b$.

109. Which of the following integrals, if either, calculates the area of the shaded region shown here? Give reasons for your answer.

a. $\displaystyle\int_{-1}^{1} (x - (-x))\, dx = \int_{-1}^{1} 2x\, dx$

b. $\displaystyle\int_{-1}^{1} (-x - (x))\, dx = \int_{-1}^{1} -2x\, dx$

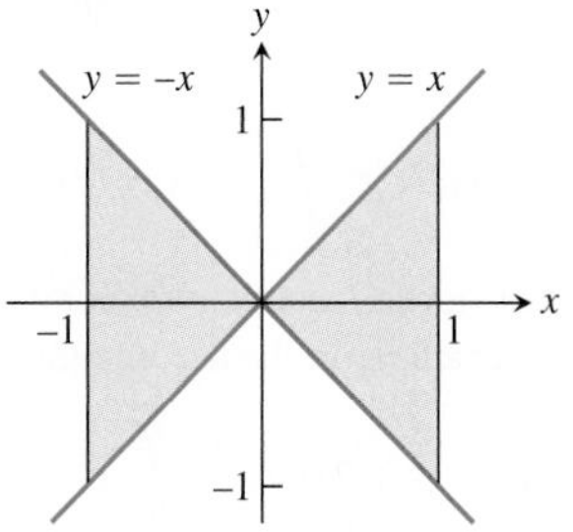

110. True, sometimes true, or never true? The area of the region between the graphs of the continuous functions $y = f(x)$ and $y = g(x)$ and the vertical lines $x = a$ and $x = b$ $(a < b)$ is

$$\int_a^b [f(x) - g(x)]\, dx.$$

Give reasons for your answer.

111. Suppose that $F(x)$ is an antiderivative of $f(x) = (\sin x)/x$, $x > 0$. Express

$$\int_1^3 \frac{\sin 2x}{x}\, dx$$

in terms of F.

112. Show that if f is continuous, then

$$\int_0^1 f(x)\, dx = \int_0^1 f(1 - x)\, dx.$$

113. Suppose that

$$\int_0^1 f(x)\, dx = 3.$$

Find

$$\int_{-1}^0 f(x)\, dx$$

if **a.** f is odd, **b.** f is even.

114. a. Show that if f is odd on $[-a, a]$, then

$$\int_{-a}^a f(x)\, dx = 0.$$

b. Test the result in part (a) with $f(x) = \sin x$ and $a = \pi/2$.

115. If f is a continuous function, find the value of the integral

$$I = \int_0^a \frac{f(x)\, dx}{f(x) + f(a - x)}$$

by making the substitution $u = a - x$ and adding the resulting integral to I.

116. By using a substitution, prove that for all positive numbers x and y,

$$\int_x^{xy} \frac{1}{t}\,dt = \int_1^y \frac{1}{t}\,dt.$$

The Shift Property for Definite Integrals A basic property of definite integrals is their invariance under translation, as expressed by the equation.

$$\int_a^b f(x)\,dx = \int_{a-c}^{b-c} f(x+c)\,dx. \qquad (1)$$

The equation holds whenever f is integrable and defined for the necessary values of x. For example in the accompanying figure, show that

$$\int_{-2}^{-1} (x+2)^3\,dx = \int_0^1 x^3\,dx$$

because the areas of the shaded regions are congruent.

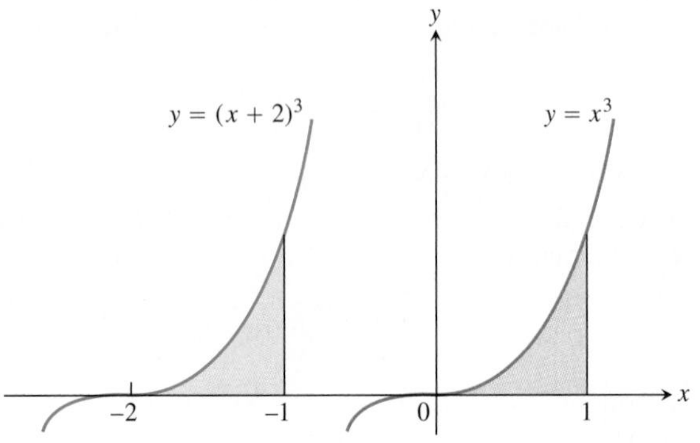

117. Use a substitution to verify Equation (1).

118. For each of the following functions, graph $f(x)$ over $[a, b]$ and $f(x+c)$ over $[a-c, b-c]$ to convince yourself that Equation (1) is reasonable.

a. $f(x) = x^2, \quad a = 0, \quad b = 1, \quad c = 1$

b. $f(x) = \sin x, \quad a = 0, \quad b = \pi, \quad c = \pi/2$

c. $f(x) = \sqrt{x-4}, \quad a = 4, \quad b = 8, \quad c = 5$

COMPUTER EXPLORATIONS

In Exercises 119–122, you will find the area between curves in the plane when you cannot find their points of intersection using simple algebra. Use a CAS to perform the following steps:

a. Plot the curves together to see what they look like and how many points of intersection they have.

b. Use the numerical equation solver in your CAS to find all the points of intersection.

c. Integrate $|f(x) - g(x)|$ over consecutive pairs of intersection values.

d. Sum together the integrals found in part (c).

119. $f(x) = \frac{x^3}{3} - \frac{x^2}{2} - 2x + \frac{1}{3}, \quad g(x) = x - 1$

120. $f(x) = \frac{x^4}{2} - 3x^3 + 10, \quad g(x) = 8 - 12x$

121. $f(x) = x + \sin(2x), \quad g(x) = x^3$

122. $f(x) = x^2 \cos x, \quad g(x) = x^3 - x$

5.7 The Logarithm Defined as an Integral

In Chapter 1 we introduced the natural logarithm function $\ln x$ as the inverse of the exponential function e^x. The function e^x was chosen as that function in the family of general exponential functions a^x, $a > 0$, whose graph has slope 1 as it crosses the y-axis. The function a^x was presented intuitively, however, based on its graph at rational values of x.

In this section we *define* the natural logarithm as an integral using the Fundamental Theorem of Calculus. The exponential function e^x is then defined as the inverse of $\ln x$. We quickly develop all of the algebraic and analytic properties seen before which were associated with these functions. While this indirect approach may at first seem strange, it provides an elegant and rigorous way to define and obtain the key characteristics of logarithmic and exponential functions.

Definition of the Natural Logarithm Function

The natural logarithm of a positive number x, written as $\ln x$, is the value of an integral.

DEFINITION

$$\ln x = \int_1^x \frac{1}{t}\,dt, \qquad x > 0 \tag{1}$$

If $x > 1$, then $\ln x$ is the area under the curve $y = 1/t$ from $t = 1$ to $t = x$ (Figure 5.29). For $0 < x < 1$, $\ln x$ gives the negative of the area under the curve from x to 1. The function is not defined for $x \le 0$. From the Zero Width Interval Rule for definite integrals, we also have

$$\ln 1 = \int_1^1 \frac{1}{t}\,dt = 0.$$

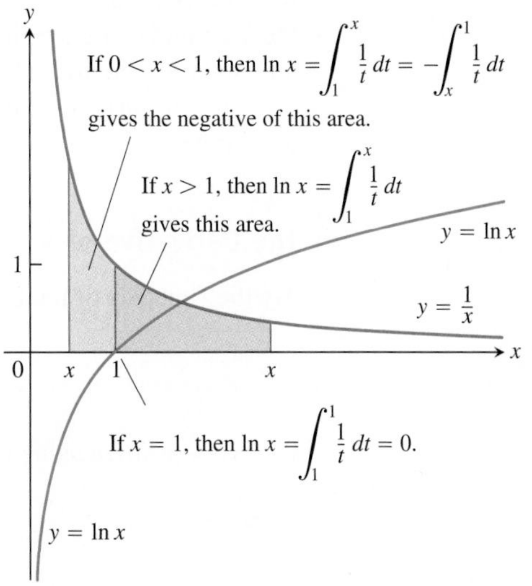

FIGURE 5.29 The graph of $y = \ln x$ and its relation to the function $y = 1/x$, $x > 0$. The graph of the logarithm rises above the x-axis as x moves from 1 to the right, and it falls below the axis as x moves from 1 to the left.

Notice that we show the graph of $y = 1/x$ in Figure 5.29 but use $y = 1/t$ in the integral. Using x for everything would have us writing

$$\ln x = \int_1^x \frac{1}{x}\,dx,$$

with x meaning two different things. Thus we change the variable of integration to t.

TABLE 5.4 Typical 2-place values of $\ln x$

x	$\ln x$
0	undefined
0.05	−3.00
0.5	−0.69
1	0
2	0.69
3	1.10
4	1.39
10	2.30

By using rectangles to obtain finite approximations of the area under the graph of $y = 1/t$ and over the interval between $t = 1$ and $t = x$, as in Section 5.1, we can approximate the values of the function $\ln x$. Several values are given in Table 5.4. There is an important number between $x = 2$ and $x = 3$ whose natural logarithm equals 1.

DEFINITION The number e is that number in the domain of the natural logarithm satisfying

$$\ln(e) = 1$$

So the number e satisfies

$$\int_1^e \frac{1}{t}\,dt = 1.$$

Interpreted geometrically, the number e corresponds to the point on the x-axis for which the area under the graph of $y = 1/t$ and above the interval $[1, e]$ equals the area of the unit square. The area of the region shaded blue in Figure 5.29 is 1 sq unit when $x = e$. We will see further on that this is the same number $e \approx 2.718281828$ we have encountered before.

The Derivative of $y = \ln x$

By the first part of the Fundamental Theorem of Calculus (Section 5.4),

$$\frac{d}{dx}\ln x = \frac{d}{dx}\int_1^x \frac{1}{t}\,dt = \frac{1}{x}.$$

For every positive value of x, we have

$$\frac{d}{dx}\ln x = \frac{1}{x},$$

and the Chain Rule gives

$$\frac{d}{dx}\ln u = \frac{1}{u}\frac{du}{dx}, \qquad u > 0 \tag{2}$$

if u is a differentiable function of x whose values are positive.

The derivative of the natural logarithm defined by the integral in Equation (1) is the same as the derivative obtained for the logarithm function defined in Section 3.7, and both functions have value 0 when $x = 1$. Therefore we know from Corollary 2 of the Mean Value Theorem (Section 4.2) that both functions are exactly the same—a single function defined in two different ways. Therefore, just as in Section 3.7, we have

$$\frac{d}{dx}\ln|x| = \frac{1}{x}, \qquad x \neq 0. \tag{3}$$

Moreover, the function $\ln x$ satisfies the following familiar algebraic properties which were proved in Section 4.2.

1. $\ln bx = \ln b + \ln x$
2. $\ln \frac{b}{x} = \ln b - \ln x$
3. $\ln \frac{1}{x} = -\ln x$
4. $\ln x^r = r \ln x, \quad r$ any rational number

Property (4) remains valid for any real number r, but we omit the proof which depends on the completeness property of the real number system (Appendix 7).

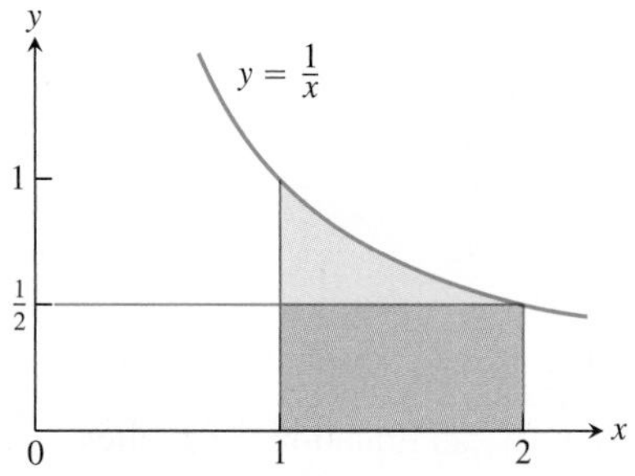

FIGURE 5.30 The rectangle of height $y = 1/2$ fits beneath the graph of $y = 1/x$ for the interval $1 \le x \le 2$.

The Graph and Range of ln *x*

The derivative $d(\ln x)/dx = 1/x$ is positive for $x > 0$, so $\ln x$ is an increasing function of x. The second derivative, $-1/x^2$, is negative, so the graph of $\ln x$ is concave down.

We can estimate the value of ln 2 by considering the area under the graph of $y = 1/x$ and above the interval [1, 2]. In Figure 5.30 a rectangle of height $1/2$ over the interval [1, 2] fits under the graph. Therefore the area under the graph, which is ln 2, is greater than the area, $1/2$, of the rectangle. So $\ln 2 > 1/2$. Knowing this we have,

$$\ln 2^n = n \ln 2 > n\left(\frac{1}{2}\right) = \frac{n}{2}.$$

This result shows that $\ln(2^n) \to \infty$ as $n \to \infty$. Since $\ln x$ is an increasing function, we get that

$$\lim_{x\to\infty} \ln x = \infty.$$

We also have

$$\lim_{x\to 0^+} \ln x = \lim_{t\to\infty} \ln t^{-1} = \lim_{t\to\infty} (-\ln t) = -\infty. \qquad x = 1/t = t^{-1}$$

We defined $\ln x$ for $x > 0$, so the domain of $\ln x$ is the set of positive real numbers. The above discussion and the Intermediate Value Theorem show that its range is the entire real line, giving the graph of $y = \ln x$ shown in Figure 5.29.

The Integral $\int (1/u)\, du$

Equation (3) leads to the following integral formula.

If u is a differentiable function that is never zero,

$$\int \frac{1}{u}\, du = \ln |u| + C. \tag{4}$$

Equation (4) says integrals of a certain form lead to logarithms. If $u = f(x)$, then $du = f'(x)\, dx$ and

$$\int \frac{1}{u}\, du = \int \frac{f'(x)}{f(x)}\, dx.$$

So Equation (4) gives

$$\int \frac{f'(x)}{f(x)}\,dx = \ln|f(x)| + C$$

whenever $f(x)$ is a differentiable function that maintains a constant sign on the given interval of interest.

EXAMPLE 1

(a) $$\int_0^2 \frac{2x}{x^2-5}\,dx = \int_{-5}^{-1} \frac{du}{u} = \ln|u|\Big]_{-5}^{-1}$$ $u = x^2 - 5,\quad du = 2x\,dx,$ $u(0) = -5,\quad u(2) = -1$

$$= \ln|-1| - \ln|-5| = \ln 1 - \ln 5 = -\ln 5$$

(b) $$\int_{-\pi/2}^{\pi/2} \frac{4\cos\theta}{3+2\sin\theta}\,d\theta = \int_1^5 \frac{2}{u}\,du$$ $u = 3 + 2\sin\theta,\quad du = 2\cos\theta\,d\theta,$ $u(-\pi/2) = 1,\quad u(\pi/2) = 5$

$$= 2\ln|u|\Big]_1^5$$

$$= 2\ln|5| - 2\ln|1| = 2\ln 5$$

Note that $u = 3 + 2\sin\theta$ is always positive on $[-\pi/2, \pi/2]$, so Equation (4) applies. ■

The Inverse of ln *x* and the Number *e*

The function $\ln x$, being an increasing function of x with domain $(0, \infty)$ and range $(-\infty, \infty)$, has an inverse $\ln^{-1} x$ with domain $(-\infty, \infty)$ and range $(0, \infty)$. The graph of $\ln^{-1} x$ is the graph of $\ln x$ reflected across the line $y = x$. As you can see in Figure 5.31,

$$\lim_{x\to\infty} \ln^{-1} x = \infty \qquad \text{and} \qquad \lim_{x\to-\infty} \ln^{-1} x = 0.$$

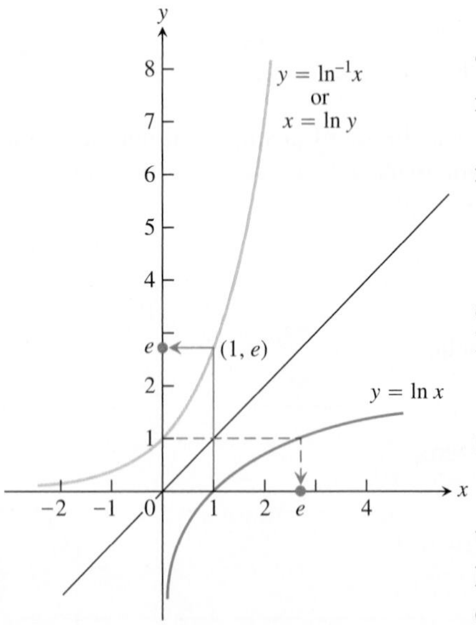

FIGURE 5.31 The graphs of $y = \ln x$ and $y = \ln^{-1} x = \exp x$. The number e is $\ln^{-1} 1 = \exp(1)$.

The function $\ln^{-1} x$ is also denoted by $\exp x$. We now show that $\ln^{-1} x = \exp x$ is an exponential function with base e.

The number e satisfies the equation $\ln(e) = 1$, so $e = \ln^{-1}(1) = \exp(1)$. We can raise the number e to a rational power r in the usual way:

$$e^2 = e \cdot e, \qquad e^{-2} = \frac{1}{e^2}, \qquad e^{1/2} = \sqrt{e},$$

and so on. Since e is positive, e^r is positive too. Thus, e^r has a logarithm. When we take the logarithm, we find that

$$\ln e^r = r\ln e = r \cdot 1 = r.$$

Since $\ln x$ is one-to-one and $\ln(\ln^{-1} r) = r$, this equation tells us that

$$e^r = \ln^{-1} r = \exp r \qquad \text{for } r \text{ rational}. \tag{5}$$

We have not yet found a way to give an obvious meaning to e^x for x irrational. But $\ln^{-1} x$ has meaning for any x, rational or irrational. So Equation (5) provides a way to extend the definition of e^x to irrational values of x. The function $\ln^{-1} x$ is defined for all x, so we use it to assign a value to e^x at every point where e^x had no previous definition.

DEFINITION For every real number x, $e^x = \ln^{-1} x = \exp x$.

Typical values of e^x

x	e^x (rounded)
-1	0.37
0	1
1	2.72
2	7.39
10	22026
100	2.6881×10^{43}

For the first time we have a precise meaning for an irrational exponent. Usually the exponential function is denoted by e^x rather than $\exp x$. Since $\ln x$ and e^x are inverses of one another, we have the following relationships.

Inverse Equations for e^x and $\ln x$

$$e^{\ln x} = x \qquad (\text{all } x > 0)$$
$$\ln (e^x) = x \qquad (\text{all } x)$$

The Derivative and Integral of e^x

The exponential function is differentiable because it is the inverse of a differentiable function whose derivative is never zero. We calculate its derivative using Theorem 4 of Section 3.7 and our knowledge of the derivative of $\ln x$. Let

$$f(x) = \ln x \qquad \text{and} \qquad y = e^x = \ln^{-1} x = f^{-1}(x).$$

Then,

$$\begin{aligned}
\frac{dy}{dx} = \frac{d}{dx}(e^x) &= \frac{d}{dx}\ln^{-1} x \\
&= \frac{d}{dx} f^{-1}(x) \\
&= \frac{1}{f'(f^{-1}(x))} && \text{Theorem 4, Section 3.7} \\
&= \frac{1}{f'(e^x)} && f^{-1}(x) = e^x \\
&= \frac{1}{\left(\frac{1}{e^x}\right)} && f'(z) = \frac{1}{z} \text{ with } z = e^x \\
&= e^x.
\end{aligned}$$

That is, for $y = e^x$, we find that $dy/dx = e^x$ so the natural exponential function e^x is its own derivative. Therefore if $f(x) = e^x$, then $f'(0) = e^0 = 1$. This means that the exponential function $e^x = \exp x = \ln^{-1} x$ has slope 1 as it crosses the y-axis at $x = 0$. This agrees with our assertion for the natural exponential function in Section 3.1 and confirms that the number e defined in this section is exactly the same number we defined in Chapter 1. (We expressed e as a limit in one way in Theorem 5, Section 3.7).

The Chain Rule extends the derivative result for the natural exponential function in the usual way to a more general form.

If u is any differentiable function of x, then

$$\frac{d}{dx} e^u = e^u \frac{du}{dx}. \tag{6}$$

Since $e^x > 0$, its derivative is also everywhere positive, so it is an increasing and continuous function for all x, having limits

$$\lim_{x\to-\infty} e^x = 0 \quad \text{and} \quad \lim_{x\to\infty} e^x = \infty.$$

It follows that the x-axis ($y = 0$) is a horizontal asymptote of the graph $y = e^x$.

The integral equivalent to Equation (6) is

$$\int e^u \, du = e^u + C.$$

Laws of Exponents

Even though e^x is defined in a seemingly roundabout way as $\ln^{-1} x$, it obeys the familiar laws of exponents from algebra. Theorem 8 shows us that these laws are consequences of the definitions of $\ln x$ and e^x.

THEOREM 8 For all numbers x, x_1, and x_2, the natural exponential e^x obeys the following laws:

1. $e^{x_1} \cdot e^{x_2} = e^{x_1 + x_2}$
2. $e^{-x} = \dfrac{1}{e^x}$
3. $\dfrac{e^{x_1}}{e^{x_2}} = e^{x_1 - x_2}$
4. $(e^{x_1})^r = e^{r x_1}$, if r is rational

Proof of Law 4 Let $y = (e^{x_1})^r$. Then

$$\begin{aligned} \ln y &= \ln (e^{x_1})^r \\ &= r \ln (e^{x_1}) && \text{Power Rule for logarithms} \\ &= r x_1 && \ln e^u = u \text{ with } u = x_1 \end{aligned}$$

Thus, exponentiating each side,

$$y = e^{r x_1}. \qquad e^{\ln y} = y$$ ■

Laws 2 and 3 follow from Law 1, which was proved in Section 4.2.

Law 4 is actually true for any real number r. As is the case with logarithms, extension of the law from the rationals to the reals depends on the completeness property of the real number system (stated informally in Appendix 7). The proof is found in more advanced texts.

The General Exponential Function a^x

Since $a = e^{\ln a}$ for any positive number a, we can think of a^x as $(e^{\ln a})^x = e^{x \ln a}$. We therefore make the following definition.

> **DEFINITION** For any numbers $a > 0$ and x, the exponential function with base a is
>
> $$a^x = e^{x \ln a}.$$

When $a = e$, the definition gives $a^x = e^{x \ln a} = e^{x \ln e} = e^{x \cdot 1} = e^x$.

Theorem 8 is also valid for a^x, the exponential function with base a. For example,

$$\begin{aligned} a^{x_1} \cdot a^{x_2} &= e^{x_1 \ln a} \cdot e^{x_2 \ln a} && \text{Definition of } a^x \\ &= e^{x_1 \ln a + x_2 \ln a} && \text{Law 1} \\ &= e^{(x_1 + x_2)\ln a} && \text{Factor } \ln a \\ &= a^{x_1 + x_2}. && \text{Definition of } a^x \end{aligned}$$

We can now define x^n for any $x > 0$ and any real number n as $x^n = e^{n \ln x}$. Therefore, the value of n in the equation $\ln x^n = n \ln x$ no longer needs to be rational—it can be any number as long as $x > 0$:

$$\ln x^n = \ln (e^{n \ln x}) = n \ln x \qquad \ln e^u = u, \text{ any } u$$

Together, the law $a^x/a^y = a^{x-y}$ and the definition $x^n = e^{n \ln x}$ enable us to establish the Power Rule for differentiation in its final form, valid for all real exponents r:

$$\frac{d}{dx} x^r = \frac{d}{dx} e^{r \ln x} = (e^{r \ln x}) \frac{d}{dx}(r \ln x) = x^r \cdot \frac{r}{x} = r x^{r-1}.$$

Starting with the definition $a^x = e^{x \ln a}$, $a > 0$, we get the derivative

$$\frac{d}{dx} a^x = \frac{d}{dx} e^{x \ln a} = (\ln a)\, e^{x \ln a} = (\ln a)\, a^x,$$

so

$$\frac{d}{dx} a^x = a^x \ln a.$$

Alternatively, we get the same derivative rule by applying logarithmic differentiation:

$$\begin{aligned} y &= a^x \\ \ln y &= x \ln a && \text{Taking logarithms} \\ \frac{1}{y}\frac{dy}{dx} &= \ln a && \text{Differentiating with respect to } x \\ \frac{dy}{dx} &= y \ln a = a^x \ln a. \end{aligned}$$

We get a more general form by applying the Chain Rule.

If $a > 0$ and u is a differentiable function of x, then a^u is a differentiable function of x and

$$\frac{d}{dx} a^u = a^u \ln a \frac{du}{dx}.$$

The integral equivalent of this last result is

$$\int a^u \, du = \frac{a^u}{\ln a} + C.$$

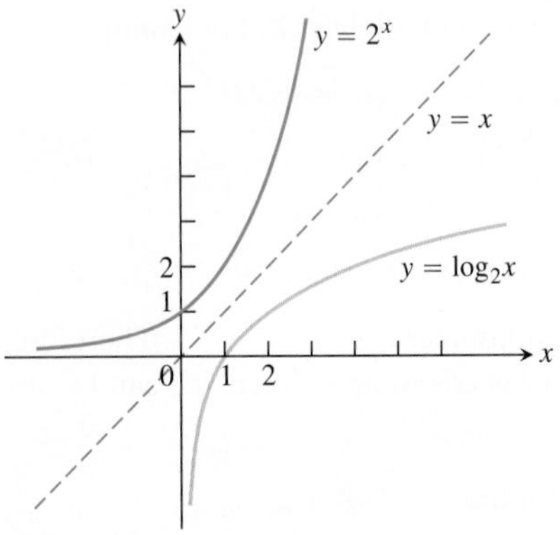

FIGURE 5.32 The graph of 2^x and its inverse, $\log_2 x$.

Logarithms with Base a

If a is any positive number other than 1, the function a^x is one-to-one and has a nonzero derivative at every point. It therefore has a differentiable inverse. We call the inverse the **logarithm of x with base a** and denote it by $\log_a x$.

DEFINITION For any positive number $a \neq 1$,

$\log_a x$ is the inverse function of a^x.

The graph of $y = \log_a x$ can be obtained by reflecting the graph of $y = a^x$ across the 45° line $y = x$ (Figure 5.32). When $a = e$, we have $\log_e x =$ inverse of $e^x = \ln x$. Since $\log_a x$ and a^x are inverses of one another, composing them in either order gives the identity function.

Inverse Equations for a^x and $\log_a x$

$$a^{\log_a x} = x \qquad (x > 0)$$
$$\log_a (a^x) = x \qquad (\text{all } x)$$

The function $\log_a x$ is actually just a numerical multiple of $\ln x$. To see this, we let $y = \log_a x$ and then take the natural logarithm of both sides of the equivalent equation $a^y = x$ to obtain $y \ln a = \ln x$. Solving for y gives

$$\log_a x = \frac{\ln x}{\ln a}.$$

It then follows easily that the arithmetic rules satisfied by $\log_a x$ are the same as the ones for $\ln x$. These rules, given in Table 5.5, can be proved by dividing the corresponding rules for the natural logarithm function by $\ln a$. For example,

$$\ln xy = \ln x + \ln y \qquad \text{Rule 1 for natural logarithms} \ldots$$
$$\frac{\ln xy}{\ln a} = \frac{\ln x}{\ln a} + \frac{\ln y}{\ln a} \qquad \ldots \text{divided by } \ln a \ldots$$
$$\log_a xy = \log_a x + \log_a y. \qquad \ldots \text{gives Rule 1 for base } a \text{ logarithms.}$$

TABLE 5.5 Rules for base a logarithms

For any numbers $x > 0$ and $y > 0$,

1. *Product Rule:*
   $\log_a xy = \log_a x + \log_a y$
2. *Quotient Rule:*
   $\log_a \frac{x}{y} = \log_a x - \log_a y$
3. *Reciprocal Rule:*
   $\log_a \frac{1}{y} = -\log_a y$
4. *Power Rule:*
   $\log_a x^y = y \log_a x$

Derivatives and Integrals Involving $\log_a x$

To find derivatives or integrals involving base a logarithms, we convert them to natural logarithms. If u is a positive differentiable function of x, then

$$\frac{d}{dx}(\log_a u) = \frac{d}{dx}\left(\frac{\ln u}{\ln a}\right) = \frac{1}{\ln a}\frac{d}{dx}(\ln u) = \frac{1}{\ln a} \cdot \frac{1}{u}\frac{du}{dx}.$$

$$\frac{d}{dx}(\log_a u) = \frac{1}{\ln a} \cdot \frac{1}{u}\frac{du}{dx}$$

EXAMPLE 2

(a) $\dfrac{d}{dx}\log_{10}(3x+1) = \dfrac{1}{\ln 10} \cdot \dfrac{1}{3x+1}\dfrac{d}{dx}(3x+1) = \dfrac{3}{(\ln 10)(3x+1)}$

(b)
$$\begin{aligned}\int \frac{\log_2 x}{x}\,dx &= \frac{1}{\ln 2}\int \frac{\ln x}{x}\,dx && \log_2 x = \frac{\ln x}{\ln 2}\\ &= \frac{1}{\ln 2}\int u\,du && u = \ln x, \quad du = \frac{1}{x}\,dx\\ &= \frac{1}{\ln 2}\frac{u^2}{2} + C = \frac{1}{\ln 2}\frac{(\ln x)^2}{2} + C = \frac{(\ln x)^2}{2\ln 2} + C\end{aligned}$$
■

Summary

In this section we used the calculus to give the very definitions of the logarithmic and exponential functions. This approach is somewhat different from our earlier treatments of the polynomial, rational, and trigonometric functions. There we first defined the function and then we studied its derivatives and integrals. Here we started with an integral from which the functions of interest were obtained. The motivation behind this approach was to avoid mathematical difficulties that arise when we attempt to define functions such as a^x for any real number x, rational or irrational. By defining $\ln x$ as the integral of the function $1/t$ from $t = 1$ to $t = x$, we could go on to define all of the exponential and logarithmic functions, and then derive their key algebraic and analytic properties.

EXERCISES 5.7

Evaluate the integrals in Exercises 1–46.

1. $\displaystyle\int_{-3}^{-2}\frac{dx}{x}$

2. $\displaystyle\int_{-1}^{0}\frac{3\,dx}{3x-2}$

3. $\displaystyle\int\frac{2y\,dy}{y^2-25}$

4. $\displaystyle\int\frac{8r\,dr}{4r^2-5}$

5. $\displaystyle\int\frac{3\sec^2 t}{6+3\tan t}\,dt$

6. $\displaystyle\int\frac{\sec y\tan y}{2+\sec y}\,dy$

7. $\displaystyle\int\frac{dx}{2\sqrt{x}+2x}$

8. $\displaystyle\int\frac{\sec x\,dx}{\sqrt{\ln(\sec x+\tan x)}}$

9. $\int_{\ln 2}^{\ln 3} e^x\,dx$

10. $\int_{-\ln 2}^{0} e^{-x}\,dx$

11. $\int 8e^{(x+1)}\,dx$

12. $\int 2e^{(2x-1)}\,dx$

13. $\int_{\ln 4}^{\ln 9} e^{x/2}\,dx$

14. $\int_{0}^{\ln 16} e^{x/4}\,dx$

15. $\int \frac{e^{\sqrt{r}}}{\sqrt{r}}\,dr$

16. $\int \frac{e^{-\sqrt{r}}}{\sqrt{r}}\,dr$

17. $\int 2t\,e^{-t^2}\,dt$

18. $\int t^3 e^{(t^4)}\,dt$

19. $\int \frac{e^{1/x}}{x^2}\,dx$

20. $\int \frac{e^{-1/x^2}}{x^3}\,dx$

21. $\int e^{\sec \pi t} \sec \pi t \tan \pi t\,dt$

22. $\int e^{\csc(\pi+t)} \csc(\pi + t) \cot(\pi + t)\,dt$

23. $\int_{\ln(\pi/6)}^{\ln(\pi/2)} 2e^v \cos e^v\,dv$

24. $\int_0^{\sqrt{\ln \pi}} 2xe^{x^2} \cos(e^{x^2})\,dx$

25. $\int \frac{e^r}{1 + e^r}\,dr$

26. $\int \frac{dx}{1 + e^x}$

27. $\int_0^1 2^{-\theta}\,d\theta$

28. $\int_{-2}^{0} 5^{-\theta}\,d\theta$

29. $\int_1^{\sqrt{2}} x2^{(x^2)}\,dx$

30. $\int_1^4 \frac{2^{\sqrt{x}}}{\sqrt{x}}\,dx$

31. $\int_0^{\pi/2} 7^{\cos t} \sin t\,dt$

32. $\int_0^{\pi/4} \left(\frac{1}{3}\right)^{\tan t} \sec^2 t\,dt$

33. $\int_2^4 x^{2x}(1 + \ln x)\,dx$

34. $\int_1^2 \frac{2^{\ln x}}{x}\,dx$

35. $\int_0^3 (\sqrt{2} + 1)x^{\sqrt{2}}\,dx$

36. $\int_1^e x^{(\ln 2)-1}\,dx$

37. $\int \frac{\log_{10} x}{x}\,dx$

38. $\int_1^4 \frac{\log_2 x}{x}\,dx$

39. $\int_1^4 \frac{\ln 2 \log_2 x}{x}\,dx$

40. $\int_1^e \frac{2 \ln 10 \log_{10} x}{x}\,dx$

41. $\int_0^2 \frac{\log_2(x + 2)}{x + 2}\,dx$

42. $\int_{1/10}^{10} \frac{\log_{10}(10x)}{x}\,dx$

43. $\int_0^9 \frac{2 \log_{10}(x + 1)}{x + 1}\,dx$

44. $\int_2^3 \frac{2 \log_2(x - 1)}{x - 1}\,dx$

45. $\int \frac{dx}{x \log_{10} x}$

46. $\int \frac{dx}{x(\log_8 x)^2}$

Solve the initial value problems in Exercises 47–52.

47. $\frac{dy}{dt} = e^t \sin(e^t - 2),\quad y(\ln 2) = 0$

48. $\frac{dy}{dt} = e^{-t} \sec^2(\pi e^{-t}),\quad y(\ln 4) = 2/\pi$

49. $\frac{d^2y}{dx^2} = 2e^{-x},\quad y(0) = 1$ and $y'(0) = 0$

50. $\frac{d^2y}{dt^2} = 1 - e^{2t},\quad y(1) = -1$ and $y'(1) = 0$

51. $\frac{dy}{dx} = 1 + \frac{1}{x},\quad y(1) = 3$

52. $\frac{d^2y}{dx^2} = \sec^2 x,\quad y(0) = 0$ and $y'(0) = 1$

T 53. **The linearization of $\ln(1 + x)$ at $x = 0$** Instead of approximating $\ln x$ near $x = 1$, we approximate $\ln(1 + x)$ near $x = 0$. We get a simpler formula this way.

a. Derive the linearization $\ln(1 + x) \approx x$ at $x = 0$.

b. Estimate to five decimal places the error involved in replacing $\ln(1 + x)$ by x on the interval $[0, 0.1]$.

c. Graph $\ln(1 + x)$ and x together for $0 \le x \le 0.5$. Use different colors, if available. At what points does the approximation of $\ln(1 + x)$ seem best? Least good? By reading coordinates from the graphs, find as good an upper bound for the error as your grapher will allow.

54. **The linearization of e^x at $x = 0$**

a. Derive the linear approximation $e^x \approx 1 + x$ at $x = 0$.

T **b.** Estimate to five decimal places the magnitude of the error involved in replacing e^x by $1 + x$ on the interval $[0, 0.2]$.

T **c.** Graph e^x and $1 + x$ together for $-2 \le x \le 2$. Use different colors, if available. On what intervals does the approximation appear to overestimate e^x? Underestimate e^x?

55. Show that for any number $a > 1$

$$\int_1^a \ln x\,dx + \int_0^{\ln a} e^y\,dy = a \ln a.$$

(See accompanying figure.)

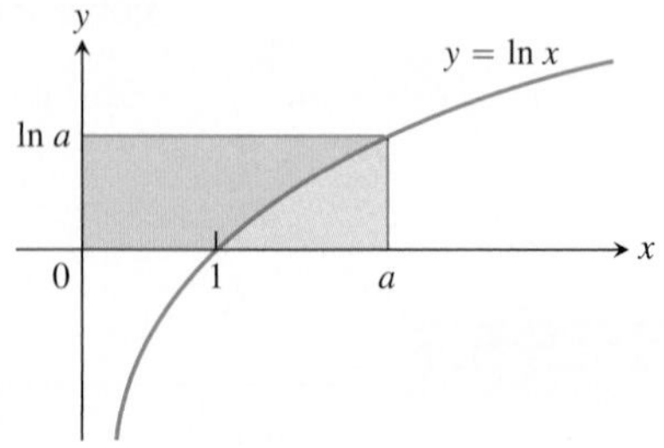

56. **The geometric, logarithmic, and arithmetic mean inequality**

a. Show that the graph of e^x is concave up over every interval of x-values.

b. Show, by reference to the accompanying figure, that if $0 < a < b$ then

$$e^{(\ln a+\ln b)/2} \cdot (\ln b - \ln a) < \int_{\ln a}^{\ln b} e^x \, dx < \frac{e^{\ln a} + e^{\ln b}}{2} \cdot (\ln b - \ln a).$$

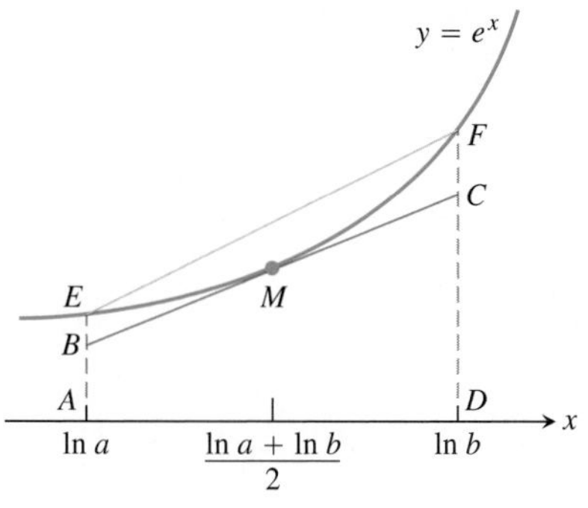

c. Use the inequality in part (b) to conclude that

$$\sqrt{ab} < \frac{b - a}{\ln b - \ln a} < \frac{a + b}{2}.$$

This inequality says that the geometric mean of two positive numbers is less than their logarithmic mean, which in turn is less than their arithmetic mean.

(For more about this inequality, see "The Geometric, Logarithmic, and Arithmetic Mean Inequality" by Frank Burk, *American Mathematical Monthly*, Vol. 94, No. 6, June–July 1987, pp. 527–528.)

T **57. Which is bigger, π^e or e^π?** Calculators have taken some of the mystery out of this once-challenging question. (Go ahead and check; you will see that it is a surprisingly close call.) You can answer the question without a calculator, though.

a. Find an equation for the line through the origin tangent to the graph of $y = \ln x$.

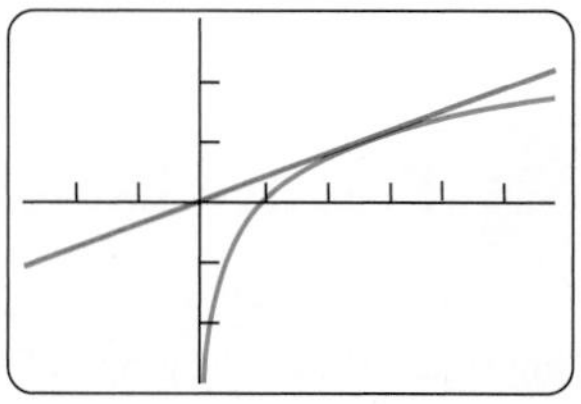

[–3, 6] by [–3, 3]

b. Give an argument based on the graphs of $y = \ln x$ and the tangent line to explain why $\ln x < x/e$ for all positive $x \neq e$.

c. Show that $\ln(x^e) < x$ for all positive $x \neq e$.

d. Conclude that $x^e < e^x$ for all positive $x \neq e$.

e. So which is bigger, π^e or e^π?

T **58. A decimal representation of e** Find e to as many decimal places as your calculator allows by solving the equation $\ln x = 1$ using Newton's method in Section 4.7.

Chapter 5 Questions to Guide Your Review

1. How can you sometimes estimate quantities like distance traveled, area, and average value with finite sums? Why might you want to do so?
2. What is sigma notation? What advantage does it offer? Give examples.
3. What is a Riemann sum? Why might you want to consider such a sum?
4. What is the norm of a partition of a closed interval?
5. What is the definite integral of a function f over a closed interval $[a, b]$? When can you be sure it exists?
6. What is the relation between definite integrals and area? Describe some other interpretations of definite integrals.
7. What is the average value of an integrable function over a closed interval? Must the function assume its average value? Explain.
8. Describe the rules for working with definite integrals (Table 5.3). Give examples.
9. What is the Fundamental Theorem of Calculus? Why is it so important? Illustrate each part of the theorem with an example.
10. How does the Fundamental Theorem provide a solution to the initial value problem $dy/dx = f(x)$, $y(x_0) = y_0$, when f is continuous?
11. How is integration by substitution related to the Chain Rule?
12. How can you sometimes evaluate indefinite integrals by substitution? Give examples.
13. How does the method of substitution work for definite integrals? Give examples.
14. How do you define and calculate the area of the region between the graphs of two continuous functions? Give an example.

15. How is the natural logarithm function defined as an integral? What are its domain, range, and derivative? What arithmetic properties does it have? Comment on its graph.

16. What integrals lead to logarithms? Give examples.

17. How is the exponential function e^x defined? What are its domain, range, and derivative? What laws of exponents does it obey? Comment on its graph.

18. How are the functions e^x and $\log_a x$ defined? Are there any restrictions on a? How is the graph of $\log_a x$ related to the graph of $\ln x$? What truth is there in the statement that there is really only one exponential function and one logarithmic function?

Chapter 5 Practice Exercises

1. The accompanying figure shows the graph of the velocity (ft/sec) of a model rocket for the first 8 sec after launch. The rocket accelerated straight up for the first 2 sec and then coasted to reach its maximum height at $t = 8$ sec.

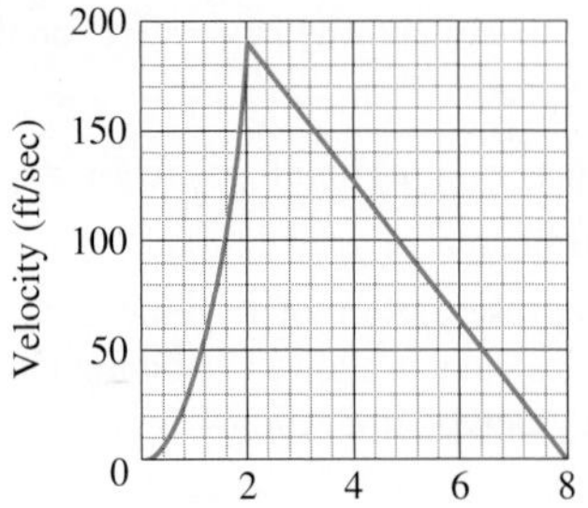

a. Assuming that the rocket was launched from ground level, about how high did it go? (This is the rocket in Section 3.3, Exercise 17, but you do not need to do Exercise 17 to do the exercise here.)

b. Sketch a graph of the rocket's height aboveground as a function of time for $0 \le t \le 8$.

2. a. The accompanying figure shows the velocity (m/sec) of a body moving along the s-axis during the time interval from $t = 0$ to $t = 10$ sec. About how far did the body travel during those 10 sec?

b. Sketch a graph of s as a function of t for $0 \le t \le 10$ assuming $s(0) = 0$.

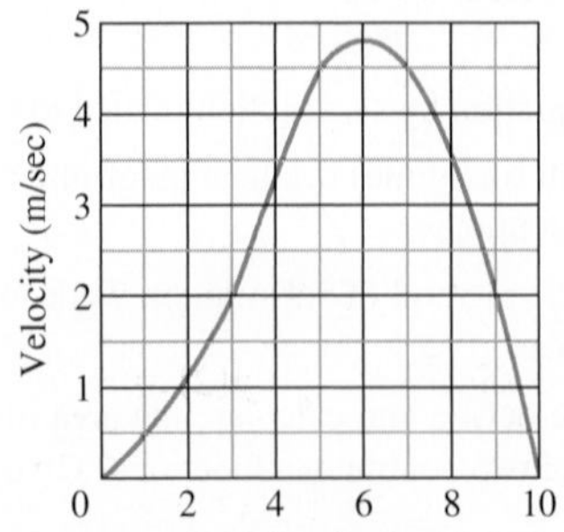

3. Suppose that $\sum_{k=1}^{10} a_k = -2$ and $\sum_{k=1}^{10} b_k = 25$. Find the value of

a. $\sum_{k=1}^{10} \frac{a_k}{4}$

b. $\sum_{k=1}^{10} (b_k - 3a_k)$

c. $\sum_{k=1}^{10} (a_k + b_k - 1)$

d. $\sum_{k=1}^{10} \left(\frac{5}{2} - b_k\right)$

4. Suppose that $\sum_{k=1}^{20} a_k = 0$ and $\sum_{k=1}^{20} b_k = 7$. Find the values of

a. $\sum_{k=1}^{20} 3a_k$

b. $\sum_{k=1}^{20} (a_k + b_k)$

c. $\sum_{k=1}^{20} \left(\frac{1}{2} - \frac{2b_k}{7}\right)$

d. $\sum_{k=1}^{20} (a_k - 2)$

In Exercises 5–8, express each limit as a definite integral. Then evaluate the integral to find the value of the limit. In each case, P is a partition of the given interval and the numbers c_k are chosen from the subintervals of P.

5. $\lim_{\|P\|\to 0} \sum_{k=1}^{n} (2c_k - 1)^{-1/2}\,\Delta x_k$, where P is a partition of $[1, 5]$

6. $\lim_{\|P\|\to 0} \sum_{k=1}^{n} c_k(c_k^2 - 1)^{1/3}\,\Delta x_k$, where P is a partition of $[1, 3]$

7. $\lim_{\|P\|\to 0} \sum_{k=1}^{n} \left(\cos\left(\frac{c_k}{2}\right)\right)\Delta x_k$, where P is a partition of $[-\pi, 0]$

8. $\lim_{\|P\|\to 0} \sum_{k=1}^{n} (\sin c_k)(\cos c_k)\,\Delta x_k$, where P is a partition of $[0, \pi/2]$

9. If $\int_{-2}^{2} 3f(x)\,dx = 12$, $\int_{-2}^{5} f(x)\,dx = 6$, and $\int_{-2}^{5} g(x)\,dx = 2$, find the values of the following.

a. $\int_{-2}^{2} f(x)\,dx$

b. $\int_{2}^{5} f(x)\,dx$

c. $\int_{5}^{-2} g(x)\,dx$

d. $\int_{-2}^{5} (-\pi g(x))\,dx$

e. $\int_{-2}^{5} \left(\frac{f(x) + g(x)}{5}\right) dx$

10. If $\int_0^2 f(x)\,dx = \pi$, $\int_0^2 7g(x)\,dx = 7$, and $\int_0^1 g(x)\,dx = 2$, find the values of the following.

a. $\int_0^2 g(x)\,dx$ b. $\int_1^2 g(x)\,dx$

c. $\int_2^0 f(x)\,dx$ d. $\int_0^2 \sqrt{2}\,f(x)\,dx$

e. $\int_0^2 (g(x) - 3f(x))\,dx$

In Exercise 11–14, find the total area of the region between the graph of f and the x-axis.

11. $f(x) = x^2 - 4x + 3, \quad 0 \le x \le 3$
12. $f(x) = 1 - (x^2/4), \quad -2 \le x \le 3$
13. $f(x) = 5 - 5x^{2/3}, \quad -1 \le x \le 8$
14. $f(x) = 1 - \sqrt{x}, \quad 0 \le x \le 4$

Find the areas of the regions enclosed by the curves and lines in Exercises 15–26.

15. $y = x, \quad y = 1/x^2, \quad x = 2$
16. $y = x, \quad y = 1/\sqrt{x}, \quad x = 2$
17. $\sqrt{x} + \sqrt{y} = 1, \quad x = 0, \quad y = 0$

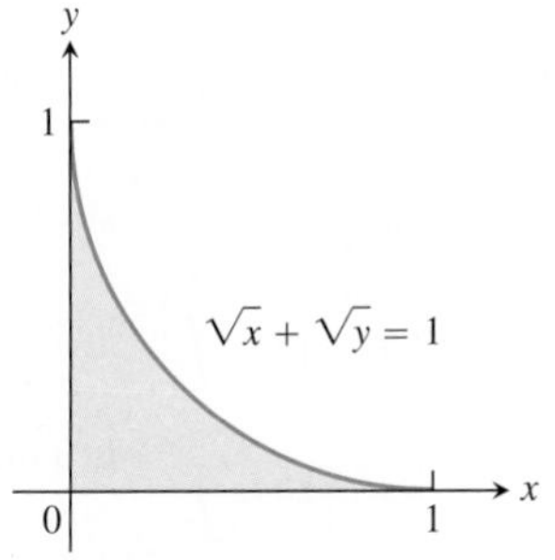

18. $x^3 + \sqrt{y} = 1, \quad x = 0, \quad y = 0, \quad \text{for} \quad 0 \le x \le 1$

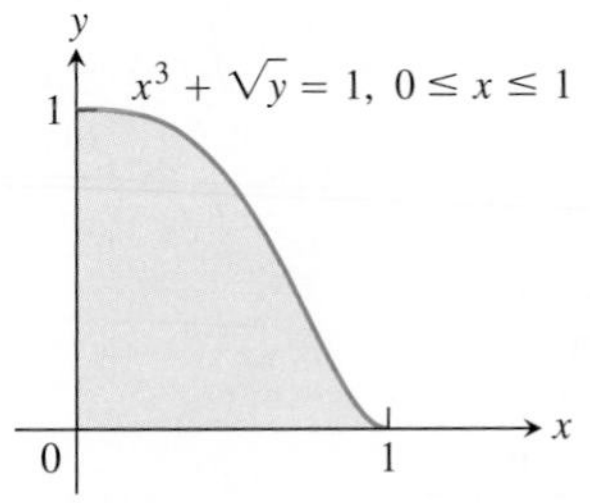

19. $x = 2y^2, \quad x = 0, \quad y = 3$ 20. $x = 4 - y^2, \quad x = 0$
21. $y^2 = 4x, \quad y = 4x - 2$
22. $y^2 = 4x + 4, \quad y = 4x - 16$
23. $y = \sin x, \quad y = x, \quad 0 \le x \le \pi/4$
24. $y = |\sin x|, \quad y = 1, \quad -\pi/2 \le x \le \pi/2$
25. $y = 2\sin x, \quad y = \sin 2x, \quad 0 \le x \le \pi$
26. $y = 8\cos x, \quad y = \sec^2 x, \quad -\pi/3 \le x \le \pi/3$
27. Find the area of the "triangular" region bounded on the left by $x + y = 2$, on the right by $y = x^2$, and above by $y = 2$.
28. Find the area of the "triangular" region bounded on the left by $y = \sqrt{x}$, on the right by $y = 6 - x$, and below by $y = 1$.
29. Find the extreme values of $f(x) = x^3 - 3x^2$ and find the area of the region enclosed by the graph of f and the x-axis.
30. Find the area of the region cut from the first quadrant by the curve $x^{1/2} + y^{1/2} = a^{1/2}$.
31. Find the total area of the region enclosed by the curve $x = y^{2/3}$ and the lines $x = y$ and $y = -1$.
32. Find the total area of the region between the curves $y = \sin x$ and $y = \cos x$ for $0 \le x \le 3\pi/2$.
33. **Area** Find the area between the curve $y = 2(\ln x)/x$ and the x-axis from $x = 1$ to $x = e$.
34. **a.** Show that the area between the curve $y = 1/x$ and the x-axis from $x = 10$ to $x = 20$ is the same as the area between the curve and the x-axis from $x = 1$ to $x = 2$.

b. Show that the area between the curve $y = 1/x$ and the x-axis from ka to kb is the same as the area between the curve and the x-axis from $x = a$ to $x = b$ $(0 < a < b, k > 0)$.

35. Show that $y = x^2 + \int_1^x \frac{1}{t}\,dt$ solves the initial value problem

$$\frac{d^2y}{dx^2} = 2 - \frac{1}{x^2}; \quad y'(1) = 3, \quad y(1) = 1.$$

36. Show that $y = \int_0^x \left(1 + 2\sqrt{\sec t}\right) dt$ solves the initial value problem

$$\frac{d^2y}{dx^2} = \sqrt{\sec x}\tan x; \quad y'(0) = 3, \quad y(0) = 0.$$

Express the solutions of the initial value problems in Exercises 37 and 38 in terms of integrals.

37. $\frac{dy}{dx} = \frac{\sin x}{x}, \quad y(5) = -3$
38. $\frac{dy}{dx} = \sqrt{2 - \sin^2 x}, \quad y(-1) = 2$

Solve the initial value problems in Exercises 39–42.

39. $\frac{dy}{dx} = \frac{1}{\sqrt{1 - x^2}}, \quad y(0) = 0$
40. $\frac{dy}{dx} = \frac{1}{x^2 + 1} - 1, \quad y(0) = 1$
41. $\frac{dy}{dx} = \frac{1}{x\sqrt{x^2 - 1}}, \quad x > 1; \quad y(2) = \pi$
42. $\frac{dy}{dx} = \frac{1}{1 + x^2} - \frac{2}{\sqrt{1 - x^2}}, \quad y(0) = 2$

Evaluate the integrals in Exercises 43–72.

43. $\int 2(\cos x)^{-1/2} \sin x\, dx$

44. $\int (\tan x)^{-3/2} \sec^2 x\, dx$

45. $\int (2\theta + 1 + 2\cos(2\theta + 1))\, d\theta$

46. $\int \left(\frac{1}{\sqrt{2\theta - \pi}} + 2\sec^2(2\theta - \pi)\right) d\theta$

47. $\int \left(t - \frac{2}{t}\right)\left(t + \frac{2}{t}\right) dt$

48. $\int \frac{(t+1)^2 - 1}{t^4}\, dt$

49. $\int \sqrt{t} \sin(2t^{3/2})\, dt$

50. $\int \sec\theta \tan\theta \sqrt{1 + \sec\theta}\, d\theta$

51. $\int e^x \sec^2(e^x - 7)\, dx$

52. $\int e^y \csc(e^y + 1) \cot(e^y + 1)\, dy$

53. $\int \sec^2(x) e^{\tan x}\, dx$

54. $\int \csc^2 x\, e^{\cot x}\, dx$

55. $\int_{-1}^{1} \frac{dx}{3x - 4}$

56. $\int_1^e \frac{\sqrt{\ln x}}{x}\, dx$

57. $\int_0^4 \frac{2t}{t^2 - 25}\, dt$

58. $\int \frac{\tan(\ln v)}{v}\, dv$

59. $\int \frac{(\ln x)^{-3}}{x}\, dx$

60. $\int \frac{1}{r} \csc^2(1 + \ln r)\, dr$

61. $\int x 3^{x^2}\, dx$

62. $\int 2^{\tan x} \sec^2 x\, dx$

63. $\int \frac{3\, dr}{\sqrt{1 - 4(r-1)^2}}$

64. $\int \frac{6\, dr}{\sqrt{4 - (r+1)^2}}$

65. $\int \frac{dx}{2 + (x-1)^2}$

66. $\int \frac{dx}{1 + (3x+1)^2}$

67. $\int \frac{dx}{(2x-1)\sqrt{(2x-1)^2 - 4}}$

68. $\int \frac{dx}{(x+3)\sqrt{(x+3)^2 - 25}}$

69. $\int \frac{e^{\sin^{-1}\sqrt{x}}\, dx}{2\sqrt{x - x^2}}$

70. $\int \frac{\sqrt{\sin^{-1} x}\, dx}{\sqrt{1 - x^2}}$

71. $\int \frac{dy}{\sqrt{\tan^{-1} y}\,(1 + y^2)}$

72. $\int \frac{(\tan^{-1} x)^2\, dx}{1 + x^2}$

Evaluate the integrals in Exercises 73–112.

73. $\int_{-1}^{1} (3x^2 - 4x + 7)\, dx$

74. $\int_0^1 (8s^3 - 12s^2 + 5)\, ds$

75. $\int_1^2 \frac{4}{v^2}\, dv$

76. $\int_1^{27} x^{-4/3}\, dx$

77. $\int_1^4 \frac{dt}{t\sqrt{t}}$

78. $\int_1^4 \frac{(1 + \sqrt{u})^{1/2}}{\sqrt{u}}\, du$

79. $\int_0^1 \frac{36\, dx}{(2x+1)^3}$

80. $\int_0^1 \frac{dr}{\sqrt[3]{(7 - 5r)^2}}$

81. $\int_{1/8}^{1} x^{-1/3}(1 - x^{2/3})^{3/2}\, dx$

82. $\int_0^{1/2} x^3(1 + 9x^4)^{-3/2}\, dx$

83. $\int_0^{\pi} \sin^2 5r\, dr$

84. $\int_0^{\pi/4} \cos^2\left(4t - \frac{\pi}{4}\right) dt$

85. $\int_0^{\pi/3} \sec^2\theta\, d\theta$

86. $\int_{\pi/4}^{3\pi/4} \csc^2 x\, dx$

87. $\int_{\pi}^{3\pi} \cot^2 \frac{x}{6}\, dx$

88. $\int_0^{\pi} \tan^2 \frac{\theta}{3}\, d\theta$

89. $\int_{-\pi/3}^{0} \sec x \tan x\, dx$

90. $\int_{\pi/4}^{3\pi/4} \csc z \cot z\, dz$

91. $\int_0^{\pi/2} 5(\sin x)^{3/2} \cos x\, dx$

92. $\int_{-\pi/2}^{\pi/2} 15 \sin^4 3x \cos 3x\, dx$

93. $\int_0^{\pi/2} \frac{3 \sin x \cos x}{\sqrt{1 + 3\sin^2 x}}\, dx$

94. $\int_0^{\pi/4} \frac{\sec^2 x}{(1 + 7\tan x)^{2/3}}\, dx$

95. $\int_1^4 \left(\frac{x}{8} + \frac{1}{2x}\right) dx$

96. $\int_1^8 \left(\frac{2}{3x} - \frac{8}{x^2}\right) dx$

97. $\int_{-2}^{-1} e^{-(x+1)}\, dx$

98. $\int_{-\ln 2}^{0} e^{2w}\, dw$

99. $\int_0^{\ln 5} e^r(3e^r + 1)^{-3/2}\, dr$

100. $\int_0^{\ln 9} e^{\theta}(e^{\theta} - 1)^{1/2}\, d\theta$

101. $\int_1^e \frac{1}{x}(1 + 7\ln x)^{-1/3}\, dx$

102. $\int_1^3 \frac{(\ln(v+1))^2}{v+1}\, dv$

103. $\int_1^8 \frac{\log_4 \theta}{\theta}\, d\theta$

104. $\int_1^e \frac{8 \ln 3 \log_3 \theta}{\theta}\, d\theta$

105. $\int_{-3/4}^{3/4} \frac{6\, dx}{\sqrt{9 - 4x^2}}$

106. $\int_{-1/5}^{1/5} \frac{6\, dx}{\sqrt{4 - 25x^2}}$

107. $\int_{-2}^{2} \frac{3\, dt}{4 + 3t^2}$

108. $\int_{\sqrt{3}}^{3} \frac{dt}{3 + t^2}$

109. $\int \frac{dy}{y\sqrt{4y^2 - 1}}$

110. $\int \frac{24\, dy}{y\sqrt{y^2 - 16}}$

111. $\int_{\sqrt{2}/3}^{2/3} \frac{dy}{|y|\sqrt{9y^2 - 1}}$

112. $\int_{-2/\sqrt{5}}^{-\sqrt{6}/\sqrt{5}} \frac{dy}{|y|\sqrt{5y^2 - 3}}$

113. Find the average value of $f(x) = mx + b$

a. over $[-1, 1]$

b. over $[-k, k]$

114. Find the average value of

a. $y = \sqrt{3x}$ over $[0, 3]$

b. $y = \sqrt{ax}$ over $[0, a]$

115. Let f be a function that is differentiable on $[a, b]$. In Chapter 2 we defined the average rate of change of f over $[a, b]$ to be

$$\frac{f(b) - f(a)}{b - a}$$

and the instantaneous rate of change of f at x to be $f'(x)$. In this chapter we defined the average value of a function. For the new definition of average to be consistent with the old one, we should have

$$\frac{f(b) - f(a)}{b - a} = \text{average value of } f' \text{ on } [a, b].$$

Is this the case? Give reasons for your answer.

116. Is it true that the average value of an integrable function over an interval of length 2 is half the function's integral over the interval? Give reasons for your answer.

117. a. Show that $\int \ln x \, dx = x \ln x - x + C$.

b. Find the average value of $\ln x$ over $[1, e]$.

118. Find the average value of $f(x) = 1/x$ on $[1, 2]$.

T **119.** Compute the average value of the temperature function

$$f(x) = 37 \sin\left(\frac{2\pi}{365}(x - 101)\right) + 25$$

for a 365-day year. This is one way to estimate the annual mean air temperature in Fairbanks, Alaska. The National Weather Service's official figure, a numerical average of the daily normal mean air temperatures for the year, is 25.7°F, which is slightly higher than the average value of $f(x)$. Figure 3.28 shows why.

T **120. Specific heat of a gas** Specific heat C_v is the amount of heat required to raise the temperature of a given mass of gas with constant volume by 1°C, measured in units of cal/deg-mole (calories per degree gram molecule). The specific heat of oxygen depends on its temperature T and satisfies the formula

$$C_v = 8.27 + 10^{-5}(26T - 1.87T^2).$$

Find the average value of C_v for $20° \le T \le 675°\text{C}$ and the temperature at which it is attained.

In Exercises 121–128, find dy/dx.

121. $y = \int_2^x \sqrt{2 + \cos^3 t}\, dt$

122. $y = \int_2^{7x^2} \sqrt{2 + \cos^3 t}\, dt$

123. $y = \int_x^1 \frac{6}{3 + t^4}\, dt$

124. $y = \int_{\sec x}^2 \frac{1}{t^2 + 1}\, dt$

125. $y = \int_{\ln x^2}^0 e^{\cos t}\, dt$

126. $y = \int_1^{e^{\sqrt{x}}} \ln(t^2 + 1)\, dt$

127. $y = \int_0^{\sin^{-1} x} \frac{dt}{\sqrt{1 - 2t^2}}$

128. $y = \int_{\tan^{-1} x}^{\pi/4} e^{\sqrt{t}}\, dt$

129. Is it true that every function $y = f(x)$ that is differentiable on $[a, b]$ is itself the derivative of some function on $[a, b]$? Give reasons for your answer.

130. Suppose that $F(x)$ is an antiderivative of $f(x) = \sqrt{1 + x^4}$. Express $\int_0^1 \sqrt{1 + x^4}\, dx$ in terms of F and give a reason for your answer.

131. Find dy/dx if $y = \int_x^1 \sqrt{1 + t^2}\, dt$. Explain the main steps in your calculation.

132. Find dy/dx if $y = \int_{\cos x}^0 (1/(1 - t^2))\, dt$. Explain the main steps in your calculation.

133. A new parking lot To meet the demand for parking, your town has allocated the area shown here. As the town engineer, you have been asked by the town council to find out if the lot can be built for \$10,000. The cost to clear the land will be \$0.10 a square foot, and the lot will cost \$2.00 a square foot to pave. Can the job be done for \$10,000? Use a lower sum estimate to see. (Answers may vary slightly, depending on the estimate used.)

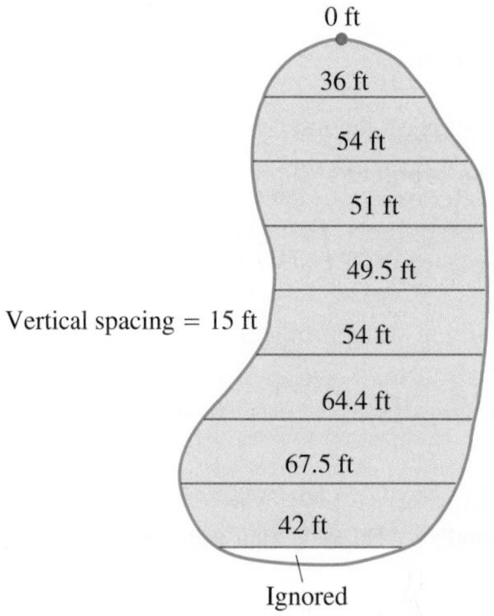

134. Skydivers A and B are in a helicopter hovering at 6400 ft. Skydiver A jumps and descends for 4 sec before opening her parachute. The helicopter then climbs to 7000 ft and hovers there. Forty-five seconds after A leaves the aircraft, B jumps and descends for 13 sec before opening his parachute. Both skydivers descend at 16 ft/sec with parachutes open. Assume that the skydivers fall freely (no effective air resistance) before their parachutes open.

a. At what altitude does A's parachute open?

b. At what altitude does B's parachute open?

c. Which skydiver lands first?

135. A particle is traveling upward and to the right along the curve $y = \ln x$. Its x-coordinate is increasing at the rate $(dx/dt) = \sqrt{x}$ m/sec. At what rate is the y-coordinate changing at the point $(e^2, 2)$?

136. A girl is sliding down a slide shaped like the curve $y = 9e^{-x/3}$. Her y-coordinate is changing at the rate $dy/dt = (-1/4)\sqrt{9 - y}$ ft/sec. At approximately what rate is her x-coordinate changing when she reaches the bottom of the slide at $x = 9$ ft? (Take e^3 to be 20 and round your answer to the nearest ft/sec.)

Chapter 5 Additional and Advanced Exercises

1. a. If $\int_0^1 7f(x)\,dx = 7$, does $\int_0^1 f(x)\,dx = 1$?

b. If $\int_0^1 f(x)\,dx = 4$ and $f(x) \geq 0$, does

$$\int_0^1 \sqrt{f(x)}\,\mathrm{dx} = \sqrt{4} = 2?$$

Give reasons for your answers.

2. Suppose $\int_{-2}^{2} f(x)\,dx = 4$, $\int_{2}^{5} f(x)\,dx = 3$, $\int_{-2}^{5} g(x)\,dx = 2$.
Which, if any, of the following statements are true?

a. $\int_5^2 f(x)\,dx = -3$ **b.** $\int_{-2}^{5} (f(x) + g(x)) = 9$

c. $f(x) \leq g(x)$ on the interval $-2 \leq x \leq 5$

3. Initial value problem Show that

$$y = \frac{1}{a}\int_0^x f(t)\sin a(x - t)\,dt$$

solves the initial value problem

$$\frac{d^2y}{dx^2} + a^2y = f(x), \quad \frac{dy}{dx} = 0 \text{ and } y = 0 \text{ when } x = 0.$$

(*Hint:* $\sin(ax - at) = \sin ax \cos at - \cos ax \sin at$.)

4. Proportionality Suppose that x and y are related by the equation

$$x = \int_0^y \frac{1}{\sqrt{1 + 4t^2}}\,dt.$$

Show that d^2y/dx^2 is proportional to y and find the constant of proportionality.

5. Find $f(4)$ if

a. $\int_0^{x^2} f(t)\,dt = x\cos \pi x$ **b.** $\int_0^{f(x)} t^2\,dt = x\cos \pi x$.

6. Find $f(\pi/2)$ from the following information.

i. f is positive and continuous.

ii. The area under the curve $y = f(x)$ from $x = 0$ to $x = a$ is

$$\frac{a^2}{2} + \frac{a}{2}\sin a + \frac{\pi}{2}\cos a.$$

7. The area of the region in the xy-plane enclosed by the x-axis, the curve $y = f(x)$, $f(x) \geq 0$, and the lines $x = 1$ and $x = b$ is equal to $\sqrt{b^2 + 1} - \sqrt{2}$ for all $b > 1$. Find $f(x)$.

8. Prove that

$$\int_0^x \left(\int_0^u f(t)\,dt\right) du = \int_0^x f(u)(x - u)\,du.$$

(*Hint:* Express the integral on the right-hand side as the difference of two integrals. Then show that both sides of the equation have the same derivative with respect to x.)

9. Finding a curve Find the equation for the curve in the xy-plane that passes through the point $(1, -1)$ if its slope at x is always $3x^2 + 2$.

10. Shoveling dirt You sling a shovelful of dirt up from the bottom of a hole with an initial velocity of 32 ft/sec. The dirt must rise 17 ft above the release point to clear the edge of the hole. Is that enough speed to get the dirt out, or had you better duck?

Piecewise Continuous Functions Although we are mainly interested in continuous functions, many functions in applications are piecewise continuous. A function $f(x)$ is **piecewise continuous on a closed interval I** if f has only finitely many discontinuities in I, the limits

$$\lim_{x\to c^-} f(x) \text{ and } \lim_{x\to c^+} f(x)$$

exist and are finite at every interior point of I, and the appropriate one-sided limits exist and are finite at the endpoints of I. All piecewise continuous functions are integrable. The points of discontinuity subdivide I into open and half-open subintervals on which f is continuous, and the limit criteria above guarantee that f has a continuous extension to the closure of each subinterval. To integrate a piecewise continuous function, we integrate the individual extensions and add the results. The integral of

$$f(x) = \begin{cases} 1 - x, & -1 \leq x < 0 \\ x^2, & 0 \leq x < 2 \\ -1, & 2 \leq x \leq 3 \end{cases}$$

(Figure 5.33) over $[-1, 3]$ is

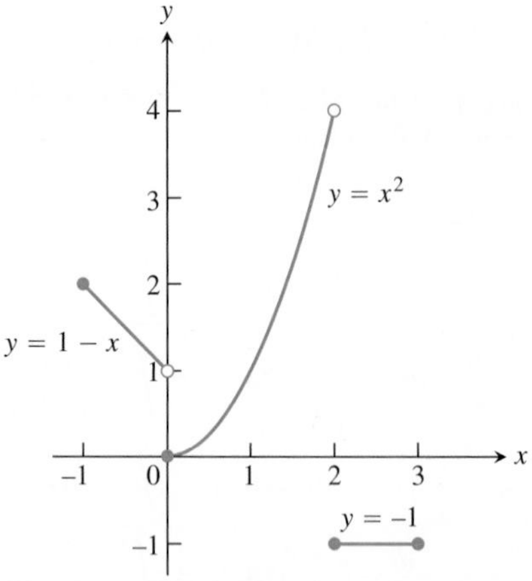

FIGURE 5.33 Piecewise continuous functions like this are integrated piece by piece.

$$\begin{aligned}\int_{-1}^{3} f(x)\,dx &= \int_{-1}^{0}(1-x)\,dx + \int_{0}^{2} x^2\,dx + \int_{2}^{3}(-1)\,dx \\ &= \left[x - \frac{x^2}{2}\right]_{-1}^{0} + \left[\frac{x^3}{3}\right]_{0}^{2} + \left[-x\right]_{2}^{3} \\ &= \frac{3}{2} + \frac{8}{3} - 1 = \frac{19}{6}.\end{aligned}$$

The Fundamental Theorem applies to piecewise continuous functions with the restriction that $(d/dx)\int_a^x f(t)\,dt$ is expected to equal $f(x)$ only at values of x at which f is continuous. There is a similar restriction on Leibniz's Rule (see page 389).

Graph the functions in Exercises 11–16 and integrate them over their domains.

11. $f(x) = \begin{cases} x^{2/3}, & -8 \le x < 0 \\ -4, & 0 \le x \le 3 \end{cases}$

12. $f(x) = \begin{cases} \sqrt{-x}, & -4 \le x < 0 \\ x^2 - 4, & 0 \le x \le 3 \end{cases}$

13. $g(t) = \begin{cases} t, & 0 \le t < 1 \\ \sin \pi t, & 1 \le t \le 2 \end{cases}$

14. $h(z) = \begin{cases} \sqrt{1 - z}, & 0 \le z < 1 \\ (7z - 6)^{-1/3}, & 1 \le z \le 2 \end{cases}$

15. $f(x) = \begin{cases} 1, & -2 \le x < -1 \\ 1 - x^2, & -1 \le x < 1 \\ 2, & 1 \le x \le 2 \end{cases}$

16. $h(r) = \begin{cases} r, & -1 \le r < 0 \\ 1 - r^2, & 0 \le r < 1 \\ 1, & 1 \le r \le 2 \end{cases}$

17. Find the average value of the function graphed in the accompanying figure.

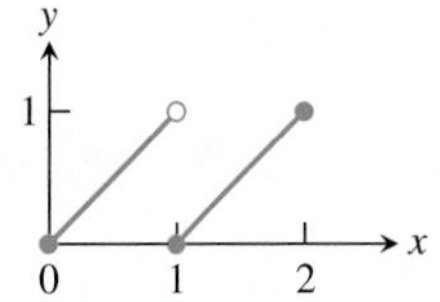

18. Find the average value of the function graphed in the accompanying figure.

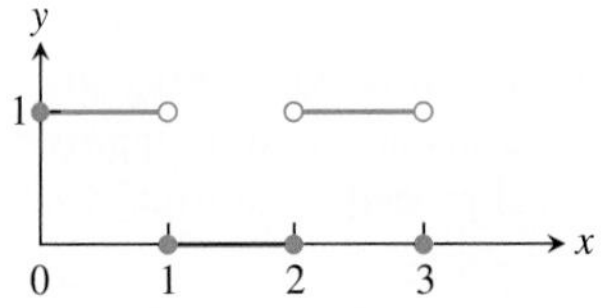

19. Verify the integral formulas in Table 5.6.

20. Verify the integral formulas in Table 5.7.

Evaluate the integrals in Exercises 21–28 in terms of

a. inverse hyperbolic functions.

b. natural logarithms.

21. $\displaystyle\int_0^{2\sqrt{3}} \frac{dx}{\sqrt{4 + x^2}}$

22. $\displaystyle\int_0^{1/3} \frac{6\,dx}{\sqrt{1 + 9x^2}}$

23. $\displaystyle\int_{5/4}^{2} \frac{dx}{1 - x^2}$

24. $\displaystyle\int_0^{1/2} \frac{dx}{1 - x^2}$

25. $\displaystyle\int_{1/5}^{3/13} \frac{dx}{x\sqrt{1 - 16x^2}}$

26. $\displaystyle\int_1^{2} \frac{dx}{x\sqrt{4 + x^2}}$

TABLE 5.6 Integral formulas for hyperbolic functions

$$\int \sinh u\,du = \cosh u + C$$

$$\int \cosh u\,du = \sinh u + C$$

$$\int \operatorname{sech}^2 u\,du = \tanh u + C$$

$$\int \operatorname{csch}^2 u\,du = -\coth u + C$$

$$\int \operatorname{sech} u \tanh u\,du = -\operatorname{sech} u + C$$

$$\int \operatorname{csch} u \coth u\,du = -\operatorname{csch} u + C$$

TABLE 5.7 Integral formulas for inverse hyperbolic functions

$$\int \frac{du}{\sqrt{a^2 + u^2}} = \sinh^{-1}\left(\frac{u}{a}\right) + C, \qquad a > 0$$

$$\int \frac{du}{\sqrt{u^2 - a^2}} = \cosh^{-1}\left(\frac{u}{a}\right) + C, \qquad u > a > 0$$

$$\int \frac{du}{a^2 - u^2} = \begin{cases} \dfrac{1}{a}\tanh^{-1}\left(\dfrac{u}{a}\right) + C & \text{if } u^2 < a^2 \\ \dfrac{1}{a}\coth^{-1}\left(\dfrac{u}{a}\right) + C, & \text{if } u^2 > a^2 \end{cases}$$

$$\int \frac{du}{u\sqrt{a^2 - u^2}} = -\frac{1}{a}\operatorname{sech}^{-1}\left(\frac{u}{a}\right) + C, \qquad 0 < u < a$$

$$\int \frac{du}{u\sqrt{a^2 + u^2}} = -\frac{1}{a}\operatorname{csch}^{-1}\left|\frac{u}{a}\right| + C, \qquad u \ne 0 \text{ and } a > 0$$

27. $\displaystyle\int_0^{\pi} \frac{\cos x\, dx}{\sqrt{1 + \sin^2 x}}$

28. $\displaystyle\int_1^{e} \frac{dx}{x\sqrt{1 + (\ln x)^2}}$

Find the limits in Exercises 29–32.

29. $\displaystyle\lim_{b \to 1^-} \int_0^b \frac{dx}{\sqrt{1 - x^2}}$

30. $\displaystyle\lim_{x \to \infty} \frac{1}{x} \int_0^x \tan^{-1} t\, dt$

31. $\displaystyle\lim_{n \to \infty} \left(\frac{1}{n+1} + \frac{1}{n+2} + \cdots + \frac{1}{2n} \right)$

32. $\displaystyle\lim_{n \to \infty} \frac{1}{n} \left(e^{1/n} + e^{2/n} + \cdots + e^{(n-1)/n} + e^{n/n} \right)$

Approximating Finite Sums with Integrals In many applications of calculus, integrals are used to approximate finite sums—the reverse of the usual procedure of using finite sums to approximate integrals.

For example, let's estimate the sum of the square roots of the first n positive integers, $\sqrt{1} + \sqrt{2} + \cdots + \sqrt{n}$. The integral

$$\int_0^1 \sqrt{x}\, dx = \frac{2}{3} x^{3/2} \Big]_0^1 = \frac{2}{3}$$

is the limit of the upper sums

$$S_n = \sqrt{\frac{1}{n}} \cdot \frac{1}{n} + \sqrt{\frac{2}{n}} \cdot \frac{1}{n} + \cdots + \sqrt{\frac{n}{n}} \cdot \frac{1}{n}$$
$$= \frac{\sqrt{1} + \sqrt{2} + \cdots + \sqrt{n}}{n^{3/2}}.$$

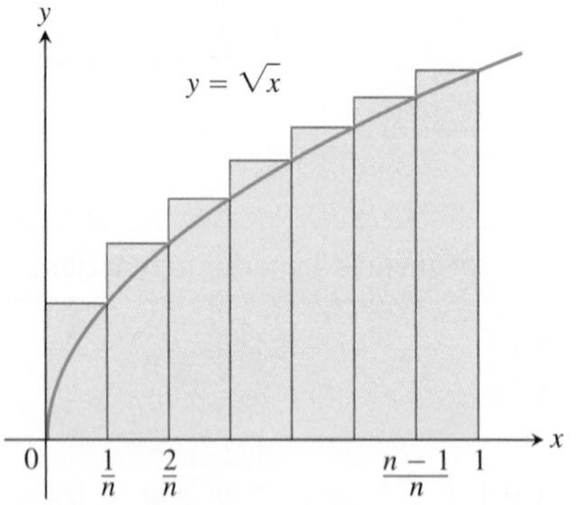

Therefore, when n is large, S_n will be close to $2/3$ and we will have

$$\text{Root sum} = \sqrt{1} + \sqrt{2} + \cdots + \sqrt{n} = S_n \cdot n^{3/2} \approx \frac{2}{3} n^{3/2}.$$

The following table shows how good the approximation can be.

n	Root sum	$(2/3)n^{3/2}$	Relative error
10	22.468	21.082	$1.386/22.468 \approx 6\%$
50	239.04	235.70	1.4%
100	671.46	666.67	0.7%
1000	21,097	21,082	0.07%

33. Evaluate

$$\lim_{n \to \infty} \frac{1^5 + 2^5 + 3^5 + \cdots + n^5}{n^6}$$

by showing that the limit is

$$\int_0^1 x^5\, dx$$

and evaluating the integral.

34. See Exercise 33. Evaluate

$$\lim_{n \to \infty} \frac{1}{n^4} (1^3 + 2^3 + 3^3 + \cdots + n^3).$$

35. Let $f(x)$ be a continuous function. Express

$$\lim_{n \to \infty} \frac{1}{n} \left[f\left(\frac{1}{n}\right) + f\left(\frac{2}{n}\right) + \cdots + f\left(\frac{n}{n}\right) \right]$$

as a definite integral.

36. Use the result of Exercise 35 to evaluate

a. $\displaystyle\lim_{n \to \infty} \frac{1}{n^2} (2 + 4 + 6 + \cdots + 2n),$

b. $\displaystyle\lim_{n \to \infty} \frac{1}{n^{16}} (1^{15} + 2^{15} + 3^{15} + \cdots + n^{15}),$

c. $\displaystyle\lim_{n \to \infty} \frac{1}{n} \left(\sin\frac{\pi}{n} + \sin\frac{2\pi}{n} + \sin\frac{3\pi}{n} + \cdots + \sin\frac{n\pi}{n} \right).$

What can be said about the following limits?

d. $\displaystyle\lim_{n \to \infty} \frac{1}{n^{17}} (1^{15} + 2^{15} + 3^{15} + \cdots + n^{15})$

e. $\displaystyle\lim_{n \to \infty} \frac{1}{n^{15}} (1^{15} + 2^{15} + 3^{15} + \cdots + n^{15})$

37. **a.** Show that the area A_n of an n-sided regular polygon in a circle of radius r is

$$A_n = \frac{nr^2}{2} \sin\frac{2\pi}{n}.$$

b. Find the limit of A_n as $n \to \infty$. Is this answer consistent with what you know about the area of a circle?

38. Let

$$S_n = \frac{1^2}{n^3} + \frac{2^2}{n^3} + \cdots + \frac{(n-1)^2}{n^3}.$$

To calculate $\lim_{n \to \infty} S_n$, show that

$$S_n = \frac{1}{n} \left[\left(\frac{1}{n}\right)^2 + \left(\frac{2}{n}\right)^2 + \cdots + \left(\frac{n-1}{n}\right)^2 \right]$$

and interpret S_n as an approximating sum of the integral

$$\int_0^1 x^2\, dx.$$

(*Hint:* Partition [0, 1] into n intervals of equal length and write out the approximating sum for inscribed rectangles.)

39. Find the areas between the curves $y = 2(\log_2 x)/x$ and $y = 2(\log_4 x)/x$ and the x-axis from $x = 1$ to $x = e$. What is the ratio of the larger area to the smaller?

40. For what $x > 0$ does $x^{(x^x)} = (x^x)^x$? Give reasons for your answer.

41. Find $f'(2)$ if $f(x) = e^{g(x)}$ and $g(x) = \int_2^x \frac{t}{1 + t^4}\, dt$.

42. **a.** Find df/dx if

$$f(x) = \int_1^{e^x} \frac{2 \ln t}{t}\, dt.$$

b. Find $f(0)$.

c. What can you conclude about the graph of f? Give reasons for your answer.

43. **A function defined by an integral** The graph of a function f consists of a semicircle and two line segments as shown. Let $g(x) = \int_1^x f(t)\, dt$.

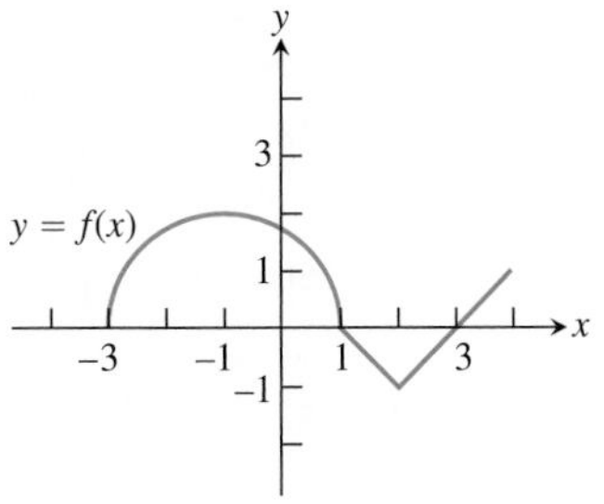

a. Find $g(1)$.

b. Find $g(3)$.

c. Find $g(-1)$.

d. Find all values of x on the open interval $(-3, 4)$ at which g has a relative maximum.

e. Write an equation for the line tangent to the graph of g at $x = -1$.

f. Find the x-coordinate of each point of inflection of the graph of g on the open interval $(-3, 4)$.

g. Find the range of g.

44. **A differential equation** Show that $y = \sin x + \int_x^{\pi} \cos 2t\, dt + 1$ satisfies both of the following conditions:

i. $y'' = -\sin x + 2 \sin 2x$

ii. $y = 1$ and $y' = -2$ when $x = \pi$.

45. Use the accompanying figure to show that

$$\int_0^{\pi/2} \sin x\, dx = \frac{\pi}{2} - \int_0^1 \sin^{-1} x\, dx.$$

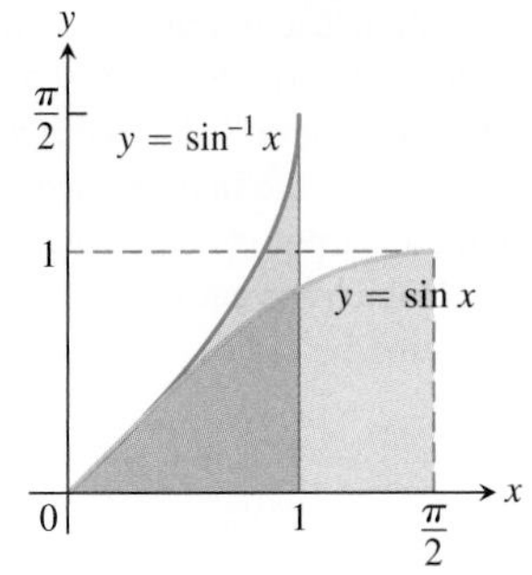

46. **Napier's inequality** Here are two pictorial proofs that

$$b > a > 0 \quad \Rightarrow \quad \frac{1}{b} < \frac{\ln b - \ln a}{b - a} < \frac{1}{a}.$$

Explain what is going on in each case.

a.

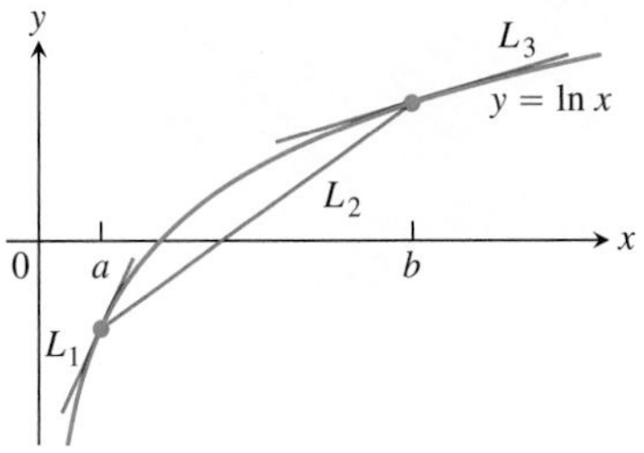

b.

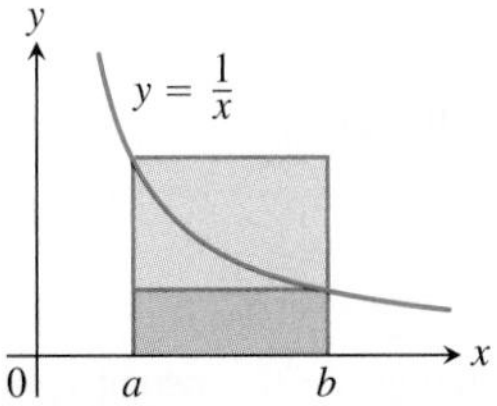

(*Source:* Roger B. Nelson, *College Mathematics Journal*, Vol. 24, No. 2, March 1993, p. 165.)

Leibniz's Rule In applications, we sometimes encounter functions like

$$f(x) = \int_{\sin x}^{x^2} (1 + t)\, dt \qquad \text{and} \qquad g(x) = \int_{\sqrt{x}}^{2\sqrt{x}} \sin t^2\, dt,$$

defined by integrals that have variable upper limits of integration and variable lower limits of integration at the same time. The first integral can be evaluated directly, but the second cannot. We may find the derivative of either integral, however, by a formula called **Leibniz's Rule**.

Leibniz's Rule

If f is continuous on $[a, b]$ and if $u(x)$ and $v(x)$ are differentiable functions of x whose values lie in $[a, b]$, then

$$\frac{d}{dx} \int_{u(x)}^{v(x)} f(t)\, dt = f(v(x)) \frac{dv}{dx} - f(u(x)) \frac{du}{dx}.$$

Figure 5.34 gives a geometric interpretation of Leibniz's Rule. It shows a carpet of variable width $f(t)$ that is being rolled up at the left at the same time x as it is being unrolled at the right. (In this interpretation, time is x, not t.) At time x, the floor is covered from $u(x)$ to $v(x)$. The rate du/dx at which the carpet is being rolled up need not be the same as the rate dv/dx at which the carpet is being laid down. At any given time x, the area covered by carpet is

$$A(x) = \int_{u(x)}^{v(x)} f(t)\,dt.$$

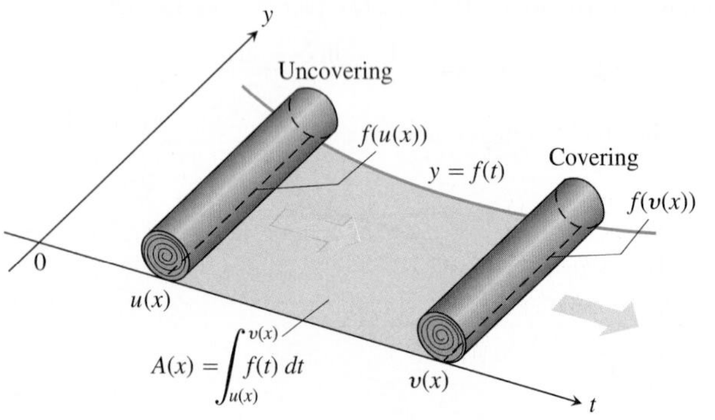

FIGURE 5.34 Rolling and unrolling a carpet: a geometric interpretation of Leibniz's Rule:

$$\frac{dA}{dx} = f(v(x))\frac{dv}{dx} - f(u(x))\frac{du}{dx}.$$

At what rate is the covered area changing? At the instant x, $A(x)$ is increasing by the width $f(v(x))$ of the unrolling carpet times the rate dv/dx at which the carpet is being unrolled. That is, $A(x)$ is being increased at the rate

$$f(v(x))\frac{dv}{dx}.$$

At the same time, A is being decreased at the rate

$$f(u(x))\frac{du}{dx},$$

the width at the end that is being rolled up times the rate du/dx. The net rate of change in A is

$$\frac{dA}{dx} = f(v(x))\frac{dv}{dx} - f(u(x))\frac{du}{dx},$$

which is precisely Leibniz's Rule.

To prove the rule, let F be an antiderivative of f on $[a, b]$. Then

$$\int_{u(x)}^{v(x)} f(t)\,dt = F(v(x)) - F(u(x)).$$

Differentiating both sides of this equation with respect to x gives the equation we want:

$$\begin{aligned}\frac{d}{dx}\int_{u(x)}^{v(x)} f(t)\,dt &= \frac{d}{dx}\Big[F(v(x)) - F(u(x))\Big]\\ &= F'(v(x))\frac{dv}{dx} - F'(u(x))\frac{du}{dx} \qquad \text{Chain Rule}\\ &= f(v(x))\frac{dv}{dx} - f(u(x))\frac{du}{dx}.\end{aligned}$$

Use Leibniz's Rule to find the derivatives of the functions in Exercises 47–54.

47. $f(x) = \int_{1/x}^{x} \frac{1}{t}\,dt$

48. $f(x) = \int_{\cos x}^{\sin x} \frac{1}{1 - t^2}\,dt$

49. $g(y) = \int_{\sqrt{y}}^{2\sqrt{y}} \sin t^2\,dt$

50. $g(y) = \int_{\sqrt{y}}^{y^2} \frac{e^t}{t}\,dt$

51. $y = \int_{x^2/2}^{x^2} \ln\sqrt{t}\,dt$

52. $y = \int_{\sqrt{x}}^{\sqrt[3]{x}} \ln t\,dt$

53. $y = \int_{0}^{\ln x} \sin e^t\,dt$

54. $y = \int_{e^{4\sqrt{x}}}^{e^{2x}} \ln t\,dt$

55. Use Leibniz's Rule to find the value of x that maximizes the value of the integral

$$\int_{x}^{x+3} t(5 - t)\,dt.$$

Problems like this arise in the mathematical theory of political elections. See "The Entry Problem in a Political Race," by Steven J. Brams and Philip D. Straffin, Jr., in *Political Equilibrium*, Peter Ordeshook and Kenneth Shepfle, Editors, Kluwer-Nijhoff, Boston, 1982, pp. 181–195.

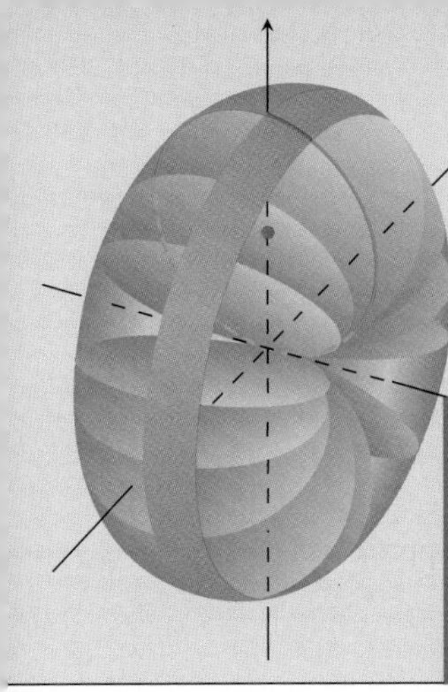

Chapter 6

APPLICATIONS OF DEFINITE INTEGRALS

OVERVIEW In Chapter 5 we saw that a continuous function over a closed interval has a definite integral, which is the limit of any Riemann sum for the function. We proved that we could evaluate definite integrals using the Fundamental Theorem of Calculus. We also found that the area under a curve or the area between two curves could be computed as definite integrals.

In this chapter we extend the applications of definite integrals to finding volumes, lengths of plane curves, and areas of surfaces of revolution. We also use integrals to solve problems involving exponential growth and decay, the work done by a force, the location of an object's center of mass, and a simple type of differential equation.

6.1 Volumes by Slicing and Rotation About an Axis

In this section we define volumes of solids whose cross-sections are plane regions. A **cross-section** of a solid S is the plane region formed by intersecting S with a plane (Figure 6.1).

Suppose we want to find the volume of a solid S like the one in Figure 6.1. We begin by extending the definition of a cylinder from classical geometry to cylindrical solids with arbitrary bases (Figure 6.2). If the cylindrical solid has a known base area A and height h, then the volume of the cylindrical solid is

$$\text{Volume} = \text{area} \times \text{height} = A \cdot h.$$

This equation forms the basis for defining the volumes of many solids that are not cylindrical, like the one in Figure 6.1, by the *method of slicing*.

If the cross-section of the solid S at each point x in the interval $[a, b]$ is a region $R(x)$ of area $A(x)$, and A is a continuous function of x, we can define and calculate the volume of the solid S as a definite integral in the following way.

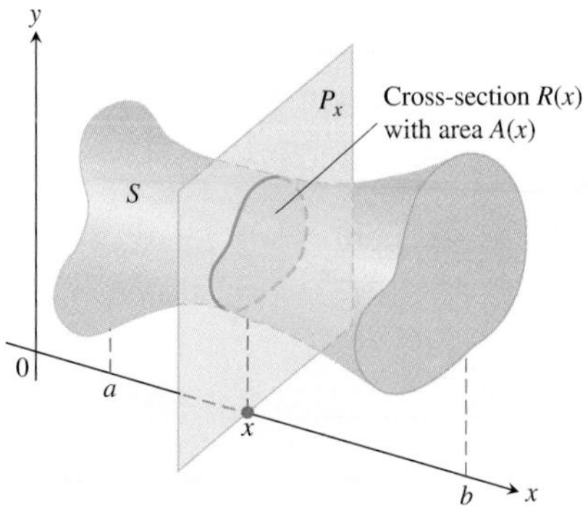

FIGURE 6.1 A cross-section of the solid S formed by intersecting S with a plane P_x perpendicular to the x-axis through the point x in the interval $[a, b]$.

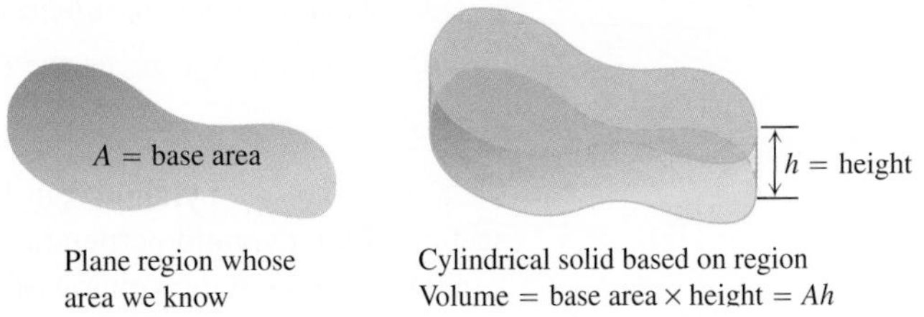

FIGURE 6.2 The volume of a cylindrical solid is always defined to be its base area times its height.

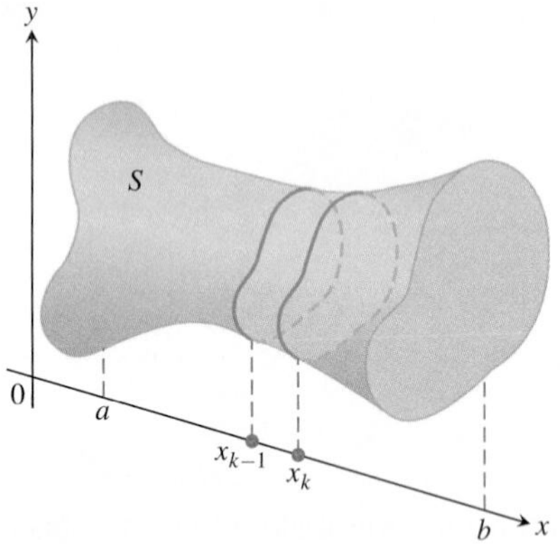

FIGURE 6.3 A typical thin slab in the solid S.

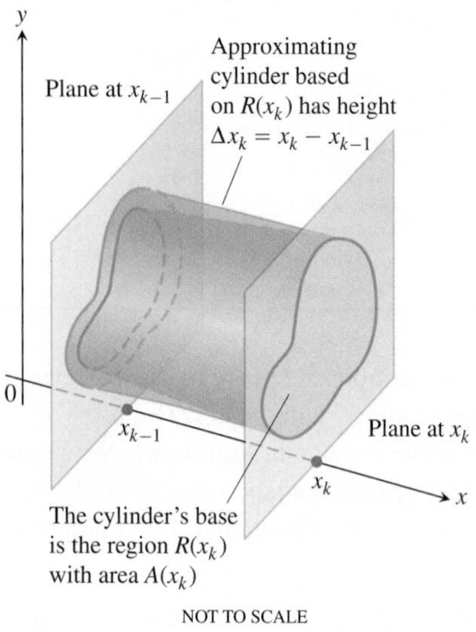

FIGURE 6.4 The solid thin slab in Figure 6.3 is approximated by the cylindrical solid with base $R(x_k)$ having area $A(x_k)$ and height $\Delta x_k = x_k - x_{k-1}$.

We partition $[a, b]$ into subintervals of width (length) Δx_k and slice the solid, as we would a loaf of bread, by planes perpendicular to the x-axis at the partition points $a = x_0 < x_1 < \cdots < x_n = b$. The planes P_{x_k}, perpendicular to the x-axis at the partition points, slice S into thin "slabs" (like thin slices of a loaf of bread). A typical slab is shown in Figure 6.3. We approximate the slab between the plane at x_{k-1} and the plane at x_k by a cylindrical solid with base area $A(x_k)$ and height $\Delta x_k = x_k - x_{k-1}$ (Figure 6.4). The volume V_k of this cylindrical solid is $A(x_k) \cdot \Delta x_k$, which is approximately the same volume as that of the slab:

$$\text{Volume of the } k\text{th slab} \approx V_k = A(x_k)\, \Delta x_k.$$

The volume V of the entire solid S is therefore approximated by the sum of these cylindrical volumes,

$$V \approx \sum_{k=1}^{n} V_k = \sum_{k=1}^{n} A(x_k)\, \Delta x_k.$$

This is a Riemann sum for the function $A(x)$ on $[a, b]$. We expect the approximations from these sums to improve as the norm of the partition of $[a, b]$ goes to zero. Taking a partition of $[a, b]$ into n subintervals with $\|P\| \to 0$ gives

$$\lim_{n\to\infty} \sum_{k=1}^{n} A(x_k)\, \Delta x_k = \int_a^b A(x)\, dx.$$

So we define their limiting definite integral to be the volume of the solid S.

DEFINITION The **volume** of a solid of known integrable cross-sectional area $A(x)$ from $x = a$ to $x = b$ is the integral of A from a to b,

$$V = \int_a^b A(x)\, dx.$$

This definition applies whenever $A(x)$ is continuous, or more generally, when it is integrable. To apply the formula in the definition to calculate the volume of a solid, take the following steps:

Calculating the Volume of a Solid

1. *Sketch the solid and a typical cross-section.*
2. *Find a formula for* $A(x)$, the area of a typical cross-section.
3. *Find the limits of integration.*
4. *Integrate* $A(x)$ using the Fundamental Theorem.

EXAMPLE 1 A pyramid 3 m high has a square base that is 3 m on a side. The cross-section of the pyramid perpendicular to the altitude x m down from the vertex is a square x m on a side. Find the volume of the pyramid.

Solution

1. *A sketch.* We draw the pyramid with its altitude along the x-axis and its vertex at the origin and include a typical cross-section (Figure 6.5).

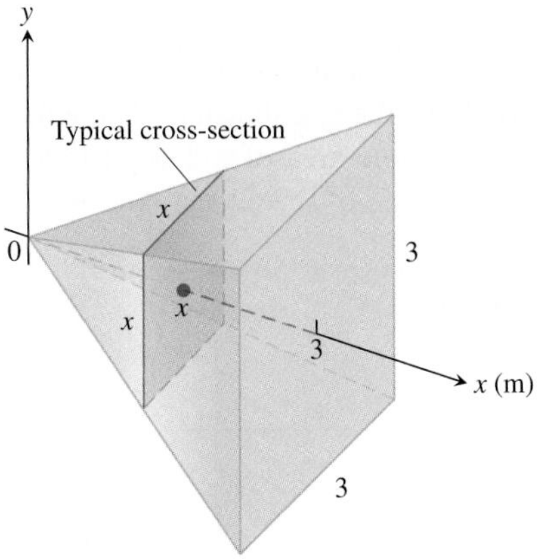

FIGURE 6.5 The cross-sections of the pyramid in example 1 are squares.

2. *A formula for $A(x)$.* The cross-section at x is a square x meters on a side, so its area is

$$A(x) = x^2.$$

3. *The limits of integration.* The squares lie on the planes from $x = 0$ to $x = 3$.
4. *Integrate to find the volume.*

$$V = \int_0^3 A(x)\,dx = \int_0^3 x^2\,dx = \frac{x^3}{3}\bigg]_0^3 = 9 \text{ m}^3$$ ∎

HISTORICAL BIOGRAPHY

Bonaventura Cavalieri
(1598–1647)

EXAMPLE 2 Cavalieri's principle says that solids with equal altitudes and identical cross-sectional areas at each height have the same volume (Figure 6.6). This follows immediately from the definition of volume, because the cross-sectional area function $A(x)$ and the interval $[a, b]$ are the same for both solids.

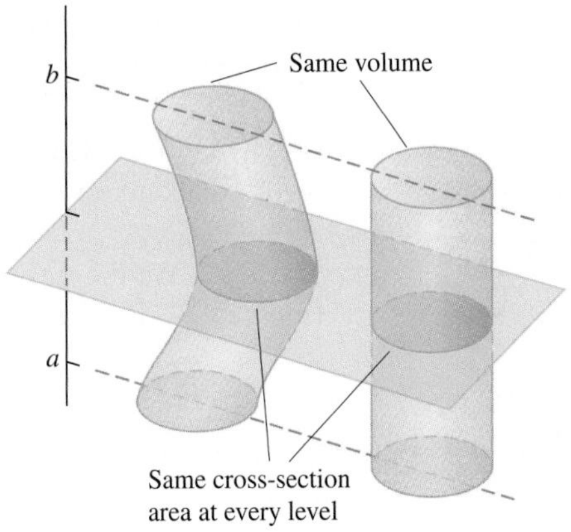

FIGURE 6.6 *Cavalieri's principle:* These solids have the same volume, which can be illustrated with stacks of coins. ∎

EXAMPLE 3 A curved wedge is cut from a circular cylinder of radius 3 by two planes. One plane is perpendicular to the axis of the cylinder. The second plane crosses the first plane at a 45° angle at the center of the cylinder. Find the volume of the wedge.

Solution We draw the wedge and sketch a typical cross-section perpendicular to the x-axis (Figure 6.7). The cross-section at x is a rectangle of area

$$A(x) = (\text{height})(\text{width}) = (x)\left(2\sqrt{9 - x^2}\right)$$
$$= 2x\sqrt{9 - x^2}.$$

The rectangles run from $x = 0$ to $x = 3$, so we have

$$V = \int_a^b A(x)\,dx = \int_0^3 2x\sqrt{9 - x^2}\,dx$$
$$= -\frac{2}{3}(9 - x^2)^{3/2}\bigg]_0^3$$
$$= 0 + \frac{2}{3}(9)^{3/2}$$
$$= 18.$$ ∎

Let $u = 9 - x^2$, $du = -2x\,dx$, integrate, and substitute back.

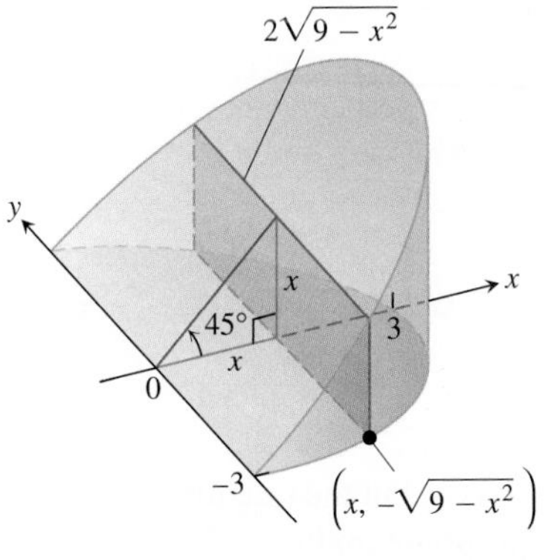

FIGURE 6.7 The wedge of Example 3, sliced perpendicular to the x-axis. The cross-sections are rectangles.

Solids of Revolution: The Disk Method

The solid generated by rotating (or revolving) a plane region about an axis in its plane is called a **solid of revolution**. To find the volume of a solid like the one shown in Figure 6.8, we need only observe that the cross-sectional area $A(x)$ is the area of a disk of radius $R(x)$, the distance of the planar region's boundary from the axis of revolution. The area is then

$$A(x) = \pi(\text{radius})^2 = \pi[R(x)]^2.$$

So the definition of volume gives

$$V = \int_a^b A(x)\,dx = \int_a^b \pi[R(x)]^2\,dx.$$

This method for calculating the volume of a solid of revolution is often called the **disk method** because a cross-section is a circular disk of radius $R(x)$.

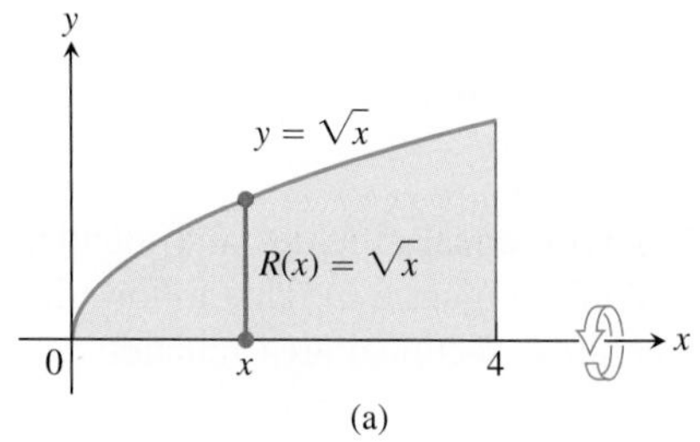

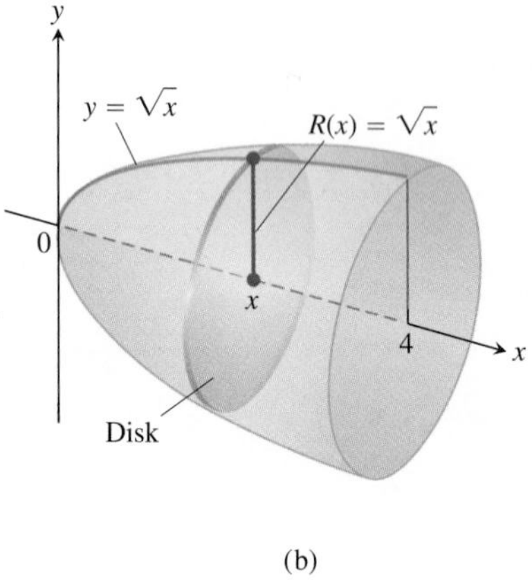

FIGURE 6.8 The region (a) and solid of revolution (b) in Example 4.

EXAMPLE 4 The region between the curve $y = \sqrt{x}, 0 \le x \le 4$, and the x-axis is revolved about the x-axis to generate a solid. Find its volume.

Solution We draw figures showing the region, a typical radius, and the generated solid (Figure 6.8). The volume is

$$\begin{aligned} V &= \int_a^b \pi[R(x)]^2\,dx \\ &= \int_0^4 \pi\left[\sqrt{x}\right]^2 dx \qquad R(x) = \sqrt{x} \\ &= \pi\int_0^4 x\,dx = \pi\frac{x^2}{2}\bigg]_0^4 = \pi\frac{(4)^2}{2} = 8\pi. \end{aligned}$$

■

EXAMPLE 5 The circle

$$x^2 + y^2 = a^2$$

is rotated about the x-axis to generate a sphere. Find its volume.

Solution We imagine the sphere cut into thin slices by planes perpendicular to the x-axis (Figure 6.9). The cross-sectional area at a typical point x between $-a$ and a is

$$A(x) = \pi y^2 = \pi(a^2 - x^2).$$

Therefore, the volume is

$$V = \int_{-a}^{a} A(x)\,dx = \int_{-a}^{a} \pi(a^2 - x^2)\,dx = \pi\left[a^2x - \frac{x^3}{3}\right]_{-a}^{a} = \frac{4}{3}\pi a^3.$$

■

The axis of revolution in the next example is not the x-axis, but the rule for calculating the volume is the same: Integrate $\pi(\text{radius})^2$ between appropriate limits.

EXAMPLE 6 Find the volume of the solid generated by revolving the region bounded by $y = \sqrt{x}$ and the lines $y = 1, x = 4$ about the line $y = 1$.

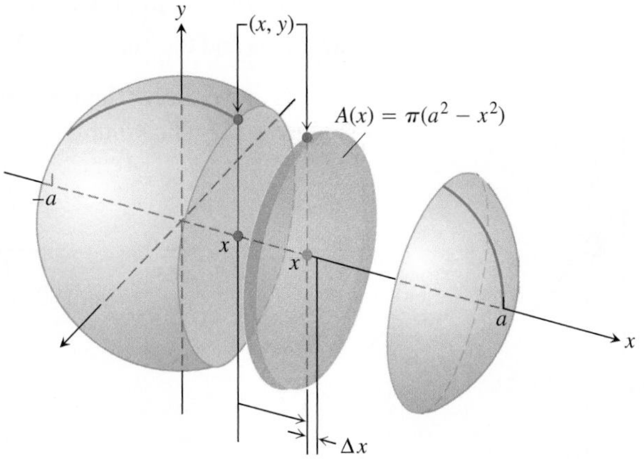

FIGURE 6.9 The sphere generated by rotating the circle $x^2 + y^2 = a^2$ about the x-axis. The radius is $R(x) = y = \sqrt{a^2 - x^2}$ (Example 5).

Solution We draw figures showing the region, a typical radius, and the generated solid (Figure 6.10). The volume is

$$\begin{aligned} V &= \int_1^4 \pi[R(x)]^2\,dx \\ &= \int_1^4 \pi\left[\sqrt{x} - 1\right]^2 dx \\ &= \pi\int_1^4 \left[x - 2\sqrt{x} + 1\right] dx \\ &= \pi\left[\frac{x^2}{2} - 2\cdot\frac{2}{3}x^{3/2} + x\right]_1^4 = \frac{7\pi}{6}. \end{aligned}$$

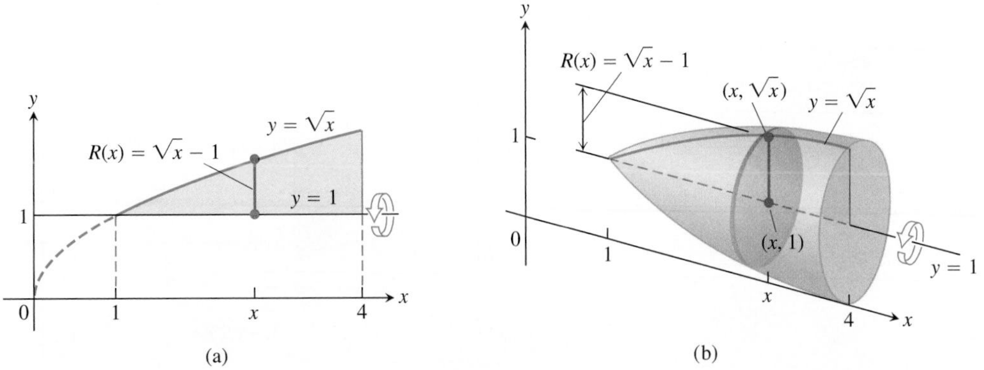

FIGURE 6.10 The region (a) and solid of revolution (b) in Example 6. ■

To find the volume of a solid generated by revolving a region between the y-axis and a curve $x = R(y)$, $c \le y \le d$, about the y-axis, we use the same method with x replaced by y. In this case, the circular cross-section is

$$A(y) = \pi[\text{radius}]^2 = \pi[R(y)]^2.$$

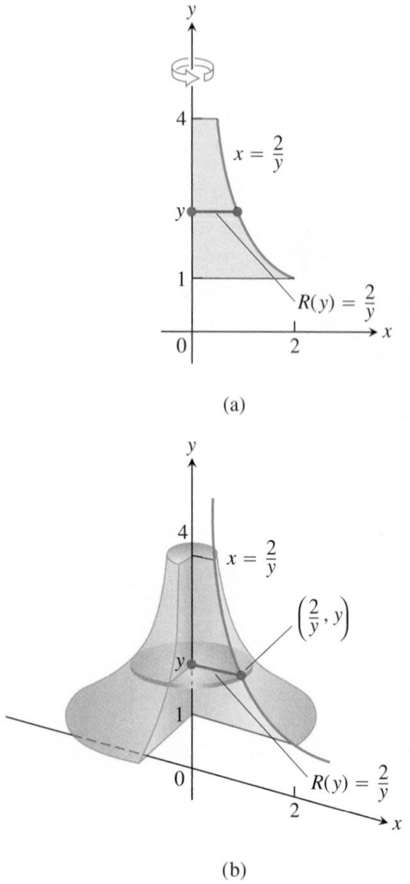

FIGURE 6.11 The region (a) and part of the solid of revolution (b) in Example 7.

EXAMPLE 7 Find the volume of the solid generated by revolving the region between the y-axis and the curve $x = 2/y$, $1 \le y \le 4$, about the y-axis.

Solution We draw figures showing the region, a typical radius, and the generated solid (Figure 6.11). The volume is

$$\begin{aligned} V &= \int_1^4 \pi[R(y)]^2\, dy \\ &= \int_1^4 \pi\left(\frac{2}{y}\right)^2 dy \\ &= \pi\int_1^4 \frac{4}{y^2}\, dy = 4\pi\left[-\frac{1}{y}\right]_1^4 = 4\pi\left[\frac{3}{4}\right] \\ &= 3\pi. \end{aligned}$$

■

EXAMPLE 8 Find the volume of the solid generated by revolving the region between the parabola $x = y^2 + 1$ and the line $x = 3$ about the line $x = 3$.

Solution We draw figures showing the region, a typical radius, and the generated solid (Figure 6.12). Note that the cross-sections are perpendicular to the line $x = 3$ and have y-coordinates from $y = -\sqrt{2}$ to $y = \sqrt{2}$. The volume is

$$\begin{aligned} V &= \int_{-\sqrt{2}}^{\sqrt{2}} \pi[R(y)]^2\, dy && (y) = \pm\sqrt{2} \text{ when } x = 3 \\ &= \int_{-\sqrt{2}}^{\sqrt{2}} \pi[2 - y^2]^2\, dy && R(y) = 3 - (y^2 + 1) = 2 - y^2 \\ &= \pi\int_{-\sqrt{2}}^{\sqrt{2}} [4 - 4y^2 + y^4]\, dy \\ &= \pi\left[4y - \frac{4}{3}y^3 + \frac{y^5}{5}\right]_{-\sqrt{2}}^{\sqrt{2}} \\ &= \frac{64\pi\sqrt{2}}{15}. \end{aligned}$$

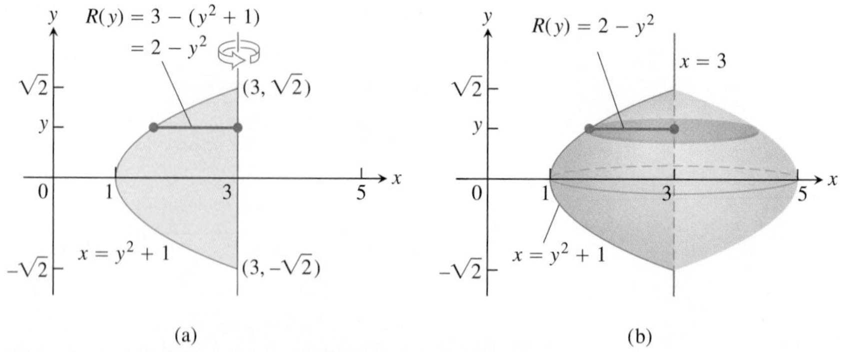

FIGURE 6.12 The region (a) and solid of revolution (b) in Example 8. ■

Solids of Revolution: The Washer Method

If the region we revolve to generate a solid does not border on or cross the axis of revolution, the solid has a hole in it (Figure 6.13). The cross-sections perpendicular to the axis of

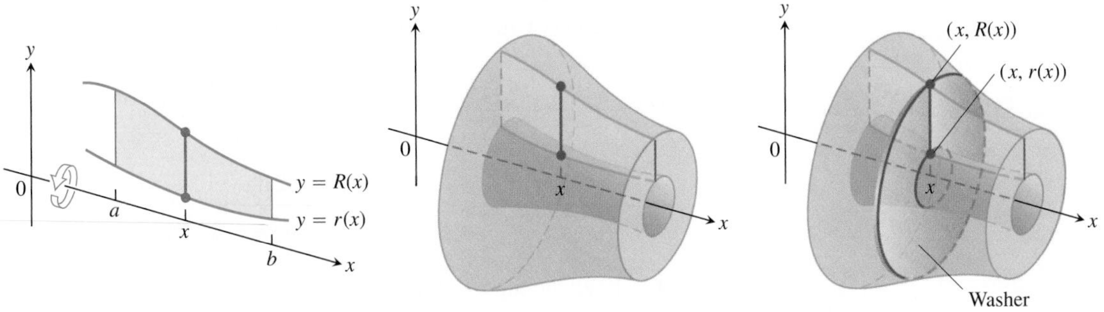

FIGURE 6.13 The cross-sections of the solid of revolution generated here are washers, not disks, so the integral $\int_a^b A(x)\,dx$ leads to a slightly different formula.

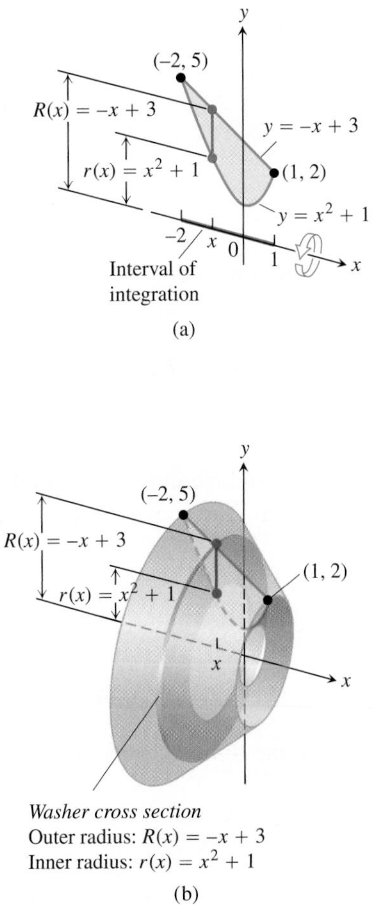

FIGURE 6.14 (a) The region in Example 9 spanned by a line segment perpendicular to the axis of revolution. (b) When the region is revolved about the x-axis, the line segment generates a washer.

revolution are *washers* (the purplish circular surface in Figure 6.13) instead of disks. The dimensions of a typical washer are

Outer radius: $R(x)$

Inner radius: $r(x)$

The washer's area is

$$A(x) = \pi[R(x)]^2 - \pi[r(x)]^2 = \pi([R(x)]^2 - [r(x)]^2).$$

Consequently, the definition of volume gives

$$V = \int_a^b A(x)\,dx = \int_a^b \pi([R(x)]^2 - [r(x)]^2)\,dx.$$

This method for calculating the volume of a solid of revolution is called the **washer method** because a slab is a circular washer of outer radius $R(x)$ and inner radius $r(x)$.

EXAMPLE 9 The region bounded by the curve $y = x^2 + 1$ and the line $y = -x + 3$ is revolved about the x-axis to generate a solid. Find the volume of the solid.

Solution

1. Draw the region and sketch a line segment across it perpendicular to the axis of revolution (the red segment in Figure 6.14).
2. Find the outer and inner radii of the washer that would be swept out by the line segment if it were revolved about the x-axis along with the region.

   These radii are the distances of the ends of the line segment from the axis of revolution (Figure 6.14).

Outer radius: $R(x) = -x + 3$

Inner radius: $r(x) = x^2 + 1$

3. Find the limits of integration by finding the x-coordinates of the intersection points of the curve and line in Figure 6.14a.

$$\begin{aligned} x^2 + 1 &= -x + 3 \\ x^2 + x - 2 &= 0 \\ (x + 2)(x - 1) &= 0 \\ x = -2, \quad x &= 1 \end{aligned}$$

4. Evaluate the volume integral.

$$\begin{aligned} V &= \int_a^b \pi([R(x)]^2 - [r(x)]^2)\,dx \\ &= \int_{-2}^{1} \pi((-x + 3)^2 - (x^2 + 1)^2)\,dx \qquad \text{Values from Steps 2 and 3} \\ &= \int_{-2}^{1} \pi(8 - 6x - x^2 - x^4)\,dx \\ &= \pi\left[8x - 3x^2 - \frac{x^3}{3} - \frac{x^5}{5}\right]_{-2}^{1} = \frac{117\pi}{5} \end{aligned}$$

■

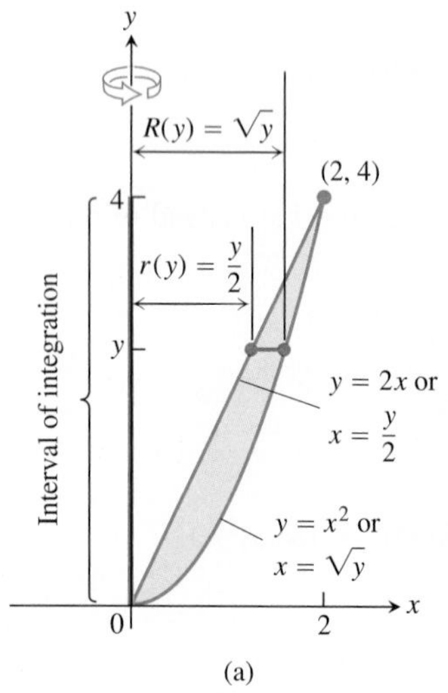

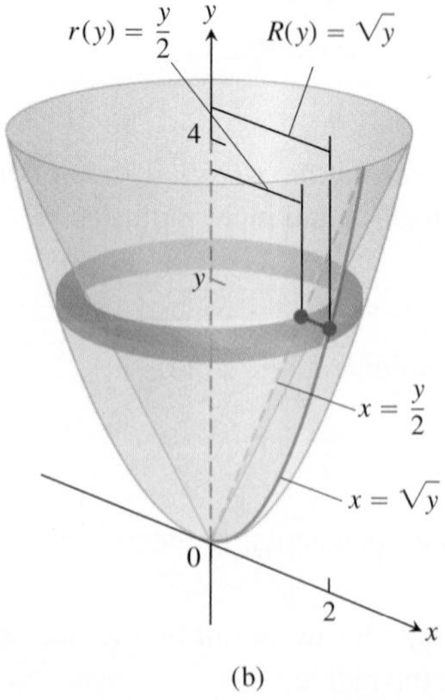

FIGURE 6.15 (a) The region being rotated about the y-axis, the washer radii, and limits of integration in Example 10. (b) The washer swept out by the line segment in part (a).

To find the volume of a solid formed by revolving a region about the y-axis, we use the same procedure as in Example 9, but integrate with respect to y instead of x. In this situation the line segment sweeping out a typical washer is perpendicular to the y-axis (the axis of revolution), and the outer and inner radii of the washer are functions of y.

EXAMPLE 10 The region bounded by the parabola $y = x^2$ and the line $y = 2x$ in the first quadrant is revolved about the y-axis to generate a solid. Find the volume of the solid.

Solution First we sketch the region and draw a line segment across it perpendicular to the axis of revolution (the y-axis). See Figure 6.15a.

The radii of the washer swept out by the line segment are $R(y) = \sqrt{y}$, $r(y) = y/2$ (Figure 6.15).

The line and parabola intersect at $y = 0$ and $y = 4$, so the limits of integration are $c = 0$ and $d = 4$. We integrate to find the volume:

$$\begin{aligned} V &= \int_c^d \pi([R(y)]^2 - [r(y)]^2)\,dy \\ &= \int_0^4 \pi\left(\left[\sqrt{y}\right]^2 - \left[\frac{y}{2}\right]^2\right) dy \\ &= \pi\int_0^4 \left(y - \frac{y^2}{4}\right) dy = \pi\left[\frac{y^2}{2} - \frac{y^3}{12}\right]_0^4 = \frac{8}{3}\pi. \end{aligned}$$

■

EXERCISES 6.1

Find the volumes of the solids in Exercises 1–10.

1. The solid lies between planes perpendicular to the x-axis at $x = 0$ and $x = 4$. The cross-sections perpendicular to the axis on the interval $0 \le x \le 4$ are squares whose diagonals run from the parabola $y = -\sqrt{x}$ to the parabola $y = \sqrt{x}$.

2. The solid lies between planes perpendicular to the x-axis at $x = -1$ and $x = 1$. The cross-sections perpendicular to the x-axis are circular disks whose diameters run from the parabola $y = x^2$ to the parabola $y = 2 - x^2$.

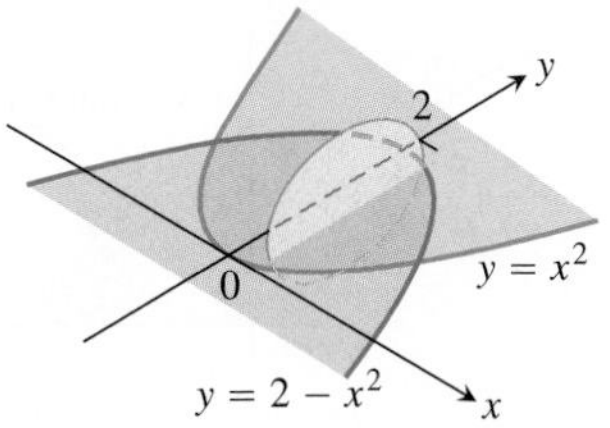

3. The solid lies between planes perpendicular to the x-axis at $x = -1$ and $x = 1$. The cross-sections perpendicular to the x-axis between these planes are squares whose bases run from the semicircle $y = -\sqrt{1 - x^2}$ to the semicircle $y = \sqrt{1 - x^2}$.

4. The solid lies between planes perpendicular to the x-axis at $x = -1$ and $x = 1$. The cross-sections perpendicular to the x-axis between these planes are squares whose diagonals run from the semicircle $y = -\sqrt{1 - x^2}$ to the semicircle $y = \sqrt{1 - x^2}$.

5. The base of a solid is the region between the curve $y = 2\sqrt{\sin x}$ and the interval $[0, \pi]$ on the x-axis. The cross-sections perpendicular to the x-axis are

a. equilateral triangles with bases running from the x-axis to the curve as shown in the figure.

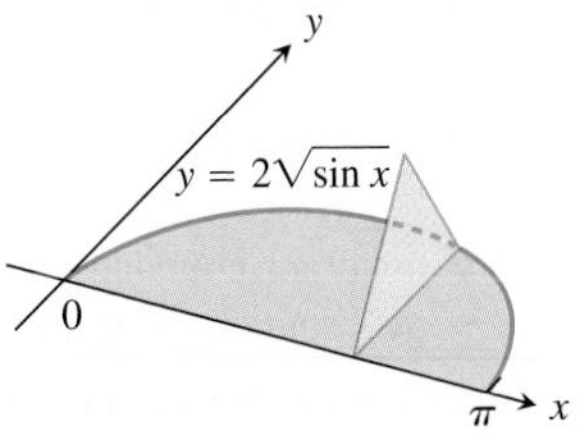

b. squares with bases running from the x-axis to the curve.

6. The solid lies between planes perpendicular to the x-axis at $x = -\pi/3$ and $x = \pi/3$. The cross-sections perpendicular to the x-axis are

a. circular disks with diameters running from the curve $y = \tan x$ to the curve $y = \sec x$.

b. squares whose bases run from the curve $y = \tan x$ to the curve $y = \sec x$.

7. The solid lies between planes perpendicular to the y-axis at $y = 0$ and $y = 2$. The cross-sections perpendicular to the y-axis are circular disks with diameters running from the y-axis to the parabola $x = \sqrt{5}y^2$.

8. The base of the solid is the disk $x^2 + y^2 \le 1$. The cross-sections by planes perpendicular to the y-axis between $y = -1$ and $y = 1$ are isosceles right triangles with one leg in the disk.

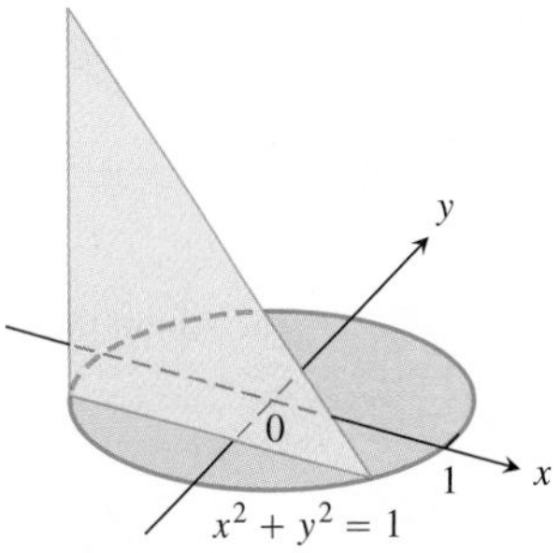

9. The solid lies between planes perpendicular to the x-axis at $x = -1$ and $x = 1$. The cross-sections perpendicular to the x-axis are

a. circles whose diameters stretch from the curve $y = -1/\sqrt{1 + x^2}$ to the curve $y = 1/\sqrt{1 + x^2}$.

b. vertical squares whose base edges run from the curve $y = -1/\sqrt{1 + x^2}$ to the curve $y = 1/\sqrt{1 + x^2}$.

10. The solid lies between planes perpendicular to the x-axis at $x = -\sqrt{2}/2$ and $x = \sqrt{2}/2$. The cross-sections perpendicular to the x-axis are

a. circles whose diameters stretch from the x-axis to the curve $y = 2/\sqrt[4]{1 - x^2}$.

b. squares whose diagonals stretch from the x-axis to the curve $y = 2/\sqrt[4]{1 - x^2}$.

11. A twisted solid A square of side length s lies in a plane perpendicular to a line L. One vertex of the square lies on L. As this square moves a distance h along L, the square turns one revolution about L to generate a corkscrew-like column with square cross-sections.

a. Find the volume of the column.

b. What will the volume be if the square turns twice instead of once? Give reasons for your answer.

12. Cavalieri's principle A solid lies between planes perpendicular to the x-axis at $x = 0$ and $x = 12$. The cross-sections by planes perpendicular to the x-axis are circular disks whose diameters run from the line $y = x/2$ to the line $y = x$ as shown in the accompanying figure. Explain why the solid has the same volume as a right circular cone with base radius 3 and height 12.

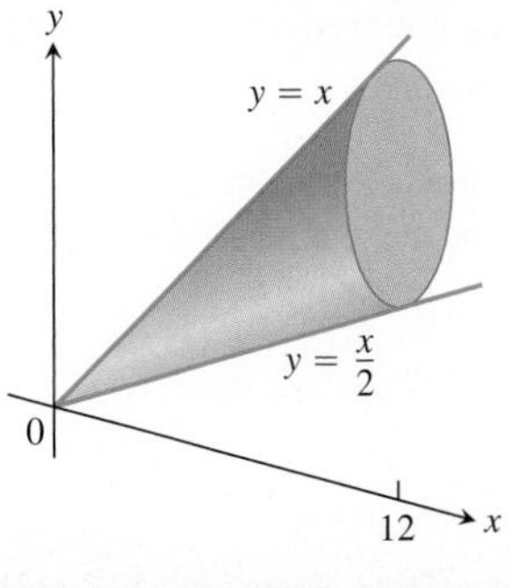

In Exercises 13–16, find the volume of the solid generated by revolving the shaded region about the given axis.

13. About the x-axis

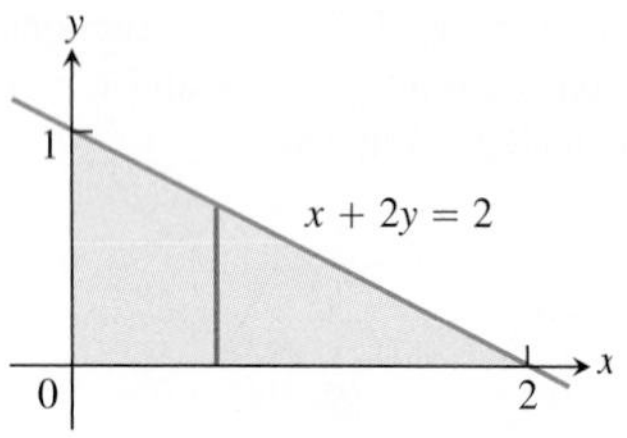

14. About the y-axis

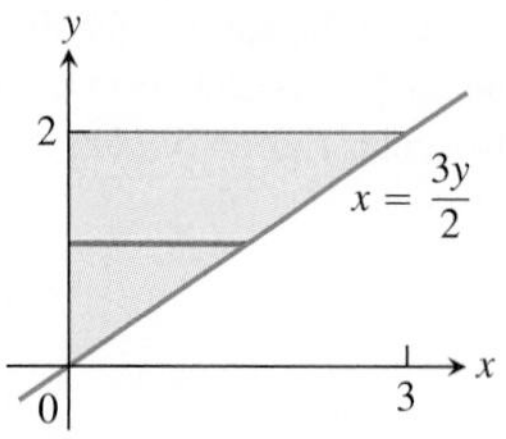

15. About the y-axis

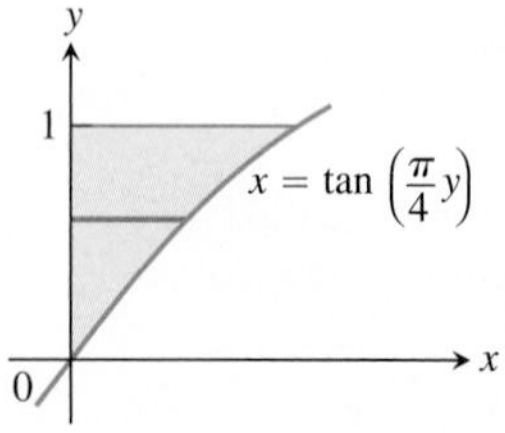

16. About the x-axis

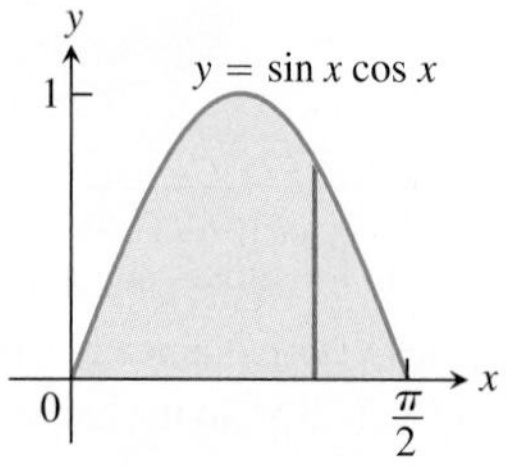

Find the volumes of the solids generated by revolving the regions bounded by the lines and curves in Exercises 17–26 about the x-axis.

17. $y = x^2, \quad y = 0, \quad x = 2$

18. $y = x^3, \quad y = 0, \quad x = 2$

19. $y = \sqrt{9 - x^2}, \quad y = 0$

20. $y = x - x^2, \quad y = 0$

21. $y = \sqrt{\cos x}, \quad 0 \le x \le \pi/2, \quad y = 0, \quad x = 0$

22. $y = \sec x, \quad y = 0, \quad x = -\pi/4, \quad x = \pi/4$

23. $y = e^{-x}, \quad y = 0, \quad x = 0, \quad x = 1$

24. The region between the curve $y = \sqrt{\cot x}$ and the x-axis from $x = \pi/6$ to $x = \pi/2$.

25. The region between the curve $y = 1/(2\sqrt{x})$ and the x-axis from $x = 1/4$ to $x = 4$.

26. The region bounded by the x-axis and one arch of the cycloid $x = \theta - \sin\theta, y = 1 - \cos\theta$.
(*Hint:* $dV = \pi y^2\,dx = \pi y^2\,(dx/d\theta)\,d\theta$.)

In Exercises 27 and 28, find the volume of the solid generated by revolving the region about the given line.

27. The region in the first quadrant bounded above by the line $y = \sqrt{2}$, below by the curve $y = \sec x \tan x$, and on the left by the y-axis, about the line $y = \sqrt{2}$

28. The region in the first quadrant bounded above by the line $y = 2$, below by the curve $y = 2\sin x$, $0 \le x \le \pi/2$, and on the left by the y-axis, about the line $y = 2$

Find the volumes of the solids generated by revolving the regions bounded by the lines and curves in Exercises 29–34 about the y-axis.

29. The region enclosed by $x = \sqrt{5}\,y^2, \quad x = 0, \quad y = -1, \quad y = 1$

30. The region enclosed by $x = y^{3/2}, \quad x = 0, \quad y = 2$

31. The region enclosed by $x = \sqrt{2\sin 2y}, \quad 0 \le y \le \pi/2, \quad x = 0$

32. The region enclosed by $x = \sqrt{\cos(\pi y/4)}, \quad -2 \le y \le 0, \quad x = 0$

33. The region in the first quadrant bounded by the coordinate axes, the line $y = 3$, and the curve $x = 2/\sqrt{y + 1}$

34. $x = \sqrt{2}y/(y^2 + 1), \quad x = 0, \quad y = 1$

Find the volumes of the solids generated by revolving the shaded regions in Exercises 35 and 36 about the indicated axes.

35. The x-axis

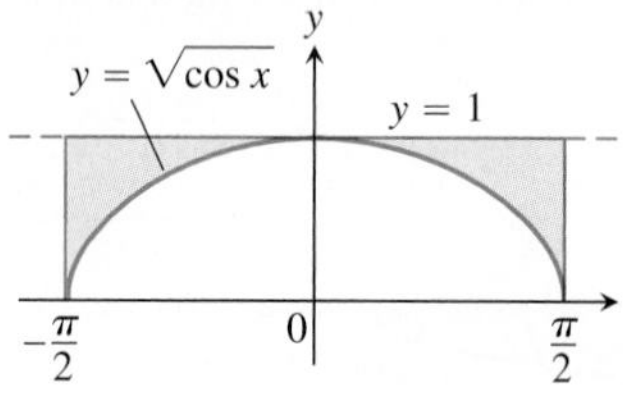

36. The y-axis

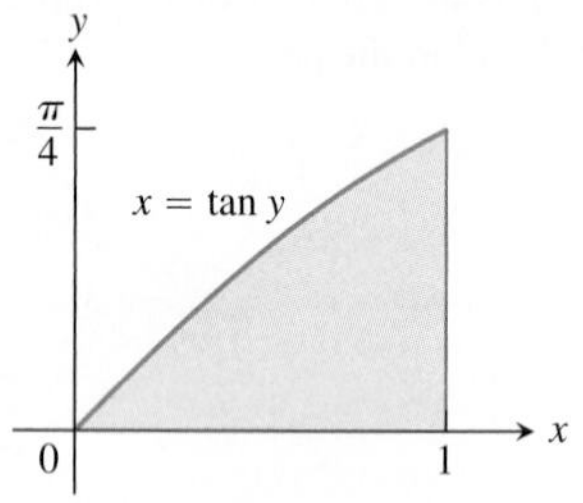

Find the volumes of the solids generated by revolving the regions bounded by the lines and curves in Exercises 37–42 about the x-axis.

37. $y = x, \quad y = 1, \quad x = 0$

38. $y = 2\sqrt{x}, \quad y = 2, \quad x = 0$

39. $y = x^2 + 1, \quad y = x + 3$

40. $y = 4 - x^2, \quad y = 2 - x$

41. $y = \sec x, \quad y = \sqrt{2}, \quad -\pi/4 \le x \le \pi/4$

42. $y = \sec x, \quad y = \tan x, \quad x = 0, \quad x = 1$

In Exercises 43–46, find the volume of the solid generated by revolving each region about the y-axis.

43. The region enclosed by the triangle with vertices (1, 0), (2, 1), and (1, 1)

44. The region enclosed by the triangle with vertices (0, 1), (1, 0), and (1, 1)

45. The region in the first quadrant bounded above by the parabola $y = x^2$, below by the x-axis, and on the right by the line $x = 2$

46. The region in the first quadrant bounded on the left by the circle $x^2 + y^2 = 3$, on the right by the line $x = \sqrt{3}$, and above by the line $y = \sqrt{3}$

In Exercises 47 and 48, find the volume of the solid generated by revolving each region about the given axis.

47. The region in the first quadrant bounded above by the curve $y = x^2$, below by the x-axis, and on the right by the line $x = 1$, about the line $x = -1$

48. The region in the second quadrant bounded above by the curve $y = -x^3$, below by the x-axis, and on the left by the line $x = -1$, about the line $x = -2$

49. Find the volume of the solid generated by revolving the region bounded by $y = \sqrt{x}$ and the lines $y = 2$ and $x = 0$ about

a. the x-axis. **b.** the y-axis.

c. the line $y = 2$. **d.** the line $x = 4$.

50. Find the volume of the solid generated by revolving the triangular region bounded by the lines $y = 2x$, $y = 0$, and $x = 1$ about

a. the line $x = 1$. **b.** the line $x = 2$.

51. Find the volume of the solid generated by revolving the region bounded by the parabola $y = x^2$ and the line $y = 1$ about

a. the line $y = 1$. **b.** the line $y = 2$.

c. the line $y = -1$.

52. By integration, find the volume of the solid generated by revolving the triangular region with vertices $(0, 0)$, $(b, 0)$, $(0, h)$ about

a. the x-axis. **b.** the y-axis.

6.2 Volumes by Cylindrical Shells

In Section 6.1 we defined the volume of a solid as the definite integral $V = \int_a^b A(x)\, dx$, where $A(x)$ is an integrable cross-sectional area of the solid from $x = a$ to $x = b$. The area $A(x)$ was obtained by slicing through the solid with a plane perpendicular to the x-axis. However, this method of slicing is sometimes awkward to apply, as we will illustrate in our first example. To overcome this difficulty, we use the same integral definition for volume, but obtain the area by slicing through the solid in a different way.

In this section we slice through the solid using circular cylinders of increasing radii, like cookie cutters. We slice straight down through the solid so that the axis of each cylinder is parallel to the y-axis. The vertical axis of each cylinder is the same line, but the radii of the cylinders increase with each slice. In this way the solid is sliced up into thin cylindrical shells of constant thickness that grow outward from their common axis, like circular tree rings. Unrolling a cylindrical shell shows that its volume is approximately that of a rectangular slab with area $A(x)$ and thickness Δx. This allows us to apply the same integral definition for volume as before. The following example provides some insight before we derive the method in general.

EXAMPLE 1 The region enclosed by the x-axis and the parabola $y = f(x) = 3x - x^2$ is revolved about the vertical line $x = -1$ to generate the shape of a solid (Figure 6.16). Find the volume of the solid.

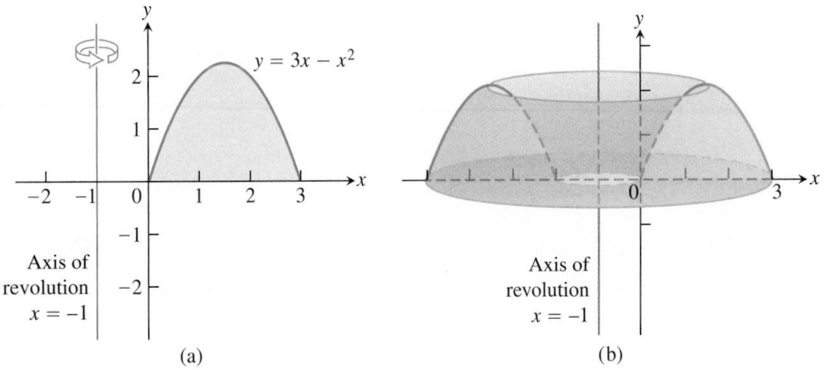

FIGURE 6.16 (a) The graph of the region in Example 1, before revolution. (b) The solid formed when the region in part (a) is revolved about the axis of revolution $x = -1$.

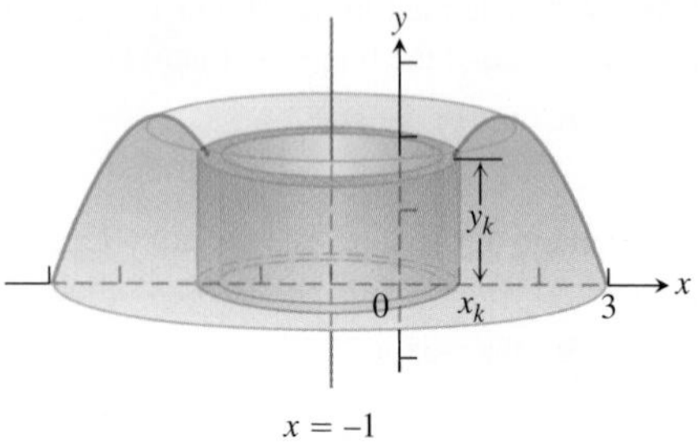

FIGURE 6.17 A cylindrical shell of height y_k obtained by rotating a vertical strip of thickness Δx about the line $x = -1$. The outer radius of the cylinder occurs at x_k, where the height of the parabola is $y_k = 3x_k - x_k^2$ (Example 1).

Solution Using the washer method from Section 6.1 would be awkward here because we would need to express the x-values of the left and right branches of the parabola in terms of y. (These x-values are the inner and outer radii for a typical washer, leading to complicated formulas.) Instead of rotating a horizontal strip of thickness Δy, we rotate a *vertical strip* of thickness Δx. This rotation produces a *cylindrical shell* of height y_k above a point x_k within the base of the vertical strip, and of thickness Δx. An example of a cylindrical shell is shown as the orange-shaded region in Figure 6.17. We can think of the cylindrical shell shown in the figure as approximating a slice of the solid obtained by cutting straight down through it, parallel to the axis of revolution, all the way around close to the inside hole. We then cut another cylindrical slice around the enlarged hole, then another, and so on, obtaining n cylinders. The radii of the cylinders gradually increase, and the heights of the cylinders follow the contour of the parabola: shorter to taller, then back to shorter (Figure 6.16a).

Each slice is sitting over a subinterval of the x-axis of length (width) Δx. Its radius is approximately $(1 + x_k)$, and its height is approximately $3x_k - x_k^2$. If we unroll the cylinder at x_k and flatten it out, it becomes (approximately) a rectangular slab with thickness Δx (Figure 6.18). The outer circumference of the kth cylinder is $2\pi \cdot \text{radius} = 2\pi(1 + x_k)$, and this is the length of the rolled-out rectangular slab. Its volume is approximated by that of a rectangular solid,

$$\begin{aligned}\Delta V_k &= \text{circumference} \times \text{height} \times \text{thickness}\\ &= 2\pi(1 + x_k) \cdot \left(3x_k - x_k^2\right) \cdot \Delta x.\end{aligned}$$

Summing together the volumes ΔV_k of the individual cylindrical shells over the interval $[0, 3]$ gives the Riemann sum

$$\sum_{k=1}^{n} \Delta V_k = \sum_{k=1}^{n} 2\pi(x_k + 1)\left(3x_k - x_k^2\right) \Delta x.$$

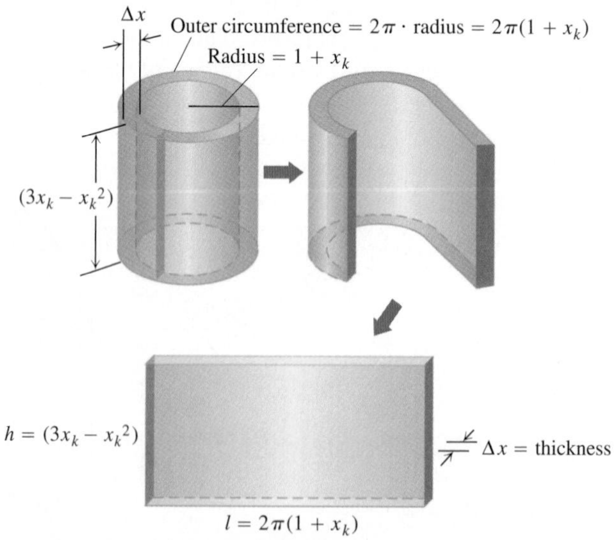

FIGURE 6.18 Imagine cutting and unrolling a cylindrical shell to get a flat (nearly) rectangular solid (Example 1).

Taking the limit as the thickness $\Delta x \to 0$ gives the volume integral

$$\begin{aligned} V &= \lim_{n\to\infty} \sum_{k=1}^{n} 2\pi(x_k + 1)(3x_k - x_k^2)\,\Delta x \\ &= \int_0^3 2\pi(x+1)(3x - x^2)\,dx \\ &= \int_0^3 2\pi(3x^2 + 3x - x^3 - x^2)\,dx \\ &= 2\pi\int_0^3 (2x^2 + 3x - x^3)\,dx \\ &= 2\pi\left[\frac{2}{3}x^3 + \frac{3}{2}x^2 - \frac{1}{4}x^4\right]_0^3 = \frac{45\pi}{2}. \end{aligned}$$

We now generalize the procedure used in Example 1.

The Shell Method

Suppose the region bounded by the graph of a nonnegative continuous function $y = f(x)$ and the x-axis over the finite closed interval $[a, b]$ lies to the right of the vertical line $x = L$ (Figure 6.19a). We assume $a \geq L$, so the vertical line may touch the region, but not pass through it. We generate a solid S by rotating this region about the vertical line L.

Let P be a partition of the interval $[a, b]$ by the points $a = x_0 < x_1 < \cdots < x_n = b$, and let c_k be the midpoint of the kth subinterval $[x_{k-1}, x_k]$. We approximate the region in Figure 6.19a with rectangles based on this partition of $[a, b]$. A typical approximating rectangle has height $f(c_k)$ and width $\Delta x_k = x_k - x_{k-1}$. If this rectangle is rotated about the vertical line $x = L$, then a shell is swept out, as in Figure 6.19b. A formula from geometry tells us that the volume of the shell swept out by the rectangle is

$$\begin{aligned} \Delta V_k &= 2\pi \times \text{average shell radius} \times \text{shell height} \times \text{thickness} \\ &= 2\pi \cdot (c_k - L) \cdot f(c_k) \cdot \Delta x_k. \end{aligned}$$

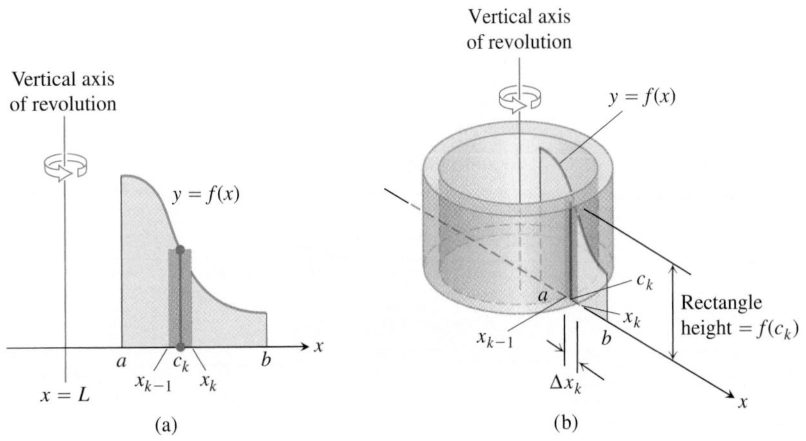

FIGURE 6.19 When the region shown in (a) is revolved about the vertical line $x = L$, a solid is produced which can be sliced into cylindrical shells. A typical shell is shown in (b).

We approximate the volume of the solid S by summing the volumes of the shells swept out by the n rectangles based on P:

$$V \approx \sum_{k=1}^{n} \Delta V_k.$$

The limit of this Riemann sum as $\|P\| \rightarrow 0$ gives the volume of the solid as a definite integral:

$$V = \lim_{\|P\| \rightarrow 0} \sum_{k=1}^{n} \Delta V_k = \int_a^b 2\pi(\text{shell radius})(\text{shell height})\, dx.$$

$$= \int_a^b 2\pi(x - L) f(x)\, dx.$$

We refer to the variable of integration, here x, as the **thickness variable**. We use the first integral, rather than the second containing a formula for the integrand, to emphasize the *process* of the shell method. This will allow for rotations about a horizontal line L as well.

Shell Formula for Revolution About a Vertical Line

The volume of the solid generated by revolving the region between the x-axis and the graph of a continuous function $y = f(x) \geq 0$, $L \leq a \leq x \leq b$, about a vertical line $x = L$ is

$$V = \int_a^b 2\pi \begin{pmatrix}\text{shell} \\ \text{radius}\end{pmatrix} \begin{pmatrix}\text{shell} \\ \text{height}\end{pmatrix} dx.$$

EXAMPLE 2 The region bounded by the curve $y = \sqrt{x}$, the x-axis, and the line $x = 4$ is revolved about the y-axis to generate a solid. Find the volume of the solid.

Solution Sketch the region and draw a line segment across it *parallel* to the axis of revolution (Figure 6.20a). Label the segment's height (shell height) and distance from the axis of revolution (shell radius). (We drew the shell in Figure 6.20b, but you need not do that.)

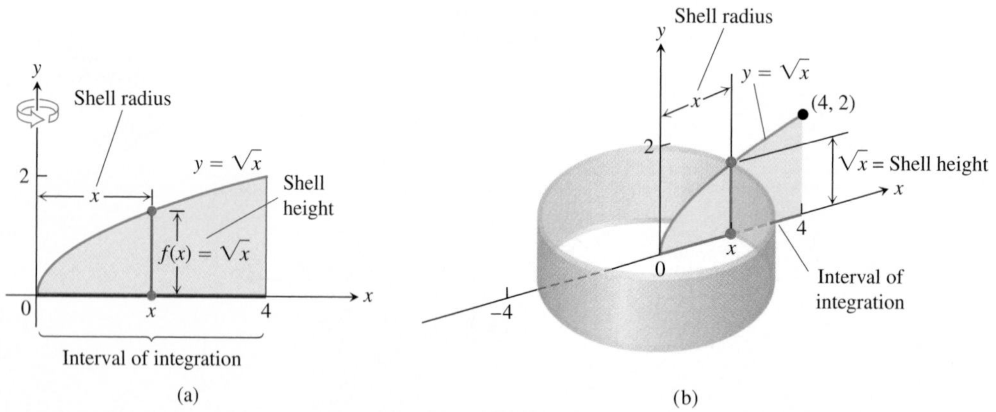

FIGURE 6.20 (a) The region, shell dimensions, and interval of integration in Example 2. (b) The shell swept out by the vertical segment in part (a) with a width Δx.

The shell thickness variable is x, so the limits of integration for the shell formula are $a = 0$ and $b = 4$ (Figure 6.20). The volume is then

$$\begin{aligned} V &= \int_a^b 2\pi \binom{\text{shell}}{\text{radius}} \binom{\text{shell}}{\text{height}} dx \\ &= \int_0^4 2\pi(x)\left(\sqrt{x}\right) dx \\ &= 2\pi \int_0^4 x^{3/2}\, dx = 2\pi\left[\frac{2}{5}x^{5/2}\right]_0^4 = \frac{128\pi}{5}. \end{aligned}$$

■

So far, we have used vertical axes of revolution. For horizontal axes, we replace the x's with y's.

EXAMPLE 3 The region bounded by the curve $y = \sqrt{x}$, the x-axis, and the line $x = 4$ is revolved about the x-axis to generate a solid. Find the volume of the solid by the shell method.

Solution This is the solid whose volume was found by the disk method in Example 4 of Section 6.1. Now we find its volume by the shell method. First, sketch the region and draw a line segment across it *parallel* to the axis of revolution (Figure 6.21a). Label the segment's length (shell height) and distance from the axis of revolution (shell radius). (We drew the shell in Figure 6.21b, but you need not do that.)

In this case, the shell thickness variable is y, so the limits of integration for the shell formula method are $a = 0$ and $b = 2$ (along the y-axis in Figure 6.21). The volume of the solid is

$$\begin{aligned} V &= \int_a^b 2\pi \binom{\text{shell}}{\text{radius}} \binom{\text{shell}}{\text{height}} dy \\ &= \int_0^2 2\pi(y)(4 - y^2)\, dy \\ &= \int_0^2 2\pi(4y - y^3)\, dy \\ &= 2\pi\left[2y^2 - \frac{y^4}{4}\right]_0^2 = 8\pi. \end{aligned}$$

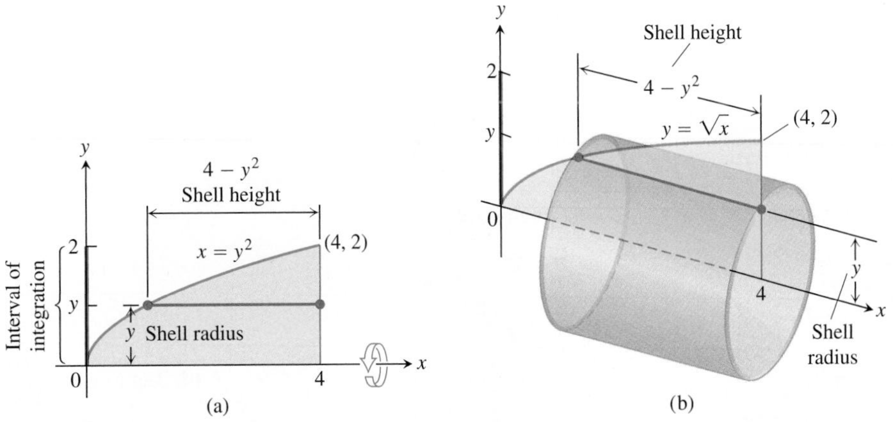

FIGURE 6.21 (a) The region, shell dimensions, and interval of integration in Example 3. (b) The shell swept out by the horizontal segment in part (a) with a width Δy.

■

Summary of the Shell Method

Regardless of the position of the axis of revolution (horizontal or vertical), the steps for implementing the shell method are these.

1. *Draw the region and sketch a line segment* across it *parallel* to the axis of revolution. *Label* the segment's height or length (shell height) and distance from the axis of revolution (shell radius).
2. *Find* the limits of integration for the thickness variable.
3. *Integrate* the product 2π (shell radius) (shell height) with respect to the thickness variable (x or y) to find the volume.

The shell method gives the same answer as the washer method when both are used to calculate the volume of a region. We do not prove that result here, but the proof is outlined in Exercise 37. Both volume formulas are actually special cases of a general volume formula we look at in studying double and triple integrals in Chapter 13. That general formula also allows for computing volumes of solids other than those swept out by regions of revolution.

EXERCISES 6.2

In Exercises 1–6, use the shell method to find the volumes of the solids generated by revolving the shaded region about the indicated axis.

1.

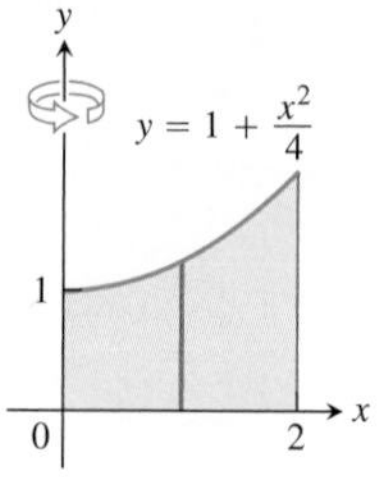

2.

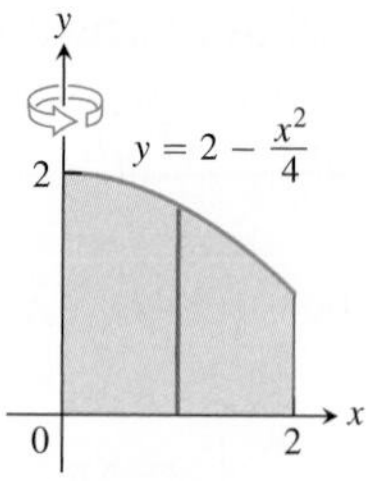

3.

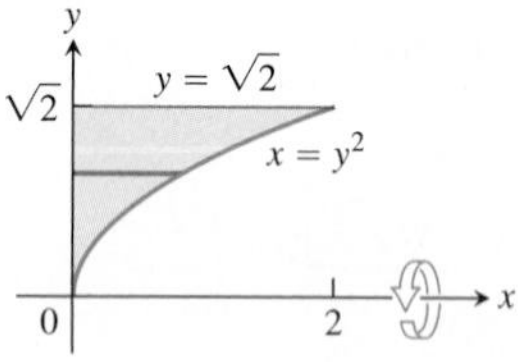

4.

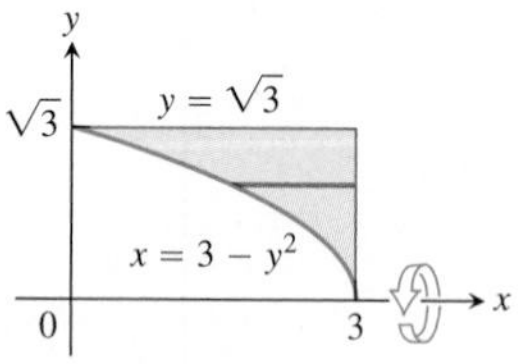

5. The y-axis

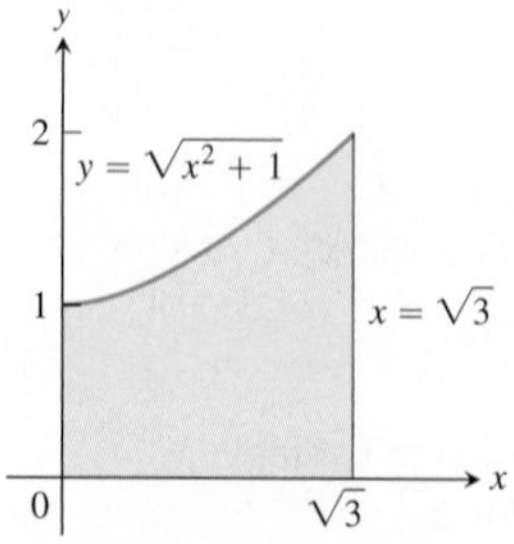

6. The y-axis

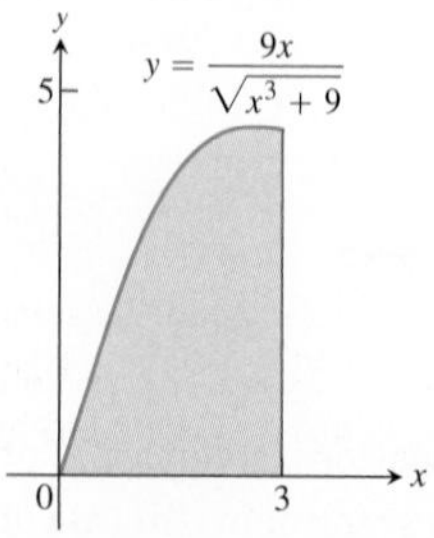

Use the shell method to find the volumes of the solids generated by revolving the regions bounded by the curves and lines in Exercises 7–14 about the y-axis.

7. $y = x, \quad y = -x/2, \quad x = 2$

8. $y = 2x, \quad y = x/2, \quad x = 1$

9. $y = x^2, \quad y = 2 - x, \quad x = 0$, for $x \geq 0$

10. $y = 2 - x^2, \quad y = x^2, \quad x = 0$

11. $y = 2x - 1, \quad y = \sqrt{x}, \quad x = 0$

12. $y = 3/\left(2\sqrt{x}\right), \quad y = 0, \quad x = 1, \quad x = 4$

13. Let $f(x) = \begin{cases} (\sin x)/x, & 0 < x \leq \pi \\ 1, & x = 0 \end{cases}$

a. Show that $x f(x) = \sin x,\ 0 \leq x \leq \pi$.

b. Find the volume of the solid generated by revolving the accompanying shaded region about the y-axis.

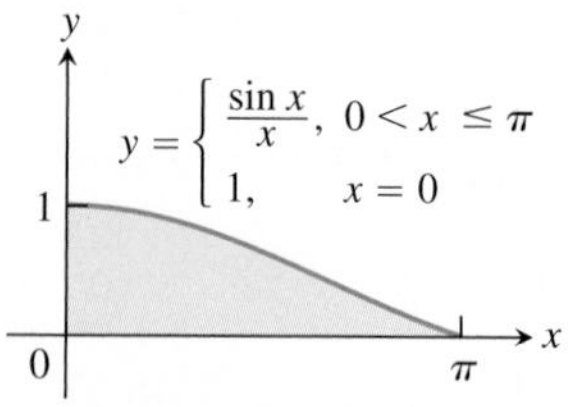

14. Let $g(x) = \begin{cases} (\tan x)^2/x, & 0 < x \leq \pi/4 \\ 0, & x = 0 \end{cases}$

a. Show that $x g(x) = (\tan x)^2,\ 0 \leq x \leq \pi/4$.

b. Find the volume of the solid generated by revolving the accompanying shaded region about the y-axis.

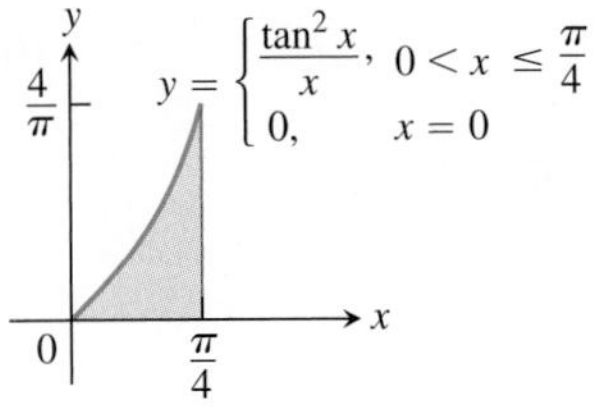

Use the shell method to find the volumes of the solids generated by revolving the regions bounded by the curves and lines in Exercises 15–22 about the x-axis.

15. $x = \sqrt{y}, \quad x = -y, \quad y = 2$

16. $x = y^2, \quad x = -y, \quad y = 2, \quad y \ge 0$

17. $x = 2y - y^2, \quad x = 0$

18. $x = 2y - y^2, \quad x = y$

19. $y = |x|, \quad y = 1$

20. $y = x, \quad y = 2x, \quad y = 2$

21. $y = \sqrt{x}, \quad y = 0, \quad y = x - 2$

22. $y = \sqrt{x}, \quad y = 0, \quad y = 2 - x$

In Exercises 23 and 24, use the shell method to find the volumes of the solids generated by revolving the shaded regions about the indicated axes.

23. a. The x-axis **b.** The line $y = 1$

c. The line $y = 8/5$ **d.** The line $y = -2/5$

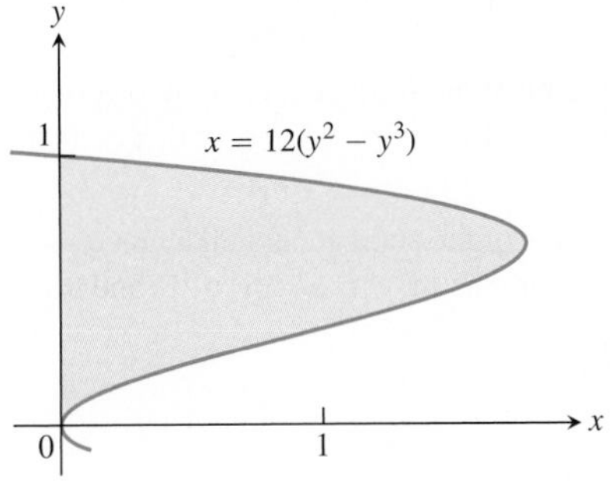

24. a. The x-axis **b.** The line $y = 2$

c. The line $y = 5$ **d.** The line $y = -5/8$

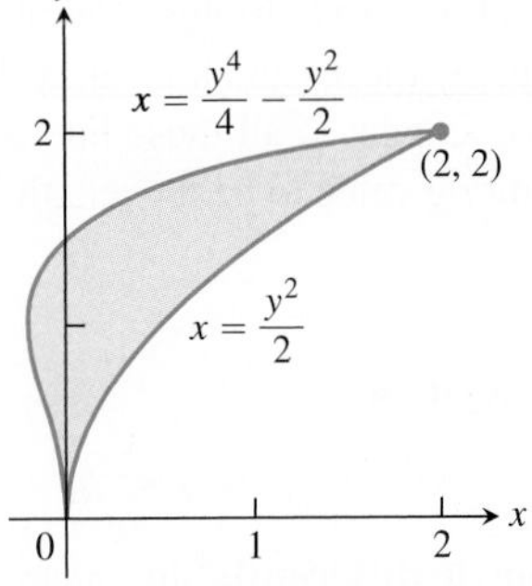

For some regions, both the washer and shell methods work well for the solid generated by revolving the region about the coordinate axes, but this is not always the case. When a region is revolved about the y-axis, for example, and washers are used, we must integrate with respect to y. It may not be possible, however, to express the integrand in terms of y. In such a case, the shell method allows us to integrate with respect to x instead. Exercises 25 and 26 provide some insight.

25. Compute the volume of the solid generated by revolving the region bounded by $y = x$ and $y = x^2$ about each coordinate axis using

a. the shell method. **b.** the washer method.

26. Compute the volume of the solid generated by revolving the triangular region bounded by the lines $2y = x + 4$, $y = x$, and $x = 0$ about

a. the x-axis using the washer method.

b. the y-axis using the shell method.

c. the line $x = 4$ using the shell method.

d. the line $y = 8$ using the washer method.

In Exercises 27–32, find the volumes of the solids generated by revolving the regions about the given axes. If you think it would be better to use washers in any given instance, feel free to do so.

27. The triangle with vertices (1, 1), (1, 2), and (2, 2) about

a. the x-axis **b.** the y-axis

c. the line $x = 10/3$ **d.** the line $y = 1$

28. The region bounded by $y = \sqrt{x}$, $y = 2$, $x = 0$ about

a. the x-axis **b.** the y-axis

c. the line $x = 4$ **d.** the line $y = 2$

29. The region in the first quadrant bounded by the curve $x = y - y^3$ and the y-axis about

a. the x-axis **b.** the line $y = 1$

30. The region in the first quadrant bounded by $x = y - y^3$, $x = 1$, and $y = 1$ about

a. the x-axis **b.** the y-axis

c. the line $x = 1$ **d.** the line $y = 1$

31. The region bounded by $y = \sqrt{x}$ and $y = x^2/8$ about

a. the x-axis **b.** the y-axis

32. The region bounded by $y = 2x - x^2$ and $y = x$ about

a. the y-axis **b.** the line $x = 1$

33. The region in the first quadrant that is bounded above by the curve $y = 1/x^{1/4}$, on the left by the line $x = 1/16$, and below by the line $y = 1$ is revolved about the x-axis to generate a solid. Find the volume of the solid by

a. the washer method. **b.** the shell method.

34. The region in the first quadrant that is bounded above by the curve $y = 1/\sqrt{x}$, on the left by the line $x = 1/4$, and below by the line $y = 1$ is revolved about the y-axis to generate a solid. Find the volume of the solid by

a. the washer method. **b.** the shell method.

35. The region shown here is to be revolved about the x-axis to generate a solid. Which of the methods (disk, washer, shell) could you use to find the volume of the solid? How many integrals would be required in each case? Explain.

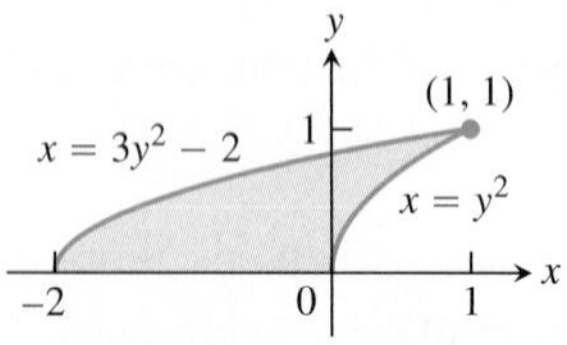

36. The region shown here is to be revolved about the y-axis to generate a solid. Which of the methods (disk, washer, shell) could you use to find the volume of the solid? How many integrals would be required in each case? Give reasons for your answers.

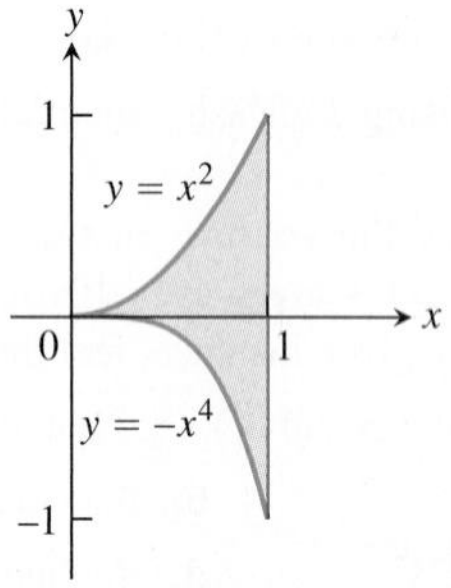

37. Equivalence of the washer and shell methods for finding volume Let f be differentiable and increasing on the interval $a \le x \le b$, with $a > 0$, and suppose that f has a differentiable inverse, f^{-1}. Revolve about the y-axis the region bounded by the graph of f and the lines $x = a$ and $y = f(b)$ to generate a solid. Then the values of the integrals given by the washer and shell methods for the volume have identical values:

$$\int_{f(a)}^{f(b)} \pi((f^{-1}(y))^2 - a^2)\,dy = \int_a^b 2\pi x(f(b) - f(x))\,dx.$$

To prove this equality, define

$$W(t) = \int_{f(a)}^{f(t)} \pi((f^{-1}(y))^2 - a^2)\,dy$$

$$S(t) = \int_a^t 2\pi x(f(t) - f(x))\,dx.$$

Then show that the functions W and S agree at a point of $[a, b]$ and have identical derivatives on $[a, b]$. As you saw in Section 4.8, Exercise 126, this will guarantee $W(t) = S(t)$ for all t in $[a, b]$. In particular, $W(b) = S(b)$. (*Source:* "Disks and Shells Revisited," by Walter Carlip, *American Mathematical Monthly*, Vol. 98, No. 2, Feb. 1991, pp. 154–156.)

38. The region between the curve $y = \sec^{-1} x$ and the x-axis from $x = 1$ to $x = 2$ (shown here) is revolved about the y-axis to generate a solid. Find the volume of the solid.

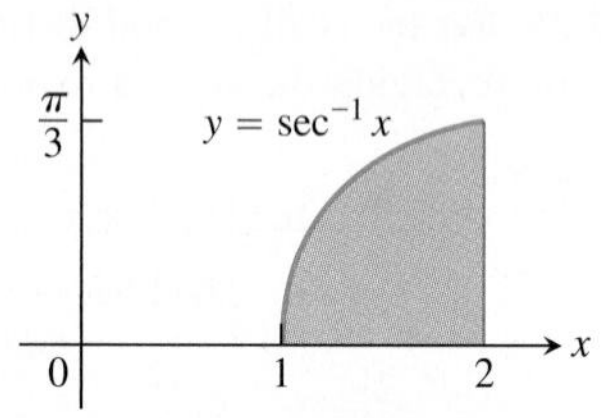

39. Find the volume of the solid generated by revolving the region enclosed by the graphs of $y = e^{-x^2}$, $y = 0$, $x = 0$, and $x = 1$ about the y-axis.

40. Find the volume of the solid generated by revolving the region enclosed by the graphs of $y = e^{x/2}$, $y = 1$, and $x = \ln 3$ about the x-axis.

6.3 Lengths of Plane Curves

We know what is meant by the length of a straight line segment, but without calculus, we have no precise notion of the length of a general winding curve. In this section we first subdivide the curve running from point A to point B into many pieces and join successive points of division by straight line segments. We then sum the lengths of all these line segments, go to the limit as their number increases, and take the limiting value to be the length of the curve.

Length of a Parametrically Defined Curve

Let C be a curve given parametrically by the equations

$$x = f(t) \quad \text{and} \quad y = g(t), \qquad a \le t \le b.$$

We assume the functions f and g are **continuously differentiable** (meaning they have continuous first derivatives) on the interval $[a, b]$. We also assume that the derivatives $f'(t)$ and $g'(t)$ are not simultaneously zero, which prevents the curve C from having any corners or cusps. Such a curve is called a **smooth curve**. It may be helpful to imagine the curve as the path of a particle moving from point $A = (f(a), g(a))$ at time $t = a$ to point

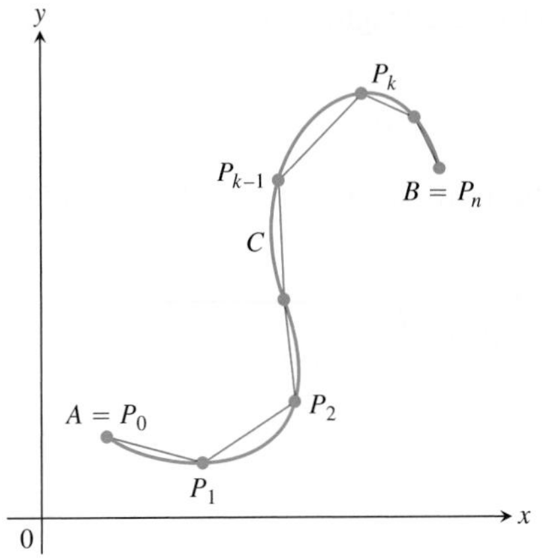

FIGURE 6.22 The curve C defined parametrically by the equations $x = f(t)$ and $y = g(t)$, $a \le t \le b$. The length of the curve from A to B is approximated by the sum of the lengths of the polygonal path (straight line segments) starting at $A = P_0$, then to P_1, and so on, ending at $B = P_n$.

$B = (f(b), g(b))$ at time $t = b$ in Figure 6.22. We subdivide the path (or arc) AB into n pieces at points $A = P_0, P_1, P_2, \dots, P_n = B$. These points correspond to a partition of the interval $[a, b]$ by $a = t_0 < t_1 < t_2 < \cdots < t_n = b$, where $P_k = (f(t_k), g(t_k))$. Join successive points of this subdivision by straight line segments (Figure 6.22). A representative line segment has length

$$\begin{aligned} L_k &= \sqrt{(\Delta x_k)^2 + (\Delta y_k)^2} \\ &= \sqrt{[f(t_k) - f(t_{k-1})]^2 + [g(t_k) - g(t_{k-1})]^2} \end{aligned}$$

(see Figure 6.23). If Δt_k is small, the length L_k is approximately the length of arc $P_{k-1}P_k$. By the Mean Value Theorem there are numbers t_k^* and t_k^{**} in $[t_{k-1}, t_k]$ such that

$$\begin{aligned} \Delta x_k &= f(t_k) - f(t_{k-1}) = f'(t_k^*)\,\Delta t_k, \\ \Delta y_k &= g(t_k) - g(t_{k-1}) = g'(t_k^{**})\,\Delta t_k. \end{aligned}$$

Assuming the path from A to B is traversed exactly once as t increases from $t = a$ to $t = b$, with no doubling back or retracing, an approximation to the "length" of the curve AB is the sum of all the lengths L_k:

$$\begin{aligned} \sum_{k=1}^{n} L_k &= \sum_{k=1}^{n} \sqrt{(\Delta x_k)^2 + (\Delta y_k)^2} \\ &= \sum_{k=1}^{n} \sqrt{[f'(t_k^*)]^2 + [g'(t_k^{**})]^2}\,\Delta t_k. \end{aligned}$$

Although this last sum on the right is not exactly a Riemann sum (because f' and g' are evaluated at different points), it can be shown that its limit, as the norm of the partition tends to zero, is the definite integral

$$\lim_{\|P\| \to 0} \sum_{k=1}^{n} \sqrt{[f'(t_k^*)]^2 + [g'(t_k^{**})]^2}\,\Delta t_k = \int_a^b \sqrt{[f'(t)]^2 + [g'(t)]^2}\,dt.$$

Therefore, it is reasonable to define the length of the curve from A to B as this integral.

DEFINITION If a curve C is defined parametrically by $x = f(t)$ and $y = g(t)$, $a \le t \le b$, where f' and g' are continuous and not simultaneously zero on $[a, b]$, and C is traversed exactly once as t increases from $t = a$ to $t = b$, then **the length of C** is the definite integral

$$L = \int_a^b \sqrt{[f'(t)]^2 + [g'(t)]^2}\,dt.$$

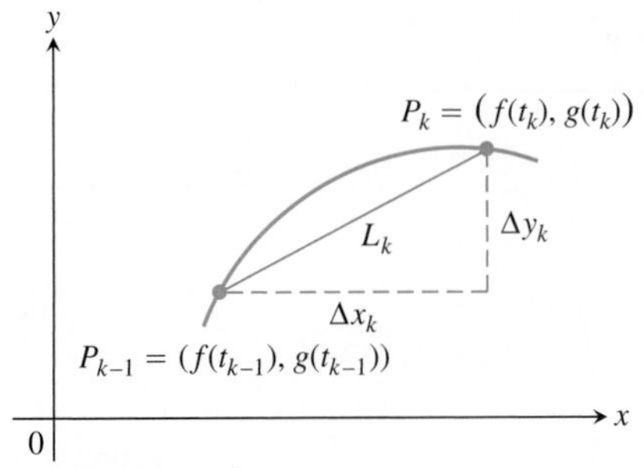

FIGURE 6.23 The arc $P_{k-1}P_k$ is approximated by the straight line segment shown here, which has length $L_k = \sqrt{(\Delta x_k)^2 + (\Delta y_k)^2}$.

A smooth curve C does not double back or reverse the direction of motion over the time interval $[a, b]$ since $(f')^2 + (g')^2 > 0$ throughout the interval.

If $x = f(t)$ and $y = g(t)$, then using the Leibniz notation we have the following result for arc length:

$$L = \int_a^b \sqrt{\left(\frac{dx}{dt}\right)^2 + \left(\frac{dy}{dt}\right)^2}\,dt. \tag{1}$$

What if there are two different parametrizations for a curve C whose length we want to find; does it matter which one we use? The answer is no, as long as the parametrization we choose meets the conditions stated in the definition of the length of C (see Exercise 36 for an example).

EXAMPLE 1 We use the definition of length to find the length of the circle of radius r defined parametrically by

$$x = r\cos t \qquad \text{and} \qquad y = r\sin t, \qquad 0 \le t \le 2\pi.$$

Solution As t varies from 0 to 2π, the circle is traversed exactly once, so the circumference is

$$L = \int_0^{2\pi} \sqrt{\left(\frac{dx}{dt}\right)^2 + \left(\frac{dy}{dt}\right)^2}\, dt.$$

We find

$$\frac{dx}{dt} = -r\sin t, \quad \frac{dy}{dt} = r\cos t$$

and

$$\left(\frac{dx}{dt}\right)^2 + \left(\frac{dy}{dt}\right)^2 = r^2(\sin^2 t + \cos^2 t) = r^2.$$

So

$$L = \int_0^{2\pi} \sqrt{r^2}\, dt = r\left[t\right]_0^{2\pi} = 2\pi r.$$ ■

EXAMPLE 2 Find the length of the astroid (Figure 6.24)

$$x = \cos^3 t, \qquad y = \sin^3 t, \qquad 0 \le t \le 2\pi.$$

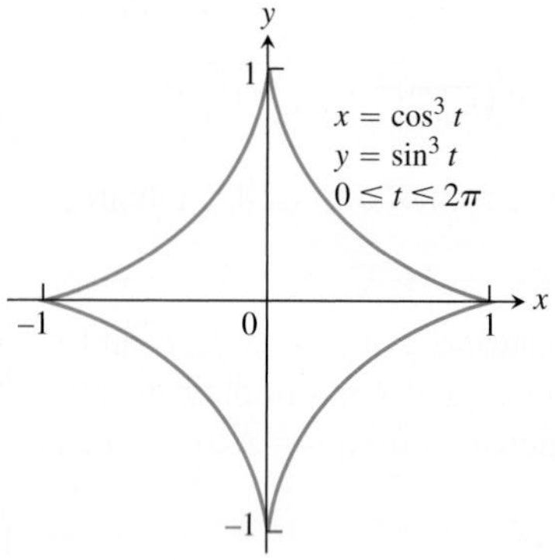

FIGURE 6.24 The astroid in Example 2.

Solution Because of the curve's symmetry with respect to the coordinate axes, its length is four times the length of the first-quadrant portion. We have

$$x = \cos^3 t, \qquad y = \sin^3 t$$

$$\left(\frac{dx}{dt}\right)^2 = [3\cos^2 t(-\sin t)]^2 = 9\cos^4 t\sin^2 t$$

$$\left(\frac{dy}{dt}\right)^2 = [3\sin^2 t(\cos t)]^2 = 9\sin^4 t\cos^2 t$$

$$\sqrt{\left(\frac{dx}{dt}\right)^2 + \left(\frac{dy}{dt}\right)^2} = \sqrt{9\cos^2 t\sin^2 t\underbrace{(\cos^2 t + \sin^2 t)}_{1}}$$

$$= \sqrt{9\cos^2 t\sin^2 t}$$

$$= 3|\cos t\sin t|$$

$$= 3\cos t\sin t. \qquad \begin{array}{l}\cos t\sin t \ge 0 \text{ for} \\ 0 \le t \le \pi/2\end{array}$$

Therefore,

$$\text{Length of first-quadrant portion} = \int_0^{\pi/2} 3\cos t\sin t\, dt$$

$$= \frac{3}{2}\int_0^{\pi/2} \sin 2t\, dt \qquad \begin{array}{l}\cos t\sin t = \\ (1/2)\sin 2t\end{array}$$

$$= -\frac{3}{4}\cos 2t\Big]_0^{\pi/2} = \frac{3}{2}.$$

The length of the astroid is four times this: $4(3/2) = 6$. ■

HISTORICAL BIOGRAPHY

Gregory St. Vincent
(1584–1667)

Length of a Curve $y = f(x)$

Given a continuously differentiable function $y = f(x)$, $a \le x \le b$, we can assign $x = t$ as a parameter. The graph of the function f is then the curve C defined parametrically by

$$x = t \quad \text{and} \quad y = f(t), \qquad a \le t \le b,$$

a special case of what we considered before. Then,

$$\frac{dx}{dt} = 1 \quad \text{and} \quad \frac{dy}{dt} = f'(t).$$

From our calculations in Section 3.5, we have

$$\frac{dy}{dx} = \frac{dy/dt}{dx/dt} = f'(t)$$

giving

$$\begin{aligned}\left(\frac{dx}{dt}\right)^2 + \left(\frac{dy}{dt}\right)^2 &= 1 + [f'(t)]^2 \\ &= 1 + \left(\frac{dy}{dx}\right)^2 \\ &= 1 + [f'(x)]^2.\end{aligned}$$

Substitution into Equation (1) gives the arc length formula for the graph of $y = f(x)$.

Formula for the Length of $y = f(x)$, $\quad a \le x \le b$

If f is continuously differentiable on the closed interval $[a, b]$, the length of the curve (graph) $y = f(x)$ from $x = a$ to $x = b$ is

$$L = \int_a^b \sqrt{1 + \left(\frac{dy}{dx}\right)^2}\, dx = \int_a^b \sqrt{1 + [f'(x)]^2}\, dx. \tag{2}$$

EXAMPLE 3 Find the length of the curve

$$y = \frac{1}{2}(e^x + e^{-x}), \qquad 0 \le x \le 2.$$

Solution We use Equation (2) with $a = 0$, $b = 2$, and

$$\begin{aligned}y &= \frac{1}{2}(e^x + e^{-x}) \\ \frac{dy}{dx} &= \frac{1}{2}(e^x - e^{-x}) \\ \left(\frac{dy}{dx}\right)^2 &= \frac{1}{4}(e^{2x} - 2 + e^{-2x}) \\ 1 + \left(\frac{dy}{dx}\right)^2 &= \frac{1}{4}(e^{2x} + 2 + e^{-2x}) = \left[\frac{1}{2}(e^x + e^{-x})\right]^2.\end{aligned}$$

The length of the curve from $x = 0$ to $x = 2$ is

$$L = \int_0^2 \sqrt{1 + \left(\frac{dy}{dx}\right)^2}\, dx = \int_0^2 \frac{1}{2}(e^x + e^{-x})\, dx \qquad \text{Eq. (2) with } a = 0, b = 2$$

$$= \frac{1}{2}\left[e^x - e^{-x}\right]_0^2 = \frac{1}{2}(e^2 - e^{-2}) \approx 3.63.$$

■

Dealing with Discontinuities in dy/dx

At a point on a curve where dy/dx fails to exist, dx/dy may exist and we may be able to find the curve's length by expressing x as a function of y and applying the following analogue of Equation (2):

Formula for the Length of $x = g(y)$, $c \le y \le d$
If g is continuously differentiable on $[c, d]$, the length of the curve $x = g(y)$ from $y = c$ to $y = d$ is

$$L = \int_c^d \sqrt{1 + \left(\frac{dx}{dy}\right)^2}\, dy = \int_c^d \sqrt{1 + [g'(y)]^2}\, dy. \tag{3}$$

EXAMPLE 4 Find the length of the curve $y = (x/2)^{2/3}$ from $x = 0$ to $x = 2$.

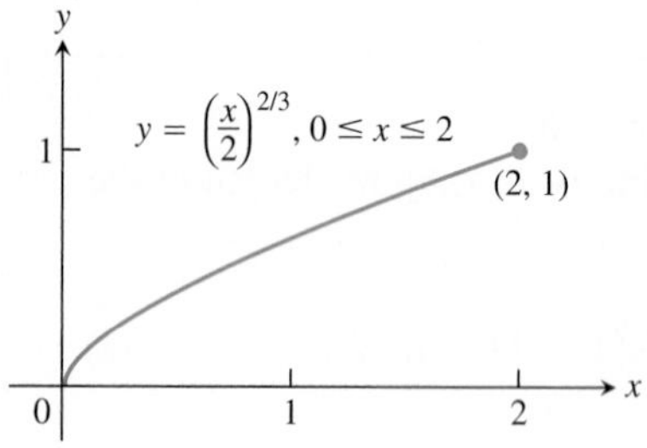

FIGURE 6.25 The graph of $y = (x/2)^{2/3}$ from $x = 0$ to $x = 2$ is also the graph of $x = 2y^{3/2}$ from $y = 0$ to $y = 1$ (Example 4).

Solution The derivative

$$\frac{dy}{dx} = \frac{2}{3}\left(\frac{x}{2}\right)^{-1/3}\left(\frac{1}{2}\right) = \frac{1}{3}\left(\frac{2}{x}\right)^{1/3}$$

is not defined at $x = 0$, so we cannot find the curve's length with Equation (2).

We therefore rewrite the equation to express x in terms of y:

$$y = \left(\frac{x}{2}\right)^{2/3}$$

$$y^{3/2} = \frac{x}{2} \qquad \text{Raise both sides to the power 3/2.}$$

$$x = 2y^{3/2}. \qquad \text{Solve for } x.$$

From this we see that the curve whose length we want is also the graph of $x = 2y^{3/2}$ from $y = 0$ to $y = 1$ (Figure 6.25).

The derivative

$$\frac{dx}{dy} = 2\left(\frac{3}{2}\right)y^{1/2} = 3y^{1/2}$$

is continuous on $[0, 1]$. We may therefore use Equation (3) to find the curve's length:

$$L = \int_c^d \sqrt{1 + \left(\frac{dx}{dy}\right)^2}\, dy = \int_0^1 \sqrt{1 + 9y}\, dy \qquad \text{Eq. (3) with } c = 0, d = 1. \text{ Let } u = 1 + 9y,\ du/9 = dy, \text{ integrate, and substitute back.}$$

$$= \frac{1}{9}\cdot\frac{2}{3}(1 + 9y)^{3/2}\Big]_0^1$$

$$= \frac{2}{27}\left(10\sqrt{10} - 1\right) \approx 2.27.$$

■

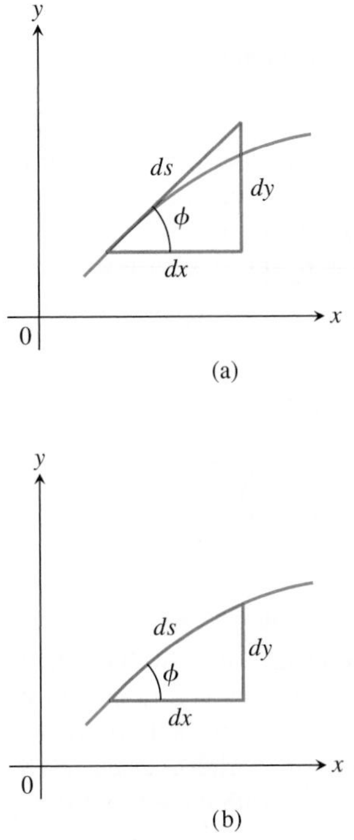

FIGURE 6.26 Diagrams for remembering the equation $ds = \sqrt{dx^2 + dy^2}$.

The Short Differential Formula

Equation (1) is frequently written in terms of differentials in place of derivatives. This is done formally by writing $(dt)^2$ under the radical in place of the dt outside the radical, and then writing

$$\left(\frac{dx}{dt}\right)^2 (dt)^2 = \left(\frac{dx}{dt}\,dt\right)^2 = (dx)^2$$

and

$$\left(\frac{dy}{dt}\right)^2 (dt)^2 = \left(\frac{dy}{dt}\,dt\right)^2 = (dy)^2.$$

It is also customary to eliminate the parentheses in $(dx)^2$ and write dx^2 instead, so that Equation (1) is written

$$L = \int \sqrt{dx^2 + dy^2}. \tag{4}$$

To compute an integral, dx and dy must both be expressed in terms of one and the same variable, and appropriate limits must be supplied in Equation (4).

A useful way to remember Equation (4) is to write

$$ds = \sqrt{dx^2 + dy^2} \tag{5}$$

and treat ds as the differential of arc length, which can be integrated between appropriate limits to give the total length of a curve. From this point of view, all the arc length formulas are simply different expressions for the equation $L = \int ds$. Figure 6.26a gives the exact interpretation of ds corresponding to Equation (5). Figure 6.26b is not strictly accurate, but is to be thought of as a simplified approximation of Figure 6.26a.

EXERCISES 6.3

Find the lengths of the curves in Exercises 1–8.

1. $x = 1 - t, \quad y = 2 + 3t, \quad -2/3 \le t \le 1$
2. $x = \cos t, \quad y = t + \sin t, \quad 0 \le t \le \pi$
3. $x = t^3, \quad y = 3t^2/2, \quad 0 \le t \le \sqrt{3}$
4. $x = t^2/2, \quad y = (2t + 1)^{3/2}/3, \quad 0 \le t \le 4$
5. $x = (2t + 3)^{3/2}/3, \quad y = t + t^2/2, \quad 0 \le t \le 3$
6. $x = 8\cos t + 8t\sin t, \quad y = 8\sin t - 8t\cos t, \quad 0 \le t \le \pi/2$
7. $x = e^t - t, \quad y = 4e^{t/2}, \quad 0 \le t \le 3$
8. $x = e^t\cos t, \quad y = e^t\sin t, \quad 0 \le t \le \pi$

Find the lengths of the curves in Exercises 9–18. If you have a grapher, you may want to graph these curves to see what they look like.

9. $y = (1/3)(x^2 + 2)^{3/2}$ from $x = 0$ to $x = 3$
10. $y = x^{3/2}$ from $x = 0$ to $x = 4$
11. $x = (y^3/3) + 1/(4y)$ from $y = 1$ to $y = 3$
    (*Hint:* $1 + (dx/dy)^2$ is a perfect square.)
12. $x = (y^{3/2}/3) - y^{1/2}$ from $y = 1$ to $y = 9$
    (*Hint:* $1 + (dx/dy)^2$ is a perfect square.)
13. $x = (y^4/4) + 1/(8y^2)$ from $y = 1$ to $y = 2$
    (*Hint:* $1 + (dx/dy)^2$ is a perfect square.)
14. $x = (y^3/6) + 1/(2y)$ from $y = 2$ to $y = 3$
    (*Hint:* $1 + (dx/dy)^2$ is a perfect square.)
15. $y = (3/4)x^{4/3} - (3/8)x^{2/3} + 5, \quad 1 \le x \le 8$
16. $y = (x^3/3) + x^2 + x + 1/(4x + 4), \quad 0 \le x \le 2$
17. $y = \sqrt{1 - x^2}, \quad -1/2 \le x \le 1/2$
18. $x = \int_0^y \sqrt{\sec^4 t - 1}\,dt, \quad -\pi/4 \le y \le \pi/4$

T In Exercises 19–26, do the following.

a. Set up an integral for the length of the curve.
b. Graph the curve to see what it looks like.
c. Use your grapher's or computer's integral evaluator to find the curve's length numerically.

19. $y = x^2, \quad -1 \le x \le 2$
20. $y = \tan x, \quad -\pi/3 \le x \le 0$
21. $x = \sin y, \quad 0 \le y \le \pi$
22. $x = \sqrt{1 - y^2}, \quad -1/2 \le y \le 1/2$
23. $y^2 + 2y = 2x + 1$ from $(-1, -1)$ to $(7, 3)$

24. $y = \sin x - x\cos x, \quad 0 \le x \le \pi$

25. $y = \int_0^x \tan t\,dt, \quad 0 \le x \le \pi/6$

26. $x = \int_0^y \sqrt{\sec^2 t - 1}\,dt, \quad -\pi/3 \le y \le \pi/4$

27. Is there a smooth (continuously differentiable) curve $y = f(x)$ whose length over the interval $0 \le x \le a$ is always $\sqrt{2}a$? Give reasons for your answer.

28. Using tangent fins to derive the length formula for curves Assume that f is smooth on $[a, b]$ and partition the interval $[a, b]$ in the usual way. In each subinterval $[x_{k-1}, x_k]$, construct the *tangent fin* at the point $(x_{k-1}, f(x_{k-1}))$, as shown in the accompanying figure.

a. Show that the length of the kth tangent fin over the interval $[x_{k-1}, x_k]$ equals $\sqrt{(\Delta x_k)^2 + (f'(x_{k-1})\,\Delta x_k)^2}$.

b. Show that

$$\lim_{n\to\infty}\sum_{k=1}^{n}(\text{length of } k\text{th tangent fin}) = \int_a^b \sqrt{1 + (f'(x))^2}\,dx,$$

which is the length L of the curve $y = f(x)$ from a to b.

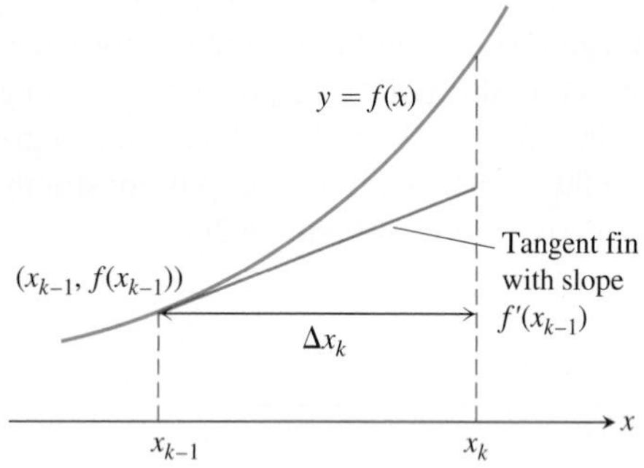

29. a. Find a curve through the point (1, 1) whose length integral is

$$L = \int_1^4 \sqrt{1 + \frac{1}{4x}}\,dx.$$

b. How many such curves are there? Give reasons for your answer.

30. a. Find a curve through the point (0, 1) whose length integral is

$$L = \int_1^2 \sqrt{1 + \frac{1}{y^4}}\,dy.$$

b. How many such curves are there? Give reasons for your answer.

31. Find a curve through the origin in the xy-plane whose length from $x = 0$ to $x = 1$ is

$$L = \int_0^1 \sqrt{1 + \frac{1}{4}e^x}\,dx.$$

32. Find a curve through the point (1, 0) whose length from $x = 1$ to $x = 2$ is

$$L = \int_1^2 \sqrt{1 + \frac{1}{x^2}}\,dx.$$

33. Find the length of the curve

$$x = \ln(\sec t + \tan t) - \sin t$$
$$y = \cos t, \quad 0 \le t \le \pi/3$$

34. Find the length of one arch of the cycloid $x = a(\theta - \sin\theta)$, $y = a(1 - \cos\theta)$, $0 \le \theta \le 2\pi$, shown in the accompanying figure. A **cycloid** is the curve traced out by a point P on the circumference of a circle rolling along a straight line, such as the x-axis.

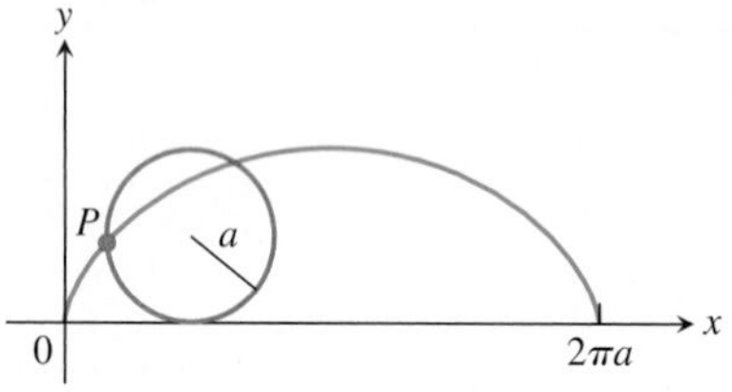

35. Find the length of the curve

$$x = e^t + e^{-t}, \quad y = 3 - 2t, \quad 0 \le t \le 3.$$

36. Length is independent of parametrization To illustrate the fact that the numbers we get for length do not depend on the way we parametrize our curves (except for the mild restrictions preventing doubling back mentioned earlier), calculate the length of the semicircle $y = \sqrt{1 - x^2}$ with these two different parametrizations:

a. $x = \cos 2t, \quad y = \sin 2t, \quad 0 \le t \le \pi/2$

b. $x = \sin \pi t, \quad y = \cos \pi t, \quad -1/2 \le t \le 1/2$

COMPUTER EXPLORATIONS

In Exercises 37–46, use a CAS to perform the following steps for the given curve over the closed interval.

a. Plot the curve together with the polygonal path approximations for $n = 2, 4, 8$ partition points over the interval. (See Figure 6.22.)

b. Find the corresponding approximation to the length of the curve by summing the lengths of the line segments.

c. Evaluate the length of the curve using an integral. Compare your approximations for $n = 2, 4, 8$ with the actual length given by the integral. How does the actual length compare with the approximations as n increases? Explain your answer.

37. $f(x) = \sqrt{1 - x^2}, \quad -1 \le x \le 1$

38. $f(x) = x^{1/3} + x^{2/3}, \quad 0 \le x \le 2$

39. $f(x) = \sin(\pi x^2), \quad 0 \le x \le \sqrt{2}$

40. $f(x) = x^2 \cos x, \quad 0 \le x \le \pi$

41. $f(x) = \dfrac{x - 1}{4x^2 + 1}, \quad -\dfrac{1}{2} \le x \le 1$

42. $f(x) = x^3 - x^2, \quad -1 \le x \le 1$

43. $x = \dfrac{1}{3}t^3, \quad y = \dfrac{1}{2}t^2, \quad 0 \le t \le 1$

44. $x = 2t^3 - 16t^2 + 25t + 5, \quad y = t^2 + t - 3, \quad 0 \le t \le 6$

45. $x = t - \cos t, \quad y = 1 + \sin t, \quad -\pi \le t \le \pi$

46. $x = \ln t, \quad y = \sqrt{t + 2}, \quad 1 \le t \le 4$

6.4 Areas of Surfaces of Revolution

When you jump rope, the rope sweeps out a surface in the space around you similar to what is called a *surface of revolution*. The "area" of this surface depends on the length of the rope and the distance of each of its segments from the axis of revolution. In this section we define areas of surfaces of revolution. More complicated surfaces are treated in Chapter 14.

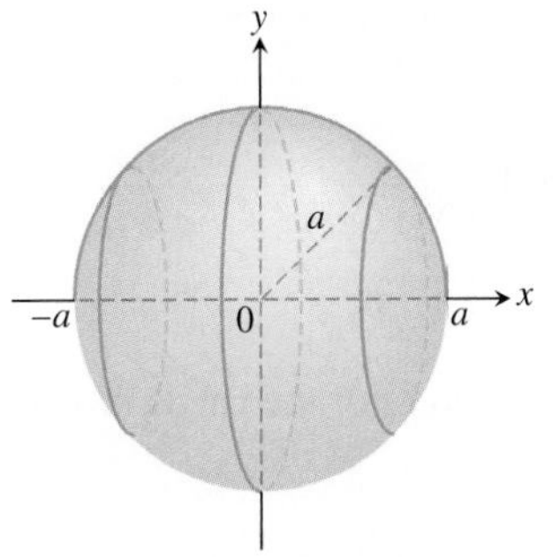

FIGURE 6.27 Rotating the semicircle $y = \sqrt{a^2 - x^2}$ of radius a with center at the origin generates a spherical surface with area $4\pi a^2$.

Defining Surface Area

We want our definition of the area of a surface of revolution to be consistent with known results from classical geometry for the surface areas of spheres, circular cylinders, and cones. So if the jump rope discussed in the introduction takes the shape of a semicircle with radius a rotated about the x-axis (Figure 6.27), it generates a sphere with surface area $4\pi a^2$.

Before considering general curves, we begin by rotating horizontal and slanted line segments about the x-axis. If we rotate the horizontal line segment AB having length Δx about the x-axis (Figure 6.28a), we generate a cylinder with surface area $2\pi y \Delta x$. This area is the same as that of a rectangle with side lengths Δx and $2\pi y$ (Figure 6.28b). The length $2\pi y$ is the circumference of the circle of radius y generated by rotating the point (x, y) on the line AB about the x-axis.

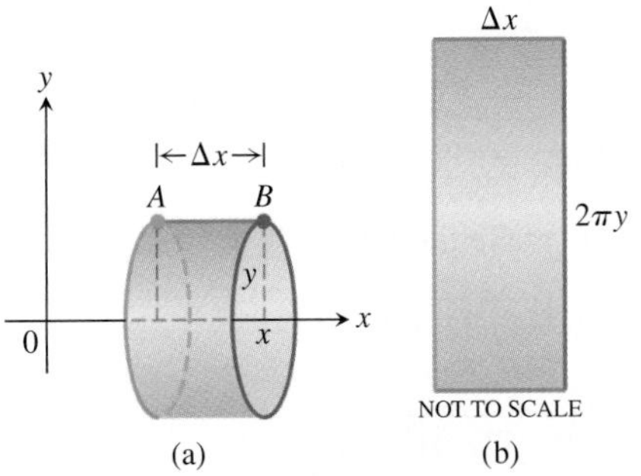

FIGURE 6.28 (a) A cylindrical surface generated by rotating the horizontal line segment AB of length Δx about the x-axis has area $2\pi y \Delta x$. (b) The cut and rolled out cylindrical surface as a rectangle.

Suppose the line segment AB has length Δs and is slanted rather than horizontal. Now when AB is rotated about the x-axis, it generates a frustum of a cone (Figure 6.29a). From classical geometry, the surface area of this frustum is $2\pi y^* \Delta s$, where $y^* = (y_1 + y_2)/2$ is the average height of the slanted segment AB above the x-axis. This surface area is the same as that of a rectangle with side lengths Δs and $2\pi y^*$ (Figure 6.29b).

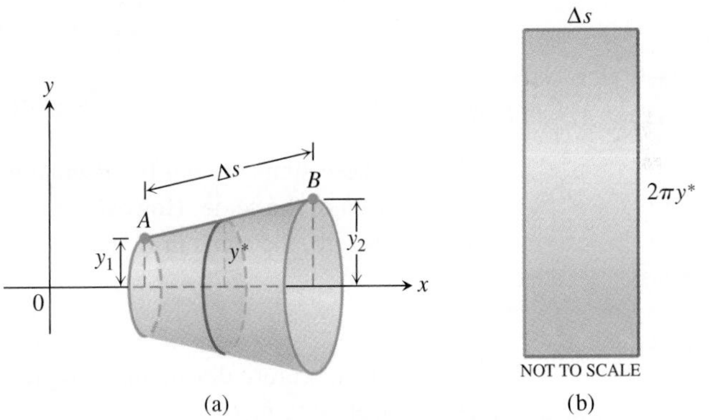

FIGURE 6.29 (a) The frustum of a cone generated by rotating the slanted line segment AB of length Δs about the x-axis has area $2\pi y^* \Delta s$. (b) The area of the rectangle for $y^* = \dfrac{y_1 + y_2}{2}$, the average height of AB above the x-axis.

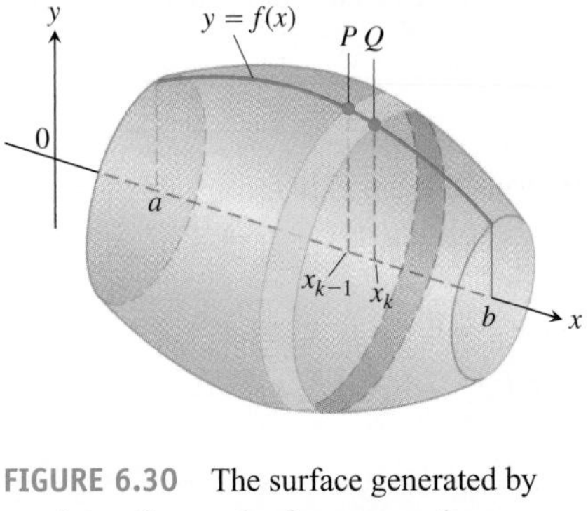

FIGURE 6.30 The surface generated by revolving the graph of a nonnegative function $y = f(x)$, $a \le x \le b$, about the x-axis. The surface is a union of bands like the one swept out by the arc PQ.

Let's build on these geometric principles to define the area of a surface swept out by revolving more general curves about the x-axis. Suppose we want to find the area of the surface swept out by revolving the graph of a nonnegative continuous function $y = f(x)$, $a \le x \le b$, about the x-axis. We partition the closed interval $[a, b]$ in the usual way and use the points in the partition to subdivide the graph into short arcs. Figure 6.30 shows a typical arc PQ and the band it sweeps out as part of the graph of f.

As the arc PQ revolves about the x-axis, the line segment joining P and Q sweeps out a frustum of a cone whose axis lies along the x-axis (Figure 6.31). The surface area

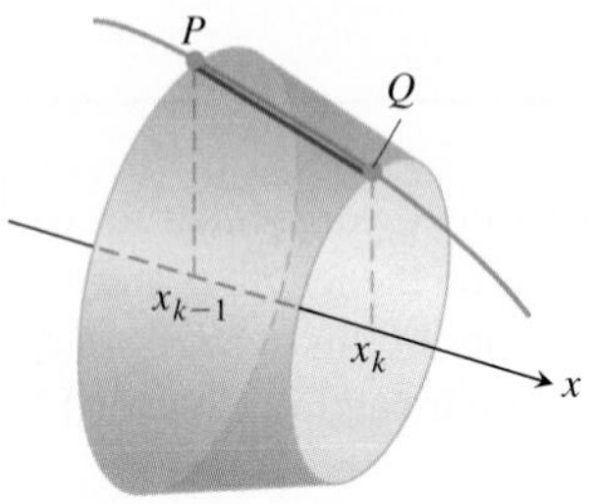

FIGURE 6.31 The line segment joining P and Q sweeps out a frustum of a cone.

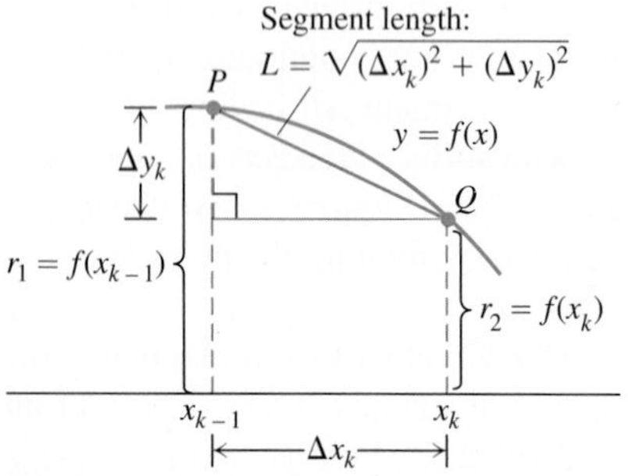

FIGURE 6.32 Dimensions associated with the arc and line segment PQ.

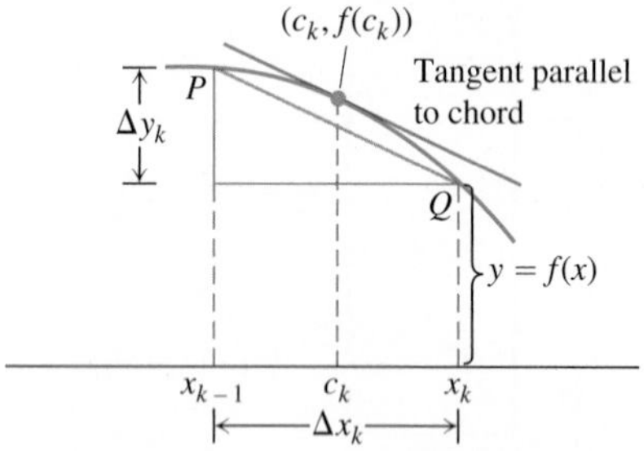

FIGURE 6.33 If f is smooth, the Mean Value Theorem guarantees the existence of a point c_k where the tangent is parallel to segment PQ.

of this frustum approximates the surface area of the band swept out by the arc PQ. The surface area of the frustum of the cone shown in Figure 6.31 is $2\pi y^* L$, where y^* is the average height of the line segment joining P and Q, and L is its length (just as before). Since $f \geq 0$, from Figure 6.32 we see that the average height of the line segment is $y^* = (f(x_{k-1}) + f(x_k))/2$, and the slant length is $L = \sqrt{(\Delta x_k)^2 + (\Delta y_k)^2}$. Therefore,

$$\begin{aligned}\text{Frustum surface area} &= 2\pi \cdot \frac{f(x_{k-1}) + f(x_k)}{2} \cdot \sqrt{(\Delta x_k)^2 + (\Delta y_k)^2} \\ &= \pi(f(x_{k-1}) + f(x_k))\sqrt{(\Delta x_k)^2 + (\Delta y_k)^2}.\end{aligned}$$

The area of the original surface, being the sum of the areas of the bands swept out by arcs like arc PQ, is approximated by the frustum area sum

$$\sum_{k=1}^{n} \pi(f(x_{k-1}) + f(x_k))\sqrt{(\Delta x_k)^2 + (\Delta y_k)^2}. \qquad (1)$$

We expect the approximation to improve as the partition of $[a, b]$ becomes finer. Moreover, if the function f is differentiable, then by the Mean Value Theorem, there is a point $(c_k, f(c_k))$ on the curve between P and Q where the tangent is parallel to the segment PQ (Figure 6.33). At this point,

$$\begin{aligned} f'(c_k) &= \frac{\Delta y_k}{\Delta x_k}, \\ \Delta y_k &= f'(c_k)\,\Delta x_k. \end{aligned}$$

With this substitution for Δy_k, the sums in Equation (1) take the form

$$\begin{aligned} &\sum_{k=1}^{n} \pi(f(x_{k-1}) + f(x_k))\sqrt{(\Delta x_k)^2 + (f'(c_k)\,\Delta x_k)^2} \\ &= \sum_{k=1}^{n} \pi(f(x_{k-1}) + f(x_k))\sqrt{1 + (f'(c_k))^2}\,\Delta x_k. \qquad (2)\end{aligned}$$

These sums are not the Riemann sums of any function because the points x_{k-1}, x_k, and c_k are not the same. However, it can be proved that as the norm of the partition of $[a, b]$ goes to zero, the sums in Equation (2) converge to the integral

$$\int_a^b 2\pi f(x)\sqrt{1 + (f'(x))^2}\,dx.$$

We therefore define this integral to be the area of the surface swept out by the graph of f from a to b.

DEFINITION If the function $f(x) \geq 0$ is continuously differentiable on $[a, b]$, the **area** of the surface generated by revolving the curve $y = f(x)$ about the x-axis is

$$S = \int_a^b 2\pi y\sqrt{1 + \left(\frac{dy}{dx}\right)^2}\,dx = \int_a^b 2\pi f(x)\sqrt{1 + (f'(x))^2}\,dx. \qquad (3)$$

The square root in Equation (3) is the same one that appears in the formula for the length of the generating curve in Equation (2) of Section 6.3.

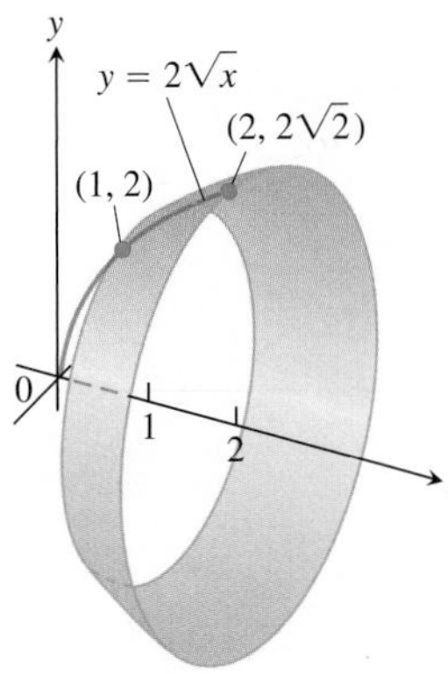

FIGURE 6.34 In Example 1 we calculate the area of this surface.

EXAMPLE 1 Find the area of the surface generated by revolving the curve $y = 2\sqrt{x}$, $1 \le x \le 2$, about the x-axis (Figure 6.34).

Solution We evaluate the formula

$$S = \int_a^b 2\pi y \sqrt{1 + \left(\frac{dy}{dx}\right)^2}\, dx \qquad \text{Eq. (3)}$$

with

$$a = 1, \qquad b = 2, \qquad y = 2\sqrt{x}, \qquad \frac{dy}{dx} = \frac{1}{\sqrt{x}},$$

$$\sqrt{1 + \left(\frac{dy}{dx}\right)^2} = \sqrt{1 + \left(\frac{1}{\sqrt{x}}\right)^2}$$

$$= \sqrt{1 + \frac{1}{x}} = \sqrt{\frac{x+1}{x}} = \frac{\sqrt{x+1}}{\sqrt{x}}.$$

With these substitutions,

$$S = \int_1^2 2\pi \cdot 2\sqrt{x}\frac{\sqrt{x+1}}{\sqrt{x}}\, dx = 4\pi \int_1^2 \sqrt{x+1}\, dx$$

$$= 4\pi \cdot \frac{2}{3}(x+1)^{3/2}\Big]_1^2 = \frac{8\pi}{3}\left(3\sqrt{3} - 2\sqrt{2}\right).$$

■

Revolution About the y-Axis

For revolution about the y-axis, we interchange x and y in Equation (3).

Surface Area for Revolution About the y-Axis

If $x = g(y) \ge 0$ is continuously differentiable on $[c, d]$, the area of the surface generated by revolving the curve $x = g(y)$ about the y-axis is

$$S = \int_c^d 2\pi x \sqrt{1 + \left(\frac{dx}{dy}\right)^2}\, dy = \int_c^d 2\pi g(y)\sqrt{1 + (g'(y))^2}\, dy. \qquad (4)$$

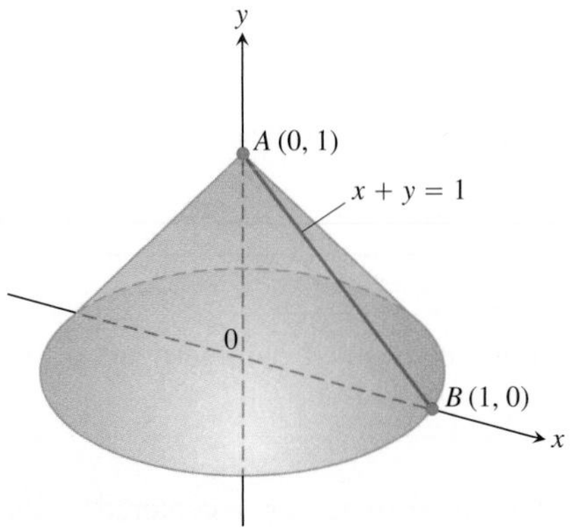

FIGURE 6.35 Revolving line segment AB about the y-axis generates a cone whose lateral surface area we can now calculate in two different ways (Example 2).

EXAMPLE 2 The line segment $x = 1 - y$, $0 \le y \le 1$, is revolved about the y-axis to generate the cone in Figure 6.35. Find its lateral surface area (which excludes the base area).

Solution Here we have a calculation we can check with a formula from geometry:

$$\text{Lateral surface area} = \frac{\text{base circumference}}{2} \times \text{slant height} = \pi\sqrt{2}.$$

To see how Equation (4) gives the same result, we take

$$c = 0, \qquad d = 1, \qquad x = 1 - y, \qquad \frac{dx}{dy} = -1,$$

$$\sqrt{1 + \left(\frac{dx}{dy}\right)^2} = \sqrt{1 + (-1)^2} = \sqrt{2}$$

and calculate

$$\begin{aligned} S &= \int_c^d 2\pi x \sqrt{1 + \left(\frac{dx}{dy}\right)^2}\, dy = \int_0^1 2\pi(1 - y)\sqrt{2}\, dy \\ &= 2\pi\sqrt{2}\left[y - \frac{y^2}{2}\right]_0^1 = 2\pi\sqrt{2}\left(1 - \frac{1}{2}\right) \\ &= \pi\sqrt{2}. \end{aligned}$$

The results agree, as they should. ■

Parametrized Curves

Regardless of the coordinate axis of revolution, the square roots appearing in Equations (3) and (4) are the same ones that appear in the formulas for arc length in Section 6.3. If the curve is parametrized by the equations $x = f(t)$ and $y = g(t)$, $a \le t \le b$, where f and g are continuously differentiable and $(f')^2 + (g')^2 > 0$ on $[a, b]$, then the corresponding square root appearing in the arc length formula is

$$\sqrt{[f'(t)]^2 + [g'(t)]^2} = \sqrt{\left(\frac{dx}{dt}\right)^2 + \left(\frac{dy}{dt}\right)^2}.$$

This observation leads to the following formulas for area of surfaces of revolution for smooth parametrized curves.

Surface Area of Revolution for Parametrized Curves

If a smooth curve $x = f(t)$, $y = g(t)$, $a \le t \le b$, is traversed exactly once as t increases from a to b, then the areas of the surfaces generated by revolving the curve about the coordinate axes are as follows.

1. Revolution about the x-axis ($y \ge 0$):

$$S = \int_a^b 2\pi y \sqrt{\left(\frac{dx}{dt}\right)^2 + \left(\frac{dy}{dt}\right)^2}\, dt \qquad (5)$$

2. Revolution about the y-axis ($x \ge 0$):

$$S = \int_a^b 2\pi x \sqrt{\left(\frac{dx}{dt}\right)^2 + \left(\frac{dy}{dt}\right)^2}\, dt \qquad (6)$$

As with length, we can calculate surface area from any convenient parametrization that meets the stated criteria.

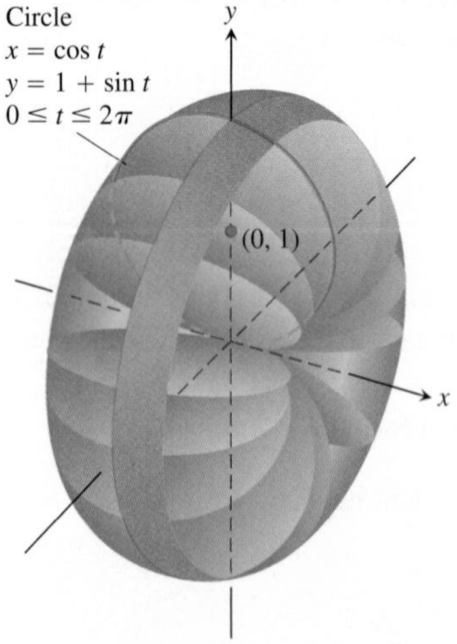

FIGURE 6.36 In Example 3 we calculate the area of the surface of revolution swept out by this parametrized curve.

EXAMPLE 3 The standard parametrization of the circle of radius 1 centered at the point (0, 1) in the xy-plane is

$$x = \cos t, \qquad y = 1 + \sin t, \qquad 0 \le t \le 2\pi.$$

Use this parametrization to find the area of the surface swept out by revolving the circle about the x-axis (Figure 6.36).

Solution We evaluate the formula

$$S = \int_a^b 2\pi y \sqrt{\left(\frac{dx}{dt}\right)^2 + \left(\frac{dy}{dt}\right)^2}\, dt$$

Eq. (5) for revolution about the x-axis; $y = 1 + \sin t > 0$

$$= \int_0^{2\pi} 2\pi(1 + \sin t)\underbrace{\sqrt{(-\sin t)^2 + (\cos t)^2}}_{1}\, dt$$

$$= 2\pi \int_0^{2\pi} (1 + \sin t)\, dt$$

$$= 2\pi\Big[t - \cos t\Big]_0^{2\pi} = 4\pi^2.$$

EXERCISES 6.4

In Exercises 1–8:

a. Set up an integral for the area of the surface generated by revolving the given curve about the indicated axis.

T **b.** Graph the curve to see what it looks like. If you can, graph the surface, too.

T **c.** Use your grapher's or computer's integral evaluator to find the surface's area numerically.

1. $y = \tan x, \quad 0 \le x \le \pi/4; \quad x$-axis

2. $y = x^2, \quad 0 \le x \le 2; \quad x$-axis

3. $xy = 1, \quad 1 \le y \le 2; \quad y$-axis

4. $x = \sin y, \quad 0 \le y \le \pi; \quad y$-axis

5. $x^{1/2} + y^{1/2} = 3$ from $(4, 1)$ to $(1, 4)$; x-axis

6. $y + 2\sqrt{y} = x, \quad 1 \le y \le 2; \quad y$-axis

7. $x = \int_0^y \tan t\, dt, \quad 0 \le y \le \pi/3; \quad y$-axis

8. $y = \int_1^x \sqrt{t^2 - 1}\, dt, \quad 1 \le x \le \sqrt{5}; \quad x$-axis

9. Find the lateral (side) surface area of the cone generated by revolving the line segment $y = x/2, 0 \le x \le 4$, about the x-axis. Check your answer with the geometry formula

$$\text{Lateral surface area} = \frac{1}{2} \times \text{base circumference} \times \text{slant height}.$$

10. Find the lateral surface area of the cone generated by revolving the line segment $y = x/2, 0 \le x \le 4$ about the y-axis. Check your answer with the geometry formula

$$\text{Lateral surface area} = \frac{1}{2} \times \text{base circumference} \times \text{slant height}.$$

11. Find the surface area of the cone frustum generated by revolving the line segment $y = (x/2) + (1/2), 1 \le x \le 3$, about the x-axis. Check your result with the geometry formula

$$\text{Frustum surface area} = \pi(r_1 + r_2) \times \text{slant height}.$$

12. Find the surface area of the cone frustum generated by revolving the line segment $y = (x/2) + (1/2), 1 \le x \le 3$, about the y-axis. Check your result with the geometry formula

$$\text{Frustum surface area} = \pi(r_1 + r_2) \times \text{slant height}.$$

Find the areas of the surfaces generated by revolving the curves in Exercises 13–23 about the indicated axes. If you have a grapher, you may want to graph these curves to see what they look like.

13. $y = x^3/9, \quad 0 \le x \le 2; \quad x$-axis

14. $y = \sqrt{x}, \quad 3/4 \le x \le 15/4; \quad x$-axis

15. $y = \sqrt{2x - x^2}, \quad 0.5 \le x \le 1.5; \quad x$-axis

16. $y = \sqrt{x + 1}, \quad 1 \le x \le 5; \quad x$-axis

17. $x = y^3/3, \quad 0 \le y \le 1; \quad y$-axis

18. $x = (1/3)y^{3/2} - y^{1/2}, \quad 1 \le y \le 3; \quad y$-axis

19. $x = 2\sqrt{4 - y}, \quad 0 \le y \le 15/4; \quad y$-axis

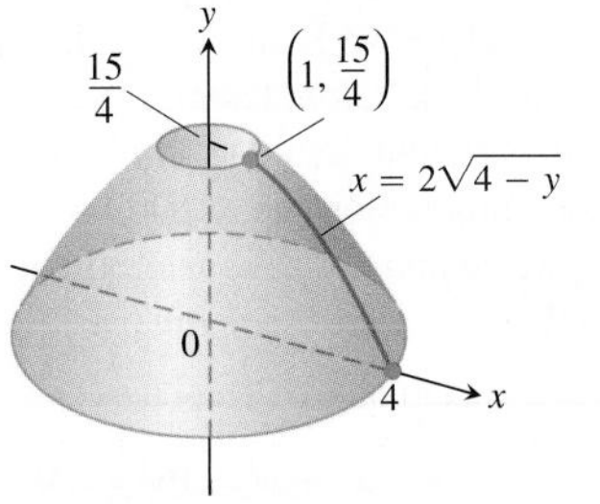

20. $x = \sqrt{2y - 1}, \quad 5/8 \le y \le 1; \quad y$-axis

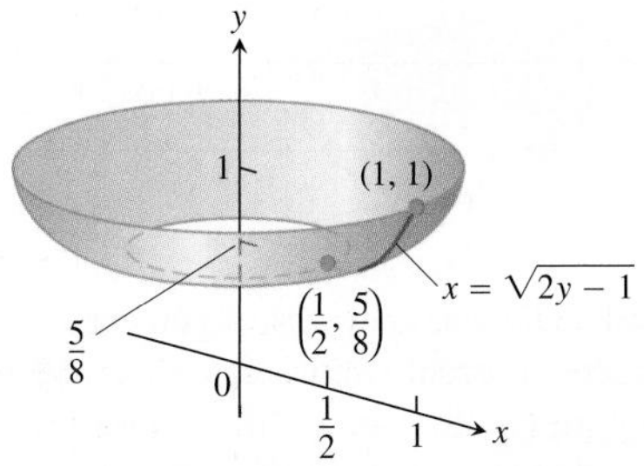

21. $x = (e^y + e^{-y})/2, \quad 0 \le y \le \ln 2; \quad y$-axis

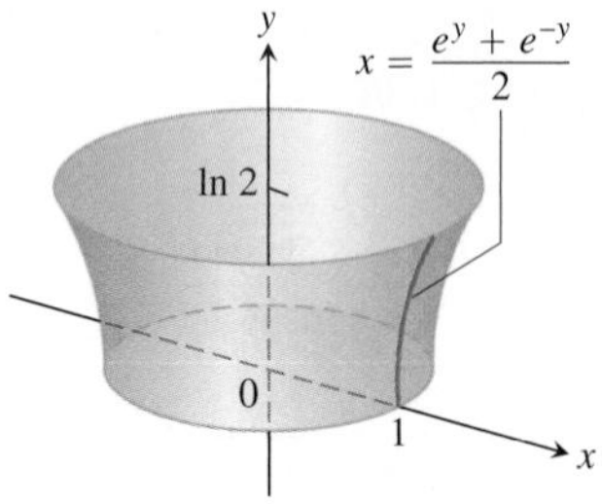

22. $y = (1/3)(x^2 + 2)^{3/2}, \quad 0 \le x \le \sqrt{2}; \quad y$-axis (*Hint:* Express $ds = \sqrt{dx^2 + dy^2}$ in terms of dx, and evaluate the integral $S = \int 2\pi x\, ds$ with appropriate limits.)

23. $x = (y^4/4) + 1/(8y^2), \quad 1 \le y \le 2; \quad x$-axis (*Hint:* Express $ds = \sqrt{dx^2 + dy^2}$ in terms of dy, and evaluate the integral $S = \int 2\pi y\, ds$ with appropriate limits.)

24. Write an integral for the area of the surface generated by revolving the curve $y = \cos x$, $-\pi/2 \le x \le \pi/2$, about the x-axis. In Section 7.3 we will see how to evaluate such integrals.

25. Testing the new definition Show that the surface area of a sphere of radius a is still $4\pi a^2$ by using Equation (3) to find the area of the surface generated by revolving the curve $y = \sqrt{a^2 - x^2}$, $-a \le x \le a$, about the x-axis.

26. Testing the new definition The lateral (side) surface area of a cone of height h and base radius r should be $\pi r\sqrt{r^2 + h^2}$, the semiperimeter of the base times the slant height. Show that this is still the case by finding the area of the surface generated by revolving the line segment $y = (r/h)x$, $0 \le x \le h$, about the x-axis.

T **27. Enameling woks** Your company decided to put out a deluxe version of a wok you designed. The plan is to coat it inside with white enamel and outside with blue enamel. Each enamel will be sprayed on 0.5 mm thick before baking. (See diagram here.) Your manufacturing department wants to know how much enamel to have on hand for a production run of 5000 woks. What do you tell them? (Neglect waste and unused material and give your answer in liters. Remember that 1 cm^3 = 1 mL, so 1 L = 1000 cm^3.)

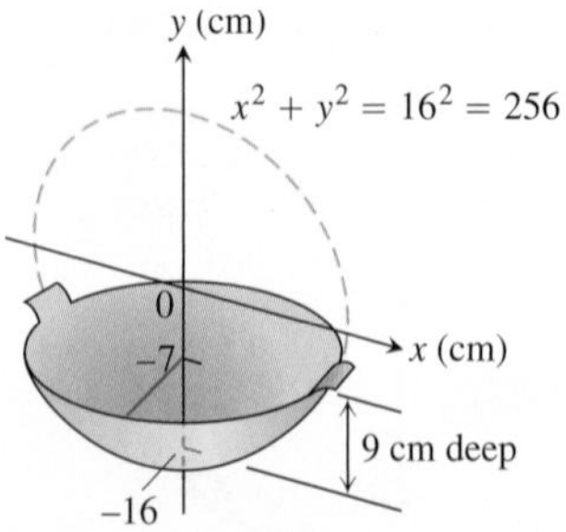

28. Slicing bread Did you know that if you cut a spherical loaf of bread into slices of equal width, each slice will have the same amount of crust? To see why, suppose the semicircle $y = \sqrt{r^2 - x^2}$ shown here is revolved about the x-axis to generate a sphere. Let AB be an arc of the semicircle that lies above an interval of length h on the x-axis. Show that the area swept out by AB does not depend on the location of the interval. (It does depend on the length of the interval.)

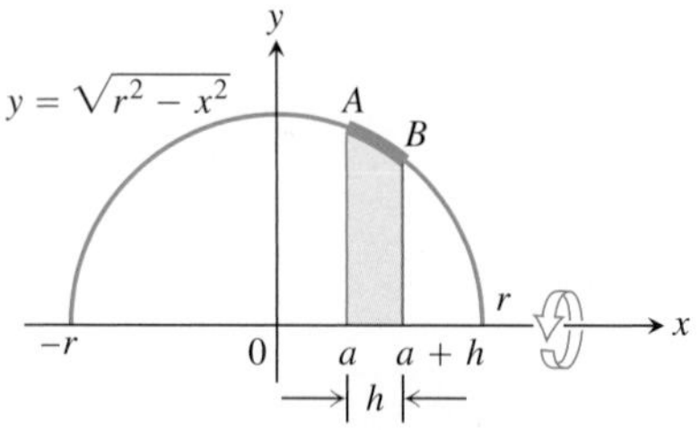

29. The shaded band shown here is cut from a sphere of radius R by parallel planes h units apart. Show that the surface area of the band is $2\pi Rh$.

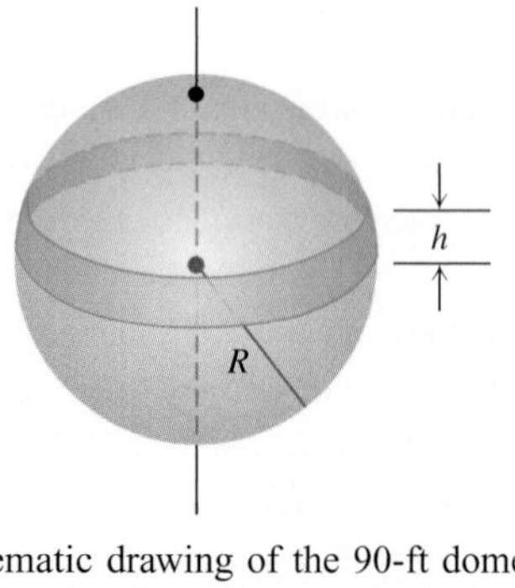

30. Here is a schematic drawing of the 90-ft dome used by the U.S. National Weather Service to house radar in Bozeman, Montana.

a. How much outside surface is there to paint (not counting the bottom)?

T **b.** Express the answer to the nearest square foot.

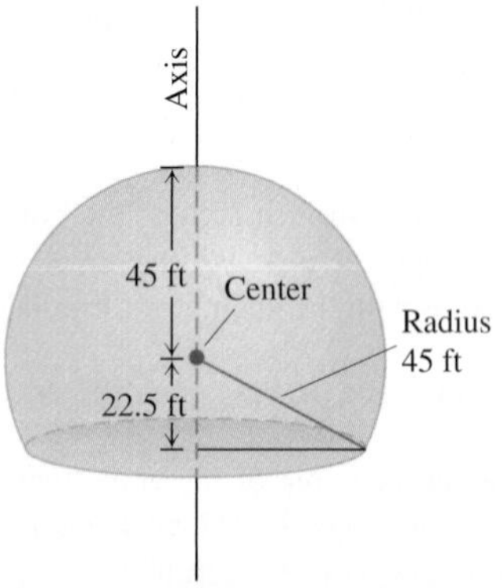

31. An alternative derivation of the surface area formula Assume f is smooth on $[a, b]$ and partition $[a, b]$ in the usual way. In the kth subinterval $[x_{k-1}, x_k]$ construct the tangent line to the curve at the midpoint $m_k = (x_{k-1} + x_k)/2$, as in the figure here.

a. Show that $r_1 = f(m_k) - f'(m_k)\dfrac{\Delta x_k}{2}$ and $r_2 = f(m_k) + f'(m_k)\dfrac{\Delta x_k}{2}$.

b. Show that the length L_k of the tangent line segment in the kth subinterval is $L_k = \sqrt{(\Delta x_k)^2 + (f'(m_k)\,\Delta x_k)^2}$.

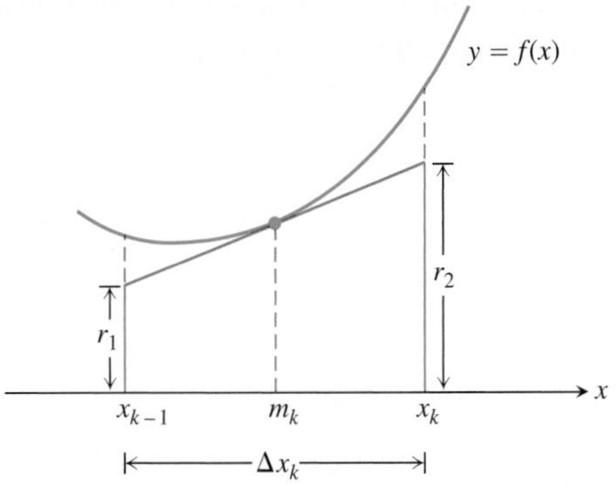

c. Show that the lateral surface area of the frustum of the cone swept out by the tangent line segment as it revolves about the x-axis is $2\pi f(m_k)\sqrt{1 + (f'(m_k))^2}\,\Delta x_k$.

d. Show that the area of the surface generated by revolving $y = f(x)$ about the x-axis over $[a, b]$ is

$$\lim_{n\to\infty} \sum_{k=1}^{n} \begin{pmatrix}\text{lateral surface area} \\ \text{of } k\text{th frustum}\end{pmatrix} = \int_a^b 2\pi f(x)\sqrt{1 + (f'(x))^2}\,dx.$$

32. The surface of an astroid Find the area of the surface generated by revolving about the x-axis the portion of the astroid $x^{2/3} + y^{2/3} = 1$ shown in the accompanying figure. (*Hint*: Revolve the first-quadrant portion $y = (1 - x^{2/3})^{3/2}$, $0 \le x \le 1$, about the x-axis and double your result.)

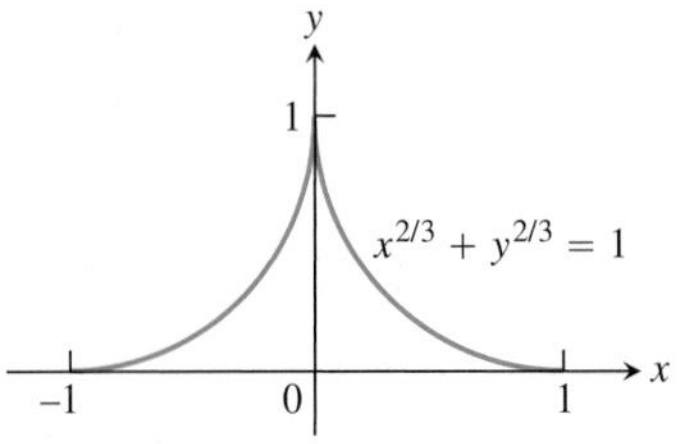

Find the areas of the surfaces generated by revolving the curves in Exercises 33–38 about the indicated axes.

33. $x = \cos t, \quad y = 2 + \sin t, \quad 0 \le t \le 2\pi;$ x-axis

34. $x = (2/3)t^{3/2}, \quad y = 2\sqrt{t}, \quad 0 \le t \le \sqrt{3};$ y-axis

35. $x = t + \sqrt{2}, \quad y = (t^2/2) + \sqrt{2}t, \quad -\sqrt{2} \le t \le \sqrt{2};$ y-axis

36. $x = a(t - \sin t), \quad y = a(1 - \cos t), \quad 0 \le t \le 2\pi;$ x-axis

37. $x = e^t - t, \quad y = 4e^{t/2}, \quad 0 \le t \le 1;$ x-axis

38. $x = \ln(\sec t + \tan t) - \sin t,\ y = \cos t,\ 0 \le t \le \pi/3;$ x-axis

39. A cone frustum The line segment joining the points (0, 1) and (2, 2) is revolved about the x-axis to generate a frustum of a cone. Find the surface area of the frustum using the parametrization $x = 2t, y = t + 1, 0 \le t \le 1$. Check your result with the geometry formula: Area $= \pi(r_1 + r_2)$(slant height).

40. A cone The line segment joining the origin to the point (h, r) is revolved about the x-axis to generate a cone of height h and base radius r. Find the cone's surface area with the parametric equations $x = ht, y = rt, 0 \le t \le 1$. Check your result with the geometry formula: Area $= \pi r$(slant height).

6.5 Exponential Change and Separable Differential Equations

In Section 1.4 we introduced graphically the idea of exponential growth and decay: $y = y_0e^{kt}$ models *growth* if $k > 0$ and *decay* if $k < 0$. We now investigate this idea by integrating an equation defining the change dy/dt, enabling us to recover the exponential expression for y.

Exponential Change

In modeling many real-world situations, a quantity y increases or decreases at a rate proportional to its size at a given time t. Examples of such quantities include the amount of a decaying radioactive material, the size of a population, and the temperature difference between a hot object and its surrounding medium. Such quantities are said to undergo *exponential change*.

If the amount present at time $t = 0$ is called y_0, then we can find y as a function of t by solving the following initial value problem:

$$\text{Differential equation:} \quad \frac{dy}{dt} = ky$$

$$\text{Initial condition:} \quad y = y_0 \text{ when } t = 0. \tag{1}$$

If y is positive and increasing, then k is positive, and we use Equation (1) to say that the rate of growth is proportional to what has already been accumulated. If y is positive and decreasing, then k is negative, and we use Equation (1) to say that the rate of decay is proportional to the amount still left.

We see right away that the constant function $y = 0$ is a solution of Equation (1) if $y_0 = 0$. To find the nonzero solutions, we divide Equation (1) by y:

$$\frac{1}{y} \cdot \frac{dy}{dt} = k \qquad y \neq 0$$

$$\int \frac{1}{y}\frac{dy}{dt}\,dt = \int k\,dt \qquad \text{Integrate with respect to } t;$$

$$\ln|y| = kt + C \qquad \int (1/u)\,du = \ln|u| + C.$$

$$|y| = e^{kt+C} \qquad \text{Exponentiate.}$$

$$|y| = e^{C} \cdot e^{kt} \qquad e^{a+b} = e^a \cdot e^b$$

$$y = \pm e^{C} e^{kt} \qquad \text{If } |y| = r, \text{ then } y = \pm r.$$

$$y = Ae^{kt}. \qquad A \text{ is a shorter name for } \pm e^C.$$

By allowing A to take on the value 0 in addition to all possible values $\pm e^C$, we can include the solution $y = 0$ in the formula.

We find the value of A for the initial value problem by solving for A when $y = y_0$ and $t = 0$:

$$y_0 = Ae^{k \cdot 0} = A.$$

The solution of the initial value problem is therefore

$$y = y_0 e^{kt}. \tag{2}$$

Quantities changing in this way are said to undergo **exponential growth** if $k > 0$, and **exponential decay** if $k < 0$. The number k is called the **rate constant** of the change.

The derivation of Equation (2) shows also that the only functions that are their own derivatives are constant multiples of the exponential function.

Before presenting several examples of exponential change, let's consider the process we used to derive it.

Separable Differential Equations

Exponential change is modeled by a differential equation of the form $dy/dx = ky$, for some nonzero constant k. More generally, suppose we have a differential equation of the form

$$\frac{dy}{dx} = f(x, y), \tag{3}$$

where f is a function of *both* the independent and dependent variables. A **solution** of the equation is a differentiable function $y = y(x)$ defined on an interval of x-values (perhaps infinite) such that

$$\frac{d}{dx}\,y(x) = f(x, y(x))$$

on that interval. That is, when $y(x)$ and its derivative $y'(x)$ are substituted into the differential equation, the resulting equation is true for all x in the solution interval. The **general solution** is a solution $y(x)$ that contains all possible solutions and it always contains an arbitrary constant.

Equation (3) is **separable** if f can be expressed as a product of a function of x and a function of y. The differential equation then has the form

$$\frac{dy}{dx} = g(x)H(y). \qquad \text{g is a function of x, H is a function of y}$$

When we rewrite this equation in the form

$$\frac{dy}{dx} = \frac{g(x)}{h(y)}, \qquad H(y) = \frac{1}{h(y)}$$

its differential form allows us to collect all y terms with dy and all x terms with dx:

$$h(y)\,dy = g(x)\,dx.$$

Now we simply integrate both sides of this equation:

$$\int h(y)\,dy = \int g(x)\,dx. \tag{4}$$

After completing the integrations we obtain the solution y defined implicitly as a function of x.

The justification that we can simply integrate both sides in Equation (4) is based on the Substitution Rule (Section 5.5):

$$\begin{aligned}\int h(y)\,dy &= \int h(y(x))\frac{dy}{dx}\,dx \\ &= \int h(y(x))\frac{g(x)}{h(y(x))}\,dx \qquad \frac{dy}{dx} = \frac{g(x)}{h(y)} \\ &= \int g(x)\,dx.\end{aligned}$$

EXAMPLE 1 Solve the differential equation

$$\frac{dy}{dx} = (1 + y^2)e^x.$$

Solution Since $1 + y^2$ is never zero, we can solve the equation by separating the variables.

$$\begin{aligned}\frac{dy}{dx} &= (1 + y^2)e^x \\ dy &= (1 + y^2)e^x\,dx && \text{Treat dy/dx as a quotient of differentials and multiply both sides by dx.} \\ \frac{dy}{1 + y^2} &= e^x\,dx && \text{Divide by $(1 + y^2)$.} \\ \int \frac{dy}{1 + y^2} &= \int e^x\,dx && \text{Integrate both sides.} \\ \tan^{-1} y &= e^x + C && \text{C represents the combined constants of integration.}\end{aligned}$$

The equation $\tan^{-1} y = e^x + C$ gives y as an implicit function of x. When $-\pi/2 < e^x + C < \pi/2$, we can solve for y as an explicit function of x by taking the tangent of both sides:

$$\begin{aligned}\tan(\tan^{-1} y) &= \tan(e^x + C) \\ y &= \tan(e^x + C).\end{aligned}$$

■

EXAMPLE 2 Solve the equation

$$(x+1)\frac{dy}{dx} = x(y^2+1).$$

Solution We change to differential form, separate the variables, and integrate:

$$(x+1)\,dy = x(y^2+1)\,dx$$

$$\frac{dy}{y^2+1} = \frac{x\,dx}{x+1} \qquad x \neq -1$$

$$\int \frac{dy}{1+y^2} = \int \left(1 - \frac{1}{x+1}\right) dx$$

$$\tan^{-1} y = x - \ln|x+1| + C.$$

■

The initial value problem

$$\frac{dy}{dt} = ky, \qquad y(0) = y_0$$

involves a separable differential equation, and the solution $y = y_0 e^{kt}$ expresses exponential change. We now present several examples of such change.

Unlimited Population Growth

Strictly speaking, the number of individuals in a population (of people, plants, animals, or bacteria, for example) is a discontinuous function of time because it takes on discrete values. However, when the number of individuals becomes large enough, the population can be approximated by a continuous function. Differentiability of the approximating function is another reasonable hypothesis in many settings, allowing for the use of calculus to model and predict population sizes.

If we assume that the proportion of reproducing individuals remains constant and assume a constant fertility, then at any instant t the birth rate is proportional to the number $y(t)$ of individuals present. Let's assume, too, that the death rate of the population is stable and proportional to $y(t)$. If, further, we neglect departures and arrivals, the growth rate dy/dt is the birth rate minus the death rate, which is the difference of the two proportionalities under our assumptions. In other words, $dy/dt = ky$, so that $y = y_0 e^{kt}$, where y_0 is the size of the population at time $t = 0$. As with all kinds of growth, there may be limitations imposed by the surrounding environment, but we will not go into these here. The proportionality $dy/dt = ky$ models *unlimited population growth.*

In the following example we assume this population model to look at how the number of individuals infected by a disease within a given population decreases as the disease is appropriately treated.

EXAMPLE 3 One model for the way diseases die out when properly treated assumes that the rate dy/dt at which the number of infected people changes is proportional to the number y. The number of people cured is proportional to the number y that are infected with the disease. Suppose that in the course of any given year the number of cases of a disease is reduced by 20%. If there are 10,000 cases today, how many years will it take to reduce the number to 1000?

Solution We use the equation $y = y_0 e^{kt}$. There are three things to find: the value of y_0, the value of k, and the time t when $y = 1000$.

The value of y_0. We are free to count time beginning anywhere we want. If we count from today, then $y = 10{,}000$ when $t = 0$, so $y_0 = 10{,}000$. Our equation is now

$$y = 10{,}000 e^{kt}. \tag{5}$$

The value of k. When $t = 1$ year, the number of cases will be 80% of its present value, or 8000. Hence,

$$\begin{aligned} 8000 &= 10{,}000 e^{k(1)} && \text{Eq. (5) with } t = 1 \text{ and } y = 8000 \\ e^k &= 0.8 \\ \ln(e^k) &= \ln 0.8 && \text{Logs of both sides} \\ k &= \ln 0.8 < 0. \end{aligned}$$

At any given time t,

$$y = 10{,}000 e^{(\ln 0.8)t}. \tag{6}$$

The value of t that makes $y = 1000$. We set y equal to 1000 in Equation (6) and solve for t:

$$\begin{aligned} 1000 &= 10{,}000 e^{(\ln 0.8)t} \\ e^{(\ln 0.8)t} &= 0.1 \\ (\ln 0.8)t &= \ln 0.1 && \text{Logs of both sides} \\ t &= \frac{\ln 0.1}{\ln 0.8} \approx 10.32 \text{ years}. \end{aligned}$$

It will take a little more than 10 years to reduce the number of cases to 1000. ■

Radioactivity

Some atoms are unstable and can spontaneously emit mass or radiation. This process is called **radioactive decay**, and an element whose atoms go spontaneously through this process is called **radioactive**. Sometimes when an atom emits some of its mass through this process of radioactivity, the remainder of the atom re-forms to make an atom of some new element. For example, radioactive carbon-14 decays into nitrogen; radium, through a number of intermediate radioactive steps, decays into lead.

For radon-222 gas, t is measured in days and $k = 0.18$. For radium-226, which used to be painted on watch dials to make them glow at night (a dangerous practice), t is measured in years and $k = 4.3 \times 10^{-4}$.

Experiments have shown that at any given time the rate at which a radioactive element decays (as measured by the number of nuclei that change per unit time) is approximately proportional to the number of radioactive nuclei present. Thus, the decay of a radioactive element is described by the equation $dy/dt = -ky$, $k > 0$. It is conventional to use $-k$, with $k > 0$, to emphasize that y is decreasing. If y_0 is the number of radioactive nuclei present at time zero, the number still present at any later time t will be

$$y = y_0 e^{-kt}, \qquad k > 0.$$

Recall from Section 1.5 that the **half-life** of a radioactive element is the time required for half of the radioactive nuclei present in a sample to decay. We found that the half-life of an element depends only on the value of the rate constant, and is given by the formula

$$\text{Half-life} = \frac{\ln 2}{k}. \tag{7}$$

For example, the half-life for radon-222 is

$$\text{Half-life} = \frac{\ln 2}{0.18} \approx 3.9 \text{ days.}$$

EXAMPLE 4 The decay of radioactive elements can sometimes be used to date events from the Earth's past. In a living organism, the ratio of radioactive carbon, carbon-14, to ordinary carbon stays fairly constant during the lifetime of the organism, being approximately equal to the ratio in the organism's surroundings at the time. After the organism's death, however, no new carbon is ingested, and the proportion of carbon-14 in the organism's remains decreases as the carbon-14 decays.

Scientists who do carbon-14 dating use a figure of 5700 years for its half-life. Find the age of a sample in which 10% of the radioactive nuclei originally present have decayed.

Solution We use the decay equation $y = y_0 e^{-kt}$. There are two things to find: the value of k and the value of t when y is $0.9y_0$ (90% of the radioactive nuclei are still present). That is, find t when $y_0 e^{-kt} = 0.9y_0$, or $e^{-kt} = 0.9$.

The value of k. We use the half-life Equation (7):

$$k = \frac{\ln 2}{\text{half-life}} = \frac{\ln 2}{5700} \qquad (\text{about } 1.2 \times 10^{-4})$$

The value of t that makes $e^{-kt} = 0.9$:

$$e^{-kt} = 0.9$$

$$e^{-(\ln 2/5700)t} = 0.9$$

$$-\frac{\ln 2}{5700} t = \ln 0.9 \qquad \text{Logs of both sides}$$

$$t = -\frac{5700 \ln 0.9}{\ln 2} \approx 866 \text{ years.}$$

The sample is about 866 years old. ■

Heat Transfer: Newton's Law of Cooling

Hot soup left in a tin cup cools to the temperature of the surrounding air. A hot silver ingot immersed in a large tub of water cools to the temperature of the surrounding water. In situations like these, the rate at which an object's temperature is changing at any given time is roughly proportional to the difference between its temperature and the temperature of the surrounding medium. This observation is called *Newton's law of cooling*, although it applies to warming as well.

If H is the temperature of the object at time t and H_S is the constant surrounding temperature, then the differential equation is

$$\frac{dH}{dt} = -k(H - H_S). \tag{8}$$

If we substitute y for $(H - H_S)$, then

$$\begin{aligned}
\frac{dy}{dt} &= \frac{d}{dt}(H - H_S) = \frac{dH}{dt} - \frac{d}{dt}(H_S) \\
&= \frac{dH}{dt} - 0 && H_S \text{ is a constant.} \\
&= \frac{dH}{dt} \\
&= -k(H - H_S) && \text{Eq. (8)} \\
&= -ky. && H - H_S = y.
\end{aligned}$$

Now we know that the solution of $dy/dt = -ky$ is $y = y_0 e^{-kt}$, where $y(0) = y_0$. Substituting $(H - H_S)$ for y, this says that

$$H - H_S = (H_0 - H_S)e^{-kt}, \tag{9}$$

where H_0 is the temperature at $t = 0$. This equation is the solution to Newton's Law of Cooling.

EXAMPLE 5 A hard-boiled egg at 98°C is put in a sink of 18°C water. After 5 min, the egg's temperature is 38°C. Assuming that the water has not warmed appreciably, how much longer will it take the egg to reach 20°C?

Solution We find how long it would take the egg to cool from 98°C to 20°C and subtract the 5 min that have already elapsed. Using Equation (9) with $H_S = 18$ and $H_0 = 98$, the egg's temperature t min after it is put in the sink is

$$H = 18 + (98 - 18)e^{-kt} = 18 + 80e^{-kt}.$$

To find k, we use the information that $H = 38$ when $t = 5$:

$$\begin{aligned}
38 &= 18 + 80e^{-5k} \\
e^{-5k} &= \frac{1}{4} \\
-5k &= \ln\frac{1}{4} = -\ln 4 \\
k &= \frac{1}{5}\ln 4 = 0.2\ln 4 \qquad (\text{about } 0.28).
\end{aligned}$$

The egg's temperature at time t is $H = 18 + 80e^{-(0.2\ln 4)t}$. Now find the time t when $H = 20$:

$$\begin{aligned}
20 &= 18 + 80e^{-(0.2\ln 4)t} \\
80e^{-(0.2\ln 4)t} &= 2 \\
e^{-(0.2\ln 4)t} &= \frac{1}{40} \\
-(0.2\ln 4)t &= \ln\frac{1}{40} = -\ln 40 \\
t &= \frac{\ln 40}{0.2\ln 4} \approx 13 \text{ min}.
\end{aligned}$$

The egg's temperature will reach 20°C about 13 min after it is put in the water to cool. Since it took 5 min to reach 38°C, it will take about 8 min more to reach 20°C. ■

EXERCISES 6.5

In Exercises 1 and 2, show that each function $y = f(x)$ is a solution of the accompanying differential equation.

1. $2y' + 3y = e^{-x}$

   a. $y = e^{-x}$ b. $y = e^{-x} + e^{-(3/2)x}$

   c. $y = e^{-x} + Ce^{-(3/2)x}$

2. $y' = y^2$

   a. $y = -\dfrac{1}{x}$ b. $y = -\dfrac{1}{x+3}$ c. $y = -\dfrac{1}{x+C}$

In Exercises 3 and 4, show that the function $y = f(x)$ is a solution of the given differential equation.

3. $y = \dfrac{1}{x}\displaystyle\int_1^x \frac{e^t}{t}\,dt, \quad x^2y' + xy = e^x$

4. $y = \dfrac{1}{\sqrt{1+x^4}}\displaystyle\int_1^x \sqrt{1+t^4}\,dt, \quad y' + \frac{2x^3}{1+x^4}y = 1$

In Exercises 5–8, show that each function is a solution of the given initial value problem.

Differential equation	Initial condition	Solution candidate
5. $y' + y = \dfrac{2}{1+4e^{2x}}$	$y(-\ln 2) = \dfrac{\pi}{2}$	$y = e^{-x}\tan^{-1}(2e^x)$
6. $y' = e^{-x^2} - 2xy$	$y(2) = 0$	$y = (x-2)e^{-x^2}$
7. $xy' + y = -\sin x,\ x > 0$	$y\left(\dfrac{\pi}{2}\right) = 0$	$y = \dfrac{\cos x}{x}$
8. $x^2y' = xy - y^2,\ x > 1$	$y(e) = e$	$y = \dfrac{x}{\ln x}$

Solve the differential equation in Exercises 9–18.

9. $2\sqrt{xy}\dfrac{dy}{dx} = 1, \quad x, y > 0$

10. $\dfrac{dy}{dx} = x^2\sqrt{y}, \quad y > 0$

11. $\dfrac{dy}{dx} = e^{x-y}$

12. $\dfrac{dy}{dx} = 3x^2 e^{-y}$

13. $\dfrac{dy}{dx} = \sqrt{y}\cos^2\sqrt{y}$

14. $\sqrt{2xy}\dfrac{dy}{dx} = 1$

15. $\sqrt{x}\dfrac{dy}{dx} = e^{y+\sqrt{x}}, \quad x > 0$

16. $(\sec x)\dfrac{dy}{dx} = e^{y+\sin x}$

17. $\dfrac{dy}{dx} = 2x\sqrt{1-y^2}, \quad -1 < y < 1$

18. $\dfrac{dy}{dx} = \dfrac{e^{2x-y}}{e^{x+y}}$

T The answers to most of the following exercises are in terms of logarithms and exponentials. A calculator can be helpful, enabling you to express the answers in decimal form.

19. **Human evolution continues** The analysis of tooth shrinkage by C. Loring Brace and colleagues at the University of Michigan's Museum of Anthropology indicates that human tooth size is continuing to decrease and that the evolutionary process did not come to a halt some 30,000 years ago as many scientists contend. In northern Europeans, for example, tooth size reduction now has a rate of 1% per 1000 years.

    a. If t represents time in years and y represents tooth size, use the condition that $y = 0.99y_0$ when $t = 1000$ to find the value of k in the equation $y = y_0e^{kt}$. Then use this value of k to answer the following questions.

    b. In about how many years will human teeth be 90% of their present size?

    c. What will be our descendants' tooth size 20,000 years from now (as a percentage of our present tooth size)?

    (*Source: LSA Magazine*, Spring 1989, Vol. 12, No. 2, p. 19, Ann Arbor, MI.)

20. **Atmospheric pressure** The earth's atmospheric pressure p is often modeled by assuming that the rate dp/dh at which p changes with the altitude h above sea level is proportional to p. Suppose that the pressure at sea level is 1013 millibars (about 14.7 pounds per square inch) and that the pressure at an altitude of 20 km is 90 millibars.

    a. Solve the initial value problem

    Differential equation: $dp/dh = kp$ (k a constant)
    Initial condition: $p = p_0$ when $h = 0$

    to express p in terms of h. Determine the values of p_0 and k from the given altitude-pressure data.

    b. What is the atmospheric pressure at $h = 50$ km?

    c. At what altitude does the pressure equal 900 millibars?

21. **First-order chemical reactions** In some chemical reactions, the rate at which the amount of a substance changes with time is proportional to the amount present. For the change of δ-glucono lactone into gluconic acid, for example,

$$\frac{dy}{dt} = -0.6y$$

when t is measured in hours. If there are 100 grams of δ-glucono lactone present when $t = 0$, how many grams will be left after the first hour?

22. **The inversion of sugar** The processing of raw sugar has a step called "inversion" that changes the sugar's molecular structure. Once the process has begun, the rate of change of the amount of raw sugar is proportional to the amount of raw sugar remaining. If 1000 kg of raw sugar reduces to 800 kg of raw sugar during the first 10 hours, how much raw sugar will remain after another 14 hours?

23. Working underwater The intensity $L(x)$ of light x feet beneath the surface of the ocean satisfies the differential equation

$$\frac{dL}{dx} = -kL.$$

As a diver, you know from experience that diving to 18 ft in the Caribbean Sea cuts the intensity in half. You cannot work without artificial light when the intensity falls below one-tenth of the surface value. About how deep can you expect to work without artificial light?

24. Voltage in a discharging capacitor Suppose that electricity is draining from a capacitor at a rate that is proportional to the voltage V across its terminals and that, if t is measured in seconds,

$$\frac{dV}{dt} = -\frac{1}{40}V.$$

Solve this equation for V, using V_0 to denote the value of V when $t = 0$. How long will it take the voltage to drop to 10% of its original value?

25. Cholera bacteria Suppose that the bacteria in a colony can grow unchecked, by the law of exponential change. The colony starts with 1 bacterium and doubles every half-hour. How many bacteria will the colony contain at the end of 24 hours? (Under favorable laboratory conditions, the number of cholera bacteria can double every 30 min. In an infected person, many bacteria are destroyed, but this example helps explain why a person who feels well in the morning may be dangerously ill by evening.)

26. Growth of bacteria A colony of bacteria is grown under ideal conditions in a laboratory so that the population increases exponentially with time. At the end of 3 hours there are 10,000 bacteria. At the end of 5 hours there are 40,000. How many bacteria were present initially?

27. The incidence of a disease (*Continuation of Example 3.*) Suppose that in any given year the number of cases can be reduced by 25% instead of 20%.

a. How long will it take to reduce the number of cases to 1000?

b. How long will it take to eradicate the disease, that is, reduce the number of cases to less than 1?

28. The U.S. population The Museum of Science in Boston displays a running total of the U.S. population. On May 11, 1993, the total was increasing at the rate of 1 person every 14 sec. The displayed population figure for 3:45 P.M. that day was 257,313,431.

a. Assuming exponential growth at a constant rate, find the rate constant for the population's growth (people per 365-day year).

b. At this rate, what will the U.S. population be at 3:45 P.M. Boston time on May 11, 2008?

29. Oil depletion Suppose the amount of oil pumped from one of the canyon wells in Whittier, California, decreases at the continuous rate of 10% per year. When will the well's output fall to one-fifth of its present value?

30. Continuous price discounting To encourage buyers to place 100-unit orders, your firm's sales department applies a continuous discount that makes the unit price a function $p(x)$ of the number of units x ordered. The discount decreases the price at the rate of \$0.01 per unit ordered. The price per unit for a 100-unit order is $p(100) = \$20.09$.

a. Find $p(x)$ by solving the following initial value problem:

Differential equation: $\dfrac{dp}{dx} = -\dfrac{1}{100}p$

Initial condition: $p(100) = 20.09.$

b. Find the unit price $p(10)$ for a 10-unit order and the unit price $p(90)$ for a 90-unit order.

c. The sales department has asked you to find out if it is discounting so much that the firm's revenue, $r(x) = x \cdot p(x)$, will actually be less for a 100-unit order than, say, for a 90-unit order. Reassure them by showing that r has its maximum value at $x = 100$.

d. Graph the revenue function $r(x) = xp(x)$ for $0 \le x \le 200$.

31. Plutonium-239 The half-life of the plutonium isotope is 24,360 years. If 10 g of plutonium is released into the atmosphere by a nuclear accident, how many years will it take for 80% of the isotope to decay?

32. Polonium-210 The half-life of polonium is 139 days, but your sample will not be useful to you after 95% of the radioactive nuclei present on the day the sample arrives has disintegrated. For about how many days after the sample arrives will you be able to use the polonium?

33. The mean life of a radioactive nucleus Physicists using the radioactivity equation $y = y_0e^{-kt}$ call the number $1/k$ the *mean life* of a radioactive nucleus. The mean life of a radon nucleus is about $1/0.18 = 5.6$ days. The mean life of a carbon-14 nucleus is more than 8000 years. Show that 95% of the radioactive nuclei originally present in a sample will disintegrate within three mean lifetimes, i.e., by time $t = 3/k$. Thus, the mean life of a nucleus gives a quick way to estimate how long the radioactivity of a sample will last.

34. Californium-252 What costs \$27 million per gram and can be used to treat brain cancer, analyze coal for its sulfur content, and detect explosives in luggage? The answer is californium-252, a radioactive isotope so rare that only 8 g of it have been made in the western world since its discovery by Glenn Seaborg in 1950. The half-life of the isotope is 2.645 years—long enough for a useful service life and short enough to have a high radioactivity per unit mass. One microgram of the isotope releases 170 million neutrons per second.

a. What is the value of k in the decay equation for this isotope?

b. What is the isotope's mean life? (See Exercise 33.)

c. How long will it take 95% of a sample's radioactive nuclei to disintegrate?

35. Cooling soup Suppose that a cup of soup cooled from 90°C to 60°C after 10 min in a room whose temperature was 20°C. Use Newton's law of cooling to answer the following questions.

a. How much longer would it take the soup to cool to 35°C?

b. Instead of being left to stand in the room, the cup of 90°C soup is put in a freezer whose temperature is -15°C. How long will it take the soup to cool from 90°C to 35°C?

36. **A beam of unknown temperature** An aluminum beam was brought from the outside cold into a machine shop where the temperature was held at 65°F. After 10 min, the beam warmed to 35°F and after another 10 min it was 50°F. Use Newton's law of cooling to estimate the beam's initial temperature.

37. **Surrounding medium of unknown temperature** A pan of warm water (46°C) was put in a refrigerator. Ten minutes later, the water's temperature was 39°C; 10 min after that, it was 33°C. Use Newton's law of cooling to estimate how cold the refrigerator was.

38. **Silver cooling in air** The temperature of an ingot of silver is 60°C above room temperature right now. Twenty minutes ago, it was 70°C above room temperature. How far above room temperature will the silver be

    a. 15 min from now? **b.** 2 hours from now?

    c. When will the silver be 10°C above room temperature?

39. **The age of Crater Lake** The charcoal from a tree killed in the volcanic eruption that formed Crater Lake in Oregon contained 44.5% of the carbon-14 found in living matter. About how old is Crater Lake?

40. **The sensitivity of carbon-14 dating to measurement** To see the effect of a relatively small error in the estimate of the amount of carbon-14 in a sample being dated, consider this hypothetical situation:

    a. A fossilized bone found in central Illinois in the year A.D. 2000 contains 17% of its original carbon-14 content. Estimate the year the animal died.

    b. Repeat part (a) assuming 18% instead of 17%.

    c. Repeat part (a) assuming 16% instead of 17%.

41. **Art forgery** A painting attributed to Vermeer (1632–1675), which should contain no more than 96.2% of its original carbon-14, contains 99.5% instead. About how old is the forgery?

6.6 Work

In everyday life, *work* means an activity that requires muscular or mental effort. In science, the term refers specifically to a force acting on a body (or object) and the body's subsequent displacement. This section shows how to calculate work. The applications run from compressing railroad car springs and emptying subterranean tanks to forcing electrons together and lifting satellites into orbit.

Work Done by a Constant Force

When a body moves a distance d along a straight line as a result of being acted on by a force of constant magnitude F in the direction of motion, we define the **work** W done by the force on the body with the formula

$$W = Fd \qquad \text{(Constant-force formula for work).} \qquad (1)$$

From Equation (1) we see that the unit of work in any system is the unit of force multiplied by the unit of distance. In SI units (SI stands for *Système International*, or International System), the unit of force is a newton, the unit of distance is a meter, and the unit of work is a newton-meter $(\text{N} \cdot \text{m})$. This combination appears so often it has a special name, the **joule**. In the British system, the unit of work is the foot-pound, a unit frequently used by engineers.

Joules

The joule, abbreviated J and pronounced "jewel," is named after the English physicist James Prescott Joule (1818–1889). The defining equation is

$$1 \text{ joule} = (1 \text{ newton})(1 \text{ meter}).$$

In symbols, $1 \text{ J} = 1 \text{ N} \cdot \text{m}$.

EXAMPLE 1 If you jack up the side of a 2000-lb car 1.25 ft to change a tire (you have to apply a constant vertical force of about 1000 lb) you will perform $1000 \times 1.25 = 1250$ ft-lb of work on the car. In SI units, you have applied a force of 4448 N through a distance of 0.381 m to do $4448 \times 0.381 \approx 1695$ J of work. ■

Work Done by a Variable Force Along a Line

If the force you apply varies along the way, as it will if you are compressing a spring, the formula $W = Fd$ has to be replaced by an integral formula that takes the variation in F into account.

Suppose that the force performing the work acts on an object moving along a straight line, which we take to be the x-axis. We assume that the magnitude of the force is a continuous function F of the object's position x. We want to find the work done over the interval from $x = a$ to $x = b$. We partition $[a, b]$ in the usual way and choose an arbitrary point c_k in each subinterval $[x_{k-1}, x_k]$. If the subinterval is short enough, F, being continuous, will not vary much from x_{k-1} to x_k. The amount of work done across the interval will be about $F(c_k)$ times the distance Δx_k, the same as it would be if F were constant and we could apply Equation (1). The total work done from a to b is therefore approximated by the Riemann sum

$$\text{Work} \approx \sum_{k=1}^{n} F(c_k)\, \Delta x_k.$$

We expect the approximation to improve as the norm of the partition goes to zero, so we define the work done by the force from a to b to be the integral of F from a to b:

$$\lim_{n\to\infty} \sum_{k=1}^{n} F(c_k)\, \Delta x_k = \int_a^b F(x)\, dx.$$

DEFINITION The **work** done by a variable force $F(x)$ in the direction of motion along the x-axis from $x = a$ to $x = b$ is

$$W = \int_a^b F(x)\, dx. \tag{2}$$

The units of the integral are joules if F is in newtons and x is in meters, and foot-pounds if F is in pounds and x in feet. So, the work done by a force of $F(x) = 1/x^2$ newtons in moving an object along the x-axis from $x = 1$ m to $x = 10$ m is

$$W = \int_1^{10} \frac{1}{x^2}\, dx = -\frac{1}{x}\bigg]_1^{10} = -\frac{1}{10} + 1 = 0.9 \text{ J}.$$

Hooke's Law for Springs: $F = kx$

Hooke's Law says that the force it takes to stretch or compress a spring x length units from its natural (unstressed) length is proportional to x. In symbols,

$$F = kx. \tag{3}$$

The constant k, measured in force units per unit length, is a characteristic of the spring, called the **force constant** (or **spring constant**) of the spring. Hooke's Law, Equation (3), gives good results as long as the force doesn't distort the metal in the spring. We assume that the forces in this section are too small to do that.

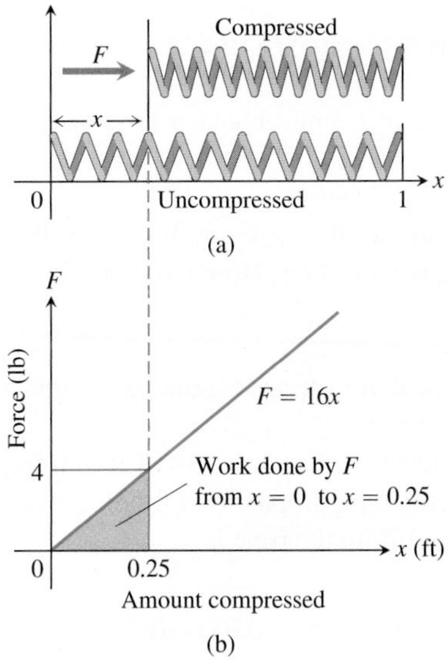

FIGURE 6.37 The force F needed to hold a spring under compression increases linearly as the spring is compressed (Example 2).

EXAMPLE 2 Find the work required to compress a spring from its natural length of 1 ft to a length of 0.75 ft if the force constant is $k = 16$ lb/ft.

Solution We picture the uncompressed spring laid out along the x-axis with its movable end at the origin and its fixed end at $x = 1$ ft (Figure 6.37). This enables us to describe the force required to compress the spring from 0 to x with the formula $F = 16x$. To compress the spring from 0 to 0.25 ft, the force must increase from

$$F(0) = 16 \cdot 0 = 0 \text{ lb} \qquad \text{to} \qquad F(0.25) = 16 \cdot 0.25 = 4 \text{ lb}.$$

The work done by F over this interval is

$$W = \int_0^{0.25} 16x\, dx = 8x^2\bigg]_0^{0.25} = 0.5 \text{ ft-lb}.$$

Eq. (2) with $a = 0, b = 0.25$, $F(x) = 16x$ ■

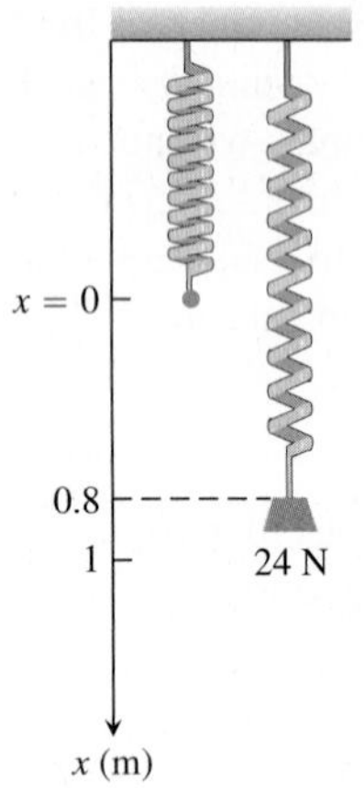

FIGURE 6.38 A 24-N weight stretches this spring 0.8 m beyond its unstressed length (Example 3).

EXAMPLE 3 A spring has a natural length of 1 m. A force of 24 N stretches the spring to a length of 1.8 m.

(a) Find the force constant k.

(b) How much work will it take to stretch the spring 2 m beyond its natural length?

(c) How far will a 45-N force stretch the spring?

Solution

(a) *The force constant.* We find the force constant from Equation (3). A force of 24 N stretches the spring 0.8 m, so

$$24 = k(0.8) \qquad \text{Eq. (3) with } F = 24, x = 0.8$$
$$k = 24/0.8 = 30 \text{ N/m}.$$

(b) *The work to stretch the spring* 2 m. We imagine the unstressed spring hanging along the x-axis with its free end at $x = 0$ (Figure 6.38). The force required to stretch the spring x m beyond its natural length is the force required to pull the free end of the spring x units from the origin. Hooke's Law with $k = 30$ says that this force is

$$F(x) = 30x.$$

The work done by F on the spring from $x = 0$ m to $x = 2$ m is

$$W = \int_0^2 30x\,dx = 15x^2\Big]_0^2 = 60 \text{ J}.$$

(c) *How far will a* 45-N *force stretch the spring?* We substitute $F = 45$ in the equation $F = 30x$ to find

$$45 = 30x, \qquad \text{or} \qquad x = 1.5 \text{ m}.$$

A 45-N force will stretch the spring 1.5 m. No calculus is required to find this. ■

The work integral is useful to calculate the work done in lifting objects whose weights vary with their elevation.

EXAMPLE 4 A 5-lb bucket is lifted from the ground into the air by pulling in 20 ft of rope at a constant speed (Figure 6.39). The rope weighs 0.08 lb/ft. How much work was spent lifting the bucket and rope?

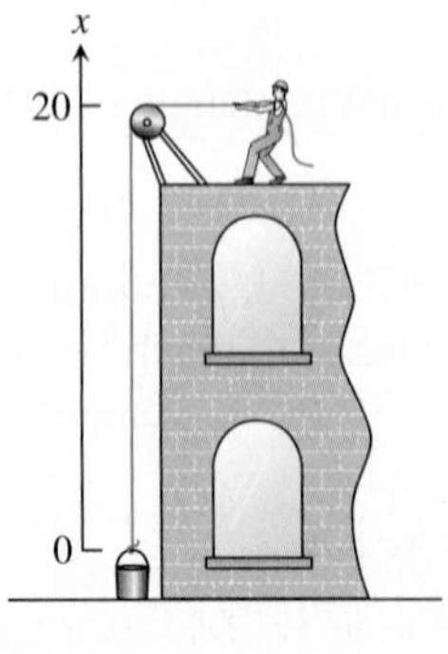

FIGURE 6.39 Lifting the bucket in Example 4.

Solution The bucket has constant weight so the work done lifting it alone is weight × distance $= 5 \cdot 20 = 100$ ft-lb.

The weight of the rope varies with the bucket's elevation, because less of it is freely hanging. When the bucket is x ft off the ground, the remaining proportion of the rope still being lifted weighs $(0.08) \cdot (20 - x)$ lb. So the work in lifting the rope is

$$\text{Work on rope} = \int_0^{20} (0.08)(20 - x)\,dx = \int_0^{20} (1.6 - 0.08x)\,dx$$
$$= \left[1.6x - 0.04x^2\right]_0^{20} = 32 - 16 = 16 \text{ ft-lb}.$$

The total work for the bucket and rope combined is

$$100 + 16 = 116 \text{ ft-lb}.$$

■

Pumping Liquids from Containers

How much work does it take to pump all or part of the liquid from a container? To find out, we imagine lifting the liquid out one thin horizontal slab at a time and applying the equation $W = Fd$ to each slab. We then evaluate the integral this leads to as the slabs become thinner and more numerous. The integral we get each time depends on the weight of the liquid and the dimensions of the container, but the way we find the integral is always the same. The next example shows what to do.

EXAMPLE 5 The conical tank in Figure 6.40 is filled to within 2 ft of the top with olive oil weighing 57 lb/ft^3. How much work does it take to pump the oil to the rim of the tank?

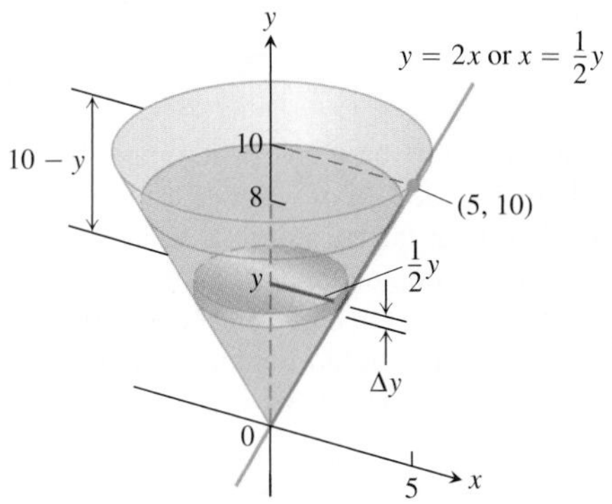

FIGURE 6.40 The olive oil and tank in Example 5.

Solution We imagine the oil divided into thin slabs by planes perpendicular to the y-axis at the points of a partition of the interval $[0, 8]$.

The typical slab between the planes at y and $y + \Delta y$ has a volume of about

$$\Delta V = \pi(\text{radius})^2(\text{thickness}) = \pi\left(\frac{1}{2}y\right)^2 \Delta y = \frac{\pi}{4}y^2\,\Delta y \text{ ft}^3.$$

The force $F(y)$ required to lift this slab is equal to its weight,

$$F(y) = 57\,\Delta V = \frac{57\pi}{4}y^2\,\Delta y \text{ lb.}$$

Weight = weight per unit volume × volume

The distance through which $F(y)$ must act to lift this slab to the level of the rim of the cone is about $(10 - y)$ ft, so the work done lifting the slab is about

$$\Delta W = \frac{57\pi}{4}(10 - y)y^2\,\Delta y \text{ ft-lb.}$$

Assuming there are n slabs associated with the partition of $[0, 8]$, and that $y = y_k$ denotes the plane associated with the kth slab of thickness Δy_k, we can approximate the work done lifting all of the slabs with the Riemann sum

$$W \approx \sum_{k=1}^{n} \frac{57\pi}{4}(10 - y_k)y_k^{\,2}\,\Delta y_k \text{ ft-lb.}$$

The work of pumping the oil to the rim is the limit of these sums as the norm of the partition goes to zero.

$$\begin{aligned} W = \lim_{n\to\infty} \sum_{k=1}^{n} \frac{57\pi}{4}(10 - y_k)y_k^{\,2}\,\Delta y_k &= \int_0^8 \frac{57\pi}{4}(10 - y)y^2\,dy \\ &= \frac{57\pi}{4}\int_0^8 (10y^2 - y^3)\,dy \\ &= \frac{57\pi}{4}\left[\frac{10y^3}{3} - \frac{y^4}{4}\right]_0^8 \approx 30{,}561 \text{ ft-lb.} \end{aligned}$$

■

EXERCISES 6.6

1. **Spring constant** It took 1800 J of work to stretch a spring from its natural length of 2 m to a length of 5 m. Find the spring's force constant.

2. **Stretching a spring** A spring has a natural length of 10 in. An 800-lb force stretches the spring to 14 in.

   a. Find the force constant.

   b. How much work is done in stretching the spring from 10 in. to 12 in.?

   c. How far beyond its natural length will a 1600-lb force stretch the spring?

3. **Stretching a rubber band** A force of 2 N will stretch a rubber band 2 cm (0.02 m). Assuming that Hooke's Law applies, how far will a 4-N force stretch the rubber band? How much work does it take to stretch the rubber band this far?

4. **Stretching a spring** If a force of 90 N stretches a spring 1 m beyond its natural length, how much work does it take to stretch the spring 5 m beyond its natural length?

5. **Subway car springs** It takes a force of 21,714 lb to compress a coil spring assembly on a New York City Transit Authority subway car from its free height of 8 in. to its fully compressed height of 5 in.
   a. What is the assembly's force constant?
   b. How much work does it take to compress the assembly the first half inch? the second half inch? Answer to the nearest in.-lb.

   (Data courtesy of Bombardier, Inc., Mass Transit Division, for spring assemblies in subway cars delivered to the New York City Transit Authority from 1985 to 1987.)

6. **Bathroom scale** A bathroom scale is compressed $1/16$ in. when a 150-lb person stands on it. Assuming that the scale behaves like a spring that obeys Hooke's Law, how much does someone who compresses the scale $1/8$ in. weigh? How much work is done compressing the scale $1/8$ in.?

7. **Lifting a rope** A mountain climber is about to haul up a 50 m length of hanging rope. How much work will it take if the rope weighs $0.624\ \text{N/m}$?

8. **Leaky sandbag** A bag of sand originally weighing 144 lb was lifted at a constant rate. As it rose, sand also leaked out at a constant rate. The sand was half gone by the time the bag had been lifted to 18 ft. How much work was done lifting the sand this far? (Neglect the weight of the bag and lifting equipment.)

9. **Lifting an elevator cable** An electric elevator with a motor at the top has a multistrand cable weighing $4.5\ \text{lb/ft}$. When the car is at the first floor, 180 ft of cable are paid out, and effectively 0 ft are out when the car is at the top floor. How much work does the motor do just lifting the cable when it takes the car from the first floor to the top?

10. **Force of attraction** When a particle of mass m is at $(x, 0)$, it is attracted toward the origin with a force whose magnitude is k/x^2. If the particle starts from rest at $x = b$ and is acted on by no other forces, find the work done on it by the time it reaches $x = a$, $0 < a < b$.

11. **Compressing gas** Suppose that the gas in a circular cylinder of cross-sectional area A is being compressed by a piston. If p is the pressure of the gas in pounds per square inch and V is the volume in cubic inches, show that the work done in compressing the gas from state (p_1, V_1) to state (p_2, V_2) is given by the equation

$$\text{Work} = \int_{(p_1, V_1)}^{(p_2, V_2)} p\, dV.$$

   (*Hint:* In the coordinates suggested in the figure here, $dV = A\, dx$. The force against the piston is pA.)

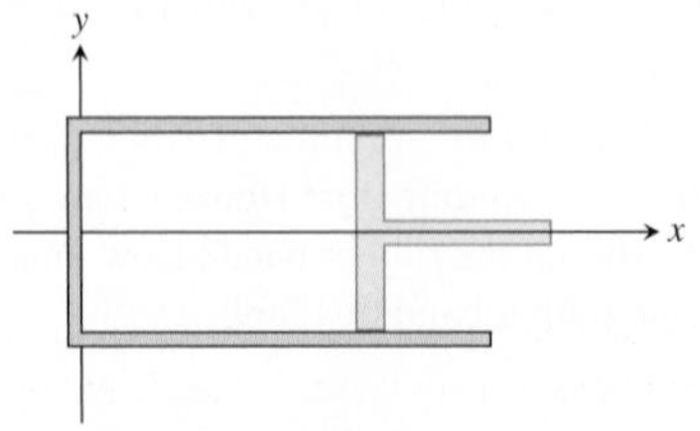

12. (*Continuation of Exercise 11.*) Use the integral in Exercise 11 to find the work done in compressing the gas from $V_1 = 243\ \text{in.}^3$ to $V_2 = 32\ \text{in.}^3$ if $p_1 = 50\ \text{lb/in.}^3$ and p and V obey the gas law $pV^{1.4} = \text{constant}$ (for adiabatic processes).

13. **Leaky bucket** Assume the bucket in Example 4 is leaking. It starts with 2 gal of water (16 lb) and leaks at a constant rate. It finishes draining just as it reaches the top. How much work was spent lifting the water alone? (*Hint:* Do not include the rope and bucket, and find the proportion of water left at elevation x ft.)

14. (*Continuation of Exercise 13.*) The workers in Example 4 and Exercise 13 changed to a larger bucket that held 5 gal (40 lb) of water, but the new bucket had an even larger leak so that it, too, was empty by the time it reached the top. Assuming that the water leaked out at a steady rate, how much work was done lifting the water alone? (Do not include the rope and bucket.)

> **The Weight of Water**
> Because of Earth's rotation and variations in its gravitational field, the weight of a cubic foot of water at sea level can vary from about 62.26 lb at the equator to as much as 62.59 lb near the poles, a variation of about 0.5%. A cubic foot that weighs about 62.4 lb in Melbourne and New York City will weigh 62.5 lb in Juneau and Stockholm. Although 62.4 is a typical figure and common textbook value, there is considerable variation.

15. **Pumping water** The rectangular tank shown here, with its top at ground level, is used to catch runoff water. Assume that the water weighs $62.4\ \text{lb/ft}^3$.
   a. How much work does it take to empty the tank by pumping the water back to ground level once the tank is full?
   b. If the water is pumped to ground level with a $(5/11)$-horsepower (hp) motor (work output $250\ \text{ft-lb/sec}$), how long will it take to empty the full tank (to the nearest minute)?
   c. Show that the pump in part (b) will lower the water level 10 ft (halfway) during the first 25 min of pumping.
   d. **The weight of water** What are the answers to parts (a) and (b) in a location where water weighs $62.26\ \text{lb/ft}^3$? $62.59\ \text{lb/ft}^3$?

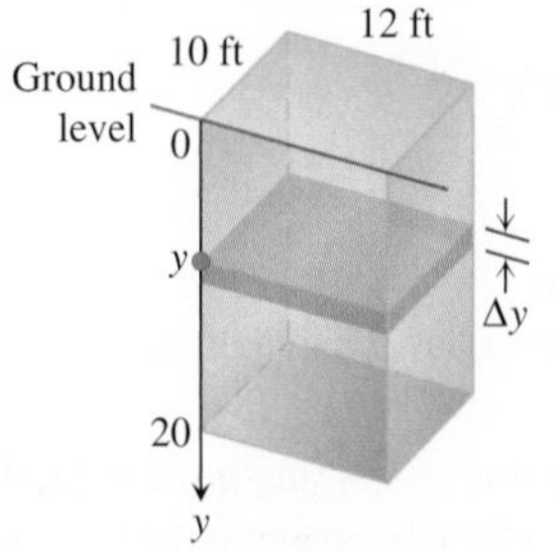

16. **Emptying a cistern** The rectangular cistern (storage tank for rainwater) shown has its top 10 ft below ground level. The cistern,

currently full, is to be emptied for inspection by pumping its contents to ground level.

a. How much work will it take to empty the cistern?

b. How long will it take a 1/2 hp pump, rated at 275 ft-lb/sec, to pump the tank dry?

c. How long will it take the pump in part (b) to empty the tank halfway? (It will be less than half the time required to empty the tank completely.)

d. The weight of water What are the answers to parts (a) through (c) in a location where water weighs 62.26 lb/ft^3? 62.59 lb/ft^3?

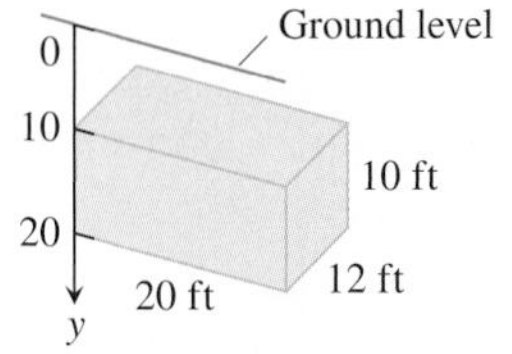

17. Pumping oil How much work would it take to pump oil from the tank in Example 5 to the level of the top of the tank if the tank were completely full?

18. Pumping a half-full tank Suppose that, instead of being full, the tank in Example 5 is only half full. How much work does it take to pump the remaining oil to a level 4 ft above the top of the tank?

19. Emptying a tank A vertical right circular cylindrical tank measures 30 ft high and 20 ft in diameter. It is full of kerosene weighing 51.2 lb/ft^3. How much work does it take to pump the kerosene to the level of the top of the tank?

20. The cylindrical tank shown here can be filled by pumping water from a lake 15 ft below the bottom of the tank. There are two ways to go about it. One is to pump the water through a hose attached to a valve in the bottom of the tank. The other is to attach the hose to the rim of the tank and let the water pour in. Which way will be faster? Give reasons for your answer.

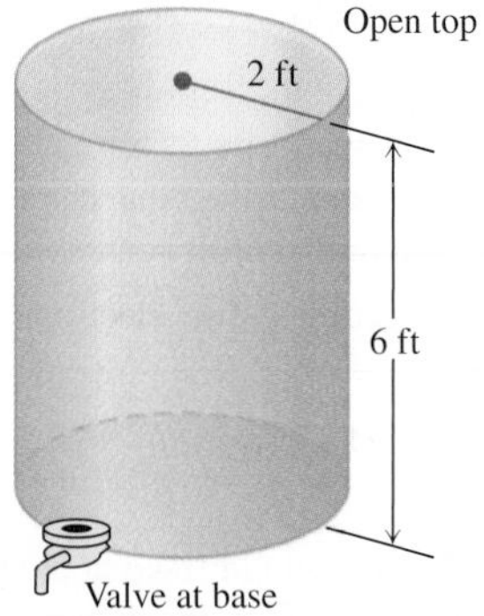

21. a. Pumping milk Suppose that the conical container in Example 5 contains milk (weighing 64.5 lb/ft^3) instead of olive oil. How much work will it take to pump the contents to the rim?

b. Pumping oil How much work will it take to pump the oil in Example 5 to a level 3 ft above the cone's rim?

22. Pumping seawater To design the interior surface of a huge stainless-steel tank, you revolve the curve $y = x^2, 0 \le x \le 4$, about the y-axis. The container, with dimensions in meters, is to be filled with seawater, which weighs 10,000 N/m^3. How much work will it take to empty the tank by pumping the water to the tank's top?

23. Emptying a water reservoir We model pumping from spherical containers the way we do from other containers, with the axis of integration along the vertical axis of the sphere. Use the figure here to find how much work it takes to empty a full hemispherical water reservoir of radius 5 m by pumping the water to a height of 4 m above the top of the reservoir. Water weighs 9800 N/m^3.

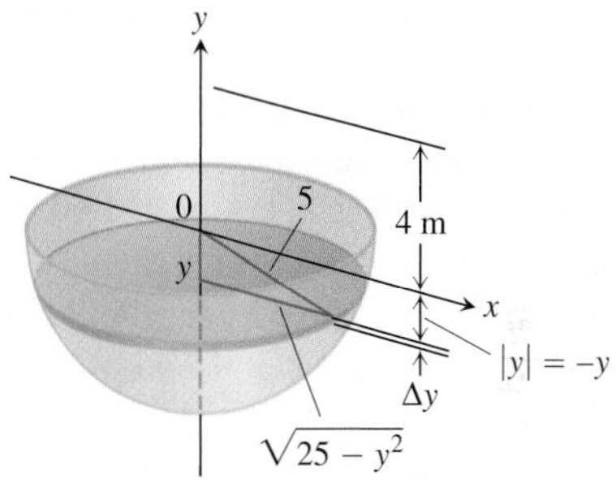

24. You are in charge of the evacuation and repair of the storage tank shown here. The tank is a hemisphere of radius 10 ft and is full of benzene weighing 56 lb/ft^3. A firm you contacted says it can empty the tank for 1/2¢ per foot-pound of work. Find the work required to empty the tank by pumping the benzene to an outlet 2 ft above the top of the tank. If you have $5000 budgeted for the job, can you afford to hire the firm?

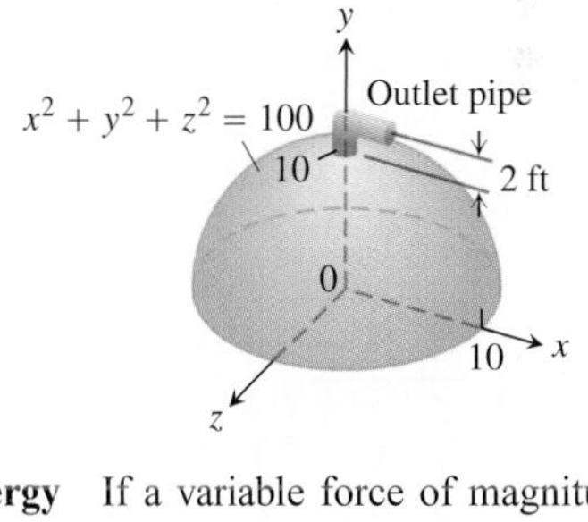

25. Kinetic energy If a variable force of magnitude $F(x)$ moves a body of mass m along the x-axis from x_1 to x_2, the body's velocity v can be written as dx/dt (where t represents time). Use Newton's second law of motion $F = m(dv/dt)$ and the Chain Rule

$$\frac{dv}{dt} = \frac{dv}{dx}\frac{dx}{dt} = v\frac{dv}{dx}$$

to show that the net work done by the force in moving the body from x_1 to x_2 is

$$W = \int_{x_1}^{x_2} F(x)\,dx = \frac{1}{2}mv_2{}^2 - \frac{1}{2}mv_1{}^2,$$

where v_1 and v_2 are the body's velocities at x_1 and x_2. In physics, the expression $(1/2)mv^2$ is called the *kinetic energy* of a body of mass m moving with velocity v. Therefore, *the work done by the force equals the change in the body's kinetic energy*, and we can find the work by calculating this change.

In Exercises 26–32, use the result of Exercise 25.

26. **Tennis** A 2-oz tennis ball was served at 160 ft/sec (about 109 mph). How much work was done on the ball to make it go this fast? (To find the ball's mass from its weight, express the weight in pounds and divide by 32 ft/sec^2, the acceleration of gravity.)

27. **Baseball** How many foot-pounds of work does it take to throw a baseball 90 mph? A baseball weighs 5 oz, or 0.3125 lb.

28. **Golf** A 1.6-oz golf ball is driven off the tee at a speed of 280 ft/sec (about 191 mph). How many foot-pounds of work are done on the ball getting it into the air?

29. **Tennis** During the match in which Pete Sampras won the 1990 U.S. Open men's tennis championship, Sampras hit a serve that was clocked at a phenomenal 124 mph. How much work did Sampras have to do on the 2-oz ball to get it to that speed?

30. **Football** A quarterback threw a 14.5-oz football 88 ft/sec (60 mph). How many foot-pounds of work were done on the ball to get it to this speed?

31. **Softball** How much work has to be performed on a 6.5-oz softball to pitch it 132 ft/sec (90 mph)?

32. **A ball bearing** A 2-oz steel ball bearing is placed on a vertical spring whose force constant is $k = 18$ lb/ft. The spring is compressed 2 in. and released. About how high does the ball bearing go?

33. **Drinking a milkshake** The truncated conical container shown here is full of strawberry milkshake that weighs 4/9 oz/in.^{3} As you can see, the container is 7 in. deep, 2.5 in. across at the base, and 3.5 in. across at the top (a standard size at Brigham's in Boston). The straw sticks up an inch above the top. About how much work does it take to suck up the milkshake through the straw (neglecting friction)? Answer in inch-ounces.

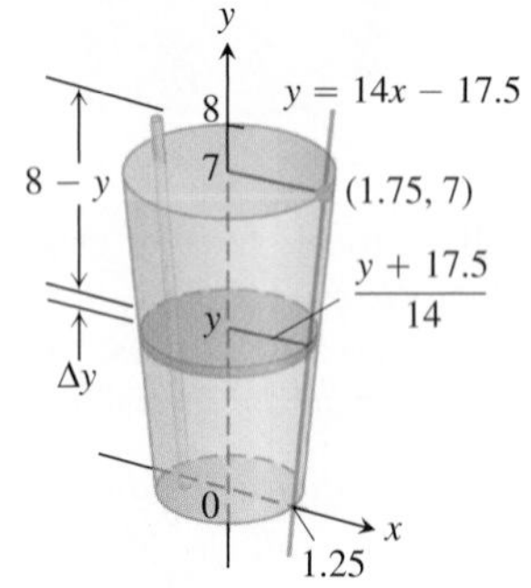

Dimensions in inches

34. **Water tower** Your town has decided to drill a well to increase its water supply. As the town engineer, you have determined that a water tower will be necessary to provide the pressure needed for distribution, and you have designed the system shown here. The water is to be pumped from a 300 ft well through a vertical 4 in. pipe into the base of a cylindrical tank 20 ft in diameter and 25 ft high. The base of the tank will be 60 ft above ground. The pump is a 3 hp pump, rated at 1650 ft · lb/sec. To the nearest hour, how long will it take to fill the tank the first time? (Include the time it takes to fill the pipe.) Assume that water weighs 62.4 lb/ft^3.

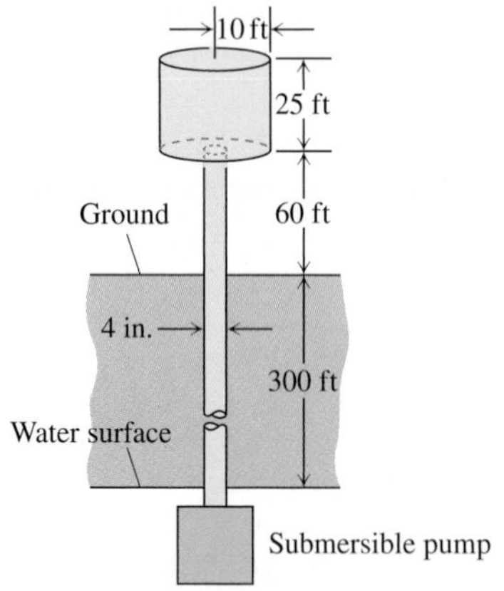

35. **Putting a satellite in orbit** The strength of Earth's gravitational field varies with the distance r from Earth's center, and the magnitude of the gravitational force experienced by a satellite of mass m during and after launch is

$$F(r) = \frac{mMG}{r^2}.$$

Here, $M = 5.975 \times 10^{24}$ kg is Earth's mass, $G = 6.6720 \times 10^{-11}\ \text{N} \cdot \text{m}^2\,\text{kg}^{-2}$ is the universal gravitational constant, and r is measured in meters. The work it takes to lift a 1000-kg satellite from Earth's surface to a circular orbit 35,780 km above Earth's center is therefore given by the integral

$$\text{Work} = \int_{6{,}370{,}000}^{35{,}780{,}000} \frac{1000MG}{r^2}\,dr \text{ joules.}$$

Evaluate the integral. The lower limit of integration is Earth's radius in meters at the launch site. (This calculation does not take into account energy spent lifting the launch vehicle or energy spent bringing the satellite to orbit velocity.)

36. **Forcing electrons together** Two electrons r meters apart repel each other with a force of

$$F = \frac{23 \times 10^{-29}}{r^2} \text{ newtons.}$$

a. Suppose one electron is held fixed at the point (1, 0) on the x-axis (units in meters). How much work does it take to move a second electron along the x-axis from the point $(-1, 0)$ to the origin?

b. Suppose an electron is held fixed at each of the points $(-1, 0)$ and (1, 0). How much work does it take to move a third electron along the x-axis from (5, 0) to (3, 0)?

6.7 Moments and Centers of Mass

Many structures and mechanical systems behave as if their masses were concentrated at a single point, called the *center of mass* (Figure 6.41). It is important to know how to locate this point, and doing so is basically a mathematical enterprise. For the moment, we deal with one- and two-dimensional objects. Three-dimensional objects are best done with the multiple integrals of Chapter 13.

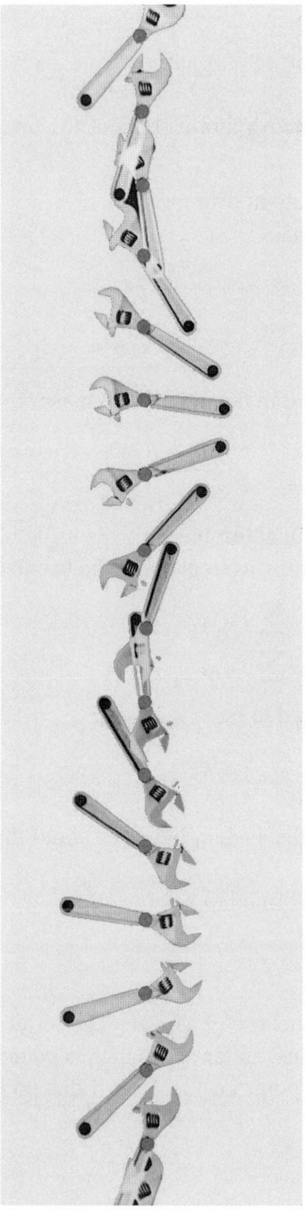

FIGURE 6.41 A wrench gliding on ice turning about its center of mass as the center glides in a straight line.

Masses Along a Line

We develop our mathematical model in stages. The first stage is to imagine masses m_1, m_2, and m_3 on a rigid x-axis supported by a fulcrum at the origin.

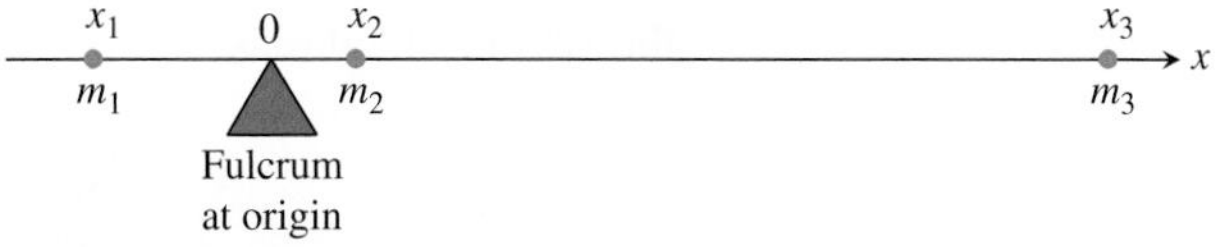

The resulting system might balance, or it might not, depending on how large the masses are and how they are arranged.

Each mass m_k exerts a downward force $m_k g$ (the weight of m_k) equal to the magnitude of the mass times the acceleration due to gravity. Each of these forces has a tendency to turn the axis about the origin, the way you turn a seesaw. This turning effect, called a **torque**, is measured by multiplying the force $m_k g$ by the signed distance x_k from the point of application to the origin. Masses to the left of the origin exert negative (counterclockwise) torque. Masses to the right of the origin exert positive (clockwise) torque.

The sum of the torques measures the tendency of a system to rotate about the origin. This sum is called the **system torque**.

$$\text{System torque} = m_1 g x_1 + m_2 g x_2 + m_3 g x_3 \tag{1}$$

The system will balance if and only if its torque is zero.

If we factor out the g in Equation (1), we see that the system torque is

$$\underbrace{g}_{\substack{\text{a feature of the}\\ \text{environment}}} \cdot \underbrace{(m_1 x_1 + m_2 x_2 + m_3 x_3)}_{\substack{\text{a feature of}\\ \text{the system}}}$$

Thus, the torque is the product of the gravitational acceleration g, which is a feature of the environment in which the system happens to reside, and the number $(m_1 x_1 + m_2 x_2 + m_3 x_3)$, which is a feature of the system itself, a constant that stays the same no matter where the system is placed.

The number $(m_1 x_1 + m_2 x_2 + m_3 x_3)$ is called the **moment of the system about the origin**. It is the sum of the **moments** $m_1 x_1$, $m_2 x_2$, $m_3 x_3$ of the individual masses.

$$M_0 = \text{Moment of system about origin} = \sum m_k x_k.$$

(We shift to sigma notation here to allow for sums with more terms.)

We usually want to know where to place the fulcrum to make the system balance, that is, at what point $\bar{x}$ to place it to make the torques add to zero.

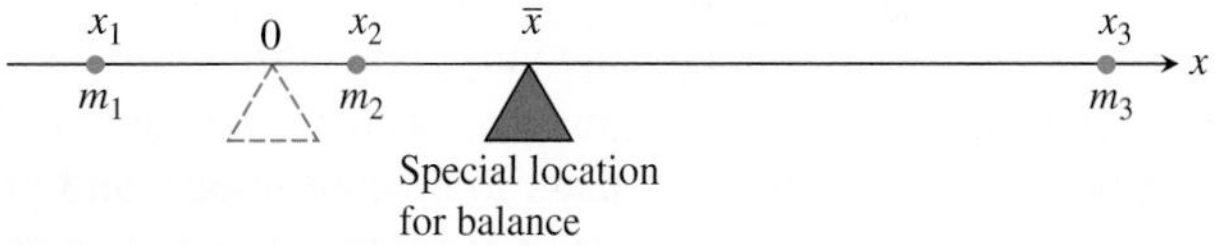

The torque of each mass about the fulcrum in this special location is

$$\begin{aligned}\text{Torque of } m_k \text{ about } \bar{x} &= \begin{pmatrix}\text{signed distance}\\ \text{of } m_k \text{ from } \bar{x}\end{pmatrix}\begin{pmatrix}\text{downward}\\ \text{force}\end{pmatrix}\\ &= (x_k - \bar{x})m_k g.\end{aligned}$$

When we write the equation that says that the sum of these torques is zero, we get an equation we can solve for $\bar{x}$:

$$\sum (x_k - \bar{x})m_k g = 0 \qquad \text{Sum of the torques equals zero}$$

$$\bar{x} = \frac{\sum m_k x_k}{\sum m_k}. \qquad \text{Solved for } \bar{x}$$

This last equation tells us to find $\bar{x}$ by dividing the system's moment about the origin by the system's total mass:

$$\bar{x} = \frac{\sum m_k x_k}{\sum m_k} = \frac{\text{system moment about origin}}{\text{system mass}}. \tag{2}$$

The point $\bar{x}$ is called the system's **center of mass**.

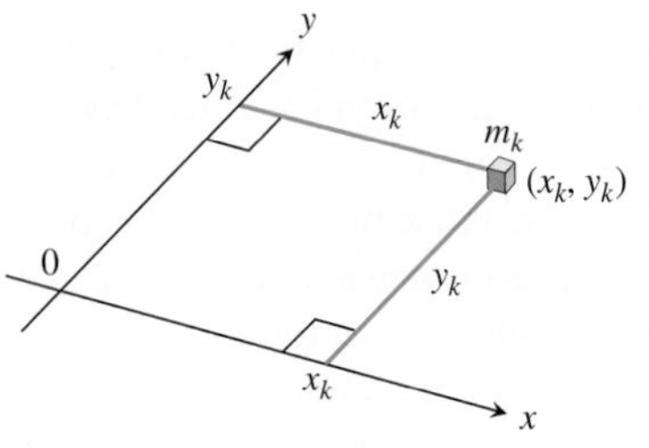

FIGURE 6.42 Each mass m_k has a moment about each axis.

Masses Distributed over a Plane Region

Suppose that we have a finite collection of masses located in the plane, with mass m_k at the point (x_k, y_k) (see Figure 6.42). The mass of the system is

$$\text{System mass: } M = \sum m_k.$$

Each mass m_k has a moment about each axis. Its moment about the x-axis is $m_k y_k$, and its moment about the y-axis is $m_k x_k$. The moments of the entire system about the two axes are

$$\text{Moment about } x\text{-axis:} \quad M_x = \sum m_k y_k,$$

$$\text{Moment about } y\text{-axis:} \quad M_y = \sum m_k x_k.$$

The x-coordinate of the system's center of mass is defined to be

$$\bar{x} = \frac{M_y}{M} = \frac{\sum m_k x_k}{\sum m_k}. \tag{3}$$

With this choice of $\bar{x}$, as in the one-dimensional case, the system balances about the line $x = \bar{x}$ (Figure 6.43).

The y-coordinate of the system's center of mass is defined to be

$$\bar{y} = \frac{M_x}{M} = \frac{\sum m_k y_k}{\sum m_k}. \tag{4}$$

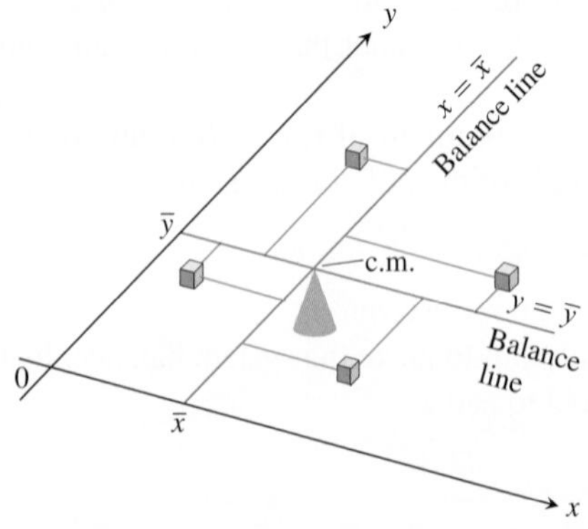

FIGURE 6.43 A two-dimensional array of masses balances on its center of mass.

With this choice of $\bar{y}$, the system balances about the line $y = \bar{y}$ as well. The torques exerted by the masses about the line $y = \bar{y}$ cancel out. Thus, as far as balance is concerned, the system behaves as if all its mass were at the single point $(\bar{x}, \bar{y})$. We call this point the system's **center of mass**.

Thin, Flat Plates

In many applications, we need to find the center of mass of a thin, flat plate: a disk of aluminum, say, or a triangular sheet of steel. In such cases, we assume the distribution of mass to be continuous, and the formulas we use to calculate $\bar{x}$ and $\bar{y}$ contain integrals instead of finite sums. The integrals arise in the following way.

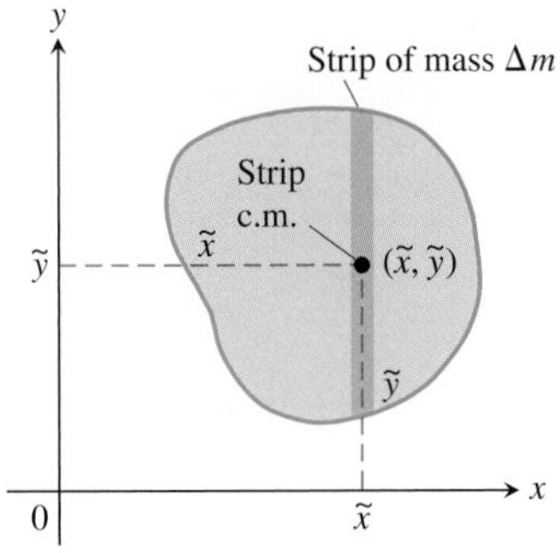

FIGURE 6.44 A plate cut into thin strips parallel to the y-axis. The moment exerted by a typical strip about each axis is the moment its mass Δm would exert if concentrated at the strip's center of mass $(\tilde{x}, \tilde{y})$.

Imagine the plate occupying a region in the xy-plane, cut into thin strips parallel to one of the axes (in Figure 6.44, the y-axis). The center of mass of a typical strip is $(\tilde{x}, \tilde{y})$. We treat the strip's mass Δm as if it were concentrated at $(\tilde{x}, \tilde{y})$. The moment of the strip about the y-axis is then $\tilde{x}\ \Delta m$. The moment of the strip about the x-axis is $\tilde{y}\ \Delta m$. Equations (3) and (4) then become

$$\bar{x} = \frac{M_y}{M} = \frac{\sum \tilde{x}\ \Delta m}{\sum \Delta m}, \qquad \bar{y} = \frac{M_x}{M} = \frac{\sum \tilde{y}\ \Delta m}{\sum \Delta m}.$$

The sums are Riemann sums for integrals and approach these integrals as limiting values as the strips into which the plate is cut become narrower and narrower. We write these integrals symbolically as

$$\bar{x} = \frac{\int \tilde{x}\ dm}{\int dm} \quad \text{and} \quad \bar{y} = \frac{\int \tilde{y}\ dm}{\int dm}.$$

Moments, Mass, and Center of Mass of a Thin Plate Covering a Region in the xy-Plane

Moment about the x-axis: $\quad M_x = \int \tilde{y}\ dm$

Moment about the y-axis: $\quad M_y = \int \tilde{x}\ dm \qquad (5)$

Mass: $\quad M = \int dm$

Center of mass: $\quad \bar{x} = \frac{M_y}{M}, \quad \bar{y} = \frac{M_x}{M}$

Density
A material's density is its mass per unit area. For wires, rods, and narrow strips, we use mass per unit length.

The differential dm is the mass of the strip. Assuming the density δ of the plate to be a continuous function, the mass differential dm equals the product $\delta\ dA$ (mass per unit area times area). Here dA represents the area of the strip.

To evaluate the integrals in Equations (5), we picture the plate in the coordinate plane and sketch a strip of mass parallel to one of the coordinate axes. We then express the strip's mass dm and the coordinates $(\tilde{x}, \tilde{y})$ of the strip's center of mass in terms of x or y. Finally, we integrate $\tilde{y}\ dm$, $\tilde{x}\ dm$, and dm between limits of integration determined by the plate's location in the plane.

EXAMPLE 1 The triangular plate shown in Figure 6.45 has a constant density of $\delta = 3\ \text{g/cm}^2$. Find

(a) the plate's moment M_y about the y-axis. **(b)** the plate's mass M.

(c) the x-coordinate of the plate's center of mass (c.m.).

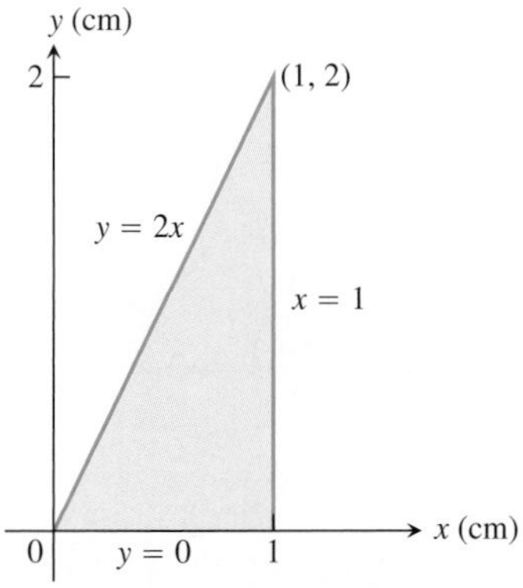

FIGURE 6.45 The plate in Example 1.

Solution **Method 1: Vertical Strips** (Figure 6.46)

(a) The moment M_y: The typical vertical strip has

center of mass (c.m.): $(\tilde{x}, \tilde{y}) = (x, x)$
length: $2x$
width: dx
area: $dA = 2x\ dx$
mass: $dm = \delta\ dA = 3 \cdot 2x\ dx = 6x\ dx$
distance of c.m. from y-axis: $\tilde{x} = x.$

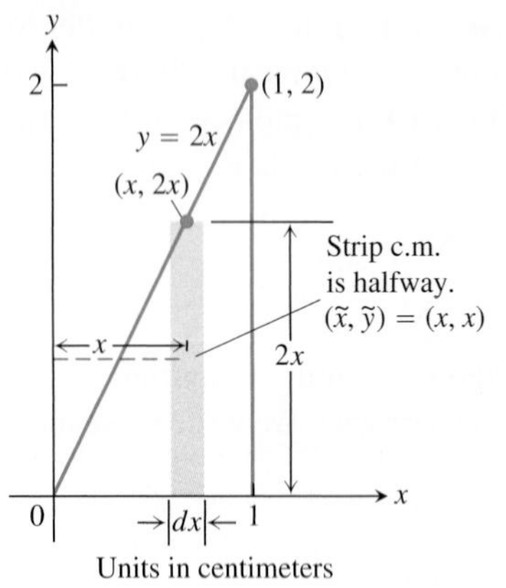

FIGURE 6.46 Modeling the plate in Example 1 with vertical strips.

The moment of the strip about the y-axis is

$$\tilde{x}\, dm = x \cdot 6x\, dx = 6x^2\, dx.$$

The moment of the plate about the y-axis is therefore

$$M_y = \int \tilde{x}\, dm = \int_0^1 6x^2\, dx = 2x^3\Big]_0^1 = 2\ \text{g} \cdot \text{cm}.$$

(b) The plate's mass:

$$M = \int dm = \int_0^1 6x\, dx = 3x^2\Big]_0^1 = 3\ \text{g}.$$

(c) The x-coordinate of the plate's center of mass:

$$\bar{x} = \frac{M_y}{M} = \frac{2\ \text{g} \cdot \text{cm}}{3\ \text{g}} = \frac{2}{3}\ \text{cm}.$$

By a similar computation, we could find M_x and $\bar{y} = M_x/M$.

Method 2: Horizontal Strips (Figure 6.47)

(a) The moment M_y: The y-coordinate of the center of mass of a typical horizontal strip is y (see the figure), so

$$\tilde{y} = y.$$

The x-coordinate is the x-coordinate of the point halfway across the triangle. This makes it the average of $y/2$ (the strip's left-hand x-value) and 1 (the strip's right-hand x-value):

$$\tilde{x} = \frac{(y/2) + 1}{2} = \frac{y}{4} + \frac{1}{2} = \frac{y+2}{4}.$$

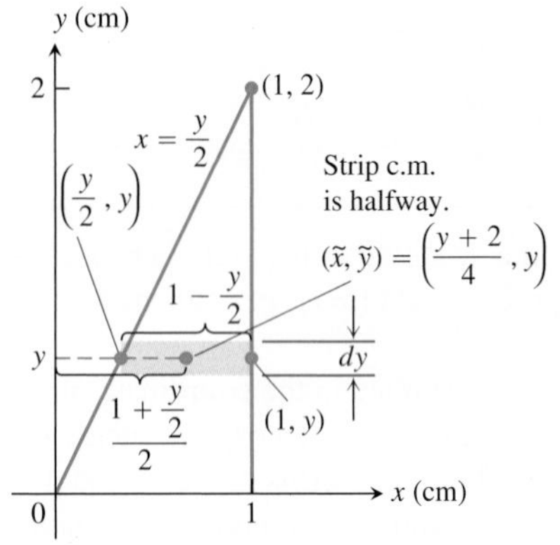

FIGURE 6.47 Modeling the plate in Example 1 with horizontal strips.

We also have

length: $1 - \dfrac{y}{2} = \dfrac{2-y}{2}$

width: dy

area: $dA = \dfrac{2-y}{2}\, dy$

mass: $dm = \delta\, dA = 3 \cdot \dfrac{2-y}{2}\, dy$

distance of c.m. to y-axis: $\tilde{x} = \dfrac{y+2}{4}.$

The moment of the strip about the y-axis is

$$\tilde{x}\, dm = \frac{y+2}{4} \cdot 3 \cdot \frac{2-y}{2}\, dy = \frac{3}{8}(4 - y^2)\, dy.$$

The moment of the plate about the y-axis is

$$M_y = \int \tilde{x}\, dm = \int_0^2 \frac{3}{8}(4 - y^2)\, dy = \frac{3}{8}\left[4y - \frac{y^3}{3}\right]_0^2 = \frac{3}{8}\left(\frac{16}{3}\right) = 2\ \text{g} \cdot \text{cm}.$$

(b) The plate's mass:

$$M = \int dm = \int_0^2 \frac{3}{2}(2 - y)\, dy = \frac{3}{2}\left[2y - \frac{y^2}{2}\right]_0^2 = \frac{3}{2}(4 - 2) = 3\ \text{g}.$$

(c) The x-coordinate of the plate's center of mass:

$$\bar{x} = \frac{M_y}{M} = \frac{2\text{ g}\cdot\text{cm}}{3\text{ g}} = \frac{2}{3}\text{ cm}.$$

By a similar computation, we could find M_x and $\bar{y}$. ■

If the distribution of mass in a thin, flat plate has an axis of symmetry, the center of mass will lie on this axis. If there are two axes of symmetry, the center of mass will lie at their intersection. These facts often help to simplify our work.

EXAMPLE 2 Find the center of mass of a thin plate covering the region bounded above by the parabola $y = 4 - x^2$ and below by the x-axis (Figure 6.48). Assume the density of the plate at the point (x, y) is $\delta = 2x^2$, which is twice the square of the distance from the point to the y-axis.

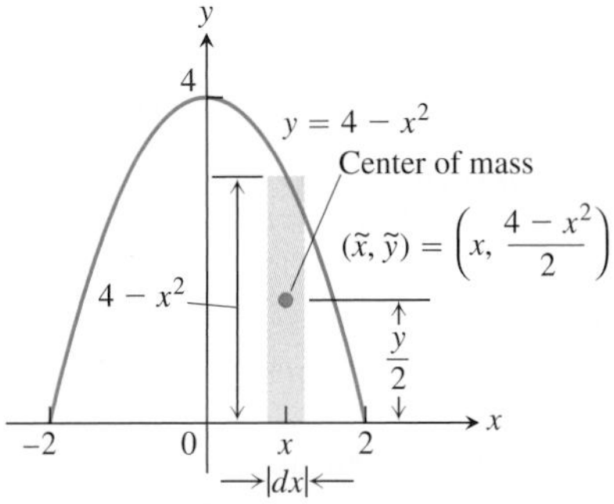

FIGURE 6.48 Modeling the plate in Example 2 with vertical strips.

Solution The mass distribution is symmetric about the y-axis, so $\bar{x} = 0$. We model the distribution of mass with vertical strips since the density is given as a function of the variable x. The typical vertical strip (see Figure 6.48) has

center of mass (c.m.): $(\tilde{x}, \tilde{y}) = \left(x, \frac{4 - x^2}{2}\right)$

length: $4 - x^2$

width: dx

area: $dA = (4 - x^2)\,dx$

mass: $dm = \delta\,dA = \delta(4 - x^2)\,dx$

distance from c.m. to x-axis: $\tilde{y} = \frac{4 - x^2}{2}$.

The moment of the strip about the x-axis is

$$\tilde{y}\,dm = \frac{4 - x^2}{2}\cdot\delta(4 - x^2)\,dx = \frac{\delta}{2}(4 - x^2)^2\,dx.$$

The moment of the plate about the x-axis is

$$M_x = \int \tilde{y}\,dm = \int_{-2}^{2}\frac{\delta}{2}(4 - x^2)^2\,dx = \int_{-2}^{2} x^2(4 - x^2)^2\,dx$$

$$= \int_{-2}^{2}(16x^2 - 8x^4 + x^6)\,dx = \frac{2048}{105}$$

$$M = \int dm = \int_{-2}^{2}\delta(4 - x^2)\,dx = \int_{-2}^{2} 2x^2(4 - x^2)\,dx$$

$$= \int_{-2}^{2}(8x^2 - 2x^4)\,dx = \frac{256}{15}.$$

Therefore,

$$\bar{y} = \frac{M_x}{M} = \frac{2048}{105}\cdot\frac{15}{256} = \frac{8}{7}.$$

The plate's center of mass is

$$(\bar{x}, \bar{y}) = \left(0, \frac{8}{7}\right).$$ ■

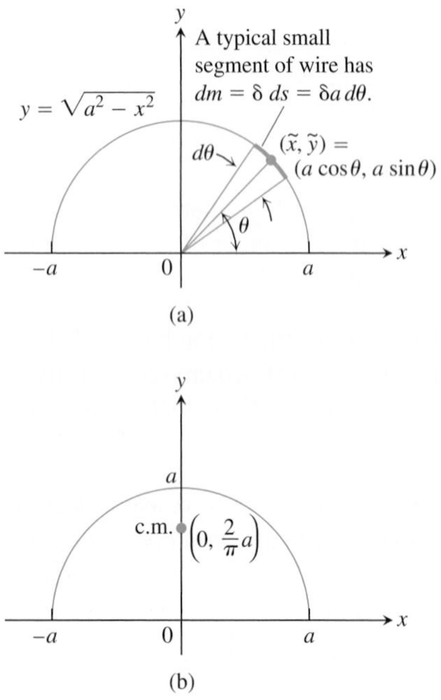

FIGURE 6.49 The semicircular wire in Example 3. (a) The dimensions and variables used in finding the center of mass. (b) The center of mass does not lie on the wire.

Centroids

When the density function is constant, it cancels out of the numerator and denominator of the formulas for $\bar{x}$ and $\bar{y}$. Thus, when the density is constant, the location of the center of mass is a feature of the geometry of the object and not of the material from which it is made. In such cases, engineers may call the center of mass the **centroid** of the shape, as in "Find the centroid of a triangle or a solid cone." To do so, just set δ equal to 1 and proceed to find $\bar{x}$ and $\bar{y}$ as before, by dividing moments by masses.

EXAMPLE 3 Find the center of mass (centroid) of a wire of constant density δ shaped like a semicircle of radius a.

Solution We model the wire with the semicircle $y = \sqrt{a^2 - x^2}$ (Figure 6.49). The distribution of mass is symmetric about the y-axis, so $\bar{x} = 0$. To find $\bar{y}$, we imagine the wire divided into short segments. The typical segment (Figure 6.49a) has

$$\text{length:} \quad ds = a\, d\theta$$

$$\text{mass:} \quad dm = \delta\, ds = \delta a\, d\theta \qquad \text{Mass per unit length times length}$$

$$\text{distance of c.m. to } x\text{-axis:} \quad \tilde{y} = a \sin\theta.$$

Hence,

$$\bar{y} = \frac{\int \tilde{y}\, dm}{\int dm} = \frac{\int_0^{\pi} a\sin\theta \cdot \delta a\, d\theta}{\int_0^{\pi} \delta a\, d\theta} = \frac{\delta a^2 \big[-\cos\theta\big]_0^{\pi}}{\delta a \pi} = \frac{2}{\pi} a.$$

The center of mass lies on the axis of symmetry at the point $(0, 2a/\pi)$, about two-thirds of the way up from the origin (Figure 6.49b). Notice how δ cancels in the equation for $\bar{y}$, so we could have set $\delta = 1$ everywhere and obtained the same value for $\bar{y}$. ■

EXERCISES 6.7

In Exercises 1–14, find the center of mass of a thin plate of constant density δ covering the given region.

1. The region bounded by the parabola $y = x^2$ and the line $y = 4$
2. The region bounded by the parabola $y = 25 - x^2$ and the x-axis
3. The region bounded by the parabola $y = x - x^2$ and the line $y = -x$
4. The region enclosed by the parabolas $y = x^2 - 3$ and $y = -2x^2$
5. The region bounded by the y-axis and the curve $x = y - y^3$, $0 \le y \le 1$
6. The region bounded by the parabola $x = y^2 - y$ and the line $y = x$
7. The region bounded by the x-axis and the curve $y = \cos x$, $-\pi/2 \le x \le \pi/2$
8. The region between the x-axis and the curve $y = \sec^2 x$, $-\pi/4 \le x \le \pi/4$
9. T The region between the curve $y = 1/x$ and the x-axis from $x = 1$ to $x = 2$. Give the coordinates to two decimal places.
10. **a.** The region cut from the first quadrant by the circle $x^2 + y^2 = 9$
    b. The region bounded by the x-axis and the semicircle $y = \sqrt{9 - x^2}$
    Compare your answer in part (b) with the answer in part (a).
11. The region in the first and fourth quadrants enclosed by the curves $y = 1/(1 + x^2)$ and $y = -1/(1 + x^2)$ and by the lines $x = 0$ and $x = 1$
12. The region bounded by the parabolas $y = 2x^2 - 4x$ and $y = 2x - x^2$
13. The region between the curve $y = 1/\sqrt{x}$ and the x-axis from $x = 1$ to $x = 16$
14. The region bounded above by the curve $y = 1/x^3$, below by the curve $y = -1/x^3$, and on the left and right by the lines $x = 1$ and $x = a > 1$. Also, find $\lim_{a\to\infty} \bar{x}$.
15. Find the center of mass of a thin plate covering the region between the x-axis and the curve $y = 2/x^2$, $1 \le x \le 2$, if the plate's density at the point (x, y) is $\delta(x) = x^2$.

16. Find the center of mass of a thin plate covering the region bounded below by the parabola $y = x^2$ and above by the line $y = x$ if the plate's density at the point (x, y) is $\delta(x) = 12x$.

17. Find the center of mass of the thin plate in Exercise 13 if, instead of being constant, the density function is $\delta(x) = 4/\sqrt{x}$.

18. The region between the curve $y = 2/x$ and the x-axis from $x = 1$ to $x = 4$ is revolved about the x-axis to generate a solid.

a. Find the volume of the solid.

b. Find the center of mass of a thin plate covering the region if the plate's density at the point (x, y) is $\delta(x) = \sqrt{x}$.

c. Sketch the plate and show the center of mass in your sketch.

19. The region bounded by the curves $y = \pm 4/\sqrt{x}$ and the lines $x = 1$ and $x = 4$ is revolved about the y-axis to generate a solid.

a. Find the volume of the solid.

b. Find the center of mass of a thin plate covering the region if the plate's density at the point (x, y) is $\delta(x) = 1/x$.

c. Sketch the plate and show the center of mass in your sketch.

20. The region between the curve $y = 1/(2\sqrt{x})$ and the x-axis from $x = 1/4$ to $x = 4$ is revolved about the x-axis to generate a solid.

a. Find the volume of the solid.

b. Find the centroid of the region.

21. The centroid of a triangle lies at the intersection of the triangle's medians (*Figure 6.50a*) You may recall that the point inside a triangle that lies one-third of the way from each side toward the opposite vertex is the point where the triangle's three medians intersect. Show that the centroid lies at the intersection of the medians by showing that it too lies one-third of the way from each side toward the opposite vertex. To do so, take the following steps.

i. Stand one side of the triangle on the x-axis as in Figure 6.50b. Express dm in terms of L and dy.

ii. Use similar triangles to show that $L = (b/h)(h - y)$. Substitute this expression for L in your formula for dm.

iii. Show that $\bar{y} = h/3$.

iv. Extend the argument to the other sides.

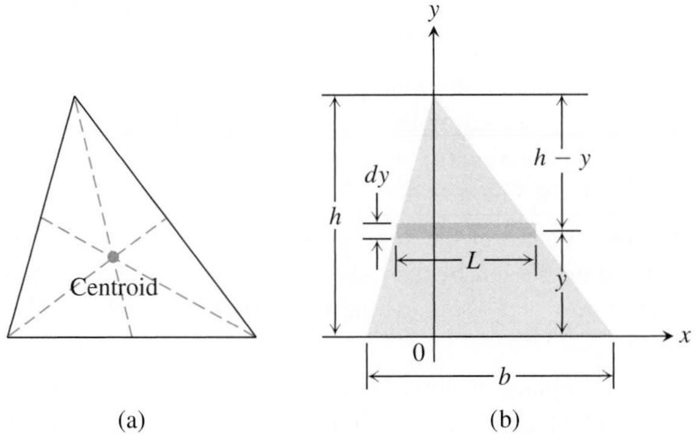

FIGURE 6.50 The triangle in Exercise 21. (a) The centroid. (b) The dimensions and variables to use in locating the center of mass.

Use the result in Exercise 21 to find the centroids of the triangles whose vertices appear in Exercises 22–26. Assume $a, b > 0$.

22. $(-1, 0), (1, 0), (0, 3)$

23. $(0, 0), (1, 0), (0, 1)$

24. $(0, 0), (a, 0), (0, a)$

25. $(0, 0), (a, 0), (0, b)$

26. $(0, 0), (a, 0), (a/2, b)$

27. Constant density Find the moment about the x-axis of a wire of constant density that lies along the curve $y = \sqrt{x}$ from $x = 0$ to $x = 2$.

28. Constant density Find the moment about the x-axis of a wire of constant density that lies along the curve $y = x^3$ from $x = 0$ to $x = 1$.

29. Variable density Suppose that the density of the wire in Example 3 is $\delta = k \sin \theta$ (k constant). Find the center of mass.

30. Variable density Suppose that the density of the wire in Example 3 is $\delta = 1 + k|\cos \theta|$ (k constant). Find the center of mass.

Verify the statements and formulas in Exercises 31 and 32.

31. The coordinates of the centroid of a differentiable plane curve are

$$\bar{x} = \frac{\int x\, ds}{\text{length}}, \qquad \bar{y} = \frac{\int y\, ds}{\text{length}}.$$

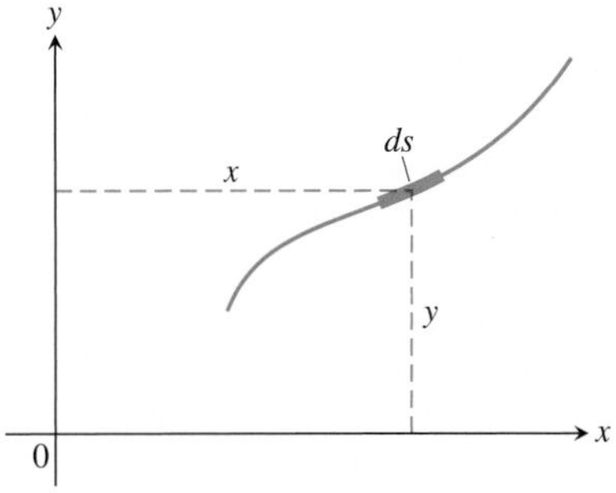

32. Whatever the value of $p > 0$ in the equation $y = x^2/(4p)$, the y-coordinate of the centroid of the parabolic segment shown here is $\bar{y} = (3/5)a$.

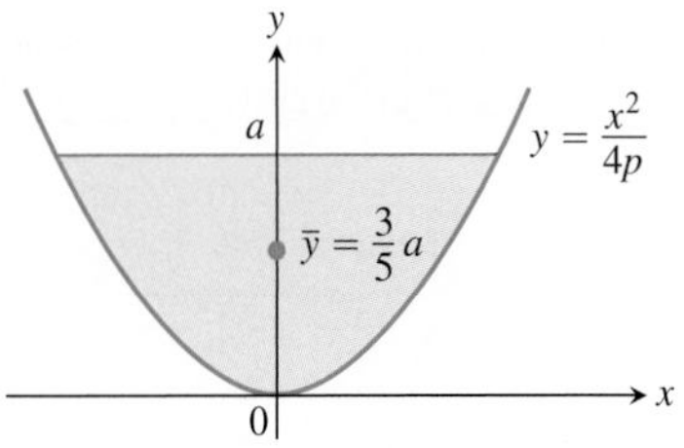

Chapter 6 Questions to Guide Your Review

1. How do you define and calculate the volumes of solids by the method of slicing? Give an example.
2. How are the disk and washer methods for calculating volumes derived from the method of slicing? Give examples of volume calculations by these methods.
3. Describe the method of cylindrical shells. Give an example.
4. How do you define the length of a smooth parametrized curve $x = f(t), y = g(t), a \leq t \leq b$? What does smoothness have to do with length? What else do you need to know about the parametrization to find the curve's length? Give examples.
5. How do you find the length of the graph of a smooth function over a closed interval? Give an example. What about functions that do not have continuous first derivatives?
6. How do you define and calculate the area of the surface swept out by revolving the graph of a smooth function $y = f(x)$, $a \leq x \leq b$, about the x-axis? Give an example.
7. Under what conditions can you find the area of the surface generated by revolving a curve $x = f(t), y = g(t), a \leq t \leq b$, about the x-axis? The y-axis? Give examples.
8. How do you solve separable first-order differential equations?
9. What is the law of exponential change? How can it be derived from an initial value problem? What are some of the applications of the law?
10. How do you define and calculate the work done by a variable force directed along a portion of the x-axis? How do you calculate the work it takes to pump a liquid from a tank? Give examples.
11. What is a center of mass?
12. How do you locate the center of mass of a thin flat plate of material? Give an example.

Chapter 6 Practice Exercises

Find the volumes of the solids in Exercises 1–16.

1. The solid lies between planes perpendicular to the x-axis at $x = 0$ and $x = 1$. The cross-sections perpendicular to the x-axis between these planes are circular disks whose diameters run from the parabola $y = x^2$ to the parabola $y = \sqrt{x}$.
2. The base of the solid is the region in the first quadrant between the line $y = x$ and the parabola $y = 2\sqrt{x}$. The cross-sections of the solid perpendicular to the x-axis are equilateral triangles whose bases stretch from the line to the curve.
3. The solid lies between planes perpendicular to the x-axis at $x = \pi/4$ and $x = 5\pi/4$. The cross-sections between these planes are circular disks whose diameters run from the curve $y = 2\cos x$ to the curve $y = 2\sin x$.
4. The solid lies between planes perpendicular to the x-axis at $x = 0$ and $x = 6$. The cross-sections between these planes are squares whose bases run from the x-axis up to the curve $x^{1/2} + y^{1/2} = \sqrt{6}$.

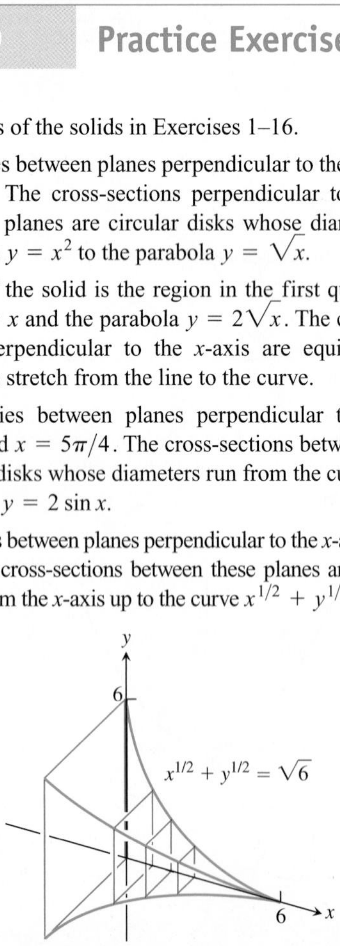

5. The solid lies between planes perpendicular to the x-axis at $x = 0$ and $x = 4$. The cross-sections of the solid perpendicular to the x-axis between these planes are circular disks whose diameters run from the curve $x^2 = 4y$ to the curve $y^2 = 4x$.
6. The base of the solid is the region bounded by the parabola $y^2 = 4x$ and the line $x = 1$ in the xy-plane. Each cross-section perpendicular to the x-axis is an equilateral triangle with one edge in the plane. (The triangles all lie on the same side of the plane.)
7. Find the volume of the solid generated by revolving the region bounded by the x-axis, the curve $y = 3x^4$, and the lines $x = 1$ and $x = -1$ about **(a)** the x-axis; **(b)** the y-axis; **(c)** the line $x = 1$; **(d)** the line $y = 3$.
8. Find the volume of the solid generated by revolving the "triangular" region bounded by the curve $y = 4/x^3$ and the lines $x = 1$ and $y = 1/2$ about **(a)** the x-axis; **(b)** the y-axis; **(c)** the line $x = 2$; **(d)** the line $y = 4$.
9. Find the volume of the solid generated by revolving the region bounded on the left by the parabola $x = y^2 + 1$ and on the right by the line $x = 5$ about **(a)** the x-axis; **(b)** the y-axis; **(c)** the line $x = 5$.
10. Find the volume of the solid generated by revolving the region bounded by the parabola $y^2 = 4x$ and the line $y = x$ about **(a)** the x-axis; **(b)** the y-axis; **(c)** the line $x = 4$; **(d)** the line $y = 4$.
11. Find the volume of the solid generated by revolving the "triangular" region bounded by the x-axis, the line $x = \pi/3$, and the curve $y = \tan x$ in the first quadrant about the x-axis.

12. Find the volume of the solid generated by revolving the region bounded by the curve $y = \sin x$ and the lines $x = 0, x = \pi$, and $y = 2$ about the line $y = 2$.

13. Find the volume of the solid generated by revolving the region bounded by the curve $x = e^{y^2}$ and the lines $y = 0$, $x = 0$, and $y = 1$ about the x-axis.

14. Find the volume of the solid generated by revolving about the x-axis the region bounded by $y = 2\tan x, y = 0, x = -\pi/4$, and $x = \pi/4$. (The region lies in the first and third quadrants and resembles a skewed bowtie.)

15. Volume of a solid sphere hole A round hole of radius $\sqrt{3}$ ft is bored through the center of a solid sphere of a radius 2 ft. Find the volume of material removed from the sphere.

16. Volume of a football The profile of a football resembles the ellipse shown here. Find the football's volume to the nearest cubic inch.

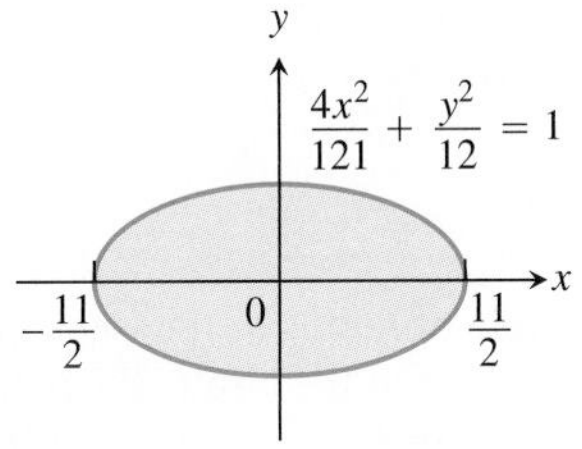

Find the lengths of the curves in Exercises 17–23.

17. $y = x^{1/2} - (1/3)x^{3/2}, \quad 1 \le x \le 4$

18. $x = y^{2/3}, \quad 1 \le y \le 8$

19. $y = x^2 - (\ln x)/8, \quad 1 \le x \le 2$

20. $x = (y^3/12) + (1/y), \quad 1 \le y \le 2$

21. $x = 5\cos t - \cos 5t, \quad y = 5\sin t - \sin 5t, \quad 0 \le t \le \pi/2$

22. $x = t^3 - 6t^2, \quad y = t^3 + 6t^2, \quad 0 \le t \le 1$

23. $x = 3\cos\theta, \quad y = 3\sin\theta, \quad 0 \le \theta \le \dfrac{3\pi}{2}$

24. Find the length of the enclosed loop $x = t^2, y = (t^3/3) - t$ shown here. The loop starts at $t = -\sqrt{3}$ and ends at $t = \sqrt{3}$.

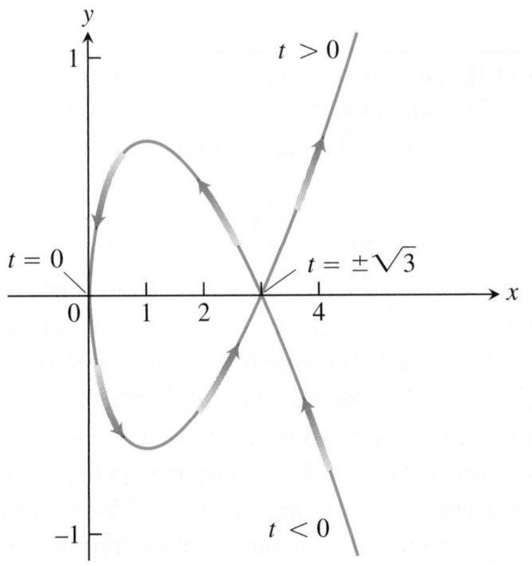

In Exercises 25–30, find the areas of the surfaces generated by revolving the curves about the given axes.

25. $y = \sqrt{2x + 1}, \quad 0 \le x \le 3; \quad x$-axis

26. $y = x^3/3, \quad 0 \le x \le 1; \quad x$-axis

27. $x = \sqrt{4y - y^2}, \quad 1 \le y \le 2; \quad y$-axis

28. $x = \sqrt{y}, \quad 2 \le y \le 6; \quad y$-axis

29. $x = t^2/2, \quad y = 2t, \quad 0 \le t \le \sqrt{5}; \quad x$-axis

30. $x = t^2 + 1/(2t), \quad y = 4\sqrt{t}, \quad 1/\sqrt{2} \le t \le 1; \quad y$-axis

In Exercises 31–34 solve the differential equation.

31. $\dfrac{dy}{dx} = \sqrt{y}\cos^2\sqrt{y}$

32. $y' = \dfrac{3y(x+1)^2}{y - 1}$

33. $yy' = \sec y^2 \sec^2 x$

34. $y\cos^2 x\,dy + \sin x\,dx = 0$

In Exercises 35–38 solve the initial value problem.

35. $\dfrac{dy}{dx} = e^{-x-y-2}, \quad y(0) = -2$

36. $\dfrac{dy}{dx} = \dfrac{y\ln y}{1 + x^2}, \quad y(0) = e^2$

37. $x\,dy - \left(y + \sqrt{y}\right)dx = 0, \quad y(1) = 1$

38. $y^{-2}\dfrac{dx}{dy} = \dfrac{e^x}{e^{2x} + 1}, \quad y(0) = 1$

39. What is the age of a sample of charcoal in which 90% of the carbon-14 originally present has decayed?

40. Cooling a pie A deep-dish apple pie, whose internal temperature was 220°F when removed from the oven, was set out on a breezy 40°F porch to cool. Fifteen minutes later, the pie's internal temperature was 180°F. How long did it take the pie to cool from there to 70°F?

41. Lifting equipment A rock climber is about to haul up 100 N (about 22.5 lb) of equipment that has been hanging beneath her on 40 m of rope that weighs 0.8 newton per meter. How much work will it take? (*Hint:* Solve for the rope and equipment separately, then add.)

42. Leaky tank truck You drove an 800-gal tank truck of water from the base of Mt. Washington to the summit and discovered on arrival that the tank was only half full. You started with a full tank, climbed at a steady rate, and accomplished the 4750-ft elevation change in 50 min. Assuming that the water leaked out at a steady rate, how much work was spent in carrying water to the top? Do not count the work done in getting yourself and the truck there. Water weighs 8 lb/U.S. gal.

43. Stretching a spring If a force of 20 lb is required to hold a spring 1 ft beyond its unstressed length, how much work does it take to stretch the spring this far? An additional foot?

44. Garage door spring A force of 200 N will stretch a garage door spring 0.8 m beyond its unstressed length. How far will a 300-N force stretch the spring? How much work does it take to stretch the spring this far from its unstressed length?

45. Pumping a reservoir A reservoir shaped like a right circular cone, point down, 20 ft across the top and 8 ft deep, is full of water. How much work does it take to pump the water to a level 6 ft above the top?

46. Pumping a reservoir (*Continuation of Exercise 45.*) The reservoir is filled to a depth of 5 ft, and the water is to be pumped to the same level as the top. How much work does it take?

47. Pumping a conical tank A right circular conical tank, point down, with top radius 5 ft and height 10 ft is filled with a liquid whose weight-density is 60 lb/ft^3. How much work does it take to pump the liquid to a point 2 ft above the tank? If the pump is driven by a motor rated at 275 ft-lb/sec (1/2 hp), how long will it take to empty the tank?

48. Pumping a cylindrical tank A storage tank is a right circular cylinder 20 ft long and 8 ft in diameter with its axis horizontal. If the tank is half full of olive oil weighing 57 lb/ft^3, find the work done in emptying it through a pipe that runs from the bottom of the tank to an outlet that is 6 ft above the top of the tank.

49. Find the centroid of a thin, flat plate covering the region enclosed by the parabolas $y = 2x^2$ and $y = 3 - x^2$.

50. Find the centroid of a thin, flat plate covering the region enclosed by the x-axis, the lines $x = 2$ and $x = -2$, and the parabola $y = x^2$.

51. Find the centroid of a thin, flat plate covering the "triangular" region in the first quadrant bounded by the y-axis, the parabola $y = x^2/4$, and the line $y = 4$.

52. Find the centroid of a thin, flat plate covering the region enclosed by the parabola $y^2 = x$ and the line $x = 2y$.

53. Find the center of mass of a thin, flat plate covering the region enclosed by the parabola $y^2 = x$ and the line $x = 2y$ if the density function is $\delta(y) = 1 + y$. (Use horizontal strips.)

54. a. Find the center of mass of a thin plate of constant density covering the region between the curve $y = 3/x^{3/2}$ and the x-axis from $x = 1$ to $x = 9$.

b. Find the plate's center of mass if, instead of being constant, the density is $\delta(x) = x$. (Use vertical strips.)

Chapter 6 Additional and Advanced Exercises

1. A solid is generated by revolving about the x-axis the region bounded by the graph of the positive continuous function $y = f(x)$, the x-axis, and the fixed line $x = a$ and the variable line $x = b$, $b > a$. Its volume, for all b, is $b^2 - ab$. Find $f(x)$.

2. A solid is generated by revolving about the x-axis the region bounded by the graph of the positive continuous function $y = f(x)$, the x-axis, and the lines $x = 0$ and $x = a$. Its volume, for all $a > 0$, is $a^2 + a$. Find $f(x)$.

3. Suppose that the increasing function $f(x)$ is smooth for $x \geq 0$ and that $f(0) = a$. Let $s(x)$ denote the length of the graph of f from $(0, a)$ to $(x, f(x))$, $x > 0$. Find $f(x)$ if $s(x) = Cx$ for some constant C. What are the allowable values for C?

4. a. Show that for $0 < \alpha \leq \pi/2$,

$$\int_0^\alpha \sqrt{1 + \cos^2\theta}\, d\theta > \sqrt{\alpha^2 + \sin^2\alpha}.$$

b. Generalize the result in part (a).

5. At points on the curve $y = 2\sqrt{x}$, line segments of length $h = y$ are drawn perpendicular to the xy-plane. (See accompanying figure.) Find the area of the surface formed by these perpendiculars from $(0, 0)$ to $(3, 2\sqrt{3})$.

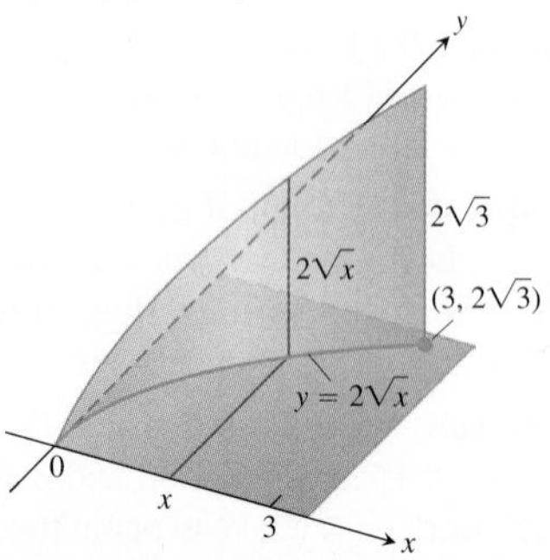

6. At points on a circle of radius a, line segments are drawn perpendicular to the plane of the circle, the perpendicular at each point P being of length ks, where s is the length of the arc of the circle measured counterclockwise from $(a, 0)$ to P and k is a positive constant, as shown here. Find the area of the surface formed by the perpendiculars along the arc beginning at $(a, 0)$ and extending once around the circle.

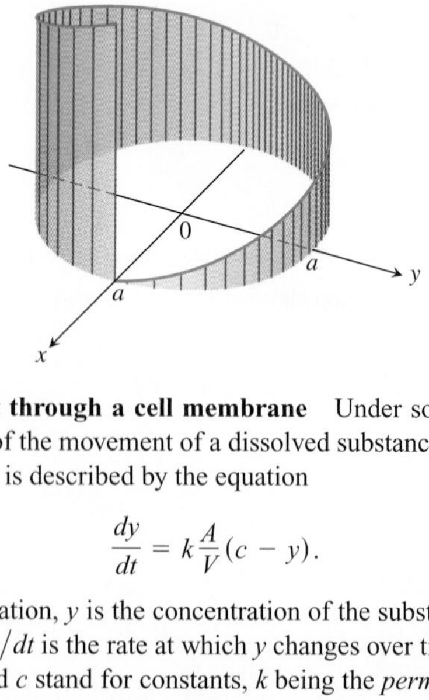

7. Transport through a cell membrane Under some conditions, the result of the movement of a dissolved substance across a cell's membrane is described by the equation

$$\frac{dy}{dt} = k\frac{A}{V}(c - y).$$

In this equation, y is the concentration of the substance inside the cell and dy/dt is the rate at which y changes over time. The letters k, A, V, and c stand for constants, k being the *permeability coefficient* (a property of the membrane), A the surface area of the membrane, V the cell's volume, and c the concentration of the substance outside the cell. The equation says that the rate at which the concentration changes within the cell is proportional to the difference between it and the outside concentration.

a. Solve the equation for $y(t)$, using y_0 to denote $y(0)$.

b. Find the steady-state concentration, $\lim_{t\to\infty} y(t)$. (Based on *Some Mathematical Models in Biology*, edited by R. M. Thrall, J. A. Mortimer, K. R. Rebman, and R. F. Baum, rev. ed., Dec. 1967, PB-202 364, pp. 101–103; distributed by N.T.I.S., U.S. Department of Commerce.)

8. Oxygen flow mixture Oxygen flows through one tube into a liter flask filled with air, and the mixture of oxygen and air (considered well stirred) escapes through another tube. Assuming that air contains 21% oxygen, what percentage of oxygen will the flask contain after 5 L have passed through the intake tube?

9. A particle of mass m starts from rest at time $t = 0$ and is moved along the x-axis with constant acceleration a from $x = 0$ to $x = h$ against a variable force of magnitude $F(t) = t^2$. Find the work done.

10. Work and kinetic energy Suppose a 1.6-oz golf ball is placed on a vertical spring with force constant $k = 2$ lb/in. The spring is compressed 6 in. and released. About how high does the ball go (measured from the spring's rest position)?

11. Find the centroid of the region bounded below by the x-axis and above by the curve $y = 1 - x^n$, n an even positive integer. What is the limiting position of the centroid as $n \to \infty$?

12. If you haul a telephone pole on a two-wheeled carriage behind a truck, you want the wheels to be 3 ft or so behind the pole's center of mass to provide an adequate "tongue" weight. NYNEX's class 1.40-ft wooden poles have a 27-in. circumference at the top and a 43.5-in. circumference at the base. About how far from the top is the center of mass?

13. Suppose that a thin metal plate of area A and constant density δ occupies a region R in the xy-plane, and let M_y be the plate's moment about the y-axis. Show that the plate's moment about the line $x = b$ is

a. $M_y - b\delta A$ if the plate lies to the right of the line, and

b. $b\delta A - M_y$ if the plate lies to the left of the line.

14. Find the center of mass of a thin plate covering the region bounded by the curve $y^2 = 4ax$ and the line $x = a$, $a =$ positive constant, if the density at (x, y) is directly proportional to **(a)** x, **(b)** $|y|$.

15. a. Find the centroid of the region in the first quadrant bounded by two concentric circles and the coordinate axes, if the circles have radii a and b, $0 < a < b$, and their centers are at the origin.

b. Find the limits of the coordinates of the centroid as a approaches b and discuss the meaning of the result.

16. A triangular corner is cut from a square 1 ft on a side. The area of the triangle removed is 36 in.^{2}. If the centroid of the remaining region is 7 in. from one side of the original square, how far is it from the remaining sides?

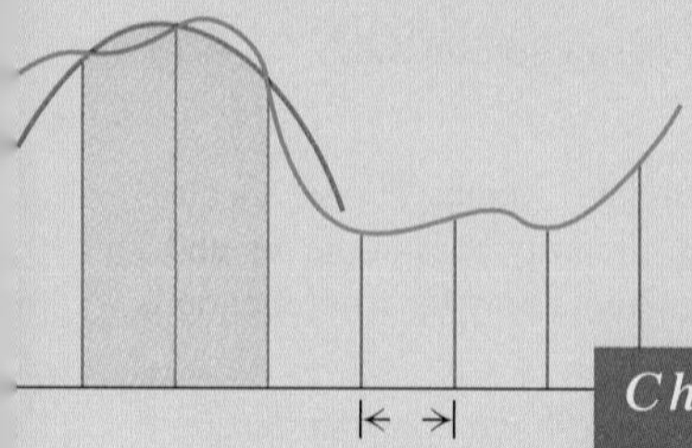

Chapter

7 TECHNIQUES OF INTEGRATION

OVERVIEW The Fundamental Theorem tells us how to evaluate a definite integral once we have an antiderivative for the integrand function. Table 4.2 shows the forms of antiderivatives for the functions we have studied so far, and the substitution method helps us use the table to evaluate more complicated functions involving the basic ones. In this chapter we study a number of other important techniques for finding antiderivatives (or indefinite integrals) for even more functions.

7.1 Integration by Parts

Integration by parts is a technique for simplifying integrals of the form

$$\int f(x)g(x)\,dx.$$

It is useful when f can be differentiated repeatedly and g can be integrated repeatedly without difficulty. The integral

$$\int xe^x\,dx$$

is such an integral because $f(x) = x$ can be differentiated twice to become zero and $g(x) = e^x$ can be integrated repeatedly without difficulty. Integration by parts also applies to integrals like

$$\int e^x \sin x\,dx$$

in which each part of the integrand appears again after repeated differentiation or integration.

Product Rule in Integral Form

If f and g are differentiable functions of x, the Product Rule says

$$\frac{d}{dx}[f(x)g(x)] = f'(x)g(x) + f(x)g'(x).$$

In terms of indefinite integrals, this equation becomes

$$\int \frac{d}{dx}[f(x)g(x)]\,dx = \int [f'(x)g(x) + f(x)g'(x)]\,dx$$

or

$$\int \frac{d}{dx}[f(x)g(x)]\,dx = \int f'(x)g(x)\,dx + \int f(x)g'(x)\,dx.$$

Rearranging the terms of this last equation, we get

$$\int f(x)g'(x)\,dx = \int \frac{d}{dx}[f(x)g(x)]\,dx - \int f'(x)g(x)\,dx$$

leading to the **integration by parts** formula

$$\int f(x)g'(x)\,dx = f(x)g(x) - \int f'(x)g(x)\,dx \qquad (1)$$

Sometimes it is easier to remember the formula if we write it in differential form. Let $u = f(x)$ and $v = g(x)$. Then $du = f'(x)\,dx$ and $dv = g'(x)\,dx$. Using the Substitution Rule, the integration by parts formula becomes

Integration by Parts Formula

$$\int u\,dv = uv - \int v\,du \qquad (2)$$

This formula expresses one integral, $\int u\,dv$, in terms of a second integral, $\int v\,du$. With a proper choice of u and v, the second integral may be easier to evaluate than the first. In using the formula, various choices may be available for u and dv. The next examples illustrate the technique.

EXAMPLE 1 Find

$$\int x \cos x\,dx.$$

Solution We use the formula $\int u\,dv = uv - \int v\,du$ with

$$u = x, \qquad dv = \cos x\,dx,$$
$$du = dx, \qquad v = \sin x. \qquad \text{Simplest antiderivative of } \cos x$$

Then

$$\int x \cos x\,dx = x \sin x - \int \sin x\,dx = x \sin x + \cos x + C.$$ ■

There are four choices available for u and dv in Example 1:

1. Let $u = 1$ and $dv = x \cos x\,dx$.
2. Let $u = x$ and $dv = \cos x\,dx$.
3. Let $u = x \cos x$ and $dv = dx$.
4. Let $u = \cos x$ and $dv = x\,dx$.

Choice 2 was used in Example 1. The other three choices lead to integrals we don't know how to integrate. For instance, Choice 3 leads to the integral

$$\int (x \cos x - x^2 \sin x)\, dx.$$

The goal of integration by parts is to go from an integral $\int u\, dv$ that we don't see how to evaluate to an integral $\int v\, du$ that we can evaluate. Generally, you choose dv first to be as much of the integrand, including dx, as you can readily integrate; u is the leftover part. Keep in mind that integration by parts does not always work.

EXAMPLE 2 Find

$$\int \ln x\, dx.$$

Solution Since $\int \ln x\, dx$ can be written as $\int \ln x \cdot 1\, dx$, we use the formula $\int u\, dv = uv - \int v\, du$ with

$u = \ln x$ Simplifies when differentiated $\qquad dv = dx$ Easy to integrate

$du = \frac{1}{x}\, dx,$ $\qquad v = x.$ Simplest antiderivative

Then

$$\int \ln x\, dx = x \ln x - \int x \cdot \frac{1}{x}\, dx = x \ln x - \int dx = x \ln x - x + C. \qquad \blacksquare$$

Sometimes we have to use integration by parts more than once.

EXAMPLE 3 Evaluate

$$\int x^2 e^x\, dx.$$

Solution With $u = x^2$, $dv = e^x\, dx$, $du = 2x\, dx$, and $v = e^x$, we have

$$\int x^2 e^x\, dx = x^2 e^x - 2 \int x e^x\, dx.$$

The new integral is less complicated than the original because the exponent on x is reduced by one. To evaluate the integral on the right, we integrate by parts again with $u = x$, $dv = e^x\, dx$. Then $du = dx$, $v = e^x$, and

$$\int x e^x\, dx = x e^x - \int e^x\, dx = x e^x - e^x + C.$$

Hence,

$$\begin{aligned} \int x^2 e^x\, dx &= x^2 e^x - 2 \int x e^x\, dx \\ &= x^2 e^x - 2x e^x + 2e^x + C. \end{aligned} \qquad \blacksquare$$

The technique of Example 3 works for any integral $\int x^n e^x\,dx$ in which n is a positive integer, because differentiating x^n will eventually lead to zero and integrating e^x is easy.

Integrals like the one in the next example occur in electrical engineering. Their evaluation requires two integrations by parts, followed by solving for the unknown integral.

EXAMPLE 4 Evaluate

$$\int e^x \cos x\,dx.$$

Solution Let $u = e^x$ and $dv = \cos x\,dx$. Then $du = e^x\,dx$, $v = \sin x$, and

$$\int e^x \cos x\,dx = e^x \sin x - \int e^x \sin x\,dx.$$

The second integral is like the first except that it has $\sin x$ in place of $\cos x$. To evaluate it, we use integration by parts with

$$u = e^x, \qquad dv = \sin x\,dx, \qquad v = -\cos x, \qquad du = e^x\,dx.$$

Then

$$\int e^x \cos x\,dx = e^x \sin x - \left(-e^x \cos x - \int (-\cos x)(e^x\,dx)\right)$$

$$= e^x \sin x + e^x \cos x - \int e^x \cos x\,dx.$$

The unknown integral now appears on both sides of the equation. Adding the integral to both sides and adding the constant of integration gives

$$2\int e^x \cos x\,dx = e^x \sin x + e^x \cos x + C_1.$$

Dividing by 2 and renaming the constant of integration gives

$$\int e^x \cos x\,dx = \frac{e^x \sin x + e^x \cos x}{2} + C.$$ ■

EXAMPLE 5 Obtain a formula that expresses the integral

$$\int \cos^n x\,dx$$

in terms of an integral of a lower power of $\cos x$.

Solution We may think of $\cos^n x$ as $\cos^{n-1} x \cdot \cos x$. Then we let

$$u = \cos^{n-1} x \qquad \text{and} \qquad dv = \cos x\,dx,$$

so that

$$du = (n-1)\cos^{n-2} x\,(-\sin x\,dx) \qquad \text{and} \qquad v = \sin x.$$

Hence

$$\begin{aligned}\int \cos^n x\,dx &= \cos^{n-1} x \sin x + (n-1)\int \sin^2 x \cos^{n-2} x\,dx \\ &= \cos^{n-1} x \sin x + (n-1)\int (1-\cos^2 x)\cos^{n-2} x\,dx, \\ &= \cos^{n-1} x \sin x + (n-1)\int \cos^{n-2} x\,dx - (n-1)\int \cos^n x\,dx.\end{aligned}$$

If we add

$$(n-1)\int \cos^n x\,dx$$

to both sides of this equation, we obtain

$$n\int \cos^n x\,dx = \cos^{n-1} x \sin x + (n-1)\int \cos^{n-2} x\,dx.$$

We then divide through by n, and the final result is

$$\int \cos^n x\,dx = \frac{\cos^{n-1} x \sin x}{n} + \frac{n-1}{n}\int \cos^{n-2} x\,dx.$$

This allows us to reduce the exponent on $\cos x$ by 2 and is a very useful formula. When n is a positive integer, we may apply the formula repeatedly until the remaining integral is either

$$\int \cos x\,dx = \sin x + C \qquad \text{or} \qquad \int \cos^0 x\,dx = \int dx = x + C. \qquad \blacksquare$$

For example, the result in Example 5 tells us,

$$\begin{aligned}\int \cos^3 x\,dx &= \frac{\cos^2 x \sin x}{3} + \frac{2}{3}\int \cos x\,dx \\ &= \frac{1}{3}\cos^2 x \sin x + \frac{2}{3}\sin x + C.\end{aligned}$$

Evaluating Definite Integrals by Parts

The integration by parts formula in Equation (1) can be combined with Part 2 of the Fundamental Theorem in order to evaluate definite integrals by parts. Assuming that both f' and g' are continuous over the interval $[a, b]$, Part 2 of the Fundamental Theorem gives

Integration by Parts Formula for Definite Integrals

$$\int_a^b f(x)g'(x)\,dx = f(x)g(x)\Big]_a^b - \int_a^b f'(x)g(x)\,dx \qquad (3)$$

In applying Equation (3), we normally use the u and v notation from Equation (2) because it is easier to remember. Here is an example.

EXAMPLE 6 Find the area of the region bounded by the curve $y = xe^{-x}$ and the x-axis from $x = 0$ to $x = 4$.

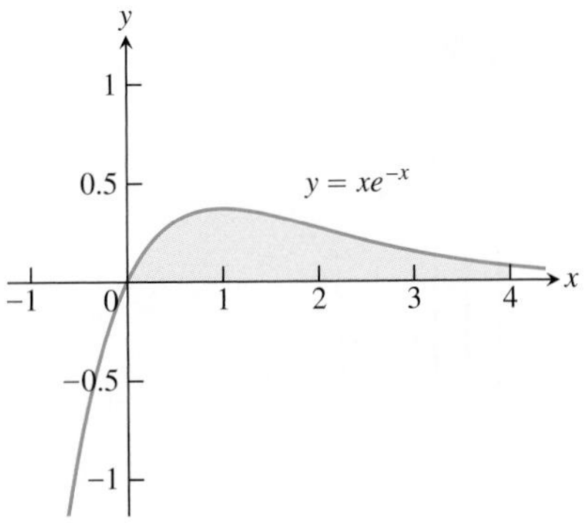

FIGURE 7.1 The region in Example 6.

Solution The region is shaded in Figure 7.1. Its area is

$$\int_0^4 xe^{-x}\, dx.$$

Let $u = x$, $dv = e^{-x}\, dx$, $v = -e^{-x}$, and $du = dx$. Then,

$$\begin{aligned}\int_0^4 xe^{-x}\, dx &= -xe^{-x}\Big]_0^4 - \int_0^4 (-e^{-x})\, dx \\ &= [-4e^{-4} - (0)] + \int_0^4 e^{-x}\, dx \\ &= -4e^{-4} - e^{-x}\Big]_0^4 \\ &= -4e^{-4} - e^{-4} - (-e^0) = 1 - 5e^{-4} \approx 0.91.\end{aligned}$$

■

EXERCISES 7.1

Evaluate the integrals in Exercises 1–24.

1. $\int x \sin \frac{x}{2}\, dx$

2. $\int \theta \cos \pi\theta\, d\theta$

3. $\int t^2 \cos t\, dt$

4. $\int x^2 \sin x\, dx$

5. $\int_1^2 x \ln x\, dx$

6. $\int_1^e x^3 \ln x\, dx$

7. $\int \tan^{-1} y\, dy$

8. $\int \sin^{-1} y\, dy$

9. $\int x \sec^2 x\, dx$

10. $\int 4x \sec^2 2x\, dx$

11. $\int x^3 e^x\, dx$

12. $\int p^4 e^{-p}\, dp$

13. $\int (x^2 - 5x)e^x\, dx$

14. $\int (r^2 + r + 1)e^r\, dr$

15. $\int x^5 e^x\, dx$

16. $\int t^2 e^{4t}\, dt$

17. $\int_0^{\pi/2} \theta^2 \sin 2\theta\, d\theta$

18. $\int_0^{\pi/2} x^3 \cos 2x\, dx$

19. $\int_{2/\sqrt{3}}^2 t \sec^{-1} t\, dt$

20. $\int_0^{1/\sqrt{2}} 2x \sin^{-1}(x^2)\, dx$

21. $\int e^\theta \sin \theta\, d\theta$

22. $\int e^{-y} \cos y\, dy$

23. $\int e^{2x} \cos 3x\, dx$

24. $\int e^{-2x} \sin 2x\, dx$

Evaluate the integrals in Exercises 25–30 by using a substitution prior to integration by parts.

25. $\int e^{\sqrt{3s+9}}\, ds$

26. $\int_0^1 x\sqrt{1 - x}\, dx$

27. $\int_0^{\pi/3} x \tan^2 x\, dx$

28. $\int \ln(x + x^2)\, dx$

29. $\int \sin(\ln x)\, dx$

30. $\int z(\ln z)^2\, dz$

31. Finding area Find the area of the region enclosed by the curve $y = x \sin x$ and the x-axis (see the accompanying figure) for

a. $0 \le x \le \pi$

b. $\pi \le x \le 2\pi$

c. $2\pi \le x \le 3\pi$.

d. What pattern do you see here? What is the area between the curve and the x-axis for $n\pi \le x \le (n + 1)\pi$, n an arbitrary nonnegative integer? Give reasons for your answer.

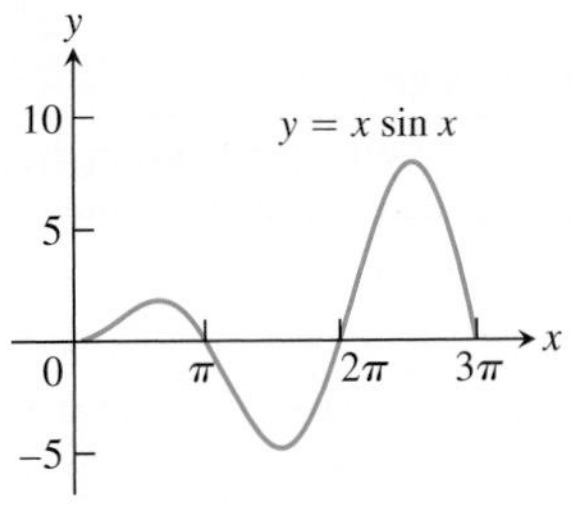

32. Finding area Find the area of the region enclosed by the curve $y = x \cos x$ and the x-axis (see the accompanying figure) for

a. $\pi/2 \le x \le 3\pi/2$

b. $3\pi/2 \le x \le 5\pi/2$

c. $5\pi/2 \le x \le 7\pi/2$.

d. What pattern do you see? What is the area between the curve and the x-axis for

$$\left(\frac{2n-1}{2}\right)\pi \le x \le \left(\frac{2n+1}{2}\right)\pi,$$

n an arbitrary positive integer? Give reasons for your answer.

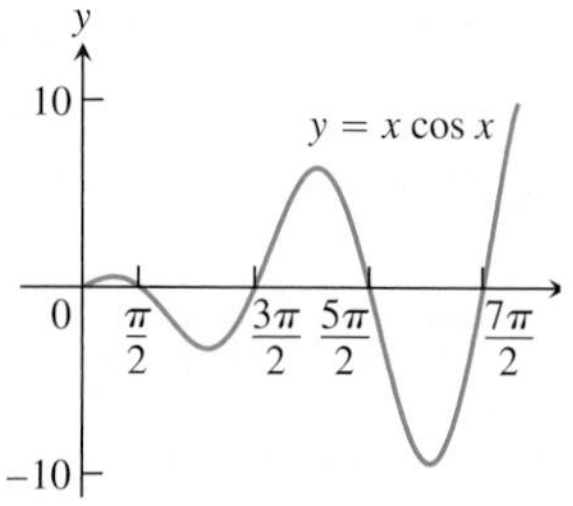

33. Finding volume Find the volume of the solid generated by revolving the region in the first quadrant bounded by the coordinate axes, the curve $y = e^x$, and the line $x = \ln 2$ about the line $x = \ln 2$.

34. Finding volume Find the volume of the solid generated by revolving the region in the first quadrant bounded by the coordinate axes, the curve $y = e^{-x}$, and the line $x = 1$

a. about the y-axis. **b.** about the line $x = 1$.

35. Finding volume Find the volume of the solid generated by revolving the region in the first quadrant bounded by the coordinate axes and the curve $y = \cos x$, $0 \le x \le \pi/2$, about

a. the y-axis. **b.** the line $x = \pi/2$.

36. Finding volume Find the volume of the solid generated by revolving the region bounded by the x-axis and the curve $y = x \sin x$, $0 \le x \le \pi$, about

a. the y-axis. **b.** the line $x = \pi$.

(See Exercise 31 for a graph.)

37. Average value A retarding force, symbolized by the dashpot in the figure, slows the motion of the weighted spring so that the mass's position at time t is

$$y = 2e^{-t}\cos t, \qquad t \ge 0.$$

Find the average value of y over the interval $0 \le t \le 2\pi$.

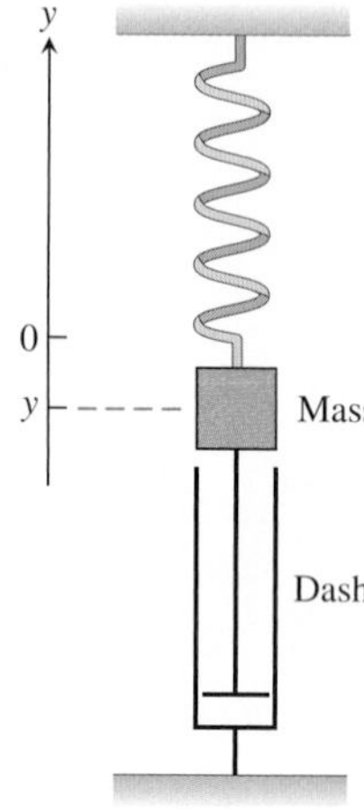

38. Average value In a mass-spring-dashpot system like the one in Exercise 37, the mass's position at time t is

$$y = 4e^{-t}(\sin t - \cos t), \qquad t \ge 0.$$

Find the average value of y over the interval $0 \le t \le 2\pi$.

Reduction Formulas In Exercises 39–42, use integration by parts to establish the *reduction formula*.

39. $\displaystyle\int x^n \cos x\,dx = x^n \sin x - n\int x^{n-1}\sin x\,dx$

40. $\displaystyle\int x^n \sin x\,dx = -x^n \cos x + n\int x^{n-1}\cos x\,dx$

41. $\displaystyle\int x^n e^{ax}\,dx = \frac{x^n e^{ax}}{a} - \frac{n}{a}\int x^{n-1}e^{ax}\,dx, \quad a \ne 0$

42. $\displaystyle\int (\ln x)^n\,dx = x(\ln x)^n - n\int (\ln x)^{n-1}\,dx$

Integrating Inverses of Functions Integration by parts leads to a rule for integrating inverses that usually gives good results:

$$\int f^{-1}(x)\,dx = \int yf'(y)\,dy \qquad \begin{array}{l} y = f^{-1}(x), \quad x = f(y) \\ dx = f'(y)\,dy \end{array}$$

$$= yf(y) - \int f(y)\,dy \qquad \begin{array}{l} \text{Integration by parts with} \\ u = y,\ dv = f'(y)\,dy \end{array}$$

$$= xf^{-1}(x) - \int f(y)\,dy$$

The idea is to take the most complicated part of the integral, in this case $f^{-1}(x)$, and simplify it first. For the integral of $\ln x$, we get

$$\int \ln x\,dx = \int ye^y\,dy \qquad \begin{array}{l} y = \ln x, \quad x = e^y \\ dx = e^y\,dy \end{array}$$

$$= ye^y - e^y + C$$

$$= x\ln x - x + C.$$

For the integral of $\cos^{-1} x$ we get

$$\begin{aligned}\int \cos^{-1} x\, dx &= x\cos^{-1} x - \int \cos y\, dy \qquad y = \cos^{-1} x\\ &= x\cos^{-1} x - \sin y + C\\ &= x\cos^{-1} x - \sin(\cos^{-1} x) + C.\end{aligned}$$

Use the formula

$$\int f^{-1}(x)\, dx = xf^{-1}(x) - \int f(y)\, dy \qquad y = f^{-1}(x) \tag{4}$$

to evaluate the integrals in Exercises 43–46. Express your answers in terms of x.

43. $\int \sin^{-1} x\, dx$

44. $\int \tan^{-1} x\, dx$

45. $\int \sec^{-1} x\, dx$

46. $\int \log_2 x\, dx$

Another way to integrate $f^{-1}(x)$ (when f^{-1} is integrable, of course) is to use integration by parts with $u = f^{-1}(x)$ and $dv = dx$ to rewrite the integral of f^{-1} as

$$\int f^{-1}(x)\, dx = xf^{-1}(x) - \int x\left(\frac{d}{dx} f^{-1}(x)\right) dx. \tag{5}$$

Exercises 47 and 48 compare the results of using Equations (4) and (5).

47. Equations (4) and (5) give different formulas for the integral of $\cos^{-1} x$:

a. $\int \cos^{-1} x\, dx = x\cos^{-1} x - \sin(\cos^{-1} x) + C$ Eq. (4)

b. $\int \cos^{-1} x\, dx = x\cos^{-1} x - \sqrt{1 - x^2} + C$ Eq. (5)

Can both integrations be correct? Explain.

48. Equations (4) and (5) lead to different formulas for the integral of $\tan^{-1} x$:

a. $\int \tan^{-1} x\, dx = x\tan^{-1} x - \ln \sec(\tan^{-1} x) + C$ Eq. (4)

b. $\int \tan^{-1} x\, dx = x\tan^{-1} x - \ln \sqrt{1 + x^2} + C$ Eq. (5)

Can both integrations be correct? Explain.

Evaluate the integrals in Exercises 49 and 50 with **(a)** Eq. (4) and **(b)** Eq. (5). In each case, check your work by differentiating your answer with respect to x.

49. $\int \sinh^{-1} x\, dx$

50. $\int \tanh^{-1} x\, dx$

7.2 Trigonometric Integrals

Trigonometric integrals involve algebraic combinations of the six basic trigonometric functions. In principle, we can always express such integrals in terms of sines and cosines, but it is often simpler to work with other functions, as in the integral

$$\int \sec^2 x\, dx = \tan x + C.$$

The general idea is to use identities to transform the integrals we have to find into integrals that are easier to work with.

Products of Powers of Sines and Cosines

We begin with integrals of the form:

$$\int \sin^m x \cos^n x\, dx,$$

where m and n are nonnegative integers (positive or zero). We can divide the appropriate substitution into three cases.

Case 1 If m is odd, we write m as $2k + 1$ and use the identity $\sin^2 x = 1 - \cos^2 x$ to obtain

$$\sin^m x = \sin^{2k+1} x = (\sin^2 x)^k \sin x = (1 - \cos^2 x)^k \sin x. \tag{1}$$

Then we combine the single $\sin x$ with dx in the integral and set $\sin x\,dx$ equal to $-d(\cos x)$.

Case 2 If m is even and n is odd in $\int \sin^m x \cos^n x\,dx$, we write n as $2k+1$ and use the identity $\cos^2 x = 1 - \sin^2 x$ to obtain

$$\cos^n x = \cos^{2k+1} x = (\cos^2 x)^k \cos x = (1 - \sin^2 x)^k \cos x.$$

We then combine the single $\cos x$ with dx and set $\cos x\,dx$ equal to $d(\sin x)$.

Case 3 If both m and n are even in $\int \sin^m x \cos^n x\,dx$, we substitute

$$\sin^2 x = \frac{1 - \cos 2x}{2}, \qquad \cos^2 x = \frac{1 + \cos 2x}{2} \tag{2}$$

to reduce the integrand to one in lower powers of $\cos 2x$.

Here are some examples illustrating each case.

EXAMPLE 1 Evaluate

$$\int \sin^3 x \cos^2 x\,dx.$$

Solution

$$\begin{aligned}
\int \sin^3 x \cos^2 x\,dx &= \int \sin^2 x \cos^2 x \sin x\,dx && m \text{ is odd}\\
&= \int (1 - \cos^2 x)\cos^2 x\,(-d(\cos x))\\
&= \int (1 - u^2)(u^2)(-du) && u = \cos x\\
&= \int (u^4 - u^2)\,du\\
&= \frac{u^5}{5} - \frac{u^3}{3} + C\\
&= \frac{\cos^5 x}{5} - \frac{\cos^3 x}{3} + C.
\end{aligned}$$

■

EXAMPLE 2 Evaluate

$$\int \cos^5 x\,dx.$$

Solution

$$\begin{aligned}
\int \cos^5 x\,dx &= \int \cos^4 x \cos x\,dx = \int (1 - \sin^2 x)^2\,d(\sin x) && m = 0,\ n = 5\\
&= \int (1 - u^2)^2\,du && u = \sin x
\end{aligned}$$

$$= \int (1 - 2u^2 + u^4)\, du$$

$$= u - \frac{2}{3}u^3 + \frac{1}{5}u^5 + C = \sin x - \frac{2}{3}\sin^3 x + \frac{1}{5}\sin^5 x + C.$$ ■

EXAMPLE 3 Evaluate

$$\int \sin^2 x \cos^4 x\, dx.$$

Solution

$$\int \sin^2 x \cos^4 x\, dx = \int \left(\frac{1 - \cos 2x}{2}\right)\left(\frac{1 + \cos 2x}{2}\right)^2 dx \qquad m \text{ and } n \text{ both even}$$

$$= \frac{1}{8}\int (1 - \cos 2x)(1 + 2\cos 2x + \cos^2 2x)\, dx$$

$$= \frac{1}{8}\int (1 + \cos 2x - \cos^2 2x - \cos^3 2x)\, dx$$

$$= \frac{1}{8}\left[x + \frac{1}{2}\sin 2x - \int (\cos^2 2x + \cos^3 2x)\, dx\right].$$

For the term involving $\cos^2 2x$ we use

$$\int \cos^2 2x\, dx = \frac{1}{2}\int (1 + \cos 4x)\, dx$$

$$= \frac{1}{2}\left(x + \frac{1}{4}\sin 4x\right). \qquad \text{Omitting the constant of integration until the final result}$$

For the $\cos^3 2x$ term we have

$$\int \cos^3 2x\, dx = \int (1 - \sin^2 2x)\cos 2x\, dx \qquad u = \sin 2x,\ du = 2\cos 2x\, dx$$

$$= \frac{1}{2}\int (1 - u^2)\, du = \frac{1}{2}\left(\sin 2x - \frac{1}{3}\sin^3 2x\right). \qquad \text{Again omitting } C$$

Combining everything and simplifying we get

$$\int \sin^2 x \cos^4 x\, dx = \frac{1}{16}\left(x - \frac{1}{4}\sin 4x + \frac{1}{3}\sin^3 2x\right) + C.$$ ■

Eliminating Square Roots

In the next example, we use the identity $\cos^2\theta = (1 + \cos 2\theta)/2$ to eliminate a square root.

EXAMPLE 4 Evaluate

$$\int_0^{\pi/4} \sqrt{1 + \cos 4x}\, dx.$$

Solution To eliminate the square root we use the identity

$$\cos^2\theta = \frac{1+\cos 2\theta}{2}, \qquad \text{or} \qquad 1+\cos 2\theta = 2\cos^2\theta.$$

With $\theta = 2x$, this becomes

$$1+\cos 4x = 2\cos^2 2x.$$

Therefore,

$$\begin{aligned}\int_0^{\pi/4}\sqrt{1+\cos 4x}\,dx &= \int_0^{\pi/4}\sqrt{2\cos^2 2x}\,dx = \int_0^{\pi/4}\sqrt{2}\sqrt{\cos^2 2x}\,dx\\ &= \sqrt{2}\int_0^{\pi/4}|\cos 2x|\,dx = \sqrt{2}\int_0^{\pi/4}\cos 2x\,dx \qquad \begin{matrix}\cos 2x \ge 0\\ \text{on } [0, \pi/4]\end{matrix}\\ &= \sqrt{2}\left[\frac{\sin 2x}{2}\right]_0^{\pi/4} = \frac{\sqrt{2}}{2}[1-0] = \frac{\sqrt{2}}{2}.\end{aligned}$$

■

Integrals of Powers of tan *x* and sec *x*

We know how to integrate the tangent and secant and their squares. To integrate higher powers we use the identities $\tan^2 x = \sec^2 x - 1$ and $\sec^2 x = \tan^2 x + 1$, and integrate by parts when necessary to reduce the higher powers to lower powers.

EXAMPLE 5 Evaluate

$$\int \tan^4 x\,dx.$$

Solution

$$\begin{aligned}\int \tan^4 x\,dx &= \int \tan^2 x\cdot\tan^2 x\,dx = \int \tan^2 x\cdot(\sec^2 x - 1)\,dx\\ &= \int \tan^2 x\sec^2 x\,dx - \int \tan^2 x\,dx\\ &= \int \tan^2 x\sec^2 x\,dx - \int (\sec^2 x - 1)\,dx\\ &= \int \tan^2 x\sec^2 x\,dx - \int \sec^2 x\,dx + \int dx.\end{aligned}$$

In the first integral, we let

$$u = \tan x, \qquad du = \sec^2 x\,dx$$

and have

$$\int u^2\,du = \frac{1}{3}u^3 + C_1.$$

The remaining integrals are standard forms, so

$$\int \tan^4 x\,dx = \frac{1}{3}\tan^3 x - \tan x + x + C.$$

■

EXAMPLE 6 Evaluate

$$\int \sec^3 x\, dx.$$

Solution We integrate by parts, using

$$u = \sec x, \qquad dv = \sec^2 x\, dx, \qquad v = \tan x, \qquad du = \sec x \tan x\, dx.$$

Then

$$\begin{aligned}\int \sec^3 x\, dx &= \sec x \tan x - \int (\tan x)(\sec x \tan x\, dx) \\ &= \sec x \tan x - \int (\sec^2 x - 1) \sec x\, dx \qquad \tan^2 x = \sec^2 x - 1 \\ &= \sec x \tan x + \int \sec x\, dx - \int \sec^3 x\, dx.\end{aligned}$$

Combining the two secant-cubed integrals gives

$$2\int \sec^3 x\, dx = \sec x \tan x + \int \sec x\, dx$$

and

$$\int \sec^3 x\, dx = \frac{1}{2} \sec x \tan x + \frac{1}{2} \ln |\sec x + \tan x| + C.$$ ■

Products of Sines and Cosines

The integrals

$$\int \sin mx \sin nx\, dx, \qquad \int \sin mx \cos nx\, dx, \qquad \text{and} \qquad \int \cos mx \cos nx\, dx$$

arise in many places where trigonometric functions are applied to problems in mathematics and science. We can evaluate these integrals through integration by parts, but two such integrations are required in each case. It is simpler to use the identities

$$\sin mx \sin nx = \frac{1}{2}[\cos (m - n)x - \cos (m + n)x], \tag{3}$$

$$\sin mx \cos nx = \frac{1}{2}[\sin (m - n)x + \sin (m + n)x], \tag{4}$$

$$\cos mx \cos nx = \frac{1}{2}[\cos (m - n)x + \cos (m + n)x]. \tag{5}$$

These identities come from the angle sum formulas for the sine and cosine functions (Section 1.3). They give functions whose antiderivatives are easily found.

EXAMPLE 7 Evaluate

$$\int \sin 3x \cos 5x\, dx.$$

Solution From Equation (4) with $m = 3$ and $n = 5$ we get

$$\begin{aligned}\int \sin 3x \cos 5x\, dx &= \frac{1}{2}\int [\sin(-2x) + \sin 8x]\, dx \\ &= \frac{1}{2}\int (\sin 8x - \sin 2x)\, dx \\ &= -\frac{\cos 8x}{16} + \frac{\cos 2x}{4} + C.\end{aligned}$$

EXERCISES 7.2

Evaluate the integrals in Exercises 1–14.

1. $\int_0^{\pi/2} \sin^5 x\, dx$

2. $\int_0^{\pi} \sin^5 \frac{x}{2}\, dx$

3. $\int_{-\pi/2}^{\pi/2} \cos^3 x\, dx$

4. $\int_0^{\pi/6} 3\cos^5 3x\, dx$

5. $\int_0^{\pi/2} \sin^7 y\, dy$

6. $\int_0^{\pi/2} 7\cos^7 t\, dt$

7. $\int_0^{\pi} 8\sin^4 x\, dx$

8. $\int_0^{1} 8\cos^4 2\pi x\, dx$

9. $\int_{-\pi/4}^{\pi/4} 16\sin^2 x\cos^2 x\, dx$

10. $\int_0^{\pi} 8\sin^4 y\cos^2 y\, dy$

11. $\int_0^{\pi/2} 35\sin^4 x\cos^3 x\, dx$

12. $\int_0^{\pi} \sin 2x\cos^2 2x\, dx$

13. $\int_0^{\pi/4} 8\cos^3 2\theta\sin 2\theta\, d\theta$

14. $\int_0^{\pi/2} \sin^2 2\theta\cos^3 2\theta\, d\theta$

Evaluate the integrals in Exercises 15–22.

15. $\int_0^{2\pi} \sqrt{\frac{1-\cos x}{2}}\, dx$

16. $\int_0^{\pi} \sqrt{1-\cos 2x}\, dx$

17. $\int_0^{\pi} \sqrt{1-\sin^2 t}\, dt$

18. $\int_0^{\pi} \sqrt{1-\cos^2 \theta}\, d\theta$

19. $\int_{-\pi/4}^{\pi/4} \sqrt{1+\tan^2 x}\, dx$

20. $\int_{-\pi/4}^{\pi/4} \sqrt{\sec^2 x - 1}\, dx$

21. $\int_0^{\pi/2} \theta\sqrt{1-\cos 2\theta}\, d\theta$

22. $\int_{-\pi}^{\pi} (1-\cos^2 t)^{3/2}\, dt$

Evaluate the integrals in Exercises 23–32.

23. $\int_{-\pi/3}^{0} 2\sec^3 x\, dx$

24. $\int e^x \sec^3 e^x\, dx$

25. $\int_0^{\pi/4} \sec^4 \theta\, d\theta$

26. $\int_0^{\pi/12} 3\sec^4 3x\, dx$

27. $\int_{\pi/4}^{\pi/2} \csc^4 \theta\, d\theta$

28. $\int_{\pi/2}^{\pi} 3\csc^4 \frac{\theta}{2}\, d\theta$

29. $\int_0^{\pi/4} 4\tan^3 x\, dx$

30. $\int_{-\pi/4}^{\pi/4} 6\tan^4 x\, dx$

31. $\int_{\pi/6}^{\pi/3} \cot^3 x\, dx$

32. $\int_{\pi/4}^{\pi/2} 8\cot^4 t\, dt$

Evaluate the integrals in Exercises 33–38.

33. $\int_{-\pi}^{0} \sin 3x\cos 2x\, dx$

34. $\int_0^{\pi/2} \sin 2x\cos 3x\, dx$

35. $\int_{-\pi}^{\pi} \sin 3x\sin 3x\, dx$

36. $\int_0^{\pi/2} \sin x\cos x\, dx$

37. $\int_0^{\pi} \cos 3x\cos 4x\, dx$

38. $\int_{-\pi/2}^{\pi/2} \cos x\cos 7x\, dx$

39. Surface area Find the area of the surface generated by revolving the arc

$$x = t^{2/3}, \quad y = t^2/2, \quad 0 \le t \le 2,$$

about the x-axis.

40. Arc length Find the length of the curve

$$y = \ln(\cos x), \quad 0 \le x \le \pi/3.$$

41. Arc length Find the length of the curve

$$y = \ln(\sec x), \quad 0 \le x \le \pi/4.$$

42. Center of gravity Find the center of gravity of the region bounded by the x-axis, the curve $y = \sec x$, and the lines $x = -\pi/4, x = \pi/4$.

43. Volume Find the volume generated by revolving one arch of the curve $y = \sin x$ about the x-axis.

44. Area Find the area between the x-axis and the curve $y = \sqrt{1+\cos 4x}$, $0 \le x \le \pi$.

7.3 Trigonometric Substitutions

Trigonometric substitutions can be effective in transforming integrals involving $\sqrt{a^2 - x^2}$, $\sqrt{a^2 + x^2}$, and $\sqrt{x^2 - a^2}$ into integrals we can evaluate directly.

The most common substitutions are $x = a \tan \theta$, $x = a \sin \theta$, and $x = a \sec \theta$. They come from the reference right triangles in Figure 7.2.

With $x = a \tan \theta$,

$$a^2 + x^2 = a^2 + a^2 \tan^2 \theta = a^2(1 + \tan^2 \theta) = a^2 \sec^2 \theta.$$

With $x = a \sin \theta$,

$$a^2 - x^2 = a^2 - a^2 \sin^2 \theta = a^2(1 - \sin^2 \theta) = a^2 \cos^2 \theta.$$

With $x = a \sec \theta$,

$$x^2 - a^2 = a^2 \sec^2 \theta - a^2 = a^2(\sec^2 \theta - 1) = a^2 \tan^2 \theta.$$

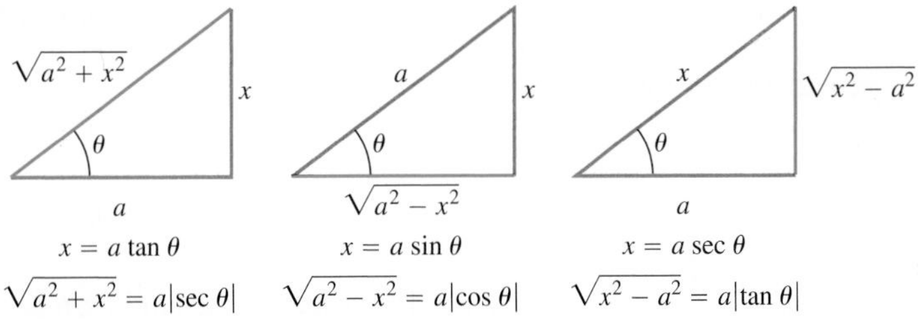

FIGURE 7.2 Reference triangles for the three basic substitutions identifying the sides labeled x and a for each substitution.

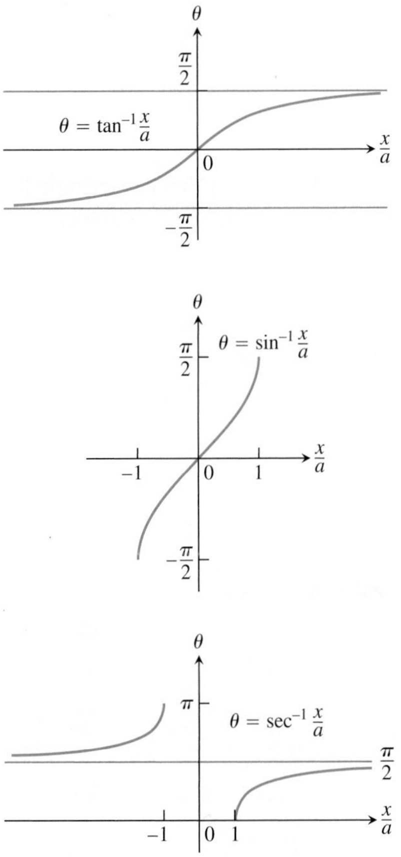

FIGURE 7.3 The arctangent, arcsine, and arcsecant of x/a, graphed as functions of x/a.

We want any substitution we use in an integration to be reversible so that we can change back to the original variable afterward. For example, if $x = a \tan \theta$, we want to be able to set $\theta = \tan^{-1}(x/a)$ after the integration takes place. If $x = a \sin \theta$, we want to be able to set $\theta = \sin^{-1}(x/a)$ when we're done, and similarly for $x = a \sec \theta$.

As we know from Section 1.5, the functions in these substitutions have inverses only for selected values of θ (Figure 7.3). For reversibility,

$$x = a \tan \theta \quad \text{requires} \quad \theta = \tan^{-1}\left(\frac{x}{a}\right) \quad \text{with} \quad -\frac{\pi}{2} < \theta < \frac{\pi}{2},$$

$$x = a \sin \theta \quad \text{requires} \quad \theta = \sin^{-1}\left(\frac{x}{a}\right) \quad \text{with} \quad -\frac{\pi}{2} \le \theta \le \frac{\pi}{2},$$

$$x = a \sec \theta \quad \text{requires} \quad \theta = \sec^{-1}\left(\frac{x}{a}\right) \quad \text{with} \quad \begin{cases} 0 \le \theta < \dfrac{\pi}{2} & \text{if } \dfrac{x}{a} \ge 1, \\ \dfrac{\pi}{2} < \theta \le \pi & \text{if } \dfrac{x}{a} \le -1. \end{cases}$$

To simplify calculations with the substitution $x = a \sec \theta$, we will restrict its use to integrals in which $x/a \ge 1$. This will place θ in $[0, \pi/2)$ and make $\tan \theta \ge 0$. We will then have $\sqrt{x^2 - a^2} = \sqrt{a^2 \tan^2 \theta} = |a \tan \theta| = a \tan \theta$, free of absolute values, provided $a > 0$.

EXAMPLE 1 Evaluate

$$\int \frac{dx}{\sqrt{4 + x^2}}.$$

Solution We set

$$x = 2\tan\theta, \qquad dx = 2\sec^2\theta\, d\theta, \qquad -\frac{\pi}{2} < \theta < \frac{\pi}{2},$$
$$4 + x^2 = 4 + 4\tan^2\theta = 4(1 + \tan^2\theta) = 4\sec^2\theta.$$

Then

$$\int \frac{dx}{\sqrt{4 + x^2}} = \int \frac{2\sec^2\theta\, d\theta}{\sqrt{4\sec^2\theta}} = \int \frac{\sec^2\theta\, d\theta}{|\sec\theta|} \qquad \sqrt{\sec^2\theta} = |\sec\theta|$$
$$= \int \sec\theta\, d\theta \qquad \sec\theta > 0 \text{ for } -\frac{\pi}{2} < \theta < \frac{\pi}{2}$$
$$= \ln|\sec\theta + \tan\theta| + C$$
$$= \ln\left|\frac{\sqrt{4 + x^2}}{2} + \frac{x}{2}\right| + C \qquad \text{From Fig. 7.4}$$
$$= \ln\left|\sqrt{4 + x^2} + x\right| + C'. \qquad \text{Taking } C' = C - \ln 2$$

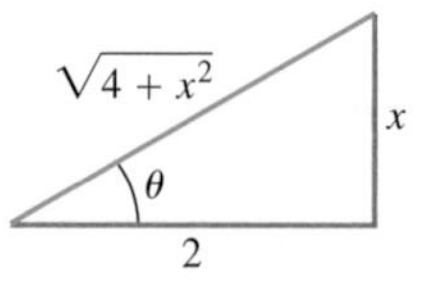

FIGURE 7.4 Reference triangle for $x = 2\tan\theta$ (Example 1):

$$\tan\theta = \frac{x}{2}$$

and

$$\sec\theta = \frac{\sqrt{4 + x^2}}{2}.$$

Notice how we expressed $\ln|\sec\theta + \tan\theta|$ in terms of x: We drew a reference triangle for the original substitution $x = 2\tan\theta$ (Figure 7.4) and read the ratios from the triangle. ■

EXAMPLE 2 Evaluate

$$\int \frac{x^2\, dx}{\sqrt{9 - x^2}}.$$

Solution We set

$$x = 3\sin\theta, \qquad dx = 3\cos\theta\, d\theta, \qquad -\frac{\pi}{2} < \theta < \frac{\pi}{2}$$
$$9 - x^2 = 9 - 9\sin^2\theta = 9(1 - \sin^2\theta) = 9\cos^2\theta.$$

Then

$$\int \frac{x^2\, dx}{\sqrt{9 - x^2}} = \int \frac{9\sin^2\theta \cdot 3\cos\theta\, d\theta}{|3\cos\theta|}$$
$$= 9\int \sin^2\theta\, d\theta \qquad \cos\theta > 0 \text{ for } -\frac{\pi}{2} < \theta < \frac{\pi}{2}$$
$$= 9\int \frac{1 - \cos 2\theta}{2}\, d\theta$$
$$= \frac{9}{2}\left(\theta - \frac{\sin 2\theta}{2}\right) + C$$

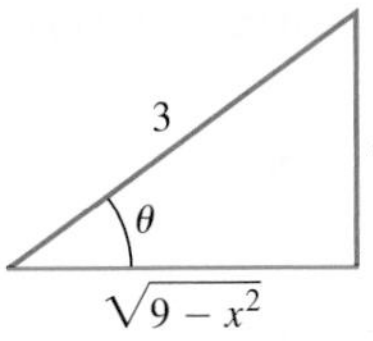

FIGURE 7.5 Reference triangle for $x = 3 \sin\theta$ (Example 2):

$$\sin\theta = \frac{x}{3}$$

and

$$\cos\theta = \frac{\sqrt{9 - x^2}}{3}.$$

$$= \frac{9}{2}(\theta - \sin\theta\cos\theta) + C \qquad \sin 2\theta = 2\sin\theta\cos\theta$$

$$= \frac{9}{2}\left(\sin^{-1}\frac{x}{3} - \frac{x}{3}\cdot\frac{\sqrt{9 - x^2}}{3}\right) + C \qquad \text{Fig. 7.5}$$

$$= \frac{9}{2}\sin^{-1}\frac{x}{3} - \frac{x}{2}\sqrt{9 - x^2} + C.$$

■

EXAMPLE 3 Evaluate

$$\int \frac{dx}{\sqrt{25x^2 - 4}}, \qquad x > \frac{2}{5}.$$

Solution We first rewrite the radical as

$$\sqrt{25x^2 - 4} = \sqrt{25\left(x^2 - \frac{4}{25}\right)}$$

$$= 5\sqrt{x^2 - \left(\frac{2}{5}\right)^2}$$

to put the radicand in the form $x^2 - a^2$. We then substitute

$$x = \frac{2}{5}\sec\theta, \qquad dx = \frac{2}{5}\sec\theta\tan\theta\,d\theta, \qquad 0 < \theta < \frac{\pi}{2}$$

$$x^2 - \left(\frac{2}{5}\right)^2 = \frac{4}{25}\sec^2\theta - \frac{4}{25}$$

$$= \frac{4}{25}(\sec^2\theta - 1) = \frac{4}{25}\tan^2\theta$$

$$\sqrt{x^2 - \left(\frac{2}{5}\right)^2} = \frac{2}{5}|\tan\theta| = \frac{2}{5}\tan\theta. \qquad \tan\theta > 0 \text{ for } 0 < \theta < \pi/2$$

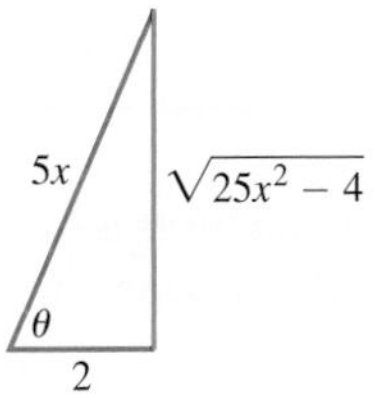

FIGURE 7.6 If $x = (2/5)\sec\theta$, $0 < \theta < \pi/2$, then $\theta = \sec^{-1}(5x/2)$, and we can read the values of the other trigonometric functions of θ from this right triangle (Example 3).

With these substitutions, we have

$$\int \frac{dx}{\sqrt{25x^2 - 4}} = \int \frac{dx}{5\sqrt{x^2 - (4/25)}} = \int \frac{(2/5)\sec\theta\tan\theta\,d\theta}{5\cdot(2/5)\tan\theta}$$

$$= \frac{1}{5}\int \sec\theta\,d\theta = \frac{1}{5}\ln|\sec\theta + \tan\theta| + C$$

$$= \frac{1}{5}\ln\left|\frac{5x}{2} + \frac{\sqrt{25x^2 - 4}}{2}\right| + C. \qquad \text{Fig. 7.6}$$

■

EXERCISES 7.3

Evaluate the integrals in Exercises 1–28.

1. $\displaystyle\int \frac{dy}{\sqrt{9 + y^2}}$

2. $\displaystyle\int \frac{3\,dy}{\sqrt{1 + 9y^2}}$

3. $\displaystyle\int_{-2}^{2} \frac{dx}{4 + x^2}$

4. $\displaystyle\int_{0}^{2} \frac{dx}{8 + 2x^2}$

5. $\displaystyle\int_{0}^{3/2} \frac{dx}{\sqrt{9 - x^2}}$

6. $\displaystyle\int_{0}^{1/2\sqrt{2}} \frac{2\,dx}{\sqrt{1 - 4x^2}}$

7. $\int \sqrt{25 - t^2}\, dt$

8. $\int \sqrt{1 - 9t^2}\, dt$

9. $\int \frac{dx}{\sqrt{4x^2 - 49}}, \quad x > \frac{7}{2}$

10. $\int \frac{5\, dx}{\sqrt{25x^2 - 9}}, \quad x > \frac{3}{5}$

11. $\int \frac{\sqrt{y^2 - 49}}{y}\, dy, \quad y > 7$

12. $\int \frac{\sqrt{y^2 - 25}}{y^3}\, dy, \quad y > 5$

13. $\int \frac{dx}{x^2\sqrt{x^2 - 1}}, \quad x > 1$

14. $\int \frac{2\, dx}{x^3\sqrt{x^2 - 1}}, \quad x > 1$

15. $\int \frac{x^3\, dx}{\sqrt{x^2 + 4}}$

16. $\int \frac{dx}{x^2\sqrt{x^2 + 1}}$

17. $\int \frac{8\, dw}{w^2\sqrt{4 - w^2}}$

18. $\int \frac{\sqrt{9 - w^2}}{w^2}\, dw$

19. $\int_0^{\sqrt{3}/2} \frac{4x^2\, dx}{(1 - x^2)^{3/2}}$

20. $\int_0^1 \frac{dx}{(4 - x^2)^{3/2}}$

21. $\int \frac{dx}{(x^2 - 1)^{3/2}}, \quad x > 1$

22. $\int \frac{x^2\, dx}{(x^2 - 1)^{5/2}}, \quad x > 1$

23. $\int \frac{(1 - x^2)^{3/2}}{x^6}\, dx$

24. $\int \frac{(1 - x^2)^{1/2}}{x^4}\, dx$

25. $\int \frac{8\, dx}{(4x^2 + 1)^2}$

26. $\int \frac{6\, dt}{(9t^2 + 1)^2}$

27. $\int \frac{v^2\, dv}{(1 - v^2)^{5/2}}$

28. $\int \frac{(1 - r^2)^{5/2}}{r^8}\, dr$

In Exercises 29–36, use an appropriate substitution and then a trigonometric substitution to evaluate the integrals.

29. $\int_0^{\ln 4} \frac{e^t\, dt}{\sqrt{e^{2t} + 9}}$

30. $\int_{\ln(3/4)}^{\ln(4/3)} \frac{e^t\, dt}{(1 + e^{2t})^{3/2}}$

31. $\int_{1/12}^{1/4} \frac{2\, dt}{\sqrt{t} + 4t\sqrt{t}}$

32. $\int_1^e \frac{dy}{y\sqrt{1 + (\ln y)^2}}$

33. $\int \frac{dx}{x\sqrt{x^2 - 1}}$

34. $\int \frac{dx}{1 + x^2}$

35. $\int \frac{x\, dx}{\sqrt{x^2 - 1}}$

36. $\int \frac{dx}{\sqrt{1 - x^2}}$

Solve the initial value problems in Exercises 37–40 for y as a function of x.

37. $x\frac{dy}{dx} = \sqrt{x^2 - 4}, \quad x \ge 2, \quad y(2) = 0$

38. $\sqrt{x^2 - 9}\frac{dy}{dx} = 1, \quad x > 3, \quad y(5) = \ln 3$

39. $(x^2 + 4)\frac{dy}{dx} = 3, \quad y(2) = 0$

40. $(x^2 + 1)^2\frac{dy}{dx} = \sqrt{x^2 + 1}, \quad y(0) = 1$

41. **Area** Find the area of the region in the first quadrant that is enclosed by the coordinate axes and the curve $y = \sqrt{9 - x^2}/3$.

42. **Volume** Find the volume of the solid generated by revolving about the x-axis the region in the first quadrant enclosed by the coordinate axes, the curve $y = 2/(1 + x^2)$, and the line $x = 1$.

7.4 Integration of Rational Functions by Partial Fractions

This section shows how to express a rational function (a quotient of polynomials) as a sum of simpler fractions, called *partial fractions*, which are easily integrated. For instance, the rational function $(5x - 3)/(x^2 - 2x - 3)$ can be rewritten as

$$\frac{5x - 3}{x^2 - 2x - 3} = \frac{2}{x + 1} + \frac{3}{x - 3},$$

which can be verified algebraically by placing the fractions on the right side over a common denominator $(x + 1)(x - 3)$. The skill acquired in writing rational functions as such a sum is useful in other settings as well (for instance, when using certain transform methods to solve differential equations). To integrate the rational function $(5x - 3)/(x^2 - 2x - 3)$ on the left side of our previous expression, we simply sum the integrals of the fractions on the right side:

$$\int \frac{5x - 3}{(x + 1)(x - 3)}\, dx = \int \frac{2}{x + 1}\, dx + \int \frac{3}{x - 3}\, dx$$
$$= 2\ln|x + 1| + 3\ln|x - 3| + C.$$

The method for rewriting rational functions as a sum of simpler fractions is called **the method of partial fractions**. In the case of the above example, it consists of finding constants A and B such that

$$\frac{5x-3}{x^2-2x-3} = \frac{A}{x+1} + \frac{B}{x-3}. \tag{1}$$

(Pretend for a moment that we do not know that $A = 2$ and $B = 3$ will work.) We call the fractions $A/(x+1)$ and $B/(x-3)$ **partial fractions** because their denominators are only part of the original denominator $x^2 - 2x - 3$. We call A and B **undetermined coefficients** until proper values for them have been found.

To find A and B, we first clear Equation (1) of fractions and regroup in powers of x, obtaining

$$5x - 3 = A(x-3) + B(x+1) = (A+B)x - 3A + B.$$

This will be an identity in x if and only if the coefficients of like powers of x on the two sides are equal:

$$A + B = 5, \qquad -3A + B = -3.$$

Solving these equations simultaneously gives $A = 2$ and $B = 3$.

General Description of the Method

Success in writing a rational function $f(x)/g(x)$ as a sum of partial fractions depends on two things:

- *The degree of $f(x)$ must be less than the degree of $g(x)$.* That is, the fraction must be proper. If it isn't, divide $f(x)$ by $g(x)$ and work with the remainder term. See Example 3 of this section.
- *We must know the factors of $g(x)$.* In theory, any polynomial with real coefficients can be written as a product of real linear factors and real quadratic factors. In practice, the factors may be hard to find.

Here is how we find the partial fractions of a proper fraction $f(x)/g(x)$ when the factors of g are known.

Method of Partial Fractions ($f(x)/g(x)$ Proper)

1. Let $x - r$ be a linear factor of $g(x)$. Suppose that $(x-r)^m$ is the highest power of $x - r$ that divides $g(x)$. Then, to this factor, assign the sum of the m partial fractions:

$$\frac{A_1}{x-r} + \frac{A_2}{(x-r)^2} + \cdots + \frac{A_m}{(x-r)^m}.$$

Do this for each distinct linear factor of $g(x)$.

continued

2. Let $x^2 + px + q$ be a quadratic factor of $g(x)$. Suppose that $(x^2 + px + q)^n$ is the highest power of this factor that divides $g(x)$ and that $x^2 + px + q$ has no real roots. Then, to this factor, assign the sum of the n partial fractions:

$$\frac{B_1x + C_1}{x^2 + px + q} + \frac{B_2x + C_2}{(x^2 + px + q)^2} + \cdots + \frac{B_nx + C_n}{(x^2 + px + q)^n}.$$

Do this for each distinct quadratic factor of $g(x)$.

3. Set the original fraction $f(x)/g(x)$ equal to the sum of all these partial fractions. Clear the resulting equation of fractions and arrange the terms in decreasing powers of x.

4. Equate the coefficients of corresponding powers of x and solve the resulting equations for the undetermined coefficients.

EXAMPLE 1 Evaluate

$$\int \frac{x^2 + 4x + 1}{(x - 1)(x + 1)(x + 3)}\,dx$$

using partial fractions.

Solution The partial fraction decomposition has the form

$$\frac{x^2 + 4x + 1}{(x - 1)(x + 1)(x + 3)} = \frac{A}{x - 1} + \frac{B}{x + 1} + \frac{C}{x + 3}.$$

To find the values of the undetermined coefficients A, B, and C we clear fractions and get

$$\begin{aligned} x^2 + 4x + 1 &= A(x + 1)(x + 3) + B(x - 1)(x + 3) + C(x - 1)(x + 1) \\ &= (A + B + C)x^2 + (4A + 2B)x + (3A - 3B - C). \end{aligned}$$

The polynomials on both sides of the above equation are identical, so we equate coefficients of like powers of x obtaining

$$\begin{aligned} &\text{Coefficient of } x^2: && A + B + C = 1 \\ &\text{Coefficient of } x^1: && 4A + 2B \quad\;\; = 4 \\ &\text{Coefficient of } x^0: && 3A - 3B - C = 1 \end{aligned}$$

There are several ways for solving such a system of linear equations for the unknowns A, B, and C, including elimination of variables, or the use of a calculator or computer. Whatever method is used, the solution is $A = 3/4$, $B = 1/2$, and $C = -1/4$. Hence we have

$$\begin{aligned} \int \frac{x^2 + 4x + 1}{(x - 1)(x + 1)(x + 3)}\,dx &= \int \left[\frac{3}{4}\frac{1}{x - 1} + \frac{1}{2}\frac{1}{x + 1} - \frac{1}{4}\frac{1}{x + 3}\right] dx \\ &= \frac{3}{4}\ln|x - 1| + \frac{1}{2}\ln|x + 1| - \frac{1}{4}\ln|x + 3| + K, \end{aligned}$$

where K is the arbitrary constant of integration (to avoid confusion with the undetermined coefficient we labeled as C). ■

EXAMPLE 2 Evaluate

$$\int \frac{6x+7}{(x+2)^2}\,dx.$$

Solution First we express the integrand as a sum of partial fractions with undetermined coefficients.

$$\begin{aligned}
\frac{6x+7}{(x+2)^2} &= \frac{A}{x+2} + \frac{B}{(x+2)^2} \\
6x+7 &= A(x+2)+B \qquad \text{Multiply both sides by } (x+2)^2. \\
&= Ax + (2A+B)
\end{aligned}$$

Equating coefficients of corresponding powers of x gives

$$A = 6 \quad \text{and} \quad 2A + B = 12 + B = 7, \quad \text{or} \quad A = 6 \quad \text{and} \quad B = -5.$$

Therefore,

$$\begin{aligned}
\int \frac{6x+7}{(x+2)^2}\,dx &= \int \left(\frac{6}{x+2} - \frac{5}{(x+2)^2}\right) dx \\
&= 6\int \frac{dx}{x+2} - 5\int (x+2)^{-2}\,dx \\
&= 6 \ln|x+2| + 5(x+2)^{-1} + C
\end{aligned}$$

■

EXAMPLE 3 Evaluate

$$\int \frac{2x^3 - 4x^2 - x - 3}{x^2 - 2x - 3}\,dx.$$

Solution First we divide the denominator into the numerator to get a polynomial plus a proper fraction.

$$\begin{array}{r}
2x \phantom{{}-4x^2-x-3} \\
x^2-2x-3 \overline{\smash{)}\,2x^3 - 4x^2 - x - 3} \\
\underline{2x^3 - 4x^2 - 6x} \phantom{{}-3} \\
5x - 3
\end{array}$$

Then we write the improper fraction as a polynomial plus a proper fraction.

$$\frac{2x^3 - 4x^2 - x - 3}{x^2 - 2x - 3} = 2x + \frac{5x - 3}{x^2 - 2x - 3}$$

We found the partial fraction decomposition of the fraction on the right in the opening example, so

$$\begin{aligned}
\int \frac{2x^3 - 4x^2 - x - 3}{x^2 - 2x - 3}\,dx &= \int 2x\,dx + \int \frac{5x-3}{x^2-2x-3}\,dx \\
&= \int 2x\,dx + \int \frac{2}{x+1}\,dx + \int \frac{3}{x-3}\,dx \\
&= x^2 + 2\ln|x+1| + 3\ln|x-3| + C.
\end{aligned}$$

■

A quadratic polynomial is **irreducible** if it cannot be written as the product of two linear factors with real coefficients. That is, the polynomial has no real roots.

EXAMPLE 4 Evaluate

$$\int \frac{-2x + 4}{(x^2 + 1)(x - 1)^2}\,dx$$

using partial fractions.

Solution The denominator has an irreducible quadratic factor as well as a repeated linear factor, so we write

$$\frac{-2x + 4}{(x^2 + 1)(x - 1)^2} = \frac{Ax + B}{x^2 + 1} + \frac{C}{x - 1} + \frac{D}{(x - 1)^2}. \tag{2}$$

Clearing the equation of fractions gives

$$\begin{aligned} -2x + 4 &= (Ax + B)(x - 1)^2 + C(x - 1)(x^2 + 1) + D(x^2 + 1) \\ &= (A + C)x^3 + (-2A + B - C + D)x^2 \\ &\quad + (A - 2B + C)x + (B - C + D). \end{aligned}$$

Equating coefficients of like terms gives

$$\begin{aligned} &\text{Coefficients of } x^3: & 0 &= A + C \\ &\text{Coefficients of } x^2: & 0 &= -2A + B - C + D \\ &\text{Coefficients of } x^1: & -2 &= A - 2B + C \\ &\text{Coefficients of } x^0: & 4 &= B - C + D \end{aligned}$$

We solve these equations simultaneously to find the values of A, B, C, and D:

$$\begin{aligned} &-4 = -2A, \quad A = 2 && \text{Subtract fourth equation from second.} \\ &C = -A = -2 && \text{From the first equation} \\ &B = 1 && A = 2 \text{ and } C = -2 \text{ in third equation.} \\ &D = 4 - B + C = 1. && \text{From the fourth equation} \end{aligned}$$

We substitute these values into Equation (2), obtaining

$$\frac{-2x + 4}{(x^2 + 1)(x - 1)^2} = \frac{2x + 1}{x^2 + 1} - \frac{2}{x - 1} + \frac{1}{(x - 1)^2}.$$

Finally, using the expansion above we can integrate:

$$\begin{aligned} \int \frac{-2x + 4}{(x^2 + 1)(x - 1)^2}\,dx &= \int \left(\frac{2x + 1}{x^2 + 1} - \frac{2}{x - 1} + \frac{1}{(x - 1)^2}\right) dx \\ &= \int \left(\frac{2x}{x^2 + 1} + \frac{1}{x^2 + 1} - \frac{2}{x - 1} + \frac{1}{(x - 1)^2}\right) dx \\ &= \ln(x^2 + 1) + \tan^{-1} x - 2\ln|x - 1| - \frac{1}{x - 1} + C. \quad \blacksquare \end{aligned}$$

EXAMPLE 5 Evaluate

$$\int \frac{dx}{x(x^2+1)^2}.$$

Solution The form of the partial fraction decomposition is

$$\frac{1}{x(x^2+1)^2} = \frac{A}{x} + \frac{Bx+C}{x^2+1} + \frac{Dx+E}{(x^2+1)^2}$$

Multiplying by $x(x^2+1)^2$, we have

$$\begin{aligned} 1 &= A(x^2+1)^2 + (Bx+C)x(x^2+1) + (Dx+E)x \\ &= A(x^4+2x^2+1) + B(x^4+x^2) + C(x^3+x) + Dx^2 + Ex \\ &= (A+B)x^4 + Cx^3 + (2A+B+D)x^2 + (C+E)x + A \end{aligned}$$

If we equate coefficients, we get the system

$$A+B=0, \qquad C=0, \qquad 2A+B+D=0, \qquad C+E=0, \qquad A=1.$$

Solving this system gives $A=1$, $B=-1$, $C=0$, $D=-1$, and $E=0$. Thus,

$$\begin{aligned} \int \frac{dx}{x(x^2+1)^2} &= \int \left[\frac{1}{x} + \frac{-x}{x^2+1} + \frac{-x}{(x^2+1)^2}\right] dx \\ &= \int \frac{dx}{x} - \int \frac{x\,dx}{x^2+1} - \int \frac{x\,dx}{(x^2+1)^2} \\ &= \int \frac{dx}{x} - \frac{1}{2}\int \frac{du}{u} - \frac{1}{2}\int \frac{du}{u^2} \qquad \begin{array}{l} u = x^2+1, \\ du = 2x\,dx \end{array} \\ &= \ln|x| - \frac{1}{2}\ln|u| + \frac{1}{2u} + K \\ &= \ln|x| - \frac{1}{2}\ln(x^2+1) + \frac{1}{2(x^2+1)} + K \\ &= \ln\frac{|x|}{\sqrt{x^2+1}} + \frac{1}{2(x^2+1)} + K. \end{aligned}$$

EXERCISES 7.4

Expand the quotients in Exercises 1–8 by partial fractions.

1. $\dfrac{5x-13}{(x-3)(x-2)}$

2. $\dfrac{5x-7}{x^2-3x+2}$

3. $\dfrac{x+4}{(x+1)^2}$

4. $\dfrac{2x+2}{x^2-2x+1}$

5. $\dfrac{z+1}{z^2(z-1)}$

6. $\dfrac{z}{z^3-z^2-6z}$

7. $\dfrac{t^2+8}{t^2-5t+6}$

8. $\dfrac{t^4+9}{t^4+9t^2}$

In Exercises 9–16, express the integrands as a sum of partial fractions and evaluate the integrals.

9. $\displaystyle\int \frac{dx}{1-x^2}$

10. $\displaystyle\int \frac{dx}{x^2+2x}$

11. $\displaystyle\int \frac{x+4}{x^2+5x-6}\,dx$

12. $\displaystyle\int \frac{2x+1}{x^2-7x+12}\,dx$

13. $\displaystyle\int_4^8 \frac{y\,dy}{y^2 - 2y - 3}$

14. $\displaystyle\int_{1/2}^1 \frac{y + 4}{y^2 + y}\,dy$

15. $\displaystyle\int \frac{dt}{t^3 + t^2 - 2t}$

16. $\displaystyle\int \frac{x + 3}{2x^3 - 8x}\,dx$

In Exercises 17–20, express the integrands as a sum of partial fractions and evaluate the integrals.

17. $\displaystyle\int_0^1 \frac{x^3\,dx}{x^2 + 2x + 1}$

18. $\displaystyle\int_{-1}^0 \frac{x^3\,dx}{x^2 - 2x + 1}$

19. $\displaystyle\int \frac{dx}{(x^2 - 1)^2}$

20. $\displaystyle\int \frac{x^2\,dx}{(x - 1)(x^2 + 2x + 1)}$

In Exercises 21–28, express the integrands as a sum of partial fractions and evaluate the integrals.

21. $\displaystyle\int_0^1 \frac{dx}{(x + 1)(x^2 + 1)}$

22. $\displaystyle\int_1^{\sqrt{3}} \frac{3t^2 + t + 4}{t^3 + t}\,dt$

23. $\displaystyle\int \frac{y^2 + 2y + 1}{(y^2 + 1)^2}\,dy$

24. $\displaystyle\int \frac{8x^2 + 8x + 2}{(4x^2 + 1)^2}\,dx$

25. $\displaystyle\int \frac{2s + 2}{(s^2 + 1)(s - 1)^3}\,ds$

26. $\displaystyle\int \frac{s^4 + 81}{s(s^2 + 9)^2}\,ds$

27. $\displaystyle\int \frac{2\theta^3 + 5\theta^2 + 8\theta + 4}{(\theta^2 + 2\theta + 2)^2}\,d\theta$

28. $\displaystyle\int \frac{\theta^4 - 4\theta^3 + 2\theta^2 - 3\theta + 1}{(\theta^2 + 1)^3}\,d\theta$

In Exercises 29–34, perform long division on the integrand, write the proper fraction as a sum of partial fractions, and then evaluate the integral.

29. $\displaystyle\int \frac{2x^3 - 2x^2 + 1}{x^2 - x}\,dx$

30. $\displaystyle\int \frac{x^4}{x^2 - 1}\,dx$

31. $\displaystyle\int \frac{9x^3 - 3x + 1}{x^3 - x^2}\,dx$

32. $\displaystyle\int \frac{16x^3}{4x^2 - 4x + 1}\,dx$

33. $\displaystyle\int \frac{y^4 + y^2 - 1}{y^3 + y}\,dy$

34. $\displaystyle\int \frac{2y^4}{y^3 - y^2 + y - 1}\,dy$

Evaluate the integrals in Exercises 35–40.

35. $\displaystyle\int \frac{e^t\,dt}{e^{2t} + 3e^t + 2}$

36. $\displaystyle\int \frac{e^{4t} + 2e^{2t} - e^t}{e^{2t} + 1}\,dt$

37. $\displaystyle\int \frac{\cos y\,dy}{\sin^2 y + \sin y - 6}$

38. $\displaystyle\int \frac{\sin\theta\,d\theta}{\cos^2\theta + \cos\theta - 2}$

39. $\displaystyle\int \frac{(x - 2)^2 \tan^{-1}(2x) - 12x^3 - 3x}{(4x^2 + 1)(x - 2)^2}\,dx$

40. $\displaystyle\int \frac{(x + 1)^2 \tan^{-1}(3x) + 9x^3 + x}{(9x^2 + 1)(x + 1)^2}\,dx$

Solve the initial value problems in Exercises 41–44 for x as a function of t.

41. $(t^2 - 3t + 2)\dfrac{dx}{dt} = 1 \quad (t > 2), \quad x(3) = 0$

42. $(3t^4 + 4t^2 + 1)\dfrac{dx}{dt} = 2\sqrt{3}, \quad x(1) = -\pi\sqrt{3}/4$

43. $(t^2 + 2t)\dfrac{dx}{dt} = 2x + 2 \quad (t, x > 0), \quad x(1) = 1$

44. $(t + 1)\dfrac{dx}{dt} = x^2 + 1 \quad (t > -1), \quad x(0) = \pi/4$

In Exercises 45 and 46, find the volume of the solid generated by revolving the shaded region about the indicated axis.

45. The x-axis

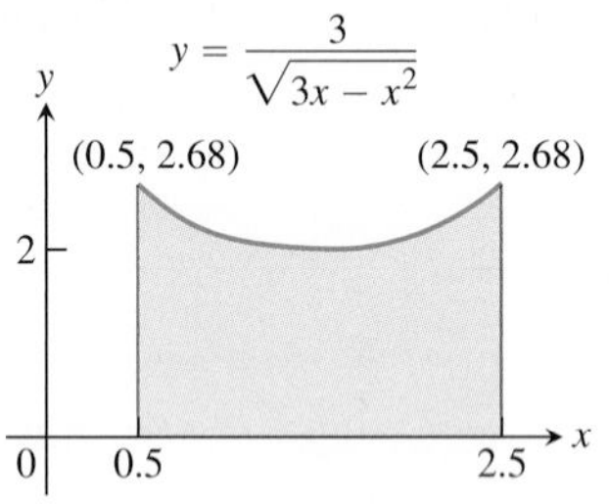

46. The y-axis

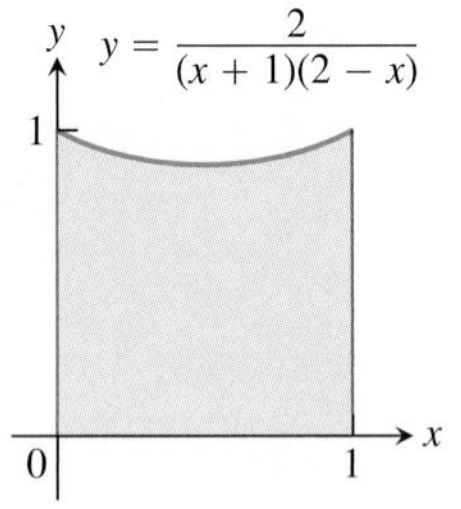

T **47.** Find, to two decimal places, the x-coordinate of the centroid of the region in the first quadrant bounded by the x-axis, the curve $y = \tan^{-1} x$, and the line $x = \sqrt{3}$.

T **48.** Find the x-coordinate of the centroid of this region to two decimal places.

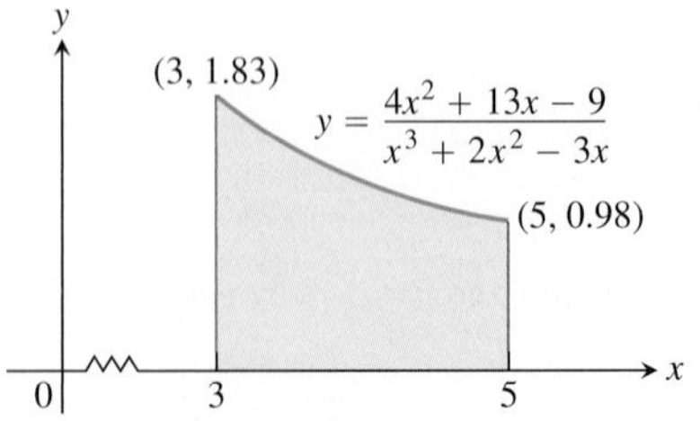

49. Social diffusion Sociologists sometimes use the phrase "social diffusion" to describe the way information spreads through a population. The information might be a rumor, a cultural fad, or news about a technical innovation. In a sufficiently large population, the number of people x who have the information is treated as a differentiable function of time t, and the rate of diffusion, dx/dt, is assumed to be proportional to the number of people who have the information times the number of people who do not. This leads to the equation

$$\frac{dx}{dt} = kx(N - x),$$

where N is the number of people in the population.

Suppose t is in days, $k = 1/250$, and two people start a rumor at time $t = 0$ in a population of $N = 1000$ people.

a. Find x as a function of t.

b. When will half the population have heard the rumor? (This is when the rumor will be spreading the fastest.)

50. Second-order chemical reactions Many chemical reactions are the result of the interaction of two molecules that undergo a change to produce a new product. The rate of the reaction typically depends on the concentrations of the two kinds of molecules. If a is the amount of substance A and b is the amount of substance B at time $t = 0$, and if x is the amount of product at time t, then the rate of formation of x may be given by the differential equation

$$\frac{dx}{dt} = k(a - x)(b - x),$$

or

$$\frac{1}{(a - x)(b - x)}\frac{dx}{dt} = k,$$

where k is a constant for the reaction. Integrate both sides of this equation to obtain a relation between x and t (**a**) if $a = b$, and (**b**) if $a \neq b$. Assume in each case that $x = 0$ when $t = 0$.

7.5 Integral Tables and Computer Algebra Systems

In this section we discuss how to use tables and computer algebra systems to evaluate integrals.

Integral Tables

A Brief Table of Integrals is provided at the back of the book, after the index. (More extensive tables appear in compilations such as *CRC Mathematical Tables*, which contain thousands of integrals.) The integration formulas are stated in terms of constants a, b, c, m, n, and so on. These constants can usually assume any real value and need not be integers. Occasional limitations on their values are stated with the formulas. Formula 5 requires $n \neq -1$, for example, and Formula 11 requires $n \neq 2$.

The formulas also assume that the constants do not take on values that require dividing by zero or taking even roots of negative numbers. For example, Formula 8 assumes that $a \neq 0$, and Formulas 13(a) and (b) cannot be used unless b is positive.

EXAMPLE 1 Find

$$\int x(2x + 5)^{-1}\,dx.$$

Solution We use Formula 8 (not 7, which requires $n \neq -1$):

$$\int x(ax + b)^{-1}\,dx = \frac{x}{a} - \frac{b}{a^2}\ln|ax + b| + C.$$

With $a = 2$ and $b = 5$, we have

$$\int x(2x + 5)^{-1}\,dx = \frac{x}{2} - \frac{5}{4}\ln|2x + 5| + C.$$ ■

EXAMPLE 2 Find

$$\int \frac{dx}{x\sqrt{2x - 4}}.$$

Solution We use Formula 13(a):

$$\int \frac{dx}{x\sqrt{ax - b}} = \frac{2}{\sqrt{b}} \tan^{-1} \sqrt{\frac{ax - b}{b}} + C.$$

With $a = 2$ and $b = 4$, we have

$$\int \frac{dx}{x\sqrt{2x - 4}} = \frac{2}{\sqrt{4}} \tan^{-1} \sqrt{\frac{2x - 4}{4}} + C = \tan^{-1} \sqrt{\frac{x - 2}{2}} + C. \qquad \blacksquare$$

EXAMPLE 3 Find

$$\int x \sin^{-1} x \, dx.$$

Solution We use Formula 99:

$$\int x^n \sin^{-1} ax \, dx = \frac{x^{n+1}}{n + 1} \sin^{-1} ax - \frac{a}{n + 1} \int \frac{x^{n+1} \, dx}{\sqrt{1 - a^2x^2}}, \qquad n \neq -1.$$

With $n = 1$ and $a = 1$, we have

$$\int x \sin^{-1} x \, dx = \frac{x^2}{2} \sin^{-1} x - \frac{1}{2} \int \frac{x^2 \, dx}{\sqrt{1 - x^2}}.$$

The integral on the right is found in the table as Formula 33:

$$\int \frac{x^2}{\sqrt{a^2 - x^2}} \, dx = \frac{a^2}{2} \sin^{-1}\left(\frac{x}{a}\right) - \frac{1}{2} x\sqrt{a^2 - x^2} + C.$$

With $a = 1$,

$$\int \frac{x^2 \, dx}{\sqrt{1 - x^2}} = \frac{1}{2} \sin^{-1} x - \frac{1}{2} x\sqrt{1 - x^2} + C.$$

The combined result is

$$\begin{aligned}
\int x \sin^{-1} x \, dx &= \frac{x^2}{2} \sin^{-1} x - \frac{1}{2}\left(\frac{1}{2} \sin^{-1} x - \frac{1}{2} x\sqrt{1 - x^2} + C\right) \\
&= \left(\frac{x^2}{2} - \frac{1}{4}\right) \sin^{-1} x + \frac{1}{4} x\sqrt{1 - x^2} + C'. \qquad \blacksquare
\end{aligned}$$

Reduction Formulas

The time required for repeated integrations by parts can sometimes be shortened by applying formulas like

$$\int \tan^n x \, dx = \frac{1}{n - 1} \tan^{n-1} x - \int \tan^{n-2} x \, dx \tag{1}$$

$$\int (\ln x)^n\,dx = x(\ln x)^n - n\int (\ln x)^{n-1}\,dx \tag{2}$$

$$\int \sin^n x \cos^m x\,dx = -\frac{\sin^{n-1} x \cos^{m+1} x}{m+n} + \frac{n-1}{m+n}\int \sin^{n-2} x \cos^m x\,dx \qquad (n \neq -m). \tag{3}$$

Formulas like these are called **reduction formulas** because they replace an integral containing some power of a function with an integral of the same form with the power reduced. By applying such a formula repeatedly, we can eventually express the original integral in terms of a power low enough to be evaluated directly.

EXAMPLE 4 Find

$$\int \tan^5 x\,dx.$$

Solution We apply Equation (1) with $n = 5$ to get

$$\int \tan^5 x\,dx = \frac{1}{4}\tan^4 x - \int \tan^3 x\,dx.$$

We then apply Equation (1) again, with $n = 3$, to evaluate the remaining integral:

$$\int \tan^3 x\,dx = \frac{1}{2}\tan^2 x - \int \tan x\,dx = \frac{1}{2}\tan^2 x + \ln|\cos x| + C.$$

The combined result is

$$\int \tan^5 x\,dx = \frac{1}{4}\tan^4 x - \frac{1}{2}\tan^2 x - \ln|\cos x| + C'.$$

As their form suggests, reduction formulas are derived by integration by parts. (See Example 5 in Section 7.1.)

Integration with a CAS

A powerful capability of computer algebra systems is their ability to integrate symbolically. This is performed with the **integrate command** specified by the particular system (for example, **int** in Maple, **Integrate** in Mathematica).

EXAMPLE 5 Suppose that you want to evaluate the indefinite integral of the function

$$f(x) = x^2\sqrt{a^2 + x^2}.$$

Using Maple, you first define or name the function:

```
> f := x^2 * sqrt (a^2 + x^2);
```

Then you use the integrate command on f, identifying the variable of integration:

```
> int(f, x);
```

Maple returns the answer

$$\frac{1}{4}x(a^2 + x^2)^{3/2} - \frac{1}{8}a^2x\sqrt{a^2 + x^2} - \frac{1}{8}a^4 \ln\left(x + \sqrt{a^2 + x^2}\right).$$

If you want to see if the answer can be simplified, enter

> simplify(%);

Maple returns

$$\frac{1}{8}a^2x\sqrt{a^2 + x^2} + \frac{1}{4}x^3\sqrt{a^2 + x^2} - \frac{1}{8}a^4 \ln\left(x + \sqrt{a^2 + x^2}\right).$$

If you want the definite integral for $0 \le x \le \pi/2$, you can use the format

> int(f, x = 0..Pi/2);

Maple will return the expression

$$\frac{1}{64}\pi(4a^2 + \pi^2)^{(3/2)} - \frac{1}{32}a^2\pi\sqrt{4a^2 + \pi^2} + \frac{1}{8}a^4 \ln(2) - \frac{1}{8}a^4 \ln\left(\pi + \sqrt{4a^2 + \pi^2}\right) + \frac{1}{16}a^4 \ln(a^2).$$

You can also find the definite integral for a particular value of the constant a:

> a:= 1;
> int(f, x = 0..1);

Maple returns the numerical answer

$$\frac{3}{8}\sqrt{2} + \frac{1}{8}\ln\left(\sqrt{2} - 1\right).$$ ■

EXAMPLE 6 Use a CAS to find

$$\int \sin^2 x \cos^3 x \, dx.$$

Solution With Maple, we have the entry

> int ((sin^2)(x) * (cos^3)(x), x);

with the immediate return

$$-\frac{1}{5}\sin(x)\cos(x)^4 + \frac{1}{15}\cos(x)^2\sin(x) + \frac{2}{15}\sin(x).$$ ■

Computer algebra systems vary in how they process integrations. We used Maple in Examples 5 and 6. Mathematica would have returned somewhat different results:

1. In Example 5, given

   In [1]:= Integrate [x^2 * Sqrt [a^2 + x^2], x]

   Mathematica returns

   $$Out\ [1]= \sqrt{a^2 + x^2}\left(\frac{a^2x}{8} + \frac{x^3}{4}\right) - \frac{1}{8}a^4 \operatorname{Log}\left[x + \sqrt{a^2 + x^2}\right]$$

without having to simplify an intermediate result. The answer is close to Formula 22 in the integral tables.

2. The Mathematica answer to the integral

In [2]:= Integrate [Sin [*x*]^2 * Cos [*x*]^3, *x*]

in Example 6 is

$$\textit{Out [2]=}\ \frac{\text{Sin}\,[x]}{8} - \frac{1}{48}\,\text{Sin}\,[3\,x] - \frac{1}{80}\,\text{Sin}\,[5\,x]$$

differing from the Maple answer.

Although a CAS is very powerful and can aid us in solving difficult problems, each CAS has its own limitations. There are even situations where a CAS may further complicate a problem (in the sense of producing an answer that is extremely difficult to use or interpret). Note, too, that neither Maple nor Mathematica return an arbitrary constant $+C$. On the other hand, a little mathematical thinking on your part may reduce the problem to one that is quite easy to handle. We provide an example in Exercise 63.

Nonelementary Integrals

The development of computers and calculators that find antiderivatives by symbolic manipulation has led to a renewed interest in determining which antiderivatives can be expressed as finite combinations of elementary functions (the functions we have been studying) and which cannot. Integrals of functions that do not have elementary antiderivatives are called **nonelementary** integrals. They require infinite series (Chapter 8) or numerical methods for their evaluation, which give only an approximation. Examples of nonelementary integrals include the error function (which measures the probability of random errors)

$$\text{erf}\,(x) = \frac{2}{\sqrt{\pi}}\int_0^x e^{-t^2}\,dt$$

and integrals such as

$$\int \sin x^2\,dx \qquad \text{and} \qquad \int \sqrt{1 + x^4}\,dx$$

that arise in engineering and physics. These and a number of others, such as

$$\int \frac{e^x}{x}\,dx, \qquad \int e^{(e^x)}\,dx, \qquad \int \frac{1}{\ln x}\,dx, \qquad \int \ln\,(\ln x)\,dx, \qquad \int \frac{\sin x}{x}\,dx,$$

$$\int \sqrt{1 - k^2 \sin^2 x}\,dx, \qquad 0 < k < 1,$$

look so easy they tempt us to try them just to see how they turn out. It can be proved, however, that there is no way to express these integrals as finite combinations of elementary functions. The same applies to integrals that can be changed into these by substitution. The integrands all have antiderivatives, as a consequence of the Fundamental Theorem of Calculus, Part 1, because they are continuous. However, none of the antiderivatives is elementary.

None of the integrals you are asked to evaluate in the present chapter falls into this category, but you may encounter nonelementary integrals in your other work.

EXERCISES 7.5

Use the table of integrals at the back of the book to evaluate the integrals in Exercises 1–26.

1. $\int \frac{dx}{x\sqrt{x-3}}$

2. $\int \frac{dx}{x\sqrt{x+4}}$

3. $\int \frac{x\,dx}{\sqrt{x-2}}$

4. $\int \frac{x\,dx}{(2x+3)^{3/2}}$

5. $\int x\sqrt{2x-3}\,dx$

6. $\int x(7x+5)^{3/2}\,dx$

7. $\int \frac{\sqrt{9-4x}}{x^2}\,dx$

8. $\int \frac{dx}{x^2\sqrt{4x-9}}$

9. $\int x\sqrt{4x-x^2}\,dx$

10. $\int \frac{\sqrt{x-x^2}}{x}\,dx$

11. $\int \frac{dx}{x\sqrt{7+x^2}}$

12. $\int \frac{dx}{x\sqrt{7-x^2}}$

13. $\int \frac{\sqrt{4-x^2}}{x}\,dx$

14. $\int \frac{\sqrt{x^2-4}}{x}\,dx$

15. $\int e^{2t}\cos 3t\,dt$

16. $\int e^{-3t}\sin 4t\,dt$

17. $\int x\cos^{-1}x\,dx$

18. $\int x\tan^{-1}x\,dx$

19. $\int x^2\tan^{-1}x\,dx$

20. $\int \frac{\tan^{-1}x}{x^2}\,dx$

21. $\int \sin 3x\cos 2x\,dx$

22. $\int \sin 2x\cos 3x\,dx$

23. $\int 8\sin 4t\sin\frac{t}{2}\,dt$

24. $\int \sin\frac{t}{3}\sin\frac{t}{6}\,dt$

25. $\int \cos\frac{\theta}{3}\cos\frac{\theta}{4}\,d\theta$

26. $\int \cos\frac{\theta}{2}\cos 7\theta\,d\theta$

In Exercises 27–36, use a substitution to change the integral into one you can find in the table. Then evaluate the integral.

27. $\int \frac{x^3+x+1}{(x^2+1)^2}\,dx$

28. $\int \frac{x^2+6x}{(x^2+3)^2}\,dx$

29. $\int \sin^{-1}\sqrt{x}\,dx$

30. $\int \frac{\cos^{-1}\sqrt{x}}{\sqrt{x}}\,dx$

31. $\int \frac{\sqrt{x}}{\sqrt{1-x}}\,dx$

32. $\int \frac{\sqrt{2-x}}{\sqrt{x}}\,dx$

33. $\int \cot t\sqrt{1-\sin^2 t}\,dt, \quad 0 < t < \pi/2$

34. $\int \frac{dt}{\tan t\sqrt{4-\sin^2 t}}$

35. $\int \frac{dy}{y\sqrt{3+(\ln y)^2}}$

36. $\int \tan^{-1}\sqrt{y}\,dy$

Use reduction formulas to evaluate the integrals in Exercises 37–46.

37. $\int \sin^5 2x\,dx$

38. $\int 8\cos^4 2\pi t\,dt$

39. $\int \sin^2 2\theta\cos^3 2\theta\,d\theta$

40. $\int 2\sin^2 t\sec^4 t\,dt$

41. $\int 4\tan^3 2x\,dx$

42. $\int 8\cot^4 t\,dt$

43. $\int 2\sec^3 \pi x\,dx$

44. $\int 3\sec^4 3x\,dx$

45. $\int \csc^5 x\,dx$

46. $\int 16x^3(\ln x)^2\,dx$

Evaluate the integrals in Exercises 47–52 by making a substitution (possibly trigonometric) and then applying a reduction formula.

47. $\int e^t\sec^3(e^t-1)\,dt$

48. $\int \frac{\csc^3\sqrt{\theta}}{\sqrt{\theta}}\,d\theta$

49. $\int_0^1 2\sqrt{x^2+1}\,dx$

50. $\int_0^{\sqrt{3}/2} \frac{dy}{(1-y^2)^{5/2}}$

51. $\int_1^2 \frac{(r^2-1)^{3/2}}{r}\,dr$

52. $\int_0^{1/\sqrt{3}} \frac{dt}{(t^2+1)^{7/2}}$

53. **Surface area** Find the area of the surface generated by revolving the curve $y = \sqrt{x^2+2}$, $0 \le x \le \sqrt{2}$, about the x-axis.

54. **Arc length** Find the length of the curve $y = x^2$, $0 \le x \le \sqrt{3}/2$.

55. **Centroid** Find the centroid of the region cut from the first quadrant by the curve $y = 1/\sqrt{x+1}$ and the line $x = 3$.

56. **Moment about y-axis** A thin plate of constant density $\delta = 1$ occupies the region enclosed by the curve $y = 36/(2x+3)$ and the line $x = 3$ in the first quadrant. Find the moment of the plate about the y-axis.

T 57. Use the integral table and a calculator to find to two decimal places the area of the surface generated by revolving the curve $y = x^2$, $-1 \le x \le 1$, about the x-axis.

58. **Volume** The head of your firm's accounting department has asked you to find a formula she can use in a computer program to calculate the year-end inventory of gasoline in the company's tanks. A typical tank is shaped like a right circular cylinder of radius r and length L, mounted horizontally, as shown here. The data come to the accounting office as depth measurements taken with a vertical measuring stick marked in centimeters.

a. Show, in the notation of the figure here, that the volume of gasoline that fills the tank to a depth d is

$$V = 2L\int_{-r}^{-r+d} \sqrt{r^2-y^2}\,dy.$$

b. Evaluate the integral.

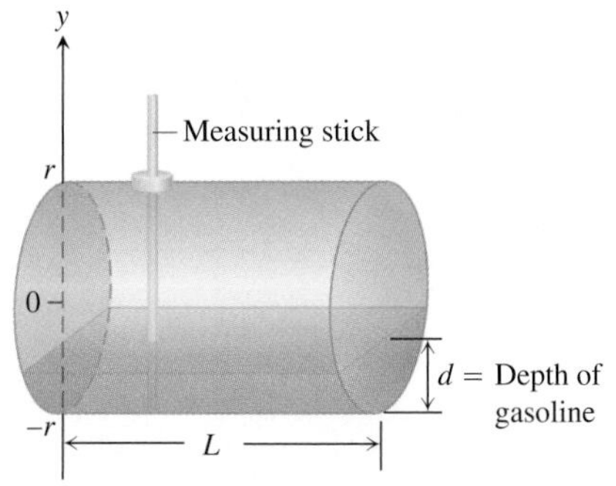

59. What is the largest value

$$\int_a^b \sqrt{x - x^2}\, dx$$

can have for any a and b? Give reasons for your answer.

60. What is the largest value

$$\int_a^b x\sqrt{2x - x^2}\, dx$$

can have for any a and b? Give reasons for your answer.

COMPUTER EXPLORATIONS

In Exercises 61 and 62, use a CAS to perform the integrations.

61. Evaluate the integrals

a. $\int x \ln x\, dx$ **b.** $\int x^2 \ln x\, dx$ **c.** $\int x^3 \ln x\, dx.$

d. What pattern do you see? Predict the formula for $\int x^4 \ln x\, dx$ and then see if you are correct by evaluating it with a CAS.

e. What is the formula for $\int x^n \ln x\, dx$, $n \geq 1$? Check your answer using a CAS.

62. Evaluate the integrals

a. $\int \frac{\ln x}{x^2}\, dx$ **b.** $\int \frac{\ln x}{x^3}\, dx$ **c.** $\int \frac{\ln x}{x^4}\, dx.$

d. What pattern do you see? Predict the formula for

$$\int \frac{\ln x}{x^5}\, dx$$

and then see if you are correct by evaluating it with a CAS.

e. What is the formula for

$$\int \frac{\ln x}{x^n}\, dx, \quad n \geq 2?$$

Check your answer using a CAS.

63. a. Use a CAS to evaluate

$$\int_0^{\pi/2} \frac{\sin^n x}{\sin^n x + \cos^n x}\, dx$$

where n is an arbitrary positive integer. Does your CAS find the result?

b. In succession, find the integral when $n = 1, 2, 3, 5, 7$. Comment on the complexity of the results.

c. Now substitute $x = (\pi/2) - u$ and add the new and old integrals. What is the value of

$$\int_0^{\pi/2} \frac{\sin^n x}{\sin^n x + \cos^n x}\, dx?$$

This exercise illustrates how a little mathematical ingenuity solves a problem not immediately amenable to solution by a CAS.

7.6 Numerical Integration

The antiderivatives of some functions, like $\sin(x^2)$, $1/\ln x$, and $\sqrt{1 + x^4}$, have no elementary formulas. When we cannot find a workable antiderivative for a function f that we have to integrate, we can partition the interval of integration, replace f by a closely fitting polynomial on each subinterval, integrate the polynomials, and add the results to approximate the integral of f. This procedure is an example of numerical integration. In this section we study two such methods, the *Trapezoidal Rule* and *Simpson's Rule*. In our presentation we assume that f is positive, but the only requirement is for it to be continuous over the interval of integration $[a, b]$.

Trapezoidal Approximations

The Trapezoidal Rule for the value of a definite integral is based on approximating the region between a curve and the x-axis with trapezoids instead of rectangles, as in Figure 7.7.

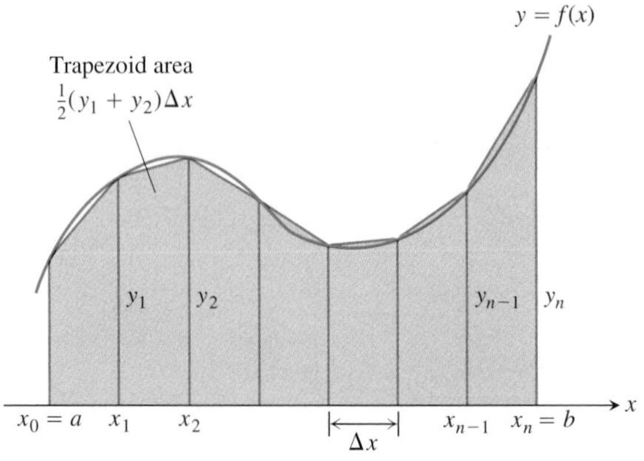

FIGURE 7.7 The Trapezoidal Rule approximates short stretches of the curve $y = f(x)$ with line segments. To approximate the integral of f from a to b, we add the areas of the trapezoids made by joining the ends of the segments to the x-axis.

It is not necessary for the subdivision points $x_0, x_1, x_2, \ldots, x_n$ in the figure to be evenly spaced, but the resulting formula is simpler if they are. We therefore assume that the length of each subinterval is

$$\Delta x = \frac{b - a}{n}.$$

The length $\Delta x = (b - a)/n$ is called the **step size** or **mesh size**. The area of the trapezoid that lies above the ith subinterval is

$$\Delta x\left(\frac{y_{i-1} + y_i}{2}\right) = \frac{\Delta x}{2}(y_{i-1} + y_i),$$

where $y_{i-1} = f(x_{i-1})$ and $y_i = f(x_i)$. This area is the length Δx of the trapezoid's horizontal "altitude" times the average of its two vertical "bases." (See Figure 7.7.) The area below the curve $y = f(x)$ and above the x-axis is then approximated by adding the areas of all the trapezoids:

$$\begin{aligned}
T &= \frac{1}{2}(y_0 + y_1)\Delta x + \frac{1}{2}(y_1 + y_2)\Delta x + \cdots \\
&\quad + \frac{1}{2}(y_{n-2} + y_{n-1})\Delta x + \frac{1}{2}(y_{n-1} + y_n)\Delta x \\
&= \Delta x\left(\frac{1}{2}y_0 + y_1 + y_2 + \cdots + y_{n-1} + \frac{1}{2}y_n\right) \\
&= \frac{\Delta x}{2}(y_0 + 2y_1 + 2y_2 + \cdots + 2y_{n-1} + y_n),
\end{aligned}$$

where

$$y_0 = f(a), \qquad y_1 = f(x_1), \qquad \ldots, \qquad y_{n-1} = f(x_{n-1}), \qquad y_n = f(b).$$

The Trapezoidal Rule says: Use T to estimate the integral of f from a to b.

TABLE 7.1

x	$y = x^2$
1	1
$\frac{5}{4}$	$\frac{25}{16}$
$\frac{6}{4}$	$\frac{36}{16}$
$\frac{7}{4}$	$\frac{49}{16}$
2	4

The Trapezoidal Rule

To approximate $\int_a^b f(x)\,dx$, use

$$T = \frac{\Delta x}{2}\left(y_0 + 2y_1 + 2y_2 + \cdots + 2y_{n-1} + y_n\right).$$

The y's are the values of f at the partition points

$$x_0 = a, x_1 = a + \Delta x, x_2 = a + 2\Delta x, \ldots, x_{n-1} = a + (n-1)\Delta x, x_n = b,$$

where $\Delta x = (b - a)/n$.

EXAMPLE 1 Use the Trapezoidal Rule with $n = 4$ to estimate $\int_1^2 x^2\,dx$. Compare the estimate with the exact value.

Solution Partition [1, 2] into four subintervals of equal length (Figure 7.8). Then evaluate $y = x^2$ at each partition point (Table 7.1).

Using these y values, $n = 4$, and $\Delta x = (2 - 1)/4 = 1/4$ in the Trapezoidal Rule, we have

$$\begin{aligned} T &= \frac{\Delta x}{2}\left(y_0 + 2y_1 + 2y_2 + 2y_3 + y_4\right) \\ &= \frac{1}{8}\left(1 + 2\left(\frac{25}{16}\right) + 2\left(\frac{36}{16}\right) + 2\left(\frac{49}{16}\right) + 4\right) \\ &= \frac{75}{32} = 2.34375. \end{aligned}$$

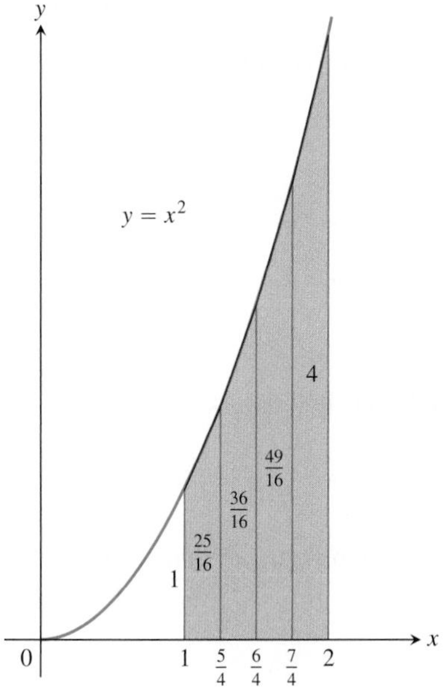

FIGURE 7.8 The trapezoidal approximation of the area under the graph of $y = x^2$ from $x = 1$ to $x = 2$ is a slight overestimate (Example 1).

Since the parabola is concave *up*, the approximating segments lie above the curve, giving each trapezoid slightly more area than the corresponding strip under the curve. The exact value of the integral is

$$\int_1^2 x^2\,dx = \frac{x^3}{3}\bigg]_1^2 = \frac{8}{3} - \frac{1}{3} = \frac{7}{3}.$$

The T approximation overestimates the integral by about half a percent of its true value of $7/3$. The percentage error is $(2.34375 - 7/3)/(7/3) \approx 0.00446$, or 0.446%. ■

Simpson's Rule: Approximations Using Parabolas

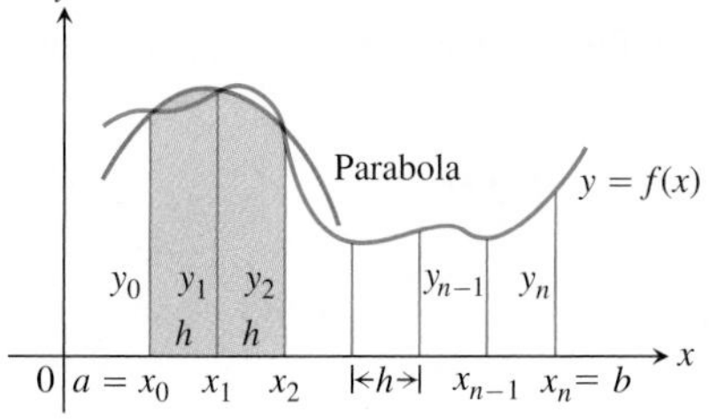

FIGURE 7.9 Simpson's Rule approximates short stretches of the curve with parabolas.

Another rule for approximating the definite integral of a continuous function results from using parabolas instead of the straight line segments that produced trapezoids. As before, we partition the interval $[a, b]$ into n subintervals of equal length $h = \Delta x = (b - a)/n$, but this time we require that n be an *even* number. On each consecutive pair of intervals we approximate the curve $y = f(x) \geq 0$ by a parabola, as shown in Figure 7.9. A typical parabola passes through three consecutive points (x_{i-1}, y_{i-1}), (x_i, y_i), and (x_{i+1}, y_{i+1}) on the curve.

Let's calculate the shaded area beneath a parabola passing through three consecutive points. To simplify our calculations, we first take the case where $x_0 = -h$, $x_1 = 0$, and

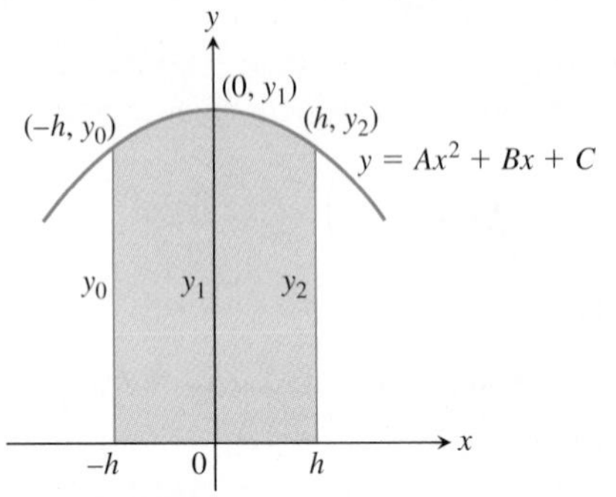

FIGURE 7.10 By integrating from $-h$ to h, we find the shaded area to be

$$\frac{h}{3}(y_0 + 4y_1 + y_2).$$

$x_2 = h$ (Figure 7.10), where $h = \Delta x = (b - a)/n$. The area under the parabola will be the same if we shift the y-axis to the left or right. The parabola has an equation of the form

$$y = Ax^2 + Bx + C,$$

so the area under it from $x = -h$ to $x = h$ is

$$\begin{aligned} A_p &= \int_{-h}^{h} (Ax^2 + Bx + C)\,dx \\ &= \frac{Ax^3}{3} + \frac{Bx^2}{2} + Cx\bigg]_{-h}^{h} \\ &= \frac{2Ah^3}{3} + 2Ch = \frac{h}{3}(2Ah^2 + 6C). \end{aligned}$$

Since the curve passes through the three points $(-h, y_0)$, $(0, y_1)$, and (h, y_2), we also have

$$y_0 = Ah^2 - Bh + C, \qquad y_1 = C, \qquad y_2 = Ah^2 + Bh + C,$$

from which we obtain

$$\begin{aligned} C &= y_1, \\ Ah^2 - Bh &= y_0 - y_1, \\ Ah^2 + Bh &= y_2 - y_1, \\ 2Ah^2 &= y_0 + y_2 - 2y_1. \end{aligned}$$

Hence, expressing the area A_p in terms of the ordinates y_0, y_1, and y_2, we have

$$A_p = \frac{h}{3}(2Ah^2 + 6C) = \frac{h}{3}((y_0 + y_2 - 2y_1) + 6y_1) = \frac{h}{3}(y_0 + 4y_1 + y_2).$$

Now shifting the parabola horizontally to its shaded position in Figure 7.9 does not change the area under it. Thus the area under the parabola through (x_0, y_0), (x_1, y_1), and (x_2, y_2) in Figure 7.9 is still

$$\frac{h}{3}(y_0 + 4y_1 + y_2).$$

Similarly, the area under the parabola through the points (x_2, y_2), (x_3, y_3), and (x_4, y_4) is

$$\frac{h}{3}(y_2 + 4y_3 + y_4).$$

Computing the areas under all the parabolas and adding the results gives the approximation

$$\begin{aligned} \int_a^b f(x)\,dx &\approx \frac{h}{3}(y_0 + 4y_1 + y_2) + \frac{h}{3}(y_2 + 4y_3 + y_4) + \cdots \\ &\quad + \frac{h}{3}(y_{n-2} + 4y_{n-1} + y_n) \\ &= \frac{h}{3}(y_0 + 4y_1 + 2y_2 + 4y_3 + 2y_4 + \cdots + 2y_{n-2} + 4y_{n-1} + y_n). \end{aligned}$$

HISTORICAL BIOGRAPHY

Thomas Simpson
(1720–1761)

The result is known as Simpson's Rule. The function need not be positive, as in our derivation, but the number n of subintervals must be even to apply the rule because each parabolic arc uses two subintervals.

Simpson's Rule

To approximate $\int_a^b f(x)\,dx$, use

$$S = \frac{\Delta x}{3}(y_0 + 4y_1 + 2y_2 + 4y_3 + \cdots + 2y_{n-2} + 4y_{n-1} + y_n).$$

The y's are the values of f at the partition points

$$x_0 = a, x_1 = a + \Delta x, x_2 = a + 2\Delta x, \ldots, x_{n-1} = a + (n-1)\Delta x, x_n = b.$$

The number n is even, and $\Delta x = (b - a)/n$.

Note the pattern of the coefficients in the above rule: 1, 4, 2, 4, 2, 4, 2, . . . , 4, 2, 1.

EXAMPLE 2 Use Simpson's Rule with $n = 4$ to approximate $\int_0^2 5x^4\,dx$.

TABLE 7.2

x	$y = 5x^4$
0	0
$\frac{1}{2}$	$\frac{5}{16}$
1	5
$\frac{3}{2}$	$\frac{405}{16}$
2	80

Solution Partition [0, 2] into four subintervals and evaluate $y = 5x^4$ at the partition points (Table 7.2). Then apply Simpson's Rule with $n = 4$ and $\Delta x = 1/2$:

$$\begin{aligned} S &= \frac{\Delta x}{3}\left(y_0 + 4y_1 + 2y_2 + 4y_3 + y_4\right) \\ &= \frac{1}{6}\left(0 + 4\left(\frac{5}{16}\right) + 2(5) + 4\left(\frac{405}{16}\right) + 80\right) \\ &= 32\frac{1}{12}. \end{aligned}$$

This estimate differs from the exact value (32) by only 1/12, a percentage error of less than three-tenths of one percent, and this was with just four subintervals. ■

Error Analysis

Whenever we use an approximation technique, the issue arises as to how accurate the approximation might be. The following theorem gives formulas for estimating the errors when using the Trapezoidal Rule and Simpson's Rule. The **error** is the difference between the approximation obtained by the rule and the actual value of the definite integral $\int_a^b f(x)\,dx$.

THEOREM 1—Error Estimates in the Trapezoidal and Simpson's Rules If f'' is continuous and M is any upper bound for the values of $|f''|$ on $[a, b]$, then the error E_T in the trapezoidal approximation of the integral of f from a to b for n steps satisfies the inequality

$$|E_T| \le \frac{M(b-a)^3}{12n^2}. \qquad \text{Trapezoidal Rule}$$

If $f^{(4)}$ is continuous and M is any upper bound for the values of $|f^{(4)}|$ on $[a, b]$, then the error E_S in the Simpson's Rule approximation of the integral of f from a to b for n steps satisfies the inequality

$$|E_S| \le \frac{M(b-a)^5}{180n^4}. \qquad \text{Simpson's Rule}$$

Theorem 1 tells us how large the step size $\Delta x = (b - a)/n$ should be for a given tolerance of error. To see why the theorem is true in the case of the Trapezoidal Rule, we begin with a result from advanced calculus, which says that if f'' is continuous on the interval $[a, b]$, then

$$\int_a^b f(x)\,dx = T - \frac{b-a}{12} \cdot f''(c)(\Delta x)^2$$

for some number c between a and b. Thus, as Δx approaches zero, the error defined by

$$E_T = -\frac{b-a}{12} \cdot f''(c)(\Delta x)^2$$

approaches zero as the *square* of Δx.

The inequality

$$|E_T| \le \frac{b-a}{12} \max|f''(x)|(\Delta x)^2,$$

where max refers to the interval $[a, b]$, gives an upper bound for the magnitude of the error. In practice, we usually cannot find the exact value of $\max|f''(x)|$ and have to estimate an upper bound or "worst case" value for it instead. If M is any upper bound for the values of $|f''(x)|$ on $[a, b]$, so that $|f''(x)| \le M$ on $[a, b]$, then

$$|E_T| \le \frac{b-a}{12} M(\Delta x)^2.$$

If we substitute $(b - a)/n$ for Δx, we get

$$|E_T| \le \frac{M(b-a)^3}{12n^2}.$$

To estimate the error in Simpson's rule, we start with a result from advanced calculus that says that if the fourth derivative $f^{(4)}$ is continuous, then

$$\int_a^b f(x)\,dx = S - \frac{b-a}{180} \cdot f^{(4)}(c)(\Delta x)^4$$

for some point c between a and b. Thus, as Δx approaches zero, the error,

$$E_S = -\frac{b-a}{180} \cdot f^{(4)}(c)(\Delta x)^4,$$

approaches zero as the *fourth power* of Δx. (This helps to explain why Simpson's Rule is likely to give better results than the Trapezoidal Rule.)

The inequality

$$|E_S| \le \frac{b-a}{180} \max|f^{(4)}(x)|\,(\Delta x)^4$$

where max refers to the interval $[a, b]$, gives an upper bound for the magnitude of the error. As with $\max|f''|$ in the error formula for the Trapezoidal Rule, we usually cannot find the exact value of $\max|f^{(4)}(x)|$ and have to replace it with an upper bound. If M is any upper bound for the values of $|f^{(4)}|$ on $[a, b]$, then

$$|E_S| \le \frac{b-a}{180} M(\Delta x)^4.$$

Substituting $(b - a)/n$ for Δx in this last expression gives

$$|E_S| \le \frac{M(b-a)^5}{180n^4}.$$

Here is an example using the error estimate for Simpson's Rule.

EXAMPLE 3 Find an upper bound for the error in estimating $\int_0^2 5x^4\,dx$ using Simpson's Rule with $n = 4$ (Example 2).

Solution To estimate the error, we first find an upper bound M for the magnitude of the fourth derivative of $f(x) = 5x^4$ on the interval $0 \le x \le 2$. Since the fourth derivative has the constant value $f^{(4)}(x) = 120$, we take $M = 120$. With $b - a = 2$ and $n = 4$, the error estimate for Simpson's Rule gives

$$|E_S| \le \frac{M(b-a)^5}{180n^4} = \frac{120(2)^5}{180 \cdot 4^4} = \frac{1}{12}.$$ ■

EXAMPLE 4 As we saw in Chapter 5, the value of ln 2 can be calculated from the integral

$$\ln 2 = \int_1^2 \frac{1}{x}\,dx.$$

Table 7.3 shows T and S values for approximations of $\int_1^2 (1/x)\,dx$ using various values of n. Notice how Simpson's Rule dramatically improves over the Trapezoidal Rule. In particular, notice that when we double the value of n (thereby halving the value of $h = \Delta x$), the T error is divided by 2 *squared*, whereas the S error is divided by 2 *to the fourth*.

This has a dramatic effect as $\Delta x = (2 - 1)/n$ gets very small. The Simpson approximation for $n = 50$ rounds accurately to seven places and for $n = 100$ agrees to nine decimal places (billionths)! ■

If $f(x)$ is a polynomial of degree less than four, then its fourth derivative is zero, and

$$E_S = -\frac{b-a}{180} f^{(4)}(c)(\Delta x)^4 = -\frac{b-a}{180}(0)(\Delta x)^4 = 0.$$

TABLE 7.3 Trapezoidal Rule approximations (T_n) and Simpson's Rule approximations (S_n) of $\ln 2 = \int_1^2 (1/x)\,dx$

n	T_n	|Error| less than . . .	S_n	|Error| less than . . .
10	0.6937714032	0.0006242227	0.6931502307	0.0000030502
20	0.6933033818	0.0001562013	0.6931473747	0.0000001942
30	0.6932166154	0.0000694349	0.6931472190	0.0000000385
40	0.6931862400	0.0000390595	0.6931471927	0.0000000122
50	0.6931721793	0.0000249988	0.6931471856	0.0000000050
100	0.6931534305	0.0000062500	0.6931471809	0.0000000004

Thus, there will be no error in the Simpson approximation of any integral of f. In other words, if f is a constant, a linear function, or a quadratic or cubic polynomial, Simpson's Rule will give the value of any integral of f exactly, whatever the number of subdivisions. Similarly, if f is a constant or a linear function, then its second derivative is zero and

$$E_T = -\frac{b-a}{12} f''(c)(\Delta x)^2 = -\frac{b-a}{12}(0)(\Delta x)^2 = 0.$$

The Trapezoidal Rule will therefore give the exact value of any integral of f. This is no surprise, for the trapezoids fit the graph perfectly. Although decreasing the step size Δx reduces the error in the Simpson and Trapezoidal approximations in theory, it may fail to do so in practice.

When Δx is very small, say $\Delta x = 10^{-5}$, computer or calculator round-off errors in the arithmetic required to evaluate S and T may accumulate to such an extent that the error formulas no longer describe what is going on. Shrinking Δx below a certain size can actually make things worse. Although this is not an issue in this book, you should consult a text on numerical analysis for alternative methods if you are having problems with round-off.

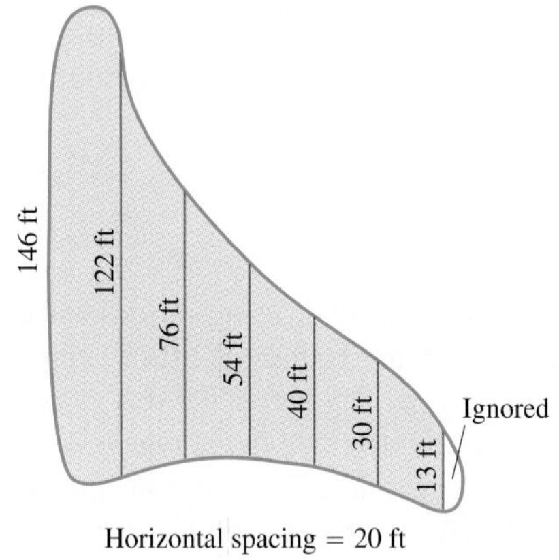

FIGURE 7.11 The dimensions of the swamp in Example 5.

EXAMPLE 5 A town wants to drain and fill a small polluted swamp (Figure 7.11). The swamp averages 5 ft deep. About how many cubic yards of dirt will it take to fill the area after the swamp is drained?

Solution To calculate the volume of the swamp, we estimate the surface area and multiply by 5. To estimate the area, we use Simpson's Rule with $\Delta x = 20$ ft and the y's equal to the distances measured across the swamp, as shown in Figure 7.11.

$$\begin{aligned} S &= \frac{\Delta x}{3}(y_0 + 4y_1 + 2y_2 + 4y_3 + 2y_4 + 4y_5 + y_6) \\ &= \frac{20}{3}(146 + 488 + 152 + 216 + 80 + 120 + 13) = 8100 \end{aligned}$$

The volume is about $(8100)(5) = 40{,}500$ ft^3 or 1500 yd^3. ■

EXERCISES 7.6

The instructions for the integrals in Exercises 1–10 have two parts, one for the Trapezoidal Rule and one for Simpson's Rule.

I. Using the Trapezoidal Rule

a. Estimate the integral with $n = 4$ steps and find an upper bound for $|E_T|$.

b. Evaluate the integral directly and find $|E_T|$.

c. Use the formula $(|E_T|/(\text{true value})) \times 100$ to express $|E_T|$ as a percentage of the integral's true value.

II. Using Simpson's Rule

a. Estimate the integral with $n = 4$ steps and find an upper bound for $|E_S|$.

b. Evaluate the integral directly and find $|E_S|$.

c. Use the formula $(|E_S|/(\text{true value})) \times 100$ to express $|E_S|$ as a percentage of the integral's true value.

1. $\displaystyle\int_1^2 x\,dx$

2. $\displaystyle\int_1^3 (2x-1)\,dx$

3. $\displaystyle\int_{-1}^1 (x^2+1)\,dx$

4. $\displaystyle\int_{-2}^0 (x^2-1)\,dx$

5. $\displaystyle\int_0^2 (t^3+t)\,dt$

6. $\displaystyle\int_{-1}^1 (t^3+1)\,dt$

7. $\displaystyle\int_1^2 \frac{1}{s^2}\,ds$

8. $\displaystyle\int_2^4 \frac{1}{(s-1)^2}\,ds$

9. $\displaystyle\int_0^\pi \sin t\,dt$

10. $\displaystyle\int_0^1 \sin \pi t\,dt$

In Exercises 11–22, estimate the minimum number of subintervals needed to approximate the integrals with an error of magnitude less than 10^{-4} by **(a)** the Trapezoidal Rule and **(b)** Simpson's Rule. (The integrals in Exercises 11–18 are the integrals from Exercises 1–8.)

11. $\int_1^2 x\,dx$

12. $\int_1^3 (2x-1)\,dx$

13. $\int_{-1}^1 (x^2+1)\,dx$

14. $\int_{-2}^0 (x^2-1)\,dx$

15. $\int_0^2 (t^3+t)\,dt$

16. $\int_{-1}^1 (t^3+1)\,dt$

17. $\int_1^2 \frac{1}{s^2}\,ds$

18. $\int_2^4 \frac{1}{(s-1)^2}\,ds$

19. $\int_0^3 \sqrt{x+1}\,dx$

20. $\int_0^3 \frac{1}{\sqrt{x+1}}\,dx$

21. $\int_0^2 \sin(x+1)\,dx$

22. $\int_{-1}^1 \cos(x+\pi)\,dx$

23. Volume of water in a swimming pool A rectangular swimming pool is 30 ft wide and 50 ft long. The table shows the depth $h(x)$ of the water at 5-ft intervals from one end of the pool to the other. Estimate the volume of water in the pool using the Trapezoidal Rule with $n = 10$, applied to the integral

$$V = \int_0^{50} 30 \cdot h(x)\,dx.$$

Position (ft) x	Depth (ft) $h(x)$	Position (ft) x	Depth (ft) $h(x)$
0	6.0	30	11.5
5	8.2	35	11.9
10	9.1	40	12.3
15	9.9	45	12.7
20	10.5	50	13.0
25	11.0		

24. Distance traveled The accompanying table shows time-to-speed data for a sports car accelerating from rest to 130 mph. How far had the car traveled by the time it reached this speed? (Use trapezoids to estimate the area under the velocity curve, but be careful: The time intervals vary in length.)

Speed change	Time (sec)
Zero to 30 mph	2.2
40 mph	3.2
50 mph	4.5
60 mph	5.9
70 mph	7.8
80 mph	10.2
90 mph	12.7
100 mph	16.0
110 mph	20.6
120 mph	26.2
130 mph	37.1

25. Wing design The design of a new airplane requires a gasoline tank of constant cross-sectional area in each wing. A scale drawing of a cross-section is shown here. The tank must hold 5000 lb of gasoline, which has a density of 42 lb/ft^3. Estimate the length of the tank.

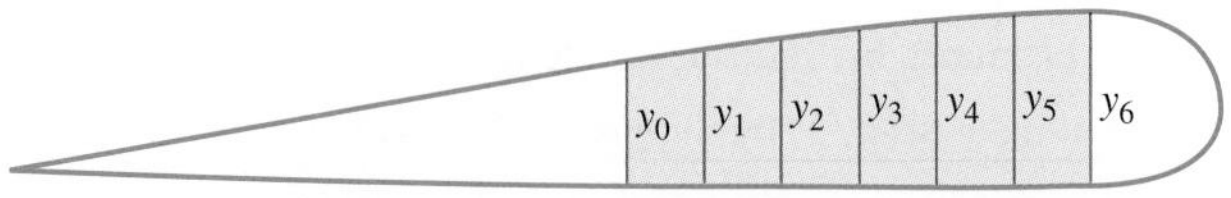

$y_0 = 1.5$ ft, $y_1 = 1.6$ ft, $y_2 = 1.8$ ft, $y_3 = 1.9$ ft,
$y_4 = 2.0$ ft, $y_5 = y_6 = 2.1$ ft   Horizontal spacing = 1 ft

26. Oil consumption on Pathfinder Island A diesel generator runs continuously, consuming oil at a gradually increasing rate until it must be temporarily shut down to have the filters replaced. Use the Trapezoidal Rule to estimate the amount of oil consumed by the generator during that week.

Day	Oil consumption rate (liters/h)
Sun	0.019
Mon	0.020
Tue	0.021
Wed	0.023
Thu	0.025
Fri	0.028
Sat	0.031
Sun	0.035

27. Usable values of the sine-integral function *The sine-integral function,*

$$\mathrm{Si}(x) = \int_0^x \frac{\sin t}{t}\,dt, \qquad \text{"Sine integral of } x\text{"}$$

is one of the many functions in engineering whose formulas cannot be simplified. There is no elementary formula for the antiderivative of $(\sin t)/t$. The values of $\mathrm{Si}(x)$, however, are readily estimated by numerical integration.

Although the notation does not show it explicitly, the function being integrated is

$$f(t) = \begin{cases} \frac{\sin t}{t}, & t \neq 0 \\ 1, & t = 0, \end{cases}$$

the continuous extension of $(\sin t)/t$ to the interval $[0, x]$. The function has derivatives of all orders at every point of its domain. Its graph is smooth, and you can expect good results from Simpson's Rule.

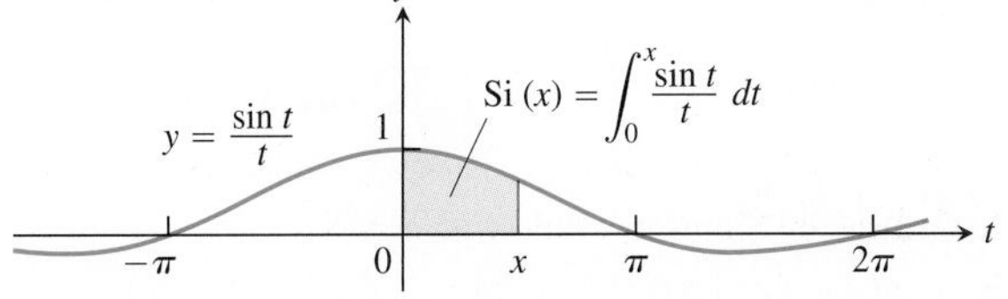

a. Use the fact that $|f^{(4)}| \le 1$ on $[0, \pi/2]$ to give an upper bound for the error that will occur if

$$\mathrm{Si}\left(\frac{\pi}{2}\right) = \int_0^{\pi/2} \frac{\sin t}{t}\, dt$$

is estimated by Simpson's Rule with $n = 4$.

b. Estimate $\mathrm{Si}(\pi/2)$ by Simpson's Rule with $n = 4$.

c. Express the error bound you found in part (a) as a percentage of the value you found in part (b).

28. The error function *The error function,*

$$\mathrm{erf}(x) = \frac{2}{\sqrt{\pi}} \int_0^x e^{-t^2}\, dt,$$

important in probability and in the theories of heat flow and signal transmission, must be evaluated numerically because there is no elementary expression for the antiderivative of e^{-t^2}.

a. Use Simpson's Rule with $n = 10$ to estimate $\mathrm{erf}(1)$.

b. In $[0, 1]$,

$$\left| \frac{d^4}{dt^4}\left(e^{-t^2}\right) \right| \le 12.$$

Give an upper bound for the magnitude of the error of the estimate in part (a).

29. Prove that the sum T in the Trapezoidal Rule for $\int_a^b f(x)\, dx$ is a Riemann sum for f continuous on $[a, b]$. (*Hint:* Use the Intermediate Value Theorem to show the existence of c_k in the subinterval $[x_{k-1}, x_k]$ satisfying $f(c_k) = (f(x_{k-1}) + f(x_k))/2$.)

30. Prove that the sum S in Simpson's Rule for $\int_a^b f(x)\, dx$ is a Riemann sum for f continuous on $[a, b]$. (See Exercise 29.)

T **31. Elliptic integrals** The length of the ellipse

$$x = a\cos t, \quad y = b\sin t, \quad 0 \le t \le 2\pi$$

turns out to be

$$\text{Length} = 4a \int_0^{\pi/2} \sqrt{1 - e^2\cos^2 t}\, dt,$$

where e is the ellipse's eccentricity. The integral in this formula, called an *elliptic integral,* is nonelementary except when $e = 0$ or 1.

a. Use the Trapezoidal Rule with $n = 10$ to estimate the length of the ellipse when $a = 1$ and $e = 1/2$.

b. Use the fact that the absolute value of the second derivative of $f(t) = \sqrt{1 - e^2\cos^2 t}$ is less than 1 to find an upper bound for the error in the estimate you obtained in part (a).

T **32.** The length of one arch of the curve $y = \sin x$ is given by

$$L = \int_0^{\pi} \sqrt{1 + \cos^2 x}\, dx.$$

Estimate L by Simpson's Rule with $n = 8$.

T **33.** Your metal fabrication company is bidding for a contract to make sheets of corrugated iron roofing like the one shown here. The cross-sections of the corrugated sheets are to conform to the curve

$$y = \sin \frac{3\pi}{20}x, \quad 0 \le x \le 20 \text{ in.}$$

If the roofing is to be stamped from flat sheets by a process that does not stretch the material, how wide should the original material be? To find out, use numerical integration to approximate the length of the sine curve to two decimal places.

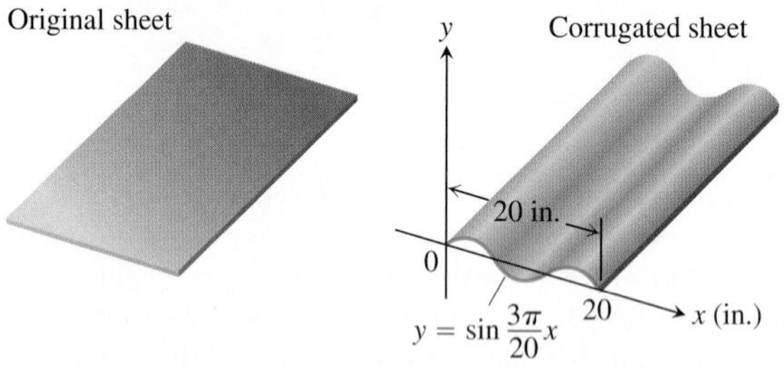

T **34.** Your engineering firm is bidding for the contract to construct the tunnel shown here. The tunnel is 300 ft long and 50 ft wide at the base. The cross-section is shaped like one arch of the curve $y = 25\cos(\pi x/50)$. Upon completion, the tunnel's inside surface (excluding the roadway) will be treated with a waterproof sealer that costs \$1.75 per square foot to apply. How much will it cost to apply the sealer? (*Hint:* Use numerical integration to find the length of the cosine curve.)

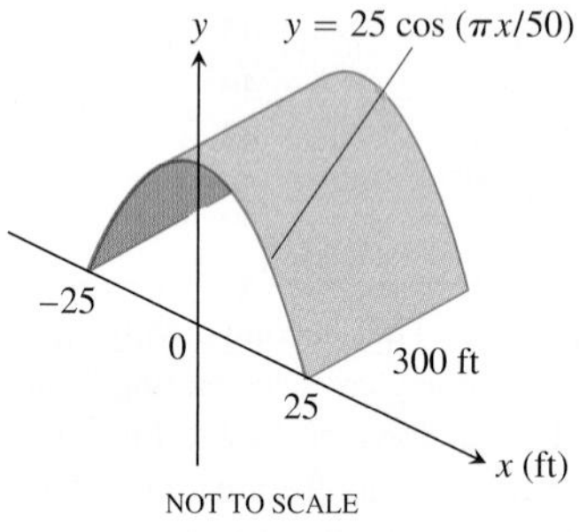

Find, to two decimal places, the areas of the surfaces generated by revolving the curves in Exercises 35 and 36 about the x-axis.

35. $y = \sin x, \quad 0 \le x \le \pi$

36. $y = x^2/4, \quad 0 \le x \le 2$

37. Use numerical integration to estimate the value of

$$\sin^{-1} 0.6 = \int_0^{0.6} \frac{dx}{\sqrt{1 - x^2}}.$$

For reference, $\sin^{-1} 0.6 = 0.64350$ to five decimal places.

38. Use numerical integration to estimate the value of

$$\pi = 4\int_0^1 \frac{1}{1 + x^2}\, dx.$$

7.7 Improper Integrals

Up to now, we have required definite integrals to have two properties. First, that the domain of integration $[a, b]$ be finite. Second, that the range of the integrand be finite on this domain. In practice, we may encounter problems that fail to meet one or both of these conditions. The integral for the area under the curve $y = (\ln x)/x^2$ from $x = 1$ to $x = \infty$ is an example for which the domain is infinite (Figure 7.12a). The integral for the area under the curve of $y = 1/\sqrt{x}$ between $x = 0$ and $x = 1$ is an example for which the range of the integrand is infinite (Figure 7.12b). In either case, the integrals are said to be *improper* and are calculated as limits. We will see in Chapter 8 that improper integrals play an important role when investigating the convergence of certain infinite series.

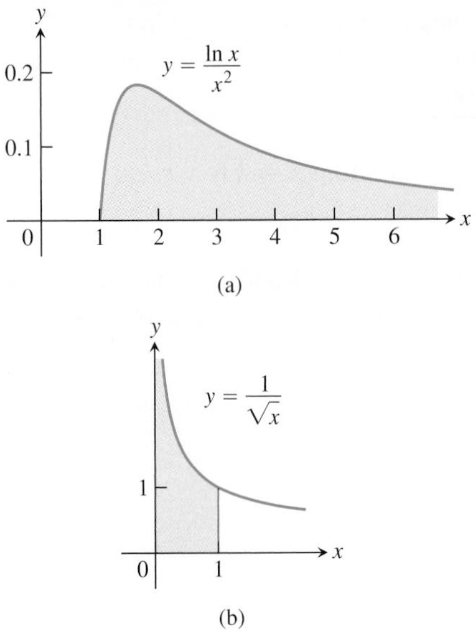

FIGURE 7.12 Are the areas under these infinite curves finite?

Infinite Limits of Integration

Consider the infinite region that lies under the curve $y = e^{-x/2}$ in the first quadrant (Figure 7.13a). You might think this region has infinite area, but we will see that the value is finite. Here is how to assign a value to the area. First find the area $A(b)$ of the portion of the region that is bounded on the right by $x = b$ (Figure 7.13b).

$$A(b) = \int_0^b e^{-x/2}\,dx = -2e^{-x/2}\Big]_0^b = -2e^{-b/2} + 2$$

Then find the limit of $A(b)$ as $b \to \infty$

$$\lim_{b\to\infty} A(b) = \lim_{b\to\infty} (-2e^{-b/2} + 2) = 2.$$

The value we assign to the area under the curve from 0 to ∞ is

$$\int_0^\infty e^{-x/2}\,dx = \lim_{b\to\infty}\int_0^b e^{-x/2}\,dx = 2.$$

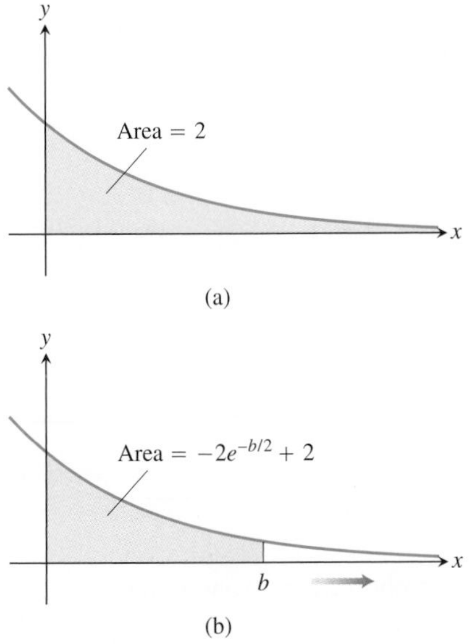

FIGURE 7.13 (a) The area in the first quadrant under the curve $y = e^{-x/2}$ (b) The area is an improper integral of the first type.

DEFINITION Integrals with infinite limits of integration are **improper integrals of Type I**.

1. If $f(x)$ is continuous on $[a, \infty)$, then
$$\int_a^\infty f(x)\,dx = \lim_{b\to\infty}\int_a^b f(x)\,dx.$$
2. If $f(x)$ is continuous on $(-\infty, b]$, then
$$\int_{-\infty}^b f(x)\,dx = \lim_{a\to-\infty}\int_a^b f(x)\,dx.$$
3. If $f(x)$ is continuous on $(-\infty, \infty)$, then
$$\int_{-\infty}^\infty f(x)\,dx = \int_{-\infty}^c f(x)\,dx + \int_c^\infty f(x)\,dx,$$
where c is any real number.

In each case, if the limit is finite we say that the improper integral **converges** and that the limit is the **value** of the improper integral. If the limit fails to exist, the improper integral **diverges**.

It can be shown that the choice of c in Part 3 of the definition is unimportant. We can evaluate or determine the convergence or divergence of $\int_{-\infty}^{\infty} f(x)\,dx$ with any convenient choice.

Any of the integrals in the above definition can be interpreted as an area if $f \geq 0$ on the interval of integration. For instance, we interpreted the improper integral in Figure 7.13 as an area. In that case, the area has the finite value 2. If $f \geq 0$ and the improper integral diverges, we say the area under the curve is **infinite**.

EXAMPLE 1 Is the area under the curve $y = (\ln x)/x^2$ from $x = 1$ to $x = \infty$ finite? If so, what is its value?

Solution We find the area under the curve from $x = 1$ to $x = b$ and examine the limit as $b \to \infty$. If the limit is finite, we take it to be the area under the curve (Figure 7.14). The area from 1 to b is

$$\begin{aligned}\int_1^b \frac{\ln x}{x^2}\,dx &= \left[(\ln x)\left(-\frac{1}{x}\right)\right]_1^b - \int_1^b \left(-\frac{1}{x}\right)\left(\frac{1}{x}\right)dx \\ &= -\frac{\ln b}{b} - \left[\frac{1}{x}\right]_1^b \\ &= -\frac{\ln b}{b} - \frac{1}{b} + 1.\end{aligned}$$

Integration by parts with $u = \ln x$, $dv = dx/x^2$, $du = dx/x$, $v = -1/x$.

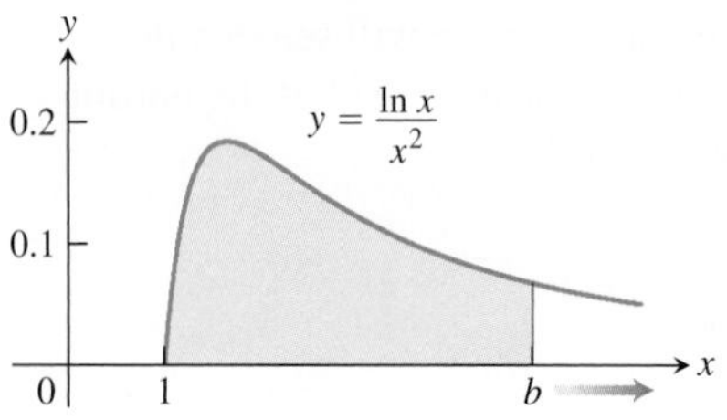

FIGURE 7.14 The area under this curve is an improper integral (Example 1).

The limit of the area as $b \to \infty$ is

$$\begin{aligned}\int_1^{\infty} \frac{\ln x}{x^2}\,dx &= \lim_{b\to\infty} \int_1^b \frac{\ln x}{x^2}\,dx \\ &= \lim_{b\to\infty}\left[-\frac{\ln b}{b} - \frac{1}{b} + 1\right] \\ &= -\left[\lim_{b\to\infty}\frac{\ln b}{b}\right] - 0 + 1 \\ &= -\left[\lim_{b\to\infty}\frac{1/b}{1}\right] + 1 = 0 + 1 = 1.\end{aligned}$$

l'Hôpital's Rule

Thus, the improper integral converges and the area has finite value 1. ■

EXAMPLE 2 Evaluate

$$\int_{-\infty}^{\infty} \frac{dx}{1 + x^2}.$$

Solution According to the definition (Part 3), we can choose $c = 0$ and write

$$\int_{-\infty}^{\infty} \frac{dx}{1 + x^2} = \int_{-\infty}^{0} \frac{dx}{1 + x^2} + \int_{0}^{\infty} \frac{dx}{1 + x^2}.$$

Next we evaluate each improper integral on the right side of the equation above.

$$\int_{-\infty}^{0} \frac{dx}{1 + x^2} = \lim_{a\to-\infty} \int_{a}^{0} \frac{dx}{1 + x^2}$$

HISTORICAL BIOGRAPHY

Lejeune Dirichlet (1805–1859)

$$= \lim_{a\to-\infty} \tan^{-1} x \Big]_a^0$$

$$= \lim_{a\to-\infty} (\tan^{-1} 0 - \tan^{-1} a) = 0 - \left(-\frac{\pi}{2}\right) = \frac{\pi}{2}$$

$$\int_0^\infty \frac{dx}{1+x^2} = \lim_{b\to\infty} \int_0^b \frac{dx}{1+x^2}$$

$$= \lim_{b\to\infty} \tan^{-1} x \Big]_0^b$$

$$= \lim_{b\to\infty} (\tan^{-1} b - \tan^{-1} 0) = \frac{\pi}{2} - 0 = \frac{\pi}{2}$$

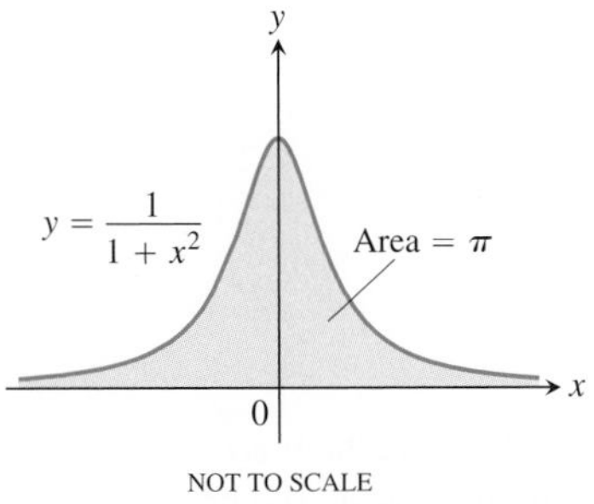

FIGURE 7.15 The area under this curve is finite (Example 2).

Thus,

$$\int_{-\infty}^\infty \frac{dx}{1+x^2} = \frac{\pi}{2} + \frac{\pi}{2} = \pi.$$

Since $1/(1 + x^2) > 0$, the improper integral can be interpreted as the (finite) area beneath the curve and above the x-axis (Figure 7.15). ■

The Integral $\int_1^\infty \frac{dx}{x^p}$

The function $y = 1/x$ is the boundary between the convergent and divergent improper integrals with integrands of the form $y = 1/x^p$. As the next example shows, the improper integral converges if $p > 1$ and diverges if $p \le 1$.

EXAMPLE 3 For what values of p does the integral $\int_1^\infty dx/x^p$ converge? When the integral does converge, what is its value?

Solution If $p \neq 1$,

$$\int_1^b \frac{dx}{x^p} = \frac{x^{-p+1}}{-p+1}\Big]_1^b = \frac{1}{1-p}(b^{-p+1} - 1) = \frac{1}{1-p}\left(\frac{1}{b^{p-1}} - 1\right).$$

Thus,

$$\int_1^\infty \frac{dx}{x^p} = \lim_{b\to\infty} \int_1^b \frac{dx}{x^p}$$

$$= \lim_{b\to\infty} \left[\frac{1}{1-p}\left(\frac{1}{b^{p-1}} - 1\right)\right] = \begin{cases} \frac{1}{p-1}, & p > 1 \\ \infty, & p < 1 \end{cases}$$

because

$$\lim_{b\to\infty} \frac{1}{b^{p-1}} = \begin{cases} 0, & p > 1 \\ \infty, & p < 1. \end{cases}$$

Therefore, the integral converges to the value $1/(p - 1)$ if $p > 1$ and it diverges if $p < 1$.

If $p = 1$, the integral also diverges:

$$\begin{aligned}\int_1^{\infty} \frac{dx}{x^p} &= \int_1^{\infty} \frac{dx}{x} \\ &= \lim_{b \to \infty} \int_1^b \frac{dx}{x} \\ &= \lim_{b \to \infty} \ln x \Big]_1^b \\ &= \lim_{b \to \infty} (\ln b - \ln 1) = \infty .\end{aligned}$$

■

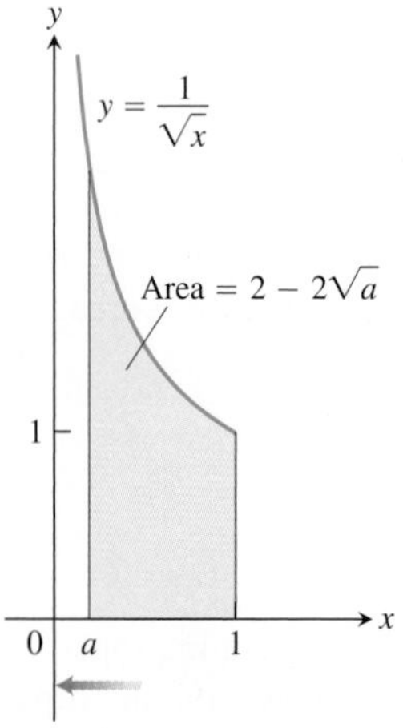

FIGURE 7.16 The area under this curve is an example of an improper integral of the second kind.

Integrands with Vertical Asymptotes

Another type of improper integral arises when the integrand has a vertical asymptote—an infinite discontinuity—at a limit of integration or at some point between the limits of integration. If the integrand f is positive over the interval of integration, we can again interpret the improper integral as the area under the graph of f and above the x-axis between the limits of integration.

Consider the region in the first quadrant that lies under the curve $y = 1/\sqrt{x}$ from $x = 0$ to $x = 1$ (Figure 7.12b). First we find the area of the portion from a to 1 (Figure 7.16).

$$\int_a^1 \frac{dx}{\sqrt{x}} = 2\sqrt{x}\Big]_a^1 = 2 - 2\sqrt{a}$$

Then we find the limit of this area as $a \to 0^+$:

$$\lim_{a \to 0^+} \int_a^1 \frac{dx}{\sqrt{x}} = \lim_{a \to 0^+} \left(2 - 2\sqrt{a}\right) = 2.$$

The area under the curve from 0 to 1 is finite and equals

$$\int_0^1 \frac{dx}{\sqrt{x}} = \lim_{a \to 0^+} \int_a^1 \frac{dx}{\sqrt{x}} = 2.$$

DEFINITION Integrals of functions that become infinite at a point within the interval of integration are **improper integrals of Type II**.

1. If $f(x)$ is continuous on $(a, b]$ and is discontinuous at a then

$$\int_a^b f(x)\,dx = \lim_{c \to a^+} \int_c^b f(x)\,dx .$$

2. If $f(x)$ is continuous on $[a, b)$ and is discontinuous at b, then

$$\int_a^b f(x)\,dx = \lim_{c \to b^-} \int_a^c f(x)\,dx .$$

continued

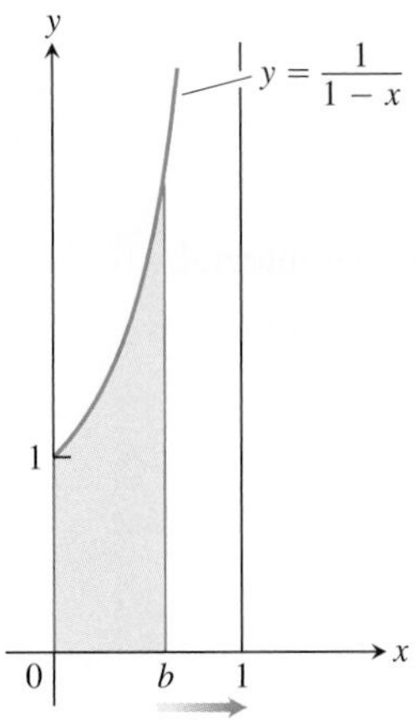

FIGURE 7.17 The area beneath the curve and above the x-axis for $[0, 1)$ is not a real number (Example 4).

3. If $f(x)$ is discontinuous at c, where $a < c < b$, and continuous on $[a, c) \cup (c, b]$, then

$$\int_a^b f(x)\,dx = \int_a^c f(x)\,dx + \int_c^b f(x)\,dx.$$

In each case, if the limit is finite we say the improper integral **converges** and that the limit is the **value** of the improper integral. If the limit does not exist, the integral **diverges**.

In Part 3 of the definition, the integral on the left side of the equation converges if *both* integrals on the right side converge; otherwise it diverges.

EXAMPLE 4 Investigate the convergence of

$$\int_0^1 \frac{1}{1-x}\,dx.$$

Solution The integrand $f(x) = 1/(1-x)$ is continuous on $[0, 1)$ but is discontinuous at $x = 1$ and becomes infinite as $x \to 1^-$ (Figure 7.17). We evaluate the integral as

$$\begin{aligned}\lim_{b\to 1^-} \int_0^b \frac{1}{1-x}\,dx &= \lim_{b\to 1^-} \Big[-\ln|1-x|\Big]_0^b \\ &= \lim_{b\to 1^-} [-\ln(1-b) + 0] = \infty.\end{aligned}$$

The limit is infinite, so the integral diverges. ■

EXAMPLE 5 Evaluate

$$\int_0^3 \frac{dx}{(x-1)^{2/3}}.$$

Solution The integrand has a vertical asymptote at $x = 1$ and is continuous on $[0, 1)$ and $(1, 3]$ (Figure 7.18). Thus, by Part 3 of the definition above,

$$\int_0^3 \frac{dx}{(x-1)^{2/3}} = \int_0^1 \frac{dx}{(x-1)^{2/3}} + \int_1^3 \frac{dx}{(x-1)^{2/3}}.$$

Next, we evaluate each improper integral on the right-hand side of this equation.

$$\begin{aligned}\int_0^1 \frac{dx}{(x-1)^{2/3}} &= \lim_{b\to 1^-} \int_0^b \frac{dx}{(x-1)^{2/3}} \\ &= \lim_{b\to 1^-} 3(x-1)^{1/3}\Big]_0^b \\ &= \lim_{b\to 1^-} [3(b-1)^{1/3} + 3] = 3\end{aligned}$$

$$\begin{aligned}\int_1^3 \frac{dx}{(x-1)^{2/3}} &= \lim_{c\to 1^+} \int_c^3 \frac{dx}{(x-1)^{2/3}} \\ &= \lim_{c\to 1^+} 3(x-1)^{1/3}\Big]_c^3 \\ &= \lim_{c\to 1^+} \Big[3(3-1)^{1/3} - 3(c-1)^{1/3}\Big] = 3\sqrt[3]{2}\end{aligned}$$

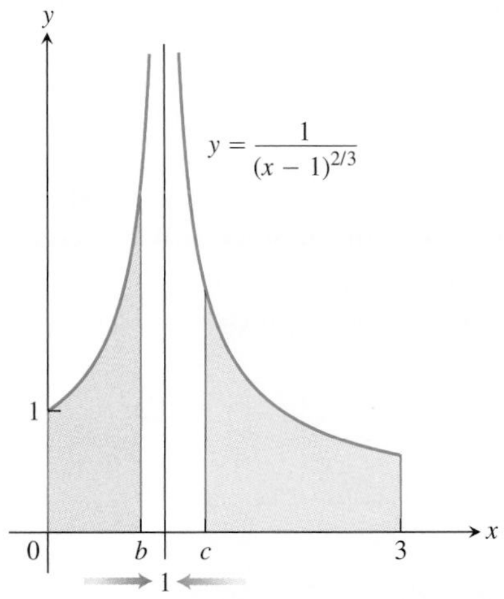

FIGURE 7.18 Example 5 shows that the area under the curve exists (so it is a real number).

We conclude that

$$\int_0^3 \frac{dx}{(x-1)^{2/3}} = 3 + 3\sqrt[3]{2}.$$ ■

Computer algebra systems can evaluate many convergent improper integrals. To evaluate the integral

$$\int_2^\infty \frac{x+3}{(x-1)(x^2+1)}\,dx$$

(which converges) using Maple, enter

$$> f := (x+3)/((x-1)*(x\char`^2+1));$$

Then use the integration command

$$> \text{int}(f, x = 2..\text{infinity});$$

Maple returns the answer

$$-\frac{1}{2}\pi + \ln(5) + \arctan(2).$$

To obtain a numerical result, use the evaluation command **evalf** and specify the number of digits, as follows:

$$> \text{evalf}(\%, 6);$$

The symbol % instructs the computer to evaluate the last expression on the screen, in this case $(-1/2)\pi + \ln(5) + \arctan(2)$. Maple returns 1.14579.

Using Mathematica, entering

$$\textit{In [1]:=} \text{ Integrate } [(x+3)/((x-1)(x\char`^2+1)), \{x, 2, \text{Infinity}\}]$$

returns

$$\textit{Out [1]=} \frac{-\pi}{2} + \text{ArcTan}[2] + \text{Log}[5].$$

To obtain a numerical result with six digits, use the command "N[%, 6]"; it also yields 1.14579.

Tests for Convergence and Divergence

When we cannot evaluate an improper integral directly, we try to determine whether it converges or diverges. If the integral diverges, that's the end of the story. If it converges, we can use numerical methods to approximate its value. The principal tests for convergence or divergence are the Direct Comparison Test and the Limit Comparison Test.

EXAMPLE 6 Does the integral $\int_1^\infty e^{-x^2}\,dx$ converge?

Solution By definition,

$$\int_1^\infty e^{-x^2}\,dx = \lim_{b\to\infty}\int_1^b e^{-x^2}\,dx.$$

We cannot evaluate this integral directly because it is nonelementary. But we *can* show that its limit as $b \to \infty$ is finite. We know that $\int_1^b e^{-x^2}\,dx$ is an increasing function of

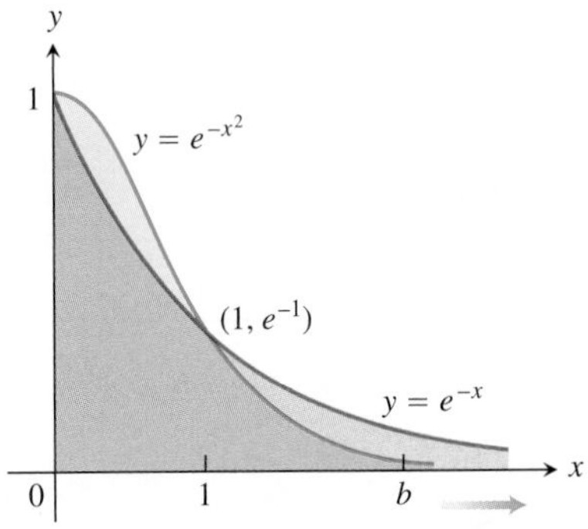

FIGURE 7.19 The graph of e^{-x^2} lies below the graph of e^{-x} for $x > 1$ (Example 6).

b. Therefore either it becomes infinite as $b \to \infty$ or it has a finite limit as $b \to \infty$. It does not become infinite: For every value of $x \geq 1$ we have $e^{-x^2} \leq e^{-x}$ (Figure 7.19), so that

$$\int_1^b e^{-x^2}\,dx \leq \int_1^b e^{-x}\,dx = -e^{-b} + e^{-1} < e^{-1} \approx 0.36788.$$

Hence

$$\int_1^\infty e^{-x^2}\,dx = \lim_{b\to\infty} \int_1^b e^{-x^2}\,dx$$

converges to some definite finite value. We do not know exactly what the value is except that it is something positive and less than 0.37. Here we are relying on the completeness property of the real numbers, discussed in Appendix 7. ■

The comparison of e^{-x^2} and e^{-x} in Example 6 is a special case of the following test.

Historical Biography

Karl Weierstrass
(1815–1897)

THEOREM 2—Direct Comparison Test Let f and g be continuous on $[a, \infty)$ with $0 \leq f(x) \leq g(x)$ for all $x \geq a$. Then

1. $\displaystyle\int_a^\infty f(x)\,dx$ converges if $\displaystyle\int_a^\infty g(x)\,dx$ converges.

2. $\displaystyle\int_a^\infty g(x)\,dx$ diverges if $\displaystyle\int_a^\infty f(x)\,dx$ diverges.

Proof The reasoning behind the argument establishing Theorem 2 is similar to that in Example 6. If $0 \leq f(x) \leq g(x)$ for $x \geq a$, then

$$\int_a^b f(x)\,dx \leq \int_a^b g(x)\,dx, \qquad b > a.$$

From this it can be argued, as in Example 6, that

$$\int_a^\infty f(x)\,dx \quad \text{converges if} \quad \int_a^\infty g(x)\,dx \quad \text{converges.}$$

Turning this around says that

$$\int_a^\infty g(x)\,dx \quad \text{diverges if} \quad \int_a^\infty f(x)\,dx \quad \text{diverges.}$$ ■

EXAMPLE 7

(a) $\displaystyle\int_1^\infty \frac{\sin^2 x}{x^2}\,dx$ converges because

$$0 \leq \frac{\sin^2 x}{x^2} \leq \frac{1}{x^2} \text{ on } [1, \infty) \quad \text{and} \quad \int_1^\infty \frac{1}{x^2}\,dx \quad \text{converges.}$$ Example 3

(b) $\displaystyle\int_1^\infty \frac{1}{\sqrt{x^2 - 0.1}}\,dx$ diverges because

$$\frac{1}{\sqrt{x^2 - 0.1}} \geq \frac{1}{x} \text{ on } [1, \infty) \quad \text{and} \quad \int_1^\infty \frac{1}{x}\,dx \quad \text{diverges.} \qquad \text{Example 3}$$

■

> **THEOREM 3—Limit Comparison Test** If the positive functions f and g are continuous on $[a, \infty)$ and if
>
> $$\lim_{x\to\infty} \frac{f(x)}{g(x)} = L, \qquad 0 < L < \infty,$$
>
> then
>
> $$\int_a^\infty f(x)\,dx \quad \text{and} \quad \int_a^\infty g(x)\,dx$$
>
> both converge or both diverge.

A proof of Theorem 3 is given in advanced calculus.

Although the improper integrals of two functions from a to ∞ may both converge, this does not mean that their integrals necessarily have the same value, as the next example shows.

EXAMPLE 8 Show that

$$\int_1^\infty \frac{dx}{1 + x^2}$$

converges by comparison with $\int_1^\infty (1/x^2)\,dx$. Find and compare the two integral values.

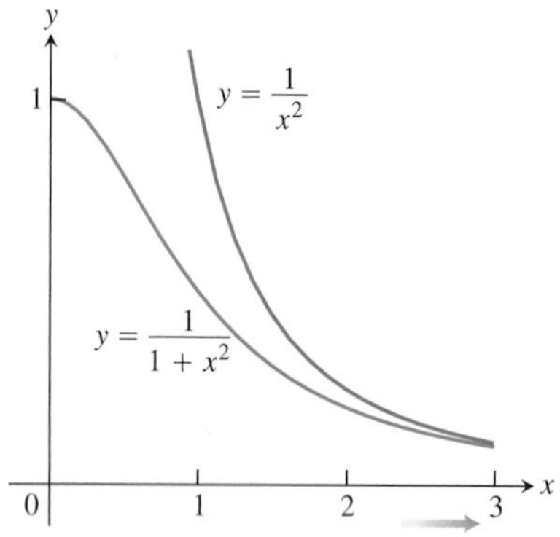

FIGURE 7.20 The functions in Example 8.

Solution The functions $f(x) = 1/x^2$ and $g(x) = 1/(1 + x^2)$ are positive and continuous on $[1, \infty)$. Also,

$$\begin{aligned}\lim_{x\to\infty} \frac{f(x)}{g(x)} &= \lim_{x\to\infty} \frac{1/x^2}{1/(1 + x^2)} = \lim_{x\to\infty} \frac{1 + x^2}{x^2} \\ &= \lim_{x\to\infty} \left(\frac{1}{x^2} + 1\right) = 0 + 1 = 1,\end{aligned}$$

a positive finite limit (Figure 7.20). Therefore, $\displaystyle\int_1^\infty \frac{dx}{1 + x^2}$ converges because $\displaystyle\int_1^\infty \frac{dx}{x^2}$ converges.

The integrals converge to different values, however.

$$\int_1^\infty \frac{dx}{x^2} = \frac{1}{2 - 1} = 1 \qquad \text{Example 3}$$

and

$$\begin{aligned}\int_1^\infty \frac{dx}{1 + x^2} &= \lim_{b\to\infty} \int_1^b \frac{dx}{1 + x^2} \\ &= \lim_{b\to\infty} [\tan^{-1} b - \tan^{-1} 1] = \frac{\pi}{2} - \frac{\pi}{4} = \frac{\pi}{4}\end{aligned}$$

■

EXERCISES 7.7

Evaluate the integrals in Exercises 1–34 without using tables.

1. $\int_0^\infty \frac{dx}{x^2+1}$
2. $\int_1^\infty \frac{dx}{x^{1.001}}$
3. $\int_0^1 \frac{dx}{\sqrt{x}}$
4. $\int_0^4 \frac{dx}{\sqrt{4-x}}$
5. $\int_{-1}^1 \frac{dx}{x^{2/3}}$
6. $\int_{-8}^1 \frac{dx}{x^{1/3}}$
7. $\int_0^1 \frac{dx}{\sqrt{1-x^2}}$
8. $\int_0^1 \frac{dr}{r^{0.999}}$
9. $\int_{-\infty}^{-2} \frac{2\,dx}{x^2-1}$
10. $\int_{-\infty}^2 \frac{2\,dx}{x^2+4}$
11. $\int_2^\infty \frac{2}{v^2-v}\,dv$
12. $\int_2^\infty \frac{2\,dt}{t^2-1}$
13. $\int_{-\infty}^\infty \frac{2x\,dx}{(x^2+1)^2}$
14. $\int_{-\infty}^\infty \frac{x\,dx}{(x^2+4)^{3/2}}$
15. $\int_0^1 \frac{\theta+1}{\sqrt{\theta^2+2\theta}}\,d\theta$
16. $\int_0^2 \frac{s+1}{\sqrt{4-s^2}}\,ds$
17. $\int_0^\infty \frac{dx}{(1+x)\sqrt{x}}$
18. $\int_1^\infty \frac{1}{x\sqrt{x^2-1}}\,dx$
19. $\int_0^\infty \frac{dv}{(1+v^2)(1+\tan^{-1} v)}$
20. $\int_0^\infty \frac{16\tan^{-1} x}{1+x^2}\,dx$
21. $\int_{-\infty}^0 \theta e^\theta\,d\theta$
22. $\int_0^\infty 2e^{-\theta}\sin\theta\,d\theta$
23. $\int_{-\infty}^0 e^{-|x|}\,dx$
24. $\int_{-\infty}^\infty 2xe^{-x^2}\,dx$
25. $\int_0^1 x\ln x\,dx$
26. $\int_0^1 (-\ln x)\,dx$
27. $\int_0^2 \frac{ds}{\sqrt{4-s^2}}$
28. $\int_0^1 \frac{4r\,dr}{\sqrt{1-r^4}}$
29. $\int_1^2 \frac{ds}{s\sqrt{s^2-1}}$
30. $\int_2^4 \frac{dt}{t\sqrt{t^2-4}}$
31. $\int_{-1}^4 \frac{dx}{\sqrt{|x|}}$
32. $\int_0^2 \frac{dx}{\sqrt{|x-1|}}$
33. $\int_{-1}^\infty \frac{d\theta}{\theta^2+5\theta+6}$
34. $\int_0^\infty \frac{dx}{(x+1)(x^2+1)}$

In Exercises 35–64, use integration, the Direct Comparison Test, or the Limit Comparison Test to test the integrals for convergence. If more than one method applies, use whatever method you prefer.

35. $\int_0^{\pi/2} \tan\theta\,d\theta$
36. $\int_0^{\pi/2} \cot\theta\,d\theta$
37. $\int_0^\pi \frac{\sin\theta\,d\theta}{\sqrt{\pi-\theta}}$
38. $\int_{-\pi/2}^{\pi/2} \frac{\cos\theta\,d\theta}{(\pi-2\theta)^{1/3}}$
39. $\int_0^{\ln 2} x^{-2}e^{-1/x}\,dx$
40. $\int_0^1 \frac{e^{-\sqrt{x}}}{\sqrt{x}}\,dx$
41. $\int_0^\pi \frac{dt}{\sqrt{t}+\sin t}$
42. $\int_0^1 \frac{dt}{t-\sin t}$ (*Hint:* $t \ge \sin t$ for $t \ge 0$)
43. $\int_0^2 \frac{dx}{1-x^2}$
44. $\int_0^2 \frac{dx}{1-x}$
45. $\int_{-1}^1 \ln|x|\,dx$
46. $\int_{-1}^1 -x\ln|x|\,dx$
47. $\int_1^\infty \frac{dx}{x^3+1}$
48. $\int_4^\infty \frac{dx}{\sqrt{x}-1}$
49. $\int_2^\infty \frac{dv}{\sqrt{v-1}}$
50. $\int_0^\infty \frac{d\theta}{1+e^\theta}$
51. $\int_0^\infty \frac{dx}{\sqrt{x^6+1}}$
52. $\int_2^\infty \frac{dx}{\sqrt{x^2-1}}$
53. $\int_1^\infty \frac{\sqrt{x+1}}{x^2}\,dx$
54. $\int_2^\infty \frac{x\,dx}{\sqrt{x^4-1}}$
55. $\int_\pi^\infty \frac{2+\cos x}{x}\,dx$
56. $\int_\pi^\infty \frac{1+\sin x}{x^2}\,dx$
57. $\int_4^\infty \frac{2\,dt}{t^{3/2}-1}$
58. $\int_2^\infty \frac{1}{\ln x}\,dx$
59. $\int_1^\infty \frac{e^x}{x}\,dx$
60. $\int_{e^e}^\infty \ln(\ln x)\,dx$
61. $\int_1^\infty \frac{1}{\sqrt{e^x-x}}\,dx$
62. $\int_1^\infty \frac{1}{e^x-2^x}\,dx$
63. $\int_{-\infty}^\infty \frac{dx}{\sqrt{x^4+1}}$
64. $\int_{-\infty}^\infty \frac{dx}{e^x+e^{-x}}$

65. Find the values of p for which each integral converges.

 a. $\int_1^2 \frac{dx}{x(\ln x)^p}$ b. $\int_2^\infty \frac{dx}{x(\ln x)^p}$

66. **$\int_{-\infty}^\infty f(x)\,dx$ may not equal $\lim_{b\to\infty}\int_{-b}^b f(x)\,dx$** Show that

$$\int_0^\infty \frac{2x\,dx}{x^2+1}$$

diverges and hence that

$$\int_{-\infty}^\infty \frac{2x\,dx}{x^2+1}$$

diverges. Then show that

$$\lim_{b\to\infty}\int_{-b}^b \frac{2x\,dx}{x^2+1} = 0.$$

Exercises 67–70 are about the infinite region in the first quadrant between the curve $y = e^{-x}$ and the x-axis.

67. Find the area of the region.

68. Find the centroid of the region.

69. Find the volume of the solid generated by revolving the region about the y-axis.

70. Find the volume of the solid generated by revolving the region about the x-axis.

71. Find the area of the region that lies between the curves $y = \sec x$ and $y = \tan x$ from $x = 0$ to $x = \pi/2$.

72. The region in Exercise 71 is revolved about the x-axis to generate a solid.

a. Find the volume of the solid.

b. Show that the inner and outer surfaces of the solid have infinite area.

73. Estimating the value of a convergent improper integral whose domain is infinite

a. Show that

$$\int_3^\infty e^{-3x}\,dx = \frac{1}{3}e^{-9} < 0.000042,$$

and hence that $\int_3^\infty e^{-x^2}\,dx < 0.000042$. Explain why this means that $\int_0^\infty e^{-x^2}\,dx$ can be replaced by $\int_0^3 e^{-x^2}\,dx$ without introducing an error of magnitude greater than 0.000042.

T **b.** Evaluate $\int_0^3 e^{-x^2}\,dx$ numerically.

74. The infinite paint can or Gabriel's horn As Example 3 shows, the integral $\int_1^\infty (dx/x)$ diverges. This means that the integral

$$\int_1^\infty 2\pi \frac{1}{x}\sqrt{1 + \frac{1}{x^4}}\,dx,$$

which measures the *surface area* of the solid of revolution traced out by revolving the curve $y = 1/x$, $1 \le x$, about the x-axis, diverges also. By comparing the two integrals, we see that, for every finite value $b > 1$,

$$\int_1^b 2\pi \frac{1}{x}\sqrt{1 + \frac{1}{x^4}}\,dx > 2\pi \int_1^b \frac{1}{x}\,dx.$$

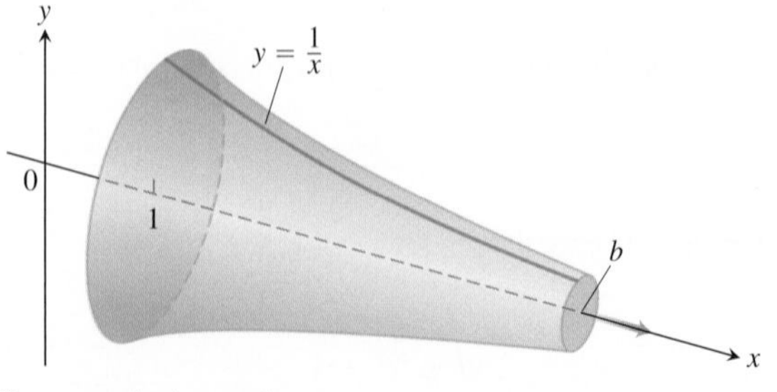

However, the integral

$$\int_1^\infty \pi\left(\frac{1}{x}\right)^2 dx$$

for the *volume* of the solid converges. **(a)** Calculate it. **(b)** This solid of revolution is sometimes described as a can that does not hold enough paint to cover its own interior. Think about that for a moment. It is common sense that a finite amount of paint cannot cover an infinite surface. But if we fill the horn with paint (a finite amount), then we *will* have covered an infinite surface. Explain the apparent contradiction.

75. Sine-integral function The integral

$$\text{Si}(x) = \int_0^x \frac{\sin t}{t}\,dt,$$

called the *sine-integral function*, has important applications in optics.

T **a.** Plot the integrand $(\sin t)/t$ for $t > 0$. Is the Si function everywhere increasing or decreasing? Do you think $\text{Si}(x) = 0$ for $x > 0$? Check your answers by graphing the function $\text{Si}(x)$ for $0 \le x \le 25$.

b. Explore the convergence of

$$\int_0^\infty \frac{\sin t}{t}\,dt.$$

If it converges, what is its value?

76. Error function The function

$$\text{erf}(x) = \int_0^x \frac{2e^{-t^2}}{\sqrt{\pi}}\,dt,$$

called the *error function*, has important applications in probability and statistics.

T **a.** Plot the error function for $0 \le x \le 25$.

b. Explore the convergence of

$$\int_0^\infty \frac{2e^{-t^2}}{\sqrt{\pi}}\,dt.$$

If it converges, what appears to be its value? You will see how to confirm your estimate in Section 13.4, Exercise 31.

77. Normal probability distribution function The function

$$f(x) = \frac{1}{\sigma\sqrt{2\pi}}e^{-\frac{1}{2}\left(\frac{x-\mu}{\sigma}\right)^2}$$

is called the *normal probability density function* with mean μ and standard deviation σ. The number μ tells where the distribution is centered, and σ measures the "scatter" around the mean.

From the theory of probability, it is known that

$$\int_{-\infty}^\infty f(x)\,dx = 1.$$

In what follows, let $\mu = 0$ and $\sigma = 1$.

T **a.** Draw the graph of f. Find the intervals on which f is increasing, the intervals on which f is decreasing, and any local extreme values and where they occur.

b. Evaluate

$$\int_{-n}^{n} f(x)\,dx$$

for $n = 1, 2, 3$.

c. Give a convincing argument that

$$\int_{-\infty}^{\infty} f(x)\,dx = 1.$$

(*Hint:* Show that $0 < f(x) < e^{-x/2}$ for $x > 1$, and for $b > 1$,

$$\int_{b}^{\infty} e^{-x/2}\,dx \to 0 \quad \text{as} \quad b \to \infty.)$$

78. Show that if $f(x)$ is integrable on every interval of real numbers and a and b are real numbers with $a < b$, then

a. $\int_{-\infty}^{a} f(x)\,dx$ and $\int_{a}^{\infty} f(x)\,dx$ both converge if and only if $\int_{-\infty}^{b} f(x)\,dx$ and $\int_{b}^{\infty} f(x)\,dx$ both converge.

b. $\int_{-\infty}^{a} f(x)\,dx + \int_{a}^{\infty} f(x)\,dx = \int_{-\infty}^{b} f(x)\,dx + \int_{b}^{\infty} f(x)\,dx$ when the integrals involved converge.

COMPUTER EXPLORATIONS

In Exercises 79–82, use a CAS to explore the integrals for various values of p (include noninteger values). For what values of p does the integral converge? What is the value of the integral when it does converge? Plot the integrand for various values of p.

79. $\displaystyle\int_{0}^{e} x^p \ln x\,dx$

80. $\displaystyle\int_{e}^{\infty} x^p \ln x\,dx$

81. $\displaystyle\int_{0}^{\infty} x^p \ln x\,dx$

82. $\displaystyle\int_{-\infty}^{\infty} x^p \ln |x|\,dx$

Chapter 7 Questions to Guide Your Review

1. What is the formula for integration by parts? Where does it come from? Why might you want to use it?
2. When applying the formula for integration by parts, how do you choose the u and dv? How can you apply integration by parts to an integral of the form $\int f(x)\,dx$?
3. What is the goal of the method of partial fractions?
4. When the degree of a polynomial $f(x)$ is less than the degree of a polynomial $g(x)$, how do you write $f(x)/g(x)$ as a sum of partial fractions if $g(x)$
   a. is a product of distinct linear factors?
   b. consists of a repeated linear factor?
   c. contains an irreducible quadratic factor?
   What do you do if the degree of f is *not* less than the degree of g?
5. If an integrand is a product of the form $\sin^n x \cos^m x$, where m and n are nonnegative integers, how do you evaluate the integral? Give a specific example of each case.
6. What substitutions are made to evaluate integrals of $\sin mx \sin nx$, $\sin mx \cos nx$, and $\cos mx \cos nx$? Give an example of each case.
7. What substitutions are sometimes used to transform integrals involving $\sqrt{a^2 - x^2}$, $\sqrt{a^2 + x^2}$, and $\sqrt{x^2 - a^2}$ into integrals that can be evaluated directly? Give an example of each case.
8. What restrictions can you place on the variables involved in the three basic trigonometric substitutions to make sure the substitutions are reversible (have inverses)?
9. How are integral tables typically used? What do you do if a particular integral you want to evaluate is not listed in the table?
10. What is a reduction formula? How are reduction formulas used? Give an example.
11. You are collaborating to produce a short "how-to" manual for numerical integration, and you are writing about the Trapezoidal Rule. **(a)** What would you say about the rule itself and how to use it? How to achieve accuracy? **(b)** What would you say if you were writing about Simpson's Rule instead?
12. How would you compare the relative merits of Simpson's Rule and the Trapezoidal Rule?
13. What is an improper integral of Type I? Type II? How are the values of various types of improper integrals defined? Give examples.
14. What tests are available for determining the convergence and divergence of improper integrals that cannot be evaluated directly? Give examples of their use.

Chapter 7 Practice Exercises

Evaluate the integrals in Exercises 1–8 using integration by parts.

1. $\displaystyle\int \ln(x+1)\,dx$

2. $\displaystyle\int x^2 \ln x\,dx$

3. $\displaystyle\int \tan^{-1} 3x\,dx$

4. $\displaystyle\int \cos^{-1}\left(\frac{x}{2}\right) dx$

5. $\int (x+1)^2 e^x\,dx$

6. $\int x^2 \sin(1-x)\,dx$

7. $\int e^x \cos 2x\,dx$

8. $\int e^{-2x} \sin 3x\,dx$

Evaluate the integrals in Exercises 9–28. It may be necessary to use a substitution first.

9. $\int \frac{x\,dx}{x^2-3x+2}$

10. $\int \frac{x\,dx}{x^2+4x+3}$

11. $\int \frac{dx}{x(x+1)^2}$

12. $\int \frac{x+1}{x^2(x-1)}\,dx$

13. $\int \frac{\sin\theta\,d\theta}{\cos^2\theta+\cos\theta-2}$

14. $\int \frac{\cos\theta\,d\theta}{\sin^2\theta+\sin\theta-6}$

15. $\int \frac{3x^2+4x+4}{x^3+x}\,dx$

16. $\int \frac{4x\,dx}{x^3+4x}$

17. $\int \frac{v+3}{2v^3-8v}\,dv$

18. $\int \frac{(3v-7)\,dv}{(v-1)(v-2)(v-3)}$

19. $\int \frac{dt}{t^4+4t^2+3}$

20. $\int \frac{t\,dt}{t^4-t^2-2}$

21. $\int \frac{x^3+x^2}{x^2+x-2}\,dx$

22. $\int \frac{x^3+1}{x^3-x}\,dx$

23. $\int \frac{x^3+4x^2}{x^2+4x+3}\,dx$

24. $\int \frac{2x^3+x^2-21x+24}{x^2+2x-8}\,dx$

25. $\int \frac{dx}{x\left(3\sqrt{x+1}\right)}$

26. $\int \frac{dx}{x\left(1+\sqrt[3]{x}\right)}$

27. $\int \frac{ds}{e^s-1}$

28. $\int \frac{ds}{\sqrt{e^s+1}}$

Evaluate the integrals in Exercises 29–32 **(a)** without using a trigonometric substitution, **(b)** using a trigonometric substitution.

29. $\int \frac{y\,dy}{\sqrt{16-y^2}}$

30. $\int \frac{x\,dx}{\sqrt{4+x^2}}$

31. $\int \frac{x\,dx}{4-x^2}$

32. $\int \frac{t\,dt}{\sqrt{4t^2-1}}$

Evaluate the integrals in Exercises 33–36.

33. $\int \frac{x\,dx}{9-x^2}$

34. $\int \frac{dx}{x(9-x^2)}$

35. $\int \frac{dx}{9-x^2}$

36. $\int \frac{dx}{\sqrt{9-x^2}}$

Evaluate the integrals in Exercises 37–44.

37. $\int \sin^3 x \cos^4 x\,dx$

38. $\int \cos^5 x \sin^5 x\,dx$

39. $\int \tan^4 x \sec^2 x\,dx$

40. $\int \tan^3 x \sec^3 x\,dx$

41. $\int \sin 5\theta \cos 6\theta\,d\theta$

42. $\int \cos 3\theta \cos 3\theta\,d\theta$

43. $\int \sqrt{1+\cos(t/2)}\,dt$

44. $\int e^t\sqrt{\tan^2 e^t+1}\,dt$

45. According to the error-bound formula for Simpson's Rule, how many subintervals should you use to be sure of estimating the value of

$$\ln 3 = \int_1^3 \frac{1}{x}\,dx$$

by Simpson's Rule with an error of no more than 10^{-4} in absolute value? (Remember that for Simpson's Rule, the number of subintervals has to be even.)

46. A brief calculation shows that if $0 \le x \le 1$, then the second derivative of $f(x) = \sqrt{1+x^4}$ lies between 0 and 8. Based on this, about how many subdivisions would you need to estimate the integral of f from 0 to 1 with an error no greater than 10^{-3} in absolute value using the Trapezoidal Rule?

47. A direct calculation shows that

$$\int_0^{\pi} 2\sin^2 x\,dx = \pi.$$

How close do you come to this value by using the Trapezoidal Rule with $n = 6$? Simpson's Rule with $n = 6$? Try them and find out.

48. You are planning to use Simpson's Rule to estimate the value of the integral

$$\int_1^2 f(x)\,dx$$

with an error magnitude less than 10^{-5}. You have determined that $|f^{(4)}(x)| \le 3$ throughout the interval of integration. How many subintervals should you use to assure the required accuracy? (Remember that for Simpson's Rule the number has to be even.)

49. **Mean temperature** Compute the average value of the temperature function

$$f(x) = 37\sin\left(\frac{2\pi}{365}(x-101)\right) + 25$$

for a 365-day year. This is one way to estimate the annual mean air temperature in Fairbanks, Alaska. The National Weather Service's official figure, a numerical average of the daily normal mean air temperatures for the year, is 25.7°F, which is slightly higher than the average value of $f(x)$.

50. **Heat capacity of a gas** Heat capacity C_v is the amount of heat required to raise the temperature of a given mass of gas with constant volume by 1°C, measured in units of cal/deg-mol (calories per degree gram molecular weight). The heat capacity of oxygen depends on its temperature T and satisfies the formula

$$C_v = 8.27 + 10^{-5}(26T - 1.87T^2).$$

Find the average value of C_v for $20° \le T \le 675°$C and the temperature at which it is attained.

51. **Fuel efficiency** An automobile computer gives a digital readout of fuel consumption in gallons per hour. During a trip, a passenger recorded the fuel consumption every 5 min for a full hour of travel.

Time	Gal/h	Time	Gal/h
0	2.5	35	2.5
5	2.4	40	2.4
10	2.3	45	2.3
15	2.4	50	2.4
20	2.4	55	2.4
25	2.5	60	2.3
30	2.6		

a. Use the Trapezoidal Rule to approximate the total fuel consumption during the hour.

b. If the automobile covered 60 mi in the hour, what was its fuel efficiency (in miles per gallon) for that portion of the trip?

52. A new parking lot To meet the demand for parking, your town has allocated the area shown here. As the town engineer, you have been asked by the town council to find out if the lot can be built for \$11,000. The cost to clear the land will be \$0.10 a square foot, and the lot will cost \$2.00 a square foot to pave. Use Simpson's Rule to find out if the job can be done for \$11,000.

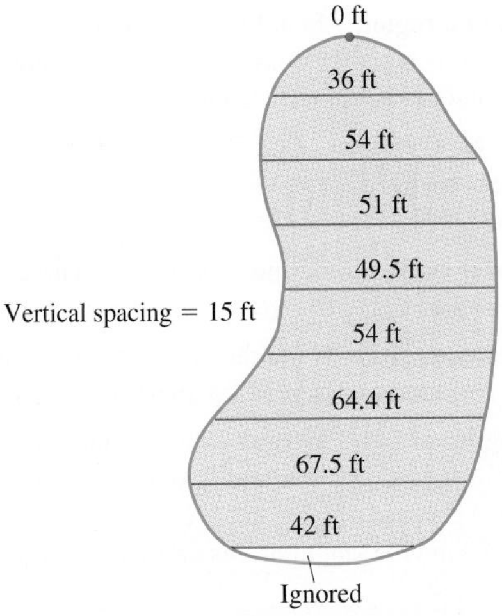

Evaluate the improper integrals in Exercises 53–62.

53. $\displaystyle\int_0^3 \frac{dx}{\sqrt{9-x^2}}$ **54.** $\displaystyle\int_0^1 \ln x\,dx$

55. $\displaystyle\int_{-1}^1 \frac{dy}{y^{2/3}}$ **56.** $\displaystyle\int_{-2}^0 \frac{d\theta}{(\theta+1)^{3/5}}$

57. $\displaystyle\int_3^\infty \frac{2\,du}{u^2-2u}$ **58.** $\displaystyle\int_1^\infty \frac{3v-1}{4v^3-v^2}\,dv$

59. $\displaystyle\int_0^\infty x^2e^{-x}\,dx$ **60.** $\displaystyle\int_{-\infty}^0 xe^{3x}\,dx$

61. $\displaystyle\int_{-\infty}^\infty \frac{dx}{4x^2+9}$ **62.** $\displaystyle\int_{-\infty}^\infty \frac{4dx}{x^2+16}$

Which of the improper integrals in Exercises 63–68 converge and which diverge?

63. $\displaystyle\int_6^\infty \frac{d\theta}{\sqrt{\theta^2+1}}$ **64.** $\displaystyle\int_0^\infty e^{-u}\cos u\,du$

65. $\displaystyle\int_1^\infty \frac{\ln z}{z}\,dz$ **66.** $\displaystyle\int_1^\infty \frac{e^{-t}}{\sqrt{t}}\,dt$

67. $\displaystyle\int_{-\infty}^\infty \frac{2\,dx}{e^x+e^{-x}}$ **68.** $\displaystyle\int_{-\infty}^\infty \frac{dx}{x^2(1+e^x)}$

Evaluate the integrals in Exercises 69–98. The integrals are listed in random order.

69. $\displaystyle\int \frac{x\,dx}{1+\sqrt{x}}$ **70.** $\displaystyle\int \frac{x^3+2}{4-x^2}\,dx$

71. $\displaystyle\int \frac{dx}{x(x^2+1)^2}$ **72.** $\displaystyle\int \frac{dx}{\sqrt{-2x-x^2}}$

73. $\displaystyle\int \frac{2-\cos x+\sin x}{\sin^2 x}\,dx$ **74.** $\displaystyle\int \frac{\sin^2\theta}{\cos^2\theta}\,d\theta$

75. $\displaystyle\int \frac{9\,dv}{81-v^4}$ **76.** $\displaystyle\int_2^\infty \frac{dx}{(x-1)^2}$

77. $\displaystyle\int \theta\cos(2\theta+1)\,d\theta$ **78.** $\displaystyle\int \frac{x^3\,dx}{x^2-2x+1}$

79. $\displaystyle\int \frac{\sin 2\theta\,d\theta}{(1+\cos 2\theta)^2}$ **80.** $\displaystyle\int_{\pi/4}^{\pi/2} \sqrt{1+\cos 4x}\,dx$

81. $\displaystyle\int \frac{x\,dx}{\sqrt{2-x}}$ **82.** $\displaystyle\int \frac{\sqrt{1-v^2}}{v^2}\,dv$

83. $\displaystyle\int \frac{dy}{y^2-2y+2}$ **84.** $\displaystyle\int \frac{x\,dx}{\sqrt{8-2x^2-x^4}}$

85. $\displaystyle\int \frac{z+1}{z^2(z^2+4)}\,dz$ **86.** $\displaystyle\int x^3e^{(x^2)}\,dx$

87. $\displaystyle\int \frac{t\,dt}{\sqrt{9-4t^2}}$ **88.** $\displaystyle\int \frac{\tan^{-1}x}{x^2}\,dx$

89. $\displaystyle\int \frac{e^t\,dt}{e^{2t}+3e^t+2}$ **90.** $\displaystyle\int \tan^3 t\,dt$

91. $\displaystyle\int_1^\infty \frac{\ln y}{y^3}\,dy$ **92.** $\displaystyle\int \frac{\cot v\,dv}{\ln\sin v}$

93. $\displaystyle\int e^{\ln\sqrt{x}}\,dx$ **94.** $\displaystyle\int e^\theta\sqrt{3+4e^\theta}\,d\theta$

95. $\displaystyle\int \frac{\sin 5t\,dt}{1+(\cos 5t)^2}$ **96.** $\displaystyle\int \frac{dv}{\sqrt{e^{2v}-1}}$

97. $\displaystyle\int \frac{dr}{1+\sqrt{r}}$ **98.** $\displaystyle\int \frac{4x^3-20x}{x^4-10x^2+9}\,dx$

Chapter 7 Additional and Advanced Exercises

Evaluate the integrals in Exercises 1–6.

1. $\int (\sin^{-1} x)^2 \, dx$

2. $\int \frac{dx}{x(x+1)(x+2)\cdots(x+m)}$

3. $\int x \sin^{-1} x \, dx$

4. $\int \sin^{-1} \sqrt{y} \, dy$

5. $\int \frac{dt}{t - \sqrt{1 - t^2}}$

6. $\int \frac{dx}{x^4 + 4}$

Evaluate the limits in Exercises 7 and 8.

7. $\lim_{x \to \infty} \int_{-x}^{x} \sin t \, dt$

8. $\lim_{x \to 0^+} x \int_{x}^{1} \frac{\cos t}{t^2} \, dt$

Evaluate the limits in Exercises 9 and 10 by identifying them with definite integrals and evaluating the integrals.

9. $\lim_{n \to \infty} \sum_{k=1}^{n} \ln \sqrt[n]{1 + \frac{k}{n}}$

10. $\lim_{n \to \infty} \sum_{k=0}^{n-1} \frac{1}{\sqrt{n^2 - k^2}}$

11. **Finding arc length** Find the length of the curve

$$y = \int_0^x \sqrt{\cos 2t} \, dt, \quad 0 \le x \le \pi/4.$$

12. **Finding arc length** Find the length of the curve $y = \ln(1 - x^2)$, $0 \le x \le 1/2$.

13. **Finding volume** The region in the first quadrant that is enclosed by the x-axis and the curve $y = 3x\sqrt{1 - x}$ is revolved about the y-axis to generate a solid. Find the volume of the solid.

14. **Finding volume** The region in the first quadrant that is enclosed by the x-axis, the curve $y = 5/\left(x\sqrt{5 - x}\right)$, and the lines $x = 1$ and $x = 4$ is revolved about the x-axis to generate a solid. Find the volume of the solid.

15. **Finding volume** The region in the first quadrant enclosed by the coordinate axes, the curve $y = e^x$, and the line $x = 1$ is revolved about the y-axis to generate a solid. Find the volume of the solid.

16. **Finding volume** The region in the first quadrant that is bounded above by the curve $y = e^x - 1$, below by the x-axis, and on the right by the line $x = \ln 2$ is revolved about the line $x = \ln 2$ to generate a solid. Find the volume of the solid.

17. **Finding volume** Let R be the "triangular" region in the first quadrant that is bounded above by the line $y = 1$, below by the curve $y = \ln x$, and on the left by the line $x = 1$. Find the volume of the solid generated by revolving R about

   a. the x-axis. **b.** the line $y = 1$.

18. **Finding volume** *(Continuation of Exercise 17.)* Find the volume of the solid generated by revolving the region R about

   a. the y-axis. **b.** the line $x = 1$.

19. **Finding volume** The region between the x-axis and the curve

$$y = f(x) = \begin{cases} 0, & x = 0 \\ x \ln x, & 0 < x \le 2 \end{cases}$$

is revolved about the x-axis to generate the solid shown here.

   a. Show that f is continuous at $x = 0$.

   b. Find the volume of the solid.

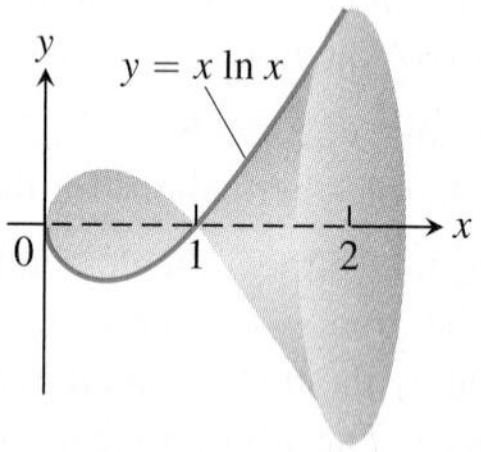

20. **Finding volume** The infinite region bounded by the coordinate axes and the curve $y = -\ln x$ in the first quadrant is revolved about the x-axis to generate a solid. Find the volume of the solid.

21. **Centroid of a region** Find the centroid of the region in the first quadrant that is bounded below by the x-axis, above by the curve $y = \ln x$, and on the right by the line $x = e$.

22. **Centroid of a region** Find the centroid of the region in the plane enclosed by the curves $y = \pm(1 - x^2)^{-1/2}$ and the lines $x = 0$ and $x = 1$.

23. **Length of a curve** Find the length of the curve $y = \ln x$ from $x = 1$ to $x = e$.

24. **Finding surface area** Find the area of the surface generated by revolving the curve in Exercise 23 about the y-axis.

25. **The length of an astroid** The graph of the equation $x^{2/3} + y^{2/3} = 1$ is one of a family of curves called *astroids* (not "asteroids") because of their starlike appearance (see accompanying figure). Find the length of this particular astroid.

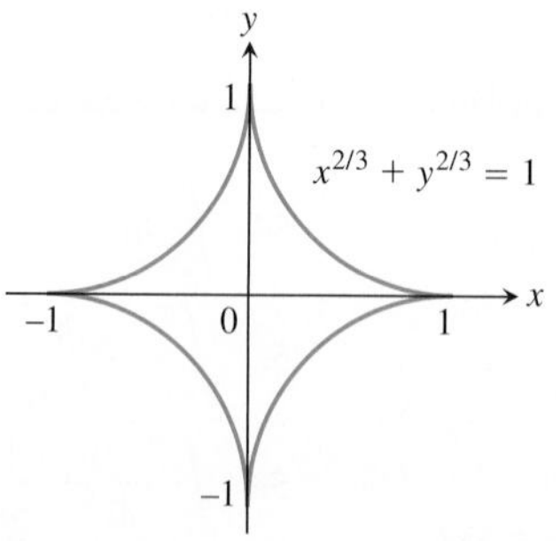

26. **The surface generated by an astroid** Find the area of the surface generated by revolving the curve in Exercise 25 about the x-axis.

27. For what value or values of a does

$$\int_1^{\infty}\left(\frac{ax}{x^2+1}-\frac{1}{2x}\right)dx$$

converge? Evaluate the corresponding integral(s).

28. For each $x > 0$, let $G(x) = \int_0^{\infty} e^{-xt}\,dt$. Prove that $xG(x) = 1$ for each $x > 0$.

29. **Infinite area and finite volume** What values of p have the following property: The area of the region between the curve $y = x^{-p}$, $1 \le x < \infty$, and the x-axis is infinite but the volume of the solid generated by revolving the region about the x-axis is finite.

30. **Infinite area and finite volume** What values of p have the following property: The area of the region in the first quadrant enclosed by the curve $y = x^{-p}$, the y-axis, the line $x = 1$, and the interval $[0, 1]$ on the x-axis is infinite but the volume of the solid generated by revolving the region about one of the coordinate axes is finite.

The Gamma Function and Stirling's Formula Euler's gamma function $\Gamma(x)$ ("gamma of x"; Γ is a Greek capital g) uses an integral to extend the factorial function from the nonnegative integers to other real values. The formula is

$$\Gamma(x) = \int_0^{\infty} t^{x-1}e^{-t}\,dt, \quad x > 0.$$

For each positive x, the number $\Gamma(x)$ is the integral of $t^{x-1}e^{-t}$ with respect to t from 0 to ∞. Figure 7.21 shows the graph of Γ near the origin. You will see how to calculate $\Gamma(1/2)$ if you do Additional Exercise 23 in Chapter 13.

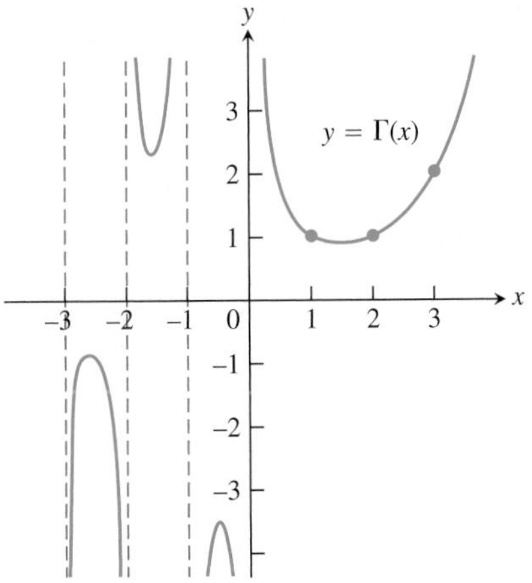

FIGURE 7.21 Euler's gamma function $\Gamma(x)$ is a continuous function of x whose value at each positive integer $n + 1$ is $n!$. The defining integral formula for Γ is valid only for $x > 0$, but we can extend Γ to negative noninteger values of x with the formula $\Gamma(x) = (\Gamma(x + 1))/x$, which is the subject of Exercise 31.

31. **If n is a nonnegative integer, $\Gamma(n + 1) = n!$**

a. Show that $\Gamma(1) = 1$.

b. Then apply integration by parts to the integral for $\Gamma(x + 1)$ to show that $\Gamma(x + 1) = x\Gamma(x)$. This gives to

$$\Gamma(2) = 1\Gamma(1) = 1$$
$$\Gamma(3) = 2\Gamma(2) = 2$$
$$\Gamma(4) = 3\Gamma(3) = 6$$
$$\vdots$$
$$\Gamma(n+1) = n\,\Gamma(n) = n! \qquad (1)$$

c. Use mathematical induction to verify Equation (1) for every nonnegative integer n.

32. **Stirling's formula** Scottish mathematician James Stirling (1692–1770) showed that

$$\lim_{x\to\infty}\left(\frac{e}{x}\right)^x\sqrt{\frac{x}{2\pi}}\,\Gamma(x) = 1,$$

so for large x,

$$\Gamma(x) = \left(\frac{x}{e}\right)^x\sqrt{\frac{2\pi}{x}}\,(1+\epsilon(x)), \qquad \epsilon(x)\to 0 \text{ as } x\to\infty. \qquad (2)$$

Dropping $\epsilon(x)$ leads to the approximation

$$\Gamma(x) \approx \left(\frac{x}{e}\right)^x\sqrt{\frac{2\pi}{x}} \qquad \textbf{(Stirling's formula)}. \qquad (3)$$

a. Stirling's approximation for $n!$ Use Equation (3) and the fact that $n! = n\Gamma(n)$ to show that

$$n! \approx \left(\frac{n}{e}\right)^n\sqrt{2n\pi} \qquad \textbf{(Stirling's approximation)}. \qquad (4)$$

As you will see if you do Exercise 90 in Section 8.1, Equation (4) leads to the approximation

$$\sqrt[n]{n!} \approx \frac{n}{e}. \qquad (5)$$

T **b.** Compare your calculator's value for n! with the value given by Stirling's approximation for $n = 10, 20, 30, \ldots$, as far as your calculator can go.

T **c.** A refinement of Equation (2) gives

$$\Gamma(x) = \left(\frac{x}{e}\right)^x\sqrt{\frac{2\pi}{x}}\,e^{1/(12x)}(1+\epsilon(x)),$$

or

$$\Gamma(x) \approx \left(\frac{x}{e}\right)^x\sqrt{\frac{2\pi}{x}}\,e^{1/(12x)}$$

which tells us that

$$n! \approx \left(\frac{n}{e}\right)^n\sqrt{2n\pi}\,e^{1/(12n)}. \qquad (6)$$

Compare the values given for 10! by your calculator, Stirling's approximation, and Equation (6).

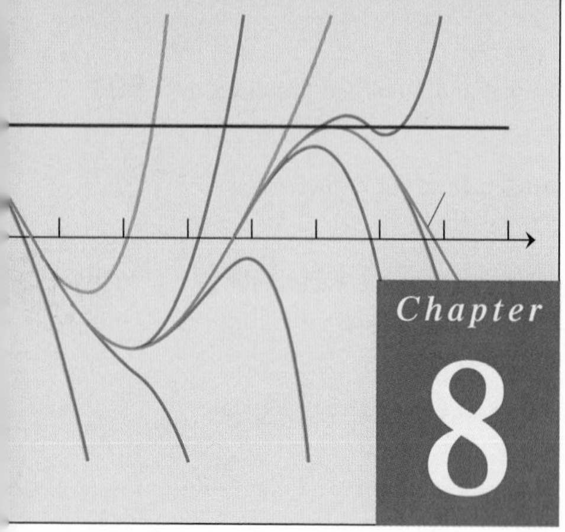

Chapter 8

INFINITE SEQUENCES AND SERIES

OVERVIEW Everyone knows how to add two numbers together, or even several. But how do you add infinitely many numbers together? In this chapter we answer this question, which is part of the theory of infinite sequences and series.

An important application of this theory is a method for representing a known differentiable function $f(x)$ as an infinite sum of powers of x, so it looks like a "polynomial with infinitely many terms." Moreover, the method extends our knowledge of how to evaluate, differentiate, and integrate polynomials, so we can work with even more general functions than those encountered so far. These new functions often solve important problems in science and engineering.

8.1 Sequences

HISTORICAL ESSAY

Sequences and Series

A sequence is a list of numbers

$$a_1, a_2, a_3, \ldots, a_n, \ldots$$

in a given order. Each of a_1, a_2, a_3 and so on represents a number. These are the **terms** of the sequence. For example the sequence

$$2, 4, 6, 8, 10, 12, \ldots, 2n, \ldots$$

has first term $a_1 = 2$, second term $a_2 = 4$ and nth term $a_n = 2n$. The integer n is called the **index** of a_n, and indicates where a_n occurs in the list. Order is important. The sequence $2, 4, 6, 8 \ldots$ is not the same as the sequence $4, 2, 6, 8 \ldots$.

We can think of the sequence

$$a_1, a_2, a_3, \ldots, a_n, \ldots$$

as a function that sends 1 to a_1, 2 to a_2, 3 to a_3, and in general sends the positive integer n to the nth term a_n. This leads to the formal definition of a sequence.

> **DEFINITION** An **infinite sequence** of numbers is a function whose domain is the set of positive integers.

The function associated with the sequence

$$2, 4, 6, 8, 10, 12, \ldots, 2n, \ldots$$

sends 1 to $a_1 = 2$, 2 to $a_2 = 4$, and so on. The general behavior of this sequence is described by the formula $a_n = 2n$.

We can equally well make the domain the integers larger than a given number n_0, and we allow sequences of this type also. For example, the sequence

$$12, 14, 16, 18, 20, 22\ldots$$

is described by the formula $a_n = 10 + 2n$. It can also be described by the simpler formula $b_n = 2n$, where the index n starts at 6 and increases. To allow such simpler formulas, we let the first index of the sequence be any integer. In the sequence above, $\{a_n\}$ starts with a_1 while $\{b_n\}$ starts with b_6.

Sequences can be described by writing rules that specify their terms, such as

$$a_n = \sqrt{n}, \qquad b_n = (-1)^{n+1}\frac{1}{n}, \qquad c_n = \frac{n-1}{n}, \qquad d_n = (-1)^{n+1}$$

or by listing terms,

$$\{a_n\} = \left\{\sqrt{1}, \sqrt{2}, \sqrt{3}, \ldots, \sqrt{n}, \ldots\right\}$$

$$\{b_n\} = \left\{1, -\frac{1}{2}, \frac{1}{3}, -\frac{1}{4}, \ldots, (-1)^{n+1}\frac{1}{n}, \ldots\right\}$$

$$\{c_n\} = \left\{0, \frac{1}{2}, \frac{2}{3}, \frac{3}{4}, \frac{4}{5}, \ldots, \frac{n-1}{n}, \ldots\right\}$$

$$\{d_n\} = \{1, -1, 1, -1, 1, -1, \ldots, (-1)^{n+1}, \ldots\}.$$

We also sometimes write

$$\{a_n\} = \left\{\sqrt{n}\right\}_{n=1}^{\infty}.$$

Figure 8.1 shows two ways to represent sequences graphically. The first marks the first few points from $a_1, a_2, a_3, \ldots, a_n, \ldots$ on the real axis. The second method shows the graph of the function defining the sequence. The function is defined only on integer inputs, and the graph consists of some points in the xy-plane, located at $(1, a_1), (2, a_2), \ldots, (n, a_n), \ldots$.

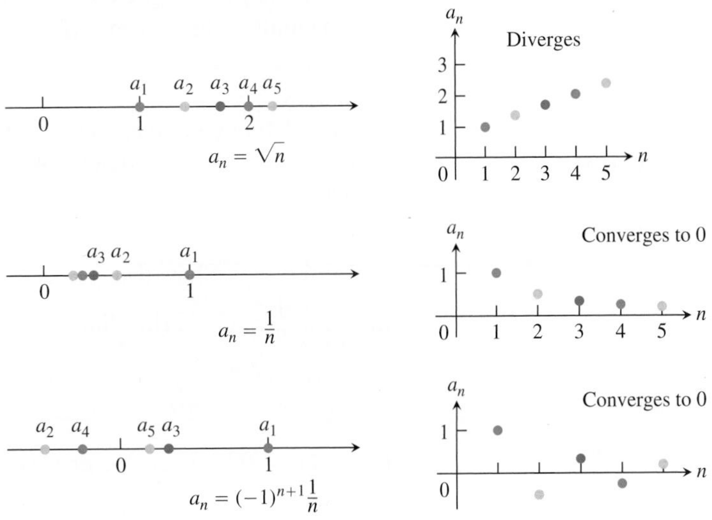

FIGURE 8.1 Sequences can be represented as points on the real line or as points in the plane where the horizontal axis n is the index number of the term and the vertical axis a_n is its value.

Convergence and Divergence

Sometimes the numbers in a sequence approach a single value as the index n increases. This happens in the sequence

$$\left\{1, \frac{1}{2}, \frac{1}{3}, \frac{1}{4}, \ldots, \frac{1}{n}, \ldots\right\}$$

whose terms approach 0 as n gets large, and in the sequence

$$\left\{0, \frac{1}{2}, \frac{2}{3}, \frac{3}{4}, \frac{4}{5}, \ldots, 1 - \frac{1}{n}, \ldots\right\}$$

whose terms approach 1. On the other hand, sequences like

$$\{\sqrt{1}, \sqrt{2}, \sqrt{3}, \ldots, \sqrt{n}, \ldots\}$$

have terms that get larger than any number as n increases, and sequences like

$$\{1, -1, 1, -1, 1, -1, \ldots, (-1)^{n+1}, \ldots\}$$

bounce back and forth between 1 and -1, never converging to a single value. The following definition captures the meaning of having a sequence converge to a limiting value. It says that if we go far enough out in the sequence, by taking the index n to be larger than some value N, the difference between a_n and the limit of the sequence becomes less than any preselected number $\epsilon > 0$.

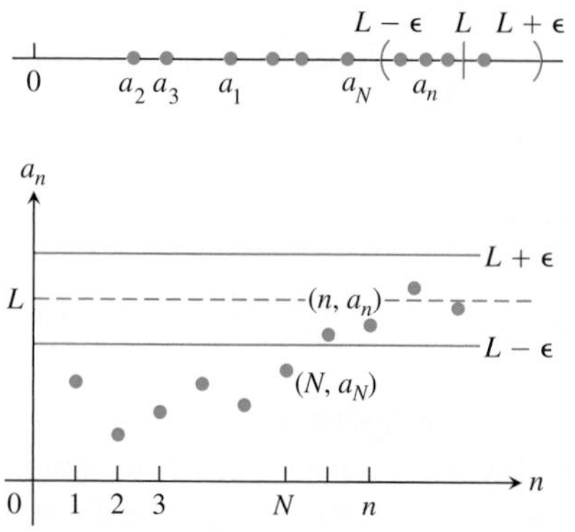

FIGURE 8.2 $a_n \rightarrow L$ if $y = L$ is a horizontal asymptote of the sequence of points $\{(n, a_n)\}$. In this figure, all the a_n's after a_N lie within ϵ of L.

DEFINITIONS The sequence $\{a_n\}$ **converges** to the number L if for every positive number ϵ there corresponds an integer N such that for all n,

$$n > N \quad \Rightarrow \quad |a_n - L| < \epsilon.$$

If no such number L exists, we say that $\{a_n\}$ **diverges.**

If $\{a_n\}$ converges to L, we write $\lim_{n\rightarrow\infty} a_n = L$, or simply $a_n \rightarrow L$, and call L the **limit** of the sequence (Figure 8.2).

The definition is very similar to the definition of the limit of a function $f(x)$ as x tends to ∞ ($\lim_{x\rightarrow\infty} f(x)$ in Section 2.4). We will exploit this connection to calculate limits of sequences.

HISTORICAL BIOGRAPHY

Nicole Oresme
(ca. 1320–1382)

EXAMPLE 1 Show that

(a) $\lim_{n\rightarrow\infty} \frac{1}{n} = 0$ **(b)** $\lim_{n\rightarrow\infty} k = k$ (any constant k)

Solution

(a) Let $\epsilon > 0$ be given. We must show that there exists an integer N such that for all n,

$$n > N \quad \Rightarrow \quad \left|\frac{1}{n} - 0\right| < \epsilon.$$

This implication will hold if $(1/n) < \epsilon$ or $n > 1/\epsilon$. If N is any integer greater than $1/\epsilon$, the implication will hold for all $n > N$. This proves that $\lim_{n\rightarrow\infty}(1/n) = 0$.

(b) Let $\epsilon > 0$ be given. We must show that there exists an integer N such that for all n,

$$n > N \quad \Rightarrow \quad |k - k| < \epsilon.$$

Since $k - k = 0$, we can use any positive integer for N and the implication will hold. This proves that $\lim_{n\to\infty} k = k$ for any constant k. ■

EXAMPLE 2 Show that the sequence $\{1, -1, 1, -1, 1, -1, \ldots, (-1)^{n+1}, \ldots\}$ diverges.

Solution Suppose the sequence converges to some number L. By choosing $\epsilon = 1/2$ in the definition of the limit, all terms a_n of the sequence with index n larger than some N must lie within $\epsilon = 1/2$ of L. Since the number 1 appears repeatedly as every other term of the sequence, we must have that the number 1 lies within the distance $\epsilon = 1/2$ of L. It follows that $|L - 1| < 1/2$, or equivalently, $1/2 < L < 3/2$. Likewise, the number -1 appears repeatedly in the sequence with arbitrarily high index. So we must also have that $|L - (-1)| < 1/2$, or equivalently, $-3/2 < L < -1/2$. But the number L cannot lie in both of the intervals $(1/2, 3/2)$ and $(-3/2, -1/2)$ because they have no overlap. Therefore, no such limit L exists and so the sequence diverges.

Note that the same argument works for any positive number ϵ smaller than 1, not just 1/2. ■

The sequence $\{\sqrt{n}\}$ also diverges, but for a different reason. As n increases, its terms become larger than any fixed number. We describe the behavior of this sequence by writing

$$\lim_{n\to\infty} \sqrt{n} = \infty.$$

In writing infinity as the limit of a sequence, we are not saying that the differences between the terms a_n and ∞ become small as n increases. Nor are we asserting that there is some number infinity that the sequence approaches. We are merely using a notation that captures the idea that a_n eventually gets and stays larger than any fixed number as n gets large.

DEFINITION The sequence $\{a_n\}$ **diverges to infinity** if for every number M there is an integer N such that for all n larger than N, $a_n > M$. If this condition holds we write

$$\lim_{n\to\infty} a_n = \infty \qquad \text{or} \qquad a_n \to \infty.$$

Similarly if for every number m there is an integer N such that for all $n > N$ we have $a_n < m$, then we say $\{a_n\}$ **diverges to negative infinity** and write

$$\lim_{n\to\infty} a_n = -\infty \qquad \text{or} \qquad a_n \to -\infty.$$

A sequence may diverge without diverging to infinity or negative infinity, as we saw in Example 2. The sequences $\{1, -2, 3, -4, 5, -6, 7, -8, \ldots\}$ and $\{1, 0, 2, 0, 3, 0, \ldots\}$ are also examples of such divergence.

Calculating Limits of Sequences

Since sequences are functions with domain restricted to the positive integers, it is not surprising that the theorems on limits of functions given in Chapter 2 have versions for sequences.

THEOREM 1 Let $\{a_n\}$ and $\{b_n\}$ be sequences of real numbers and let A and B be real numbers. The following rules hold if $\lim_{n\to\infty} a_n = A$ and $\lim_{n\to\infty} b_n = B$.

1. *Sum Rule:* $\lim_{n\to\infty}(a_n + b_n) = A + B$
2. *Difference Rule:* $\lim_{n\to\infty}(a_n - b_n) = A - B$
3. *Product Rule:* $\lim_{n\to\infty}(a_n \cdot b_n) = A \cdot B$
4. *Constant Multiple Rule:* $\lim_{n\to\infty}(k \cdot b_n) = k \cdot B$ (Any number k)
5. *Quotient Rule:* $\lim_{n\to\infty} \dfrac{a_n}{b_n} = \dfrac{A}{B}$ if $B \neq 0$

The proof is similar to that of Theorem 1 of Section 2.2, and is omitted.

EXAMPLE 3 By combining Theorem 1 with the limits of Example 1, we have:

(a) $\displaystyle \lim_{n\to\infty}\left(-\frac{1}{n}\right) = -1 \cdot \lim_{n\to\infty}\frac{1}{n} = -1 \cdot 0 = 0$ Constant Multiple Rule and Example 1a

(b) $\displaystyle \lim_{n\to\infty}\left(\frac{n-1}{n}\right) = \lim_{n\to\infty}\left(1 - \frac{1}{n}\right) = \lim_{n\to\infty} 1 - \lim_{n\to\infty}\frac{1}{n} = 1 - 0 = 1$ Difference Rule and Example 1a

(c) $\displaystyle \lim_{n\to\infty}\frac{5}{n^2} = 5 \cdot \lim_{n\to\infty}\frac{1}{n} \cdot \lim_{n\to\infty}\frac{1}{n} = 5 \cdot 0 \cdot 0 = 0$ Product Rule

(d) $\displaystyle \lim_{n\to\infty}\frac{4 - 7n^6}{n^6 + 3} = \lim_{n\to\infty}\frac{(4/n^6) - 7}{1 + (3/n^6)} = \frac{0 - 7}{1 + 0} = -7.$ Sum and Quotient rules ■

Be cautious in applying Theorem 1. It does not say, for example, that each of the sequences $\{a_n\}$ and $\{b_n\}$ have limits if their sum $\{a_n + b_n\}$ has a limit. For instance, $\{a_n\} = \{1, 2, 3, \dots\}$ and $\{b_n\} = \{-1, -2, -3, \dots\}$ both diverge, but their sum $\{a_n + b_n\} = \{0, 0, 0, \dots\}$ clearly converges to 0.

One consequence of Theorem 1 is that every nonzero multiple of a divergent sequence $\{a_n\}$ diverges. For suppose, to the contrary, that $\{ca_n\}$ converges for some number $c \neq 0$. Then, by taking $k = 1/c$ in the Constant Multiple Rule in Theorem 1, we see that the sequence

$$\left\{\frac{1}{c} \cdot ca_n\right\} = \{a_n\}$$

converges. Thus, $\{ca_n\}$ cannot converge unless $\{a_n\}$ also converges. If $\{a_n\}$ does not converge, then $\{ca_n\}$ does not converge.

The next theorem is the sequence version of the Sandwich Theorem in Section 2.2. You are asked to prove the theorem in Exercise 95.

THEOREM 2—The Sandwich Theorem for Sequences Let $\{a_n\}$, $\{b_n\}$, and $\{c_n\}$ be sequences of real numbers. If $a_n \le b_n \le c_n$ holds for all n beyond some index N, and if $\lim_{n\to\infty} a_n = \lim_{n\to\infty} c_n = L$, then $\lim_{n\to\infty} b_n = L$ also.

An immediate consequence of Theorem 2 is that, if $|b_n| \le c_n$ and $c_n \to 0$, then $b_n \to 0$ because $-c_n \le b_n \le c_n$. We use this fact in the next example.

EXAMPLE 4 Since $1/n \to 0$, we know that

(a) $\dfrac{\cos n}{n} \to 0$ because $-\dfrac{1}{n} \le \dfrac{\cos n}{n} \le \dfrac{1}{n}$;

(b) $\dfrac{1}{2^n} \to 0$ because $0 \le \dfrac{1}{2^n} \le \dfrac{1}{n}$;

(c) $(-1)^n \dfrac{1}{n} \to 0$ because $-\dfrac{1}{n} \le (-1)^n \dfrac{1}{n} \le \dfrac{1}{n}$. ■

The application of Theorems 1 and 2 is broadened by a theorem stating that applying a continuous function to a convergent sequence produces a convergent sequence. We state the theorem without proof (Exercise 96).

THEOREM 3—The Continuous Function Theorem for Sequences Let $\{a_n\}$ be a sequence of real numbers. If $a_n \to L$ and if f is a function that is continuous at L and defined at all a_n, then $f(a_n) \to f(L)$.

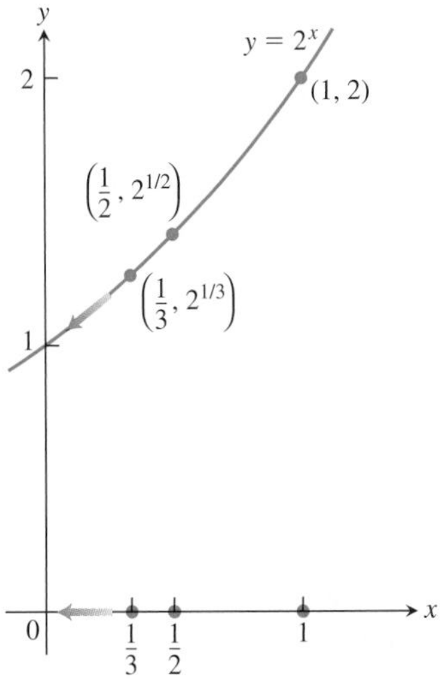

FIGURE 8.3 As $n \to \infty$, $1/n \to 0$ and $2^{1/n} \to 2^0$ (Example 6).

EXAMPLE 5 Show that $\sqrt{(n + 1)/n} \to 1$.

Solution We know that $(n + 1)/n \to 1$. Taking $f(x) = \sqrt{x}$ and $L = 1$ in Theorem 3 gives $\sqrt{(n + 1)/n} \to \sqrt{1} = 1$. ■

EXAMPLE 6 The sequence $\{1/n\}$ converges to 0. By taking $a_n = 1/n$, $f(x) = 2^x$, and $L = 0$ in Theorem 3, we see that $2^{1/n} = f(1/n) \to f(L) = 2^0 = 1$. The sequence $\{2^{1/n}\}$ converges to 1 (Figure 8.3).

Using l'Hôpital's Rule

The next theorem enables us to use l'Hôpital's Rule to find the limits of some sequences. It formalizes the connection between $\lim_{n\to\infty} a_n$ and $\lim_{x\to\infty} f(x)$.

THEOREM 4 Suppose that $f(x)$ is a function defined for all $x \ge n_0$ and that $\{a_n\}$ is a sequence of real numbers such that $a_n = f(n)$ for $n \ge n_0$. Then

$$\lim_{x\to\infty} f(x) = L \quad \Rightarrow \quad \lim_{n\to\infty} a_n = L.$$

Proof Suppose that $\lim_{x\to\infty} f(x) = L$. Then for each positive number ϵ there is a number M such that for all x,

$$x > M \quad \Rightarrow \quad |f(x) - L| < \epsilon.$$

Let N be an integer greater than M and greater than or equal to n_0. Then

$$n > N \quad \Rightarrow \quad a_n = f(n) \quad \text{and} \quad |a_n - L| = |f(n) - L| < \epsilon. \qquad ■$$

EXAMPLE 7 Show that

$$\lim_{n\to\infty} \frac{\ln n}{n} = 0.$$

Solution The function $(\ln x)/x$ is defined for all $x \geq 1$ and agrees with the given sequence at positive integers. Therefore, by Theorem 5, $\lim_{n\to\infty} (\ln n)/n$ will equal $\lim_{x\to\infty} (\ln x)/x$ if the latter exists. A single application of l'Hôpital's Rule shows that

$$\lim_{x\to\infty} \frac{\ln x}{x} = \lim_{x\to\infty} \frac{1/x}{1} = \frac{0}{1} = 0.$$

We conclude that $\lim_{n\to\infty} (\ln n)/n = 0$. ■

When we use l'Hôpital's Rule to find the limit of a sequence, we often treat n as a continuous real variable and differentiate directly with respect to n. This saves us from having to rewrite the formula for a_n as we did in Example 7.

EXAMPLE 8 Does the sequence whose nth term is

$$a_n = \left(\frac{n+1}{n-1}\right)^n$$

converge? If so, find $\lim_{n\to\infty} a_n$.

Solution The limit leads to the indeterminate form 1^∞. We can apply l'Hôpital's Rule if we first change the form to $\infty \cdot 0$ by taking the natural logarithm of a_n:

$$\begin{aligned} \ln a_n &= \ln\left(\frac{n+1}{n-1}\right)^n \\ &= n \ln\left(\frac{n+1}{n-1}\right). \end{aligned}$$

Then,

$$\begin{aligned} \lim_{n\to\infty} \ln a_n &= \lim_{n\to\infty} n \ln\left(\frac{n+1}{n-1}\right) && \infty \cdot 0 \\ &= \lim_{n\to\infty} \frac{\ln\left(\frac{n+1}{n-1}\right)}{1/n} && \frac{0}{0} \\ &= \lim_{n\to\infty} \frac{-2/(n^2-1)}{-1/n^2} && \text{l'Hôpital's Rule} \\ &= \lim_{n\to\infty} \frac{2n^2}{n^2-1} = 2. \end{aligned}$$

Since $\ln a_n \to 2$ and $f(x) = e^x$ is continuous, Theorem 4 tells us that

$$a_n = e^{\ln a_n} \to e^2.$$

The sequence $\{a_n\}$ converges to e^2. ■

Commonly Occurring Limits

The next theorem gives some limits that arise frequently.

THEOREM 5 The following six sequences converge to the limits listed below:

1. $\lim_{n\to\infty} \frac{\ln n}{n} = 0$

2. $\lim_{n\to\infty} \sqrt[n]{n} = 1$

3. $\lim_{n\to\infty} x^{1/n} = 1 \qquad (x > 0)$

4. $\lim_{n\to\infty} x^n = 0 \qquad (|x| < 1)$

5. $\lim_{n\to\infty} \left(1 + \frac{x}{n}\right)^n = e^x \qquad (\text{any } x)$

6. $\lim_{n\to\infty} \frac{x^n}{n!} = 0 \qquad (\text{any } x)$

In Formulas (3) through (6), x remains fixed as $n \to \infty$.

Factorial Notation
The notation $n!$ ("n factorial") means the product $1 \cdot 2 \cdot 3 \cdots n$ of the integers from 1 to n. Notice that $(n + 1)! = (n + 1) \cdot n!$. Thus, $4! = 1 \cdot 2 \cdot 3 \cdot 4 = 24$ and $5! = 1 \cdot 2 \cdot 3 \cdot 4 \cdot 5 = 5 \cdot 4! = 120$. We define $0!$ to be 1. Factorials grow even faster than exponentials, as the table suggests.

n	e^n (rounded)	$n!$
1	3	1
5	148	120
10	22,026	3,628,800
20	4.9×10^8	2.4×10^{18}

Proof The first limit was computed in Example 7. The next two can be proved by taking logarithms and applying Theorem 4 (Exercises 93 and 94). The remaining proofs are given in Appendix 6. ∎

EXAMPLE 9

(a) $\frac{\ln (n^2)}{n} = \frac{2 \ln n}{n} \to 2 \cdot 0 = 0$ Formula 1

(b) $\sqrt[n]{n^2} = n^{2/n} = (n^{1/n})^2 \to (1)^2 = 1$ Formula 2

(c) $\sqrt[n]{3n} = 3^{1/n}(n^{1/n}) \to 1 \cdot 1 = 1$ Formula 3 with $x = 3$ and Formula 2

(d) $\left(-\frac{1}{2}\right)^n \to 0$ Formula 4 with $x = -\frac{1}{2}$

(e) $\left(\frac{n - 2}{n}\right)^n = \left(1 + \frac{-2}{n}\right)^n \to e^{-2}$ Formula 5 with $x = -2$

(f) $\frac{100^n}{n!} \to 0$ Formula 6 with $x = 100$ ∎

Recursive Definitions

So far, we have calculated each a_n directly from the value of n. But sequences are often defined **recursively** by giving

1. The value(s) of the initial term or terms, and
2. A rule, called a **recursion formula**, for calculating any later term from terms that precede it.

EXAMPLE 10

(a) The statements $a_1 = 1$ and $a_n = a_{n-1} + 1$ define the sequence $1, 2, 3, \ldots, n, \ldots$ of positive integers. With $a_1 = 1$, we have $a_2 = a_1 + 1 = 2$, $a_3 = a_2 + 1 = 3$, and so on.

(b) The statements $a_1 = 1$ and $a_n = n \cdot a_{n-1}$ define the sequence $1, 2, 6, 24, \ldots, n!, \ldots$ of factorials. With $a_1 = 1$, we have $a_2 = 2 \cdot a_1 = 2$, $a_3 = 3 \cdot a_2 = 6$, $a_4 = 4 \cdot a_3 = 24$, and so on.

(c) The statements $a_1 = 1, a_2 = 1$, and $a_{n+1} = a_n + a_{n-1}$ define the sequence $1, 1, 2, 3, 5, \ldots$ of **Fibonacci numbers**. With $a_1 = 1$ and $a_2 = 1$, we have $a_3 = 1 + 1 = 2$, $a_4 = 2 + 1 = 3$, $a_5 = 3 + 2 = 5$, and so on.

(d) As we can see by applying Newton's method, the statements $x_0 = 1$ and $x_{n+1} = x_n - [(\sin x_n - x_n^2)/(\cos x_n - 2x_n)]$ define a sequence that, when it converges, gives a solution to the equation $\sin x - x^2 = 0$. ■

Bounded Nondecreasing Sequences

The terms of a general sequence can bounce around, sometimes getting larger, sometimes smaller. An important special kind of sequence is one for which each term is at least as large as its predecessor.

> **DEFINITION** A sequence $\{a_n\}$ with the property that $a_n \le a_{n+1}$ for all n is called a **nondecreasing sequence**.

EXAMPLE 11 The following sequences are nondecreasing.

(a) The sequence $1, 2, 3, \ldots, n, \ldots$ of natural numbers

(b) The sequence $\frac{1}{2}, \frac{2}{3}, \frac{3}{4}, \ldots, \frac{n}{n+1}, \ldots$

(c) The constant sequence $\{3\}$ ■

There are two kinds of nondecreasing sequences—those whose terms increase beyond any finite bound and those whose terms do not.

> **DEFINITIONS** A sequence $\{a_n\}$ is **bounded from above** if there exists a number M such that $a_n \le M$ for all n. The number M is an **upper bound** for $\{a_n\}$. If M is an upper bound for $\{a_n\}$ but no number less than M is an upper bound for $\{a_n\}$, then M is the **least upper bound** for $\{a_n\}$.

EXAMPLE 12

(a) The sequence $1, 2, 3, \ldots, n, \ldots$ has no upper bound.

(b) The sequence $\frac{1}{2}, \frac{2}{3}, \frac{3}{4}, \ldots, \frac{n}{n+1}, \ldots$ is bounded above by $M = 1$.

No number less than 1 is an upper bound for the sequence, so 1 is the least upper bound (Exercise 113). ■

A nondecreasing sequence that is bounded from above always has a least upper bound. This is the completeness property of the real numbers, discussed in Appendix 7. We will prove that if L is the least upper bound then the sequence converges to L.

Suppose we plot the points $(1, a_1), (2, a_2), \ldots, (n, a_n), \ldots$ in the xy-plane. If M is an upper bound of the sequence, all these points will lie on or below the line $y = M$

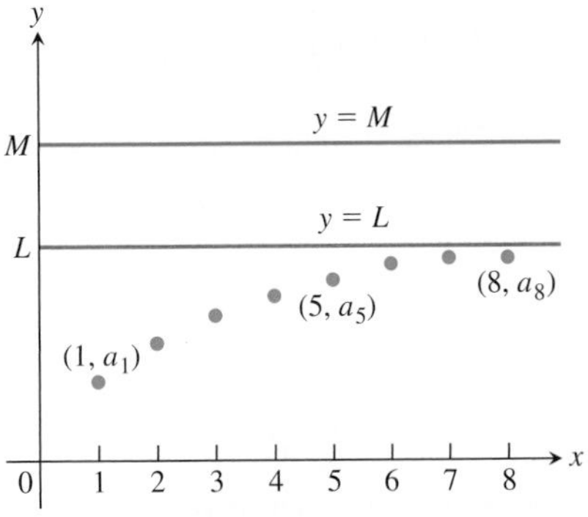

FIGURE 8.4 If the terms of a nondecreasing sequence have an upper bound M, they have a limit $L \leq M$.

(Figure 8.4). The line $y = L$ is the lowest such line. None of the points (n, a_n) lies above $y = L$, but some do lie above any lower line $y = L - \epsilon$, if ϵ is a positive number. The sequence converges to L because

(a) $a_n \leq L$ for *all* values of n and

(b) given any $\epsilon > 0$, there exists at least one integer N for which $a_N > L - \epsilon$.

The fact that $\{a_n\}$ is nondecreasing tells us further that

$$a_n \geq a_N > L - \epsilon \qquad \text{for all } n \geq N.$$

Thus, *all* the numbers a_n beyond the Nth number lie within ϵ of L. This is precisely the condition for L to be the limit of the sequence $\{a_n\}$.

The facts for nondecreasing sequences are summarized in the following theorem. A similar result holds for nonincreasing sequences (Exercise 107).

> **THEOREM 6—The Nondecreasing Sequence Theorem** A nondecreasing sequence of real numbers converges if and only if it is bounded from above. If a nondecreasing sequence converges, it converges to its least upper bound.

Theorem 6 implies that a nondecreasing sequence converges when it is bounded from above. It diverges to infinity if it is not bounded from above.

EXERCISES 8.1

Each of Exercises 1–6 gives a formula for the nth term a_n of a sequence $\{a_n\}$. Find the values of a_1, a_2, a_3, and a_4.

1. $a_n = \dfrac{1 - n}{n^2}$

2. $a_n = \dfrac{1}{n!}$

3. $a_n = \dfrac{(-1)^{n+1}}{2n - 1}$

4. $a_n = 2 + (-1)^n$

5. $a_n = \dfrac{2^n}{2^{n+1}}$

6. $a_n = \dfrac{2^n - 1}{2^n}$

Each of Exercises 7–12 gives the first term or two of a sequence along with a recursion formula for the remaining terms. Write out the first ten terms of the sequence.

7. $a_1 = 1, \quad a_{n+1} = a_n + (1/2^n)$

8. $a_1 = 1, \quad a_{n+1} = a_n/(n + 1)$

9. $a_1 = 2, \quad a_{n+1} = (-1)^{n+1}a_n/2$

10. $a_1 = -2, \quad a_{n+1} = na_n/(n + 1)$

11. $a_1 = a_2 = 1, \quad a_{n+2} = a_{n+1} + a_n$

12. $a_1 = 2, \quad a_2 = -1, \quad a_{n+2} = a_{n+1}/a_n$

In Exercises 13–22, find a formula for the nth term of the sequence.

13. The sequence $1, -1, 1, -1, 1, \ldots$ — 1's with alternating signs

14. The sequence $-1, 1, -1, 1, -1, \ldots$ — 1's with alternating signs

15. The sequence $1, -4, 9, -16, 25, \ldots$ — Squares of the positive integers; with alternating signs

16. The sequence $1, -\frac{1}{4}, \frac{1}{9}, -\frac{1}{16}, \frac{1}{25}, \ldots$ — Reciprocals of squares of the positive integers, with alternating signs

17. The sequence $0, 3, 8, 15, 24, \ldots$ — Squares of the positive integers diminished by 1

18. The sequence $-3, -2, -1, 0, 1, \ldots$ — Integers beginning with -3

19. The sequence $1, 5, 9, 13, 17, \ldots$ — Every other odd positive integer

20. The sequence $2, 6, 10, 14, 18, \ldots$ — Every other even positive integer

21. The sequence $1, 0, 1, 0, 1, \ldots$ — Alternating 1's and 0's

22. The sequence $0, 1, 1, 2, 2, 3, 3, 4, \ldots$ — Each positive integer repeated

Which of the sequences $\{a_n\}$ in Exercises 23–84 converge, and which diverge? Find the limit of each convergent sequence.

23. $a_n = 2 + (0.1)^n$

24. $a_n = \dfrac{n + (-1)^n}{n}$

25. $a_n = \dfrac{1 - 2n}{1 + 2n}$

26. $a_n = \dfrac{2n + 1}{1 - 3\sqrt{n}}$

27. $a_n = \dfrac{1 - 5n^4}{n^4 + 8n^3}$

28. $a_n = \dfrac{n + 3}{n^2 + 5n + 6}$

29. $a_n = \dfrac{n^2 - 2n + 1}{n - 1}$

30. $a_n = \dfrac{1 - n^3}{70 - 4n^2}$

31. $a_n = 1 + (-1)^n$

32. $a_n = (-1)^n\left(1 - \dfrac{1}{n}\right)$

33. $a_n = \left(\dfrac{n+1}{2n}\right)\left(1 - \dfrac{1}{n}\right)$

34. $a_n = \left(2 - \dfrac{1}{2^n}\right)\left(3 + \dfrac{1}{2^n}\right)$

35. $a_n = \dfrac{(-1)^{n+1}}{2n - 1}$

36. $a_n = \left(-\dfrac{1}{2}\right)^n$

37. $a_n = \sqrt{\dfrac{2n}{n+1}}$

38. $a_n = \dfrac{1}{(0.9)^n}$

39. $a_n = \sin\left(\dfrac{\pi}{2} + \dfrac{1}{n}\right)$

40. $a_n = n\pi\cos(n\pi)$

41. $a_n = \dfrac{\sin n}{n}$

42. $a_n = \dfrac{\sin^2 n}{2^n}$

43. $a_n = \dfrac{n}{2^n}$

44. $a_n = \dfrac{3^n}{n^3}$

45. $a_n = \dfrac{\ln(n+1)}{\sqrt{n}}$

46. $a_n = \dfrac{\ln n}{\ln 2n}$

47. $a_n = 8^{1/n}$

48. $a_n = (0.03)^{1/n}$

49. $a_n = \left(1 + \dfrac{7}{n}\right)^n$

50. $a_n = \left(1 - \dfrac{1}{n}\right)^n$

51. $a_n = \sqrt[n]{10n}$

52. $a_n = \sqrt[n]{n^2}$

53. $a_n = \left(\dfrac{3}{n}\right)^{1/n}$

54. $a_n = (n+4)^{1/(n+4)}$

55. $a_n = \dfrac{\ln n}{n^{1/n}}$

56. $a_n = \ln n - \ln(n+1)$

57. $a_n = \sqrt[n]{4^n n}$

58. $a_n = \sqrt[n]{3^{2n+1}}$

59. $a_n = \dfrac{n!}{n^n}$ (*Hint:* Compare with $1/n$.)

60. $a_n = \dfrac{(-4)^n}{n!}$

61. $a_n = \dfrac{n!}{10^{6n}}$

62. $a_n = \dfrac{n!}{2^n \cdot 3^n}$

63. $a_n = \left(\dfrac{1}{n}\right)^{1/(\ln n)}$

64. $a_n = \ln\left(1 + \dfrac{1}{n}\right)^n$

65. $a_n = \left(\dfrac{3n+1}{3n-1}\right)^n$

66. $a_n = \left(\dfrac{n}{n+1}\right)^n$

67. $a_n = \left(\dfrac{x^n}{2n+1}\right)^{1/n}, \quad x > 0$

68. $a_n = \left(1 - \dfrac{1}{n^2}\right)^n$

69. $a_n = \dfrac{3^n \cdot 6^n}{2^{-n} \cdot n!}$

70. $a_n = \dfrac{(10/11)^n}{(9/10)^n + (11/12)^n}$

71. $a_n = \tanh n$

72. $a_n = \sinh(\ln n)$

73. $a_n = \dfrac{n^2}{2n - 1}\sin\dfrac{1}{n}$

74. $a_n = n\left(1 - \cos\dfrac{1}{n}\right)$

75. $a_n = \tan^{-1} n$

76. $a_n = \dfrac{1}{\sqrt{n}}\tan^{-1} n$

77. $a_n = \left(\dfrac{1}{3}\right)^n + \dfrac{1}{\sqrt{2^n}}$

78. $a_n = \sqrt[n]{n^2 + n}$

79. $a_n = \dfrac{(\ln n)^{200}}{n}$

80. $a_n = \dfrac{(\ln n)^5}{\sqrt{n}}$

81. $a_n = n - \sqrt{n^2 - n}$

82. $a_n = \dfrac{1}{\sqrt{n^2 - 1} - \sqrt{n^2 + n}}$

83. $a_n = \dfrac{1}{n}\displaystyle\int_1^n \dfrac{1}{x}\,dx$

84. $a_n = \displaystyle\int_1^n \dfrac{1}{x^p}\,dx, \quad p > 1$

85. The first term of a sequence is $x_1 = 1$. Each succeeding term is the sum of all those that come before it:

$$x_{n+1} = x_1 + x_2 + \cdots + x_n.$$

Write out enough early terms of the sequence to deduce a general formula for x_n that holds for $n \geq 2$.

86. A sequence of rational numbers is described as follows:

$$\frac{1}{1}, \frac{3}{2}, \frac{7}{5}, \frac{17}{12}, \ldots, \frac{a}{b}, \frac{a+2b}{a+b}, \ldots.$$

Here the numerators form one sequence, the denominators form a second sequence, and their ratios form a third sequence. Let x_n and y_n be, respectively, the numerator and the denominator of the nth fraction $r_n = x_n/y_n$.

a. Verify that $x_1^2 - 2y_1^2 = -1$, $x_2^2 - 2y_2^2 = +1$ and, more generally, that if $a^2 - 2b^2 = -1$ or $+1$, then

$$(a + 2b)^2 - 2(a + b)^2 = +1 \quad \text{or} \quad -1,$$

respectively.

b. The fractions $r_n = x_n/y_n$ approach a limit as n increases. What is that limit? (*Hint:* Use part (a) to show that $r_n^2 - 2 = \pm(1/y_n)^2$ and that y_n is not less than n.)

87. Newton's method The following sequences come from the recursion formula for Newton's method,

$$x_{n+1} = x_n - \frac{f(x_n)}{f'(x_n)}.$$

Do the sequences converge? If so, to what value? In each case, begin by identifying the function f that generates the sequence.

a. $x_0 = 1, \quad x_{n+1} = x_n - \dfrac{x_n^2 - 2}{2x_n} = \dfrac{x_n}{2} + \dfrac{1}{x_n}$

b. $x_0 = 1, \quad x_{n+1} = x_n - \dfrac{\tan x_n - 1}{\sec^2 x_n}$

c. $x_0 = 1, \quad x_{n+1} = x_n - 1$

88. a. Suppose that $f(x)$ is differentiable for all x in $[0, 1]$ and that $f(0) = 0$. Define the sequence $\{a_n\}$ by the rule $a_n = nf(1/n)$. Show that $\lim_{n\to\infty} a_n = f'(0)$.

Use the result in part (a) to find the limits of the following sequences $\{a_n\}$.

b. $a_n = n \tan^{-1} \frac{1}{n}$ **c.** $a_n = n(e^{1/n} - 1)$

d. $a_n = n \ln\left(1 + \frac{2}{n}\right)$

89. Pythagorean triples A triple of positive integers a, b, and c is called a **Pythagorean triple** if $a^2 + b^2 = c^2$. Let a be an odd positive integer and let

$$b = \left\lfloor \frac{a^2}{2} \right\rfloor \quad \text{and} \quad c = \left\lceil \frac{a^2}{2} \right\rceil$$

be, respectively, the integer floor and ceiling for $a^2/2$.

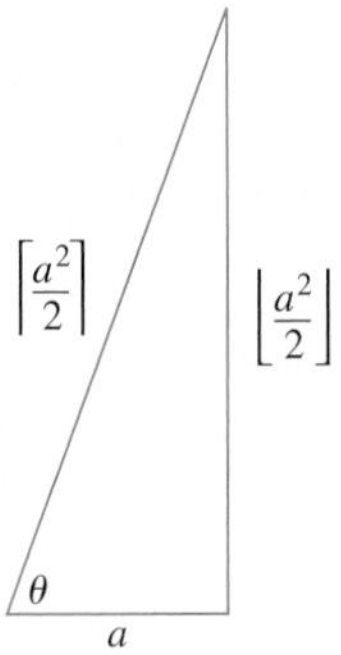

a. Show that $a^2 + b^2 = c^2$. (*Hint:* Let $a = 2n + 1$ and express b and c in terms of n.)

b. By direct calculation, or by appealing to the figure here, find

$$\lim_{a\to\infty} \frac{\left\lfloor \frac{a^2}{2} \right\rfloor}{\left\lceil \frac{a^2}{2} \right\rceil}.$$

90. The *n*th root of *n*!

a. Show that $\lim_{n\to\infty}(2n\pi)^{1/(2n)} = 1$ and hence, using Stirling's approximation (Chapter 7, Additional Exercise 32a), that

$$\sqrt[n]{n!} \approx \frac{n}{e} \quad \text{for large values of } n.$$

T **b.** Test the approximation in part (a) for $n = 40, 50, 60, \ldots$, as far as your calculator will allow.

91. a. Assuming that $\lim_{n\to\infty}(1/n^c) = 0$ if c is any positive constant, show that

$$\lim_{n\to\infty} \frac{\ln n}{n^c} = 0$$

if c is any positive constant.

b. Prove that $\lim_{n\to\infty}(1/n^c) = 0$ if c is any positive constant. (*Hint:* If $\epsilon = 0.001$ and $c = 0.04$, how large should N be to ensure that $|1/n^c - 0| < \epsilon$ if $n > N$?)

92. The zipper theorem Prove the "zipper theorem" for sequences: If $\{a_n\}$ and $\{b_n\}$ both converge to L, then the sequence

$$a_1, b_1, a_2, b_2, \ldots, a_n, b_n, \ldots$$

converges to L.

93. Prove that $\lim_{n\to\infty} \sqrt[n]{n} = 1$.

94. Prove that $\lim_{n\to\infty} x^{1/n} = 1, (x > 0)$.

95. Prove Theorem 2.

96. Prove Theorem 3.

In Exercises 97–100, determine if the sequence is nondecreasing and if it is bounded from above.

97. $a_n = \dfrac{3n + 1}{n + 1}$

98. $a_n = \dfrac{(2n + 3)!}{(n + 1)!}$

99. $a_n = \dfrac{2^n 3^n}{n!}$

100. $a_n = 2 - \dfrac{2}{n} - \dfrac{1}{2^n}$

Which of the sequences in Exercises 101–106 converge, and which diverge? Give reasons for your answers.

101. $a_n = 1 - \dfrac{1}{n}$

102. $a_n = n - \dfrac{1}{n}$

103. $a_n = \dfrac{2^n - 1}{2^n}$

104. $a_n = \dfrac{2^n - 1}{3^n}$

105. $a_n = ((-1)^n + 1)\left(\dfrac{n + 1}{n}\right)$

106. The first term of a sequence is $x_1 = \cos(1)$. The next terms are $x_2 = x_1$ or $\cos(2)$, whichever is larger; and $x_3 = x_2$ or $\cos(3)$, whichever is larger (farther to the right). In general,

$$x_{n+1} = \max\{x_n, \cos(n + 1)\}.$$

107. Nonincreasing sequences A sequence of numbers $\{a_n\}$ in which $a_n \ge a_{n+1}$ for every n is called a **nonincreasing sequence.** A sequence $\{a_n\}$ is **bounded from below** if there is a number M with $M \le a_n$ for every n. Such a number M is called a **lower bound** for the sequence. Deduce from Theorem 6 that a nonincreasing sequence that is bounded from below converges and that a nonincreasing sequence that is not bounded from below diverges.

(*Continuation of Exercise 107.*) Using the conclusion of Exercise 107, determine which of the sequences in Exercises 108–112 converge and which diverge.

108. $a_n = \dfrac{n + 1}{n}$

109. $a_n = \dfrac{1 + \sqrt{2n}}{\sqrt{n}}$

110. $a_n = \dfrac{1 - 4^n}{2^n}$

111. $a_n = \dfrac{4^{n+1} + 3^n}{4^n}$

112. $a_1 = 1, \quad a_{n+1} = 2a_n - 3$

113. The sequence $\{n/(n + 1)\}$ has a least upper bound of 1 Show that if M is a number less than 1, then the terms of $\{n/(n + 1)\}$ eventually exceed M. That is, if $M < 1$ there is an integer N such that $n/(n + 1) > M$ whenever $n > N$. Since $n/(n + 1) < 1$ for every n, this proves that 1 is a least upper bound for $\{n/(n + 1)\}$.

114. Uniqueness of least upper bounds Show that if M_1 and M_2 are least upper bounds for the sequence $\{a_n\}$, then $M_1 = M_2$. That is, a sequence cannot have two different least upper bounds.

115. Is it true that a sequence $\{a_n\}$ of positive numbers must converge if it is bounded from above? Give reasons for your answer.

116. Prove that if $\{a_n\}$ is a convergent sequence, then to every positive number ϵ there corresponds an integer N such that for all m and n,

$$m > N \quad \text{and} \quad n > N \quad \Rightarrow \quad |a_m - a_n| < \epsilon.$$

117. Uniqueness of limits Prove that limits of sequences are unique. That is, show that if L_1 and L_2 are numbers such that $a_n \to L_1$ and $a_n \to L_2$, then $L_1 = L_2$.

118. Limits and subsequences If the terms of one sequence appear in another sequence in their given order, we call the first sequence a **subsequence** of the second. Prove that if two subsequences of a sequence $\{a_n\}$ have different limits $L_1 \neq L_2$, then $\{a_n\}$ diverges.

119. For a sequence $\{a_n\}$ the terms of even index are denoted by a_{2k} and the terms of odd index by a_{2k+1}. Prove that if $a_{2k} \to L$ and $a_{2k+1} \to L$, then $a_n \to L$.

120. Prove that a sequence $\{a_n\}$ converges to 0 if and only if the sequence of absolute values $\{|a_n|\}$ converges to 0.

T In Exercises 121–124, experiment with a calculator to find a value of N that will make the inequality hold for all $n > N$. Assuming that the inequality is the one from the formal definition of the limit of a sequence, what sequence is being considered in each case and what is its limit?

121. $|\sqrt[n]{0.5} - 1| < 10^{-3}$ **122.** $|\sqrt[n]{n} - 1| < 10^{-3}$

123. $(0.9)^n < 10^{-3}$ **124.** $2^n/n! < 10^{-7}$

125. Sequences generated by Newton's method Newton's method, applied to a differentiable function $f(x)$, begins with a starting value x_0 and constructs from it a sequence of numbers $\{x_n\}$ that under favorable circumstances converges to a zero of f. The recursion formula for the sequence is

$$x_{n+1} = x_n - \frac{f(x_n)}{f'(x_n)}.$$

a. Show that the recursion formula for $f(x) = x^2 - a, a > 0$, can be written as $x_{n+1} = (x_n + a/x_n)/2$.

b. Starting with $x_0 = 1$ and $a = 3$, calculate successive terms of the sequence until the display begins to repeat. What number is being approximated? Explain.

126. (*Continuation of Exercise 125.*) Repeat part (b) of Exercise 125 with $a = 2$ in place of $a = 3$.

127. A recursive definition of $\pi/2$ If you start with $x_1 = 1$ and define the subsequent terms of $\{x_n\}$ by the rule $x_n = x_{n-1} + \cos x_{n-1}$, you generate a sequence that converges rapidly to $\pi/2$. **a.** Try it. **b.** Use the accompanying figure to explain why the convergence is so rapid.

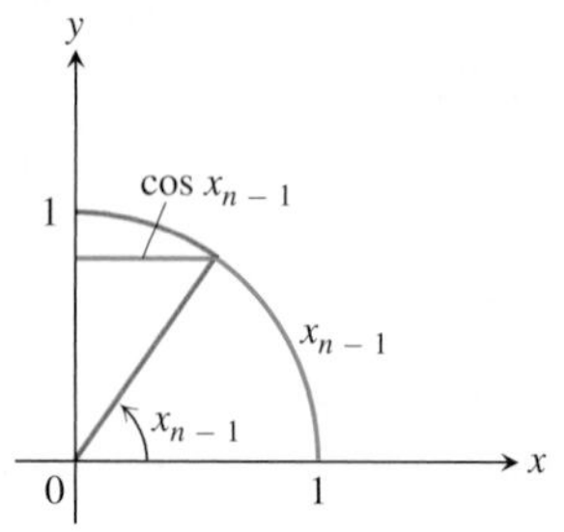

128. According to a front-page article in the December 15, 1992, issue of the *Wall Street Journal*, Ford Motor Company used about $7\frac{1}{4}$ hours of labor to produce stampings for the average vehicle, down from an estimated 15 hours in 1980. The Japanese automobile companies needed only about $3\frac{1}{2}$ hours.

Ford's improvement since 1980 represents an average decrease of 6% per year. If that rate continues, then n years from 1992 Ford will use about

$$S_n = 7.25(0.94)^n$$

hours of labor to produce stampings for the average vehicle. Assuming that the Japanese continue to spend $3\frac{1}{2}$ hours per vehicle, how many more years will it take Ford to catch up? Find out two ways:

a. Find the first term of the sequence $\{S_n\}$ that is less than or equal to 3.5.

T **b.** Graph $f(x) = 7.25(0.94)^x$ and use Trace to find where the graph crosses the line $y = 3.5$.

COMPUTER EXPLORATIONS

Use a CAS to perform the following steps for the sequences in Exercises 129–140.

a. Calculate and then plot the first 25 terms of the sequence. Does the sequence appear to be bounded from above or below? Does it appear to converge or diverge? If it does converge, what is the limit L?

b. If the sequence converges, find an integer N such that $|a_n - L| \le 0.01$ for $n \ge N$. How far in the sequence do you have to get for the terms to lie within 0.0001 of L?

129. $a_n = \sqrt[n]{n}$ **130.** $a_n = \left(1 + \dfrac{0.5}{n}\right)^n$

131. $a_1 = 1, \quad a_{n+1} = a_n + \dfrac{1}{5^n}$

132. $a_1 = 1, \quad a_{n+1} = a_n + (-2)^n$

133. $a_n = \sin n$ **134.** $a_n = n \sin \dfrac{1}{n}$

135. $a_n = \dfrac{\sin n}{n}$ **136.** $a_n = \dfrac{\ln n}{n}$

137. $a_n = (0.9999)^n$ **138.** $a_n = 123456^{1/n}$

139. $a_n = \dfrac{8^n}{n!}$ **140.** $a_n = \dfrac{n^{41}}{19^n}$

8.2 Infinite Series

An *infinite series* is the sum of an infinite sequence of numbers

$$a_1 + a_2 + a_3 + \cdots + a_n + \cdots$$

The goal of this section is to understand the meaning of such an infinite sum and to develop methods to calculate it. Since there are infinitely many terms to add in an infinite series, we cannot just keep adding to see what comes out. Instead we look at the result of summing the first n terms of the sequence and stopping. The sum of the first n terms

$$s_n = a_1 + a_2 + a_3 + \cdots + a_n$$

is an ordinary finite sum and can be calculated by normal addition. It is called the *nth partial sum*. As n gets larger, we expect the partial sums to get closer and closer to a limiting value in the same sense that the terms of a sequence approach a limit, as discussed in Section 8.1.

For example, to assign meaning to an expression like

$$1 + \frac{1}{2} + \frac{1}{4} + \frac{1}{8} + \frac{1}{16} + \cdots$$

we add the terms one at a time from the beginning and look for a pattern in how these partial sums grow.

Partial sum		**Suggestive expression for partial sum**	**Value**
First:	$s_1 = 1$	$2 - 1$	1
Second:	$s_2 = 1 + \frac{1}{2}$	$2 - \frac{1}{2}$	$\frac{3}{2}$
Third:	$s_3 = 1 + \frac{1}{2} + \frac{1}{4}$	$2 - \frac{1}{4}$	$\frac{7}{4}$
$\vdots$	$\vdots$	$\vdots$	$\vdots$
nth:	$s_n = 1 + \frac{1}{2} + \frac{1}{4} + \cdots + \frac{1}{2^{n-1}}$	$2 - \frac{1}{2^{n-1}}$	$\frac{2^n - 1}{2^{n-1}}$

Indeed there is a pattern. The partial sums form a sequence whose nth term is

$$s_n = 2 - \frac{1}{2^{n-1}}.$$

This sequence of partial sums converges to 2 because $\lim_{n\to\infty}(1/2^{n-1}) = 0$. We say

"the sum of the infinite series $1 + \frac{1}{2} + \frac{1}{4} + \cdots + \frac{1}{2^{n-1}} + \cdots$ is 2."

Is the sum of any finite number of terms in this series equal to 2? No. Can we actually add an infinite number of terms one by one? No. But we can still define their sum by defining it to be the limit of the sequence of partial sums as $n \to \infty$, in this case 2 (Figure 8.5). Our knowledge of sequences and limits enables us to break away from the confines of finite sums.

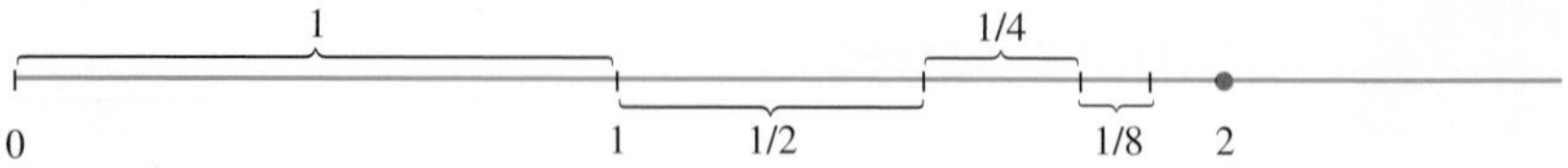

FIGURE 8.5 As the lengths 1, ½, ¼, ⅛, . . . are added one by one, the sum approaches 2.

HISTORICAL BIOGRAPHY

Blaise Pascal
(1623–1662)

DEFINITIONS Given a sequence of numbers $\{a_n\}$, an expression of the form

$$a_1 + a_2 + a_3 + \cdots + a_n + \cdots$$

is an **infinite series**. The number a_n is the ***n*th term** of the series. The sequence $\{s_n\}$ defined by

$$\begin{aligned} s_1 &= a_1 \\ s_2 &= a_1 + a_2 \\ &\vdots \\ s_n &= a_1 + a_2 + \cdots + a_n = \sum_{k=1}^{n} a_k \\ &\vdots \end{aligned}$$

is the **sequence of partial sums** of the series, the number s_n being the ***n*th partial sum**. If the sequence of partial sums converges to a limit L, we say that the series **converges** and that its **sum** is L. In this case, we also write

$$a_1 + a_2 + \cdots + a_n + \cdots = \sum_{n=1}^{\infty} a_n = L.$$

If the sequence of partial sums of the series does not converge, we say that the series **diverges**.

When we begin to study a given series $a_1 + a_2 + \cdots + a_n + \cdots$, we might not know whether it converges or diverges. In either case, it is convenient to use sigma notation to write the series as

$$\sum_{n=1}^{\infty} a_n, \qquad \sum_{k=1}^{\infty} a_k, \qquad \text{or} \qquad \sum a_n$$

A useful shorthand when summation from 1 to ∞ is understood

Geometric Series

Geometric series are series of the form

$$a + ar + ar^2 + \cdots + ar^{n-1} + \cdots = \sum_{n=1}^{\infty} ar^{n-1}$$

in which a and r are fixed real numbers and $a \neq 0$. The series can also be written as $\sum_{n=0}^{\infty} ar^n$. The **ratio** r can be positive, as in

$$1 + \frac{1}{2} + \frac{1}{4} + \cdots + \left(\frac{1}{2}\right)^{n-1} + \cdots, \qquad r = 1/2,\ a = 1$$

or negative, as in

$$1 - \frac{1}{3} + \frac{1}{9} - \cdots + \left(-\frac{1}{3}\right)^{n-1} + \cdots. \qquad r = -1/3,\ a = 1$$

If $r = 1$, the nth partial sum of the geometric series is

$$s_n = a + a(1) + a(1)^2 + \cdots + a(1)^{n-1} = na,$$

and the series diverges because $\lim_{n\to\infty} s_n = \pm\infty$, depending on the sign of a. If $r = -1$, the series diverges because the nth partial sums alternate between a and 0. If $|r| \neq 1$, we can determine the convergence or divergence of the series in the following way:

$$s_n = a + ar + ar^2 + \cdots + ar^{n-1}$$

$$rs_n = ar + ar^2 + \cdots + ar^{n-1} + ar^n \qquad \text{Multiply } s_n \text{ by } r.$$

$$s_n - rs_n = a - ar^n \qquad \text{Subtract } rs_n \text{ from } s_n\text{. Most of the terms on the right cancel.}$$

$$s_n(1 - r) = a(1 - r^n) \qquad \text{Factor.}$$

$$s_n = \frac{a(1 - r^n)}{1 - r}, \quad (r \neq 1). \qquad \text{We can solve for } s_n \text{ if } r \neq 1.$$

If $|r| < 1$, then $r^n \to 0$ as $n \to \infty$ (as in Section 8.1) and $s_n \to a/(1 - r)$. If $|r| > 1$, then $|r^n| \to \infty$ and the series diverges.

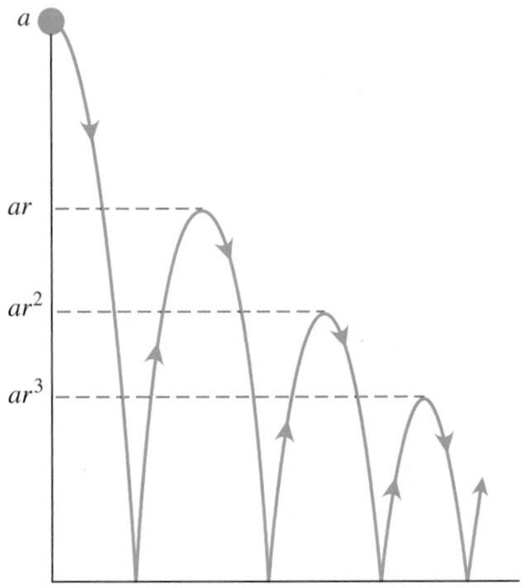

(a)

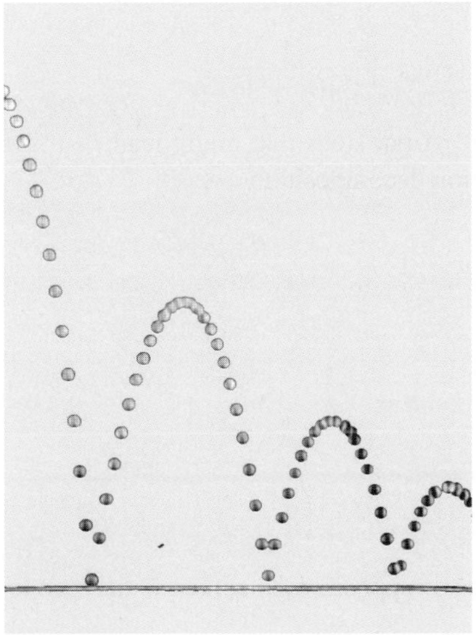

(b)

FIGURE 8.6 (a) Example 3 shows how to use a geometric series to calculate the total vertical distance traveled by a bouncing ball if the height of each rebound is reduced by the factor r. (b) A stroboscopic photo of a bouncing ball.

If $|r| < 1$, the geometric series $a + ar + ar^2 + \cdots + ar^{n-1} + \cdots$ converges to $a/(1 - r)$:

$$\sum_{n=1}^{\infty} ar^{n-1} = \frac{a}{1 - r}, \qquad |r| < 1.$$

If $|r| \geq 1$, the series diverges.

We have determined when a geometric series converges or diverges, and to what value. Often we can determine that a series converges without knowing the value to which it converges, as we will see in the next several sections. The formula $a/(1 - r)$ for the sum of a geometric series applies *only* when the summation index begins with $n = 1$ in the expression $\sum_{n=1}^{\infty} ar^{n-1}$ (or with the index $n = 0$ if we write the series as $\sum_{n=0}^{\infty} ar^n$).

EXAMPLE 1 The geometric series with $a = 1/9$ and $r = 1/3$ is

$$\frac{1}{9} + \frac{1}{27} + \frac{1}{81} + \cdots = \sum_{n=1}^{\infty} \frac{1}{9}\left(\frac{1}{3}\right)^{n-1} = \frac{1/9}{1 - (1/3)} = \frac{1}{6}.$$

■

EXAMPLE 2 The series

$$\sum_{n=0}^{\infty} \frac{(-1)^n 5}{4^n} = 5 - \frac{5}{4} + \frac{5}{16} - \frac{5}{64} + \cdots$$

is a geometric series with $a = 5$ and $r = -1/4$. It converges to

$$\frac{a}{1 - r} = \frac{5}{1 + (1/4)} = 4.$$

■

EXAMPLE 3 You drop a ball from a meters above a flat surface. Each time the ball hits the surface after falling a distance h, it rebounds a distance rh, where r is positive but less than 1. Find the total distance the ball travels up and down (Figure 8.6).

Solution The total distance is

$$s = \underbrace{a + 2ar + 2ar^2 + 2ar^3 + \cdots}_{\text{This sum is } 2ar/(1-r).} = a + \frac{2ar}{1-r} = a\frac{1+r}{1-r}.$$

If $a = 6$ m and $r = 2/3$, for instance, the distance is

$$s = 6\frac{1 + (2/3)}{1 - (2/3)} = 6\left(\frac{5/3}{1/3}\right) = 30 \text{ m}.$$

EXAMPLE 4 Express the repeating decimal 5.232323 . . . as the ratio of two integers.

Solution

$$\begin{aligned} 5.232323\ldots &= 5 + \frac{23}{100} + \frac{23}{(100)^2} + \frac{23}{(100)^3} + \cdots \\ &= 5 + \frac{23}{100}\underbrace{\left(1 + \frac{1}{100} + \left(\frac{1}{100}\right)^2 + \cdots\right)}_{1/(1-0.01)} \qquad a = 1,\ r = 1/100 \\ &= 5 + \frac{23}{100}\left(\frac{1}{0.99}\right) = 5 + \frac{23}{99} = \frac{518}{99} \end{aligned}$$

Unfortunately, formulas like the one for the sum of a convergent geometric series are rare and we usually have to settle for an estimate of a series' sum (more about this later). The next example, however, is another case in which we can find the sum exactly.

EXAMPLE 5 Find the sum of the "telescoping" series $\sum_{n=1}^{\infty} \frac{1}{n(n+1)}$.

Solution We look for a pattern in the sequence of partial sums that might lead to a formula for s_k. The key observation is the partial fraction decomposition

$$\frac{1}{n(n+1)} = \frac{1}{n} - \frac{1}{n+1},$$

so

$$\sum_{n=1}^{k} \frac{1}{n(n+1)} = \sum_{n=1}^{k}\left(\frac{1}{n} - \frac{1}{n+1}\right)$$

and

$$s_k = \left(\frac{1}{1} - \frac{1}{2}\right) + \left(\frac{1}{2} - \frac{1}{3}\right) + \left(\frac{1}{3} - \frac{1}{4}\right) + \cdots + \left(\frac{1}{k} - \frac{1}{k+1}\right).$$

Removing parentheses and canceling adjacent terms of opposite sign collapses the sum to

$$s_k = 1 - \frac{1}{k+1}.$$

We now see that $s_k \to 1$ as $k \to \infty$. The series converges, and its sum is 1:

$$\sum_{n=1}^{\infty} \frac{1}{n(n+1)} = 1.$$

Divergent Series

One reason that a series may fail to converge is that its terms don't become small.

EXAMPLE 6 The series

$$\sum_{n=1}^{\infty} \frac{n+1}{n} = \frac{2}{1} + \frac{3}{2} + \frac{4}{3} + \cdots + \frac{n+1}{n} + \cdots$$

diverges because the partial sums eventually outgrow every preassigned number. Each term is greater than 1, so the sum of n terms is greater than n. ■

The nth-Term Test for Divergence

Notice that $\lim_{n\to\infty} a_n$ must equal zero if the series $\sum_{n=1}^{\infty} a_n$ converges. To see why, let S represent the series' sum and $s_n = a_1 + a_2 + \cdots + a_n$ the nth partial sum. When n is large, both s_n and s_{n-1} are close to S, so their difference, a_n, is close to zero. More formally,

$$a_n = s_n - s_{n-1} \quad \to \quad S - S = 0.$$

Difference Rule for sequences

This establishes the following theorem.

Caution
Theorem 7 *does not say* that $\sum_{n=1}^{\infty} a_n$ converges if $a_n \to 0$. It is possible for a series to diverge when $a_n \to 0$.

THEOREM 7 If $\sum_{n=1}^{\infty} a_n$ converges, then $a_n \to 0$.

Theorem 7 leads to a test for detecting the kind of divergence that occurred in Example 6.

The nth-Term Test for Divergence

$\sum_{n=1}^{\infty} a_n$ diverges if $\lim_{n\to\infty} a_n$ fails to exist or is different from zero.

EXAMPLE 7

(a) $\sum_{n=1}^{\infty} n^2$ diverges because $n^2 \to \infty$

(b) $\sum_{n=1}^{\infty} \frac{n+1}{n}$ diverges because $\frac{n+1}{n} \to 1$ $\quad$ $\lim_{n\to\infty} a_n \neq 0$

(c) $\sum_{n=1}^{\infty} (-1)^{n+1}$ diverges because $\lim_{n\to\infty}(-1)^{n+1}$ does not exist

(d) $\sum_{n=1}^{\infty} \frac{-n}{2n+5}$ diverges because $\lim_{n\to\infty} \frac{-n}{2n+5} = -\frac{1}{2} \neq 0.$ ■

EXAMPLE 8 The series

$$1 + \underbrace{\frac{1}{2} + \frac{1}{2}}_{\text{2 terms}} + \underbrace{\frac{1}{4} + \frac{1}{4} + \frac{1}{4} + \frac{1}{4}}_{\text{4 terms}} + \cdots + \underbrace{\frac{1}{2^n} + \frac{1}{2^n} + \cdots + \frac{1}{2^n}}_{2^n \text{ terms}} + \cdots$$

diverges because the terms can be grouped into clusters that add to 1, so the partial sums increase without bound. However, the terms of the series form a sequence that converges to 0. Example 1 of Section 8.3 shows that the harmonic series also behaves in this manner. ■

Combining Series

Whenever we have two convergent series, we can add them term by term, subtract them term by term, or multiply them by constants to make new convergent series.

THEOREM 8 If $\sum a_n = A$ and $\sum b_n = B$ are convergent series, then

1. *Sum Rule:* $\sum(a_n + b_n) = \sum a_n + \sum b_n = A + B$
2. *Difference Rule:* $\sum(a_n - b_n) = \sum a_n - \sum b_n = A - B$
3. *Constant Multiple Rule:* $\sum ka_n = k\sum a_n = kA$ (Any number k).

Proof The three rules for series follow from the analogous rules for sequences in Theorem 1, Section 8.1. To prove the Sum Rule for series, let

$$A_n = a_1 + a_2 + \cdots + a_n, \quad B_n = b_1 + b_2 + \cdots + b_n.$$

Then the partial sums of $\sum(a_n + b_n)$ are

$$\begin{aligned} s_n &= (a_1 + b_1) + (a_2 + b_2) + \cdots + (a_n + b_n) \\ &= (a_1 + \cdots + a_n) + (b_1 + \cdots + b_n) \\ &= A_n + B_n. \end{aligned}$$

Since $A_n \to A$ and $B_n \to B$, we have $s_n \to A + B$ by the Sum Rule for sequences. The proof of the Difference Rule is similar.

To prove the Constant Multiple Rule for series, observe that the partial sums of $\sum ka_n$ form the sequence

$$s_n = ka_1 + ka_2 + \cdots + ka_n = k(a_1 + a_2 + \cdots + a_n) = kA_n,$$

which converges to kA by the Constant Multiple Rule for sequences. ■

As corollaries of Theorem 8, we have the following results. We omit the proofs.

1. Every nonzero constant multiple of a divergent series diverges.
2. If $\sum a_n$ converges and $\sum b_n$ diverges, then $\sum(a_n + b_n)$ and $\sum(a_n - b_n)$ both diverge.

Caution Remember that $\sum(a_n + b_n)$ can converge when $\sum a_n$ and $\sum b_n$ both diverge. For example, $\sum a_n = 1 + 1 + 1 + \cdots$ and $\sum b_n = (-1) + (-1) + (-1) + \cdots$ diverge, whereas $\sum(a_n + b_n) = 0 + 0 + 0 + \cdots$ converges to 0.

EXAMPLE 9 Find the sums of the following series.

(a)
$$\begin{aligned} \sum_{n=1}^{\infty} \frac{3^{n-1} - 1}{6^{n-1}} &= \sum_{n=1}^{\infty} \left(\frac{1}{2^{n-1}} - \frac{1}{6^{n-1}}\right) \\ &= \sum_{n=1}^{\infty} \frac{1}{2^{n-1}} - \sum_{n=1}^{\infty} \frac{1}{6^{n-1}} \qquad \text{Difference Rule} \end{aligned}$$

$$= \frac{1}{1-(1/2)} - \frac{1}{1-(1/6)}$$ Geometric series with $a = 1$ and $r = 1/2, 1/6$

$$= 2 - \frac{6}{5} = \frac{4}{5}$$

(b) $$\sum_{n=0}^{\infty} \frac{4}{2^n} = 4\sum_{n=0}^{\infty} \frac{1}{2^n}$$ Constant Multiple Rule

$$= 4\left(\frac{1}{1-(1/2)}\right)$$ Geometric series with $a = 1, r = 1/2$

$$= 8$$

■

Adding or Deleting Terms

We can add a finite number of terms to a series or delete a finite number of terms without altering the series' convergence or divergence, although in the case of convergence this will usually change the sum. If $\sum_{n=1}^{\infty} a_n$ converges, then $\sum_{n=k}^{\infty} a_n$ converges for any $k > 1$ and

$$\sum_{n=1}^{\infty} a_n = a_1 + a_2 + \cdots + a_{k-1} + \sum_{n=k}^{\infty} a_n.$$

Conversely, if $\sum_{n=k}^{\infty} a_n$ converges for any $k > 1$, then $\sum_{n=1}^{\infty} a_n$ converges. Thus,

$$\sum_{n=1}^{\infty} \frac{1}{5^n} = \frac{1}{5} + \frac{1}{25} + \frac{1}{125} + \sum_{n=4}^{\infty} \frac{1}{5^n}$$

and

$$\sum_{n=4}^{\infty} \frac{1}{5^n} = \left(\sum_{n=1}^{\infty} \frac{1}{5^n}\right) - \frac{1}{5} - \frac{1}{25} - \frac{1}{125}.$$

Reindexing

HISTORICAL BIOGRAPHY

Richard Dedekind
(1831–1916)

As long as we preserve the order of its terms, we can reindex any series without altering its convergence. To raise the starting value of the index h units, replace the n in the formula for a_n by $n - h$:

$$\sum_{n=1}^{\infty} a_n = \sum_{n=1+h}^{\infty} a_{n-h} = a_1 + a_2 + a_3 + \cdots.$$

To lower the starting value of the index h units, replace the n in the formula for a_n by $n + h$:

$$\sum_{n=1}^{\infty} a_n = \sum_{n=1-h}^{\infty} a_{n+h} = a_1 + a_2 + a_3 + \cdots.$$

It works like a horizontal shift. We saw this in starting a geometric series with the index $n = 0$ instead of the index $n = 1$, but we can use any other starting index value as well. We usually give preference to indexings that lead to simple expressions.

EXAMPLE 10 We can write the geometric series

$$\sum_{n=1}^{\infty} \frac{1}{2^{n-1}} = 1 + \frac{1}{2} + \frac{1}{4} + \cdots$$

as

$$\sum_{n=0}^{\infty} \frac{1}{2^n}, \quad \sum_{n=5}^{\infty} \frac{1}{2^{n-5}}, \quad \text{or even} \quad \sum_{n=-4}^{\infty} \frac{1}{2^{n+4}}.$$

The partial sums remain the same no matter what indexing we choose. ■

EXERCISES 8.2

In Exercises 1–6, find a formula for the nth partial sum of each series and use it to find the series' sum if the series converges.

1. $2 + \frac{2}{3} + \frac{2}{9} + \frac{2}{27} + \cdots + \frac{2}{3^{n-1}} + \cdots$

2. $\frac{9}{100} + \frac{9}{100^2} + \frac{9}{100^3} + \cdots + \frac{9}{100^n} + \cdots$

3. $1 - \frac{1}{2} + \frac{1}{4} - \frac{1}{8} + \cdots + (-1)^{n-1}\frac{1}{2^{n-1}} + \cdots$

4. $1 - 2 + 4 - 8 + \cdots + (-1)^{n-1}2^{n-1} + \cdots$

5. $\frac{1}{2\cdot 3} + \frac{1}{3\cdot 4} + \frac{1}{4\cdot 5} + \cdots + \frac{1}{(n+1)(n+2)} + \cdots$

6. $\frac{5}{1\cdot 2} + \frac{5}{2\cdot 3} + \frac{5}{3\cdot 4} + \cdots + \frac{5}{n(n+1)} + \cdots$

In Exercises 7–14, write out the first few terms of each series to show how the series starts. Then find the sum of the series.

7. $\sum_{n=0}^{\infty} \frac{(-1)^n}{4^n}$

8. $\sum_{n=2}^{\infty} \frac{1}{4^n}$

9. $\sum_{n=1}^{\infty} \frac{7}{4^n}$

10. $\sum_{n=0}^{\infty} (-1)^n \frac{5}{4^n}$

11. $\sum_{n=0}^{\infty} \left(\frac{5}{2^n} + \frac{1}{3^n}\right)$

12. $\sum_{n=0}^{\infty} \left(\frac{5}{2^n} - \frac{1}{3^n}\right)$

13. $\sum_{n=0}^{\infty} \left(\frac{1}{2^n} + \frac{(-1)^n}{5^n}\right)$

14. $\sum_{n=0}^{\infty} \left(\frac{2^{n+1}}{5^n}\right)$

Find the sum of each series in Exercises 15–22.

15. $\sum_{n=1}^{\infty} \frac{4}{(4n-3)(4n+1)}$

16. $\sum_{n=1}^{\infty} \frac{6}{(2n-1)(2n+1)}$

17. $\sum_{n=1}^{\infty} \frac{40n}{(2n-1)^2(2n+1)^2}$

18. $\sum_{n=1}^{\infty} \frac{2n+1}{n^2(n+1)^2}$

19. $\sum_{n=1}^{\infty} \left(\frac{1}{\sqrt{n}} - \frac{1}{\sqrt{n+1}}\right)$

20. $\sum_{n=1}^{\infty} \left(\frac{1}{2^{1/n}} - \frac{1}{2^{1/(n+1)}}\right)$

21. $\sum_{n=1}^{\infty} \left(\frac{1}{\ln(n+2)} - \frac{1}{\ln(n+1)}\right)$

22. $\sum_{n=1}^{\infty} (\tan^{-1}(n) - \tan^{-1}(n+1))$

Which series in Exercises 23–40 converge, and which diverge? Give reasons for your answers. If a series converges, find its sum.

23. $\sum_{n=0}^{\infty} \left(\frac{1}{\sqrt{2}}\right)^n$

24. $\sum_{n=0}^{\infty} (\sqrt{2})^n$

25. $\sum_{n=1}^{\infty} (-1)^{n+1}\frac{3}{2^n}$

26. $\sum_{n=1}^{\infty} (-1)^{n+1} n$

27. $\sum_{n=0}^{\infty} \cos n\pi$

28. $\sum_{n=0}^{\infty} \frac{\cos n\pi}{5^n}$

29. $\sum_{n=0}^{\infty} e^{-2n}$

30. $\sum_{n=1}^{\infty} \ln\frac{1}{n}$

31. $\sum_{n=1}^{\infty} \frac{2}{10^n}$

32. $\sum_{n=0}^{\infty} \frac{1}{x^n}, \quad |x| > 1$

33. $\sum_{n=0}^{\infty} \frac{2^n - 1}{3^n}$

34. $\sum_{n=1}^{\infty} \left(1 - \frac{1}{n}\right)^n$

35. $\sum_{n=0}^{\infty} \frac{n!}{1000^n}$

36. $\sum_{n=1}^{\infty} \frac{n^n}{n!}$

37. $\sum_{n=1}^{\infty} \ln\left(\frac{n}{n+1}\right)$

38. $\sum_{n=1}^{\infty} \ln\left(\frac{n}{2n+1}\right)$

39. $\sum_{n=0}^{\infty} \left(\frac{e}{\pi}\right)^n$

40. $\sum_{n=0}^{\infty} \frac{e^{n\pi}}{\pi^{ne}}$

In each of the geometric series in Exercises 41–44, write out the first few terms of the series to find a and r, and find the sum of the series. Then express the inequality $|r| < 1$ in terms of x and find the values of x for which the inequality holds and the series converges.

41. $\sum_{n=0}^{\infty} (-1)^n x^n$

42. $\sum_{n=0}^{\infty} (-1)^n x^{2n}$

43. $\sum_{n=0}^{\infty} 3\left(\frac{x-1}{2}\right)^n$

44. $\sum_{n=0}^{\infty} \frac{(-1)^n}{2}\left(\frac{1}{3+\sin x}\right)^n$

In Exercises 45–50, find the values of x for which the given geometric series converges. Also, find the sum of the series (as a function of x) for those values of x.

45. $\sum_{n=0}^{\infty} 2^n x^n$

46. $\sum_{n=0}^{\infty} (-1)^n x^{-2n}$

47. $\sum_{n=0}^{\infty} (-1)^n (x+1)^n$

48. $\sum_{n=0}^{\infty} \left(-\frac{1}{2}\right)^n (x-3)^n$

49. $\sum_{n=0}^{\infty} \sin^n x$

50. $\sum_{n=0}^{\infty} (\ln x)^n$

Express each of the numbers in Exercises 51–58 as the ratio of two integers.

51. $0.\overline{23} = 0.23\ 23\ 23\ldots$

52. $0.\overline{234} = 0.234\ 234\ 234\ldots$

53. $0.\overline{7} = 0.7777\ldots$

54. $0.\overline{d} = 0.dddd\ldots$, where d is a digit

55. $0.0\overline{6} = 0.06666\ldots$

56. $1.\overline{414} = 1.414\ 414\ 414\ldots$

57. $1.24\overline{123} = 1.24\ 123\ 123\ 123\ldots$

58. $3.\overline{142857} = 3.142857\,142857\ldots$

59. The series in Exercise 5 can also be written as

$$\sum_{n=1}^{\infty} \frac{1}{(n+1)(n+2)} \quad \text{and} \quad \sum_{n=-1}^{\infty} \frac{1}{(n+3)(n+4)}.$$

Write it as a sum beginning with **(a)** $n = -2$, **(b)** $n = 0$, **(c)** $n = 5$.

60. The series in Exercise 6 can also be written as

$$\sum_{n=1}^{\infty} \frac{5}{n(n+1)} \quad \text{and} \quad \sum_{n=0}^{\infty} \frac{5}{(n+1)(n+2)}.$$

Write it as a sum beginning with **(a)** $n = -1$, **(b)** $n = 3$, **(c)** $n = 20$.

61. Make up an infinite series of nonzero terms whose sum is

a. 1 **b.** -3 **c.** 0.

62. (*Continuation of Exercise 61.*) Can you make an infinite series of nonzero terms that converges to any number you want? Explain.

63. Show by example that $\sum(a_n/b_n)$ may diverge even though $\sum a_n$ and $\sum b_n$ converge and no b_n equals 0.

64. Find convergent geometric series $A = \sum a_n$ and $B = \sum b_n$ that illustrate the fact that $\sum a_n b_n$ may converge without being equal to AB.

65. Show by example that $\sum(a_n/b_n)$ may converge to something other than A/B even when $A = \sum a_n$, $B = \sum b_n \neq 0$, and no b_n equals 0.

66. If $\sum a_n$ converges and $a_n > 0$ for all n, can anything be said about $\sum(1/a_n)$? Give reasons for your answer.

67. What happens if you add a finite number of terms to a divergent series or delete a finite number of terms from a divergent series? Give reasons for your answer.

68. If $\sum a_n$ converges and $\sum b_n$ diverges, can anything be said about their term-by-term sum $\sum(a_n + b_n)$? Give reasons for your answer.

69. Make up a geometric series $\sum ar^{n-1}$ that converges to the number 5 if

a. $a = 2$ **b.** $a = 13/2$.

70. Find the value of b for which

$$1 + e^b + e^{2b} + e^{3b} + \cdots = 9.$$

71. For what values of r does the infinite series

$$1 + 2r + r^2 + 2r^3 + r^4 + 2r^5 + r^6 + \cdots$$

converge? Find the sum of the series when it converges.

72. Show that the error $(L - s_n)$ obtained by replacing a convergent geometric series with one of its partial sums s_n is $ar^n/(1 - r)$.

8.3 The Integral Test

Given a series, we want to know whether it converges or not. In this section and the next two, we study series with nonnegative terms. Such a series converges if its sequence of partial sums is bounded. If we establish that a given series does converge, we generally do not have a formula available for its sum, so we investigate methods to approximate the sum instead.

Nondecreasing Partial Sums

Suppose that $\sum_{n=1}^{\infty} a_n$ is an infinite series with $a_n \geq 0$ for all n. Then each partial sum is greater than or equal to its predecessor because $s_{n+1} = s_n + a_n$:

$$s_1 \leq s_2 \leq s_3 \leq \cdots \leq s_n \leq s_{n+1} \leq \cdots.$$

Since the partial sums form a nondecreasing sequence, the Nondecreasing Sequence Theorem (Theorem 6, Section 8.1) tells us that the series will converge if and only if the partial sums are bounded from above.

Corollary of Theorem 6 A series $\sum_{n=1}^{\infty} a_n$ of nonnegative terms converges if and only if its partial sums are bounded from above.

EXAMPLE 1 The series

$$\sum_{n=1}^{\infty} \frac{1}{n} = 1 + \frac{1}{2} + \frac{1}{3} + \cdots + \frac{1}{n} + \cdots$$

is called the **harmonic series**. The harmonic series is divergent, but this doesn't follow from the *n*th-Term Test. The *n*th term $1/n$ does go to zero, but the series still diverges. The reason it diverges is because there is no upper bound for its partial sums. To see why, group the terms of the series in the following way:

$$1 + \frac{1}{2} + \underbrace{\left(\frac{1}{3} + \frac{1}{4}\right)}_{> \frac{2}{4} = \frac{1}{2}} + \underbrace{\left(\frac{1}{5} + \frac{1}{6} + \frac{1}{7} + \frac{1}{8}\right)}_{> \frac{4}{8} = \frac{1}{2}} + \underbrace{\left(\frac{1}{9} + \frac{1}{10} + \cdots + \frac{1}{16}\right)}_{> \frac{8}{16} = \frac{1}{2}} + \cdots.$$

The sum of the first two terms is 1.5. The sum of the next two terms is $1/3 + 1/4$, which is greater than $1/4 + 1/4 = 1/2$. The sum of the next four terms is $1/5 + 1/6 + 1/7 + 1/8$, which is greater than $1/8 + 1/8 + 1/8 + 1/8 = 1/2$. The sum of the next eight terms is $1/9 + 1/10 + 1/11 + 1/12 + 1/13 + 1/14 + 1/15 + 1/16$, which is greater than $8/16 = 1/2$. The sum of the next 16 terms is greater than $16/32 = 1/2$, and so on. In general, the sum of 2^n terms ending with $1/2^{n+1}$ is greater than $2^n/2^{n+1} = 1/2$. The sequence of partial sums is not bounded from above: If $n = 2^k$, the partial sum s_n is greater than $k/2$. The harmonic series diverges. ■

The Integral Test

We introduce the Integral Test with a series that is related to the harmonic series, but whose *n*th term is $1/n^2$ instead of $1/n$.

EXAMPLE 2 Does the following series converge?

$$\sum_{n=1}^{\infty} \frac{1}{n^2} = 1 + \frac{1}{4} + \frac{1}{9} + \frac{1}{16} + \cdots + \frac{1}{n^2} + \cdots$$

Solution We determine the convergence of $\sum_{n=1}^{\infty}(1/n^2)$ by comparing it with $\int_1^{\infty}(1/x^2)\,dx$. To carry out the comparison, we think of the terms of the series as values of the function $f(x) = 1/x^2$ and interpret these values as the areas of rectangles under the curve $y = 1/x^2$.

As Figure 8.7 shows,

$$\begin{aligned} s_n &= \frac{1}{1^2} + \frac{1}{2^2} + \frac{1}{3^2} + \cdots + \frac{1}{n^2} \\ &= f(1) + f(2) + f(3) + \cdots + f(n) \\ &< f(1) + \int_1^n \frac{1}{x^2}\,dx && \text{Rectangle areas sum to less than area under graph.} \\ &< 1 + \int_1^{\infty} \frac{1}{x^2}\,dx && \int_1^n (1/x^2)\,dx < \int_1^{\infty}(1/x^2)\,dx \\ &< 1 + 1 = 2. && \text{As in Section 7.7, Example 3, } \int_1^{\infty}(1/x^2)\,dx = 1. \end{aligned}$$

Thus the partial sums of $\sum_{n=1}^{\infty} 1/n^2$ are bounded from above (by 2) and the series converges. The sum of the series is known to be $\pi^2/6 \approx 1.64493$. ■

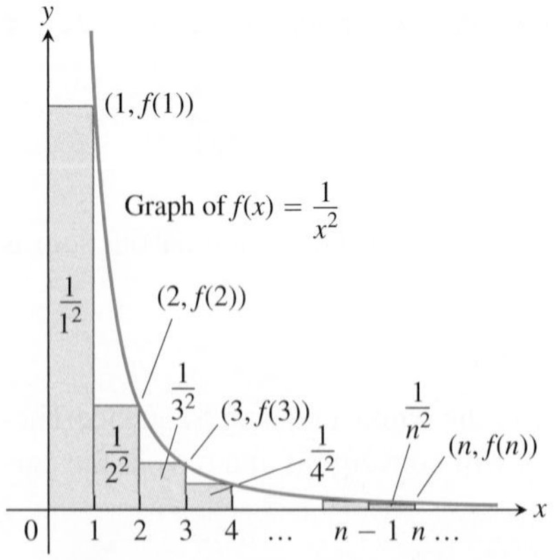

FIGURE 8.7 The sum of the areas of the rectangles under the graph of $f(x) = 1/x^2$ is less than the area under the graph (Example 2).

Caution
The series and integral need not have the same value in the convergent case. As we noted in Example 2, $\sum_{n=1}^{\infty}(1/n^2) = \pi^2/6$ while $\int_1^{\infty}(1/x^2)\,dx = 1$.

THEOREM 9—The Integral Test Let $\{a_n\}$ be a sequence of positive terms. Suppose that $a_n = f(n)$, where f is a continuous, positive, decreasing function of x for all $x \geq N$ (N a positive integer). Then the series $\sum_{n=N}^{\infty} a_n$ and the integral $\int_N^{\infty} f(x)\,dx$ both converge or both diverge.

Proof We establish the test for the case $N = 1$. The proof for general N is similar.

We start with the assumption that f is a decreasing function with $f(n) = a_n$ for every n. This leads us to observe that the rectangles in Figure 8.8a, which have areas $a_1, a_2, \ldots, a_n$, collectively enclose more area than that under the curve $y = f(x)$ from $x = 1$ to $x = n + 1$. That is,

$$\int_1^{n+1} f(x)\,dx \leq a_1 + a_2 + \cdots + a_n.$$

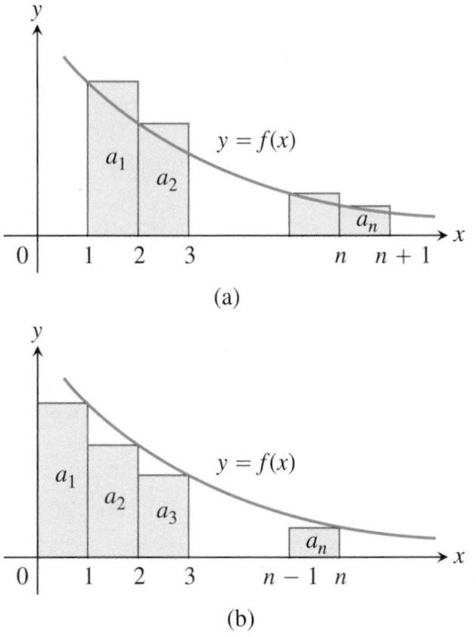

FIGURE 8.8 Subject to the conditions of the Integral Test, the series $\sum_{n=1}^{\infty} a_n$ and the integral $\int_1^{\infty}(x)\,dx$ both converge or both diverge.

In Figure 8.8b the rectangles have been faced to the left instead of to the right. If we momentarily disregard the first rectangle, of area a_1, we see that

$$a_2 + a_3 + \cdots + a_n \leq \int_1^n f(x)\,dx.$$

If we include a_1, we have

$$a_1 + a_2 + \cdots + a_n \leq a_1 + \int_1^n f(x)\,dx.$$

Combining these results gives

$$\int_1^{n+1} f(x)\,dx \leq a_1 + a_2 + \cdots + a_n \leq a_1 + \int_1^n f(x)\,dx.$$

These inequalities hold for each n, and continue to hold as $n \to \infty$.

If $\int_1^{\infty} f(x)\,dx$ is finite, the right-hand inequality shows that $\sum a_n$ is finite. If $\int_1^{\infty} f(x)\,dx$ is infinite, the left-hand inequality shows that $\sum a_n$ is infinite. Hence the series and the integral are both finite or both infinite. ■

EXAMPLE[redacted]w that the ***p*-series**

$$\sum_{n=1}^{\infty} \frac{1}{n^p} = \frac{1}{1^p} + \frac{1}{2^p} + \frac{1}{3^p} + \cdots + \frac{1}{n^p} + \cdots$$

(p a real constant) converges if $p > 1$, and diverges if $p \leq 1$.

Solution If $p > 1$, then $f(x) = 1/x^p$ is a positive decreasing function of x. Since

$$\begin{aligned}\int_1^{\infty} \frac{1}{x^p}\,dx = \int_1^{\infty} x^{-p}\,dx &= \lim_{b\to\infty}\left[\frac{x^{-p+1}}{-p+1}\right]_1^b \\ &= \frac{1}{1-p}\lim_{b\to\infty}\left(\frac{1}{b^{p-1}} - 1\right) \\ &= \frac{1}{1-p}(0-1) = \frac{1}{p-1},\end{aligned}$$

$b^{p-1} \to \infty$ as $b \to \infty$ because $p - 1 > 0$.

the series converges by the Integral Test. We emphasize that the sum of the p-series is *not* $1/(p-1)$. The series converges, but we don't know the value it converges to.

If $p < 1$, then $1 - p > 0$ and

$$\int_1^\infty \frac{1}{x^p}\,dx = \frac{1}{1-p}\lim_{b\to\infty}(b^{1-p} - 1) = \infty .$$

The series diverges by the Integral Test.

If $p = 1$, we have the (divergent) harmonic series

$$1 + \frac{1}{2} + \frac{1}{3} + \cdots + \frac{1}{n} + \cdots .$$

We have convergence for $p > 1$ but divergence for every other value of p. ■

The p-series with $p = 1$ is the **harmonic series** (Example 1). The p-Series Test shows that the harmonic series is just *barely* divergent; if we increase p to 1.000000001, for instance, the series converges!

The slowness with which the partial sums of the harmonic series approaches infinity is impressive. For instance, it takes more than 178 million terms of the harmonic series to move the partial sums beyond 20. (See also Exercise 33b.)

Error Estimation

If a series Σa_n is shown to be convergent by the integral test, we may want to estimate the size of the **remainder** R_n between the total sum S of the series and its nth partial sum s_n. That is, we wish to estimate

$$R_n = S - s_n = a_{n+1} + a_{n+2} + a_{n+3} + \cdots .$$

To get a lower bound for the remainder, we compare the sum of the areas of the rectangles with the area under the curve $y = f(x)$ for $x \geq n$ (see Figure 8.8a). We see that

$$R_n = a_{n+1} + a_{n+2} + a_{n+3} + \cdots \geq \int_{n+1}^\infty f(x)\,dx.$$

Similarly, from Figure 8.8b, we find an upper bound with

$$R_n = a_{n+1} + a_{n+2} + a_{n+3} + \cdots \leq \int_n^\infty f(x)\,dx.$$

These comparisons prove the following result giving bounds on the size of the remainder.

Bounds for the Remainder in the Integral Test

Suppose $\{a_k\}$ is a sequence of positive terms with $a_k = f(k)$, where f is a continuous positive decreasing function of x for all $x \geq n$, and that Σa_n converges to S. Then the remainder $R_n = S - s_n$ satisfies the inequalities

$$\int_{n+1}^\infty f(x)\,dx \leq R_n \leq \int_n^\infty f(x)\,dx. \qquad (1)$$

If we add the partial sum s_n to each side of the inequalities in (1), we get

$$s_n + \int_{n+1}^{\infty} f(x)\,dx \le S \le s_n + \int_{n}^{\infty} f(x)\,dx \tag{2}$$

since $s_n + R_n = S$. The inequalities in (2) are useful for estimating the error in approximating the sum of a convergent series. The error can be no larger than the length of the interval containing S, as given by (2).

EXAMPLE 4 Estimate the sum of the series $\Sigma\left(1/n^2\right)$ using the inequalities in (2) and $n = 10$.

Solution We have that

$$\int_n^{\infty} \frac{1}{x^2}\,dx = \lim_{b\to\infty}\left[-\frac{1}{x}\right]_n^b = \lim_{b\to\infty}\left(-\frac{1}{b} + \frac{1}{n}\right) = \frac{1}{n}.$$

Using this result with the inequalities in (2), we get

$$s_{10} + \frac{1}{11} \le S \le s_{10} + \frac{1}{10}.$$

Taking $s_{10} = 1 + (1/4) + (1/9) + (1/16) + \cdots + (1/100) \approx 1.54977$, these last inequalities give

$$1.64068 \le S \le 1.64997.$$

If we approximate the sum S by the midpoint of this interval, we find that

$$\sum_{n=1}^{\infty} \frac{1}{n^2} \approx 1.6453.$$

The error in this approximation is less than half the length of the interval, so the error is less than 0.005. ∎

EXERCISES 8.3

Which of the series in Exercises 1–30 converge, and which diverge? Give reasons for your answers. (When you check an answer, remember that there may be more than one way to determine the series' convergence or divergence.)

1. $\sum_{n=1}^{\infty} \frac{1}{10^n}$
2. $\sum_{n=1}^{\infty} e^{-n}$
3. $\sum_{n=1}^{\infty} \frac{n}{n+1}$
4. $\sum_{n=1}^{\infty} \frac{5}{n+1}$
5. $\sum_{n=1}^{\infty} \frac{3}{\sqrt{n}}$
6. $\sum_{n=1}^{\infty} \frac{-2}{n\sqrt{n}}$
7. $\sum_{n=1}^{\infty} -\frac{1}{8^n}$
8. $\sum_{n=1}^{\infty} \frac{-8}{n}$
9. $\sum_{n=2}^{\infty} \frac{\ln n}{n}$
10. $\sum_{n=2}^{\infty} \frac{\ln n}{\sqrt{n}}$
11. $\sum_{n=1}^{\infty} \frac{2^n}{3^n}$
12. $\sum_{n=1}^{\infty} \frac{5^n}{4^n + 3}$
13. $\sum_{n=0}^{\infty} \frac{-2}{n+1}$
14. $\sum_{n=1}^{\infty} \frac{1}{2n-1}$
15. $\sum_{n=1}^{\infty} \frac{2^n}{n+1}$
16. $\sum_{n=1}^{\infty} \frac{1}{\sqrt{n}\left(\sqrt{n}+1\right)}$
17. $\sum_{n=2}^{\infty} \frac{\sqrt{n}}{\ln n}$
18. $\sum_{n=1}^{\infty} \left(1 + \frac{1}{n}\right)^n$
19. $\sum_{n=1}^{\infty} \frac{1}{(\ln 2)^n}$
20. $\sum_{n=1}^{\infty} \frac{1}{(\ln 3)^n}$
21. $\sum_{n=3}^{\infty} \frac{(1/n)}{(\ln n)\sqrt{\ln^2 n - 1}}$
22. $\sum_{n=1}^{\infty} \frac{1}{n(1 + \ln^2 n)}$
23. $\sum_{n=1}^{\infty} n \sin\frac{1}{n}$
24. $\sum_{n=1}^{\infty} n \tan\frac{1}{n}$
25. $\sum_{n=1}^{\infty} \frac{e^n}{1 + e^{2n}}$
26. $\sum_{n=1}^{\infty} \frac{2}{1 + e^n}$
27. $\sum_{n=1}^{\infty} \frac{8 \tan^{-1} n}{1 + n^2}$
28. $\sum_{n=1}^{\infty} \frac{n}{n^2 + 1}$
29. $\sum_{n=1}^{\infty} \operatorname{sech} n$
30. $\sum_{n=1}^{\infty} \operatorname{sech}^2 n$

For what values of a, if any, do the series in Exercises 31 and 32 converge?

31. $\sum_{n=1}^{\infty}\left(\frac{a}{n+2}-\frac{1}{n+4}\right)$ **32.** $\sum_{n=3}^{\infty}\left(\frac{1}{n-1}-\frac{2a}{n+1}\right)$

33. a. Draw illustrations like those in Figures 8.7 and 8.8 to show that the partial sums of the harmonic series satisfy the inequalities

$$\ln(n+1)=\int_1^{n+1}\frac{1}{x}\,dx \le 1+\frac{1}{2}+\cdots+\frac{1}{n}$$
$$\le 1+\int_1^n\frac{1}{x}\,dx = 1+\ln n.$$

T **b.** There is absolutely no empirical evidence for the divergence of the harmonic series even though we know it diverges. The partial sums just grow too slowly. To see what we mean, suppose you had started with $s_1 = 1$ the day the universe was formed, 13 billion years ago, and added a new term every *second*. About how large would the partial sum s_n be today, assuming a 365-day year?

34. Are there any values of x for which $\sum_{n=1}^{\infty}(1/(nx))$ converges? Give reasons for your answer.

35. Is it true that if $\sum_{n=1}^{\infty} a_n$ is a divergent series of positive numbers then there is also a divergent series $\sum_{n=1}^{\infty} b_n$ of positive numbers with $b_n < a_n$ for every n? Is there a "smallest" divergent series of positive numbers? Give reasons for your answers.

36. (*Continuation of Exercise 35.*) Is there a "largest" convergent series of positive numbers? Explain.

37. The Cauchy condensation test The Cauchy condensation test says: Let $\{a_n\}$ be a nonincreasing sequence ($a_n \ge a_{n+1}$ for all n) of positive terms that converges to 0. Then $\sum a_n$ converges if and only if $\sum 2^n a_{2^n}$ converges. For example, $\sum(1/n)$ diverges because $\sum 2^n \cdot (1/2^n) = \sum 1$ diverges. Show why the test works.

38. Use the Cauchy condensation test from Exercise 37 to show that

a. $\sum_{n=2}^{\infty}\frac{1}{n\ln n}$ diverges;

b. $\sum_{n=1}^{\infty}\frac{1}{n^p}$ converges if $p > 1$ and diverges if $p \le 1$.

39. Logarithmic p-series

a. Show that

$$\int_2^{\infty}\frac{dx}{x(\ln x)^p} \quad (p \text{ a positive constant})$$

converges if and only if $p > 1$.

b. What implications does the fact in part (a) have for the convergence of the series

$$\sum_{n=2}^{\infty}\frac{1}{n(\ln n)^p}\,?$$

Give reasons for your answer.

40. (*Continuation of Exercise 39.*) Use the result in Exercise 39 to determine which of the following series converge and which diverge. Support your answer in each case.

a. $\sum_{n=2}^{\infty}\frac{1}{n(\ln n)}$ **b.** $\sum_{n=2}^{\infty}\frac{1}{n(\ln n)^{1.01}}$

c. $\sum_{n=2}^{\infty}\frac{1}{n\ln(n^3)}$ **d.** $\sum_{n=2}^{\infty}\frac{1}{n(\ln n)^3}$

41. Euler's constant Graphs like those in Figure 8.8 suggest that as n increases there is little change in the difference between the sum

$$1+\frac{1}{2}+\cdots+\frac{1}{n}$$

and the integral

$$\ln n = \int_1^n\frac{1}{x}\,dx.$$

To explore this idea, carry out the following steps.

a. By taking $f(x) = 1/x$ in the proof of Theorem 9, show that

$$\ln(n+1) \le 1+\frac{1}{2}+\cdots+\frac{1}{n} \le 1+\ln n$$

or

$$0 < \ln(n+1)-\ln n \le 1+\frac{1}{2}+\cdots+\frac{1}{n}-\ln n \le 1.$$

Thus, the sequence

$$a_n = 1+\frac{1}{2}+\cdots+\frac{1}{n}-\ln n$$

is bounded from below and from above.

b. Show that

$$\frac{1}{n+1} < \int_n^{n+1}\frac{1}{x}\,dx = \ln(n+1)-\ln n,$$

and use this result to show that the sequence $\{a_n\}$ in part (a) is decreasing.

Since a decreasing sequence that is bounded from below converges (Exercise 107 in Section 8.1), the numbers a_n defined in part (a) converge:

$$1+\frac{1}{2}+\cdots+\frac{1}{n}-\ln n \to \gamma.$$

The number γ, whose value is $0.5772\ldots$, is called *Euler's constant*. In contrast to other special numbers like π and e, no other expression with a simple law of formulation has ever been found for γ.

42. Use the integral test to show that

$$\sum_{n=0}^{\infty} e^{-n^2}$$

converges.

43. a. For the series $\sum(1/n^3)$, use the inequalities in (2) with $n = 10$ to find an interval containing the sum S.

b. As in Example 4, use the midpoint of the interval found in part (a) to approximate the sum of the series. What is the maximum error for your approximation?

44. Repeat Exercise 43 using the series $\sum(1/n^4)$.

8.4 Comparison Tests

We have seen how to determine the convergence of geometric series, p-series, and a few others. We can test the convergence of many more series by comparing their terms to those of a series whose convergence is known.

THEOREM 10—The Comparison Test Let $\sum a_n$ be a series with nonnegative terms.

(a) $\sum a_n$ converges if there is a convergent series $\sum c_n$ with $a_n \leq c_n$ for all $n > N$, for some integer N.

(b) $\sum a_n$ diverges if there is a divergent series of nonnegative terms $\sum d_n$ with $a_n \geq d_n$ for all $n > N$, for some integer N.

HISTORICAL BIOGRAPHY

Albert of Saxony
(ca. 1316–1390)

Proof In Part (a), the partial sums of $\sum a_n$ are bounded above by

$$M = a_1 + a_2 + \cdots + a_N + \sum_{n=N+1}^{\infty} c_n.$$

They therefore form a nondecreasing sequence with a limit $L \leq M$.

In Part (b), the partial sums of $\sum a_n$ are not bounded from above. If they were, the partial sums for $\sum d_n$ would be bounded by

$$M^* = d_1 + d_2 + \cdots + d_N + \sum_{n=N+1}^{\infty} a_n$$

and $\sum d_n$ would have to converge instead of diverge. ■

EXAMPLE 1

(a) The series

$$\sum_{n=1}^{\infty} \frac{5}{5n - 1}$$

diverges because its nth term

$$\frac{5}{5n - 1} = \frac{1}{n - \frac{1}{5}} > \frac{1}{n}$$

is greater than the nth term of the divergent harmonic series.

(b) The series

$$\sum_{n=0}^{\infty} \frac{1}{n!} = 1 + \frac{1}{1!} + \frac{1}{2!} + \frac{1}{3!} + \cdots$$

converges because its terms are all positive and less than or equal to the corresponding terms of

$$1 + \sum_{n=0}^{\infty} \frac{1}{2^n} = 1 + 1 + \frac{1}{2} + \frac{1}{2^2} + \cdots.$$

The geometric series on the left converges and we have

$$1 + \sum_{n=0}^{\infty} \frac{1}{2^n} = 1 + \frac{1}{1 - (1/2)} = 3.$$

The fact that 3 is an upper bound for the partial sums of $\sum_{n=0}^{\infty}(1/n!)$ does not mean that the series converges to 3. As we will see in Section 8.9, the series converges to e.

(c) The series

$$5 + \frac{2}{3} + \frac{1}{7} + 1 + \frac{1}{2+\sqrt{1}} + \frac{1}{4+\sqrt{2}} + \frac{1}{8+\sqrt{3}} + \cdots + \frac{1}{2^n+\sqrt{n}} + \cdots$$

converges. To see this, we ignore the first three terms and compare the remaining terms with those of the convergent geometric series $\sum_{n=0}^{\infty}(1/2^n)$. The term $1/(2^n + \sqrt{n})$ of the truncated sequence is less than the corresponding term $1/2^n$ of the geometric series. We see that term by term we have the comparison,

$$1 + \frac{1}{2+\sqrt{1}} + \frac{1}{4+\sqrt{2}} + \frac{1}{8+\sqrt{3}} + \cdots \leq 1 + \frac{1}{2} + \frac{1}{4} + \frac{1}{8} + \cdots$$

So the truncated series and the original series converge by an application of the Comparison Test. ■

The Limit Comparison Test

We now introduce a comparison test that is particularly useful for series in which a_n is a rational function of n.

THEOREM 11—Limit Comparison Test Suppose that $a_n > 0$ and $b_n > 0$ for all $n \geq N$ (N an integer).

1. If $\lim_{n\to\infty} \frac{a_n}{b_n} = c > 0$, then $\sum a_n$ and $\sum b_n$ both converge or both diverge.
2. If $\lim_{n\to\infty} \frac{a_n}{b_n} = 0$ and $\sum b_n$ converges, then $\sum a_n$ converges.
3. If $\lim_{n\to\infty} \frac{a_n}{b_n} = \infty$ and $\sum b_n$ diverges, then $\sum a_n$ diverges.

Proof We will prove Part 1. Parts 2 and 3 are left as Exercises 37(a) and (b).

Since $c/2 > 0$, there exists an integer N such that for all n

$$n > N \Rightarrow \left|\frac{a_n}{b_n} - c\right| < \frac{c}{2}.$$

Limit definition with $\epsilon = c/2$, $L = c$, and a_n replaced by a_n/b_n

Thus, for $n > N$,

$$-\frac{c}{2} < \frac{a_n}{b_n} - c < \frac{c}{2},$$

$$\frac{c}{2} < \frac{a_n}{b_n} < \frac{3c}{2},$$

$$\left(\frac{c}{2}\right)b_n < a_n < \left(\frac{3c}{2}\right)b_n.$$

If $\sum b_n$ converges, then $\sum(3c/2)b_n$ converges and $\sum a_n$ converges by the Direct Comparison Test. If $\sum b_n$ diverges, then $\sum(c/2)b_n$ diverges and $\sum a_n$ diverges by the Direct Comparison Test. ■

EXAMPLE 2 Which of the following series converge, and which diverge?

(a) $\frac{3}{4} + \frac{5}{9} + \frac{7}{16} + \frac{9}{25} + \cdots = \sum_{n=1}^{\infty} \frac{2n+1}{(n+1)^2} = \sum_{n=1}^{\infty} \frac{2n+1}{n^2+2n+1}$

(b) $\frac{1}{1} + \frac{1}{3} + \frac{1}{7} + \frac{1}{15} + \cdots = \sum_{n=1}^{\infty} \frac{1}{2^n - 1}$

(c) $\frac{1 + 2\ln 2}{9} + \frac{1 + 3\ln 3}{14} + \frac{1 + 4\ln 4}{21} + \cdots = \sum_{n=2}^{\infty} \frac{1 + n\ln n}{n^2 + 5}$

Solution

(a) Let $a_n = (2n+1)/(n^2+2n+1)$. For large n, we expect a_n to behave like $2n/n^2 = 2/n$ since the leading terms dominate for large n, so we let $b_n = 1/n$. Since

$$\sum_{n=1}^{\infty} b_n = \sum_{n=1}^{\infty} \frac{1}{n} \text{ diverges}$$

and

$$\lim_{n\to\infty} \frac{a_n}{b_n} = \lim_{n\to\infty} \frac{2n^2+n}{n^2+2n+1} = 2,$$

$\sum a_n$ diverges by Part 1 of the Limit Comparison Test. We could just as well have taken $b_n = 2/n$, but $1/n$ is simpler.

(b) Let $a_n = 1/(2^n - 1)$. For large n, we expect a_n to behave like $1/2^n$, so we let $b_n = 1/2^n$. Since

$$\sum_{n=1}^{\infty} b_n = \sum_{n=1}^{\infty} \frac{1}{2^n} \text{ converges}$$

and

$$\begin{aligned} \lim_{n\to\infty} \frac{a_n}{b_n} &= \lim_{n\to\infty} \frac{2^n}{2^n - 1} \\ &= \lim_{n\to\infty} \frac{1}{1 - (1/2^n)} \\ &= 1, \end{aligned}$$

$\sum a_n$ converges by Part 1 of the Limit Comparison Test.

(c) Let $a_n = (1 + n\ln n)/(n^2+5)$. For large n, we expect a_n to behave like $(n\ln n)/n^2 = (\ln n)/n$, which is greater than $1/n$ for $n \geq 3$, so we take $b_n = 1/n$. Since

$$\sum_{n=2}^{\infty} b_n = \sum_{n=2}^{\infty} \frac{1}{n} \text{ diverges}$$

and

$$\begin{aligned} \lim_{n\to\infty} \frac{a_n}{b_n} &= \lim_{n\to\infty} \frac{n + n^2\ln n}{n^2+5} \\ &= \infty, \end{aligned}$$

$\sum a_n$ diverges by Part 3 of the Limit Comparison Test. ∎

EXAMPLE 3 Does $\sum_{n=1}^{\infty} \frac{\ln n}{n^{3/2}}$ converge?

Solution Because $\ln n$ grows more slowly than n^c for any positive constant c (Section 8.1, Exercise 91), we would expect to have

$$\frac{\ln n}{n^{3/2}} < \frac{n^{1/4}}{n^{3/2}} = \frac{1}{n^{5/4}}$$

for n sufficiently large. Indeed, taking $a_n = (\ln n)/n^{3/2}$ and $b_n = 1/n^{5/4}$, we have

$$\begin{aligned}\lim_{n\to\infty} \frac{a_n}{b_n} &= \lim_{n\to\infty} \frac{\ln n}{n^{1/4}} \\ &= \lim_{n\to\infty} \frac{1/n}{(1/4)n^{-3/4}} \qquad \text{l'Hôpital's Rule} \\ &= \lim_{n\to\infty} \frac{4}{n^{1/4}} = 0.\end{aligned}$$

Since $\Sigma b_n = \Sigma(1/n^{5/4})$ (a p-series with $p > 1$) converges, Σa_n converges by Part 2 of the Limit Comparison Test. ■

EXERCISES 8.4

Which of the series in Exercises 1–36 converge, and which diverge? Give reasons for your answers.

1. $\displaystyle\sum_{n=1}^{\infty} \frac{1}{2\sqrt{n} + \sqrt[3]{n}}$
2. $\displaystyle\sum_{n=1}^{\infty} \frac{3}{n + \sqrt{n}}$
3. $\displaystyle\sum_{n=1}^{\infty} \frac{\sin^2 n}{2^n}$
4. $\displaystyle\sum_{n=1}^{\infty} \frac{1 + \cos n}{n^2}$
5. $\displaystyle\sum_{n=1}^{\infty} \frac{2n}{3n - 1}$
6. $\displaystyle\sum_{n=1}^{\infty} \frac{n + 1}{n^2\sqrt{n}}$
7. $\displaystyle\sum_{n=1}^{\infty} \left(\frac{n}{3n + 1}\right)^n$
8. $\displaystyle\sum_{n=1}^{\infty} \frac{1}{\sqrt{n^3 + 2}}$
9. $\displaystyle\sum_{n=3}^{\infty} \frac{1}{\ln(\ln n)}$
10. $\displaystyle\sum_{n=2}^{\infty} \frac{1}{(\ln n)^2}$
11. $\displaystyle\sum_{n=1}^{\infty} \frac{(\ln n)^2}{n^3}$
12. $\displaystyle\sum_{n=1}^{\infty} \frac{(\ln n)^3}{n^3}$
13. $\displaystyle\sum_{n=2}^{\infty} \frac{1}{\sqrt{n}\ln n}$
14. $\displaystyle\sum_{n=1}^{\infty} \frac{(\ln n)^2}{n^{3/2}}$
15. $\displaystyle\sum_{n=1}^{\infty} \frac{1}{1 + \ln n}$
16. $\displaystyle\sum_{n=1}^{\infty} \frac{1}{(1 + \ln n)^2}$
17. $\displaystyle\sum_{n=2}^{\infty} \frac{\ln(n + 1)}{n + 1}$
18. $\displaystyle\sum_{n=1}^{\infty} \frac{1}{(1 + \ln^2 n)}$
19. $\displaystyle\sum_{n=2}^{\infty} \frac{1}{n\sqrt{n^2 - 1}}$
20. $\displaystyle\sum_{n=1}^{\infty} \frac{\sqrt{n}}{n^2 + 1}$
21. $\displaystyle\sum_{n=1}^{\infty} \frac{1 - n}{n2^n}$
22. $\displaystyle\sum_{n=1}^{\infty} \frac{n + 2^n}{n^2 2^n}$
23. $\displaystyle\sum_{n=1}^{\infty} \frac{1}{3^{n-1} + 1}$
24. $\displaystyle\sum_{n=1}^{\infty} \frac{3^{n-1} + 1}{3^n}$
25. $\displaystyle\sum_{n=1}^{\infty} \sin\frac{1}{n}$
26. $\displaystyle\sum_{n=1}^{\infty} \tan\frac{1}{n}$
27. $\displaystyle\sum_{n=1}^{\infty} \frac{10n + 1}{n(n + 1)(n + 2)}$
28. $\displaystyle\sum_{n=3}^{\infty} \frac{5n^3 - 3n}{n^2(n - 2)(n^2 + 5)}$
29. $\displaystyle\sum_{n=1}^{\infty} \frac{\tan^{-1} n}{n^{1.1}}$
30. $\displaystyle\sum_{n=1}^{\infty} \frac{\sec^{-1} n}{n^{1.3}}$
31. $\displaystyle\sum_{n=1}^{\infty} \frac{\coth n}{n^2}$
32. $\displaystyle\sum_{n=1}^{\infty} \frac{\tanh n}{n^2}$
33. $\displaystyle\sum_{n=1}^{\infty} \frac{1}{n\sqrt[n]{n}}$
34. $\displaystyle\sum_{n=1}^{\infty} \frac{\sqrt[n]{n}}{n^2}$
35. $\displaystyle\sum_{n=1}^{\infty} \frac{1}{1 + 2 + 3 + \cdots + n}$
36. $\displaystyle\sum_{n=1}^{\infty} \frac{1}{1 + 2^2 + 3^2 + \cdots + n^2}$

37. Prove **(a)** Part 2 and **(b)** Part 3 of the Limit Comparison Test.

38. If $\sum_{n=1}^{\infty} a_n$ is a convergent series of nonnegative numbers, can anything be said about $\sum_{n=1}^{\infty}(a_n/n)$? Explain.

39. Suppose that $a_n > 0$ and $b_n > 0$ for $n \geq N$ (N an integer). If $\lim_{n\to\infty}(a_n/b_n) = \infty$ and Σa_n converges, can anything be said about $\Sigma\, b_n$? Give reasons for your answer.

40. Prove that if Σa_n is a convergent series of nonnegative terms, then $\Sigma {a_n}^2$ converges.

COMPUTER EXPLORATION

41. It is not yet known whether the series

$$\sum_{n=1}^{\infty} \frac{1}{n^3 \sin^2 n}$$

converges or diverges. Use a CAS to explore the behavior of the series by performing the following steps.

a. Define the sequence of partial sums

$$s_k = \sum_{n=1}^{k} \frac{1}{n^3 \sin^2 n}.$$

What happens when you try to find the limit of s_k as $k \to \infty$? Does your CAS find a closed form answer for this limit?

b. Plot the first 100 points (k, s_k) for the sequence of partial sums. Do they appear to converge? What would you estimate the limit to be?

c. Next plot the first 200 points (k, s_k). Discuss the behavior in your own words.

d. Plot the first 400 points (k, s_k). What happens when $k = 355$? Calculate the number 355/113. Explain from your calculation what happened at $k = 355$. For what values of k would you guess this behavior might occur again?

You will find an interesting discussion of this series in Chapter 72 of *Mazes for the Mind* by Clifford A. Pickover, St. Martin's Press, Inc., New York, 1992.

8.5 The Ratio and Root Tests

The Ratio Test measures the rate of growth (or decline) of a series by examining the ratio a_{n+1}/a_n. For a geometric series Σar^n, this rate is a constant $((ar^{n+1})/(ar^n) = r)$, and the series converges if and only if its ratio is less than 1 in absolute value. The Ratio Test is a powerful rule extending that result.

> **THEOREM 12—The Ratio Test** Let Σa_n be a series with positive terms and suppose that
>
> $$\lim_{n\to\infty} \frac{a_{n+1}}{a_n} = \rho.$$
>
> Then **(a)** the series *converges* if $\rho < 1$, **(b)** the series *diverges* if $\rho > 1$ or ρ is infinite, **(c)** the test is *inconclusive* if $\rho = 1$.

Proof

(a) $\boldsymbol{\rho < 1}$**.** Let r be a number between ρ and 1. Then the number $\epsilon = r - \rho$ is positive. Since

$$\frac{a_{n+1}}{a_n} \to \rho,$$

a_{n+1}/a_n must lie within ϵ of ρ when n is large enough, say for all $n \geq N$. In particular

$$\frac{a_{n+1}}{a_n} < \rho + \epsilon = r, \qquad \text{when } n \geq N.$$

That is,

$$\begin{aligned} a_{N+1} &< ra_N, \\ a_{N+2} &< ra_{N+1} < r^2 a_N, \\ a_{N+3} &< ra_{N+2} < r^3 a_N, \\ &\vdots \\ a_{N+m} &< ra_{N+m-1} < r^m a_N. \end{aligned}$$

These inequalities show that the terms of our series, after the Nth term, approach zero more rapidly than the terms in a geometric series with ratio $r < 1$. More precisely, consider the series Σc_n, where $c_n = a_n$ for $n = 1, 2, \ldots, N$ and $c_{N+1} = ra_N$, $c_{N+2} = r^2 a_N, \ldots, c_{N+m} = r^m a_N, \ldots$. Now $a_n \leq c_n$ for all n, and

$$\begin{aligned} \sum_{n=1}^{\infty} c_n &= a_1 + a_2 + \cdots + a_{N-1} + a_N + ra_N + r^2 a_N + \cdots \\ &= a_1 + a_2 + \cdots + a_{N-1} + a_N(1 + r + r^2 + \cdots). \end{aligned}$$

The geometric series $1 + r + r^2 + \cdots$ converges because $|r| < 1$, so Σc_n converges. Since $a_n \leq c_n$, Σa_n also converges.

(b) $\boldsymbol{1 < \rho \leq \infty}$**.** From some index M on,

$$\frac{a_{n+1}}{a_n} > 1 \qquad \text{and} \qquad a_M < a_{M+1} < a_{M+2} < \cdots.$$

The terms of the series do not approach zero as n becomes infinite, and the series diverges by the nth-Term Test.

(c) $\boldsymbol{\rho = 1}$**.** The two series

$$\sum_{n=1}^{\infty} \frac{1}{n} \quad \text{and} \quad \sum_{n=1}^{\infty} \frac{1}{n^2}$$

show that some other test for convergence must be used when $\rho = 1$.

$$\text{For } \sum_{n=1}^{\infty} \frac{1}{n}: \quad \frac{a_{n+1}}{a_n} = \frac{1/(n+1)}{1/n} = \frac{n}{n+1} \to 1.$$

$$\text{For } \sum_{n=1}^{\infty} \frac{1}{n^2}: \quad \frac{a_{n+1}}{a_n} = \frac{1/(n+1)^2}{1/n^2} = \left(\frac{n}{n+1}\right)^2 \to 1^2 = 1.$$

In both cases, $\rho = 1$, yet the first series diverges, whereas the second converges. ■

The Ratio Test is often effective when the terms of a series contain factorials of expressions involving n or expressions raised to a power involving n.

EXAMPLE 1 Investigate the convergence of the following series.

(a) $\displaystyle\sum_{n=0}^{\infty} \frac{2^n + 5}{3^n}$ **(b)** $\displaystyle\sum_{n=1}^{\infty} \frac{(2n)!}{n!n!}$ **(c)** $\displaystyle\sum_{n=1}^{\infty} \frac{4^n n! n!}{(2n)!}$

Solution

(a) For the series $\sum_{n=0}^{\infty} (2^n + 5)/3^n$,

$$\frac{a_{n+1}}{a_n} = \frac{(2^{n+1} + 5)/3^{n+1}}{(2^n + 5)/3^n} = \frac{1}{3} \cdot \frac{2^{n+1} + 5}{2^n + 5} = \frac{1}{3} \cdot \left(\frac{2 + 5 \cdot 2^{-n}}{1 + 5 \cdot 2^{-n}}\right) \to \frac{1}{3} \cdot \frac{2}{1} = \frac{2}{3}.$$

The series converges because $\rho = 2/3$ is less than 1. This does *not* mean that 2/3 is the sum of the series. In fact,

$$\sum_{n=0}^{\infty} \frac{2^n + 5}{3^n} = \sum_{n=0}^{\infty} \left(\frac{2}{3}\right)^n + \sum_{n=0}^{\infty} \frac{5}{3^n} = \frac{1}{1 - (2/3)} + \frac{5}{1 - (1/3)} = \frac{21}{2}.$$

(b) If $a_n = \dfrac{(2n)!}{n!n!}$, then $a_{n+1} = \dfrac{(2n+2)!}{(n+1)!(n+1)!}$ and

$$\begin{aligned} \frac{a_{n+1}}{a_n} &= \frac{n!n!(2n+2)(2n+1)(2n)!}{(n+1)!(n+1)!(2n)!} \\ &= \frac{(2n+2)(2n+1)}{(n+1)(n+1)} = \frac{4n+2}{n+1} \to 4. \end{aligned}$$

The series diverges because $\rho = 4$ is greater than 1.

(c) If $a_n = 4^n n! n!/(2n)!$, then

$$\begin{aligned} \frac{a_{n+1}}{a_n} &= \frac{4^{n+1}(n+1)!(n+1)!}{(2n+2)(2n+1)(2n)!} \cdot \frac{(2n)!}{4^n n! n!} \\ &= \frac{4(n+1)(n+1)}{(2n+2)(2n+1)} = \frac{2(n+1)}{2n+1} \to 1. \end{aligned}$$

Because the limit is $\rho = 1$, we cannot decide from the Ratio Test whether the series converges. When we notice that $a_{n+1}/a_n = (2n+2)/(2n+1)$, we conclude that a_{n+1} is always greater than a_n because $(2n+2)/(2n+1)$ is always greater than 1.

Therefore, all terms are greater than or equal to $a_1 = 2$, and the nth term does not approach zero as $n \to \infty$. The series diverges. ■

The Root Test

The convergence tests we have so far for $\sum a_n$ work best when the formula for a_n is relatively simple. However, consider the following series.

EXAMPLE 2 Let $a_n = \begin{cases} n/2^n, & n \text{ odd} \\ 1/2^n, & n \text{ even.} \end{cases}$ Does $\sum a_n$ converge?

Solution We write out several terms of the series:

$$\sum_{n=1}^{\infty} a_n = \frac{1}{2^1} + \frac{1}{2^2} + \frac{3}{2^3} + \frac{1}{2^4} + \frac{5}{2^5} + \frac{1}{2^6} + \frac{7}{2^7} + \cdots$$

$$= \frac{1}{2} + \frac{1}{4} + \frac{3}{8} + \frac{1}{16} + \frac{5}{32} + \frac{1}{64} + \frac{7}{128} + \cdots.$$

Clearly, this is not a geometric series. The nth term approaches zero as $n \to \infty$, so we do not know if the series diverges. The Integral Test does not look promising. The Ratio Test produces

$$\frac{a_{n+1}}{a_n} = \begin{cases} \dfrac{1}{2n}, & n \text{ odd} \\ \dfrac{n+1}{2}, & n \text{ even.} \end{cases}$$

As $n \to \infty$, the ratio is alternately small and large and has no limit.

A test that will answer the question (the series converges) is the Root Test. ■

THEOREM 13—The Root Test Let $\sum a_n$ be a series with $a_n \geq 0$ for $n \geq N$, and suppose that

$$\lim_{n\to\infty} \sqrt[n]{a_n} = \rho.$$

Then **(a)** the series *converges* if $\rho < 1$, **(b)** the series *diverges* if $\rho > 1$ or ρ is infinite, **(c)** the test is *inconclusive* if $\rho = 1$.

Proof

(a) $\boldsymbol{\rho < 1}$**.** Choose an $\epsilon > 0$ so small that $\rho + \epsilon < 1$. Since $\sqrt[n]{a_n} \to \rho$, the terms $\sqrt[n]{a_n}$ eventually get closer than ϵ to ρ. In other words, there exists an index $M \geq N$ such that

$$\sqrt[n]{a_n} < \rho + \epsilon \qquad \text{when } n \geq M.$$

Then it is also true that

$$a_n < (\rho + \epsilon)^n \qquad \text{for } n \geq M.$$

Now, $\sum_{n=M}^{\infty} (\rho + \epsilon)^n$, a geometric series with ratio $(\rho + \epsilon) < 1$, converges. By comparison, $\sum_{n=M}^{\infty} a_n$ converges, from which it follows that

$$\sum_{n=1}^{\infty} a_n = a_1 + \cdots + a_{M-1} + \sum_{n=M}^{\infty} a_n$$

converges.

(b) $1 < \rho \le \infty$. For all indices beyond some integer M, we have $\sqrt[n]{a_n} > 1$, so that $a_n > 1$ for $n > M$. The terms of the series do not converge to zero. The series diverges by the nth-Term Test.

(c) $\rho = 1$. The series $\sum_{n=1}^{\infty}(1/n)$ and $\sum_{n=1}^{\infty}(1/n^2)$ show that the test is not conclusive when $\rho = 1$. The first series diverges and the second converges, but in both cases $\sqrt[n]{a_n} \to 1$. ■

EXAMPLE 3 Which of the following series converge, and which diverge?

$$\text{(a)}\ \sum_{n=1}^{\infty}\frac{n^2}{2^n} \qquad \text{(b)}\ \sum_{n=1}^{\infty}\frac{2^n}{n^2} \qquad \text{(c)}\ \sum_{n=1}^{\infty}\left(\frac{1}{1+n}\right)^n$$

Solution

(a) $\displaystyle\sum_{n=1}^{\infty}\frac{n^2}{2^n}$ converges because $\displaystyle\sqrt[n]{\frac{n^2}{2^n}} = \frac{\sqrt[n]{n^2}}{\sqrt[n]{2^n}} = \frac{\left(\sqrt[n]{n}\right)^2}{2} \to \frac{1}{2} < 1.$

(b) $\displaystyle\sum_{n=1}^{\infty}\frac{2^n}{n^2}$ diverges because $\displaystyle\sqrt[n]{\frac{2^n}{n^2}} = \frac{2}{\left(\sqrt[n]{n}\right)^2} \to \frac{2}{1} > 1.$

(c) $\displaystyle\sum_{n=1}^{\infty}\left(\frac{1}{1+n}\right)^n$ converges because $\displaystyle\sqrt[n]{\left(\frac{1}{1+n}\right)^n} = \frac{1}{1+n} \to 0 < 1.$ ■

EXAMPLE 4 (Example 2 Revisited)

Let $a_n = \begin{cases} n/2^n, & n \text{ odd} \\ 1/2^n, & n \text{ even.} \end{cases}$ Does $\sum a_n$ converge?

Solution We apply the Root Test, finding that

$$\sqrt[n]{a_n} = \begin{cases} \sqrt[n]{n}/2, & n \text{ odd} \\ 1/2, & n \text{ even.} \end{cases}$$

Therefore,

$$\frac{1}{2} \le \sqrt[n]{a_n} \le \frac{\sqrt[n]{n}}{2}.$$

Since $\sqrt[n]{n} \to 1$ (Section 8.1, Theorem 5), we have $\lim_{n\to\infty}\sqrt[n]{a_n} = 1/2$ by the Sandwich Theorem. The limit is less than 1, so the series converges by the Root Test. ■

EXERCISES 8.5

Which of the series in Exercises 1–26 converge, and which diverge? Give reasons for your answers. (When checking your answers, remember there may be more than one way to determine a series' convergence or divergence.)

1. $\displaystyle\sum_{n=1}^{\infty}\frac{n^{\sqrt{2}}}{2^n}$

2. $\displaystyle\sum_{n=1}^{\infty}n^2e^{-n}$

3. $\displaystyle\sum_{n=1}^{\infty}n!e^{-n}$

4. $\displaystyle\sum_{n=1}^{\infty}\frac{n!}{10^n}$

5. $\displaystyle\sum_{n=1}^{\infty}\frac{n^{10}}{10^n}$

6. $\displaystyle\sum_{n=1}^{\infty}\left(\frac{n-2}{n}\right)^n$

7. $\displaystyle\sum_{n=1}^{\infty}\frac{2+(-1)^n}{1.25^n}$

8. $\displaystyle\sum_{n=1}^{\infty}\frac{(-2)^n}{3^n}$

9. $\displaystyle\sum_{n=1}^{\infty}\left(1-\frac{3}{n}\right)^n$

10. $\displaystyle\sum_{n=1}^{\infty}\left(1-\frac{1}{3n}\right)^n$

11. $\displaystyle\sum_{n=1}^{\infty}\frac{\ln n}{n^3}$

12. $\displaystyle\sum_{n=1}^{\infty}\frac{(\ln n)^n}{n^n}$

13. $\sum_{n=1}^{\infty}\left(\frac{1}{n}-\frac{1}{n^2}\right)$

14. $\sum_{n=1}^{\infty}\left(\frac{1}{n}-\frac{1}{n^2}\right)^n$

15. $\sum_{n=1}^{\infty}\frac{\ln n}{n}$

16. $\sum_{n=1}^{\infty}\frac{n\ln n}{2^n}$

17. $\sum_{n=1}^{\infty}\frac{(n+1)(n+2)}{n!}$

18. $\sum_{n=1}^{\infty}e^{-n}(n^3)$

19. $\sum_{n=1}^{\infty}\frac{(n+3)!}{3!n!3^n}$

20. $\sum_{n=1}^{\infty}\frac{n2^n(n+1)!}{3^n n!}$

21. $\sum_{n=1}^{\infty}\frac{n!}{(2n+1)!}$

22. $\sum_{n=1}^{\infty}\frac{n!}{n^n}$

23. $\sum_{n=2}^{\infty}\frac{n}{(\ln n)^n}$

24. $\sum_{n=2}^{\infty}\frac{n}{(\ln n)^{(n/2)}}$

25. $\sum_{n=1}^{\infty}\frac{n!\ln n}{n(n+2)!}$

26. $\sum_{n=1}^{\infty}\frac{3^n}{n^3 2^n}$

Which of the series $\sum_{n=1}^{\infty}a_n$ defined by the formulas in Exercises 27–38 converge, and which diverge? Give reasons for your answers.

27. $a_1=2,\quad a_{n+1}=\frac{1+\sin n}{n}a_n$

28. $a_1=1,\quad a_{n+1}=\frac{1+\tan^{-1}n}{n}a_n$

29. $a_1=\frac{1}{3},\quad a_{n+1}=\frac{3n-1}{2n+5}a_n$

30. $a_1=3,\quad a_{n+1}=\frac{n}{n+1}a_n$

31. $a_1=2,\quad a_{n+1}=\frac{2}{n}a_n$

32. $a_1=5,\quad a_{n+1}=\frac{\sqrt[n]{n}}{2}a_n$

33. $a_1=1,\quad a_{n+1}=\frac{1+\ln n}{n}a_n$

34. $a_1=\frac{1}{2},\quad a_{n+1}=\frac{n+\ln n}{n+10}a_n$

35. $a_1=\frac{1}{3},\quad a_{n+1}=\sqrt[n]{a_n}$

36. $a_1=\frac{1}{2},\quad a_{n+1}=(a_n)^{n+1}$

37. $a_n=\frac{2^n n!n!}{(2n)!}$

38. $a_n=\frac{(3n)!}{n!(n+1)!(n+2)!}$

Which of the series in Exercises 39–44 converge, and which diverge? Give reasons for your answers.

39. $\sum_{n=1}^{\infty}\frac{(n!)^n}{(n^n)^2}$

40. $\sum_{n=1}^{\infty}\frac{(n!)^n}{n^{(n^2)}}$

41. $\sum_{n=1}^{\infty}\frac{n^n}{2^{(n^2)}}$

42. $\sum_{n=1}^{\infty}\frac{n^n}{(2^n)^2}$

43. $\sum_{n=1}^{\infty}\frac{1\cdot 3\cdot\cdots\cdot(2n-1)}{4^n 2^n n!}$

44. $\sum_{n=1}^{\infty}\frac{1\cdot 3\cdot\cdots\cdot(2n-1)}{[2\cdot 4\cdot\cdots\cdot(2n)](3^n+1)}$

45. Neither the Ratio nor the Root Test helps with p-series. Try them on

$$\sum_{n=1}^{\infty}\frac{1}{n^p}$$

and show that both tests fail to provide information about convergence.

46. Show that neither the Ratio Test nor the Root Test provides information about the convergence of

$$\sum_{n=2}^{\infty}\frac{1}{(\ln n)^p}\qquad (p\text{ constant}).$$

47. Let $a_n=\begin{cases} n/2^n, & \text{if } n \text{ is a prime number}\\ 1/2^n, & \text{otherwise.}\end{cases}$

Does $\sum a_n$ converge? Give reasons for your answer.

8.6 Alternating Series, Absolute and Conditional Convergence

A series in which the terms are alternately positive and negative is an **alternating series**. Here are three examples:

$$1-\frac{1}{2}+\frac{1}{3}-\frac{1}{4}+\frac{1}{5}-\cdots+\frac{(-1)^{n+1}}{n}+\cdots \tag{1}$$

$$-2+1-\frac{1}{2}+\frac{1}{4}-\frac{1}{8}+\cdots+\frac{(-1)^n 4}{2^n}+\cdots \tag{2}$$

$$1-2+3-4+5-6+\cdots+(-1)^{n+1}n+\cdots \tag{3}$$

Series (1), called the **alternating harmonic series**, converges, as we will see in a moment. Series (2), a geometric series with ratio $r = -1/2$, converges to $-2/[1 + (1/2)] = -4/3$. Series (3) diverges because the nth term does not approach zero.

We prove the convergence of the alternating harmonic series by applying the Alternating Series Test.

THEOREM 14—The Alternating Series Test (Leibniz's Theorem) The series

$$\sum_{n=1}^{\infty}(-1)^{n+1}u_n = u_1 - u_2 + u_3 - u_4 + \cdots$$

converges if all three of the following conditions are satisfied:

1. The u_n's are all positive.
2. $u_n \geq u_{n+1}$ for all $n \geq N$, for some integer N.
3. $u_n \to 0$.

Proof Assume $N = 1$. If n is an even integer, say $n = 2m$, then the sum of the first n terms is

$$\begin{aligned} s_{2m} &= (u_1 - u_2) + (u_3 - u_4) + \cdots + (u_{2m-1} - u_{2m}) \\ &= u_1 - (u_2 - u_3) - (u_4 - u_5) - \cdots - (u_{2m-2} - u_{2m-1}) - u_{2m}. \end{aligned}$$

The first equality shows that s_{2m} is the sum of m nonnegative terms, since each term in parentheses is positive or zero. Hence $s_{2m+2} \geq s_{2m}$, and the sequence $\{s_{2m}\}$ is nondecreasing. The second equality shows that $s_{2m} \leq u_1$. Since $\{s_{2m}\}$ is nondecreasing and bounded from above, it has a limit, say

$$\lim_{m\to\infty} s_{2m} = L. \tag{4}$$

If n is an odd integer, say $n = 2m + 1$, then the sum of the first n terms is $s_{2m+1} = s_{2m} + u_{2m+1}$. Since $u_n \to 0$,

$$\lim_{m\to\infty} u_{2m+1} = 0$$

and, as $m \to \infty$,

$$s_{2m+1} = s_{2m} + u_{2m+1} \to L + 0 = L. \tag{5}$$

Combining the results of Equations (4) and (5) gives $\lim_{n\to\infty} s_n = L$ (Section 8.1, Exercise 119). ■

EXAMPLE 1 The alternating harmonic series

$$\sum_{n=1}^{\infty}(-1)^{n+1}\frac{1}{n} = 1 - \frac{1}{2} + \frac{1}{3} - \frac{1}{4} + \cdots$$

satisfies the three requirements of Theorem 14 with $N = 1$; it therefore converges. ■

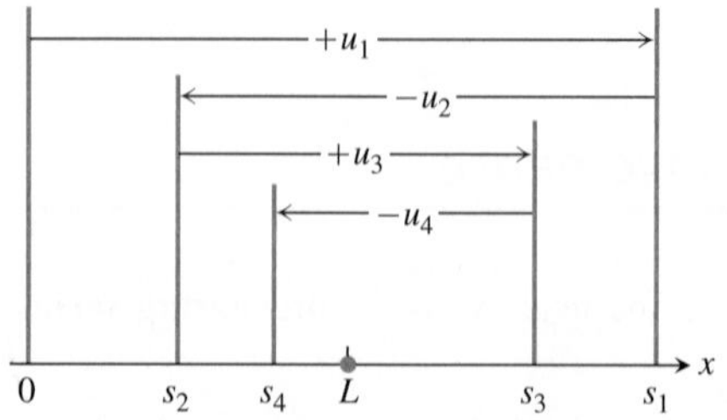

FIGURE 8.9 The partial sums of an alternating series that satisfies the hypotheses of Theorem 14 for $N = 1$ straddle the limit from the beginning.

A graphical interpretation of the partial sums (Figure 8.9) shows how an alternating series converges to its limit L when the three conditions of Theorem 14 are satisfied with $N = 1$. Starting from the origin of the x-axis, we lay off the positive distance $s_1 = u_1$. To find the point corresponding to $s_2 = u_1 - u_2$, we back up a distance equal to u_2. Since

$u_2 \leq u_1$, we do not back up any farther than the origin. We continue in this seesaw fashion, backing up or going forward as the signs in the series demand. But for $n \geq N$, each forward or backward step is shorter than (or at most the same size as) the preceding step, because $u_{n+1} \leq u_n$. And since the nth term approaches zero as n increases, the size of step we take forward or backward gets smaller and smaller. We oscillate across the limit L, and the amplitude of oscillation approaches zero. The limit L lies between any two successive sums s_n and s_{n+1} and hence differs from s_n by an amount less than u_{n+1}.

Because

$$|L - s_n| < u_{n+1} \qquad \text{for } n \geq N,$$

we can make useful estimates of the sums of convergent alternating series.

THEOREM 15—The Alternating Series Estimation Theorem If the alternating series $\sum_{n=1}^{\infty}(-1)^{n+1}u_n$ satisfies the three conditions of Theorem 14, then for $n \geq N$,

$$s_n = u_1 - u_2 + \cdots + (-1)^{n+1}u_n$$

approximates the sum L of the series with an error whose absolute value is less than u_{n+1}, the absolute value of the first unused term. Furthermore, the remainder, $L - s_n$, has the same sign as the first unused term.

We leave the verification of the sign of the remainder for Exercise 53.

EXAMPLE 2 We try Theorem 15 on a series whose sum we know:

$$\sum_{n=0}^{\infty}(-1)^n\frac{1}{2^n} = 1 - \frac{1}{2} + \frac{1}{4} - \frac{1}{8} + \frac{1}{16} - \frac{1}{32} + \frac{1}{64} - \frac{1}{128} \;\vdots\; + \frac{1}{256} - \cdots.$$

The theorem says that if we truncate the series after the eighth term, we throw away a total that is positive and less than $1/256$. The sum of the first eight terms is 0.6640625. The sum of the series is

$$\frac{1}{1-(-1/2)} = \frac{1}{3/2} = \frac{2}{3}.$$

The difference, $(2/3) - 0.6640625 = 0.0026041666\ldots$, is positive and less than $(1/256) = 0.00390625$. ■

Absolute and Conditional Convergence

DEFINITION A series $\sum a_n$ **converges absolutely** (is **absolutely convergent**) if the corresponding series of absolute values, $\sum|a_n|$, converges.

The geometric series in Example 2 converges absolutely because the corresponding series of absolute values

$$1 + \frac{1}{2} + \frac{1}{4} + \frac{1}{8} + \cdots$$

converges. The alternating harmonic series does not converge absolutely. The corresponding series of absolute values is the (divergent) harmonic series.

DEFINITION A series that converges but does not converge absolutely **converges conditionally**.

The alternating harmonic series converges conditionally.

Absolute convergence is important for two reasons. First, we have good tests for convergence of series of positive terms. Second, if a series converges absolutely, then it converges, as we now prove.

THEOREM 16—The Absolute Convergence Test If $\sum_{n=1}^{\infty} |a_n|$ converges, then $\sum_{n=1}^{\infty} a_n$ converges.

Proof For each n,

$$-|a_n| \le a_n \le |a_n|, \qquad \text{so} \qquad 0 \le a_n + |a_n| \le 2|a_n|.$$

If $\sum_{n=1}^{\infty} |a_n|$ converges, then $\sum_{n=1}^{\infty} 2|a_n|$ converges and, by the Direct Comparison Test, the nonnegative series $\sum_{n=1}^{\infty} (a_n + |a_n|)$ converges. The equality $a_n = (a_n + |a_n|) - |a_n|$ now lets us express $\sum_{n=1}^{\infty} a_n$ as the difference of two convergent series:

$$\sum_{n=1}^{\infty} a_n = \sum_{n=1}^{\infty} (a_n + |a_n| - |a_n|) = \sum_{n=1}^{\infty} (a_n + |a_n|) - \sum_{n=1}^{\infty} |a_n|.$$

Therefore, $\sum_{n=1}^{\infty} a_n$ converges. ■

Caution We can rephrase Theorem 16 to say that every absolutely convergent series converges. However, the converse statement is false: Many convergent series do not converge absolutely (such as the alternating harmonic series in Example 1).

EXAMPLE 3

(a) For $\sum_{n=1}^{\infty} (-1)^{n+1} \frac{1}{n^2} = 1 - \frac{1}{4} + \frac{1}{9} - \frac{1}{16} + \cdots$, the corresponding series of absolute values is the convergent series

$$\sum_{n=1}^{\infty} \frac{1}{n^2} = 1 + \frac{1}{4} + \frac{1}{9} + \frac{1}{16} + \cdots.$$

The original series converges because it converges absolutely.

(b) For $\sum_{n=1}^{\infty} \frac{\sin n}{n^2} = \frac{\sin 1}{1} + \frac{\sin 2}{4} + \frac{\sin 3}{9} + \cdots$, the corresponding series of absolute values is

$$\sum_{n=1}^{\infty} \left| \frac{\sin n}{n^2} \right| = \frac{|\sin 1|}{1} + \frac{|\sin 2|}{4} + \cdots,$$

which converges by comparison with $\sum_{n=1}^{\infty}(1/n^2)$ because $|\sin n| \leq 1$ for every n. The original series converges absolutely; therefore it converges. ■

EXAMPLE 4 If p is a positive constant, the sequence $\{1/n^p\}$ is a decreasing sequence with limit zero. Therefore the alternating p-series

$$\sum_{n=1}^{\infty} \frac{(-1)^{n-1}}{n^p} = 1 - \frac{1}{2^p} + \frac{1}{3^p} - \frac{1}{4^p} + \cdots, \qquad p > 0$$

converges.

If $p > 1$, the series converges absolutely. If $0 < p \leq 1$, the series converges conditionally.

$$\text{Conditional convergence:} \quad 1 - \frac{1}{\sqrt{2}} + \frac{1}{\sqrt{3}} - \frac{1}{\sqrt{4}} + \cdots$$

$$\text{Absolute convergence:} \quad 1 - \frac{1}{2^{3/2}} + \frac{1}{3^{3/2}} - \frac{1}{4^{3/2}} + \cdots$$ ■

Rearranging Series

We can always rearrange the terms of a *finite* sum. The same result is true for an infinite series that is absolutely convergent (see Exercise 60 for an outline of the proof).

THEOREM 17—The Rearrangement Theorem for Absolutely Convergent Series If $\sum_{n=1}^{\infty} a_n$ converges absolutely, and $b_1, b_2, \ldots, b_n, \ldots$ is any arrangement of the sequence $\{a_n\}$, then $\sum b_n$ converges absolutely and

$$\sum_{n=1}^{\infty} b_n = \sum_{n=1}^{\infty} a_n.$$

If we rearrange the terms of a conditionally convergent series, we get different results. In fact, it can be proved that for any real number r, a given conditionally convergent series can be rearranged so its sum is equal to r. (We omit the proof of this fact.) Therefore we must always add the terms of a conditionally convergent series in the order given.

We have now developed several tests for convergence and divergence of series. In summary:

1. **The *n*th-Term Test:** Unless $a_n \to 0$, the series diverges.
2. **Geometric series:** $\sum ar^n$ converges if $|r| < 1$; otherwise it diverges.
3. ***p*-series:** $\sum 1/n^p$ converges if $p > 1$; otherwise it diverges.
4. **Series with nonnegative terms:** Try the Integral Test, Ratio Test, or Root Test. Try comparing to a known series with the Comparison Test.
5. **Series with some negative terms:** Does $\sum |a_n|$ converge? If yes, so does $\sum a_n$, since absolute convergence implies convergence.
6. **Alternating series:** $\sum a_n$ converges if the series satisfies the conditions of the Alternating Series Test.

EXERCISES 8.6

Which of the alternating series in Exercises 1–10 converge, and which diverge? Give reasons for your answers.

1. $\sum_{n=1}^{\infty}(-1)^{n+1}\frac{1}{n^2}$

2. $\sum_{n=1}^{\infty}(-1)^{n+1}\frac{1}{n^{3/2}}$

3. $\sum_{n=1}^{\infty}(-1)^{n+1}\left(\frac{n}{10}\right)^n$

4. $\sum_{n=1}^{\infty}(-1)^{n+1}\frac{10^n}{n^{10}}$

5. $\sum_{n=2}^{\infty}(-1)^{n+1}\frac{1}{\ln n}$

6. $\sum_{n=1}^{\infty}(-1)^{n+1}\frac{\ln n}{n}$

7. $\sum_{n=2}^{\infty}(-1)^{n+1}\frac{\ln n}{\ln n^2}$

8. $\sum_{n=1}^{\infty}(-1)^{n}\ln\left(1+\frac{1}{n}\right)$

9. $\sum_{n=1}^{\infty}(-1)^{n+1}\frac{\sqrt{n}+1}{n+1}$

10. $\sum_{n=1}^{\infty}(-1)^{n+1}\frac{3\sqrt{n+1}}{\sqrt{n}+1}$

Which of the series in Exercises 11–44 converge absolutely, which converge, and which diverge? Give reasons for your answers.

11. $\sum_{n=1}^{\infty}(-1)^{n+1}(0.1)^n$

12. $\sum_{n=1}^{\infty}(-1)^{n+1}\frac{(0.1)^n}{n}$

13. $\sum_{n=1}^{\infty}(-1)^{n}\frac{1}{\sqrt{n}}$

14. $\sum_{n=1}^{\infty}\frac{(-1)^n}{1+\sqrt{n}}$

15. $\sum_{n=1}^{\infty}(-1)^{n+1}\frac{n}{n^3+1}$

16. $\sum_{n=1}^{\infty}(-1)^{n+1}\frac{n!}{2^n}$

17. $\sum_{n=1}^{\infty}(-1)^{n}\frac{1}{n+3}$

18. $\sum_{n=1}^{\infty}(-1)^{n}\frac{\sin n}{n^2}$

19. $\sum_{n=1}^{\infty}(-1)^{n+1}\frac{3+n}{5+n}$

20. $\sum_{n=2}^{\infty}(-1)^{n}\frac{1}{\ln(n^3)}$

21. $\sum_{n=1}^{\infty}(-1)^{n+1}\frac{1+n}{n^2}$

22. $\sum_{n=1}^{\infty}\frac{(-2)^{n+1}}{n+5^n}$

23. $\sum_{n=1}^{\infty}(-1)^{n}n^2(2/3)^n$

24. $\sum_{n=1}^{\infty}(-1)^{n+1}\left(\sqrt[n]{10}\right)$

25. $\sum_{n=1}^{\infty}(-1)^{n}\frac{\tan^{-1}n}{n^2+1}$

26. $\sum_{n=2}^{\infty}(-1)^{n+1}\frac{1}{n\ln n}$

27. $\sum_{n=1}^{\infty}(-1)^{n}\frac{n}{n+1}$

28. $\sum_{n=1}^{\infty}(-1)^{n}\frac{\ln n}{n-\ln n}$

29. $\sum_{n=1}^{\infty}\frac{(-100)^n}{n!}$

30. $\sum_{n=1}^{\infty}(-5)^{-n}$

31. $\sum_{n=1}^{\infty}\frac{(-1)^{n-1}}{n^2+2n+1}$

32. $\sum_{n=2}^{\infty}(-1)^{n}\left(\frac{\ln n}{\ln n^2}\right)^n$

33. $\sum_{n=1}^{\infty}\frac{\cos n\pi}{n\sqrt{n}}$

34. $\sum_{n=1}^{\infty}\frac{\cos n\pi}{n}$

35. $\sum_{n=1}^{\infty}\frac{(-1)^n(n+1)^n}{(2n)^n}$

36. $\sum_{n=1}^{\infty}\frac{(-1)^{n+1}(n!)^2}{(2n)!}$

37. $\sum_{n=1}^{\infty}(-1)^{n}\frac{(2n)!}{2^n n! n}$

38. $\sum_{n=1}^{\infty}(-1)^{n}\frac{(n!)^2 3^n}{(2n+1)!}$

39. $\sum_{n=1}^{\infty}(-1)^{n}\left(\sqrt{n+1}-\sqrt{n}\right)$

40. $\sum_{n=1}^{\infty}(-1)^{n}\left(\sqrt{n^2+n}-n\right)$

41. $\sum_{n=1}^{\infty}(-1)^{n}\left(\sqrt{n+\sqrt{n}}-\sqrt{n}\right)$

42. $\sum_{n=1}^{\infty}\frac{(-1)^n}{\sqrt{n}+\sqrt{n+1}}$

43. $\sum_{n=1}^{\infty}(-1)^{n}\operatorname{sech} n$

44. $\sum_{n=1}^{\infty}(-1)^{n}\operatorname{csch} n$

In Exercises 45–48, estimate the magnitude of the error involved in using the sum of the first four terms to approximate the sum of the entire series.

45. $\sum_{n=1}^{\infty}(-1)^{n+1}\frac{1}{n}$ It can be shown that the sum is ln 2.

46. $\sum_{n=1}^{\infty}(-1)^{n+1}\frac{1}{10^n}$

47. $\sum_{n=1}^{\infty}(-1)^{n+1}\frac{(0.01)^n}{n}$ As you will see in Section 8.7, the sum is ln(1.01).

48. $\frac{1}{1+t}=\sum_{n=0}^{\infty}(-1)^n t^n,\quad 0<t<1$

T Approximate the sums in Exercises 49 and 50 with an error of magnitude less than 5×10^{-6}.

49. $\sum_{n=0}^{\infty}(-1)^{n}\frac{1}{(2n)!}$ As you will see in Section 8.9, the sum is cos 1, the cosine of 1 radian.

50. $\sum_{n=0}^{\infty}(-1)^{n}\frac{1}{n!}$ As you will see in Section 8.9, the sum is e^{-1}.

51. **a.** The series

$$\frac{1}{3}-\frac{1}{2}+\frac{1}{9}-\frac{1}{4}+\frac{1}{27}-\frac{1}{8}+\cdots+\frac{1}{3^n}-\frac{1}{2^n}+\cdots$$

does not meet one of the conditions of Theorem 14. Which one?

b. Find the sum of the series in part (a).

T 52. The limit L of an alternating series that satisfies the conditions of Theorem 14 lies between the values of any two consecutive partial sums. This suggests using the average

$$\frac{s_n+s_{n+1}}{2}=s_n+\frac{1}{2}(-1)^{n+2}a_{n+1}$$

to estimate L. Compute

$$s_{20} + \frac{1}{2} \cdot \frac{1}{21}$$

as an approximation to the sum of the alternating harmonic series. The exact sum is $\ln 2 = 0.6931\ldots$.

53. The sign of the remainder of an alternating series that satisfies the conditions of Theorem 14 Prove the assertion in Theorem 15 that whenever an alternating series satisfying the conditions of Theorem 14 is approximated with one of its partial sums, then the remainder (sum of the unused terms) has the same sign as the first unused term. (*Hint:* Group the remainder's terms in consecutive pairs.)

54. Show that the sum of the first $2n$ terms of the series

$$1 - \frac{1}{2} + \frac{1}{2} - \frac{1}{3} + \frac{1}{3} - \frac{1}{4} + \frac{1}{4} - \frac{1}{5} + \frac{1}{5} - \frac{1}{6} + \cdots$$

is the same as the sum of the first n terms of the series

$$\frac{1}{1 \cdot 2} + \frac{1}{2 \cdot 3} + \frac{1}{3 \cdot 4} + \frac{1}{4 \cdot 5} + \frac{1}{5 \cdot 6} + \cdots.$$

Do these series converge? What is the sum of the first $2n + 1$ terms of the first series? If the series converge, what is their sum?

55. Show that if $\sum_{n=1}^{\infty} a_n$ diverges, then $\sum_{n=1}^{\infty} |a_n|$ diverges.

56. Show that if $\sum_{n=1}^{\infty} a_n$ converges absolutely, then

$$\left|\sum_{n=1}^{\infty} a_n\right| \le \sum_{n=1}^{\infty} |a_n|.$$

57. Show that if $\sum_{n=1}^{\infty} a_n$ and $\sum_{n=1}^{\infty} b_n$ both converge absolutely, then so does

a. $\sum_{n=1}^{\infty} (a_n + b_n)$ **b.** $\sum_{n=1}^{\infty} (a_n - b_n)$

c. $\sum_{n=1}^{\infty} ka_n$ (k any number)

58. Show by example that $\sum_{n=1}^{\infty} a_n b_n$ may diverge even if $\sum_{n=1}^{\infty} a_n$ and $\sum_{n=1}^{\infty} b_n$ both converge.

T **59.** In the alternating harmonic series, suppose the goal is to arrange the terms to get a new series that converges to $-1/2$. Start the new arrangement with the first negative term, which is $-1/2$. Whenever you have a sum that is less than or equal to $-1/2$, start introducing positive terms, taken in order, until the new total is greater than $-1/2$. Then add negative terms until the total is less than or equal to $-1/2$ again. Continue this process until your partial sums have been above the target at least three times and finish at or below it. If s_n is the sum of the first n terms of your new series, plot the points (n, s_n) to illustrate how the sums are behaving.

60. Outline of the proof of the Rearrangement Theorem (Theorem 17)

a. Let ϵ be a positive real number, let $L = \sum_{n=1}^{\infty} a_n$, and let $s_k = \sum_{n=1}^{k} a_n$. Show that for some index N_1 and for some index $N_2 \ge N_1$,

$$\sum_{n=N_1}^{\infty} |a_n| < \frac{\epsilon}{2} \quad \text{and} \quad |s_{N_2} - L| < \frac{\epsilon}{2}.$$

Since all the terms $a_1, a_2, \ldots, a_{N_2}$ appear somewhere in the sequence $\{b_n\}$, there is an index $N_3 \ge N_2$ such that if $n \ge N_3$, then $\left(\sum_{k=1}^{n} b_k\right) - s_{N_2}$ is at most a sum of terms a_m with $m \ge N_1$. Therefore, if $n \ge N_3$,

$$\left|\sum_{k=1}^{n} b_k - L\right| \le \left|\sum_{k=1}^{n} b_k - s_{N_2}\right| + |s_{N_2} - L|$$
$$\le \sum_{k=N_1}^{\infty} |a_k| + |s_{N_2} - L| < \epsilon.$$

b. The argument in part (a) shows that if $\sum_{n=1}^{\infty} a_n$ converges absolutely then $\sum_{n=1}^{\infty} b_n$ converges and $\sum_{n=1}^{\infty} b_n = \sum_{n=1}^{\infty} a_n$. Now show that because $\sum_{n=1}^{\infty} |a_n|$ converges, $\sum_{n=1}^{\infty} |b_n|$ converges to $\sum_{n=1}^{\infty} |a_n|$.

8.7 Power Series

Now that we can test infinite series for convergence, we can study sums that look like "infinite polynomials." We call these sums *power series* because they are defined as infinite series of powers of some variable, in our case x. Like polynomials, power series can be added, subtracted, multiplied, differentiated, and integrated to give new power series.

Power Series and Convergence

We begin with the formal definition.

DEFINITIONS A **power series about $x = 0$** is a series of the form

$$\sum_{n=0}^{\infty} c_n x^n = c_0 + c_1 x + c_2 x^2 + \cdots + c_n x^n + \cdots. \tag{1}$$

A **power series about $x = a$** is a series of the form

$$\sum_{n=0}^{\infty} c_n (x-a)^n = c_0 + c_1(x-a) + c_2(x-a)^2 + \cdots + c_n(x-a)^n + \cdots \tag{2}$$

in which the **center** a and the **coefficients** $c_0, c_1, c_2, \ldots, c_n, \ldots$ are constants.

Equation (1) is the special case obtained by taking $a = 0$ in Equation (2).

EXAMPLE 1 Taking all the coefficients to be 1 in Equation (1) gives the geometric power series

$$\sum_{n=0}^{\infty} x^n = 1 + x + x^2 + \cdots + x^n + \cdots.$$

This is the geometric series with first term 1 and ratio x. It converges to $1/(1-x)$ for $|x| < 1$. We express this fact by writing

$$\frac{1}{1-x} = 1 + x + x^2 + \cdots + x^n + \cdots, \qquad -1 < x < 1. \tag{3}$$

■

Up to now, we have used Equation (3) as a formula for the sum of the series on the right. We now change the focus: We think of the partial sums of the series on the right as polynomials $P_n(x)$ that approximate the function on the left. For values of x near zero, we need take only a few terms of the series to get a good approximation. As we move toward $x = 1$, or -1, we must take more terms. Figure 8.10 shows the graphs of $f(x) = 1/(1-x)$, and the approximating polynomials $y_n = P_n(x)$ for $n = 0, 1, 2$, and 8. The function $f(x) = 1/(1-x)$ is not continuous on intervals containing $x = 1$, where it has a vertical asymptote. The approximations do not apply when $x \geq 1$.

EXAMPLE 2 The power series

$$1 - \frac{1}{2}(x-2) + \frac{1}{4}(x-2)^2 + \cdots + \left(-\frac{1}{2}\right)^n (x-2)^n + \cdots \tag{4}$$

matches Equation (2) with $a = 2$, $c_0 = 1$, $c_1 = -1/2$, $c_2 = 1/4, \ldots, c_n = (-1/2)^n$. This is a geometric series with first term 1 and ratio $r = -\dfrac{x-2}{2}$. The series converges for

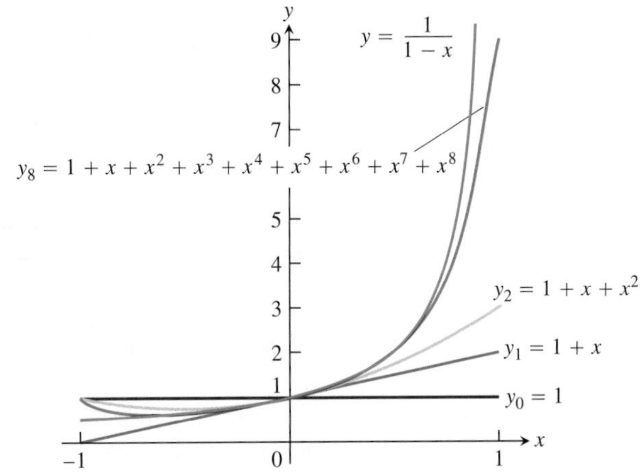

FIGURE 8.10 The graphs of $f(x) = 1/(1 - x)$ and four of its polynomial approximations (Example 1).

$\left|\frac{x-2}{2}\right| < 1$ or $0 < x < 4$. The sum is

$$\frac{1}{1-r} = \frac{1}{1 + \frac{x-2}{2}} = \frac{2}{x},$$

so

$$\frac{2}{x} = 1 - \frac{(x-2)}{2} + \frac{(x-2)^2}{4} - \cdots + \left(-\frac{1}{2}\right)^n (x-2)^n + \cdots, \qquad 0 < x < 4.$$

Series (4) generates useful polynomial approximations of $f(x) = 2/x$ for values of x near 2:

$$P_0(x) = 1$$

$$P_1(x) = 1 - \frac{1}{2}(x-2) = 2 - \frac{x}{2}$$

$$P_2(x) = 1 - \frac{1}{2}(x-2) + \frac{1}{4}(x-2)^2 = 3 - \frac{3x}{2} + \frac{x^2}{4},$$

and so on (Figure 8.11). ■

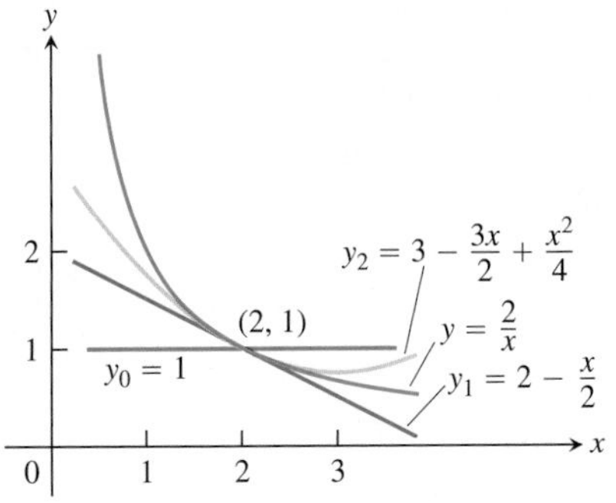

FIGURE 8.11 The graphs of $f(x) = 2/x$ and its first three polynomial approximations (Example 2).

The following example illustrates how we usually test a power series for convergence and the possible results.

EXAMPLE 3 For what values of x do the following power series converge?

(a) $\displaystyle\sum_{n=1}^{\infty} (-1)^{n-1} \frac{x^n}{n} = x - \frac{x^2}{2} + \frac{x^3}{3} - \cdots$

(b) $\displaystyle\sum_{n=1}^{\infty} (-1)^{n-1} \frac{x^{2n-1}}{2n-1} = x - \frac{x^3}{3} + \frac{x^5}{5} - \cdots$

(c) $\sum_{n=0}^{\infty} \frac{x^n}{n!} = 1 + x + \frac{x^2}{2!} + \frac{x^3}{3!} + \cdots$

(d) $\sum_{n=0}^{\infty} n!x^n = 1 + x + 2!x^2 + 3!x^3 + \cdots$

Solution Apply the Ratio Test to the series $\sum |u_n|$, where u_n is the nth term of the series in question.

(a) $\left|\frac{u_{n+1}}{u_n}\right| = \frac{n}{n+1}|x| \to |x|.$

The series converges absolutely for $|x| < 1$. It diverges if $|x| > 1$ because the nth term does not converge to zero. At $x = 1$, we get the alternating harmonic series $1 - 1/2 + 1/3 - 1/4 + \cdots$, which converges. At $x = -1$ we get $-1 - 1/2 - 1/3 - 1/4 - \cdots$, the negative of the harmonic series; it diverges. Series (a) converges for $-1 < x \le 1$ and diverges elsewhere.

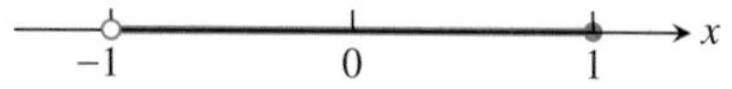

(b) $\left|\frac{u_{n+1}}{u_n}\right| = \frac{2n-1}{2n+1}x^2 \to x^2.$

The series converges absolutely for $x^2 < 1$. It diverges for $x^2 > 1$ because the nth term does not converge to zero. At $x = 1$ the series becomes $1 - 1/3 + 1/5 - 1/7 + \cdots$, which converges by the Alternating Series Theorem. It also converges at $x = -1$ because it is again an alternating series that satisfies the conditions for convergence. The value at $x = -1$ is the negative of the value at $x = 1$. Series (b) converges for $-1 \le x \le 1$ and diverges elsewhere.

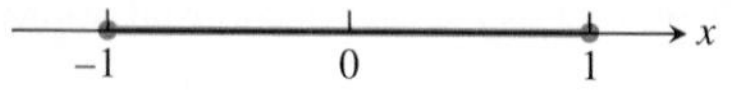

(c) $\left|\frac{u_{n+1}}{u_n}\right| = \left|\frac{x^{n+1}}{(n+1)!} \cdot \frac{n!}{x^n}\right| = \frac{|x|}{n+1} \to 0$ for every x.

The series converges absolutely for all x.

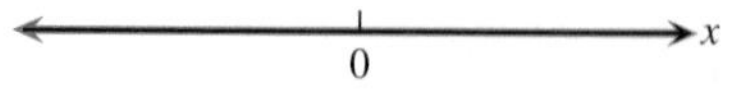

(d) $\left|\frac{u_{n+1}}{u_n}\right| = \left|\frac{(n+1)!x^{n+1}}{n!x^n}\right| = (n+1)|x| \to \infty$ unless $x = 0$.

The series diverges for all values of x except $x = 0$.

■

The previous example illustrated how a power series might converge. The next result shows that if a power series converges at more than one value, then it converges over an entire interval of values.

THEOREM 18—The Convergence Theorem for Power Series If the power series $\sum_{n=0}^{\infty} a_n x^n = a_0 + a_1 x + a_2 x^2 + \cdots$ converges for $x = c \neq 0$, then it converges absolutely for all x with $|x| < |c|$. If the series diverges for $x = d$, then it diverges for all x with $|x| > |d|$.

Proof Suppose the series $\sum_{n=0}^{\infty} a_n c^n$ converges. Then $\lim_{n\to\infty} a_n c^n = 0$. Hence, there is an integer N such that $|a_n c^n| < 1$ for all $n \geq N$. That is,

$$|a_n| < \frac{1}{|c|^n} \qquad \text{for } n \geq N. \tag{5}$$

Now take any x such that $|x| < |c|$ and consider

$$|a_0| + |a_1 x| + \cdots + |a_{N-1} x^{N-1}| + |a_N x^N| + |a_{N+1} x^{N+1}| + \cdots.$$

There are only a finite number of terms prior to $|a_N x^N|$, and their sum is finite. Starting with $|a_N x^N|$ and beyond, the terms are less than

$$\left|\frac{x}{c}\right|^N + \left|\frac{x}{c}\right|^{N+1} + \left|\frac{x}{c}\right|^{N+2} + \cdots \tag{6}$$

because of Inequality (5). But Series (6) is a geometric series with ratio $r = |x/c|$, which is less than 1, since $|x| < |c|$. Hence Series (6) converges, so the original series converges absolutely. This proves the first half of the theorem.

The second half of the theorem follows from the first. If the series diverges at $x = d$ and converges at a value x_0 with $|x_0| > |d|$, we may take $c = x_0$ in the first half of the theorem and conclude that the series converges absolutely at d. But the series cannot converge absolutely and diverge at one and the same time. Hence, if it diverges at d, it diverges for all x with $|x| > |d|$. ■

To simplify the notation, Theorem 18 deals with the convergence of series of the form $\sum a_n x^n$. For series of the form $\sum a_n(x - a)^n$ we can replace $x - a$ by x' and apply the results to the series $\sum a_n(x')^n$.

The Radius of Convergence of a Power Series

The theorem we have just proved and the examples we have studied lead to the conclusion that a power series $\sum c_n(x - a)^n$ behaves in one of three possible ways. It might converge only at $x = a$, or converge everywhere, or converge on some interval of radius R centered at $x = a$. We prove this as a Corollary to Theorem 18.

COROLLARY TO THEOREM 18 The convergence of the series $\sum c_n(x-a)^n$ is described by one of the following three possibilities:

1. There is a positive number R such that the series diverges for x with $|x-a|>R$ but converges absolutely for x with $|x-a|<R$. The series may or may not converge at either of the endpoints $x=a-R$ and $x=a+R$.
2. The series converges absolutely for every x $(R=\infty)$.
3. The series converges at $x=a$ and diverges elsewhere $(R=0)$.

Proof We assume first that $a=0$, so that the power series is centered at 0. If the series converges everywhere we are in Case 2. If it converges only at $x=0$ we are in Case 3. Otherwise there is a nonzero number d such that $\sum c_n d^n$ diverges. The set S of values of x for which the series $\sum c_n x^n$ converges is nonempty because it contains 0 and a positive number p as well. By Theorem 18, the series diverges for all x with $|x|>|d|$, so $|x|\le|d|$ for all $x\in S$, and S is a bounded set. By the Completeness Property of the real numbers (see Appendix 7) a nonempty, bounded set has a least upper bound R. (The least upper bound is the smallest number with the property that the elements $x\in S$ satisfy $x\le R$.) If $|x|>R\ge p$, then $x\notin S$ so the series $\sum c_n x^n$ diverges. If $|x|<R$, then $|x|$ is not an upper bound for S (because it's smaller than the least upper bound) so there is a number $b\in S$ such that $b>|x|$. Since $b\in S$, the series $\sum c_n b^n$ converges and therefore the series $\sum c_n|x|^n$ converges by Theorem 18. This proves the Corollary for power series centered at $a=0$.

For a power series centered at $a\ne 0$, we set $x'=(x-a)$ and repeat the argument with x'. Since $x'=0$ when $x=a$, a radius R interval of convergence for $\sum c_n(x')^n$ centered at $x'=0$ is the same as a radius R interval of convergence for $\sum c_n(x-a)^n$ centered at $x=a$. This establishes the Corollary for the general case. ■

R is called the **radius of convergence** of the power series and the interval of radius R centered at $x=a$ is called the **interval of convergence**. The interval of convergence may be open, closed, or half-open, depending on the particular series. At points x with $|x-a|<R$, the series converges absolutely. If the series converges for all values of x, we say its radius of convergence is infinite. If it converges only at $x=a$, we say its radius of convergence is zero.

How to Test a Power Series for Convergence

1. *Use the Ratio Test (or nth-Root Test) to find the interval where the series converges absolutely.* Ordinarily, this is an open interval
$$|x-a|<R \qquad \text{or} \qquad a-R<x<a+R.$$
2. *If the interval of absolute convergence is finite, test for convergence or divergence at each endpoint*, as in Examples 3a and b. Use a Comparison Test, the Integral Test, or the Alternating Series Test.
3. *If the interval of absolute convergence is $a-R<x<a+R$, the series diverges for $|x-a|>R$* (it does not even converge conditionally), because the nth term does not approach zero for those values of x.

Term-by-Term Differentiation

A theorem from advanced calculus says that a power series can be differentiated term by term at each interior point of its interval of convergence.

THEOREM 19—The Term-by-Term Differentiation Theorem If $\sum c_n(x-a)^n$ converges for $a - R < x < a + R$ for some $R > 0$, it defines a function f:

$$f(x) = \sum_{n=0}^{\infty} c_n(x-a)^n, \qquad a - R < x < a + R.$$

Such a function f has derivatives of all orders inside the interval of convergence. We can obtain the derivatives by differentiating the original series term by term:

$$f'(x) = \sum_{n=1}^{\infty} nc_n(x-a)^{n-1}$$

$$f''(x) = \sum_{n=2}^{\infty} n(n-1)c_n(x-a)^{n-2},$$

and so on. Each of these derived series converges at every interior point of the interval of convergence of the original series.

EXAMPLE 4 Find series for $f'(x)$ and $f''(x)$ if

$$f(x) = \frac{1}{1-x} = 1 + x + x^2 + x^3 + x^4 + \cdots + x^n + \cdots$$

$$= \sum_{n=0}^{\infty} x^n, \qquad -1 < x < 1$$

Solution

$$f'(x) = \frac{1}{(1-x)^2} = 1 + 2x + 3x^2 + 4x^3 + \cdots + nx^{n-1} + \cdots$$

$$= \sum_{n=1}^{\infty} nx^{n-1}, \qquad -1 < x < 1$$

$$f''(x) = \frac{2}{(1-x)^3} = 2 + 6x + 12x^2 + \cdots + n(n-1)x^{n-2} + \cdots$$

$$= \sum_{n=2}^{\infty} n(n-1)x^{n-2}, \qquad -1 < x < 1$$

■

Caution Term-by-term differentiation might not work for other kinds of series. For example, the trigonometric series

$$\sum_{n=1}^{\infty} \frac{\sin(n!x)}{n^2}$$

converges for all x. But if we differentiate term by term we get the series

$$\sum_{n=1}^{\infty} \frac{n!\cos(n!x)}{n^2},$$

which diverges for all x. This is not a power series, since it is not a sum of positive integer powers of x.

Term-by-Term Integration

It is also true that a power series can be integrated term by term throughout its interval of convergence. This result is proved in a more advanced course.

THEOREM 20—The Term-by-Term Integration Theorem Suppose that

$$f(x) = \sum_{n=0}^{\infty} c_n(x-a)^n$$

converges for $a - R < x < a + R$ $(R > 0)$. Then

$$\sum_{n=0}^{\infty} c_n \frac{(x-a)^{n+1}}{n+1}$$

converges for $a - R < x < a + R$ and

$$\int f(x)\,dx = \sum_{n=0}^{\infty} c_n \frac{(x-a)^{n+1}}{n+1} + C$$

for $a - R < x < a + R$.

EXAMPLE 5 Identify the function

$$f(x) = x - \frac{x^3}{3} + \frac{x^5}{5} - \cdots, \qquad -1 \le x \le 1.$$

Solution We differentiate the original series term by term and get

$$f'(x) = 1 - x^2 + x^4 - x^6 + \cdots, \qquad -1 < x < 1.$$

This is a geometric series with first term 1 and ratio $-x^2$, so

$$f'(x) = \frac{1}{1-(-x^2)} = \frac{1}{1+x^2}.$$

We can now integrate $f'(x) = 1/(1+x^2)$ to get

$$\int f'(x)\,dx = \int \frac{dx}{1+x^2} = \tan^{-1} x + C.$$

The series for $f(x)$ is zero when $x = 0$, so $C = 0$. Hence

$$f(x) = x - \frac{x^3}{3} + \frac{x^5}{5} - \frac{x^7}{7} + \cdots = \tan^{-1} x, \qquad -1 < x < 1. \tag{7}$$

It can be shown that the series also converges to $\tan^{-1} x$ at $x = \pm 1$, but we omit the proof. ■

Notice that the original series in Example 5 converges at both endpoints of the original interval of convergence, but Theorem 20 can guarantee the convergence of the differentiated series only inside the interval.

EXAMPLE 6 The series

$$\frac{1}{1+t} = 1 - t + t^2 - t^3 + \cdots$$

converges on the open interval $-1 < t < 1$. Therefore,

$$\ln(1+x) = \int_0^x \frac{1}{1+t}\,dt = t - \frac{t^2}{2} + \frac{t^3}{3} - \frac{t^4}{4} + \cdots \Big]_0^x \qquad \text{Theorem 20}$$

$$= x - \frac{x^2}{2} + \frac{x^3}{3} - \frac{x^4}{4} + \cdots, \qquad -1 < x < 1.$$

It can also be shown that the series converges at $x = 1$ to the number ln 2, but that was not guaranteed by the theorem. ■

Multiplication of Power Series

Another theorem states that absolutely converging power series can be multiplied the way we multiply polynomials. We again omit the proof.

THEOREM 21—The Series Multiplication Theorem for Power Series If $A(x) = \sum_{n=0}^{\infty} a_n x^n$ and $B(x) = \sum_{n=0}^{\infty} b_n x^n$ converge absolutely for $|x| < R$, and

$$c_n = a_0 b_n + a_1 b_{n-1} + a_2 b_{n-2} + \cdots + a_{n-1} b_1 + a_n b_0 = \sum_{k=0}^{n} a_k b_{n-k},$$

then $\sum_{n=0}^{\infty} c_n x^n$ converges absolutely to $A(x)B(x)$ for $|x| < R$:

$$\left(\sum_{n=0}^{\infty} a_n x^n\right) \cdot \left(\sum_{n=0}^{\infty} b_n x^n\right) = \sum_{n=0}^{\infty} c_n x^n.$$

Finding the general coefficient c_n in the product of two given power series can be very tedious. In practice, we usually find just the first few terms instead. For instance, from Examples 1 and 6, we have

$$\frac{1}{1-x}\ln(1+x) = \left(1 + x + x^2 + \cdots\right)\left(x - \frac{x^2}{2} + \frac{x^3}{3} - \cdots\right)$$

$$= x + \frac{x^2}{2} + \frac{5x^3}{6} - \frac{x^4}{6} \cdots.$$

EXERCISES 8.7

In Exercises 1–32, **(a)** find the series' radius and interval of convergence. For what values of x does the series converge **(b)** absolutely, **(c)** conditionally?

1. $\sum_{n=0}^{\infty} x^n$

2. $\sum_{n=0}^{\infty} (x+5)^n$

3. $\sum_{n=0}^{\infty} (-1)^n(4x+1)^n$

4. $\sum_{n=1}^{\infty} \frac{(3x-2)^n}{n}$

5. $\sum_{n=0}^{\infty} \frac{(x-2)^n}{10^n}$

6. $\sum_{n=0}^{\infty} (2x)^n$

7. $\sum_{n=0}^{\infty} \frac{nx^n}{n+2}$

8. $\sum_{n=1}^{\infty} \frac{(-1)^n(x+2)^n}{n}$

9. $\sum_{n=1}^{\infty} \frac{x^n}{n\sqrt{n}\,3^n}$

10. $\sum_{n=1}^{\infty} \frac{(x-1)^n}{\sqrt{n}}$

11. $\sum_{n=0}^{\infty} \frac{(-1)^n x^n}{n!}$

12. $\sum_{n=0}^{\infty} \frac{3^n x^n}{n!}$

13. $\sum_{n=0}^{\infty} \frac{x^{2n+1}}{n!}$

14. $\sum_{n=0}^{\infty} \frac{(2x+3)^{2n+1}}{n!}$

15. $\sum_{n=0}^{\infty} \frac{x^n}{\sqrt{n^2+3}}$

16. $\sum_{n=0}^{\infty} \frac{(-1)^n x^n}{\sqrt{n^2+3}}$

17. $\sum_{n=0}^{\infty} \frac{n(x+3)^n}{5^n}$

18. $\sum_{n=0}^{\infty} \frac{nx^n}{4^n(n^2+1)}$

19. $\sum_{n=0}^{\infty} \frac{\sqrt{n}x^n}{3^n}$

20. $\sum_{n=1}^{\infty} \sqrt[n]{n}(2x+5)^n$

21. $\sum_{n=1}^{\infty} \left(1+\frac{1}{n}\right)^n x^n$

22. $\sum_{n=1}^{\infty} (\ln n)x^n$

23. $\sum_{n=1}^{\infty} n^n x^n$

24. $\sum_{n=0}^{\infty} n!(x-4)^n$

25. $\sum_{n=1}^{\infty} \frac{(-1)^{n+1}(x+2)^n}{n2^n}$

26. $\sum_{n=0}^{\infty} (-2)^n(n+1)(x-1)^n$

27. $\sum_{n=2}^{\infty} \frac{x^n}{n(\ln n)^2}$ Get the information you need about $\sum 1/(n(\ln n)^2)$ from Section 8.3, Exercise 39.

28. $\sum_{n=2}^{\infty} \frac{x^n}{n \ln n}$ Get the information you need about $\sum 1/(n \ln n)$ from Section 8.3, Exercise 38.

29. $\sum_{n=1}^{\infty} \frac{(4x-5)^{2n+1}}{n^{3/2}}$

30. $\sum_{n=1}^{\infty} \frac{(3x+1)^{n+1}}{2n+2}$

31. $\sum_{n=1}^{\infty} \frac{(x+\pi)^n}{\sqrt{n}}$

32. $\sum_{n=0}^{\infty} \frac{(x-\sqrt{2})^{2n+1}}{2^n}$

In Exercises 33–38, find the series' interval of convergence and, within this interval, the sum of the series as a function of x.

33. $\sum_{n=0}^{\infty} \frac{(x-1)^{2n}}{4^n}$

34. $\sum_{n=0}^{\infty} \frac{(x+1)^{2n}}{9^n}$

35. $\sum_{n=0}^{\infty} \left(\frac{\sqrt{x}}{2}-1\right)^n$

36. $\sum_{n=0}^{\infty} (\ln x)^n$

37. $\sum_{n=0}^{\infty} \left(\frac{x^2+1}{3}\right)^n$

38. $\sum_{n=0}^{\infty} \left(\frac{x^2-1}{2}\right)^n$

39. For what values of x does the series

$$1-\frac{1}{2}(x-3)+\frac{1}{4}(x-3)^2+\cdots+\left(-\frac{1}{2}\right)^n(x-3)^n+\cdots$$

converge? What is its sum? What series do you get if you differentiate the given series term by term? For what values of x does the new series converge? What is its sum?

40. If you integrate the series in Exercise 39 term by term, what new series do you get? For what values of x does the new series converge, and what is another name for its sum?

41. The series

$$\sin x = x-\frac{x^3}{3!}+\frac{x^5}{5!}-\frac{x^7}{7!}+\frac{x^9}{9!}-\frac{x^{11}}{11!}+\cdots$$

converges to $\sin x$ for all x.

a. Find the first six terms of a series for $\cos x$. For what values of x should the series converge?

b. By replacing x by $2x$ in the series for $\sin x$, find a series that converges to $\sin 2x$ for all x.

c. Using the result in part (a) and series multiplication, calculate the first six terms of a series for $2 \sin x \cos x$. Compare your answer with the answer in part (b).

42. The series

$$e^x = 1+x+\frac{x^2}{2!}+\frac{x^3}{3!}+\frac{x^4}{4!}+\frac{x^5}{5!}+\cdots$$

converges to e^x for all x.

a. Find a series for $(d/dx)e^x$. Do you get the series for e^x? Explain your answer.

b. Find a series for $\int e^x\,dx$. Do you get the series for e^x? Explain your answer.

c. Replace x by $-x$ in the series for e^x to find a series that converges to e^{-x} for all x. Then multiply the series for e^x and e^{-x} to find the first six terms of a series for $e^{-x} \cdot e^x$.

43. The series

$$\tan x = x+\frac{x^3}{3}+\frac{2x^5}{15}+\frac{17x^7}{315}+\frac{62x^9}{2835}+\cdots$$

converges to $\tan x$ for $-\pi/2 < x < \pi/2$.

a. Find the first five terms of the series for $\ln|\sec x|$. For what values of x should the series converge?

b. Find the first five terms of the series for $\sec^2 x$. For what values of x should this series converge?

c. Check your result in part (b) by squaring the series given for $\sec x$ in Exercise 44.

44. The series

$$\sec x = 1 + \frac{x^2}{2} + \frac{5}{24}x^4 + \frac{61}{720}x^6 + \frac{277}{8064}x^8 + \cdots$$

converges to $\sec x$ for $-\pi/2 < x < \pi/2$.

a. Find the first five terms of a power series for the function $\ln|\sec x + \tan x|$. For what values of x should the series converge?

b. Find the first four terms of a series for $\sec x \tan x$. For what values of x should the series converge?

c. Check your result in part (b) by multiplying the series for $\sec x$ by the series given for $\tan x$ in Exercise 43.

45. Uniqueness of convergent power series

a. Show that if two power series $\sum_{n=0}^{\infty} a_n x^n$ and $\sum_{n=0}^{\infty} b_n x^n$ are convergent and equal for all values of x in an open interval $(-c, c)$, then $a_n = b_n$ for every n. (*Hint:* Let $f(x) = \sum_{n=0}^{\infty} a_n x^n = \sum_{n=0}^{\infty} b_n x^n$. Differentiate term by term to show that a_n and b_n both equal $f^{(n)}(0)/(n!)$.

b. Show that if $\sum_{n=0}^{\infty} a_n x^n = 0$ for all x in an open interval $(-c, c)$, then $a_n = 0$ for every n.

46. The sum of the series $\sum_{n=0}^{\infty} (n^2/2^n)$ To find the sum of this series, express $1/(1 - x)$ as a geometric series, differentiate both sides of the resulting equation with respect to x, multiply both sides of the result by x, differentiate again, multiply by x again, and set x equal to $1/2$. What do you get? (*Source*: David E. Dobbs' letter to the editor, *Illinois Mathematics Teacher*, Vol. 33, Issue 4, 1982, p. 27.)

47. Convergence at endpoints Show by examples that the convergence of a power series at an endpoint of its interval of convergence may be either conditional or absolute.

48. Make up a power series whose interval of convergence is

a. $(-3, 3)$ **b.** $(-2, 0)$ **c.** $(1, 5)$.

8.8 Taylor and Maclaurin Series

This section shows how functions that are infinitely differentiable generate power series called Taylor series. In many cases, these series can provide useful polynomial approximations of the generating functions.

Series Representations

We know from Theorem 19 that within its interval of convergence the sum of a power series is a continuous function with derivatives of all orders. But what about the other way around? If a function $f(x)$ has derivatives of all orders on an interval I, can it be expressed as a power series on I? And if it can, what will its coefficients be?

We can answer the last question readily if we assume that $f(x)$ is the sum of a power series

$$\begin{aligned} f(x) &= \sum_{n=0}^{\infty} a_n(x - a)^n \\ &= a_0 + a_1(x - a) + a_2(x - a)^2 + \cdots + a_n(x - a)^n + \cdots \end{aligned}$$

with a positive radius of convergence. By repeated term-by-term differentiation within the interval of convergence I we obtain

$$\begin{aligned} f'(x) &= a_1 + 2a_2(x - a) + 3a_3(x - a)^2 + \cdots + na_n(x - a)^{n-1} + \cdots \\ f''(x) &= 1 \cdot 2a_2 + 2 \cdot 3a_3(x - a) + 3 \cdot 4a_4(x - a)^2 + \cdots \\ f'''(x) &= 1 \cdot 2 \cdot 3a_3 + 2 \cdot 3 \cdot 4a_4(x - a) + 3 \cdot 4 \cdot 5a_5(x - a)^2 + \cdots, \end{aligned}$$

with the nth derivative, for all n, being

$$f^{(n)}(x) = n!a_n + \text{a sum of terms with } (x - a) \text{ as a factor.}$$

Since these equations all hold at $x = a$, we have

$$\begin{aligned} f'(a) &= a_1, \\ f''(a) &= 1 \cdot 2a_2, \\ f'''(a) &= 1 \cdot 2 \cdot 3a_3, \end{aligned}$$

and, in general,

$$f^{(n)}(a) = n!a_n.$$

These formulas reveal a pattern in the coefficients of any power series $\sum_{n=0}^{\infty} a_n(x - a)^n$ that converges to the values of f on I ("represents f on I"). If there *is* such a series (still an open question), then there is only one such series and its nth coefficient is

$$a_n = \frac{f^{(n)}(a)}{n!}.$$

If f has a series representation, then the series must be

$$f(x) = f(a) + f'(a)(x - a) + \frac{f''(a)}{2!}(x - a)^2 + \cdots + \frac{f^{(n)}(a)}{n!}(x - a)^n + \cdots. \tag{1}$$

But if we start with an arbitrary function f that is infinitely differentiable on an interval I centered at $x = a$ and use it to generate the series in Equation (1), will the series then converge to $f(x)$ at each x in the interior of I? The answer is maybe—for some functions it will but for other functions it will not, as we will see.

Taylor and Maclaurin Series

HISTORICAL BIOGRAPHIES

Brook Taylor (1685–1731)

Colin Maclaurin (1698–1746)

DEFINITIONS Let f be a function with derivatives of all orders throughout some interval containing a as an interior point. Then the **Taylor series generated by f at $x = a$ is**

$$\sum_{k=0}^{\infty} \frac{f^{(k)}(a)}{k!}(x - a)^k = f(a) + f'(a)(x - a) + \frac{f''(a)}{2!}(x - a)^2 + \cdots + \frac{f^{(n)}(a)}{n!}(x - a)^n + \cdots.$$

The **Maclaurin series generated by f is**

$$\sum_{k=0}^{\infty} \frac{f^{(k)}(0)}{k!}x^k = f(0) + f'(0)x + \frac{f''(0)}{2!}x^2 + \cdots + \frac{f^{(n)}(0)}{n!}x^n + \cdots,$$

the Taylor series generated by f at $x = 0$.

The Maclaurin series generated by f is often just called the Taylor series of f.

EXAMPLE 1 Find the Taylor series generated by $f(x) = 1/x$ at $a = 2$. Where, if anywhere, does the series converge to $1/x$?

Solution We need to find $f(2), f'(2), f''(2), \ldots$. Taking derivatives we get

$$f(x) = x^{-1}, \qquad f(2) = 2^{-1} = \frac{1}{2},$$

$$f'(x) = -x^{-2}, \qquad f'(2) = -\frac{1}{2^2},$$

$$f''(x) = 2!x^{-3}, \qquad \frac{f''(2)}{2!} = 2^{-3} = \frac{1}{2^3},$$

$$f'''(x) = -3!x^{-4}, \qquad \frac{f'''(2)}{3!} = -\frac{1}{2^4},$$

$$\vdots \qquad \vdots$$

$$f^{(n)}(x) = (-1)^n n! x^{-(n+1)}, \qquad \frac{f^{(n)}(2)}{n!} = \frac{(-1)^n}{2^{n+1}}.$$

The Taylor series is

$$f(2) + f'(2)(x-2) + \frac{f''(2)}{2!}(x-2)^2 + \cdots + \frac{f^{(n)}(2)}{n!}(x-2)^n + \cdots$$

$$= \frac{1}{2} - \frac{(x-2)}{2^2} + \frac{(x-2)^2}{2^3} - \cdots + (-1)^n \frac{(x-2)^n}{2^{n+1}} + \cdots.$$

This is a geometric series with first term $1/2$ and ratio $r = -(x-2)/2$. It converges absolutely for $|x-2| < 2$ and its sum is

$$\frac{1/2}{1 + (x-2)/2} = \frac{1}{2 + (x-2)} = \frac{1}{x}.$$

In this example the Taylor series generated by $f(x) = 1/x$ at $a = 2$ converges to $1/x$ for $|x-2| < 2$ or $0 < x < 4$. ■

Taylor Polynomials

The linearization of a differentiable function f at a point a is the polynomial of degree one given by

$$P_1(x) = f(a) + f'(a)(x-a).$$

In Section 3.10 we used this linearization to approximate $f(x)$ at values of x near a. If f has derivatives of higher order at a, then it has higher-order polynomial approximations as well, one for each available derivative. These polynomials are called the Taylor polynomials of f.

DEFINITION Let f be a function with derivatives of order k for $k = 1, 2, \ldots, N$ in some interval containing a as an interior point. Then for any integer n from 0 through N, the **Taylor polynomial of order *n*** generated by f at $x = a$ is the polynomial

$$P_n(x) = f(a) + f'(a)(x-a) + \frac{f''(a)}{2!}(x-a)^2 + \cdots + \frac{f^{(k)}(a)}{k!}(x-a)^k + \cdots + \frac{f^{(n)}(a)}{n!}(x-a)^n.$$

We speak of a Taylor polynomial of *order n* rather than *degree n* because $f^{(n)}(a)$ may be zero. The first two Taylor polynomials of $f(x) = \cos x$ at $x = 0$, for example, are $P_0(x) = 1$ and $P_1(x) = 1$. The first-order Taylor polynomial has degree zero, not one.

Just as the linearization of f at $x = a$ provides the best linear approximation of f in the neighborhood of a, the higher-order Taylor polynomials provide the "best" polynomial approximations of their respective degrees. (See Exercise 32.)

EXAMPLE 2 Find the Taylor series and the Taylor polynomials generated by $f(x) = e^x$ at $x = 0$.

Solution Since

$$f(x) = e^x, \quad f'(x) = e^x, \quad \ldots, \quad f^{(n)}(x) = e^x, \quad \ldots,$$

we have

$$f(0) = e^0 = 1, \quad f'(0) = 1, \quad \ldots, \quad f^{(n)}(0) = 1, \quad \ldots.$$

The Taylor series generated by f at $x = 0$ is

$$f(0) + f'(0)x + \frac{f''(0)}{2!}x^2 + \cdots + \frac{f^{(n)}(0)}{n!}x^n + \cdots$$

$$= 1 + x + \frac{x^2}{2} + \cdots + \frac{x^n}{n!} + \cdots$$

$$= \sum_{k=0}^{\infty} \frac{x^k}{k!}.$$

This is also the Maclaurin series for e^x. In Section 8.9 we will see that the series converges to e^x at every x.

The Taylor polynomial of order n at $x = 0$ is

$$P_n(x) = 1 + x + \frac{x^2}{2} + \cdots + \frac{x^n}{n!}.$$

See Figure 8.12. ■

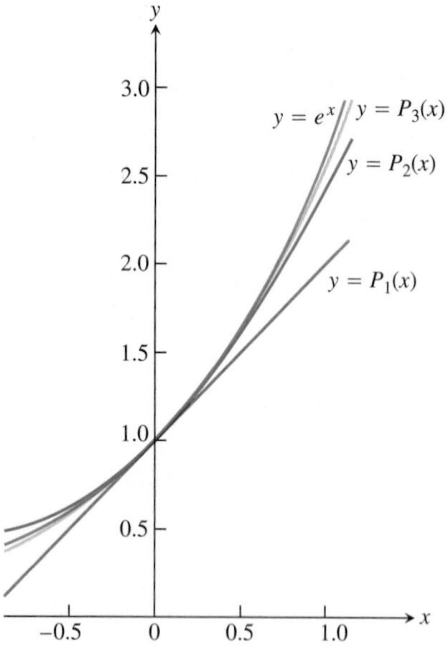

FIGURE 8.12 The graph of $f(x) = e^x$ and its Taylor polynomials

$P_1(x) = 1 + x$

$P_2(x) = 1 + x + (x^2/2!)$

$P_3(x) = 1 + x + (x^2/2!) + (x^3/3!)$.

Notice the very close agreement near the center $x = 0$ (Example 2).

EXAMPLE 3 Find the Taylor series and Taylor polynomials generated by $f(x) = \cos x$ at $x = 0$.

Solution The cosine and its derivatives are

$$\begin{aligned} f(x) &= \cos x, & f'(x) &= -\sin x, \\ f''(x) &= -\cos x, & f^{(3)}(x) &= \sin x, \\ &\vdots & &\vdots \\ f^{(2n)}(x) &= (-1)^n \cos x, & f^{(2n+1)}(x) &= (-1)^{n+1} \sin x. \end{aligned}$$

At $x = 0$, the cosines are 1 and the sines are 0, so

$$f^{(2n)}(0) = (-1)^n, \qquad f^{(2n+1)}(0) = 0.$$

The Taylor series generated by f at 0 is

$$\begin{aligned} f(0) + f'(0)x + \frac{f''(0)}{2!}x^2 + \frac{f'''(0)}{3!}x^3 + \cdots + \frac{f^{(n)}(0)}{n!}x^n + \cdots \\ = 1 + 0 \cdot x - \frac{x^2}{2!} + 0 \cdot x^3 + \frac{x^4}{4!} + \cdots + (-1)^n \frac{x^{2n}}{(2n)!} + \cdots \\ = \sum_{k=0}^{\infty} \frac{(-1)^k x^{2k}}{(2k)!}. \end{aligned}$$

This is also the Maclaurin series for $\cos x$. In Section 8.9, we will see that the series converges to $\cos x$ at every x.

Because $f^{(2n+1)}(0) = 0$, the Taylor polynomials of orders $2n$ and $2n + 1$ are identical:

$$P_{2n}(x) = P_{2n+1}(x) = 1 - \frac{x^2}{2!} + \frac{x^4}{4!} - \cdots + (-1)^n \frac{x^{2n}}{(2n)!}.$$

Figure 8.13 shows how well these polynomials approximate $f(x) = \cos x$ near $x = 0$. Only the right-hand portions of the graphs are given because the graphs are symmetric about the y-axis. ■

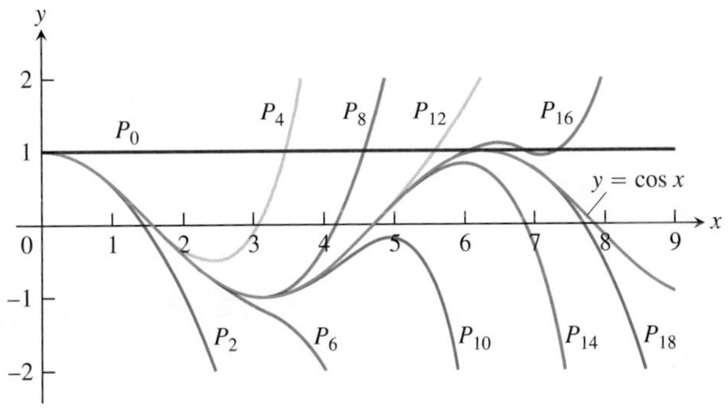

FIGURE 8.13 The polynomials

$$P_{2n}(x) = \sum_{k=0}^{n} \frac{(-1)^k x^{2k}}{(2k)!}$$

converge to $\cos x$ as $n \to \infty$. We can deduce the behavior of $\cos x$ arbitrarily far away solely from knowing the values of the cosine and its derivatives at $x = 0$ (Example 3).

EXAMPLE 4 It can be shown (though not easily) that

$$f(x) = \begin{cases} 0, & x = 0 \\ e^{-1/x^2}, & x \neq 0 \end{cases}$$

(Figure 8.14) has derivatives of all orders at $x = 0$ and that $f^{(n)}(0) = 0$ for all n. This means that the Taylor series generated by f at $x = 0$ is

$$\begin{aligned} f(0) + f'(0)x + \frac{f''(0)}{2!}x^2 + \cdots + \frac{f^{(n)}(0)}{n!}x^n + \cdots \\ = 0 + 0 \cdot x + 0 \cdot x^2 + \cdots + 0 \cdot x^n + \cdots \\ = 0 + 0 + \cdots + 0 + \cdots. \end{aligned}$$

The series converges for every x (its sum is 0) but converges to $f(x)$ only at $x = 0$. ■

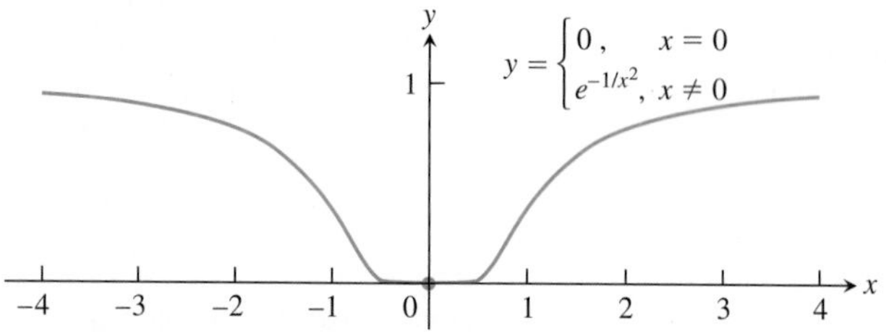

FIGURE 8.14 The graph of the continuous extension of $y = e^{-1/x^2}$ is so flat at the origin that all of its derivatives there are zero (Example 4).

Two questions still remain.

1. For what values of x can we normally expect a Taylor series to converge to its generating function?
2. How accurately do a function's Taylor polynomials approximate the function on a given interval?

The answers are provided by a theorem of Taylor in the next section.

EXERCISES 8.8

In Exercises 1–8, find the Taylor polynomials of orders 0, 1, 2, and 3 generated by f at a.

1. $f(x) = \ln x, \quad a = 1$
2. $f(x) = \ln(1 + x), \quad a = 0$
3. $f(x) = 1/x, \quad a = 2$
4. $f(x) = 1/(x + 2), \quad a = 0$
5. $f(x) = \sin x, \quad a = \pi/4$
6. $f(x) = \cos x, \quad a = \pi/4$
7. $f(x) = \sqrt{x}, \quad a = 4$
8. $f(x) = \sqrt{x + 4}, \quad a = 0$

Find the Maclaurin series for the functions in Exercises 9–20.

9. e^{-x}
10. $e^{x/2}$
11. $\dfrac{1}{1 + x}$
12. $\dfrac{1}{1 - x}$
13. $\sin 3x$
14. $\sin \dfrac{x}{2}$
15. $7 \cos(-x)$
16. $5 \cos \pi x$
17. $\cosh x = \dfrac{e^x + e^{-x}}{2}$
18. $\sinh x = \dfrac{e^x - e^{-x}}{2}$
19. $x^4 - 2x^3 - 5x + 4$
20. $(x + 1)^2$

In Exercises 21–28, find the Taylor series generated by f at $x = a$.

21. $f(x) = x^3 - 2x + 4, \quad a = 2$
22. $f(x) = 2x^3 + x^2 + 3x - 8, \quad a = 1$
23. $f(x) = x^4 + x^2 + 1, \quad a = -2$

24. $f(x) = 3x^5 - x^4 + 2x^3 + x^2 - 2, \quad a = -1$

25. $f(x) = 1/x^2, \quad a = 1$

26. $f(x) = x/(1 - x), \quad a = 0$

27. $f(x) = e^x, \quad a = 2$

28. $f(x) = 2^x, \quad a = 1$

29. Use the Taylor series generated by e^x at $x = a$ to show that

$$e^x = e^a\left[1 + (x - a) + \frac{(x - a)^2}{2!} + \cdots\right].$$

30. (*Continuation of Exercise 29.*) Find the Taylor series generated by e^x at $x = 1$. Compare your answer with the formula in Exercise 29.

31. Let $f(x)$ have derivatives through order n at $x = a$. Show that the Taylor polynomial of order n and its first n derivatives have the same values that f and its first n derivatives have at $x = a$.

32. Approximation properties of Taylor polynomials Suppose that $f(x)$ is differentiable on an interval centered at $x = a$ and that $g(x) = b_0 + b_1(x - a) + \cdots + b_n(x - a)^n$ is a polynomial of degree n with constant coefficients $b_0, \ldots, b_n$. Let $E(x) = f(x) - g(x)$. Show that if we impose on g the conditions

a. $E(a) = 0$ — The approximation error is zero at $x = a$.

b. $\lim_{x \to a} \frac{E(x)}{(x - a)^n} = 0,$ — The error is negligible when compared to $(x - a)^n$.

then

$$g(x) = f(a) + f'(a)(x - a) + \frac{f''(a)}{2!}(x - a)^2 + \cdots + \frac{f^{(n)}(a)}{n!}(x - a)^n.$$

Thus, the Taylor polynomial $P_n(x)$ is the only polynomial of degree less than or equal to n whose error is both zero at $x = a$ and negligible when compared with $(x - a)^n$.

Quadratic Approximations The Taylor polynomial of order 2 generated by a twice-differentiable function $f(x)$ at $x = a$ is called the *quadratic approximation* of f at $x = a$. In Exercises 33–38, find the **(a)** linearization (Taylor polynomial of order 1) and **(b)** quadratic approximation of f at $x = 0$.

33. $f(x) = \ln(\cos x)$

34. $f(x) = e^{\sin x}$

35. $f(x) = 1/\sqrt{1 - x^2}$

36. $f(x) = \cosh x$

37. $f(x) = \sin x$

38. $f(x) = \tan x$

8.9 Convergence of Taylor Series

In the last section, we asked when a Taylor series for a function can be expected to converge to that (generating) function. We answer the question in this section with the following theorem.

THEOREM 22—Taylor's Theorem If f and its first n derivatives $f', f'', \ldots, f^{(n)}$ are continuous on the closed interval between a and b, and $f^{(n)}$ is differentiable on the open interval between a and b, then there exists a number c between a and b such that

$$f(b) = f(a) + f'(a)(b - a) + \frac{f''(a)}{2!}(b - a)^2 + \cdots + \frac{f^{(n)}(a)}{n!}(b - a)^n + \frac{f^{(n+1)}(c)}{(n + 1)!}(b - a)^{n+1}.$$

Taylor's Theorem is a generalization of the Mean Value Theorem (Exercise 39). There is a proof of Taylor's Theorem at the end of this section.

When we apply Taylor's Theorem, we usually want to hold a fixed and treat b as an independent variable. Taylor's formula is easier to use in circumstances like these if we change b to x. Here is a version of the theorem with this change.

Taylor's Formula

If f has derivatives of all orders in an open interval I containing a, then for each positive integer n and for each x in I,

$$f(x) = f(a) + f'(a)(x-a) + \frac{f''(a)}{2!}(x-a)^2 + \cdots + \frac{f^{(n)}(a)}{n!}(x-a)^n + R_n(x), \tag{1}$$

where

$$R_n(x) = \frac{f^{(n+1)}(c)}{(n+1)!}(x-a)^{n+1} \quad \text{for some } c \text{ between } a \text{ and } x. \tag{2}$$

When we state Taylor's theorem this way, it says that for each $x \in I$,

$$f(x) = P_n(x) + R_n(x).$$

The function $R_n(x)$ is determined by the value of the $(n+1)$st derivative $f^{(n+1)}$ at a point c that depends on both a and x, and which lies somewhere between them. For any value of n we want, the equation gives both a polynomial approximation of f of that order and a formula for the error involved in using that approximation over the interval I.

Equation (1) is called **Taylor's formula**. The function $R_n(x)$ is called the **remainder of order n** or the **error term** for the approximation of f by $P_n(x)$ over I. If $R_n(x) \to 0$ as $n \to \infty$ for all $x \in I$, we say that the Taylor series generated by f at $x = a$ **converges** to f on I, and we write

$$f(x) = \sum_{k=0}^{\infty} \frac{f^{(k)}(a)}{k!}(x-a)^k.$$

Often we can estimate R_n without knowing the value of c, as the following example illustrates.

EXAMPLE 1 Show that the Taylor series generated by $f(x) = e^x$ at $x = 0$ converges to $f(x)$ for every real value of x.

Solution The function has derivatives of all orders throughout the interval $I = (-\infty, \infty)$. Equations (1) and (2) with $f(x) = e^x$ and $a = 0$ give

$$e^x = 1 + x + \frac{x^2}{2!} + \cdots + \frac{x^n}{n!} + R_n(x) \qquad \text{Polynomial from Section 8.8, Example 2}$$

and

$$R_n(x) = \frac{e^c}{(n+1)!}x^{n+1} \quad \text{for some } c \text{ between 0 and } x.$$

Since e^x is an increasing function of x, e^c lies between $e^0 = 1$ and e^x. When x is negative, so is c, and $e^c < 1$. When x is zero, $e^x = 1$ and $R_n(x) = 0$. When x is positive, so is c, and $e^c < e^x$. Thus, for $R_n(x)$ given as above,

$$|R_n(x)| \le \frac{|x|^{n+1}}{(n+1)!} \quad \text{when } x \le 0, \qquad e^c < 1$$

and

$$|R_n(x)| < e^x \frac{x^{n+1}}{(n+1)!} \qquad \text{when } x > 0. \qquad e^c < e^x$$

Finally, because

$$\lim_{n\to\infty} \frac{x^{n+1}}{(n+1)!} = 0 \qquad \text{for every } x, \qquad \text{Section 8.1}$$

$\lim_{n\to\infty} R_n(x) = 0$, and the series converges to e^x for every x. Thus,

$$e^x = \sum_{k=0}^{\infty} \frac{x^k}{k!} = 1 + x + \frac{x^2}{2!} + \cdots + \frac{x^k}{k!} + \cdots. \tag{3}$$

■

We can use the result of Example 1 with $x = 1$ to write

$$e = 1 + 1 + \frac{1}{2!} + \cdots + \frac{1}{n!} + R_n(1),$$

where for some c between 0 and 1,

$$R_n(1) = e^c \frac{1}{(n+1)!} < \frac{e}{(n+1)!}. \qquad e^c < e^1$$

Estimating the Remainder

It is often possible to estimate $R_n(x)$ as we did in Example 1. This method of estimation is so convenient that we state it as a theorem for future reference.

THEOREM 23—The Remainder Estimation Theorem If there is a positive constant M such that $|f^{(n+1)}(t)| \le M$ for all t between x and a, inclusive, then the remainder term $R_n(x)$ in Taylor's Theorem satisfies the inequality

$$|R_n(x)| \le M \frac{|x-a|^{n+1}}{(n+1)!}.$$

If this condition holds for every n and the other conditions of Taylor's Theorem are satisfied by f, then the series converges to $f(x)$.

Here's an application of Theorem 23.

EXAMPLE 2 Show that the Taylor series for $\sin x$ at $x = 0$ converges for all x.

Solution The function and its derivatives are

$$\begin{aligned} f(x) &= \sin x, & f'(x) &= \cos x, \\ f''(x) &= -\sin x, & f'''(x) &= -\cos x, \\ &\vdots & &\vdots \\ f^{(2k)}(x) &= (-1)^k \sin x, & f^{(2k+1)}(x) &= (-1)^k \cos x, \end{aligned}$$

so

$$f^{(2k)}(0) = 0 \quad \text{and} \quad f^{(2k+1)}(0) = (-1)^k.$$

The series has only odd-powered terms and, for $n = 2k + 1$, Taylor's Theorem gives

$$\sin x = x - \frac{x^3}{3!} + \frac{x^5}{5!} - \cdots + \frac{(-1)^k x^{2k+1}}{(2k + 1)!} + R_{2k+1}(x).$$

All the derivatives of $\sin x$ have absolute values less than or equal to 1, so we can apply the Remainder Estimation Theorem with $M = 1$ to obtain

$$|R_{2k+1}(x)| \le 1 \cdot \frac{|x|^{2k+2}}{(2k + 2)!}.$$

Since $(|x|^{2k+2}/(2k + 2)!) \to 0$ as $k \to \infty$, whatever the value of x, $R_{2k+1}(x) \to 0$, and the Maclaurin series for $\sin x$ converges to $\sin x$ for every x. Thus,

$$\sin x = \sum_{k=0}^{\infty} \frac{(-1)^k x^{2k+1}}{(2k + 1)!} = x - \frac{x^3}{3!} + \frac{x^5}{5!} - \frac{x^7}{7!} + \cdots. \tag{4}$$

■

EXAMPLE 3 Show that the Taylor series for $\cos x$ at $x = 0$ converges to $\cos x$ for every value of x.

Solution We add the remainder term to the Taylor polynomial for $\cos x$ (Section 8.8, Example 3) to obtain Taylor's formula for $\cos x$ with $n = 2k$:

$$\cos x = 1 - \frac{x^2}{2!} + \frac{x^4}{4!} - \cdots + (-1)^k \frac{x^{2k}}{(2k)!} + R_{2k}(x).$$

Because the derivatives of the cosine have absolute value less than or equal to 1, the Remainder Estimation Theorem with $M = 1$ gives

$$|R_{2k}(x)| \le 1 \cdot \frac{|x|^{2k+1}}{(2k + 1)!}.$$

For every value of x, $R_{2k}(x) \to 0$ as $k \to \infty$. Therefore, the series converges to $\cos x$ for every value of x. Thus,

$$\cos x = \sum_{k=0}^{\infty} \frac{(-1)^k x^{2k}}{(2k)!} = 1 - \frac{x^2}{2!} + \frac{x^4}{4!} - \frac{x^6}{6!} + \cdots. \tag{5}$$

■

We can find the Taylor series for $\cos 2x$ by substituting $2x$ for x in the Taylor series for $\cos x$:

$$\cos 2x = \sum_{k=0}^{\infty} \frac{(-1)^k (2x)^{2k}}{(2k)!} = 1 - \frac{(2x)^2}{2!} + \frac{(2x)^4}{4!} - \frac{(2x)^6}{6!} + \cdots$$

Equation (5) with $2x$ for x

$$= 1 - \frac{2^2x^2}{2!} + \frac{2^4x^4}{4!} - \frac{2^6x^6}{6!} + \cdots$$

$$= \sum_{k=0}^{\infty} (-1)^k \frac{2^{2k}x^{2k}}{(2k)!}.$$

EXAMPLE 4 For what values of x can we replace $\sin x$ by $x - (x^3/3!)$ with an error of magnitude no greater than 3×10^{-4}?

Solution Here we can take advantage of the fact that the Taylor series for $\sin x$ is an alternating series for every nonzero value of x. According to the Alternating Series Estimation Theorem (Section 8.6), the error in truncating

$$\sin x = x - \frac{x^3}{3!} \,\Big|\, + \frac{x^5}{5!} - \cdots$$

after $(x^3/3!)$ is no greater than

$$\left|\frac{x^5}{5!}\right| = \frac{|x|^5}{120}.$$

Therefore the error will be less than or equal to 3×10^{-4} if

$$\frac{|x|^5}{120} < 3 \times 10^{-4} \qquad \text{or} \qquad |x| < \sqrt[5]{360 \times 10^{-4}} \approx 0.514.$$

Rounded down, to be safe

The Alternating Series Estimation Theorem tells us something that the Remainder Estimation Theorem does not: namely, that the estimate $x - (x^3/3!)$ for $\sin x$ is an underestimate when x is positive because then $x^5/120$ is positive.

Figure 8.15 shows the graph of $\sin x$, along with the graphs of a number of its approximating Taylor polynomials. The graph of $P_3(x) = x - (x^3/3!)$ is almost indistinguishable from the sine curve when $0 \le x \le 1$. ■

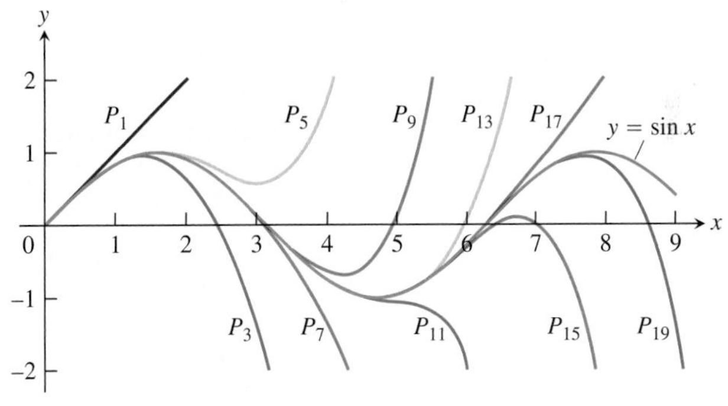

FIGURE 8.15 The polynomials

$$P_{2n+1}(x) = \sum_{k=0}^{n} \frac{(-1)^k x^{2k+1}}{(2k+1)!}$$

converge to $\sin x$ as $n \to \infty$. Notice how closely $P_3(x)$ approximates the sine curve for $x \le 1$ (Example 4).

Applying Taylor Series

On the intersection of their intervals of convergence, Taylor series can be added, subtracted, and multiplied by constants, and the results are once again Taylor series. The Taylor series for $f(x) + g(x)$ is the sum of the Taylor series for $f(x)$ and $g(x)$ because the nth derivative of $f + g$ is $f^{(n)} + g^{(n)}$, and so on. Thus we obtain the Taylor series for

$(1 + \cos 2x)/2$ by adding 1 to the Taylor series for $\cos 2x$ and dividing the combined results by 2, and the Taylor series for $\sin x + \cos x$ is the term-by-term sum of the Taylor series for $\sin x$ and $\cos x$.

Taylor series can be used to express nonelementary integrals in terms of series. For example, integrals like $\int \sin x^2\,dx$ arise in the study of the diffraction of light. However, there is no simple formula for an antiderivative of $\sin x^2$.

EXAMPLE 5 Express $\int \sin x^2\,dx$ as a power series.

Solution From the series for $\sin x$ we obtain

$$\sin x^2 = x^2 - \frac{x^6}{3!} + \frac{x^{10}}{5!} - \frac{x^{14}}{7!} + \frac{x^{18}}{9!} - \cdots.$$

Therefore,

$$\int \sin x^2\,dx = C + \frac{x^3}{3} - \frac{x^7}{7 \cdot 3!} + \frac{x^{11}}{11 \cdot 5!} - \frac{x^{15}}{15 \cdot 7!} + \frac{x^{10}}{19 \cdot 9!} - \cdots.$$ ■

EXAMPLE 6 Estimate $\int_0^1 \sin x^2\,dx$ with an error of less than 0.001.

Solution From the indefinite integral in Example 5,

$$\int_0^1 \sin x^2\,dx = \frac{1}{3} - \frac{1}{7 \cdot 3!} + \frac{1}{11 \cdot 5!} - \frac{1}{15 \cdot 7!} + \frac{1}{19 \cdot 9!} - \cdots.$$

The series alternates, and we find by experiment that

$$\frac{1}{11 \cdot 5!} \approx 0.00076$$

is the first term to be numerically less than 0.001. The sum of the preceding two terms gives

$$\int_0^1 \sin x^2\,dx \approx \frac{1}{3} - \frac{1}{42} \approx 0.310.$$ ■

We can sometimes evaluate indeterminate forms by expressing the functions involved as Taylor series.

EXAMPLE 7 Evaluate

$$\lim_{x \to 0} \frac{\sin x - \tan x}{x^3}.$$

Solution The Taylor series for $\sin x$ and $\tan x$, to terms in x^5, are

$$\sin x = x - \frac{x^3}{3!} + \frac{x^5}{5!} - \cdots, \qquad \tan x = x + \frac{x^3}{3} + \frac{2x^5}{15} + \cdots.$$

Hence,

$$\sin x - \tan x = -\frac{x^3}{2} - \frac{x^5}{8} - \cdots = x^3\left(-\frac{1}{2} - \frac{x^2}{8} - \cdots\right)$$

and

$$\lim_{x\to 0}\frac{\sin x - \tan x}{x^3} = \lim_{x\to 0}\left(-\frac{1}{2} - \frac{x^2}{8} - \cdots\right)$$
$$= -\frac{1}{2}.$$

Euler's Identity

As you may recall, a complex number is a number of the form $a + bi$, where a and b are real numbers and $i = \sqrt{-1}$. If we substitute $x = i\theta$ (θ real) in the Taylor series for e^x and use the relations

$$i^2 = -1, \qquad i^3 = i^2 i = -i, \qquad i^4 = i^2 i^2 = 1, \qquad i^5 = i^4 i = i,$$

and so on, to simplify the result, we obtain

$$e^{i\theta} = 1 + \frac{i\theta}{1!} + \frac{i^2\theta^2}{2!} + \frac{i^3\theta^3}{3!} + \frac{i^4\theta^4}{4!} + \frac{i^5\theta^5}{5!} + \frac{i^6\theta^6}{6!} + \cdots$$

$$= \left(1 - \frac{\theta^2}{2!} + \frac{\theta^4}{4!} - \frac{\theta^6}{6!} + \cdots\right) + i\left(\theta - \frac{\theta^3}{3!} + \frac{\theta^5}{5!} - \cdots\right) = \cos\theta + i\sin\theta.$$

This does not *prove* that $e^{i\theta} = \cos\theta + i\sin\theta$ because we have not yet defined what it means to raise e to an imaginary power. Rather, it says how to define $e^{i\theta}$ to be consistent with other things we know.

DEFINITION

For any real number θ, $e^{i\theta} = \cos\theta + i\sin\theta$. (6)

Equation (6), called **Euler's identity**, enables us to define e^{a+bi} to be $e^a \cdot e^{bi}$ for any complex number $a + bi$. One consequence of the identity is the equation

$$e^{i\pi} = -1.$$

When written in the form $e^{i\pi} + 1 = 0$, this equation combines five of the most important constants in mathematics.

A Proof of Taylor's Theorem

We prove Taylor's theorem assuming $a < b$. The proof for $a > b$ is nearly the same.

The Taylor polynomial

$$P_n(x) = f(a) + f'(a)(x - a) + \frac{f''(a)}{2!}(x - a)^2 + \cdots + \frac{f^{(n)}(a)}{n!}(x - a)^n$$

and its first n derivatives match the function f and its first n derivatives at $x = a$. We do not disturb that matching if we add another term of the form $K(x - a)^{n+1}$, where K is any constant, because such a term and its first n derivatives are all equal to zero at $x = a$. The new function

$$\phi_n(x) = P_n(x) + K(x - a)^{n+1}$$

and its first n derivatives still agree with f and its first n derivatives at $x = a$.

We now choose the particular value of K that makes the curve $y = \phi_n(x)$ agree with the original curve $y = f(x)$ at $x = b$. In symbols,

$$f(b) = P_n(b) + K(b - a)^{n+1}, \qquad \text{or} \qquad K = \frac{f(b) - P_n(b)}{(b - a)^{n+1}}. \tag{7}$$

With K defined by Equation (7), the function

$$F(x) = f(x) - \phi_n(x)$$

measures the difference between the original function f and the approximating function ϕ_n for each x in $[a, b]$.

We now use Rolle's Theorem (Section 4.2). First, because $F(a) = F(b) = 0$ and both F and F' are continuous on $[a, b]$, we know that

$$F'(c_1) = 0 \qquad \text{for some } c_1 \text{ in } (a, b).$$

Next, because $F'(a) = F'(c_1) = 0$ and both F' and F'' are continuous on $[a, c_1]$, we know that

$$F''(c_2) = 0 \qquad \text{for some } c_2 \text{ in } (a, c_1).$$

Rolle's Theorem, applied successively to $F'', F''', \dots, F^{(n-1)}$ implies the existence of

$$\begin{aligned}
&c_3 \quad \text{in } (a, c_2) && \text{such that } F'''(c_3) = 0,\\
&c_4 \quad \text{in } (a, c_3) && \text{such that } F^{(4)}(c_4) = 0,\\
&\quad\ \vdots\\
&c_n \quad \text{in } (a, c_{n-1}) && \text{such that } F^{(n)}(c_n) = 0.
\end{aligned}$$

Finally, because $F^{(n)}$ is continuous on $[a, c_n]$ and differentiable on (a, c_n), and $F^{(n)}(a) = F^{(n)}(c_n) = 0$, Rolle's Theorem implies that there is a number c_{n+1} in (a, c_n) such that

$$F^{(n+1)}(c_{n+1}) = 0. \tag{8}$$

If we differentiate $F(x) = f(x) - P_n(x) - K(x - a)^{n+1}$ a total of $n + 1$ times, we get

$$F^{(n+1)}(x) = f^{(n+1)}(x) - 0 - (n + 1)!K. \tag{9}$$

Equations (8) and (9) together give

$$K = \frac{f^{(n+1)}(c)}{(n + 1)!} \qquad \text{for some number } c = c_{n+1} \text{ in } (a, b). \tag{10}$$

Equations (7) and (10) give

$$f(b) = P_n(b) + \frac{f^{(n+1)}(c)}{(n + 1)!}(b - a)^{n+1}.$$

This concludes the proof. ■

EXERCISES 8.9

Use substitution (as in Example 4) to find the Taylor series at $x = 0$ of the functions in Exercises 1–6.

1. e^{-5x} **2.** $e^{-x/2}$ **3.** $5\sin(-x)$

4. $\sin\left(\frac{\pi x}{2}\right)$ **5.** $\cos\sqrt{x+1}$ **6.** $\cos\left(x^{3/2}/\sqrt{2}\right)$

Find Taylor series at $x = 0$ for the functions in Exercises 7–18.

7. xe^x **8.** $x^2\sin x$ **9.** $\frac{x^2}{2} - 1 + \cos x$

10. $\sin x - x + \frac{x^3}{3!}$ **11.** $x\cos\pi x$ **12.** $x^2\cos(x^2)$

13. $\cos^2 x$ (*Hint:* $\cos^2 x = (1 + \cos 2x)/2$.)

14. $\sin^2 x$ **15.** $\frac{x^2}{1-2x}$ **16.** $x\ln(1+2x)$

17. $\frac{1}{(1-x)^2}$ **18.** $\frac{2}{(1-x)^3}$

19. For approximately what values of x can you replace $\sin x$ by $x - (x^3/6)$ with an error of magnitude no greater than 5×10^{-4}? Give reasons for your answer.

20. If $\cos x$ is replaced by $1 - (x^2/2)$ and $|x| < 0.5$, what estimate can be made of the error? Does $1 - (x^2/2)$ tend to be too large, or too small? Give reasons for your answer.

21. How close is the approximation $\sin x = x$ when $|x| < 10^{-3}$? For which of these values of x is $x < \sin x$?

22. The estimate $\sqrt{1+x} = 1 + (x/2)$ is used when x is small. Estimate the error when $|x| < 0.01$.

23. The approximation $e^x = 1 + x + (x^2/2)$ is used when x is small. Use the Remainder Estimation Theorem to estimate the error when $|x| < 0.1$.

24. (*Continuation of Exercise 23.*) When $x < 0$, the series for e^x is an alternating series. Use the Alternating Series Estimation Theorem to estimate the error that results from replacing e^x by $1 + x + (x^2/2)$ when $-0.1 < x < 0$. Compare your estimate with the one you obtained in Exercise 23.

In Exercises 25–28, find a polynomial that will approximate $F(x)$ throughout the given interval with an error of magnitude less than 10^{-3}.

25. $F(x) = \int_0^x \sin t^2\, dt$, $[0, 1]$

26. $F(x) = \int_0^x t^2 e^{-t^2}\, dt$, $[0, 1]$

27. $F(x) = \int_0^x \tan^{-1} t\, dt$, **(a)** $[0, 0.5]$ **(b)** $[0, 1]$

28. $F(x) = \int_0^x \frac{\ln(1+t)}{t}\, dt$, **(a)** $[0, 0.5]$ **(b)** $[0, 1]$

Use series to evaluate the limits in Exercises 29–34.

29. $\lim_{x\to 0} \frac{e^x - (1+x)}{x^2}$ **30.** $\lim_{x\to 0} \frac{e^x - e^{-x}}{x}$

31. $\lim_{t\to 0} \frac{1 - \cos t - (t^2/2)}{t^4}$ **32.** $\lim_{\theta\to 0} \frac{\sin\theta - \theta + (\theta^3/6)}{\theta^5}$

33. $\lim_{y\to 0} \frac{y - \tan^{-1} y}{y^3}$ **34.** $\lim_{y\to 0} \frac{\tan^{-1} y - \sin y}{y^3 \cos y}$

35. Multiply the Maclaurin series for e^x and $\sin x$ together to find the first five nonzero terms of the Maclaurin series for $e^x \sin x$.

36. Multiply the Maclaurin series for e^x and $\cos x$ together to find the first five nonzero terms of the Maclaurin series for $e^x \cos x$.

37. Use the identity $\sin^2 x = (1 - \cos 2x)/2$ to obtain the Maclaurin series for $\sin^2 x$. Then differentiate this series to obtain the Maclaurin series for $2\sin x\cos x$. Check that this is the series for $\sin 2x$.

38. (*Continuation of Exercise 37.*) Use the identity $\cos^2 x = \cos 2x + \sin^2 x$ to obtain a power series for $\cos^2 x$.

39. Taylor's Theorem and the Mean Value Theorem Explain how the Mean Value Theorem (Section 4.2, Theorem 4) is a special case of Taylor's Theorem.

40. Linearizations at inflection points Show that if the graph of a twice-differentiable function $f(x)$ has an inflection point at $x = a$, then the linearization of f at $x = a$ is also the quadratic approximation of f at $x = a$. This explains why tangent lines fit so well at inflection points.

41. The (second) second derivative test Use the equation

$$f(x) = f(a) + f'(a)(x-a) + \frac{f''(c_2)}{2}(x-a)^2$$

to establish the following test.

Let f have continuous first and second derivatives and suppose that $f'(a) = 0$. Then

a. f has a local maximum at a if $f'' \le 0$ throughout an interval whose interior contains a;

b. f has a local minimum at a if $f'' \ge 0$ throughout an interval whose interior contains a.

42. A cubic approximation Use Taylor's formula with $a = 0$ and $n = 3$ to find the standard cubic approximation of $f(x) = 1/(1-x)$ at $x = 0$. Give an upper bound for the magnitude of the error in the approximation when $|x| \le 0.1$.

43. a. Use Taylor's formula with $n = 2$ to find the quadratic approximation of $f(x) = (1+x)^k$ at $x = 0$ (k a constant).

b. If $k = 3$, for approximately what values of x in the interval $[0, 1]$ will the error in the quadratic approximation be less than $1/100$?

44. Improving approximations to π

a. Let P be an approximation of π accurate to n decimals. Show that $P + \sin P$ gives an approximation correct to $3n$ decimals. (*Hint:* Let $P = \pi + x$.)

T b. Try it with a calculator.

45. The Taylor series generated by $f(x) = \sum_{n=0}^{\infty} a_n x^n$ is $\sum_{n=0}^{\infty} a_n x^n$ A function defined by a power series $\sum_{n=0}^{\infty} a_n x^n$ with a radius of convergence $c > 0$ has a Taylor series that converges to the function at every point of $(-c, c)$. Show this by showing that the Taylor series generated by $f(x) = \sum_{n=0}^{\infty} a_n x^n$ is the series $\sum_{n=0}^{\infty} a_n x^n$ itself.

An immediate consequence of this is that series like

$$x \sin x = x^2 - \frac{x^4}{3!} + \frac{x^6}{5!} - \frac{x^8}{7!} + \cdots$$

and

$$x^2 e^x = x^2 + x^3 + \frac{x^4}{2!} + \frac{x^5}{3!} + \cdots,$$

obtained by multiplying Taylor series by powers of x, as well as series obtained by integration and differentiation of convergent power series, are themselves the Taylor series generated by the functions they represent.

46. Taylor series for even functions and odd functions (*Continuation of Section 8.7, Exercise 45.*) Suppose that $f(x) = \sum_{n=0}^{\infty} a_n x^n$ converges for all x in an open interval $(-c, c)$. Show that

a. If f is even, then $a_1 = a_3 = a_5 = \cdots = 0$, i.e., the Taylor series for f at $x = 0$ contains only even powers of x.

b. If f is odd, then $a_0 = a_2 = a_4 = \cdots = 0$, i.e., the Taylor series for f at $x = 0$ contains only odd powers of x.

47. Taylor polynomials of periodic functions

a. Show that every continuous periodic function $f(x)$, $-\infty < x < \infty$, is bounded in magnitude by showing that there exists a positive constant M such that $|f(x)| \le M$ for all x.

b. Show that the graph of every Taylor polynomial of positive degree generated by $f(x) = \cos x$ must eventually move away from the graph of $\cos x$ as $|x|$ increases. You can see this in Figure 8.13. The Taylor polynomials of $\sin x$ behave in a similar way (Figure 8.15).

T **48.** a. Graph the curves $y = (1/3) - (x^2)/5$ and $y = (x - \tan^{-1} x)/x^3$ together with the line $y = 1/3$.

b. Use a Taylor series to explain what you see. What is

$$\lim_{x \to 0} \frac{x - \tan^{-1} x}{x^3}?$$

49. Use Equation (6) to write the following powers of e in the form $a + bi$.

a. $e^{-i\pi}$

b. $e^{i\pi/4}$

c. $e^{-i\pi/2}$

50. Use Equation (6) to show that

$$\cos\theta = \frac{e^{i\theta} + e^{-i\theta}}{2} \quad \text{and} \quad \sin\theta = \frac{e^{i\theta} - e^{-i\theta}}{2i}.$$

51. Establish the equations in Exercise 50 by combining the formal Taylor series for $e^{i\theta}$ and $e^{-i\theta}$.

52. Show that

a. $\cosh i\theta = \cos\theta$, b. $\sinh i\theta = i \sin\theta$.

53. By multiplying the Taylor series for e^x and $\sin x$, find the terms through x^5 of the Taylor series for $e^x \sin x$. This series is the imaginary part of the series for

$$e^x \cdot e^{ix} = e^{(1+i)x}.$$

Use this fact to check your answer. For what values of x should the series for $e^x \sin x$ converge?

54. When a and b are real, we define $e^{(a+ib)x}$ with the equation

$$e^{(a+ib)x} = e^{ax} \cdot e^{ibx} = e^{ax}(\cos bx + i \sin bx).$$

Differentiate the right-hand side of this equation to show that

$$\frac{d}{dx} e^{(a+ib)x} = (a + ib)e^{(a+ib)x}.$$

Thus the familiar rule $(d/dx)e^{kx} = ke^{kx}$ holds for k complex as well as real.

55. Use the definition of $e^{i\theta}$ to show that for any real numbers θ, θ_1, and θ_2,

a. $e^{i\theta_1}e^{i\theta_2} = e^{i(\theta_1+\theta_2)}$, b. $e^{-i\theta} = 1/e^{i\theta}$.

56. Two complex numbers $a + ib$ and $c + id$ are equal if and only if $a = c$ and $b = d$. Use this fact to evaluate

$$\int e^{ax} \cos bx \, dx \quad \text{and} \quad \int e^{ax} \sin bx \, dx$$

from

$$\int e^{(a+ib)x} \, dx = \frac{a - ib}{a^2 + b^2} e^{(a+ib)x} + C,$$

where $C = C_1 + iC_2$ is a complex constant of integration.

COMPUTER EXPLORATIONS

Taylor's formula with $n = 1$ and $a = 0$ gives the linearization of a function at $x = 0$. With $n = 2$ and $n = 3$ we obtain the standard quadratic and cubic approximations. In these exercises we explore the errors associated with these approximations. We seek answers to two questions:

a. For what values of x can the function be replaced by each approximation with an error less than 10^{-2}?

b. What is the maximum error we could expect if we replace the function by each approximation over the specified interval?

Using a CAS, perform the following steps to aid in answering questions (a) and (b) for the functions and intervals in Exercises 57–62.

Step 1: Plot the function over the specified interval.

Step 2: Find the Taylor polynomials $P_1(x)$, $P_2(x)$, and $P_3(x)$ at $x = 0$.

Step 3: Calculate the $(n + 1)$st derivative $f^{(n+1)}(c)$ associated with the remainder term for each Taylor polynomial. Plot the derivative as a function of c over the specified interval and estimate its maximum absolute value, M.

Step 4: Calculate the remainder $R_n(x)$ for each polynomial. Using the estimate M from Step 3 in place of $f^{(n+1)}(c)$, plot $R_n(x)$ over the specified interval. Then estimate the values of x that answer question (a).

Step 5: Compare your estimated error with the actual error $E_n(x) = |f(x) - P_n(x)|$ by plotting $E_n(x)$ over the specified interval. This will help answer question (b).

Step 6: Graph the function and its three Taylor approximations together. Discuss the graphs in relation to the information discovered in Steps 4 and 5.

57. $f(x) = \dfrac{1}{\sqrt{1 + x}}, \quad |x| \le \dfrac{3}{4}$

58. $f(x) = (1 + x)^{3/2}, \quad -\dfrac{1}{2} \le x \le 2$

59. $f(x) = \dfrac{x}{x^2 + 1}, \quad |x| \le 2$

60. $f(x) = (\cos x)(\sin 2x), \quad |x| \le 2$

61. $f(x) = e^{-x} \cos 2x, \quad |x| \le 1$

62. $f(x) = e^{x/3} \sin 2x, \quad |x| \le 2$

8.10 The Binomial Series

This section introduces the binomial series for estimating powers and roots of binomial expressions $(1 + x)^m$. This section concludes with a reference table of frequently used series.

The Binomial Series for Powers and Roots

The Taylor series generated by $f(x) = (1 + x)^m$, when m is constant, is

$$1 + mx + \frac{m(m-1)}{2!}x^2 + \frac{m(m-1)(m-2)}{3!}x^3 + \cdots + \frac{m(m-1)(m-2)\cdots(m-k+1)}{k!}x^k + \cdots. \tag{1}$$

This series, called the **binomial series**, converges absolutely for $|x| < 1$. To derive the series, we first list the function and its derivatives:

$$\begin{aligned} f(x) &= (1 + x)^m \\ f'(x) &= m(1 + x)^{m-1} \\ f''(x) &= m(m-1)(1 + x)^{m-2} \\ f'''(x) &= m(m-1)(m-2)(1 + x)^{m-3} \\ &\vdots \\ f^{(k)}(x) &= m(m-1)(m-2)\cdots(m-k+1)(1 + x)^{m-k}. \end{aligned}$$

We then evaluate these at $x = 0$ and substitute into the Taylor series formula to obtain Series (1).

If m is an integer greater than or equal to zero, the series stops after $(m + 1)$ terms because the coefficients from $k = m + 1$ on are zero.

If m is not a positive integer or zero, the series is infinite and converges for $|x| < 1$. To see why, let u_k be the term involving x^k. Then apply the Ratio Test for absolute convergence to see that

$$\left|\frac{u_{k+1}}{u_k}\right| = \left|\frac{m-k}{k+1}x\right| \to |x| \qquad \text{as } k \to \infty.$$

Our derivation of the binomial series shows only that it is generated by $(1 + x)^m$ and converges for $|x| < 1$. The derivation does not show that the series converges to $(1 + x)^m$. It does, but we omit the proof. (See Exercise 20.)

The Binomial Series

For $-1 < x < 1$,

$$(1 + x)^m = 1 + \sum_{k=1}^{\infty} \binom{m}{k} x^k,$$

where we define

$$\binom{m}{1} = m, \qquad \binom{m}{2} = \frac{m(m-1)}{2!},$$

and

$$\binom{m}{k} = \frac{m(m-1)(m-2)\cdots(m-k+1)}{k!} \quad \text{for } k \geq 3.$$

EXAMPLE 1 If $m = -1$,

$$\binom{-1}{1} = -1, \qquad \binom{-1}{2} = \frac{-1(-2)}{2!} = 1,$$

and

$$\binom{-1}{k} = \frac{-1(-2)(-3)\cdots(-1-k+1)}{k!} = (-1)^k \left(\frac{k!}{k!}\right) = (-1)^k.$$

With these coefficient values and with x replaced by $-x$, the binomial series formula gives the familiar geometric series

$$(1 + x)^{-1} = 1 + \sum_{k=1}^{\infty} (-1)^k x^k = 1 - x + x^2 - x^3 + \cdots + (-1)^k x^k + \cdots. \qquad \blacksquare$$

EXAMPLE 2 We know from Section 3.10, Example 1, that $\sqrt{1 + x} \approx 1 + (x/2)$ for $|x|$ small. With $m = 1/2$, the binomial series gives quadratic and higher-order approximations as well, along with error estimates that come from the Alternating Series Estimation Theorem:

$$(1 + x)^{1/2} = 1 + \frac{x}{2} + \frac{\left(\frac{1}{2}\right)\left(-\frac{1}{2}\right)}{2!} x^2 + \frac{\left(\frac{1}{2}\right)\left(-\frac{1}{2}\right)\left(-\frac{3}{2}\right)}{3!} x^3$$

$$+ \frac{\left(\frac{1}{2}\right)\left(-\frac{1}{2}\right)\left(-\frac{3}{2}\right)\left(-\frac{5}{2}\right)}{4!} x^4 + \cdots$$

$$= 1 + \frac{x}{2} - \frac{x^2}{8} + \frac{x^3}{16} - \frac{5x^4}{128} + \cdots.$$

Substitution for x gives still other approximations. For example,

$$\sqrt{1 - x^2} \approx 1 - \frac{x^2}{2} - \frac{x^4}{8} \qquad \text{for } |x^2| \text{ small}$$

$$\sqrt{1 - \frac{1}{x}} \approx 1 - \frac{1}{2x} - \frac{1}{8x^2} \qquad \text{for } \left|\frac{1}{x}\right| \text{ small, that is, } |x| \text{ large.}$$

■

TABLE 8.1 Frequently used Taylor series

$$\frac{1}{1-x} = 1 + x + x^2 + \cdots + x^n + \cdots = \sum_{n=0}^{\infty} x^n, \qquad |x| < 1$$

$$\frac{1}{1+x} = 1 - x + x^2 - \cdots + (-x)^n + \cdots = \sum_{n=0}^{\infty} (-1)^n x^n, \qquad |x| < 1$$

$$e^x = 1 + x + \frac{x^2}{2!} + \cdots + \frac{x^n}{n!} + \cdots = \sum_{n=0}^{\infty} \frac{x^n}{n!}, \qquad |x| < \infty$$

$$\sin x = x - \frac{x^3}{3!} + \frac{x^5}{5!} - \cdots + (-1)^n \frac{x^{2n+1}}{(2n+1)!} + \cdots = \sum_{n=0}^{\infty} \frac{(-1)^n x^{2n+1}}{(2n+1)!}, \qquad |x| < \infty$$

$$\cos x = 1 - \frac{x^2}{2!} + \frac{x^4}{4!} - \cdots + (-1)^n \frac{x^{2n}}{(2n)!} + \cdots = \sum_{n=0}^{\infty} \frac{(-1)^n x^{2n}}{(2n)!}, \qquad |x| < \infty$$

$$\ln(1 + x) = x - \frac{x^2}{2} + \frac{x^3}{3} - \cdots + (-1)^{n-1} \frac{x^n}{n} + \cdots = \sum_{n=1}^{\infty} \frac{(-1)^{n-1} x^n}{n}, \qquad -1 < x \le 1$$

$$\ln \frac{1+x}{1-x} = 2 \tanh^{-1} x = 2\left(x + \frac{x^3}{3} + \frac{x^5}{5} + \cdots + \frac{x^{2n+1}}{2n+1} + \cdots\right) = 2\sum_{n=0}^{\infty} \frac{x^{2n+1}}{2n+1}, \qquad |x| < 1$$

$$\tan^{-1} x = x - \frac{x^3}{3} + \frac{x^5}{5} - \cdots + (-1)^n \frac{x^{2n+1}}{2n+1} + \cdots = \sum_{n=0}^{\infty} \frac{(-1)^n x^{2n+1}}{2n+1}, \qquad |x| \le 1$$

Binomial Series

$$(1 + x)^m = 1 + mx + \frac{m(m-1)x^2}{2!} + \frac{m(m-1)(m-2)x^3}{3!} + \cdots + \frac{m(m-1)(m-2)\cdots(m-k+1)x^k}{k!} + \cdots$$

$$= 1 + \sum_{k=1}^{\infty} \binom{m}{k} x^k, \qquad |x| < 1,$$

where

$$\binom{m}{1} = m, \qquad \binom{m}{2} = \frac{m(m-1)}{2!}, \qquad \binom{m}{k} = \frac{m(m-1)\cdots(m-k+1)}{k!} \qquad \text{for } k \ge 3.$$

Note: To write the binomial series compactly, it is customary to define $\binom{m}{0}$ to be 1 and to take $x^0 = 1$ (even in the usually excluded case where $x = 0$), yielding $(1 + x)^m = \sum_{k=0}^{\infty} \binom{m}{k} x^k$. If m is a *positive integer*, the series terminates at x^m and the result converges for all x.

EXERCISES 8.10

Find the first four terms of the binomial series for the functions in Exercises 1–10.

1. $(1 + x)^{1/2}$ **2.** $(1 + x)^{1/3}$ **3.** $(1 - x)^{-1/2}$

4. $(1 - 2x)^{1/2}$ **5.** $\left(1 + \frac{x}{2}\right)^{-2}$ **6.** $\left(1 - \frac{x}{2}\right)^{-2}$

7. $(1 + x^3)^{-1/2}$ **8.** $(1 + x^2)^{-1/3}$

9. $\left(1 + \frac{1}{x}\right)^{1/2}$ **10.** $\left(1 - \frac{2}{x}\right)^{1/3}$

Find the binomial series for the functions in Exercises 11–14.

11. $(1 + x)^4$ **12.** $(1 + x^2)^3$

13. $(1 - 2x)^3$ **14.** $\left(1 - \frac{x}{2}\right)^4$

15. a. Use the binomial series and the fact that

$$\frac{d}{dx}\sin^{-1} x = (1 - x^2)^{-1/2}$$

to generate the first four nonzero terms of the Taylor series for $\sin^{-1} x$. What is the radius of convergence?

b. Series for $\cos^{-1} x$ Use your result in part (a) to find the first five nonzero terms of the Taylor series for $\cos^{-1} x$.

16 a. Series for $\sinh^{-1} x$ Find the first four nonzero terms of the Taylor series for

$$\sinh^{-1} x = \int_0^x \frac{dt}{\sqrt{1 + t^2}}.$$

T **b.** Use the first *three* terms of the series in part (a) to estimate $\sinh^{-1} 0.25$. Give an upper bound for the magnitude of the estimation error.

17. Obtain the Taylor series for $1/(1 + x)^2$ from the binomial series for $-1/(1 + x)$.

18. Use the binomial series for $1/(1 - x^2)$ to obtain a power series for $2x/(1 - x^2)^2$.

19. Series for $\sin^{-1} x$ Integrate the binomial series for $(1 - x^2)^{-1/2}$ to show that for $|x| < 1$,

$$\sin^{-1} x = x + \sum_{n=1}^{\infty} \frac{1 \cdot 3 \cdot 5 \cdot \cdots \cdot (2n - 1)}{2 \cdot 4 \cdot 6 \cdot \cdots \cdot (2n)} \frac{x^{2n+1}}{2n + 1}.$$

20. Use the following steps to prove Equation (1).

a. Differentiate the series

$$f(x) = 1 + \sum_{k=1}^{\infty} \binom{m}{k} x^k$$

to show that

$$f'(x) = \frac{mf(x)}{1 + x}, \quad -1 < x < 1.$$

b. Define $g(x) = (1 + x)^{-m} f(x)$ and show that $g'(x) = 0$.

c. From part (b), show that

$$f(x) = (1 + x)^m.$$

Chapter 8 Questions to Guide Your Review

1. What is an infinite sequence? What does it mean for such a sequence to converge? To diverge? Give examples.
2. What is a nondecreasing sequence? Under what circumstances does such a sequence have a limit? Give examples.
3. What theorems are available for calculating limits of sequences? Give examples.
4. What theorem sometimes enables us to use l'Hôpital's Rule to calculate the limit of a sequence? Give an example.
5. What six sequence limits are likely to arise when you work with sequences and series?
6. What is an infinite series? What does it mean for such a series to converge? To diverge? Give examples.
7. What is a geometric series? When does such a series converge? Diverge? When it does converge, what is its sum? Give examples.
8. Besides geometric series, what other convergent and divergent series do you know?
9. What is the nth-Term Test for Divergence? What is the idea behind the test?
10. What can be said about term-by-term sums and differences of convergent series? About constant multiples of convergent and divergent series?
11. What happens if you add a finite number of terms to a convergent series? A divergent series? What happens if you delete a finite number of terms from a convergent series? A divergent series?
12. How do you reindex a series? Why might you want to do this?
13. Under what circumstances will an infinite series of nonnegative terms converge? Diverge? Why study series of nonnegative terms?

14. What is the Integral Test? What is the reasoning behind it? Give an example of its use.
15. When do p-series converge? Diverge? How do you know? Give examples of convergent and divergent p-series.
16. What are the Direct Comparison Test and the Limit Comparison Test? What is the reasoning behind these tests? Give examples of their use.
17. What are the Ratio and Root Tests? Do they always give you the information you need to determine convergence or divergence? Give examples.
18. What is an alternating series? What theorem is available for determining the convergence of such a series?
19. How can you estimate the error involved in approximating the sum of an alternating series with one of the series' partial sums? What is the reasoning behind the estimate?
20. What is absolute convergence? Conditional convergence? How are the two related?
21. What do you know about rearranging the terms of an absolutely convergent series? Of a conditionally convergent series?
22. What is a power series? How do you test a power series for convergence? What are the possible outcomes?
23. What are the basic facts about
    a. term-by-term differentiation of power series?
    b. term-by-term integration of power series?
    c. multiplication of power series?

    Give examples.
24. What is the Taylor series generated by a function $f(x)$ at a point $x = a$? What information do you need about f to construct the series? Give an example.
25. What is a Maclaurin series?
26. Does a Taylor series always converge to its generating function? Explain.
27. What are Taylor polynomials? Of what use are they?
28. What is Taylor's formula? What does it say about the errors involved in using Taylor polynomials to approximate functions? In particular, what does Taylor's formula say about the error in a linearization? A quadratic approximation?
29. What is the binomial series? On what interval does it converge? How is it used?
30. How can you sometimes use power series to estimate the values of nonelementary definite integrals?
31. What are the Taylor series for $1/(1 - x)$, $1/(1 + x)$, e^x, $\sin x$, $\cos x$, $\ln(1 + x)$, $\ln[(1 + x)/(1 - x)]$, and $\tan^{-1} x$? How do you estimate the errors involved in replacing these series with their partial sums?

Chapter 8 Practice Exercises

Which of the sequences whose nth terms appear in Exercises 1–18 converge, and which diverge? Find the limit of each convergent sequence.

1. $a_n = 1 + \dfrac{(-1)^n}{n}$
2. $a_n = \dfrac{1 - (-1)^n}{\sqrt{n}}$
3. $a_n = \dfrac{1 - 2^n}{2^n}$
4. $a_n = 1 + (0.9)^n$
5. $a_n = \sin \dfrac{n\pi}{2}$
6. $a_n = \sin n\pi$
7. $a_n = \dfrac{\ln(n^2)}{n}$
8. $a_n = \dfrac{\ln(2n + 1)}{n}$
9. $a_n = \dfrac{n + \ln n}{n}$
10. $a_n = \dfrac{\ln(2n^3 + 1)}{n}$
11. $a_n = \left(\dfrac{n - 5}{n}\right)^n$
12. $a_n = \left(1 + \dfrac{1}{n}\right)^{-n}$
13. $a_n = \sqrt[n]{\dfrac{3^n}{n}}$
14. $a_n = \left(\dfrac{3}{n}\right)^{1/n}$
15. $a_n = n(2^{1/n} - 1)$
16. $a_n = \sqrt[n]{2n + 1}$
17. $a_n = \dfrac{(n + 1)!}{n!}$
18. $a_n = \dfrac{(-4)^n}{n!}$

Find the sums of the series in Exercises 19–24.

19. $\displaystyle\sum_{n=3}^{\infty} \frac{1}{(2n - 3)(2n - 1)}$
20. $\displaystyle\sum_{n=2}^{\infty} \frac{-2}{n(n + 1)}$
21. $\displaystyle\sum_{n=1}^{\infty} \frac{9}{(3n - 1)(3n + 2)}$
22. $\displaystyle\sum_{n=3}^{\infty} \frac{-8}{(4n - 3)(4n + 1)}$
23. $\displaystyle\sum_{n=0}^{\infty} e^{-n}$
24. $\displaystyle\sum_{n=1}^{\infty} (-1)^n \frac{3}{4^n}$

Which of the series in Exercises 25–40 converge absolutely, which converge conditionally, and which diverge? Give reasons for your answers.

25. $\displaystyle\sum_{n=1}^{\infty} \frac{1}{\sqrt{n}}$
26. $\displaystyle\sum_{n=1}^{\infty} \frac{-5}{n}$
27. $\displaystyle\sum_{n=1}^{\infty} \frac{(-1)^n}{\sqrt{n}}$
28. $\displaystyle\sum_{n=1}^{\infty} \frac{1}{2n^3}$
29. $\displaystyle\sum_{n=1}^{\infty} \frac{(-1)^n}{\ln(n + 1)}$
30. $\displaystyle\sum_{n=2}^{\infty} \frac{1}{n(\ln n)^2}$
31. $\displaystyle\sum_{n=1}^{\infty} \frac{\ln n}{n^3}$
32. $\displaystyle\sum_{n=3}^{\infty} \frac{\ln n}{\ln(\ln n)}$

33. $\sum_{n=1}^{\infty} \frac{(-1)^n}{n\sqrt{n^2+1}}$

34. $\sum_{n=1}^{\infty} \frac{(-1)^n 3n^2}{n^3+1}$

35. $\sum_{n=1}^{\infty} \frac{n+1}{n!}$

36. $\sum_{n=1}^{\infty} \frac{(-1)^n(n^2+1)}{2n^2+n-1}$

37. $\sum_{n=1}^{\infty} \frac{(-3)^n}{n!}$

38. $\sum_{n=1}^{\infty} \frac{2^n 3^n}{n^n}$

39. $\sum_{n=1}^{\infty} \frac{1}{\sqrt{n(n+1)(n+2)}}$

40. $\sum_{n=2}^{\infty} \frac{1}{n\sqrt{n^2-1}}$

In Exercises 41–50, **(a)** find the series' radius and interval of convergence. Then identify the values of x for which the series converges **(b)** absolutely and **(c)** conditionally.

41. $\sum_{n=1}^{\infty} \frac{(x+4)^n}{n3^n}$

42. $\sum_{n=1}^{\infty} \frac{(x-1)^{2n-2}}{(2n-1)!}$

43. $\sum_{n=1}^{\infty} \frac{(-1)^{n-1}(3x-1)^n}{n^2}$

44. $\sum_{n=0}^{\infty} \frac{(n+1)(2x+1)^n}{(2n+1)2^n}$

45. $\sum_{n=1}^{\infty} \frac{x^n}{n^n}$

46. $\sum_{n=1}^{\infty} \frac{x^n}{\sqrt{n}}$

47. $\sum_{n=0}^{\infty} \frac{(n+1)x^{2n-1}}{3^n}$

48. $\sum_{n=0}^{\infty} \frac{(-1)^n(x-1)^{2n+1}}{2n+1}$

49. $\sum_{n=1}^{\infty} (\operatorname{csch} n)x^n$

50. $\sum_{n=1}^{\infty} (\coth n)x^n$

Each of the series in Exercises 51–56 is the value of the Taylor series at $x = 0$ of a function $f(x)$ at a particular point. What function and what point? What is the sum of the series?

51. $1 - \frac{1}{4} + \frac{1}{16} - \cdots + (-1)^n \frac{1}{4^n} + \cdots$

52. $\frac{2}{3} - \frac{4}{18} + \frac{8}{81} - \cdots + (-1)^{n-1} \frac{2^n}{n3^n} + \cdots$

53. $\pi - \frac{\pi^3}{3!} + \frac{\pi^5}{5!} - \cdots + (-1)^n \frac{\pi^{2n+1}}{(2n+1)!} + \cdots$

54. $1 - \frac{\pi^2}{9 \cdot 2!} + \frac{\pi^4}{81 \cdot 4!} - \cdots + (-1)^n \frac{\pi^{2n}}{3^{2n}(2n)!} + \cdots$

55. $1 + \ln 2 + \frac{(\ln 2)^2}{2!} + \cdots + \frac{(\ln 2)^n}{n!} + \cdots$

56. $\frac{1}{\sqrt{3}} - \frac{1}{9\sqrt{3}} + \frac{1}{45\sqrt{3}} - \cdots + (-1)^{n-1} \frac{1}{(2n-1)(\sqrt{3})^{2n-1}} + \cdots$

Find Taylor series at $x = 0$ for the functions in Exercises 57–64.

57. $\frac{1}{1-2x}$

58. $\frac{1}{1+x^3}$

59. $\sin \pi x$

60. $\sin \frac{2x}{3}$

61. $\cos (x^{5/2})$

62. $\cos \sqrt{5x}$

63. $e^{(\pi x/2)}$

64. e^{-x^2}

In Exercises 65–68, find the first four nonzero terms of the Taylor series generated by f at $x = a$.

65. $f(x) = \sqrt{3 + x^2}$ at $x = -1$

66. $f(x) = 1/(1 - x)$ at $x = 2$

67. $f(x) = 1/(x + 1)$ at $x = 3$

68. $f(x) = 1/x$ at $x = a > 0$

Use series to approximate the values of the integrals in Exercises 69–72 with an error of magnitude less than 10^{-8}. (The answer section gives the integrals' values rounded to 10 decimal places.)

69. $\int_0^{1/2} e^{-x^3}\, dx$

70. $\int_0^1 x \sin (x^3)\, dx$

71. $\int_0^{1/2} \frac{\tan^{-1} x}{x}\, dx$

72. $\int_0^{1/64} \frac{\tan^{-1} x}{\sqrt{x}}\, dx$

In Exercises 73–78:

a. Use power series to evaluate the limit.

T **b.** Then use a grapher to support your calculation.

73. $\lim_{x \to 0} \frac{7 \sin x}{e^{2x} - 1}$

74. $\lim_{\theta \to 0} \frac{e^\theta - e^{-\theta} - 2\theta}{\theta - \sin \theta}$

75. $\lim_{t \to 0} \left(\frac{1}{2 - 2\cos t} - \frac{1}{t^2} \right)$

76. $\lim_{h \to 0} \frac{(\sin h)/h - \cos h}{h^2}$

77. $\lim_{z \to 0} \frac{1 - \cos^2 z}{\ln (1 - z) + \sin z}$

78. $\lim_{y \to 0} \frac{y^2}{\cos y - \cosh y}$

79. Use a series representation of $\sin 3x$ to find values of r and s for which

$$\lim_{x \to 0} \left(\frac{\sin 3x}{x^3} + \frac{r}{x^2} + s \right) = 0.$$

T 80. Compare the accuracies of the approximations $\sin x \approx x$ and $\sin x \approx 6x/(6 + x^2)$ by comparing the graphs of $f(x) = \sin x - x$ and $g(x) = \sin x - (6x/(6 + x^2))$. Describe what you find.

81. Find the radius of convergence of the series

$$\sum_{n=1}^{\infty} \frac{2 \cdot 5 \cdot 8 \cdot \cdots \cdot (3n-1)}{2 \cdot 4 \cdot 6 \cdot \cdots \cdot (2n)} x^n.$$

82. Find the radius of convergence of the series

$$\sum_{n=1}^{\infty} \frac{3 \cdot 5 \cdot 7 \cdot \cdots \cdot (2n+1)}{4 \cdot 9 \cdot 14 \cdot \cdots \cdot (5n-1)} (x-1)^n.$$

83. Find a closed-form formula for the nth partial sum of the series $\sum_{n=2}^{\infty} \ln (1 - (1/n^2))$ and use it to determine the convergence or divergence of the series.

84. Evaluate $\sum_{k=2}^{\infty} (1/(k^2 - 1))$ by finding the limits as $n \to \infty$ of the series' nth partial sum.

85. **a.** Find the interval of convergence of the series

$$y = 1 + \frac{1}{6}x^3 + \frac{1}{180}x^6 + \cdots + \frac{1 \cdot 4 \cdot 7 \cdot \cdots \cdot (3n-2)}{(3n)!} x^{3n} + \cdots.$$

b. Show that the function defined by the series satisfies a differential equation of the form

$$\frac{d^2y}{dx^2} = x^a y + b$$

and find the values of the constants a and b.

86. a. Find the Maclaurin series for the function $x^2/(1 + x)$.

b. Does the series converge at $x = 1$? Explain.

87. If $\sum_{n=1}^{\infty} a_n$ and $\sum_{n=1}^{\infty} b_n$ are convergent series of nonnegative numbers, can anything be said about $\sum_{n=1}^{\infty} a_n b_n$? Give reasons for your answer.

88. If $\sum_{n=1}^{\infty} a_n$ and $\sum_{n=1}^{\infty} b_n$ are divergent series of nonnegative numbers, can anything be said about $\sum_{n=1}^{\infty} a_n b_n$? Give reasons for your answer.

89. Prove that the sequence $\{x_n\}$ and the series $\sum_{k=1}^{\infty} (x_{k+1} - x_k)$ both converge or both diverge.

90. Prove that $\sum_{n=1}^{\infty} (a_n/(1 + a_n))$ converges if $a_n > 0$ for all n and $\sum_{n=1}^{\infty} a_n$ converges.

91. Suppose that $a_1, a_2, a_3, \ldots, a_n$ are positive numbers satisfying the following conditions:

i. $a_1 \geq a_2 \geq a_3 \geq \cdots$;

ii. the series $a_2 + a_4 + a_8 + a_{16} + \cdots$ diverges.

Show that the series

$$\frac{a_1}{1} + \frac{a_2}{2} + \frac{a_3}{3} + \cdots$$

diverges.

92. Use the result in Exercise 91 to show that

$$1 + \sum_{n=2}^{\infty} \frac{1}{n \ln n}$$

diverges.

Chapter 8 Additional and Advanced Exercises

Which of the series $\sum_{n=1}^{\infty} a_n$ defined by the formulas in Exercises 1–4 converge, and which diverge? Give reasons for your answers.

1. $\displaystyle\sum_{n=1}^{\infty} \frac{1}{(3n - 2)^{n+(1/2)}}$

2. $\displaystyle\sum_{n=1}^{\infty} \frac{(\tan^{-1} n)^2}{n^2 + 1}$

3. $\displaystyle\sum_{n=1}^{\infty} (-1)^n \tanh n$

4. $\displaystyle\sum_{n=2}^{\infty} \frac{\log_n (n!)}{n^3}$

Which of the series $\sum_{n=1}^{\infty} a_n$ defined by the formulas in Exercises 5–8 converge, and which diverge? Give reasons for your answers.

5. $a_1 = 1, \quad a_{n+1} = \dfrac{n(n + 1)}{(n + 2)(n + 3)} a_n$

(*Hint:* Write out several terms, see which factors cancel, and then generalize.)

6. $a_1 = a_2 = 7, \quad a_{n+1} = \dfrac{n}{(n - 1)(n + 1)} a_n \quad \text{if } n \geq 2$

7. $a_1 = a_2 = 1, \quad a_{n+1} = \dfrac{1}{1 + a_n} \quad \text{if } n \geq 2$

8. $a_n = 1/3^n$ if n is odd, $a_n = n/3^n$ if n is even

Taylor's formula

$$f(x) = f(a) + f'(a)(x - a) + \frac{f''(a)}{2!}(x - a)^2 + \cdots + \frac{f^{(n)}(a)}{n!}(x - a)^n + \frac{f^{(n+1)}(c)}{(n + 1)!}(x - a)^{n+1}$$

expresses the value of f at x in terms of the values of f and its derivatives at $x = a$. In numerical computations, we therefore need a to be a point where we know the values of f and its derivatives. We also need a to be close enough to the values of f we are interested in to make $(x - a)^{n+1}$ so small we can neglect the remainder.

In Exercises 9–14, what Taylor series would you choose to represent the function near the given value of x? (There may be more than one good answer.) Write out the first four nonzero terms of the series you choose.

9. $\cos x$ near $x = 1$

10. $\sin x$ near $x = 6.3$

11. e^x near $x = 0.4$

12. $\ln x$ near $x = 1.3$

13. $\cos x$ near $x = 69$

14. $\tan^{-1} x$ near $x = 2$

15. Let a and b be constants with $0 < a < b$. Does the sequence $\{(a^n + b^n)^{1/n}\}$ converge? If it does converge, what is the limit?

16. Find the sum of the infinite series

$$1 + \frac{2}{10} + \frac{3}{10^2} + \frac{7}{10^3} + \frac{2}{10^4} + \frac{3}{10^5} + \frac{7}{10^6} + \frac{2}{10^7} + \frac{3}{10^8} + \frac{7}{10^9} + \cdots.$$

17. Evaluate

$$\sum_{n=0}^{\infty} \int_n^{n+1} \frac{1}{1 + x^2}\, dx.$$

18. Find all values of x for which

$$\sum_{n=1}^{\infty} \frac{nx^n}{(n + 1)(2x + 1)^n}$$

converges absolutely.

T **19. a.** Does the value of

$$\lim_{n \to \infty} \left(1 - \frac{\cos (a/n)}{n}\right)^n, \quad a \text{ constant},$$

appear to depend on the value of a? If so, how?

b. Does the value of

$$\lim_{n\to\infty}\left(1-\frac{\cos(a/n)}{bn}\right)^n, \quad a \text{ and } b \text{ constant}, b \neq 0,$$

appear to depend on the value of b? If so, how?

c. Use calculus to confirm your findings in parts (a) and (b).

20. Show that if $\sum_{n=1}^{\infty} a_n$ converges, then

$$\sum_{n=1}^{\infty}\left(\frac{1+\sin(a_n)}{2}\right)^n$$

converges.

21. Find a value for the constant b that will make the radius of convergence of the power series

$$\sum_{n=2}^{\infty}\frac{b^n x^n}{\ln n}$$

equal to 5.

22. How do you know that the functions $\sin x$, $\ln x$, and e^x are not polynomials? Give reasons for your answer.

23. Find the value of a for which the limit

$$\lim_{x\to 0}\frac{\sin(ax)-\sin x - x}{x^3}$$

is finite and evaluate the limit.

24. Find values of a and b for which

$$\lim_{x\to 0}\frac{\cos(ax)-b}{2x^2} = -1.$$

25. Raabe's (or Gauss's) test The following test, which we state without proof, is an extension of the Ratio Test.

Raabe's test: If $\sum_{n=1}^{\infty} u_n$ is a series of positive constants and there exist constants C, K, and N such that

$$\frac{u_n}{u_{n+1}} = 1 + \frac{C}{n} + \frac{f(n)}{n^2}, \tag{1}$$

where $|f(n)| < K$ for $n \geq N$, then $\sum_{n=1}^{\infty} u_n$ converges if $C > 1$ and diverges if $C \leq 1$.

Show that the results of Raabe's test agree with what you know about the series $\sum_{n=1}^{\infty}(1/n^2)$ and $\sum_{n=1}^{\infty}(1/n)$.

26. (*Continuation of Exercise 25.*) Suppose that the terms of $\sum_{n=1}^{\infty} u_n$ are defined recursively by the formulas

$$u_1 = 1, \quad u_{n+1} = \frac{(2n-1)^2}{(2n)(2n+1)}u_n.$$

Apply Raabe's test to determine whether the series converges.

27. If $\sum_{n=1}^{\infty} a_n$ converges, and if $a_n \neq 1$ and $a_n > 0$ for all n,

a. Show that $\sum_{n=1}^{\infty} a_n^2$ converges.

b. Does $\sum_{n=1}^{\infty} a_n/(1-a_n)$ converge? Explain.

28. (*Continuation of Exercise 27.*) If $\sum_{n=1}^{\infty} a_n$ converges, and if $1 > a_n > 0$ for all n, show that $\sum_{n=1}^{\infty}\ln(1-a_n)$ converges.

(*Hint:* First show that $|\ln(1-a_n)| \leq a_n/(1-a_n)$.)

29. Nicole Oresme's Theorem Prove Nicole Oresme's Theorem that

$$1 + \frac{1}{2}\cdot 2 + \frac{1}{4}\cdot 3 + \cdots + \frac{n}{2^{n-1}} + \cdots = 4.$$

(*Hint:* Differentiate both sides of the equation $1/(1-x) = 1 + \sum_{n=1}^{\infty} x^n$.)

30. a. Show that

$$\sum_{n=1}^{\infty}\frac{n(n+1)}{x^n} = \frac{2x^2}{(x-1)^3}$$

for $|x| > 1$ by differentiating the identity

$$\sum_{n=1}^{\infty} x^{n+1} = \frac{x^2}{1-x}$$

twice, multiplying the result by x, and then replacing x by $1/x$.

b. Use part (a) to find the real solution greater than 1 of the equation

$$x = \sum_{n=1}^{\infty}\frac{n(n+1)}{x^n}.$$

31. Quality control

a. Differentiate the series

$$\frac{1}{1-x} = 1 + x + x^2 + \cdots + x^n + \cdots$$

to obtain a series for $1/(1-x)^2$.

b. In one throw of two dice, the probability of getting a roll of 7 is $p = 1/6$. If you throw the dice repeatedly, the probability that a 7 will appear for the first time at the nth throw is $q^{n-1}p$, where $q = 1 - p = 5/6$. The expected number of throws until a 7 first appears is $\sum_{n=1}^{\infty} nq^{n-1}p$. Find the sum of this series.

c. As an engineer applying statistical control to an industrial operation, you inspect items taken at random from the assembly line. You classify each sampled item as either "good" or "bad." If the probability of an item's being good is p and of an item's being bad is $q = 1 - p$, the probability that the first bad item found is the nth one inspected is $p^{n-1}q$. The average number inspected up to and including the first bad item found is $\sum_{n=1}^{\infty} np^{n-1}q$. Evaluate this sum, assuming $0 < p < 1$.

32. Expected value Suppose that a random variable X may assume the values $1, 2, 3, \ldots$, with probabilities $p_1, p_2, p_3, \ldots$, where p_k is the probability that X equals k $(k = 1, 2, 3, \ldots)$. Suppose also that $p_k \geq 0$ and that $\sum_{k=1}^{\infty} p_k = 1$. The **expected value** of X, denoted by $E(X)$, is the number $\sum_{k=1}^{\infty} kp_k$, provided the series converges. In each of the following cases, show that $\sum_{k=1}^{\infty} p_k = 1$ and find $E(X)$ if it exists. (*Hint:* See Exercise 31.)

a. $p_k = 2^{-k}$

b. $p_k = \dfrac{5^{k-1}}{6^k}$

c. $p_k = \dfrac{1}{k(k+1)} = \dfrac{1}{k} - \dfrac{1}{k+1}$

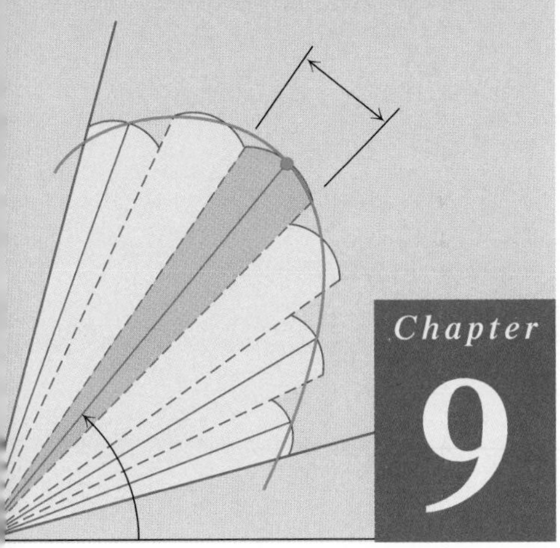

Chapter 9

Polar Coordinates and Conics

OVERVIEW In this chapter we study curves, derivatives, and integrals in polar coordinates. Polar coordinates are useful for describing rotational motion, as in planetary and satellite motion, and they can also simplify the calculations of multiple integrals (Chapter 13). Additionally, we review the geometric definitions of parabolas, ellipses, and hyperbolas and derive their standard equations. These curves are called *conic sections*, or *conics*, and model the paths traveled by projectiles, planets, and any other object moving under the sole influence of a gravitational or electromagnetic force.

9.1 Polar Coordinates

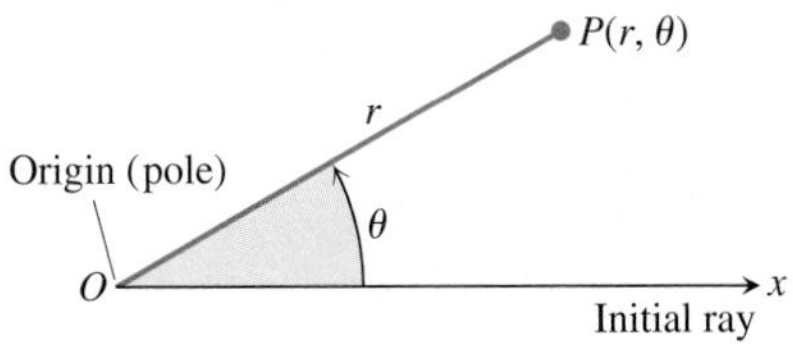

FIGURE 9.1 To define polar coordinates for the plane, we start with an origin, called the pole, and an initial ray.

In this section, we study polar coordinates and their relation to Cartesian coordinates. While a point in the plane has just one pair of Cartesian coordinates, it has infinitely many pairs of polar coordinates.

Definition of Polar Coordinates

To define polar coordinates, we first fix an **origin** O (called the **pole**) and an **initial ray** from O (Figure 9.1). Then each point P can be located by assigning to it a **polar coordinate pair** (r, θ) in which r gives the directed distance from O to P and θ gives the directed angle from the initial ray to ray OP.

> **Polar Coordinates**
>
> $P(r, \theta)$
>
> r: Directed distance from O to P
>
> θ: Directed angle from initial ray to OP

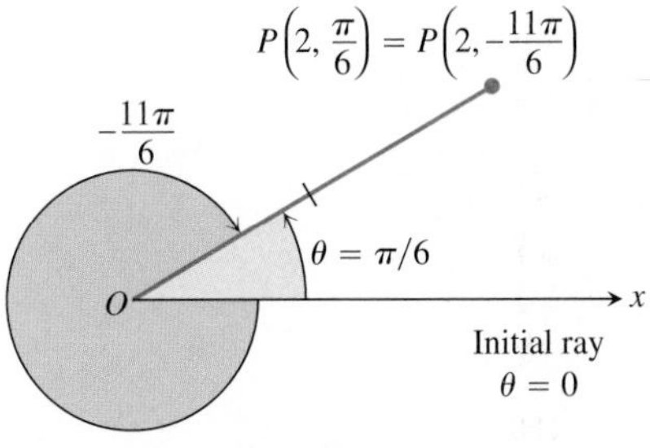

FIGURE 9.2 Polar coordinates are not unique.

As in trigonometry, θ is positive when measured counterclockwise and negative when measured clockwise. The angle associated with a given point is not unique. For instance, the point 2 units from the origin along the ray $\theta = \pi/6$ has polar coordinates $r = 2$, $\theta = \pi/6$. It also has coordinates $r = 2, \theta = -11\pi/6$ (Figure 9.2). In some situations we allow r to be negative. That is why we use directed distance in defining $P(r, \theta)$. The point $P(2, 7\pi/6)$ can be reached by turning $7\pi/6$ radians counterclockwise from the initial ray and going forward 2 units (Figure 9.3). It can also be reached by turning $\pi/6$ radians

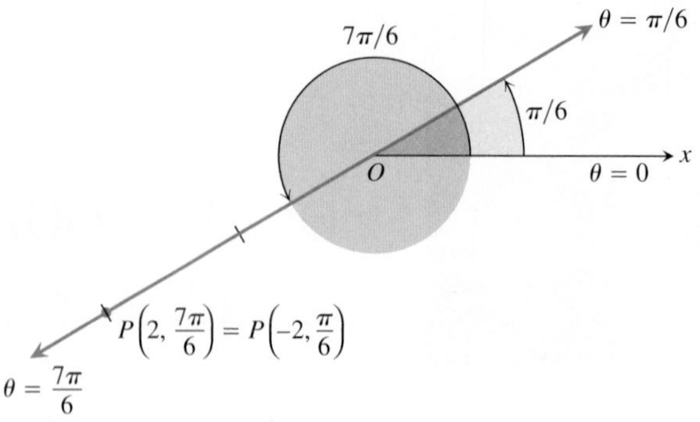

FIGURE 9.3 Polar coordinates can have negative r-values.

counterclockwise from the initial ray and going *backward* 2 units. So the point also has polar coordinates $r = -2, \theta = \pi/6$.

EXAMPLE 1 Find all the polar coordinates of the point $P(2, \pi/6)$.

Solution We sketch the initial ray of the coordinate system, draw the ray from the origin that makes an angle of $\pi/6$ radians with the initial ray, and mark the point $(2, \pi/6)$ (Figure 9.4). We then find the angles for the other coordinate pairs of P in which $r = 2$ and $r = -2$.

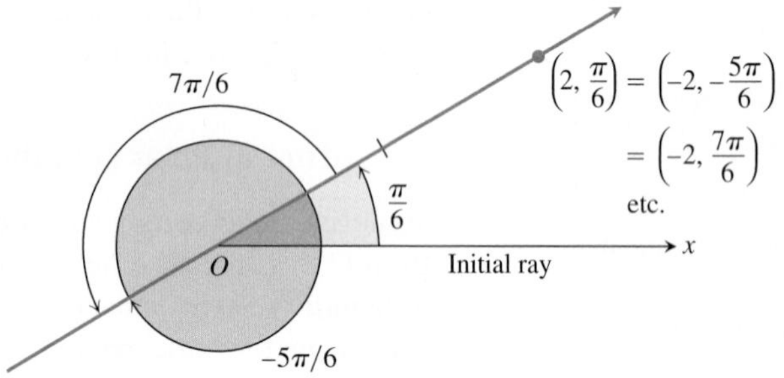

FIGURE 9.4 The point $P(2, \pi/6)$ has infinitely many polar coordinate pairs (Example 1).

For $r = 2$, the complete list of angles is

$$\frac{\pi}{6}, \quad \frac{\pi}{6} \pm 2\pi, \quad \frac{\pi}{6} \pm 4\pi, \quad \frac{\pi}{6} \pm 6\pi, \quad \ldots .$$

For $r = -2$, the angles are

$$-\frac{5\pi}{6}, \quad -\frac{5\pi}{6} \pm 2\pi, \quad -\frac{5\pi}{6} \pm 4\pi, \quad -\frac{5\pi}{6} \pm 6\pi, \quad \ldots .$$

The corresponding coordinate pairs of P are

$$\left(2, \frac{\pi}{6} + 2n\pi\right), \qquad n = 0, \pm 1, \pm 2, \ldots$$

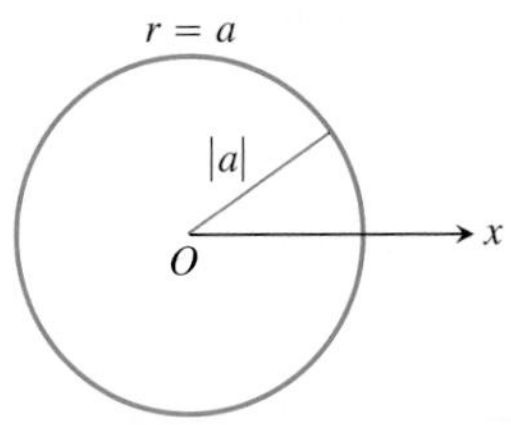

FIGURE 9.5 The polar equation for a circle is $r = a$.

and

$$\left(-2, -\frac{5\pi}{6} + 2n\pi\right), \qquad n = 0, \pm 1, \pm 2, \ldots.$$

When $n = 0$, the formulas give $(2, \pi/6)$ and $(-2, -5\pi/6)$. When $n = 1$, they give $(2, 13\pi/6)$ and $(-2, 7\pi/6)$, and so on. ■

Polar Equations and Graphs

If we hold r fixed at a constant value $r = a \neq 0$, the point $P(r, \theta)$ will lie $|a|$ units from the origin O. As θ varies over any interval of length 2π, P then traces a circle of radius $|a|$ centered at O (Figure 9.5).

If we hold θ fixed at a constant value $\theta = \theta_0$ and let r vary between $-\infty$ and ∞, the point $P(r, \theta)$ traces the line through O that makes an angle of measure θ_0 with the initial ray.

Equation	Graph
$r = a$	Circle of radius $|a|$ centered at O
$\theta = \theta_0$	Line through O making an angle θ_0 with the initial ray

EXAMPLE 2

(a) $r = 1$ and $r = -1$ are equations for the circle of radius 1 centered at O.

(b) $\theta = \pi/6$, $\theta = 7\pi/6$, and $\theta = -5\pi/6$ are equations for the line in Figure 9.4. ■

Equations of the form $r = a$ and $\theta = \theta_0$ can be combined to define regions, segments, and rays.

EXAMPLE 3 Graph the sets of points whose polar coordinates satisfy the following conditions.

(a) $1 \le r \le 2$ and $0 \le \theta \le \dfrac{\pi}{2}$

(b) $-3 \le r \le 2$ and $\theta = \dfrac{\pi}{4}$

(c) $r \le 0$ and $\theta = \dfrac{\pi}{4}$

(d) $\dfrac{2\pi}{3} \le \theta \le \dfrac{5\pi}{6}$ (no restriction on r)

Solution The graphs are shown in Figure 9.6. ■

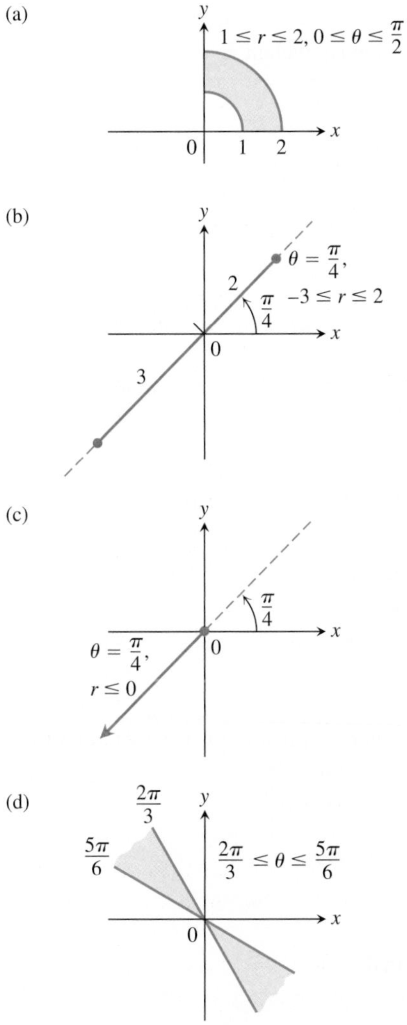

FIGURE 9.6 The graphs of typical inequalities in r and θ (Example 3).

Relating Polar and Cartesian Coordinates

When we use both polar and Cartesian coordinates in a plane, we place the two origins together and take the initial polar ray as the positive x-axis. The ray $\theta = \pi/2, r > 0$,

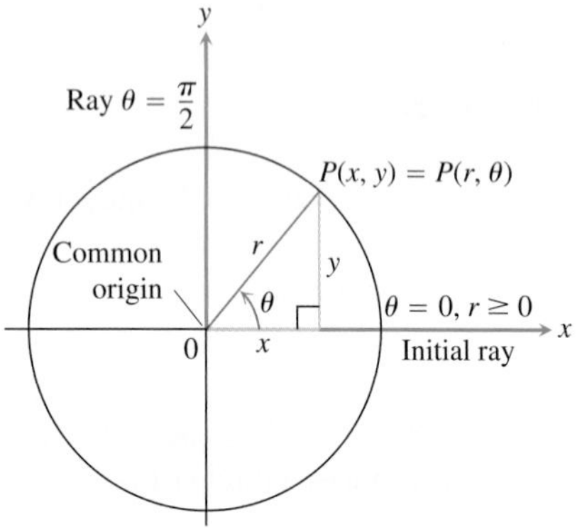

FIGURE 9.7 The usual way to relate polar and Cartesian coordinates.

becomes the positive y-axis (Figure 9.7). The two coordinate systems are then related by the following equations.

Equations Relating Polar and Cartesian Coordinates

$$x = r\cos\theta, \qquad y = r\sin\theta, \qquad x^2 + y^2 = r^2$$

The first two of these equations uniquely determine the Cartesian coordinates x and y given the polar coordinates r and θ. On the other hand, if x and y are given, the third equation gives two possible choices for r (a positive and a negative value). For each selection, there is a unique $\theta \in [0, 2\pi)$ satisfying the first two equations, each then giving a polar coordinate representation of the Cartesian point (x, y). The other polar coordinate representations for the point can be determined from these two, as in Example 1.

EXAMPLE 4 Here are some equivalent equations.

Polar equation	Cartesian equivalent
$r\cos\theta = 2$	$x = 2$
$r^2\cos\theta\sin\theta = 4$	$xy = 4$
$r^2\cos^2\theta - r^2\sin^2\theta = 1$	$x^2 - y^2 = 1$
$r = 1 + 2r\cos\theta$	$y^2 - 3x^2 - 4x - 1 = 0$
$r = 1 - \cos\theta$	$x^4 + y^4 + 2x^2y^2 + 2x^3 + 2xy^2 - y^2 = 0$

With some curves, we are better off with polar coordinates; with others, we aren't. ■

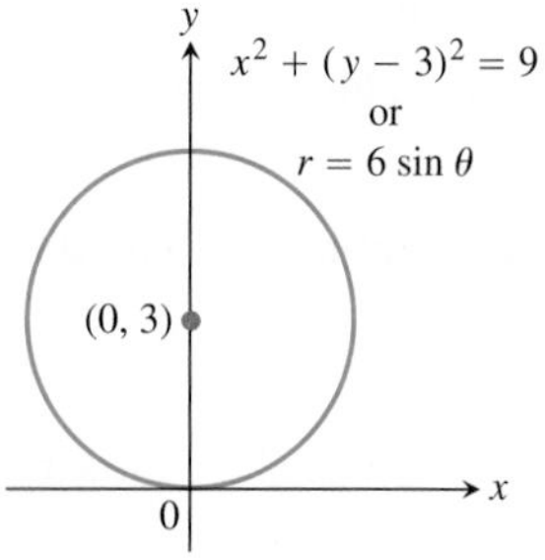

FIGURE 9.8 The circle in Example 5.

EXAMPLE 5 Find a polar equation for the circle $x^2 + (y - 3)^2 = 9$ (Figure 9.8).

Solution

$$\begin{aligned} x^2 + y^2 - 6y + 9 &= 9 && \text{Expand } (y-3)^2. \\ x^2 + y^2 - 6y &= 0 && \text{The 9's cancel.} \\ r^2 - 6r\sin\theta &= 0 && x^2 + y^2 = r^2 \\ r = 0 \quad \text{or} \quad r - 6\sin\theta &= 0 \\ r &= 6\sin\theta && \text{Includes both possibilities} \end{aligned}$$

■

EXAMPLE 6 Replace the following polar equations by equivalent Cartesian equations, and identify their graphs.

(a) $r\cos\theta = -4$

(b) $r^2 = 4r\cos\theta$

(c) $r = \dfrac{4}{2\cos\theta - \sin\theta}$

Solution We use the substitutions $r\cos\theta = x$, $r\sin\theta = y$, $r^2 = x^2 + y^2$.

(a) $r\cos\theta = -4$

The Cartesian equation: $r\cos\theta = -4$

$x = -4$

The graph: Vertical line through $x = -4$ on the x-axis

(b) $r^2 = 4r\cos\theta$

The Cartesian equation:

$$
\begin{aligned}
r^2 &= 4r\cos\theta \\
x^2 + y^2 &= 4x \\
x^2 - 4x + y^2 &= 0 \\
x^2 - 4x + 4 + y^2 &= 4 \qquad \text{Completing the square} \\
(x-2)^2 + y^2 &= 4
\end{aligned}
$$

The graph: Circle, radius 2, center $(h, k) = (2, 0)$

(c) $r = \dfrac{4}{2\cos\theta - \sin\theta}$

The Cartesian equation:

$$
\begin{aligned}
r(2\cos\theta - \sin\theta) &= 4 \\
2r\cos\theta - r\sin\theta &= 4 \\
2x - y &= 4 \\
y &= 2x - 4
\end{aligned}
$$

The graph: Line, slope $m = 2$, y-intercept $b = -4$ ■

EXERCISES 9.1

1. Which polar coordinate pairs label the same point?

a. $(3, 0)$ **b.** $(-3, 0)$ **c.** $(2, 2\pi/3)$
d. $(2, 7\pi/3)$ **e.** $(-3, \pi)$ **f.** $(2, \pi/3)$
g. $(-3, 2\pi)$ **h.** $(-2, -\pi/3)$

2. Which polar coordinate pairs label the same point?

a. $(-2, \pi/3)$ **b.** $(2, -\pi/3)$ **c.** (r, θ)
d. $(r, \theta + \pi)$ **e.** $(-r, \theta)$ **f.** $(2, -2\pi/3)$
g. $(-r, \theta + \pi)$ **h.** $(-2, 2\pi/3)$

3. Plot the following points (given in polar coordinates). Then find all the polar coordinates of each point.

a. $(2, \pi/2)$ **b.** $(2, 0)$
c. $(-2, \pi/2)$ **d.** $(-2, 0)$

4. Plot the following points (given in polar coordinates). Then find all the polar coordinates of each point.

a. $(3, \pi/4)$ **b.** $(-3, \pi/4)$
c. $(3, -\pi/4)$ **d.** $(-3, -\pi/4)$

5. Find the Cartesian coordinates of the points in Exercise 1.

6. Find the Cartesian coordinates of the following points (given in polar coordinates).

a. $(\sqrt{2}, \pi/4)$ **b.** $(1, 0)$
c. $(0, \pi/2)$ **d.** $(-\sqrt{2}, \pi/4)$
e. $(-3, 5\pi/6)$ **f.** $(5, \tan^{-1}(4/3))$
g. $(-1, 7\pi)$ **h.** $(2\sqrt{3}, 2\pi/3)$

Graph the sets of points whose polar coordinates satisfy the equations and inequalities in Exercises 7–22.

7. $r = 2$ **8.** $0 \le r \le 2$
9. $r \ge 1$ **10.** $1 \le r \le 2$
11. $0 \le \theta \le \pi/6, \quad r \ge 0$ **12.** $\theta = 2\pi/3, \quad r \le -2$
13. $\theta = \pi/3, \quad -1 \le r \le 3$ **14.** $\theta = 11\pi/4, \quad r \ge -1$
15. $\theta = \pi/2, \quad r \ge 0$ **16.** $\theta = \pi/2, \quad r \le 0$
17. $0 \le \theta \le \pi, \quad r = 1$ **18.** $0 \le \theta \le \pi, \quad r = -1$
19. $\pi/4 \le \theta \le 3\pi/4, \quad 0 \le r \le 1$
20. $-\pi/4 \le \theta \le \pi/4, \quad -1 \le r \le 1$
21. $-\pi/2 \le \theta \le \pi/2, \quad 1 \le r \le 2$
22. $0 \le \theta \le \pi/2, \quad 1 \le |r| \le 2$

Replace the polar equations in Exercises 23–48 by equivalent Cartesian equations. Then describe or identify the graph.

23. $r\cos\theta = 2$ **24.** $r\sin\theta = -1$
25. $r\sin\theta = 0$ **26.** $r\cos\theta = 0$

27. $r = 4 \csc \theta$

28. $r = -3 \sec \theta$

29. $r \cos \theta + r \sin \theta = 1$

30. $r \sin \theta = r \cos \theta$

31. $r^2 = 1$

32. $r^2 = 4r \sin \theta$

33. $r = \dfrac{5}{\sin \theta - 2 \cos \theta}$

34. $r^2 \sin 2\theta = 2$

35. $r = \cot \theta \csc \theta$

36. $r = 4 \tan \theta \sec \theta$

37. $r = \csc \theta \, e^{r \cos \theta}$

38. $r \sin \theta = \ln r + \ln \cos \theta$

39. $r^2 + 2r^2 \cos \theta \sin \theta = 1$

40. $\cos^2 \theta = \sin^2 \theta$

41. $r^2 = -4r \cos \theta$

42. $r^2 = -6r \sin \theta$

43. $r = 8 \sin \theta$

44. $r = 3 \cos \theta$

45. $r = 2 \cos \theta + 2 \sin \theta$

46. $r = 2 \cos \theta - \sin \theta$

47. $r \sin \left(\theta + \dfrac{\pi}{6}\right) = 2$

48. $r \sin \left(\dfrac{2\pi}{3} - \theta\right) = 5$

Replace the Cartesian equations in Exercises 49–62 by equivalent polar equations.

49. $x = 7$

50. $y = 1$

51. $x = y$

52. $x - y = 3$

53. $x^2 + y^2 = 4$

54. $x^2 - y^2 = 1$

55. $\dfrac{x^2}{9} + \dfrac{y^2}{4} = 1$

56. $xy = 2$

57. $y^2 = 4x$

58. $x^2 + xy + y^2 = 1$

59. $x^2 + (y - 2)^2 = 4$

60. $(x - 5)^2 + y^2 = 25$

61. $(x - 3)^2 + (y + 1)^2 = 4$

62. $(x + 2)^2 + (y - 5)^2 = 16$

63. Find all polar coordinates of the origin.

64. Vertical and horizontal lines

a. Show that every vertical line in the xy-plane has a polar equation of the form $r = a \sec \theta$.

b. Find the analogous polar equation for horizontal lines in the xy-plane.

9.2 Graphing in Polar Coordinates

This section describes techniques for graphing equations in polar coordinates.

Symmetry

Figure 9.9 illustrates the standard polar coordinate tests for symmetry.

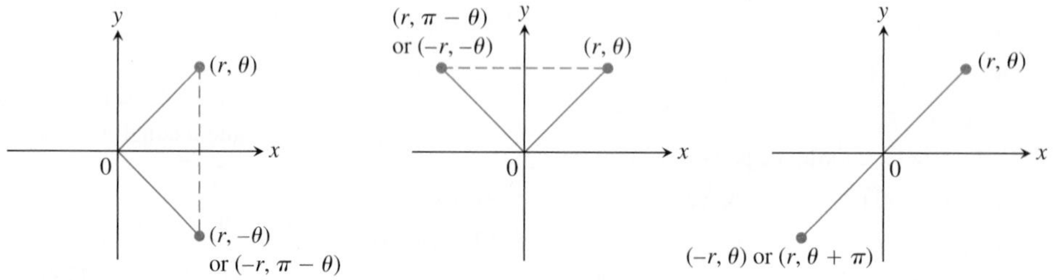

(a) About the x-axis (b) About the y-axis (c) About the origin

FIGURE 9.9 Three tests for symmetry in polar coordinates.

> **Symmetry Tests for Polar Graphs**
>
> 1. *Symmetry about the x-axis:* If the point (r, θ) lies on the graph, the point $(r, -\theta)$ or $(-r, \pi - \theta)$ lies on the graph (Figure 9.9a).
> 2. *Symmetry about the y-axis:* If the point (r, θ) lies on the graph, the point $(r, \pi - \theta)$ or $(-r, -\theta)$ lies on the graph (Figure 9.9b).
> 3. *Symmetry about the origin:* If the point (r, θ) lies on the graph, the point $(-r, \theta)$ or $(r, \theta + \pi)$ lies on the graph (Figure 9.9c).

Slope

The slope of a polar curve $r = f(\theta)$ is given by dy/dx, not by $r' = df/d\theta$. To see why, think of the graph of f as the graph of the parametric equations

$$x = r\cos\theta = f(\theta)\cos\theta, \qquad y = r\sin\theta = f(\theta)\sin\theta.$$

If f is a differentiable function of θ, then so are x and y and, when $dx/d\theta \neq 0$, we can calculate dy/dx from the parametric formula

$$\frac{dy}{dx} = \frac{dy/d\theta}{dx/d\theta} \qquad \text{Section 3.5, Equation (2) with } t = \theta$$

$$= \frac{\dfrac{d}{d\theta}(f(\theta)\cdot\sin\theta)}{\dfrac{d}{d\theta}(f(\theta)\cdot\cos\theta)}$$

$$= \frac{\dfrac{df}{d\theta}\sin\theta + f(\theta)\cos\theta}{\dfrac{df}{d\theta}\cos\theta - f(\theta)\sin\theta} \qquad \text{Product Rule for derivatives}$$

Slope of the Curve $r = f(\theta)$

$$\left.\frac{dy}{dx}\right|_{(r,\,\theta)} = \frac{f'(\theta)\sin\theta + f(\theta)\cos\theta}{f'(\theta)\cos\theta - f(\theta)\sin\theta},$$

provided $dx/d\theta \neq 0$ at (r, θ).

If the curve $r = f(\theta)$ passes through the origin at $\theta = \theta_0$, then $f(\theta_0) = 0$, and the slope equation gives

$$\left.\frac{dy}{dx}\right|_{(0,\,\theta_0)} = \frac{f'(\theta_0)\sin\theta_0}{f'(\theta_0)\cos\theta_0} = \tan\theta_0.$$

If the graph of $r = f(\theta)$ passes through the origin at the value $\theta = \theta_0$, the slope of the curve there is $\tan\theta_0$. The reason we say "slope at $(0, \theta_0)$" and not just "slope at the origin" is that a polar curve may pass through the origin (or any point) more than once, with different slopes at different θ-values. This is not the case in our first example, however.

EXAMPLE 1 Graph the curve $r = 1 - \cos\theta$.

Solution The curve is symmetric about the x-axis because

$$(r, \theta) \text{ on the graph} \Rightarrow r = 1 - \cos\theta$$

$$\Rightarrow r = 1 - \cos(-\theta) \qquad \cos\theta = \cos(-\theta)$$

$$\Rightarrow (r, -\theta) \text{ on the graph}.$$

θ	$r = 1 - \cos\theta$
0	0
$\frac{\pi}{3}$	$\frac{1}{2}$
$\frac{\pi}{2}$	1
$\frac{2\pi}{3}$	$\frac{3}{2}$
π	2

(a)

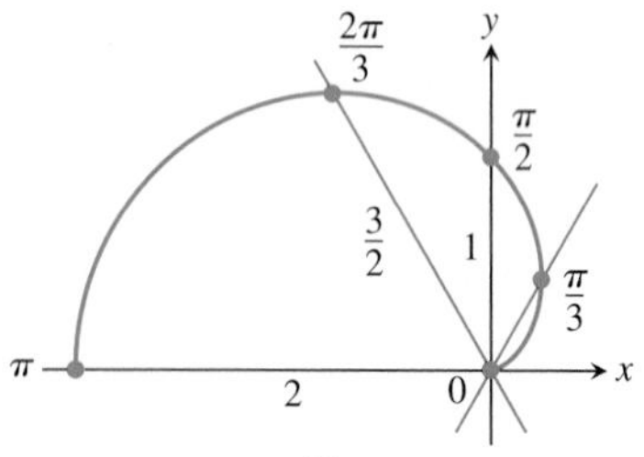

(b)

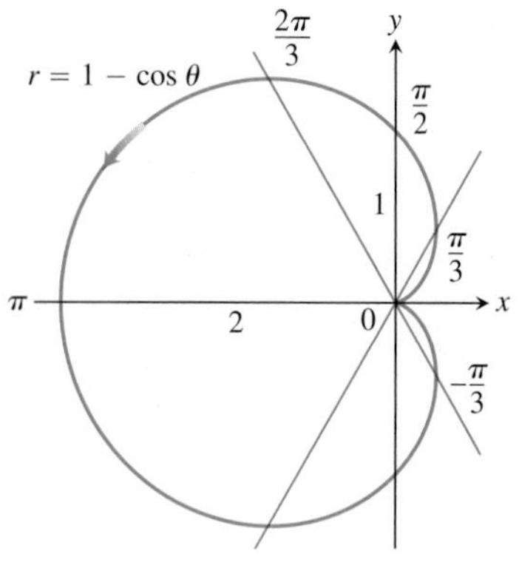

(c)

FIGURE 9.10 The steps in graphing the cardioid $r = 1 - \cos\theta$ (Example 1). The arrow shows the direction of increasing θ.

As θ increases from 0 to π, $\cos\theta$ decreases from 1 to -1, and $r = 1 - \cos\theta$ increases from a minimum value of 0 to a maximum value of 2. As θ continues on from π to 2π, $\cos\theta$ increases from -1 back to 1 and r decreases from 2 back to 0. The curve starts to repeat when $\theta = 2\pi$ because the cosine has period 2π.

The curve leaves the origin with slope $\tan(0) = 0$ and returns to the origin with slope $\tan(2\pi) = 0$.

We make a table of values from $\theta = 0$ to $\theta = \pi$, plot the points, draw a smooth curve through them with a horizontal tangent at the origin, and reflect the curve across the x-axis to complete the graph (Figure 9.10). The curve is called a *cardioid* because of its heart shape. ■

EXAMPLE 2 Graph the curve $r^2 = 4\cos\theta$.

Solution The equation $r^2 = 4\cos\theta$ requires $\cos\theta \geq 0$, so we get the entire graph by running θ from $-\pi/2$ to $\pi/2$. The curve is symmetric about the x-axis because

$$\begin{aligned}(r, \theta) \text{ on the graph} &\Rightarrow r^2 = 4\cos\theta \\ &\Rightarrow r^2 = 4\cos(-\theta) \qquad \cos\theta = \cos(-\theta) \\ &\Rightarrow (r, -\theta) \text{ on the graph.}\end{aligned}$$

The curve is also symmetric about the origin because

$$\begin{aligned}(r, \theta) \text{ on the graph} &\Rightarrow r^2 = 4\cos\theta \\ &\Rightarrow (-r)^2 = 4\cos\theta \\ &\Rightarrow (-r, \theta) \text{ on the graph.}\end{aligned}$$

Together, these two symmetries imply symmetry about the y-axis.

The curve passes through the origin when $\theta = -\pi/2$ and $\theta = \pi/2$. It has a vertical tangent both times because $\tan\theta$ is infinite.

For each value of θ in the interval between $-\pi/2$ and $\pi/2$, the formula $r^2 = 4\cos\theta$ gives two values of r:

$$r = \pm 2\sqrt{\cos\theta}.$$

θ	$\cos\theta$	$r = \pm 2\sqrt{\cos\theta}$
0	1	± 2
$\pm\frac{\pi}{6}$	$\frac{\sqrt{3}}{2}$	$\approx \pm 1.9$
$\pm\frac{\pi}{4}$	$\frac{1}{\sqrt{2}}$	$\approx \pm 1.7$
$\pm\frac{\pi}{3}$	$\frac{1}{2}$	$\approx \pm 1.4$
$\pm\frac{\pi}{2}$	0	0

(a)

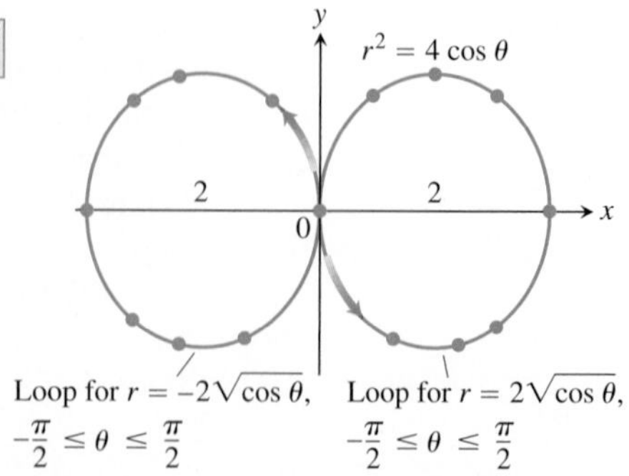

(b)

FIGURE 9.11 The graph of $r^2 = 4\cos\theta$. The arrows show the direction of increasing θ. The values of r in the table are rounded (Example 2).

We make a short table of values, plot the corresponding points, and use information about symmetry and tangents to guide us in connecting the points with a smooth curve (Figure 9.11). ■

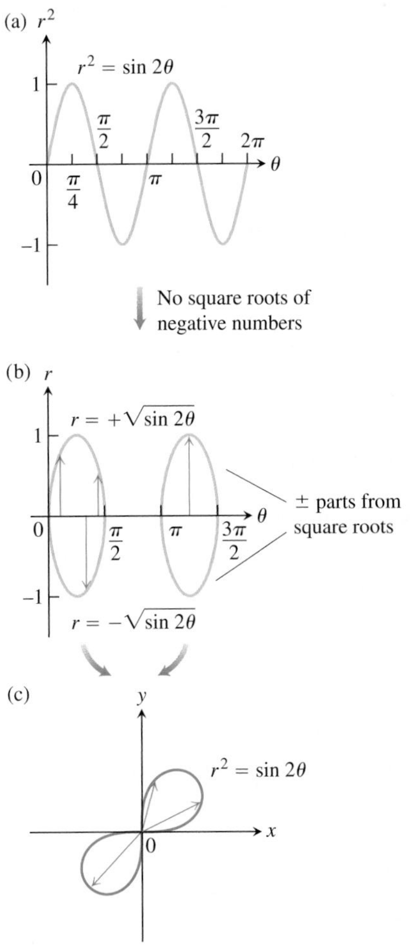

FIGURE 9.12 To plot $r = f(\theta)$ in the Cartesian $r\theta$-plane in (b), we first plot $r^2 = \sin 2\theta$ in the $r^2\theta$-plane in (a) and then ignore the values of θ for which $\sin 2\theta$ is negative. The radii from the sketch in (b) cover the polar graph of the lemniscate in (c) twice (Example 3).

A Technique for Graphing

One way to graph a polar equation $r = f(\theta)$ is to make a table of (r, θ)-values, plot the corresponding points, and connect them in order of increasing θ. This can work well if enough points have been plotted to reveal all the loops and dimples in the graph. Another method of graphing that is usually quicker and more reliable is to

1. first graph $r = f(\theta)$ in the *Cartesian* $r\theta$-plane,
2. then use the Cartesian graph as a "table" and guide to sketch the *polar* coordinate graph.

This method is better than simple point plotting because the first Cartesian graph, even when hastily drawn, shows at a glance where r is positive, negative, and nonexistent, as well as where r is increasing and decreasing. Here's an example.

EXAMPLE 3 Graph the *lemniscate* curve

$$r^2 = \sin 2\theta.$$

Solution Here we begin by plotting r^2 (not r) as a function of θ in the Cartesian $r^2\theta$-plane. See Figure 9.12a. We pass from there to the graph of $r = \pm\sqrt{\sin 2\theta}$ in the $r\theta$-plane (Figure 9.12b), and then draw the polar graph (Figure 9.12c). The graph in Figure 9.12b "covers" the final polar graph in Figure 9.12c twice. We could have managed with either loop alone, with the two upper halves, or with the two lower halves. The double covering does no harm, however, and we actually learn a little more about the behavior of the function this way. ■

USING TECHNOLOGY Graphing Polar Curves Parametrically

For complicated polar curves we may need to use a graphing calculator or computer to graph the curve. If the device does not plot polar graphs directly, we can convert $r = f(\theta)$ into parametric form using the equations

$$x = r\cos\theta = f(\theta)\cos\theta, \qquad y = r\sin\theta = f(\theta)\sin\theta.$$

Then we use the device to draw a parametrized curve in the Cartesian xy-plane. It may be necessary to use the parameter t rather than θ for the graphing device.

EXERCISES 9.2

Identify the symmetries of the curves in Exercises 1–12. Then sketch the curves.

1. $r = 1 + \cos\theta$
2. $r = 2 - 2\cos\theta$
3. $r = 1 - \sin\theta$
4. $r = 1 + \sin\theta$
5. $r = 2 + \sin\theta$
6. $r = 1 + 2\sin\theta$
7. $r = \sin(\theta/2)$
8. $r = \cos(\theta/2)$
9. $r^2 = \cos\theta$
10. $r^2 = \sin\theta$
11. $r^2 = -\sin\theta$
12. $r^2 = -\cos\theta$

Graph the lemniscates in Exercises 13–16. What symmetries do these curves have?

13. $r^2 = 4\cos 2\theta$
14. $r^2 = 4\sin 2\theta$
15. $r^2 = -\sin 2\theta$
16. $r^2 = -\cos 2\theta$

Find the slopes of the curves in Exercises 17–20 at the given points. Sketch the curves along with their tangents at these points.

17. Cardioid $r = -1 + \cos\theta;\quad \theta = \pm\pi/2$

18. Cardioid $r = -1 + \sin\theta;\quad \theta = 0, \pi$

19. Four-leaved rose $r = \sin 2\theta;\quad \theta = \pm\pi/4, \pm 3\pi/4$

20. Four-leaved rose $r = \cos 2\theta;\quad \theta = 0, \pm\pi/2, \pi$

Graph the limaçons in Exercises 21–24. Limaçon ("*lee*-ma-sahn") is Old French for "snail." You will understand the name when you graph the limaçons in Exercise 21. Equations for limaçons have the form $r = a \pm b\cos\theta$ or $r = a \pm b\sin\theta$. There are four basic shapes.

21. Limaçons with an inner loop

a. $r = \frac{1}{2} + \cos\theta$ **b.** $r = \frac{1}{2} + \sin\theta$

22. Cardioids

a. $r = 1 - \cos\theta$ **b.** $r = -1 + \sin\theta$

23. Dimpled limaçons

a. $r = \frac{3}{2} + \cos\theta$ **b.** $r = \frac{3}{2} - \sin\theta$

24. Oval limaçons

a. $r = 2 + \cos\theta$ **b.** $r = -2 + \sin\theta$

25. Sketch the region defined by the inequalities $-1 \le r \le 2$ and $-\pi/2 \le \theta \le \pi/2$.

26. Sketch the region defined by the inequalities $0 \le r \le 2\sec\theta$ and $-\pi/4 \le \theta \le \pi/4$.

In Exercises 27 and 28, sketch the region defined by the inequality.

27. $0 \le r \le 2 - 2\cos\theta$ **28.** $0 \le r^2 \le \cos\theta$

T **29.** Which of the following has the same graph as $r = 1 - \cos\theta$?

a. $r = -1 - \cos\theta$

b. $r = 1 + \cos\theta$

Confirm your answer with algebra.

T **30.** Which of the following has the same graph as $r = \cos 2\theta$?

a. $r = -\sin(2\theta + \pi/2)$

b. $r = -\cos(\theta/2)$

Confirm your answer with algebra.

T **31. A rose within a rose** Graph the equation $r = 1 - 2\sin 3\theta$.

T **32. The nephroid of Freeth** Graph the nephroid of Freeth:

$$r = 1 + 2\sin\frac{\theta}{2}.$$

T **33. Roses** Graph the roses $r = \cos m\theta$ for $m = 1/3, 2, 3$, and 7.

T **34. Spirals** Polar coordinates are just the thing for defining spirals. Graph the following spirals.

a. $r = \theta$

b. $r = -\theta$

c. *A logarithmic spiral:* $r = e^{\theta/10}$

d. *A hyperbolic spiral:* $r = 8/\theta$

e. *An equilateral hyperbola:* $r = \pm 10/\sqrt{\theta}$

(Use different colors for the two branches.)

9.3 Areas and Lengths in Polar Coordinates

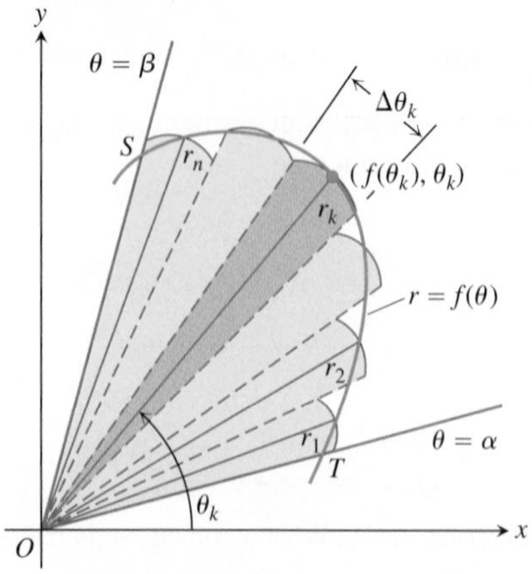

FIGURE 9.13 To derive a formula for the area of region *OTS*, we approximate the region with fan-shaped circular sectors.

This section shows how to calculate areas of plane regions and lengths of curves in polar coordinates.

Area in the Plane

The region *OTS* in Figure 9.13 is bounded by the rays $\theta = \alpha$ and $\theta = \beta$ and the curve $r = f(\theta)$. We approximate the region with n nonoverlapping fan-shaped circular sectors based on a partition P of angle TOS. The typical sector has radius $r_k = f(\theta_k)$ and central angle of radian measure $\Delta\theta_k$. Its area is $\Delta\theta_k/2\pi$ times the area of a circle of radius r_k, or

$$A_k = \frac{1}{2} r_k^2 \, \Delta\theta_k = \frac{1}{2}\left(f(\theta_k)\right)^2 \Delta\theta_k .$$

The area of region *OTS* is approximately

$$\sum_{k=1}^{n} A_k = \sum_{k=1}^{n} \frac{1}{2}\left(f(\theta_k)\right)^2 \Delta\theta_k .$$

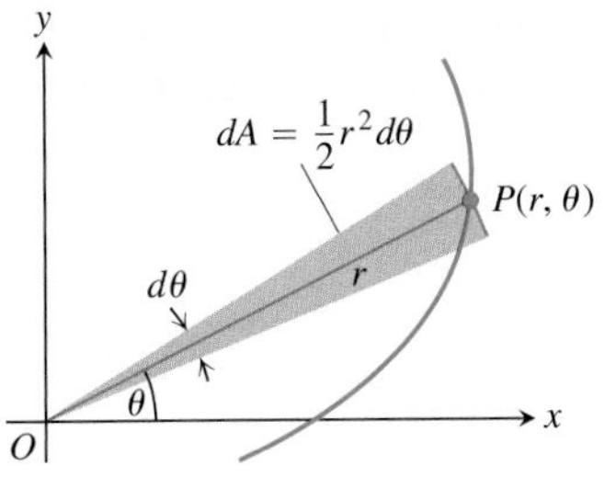

FIGURE 9.14 The area differential dA for the curve $r = f(\theta)$.

If f is continuous, we expect the approximations to improve as the norm of the partition P goes to zero, where the norm of P is the largest value of $\Delta\theta_k$. We are then led to the following formula for the region's area:

$$\begin{aligned} A &= \lim_{\|P\| \to 0} \sum_{k=1}^{n} \frac{1}{2}\left(f(\theta_k)\right)^2 \Delta\theta_k \\ &= \int_{\alpha}^{\beta} \frac{1}{2}\left(f(\theta)\right)^2 d\theta . \end{aligned}$$

Area of the Fan-Shaped Region Between the Origin and the Curve $r = f(\theta), \alpha \le \theta \le \beta$

$$A = \int_{\alpha}^{\beta} \frac{1}{2} r^2 \, d\theta .$$

This is the integral of the **area differential** (Figure 9.14)

$$dA = \frac{1}{2} r^2 \, d\theta = \frac{1}{2}\left(f(\theta)\right)^2 d\theta .$$

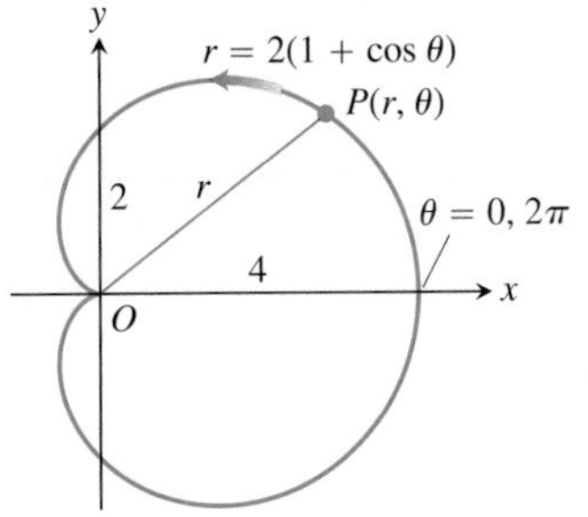

FIGURE 9.15 The cardioid in Example 1.

EXAMPLE 1 Find the area of the region in the plane enclosed by the cardioid $r = 2(1 + \cos\theta)$.

Solution We graph the cardioid (Figure 9.15) and determine that the radius OP sweeps out the region exactly once as θ runs from 0 to 2π. The area is therefore

$$\begin{aligned} \int_{\theta=0}^{\theta=2\pi} \frac{1}{2} r^2 \, d\theta &= \int_0^{2\pi} \frac{1}{2} \cdot 4(1 + \cos\theta)^2 \, d\theta \\ &= \int_0^{2\pi} 2(1 + 2\cos\theta + \cos^2\theta) \, d\theta \\ &= \int_0^{2\pi} \left(2 + 4\cos\theta + 2\,\frac{1 + \cos 2\theta}{2}\right) d\theta \\ &= \int_0^{2\pi} (3 + 4\cos\theta + \cos 2\theta) \, d\theta \\ &= \left[3\theta + 4\sin\theta + \frac{\sin 2\theta}{2}\right]_0^{2\pi} = 6\pi - 0 = 6\pi . \end{aligned}$$

■

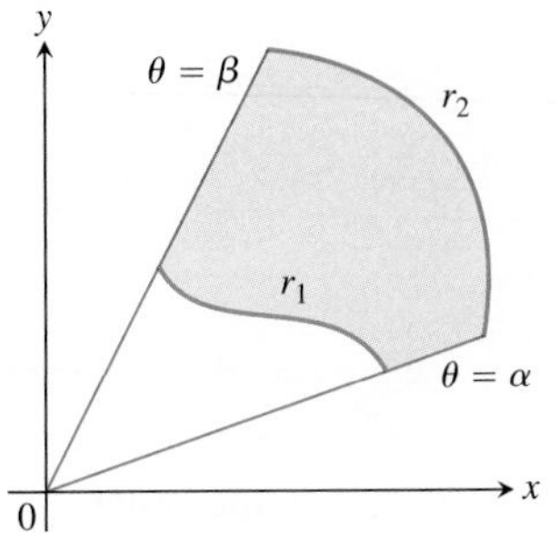

FIGURE 9.16 The area of the shaded region is calculated by subtracting the area of the region between r_1 and the origin from the area of the region between r_2 and the origin.

To find the area of a region like the one in Figure 9.16, which lies between two polar curves $r_1 = r_1(\theta)$ and $r_2 = r_2(\theta)$ from $\theta = \alpha$ to $\theta = \beta$, we subtract the integral of $(1/2)r_1^2 \, d\theta$ from the integral of $(1/2)r_2^2 \, d\theta$. This leads to the following formula.

Area of the Region $0 \le r_1(\theta) \le r \le r_2(\theta), \quad \alpha \le \theta \le \beta$

$$A = \int_{\alpha}^{\beta} \frac{1}{2} r_2^2 \, d\theta - \int_{\alpha}^{\beta} \frac{1}{2} r_1^2 \, d\theta = \int_{\alpha}^{\beta} \frac{1}{2}\left(r_2^2 - r_1^2\right) d\theta \qquad (1)$$

EXAMPLE 2 Find the area of the region that lies inside the circle $r = 1$ and outside the cardioid $r = 1 - \cos\theta$.

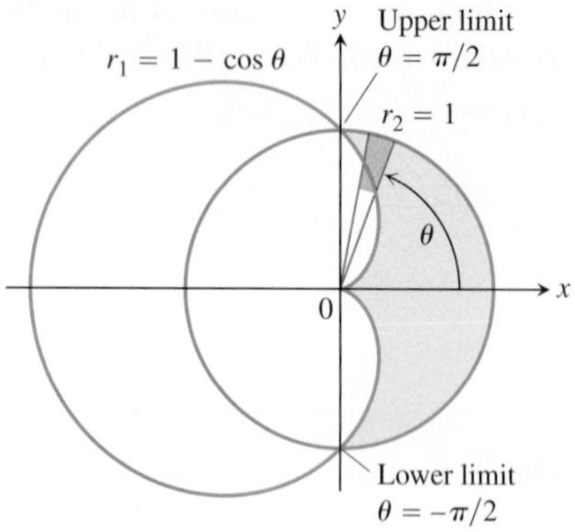

FIGURE 9.17 The region and limits of integration in Example 2.

Solution We sketch the region to determine its boundaries and find the limits of integration (Figure 9.17). The outer curve is $r_2 = 1$, the inner curve is $r_1 = 1 - \cos\theta$, and θ runs from $-\pi/2$ to $\pi/2$. The area, from Equation (1), is

$$\begin{aligned} A &= \int_{-\pi/2}^{\pi/2} \frac{1}{2}\left(r_2^2 - r_1^2\right) d\theta \\ &= 2\int_0^{\pi/2} \frac{1}{2}\left(r_2^2 - r_1^2\right) d\theta \qquad \text{Symmetry} \\ &= \int_0^{\pi/2} (1 - (1 - 2\cos\theta + \cos^2\theta))\, d\theta \\ &= \int_0^{\pi/2} (2\cos\theta - \cos^2\theta)\, d\theta = \int_0^{\pi/2} \left(2\cos\theta - \frac{1 + \cos 2\theta}{2}\right) d\theta \\ &= \left[2\sin\theta - \frac{\theta}{2} - \frac{\sin 2\theta}{4}\right]_0^{\pi/2} = 2 - \frac{\pi}{4}. \end{aligned}$$

■

The fact that we can represent a point in different ways in polar coordinates requires extra care in deciding when a point lies on the graph of a polar equation and in determining the points in which polar graphs intersect. (We needed intersection points in Example 2.) In Cartesian coordinates, we can always find the points where two curves cross by solving their equations simultaneously. In polar coordinates, the story is different. Simultaneous solution may reveal some intersection points without revealing others. One way to identify all the points of intersection is to graph the equations.

Length of a Polar Curve

We can obtain a polar coordinate formula for the length of a curve $r = f(\theta)$, $\alpha \le \theta \le \beta$, by parametrizing the curve as

$$x = r\cos\theta = f(\theta)\cos\theta, \qquad y = r\sin\theta = f(\theta)\sin\theta, \qquad \alpha \le \theta \le \beta. \tag{2}$$

The parametric length formula, Equation (1) from Section 6.3, then gives the length as

$$L = \int_\alpha^\beta \sqrt{\left(\frac{dx}{d\theta}\right)^2 + \left(\frac{dy}{d\theta}\right)^2}\, d\theta.$$

This equation becomes

$$L = \int_\alpha^\beta \sqrt{r^2 + \left(\frac{dr}{d\theta}\right)^2}\, d\theta$$

when Equations (2) are substituted for x and y (Exercise 27).

Length of a Polar Curve
If $r = f(\theta)$ has a continuous first derivative for $\alpha \le \theta \le \beta$ and if the point $P(r, \theta)$ traces the curve $r = f(\theta)$ exactly once as θ runs from α to β, then the length of the curve is

$$L = \int_\alpha^\beta \sqrt{r^2 + \left(\frac{dr}{d\theta}\right)^2}\, d\theta. \tag{3}$$

EXAMPLE 3 Find the length of the cardioid $r = 1 - \cos\theta$.

Solution We sketch the cardioid to determine the limits of integration (Figure 9.18). The point $P(r, \theta)$ traces the curve once, counterclockwise as θ runs from 0 to 2π, so these are the values we take for α and β.

With

$$r = 1 - \cos\theta, \qquad \frac{dr}{d\theta} = \sin\theta,$$

we have

$$r^2 + \left(\frac{dr}{d\theta}\right)^2 = (1 - \cos\theta)^2 + (\sin\theta)^2$$
$$= 1 - 2\cos\theta + \underbrace{\cos^2\theta + \sin^2\theta}_{1} = 2 - 2\cos\theta$$

and

$$L = \int_\alpha^\beta \sqrt{r^2 + \left(\frac{dr}{d\theta}\right)^2}\, d\theta = \int_0^{2\pi} \sqrt{2 - 2\cos\theta}\, d\theta$$
$$= \int_0^{2\pi} \sqrt{4\sin^2\frac{\theta}{2}}\, d\theta \qquad 1 - \cos\theta = 2\sin^2\frac{\theta}{2}$$
$$= \int_0^{2\pi} 2\left|\sin\frac{\theta}{2}\right| d\theta$$
$$= \int_0^{2\pi} 2\sin\frac{\theta}{2}\, d\theta \qquad \sin\frac{\theta}{2} \geq 0 \quad \text{for} \quad 0 \leq \theta \leq 2\pi$$
$$= \left[-4\cos\frac{\theta}{2}\right]_0^{2\pi} = 4 + 4 = 8.$$

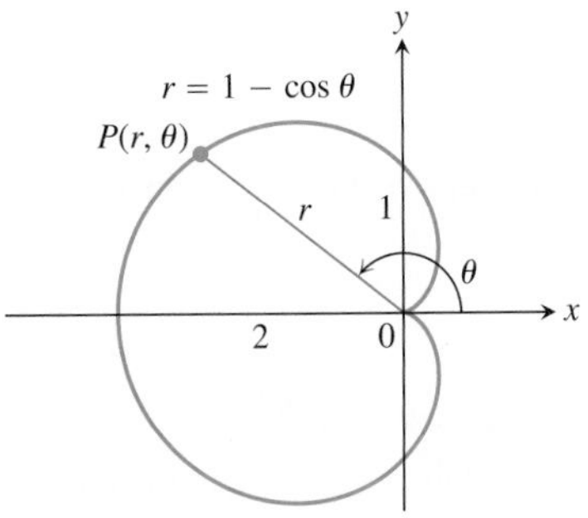

FIGURE 9.18 Calculating the length of a cardioid (Example 3).

EXERCISES 9.3

Find the areas of the regions in Exercises 1–6.

1. Inside the oval limaçon $r = 4 + 2\cos\theta$
2. Inside the cardioid $r = a(1 + \cos\theta)$, $a > 0$
3. Inside one leaf of the four-leaved rose $r = \cos 2\theta$
4. Inside the lemniscate $r^2 = 2a^2\cos 2\theta$, $a > 0$
5. Inside one loop of the lemniscate $r^2 = 4\sin 2\theta$
6. Inside the six-leaved rose $r^2 = 2\sin 3\theta$

Find the areas of the regions in Exercises 7–16.

7. Shared by the circles $r = 2\cos\theta$ and $r = 2\sin\theta$
8. Shared by the circles $r = 1$ and $r = 2\sin\theta$
9. Shared by the circle $r = 2$ and the cardioid $r = 2(1 - \cos\theta)$
10. Shared by the cardioids $r = 2(1 + \cos\theta)$ and $r = 2(1 - \cos\theta)$
11. Inside the lemniscate $r^2 = 6\cos 2\theta$ and outside the circle $r = \sqrt{3}$
12. Inside the circle $r = 3a\cos\theta$ and outside the cardioid $r = a(1 + \cos\theta)$, $a > 0$
13. Inside the circle $r = -2\cos\theta$ and outside the circle $r = 1$
14. Inside the circle $r = 6$ above the line $r = 3\csc\theta$
15. **a.** Find the area of the shaded region in the accompanying figure.

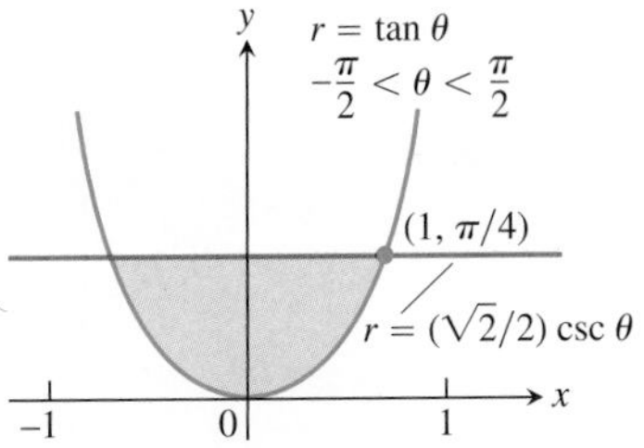

b. It looks as if the graph of $r = \tan\theta$, $-\pi/2 < \theta < \pi/2$, could be asymptotic to the lines $x = 1$ and $x = -1$. Is it? Give reasons for your answer.

16. The area of the region that lies inside the cardioid curve $r = \cos\theta + 1$ and outside the circle $r = \cos\theta$ is not

$$\frac{1}{2}\int_0^{2\pi} [(\cos\theta + 1)^2 - \cos^2\theta]\,d\theta = \pi.$$

Why not? What *is* the area? Give reasons for your answers.

Find the lengths of the curves in Exercises 17–25.

17. The spiral $r = \theta^2, \quad 0 \le \theta \le \sqrt{5}$

18. The spiral $r = e^{\theta}/\sqrt{2}, \quad 0 \le \theta \le \pi$

19. The cardioid $r = 1 + \cos\theta$

20. The curve $r = a\sin^2(\theta/2), \quad 0 \le \theta \le \pi, \quad a > 0$

21. The parabolic segment $r = 6/(1 + \cos\theta), \quad 0 \le \theta \le \pi/2$

22. The parabolic segment $r = 2/(1 - \cos\theta), \quad \pi/2 \le \theta \le \pi$

23. The curve $r = \cos^3(\theta/3), \quad 0 \le \theta \le \pi/4$

24. The curve $r = \sqrt{1 + \sin 2\theta}, \quad 0 \le \theta \le \pi\sqrt{2}$

25. The curve $r = \sqrt{1 + \cos 2\theta}, \quad 0 \le \theta \le \pi\sqrt{2}$

26. Circumferences of circles As usual, when faced with a new formula, it is a good idea to try it on familiar objects to be sure it gives results consistent with past experience. Use the length formula in Equation (3) to calculate the circumferences of the following circles $(a > 0)$:

a. $r = a$ **b.** $r = a\cos\theta$ **c.** $r = a\sin\theta$

27. The length of the curve $r = f(\theta), \alpha \le \theta \le \beta$ Assuming that the necessary derivatives are continuous, show how the substitutions

$$x = f(\theta)\cos\theta, \quad y = f(\theta)\sin\theta$$

(Equations 2 in the text) transform

$$L = \int_\alpha^\beta \sqrt{\left(\frac{dx}{d\theta}\right)^2 + \left(\frac{dy}{d\theta}\right)^2}\,d\theta$$

into

$$L = \int_\alpha^\beta \sqrt{r^2 + \left(\frac{dr}{d\theta}\right)^2}\,d\theta.$$

28. Average value If f is continuous, the average value of the polar coordinate r over the curve $r = f(\theta), \alpha \le \theta \le \beta$, with respect to θ is given by the formula

$$r_{\text{av}} = \frac{1}{\beta - \alpha}\int_\alpha^\beta f(\theta)\,d\theta.$$

Use this formula to find the average value of r with respect to θ over the following curves $(a > 0)$.

a. The cardioid $r = a(1 - \cos\theta)$

b. The circle $r = a$

c. The circle $r = a\cos\theta, \quad -\pi/2 \le \theta \le \pi/2$

29. $r = f(\theta)$ *vs.* $r = 2f(\theta)$ Can anything be said about the relative lengths of the curves $r = f(\theta), \alpha \le \theta \le \beta$, and $r = 2f(\theta), \alpha \le \theta \le \beta$? Give reasons for your answer.

30. $r = f(\theta)$ *vs.* $r = 2f(\theta)$ The curves $r = f(\theta), \alpha \le \theta \le \beta$, and $r = 2f(\theta), \alpha \le \theta \le \beta$, are revolved about the x-axis to generate surfaces. Can anything be said about the relative areas of these surfaces? Give reasons for your answer.

9.4 Conic Sections

In this section we define parabolas, ellipses, and hyperbolas geometrically and derive their standard equations. These curves are called *conic sections* or *conics* because they are formed by cutting a double cone with a plane (Figure 9.19), which is the only way they could be described by Greek mathematicians who did not have our tools of Cartesian or polar coordinates.

Parabolas

DEFINITIONS A set that consists of all the points in a plane equidistant from a given fixed point and a given fixed line in the plane is a **parabola**. The fixed point is the **focus** of the parabola. The fixed line is the **directrix**.

If the focus F lies on the directrix L, the parabola is the line through F perpendicular to L. We consider this to be a degenerate case and assume henceforth that F does not lie on L.

A parabola has its simplest equation when its focus and directrix straddle one of the coordinate axes. For example, suppose that the focus lies at the point $F(0, p)$ on the positive

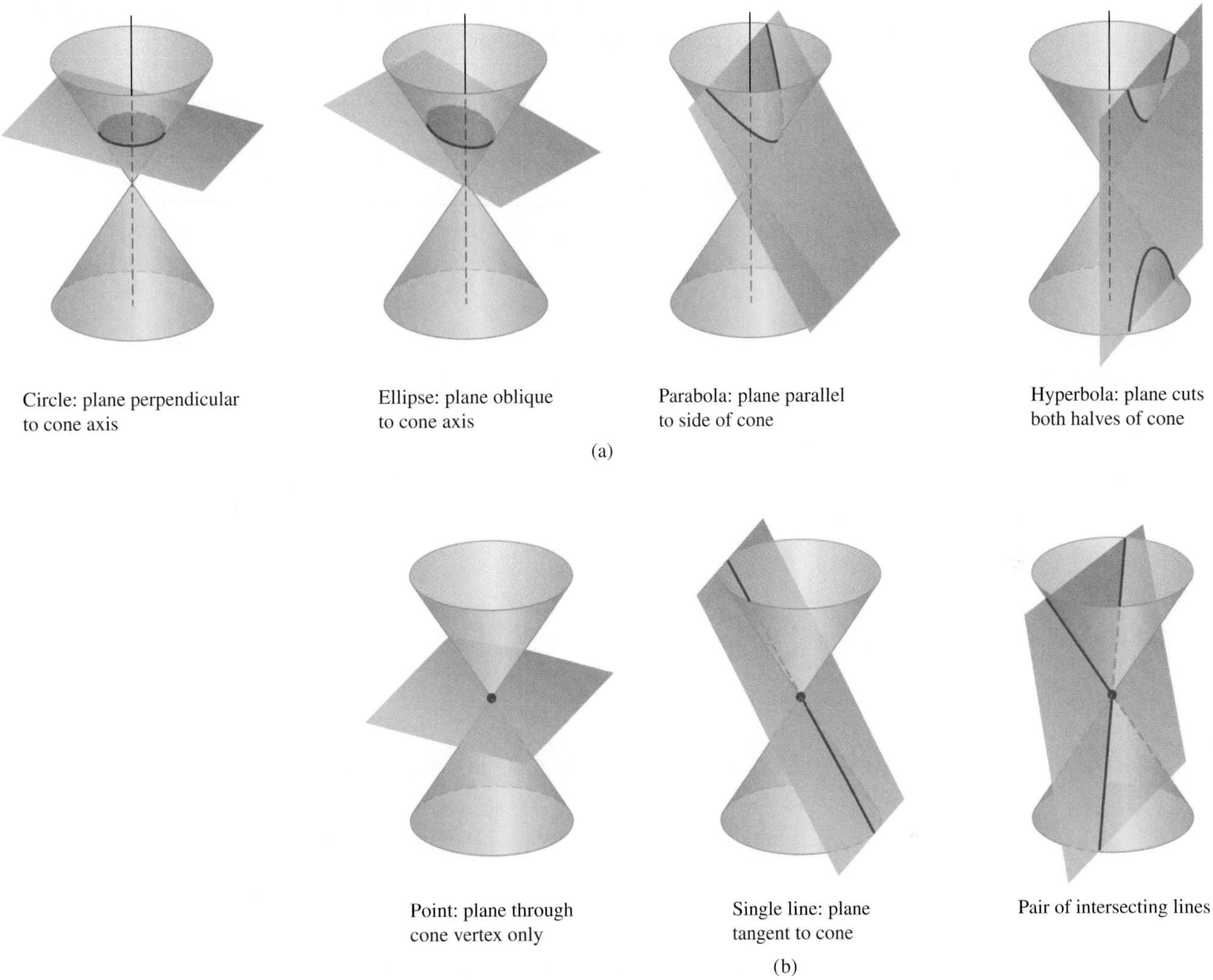

FIGURE 9.19 The standard conic sections (a) are the curves in which a plane cuts a *double* cone. Hyperbolas come in two parts, called *branches*. The point and lines obtained by passing the plane through the cone's vertex (b) are *degenerate* conic sections.

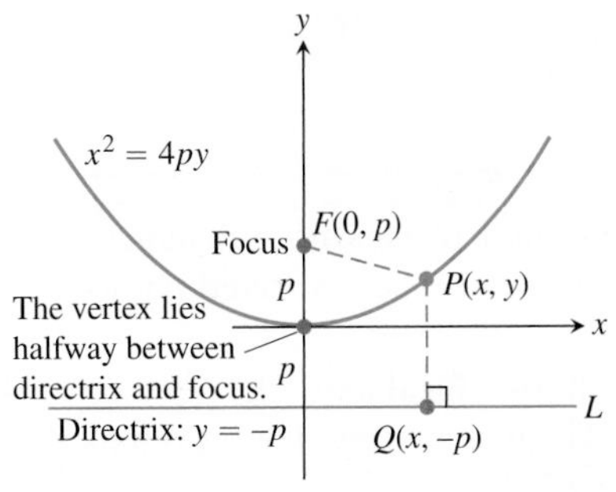

FIGURE 9.20 The standard form of the parabola $x^2 = 4py, p > 0$.

y-axis and that the directrix is the line $y = -p$ (Figure 9.20). In the notation of the figure, a point $P(x, y)$ lies on the parabola if and only if $PF = PQ$. From the distance formula,

$$PF = \sqrt{(x-0)^2 + (y-p)^2} = \sqrt{x^2 + (y-p)^2}$$

$$PQ = \sqrt{(x-x)^2 + (y-(-p))^2} = \sqrt{(y+p)^2}.$$

When we equate these expressions, square, and simplify, we get

$$y = \frac{x^2}{4p} \quad \text{or} \quad x^2 = 4py. \quad \text{Standard form} \tag{1}$$

These equations reveal the parabola's symmetry about the y-axis. We call the y-axis the **axis** of the parabola (short for "axis of symmetry").

The point where a parabola crosses its axis is the **vertex**. The vertex of the parabola $x^2 = 4py$ lies at the origin (Figure 9.20). The positive number p is the parabola's **focal length**.

If the parabola opens downward, with its focus at $(0, -p)$ and its directrix the line $y = p$, then Equations (1) become

$$y = -\frac{x^2}{4p} \qquad \text{and} \qquad x^2 = -4py.$$

By interchanging the variables x and y, we obtain similar equations for parabolas opening to the right or to the left (Figure 9.21).

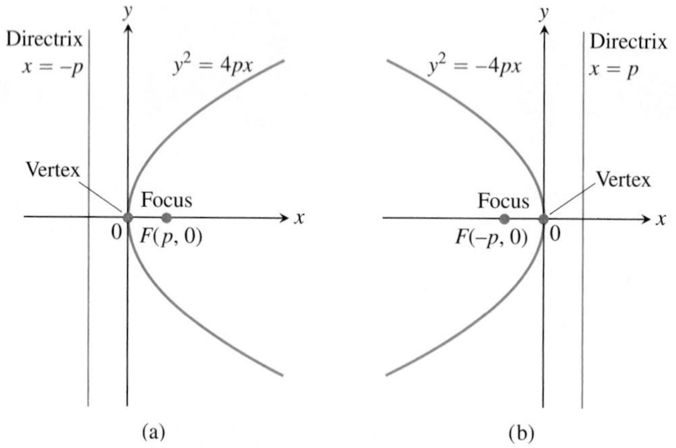

FIGURE 9.21 (a) The parabola $y^2 = 4px$. (b) The parabola $y^2 = -4px$.

EXAMPLE 1 Find the focus and directrix of the parabola $y^2 = 10x$.

Solution We find the value of p in the standard equation $y^2 = 4px$:

$$4p = 10, \qquad \text{so} \qquad p = \frac{10}{4} = \frac{5}{2}.$$

Then we find the focus and directrix for this value of p:

$$\text{Focus:} \qquad (p, 0) = \left(\frac{5}{2}, 0\right)$$

$$\text{Directrix:} \qquad x = -p \qquad \text{or} \qquad x = -\frac{5}{2}.$$

■

Ellipses

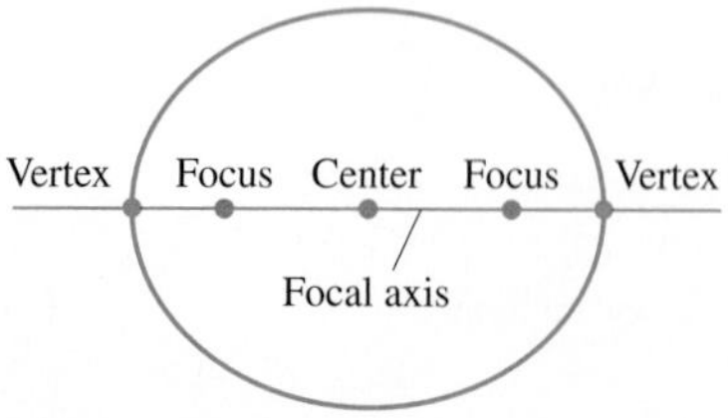

FIGURE 9.22 Points on the focal axis of an ellipse.

DEFINITIONS An **ellipse** is the set of points in a plane whose distances from two fixed points in the plane have a constant sum. The two fixed points are the **foci** of the ellipse.

The line through the foci of an ellipse is the ellipse's **focal axis**. The point on the axis halfway between the foci is the **center**. The points where the focal axis and ellipse cross are the ellipse's **vertices** (Figure 9.22).

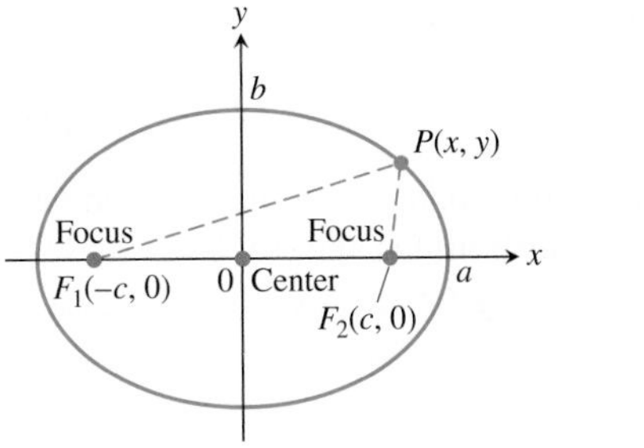

FIGURE 9.23 The ellipse defined by the equation $PF_1 + PF_2 = 2a$ is the graph of the equation $(x^2/a^2) + (y^2/b^2) = 1$, where $b^2 = a^2 - c^2$.

If the foci are $F_1(-c, 0)$ and $F_2(c, 0)$ (Figure 9.23), and $PF_1 + PF_2$ is denoted by $2a$, then the coordinates of a point P on the ellipse satisfy the equation

$$\sqrt{(x+c)^2 + y^2} + \sqrt{(x-c)^2 + y^2} = 2a.$$

To simplify this equation, we move the second radical to the right-hand side, square, isolate the remaining radical, and square again, obtaining

$$\frac{x^2}{a^2} + \frac{y^2}{a^2 - c^2} = 1. \tag{2}$$

Since $PF_1 + PF_2$ is greater than the length F_1F_2 (by the triangle inequality for triangle PF_1F_2), the number $2a$ is greater than $2c$. Accordingly, $a > c$ and the number $a^2 - c^2$ in Equation (2) is positive.

The algebraic steps leading to Equation (2) can be reversed to show that every point P whose coordinates satisfy an equation of this form with $0 < c < a$ also satisfies the equation $PF_1 + PF_2 = 2a$. A point therefore lies on the ellipse if and only if its coordinates satisfy Equation (2).

If

$$b = \sqrt{a^2 - c^2}, \tag{3}$$

then $a^2 - c^2 = b^2$ and Equation (2) takes the form

$$\frac{x^2}{a^2} + \frac{y^2}{b^2} = 1. \tag{4}$$

Equation (4) reveals that this ellipse is symmetric with respect to the origin and both coordinate axes. It lies inside the rectangle bounded by the lines $x = \pm a$ and $y = \pm b$. It crosses the axes at the points $(\pm a, 0)$ and $(0, \pm b)$. The tangents at these points are perpendicular to the axes because

$$\frac{dy}{dx} = -\frac{b^2 x}{a^2 y} \qquad \text{Obtained from Equation (4) by implicit differentiation}$$

is zero if $x = 0$ and infinite if $y = 0$.

The **major axis** of the ellipse in Equation (4) is the line segment of length $2a$ joining the points $(\pm a, 0)$. The **minor axis** is the line segment of length $2b$ joining the points $(0, \pm b)$. The number a itself is the **semimajor axis**, the number b the **semiminor axis**. The number c, found from Equation (3) as

$$c = \sqrt{a^2 - b^2},$$

is the **center-to-focus distance** of the ellipse. If $a = b$, the ellipse is a circle.

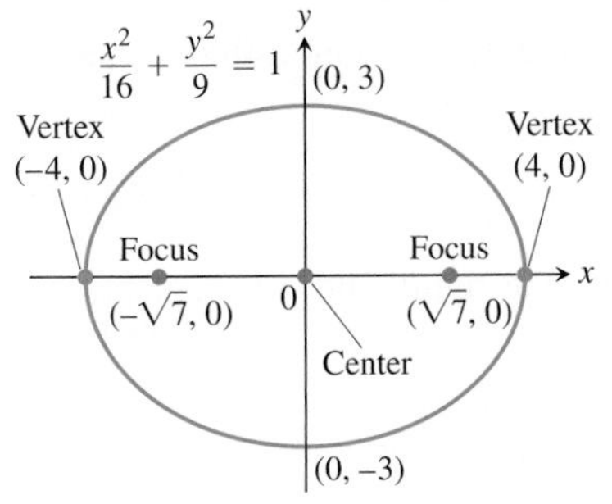

FIGURE 9.24 An ellipse with its major axis horizontal (Example 2).

EXAMPLE 2 The ellipse

$$\frac{x^2}{16} + \frac{y^2}{9} = 1 \tag{5}$$

(Figure 9.24) has

Semimajor axis: $a = \sqrt{16} = 4$, Semiminor axis: $b = \sqrt{9} = 3$

Center-to-focus distance: $c = \sqrt{16 - 9} = \sqrt{7}$

Foci: $(\pm c, 0) = \left(\pm\sqrt{7}, 0\right)$

Vertices: $(\pm a, 0) = (\pm 4, 0)$

Center: $(0, 0)$. ■

If we interchange x and y in Equation (5), we have the equation

$$\frac{x^2}{9} + \frac{y^2}{16} = 1 \tag{6}$$

The major axis of this ellipse is now vertical instead of horizontal, with the foci and vertices on the y-axis. There is no confusion in analyzing Equations (5) and (6). If we find the intercepts on the coordinate axes, we will know which way the major axis runs because it is the longer of the two axes.

Standard-Form Equations for Ellipses Centered at the Origin

Foci on the x-axis: $\frac{x^2}{a^2} + \frac{y^2}{b^2} = 1 \quad (a > b)$

Center-to-focus distance: $c = \sqrt{a^2 - b^2}$

Foci: $(\pm c, 0)$

Vertices: $(\pm a, 0)$

Foci on the y-axis: $\frac{x^2}{b^2} + \frac{y^2}{a^2} = 1 \quad (a > b)$

Center-to-focus distance: $c = \sqrt{a^2 - b^2}$

Foci: $(0, \pm c)$

Vertices: $(0, \pm a)$

In each case, a is the semimajor axis and b is the semiminor axis.

Hyperbolas

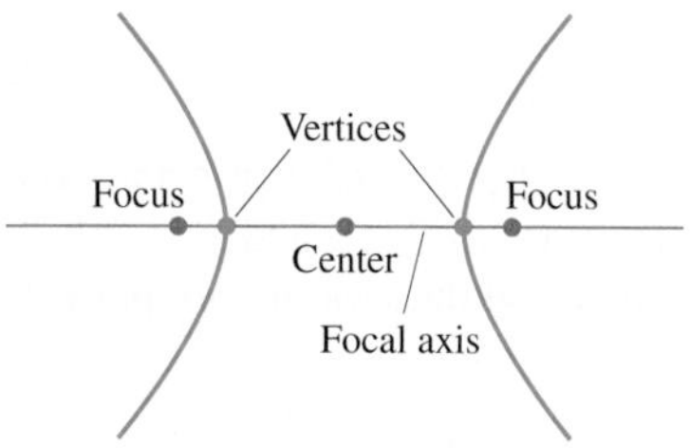

FIGURE 9.25 Points on the focal axis of a hyperbola.

DEFINITIONS A **hyperbola** is the set of points in a plane whose distances from two fixed points in the plane have a constant difference. The two fixed points are the **foci** of the hyperbola.

The line through the foci of a hyperbola is the **focal axis**. The point on the axis halfway between the foci is the hyperbola's **center**. The points where the focal axis and hyperbola cross are the **vertices** (Figure 9.25).

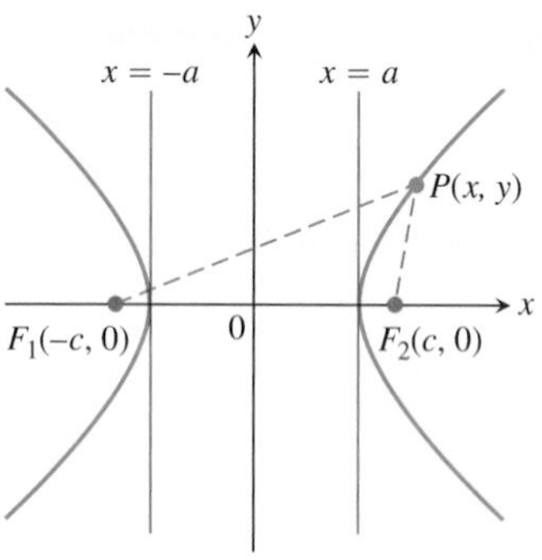

FIGURE 9.26 Hyperbolas have two branches. For points on the right-hand branch of the hyperbola shown here, $PF_1 - PF_2 = 2a$. For points on the left-hand branch, $PF_2 - PF_1 = 2a$. We then let $b = \sqrt{c^2 - a^2}$.

If the foci are $F_1(-c, 0)$ and $F_2(c, 0)$ (Figure 9.26) and the constant difference is $2a$, then a point (x, y) lies on the hyperbola if and only if

$$\sqrt{(x + c)^2 + y^2} - \sqrt{(x - c)^2 + y^2} = \pm 2a. \tag{7}$$

To simplify this equation, we move the second radical to the right-hand side, square, isolate the remaining radical, and square again, obtaining

$$\frac{x^2}{a^2} + \frac{y^2}{a^2 - c^2} = 1. \tag{8}$$

So far, this looks just like the equation for an ellipse. But now $a^2 - c^2$ is negative because $2a$, being the difference of two sides of triangle PF_1F_2, is less than $2c$, the third side.

The algebraic steps leading to Equation (8) can be reversed to show that every point P whose coordinates satisfy an equation of this form with $0 < a < c$ also satisfies Equation (7). A point therefore lies on the hyperbola if and only if its coordinates satisfy Equation (8).

If we let b denote the positive square root of $c^2 - a^2$,

$$b = \sqrt{c^2 - a^2}, \tag{9}$$

then $a^2 - c^2 = -b^2$ and Equation (8) takes the more compact form

$$\frac{x^2}{a^2} - \frac{y^2}{b^2} = 1. \tag{10}$$

The differences between Equation (10) and the equation for an ellipse (Equation 4) are the minus sign and the new relation

$$c^2 = a^2 + b^2. \quad \text{From Equation (9)}$$

Like the ellipse, the hyperbola is symmetric with respect to the origin and coordinate axes. It crosses the x-axis at the points $(\pm a, 0)$. The tangents at these points are vertical because

$$\frac{dy}{dx} = \frac{b^2 x}{a^2 y} \quad \text{Obtained from Equation (10) by implicit differentiation}$$

is infinite when $y = 0$. The hyperbola has no y-intercepts; in fact, no part of the curve lies between the lines $x = -a$ and $x = a$.

The lines

$$y = \pm\frac{b}{a}x$$

are the two **asymptotes** of the hyperbola defined by Equation (10). The fastest way to find the equations of the asymptotes is to replace the 1 in Equation (10) by 0 and solve the new equation for y:

$$\underbrace{\frac{x^2}{a^2} - \frac{y^2}{b^2} = 1}_{\text{hyperbola}} \rightarrow \underbrace{\frac{x^2}{a^2} - \frac{y^2}{b^2} = 0}_{\text{0 for 1}} \rightarrow \underbrace{y = \pm\frac{b}{a}x.}_{\text{asymptotes}}$$

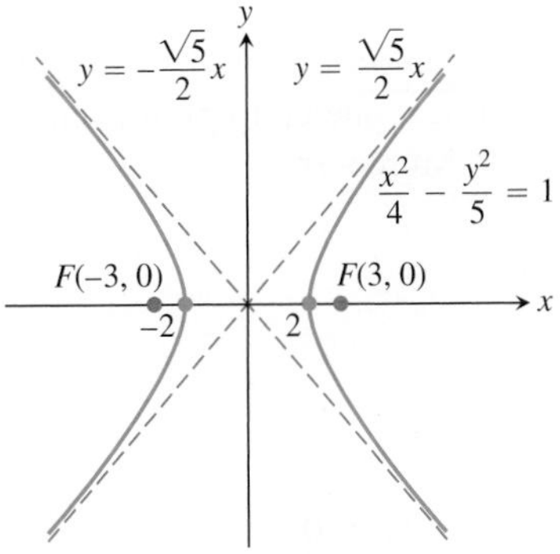

FIGURE 9.27 The hyperbola and its asymptotes in Example 3.

EXAMPLE 3 The equation

$$\frac{x^2}{4} - \frac{y^2}{5} = 1 \tag{11}$$

is Equation (10) with $a^2 = 4$ and $b^2 = 5$ (Figure 9.27). We have

Center-to-focus distance: $c = \sqrt{a^2 + b^2} = \sqrt{4 + 5} = 3$

Foci: $(\pm c, 0) = (\pm 3, 0)$, Vertices: $(\pm a, 0) = (\pm 2, 0)$

Center: $(0, 0)$

Asymptotes: $\frac{x^2}{4} - \frac{y^2}{5} = 0$ or $y = \pm\frac{\sqrt{5}}{2}x.$ ■

If we interchange x and y in Equation (11), the foci and vertices of the resulting hyperbola will lie along the y-axis. We still find the asymptotes in the same way as before, but now their equations will be $y = \pm 2x/\sqrt{5}$.

Standard-Form Equations for Hyperbolas Centered at the Origin

Foci on the x-axis: $\dfrac{x^2}{a^2} - \dfrac{y^2}{b^2} = 1$

Center-to-focus distance: $c = \sqrt{a^2 + b^2}$

Foci: $(\pm c, 0)$

Vertices: $(\pm a, 0)$

Asymptotes: $\dfrac{x^2}{a^2} - \dfrac{y^2}{b^2} = 0$ or $y = \pm \dfrac{b}{a} x$

Foci on the y-axis: $\dfrac{y^2}{a^2} - \dfrac{x^2}{b^2} = 1$

Center-to-focus distance: $c = \sqrt{a^2 + b^2}$

Foci: $(0, \pm c)$

Vertices: $(0, \pm a)$

Asymptotes: $\dfrac{y^2}{a^2} - \dfrac{x^2}{b^2} = 0$ or $y = \pm \dfrac{a}{b} x$

Notice the difference in the asymptote equations (b/a in the first, a/b in the second).

We shift conics using the principles reviewed in Section 1.2 replacing x by $x + h$ and y by $y + k$.

EXAMPLE 4 Show that the equation $x^2 - 4y^2 + 2x + 8y - 7 = 0$ represents a hyperbola. Find its center, asymptotes, and foci.

Solution We reduce the equation to standard form by completing the square in x and y as follows:

$$(x^2 + 2x) - 4(y^2 - 2y) = 7$$

$$(x^2 + 2x + 1) - 4(y^2 - 2y + 1) = 7 + 1 - 4$$

$$\frac{(x + 1)^2}{4} - (y - 1)^2 = 1.$$

This is the standard form Equation (10) of a hyperbola with x replaced by $x + 1$ and y replaced by $y - 1$. The hyperbola is shifted one unit to the left and one unit upward, and it has center $x + 1 = 0$ and $y - 1 = 0$, or $x = -1$ and $y = 1$. Moreover,

$$a^2 = 4, \quad b^2 = 1, \quad c^2 = a^2 + b^2 = 5$$

so the asymptotes are the two lines

$$\frac{x + 1}{2} - (y - 1) = 0 \quad \text{and} \quad \frac{x + 1}{2} + (y - 1) = 0.$$

The shifted foci have coordinates $\left(-1 \pm \sqrt{5}, 1\right)$. ■

EXERCISES 9.4

Match the parabolas in Exercises 1–4 with the following equations:

$$x^2 = 2y, \quad x^2 = -6y, \quad y^2 = 8x, \quad y^2 = -4x.$$

Then find the parabola's focus and directrix.

1.

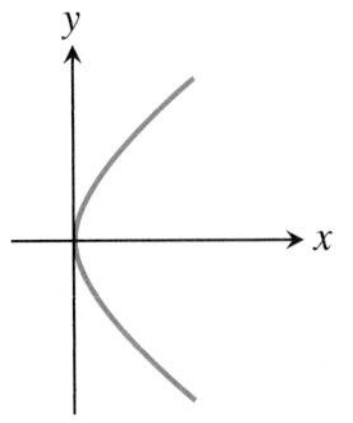

2.

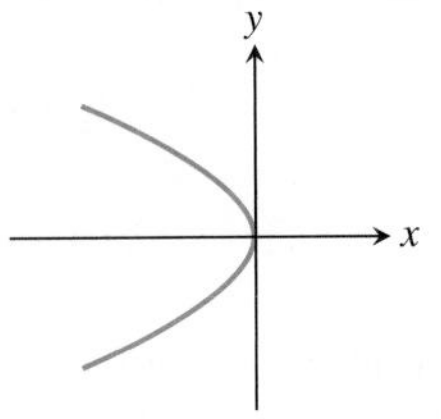

3.

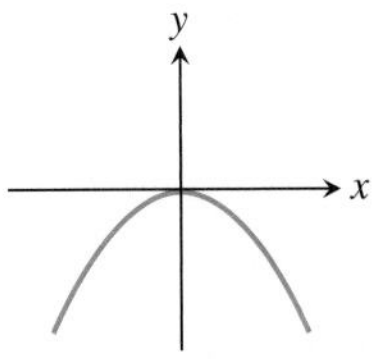

4.

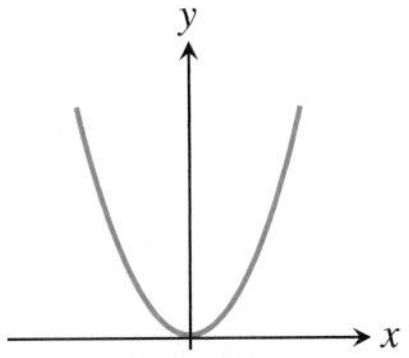

Match each conic section in Exercises 5–8 with one of these equations:

$$\frac{x^2}{4} + \frac{y^2}{9} = 1, \qquad \frac{x^2}{2} + y^2 = 1,$$

$$\frac{y^2}{4} - x^2 = 1, \qquad \frac{x^2}{4} - \frac{y^2}{9} = 1.$$

Then find the conic section's foci and vertices. If the conic section is a hyperbola, find its asymptotes as well.

5.

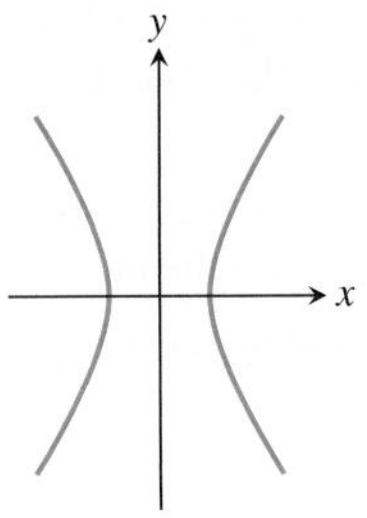

6.

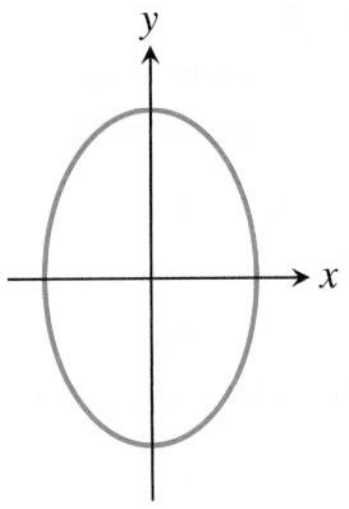

7.

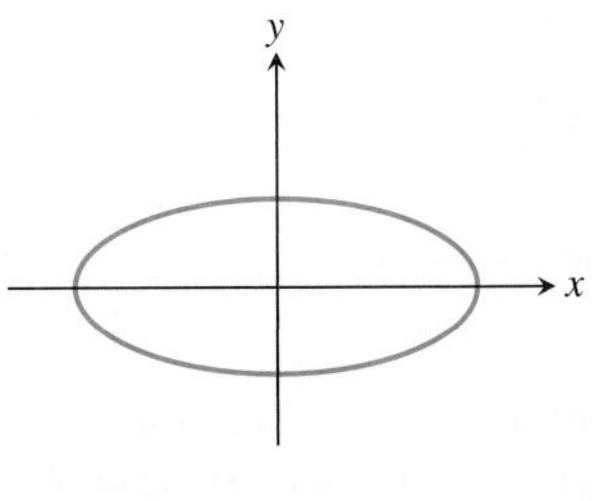

8.

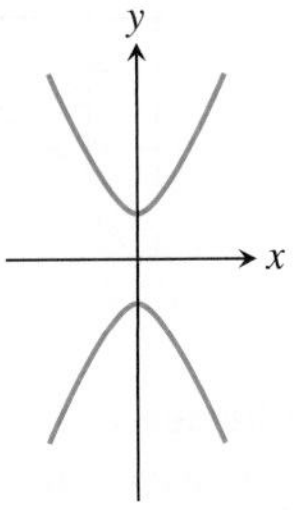

Exercises 9–16 give equations of parabolas. Find each parabola's focus and directrix. Then sketch the parabola. Include the focus and directrix in your sketch.

9. $y^2 = 12x$ **10.** $x^2 = 6y$ **11.** $x^2 = -8y$

12. $y^2 = -2x$ **13.** $y = 4x^2$ **14.** $y = -8x^2$

15. $x = -3y^2$ **16.** $x = 2y^2$

Exercises 17–24 give equations for ellipses. Put each equation in standard form. Then sketch the ellipse. Include the foci in your sketch.

17. $16x^2 + 25y^2 = 400$ **18.** $7x^2 + 16y^2 = 112$

19. $2x^2 + y^2 = 2$ **20.** $2x^2 + y^2 = 4$

21. $3x^2 + 2y^2 = 6$ **22.** $9x^2 + 10y^2 = 90$

23. $6x^2 + 9y^2 = 54$ **24.** $169x^2 + 25y^2 = 4225$

Exercises 25 and 26 give information about the foci and vertices of ellipses centered at the origin of the *xy*-plane. In each case, find the ellipse's standard-form equation from the given information.

25. Foci: $\left(\pm\sqrt{2}, 0\right)$ Vertices: $(\pm 2, 0)$

26. Foci: $(0, \pm 4)$ Vertices: $(0, \pm 5)$

Exercises 27–34 give equations for hyperbolas. Put each equation in standard form and find the hyperbola's asymptotes. Then sketch the hyperbola. Include the asymptotes and foci in your sketch.

27. $x^2 - y^2 = 1$ **28.** $9x^2 - 16y^2 = 144$

29. $y^2 - x^2 = 8$ **30.** $y^2 - x^2 = 4$

31. $8x^2 - 2y^2 = 16$ **32.** $y^2 - 3x^2 = 3$

33. $8y^2 - 2x^2 = 16$ **34.** $64x^2 - 36y^2 = 2304$

Exercises 35–38 give information about the foci, vertices, and asymptotes of hyperbolas centered at the origin of the *xy*-plane. In each case, find the hyperbola's standard-form equation from the information given.

35. Foci: $\left(0, \pm\sqrt{2}\right)$
Asymptotes: $y = \pm x$

36. Foci: $(\pm 2, 0)$
Asymptotes: $y = \pm\frac{1}{\sqrt{3}}x$

37. Vertices: $(\pm 3, 0)$
Asymptotes: $y = \pm\frac{4}{3}x$

38. Vertices: $(0, \pm 2)$
Asymptotes: $y = \pm\frac{1}{2}x$

You may wish to review Section 1.2 before solving Exercises 39–56.

39. The parabola $y^2 = 8x$ is shifted down 2 units and right 1 unit to generate the parabola $(y + 2)^2 = 8(x - 1)$.

a. Find the new parabola's vertex, focus, and directrix.

b. Plot the new vertex, focus, and directrix, and sketch in the parabola.

40. The parabola $x^2 = -4y$ is shifted left 1 unit and up 3 units to generate the parabola $(x + 1)^2 = -4(y - 3)$.

a. Find the new parabola's vertex, focus, and directrix.

b. Plot the new vertex, focus, and directrix, and sketch in the parabola.

41. The ellipse $(x^2/16) + (y^2/9) = 1$ is shifted 4 units to the right and 3 units up to generate the ellipse

$$\frac{(x-4)^2}{16} + \frac{(y-3)^2}{9} = 1.$$

a. Find the foci, vertices, and center of the new ellipse.

b. Plot the new foci, vertices, and center, and sketch in the new ellipse.

42. The ellipse $(x^2/9) + (y^2/25) = 1$ is shifted 3 units to the left and 2 units down to generate the ellipse

$$\frac{(x+3)^2}{9} + \frac{(y+2)^2}{25} = 1.$$

a. Find the foci, vertices, and center of the new ellipse.

b. Plot the new foci, vertices, and center, and sketch in the new ellipse.

43. The hyperbola $(x^2/16) - (y^2/9) = 1$ is shifted 2 units to the right to generate the hyperbola

$$\frac{(x-2)^2}{16} - \frac{y^2}{9} = 1.$$

a. Find the center, foci, vertices, and asymptotes of the new hyperbola.

b. Plot the new center, foci, vertices, and asymptotes, and sketch in the hyperbola.

44. The hyperbola $(y^2/4) - (x^2/5) = 1$ is shifted 2 units down to generate the hyperbola

$$\frac{(y+2)^2}{4} - \frac{x^2}{5} = 1.$$

a. Find the center, foci, vertices, and asymptotes of the new hyperbola.

b. Plot the new center, foci, vertices, and asymptotes, and sketch in the hyperbola.

Exercises 45–48 give equations for parabolas and tell how many units up or down and to the right or left each parabola is to be shifted. Find an equation for the new parabola, and find the new vertex, focus, and directrix.

45. $y^2 = 4x$, left 2, down 3

46. $y^2 = -12x$, right 4, up 3

47. $x^2 = 8y$, right 1, down 7

48. $x^2 = 6y$, left 3, down 2

Exercises 49–52 give equations for ellipses and tell how many units up or down and to the right or left each ellipse is to be shifted. Find an equation for the new ellipse, and find the new foci, vertices, and center.

49. $\frac{x^2}{6} + \frac{y^2}{9} = 1$, left 2, down 1

50. $\frac{x^2}{2} + y^2 = 1$, right 3, up 4

51. $\frac{x^2}{3} + \frac{y^2}{2} = 1$, right 2, up 3

52. $\frac{x^2}{16} + \frac{y^2}{25} = 1$, left 4, down 5

Exercises 53–56 give equations for hyperbolas and tell how many units up or down and to the right or left each hyperbola is to be shifted. Find an equation for the new hyperbola, and find the new center, foci, vertices, and asymptotes.

53. $\frac{x^2}{4} - \frac{y^2}{5} = 1$, right 2, up 2

54. $\frac{x^2}{16} - \frac{y^2}{9} = 1$, left 2, down 1

55. $y^2 - x^2 = 1$, left 1, down 1

56. $\frac{y^2}{3} - x^2 = 1$, right 1, up 3

Find the center, foci, vertices, asymptotes, and radius, as appropriate, of the conic sections in Exercises 57–68.

57. $x^2 + 4x + y^2 = 12$

58. $2x^2 + 2y^2 - 28x + 12y + 114 = 0$

59. $x^2 + 2x + 4y - 3 = 0$

60. $y^2 - 4y - 8x - 12 = 0$

61. $x^2 + 5y^2 + 4x = 1$

62. $9x^2 + 6y^2 + 36y = 0$

63. $x^2 + 2y^2 - 2x - 4y = -1$

64. $4x^2 + y^2 + 8x - 2y = -1$

65. $x^2 - y^2 - 2x + 4y = 4$

66. $x^2 - y^2 + 4x - 6y = 6$

67. $2x^2 - y^2 + 6y = 3$

68. $y^2 - 4x^2 + 16x = 24$

69. If lines are drawn parallel to the coordinate axes through a point P on the parabola $y^2 = kx$, $k > 0$, the parabola partitions the rectangular region bounded by these lines and the coordinate axes into two smaller regions, A and B.

a. If the two smaller regions are revolved about the y-axis, show that they generate solids whose volumes have the ratio 4:1.

b. What is the ratio of the volumes generated by revolving the regions about the x-axis?

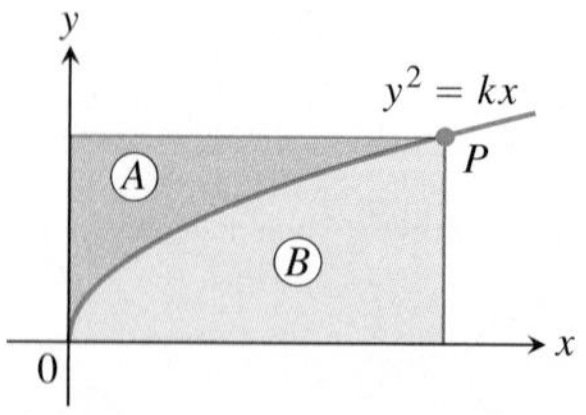

70. Suspension bridge cables hang in parabolas The suspension bridge cable shown on the next page supports a uniform load of w pounds per horizontal foot. It can be shown that if H is the horizontal tension of the cable at the origin, then the curve of the cable satisfies the equation

$$\frac{dy}{dx} = \frac{w}{H}x.$$

Show that the cable hangs in a parabola by solving this differential equation subject to the initial condition that $y = 0$ when $x = 0$.

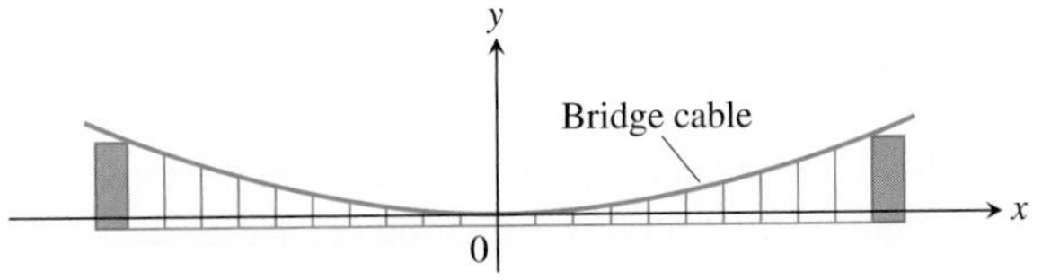

71. The width of a parabola at the focus Show that the number $4p$ is the *width* of the parabola $x^2 = 4py\ (p > 0)$ at the focus by showing that the line $y = p$ cuts the parabola at points that are $4p$ units apart.

72. The asymptotes of $(x^2/a^2) - (y^2/b^2) = 1$ Show that the vertical distance between the line $y = (b/a)x$ and the upper half of the right-hand branch $y = (b/a)\sqrt{x^2 - a^2}$ of the hyperbola $(x^2/a^2) - (y^2/b^2) = 1$ approaches 0 by showing that

$$\lim_{x\to\infty}\left(\frac{b}{a}x - \frac{b}{a}\sqrt{x^2 - a^2}\right) = \frac{b}{a}\lim_{x\to\infty}\left(x - \sqrt{x^2 - a^2}\right) = 0.$$

Similar results hold for the remaining portions of the hyperbola and the lines $y = \pm(b/a)x$.

73. Find the dimensions of the rectangle of largest area that can be inscribed in the ellipse $x^2 + 4y^2 = 4$ with its sides parallel to the coordinate axes. What is the area of the rectangle?

74. Find the volume of the solid generated by revolving the region enclosed by the ellipse $9x^2 + 4y^2 = 36$ about the **(a)** x-axis, **(b)** y-axis.

75. The "triangular" region in the first quadrant bounded by the x-axis, the line $x = 4$, and the hyperbola $9x^2 - 4y^2 = 36$ is revolved about the x-axis to generate a solid. Find the volume of the solid.

76. Show that the tangents to the curve $y^2 = 4px$ from any point on the line $x = -p$ are perpendicular.

9.5 Conics in Polar Coordinates

Polar coordinates are important in astronomy and astronautical engineering because satellites, moons, planets, and comets all move approximately along ellipses, parabolas, and hyperbolas that can be described with a single relatively simple polar coordinate equation. We develop that equation here after first introducing the idea of a conic section's *eccentricity*. The eccentricity reveals the conic section's type (circle, ellipse, parabola, or hyperbola), and the degree to which it is "squashed" or flattened.

Eccentricity

Although the center-to-focus distance c does not appear in the equation

$$\frac{x^2}{a^2} + \frac{y^2}{b^2} = 1, \qquad (a > b)$$

for an ellipse, we can still determine c from the equation $c = \sqrt{a^2 - b^2}$. If we fix a and vary c over the interval $0 \le c \le a$, the resulting ellipses will vary in shape. They are circles if $c = 0$ (so that $a = b$) and flatten as c increases. If $c = a$, the foci and vertices overlap and the ellipse degenerates into a line segment. Thus we are led to consider the ratio $e = c/a$. We use this ratio for hyperbolas as well, only in this case c equals $\sqrt{a^2 + b^2}$ instead of $\sqrt{a^2 - b^2}$, and define these ratios with the somewhat familiar term *eccentricity*.

DEFINITION

The **eccentricity** of the ellipse $(x^2/a^2) + (y^2/b^2) = 1\ (a > b)$ is

$$e = \frac{c}{a} = \frac{\sqrt{a^2 - b^2}}{a}.$$

The **eccentricity** of the hyperbola $(x^2/a^2) - (y^2/b^2) = 1$ is

$$e = \frac{c}{a} = \frac{\sqrt{a^2 + b^2}}{a}.$$

The **eccentricity** of a parabola is $e = 1$.

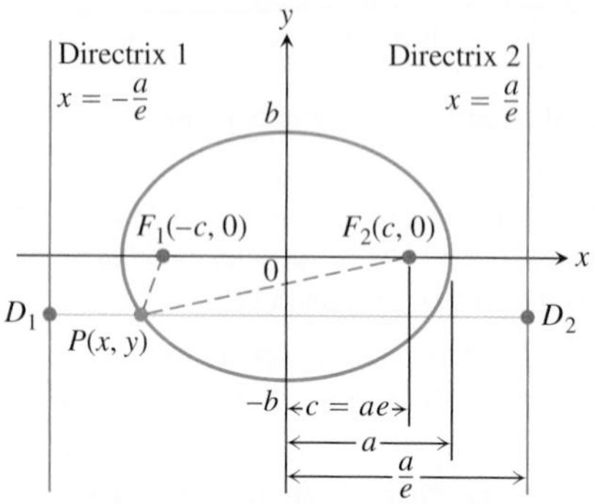

FIGURE 9.28 The foci and directrices of the ellipse $(x^2/a^2) + (y^2/b^2) = 1$. Directrix 1 corresponds to focus F_1, and directrix 2 to focus F_2.

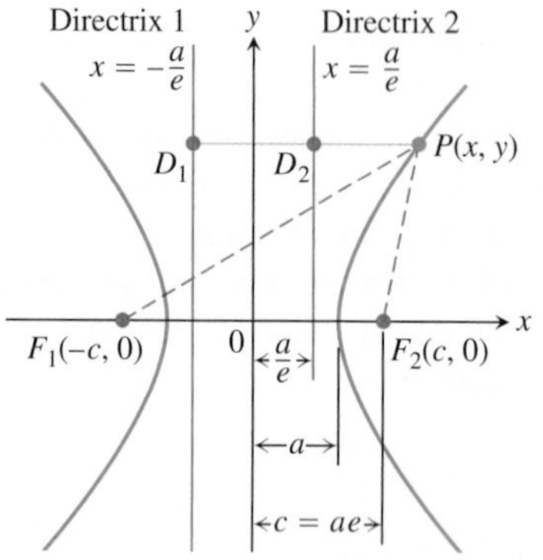

FIGURE 9.29 The foci and directrices of the hyperbola $(x^2/a^2) - (y^2/b^2) = 1$. No matter where P lies on the hyperbola, $PF_1 = e \cdot PD_1$ and $PF_2 = e \cdot PD_2$.

Whereas a parabola has one focus and one directrix, each **ellipse** has two foci and two **directrices**. These are the lines perpendicular to the major axis at distances $\pm a/e$ from the center. The parabola has the property that

$$PF = 1 \cdot PD \tag{1}$$

for any point P on it, where F is the focus and D is the point nearest P on the directrix. For an ellipse, it can be shown that the equations that replace Equation (1) are

$$PF_1 = e \cdot PD_1, \qquad PF_2 = e \cdot PD_2. \tag{2}$$

Here, e is the eccentricity, P is any point on the ellipse, F_1 and F_2 are the foci, and D_1 and D_2 are the points on the directrices nearest P (Figure 9.28).

In both Equations (2) the directrix and focus must correspond; that is, if we use the distance from P to F_1, we must also use the distance from P to the directrix at the same end of the ellipse. The directrix $x = -a/e$ corresponds to $F_1(-c, 0)$, and the directrix $x = a/e$ corresponds to $F_2(c, 0)$.

As with the ellipse, it can be shown that the lines $x = \pm a/e$ act as **directrices** for the **hyperbola** and that

$$PF_1 = e \cdot PD_1 \quad \text{and} \quad PF_2 = e \cdot PD_2. \tag{3}$$

Here P is any point on the hyperbola, F_1 and F_2 are the foci, and D_1 and D_2 are the points nearest P on the directrices (Figure 9.29).

In both the ellipse and the hyperbola, the eccentricity is the ratio of the distance between the foci to the distance between the vertices (because $c/a = 2c/2a$).

$$\text{Eccentricity} = \frac{\text{distance between foci}}{\text{distance between vertices}}$$

In an ellipse, the foci are closer together than the vertices and the ratio is less than 1. In a hyperbola, the foci are farther apart than the vertices and the ratio is greater than 1.

The "focus–directrix" equation $PF = e \cdot PD$ unites the parabola, ellipse, and hyperbola in the following way. Suppose that the distance PF of a point P from a fixed point F (the focus) is a constant multiple of its distance from a fixed line (the directrix). That is, suppose

$$PF = e \cdot PD, \tag{4}$$

where e is the constant of proportionality. Then the path traced by P is

(a) a *parabola* if $e = 1$,

(b) an *ellipse* of eccentricity e if $e < 1$, and

(c) a *hyperbola* of eccentricity e if $e > 1$.

There are no coordinates in Equation (4) and when we try to translate it into coordinate form it translates in different ways, depending on the size of e. At least, that is what happens in Cartesian coordinates. However, as we will see, in polar coordinates the equation $PF = e \cdot PD$ translates into a single equation regardless of the value of e.

Given the focus and corresponding directrix of a hyperbola centered at the origin and with foci on the x-axis, we can use the dimensions shown in Figure 9.29 to find e. Knowing

e, we can derive a Cartesian equation for the hyperbola from the equation $PF = e \cdot PD$, as in the next example. We can find equations for ellipses centered at the origin and with foci on the x-axis in a similar way, using the dimensions shown in Figure 9.28.

EXAMPLE 1 Find a Cartesian equation for the hyperbola centered at the origin that has a focus at (3, 0) and the line $x = 1$ as the corresponding directrix.

Solution We first use the dimensions shown in Figure 9.29 to find the hyperbola's eccentricity. The focus is

$$(c, 0) = (3, 0) \quad \text{so} \quad c = 3.$$

The directrix is the line

$$x = \frac{a}{e} = 1, \quad \text{so} \quad a = e.$$

When combined with the equation $e = c/a$ that defines eccentricity, these results give

$$e = \frac{c}{a} = \frac{3}{e}, \quad \text{so} \quad e^2 = 3 \quad \text{and} \quad e = \sqrt{3}.$$

Knowing e, we can now derive the equation we want from the equation $PF = e \cdot PD$. In the notation of Figure 9.30, we have

$$PF = e \cdot PD \qquad \text{Equation (4)}$$

$$\sqrt{(x-3)^2 + (y-0)^2} = \sqrt{3}\,|x - 1| \qquad e = \sqrt{3}$$

$$x^2 - 6x + 9 + y^2 = 3(x^2 - 2x + 1)$$

$$2x^2 - y^2 = 6$$

$$\frac{x^2}{3} - \frac{y^2}{6} = 1.$$

■

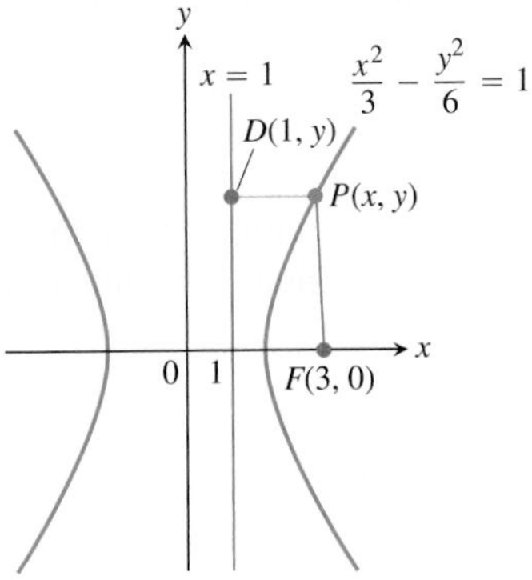

FIGURE 9.30 The hyperbola and directrix in Example 1.

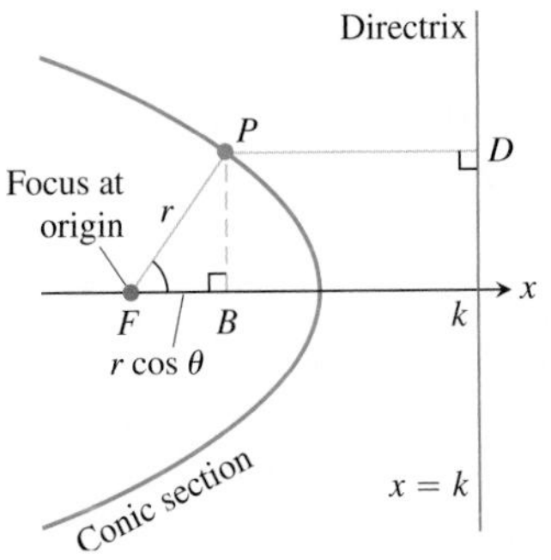

FIGURE 9.31 If a conic section is put in the position with its focus placed at the origin and a directrix perpendicular to the initial ray and right of the origin, we can find its polar equation from the conic's focus–directrix equation.

Polar Equations

To find polar equations for ellipses, parabolas, and hyperbolas, we place one focus at the origin and the corresponding directrix to the right of the origin along the vertical line $x = k$ (Figure 9.31). This makes

$$PF = r$$

and

$$PD = k - FB = k - r\cos\theta.$$

The conic's focus–directrix equation $PF = e \cdot PD$ then becomes

$$r = e(k - r\cos\theta),$$

which can be solved for r to obtain the following expression.

Polar Equation for a Conic with Eccentricity e

$$r = \frac{ke}{1 + e\cos\theta}, \qquad (5)$$

where $x = k > 0$ is the vertical directrix.

EXAMPLE 2 Here are polar equations for three conics.

$$e = \frac{1}{2}: \quad \text{ellipse} \quad r = \frac{k}{2 + \cos\theta}$$

$$e = 1: \quad \text{parabola} \quad r = \frac{k}{1 + \cos\theta}$$

$$e = 2: \quad \text{hyperbola} \quad r = \frac{2k}{1 + 2\cos\theta}$$

■

You may see variations of Equation (5), depending on the location of the directrix. If the directrix is the line $x = -k$ to the left of the origin (the origin is still a focus), we replace Equation (5) by

$$r = \frac{ke}{1 - e\cos\theta}.$$

The denominator now has a $(-)$ instead of a $(+)$. If the directrix is either of the lines $y = k$ or $y = -k$, the equations have sines in them instead of cosines, as shown in Figure 9.32.

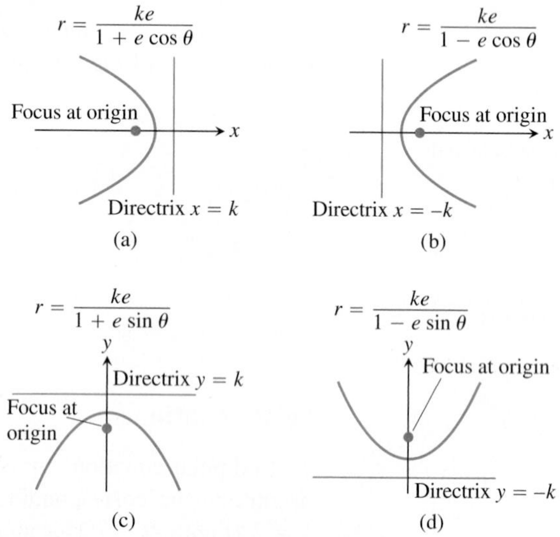

FIGURE 9.32 Equations for conic sections with eccentricity $e > 0$, but different locations of the directrix. The graphs here show a parabola, so $e = 1$.

EXAMPLE 3 Find an equation for the hyperbola with eccentricity $3/2$ and directrix $x = 2$.

Solution We use Equation (5) with $k = 2$ and $e = 3/2$:

$$r = \frac{2(3/2)}{1 + (3/2)\cos\theta} \quad \text{or} \quad r = \frac{6}{2 + 3\cos\theta}.$$

■

EXAMPLE 4 Find the directrix of the parabola

$$r = \frac{25}{10 + 10\cos\theta}.$$

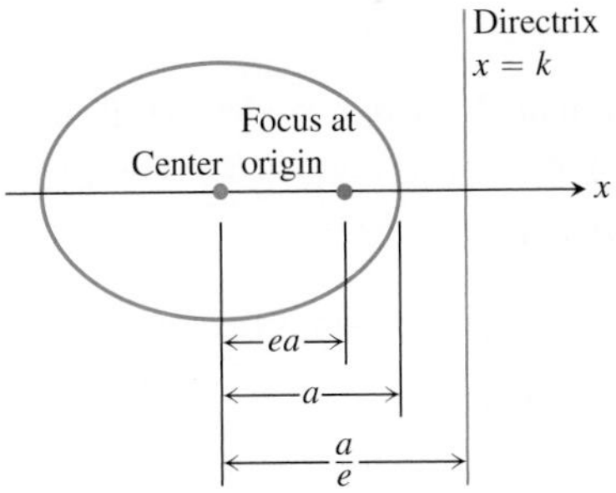

FIGURE 9.33 In an ellipse with semimajor axis a, the focus–directrix distance is $k = (a/e) - ea$, so $ke = a(1 - e^2)$.

Solution We divide the numerator and denominator by 10 to put the equation in standard polar form:

$$r = \frac{5/2}{1 + \cos\theta}.$$

This is the equation

$$r = \frac{ke}{1 + e\cos\theta}$$

with $k = 5/2$ and $e = 1$. The equation of the directrix is $x = 5/2$. ■

From the ellipse diagram in Figure 9.33, we see that k is related to the eccentricity e and the semimajor axis a by the equation

$$k = \frac{a}{e} - ea.$$

From this, we find that $ke = a(1 - e^2)$. Replacing ke in Equation (5) by $a(1 - e^2)$ gives the standard polar equation for an ellipse.

Polar Equation for the Ellipse with Eccentricity e and Semimajor Axis a

$$r = \frac{a(1 - e^2)}{1 + e\cos\theta} \qquad (6)$$

Notice that when $e = 0$, Equation (6) becomes $r = a$, which represents a circle.

Lines

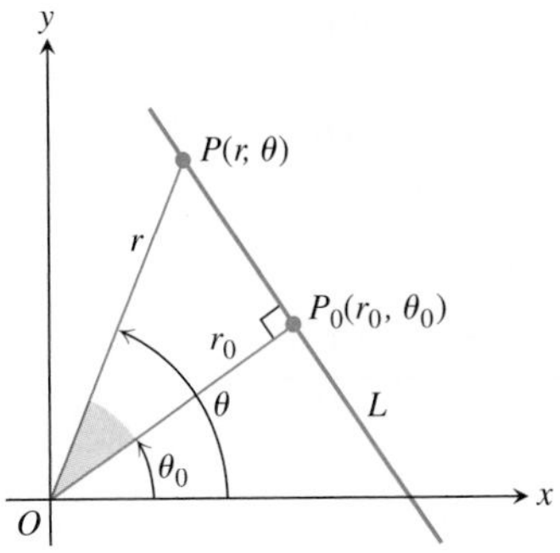

FIGURE 9.34 We can obtain a polar equation for line L by reading the relation $r_0 = r\cos(\theta - \theta_0)$ from the right triangle OP_0P.

Suppose the perpendicular from the origin to line L meets L at the point $P_0(r_0, \theta_0)$, with $r_0 \geq 0$ (Figure 9.34). Then, if $P(r, \theta)$ is any other point on L, the points P, P_0, and O are the vertices of a right triangle, from which we can read the relation

$$r_0 = r\cos(\theta - \theta_0).$$

The Standard Polar Equation for Lines

If the point $P_0(r_0, \theta_0)$ is the foot of the perpendicular from the origin to the line L, and $r_0 \geq 0$, then an equation for L is

$$r\cos(\theta - \theta_0) = r_0. \qquad (7)$$

For example, if $\theta_0 = \pi/3$, we find that

$$r\cos\left(\theta - \frac{\pi}{3}\right) = 2$$

$$r\left(\cos\theta\cos\frac{\pi}{3} + \sin\theta\sin\frac{\pi}{3}\right) = 2$$

$$\frac{1}{2}r\cos\theta + \frac{\sqrt{3}}{2}r\sin\theta = 2, \qquad \text{or} \qquad x + \sqrt{3}\,y = 4.$$

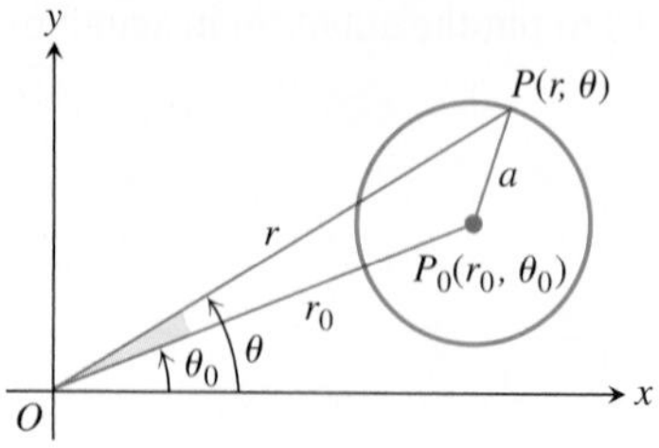

FIGURE 9.35 We can get a polar equation for this circle by applying the Law of Cosines to triangle OP_0P.

Circles

To find a polar equation for the circle of radius a centered at $P_0(r_0, \theta_0)$, we let $P(r, \theta)$ be a point on the circle and apply the Law of Cosines to triangle OP_0P (Figure 9.35). This gives

$$a^2 = r_0^2 + r^2 - 2r_0 r\cos(\theta - \theta_0).$$

If the circle passes through the origin, then $r_0 = a$ and this equation simplifies to

$$a^2 = a^2 + r^2 - 2ar\cos(\theta - \theta_0)$$
$$r^2 = 2ar\cos(\theta - \theta_0)$$
$$r = 2a\cos(\theta - \theta_0).$$

If the circle's center lies on the positive x-axis, $\theta_0 = 0$ and we get the further simplification

$$r = 2a\cos\theta. \tag{8}$$

If the center lies on the positive y-axis, $\theta = \pi/2$, $\cos(\theta - \pi/2) = \sin\theta$, and the equation $r = 2a\cos(\theta - \theta_0)$ becomes

$$r = 2a\sin\theta. \tag{9}$$

Equations for circles through the origin centered on the negative x- and y-axes can be obtained by replacing r with $-r$ in the above equations.

EXAMPLE 5 Here are several polar equations for circles through the origin.

Radius	Center (polar coordinates)	Polar equation
3	$(3, 0)$	$r = 6\cos\theta$
2	$(2, \pi/2)$	$r = 4\sin\theta$
1/2	$(-1/2, 0)$	$r = -\cos\theta$
1	$(-1, \pi/2)$	$r = -2\sin\theta$

EXERCISES 9.5

In Exercises 1–8, find the eccentricity of the ellipse. Then find and graph the ellipse's foci and directrices.

1. $16x^2 + 25y^2 = 400$
2. $7x^2 + 16y^2 = 112$
3. $2x^2 + y^2 = 2$
4. $2x^2 + y^2 = 4$
5. $3x^2 + 2y^2 = 6$
6. $9x^2 + 10y^2 = 90$
7. $6x^2 + 9y^2 = 54$
8. $169x^2 + 25y^2 = 4225$

Exercises 9–12 give the foci or vertices and the eccentricities of ellipses centered at the origin of the xy-plane. In each case, find the ellipse's standard-form equation in Cartesian coordinates.

9. Foci: $(0, \pm 3)$
   Eccentricity: 0.5
10. Foci: $(\pm 8, 0)$
    Eccentricity: 0.2
11. Vertices: $(0, \pm 70)$
    Eccentricity: 0.1
12. Vertices: $(\pm 10, 0)$
    Eccentricity: 0.24

Exercises 13–16 give foci and corresponding directrices of ellipses centered at the origin of the xy-plane. In each case, use the dimensions in Figure 9.28 to find the eccentricity of the ellipse. Then find the ellipse's standard-form equation in Cartesian coordinates.

13. Focus: $\left(\sqrt{5}, 0\right)$
    Directrix: $x = \dfrac{9}{\sqrt{5}}$
14. Focus: $(4, 0)$
    Directrix: $x = \dfrac{16}{3}$
15. Focus: $(-4, 0)$
    Directrix: $x = -16$
16. Focus: $\left(-\sqrt{2}, 0\right)$
    Directrix: $x = -2\sqrt{2}$

In Exercises 17–24, find the eccentricity of the hyperbola. Then find and graph the hyperbola's foci and directrices.

17. $x^2 - y^2 = 1$ **18.** $9x^2 - 16y^2 = 144$

19. $y^2 - x^2 = 8$ **20.** $y^2 - x^2 = 4$

21. $8x^2 - 2y^2 = 16$ **22.** $y^2 - 3x^2 = 3$

23. $8y^2 - 2x^2 = 16$ **24.** $64x^2 - 36y^2 = 2304$

Exercises 25–28 give the eccentricities and the vertices or foci of hyperbolas centered at the origin of the xy-plane. In each case, find the hyperbola's standard-form equation in Cartesian coordinates.

25. Eccentricity: 3
Vertices: $(0, \pm 1)$

26. Eccentricity: 2
Vertices: $(\pm 2, 0)$

27. Eccentricity: 3
Foci: $(\pm 3, 0)$

28. Eccentricity: 1.25
Foci: $(0, \pm 5)$

Exercises 29–36 give the eccentricities of conic sections with one focus at the origin, along with the directrix corresponding to that focus. Find a polar equation for each conic section.

29. $e = 1, \quad x = 2$ **30.** $e = 1, \quad y = 2$

31. $e = 5, \quad y = -6$ **32.** $e = 2, \quad x = 4$

33. $e = 1/2, \quad x = 1$ **34.** $e = 1/4, \quad x = -2$

35. $e = 1/5, \quad y = -10$ **36.** $e = 1/3, \quad y = 6$

Sketch the parabolas and ellipses in Exercises 37–44. Include the directrix that corresponds to the focus at the origin. Label the vertices with appropriate polar coordinates. Label the centers of the ellipses as well.

37. $r = \dfrac{1}{1 + \cos\theta}$ **38.** $r = \dfrac{6}{2 + \cos\theta}$

39. $r = \dfrac{25}{10 - 5\cos\theta}$ **40.** $r = \dfrac{4}{2 - 2\cos\theta}$

41. $r = \dfrac{400}{16 + 8\sin\theta}$ **42.** $r = \dfrac{12}{3 + 3\sin\theta}$

43. $r = \dfrac{8}{2 - 2\sin\theta}$ **44.** $r = \dfrac{4}{2 - \sin\theta}$

Sketch the lines in Exercises 45–48 and find Cartesian equations for them.

45. $r\cos\left(\theta - \dfrac{\pi}{4}\right) = \sqrt{2}$ **46.** $r\cos\left(\theta + \dfrac{3\pi}{4}\right) = 1$

47. $r\cos\left(\theta - \dfrac{2\pi}{3}\right) = 3$ **48.** $r\cos\left(\theta + \dfrac{\pi}{3}\right) = 2$

Find a polar equation in the form $r\cos(\theta - \theta_0) = r_0$ for each of the lines in Exercises 49–52.

49. $\sqrt{2}x + \sqrt{2}y = 6$ **50.** $\sqrt{3}x - y = 1$

51. $y = -5$ **52.** $x = -4$

Sketch the circles in Exercises 53–56. Give polar coordinates for their centers and identify their radii.

53. $r = 4\cos\theta$ **54.** $r = 6\sin\theta$

55. $r = -2\cos\theta$ **56.** $r = -8\sin\theta$

Find polar equations for the circles in Exercises 57–64. Sketch each circle in the coordinate plane and label it with both its Cartesian and polar equations.

57. $(x - 6)^2 + y^2 = 36$ **58.** $(x + 2)^2 + y^2 = 4$

59. $x^2 + (y - 5)^2 = 25$ **60.** $x^2 + (y + 7)^2 = 49$

61. $x^2 + 2x + y^2 = 0$ **62.** $x^2 - 16x + y^2 = 0$

63. $x^2 + y^2 + y = 0$ **64.** $x^2 + y^2 - \dfrac{4}{3}y = 0$

T Graph the lines and conic sections in Exercises 65–74.

65. $r = 3\sec(\theta - \pi/3)$ **66.** $r = 4\sec(\theta + \pi/6)$

67. $r = 4\sin\theta$ **68.** $r = -2\cos\theta$

69. $r = 8/(4 + \cos\theta)$ **70.** $r = 8/(4 + \sin\theta)$

71. $r = 1/(1 - \sin\theta)$ **72.** $r = 1/(1 + \cos\theta)$

73. $r = 1/(1 + 2\sin\theta)$ **74.** $r = 1/(1 + 2\cos\theta)$

75. Perihelion and aphelion A planet travels about its sun in an ellipse whose semimajor axis has length a. (See accompanying figure.)

a. Show that $r = a(1 - e)$ when the planet is closest to the sun and that $r = a(1 + e)$ when the planet is farthest from the sun.

b. Use the data in the table in Exercise 76 to find how close each planet in our solar system comes to the sun and how far away each planet gets from the sun.

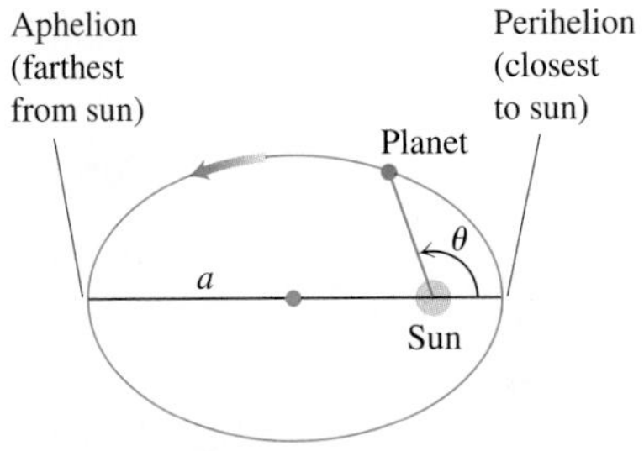

76. Planetary orbits Use the data in the table below and Equation (6) to find polar equations for the orbits of the planets.

Planet	Semimajor axis (astronomical units)	Eccentricity
Mercury	0.3871	0.2056
Venus	0.7233	0.0068
Earth	1.000	0.0167
Mars	1.524	0.0934
Jupiter	5.203	0.0484
Saturn	9.539	0.0543
Uranus	19.18	0.0460
Neptune	30.06	0.0082
Pluto	39.44	0.2481

For example, the orbit of Pluto is

$$r = \frac{39.44(1 - (0.25)^2)}{1 + 0.25\cos\theta} = \frac{147.9}{4 + \cos\theta}$$

In Exercises 77–80, find a polar equation for the given curve. In each case, sketch a typical curve.

77. $x^2 + y^2 - 2ay = 0$

78. $y^2 = 4ax + 4a^2$

79. $x \cos \alpha + y \sin \alpha = p \quad (\alpha, p \text{ constant})$

80. $(x^2 + y^2)^2 + 2ax(x^2 + y^2) - a^2y^2 = 0$

COMPUTER EXPLORATIONS

81. Use a CAS to plot the polar equation

$$r = \frac{ke}{1 + e \cos \theta}$$

for various values of k and e, $-\pi \leq \theta \leq \pi$. Answer the following questions.

a. Take $k = -2$. Describe what happens to the plots as you take e to be $3/4$, 1, and $5/4$. Repeat for $k = 2$.

b. Take $k = -1$. Describe what happens to the plots as you take e to be $7/6$, $5/4$, $4/3$, $3/2$, 2, 3, 5, 10, and 20. Repeat for $e = 1/2$, $1/3$, $1/4$, $1/10$, and $1/20$.

c. Now keep $e > 0$ fixed and describe what happens as you take k to be $-1, -2, -3, -4$, and -5. Be sure to look at graphs for parabolas, ellipses, and hyperbolas.

82. Use a CAS to plot the polar ellipse

$$r = \frac{a(1 - e^2)}{1 + e \cos \theta}$$

for various values of $a > 0$ and $0 < e < 1$, $-\pi \leq \theta \leq \pi$.

a. Take $e = 9/10$. Describe what happens to the plots as you let a equal 1, $3/2$, 2, 3, 5, and 10. Repeat with $e = 1/4$.

b. Take $a = 2$. Describe what happens as you take e to be $9/10$, $8/10$, $7/10$, $\ldots$, $1/10$, $1/20$, and $1/50$.

9.6 Conics and Parametric Equations; The Cycloid

Curves in the Cartesian plane defined by parametric equations, and the calculation of their derivatives, were introduced in Section 3.5. There we studied parametrizations of lines, circles, and ellipses. In this section we discuss parametrization of other plane curves, including parabolas, hyperbolas, cycloids, brachistocrones, and tautocrones.

Parabolas and Hyperbolas

In Section 3.5 we used the parametrization

$$x = \sqrt{t}, \qquad y = t, \qquad t \geq 0$$

to describe the motion of a particle moving along the right branch of the parabola $y = x^2$. In the following example we obtain a parametrization of the entire parabola, not just its right branch.

EXAMPLE 1 The position $P(x, y)$ of a particle moving in the xy-plane is given by the equations and parameter interval

$$x = t, \qquad y = t^2, \qquad -\infty < t < \infty.$$

Identify the particle's path and describe the motion.

Solution We identify the path by eliminating t between the equations $x = t$ and $y = t^2$, obtaining

$$y = (t)^2 = x^2.$$

The particle's position coordinates satisfy the equation $y = x^2$, so the particle moves along this curve.

In contrast to Example 10 in Section 3.5, the particle now traverses the entire parabola. As t increases from $-\infty$ to ∞, the particle comes down the left-hand side, passes through the origin, and moves up the right-hand side (Figure 9.36). ■

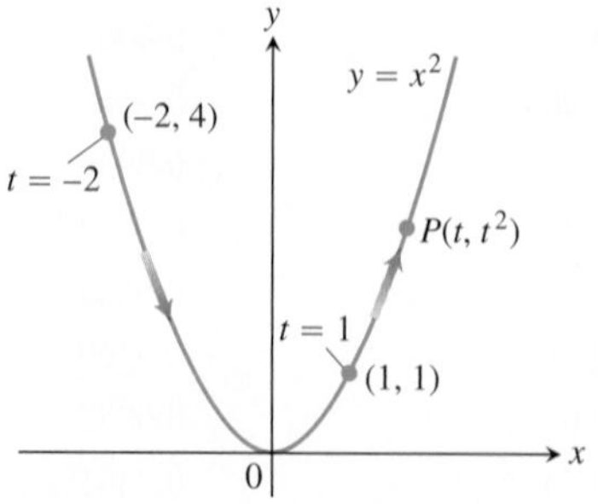

FIGURE 9.36 The path defined by $x = t, y = t^2, -\infty < t < \infty$ is the entire parabola $y = x^2$ (Example 1).

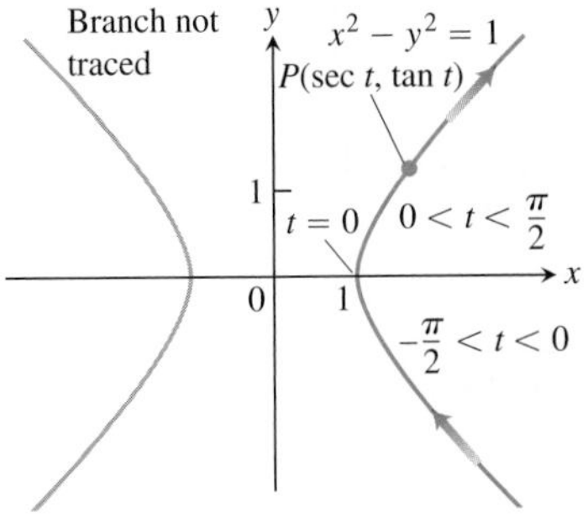

FIGURE 9.37 The equations $x = \sec t, y = \tan t$ and interval $-\pi/2 < t < \pi/2$ describe the right-hand branch of the hyperbola $x^2 - y^2 = 1$ (Example 2).

As Example 1 illustrates, any curve $y = f(x)$ has the parametrization $x = t, y = f(t)$. This is so simple we usually do not use it, but the point of view is occasionally helpful.

EXAMPLE 2 Describe the motion of the particle whose position $P(x, y)$ at time t is given by

$$x = \sec t, \qquad y = \tan t, \qquad -\frac{\pi}{2} < t < \frac{\pi}{2}.$$

Solution We find a Cartesian equation for the coordinates of P by eliminating t between the equations

$$\sec t = x, \qquad \tan t = y.$$

We accomplish this with the identity $\sec^2 t - \tan^2 t = 1$, which yields

$$x^2 - y^2 = 1.$$

Since the particle's coordinates (x, y) satisfy the equation $x^2 - y^2 = 1$, the motion takes place somewhere on this hyperbola. As t runs between $-\pi/2$ and $\pi/2$, $x = \sec t$ remains positive and $y = \tan t$ runs between $-\infty$ and ∞, so P traverses the hyperbola's right-hand branch. It comes in along the branch's lower half as $t \to 0^-$, reaches $(1, 0)$ at $t = 0$, and moves out into the first quadrant as t increases toward $\pi/2$ (Figure 9.37). ■

HISTORICAL BIOGRAPHY

Christiaan Huygens (1629–1695)

Cycloids

The problem with a pendulum clock whose bob swings in a circular arc is that the frequency of the swing depends on the amplitude of the swing. The wider the swing, the longer it takes the bob to return to center (its lowest position).

This does not happen if the bob can be made to swing in a *cycloid*. In 1673, Christiaan Huygens designed a pendulum clock whose bob would swing in a cycloid, a curve we define in Example 3. He hung the bob from a fine wire constrained by guards that caused it to draw up as it swung away from center (Figure 9.38).

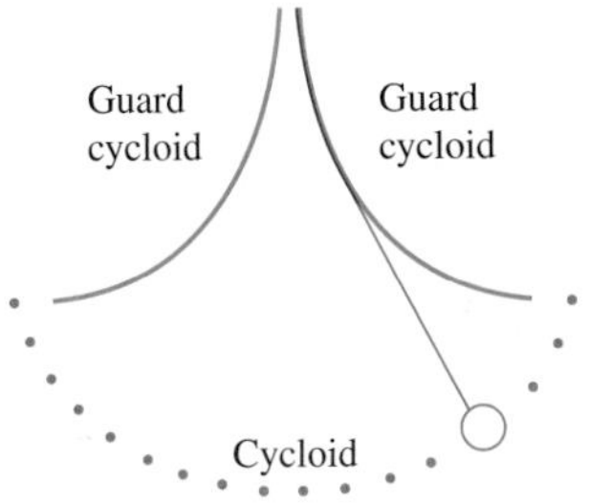

FIGURE 9.38 In Huygens' pendulum clock, the bob swings in a cycloid, so the frequency is independent of the amplitude.

EXAMPLE 3 A wheel of radius a rolls along a horizontal straight line. Find parametric equations for the path traced by a point P on the wheel's circumference. The path is called a **cycloid**.

Solution We take the line to be the x-axis, mark a point P on the wheel, start the wheel with P at the origin, and roll the wheel to the right. As parameter, we use the angle t through which the wheel turns, measured in radians. Figure 9.39 shows the wheel a short while later, when its base lies at units from the origin. The wheel's center C lies at (at, a) and the coordinates of P are

$$x = at + a\cos\theta, \qquad y = a + a\sin\theta.$$

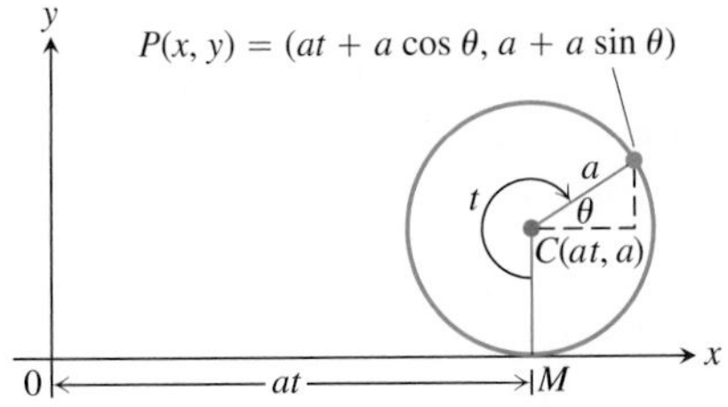

FIGURE 9.39 The position of $P(x, y)$ on the rolling wheel at angle t (Example 3).

To express θ in terms of t, we observe that $t + \theta = 3\pi/2$ in the figure, so that

$$\theta = \frac{3\pi}{2} - t.$$

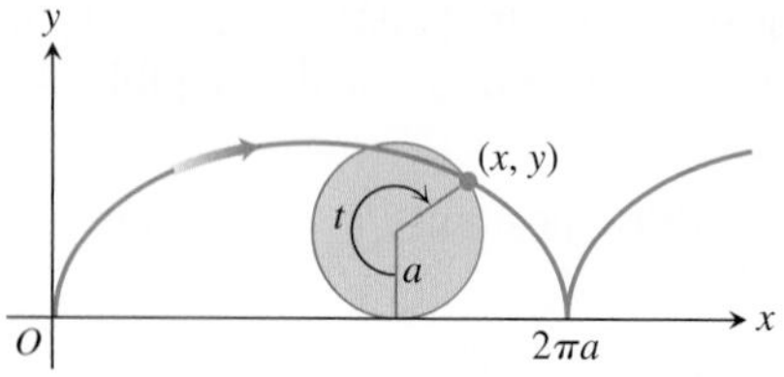

FIGURE 9.40 The cycloid $x = a(t - \sin t), y = a(1 - \cos t)$, for $t \geq 0$.

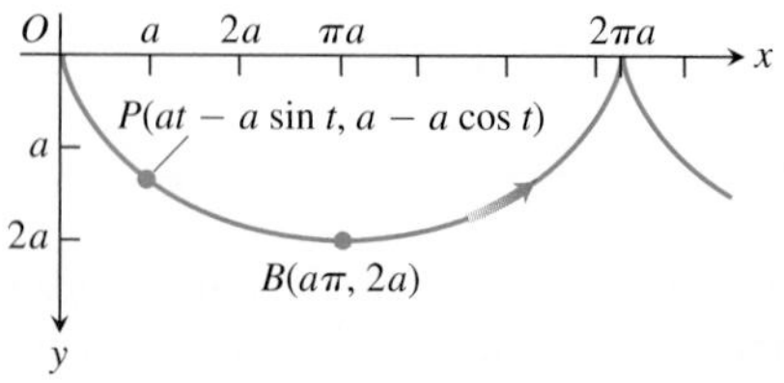

FIGURE 9.41 To study motion along an upside-down cycloid under the influence of gravity, we turn Figure 9.40 upside down. This points the y-axis in the direction of the gravitational force and makes the downward y-coordinates positive. The equations and parameter interval for the cycloid are still

$$x = a(t - \sin t),$$
$$y = a(1 - \cos t), \quad t \geq 0.$$

The arrow shows the direction of increasing t.

This makes

$$\cos\theta = \cos\left(\frac{3\pi}{2} - t\right) = -\sin t, \qquad \sin\theta = \sin\left(\frac{3\pi}{2} - t\right) = -\cos t.$$

The equations we seek are

$$x = at - a\sin t, \qquad y = a - a\cos t.$$

These are usually written with the a factored out:

$$x = a(t - \sin t), \qquad y = a(1 - \cos t). \tag{1}$$

Figure 9.40 shows the first arch of the cycloid and part of the next. ■

Brachistochrones and Tautochrones

If we turn Figure 9.40 upside down, Equations (1) still apply and the resulting curve (Figure 9.41) has two interesting physical properties. The first relates to the origin O and the point B at the bottom of the first arch. Among all smooth curves joining these points, the cycloid is the curve along which a frictionless bead, subject only to the force of gravity, will slide from O to B the fastest. This makes the cycloid a **brachistochrone** ("brah-*kiss*-toe-krone"), or shortest time curve for these points. The second property is that even if you start the bead partway down the curve toward B, it will still take the bead the same amount of time to reach B. This makes the cycloid a **tautochrone** ("*taw*-toe-krone"), or same-time curve for O and B. It can be shown that the cycloid from O to B is the one and only brachistochrone for O and B. We omit the argument here.

EXERCISE 9.6

Exercises 1–12 give parametric equations and parameter intervals for the motion of a particle in the xy-plane. Identify the particle's path by finding a Cartesian equation for it. Graph the Cartesian equation. (The graphs will vary with the equation used.) Indicate the portion of the graph traced by the particle and the direction of motion.

1. $x = \cos t, \quad y = \sin t, \quad 0 \leq t \leq \pi$
2. $x = \sin(2\pi(1 - t)), \quad y = \cos(2\pi(1 - t)); \quad 0 \leq t \leq 1$
3. $x = 4\cos t, \quad y = 5\sin t; \quad 0 \leq t \leq \pi$
4. $x = 4\sin t, \quad y = 5\cos t; \quad 0 \leq t \leq 2\pi$
5. $x = t, \quad y = \sqrt{t}; \quad t \geq 0$
6. $x = \sec^2 t - 1, \quad y = \tan t; \quad -\pi/2 < t < \pi/2$
7. $x = -\sec t, \quad y = \tan t; \quad -\pi/2 < t < \pi/2$
8. $x = \csc t, \quad y = \cot t; \quad 0 < t < \pi$
9. $x = t, \quad y = \sqrt{4 - t^2}; \quad 0 \leq t \leq 2$
10. $x = t^2, \quad y = \sqrt{t^4 + 1}; \quad t \geq 0$
11. $x = -\cosh t, \quad y = \sinh t; \quad -\infty < t < \infty$
12. $x = 2\sinh t, \quad y = 2\cosh t; \quad -\infty < t < \infty$

13. **Hypocycloids** When a circle rolls on the inside of a fixed circle, any point P on the circumference of the rolling circle describes a *hypocycloid*. Let the fixed circle be $x^2 + y^2 = a^2$, let the radius of the rolling circle be b, and let the initial position of the tracing point P be $A(a, 0)$. Find parametric equations for the hypocycloid, using as the parameter the angle θ from the positive x-axis to the line joining the circles' centers. In particular, if $b = a/4$, as in the accompanying figure, show that the hypocycloid is the astroid

$$x = a\cos^3\theta, \quad y = a\sin^3\theta.$$

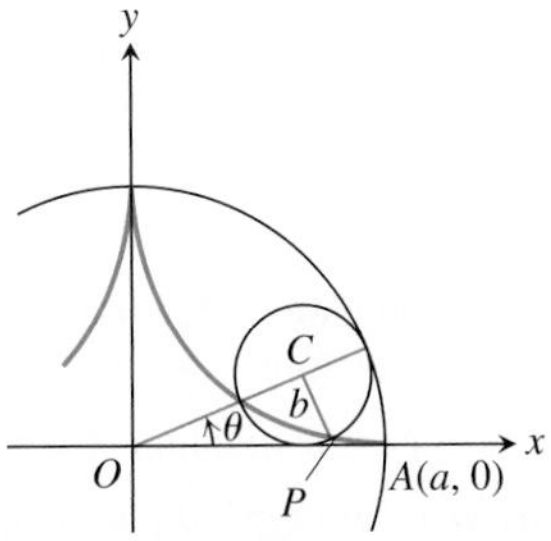

14. **More about hypocycloids** The accompanying figure shows a circle of radius a tangent to the inside of a circle of radius $2a$. The point P, shown as the point of tangency in the figure, is attached to the smaller circle. What path does P trace as the smaller circle rolls around the inside of the larger circle?

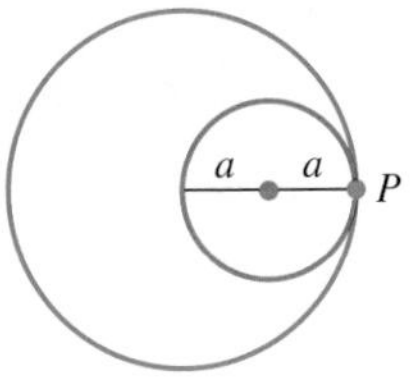

15. As the point N moves along the line $y = a$ in the accompanying figure, P moves in such a way that $OP = MN$. Find parametric equations for the coordinates of P as functions of the angle t that the line ON makes with the positive y-axis.

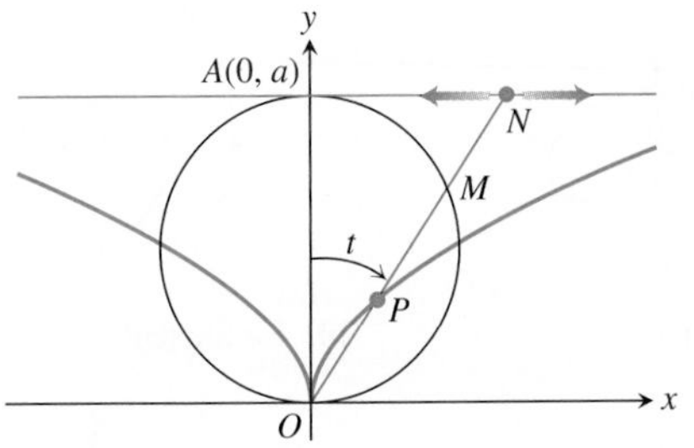

16. **Trochoids** A wheel of radius a rolls along a horizontal straight line without slipping. Find parametric equations for the curve traced out by a point P on a spoke of the wheel b units from its center. As parameter, use the angle θ through which the wheel turns. The curve is called a *trochoid*, which is a cycloid when $b = a$.

17. Find the point on the parabola $x = t, y = t^2, -\infty < t < \infty$, closest to the point $(2, 1/2)$. (*Hint:* Minimize the square of the distance as a function of t.)

18. Find the point on the ellipse $x = 2\cos t, y = \sin t, 0 \le t \le 2\pi$ closest to the point $(3/4, 0)$. (*Hint:* Minimize the square of the distance as a function of t.)

T If you have a parametric equation grapher, graph the following equations over the given intervals.

19. **Ellipse** $x = 4\cos t, \quad y = 2\sin t,$ over
   a. $0 \le t \le 2\pi$ **b.** $0 \le t \le \pi$
   c. $-\pi/2 \le t \le \pi/2$.

20. **Hyperbola branch** $x = \sec t$ (enter as $1/\cos(t)$), $y = \tan t$ (enter as $\sin(t)/\cos(t)$), over
   a. $-1.5 \le t \le 1.5$ **b.** $-0.5 \le t \le 0.5$
   c. $-0.1 \le t \le 0.1$.

21. **Parabola** $x = 2t + 3, \quad y = t^2 - 1, \quad -2 \le t \le 2$

22. **Cycloid** $x = t - \sin t, \quad y = 1 - \cos t,$ over
   a. $0 \le t \le 2\pi$ **b.** $0 \le t \le 4\pi$
   c. $\pi \le t \le 3\pi$.

23. **A nice curve (a deltoid)**

$$x = 2\cos t + \cos 2t, \quad y = 2\sin t - \sin 2t; \quad 0 \le t \le 2\pi$$

What happens if you replace 2 with -2 in the equations for x and y? Graph the new equations and find out.

24. **An even nicer curve**

$$x = 3\cos t + \cos 3t, \quad y = 3\sin t - \sin 3t; \quad 0 \le t \le 2\pi$$

What happens if you replace 3 with -3 in the equations for x and y? Graph the new equations and find out.

25. **Three beautiful curves**
   a. *Epicycloid:*

$$x = 9\cos t - \cos 9t, \quad y = 9\sin t - \sin 9t; \quad 0 \le t \le 2\pi$$

   b. *Hypocycloid:*

$$x = 8\cos t + 2\cos 4t, \quad y = 8\sin t - 2\sin 4t; \quad 0 \le t \le 2\pi$$

   c. *Hypotrochoid:*

$$x = \cos t + 5\cos 3t, \quad y = 6\cos t - 5\sin 3t; \quad 0 \le t \le 2\pi$$

26. **More beautiful curves**
   a. $x = 6\cos t + 5\cos 3t, \quad y = 6\sin t - 5\sin 3t;$ $0 \le t \le 2\pi$
   b. $x = 6\cos 2t + 5\cos 6t, \quad y = 6\sin 2t - 5\sin 6t;$ $0 \le t \le \pi$
   c. $x = 6\cos t + 5\cos 3t, \quad y = 6\sin 2t - 5\sin 3t;$ $0 \le t \le 2\pi$
   d. $x = 6\cos 2t + 5\cos 6t, \quad y = 6\sin 4t - 5\sin 6t;$ $0 \le t \le \pi$

Chapter 9 Questions to Guide Your Review

1. What are polar coordinates? What equations relate polar coordinates to Cartesian coordinates? Why might you want to change from one coordinate system to the other?
2. What consequence does the lack of uniqueness of polar coordinates have for graphing? Give an example.
3. How do you graph equations in polar coordinates? Include in your discussion symmetry, slope, behavior at the origin, and the use of Cartesian graphs. Give examples.
4. How do you find the area of a region $0 \le r_1(\theta) \le r \le r_2(\theta)$, $\alpha \le \theta \le \beta$, in the polar coordinate plane? Give examples.
5. Under what conditions can you find the length of a curve $r = f(\theta)$, $\alpha \le \theta \le \beta$, in the polar coordinate plane? Give an example of a typical calculation.
6. What is a parabola? What are the Cartesian equations for parabolas whose vertices lie at the origin and whose foci lie on the coordinate axes? How can you find the focus and directrix of such a parabola from its equation?
7. What is an ellipse? What are the Cartesian equations for ellipses centered at the origin with foci on one of the coordinate axes? How can you find the foci, vertices, and directrices of such an ellipse from its equation?
8. What is a hyperbola? What are the Cartesian equations for hyperbolas centered at the origin with foci on one of the coordinate axes? How can you find the foci, vertices, and directrices of such an ellipse from its equation?
9. What is the eccentricity of a conic section? How can you classify conic sections by eccentricity? How are an ellipse's shape and eccentricity related?
10. Explain the equation $PF = e \cdot PD$.
11. What are the standard equations for lines and conic sections in polar coordinates? Give examples.
12. What are some typical parametrizations for conic sections?
13. What is a cycloid? What are typical parametric equations for cycloids? What physical properties account for the importance of cycloids?

Chapter 9 Practice Exercises

Sketch the lines in Exercises 1–6. Also, find a Cartesian equation for each line.

1. $r \cos\left(\theta + \dfrac{\pi}{3}\right) = 2\sqrt{3}$
2. $r \cos\left(\theta - \dfrac{3\pi}{4}\right) = \dfrac{\sqrt{2}}{2}$
3. $r = 2 \sec \theta$
4. $r = -\sqrt{2} \sec \theta$
5. $r = -(3/2) \csc \theta$
6. $r = \left(3\sqrt{3}\right) \csc \theta$

Find Cartesian equations for the circles in Exercises 7–10. Sketch each circle in the coordinate plane and label it with both its Cartesian and polar equations.

7. $r = -4 \sin \theta$
8. $r = 3\sqrt{3} \sin \theta$
9. $r = 2\sqrt{2} \cos \theta$
10. $r = -6 \cos \theta$

Find polar equations for the circles in Exercises 11–14. Sketch each circle in the coordinate plane and label it with both its Cartesian and polar equations.

11. $x^2 + y^2 + 5y = 0$
12. $x^2 + y^2 - 2y = 0$
13. $x^2 + y^2 - 3x = 0$
14. $x^2 + y^2 + 4x = 0$

Sketch the regions defined by the polar coordinate inequalities in Exercises 15 and 16.

15. $0 \le r \le 6 \cos \theta$
16. $-4 \sin \theta \le r \le 0$

Match each graph in Exercises 17–24 with the appropriate equation (a)–(l). There are more equations than graphs, so some equations will not be matched.

a. $r = \cos 2\theta$
b. $r \cos \theta = 1$
c. $r = \dfrac{6}{1 - 2\cos\theta}$
d. $r = \sin 2\theta$
e. $r = \theta$
f. $r^2 = \cos 2\theta$
g. $r = 1 + \cos\theta$
h. $r = 1 - \sin\theta$
i. $r = \dfrac{2}{1 - \cos\theta}$
j. $r^2 = \sin 2\theta$
k. $r = -\sin\theta$
l. $r = 2\cos\theta + 1$

17. Four-leaved rose

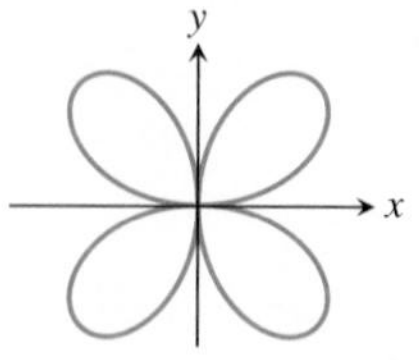

18. Spiral

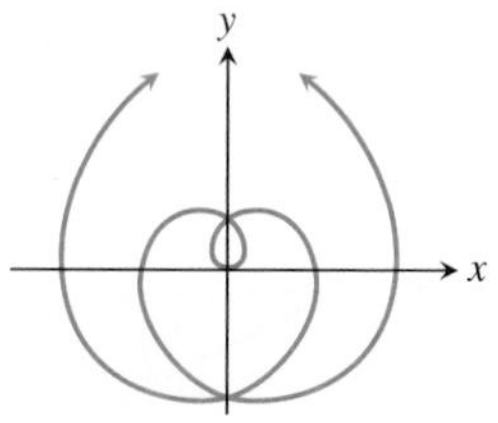

19. Limaçon

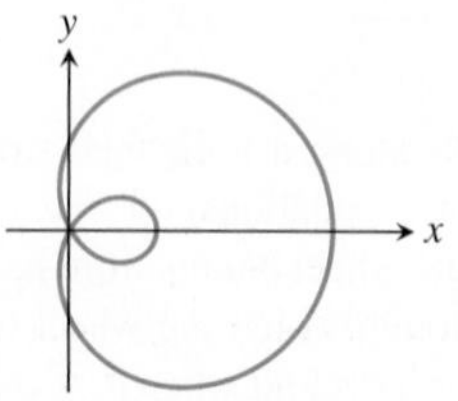

20. Lemniscate

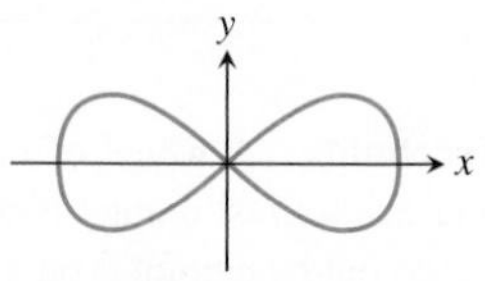

21. Circle

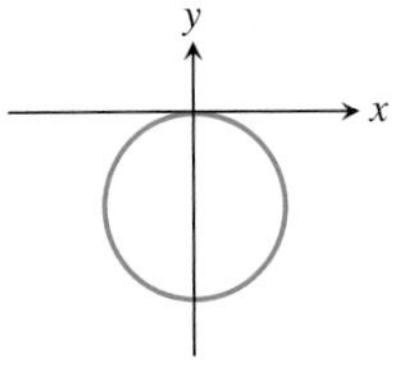

22. Cardioid

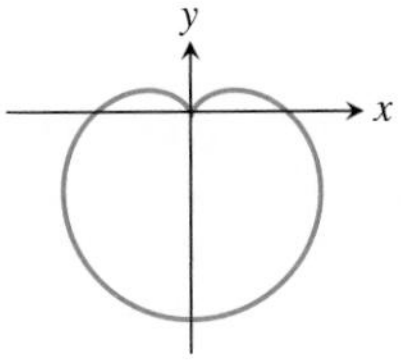

23. Parabola

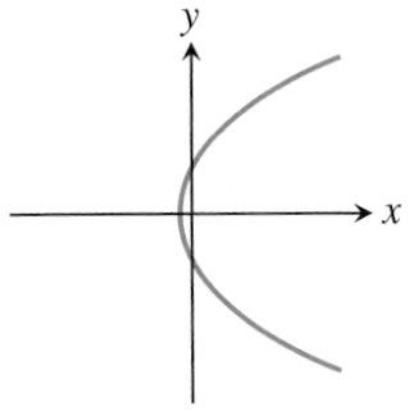

24. Lemniscate

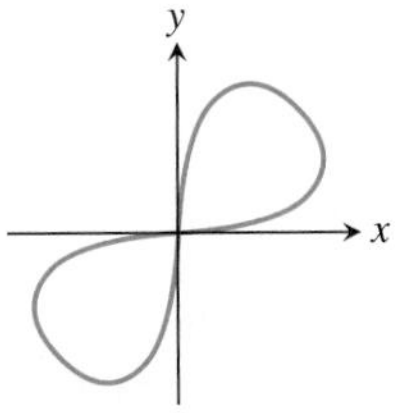

Find the areas of the regions in the polar coordinate plane described in Exercises 25–28.

25. Enclosed by the limaçon $r = 2 - \cos\theta$

26. Enclosed by one leaf of the three-leaved rose $r = \sin 3\theta$

27. Inside the "figure eight" $r = 1 + \cos 2\theta$ and outside the circle $r = 1$

28. Inside the cardioid $r = 2(1 + \sin\theta)$ and outside the circle $r = 2\sin\theta$

Find the lengths of the curves given by the polar coordinate equations in Exercises 29–32.

29. $r = -1 + \cos\theta$

30. $r = 2\sin\theta + 2\cos\theta, \quad 0 \le \theta \le \pi/2$

31. $r = 8\sin^3(\theta/3), \quad 0 \le \theta \le \pi/4$

32. $r = \sqrt{1 + \cos 2\theta}, \quad -\pi/2 \le \theta \le \pi/2$

Sketch the parabolas in Exercises 33–36. Include the focus and directrix in each sketch.

33. $x^2 = -4y$

34. $x^2 = 2y$

35. $y^2 = 3x$

36. $y^2 = -(8/3)x$

Find the eccentricities of the ellipses and hyperbolas in Exercises 37–40. Sketch each conic section. Include the foci, vertices, and asymptotes (as appropriate) in your sketch.

37. $16x^2 + 7y^2 = 112$

38. $x^2 + 2y^2 = 4$

39. $3x^2 - y^2 = 3$

40. $5y^2 - 4x^2 = 20$

Exercises 41–46 give equations for conic sections and tell how many units up or down and to the right or left each curve is to be shifted. Find an equation for the new conic section and find the new foci, vertices, centers, and asymptotes, as appropriate. If the curve is a parabola, find the new directrix as well.

41. $x^2 = -12y$, right 2, up 3

42. $y^2 = 10x$, left 1/2, down 1

43. $\dfrac{x^2}{9} + \dfrac{y^2}{25} = 1$, left 3, down 5

44. $\dfrac{x^2}{169} + \dfrac{y^2}{144} = 1$, right 5, up 12

45. $\dfrac{y^2}{8} - \dfrac{x^2}{2} = 1$, right 2, up $2\sqrt{2}$

46. $\dfrac{x^2}{36} - \dfrac{y^2}{64} = 1$, left 10, down 3

Complete the squares to identify the conic sections in Exercises 47–54. Find their foci, vertices, centers, and asymptotes (as appropriate). If the curve is a parabola, find its directrix as well.

47. $x^2 - 4x - 4y^2 = 0$

48. $4x^2 - y^2 + 4y = 8$

49. $y^2 - 2y + 16x = -49$

50. $x^2 - 2x + 8y = -17$

51. $9x^2 + 16y^2 + 54x - 64y = -1$

52. $25x^2 + 9y^2 - 100x + 54y = 44$

53. $x^2 + y^2 - 2x - 2y = 0$

54. $x^2 + y^2 + 4x + 2y = 1$

Sketch the conic sections whose polar coordinate equations are given in Exercises 55–58. Give polar coordinates for the vertices and, in the case of ellipses, for the centers as well.

55. $r = \dfrac{2}{1 + \cos\theta}$

56. $r = \dfrac{8}{2 + \cos\theta}$

57. $r = \dfrac{6}{1 - 2\cos\theta}$

58. $r = \dfrac{12}{3 + \sin\theta}$

Exercises 59–62 give the eccentricities of conic sections with one focus at the origin of the polar coordinate plane, along with the directrix for that focus. Find a polar equation for each conic section.

59. $e = 2, \quad r\cos\theta = 2$

60. $e = 1, \quad r\cos\theta = -4$

61. $e = 1/2, \quad r\sin\theta = 2$

62. $e = 1/3, \quad r\sin\theta = -6$

Exercises 63–66 give parametric equations and parameter intervals for the motion of a particle in the xy-plane. Identify the particle's path by finding a Cartesian equation for it. Graph the Cartesian equation and indicate the direction of motion and the portion traced by the particle.

63. $x = (1/2)\tan t, \quad y = (1/2)\sec t; \quad -\pi/2 < t < \pi/2$

64. $x = -2\cos t, \quad y = 2\sin t; \quad 0 \le t \le \pi$

65. $x = -\cos t, \quad y = \cos^2 t; \quad 0 \le t \le \pi$

66. $x = 4\cos t, \quad y = 9\sin t; \quad 0 \le t \le 2\pi$

67. Find the volume of the solid generated by revolving the region enclosed by the ellipse $9x^2 + 4y^2 = 36$ about **(a)** the x-axis, **(b)** the y-axis.

68. The "triangular" region in the first quadrant bounded by the x-axis, the line $x = 4$, and the hyperbola $9x^2 - 4y^2 = 36$ is revolved about the x-axis to generate a solid. Find the volume of the solid.

69. Show that the equations $x = r\cos\theta, y = r\sin\theta$ transform the polar equation

$$r = \frac{k}{1 + e\cos\theta}$$

into the Cartesian equation

$$(1 - e^2)x^2 + y^2 + 2kex - k^2 = 0.$$

70. Archimedes spirals The graph of an equation of the form $r = a\theta$, where a is a nonzero constant, is called an *Archimedes spiral*. Is there anything special about the widths between the successive turns of such a spiral?

Chapter 9 Additional and Advanced Exercises

1. Find an equation for the parabola with focus (4, 0) and directrix $x = 3$. Sketch the parabola together with its vertex, focus, and directrix.

2. Find the vertex, focus, and directrix of the parabola

$$x^2 - 6x - 12y + 9 = 0.$$

3. Find an equation for the curve traced by the point $P(x, y)$ if the distance from P to the vertex of the parabola $x^2 = 4y$ is twice the distance from P to the focus. Identify the curve.

4. A line segment of length $a + b$ runs from the x-axis to the y-axis. The point P on the segment lies a units from one end and b units from the other end. Show that P traces an ellipse as the ends of the segment slide along the axes.

5. The vertices of an ellipse of eccentricity 0.5 lie at the points $(0, \pm 2)$. Where do the foci lie?

6. Find an equation for the ellipse of eccentricity 2/3 that has the line $x = 2$ as a directrix and the point (4, 0) as the corresponding focus.

7. One focus of a hyperbola lies at the point $(0, -7)$ and the corresponding directrix is the line $y = -1$. Find an equation for the hyperbola if its eccentricity is **(a)** 2, **(b)** 5.

8. Find an equation for the hyperbola with foci $(0, -2)$ and (0, 2) that passes through the point (12, 7).

9. Show that the line

$$b^2xx_1 + a^2yy_1 - a^2b^2 = 0$$

is tangent to the ellipse $b^2x^2 + a^2y^2 - a^2b^2 = 0$ at the point (x_1, y_1) on the ellipse.

10. Show that the line

$$b^2xx_1 - a^2yy_1 - a^2b^2 = 0$$

is tangent to the hyperbola $b^2x^2 - a^2y^2 - a^2b^2 = 0$ at the point (x_1, y_1) on the hyperbola.

What points in the xy-plane satisfy the equations and inequalities in Exercises 11–16? Draw a figure for each exercise.

11. $(x^2 - y^2 - 1)(x^2 + y^2 - 25)(x^2 + 4y^2 - 4) = 0$

12. $(x + y)(x^2 + y^2 - 1) = 0$

13. $(x^2/9) + (y^2/16) \le 1$

14. $(x^2/9) - (y^2/16) \le 1$

15. $(9x^2 + 4y^2 - 36)(4x^2 + 9y^2 - 16) \le 0$

16. $(9x^2 + 4y^2 - 36)(4x^2 + 9y^2 - 16) > 0$

17. a. Find an equation in polar coordinates for the curve

$$x = e^{2t}\cos t, \quad y = e^{2t}\sin t; \quad -\infty < t < \infty.$$

b. Find the length of the curve from $t = 0$ to $t = 2\pi$.

18. Find the length of the curve $r = 2\sin^3(\theta/3), 0 \le \theta \le 3\pi$, in the polar coordinate plane.

Exercises 19–22 give the eccentricities of conic sections with one focus at the origin of the polar coordinate plane, along with the directrix for that focus. Find a polar equation for each conic section.

19. $e = 2, \quad r\cos\theta = 2$

20. $e = 1, \quad r\cos\theta = -4$

21. $e = 1/2, \quad r\sin\theta = 2$

22. $e = 1/3, \quad r\sin\theta = -6$

23. Epicycloids When a circle rolls externally along the circumference of a second, fixed circle, any point P on the circumference of the rolling circle describes an *epicycloid*, as shown here. Let the fixed circle have its center at the origin O and have radius a.

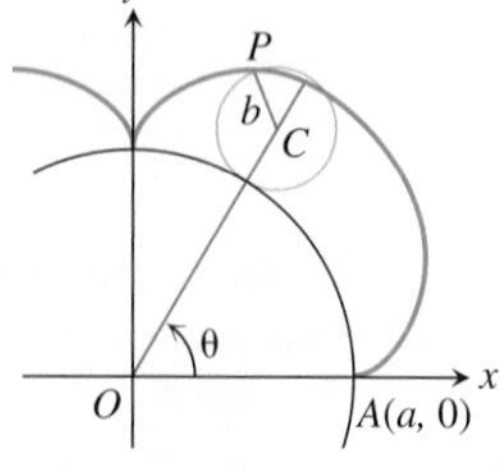

Let the radius of the rolling circle be b and let the initial position of the tracing point P be $A(a, 0)$. Find parametric equations for the epicycloid, using as the parameter the angle θ from the positive x-axis to the line through the circles' centers.

24. Find the centroid of the region enclosed by the x-axis and the cycloid arch

$$x = a(t - \sin t), \quad y = a(1 - \cos t); \quad 0 \le t \le 2\pi.$$

The Angle Between the Radius Vector and the Tangent Line to a Polar Coordinate Curve In Cartesian coordinates, when we want to discuss the direction of a curve at a point, we use the angle ϕ measured counterclockwise from the positive x-axis to the tangent line. In polar coordinates, it is more convenient to calculate the angle ψ from the *radius vector* to the tangent line (see the accompanying figure). The angle ϕ can then be calculated from the relation

$$\phi = \theta + \psi, \tag{1}$$

which comes from applying the Exterior Angle Theorem to the triangle in the accompanying figure.

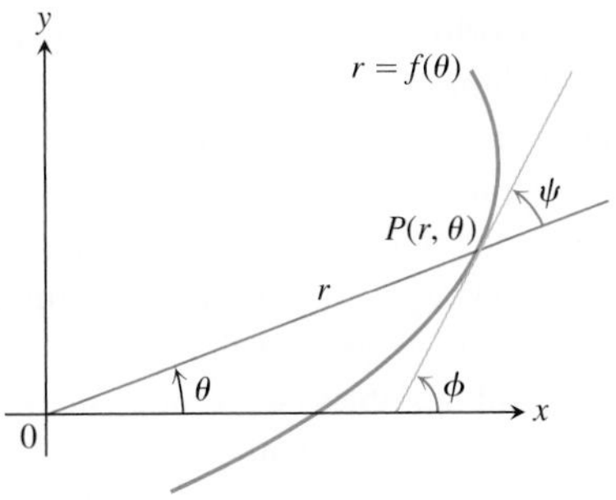

Suppose the equation of the curve is given in the form $r = f(\theta)$, where $f(\theta)$ is a differentiable function of θ. Then

$$x = r\cos\theta \quad \text{and} \quad y = r\sin\theta \tag{2}$$

are differentiable functions of θ with

$$\frac{dx}{d\theta} = -r\sin\theta + \cos\theta\frac{dr}{d\theta},$$
$$\frac{dy}{d\theta} = r\cos\theta + \sin\theta\frac{dr}{d\theta}. \tag{3}$$

Since $\psi = \phi - \theta$ from (1),

$$\tan\psi = \tan(\phi - \theta) = \frac{\tan\phi - \tan\theta}{1 + \tan\phi\tan\theta}.$$

Furthermore,

$$\tan\phi = \frac{dy}{dx} = \frac{dy/d\theta}{dx/d\theta}$$

because $\tan\phi$ is the slope of the curve at P. Also,

$$\tan\theta = \frac{y}{x}.$$

Hence

$$\tan\psi = \frac{\dfrac{dy/d\theta}{dx/d\theta} - \dfrac{y}{x}}{1 + \dfrac{y}{x}\dfrac{dy/d\theta}{dx/d\theta}} = \frac{x\dfrac{dy}{d\theta} - y\dfrac{dx}{d\theta}}{x\dfrac{dx}{d\theta} + y\dfrac{dy}{d\theta}}. \tag{4}$$

The numerator in the last expression in Equation (4) is found from Equations (2) and (3) to be

$$x\frac{dy}{d\theta} - y\frac{dx}{d\theta} = r^2.$$

Similarly, the denominator is

$$x\frac{dx}{d\theta} + y\frac{dy}{d\theta} = r\frac{dr}{d\theta}.$$

When we substitute these into Equation (4), we obtain

$$\tan\psi = \frac{r}{dr/d\theta}. \tag{5}$$

This is the equation we use for finding ψ as a function of θ.

25. Show, by reference to a figure, that the angle β between the tangents to two curves at a point of intersection may be found from the formula

$$\tan\beta = \frac{\tan\psi_2 - \tan\psi_1}{1 + \tan\psi_2\tan\psi_1}. \tag{6}$$

When will the two curves intersect at right angles?

26. Find the value of $\tan\psi$ for the curve $r = \sin^4(\theta/4)$.

27. Find the angle between the radius vector to the curve $r = 2a\sin 3\theta$ and its tangent when $\theta = \pi/6$.

T **28.** **a.** Graph the hyperbolic spiral $r\theta = 1$. What appears to happen to ψ as the spiral winds in around the origin?

b. Confirm your finding in part (a) analytically.

29. The circles $r = \sqrt{3}\cos\theta$ and $r = \sin\theta$ intersect at the point $(\sqrt{3}/2, \pi/3)$. Show that their tangents are perpendicular there.

30. Find the angle at which the cardioid $r = a(1 - \cos\theta)$ crosses the ray $\theta = \pi/2$.

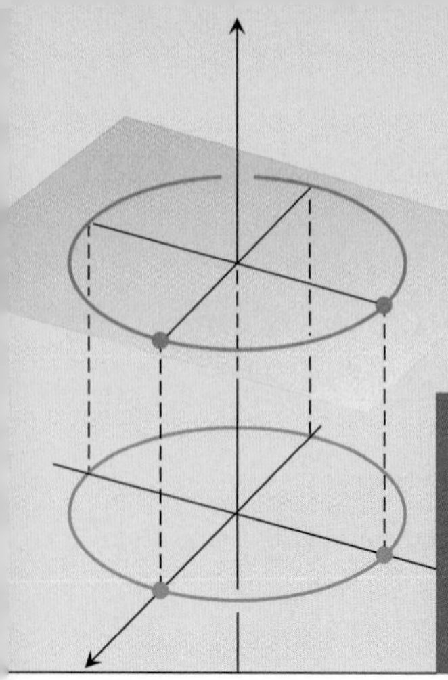

Chapter 10

Vectors and the Geometry of Space

OVERVIEW To apply calculus in many real-world situations and in higher mathematics, we need a mathematical description of three-dimensional space. In this chapter we introduce three-dimensional coordinate systems and vectors. Building on what we already know about coordinates in the xy-plane, we establish coordinates in space by adding a third axis that measures distance above and below the xy-plane. Vectors are used to study the analytic geometry of space, where they give simple ways to describe lines, planes, surfaces, and curves in space. We use these geometric ideas later in the book to study motion in space and the calculus of functions of several variables, with their many important applications in science, engineering, economics, and higher mathematics.

10.1 Three-Dimensional Coordinate Systems

To locate a point in space, we use three mutually perpendicular coordinate axes, arranged as in Figure 10.1. The axes shown there make a *right-handed* coordinate frame. When you hold your right hand so that the fingers curl from the positive x-axis toward the positive y-axis, your thumb points along the positive z-axis. So when you look down on the xy-plane from the positive direction of the z-axis, positive angles in the plane are measured counterclockwise from the positive x-axis and around the positive z-axis. (In a *left-handed* coordinate frame, the z-axis would point downward in Figure 10.1 and angles in the plane would be positive when measured clockwise from the positive x-axis. Right-handed and left-handed coordinate frames are not equivalent.)

FIGURE 10.1 The Cartesian coordinate system is right-handed.

The Cartesian coordinates (x, y, z) of a point P in space are the values at which the planes through P perpendicular to the axes cut the axes. Cartesian coordinates for space are also called **rectangular coordinates** because the axes that define them meet at right angles. Points on the x-axis have y- and z-coordinates equal to zero. That is, they have coordinates of the form $(x, 0, 0)$. Similarly, points on the y-axis have coordinates of the form $(0, y, 0)$, and points on the z-axis have coordinates of the form $(0, 0, z)$.

The planes determined by the coordinates axes are the ***xy*-plane**, whose standard equation is $z = 0$; the ***yz*-plane**, whose standard equation is $x = 0$; and the ***xz*-plane**, whose standard equation is $y = 0$. They meet at the **origin** $(0, 0, 0)$ (Figure 10.2). The origin is also identified by simply 0 or sometimes the letter O.

The three **coordinate planes** $x = 0$, $y = 0$, and $z = 0$ divide space into eight cells called **octants**. The octant in which the point coordinates are all positive is called the **first octant**; there is no convention for numbering the other seven octants.

The points in a plane perpendicular to the x-axis all have the same x-coordinate, this being the number at which that plane cuts the x-axis. The y- and z-coordinates can be any numbers.

Similarly, the points in a plane perpendicular to the y-axis have a common y-coordinate and the points in a plane perpendicular to the z-axis have a common z-coordinate. To write equations for these planes, we name the common coordinate's value. The plane $x = 2$ is the plane perpendicular to the x-axis at $x = 2$. The plane $y = 3$ is the plane perpendicular to the y-axis at $y = 3$. The plane $z = 5$ is the plane perpendicular to the z-axis at $z = 5$. Figure 10.3 shows the planes $x = 2$, $y = 3$, and $z = 5$, together with their intersection point (2, 3, 5).

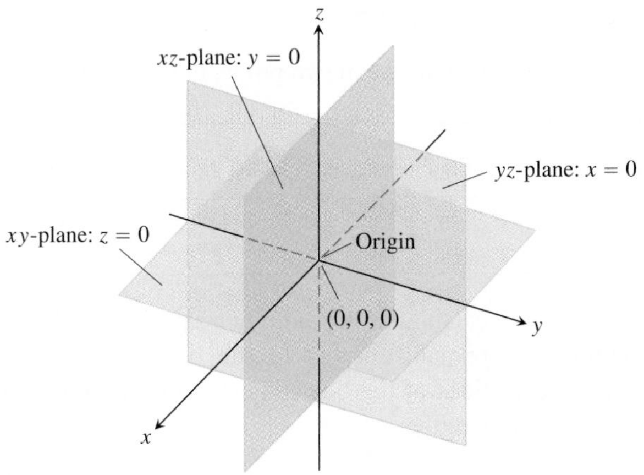

FIGURE 10.2 The planes $x = 0$, $y = 0$, and $z = 0$ divide space into eight octants.

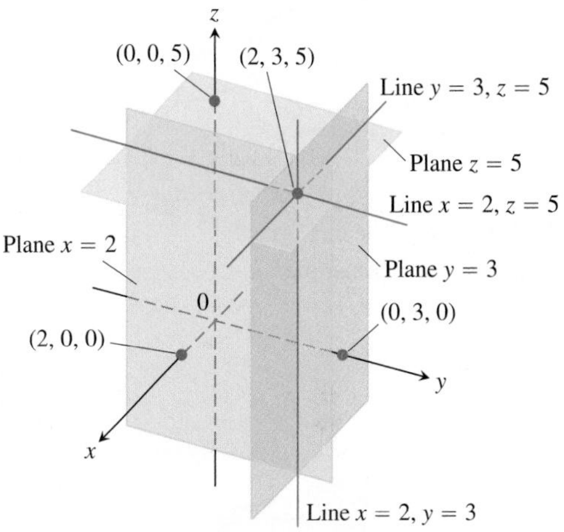

FIGURE 10.3 The planes $x = 2$, $y = 3$, and $z = 5$ determine three lines through the point (2, 3, 5).

The planes $x = 2$ and $y = 3$ in Figure 10.3 intersect in a line parallel to the z-axis. This line is described by the *pair* of equations $x = 2, y = 3$. A point (x, y, z) lies on the line if and only if $x = 2$ and $y = 3$. Similarly, the line of intersection of the planes $y = 3$ and $z = 5$ is described by the equation pair $y = 3, z = 5$. This line runs parallel to the x-axis. The line of intersection of the planes $x = 2$ and $z = 5$, parallel to the y-axis, is described by the equation pair $x = 2, z = 5$.

In the following examples, we match coordinate equations and inequalities with the sets of points they define in space.

EXAMPLE 1 We interpret these equations and inequalities geometrically.

(a) $z \geq 0$ — The half-space consisting of the points on and above the xy-plane.

(b) $x = -3$ — The plane perpendicular to the x-axis at $x = -3$. This plane lies parallel to the yz-plane and 3 units behind it.

(c) $z = 0, x \leq 0, y \geq 0$ — The second quadrant of the xy-plane.

(d) $x \geq 0, y \geq 0, z \geq 0$ — The first octant.

(e) $-1 \leq y \leq 1$ — The slab between the planes $y = -1$ and $y = 1$ (planes included).

(f) $y = -2, z = 2$ — The line in which the planes $y = -2$ and $z = 2$ intersect. Alternatively, the line through the point $(0, -2, 2)$ parallel to the x-axis. ■

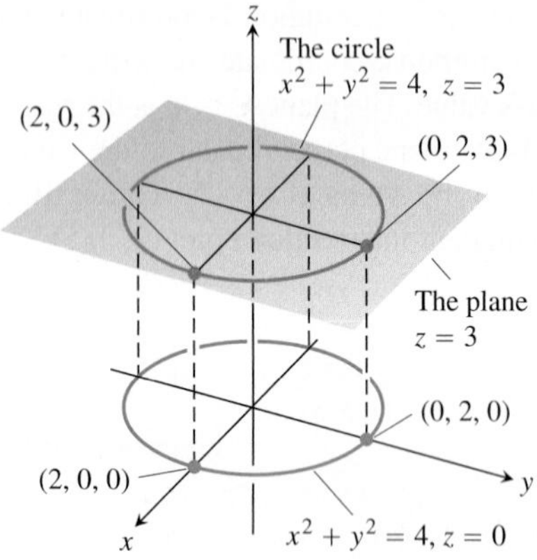

FIGURE 10.4 The circle $x^2 + y^2 = 4$ in the plane $z = 3$ (Example 2).

EXAMPLE 2 What points $P(x, y, z)$ satisfy the equations

$$x^2 + y^2 = 4 \qquad \text{and} \qquad z = 3?$$

Solution The points lie in the horizontal plane $z = 3$ and, in this plane, make up the circle $x^2 + y^2 = 4$. We call this set of points "the circle $x^2 + y^2 = 4$ in the plane $z = 3$" or, more simply, "the circle $x^2 + y^2 = 4, z = 3$" (Figure 10.4). ■

Distance and Spheres in Space

The formula for the distance between two points in the xy-plane extends to points in space.

The Distance Between $P_1(x_1, y_1, z_1)$ and $P_2(x_2, y_2, z_2)$ is

$$|P_1P_2| = \sqrt{(x_2 - x_1)^2 + (y_2 - y_1)^2 + (z_2 - z_1)^2}$$

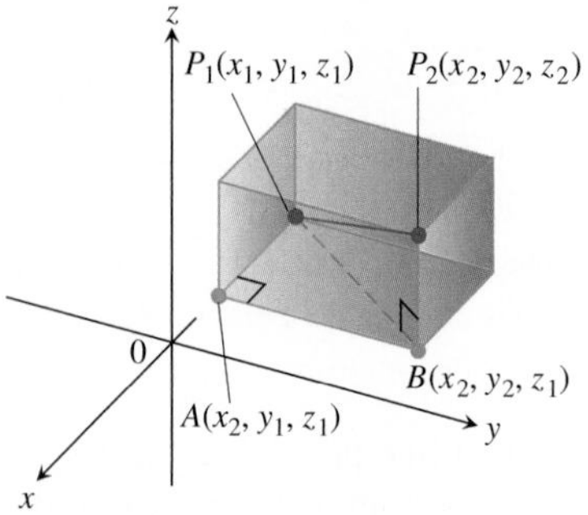

FIGURE 10.5 We find the distance between P_1 and P_2 by applying the Pythagorean theorem to the right triangles P_1AB and P_1BP_2.

Proof We construct a rectangular box with faces parallel to the coordinate planes and the points P_1 and P_2 at opposite corners of the box (Figure 10.5). If $A(x_2, y_1, z_1)$ and $B(x_2, y_2, z_1)$ are the vertices of the box indicated in the figure, then the three box edges P_1A, AB, and BP_2 have lengths

$$|P_1A| = |x_2 - x_1|, \qquad |AB| = |y_2 - y_1|, \qquad |BP_2| = |z_2 - z_1|.$$

Because triangles P_1BP_2 and P_1AB are both right-angled, two applications of the Pythagorean theorem give

$$|P_1P_2|^2 = |P_1B|^2 + |BP_2|^2 \qquad \text{and} \qquad |P_1B|^2 = |P_1A|^2 + |AB|^2$$

(see Figure 10.5).
So

$$\begin{aligned}|P_1P_2|^2 &= |P_1B|^2 + |BP_2|^2\\ &= |P_1A|^2 + |AB|^2 + |BP_2|^2 && \text{Substitute } |P_1B|^2 = |P_1A|^2 + |AB|^2.\\ &= |x_2 - x_1|^2 + |y_2 - y_1|^2 + |z_2 - z_1|^2\\ &= (x_2 - x_1)^2 + (y_2 - y_1)^2 + (z_2 - z_1)^2\end{aligned}$$

Therefore

$$|P_1P_2| = \sqrt{(x_2 - x_1)^2 + (y_2 - y_1)^2 + (z_2 - z_1)^2}$$ ■

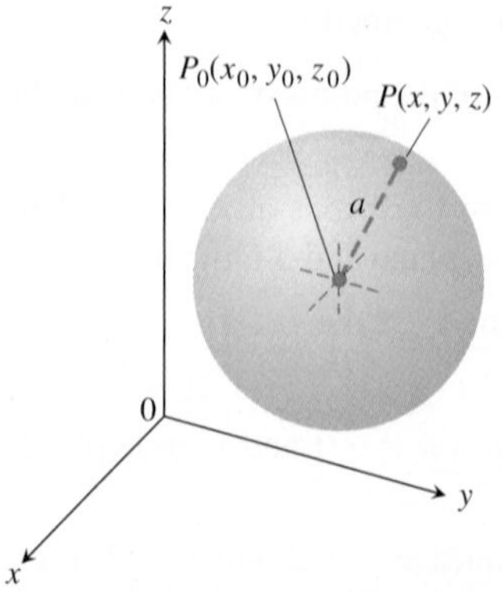

FIGURE 10.6 The sphere of radius a centered at the point (x_0, y_0, z_0).

EXAMPLE 3 The distance between $P_1(2, 1, 5)$ and $P_2(-2, 3, 0)$ is

$$\begin{aligned}|P_1P_2| &= \sqrt{(-2 - 2)^2 + (3 - 1)^2 + (0 - 5)^2}\\ &= \sqrt{16 + 4 + 25}\\ &= \sqrt{45} \approx 6.708.\end{aligned}$$ ■

We can use the distance formula to write equations for spheres in space (Figure 10.6). A point $P(x, y, z)$ lies on the sphere of radius a centered at $P_0(x_0, y_0, z_0)$ precisely when $|P_0P| = a$ or

$$(x - x_0)^2 + (y - y_0)^2 + (z - z_0)^2 = a^2.$$

The Standard Equation for the Sphere of Radius a and Center (x_0, y_0, z_0)

$$(x - x_0)^2 + (y - y_0)^2 + (z - z_0)^2 = a^2$$

EXAMPLE 4 Find the center and radius of the sphere

$$x^2 + y^2 + z^2 + 3x - 4z + 1 = 0.$$

Solution We find the center and radius of a sphere the way we find the center and radius of a circle: Complete the squares on the x-, y-, and z-terms as necessary and write each quadratic as a squared linear expression. Then, from the equation in standard form, read off the center and radius. For the sphere here, we have

$$x^2 + y^2 + z^2 + 3x - 4z + 1 = 0$$
$$(x^2 + 3x) + y^2 + (z^2 - 4z) = -1$$
$$\left(x^2 + 3x + \left(\frac{3}{2}\right)^2\right) + y^2 + \left(z^2 - 4z + \left(\frac{-4}{2}\right)^2\right) = -1 + \left(\frac{3}{2}\right)^2 + \left(\frac{-4}{2}\right)^2$$
$$\left(x + \frac{3}{2}\right)^2 + y^2 + (z - 2)^2 = -1 + \frac{9}{4} + 4 = \frac{21}{4}.$$

From this standard form, we read that $x_0 = -3/2$, $y_0 = 0$, $z_0 = 2$, and $a = \sqrt{21}/2$. The center is $(-3/2, 0, 2)$. The radius is $\sqrt{21}/2$. ■

EXAMPLE 5 Here are some geometric interpretations.

(a) $x^2 + y^2 + z^2 < 4$ The interior of the sphere $x^2 + y^2 + z^2 = 4$.

(b) $x^2 + y^2 + z^2 \leq 4$ The solid ball bounded by the sphere $x^2 + y^2 + z^2 = 4$. Alternatively, the sphere $x^2 + y^2 + z^2 = 4$ together with its interior.

(c) $x^2 + y^2 + z^2 > 4$ The exterior of the sphere $x^2 + y^2 + z^2 = 4$.

(d) $x^2 + y^2 + z^2 = 4, z \leq 0$ The lower hemisphere cut from the sphere $x^2 + y^2 + z^2 = 4$ by the xy-plane (the plane $z = 0$). ■

Just as polar coordinates give another way to locate points in the xy-plane (Section 9.1), alternative coordinate systems, different from the Cartesian coordinate system developed here, exist for three-dimensional space. We examine two of these coordinate systems in Section 13.7.

EXERCISES 10.1

In Exercises 1–12, give a geometric description of the set of points in space whose coordinates satisfy the given pairs of equations.

1. $x = 2, \quad y = 3$

2. $x = -1, \quad z = 0$

3. $y = 0, \quad z = 0$

4. $x = 1, \quad y = 0$

5. $x^2 + y^2 = 4, \quad z = 0$

6. $x^2 + y^2 = 4, \quad z = -2$

7. $x^2 + z^2 = 4, \quad y = 0$

8. $y^2 + z^2 = 1, \quad x = 0$

9. $x^2 + y^2 + z^2 = 1, \quad x = 0$

10. $x^2 + y^2 + z^2 = 25, \quad y = -4$

11. $x^2 + y^2 + (z + 3)^2 = 25, \quad z = 0$

12. $x^2 + (y - 1)^2 + z^2 = 4, \quad y = 0$

In Exercises 13–18, describe the sets of points in space whose coordinates satisfy the given inequalities or combinations of equations and inequalities.

13. **a.** $x \geq 0, \quad y \geq 0, \quad z = 0$ **b.** $x \geq 0, \quad y \leq 0, \quad z = 0$

14. **a.** $0 \leq x \leq 1$ **b.** $0 \leq x \leq 1, \quad 0 \leq y \leq 1$

c. $0 \leq x \leq 1, \quad 0 \leq y \leq 1, \quad 0 \leq z \leq 1$

15. **a.** $x^2 + y^2 + z^2 \leq 1$ **b.** $x^2 + y^2 + z^2 > 1$

16. **a.** $x^2 + y^2 \leq 1, \quad z = 0$ **b.** $x^2 + y^2 \leq 1, \quad z = 3$

c. $x^2 + y^2 \leq 1$, no restriction on z

17. **a.** $x^2 + y^2 + z^2 = 1, \quad z \geq 0$

b. $x^2 + y^2 + z^2 \leq 1, \quad z \geq 0$

18. **a.** $x = y, \quad z = 0$ **b.** $x = y$, no restriction on z

In Exercises 19–28, describe the given set with a single equation or with a pair of equations.

19. The plane perpendicular to the

a. x-axis at $(3, 0, 0)$ **b.** y-axis at $(0, -1, 0)$

c. z-axis at $(0, 0, -2)$

20. The plane through the point $(3, -1, 2)$ perpendicular to the

a. x-axis **b.** y-axis **c.** z-axis

21. The plane through the point $(3, -1, 1)$ parallel to the

a. xy-plane **b.** yz-plane **c.** xz-plane

22. The circle of radius 2 centered at $(0, 0, 0)$ and lying in the

a. xy-plane **b.** yz-plane **c.** xz-plane

23. The circle of radius 2 centered at $(0, 2, 0)$ and lying in the

a. xy-plane **b.** yz-plane **c.** plane $y = 2$

24. The circle of radius 1 centered at $(-3, 4, 1)$ and lying in a plane parallel to the

a. xy-plane **b.** yz-plane **c.** xz-plane

25. The line through the point $(1, 3, -1)$ parallel to the

a. x-axis **b.** y-axis **c.** z-axis

26. The set of points in space equidistant from the origin and the point $(0, 2, 0)$

27. The circle in which the plane through the point $(1, 1, 3)$ perpendicular to the z-axis meets the sphere of radius 5 centered at the origin

28. The set of points in space that lie 2 units from the point $(0, 0, 1)$ and, at the same time, 2 units from the point $(0, 0, -1)$

Write inequalities to describe the sets in Exercises 29–34.

29. The slab bounded by the planes $z = 0$ and $z = 1$ (planes included)

30. The solid cube in the first octant bounded by the coordinate planes and the planes $x = 2, y = 2$, and $z = 2$

31. The half-space consisting of the points on and below the xy-plane

32. The upper hemisphere of the sphere of radius 1 centered at the origin

33. The **(a)** interior and **(b)** exterior of the sphere of radius 1 centered at the point $(1, 1, 1)$

34. The closed region bounded by the spheres of radius 1 and radius 2 centered at the origin. (*Closed* means the spheres are to be included. Had we wanted the spheres left out, we would have asked for the *open* region bounded by the spheres. This is analogous to the way we use *closed* and *open* to describe intervals: *closed* means endpoints included, *open* means endpoints left out. Closed sets include boundaries; open sets leave them out.)

In Exercises 35–40, find the distance between points P_1 and P_2.

35. $P_1(1, 1, 1), \quad P_2(3, 3, 0)$

36. $P_1(-1, 1, 5), \quad P_2(2, 5, 0)$

37. $P_1(1, 4, 5), \quad P_2(4, -2, 7)$

38. $P_1(3, 4, 5), \quad P_2(2, 3, 4)$

39. $P_1(0, 0, 0), \quad P_2(2, -2, -2)$

40. $P_1(5, 3, -2), \quad P_2(0, 0, 0)$

Find the centers and radii of the spheres in Exercises 41–44.

41. $(x + 2)^2 + y^2 + (z - 2)^2 = 8$

42. $\left(x + \frac{1}{2}\right)^2 + \left(y + \frac{1}{2}\right)^2 + \left(z + \frac{1}{2}\right)^2 = \frac{21}{4}$

43. $\left(x - \sqrt{2}\right)^2 + \left(y - \sqrt{2}\right)^2 + \left(z + \sqrt{2}\right)^2 = 2$

44. $x^2 + \left(y + \frac{1}{3}\right)^2 + \left(z - \frac{1}{3}\right)^2 = \frac{29}{9}$

Find equations for the spheres whose centers and radii are given in Exercises 45–48.

	Center	Radius
45.	$(1, 2, 3)$	$\sqrt{14}$
46.	$(0, -1, 5)$	2
47.	$(-2, 0, 0)$	$\sqrt{3}$
48.	$(0, -7, 0)$	7

Find the centers and radii of the spheres in Exercises 49–52.

49. $x^2 + y^2 + z^2 + 4x - 4z = 0$

50. $x^2 + y^2 + z^2 - 6y + 8z = 0$

51. $2x^2 + 2y^2 + 2z^2 + x + y + z = 9$

52. $3x^2 + 3y^2 + 3z^2 + 2y - 2z = 9$

53. Find a formula for the distance from the point $P(x, y, z)$ to the

a. x-axis **b.** y-axis **c.** z-axis

54. Find a formula for the distance from the point $P(x, y, z)$ to the

a. xy-plane **b.** yz-plane **c.** xz-plane

55. Find the perimeter of the triangle with vertices $A(-1, 2, 1)$, $B(1, -1, 3)$, and $C(3, 4, 5)$.

56. Show that the point $P(3, 1, 2)$ is equidistant from the points $A(2, -1, 3)$ and $B(4, 3, 1)$.

10.2 Vectors

Some of the things we measure are determined simply by their magnitudes. To record mass, length, or time, for example, we need only write down a number and name an appropriate unit of measure. We need more information to describe a force, displacement, or velocity. To describe a force, we need to record the direction in which it acts as well as how large it is. To describe a body's displacement, we have to say in what direction it moved as well as how far. To describe a body's velocity, we have to know where the body is headed as well as how fast it is going. In this section we show how to represent things that have both magnitude and direction in the plane or in space.

Component Form

A quantity such as force, displacement, or velocity is called a *vector* and is represented by a **directed line segment** (Figure 10.7). The arrow points in the direction of the action and its length gives the magnitude of the action in terms of a suitably chosen unit. For example, a force vector points in the direction in which the force acts; its length is a measure of the force's strength; a velocity vector points in the direction of motion and its length is the speed of the moving object. Figure 10.8 displays the velocity vector $\mathbf{v}$ at a specific location for a particle moving along a path in the plane or in space. (This application of vectors is studied in Chapter 11.)

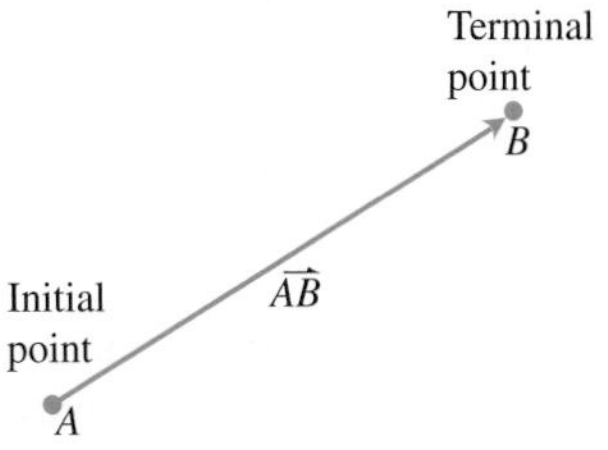

FIGURE 10.7 The directed line segment $\overrightarrow{AB}$.

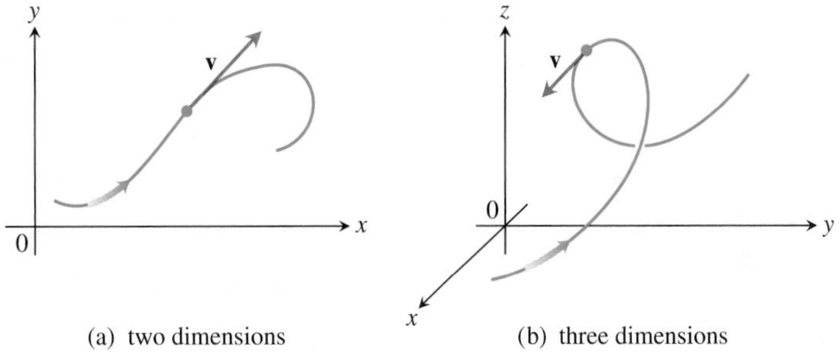

FIGURE 10.8 The velocity vector of a particle moving along a path (a) in the plane (b) in space. The arrowhead on the path indicates the direction of motion of the particle.

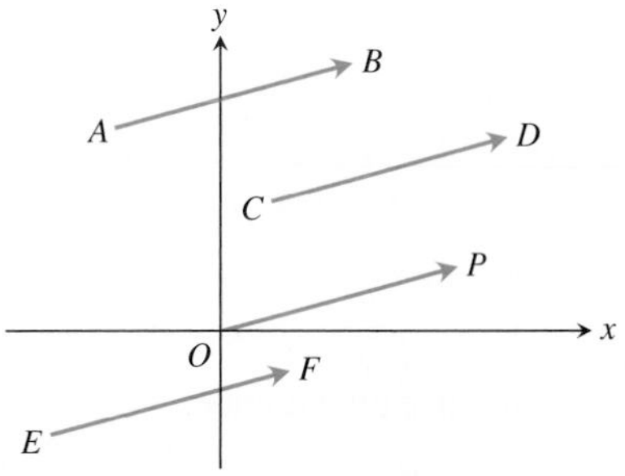

FIGURE 10.9 The four arrows in the plane (directed line segments) shown here have the same length and direction. They therefore represent the same vector, and we write $\overrightarrow{AB} = \overrightarrow{CD} = \overrightarrow{OP} = \overrightarrow{EF}$.

> **DEFINITIONS** A **vector** is a directed line segment. The directed line segment $\overrightarrow{AB}$ has **initial point** A and **terminal point** B; its **length** is denoted by $|\overrightarrow{AB}|$. Two vectors are **equal** if they have the same length and direction.

The arrows we use when we draw vectors are understood to represent the same vector if they have the same length, are parallel, and point in the same direction (Figure 10.9) regardless of the initial point.

In textbooks, vectors are usually written in lowercase, boldface letters, for example $\mathbf{u}$, $\mathbf{v}$, and $\mathbf{w}$. Sometimes we use uppercase boldface letters, such as $\mathbf{F}$, to denote a force vector. In handwritten form, it is customary to draw small arrows above the letters, for example $\vec{u}$, $\vec{v}$, $\vec{w}$, and $\vec{F}$.

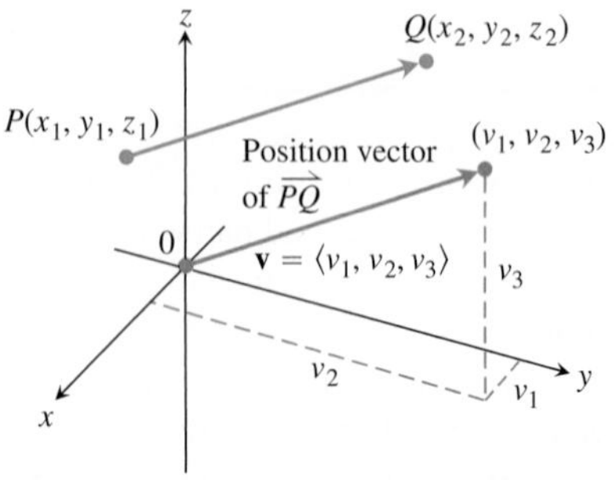

FIGURE 10.10 A vector $\overrightarrow{PQ}$ in standard position has its initial point at the origin. The directed line segments $\overrightarrow{PQ}$ and $\mathbf{v}$ are parallel and have the same length.

We need a way to represent vectors algebraically so that we can be more precise about the direction of a vector. Let $\mathbf{v} = \overrightarrow{PQ}$. There is one directed line segment equal to $\overrightarrow{PQ}$ whose initial point is the origin (Figure 10.10). It is the representative of $\mathbf{v}$ in **standard position** and is the vector we normally use to represent $\mathbf{v}$. We can specify $\mathbf{v}$ by writing the coordinates of its terminal point (v_1, v_2, v_3) when $\mathbf{v}$ is in standard position. If $\mathbf{v}$ is a vector in the plane its terminal point (v_1, v_2) has two coordinates.

DEFINITION

If $\mathbf{v}$ is a **two-dimensional** vector in the plane equal to the vector with initial point at the origin and terminal point (v_1, v_2), then the **component form** of $\mathbf{v}$ is

$$\mathbf{v} = \langle v_1, v_2 \rangle .$$

If $\mathbf{v}$ is a **three-dimensional** vector equal to the vector with initial point at the origin and terminal point (v_1, v_2, v_3), then the **component form** of $\mathbf{v}$ is

$$\mathbf{v} = \langle v_1, v_2, v_3 \rangle .$$

So a two-dimensional vector is an ordered pair $\mathbf{v} = \langle v_1, v_2 \rangle$ of real numbers, and a three-dimensional vector is an ordered triple $\mathbf{v} = \langle v_1, v_2, v_3 \rangle$ of real numbers. The numbers v_1, v_2, and v_3 are the **components** of $\mathbf{v}$.

If $\mathbf{v} = \langle v_1, v_2, v_3 \rangle$ is represented by the directed line segment $\overrightarrow{PQ}$, where the initial point is $P(x_1, y_1, z_1)$ and the terminal point is $Q(x_2, y_2, z_2)$, then $x_1 + v_1 = x_2, y_1 + v_2 = y_2$, and $z_1 + v_3 = z_2$ (see Figure 10.10). Thus, $v_1 = x_2 - x_1, v_2 = y_2 - y_1$, and $v_3 = z_2 - z_1$ are the components of $\overrightarrow{PQ}$.

In summary, given the points $P(x_1, y_1, z_1)$ and $Q(x_2, y_2, z_2)$, the standard position vector $\mathbf{v} = \langle v_1, v_2, v_3 \rangle$ equal to $\overrightarrow{PQ}$ is

$$\mathbf{v} = \langle x_2 - x_1, y_2 - y_1, z_2 - z_1 \rangle .$$

If $\mathbf{v}$ is two-dimensional with $P(x_1, y_1)$ and $Q(x_2, y_2)$ as points in the plane, then $\mathbf{v} = \langle x_2 - x_1, y_2 - y_1 \rangle$. There is no third component for planar vectors. With this understanding, we will develop the algebra of three-dimensional vectors and simply drop the third component when the vector is two-dimensional (a planar vector).

Two vectors are equal if and only if their standard position vectors are identical. Thus $\langle u_1, u_2, u_3 \rangle$ and $\langle v_1, v_2, v_3 \rangle$ are equal if and only if $u_1 = v_1, u_2 = v_2$, and $u_3 = v_3$.

The **magnitude** or **length** of the vector $\overrightarrow{PQ}$ is the length of any of its equivalent directed line segment representations. In particular, if $\mathbf{v} = \langle x_2 - x_1, y_2 - y_1, z_2 - z_1 \rangle$ is the standard position vector for $\overrightarrow{PQ}$, then the distance formula gives the magnitude or length of $\mathbf{v}$, denoted by the symbol $|\mathbf{v}|$ or $\|\mathbf{v}\|$.

The **magnitude** or **length** of the vector $\mathbf{v} = \overrightarrow{PQ}$ is the nonnegative number

$$|\mathbf{v}| = \sqrt{v_1^2 + v_2^2 + v_3^2} = \sqrt{(x_2 - x_1)^2 + (y_2 - y_1)^2 + (z_2 - z_1)^2}$$

(See Figure 10.10.)

The only vector with length 0 is the **zero vector** $\mathbf{0} = \langle 0, 0 \rangle$ or $\mathbf{0} = \langle 0, 0, 0 \rangle$. This vector is also the only vector with no specific direction.

EXAMPLE 1 Find the **(a)** component form and **(b)** length of the vector with initial point $P(-3, 4, 1)$ and terminal point $Q(-5, 2, 2)$.

Solution

(a) The standard position vector **v** representing $\overrightarrow{PQ}$ has components

$$v_1 = x_2 - x_1 = -5 - (-3) = -2, \qquad v_2 = y_2 - y_1 = 2 - 4 = -2,$$

and

$$v_3 = z_2 - z_1 = 2 - 1 = 1.$$

The component form of $\overrightarrow{PQ}$ is

$$\mathbf{v} = \langle -2, -2, 1 \rangle.$$

(b) The length or magnitude of $\mathbf{v} = \overrightarrow{PQ}$ is

$$|\mathbf{v}| = \sqrt{(-2)^2 + (-2)^2 + (1)^2} = \sqrt{9} = 3.$$ ■

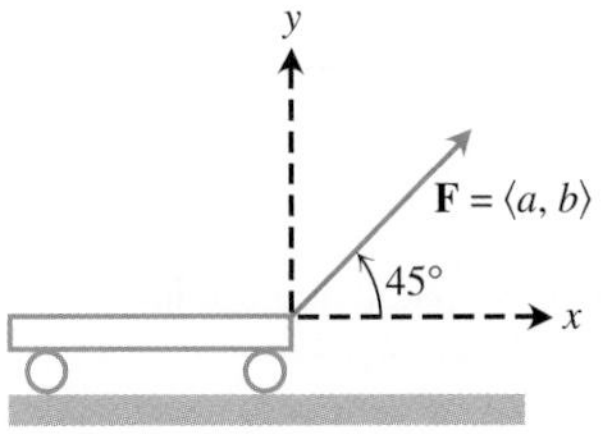

FIGURE 10.11 The force pulling the cart forward is represented by the vector **F** of magnitude 20 (pounds) making an angle of 45° with the horizontal ground (positive x-axis) (Example 2).

EXAMPLE 2 A small cart is being pulled along a smooth horizontal floor with a 20-lb force **F** making a 45° angle to the floor (Figure 10.11). What is the *effective* force moving the cart forward?

Solution The effective force is the horizontal component of $\mathbf{F} = \langle a, b \rangle$, given by

$$a = |\mathbf{F}| \cos 45^\circ = (20)\left(\frac{\sqrt{2}}{2}\right) \approx 14.14 \text{ lb}.$$

Notice that **F** is a two-dimensional vector. ■

Vector Algebra Operations

Two principal operations involving vectors are *vector addition* and *scalar multiplication*. A **scalar** is simply a real number, and is called such when we want to draw attention to its differences from vectors. Scalars can be positive, negative, or zero and are used to "scale" a vector by multiplication.

DEFINITIONS Let $\mathbf{u} = \langle u_1, u_2, u_3 \rangle$ and $\mathbf{v} = \langle v_1, v_2, v_3 \rangle$ be vectors with k a scalar.

Addition: $\mathbf{u} + \mathbf{v} = \langle u_1 + v_1, u_2 + v_2, u_3 + v_3 \rangle$

Scalar multiplication: $k\mathbf{u} = \langle ku_1, ku_2, ku_3 \rangle$

We add vectors by adding the corresponding components of the vectors. We multiply a vector by a scalar by multiplying each component by the scalar. The definitions apply to planar vectors except there are only two components, $\langle u_1, u_2 \rangle$ and $\langle v_1, v_2 \rangle$.

The definition of vector addition is illustrated geometrically for planar vectors in Figure 10.12a, where the initial point of one vector is placed at the terminal point of the other. Another interpretation is shown in Figure 10.12b (called the **parallelogram law** of addition), where the sum, called the **resultant vector**, is the diagonal of the parallelogram. In physics, forces add vectorially as do velocities, accelerations, and so on. So the force acting on a particle subject to two gravitational forces, for example, is obtained by adding the two force vectors.

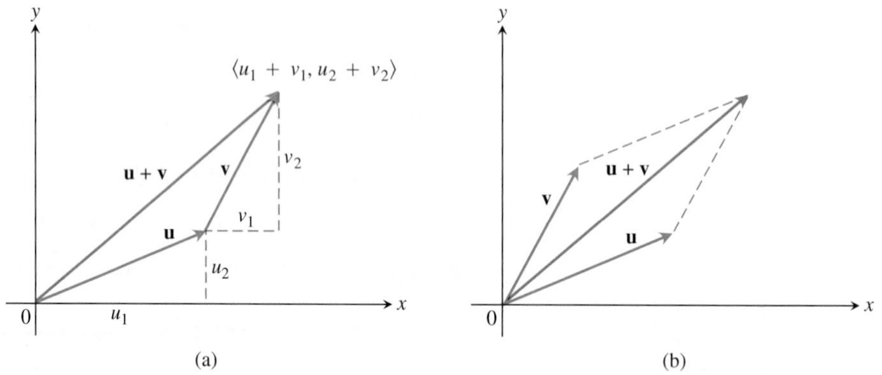

FIGURE 10.12 (a) Geometric interpretation of the vector sum. (b) The parallelogram law of vector addition.

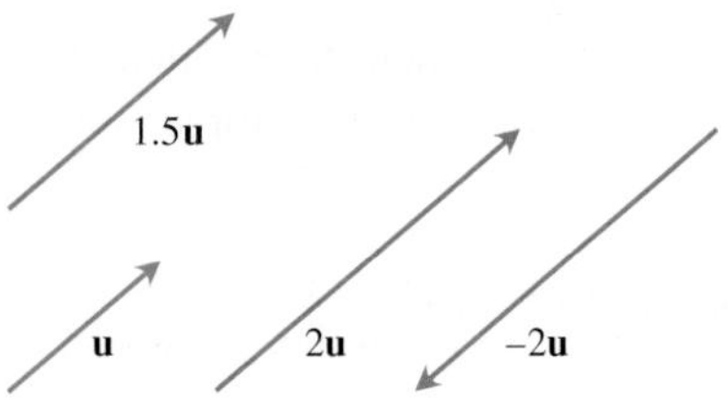

FIGURE 10.13 Scalar multiples of **u**.

Figure 10.13 displays a geometric interpretation of the product $k\mathbf{u}$ of the scalar k and vector $\mathbf{u}$. If $k > 0$, then $k\mathbf{u}$ has the same direction as $\mathbf{u}$; if $k < 0$, then the direction of $k\mathbf{u}$ is opposite to that of $\mathbf{u}$. Comparing the lengths of $\mathbf{u}$ and $k\mathbf{u}$, we see that

$$\begin{aligned} |k\mathbf{u}| &= \sqrt{(ku_1)^2 + (ku_2)^2 + (ku_3)^2} = \sqrt{k^2(u_1^2 + u_2^2 + u_3^2)} \\ &= \sqrt{k^2}\sqrt{u_1^2 + u_2^2 + u_3^2} = |k|\,|\mathbf{u}|. \end{aligned}$$

The length of $k\mathbf{u}$ is the absolute value of the scalar k times the length of $\mathbf{u}$. The vector $(-1)\mathbf{u} = -\mathbf{u}$ has the same length as $\mathbf{u}$ but points in the opposite direction.

The **difference** $\mathbf{u} - \mathbf{v}$ of two vectors is defined by

$$\mathbf{u} - \mathbf{v} = \mathbf{u} + (-\mathbf{v}).$$

If $\mathbf{u} = \langle u_1, u_2, u_3 \rangle$ and $\mathbf{v} = \langle v_1, v_2, v_3 \rangle$, then

$$\mathbf{u} - \mathbf{v} = \langle u_1 - v_1, u_2 - v_2, u_3 - v_3 \rangle.$$

Note that $(\mathbf{u} - \mathbf{v}) + \mathbf{v} = \mathbf{u}$, so adding the vector $(\mathbf{u} - \mathbf{v})$ to $\mathbf{v}$ gives $\mathbf{u}$ (Figure 10.14a). Figure 10.14b shows the difference $\mathbf{u} - \mathbf{v}$ as the sum $\mathbf{u} + (-\mathbf{v})$.

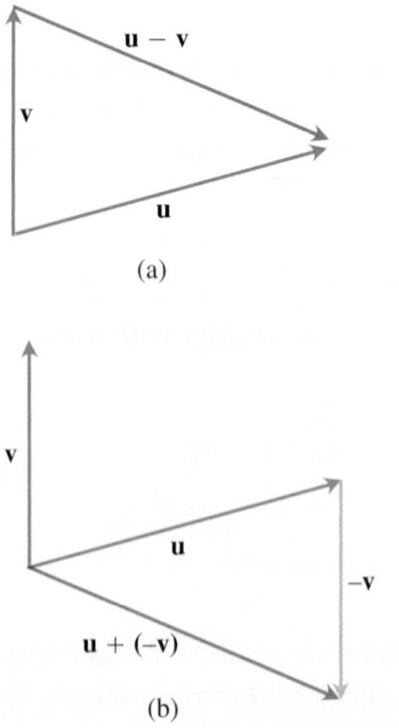

FIGURE 10.14 (a) The vector $\mathbf{u} - \mathbf{v}$, when added to $\mathbf{v}$, gives $\mathbf{u}$. (b) $\mathbf{u} - \mathbf{v} = \mathbf{u} + (-\mathbf{v})$.

EXAMPLE 3 Let $\mathbf{u} = \langle -1, 3, 1 \rangle$ and $\mathbf{v} = \langle 4, 7, 0 \rangle$. Find

(a) $2\mathbf{u} + 3\mathbf{v}$ **(b)** $\mathbf{u} - \mathbf{v}$ **(c)** $\left|\frac{1}{2}\mathbf{u}\right|$.

Solution

(a) $2\mathbf{u} + 3\mathbf{v} = 2\langle -1, 3, 1 \rangle + 3\langle 4, 7, 0 \rangle = \langle -2, 6, 2 \rangle + \langle 12, 21, 0 \rangle = \langle 10, 27, 2 \rangle$

(b) $\mathbf{u} - \mathbf{v} = \langle -1, 3, 1 \rangle - \langle 4, 7, 0 \rangle = \langle -1 - 4, 3 - 7, 1 - 0 \rangle = \langle -5, -4, 1 \rangle$

(c) $\left|\frac{1}{2}\mathbf{u}\right| = \left|\left\langle -\frac{1}{2}, \frac{3}{2}, \frac{1}{2} \right\rangle\right| = \sqrt{\left(-\frac{1}{2}\right)^2 + \left(\frac{3}{2}\right)^2 + \left(\frac{1}{2}\right)^2} = \frac{1}{2}\sqrt{11}.$ ∎

Vector operations have many of the properties of ordinary arithmetic. These properties are readily verified using the definitions of vector addition and multiplication by a scalar.

Properties of Vector Operations

Let **u**, **v**, **w** be vectors and a, b be scalars.

1. $\mathbf{u} + \mathbf{v} = \mathbf{v} + \mathbf{u}$	**2.** $(\mathbf{u} + \mathbf{v}) + \mathbf{w} = \mathbf{u} + (\mathbf{v} + \mathbf{w})$
3. $\mathbf{u} + \mathbf{0} = \mathbf{u}$	**4.** $\mathbf{u} + (-\mathbf{u}) = \mathbf{0}$
5. $0\mathbf{u} = \mathbf{0}$	**6.** $1\mathbf{u} = \mathbf{u}$
7. $a(b\mathbf{u}) = (ab)\mathbf{u}$	**8.** $a(\mathbf{u} + \mathbf{v}) = a\mathbf{u} + a\mathbf{v}$
9. $(a + b)\mathbf{u} = a\mathbf{u} + b\mathbf{u}$	

An important application of vectors occurs in navigation.

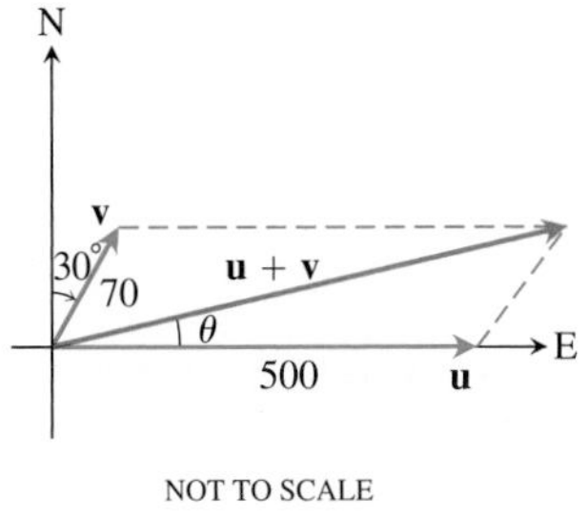

FIGURE 10.15 Vectors representing the velocities of the airplane **u** and tailwind **v** in Example 4.

EXAMPLE 4 A jet airliner, flying due east at 500 mph in still air, encounters a 70-mph tailwind blowing in the direction 60° north of east. The airplane holds its compass heading due east but, because of the wind, acquires a new ground speed and direction. What are they?

Solution If **u** = the velocity of the airplane alone and **v** = the velocity of the tailwind, then $|\mathbf{u}| = 500$ and $|\mathbf{v}| = 70$ (Figure 10.15). The velocity of the airplane with respect to the ground is given by the magnitude and direction of the *resultant vector* $\mathbf{u} + \mathbf{v}$. If we let the positive x-axis represent east and the positive y-axis represent north, then the component forms of **u** and **v** are

$$\mathbf{u} = \langle 500, 0\rangle \quad \text{and} \quad \mathbf{v} = \langle 70\cos 60°, 70\sin 60°\rangle = \langle 35, 35\sqrt{3}\rangle.$$

Therefore,

$$\mathbf{u} + \mathbf{v} = \langle 535, 35\sqrt{3}\rangle$$

$$|\mathbf{u} + \mathbf{v}| = \sqrt{535^2 + (35\sqrt{3})^2} \approx 538.4$$

and

$$\theta = \tan^{-1}\frac{35\sqrt{3}}{535} \approx 6.5°. \qquad \text{Figure 10.15}$$

The new ground speed of the airplane is about 538.4 mph, and its new direction is about 6.5° north of east. ■

Unit Vectors

A vector **v** of length 1 is called a **unit vector**. The **standard unit vectors** are

$$\mathbf{i} = \langle 1, 0, 0\rangle, \qquad \mathbf{j} = \langle 0, 1, 0\rangle, \qquad \text{and} \quad \mathbf{k} = \langle 0, 0, 1\rangle.$$

Any vector $\mathbf{v} = \langle v_1, v_2, v_3\rangle$ can be written as a *linear combination* of the standard unit vectors as follows:

$$\begin{aligned}\mathbf{v} = \langle v_1, v_2, v_3\rangle &= \langle v_1, 0, 0\rangle + \langle 0, v_2, 0\rangle + \langle 0, 0, v_3\rangle \\ &= v_1\langle 1, 0, 0\rangle + v_2\langle 0, 1, 0\rangle + v_3\langle 0, 0, 1\rangle \\ &= v_1\mathbf{i} + v_2\mathbf{j} + v_3\mathbf{k}.\end{aligned}$$

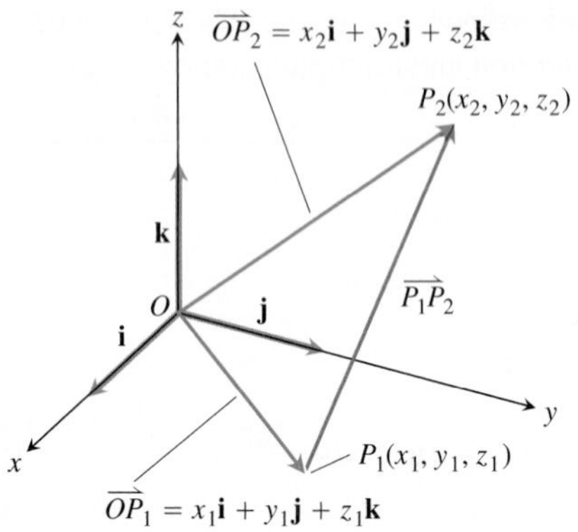

FIGURE 10.16 The vector from P_1 to P_2 is $\overrightarrow{P_1P_2} = (x_2 - x_1)\mathbf{i} + (y_2 - y_1)\mathbf{j} + (z_2 - z_1)\mathbf{k}$.

We call the scalar (or number) v_1 the **i-component** of the vector $\mathbf{v}$, v_2 the **j-component**, and v_3 the **k-component**. In component form, the vector from $P_1(x_1, y_1, z_1)$ to $P_2(x_2, y_2, z_2)$ is

$$\overrightarrow{P_1P_2} = (x_2 - x_1)\mathbf{i} + (y_2 - y_1)\mathbf{j} + (z_2 - z_1)\mathbf{k}$$

(Figure 10.16).

Whenever $\mathbf{v} \neq \mathbf{0}$, its length $|\mathbf{v}|$ is not zero and

$$\left|\frac{1}{|\mathbf{v}|}\mathbf{v}\right| = \frac{1}{|\mathbf{v}|}|\mathbf{v}| = 1.$$

That is, $\mathbf{v}/|\mathbf{v}|$ is a unit vector in the direction of $\mathbf{v}$, called **the direction** of the nonzero vector $\mathbf{v}$.

EXAMPLE 5 Find a unit vector $\mathbf{u}$ in the direction of the vector from $P_1(1, 0, 1)$ to $P_2(3, 2, 0)$.

Solution We divide $\overrightarrow{P_1P_2}$ by its length:

$$\overrightarrow{P_1P_2} = (3 - 1)\mathbf{i} + (2 - 0)\mathbf{j} + (0 - 1)\mathbf{k} = 2\mathbf{i} + 2\mathbf{j} - \mathbf{k}$$

$$|\overrightarrow{P_1P_2}| = \sqrt{(2)^2 + (2)^2 + (-1)^2} = \sqrt{4 + 4 + 1} = \sqrt{9} = 3$$

$$\mathbf{u} = \frac{\overrightarrow{P_1P_2}}{|\overrightarrow{P_1P_2}|} = \frac{2\mathbf{i} + 2\mathbf{j} - \mathbf{k}}{3} = \frac{2}{3}\mathbf{i} + \frac{2}{3}\mathbf{j} - \frac{1}{3}\mathbf{k}.$$

The unit vector $\mathbf{u}$ is the direction of $\overrightarrow{P_1P_2}$. ■

EXAMPLE 6 If $\mathbf{v} = 3\mathbf{i} - 4\mathbf{j}$ is a velocity vector, express $\mathbf{v}$ as a product of its speed times a unit vector in the direction of motion.

Solution Speed is the magnitude (length) of $\mathbf{v}$:

$$|\mathbf{v}| = \sqrt{(3)^2 + (-4)^2} = \sqrt{9 + 16} = 5.$$

The unit vector $\mathbf{v}/|\mathbf{v}|$ has the same direction as $\mathbf{v}$:

$$\frac{\mathbf{v}}{|\mathbf{v}|} = \frac{3\mathbf{i} - 4\mathbf{j}}{5} = \frac{3}{5}\mathbf{i} - \frac{4}{5}\mathbf{j}.$$

So

$$\mathbf{v} = 3\mathbf{i} - 4\mathbf{j} = \underbrace{5}_{\text{Length (speed)}}\underbrace{\left(\frac{3}{5}\mathbf{i} - \frac{4}{5}\mathbf{j}\right)}_{\text{Direction of motion}}.$$ ■

In summary, we can express any nonzero vector $\mathbf{v}$ in terms of its two important features, length and direction, by writing $\mathbf{v} = |\mathbf{v}|\frac{\mathbf{v}}{|\mathbf{v}|}$.

HISTORICAL BIOGRAPHY

Hermann Grassmann
(1809–1877)

If $\mathbf{v} \neq \mathbf{0}$, then

1. $\dfrac{\mathbf{v}}{|\mathbf{v}|}$ is a unit vector in the direction of $\mathbf{v}$;
2. the equation $\mathbf{v} = |\mathbf{v}|\dfrac{\mathbf{v}}{|\mathbf{v}|}$ expresses $\mathbf{v}$ in terms of its length and direction.

EXAMPLE 7 A force of 6 newtons is applied in the direction of the vector $\mathbf{v} = 2\mathbf{i} + 2\mathbf{j} - \mathbf{k}$. Express the force $\mathbf{F}$ as a product of its magnitude and direction.

Solution The force vector has magnitude 6 and direction $\dfrac{\mathbf{v}}{|\mathbf{v}|}$, so

$$\mathbf{F} = 6\frac{\mathbf{v}}{|\mathbf{v}|} = 6\frac{2\mathbf{i} + 2\mathbf{j} - \mathbf{k}}{\sqrt{2^2 + 2^2 + (-1)^2}} = 6\frac{2\mathbf{i} + 2\mathbf{j} - \mathbf{k}}{3}$$
$$= 6\left(\frac{2}{3}\mathbf{i} + \frac{2}{3}\mathbf{j} - \frac{1}{3}\mathbf{k}\right).$$

■

Midpoint of a Line Segment

Vectors are often useful in geometry. For example, the coordinates of the midpoint of a line segment are found by averaging.

The **midpoint** M of the line segment joining points $P_1(x_1, y_1, z_1)$ and $P_2(x_2, y_2, z_2)$ is the point

$$\left(\frac{x_1 + x_2}{2}, \frac{y_1 + y_2}{2}, \frac{z_1 + z_2}{2}\right).$$

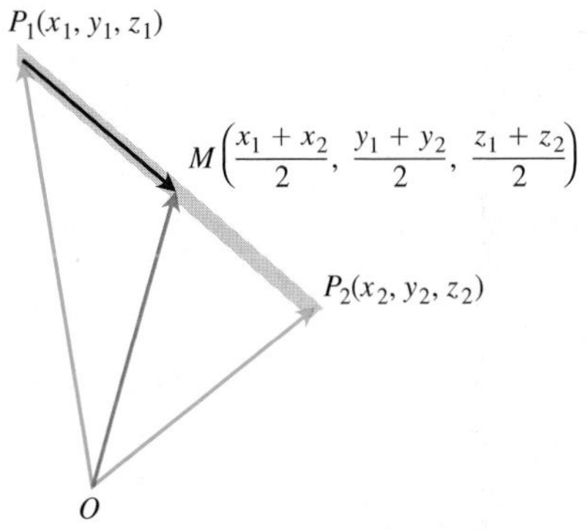

FIGURE 10.17 The coordinates of the midpoint are the averages of the coordinates of P_1 and P_2.

To see why, observe (Figure 10.17) that

$$\vec{OM} = \vec{OP}_1 + \frac{1}{2}(\vec{P_1P_2}) = \vec{OP}_1 + \frac{1}{2}(\vec{OP}_2 - \vec{OP}_1)$$
$$= \frac{1}{2}(\vec{OP}_1 + \vec{OP}_2)$$
$$= \frac{x_1 + x_2}{2}\mathbf{i} + \frac{y_1 + y_2}{2}\mathbf{j} + \frac{z_1 + z_2}{2}\mathbf{k}.$$

EXAMPLE 8 The midpoint of the segment joining $P_1(3, -2, 0)$ and $P_2(7, 4, 4)$ is

$$\left(\frac{3 + 7}{2}, \frac{-2 + 4}{2}, \frac{0 + 4}{2}\right) = (5, 1, 2).$$

■

EXERCISES 10.2

In Exercises 1–8, let $\mathbf{u} = \langle 3, -2 \rangle$ and $\mathbf{v} = \langle -2, 5 \rangle$. Find the **(a)** component form and **(b)** magnitude (length) of the vector.

1. $3\mathbf{u}$

2. $-2\mathbf{v}$

3. $\mathbf{u} + \mathbf{v}$

4. $\mathbf{u} - \mathbf{v}$

5. $2\mathbf{u} - 3\mathbf{v}$

6. $-2\mathbf{u} + 5\mathbf{v}$

7. $\frac{3}{5}\mathbf{u} + \frac{4}{5}\mathbf{v}$

8. $-\frac{5}{13}\mathbf{u} + \frac{12}{13}\mathbf{v}$

In Exercises 9–16, find the component form of the vector.

9. The vector $\overrightarrow{PQ}$, where $P = (1, 3)$ and $Q = (2, -1)$

10. The vector $\overrightarrow{OP}$ where O is the origin and P is the midpoint of segment RS, where $R = (2, -1)$ and $S = (-4, 3)$

11. The vector from the point $A = (2, 3)$ to the origin

12. The sum of $\overrightarrow{AB}$ and $\overrightarrow{CD}$, where $A = (1, -1)$, $B = (2, 0)$, $C = (-1, 3)$, and $D = (-2, 2)$

13. The unit vector that makes an angle $\theta = 2\pi/3$ with the positive x-axis

14. The unit vector that makes an angle $\theta = -3\pi/4$ with the positive x-axis

15. The unit vector obtained by rotating the vector $\langle 0, 1 \rangle$ 120° counterclockwise about the origin

16. The unit vector obtained by rotating the vector $\langle 1, 0 \rangle$ 135° counterclockwise about the origin

In Exercises 17–22, express each vector in the form $\mathbf{v} = v_1\mathbf{i} + v_2\mathbf{j} + v_3\mathbf{k}$.

17. $\overrightarrow{P_1P_2}$ if P_1 is the point $(5, 7, -1)$ and P_2 is the point $(2, 9, -2)$

18. $\overrightarrow{P_1P_2}$ if P_1 is the point $(1, 2, 0)$ and P_2 is the point $(-3, 0, 5)$

19. $\overrightarrow{AB}$ if A is the point $(-7, -8, 1)$ and B is the point $(-10, 8, 1)$

20. $\overrightarrow{AB}$ if A is the point $(1, 0, 3)$ and B is the point $(-1, 4, 5)$

21. $5\mathbf{u} - \mathbf{v}$ if $\mathbf{u} = \langle 1, 1, -1 \rangle$ and $\mathbf{v} = \langle 2, 0, 3 \rangle$

22. $-2\mathbf{u} + 3\mathbf{v}$ if $\mathbf{u} = \langle -1, 0, 2 \rangle$ and $\mathbf{v} = \langle 1, 1, 1 \rangle$

In Exercises 23 and 24, copy vectors **u**, **v**, and **w** head to tail as needed to sketch the indicated vector.

23.

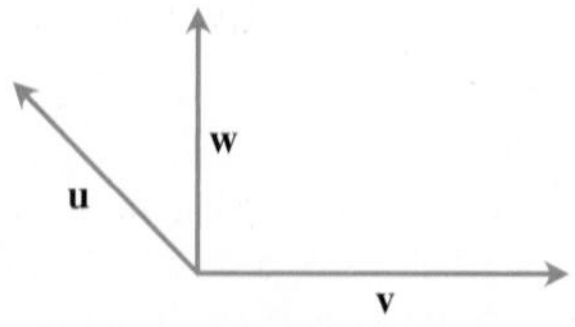

a. $\mathbf{u} + \mathbf{v}$

b. $\mathbf{u} + \mathbf{v} + \mathbf{w}$

c. $\mathbf{u} - \mathbf{v}$

d. $\mathbf{u} - \mathbf{w}$

24.

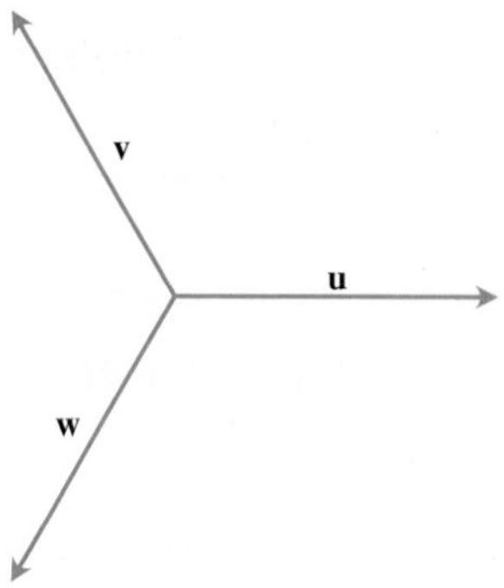

a. $\mathbf{u} - \mathbf{v}$

b. $\mathbf{u} - \mathbf{v} + \mathbf{w}$

c. $2\mathbf{u} - \mathbf{v}$

d. $\mathbf{u} + \mathbf{v} + \mathbf{w}$

In Exercises 25–30, express each vector as a product of its length and direction.

25. $2\mathbf{i} + \mathbf{j} - 2\mathbf{k}$

26. $9\mathbf{i} - 2\mathbf{j} + 6\mathbf{k}$

27. $5\mathbf{k}$

28. $\frac{3}{5}\mathbf{i} + \frac{4}{5}\mathbf{k}$

29. $\frac{1}{\sqrt{6}}\mathbf{i} - \frac{1}{\sqrt{6}}\mathbf{j} - \frac{1}{\sqrt{6}}\mathbf{k}$

30. $\frac{\mathbf{i}}{\sqrt{3}} + \frac{\mathbf{j}}{\sqrt{3}} + \frac{\mathbf{k}}{\sqrt{3}}$

31. Find the vectors whose lengths and directions are given. Try to do the calculations without writing.

Length	Direction
a. 2	$\mathbf{i}$
b. $\sqrt{3}$	$-\mathbf{k}$
c. $\frac{1}{2}$	$\frac{3}{5}\mathbf{j} + \frac{4}{5}\mathbf{k}$
d. 7	$\frac{6}{7}\mathbf{i} - \frac{2}{7}\mathbf{j} + \frac{3}{7}\mathbf{k}$

32. Find the vectors whose lengths and directions are given. Try to do the calculations without writing.

Length	Direction
a. 7	$-\mathbf{j}$
b. $\sqrt{2}$	$-\frac{3}{5}\mathbf{i} - \frac{4}{5}\mathbf{k}$
c. $\frac{13}{12}$	$\frac{3}{13}\mathbf{i} - \frac{4}{13}\mathbf{j} - \frac{12}{13}\mathbf{k}$
d. $a > 0$	$\frac{1}{\sqrt{2}}\mathbf{i} + \frac{1}{\sqrt{3}}\mathbf{j} - \frac{1}{\sqrt{6}}\mathbf{k}$

33. Find a vector of magnitude 7 in the direction of $\mathbf{v} = 12\mathbf{i} - 5\mathbf{k}$.

34. Find a vector of magnitude 3 in the direction opposite to the direction of $\mathbf{v} = (1/2)\mathbf{i} - (1/2)\mathbf{j} - (1/2)\mathbf{k}$.

In Exercises 35–38, find

a. the direction of $\overrightarrow{P_1P_2}$ and

b. the midpoint of line segment P_1P_2.

35. $P_1(-1, 1, 5)$ $P_2(2, 5, 0)$

36. $P_1(1, 4, 5)$ $P_2(4, -2, 7)$

37. $P_1(3, 4, 5)$ $P_2(2, 3, 4)$

38. $P_1(0, 0, 0)$ $P_2(2, -2, -2)$

39. If $\overrightarrow{AB} = \mathbf{i} + 4\mathbf{j} - 2\mathbf{k}$ and B is the point $(5, 1, 3)$, find A.

40. If $\overrightarrow{AB} = -7\mathbf{i} + 3\mathbf{j} + 8\mathbf{k}$ and A is the point $(-2, -3, 6)$, find B.

41. Linear combination Let $\mathbf{u} = 2\mathbf{i} + \mathbf{j}$, $\mathbf{v} = \mathbf{i} + \mathbf{j}$, and $\mathbf{w} = \mathbf{i} - \mathbf{j}$. Find scalars a and b such that $\mathbf{u} = a\mathbf{v} + b\mathbf{w}$.

42. Linear combination Let $\mathbf{u} = \mathbf{i} - 2\mathbf{j}$, $\mathbf{v} = 2\mathbf{i} + 3\mathbf{j}$, and $\mathbf{w} = \mathbf{i} + \mathbf{j}$. Write $\mathbf{u} = \mathbf{u}_1 + \mathbf{u}_2$, where $\mathbf{u}_1$ is parallel to $\mathbf{v}$ and $\mathbf{u}_2$ is parallel to $\mathbf{w}$. (See Exercise 41.)

43. Force vector You are pulling on a suitcase with a force $\mathbf{F}$ (pictured here) whose magnitude is $|\mathbf{F}| = 10$ lb. Find the $\mathbf{i}$- and $\mathbf{j}$-components of $\mathbf{F}$.

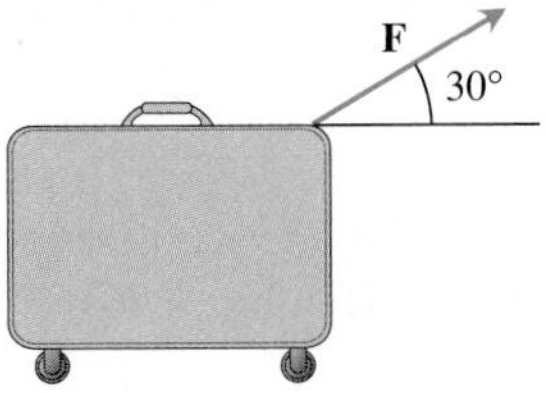

44. Force vector A kite string exerts a 12-lb pull ($|\mathbf{F}| = 12$) on a kite and makes a 45° angle with the horizontal. Find the horizontal and vertical components of $\mathbf{F}$.

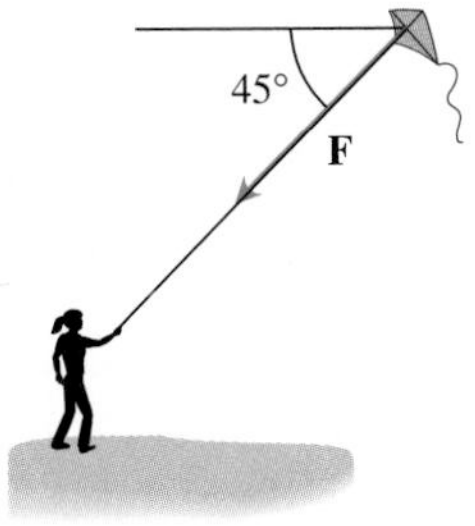

45. Velocity An airplane is flying in the direction 25° west of north at 800 km/h. Find the component form of the velocity of the airplane, assuming that the positive x-axis represents due east and the positive y-axis represents due north.

46. Velocity An airplane is flying in the direction 10° east of south at 600 km/h. Find the component form of the velocity of the airplane, assuming that the positive x-axis represents due east and the positive y-axis represents due north.

47. Location A bird flies from its nest 5 km in the direction 60° north of east, where it stops to rest on a tree. It then flies 10 km in the direction due southeast and lands atop a telephone pole. Place an xy-coordinate system so that the origin is the bird's nest, the x-axis points east, and the y-axis points north.

a. At what point is the tree located?

b. At what point is the telephone pole?

48. Use similar triangles to find the coordinates of the point Q that divides the segment from $P_1(x_1, y_1, z_1)$ to $P_2(x_2, y_2, z_2)$ into two lengths whose ratio is $p/q = r$.

49. Medians of a triangle Suppose that A, B, and C are the corner points of the thin triangular plate of constant density shown here.

a. Find the vector from C to the midpoint M of side AB.

b. Find the vector from C to the point that lies two-thirds of the way from C to M on the median CM.

c. Find the coordinates of the point in which the medians of ΔABC intersect. According to Exercise 21, Section 6.7, this point is the plate's center of mass.

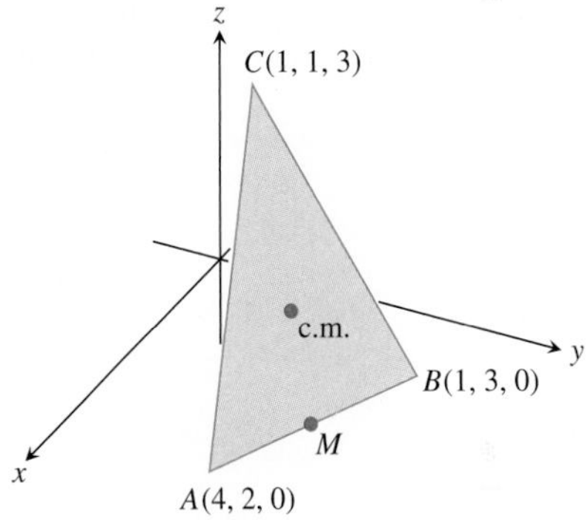

50. Find the vector from the origin to the point of intersection of the medians of the triangle whose vertices are

$$A(1, -1, 2),\quad B(2, 1, 3),\quad \text{and}\quad C(-1, 2, -1).$$

51. Let $ABCD$ be a general, not necessarily planar, quadrilateral in space. Show that the two segments joining the midpoints of opposite sides of $ABCD$ bisect each other. (*Hint:* Show that the segments have the same midpoint.)

52. Vectors are drawn from the center of a regular n-sided polygon in the plane to the vertices of the polygon. Show that the sum of the vectors is zero. (*Hint:* What happens to the sum if you rotate the polygon about its center?)

53. Suppose that A, B, and C are vertices of a triangle and that a, b, and c are, respectively, the midpoints of the opposite sides. Show that $\overrightarrow{Aa} + \overrightarrow{Bb} + \overrightarrow{Cc} = \mathbf{0}$.

54. Unit vectors in the plane Show that a unit vector in the plane can be expressed as $\mathbf{u} = (\cos\theta)\mathbf{i} + (\sin\theta)\mathbf{j}$, obtained by rotating $\mathbf{i}$ through an angle θ in the counterclockwise direction. Explain why this form gives *every* unit vector in the plane.

10.3 The Dot Product

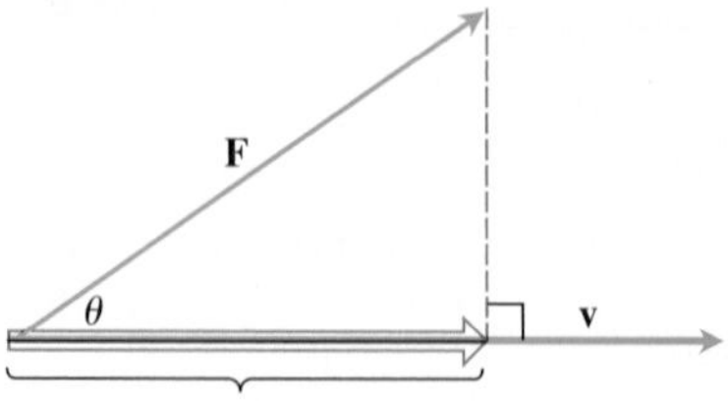

FIGURE 10.18 The magnitude of the force **F** in the direction of vector **v** is the length $|\mathbf{F}|\cos\theta$ of the projection of **F** onto **v**.

If a force **F** is applied to a particle moving along a path, we often need to know the magnitude of the force in the direction of motion. If **v** is parallel to the tangent line to the path at the point where **F** is applied, then we want the magnitude of **F** in the direction of **v**. Figure 10.18 shows that the scalar quantity we seek is the length $|\mathbf{F}|\cos\theta$, where θ is the angle between the two vectors **F** and **v**.

In this section, we show how to calculate easily the angle between two vectors directly from their components. A key part of the calculation is an expression called the *dot product*. Dot products are also called *inner* or *scalar* products because the product results in a scalar, not a vector. After investigating the dot product, we apply it to finding the projection of one vector onto another (as displayed in Figure 10.18) and to finding the work done by a constant force acting through a displacement.

Angle Between Vectors

When two nonzero vectors **u** and **v** are placed so their initial points coincide, they form an angle θ of measure $0 \le \theta \le \pi$ (Figure 10.19). If the vectors do not lie along the same line, the angle θ is measured in the plane containing both of them. If they do lie along the same line, the angle between them is 0 if they point in the same direction, and π if they point in opposite directions. The angle θ is the **angle between u and v**. Theorem 1 gives a formula to determine this angle.

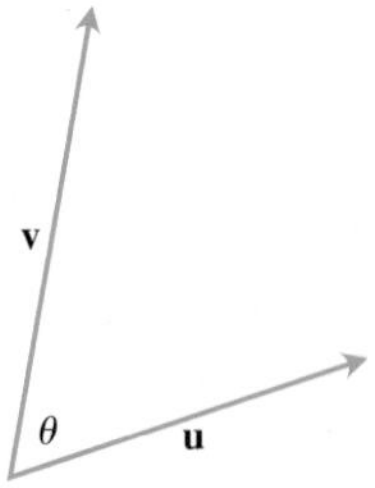

FIGURE 10.19 The angle between **u** and **v**.

THEOREM 1—Angle Between Two Vectors The angle θ between two nonzero vectors $\mathbf{u} = \langle u_1, u_2, u_3\rangle$ and $\mathbf{v} = \langle v_1, v_2, v_3\rangle$ is given by

$$\theta = \cos^{-1}\left(\frac{u_1v_1 + u_2v_2 + u_3v_3}{|\mathbf{u}|\,|\mathbf{v}|}\right).$$

Before proving Theorem 1, we focus attention on the expression $u_1v_1 + u_2v_2 + u_3v_3$ in the calculation for θ.

DEFINITION The **dot product $\mathbf{u}\cdot\mathbf{v}$** ("**u** dot **v**") of vectors $\mathbf{u} = \langle u_1, u_2, u_3\rangle$ and $\mathbf{v} = \langle v_1, v_2, v_3\rangle$ is

$$\mathbf{u}\cdot\mathbf{v} = u_1v_1 + u_2v_2 + u_3v_3.$$

EXAMPLE 1

(a) $$\langle 1, -2, -1\rangle\cdot\langle -6, 2, -3\rangle = (1)(-6) + (-2)(2) + (-1)(-3)$$
$$= -6 - 4 + 3 = -7$$

(b) $$\left(\frac{1}{2}\mathbf{i} + 3\mathbf{j} + \mathbf{k}\right)\cdot(4\mathbf{i} - \mathbf{j} + 2\mathbf{k}) = \left(\frac{1}{2}\right)(4) + (3)(-1) + (1)(2) = 1$$ ■

The dot product of a pair of two-dimensional vectors is defined in a similar fashion:

$$\langle u_1, u_2\rangle\cdot\langle v_1, v_2\rangle = u_1v_1 + u_2v_2.$$

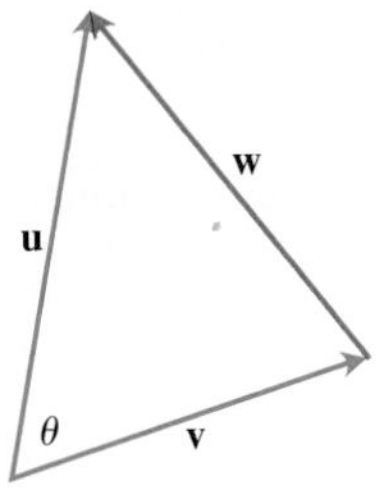

FIGURE 10.20 The parallelogram law of addition of vectors gives $\mathbf{w} = \mathbf{u} - \mathbf{v}$.

Proof of Theorem 1 Applying the law of cosines (Equation (8), Section 1.3) to the triangle in Figure 10.20, we find that

$$|\mathbf{w}|^2 = |\mathbf{u}|^2 + |\mathbf{v}|^2 - 2|\mathbf{u}||\mathbf{v}|\cos\theta \qquad \text{Law of cosines}$$

$$2|\mathbf{u}||\mathbf{v}|\cos\theta = |\mathbf{u}|^2 + |\mathbf{v}|^2 - |\mathbf{w}|^2.$$

Because $\mathbf{w} = \mathbf{u} - \mathbf{v}$, the component form of $\mathbf{w}$ is $\langle u_1 - v_1, u_2 - v_2, u_3 - v_3\rangle$. So

$$|\mathbf{u}|^2 = \left(\sqrt{u_1^2 + u_2^2 + u_3^2}\right)^2 = u_1^2 + u_2^2 + u_3^2$$

$$|\mathbf{v}|^2 = \left(\sqrt{v_1^2 + v_2^2 + v_3^2}\right)^2 = v_1^2 + v_2^2 + v_3^2$$

$$\begin{aligned}|\mathbf{w}|^2 &= \left(\sqrt{(u_1 - v_1)^2 + (u_2 - v_2)^2 + (u_3 - v_3)^2}\right)^2 \\ &= (u_1 - v_1)^2 + (u_2 - v_2)^2 + (u_3 - v_3)^2 \\ &= u_1^2 - 2u_1v_1 + v_1^2 + u_2^2 - 2u_2v_2 + v_2^2 + u_3^2 - 2u_3v_3 + v_3^2\end{aligned}$$

and

$$|\mathbf{u}|^2 + |\mathbf{v}|^2 - |\mathbf{w}|^2 = 2(u_1v_1 + u_2v_2 + u_3v_3).$$

Therefore,

$$\begin{aligned}2|\mathbf{u}||\mathbf{v}|\cos\theta &= |\mathbf{u}|^2 + |\mathbf{v}|^2 - |\mathbf{w}|^2 = 2(u_1v_1 + u_2v_2 + u_3v_3) \\ |\mathbf{u}||\mathbf{v}|\cos\theta &= u_1v_1 + u_2v_2 + u_3v_3 \\ \cos\theta &= \frac{u_1v_1 + u_2v_2 + u_3v_3}{|\mathbf{u}||\mathbf{v}|}.\end{aligned}$$

Since $0 \le \theta < \pi$, we have

$$\theta = \cos^{-1}\left(\frac{u_1v_1 + u_2v_2 + u_3v_3}{|\mathbf{u}||\mathbf{v}|}\right). \qquad \blacksquare$$

With the notation of the dot product, the angle between two vectors $\mathbf{u}$ and $\mathbf{v}$ can be written as

$$\theta = \cos^{-1}\left(\frac{\mathbf{u}\cdot\mathbf{v}}{|\mathbf{u}||\mathbf{v}|}\right).$$

EXAMPLE 2 Find the angle between $\mathbf{u} = \mathbf{i} - 2\mathbf{j} - 2\mathbf{k}$ and $\mathbf{v} = 6\mathbf{i} + 3\mathbf{j} + 2\mathbf{k}$.

Solution We use the formula above:

$$\mathbf{u}\cdot\mathbf{v} = (1)(6) + (-2)(3) + (-2)(2) = 6 - 6 - 4 = -4$$

$$|\mathbf{u}| = \sqrt{(1)^2 + (-2)^2 + (-2)^2} = \sqrt{9} = 3$$

$$|\mathbf{v}| = \sqrt{(6)^2 + (3)^2 + (2)^2} = \sqrt{49} = 7$$

$$\begin{aligned}\theta &= \cos^{-1}\left(\frac{\mathbf{u}\cdot\mathbf{v}}{|\mathbf{u}||\mathbf{v}|}\right) \\ &= \cos^{-1}\left(\frac{-4}{(3)(7)}\right) \approx 1.76 \text{ radians}.\end{aligned} \qquad \blacksquare$$

The angle formula applies to two-dimensional vectors as well.

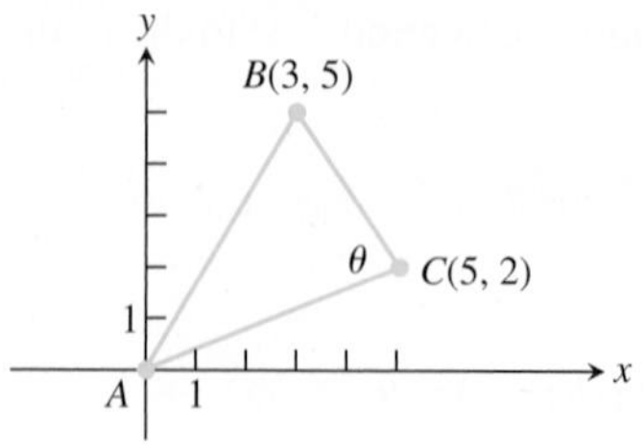

FIGURE 10.21 The triangle in Example 3.

EXAMPLE 3 Find the angle θ in the triangle ABC determined by the vertices $A = (0, 0)$, $B = (3, 5)$, and $C = (5, 2)$ (Figure 10.21).

Solution The angle θ is the angle between the vectors $\overrightarrow{CA}$ and $\overrightarrow{CB}$. The component forms of these two vectors are

$$\overrightarrow{CA} = \langle -5, -2 \rangle \qquad \text{and} \qquad \overrightarrow{CB} = \langle -2, 3 \rangle.$$

First we calculate the dot product and magnitudes of these two vectors.

$$\begin{aligned} \overrightarrow{CA} \cdot \overrightarrow{CB} &= (-5)(-2) + (-2)(3) = 4 \\ |\overrightarrow{CA}| &= \sqrt{(-5)^2 + (-2)^2} = \sqrt{29} \\ |\overrightarrow{CB}| &= \sqrt{(-2)^2 + (3)^2} = \sqrt{13} \end{aligned}$$

Then applying the angle formula, we have

$$\begin{aligned} \theta &= \cos^{-1}\left(\frac{\overrightarrow{CA} \cdot \overrightarrow{CB}}{|\overrightarrow{CA}|\,|\overrightarrow{CB}|}\right) \\ &= \cos^{-1}\left(\frac{4}{(\sqrt{29})(\sqrt{13})}\right) \\ &\approx 78.1^\circ \qquad \text{or} \qquad 1.36 \text{ radians}. \end{aligned}$$

■

Perpendicular (Orthogonal) Vectors

Two nonzero vectors **u** and **v** are perpendicular or **orthogonal** if the angle between them is $\pi/2$. For such vectors, we have $\mathbf{u} \cdot \mathbf{v} = 0$ because $\cos(\pi/2) = 0$. The converse is also true. If **u** and **v** are nonzero vectors with $\mathbf{u} \cdot \mathbf{v} = |\mathbf{u}|\,|\mathbf{v}| \cos\theta = 0$, then $\cos\theta = 0$ and $\theta = \cos^{-1} 0 = \pi/2$.

DEFINITION Vectors **u** and **v** are **orthogonal** (or **perpendicular**) if and only if $\mathbf{u} \cdot \mathbf{v} = 0$.

EXAMPLE 4

(a) $\mathbf{u} = \langle 3, -2 \rangle$ and $\mathbf{v} = \langle 4, 6 \rangle$ are orthogonal because $\mathbf{u} \cdot \mathbf{v} = (3)(4) + (-2)(6) = 0$.

(b) $\mathbf{u} = 3\mathbf{i} - 2\mathbf{j} + \mathbf{k}$ and $\mathbf{v} = 2\mathbf{j} + 4\mathbf{k}$ are orthogonal because $\mathbf{u} \cdot \mathbf{v} = (3)(0) + (-2)(2) + (1)(4) = 0$.

(c) **0** is orthogonal to every vector **u** since

$$\begin{aligned} \mathbf{0} \cdot \mathbf{u} &= \langle 0, 0, 0 \rangle \cdot \langle u_1, u_2, u_3 \rangle \\ &= (0)(u_1) + (0)(u_2) + (0)(u_3) \\ &= 0. \end{aligned}$$

■

Dot Product Properties and Vector Projections

The dot product obeys many of the laws that hold for ordinary products of real numbers (scalars).

Properties of the Dot Product

If **u**, **v**, and **w** are any vectors and c is a scalar, then

1. $\mathbf{u} \cdot \mathbf{v} = \mathbf{v} \cdot \mathbf{u}$
2. $(c\mathbf{u}) \cdot \mathbf{v} = \mathbf{u} \cdot (c\mathbf{v}) = c(\mathbf{u} \cdot \mathbf{v})$
3. $\mathbf{u} \cdot (\mathbf{v} + \mathbf{w}) = \mathbf{u} \cdot \mathbf{v} + \mathbf{u} \cdot \mathbf{w}$
4. $\mathbf{u} \cdot \mathbf{u} = |\mathbf{u}|^2$
5. $\mathbf{0} \cdot \mathbf{u} = 0.$

HISTORICAL BIOGRAPHY

Carl Friedrich Gauss
(1777–1855)

Proofs of Properties 1 and 3 The properties are easy to prove using the definition. For instance, here are the proofs of Properties 1 and 3.

1. $\mathbf{u} \cdot \mathbf{v} = u_1 v_1 + u_2 v_2 + u_3 v_3 = v_1 u_1 + v_2 u_2 + v_3 u_3 = \mathbf{v} \cdot \mathbf{u}$

3. $$\begin{aligned} \mathbf{u} \cdot (\mathbf{v} + \mathbf{w}) &= \langle u_1, u_2, u_3 \rangle \cdot \langle v_1 + w_1, v_2 + w_2, v_3 + w_3 \rangle \\ &= u_1(v_1 + w_1) + u_2(v_2 + w_2) + u_3(v_3 + w_3) \\ &= u_1 v_1 + u_1 w_1 + u_2 v_2 + u_2 w_2 + u_3 v_3 + u_3 w_3 \\ &= (u_1 v_1 + u_2 v_2 + u_3 v_3) + (u_1 w_1 + u_2 w_2 + u_3 w_3) \\ &= \mathbf{u} \cdot \mathbf{v} + \mathbf{u} \cdot \mathbf{w} \end{aligned}$$ ■

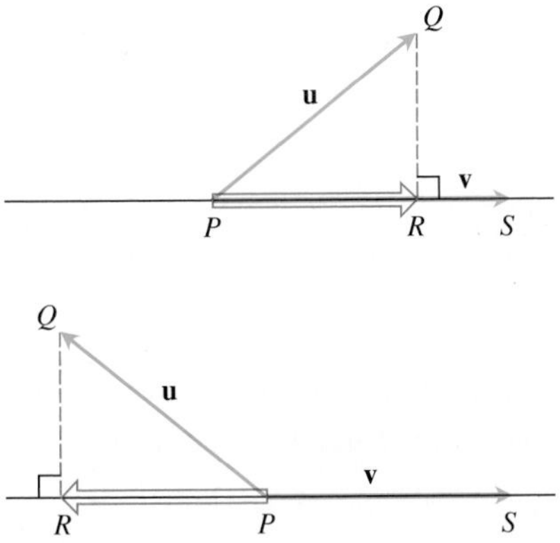

FIGURE 10.22 The vector projection of **u** onto **v**.

We now return to the problem of projecting one vector onto another, posed in the opening to this section. The **vector projection** of $\mathbf{u} = \overrightarrow{PQ}$ onto a nonzero vector $\mathbf{v} = \overrightarrow{PS}$ (Figure 10.22) is the vector $\overrightarrow{PR}$ determined by dropping a perpendicular from Q to the line PS. The notation for this vector is

$$\text{proj}_{\mathbf{v}}\, \mathbf{u} \qquad (\text{“the vector projection of } \mathbf{u} \text{ onto } \mathbf{v}\text{”}).$$

If **u** represents a force, then $\text{proj}_{\mathbf{v}}\, \mathbf{u}$ represents the effective force in the direction of **v** (Figure 10.23).

If the angle θ between **u** and **v** is acute, $\text{proj}_{\mathbf{v}}\, \mathbf{u}$ has length $|\mathbf{u}| \cos\theta$ and direction $\mathbf{v}/|\mathbf{v}|$ (Figure 10.24). If θ is obtuse, $\cos\theta < 0$ and $\text{proj}_{\mathbf{v}}\, \mathbf{u}$ has length $-|\mathbf{u}| \cos\theta$ and direction $-\mathbf{v}/|\mathbf{v}|$. In both cases,

$$\begin{aligned} \text{proj}_{\mathbf{v}}\, \mathbf{u} &= (|\mathbf{u}| \cos\theta) \frac{\mathbf{v}}{|\mathbf{v}|} \\ &= \left(\frac{\mathbf{u} \cdot \mathbf{v}}{|\mathbf{v}|}\right) \frac{\mathbf{v}}{|\mathbf{v}|} \qquad\qquad |\mathbf{u}| \cos\theta = \frac{|\mathbf{u}||\mathbf{v}| \cos\theta}{|\mathbf{v}|} = \frac{\mathbf{u} \cdot \mathbf{v}}{|\mathbf{v}|} \\ &= \left(\frac{\mathbf{u} \cdot \mathbf{v}}{|\mathbf{v}|^2}\right) \mathbf{v}. \end{aligned}$$

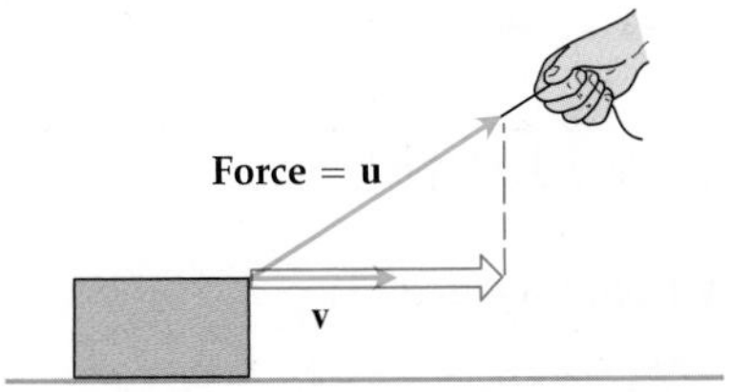

FIGURE 10.23 If we pull on the box with force **u**, the effective force moving the box forward in the direction **v** is the projection of **u** onto **v**.

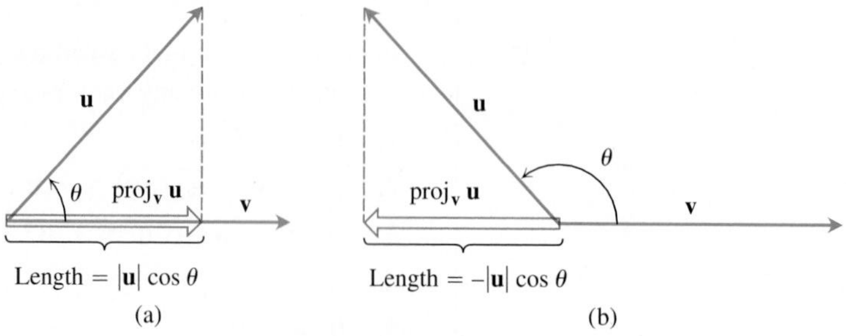

FIGURE 10.24 The length of $\text{proj}_{\mathbf{v}}\mathbf{u}$ is (a) $|\mathbf{u}|\cos\theta$ if $\cos\theta \geq 0$ and (b) $-|\mathbf{u}|\cos\theta$ if $\cos\theta < 0$.

The number $|\mathbf{u}|\cos\theta$ is called the **scalar component of u in the direction of v**. To summarize,

Vector projection of **u** onto **v**:

$$\text{proj}_{\mathbf{v}}\,\mathbf{u} = \left(\frac{\mathbf{u}\cdot\mathbf{v}}{|\mathbf{v}|^2}\right)\mathbf{v} \tag{1}$$

Scalar component of **u** in the direction of **v**:

$$|\mathbf{u}|\cos\theta = \frac{\mathbf{u}\cdot\mathbf{v}}{|\mathbf{v}|} = \mathbf{u}\cdot\frac{\mathbf{v}}{|\mathbf{v}|} \tag{2}$$

Note that both the vector projection of **u** onto **v** and the scalar component of **u** onto **v** depend only on the direction of the vector **v** and not its length (because we dot **u** with $\mathbf{v}/|\mathbf{v}|$, which is the direction of **v**).

EXAMPLE 5 Find the vector projection of $\mathbf{u} = 6\mathbf{i} + 3\mathbf{j} + 2\mathbf{k}$ onto $\mathbf{v} = \mathbf{i} - 2\mathbf{j} - 2\mathbf{k}$ and the scalar component of **u** in the direction of **v**.

Solution We find $\text{proj}_{\mathbf{v}}\,\mathbf{u}$ from Equation (1):

$$\begin{aligned}\text{proj}_{\mathbf{v}}\,\mathbf{u} &= \frac{\mathbf{u}\cdot\mathbf{v}}{\mathbf{v}\cdot\mathbf{v}}\mathbf{v} = \frac{6-6-4}{1+4+4}(\mathbf{i}-2\mathbf{j}-2\mathbf{k})\\ &= -\frac{4}{9}(\mathbf{i}-2\mathbf{j}-2\mathbf{k}) = -\frac{4}{9}\mathbf{i} + \frac{8}{9}\mathbf{j} + \frac{8}{9}\mathbf{k}.\end{aligned}$$

We find the scalar component of **u** in the direction of **v** from Equation (2):

$$\begin{aligned}|\mathbf{u}|\cos\theta &= \mathbf{u}\cdot\frac{\mathbf{v}}{|\mathbf{v}|} = (6\mathbf{i}+3\mathbf{j}+2\mathbf{k})\cdot\left(\frac{1}{3}\mathbf{i} - \frac{2}{3}\mathbf{j} - \frac{2}{3}\mathbf{k}\right)\\ &= 2 - 2 - \frac{4}{3} = -\frac{4}{3}.\end{aligned}$$

■

Equations (1) and (2) also apply to two-dimensional vectors.

EXAMPLE 6 Find the vector projection of a force $\mathbf{F} = 5\mathbf{i} + 2\mathbf{j}$ onto $\mathbf{v} = \mathbf{i} - 3\mathbf{j}$ and the scalar component of $\mathbf{F}$ in the direction of $\mathbf{v}$.

Solution The vector projection is

$$\begin{aligned}\text{proj}_{\mathbf{v}} \mathbf{F} &= \left(\frac{\mathbf{F}\cdot\mathbf{v}}{|\mathbf{v}|^2}\right)\mathbf{v} \\ &= \frac{5-6}{1+9}(\mathbf{i} - 3\mathbf{j}) = -\frac{1}{10}(\mathbf{i} - 3\mathbf{j}) \\ &= -\frac{1}{10}\mathbf{i} + \frac{3}{10}\mathbf{j}.\end{aligned}$$

The scalar component of $\mathbf{F}$ in the direction of $\mathbf{v}$ is

$$|\mathbf{F}|\cos\theta = \frac{\mathbf{F}\cdot\mathbf{v}}{|\mathbf{v}|} = \frac{5-6}{\sqrt{1+9}} = -\frac{1}{\sqrt{10}}.$$ ■

Work

In Chapter 6, we calculated the work done by a constant force of magnitude F in moving an object through a distance d as $W = Fd$. That formula holds only if the force is directed along the line of motion. If a force $\mathbf{F}$ moving an object through a displacement $\mathbf{D} = \overrightarrow{PQ}$ has some other direction, the work is performed by the component of $\mathbf{F}$ in the direction of $\mathbf{D}$. If θ is the angle between $\mathbf{F}$ and $\mathbf{D}$ (Figure 10.25), then

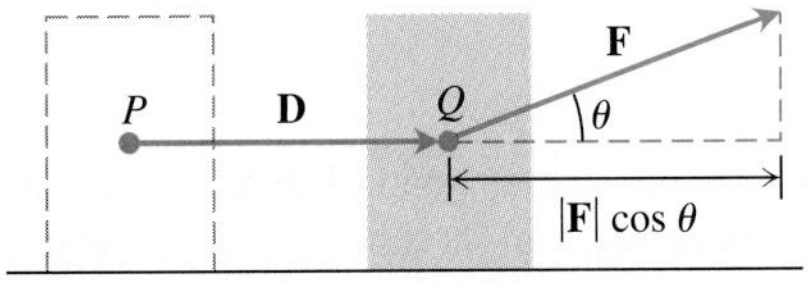

FIGURE 10.25 The work done by a constant force $\mathbf{F}$ during a displacement $\mathbf{D}$ is $(|\mathbf{F}|\cos\theta)|\mathbf{D}|$.

$$\begin{aligned}\text{Work} &= \begin{pmatrix}\text{scalar component of } \mathbf{F} \\ \text{in the direction of } \mathbf{D}\end{pmatrix}(\text{length of } \mathbf{D}) \\ &= (|\mathbf{F}|\cos\theta)|\mathbf{D}| \\ &= \mathbf{F}\cdot\mathbf{D}.\end{aligned}$$

DEFINITION The **work** done by a constant force $\mathbf{F}$ acting through a displacement $\mathbf{D} = \overrightarrow{PQ}$ is

$$W = \mathbf{F}\cdot\mathbf{D} = |\mathbf{F}||\mathbf{D}|\cos\theta,$$

where θ is the angle between $\mathbf{F}$ and $\mathbf{D}$.

EXAMPLE 7 If $|\mathbf{F}| = 40$ N (newtons), $|\mathbf{D}| = 3$ m, and $\theta = 60°$, the work done by $\mathbf{F}$ in acting from P to Q is

$$\begin{aligned}\text{Work} &= |\mathbf{F}||\mathbf{D}|\cos\theta && \text{Definition} \\ &= (40)(3)\cos 60° && \text{Given values} \\ &= (120)(1/2) \\ &= 60 \text{ J (joules)}.\end{aligned}$$ ■

We encounter more challenging work problems in Chapter 14 when we learn to find the work done by a variable force along a *path* in space.

EXERCISES 10.3

In Exercises 1–8, find

a. $\mathbf{v} \cdot \mathbf{u}$, $|\mathbf{v}|$, $|\mathbf{u}|$

b. the cosine of the angle between $\mathbf{v}$ and $\mathbf{u}$

c. the scalar component of $\mathbf{u}$ in the direction of $\mathbf{v}$

d. the vector $\text{proj}_{\mathbf{v}}\, \mathbf{u}$.

1. $\mathbf{v} = 2\mathbf{i} - 4\mathbf{j} + \sqrt{5}\mathbf{k}$, $\mathbf{u} = -2\mathbf{i} + 4\mathbf{j} - \sqrt{5}\mathbf{k}$

2. $\mathbf{v} = (3/5)\mathbf{i} + (4/5)\mathbf{k}$, $\mathbf{u} = 5\mathbf{i} + 12\mathbf{j}$

3. $\mathbf{v} = 10\mathbf{i} + 11\mathbf{j} - 2\mathbf{k}$, $\mathbf{u} = 3\mathbf{j} + 4\mathbf{k}$

4. $\mathbf{v} = 2\mathbf{i} + 10\mathbf{j} - 11\mathbf{k}$, $\mathbf{u} = 2\mathbf{i} + 2\mathbf{j} + \mathbf{k}$

5. $\mathbf{v} = 5\mathbf{j} - 3\mathbf{k}$, $\mathbf{u} = \mathbf{i} + \mathbf{j} + \mathbf{k}$

6. $\mathbf{v} = -\mathbf{i} + \mathbf{j}$, $\mathbf{u} = \sqrt{2}\mathbf{i} + \sqrt{3}\mathbf{j} + 2\mathbf{k}$

7. $\mathbf{v} = 5\mathbf{i} + \mathbf{j}$, $\mathbf{u} = 2\mathbf{i} + \sqrt{17}\mathbf{j}$

8. $\mathbf{v} = \left\langle \frac{1}{\sqrt{2}}, \frac{1}{\sqrt{3}} \right\rangle$, $\mathbf{u} = \left\langle \frac{1}{\sqrt{2}}, -\frac{1}{\sqrt{3}} \right\rangle$

T Find the angles between the vectors in Exercises 9–12 to the nearest hundredth of a radian.

9. $\mathbf{u} = 2\mathbf{i} + \mathbf{j}$, $\mathbf{v} = \mathbf{i} + 2\mathbf{j} - \mathbf{k}$

10. $\mathbf{u} = 2\mathbf{i} - 2\mathbf{j} + \mathbf{k}$, $\mathbf{v} = 3\mathbf{i} + 4\mathbf{k}$

11. $\mathbf{u} = \sqrt{3}\mathbf{i} - 7\mathbf{j}$, $\mathbf{v} = \sqrt{3}\mathbf{i} + \mathbf{j} - 2\mathbf{k}$

12. $\mathbf{u} = \mathbf{i} + \sqrt{2}\mathbf{j} - \sqrt{2}\mathbf{k}$, $\mathbf{v} = -\mathbf{i} + \mathbf{j} + \mathbf{k}$

13. Triangle Find the measures of the angles of the triangle whose vertices are $A = (-1, 0)$, $B = (2, 1)$, and $C = (1, -2)$.

14. Rectangle Find the measures of the angles between the diagonals of the rectangle whose vertices are $A = (1, 0)$, $B = (0, 3)$, $C = (3, 4)$, and $D = (4, 1)$.

15. Direction angles and direction cosines The *direction angles* α, β, and γ of a vector $\mathbf{v} = a\mathbf{i} + b\mathbf{j} + c\mathbf{k}$ are defined as follows:

α is the angle between $\mathbf{v}$ and the positive x-axis $(0 \le \alpha \le \pi)$

β is the angle between $\mathbf{v}$ and the positive y-axis $(0 \le \beta \le \pi)$

γ is the angle between $\mathbf{v}$ and the positive z-axis $(0 \le \gamma \le \pi)$.

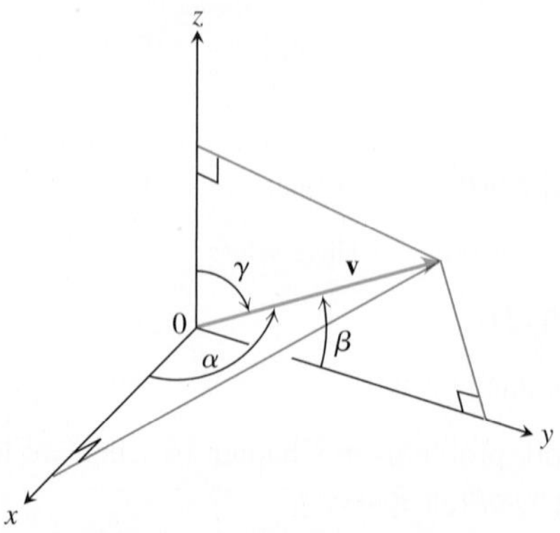

a. Show that

$$\cos\alpha = \frac{a}{|\mathbf{v}|}, \qquad \cos\beta = \frac{b}{|\mathbf{v}|}, \qquad \cos\gamma = \frac{c}{|\mathbf{v}|},$$

and $\cos^2\alpha + \cos^2\beta + \cos^2\gamma = 1$. These cosines are called the *direction cosines* of $\mathbf{v}$.

b. Unit vectors are built from direction cosines Show that if $\mathbf{v} = a\mathbf{i} + b\mathbf{j} + c\mathbf{k}$ is a unit vector, then a, b, and c are the direction cosines of $\mathbf{v}$.

16. Water main construction A water main is to be constructed with a 20% grade in the north direction and a 10% grade in the east direction. Determine the angle θ required in the water main for the turn from north to east.

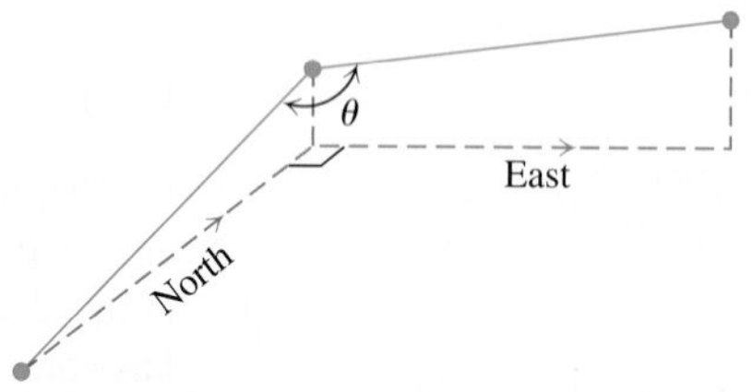

17. Sums and differences In the accompanying figure, it looks as if $\mathbf{v}_1 + \mathbf{v}_2$ and $\mathbf{v}_1 - \mathbf{v}_2$ are orthogonal. Is this mere coincidence, or are there circumstances under which we may expect the sum of two vectors to be orthogonal to their difference? Give reasons for your answer.

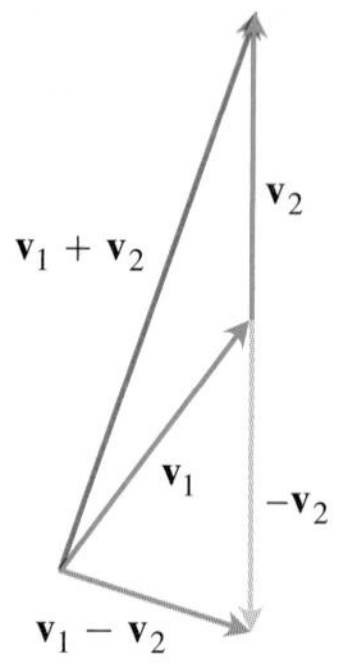

18. Orthogonality on a circle Suppose that AB is the diameter of a circle with center O and that C is a point on one of the two arcs joining A and B. Show that $\overrightarrow{CA}$ and $\overrightarrow{CB}$ are orthogonal.

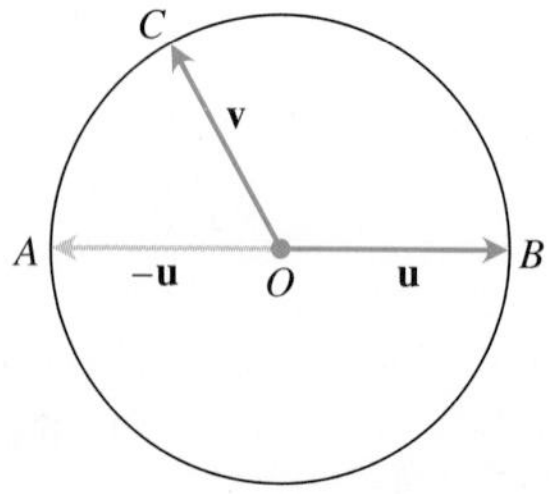

19. **Diagonals of a rhombus** Show that the diagonals of a rhombus (parallelogram with sides of equal length) are perpendicular.

20. **Perpendicular diagonals** Show that squares are the only rectangles with perpendicular diagonals.

21. **When parallelograms are rectangles** Prove that a parallelogram is a rectangle if and only if its diagonals are equal in length. (This fact is often exploited by carpenters.)

22. **Diagonal of parallelogram** Show that the indicated diagonal of the parallelogram determined by vectors **u** and **v** bisects the angle between **u** and **v** if $|\mathbf{u}| = |\mathbf{v}|$.

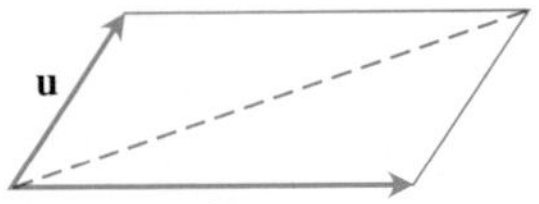

23. **Projectile motion** A gun with muzzle velocity of 1200 ft/sec is fired at an angle of 8° above the horizontal. Find the horizontal and vertical components of the velocity.

24. **Inclined plane** Suppose that a box is being towed up an inclined plane as shown in the figure. Find the force **w** needed to make the component of the force parallel to the inclined plane equal to 2.5 lb.

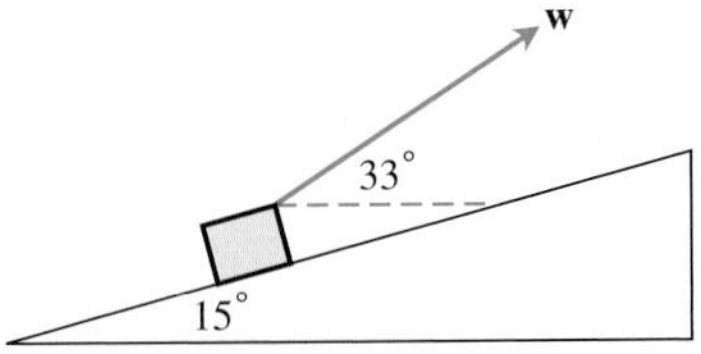

25. a. **Cauchy-Schwartz inequality** Use the fact that $\mathbf{u}\cdot\mathbf{v} = |\mathbf{u}||\mathbf{v}|\cos\theta$ to show that the inequality $|\mathbf{u}\cdot\mathbf{v}| \le |\mathbf{u}||\mathbf{v}|$ holds for any vectors **u** and **v**.

    b. Under what circumstances, if any, does $|\mathbf{u}\cdot\mathbf{v}|$ equal $|\mathbf{u}||\mathbf{v}|$? Give reasons for your answer.

26. Copy the axes and vector shown here. Then shade in the points (x, y) for which $(x\mathbf{i} + y\mathbf{j})\cdot\mathbf{v} \le 0$. Justify your answer.

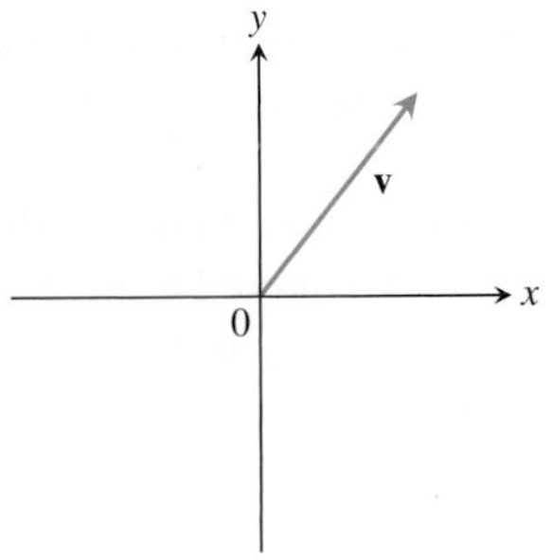

27. **Orthogonal unit vectors** If $\mathbf{u}_1$ and $\mathbf{u}_2$ are orthogonal unit vectors and $\mathbf{v} = a\mathbf{u}_1 + b\mathbf{u}_2$, find $\mathbf{v}\cdot\mathbf{u}_1$.

28. **Cancellation in dot products** In real-number multiplication, if $uv_1 = uv_2$ and $u \ne 0$, we can cancel the u and conclude that $v_1 = v_2$. Does the same rule hold for the dot product: If $\mathbf{u}\cdot\mathbf{v}_1 = \mathbf{u}\cdot\mathbf{v}_2$ and $\mathbf{u} \ne \mathbf{0}$, can you conclude that $\mathbf{v}_1 = \mathbf{v}_2$? Give reasons for your answer.

29. **Line perpendicular to a vector** Show that the vector $\mathbf{v} = a\mathbf{i} + b\mathbf{j}$ is perpendicular to the line $ax + by = c$ by establishing that the slope of **v** is the negative reciprocal of the slope of the given line.

30. **Line parallel to a vector** Show that the vector $\mathbf{v} = a\mathbf{i} + b\mathbf{j}$ is parallel to the line $bx - ay = c$ by establishing that the slope of the line segment representing **v** is the same as the slope of the given line.

In Exercises 31–34, use the result of Exercise 29 to find an equation for the line through P perpendicular to **v**. Then sketch the line. Include **v** in your sketch *as a vector starting at the origin.*

31. $P(2, 1)$, $\mathbf{v} = \mathbf{i} + 2\mathbf{j}$
32. $P(-1, 2)$, $\mathbf{v} = -2\mathbf{i} - \mathbf{j}$
33. $P(-2, -7)$, $\mathbf{v} = -2\mathbf{i} + \mathbf{j}$
34. $P(11, 10)$, $\mathbf{v} = 2\mathbf{i} - 3\mathbf{j}$

In Exercises 35–38, use the result of Exercise 30 to find an equation for the line through P parallel to **v**. Then sketch the line. Include **v** in your sketch *as a vector starting at the origin.*

35. $P(-2, 1)$, $\mathbf{v} = \mathbf{i} - \mathbf{j}$
36. $P(0, -2)$, $\mathbf{v} = 2\mathbf{i} + 3\mathbf{j}$
37. $P(1, 2)$, $\mathbf{v} = -\mathbf{i} - 2\mathbf{j}$
38. $P(1, 3)$, $\mathbf{v} = 3\mathbf{i} - 2\mathbf{j}$

39. **Work along a line** Find the work done by a force $\mathbf{F} = 5\mathbf{i}$ (magnitude 5 N) in moving an object along the line from the origin to the point (1, 1) (distance in meters).

40. **Locomotive** The Union Pacific's *Big Boy* locomotive could pull 6000-ton trains with a tractive effort (pull) of 602,148 N (135,375 lb). At this level of effort, about how much work did *Big Boy* do on the (approximately straight) 605-km journey from San Francisco to Los Angeles?

41. **Inclined plane** How much work does it take to slide a crate 20 m along a loading dock by pulling on it with a 200 N force at an angle of 30° from the horizontal?

42. **Sailboat** The wind passing over a boat's sail exerted a 1000-lb magnitude force **F** as shown here. How much work did the wind perform in moving the boat forward 1 mi? Answer in foot-pounds.

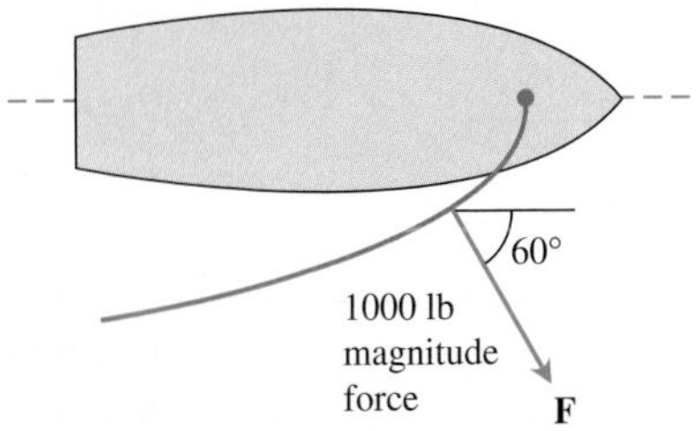

The **acute angle between intersecting lines** that do not cross at right angles is the same as the angle determined by vectors normal to the lines or by the vectors parallel to the lines.

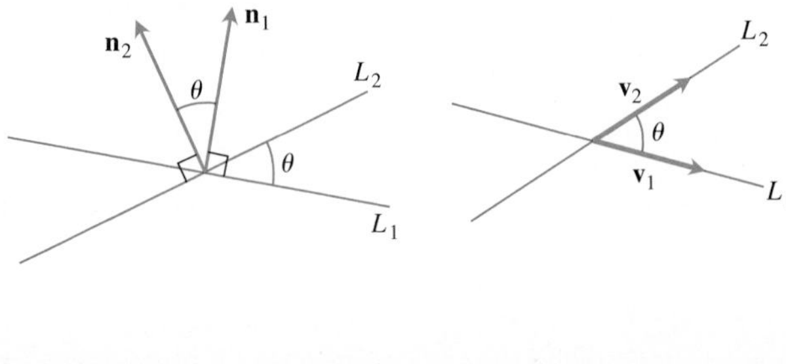

Use this fact and the results of Exercise 29 or 30 to find the acute angles between the lines in Exercises 43–48.

43. $3x + y = 5, \quad 2x - y = 4$

44. $y = \sqrt{3}x - 1, \quad y = -\sqrt{3}x + 2$

45. $\sqrt{3}x - y = -2, \quad x - \sqrt{3}y = 1$

46. $x + \sqrt{3}y = 1, \quad \left(1 - \sqrt{3}\right)x + \left(1 + \sqrt{3}\right)y = 8$

47. $3x - 4y = 3, \quad x - y = 7$

48. $12x + 5y = 1, \quad 2x - 2y = 3$

10.4 The Cross Product

In studying lines in the plane, when we needed to describe how a line was tilting, we used the notions of slope and angle of inclination. In space, we want a way to describe how a *plane* is tilting. We accomplish this by multiplying two vectors in the plane together to get a third vector perpendicular to the plane. The direction of this third vector tells us the "inclination" of the plane. The product we use to multiply the vectors together is the *vector* or *cross product*, the second of the two vector multiplication methods. We study the cross product in this section.

The Cross Product of Two Vectors in Space

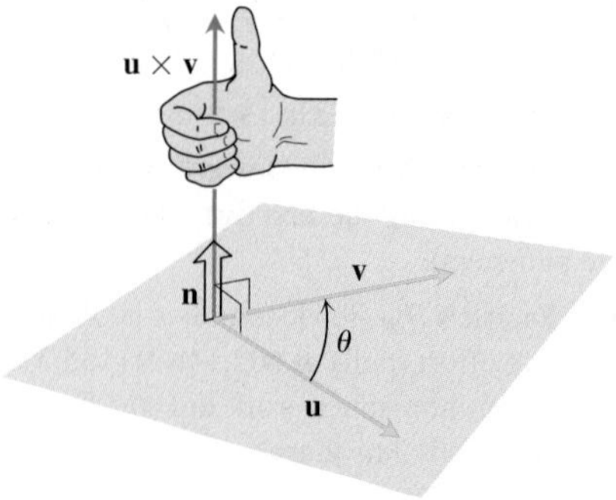

FIGURE 10.26 The construction of $\mathbf{u} \times \mathbf{v}$.

We start with two nonzero vectors **u** and **v** in space. If **u** and **v** are not parallel, they determine a plane. We select a unit vector **n** perpendicular to the plane by the **right-hand rule.** This means that we choose **n** to be the unit (normal) vector that points the way your right thumb points when your fingers curl through the angle θ from **u** to **v** (Figure 10.26). Then the **cross product u × v** ("**u** cross **v**") is the *vector* defined as follows.

DEFINITION

$$\mathbf{u} \times \mathbf{v} = (|\mathbf{u}||\mathbf{v}| \sin\theta)\,\mathbf{n}$$

Unlike the dot product, the cross product is a vector. For this reason it's also called the **vector product** of **u** and **v**, and applies *only* to vectors in space. The vector $\mathbf{u} \times \mathbf{v}$ is orthogonal to both **u** and **v** because it is a scalar multiple of **n**.

There is a straightforward way to calculate the cross product of two vectors from their components. The method does not require that we know the angle between them (as suggested by the definition), but we postpone that calculation momentarily so we can focus first on the properties of the cross product.

Since the sines of 0 and π are both zero, it makes sense to define the cross product of two parallel nonzero vectors to be **0**. If one or both of **u** and **v** are zero, we also define $\mathbf{u} \times \mathbf{v}$ to be zero. This way, the cross product of two vectors **u** and **v** is zero if and only if **u** and **v** are parallel or one or both of them are zero.

Parallel Vectors

Nonzero vectors **u** and **v** are parallel if and only if $\mathbf{u} \times \mathbf{v} = \mathbf{0}$.

The cross product obeys the following laws.

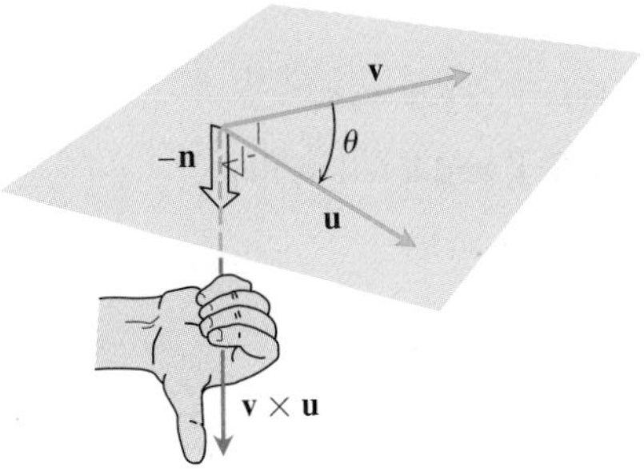

FIGURE 10.27 The construction of $\mathbf{v} \times \mathbf{u}$.

Properties of the Cross Product

If **u**, **v**, and **w** are any vectors and r, s are scalars, then

1. $(r\mathbf{u}) \times (s\mathbf{v}) = (rs)(\mathbf{u} \times \mathbf{v})$
2. $\mathbf{u} \times (\mathbf{v} + \mathbf{w}) = \mathbf{u} \times \mathbf{v} + \mathbf{u} \times \mathbf{w}$
3. $(\mathbf{v} + \mathbf{w}) \times \mathbf{u} = \mathbf{v} \times \mathbf{u} + \mathbf{w} \times \mathbf{u}$
4. $\mathbf{v} \times \mathbf{u} = -(\mathbf{u} \times \mathbf{v})$
5. $\mathbf{0} \times \mathbf{u} = \mathbf{0}$

To visualize Property 4, for example, notice that when the fingers of a right hand curl through the angle θ from **v** to **u**, the thumb points the opposite way and the unit vector we choose in forming $\mathbf{v} \times \mathbf{u}$ is the negative of the one we choose in forming $\mathbf{u} \times \mathbf{v}$ (Figure 10.27).

Property 1 can be verified by applying the definition of cross product to both sides of the equation and comparing the results. Property 2 is proved in Appendix 8. Property 3 follows by multiplying both sides of the equation in Property 2 by -1 and reversing the order of the products using Property 4. Property 5 is a definition. As a rule, cross product multiplication is *not associative* so $(\mathbf{u} \times \mathbf{v}) \times \mathbf{w}$ does not generally equal $\mathbf{u} \times (\mathbf{v} \times \mathbf{w})$. (See Additional Exercise 15.)

When we apply the definition to calculate the pairwise cross products of **i**, **j**, and **k**, we find (Figure 10.28)

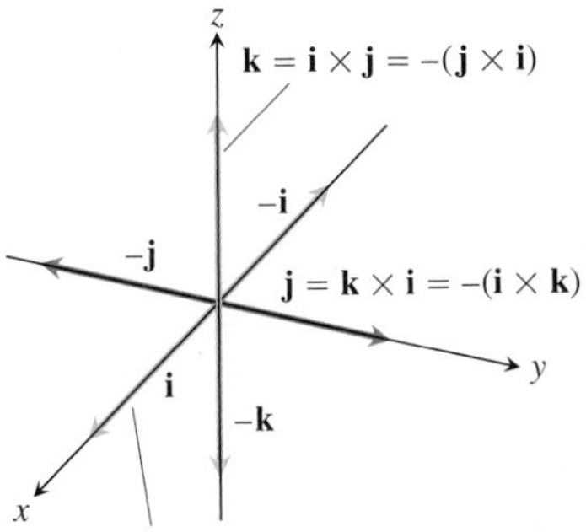

FIGURE 10.28 The pairwise cross products of **i**, **j**, and **k**.

$$\mathbf{i} \times \mathbf{j} = -(\mathbf{j} \times \mathbf{i}) = \mathbf{k}$$
$$\mathbf{j} \times \mathbf{k} = -(\mathbf{k} \times \mathbf{j}) = \mathbf{i}$$
$$\mathbf{k} \times \mathbf{i} = -(\mathbf{i} \times \mathbf{k}) = \mathbf{j}$$

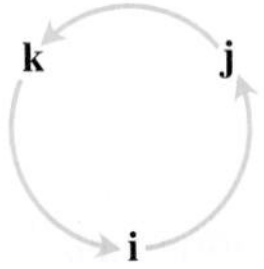

Diagram for recalling these products

and

$$\mathbf{i} \times \mathbf{i} = \mathbf{j} \times \mathbf{j} = \mathbf{k} \times \mathbf{k} = \mathbf{0}.$$

$|\mathbf{u} \times \mathbf{v}|$ Is the Area of a Parallelogram

Because **n** is a unit vector, the magnitude of $\mathbf{u} \times \mathbf{v}$ is

$$|\mathbf{u} \times \mathbf{v}| = |\mathbf{u}||\mathbf{v}||\sin\theta||\mathbf{n}| = |\mathbf{u}||\mathbf{v}|\sin\theta.$$

This is the area of the parallelogram determined by **u** and **v** (Figure 10.29), $|\mathbf{u}|$ being the base of the parallelogram and $|\mathbf{v}||\sin\theta|$ the height.

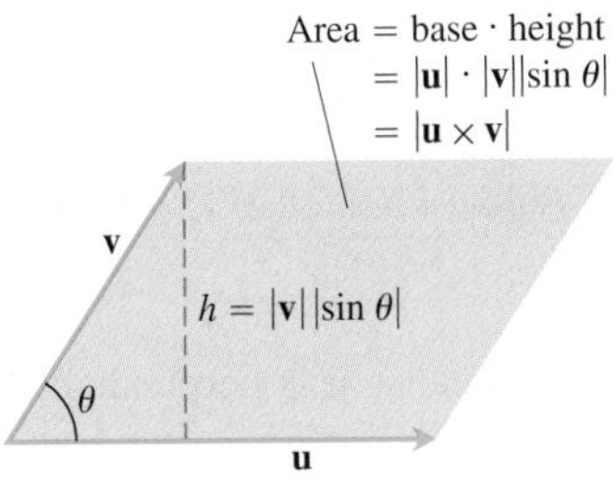

FIGURE 10.29 The parallelogram determined by **u** and **v**.

Determinant Formula for $\mathbf{u} \times \mathbf{v}$

Our next objective is to calculate $\mathbf{u} \times \mathbf{v}$ from the components of **u** and **v** relative to a Cartesian coordinate system.

Determinants

2×2 and 3×3 determinants are evaluated as follows:

$$\begin{vmatrix} a & b \\ c & d \end{vmatrix} = ad - bc$$

EXAMPLE

$$\begin{vmatrix} 2 & 1 \\ -4 & 3 \end{vmatrix} = (2)(3) - (1)(-4)$$
$$= 6 + 4 = 10$$

$$\begin{vmatrix} a_1 & a_2 & a_3 \\ b_1 & b_2 & b_3 \\ c_1 & c_2 & c_3 \end{vmatrix} = a_1\begin{vmatrix} b_2 & b_3 \\ c_2 & c_3 \end{vmatrix}$$
$$- a_2\begin{vmatrix} b_1 & b_3 \\ c_1 & c_3 \end{vmatrix} + a_3\begin{vmatrix} b_1 & b_2 \\ c_1 & c_2 \end{vmatrix}$$

EXAMPLE

$$\begin{vmatrix} -5 & 3 & 1 \\ 2 & 1 & 1 \\ -4 & 3 & 1 \end{vmatrix} = (-5)\begin{vmatrix} 1 & 1 \\ 3 & 1 \end{vmatrix}$$
$$- (3)\begin{vmatrix} 2 & 1 \\ -4 & 1 \end{vmatrix} + (1)\begin{vmatrix} 2 & 1 \\ -4 & 3 \end{vmatrix}$$
$$= -5(1 - 3) - 3(2 + 4)$$
$$+ 1(6 + 4)$$
$$= 10 - 18 + 10 = 2$$

(For more information, see the Web site at **www.aw-bc.com/thomas**.)

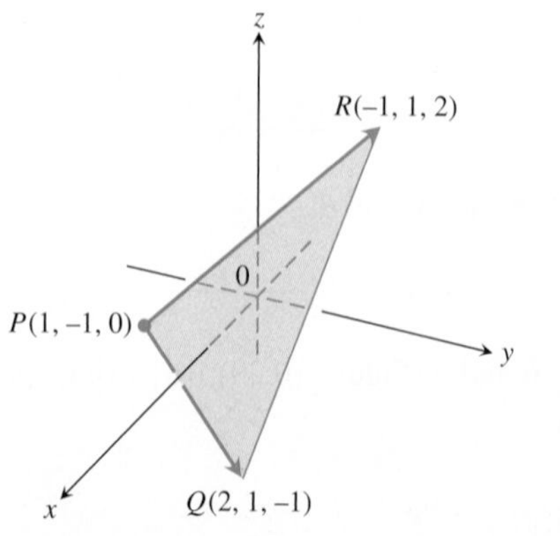

FIGURE 10.30 The area of triangle PQR is half of $|\overrightarrow{PQ} \times \overrightarrow{PR}|$ (Example 2).

Suppose that

$$\mathbf{u} = u_1\mathbf{i} + u_2\mathbf{j} + u_3\mathbf{k}, \qquad \mathbf{v} = v_1\mathbf{i} + v_2\mathbf{j} + v_3\mathbf{k}.$$

Then the distributive laws and the rules for multiplying **i**, **j**, and **k** tell us that

$$\begin{aligned} \mathbf{u} \times \mathbf{v} &= (u_1\mathbf{i} + u_2\mathbf{j} + u_3\mathbf{k}) \times (v_1\mathbf{i} + v_2\mathbf{j} + v_3\mathbf{k}) \\ &= u_1v_1\mathbf{i} \times \mathbf{i} + u_1v_2\mathbf{i} \times \mathbf{j} + u_1v_3\mathbf{i} \times \mathbf{k} \\ &\quad + u_2v_1\mathbf{j} \times \mathbf{i} + u_2v_2\mathbf{j} \times \mathbf{j} + u_2v_3\mathbf{j} \times \mathbf{k} \\ &\quad + u_3v_1\mathbf{k} \times \mathbf{i} + u_3v_2\mathbf{k} \times \mathbf{j} + u_3v_3\mathbf{k} \times \mathbf{k} \\ &= (u_2v_3 - u_3v_2)\mathbf{i} - (u_1v_3 - u_3v_1)\mathbf{j} + (u_1v_2 - u_2v_1)\mathbf{k}. \end{aligned}$$

The terms in the last line are the same as the terms in the expansion of the symbolic determinant

$$\begin{vmatrix} \mathbf{i} & \mathbf{j} & \mathbf{k} \\ u_1 & u_2 & u_3 \\ v_1 & v_2 & v_3 \end{vmatrix}.$$

We therefore have the following rule.

Calculating Cross Products Using Determinants

If $\mathbf{u} = u_1\mathbf{i} + u_2\mathbf{j} + u_3\mathbf{k}$ and $\mathbf{v} = v_1\mathbf{i} + v_2\mathbf{j} + v_3\mathbf{k}$, then

$$\mathbf{u} \times \mathbf{v} = \begin{vmatrix} \mathbf{i} & \mathbf{j} & \mathbf{k} \\ u_1 & u_2 & u_3 \\ v_1 & v_2 & v_3 \end{vmatrix}.$$

EXAMPLE 1 Find $\mathbf{u} \times \mathbf{v}$ and $\mathbf{v} \times \mathbf{u}$ if $\mathbf{u} = 2\mathbf{i} + \mathbf{j} + \mathbf{k}$ and $\mathbf{v} = -4\mathbf{i} + 3\mathbf{j} + \mathbf{k}$.

Solution

$$\mathbf{u} \times \mathbf{v} = \begin{vmatrix} \mathbf{i} & \mathbf{j} & \mathbf{k} \\ 2 & 1 & 1 \\ -4 & 3 & 1 \end{vmatrix} = \begin{vmatrix} 1 & 1 \\ 3 & 1 \end{vmatrix}\mathbf{i} - \begin{vmatrix} 2 & 1 \\ -4 & 1 \end{vmatrix}\mathbf{j} + \begin{vmatrix} 2 & 1 \\ -4 & 3 \end{vmatrix}\mathbf{k}$$
$$= -2\mathbf{i} - 6\mathbf{j} + 10\mathbf{k}$$

$$\mathbf{v} \times \mathbf{u} = -(\mathbf{u} \times \mathbf{v}) = 2\mathbf{i} + 6\mathbf{j} - 10\mathbf{k}$$

■

EXAMPLE 2 Find a vector perpendicular to the plane of $P(1, -1, 0)$, $Q(2, 1, -1)$, and $R(-1, 1, 2)$ (Figure 10.30).

Solution The vector $\overrightarrow{PQ} \times \overrightarrow{PR}$ is perpendicular to the plane because it is perpendicular to both vectors. In terms of components,

$$\overrightarrow{PQ} = (2 - 1)\mathbf{i} + (1 + 1)\mathbf{j} + (-1 - 0)\mathbf{k} = \mathbf{i} + 2\mathbf{j} - \mathbf{k}$$
$$\overrightarrow{PR} = (-1 - 1)\mathbf{i} + (1 + 1)\mathbf{j} + (2 - 0)\mathbf{k} = -2\mathbf{i} + 2\mathbf{j} + 2\mathbf{k}$$

$$\overrightarrow{PQ} \times \overrightarrow{PR} = \begin{vmatrix} \mathbf{i} & \mathbf{j} & \mathbf{k} \\ 1 & 2 & -1 \\ -2 & 2 & 2 \end{vmatrix} = \begin{vmatrix} 2 & -1 \\ 2 & 2 \end{vmatrix}\mathbf{i} - \begin{vmatrix} 1 & -1 \\ -2 & 2 \end{vmatrix}\mathbf{j} + \begin{vmatrix} 1 & 2 \\ -2 & 2 \end{vmatrix}\mathbf{k}$$

$$= 6\mathbf{i} + 6\mathbf{k}.$$

EXAMPLE 3 Find the area of the triangle with vertices $P(1, -1, 0)$, $Q(2, 1, -1)$, and $R(-1, 1, 2)$ (Figure 10.30).

Solution The area of the parallelogram determined by P, Q, and R is

$$|\overrightarrow{PQ} \times \overrightarrow{PR}| = |6\mathbf{i} + 6\mathbf{k}| \qquad \text{Values from Example 2.}$$

$$= \sqrt{(6)^2 + (6)^2} = \sqrt{2 \cdot 36} = 6\sqrt{2}.$$

The triangle's area is half of this, or $3\sqrt{2}$.

EXAMPLE 4 Find a unit vector perpendicular to the plane of $P(1, -1, 0)$, $Q(2, 1, -1)$, and $R(-1, 1, 2)$.

Solution Since $\overrightarrow{PQ} \times \overrightarrow{PR}$ is perpendicular to the plane, its direction $\mathbf{n}$ is a unit vector perpendicular to the plane. Taking values from Examples 2 and 3, we have

$$\mathbf{n} = \frac{\overrightarrow{PQ} \times \overrightarrow{PR}}{|\overrightarrow{PQ} \times \overrightarrow{PR}|} = \frac{6\mathbf{i} + 6\mathbf{k}}{6\sqrt{2}} = \frac{1}{\sqrt{2}}\mathbf{i} + \frac{1}{\sqrt{2}}\mathbf{k}.$$

For ease in calculating the cross product using determinants, we usually write vectors in the form $\mathbf{v} = v_1\mathbf{i} + v_2\mathbf{j} + v_3\mathbf{k}$ rather than as ordered triples $\mathbf{v} = \langle v_1, v_2, v_3 \rangle$.

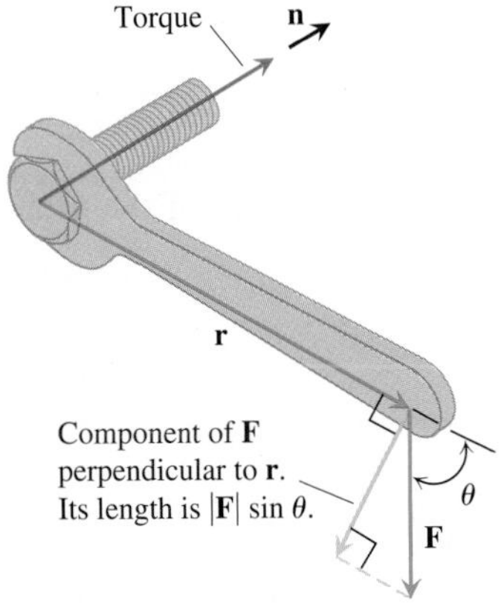

FIGURE 10.31 The torque vector describes the tendency of the force **F** to drive the bolt forward.

Torque

When we turn a bolt by applying a force **F** to a wrench (Figure 10.31), the torque we produce acts along the axis of the bolt to drive the bolt forward. The magnitude of the torque depends on how far out on the wrench the force is applied and on how much of the force is perpendicular to the wrench at the point of application. The number we use to measure the torque's magnitude is the product of the length of the lever arm **r** and the scalar component of **F** perpendicular to **r**. In the notation of Figure 10.31,

$$\text{Magnitude of torque vector} = |\mathbf{r}|\,|\mathbf{F}| \sin\theta,$$

or $|\mathbf{r} \times \mathbf{F}|$. If we let $\mathbf{n}$ be a unit vector along the axis of the bolt in the direction of the torque, then a complete description of the torque vector is $\mathbf{r} \times \mathbf{F}$, or

$$\text{Torque vector} = (|\mathbf{r}|\,|\mathbf{F}| \sin\theta)\,\mathbf{n}.$$

Recall that we defined $\mathbf{u} \times \mathbf{v}$ to be $\mathbf{0}$ when $\mathbf{u}$ and $\mathbf{v}$ are parallel. This is consistent with the torque interpretation as well. If the force **F** in Figure 10.31 is parallel to the wrench, meaning that we are trying to turn the bolt by pushing or pulling along the line of the wrench's handle, the torque produced is zero.

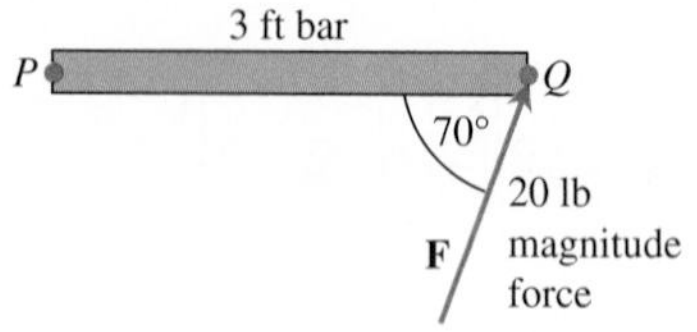

FIGURE 10.32 The magnitude of the torque exerted by **F** at P is about 56.4 ft-lb (Example 5).

EXAMPLE 5 The magnitude of the torque generated by force **F** at the pivot point P in Figure 10.32 is

$$\begin{aligned}|\overrightarrow{PQ} \times \mathbf{F}| &= |\overrightarrow{PQ}||\mathbf{F}| \sin 70^\circ \\ &\approx (3)(20)(0.94) \\ &\approx 56.4 \text{ ft-lb}.\end{aligned}$$

Triple Scalar or Box Product

The product $(\mathbf{u} \times \mathbf{v}) \cdot \mathbf{w}$ is called the **triple scalar product** of **u**, **v**, and **w** (in that order). As you can see from the formula

$$|(\mathbf{u} \times \mathbf{v}) \cdot \mathbf{w}| = |\mathbf{u} \times \mathbf{v}||\mathbf{w}||\cos \theta|,$$

the absolute value of the product is the volume of the parallelepiped (parallelogram-sided box) determined by **u**, **v**, and **w** (Figure 10.33). The number $|\mathbf{u} \times \mathbf{v}|$ is the area of the base parallelogram. The number $|\mathbf{w}||\cos \theta|$ is the parallelepiped's height. Because of this geometry, $(\mathbf{u} \times \mathbf{v}) \cdot \mathbf{w}$ is also called the **box product** of **u**, **v**, and **w**.

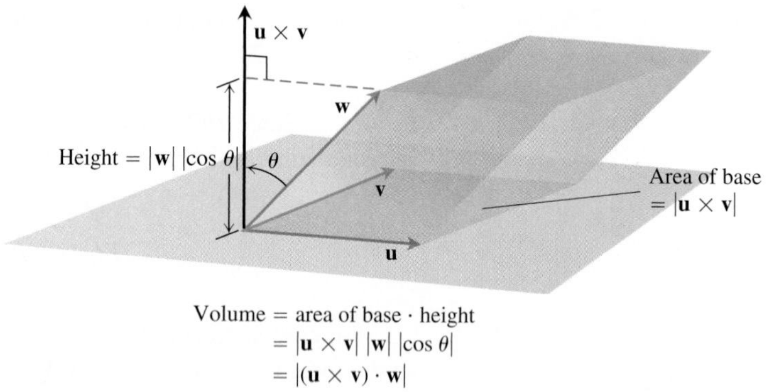

FIGURE 10.33 The number $|(\mathbf{u} \times \mathbf{v}) \cdot \mathbf{w}|$ is the volume of a parallelepiped.

By treating the planes of **v** and **w** and of **w** and **u** as the base planes of the parallelepiped determined by **u**, **v**, and **w**, we see that

$$(\mathbf{u} \times \mathbf{v}) \cdot \mathbf{w} = (\mathbf{v} \times \mathbf{w}) \cdot \mathbf{u} = (\mathbf{w} \times \mathbf{u}) \cdot \mathbf{v}.$$

Since the dot product is commutative, we also have

$$(\mathbf{u} \times \mathbf{v}) \cdot \mathbf{w} = \mathbf{u} \cdot (\mathbf{v} \times \mathbf{w}).$$

The dot and cross may be interchanged in a triple scalar product without altering its value.

The triple scalar product can be evaluated as a determinant:

$$\begin{aligned}(\mathbf{u} \times \mathbf{v}) \cdot \mathbf{w} &= \left[\begin{vmatrix} u_2 & u_3 \\ v_2 & v_3 \end{vmatrix} \mathbf{i} - \begin{vmatrix} u_1 & u_3 \\ v_1 & v_3 \end{vmatrix} \mathbf{j} + \begin{vmatrix} u_1 & u_2 \\ v_1 & v_2 \end{vmatrix} \mathbf{k} \right] \cdot \mathbf{w} \\ &= w_1 \begin{vmatrix} u_2 & u_3 \\ v_2 & v_3 \end{vmatrix} - w_2 \begin{vmatrix} u_1 & u_3 \\ v_1 & v_3 \end{vmatrix} + w_3 \begin{vmatrix} u_1 & u_2 \\ v_1 & v_2 \end{vmatrix} \\ &= \begin{vmatrix} u_1 & u_2 & u_3 \\ v_1 & v_2 & v_3 \\ w_1 & w_2 & w_3 \end{vmatrix}.\end{aligned}$$

Calculating the Triple Scalar Product

$$(\mathbf{u} \times \mathbf{v}) \cdot \mathbf{w} = \begin{vmatrix} u_1 & u_2 & u_3 \\ v_1 & v_2 & v_3 \\ w_1 & w_2 & w_3 \end{vmatrix}$$

EXAMPLE 6 Find the volume of the box (parallelepiped) determined by $\mathbf{u} = \mathbf{i} + 2\mathbf{j} - \mathbf{k}$, $\mathbf{v} = -2\mathbf{i} + 3\mathbf{k}$, and $\mathbf{w} = 7\mathbf{j} - 4\mathbf{k}$.

Solution Using the rule for calculating determinants, we find

$$(\mathbf{u} \times \mathbf{v}) \cdot \mathbf{w} = \begin{vmatrix} 1 & 2 & -1 \\ -2 & 0 & 3 \\ 0 & 7 & -4 \end{vmatrix} = -23.$$

The volume is $|(\mathbf{u} \times \mathbf{v}) \cdot \mathbf{w}| = 23$ units cubed. ■

EXERCISES 10.4

In Exercises 1–8, find the length and direction (when defined) of $\mathbf{u} \times \mathbf{v}$ and $\mathbf{v} \times \mathbf{u}$.

1. $\mathbf{u} = 2\mathbf{i} - 2\mathbf{j} - \mathbf{k}$, $\mathbf{v} = \mathbf{i} - \mathbf{k}$

2. $\mathbf{u} = 2\mathbf{i} + 3\mathbf{j}$, $\mathbf{v} = -\mathbf{i} + \mathbf{j}$

3. $\mathbf{u} = 2\mathbf{i} - 2\mathbf{j} + 4\mathbf{k}$, $\mathbf{v} = -\mathbf{i} + \mathbf{j} - 2\mathbf{k}$

4. $\mathbf{u} = \mathbf{i} + \mathbf{j} - \mathbf{k}$, $\mathbf{v} = \mathbf{0}$

5. $\mathbf{u} = 2\mathbf{i}$, $\mathbf{v} = -3\mathbf{j}$

6. $\mathbf{u} = \mathbf{i} \times \mathbf{j}$, $\mathbf{v} = \mathbf{j} \times \mathbf{k}$

7. $\mathbf{u} = -8\mathbf{i} - 2\mathbf{j} - 4\mathbf{k}$, $\mathbf{v} = 2\mathbf{i} + 2\mathbf{j} + \mathbf{k}$

8. $\mathbf{u} = \frac{3}{2}\mathbf{i} - \frac{1}{2}\mathbf{j} + \mathbf{k}$, $\mathbf{v} = \mathbf{i} + \mathbf{j} + 2\mathbf{k}$

In Exercises 9–14, sketch the coordinate axes and then include the vectors $\mathbf{u}$, $\mathbf{v}$ and $\mathbf{u} \times \mathbf{v}$ as vectors starting at the origin.

9. $\mathbf{u} = \mathbf{i}$, $\mathbf{v} = \mathbf{j}$

10. $\mathbf{u} = \mathbf{i} - \mathbf{k}$, $\mathbf{v} = \mathbf{j}$

11. $\mathbf{u} = \mathbf{i} - \mathbf{k}$, $\mathbf{v} = \mathbf{j} + \mathbf{k}$

12. $\mathbf{u} = 2\mathbf{i} - \mathbf{j}$, $\mathbf{v} = \mathbf{i} + 2\mathbf{j}$

13. $\mathbf{u} = \mathbf{i} + \mathbf{j}$, $\mathbf{v} = \mathbf{i} - \mathbf{j}$

14. $\mathbf{u} = \mathbf{j} + 2\mathbf{k}$, $\mathbf{v} = \mathbf{i}$

In Exercises 15–18,

a. Find the area of the triangle determined by the points P, Q, and R.

b. Find a unit vector perpendicular to plane PQR.

15. $P(1, -1, 2)$, $Q(2, 0, -1)$, $R(0, 2, 1)$

16. $P(1, 1, 1)$, $Q(2, 1, 3)$, $R(3, -1, 1)$

17. $P(2, -2, 1)$, $Q(3, -1, 2)$, $R(3, -1, 1)$

18. $P(-2, 2, 0)$, $Q(0, 1, -1)$, $R(-1, 2, -2)$

In Exercises 19–22, verify that $(\mathbf{u} \times \mathbf{v}) \cdot \mathbf{w} = (\mathbf{v} \times \mathbf{w}) \cdot \mathbf{u} = (\mathbf{w} \times \mathbf{u}) \cdot \mathbf{v}$ and find the volume of the parallelepiped (box) determined by $\mathbf{u}$, $\mathbf{v}$, and $\mathbf{w}$.

	u	v	w
19.	$2\mathbf{i}$	$2\mathbf{j}$	$2\mathbf{k}$
20.	$\mathbf{i} - \mathbf{j} + \mathbf{k}$	$2\mathbf{i} + \mathbf{j} - 2\mathbf{k}$	$-\mathbf{i} + 2\mathbf{j} - \mathbf{k}$
21.	$2\mathbf{i} + \mathbf{j}$	$2\mathbf{i} - \mathbf{j} + \mathbf{k}$	$\mathbf{i} + 2\mathbf{k}$
22.	$\mathbf{i} + \mathbf{j} - 2\mathbf{k}$	$-\mathbf{i} - \mathbf{k}$	$2\mathbf{i} + 4\mathbf{j} - 2\mathbf{k}$

23. Parallel and perpendicular vectors Let $\mathbf{u} = 5\mathbf{i} - \mathbf{j} + \mathbf{k}$, $\mathbf{v} = \mathbf{j} - 5\mathbf{k}$, $\mathbf{w} = -15\mathbf{i} + 3\mathbf{j} - 3\mathbf{k}$. Which vectors, if any, are **(a)** perpendicular? **(b)** Parallel? Give reasons for your answers.

24. Parallel and perpendicular vectors Let $\mathbf{u} = \mathbf{i} + 2\mathbf{j} - \mathbf{k}$, $\mathbf{v} = -\mathbf{i} + \mathbf{j} + \mathbf{k}$, $\mathbf{w} = \mathbf{i} + \mathbf{k}$, $\mathbf{r} = -(\pi/2)\mathbf{i} - \pi\mathbf{j} + (\pi/2)\mathbf{k}$. Which vectors, if any, are **(a)** perpendicular? **(b)** Parallel? Give reasons for your answers.

In Exercises 25 and 26, find the magnitude of the torque exerted by $\mathbf{F}$ on the bolt at P if $|\overrightarrow{PQ}| = 8$ in. and $|\mathbf{F}| = 30$ lb. Answer in foot-pounds.

25.

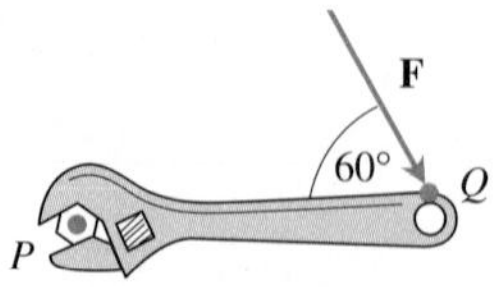

26.

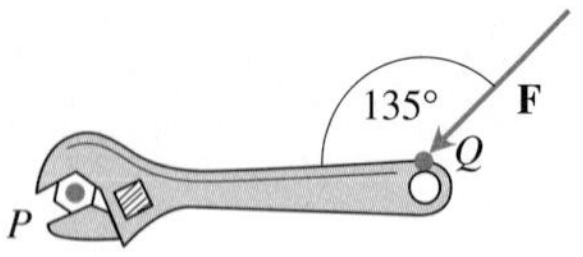

27. Which of the following are *always true*, and which are *not always true*? Give reasons for your answers.

a. $|\mathbf{u}| = \sqrt{\mathbf{u} \cdot \mathbf{u}}$

b. $\mathbf{u} \cdot \mathbf{u} = |\mathbf{u}|$

c. $\mathbf{u} \times \mathbf{0} = \mathbf{0} \times \mathbf{u} = \mathbf{0}$

d. $\mathbf{u} \times (-\mathbf{u}) = \mathbf{0}$

e. $\mathbf{u} \times \mathbf{v} = \mathbf{v} \times \mathbf{u}$

f. $\mathbf{u} \times (\mathbf{v} + \mathbf{w}) = \mathbf{u} \times \mathbf{v} + \mathbf{u} \times \mathbf{w}$

g. $(\mathbf{u} \times \mathbf{v}) \cdot \mathbf{v} = 0$

h. $(\mathbf{u} \times \mathbf{v}) \cdot \mathbf{w} = \mathbf{u} \cdot (\mathbf{v} \times \mathbf{w})$

28. Which of the following are *always true*, and which are *not always true*? Give reasons for your answers.

a. $\mathbf{u} \cdot \mathbf{v} = \mathbf{v} \cdot \mathbf{u}$

b. $\mathbf{u} \times \mathbf{v} = -(\mathbf{v} \times \mathbf{u})$

c. $(-\mathbf{u}) \times \mathbf{v} = -(\mathbf{u} \times \mathbf{v})$

d. $(c\mathbf{u}) \cdot \mathbf{v} = \mathbf{u} \cdot (c\mathbf{v}) = c(\mathbf{u} \cdot \mathbf{v})$ (any number c)

e. $c(\mathbf{u} \times \mathbf{v}) = (c\mathbf{u}) \times \mathbf{v} = \mathbf{u} \times (c\mathbf{v})$ (any number c)

f. $\mathbf{u} \cdot \mathbf{u} = |\mathbf{u}|^2$

g. $(\mathbf{u} \times \mathbf{u}) \cdot \mathbf{u} = 0$

h. $(\mathbf{u} \times \mathbf{v}) \cdot \mathbf{u} = \mathbf{v} \cdot (\mathbf{u} \times \mathbf{v})$

29. Given nonzero vectors $\mathbf{u}$, $\mathbf{v}$, and $\mathbf{w}$, use dot product and cross product notation, as appropriate, to describe the following.

a. The vector projection of $\mathbf{u}$ onto $\mathbf{v}$

b. A vector orthogonal to $\mathbf{u}$ and $\mathbf{v}$

c. A vector orthogonal to $\mathbf{u} \times \mathbf{v}$ and $\mathbf{w}$

d. The volume of the parallelepiped determined by $\mathbf{u}$, $\mathbf{v}$, and $\mathbf{w}$

30. Given nonzero vectors $\mathbf{u}$, $\mathbf{v}$, and $\mathbf{w}$, use dot product and cross product notation to describe the following.

a. A vector orthogonal to $\mathbf{u} \times \mathbf{v}$ and $\mathbf{u} \times \mathbf{w}$

b. A vector orthogonal to $\mathbf{u} + \mathbf{v}$ and $\mathbf{u} - \mathbf{v}$

c. A vector of length $|\mathbf{u}|$ in the direction of $\mathbf{v}$

d. The area of the parallelogram determined by $\mathbf{u}$ and $\mathbf{w}$

31. Let $\mathbf{u}$, $\mathbf{v}$, and $\mathbf{w}$ be vectors. Which of the following make sense, and which do not? Give reasons for your answers.

a. $(\mathbf{u} \times \mathbf{v}) \cdot \mathbf{w}$

b. $\mathbf{u} \times (\mathbf{v} \cdot \mathbf{w})$

c. $\mathbf{u} \times (\mathbf{v} \times \mathbf{w})$

d. $\mathbf{u} \cdot (\mathbf{v} \cdot \mathbf{w})$

32. Cross products of three vectors Show that except in degenerate cases, $(\mathbf{u} \times \mathbf{v}) \times \mathbf{w}$ lies in the plane of $\mathbf{u}$ and $\mathbf{v}$, whereas $\mathbf{u} \times (\mathbf{v} \times \mathbf{w})$ lies in the plane of $\mathbf{v}$ and $\mathbf{w}$. What *are* the degenerate cases?

33. Cancellation in cross products If $\mathbf{u} \times \mathbf{v} = \mathbf{u} \times \mathbf{w}$ and $\mathbf{u} \neq \mathbf{0}$, then does $\mathbf{v} = \mathbf{w}$? Give reasons for your answer.

34. Double cancellation If $\mathbf{u} \neq \mathbf{0}$ and if $\mathbf{u} \times \mathbf{v} = \mathbf{u} \times \mathbf{w}$ and $\mathbf{u} \cdot \mathbf{v} = \mathbf{u} \cdot \mathbf{w}$, then does $\mathbf{v} = \mathbf{w}$? Give reasons for your answer.

Find the areas of the parallelograms whose vertices are given in Exercises 35–38.

35. $A(1, 0)$, $B(0, 1)$, $C(-1, 0)$, $D(0, -1)$

36. $A(0, 0)$, $B(7, 3)$, $C(9, 8)$, $D(2, 5)$

37. $A(-1, 2)$, $B(2, 0)$, $C(7, 1)$, $D(4, 3)$

38. $A(-6, 0)$, $B(1, -4)$, $C(3, 1)$, $D(-4, 5)$

Find the areas of the triangles whose vertices are given in Exercises 39–42.

39. $A(0, 0)$, $B(-2, 3)$, $C(3, 1)$

40. $A(-1, -1)$, $B(3, 3)$, $C(2, 1)$

41. $A(-5, 3)$, $B(1, -2)$, $C(6, -2)$

42. $A(-6, 0)$, $B(10, -5)$, $C(-2, 4)$

43. Triangle area Find a formula for the area of the triangle in the xy-plane with vertices at $(0, 0)$, (a_1, a_2), and (b_1, b_2). Explain your work.

44. Triangle area Find a concise formula for the area of a triangle with vertices (a_1, a_2), (b_1, b_2), and (c_1, c_2).

10.5 Lines and Planes in Space

This section shows how to use scalar and vector products to write equations for lines, line segments, and planes in space. We will use these representations throughout the rest of the book.

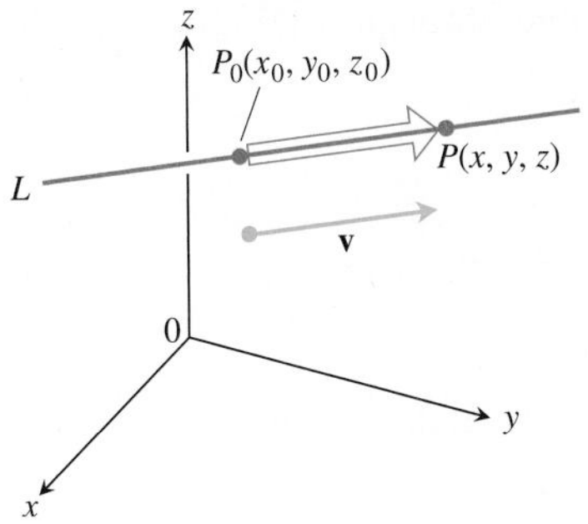

FIGURE 10.34 A point P lies on L through P_0 parallel to $\mathbf{v}$ if and only if $\overrightarrow{P_0P}$ is a scalar multiple of $\mathbf{v}$.

Lines and Line Segments in Space

In the plane, a line is determined by a point and a number giving the slope of the line. In space a line is determined by a point and a *vector* giving the direction of the line.

Suppose that L is a line in space passing through a point $P_0(x_0, y_0, z_0)$ parallel to a vector $\mathbf{v} = v_1\mathbf{i} + v_2\mathbf{j} + v_3\mathbf{k}$. Then L is the set of all points $P(x, y, z)$ for which $\overrightarrow{P_0P}$ is parallel to $\mathbf{v}$ (Figure 10.34). Thus, $\overrightarrow{P_0P} = t\mathbf{v}$ for some scalar parameter t. The value of t depends on the location of the point P along the line, and the domain of t is $(-\infty, \infty)$. The expanded form of the equation $\overrightarrow{P_0P} = t\mathbf{v}$ is

$$(x - x_0)\mathbf{i} + (y - y_0)\mathbf{j} + (z - z_0)\mathbf{k} = t(v_1\mathbf{i} + v_2\mathbf{j} + v_3\mathbf{k}),$$

which can be rewritten as

$$x\mathbf{i} + y\mathbf{j} + z\mathbf{k} = x_0\mathbf{i} + y_0\mathbf{j} + z_0\mathbf{k} + t(v_1\mathbf{i} + v_2\mathbf{j} + v_3\mathbf{k}). \tag{1}$$

If $\mathbf{r}(t)$ is the position vector of a point $P(x, y, z)$ on the line and $\mathbf{r}_0$ is the position vector of the point $P_0(x_0, y_0, z_0)$, then Equation (1) gives the following vector form for the equation of a line in space.

> **Vector Equation for a Line**
> **A vector equation for the line L through $P_0(x_0, y_0, z_0)$ parallel to $\mathbf{v}$ is**
>
> $$\mathbf{r}(t) = \mathbf{r}_0 + t\mathbf{v}, \qquad -\infty < t < \infty, \tag{2}$$
>
> where $\mathbf{r}$ is the position vector of a point $P(x, y, z)$ on L and $\mathbf{r}_0$ is the position vector of $P_0(x_0, y_0, z_0)$.

Equating the corresponding components of the two sides of Equation (1) gives three scalar equations involving the parameter t:

$$x = x_0 + tv_1, \qquad y = y_0 + tv_2, \qquad z = z_0 + tv_3.$$

These equations give us the standard parametrization of the line for the parameter interval $-\infty < t < \infty$.

> **Parametric Equations for a Line**
> **The standard parametrization of the line through $P_0(x_0, y_0, z_0)$ parallel to $\mathbf{v} = v_1\mathbf{i} + v_2\mathbf{j} + v_3\mathbf{k}$ is**
>
> $$x = x_0 + tv_1, \quad y = y_0 + tv_2, \quad z = z_0 + tv_3, \quad -\infty < t < \infty \tag{3}$$

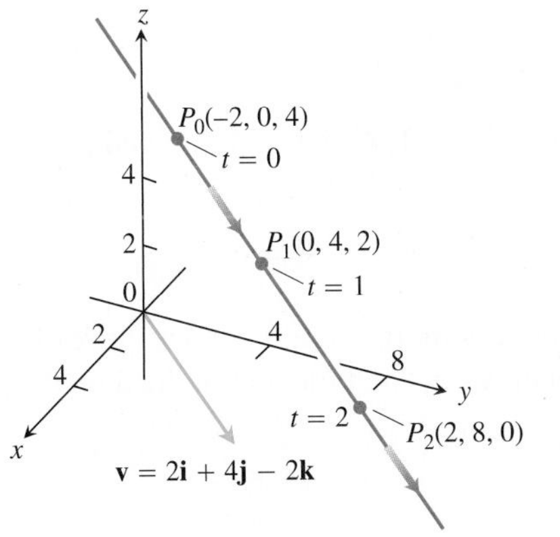

FIGURE 10.35 Selected points and parameter values on the line in Example 1. The arrows show the direction of increasing t.

EXAMPLE 1 Find parametric equations for the line through $(-2, 0, 4)$ parallel to $\mathbf{v} = 2\mathbf{i} + 4\mathbf{j} - 2\mathbf{k}$ (Figure 10.35).

Solution With $P_0(x_0, y_0, z_0)$ equal to $(-2, 0, 4)$ and $v_1\mathbf{i} + v_2\mathbf{j} + v_3\mathbf{k}$ equal to $2\mathbf{i} + 4\mathbf{j} - 2\mathbf{k}$, Equations (3) become

$$x = -2 + 2t, \qquad y = 4t, \qquad z = 4 - 2t. \qquad \blacksquare$$

EXAMPLE 2 Find parametric equations for the line through $P(-3, 2, -3)$ and $Q(1, -1, 4)$.

Solution The vector

$$\begin{aligned}\overrightarrow{PQ} &= (1 - (-3))\mathbf{i} + (-1 - 2)\mathbf{j} + (4 - (-3))\mathbf{k} \\ &= 4\mathbf{i} - 3\mathbf{j} + 7\mathbf{k}\end{aligned}$$

is parallel to the line, and Equations (3) with $(x_0, y_0, z_0) = (-3, 2, -3)$ give

$$x = -3 + 4t, \qquad y = 2 - 3t, \qquad z = -3 + 7t.$$

We could have chosen $Q(1, -1, 4)$ as the "base point" and written

$$x = 1 + 4t, \quad y = -1 - 3t, \quad z = 4 + 7t.$$

These equations serve as well as the first; they simply place you at a different point on the line for a given value of t. ■

Notice that parametrizations are not unique. Not only can the "base point" change, but so can the parameter. The equations $x = -3 + 4t^3$, $y = 2 - 3t^3$, and $z = -3 + 7t^3$ also parametrize the line in Example 2.

To parametrize a line segment joining two points, we first parametrize the line through the points. We then find the t-values for the endpoints and restrict t to lie in the closed interval bounded by these values. The line equations together with this added restriction parametrize the segment.

EXAMPLE 3 Parametrize the line segment joining the points $P(-3, 2, -3)$ and $Q(1, -1, 4)$ (Figure 10.36).

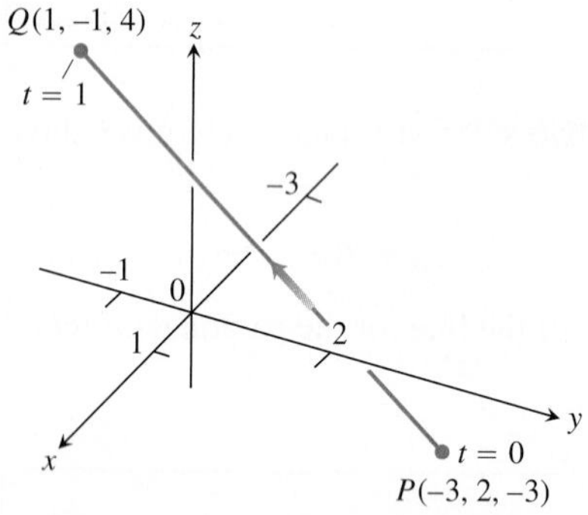

FIGURE 10.36 Example 3 derives a parametrization of line segment PQ. The arrow shows the direction of increasing t.

Solution We begin with equations for the line through P and Q, taking them, in this case, from Example 2:

$$x = -3 + 4t, \qquad y = 2 - 3t, \qquad z = -3 + 7t.$$

We observe that the point

$$(x, y, z) = (-3 + 4t, 2 - 3t, -3 + 7t)$$

on the line passes through $P(-3, 2, -3)$ at $t = 0$ and $Q(1, -1, 4)$ at $t = 1$. We add the restriction $0 \le t \le 1$ to parametrize the segment:

$$x = -3 + 4t, \qquad y = 2 - 3t, \qquad z = -3 + 7t, \qquad 0 \le t \le 1.$$ ■

The vector form (Equation (2)) for a line in space is more revealing if we think of a line as the path of a particle starting at position $P_0(x_0, y_0, z_0)$ and moving in the direction of vector $\mathbf{v}$. Rewriting Equation (2), we have

$$\begin{aligned}\mathbf{r}(t) &= \mathbf{r}_0 + t\mathbf{v} \\ &= \underbrace{\mathbf{r}_0}_{\text{Initial position}} + \underbrace{t}_{\text{Time}}\underbrace{|\mathbf{v}|}_{\text{Speed}}\underbrace{\frac{\mathbf{v}}{|\mathbf{v}|}}_{\text{Direction}}.\end{aligned} \tag{4}$$

In other words, the position of the particle at time t is its initial position plus its distance moved (speed × time) in the direction $\mathbf{v}/|\mathbf{v}|$ of its straight-line motion.

EXAMPLE 4 A helicopter is to fly directly from a helipad at the origin in the direction of the point (1, 1, 1) at a speed of 60 ft/sec. What is the position of the helicopter after 10 sec?

Solution We place the origin at the starting position (helipad) of the helicopter. Then the unit vector

$$\mathbf{u} = \frac{1}{\sqrt{3}}\mathbf{i} + \frac{1}{\sqrt{3}}\mathbf{j} + \frac{1}{\sqrt{3}}\mathbf{k}$$

gives the flight direction of the helicopter. From Equation (4), the position of the helicopter at any time t is

$$\begin{aligned} \mathbf{r}(t) &= \mathbf{r}_0 + t(\text{speed})\mathbf{u} \\ &= \mathbf{0} + t(60)\left(\frac{1}{\sqrt{3}}\mathbf{i} + \frac{1}{\sqrt{3}}\mathbf{j} + \frac{1}{\sqrt{3}}\mathbf{k}\right) \\ &= 20\sqrt{3}t(\mathbf{i} + \mathbf{j} + \mathbf{k}). \end{aligned}$$

When $t = 10$ sec,

$$\begin{aligned} \mathbf{r}(10) &= 200\sqrt{3}\,(\mathbf{i} + \mathbf{j} + \mathbf{k}) \\ &= \left\langle 200\sqrt{3}, 200\sqrt{3}, 200\sqrt{3} \right\rangle. \end{aligned}$$

After 10 sec of flight from the origin toward (1, 1, 1), the helicopter is located at the point $(200\sqrt{3}, 200\sqrt{3}, 200\sqrt{3})$ in space. It has traveled a distance of (60 ft/sec)(10 sec) = 600 ft, which is the length of the vector $\mathbf{r}(10)$. ■

The Distance from a Point to a Line in Space

To find the distance from a point S to a line that passes through a point P parallel to a vector $\mathbf{v}$, we find the absolute value of the scalar component of $\overrightarrow{PS}$ in the direction of a vector normal to the line (Figure 10.37). In the notation of the figure, the absolute value of the scalar component is $|\overrightarrow{PS}|\sin\theta$, which is $\dfrac{|\overrightarrow{PS} \times \mathbf{v}|}{|\mathbf{v}|}$.

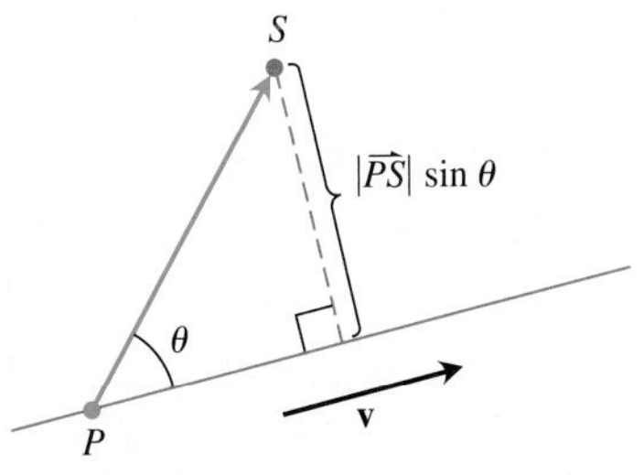

FIGURE 10.37 The distance from S to the line through P parallel to $\mathbf{v}$ is $|\overrightarrow{PS}|\sin\theta$, where θ is the angle between $\overrightarrow{PS}$ and $\mathbf{v}$.

Distance from a Point S to a Line Through P Parallel to v

$$d = \frac{|\overrightarrow{PS} \times \mathbf{v}|}{|\mathbf{v}|} \tag{5}$$

EXAMPLE 5 Find the distance from the point $S(1, 1, 5)$ to the line

$$L: \quad x = 1 + t, \quad y = 3 - t, \quad z = 2t.$$

Solution We see from the equations for L that L passes through $P(1, 3, 0)$ parallel to $\mathbf{v} = \mathbf{i} - \mathbf{j} + 2\mathbf{k}$. With

$$\overrightarrow{PS} = (1 - 1)\mathbf{i} + (1 - 3)\mathbf{j} + (5 - 0)\mathbf{k} = -2\mathbf{j} + 5\mathbf{k}$$

and

$$\overrightarrow{PS} \times \mathbf{v} = \begin{vmatrix} \mathbf{i} & \mathbf{j} & \mathbf{k} \\ 0 & -2 & 5 \\ 1 & -1 & 2 \end{vmatrix} = \mathbf{i} + 5\mathbf{j} + 2\mathbf{k},$$

Equation (5) gives

$$d = \frac{|\overrightarrow{PS} \times \mathbf{v}|}{|\mathbf{v}|} = \frac{\sqrt{1 + 25 + 4}}{\sqrt{1 + 1 + 4}} = \frac{\sqrt{30}}{\sqrt{6}} = \sqrt{5}.$$ ■

An Equation for a Plane in Space

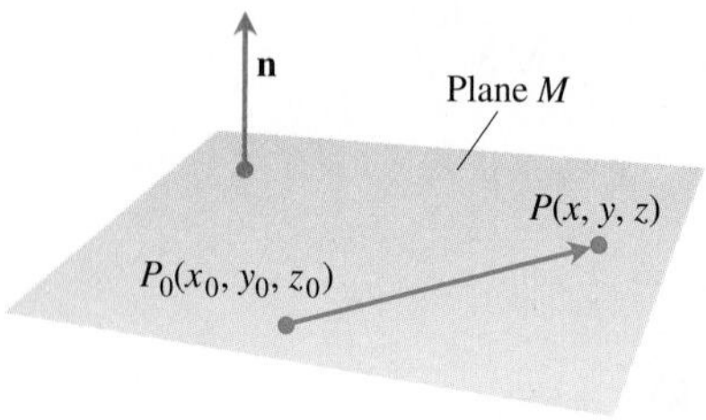

FIGURE 10.38 The standard equation for a plane in space is defined in terms of a vector normal to the plane: A point P lies in the plane through P_0 normal to $\mathbf{n}$ if and only if $\mathbf{n} \cdot \overrightarrow{P_0P} = 0$.

A plane in space is determined by knowing a point on the plane and its "tilt" or orientation. This "tilt" is defined by specifying a vector that is perpendicular or normal to the plane.

Suppose that plane M passes through a point $P_0(x_0, y_0, z_0)$ and is normal to the nonzero vector $\mathbf{n} = A\mathbf{i} + B\mathbf{j} + C\mathbf{k}$. Then M is the set of all points $P(x, y, z)$ for which $\overrightarrow{P_0P}$ is orthogonal to $\mathbf{n}$ (Figure 10.38). Thus, the dot product $\mathbf{n} \cdot \overrightarrow{P_0P} = 0$. This equation is equivalent to

$$(A\mathbf{i} + B\mathbf{j} + C\mathbf{k}) \cdot [(x - x_0)\mathbf{i} + (y - y_0)\mathbf{j} + (z - z_0)\mathbf{k}] = 0$$

or

$$A(x - x_0) + B(y - y_0) + C(z - z_0) = 0.$$

> **Equation for a Plane**
> The plane through $P_0(x_0, y_0, z_0)$ normal to $\mathbf{n} = A\mathbf{i} + B\mathbf{j} + C\mathbf{k}$ has
>
> Vector equation: $\mathbf{n} \cdot \overrightarrow{P_0P} = 0$
> Component equation: $A(x - x_0) + B(y - y_0) + C(z - z_0) = 0$
> Component equation simplified: $Ax + By + Cz = D$, where $D = Ax_0 + By_0 + Cz_0$

EXAMPLE 6 Find an equation for the plane through $P_0(-3, 0, 7)$ perpendicular to $\mathbf{n} = 5\mathbf{i} + 2\mathbf{j} - \mathbf{k}$.

Solution The component equation is

$$5(x - (-3)) + 2(y - 0) + (-1)(z - 7) = 0.$$

Simplifying, we obtain

$$5x + 15 + 2y - z + 7 = 0$$
$$5x + 2y - z = -22.$$ ■

Notice in Example 6 how the components of $\mathbf{n} = 5\mathbf{i} + 2\mathbf{j} - \mathbf{k}$ became the coefficients of x, y, and z in the equation $5x + 2y - z = -22$. The vector $\mathbf{n} = A\mathbf{i} + B\mathbf{j} + C\mathbf{k}$ is normal to the plane $Ax + By + Cz = D$.

EXAMPLE 7 Find an equation for the plane through $A(0, 0, 1)$, $B(2, 0, 0)$, and $C(0, 3, 0)$.

Solution We find a vector normal to the plane and use it with one of the points (it does not matter which) to write an equation for the plane.

The cross product

$$\overrightarrow{AB} \times \overrightarrow{AC} = \begin{vmatrix} \mathbf{i} & \mathbf{j} & \mathbf{k} \\ 2 & 0 & -1 \\ 0 & 3 & -1 \end{vmatrix} = 3\mathbf{i} + 2\mathbf{j} + 6\mathbf{k}$$

is normal to the plane. We substitute the components of this vector and the coordinates of $A(0, 0, 1)$ into the component form of the equation to obtain

$$3(x - 0) + 2(y - 0) + 6(z - 1) = 0$$
$$3x + 2y + 6z = 6.$$ ■

Lines of Intersection

Just as lines are parallel if and only if they have the same direction, two planes are **parallel** if and only if their normals are parallel, or $\mathbf{n}_1 = k\mathbf{n}_2$ for some scalar k. Two planes that are not parallel intersect in a line.

EXAMPLE 8 Find a vector parallel to the line of intersection of the planes $3x - 6y - 2z = 15$ and $2x + y - 2z = 5$.

Solution The line of intersection of two planes is perpendicular to both planes' normal vectors $\mathbf{n}_1$ and $\mathbf{n}_2$ (Figure 10.39) and therefore parallel to $\mathbf{n}_1 \times \mathbf{n}_2$. Turning this around, $\mathbf{n}_1 \times \mathbf{n}_2$ is a vector parallel to the planes' line of intersection. In our case,

$$\mathbf{n}_1 \times \mathbf{n}_2 = \begin{vmatrix} \mathbf{i} & \mathbf{j} & \mathbf{k} \\ 3 & -6 & -2 \\ 2 & 1 & -2 \end{vmatrix} = 14\mathbf{i} + 2\mathbf{j} + 15\mathbf{k}.$$

Any nonzero scalar multiple of $\mathbf{n}_1 \times \mathbf{n}_2$ will do as well. ■

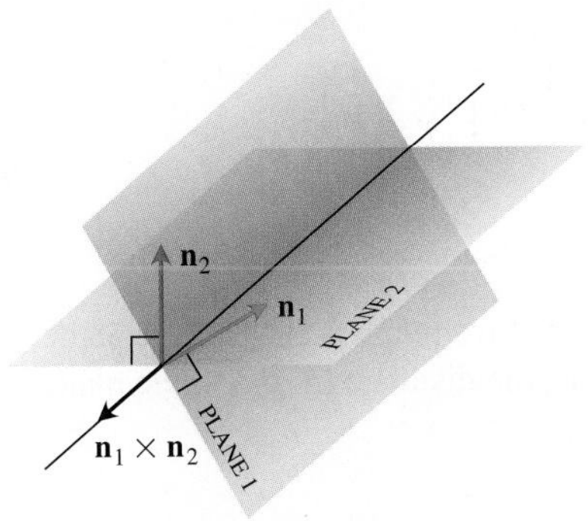

FIGURE 10.39 How the line of intersection of two planes is related to the planes' normal vectors (Example 8).

EXAMPLE 9 Find parametric equations for the line in which the planes $3x - 6y - 2z = 15$ and $2x + y - 2z = 5$ intersect.

Solution We find a vector parallel to the line and a point on the line and use Equations (3).

Example 8 identifies $\mathbf{v} = 14\mathbf{i} + 2\mathbf{j} + 15\mathbf{k}$ as a vector parallel to the line. To find a point on the line, we can take any point common to the two planes. Substituting $z = 0$ in the plane equations and solving for x and y simultaneously identifies one of these points as $(3, -1, 0)$. The line is

$$x = 3 + 14t, \qquad y = -1 + 2t, \qquad z = 15t.$$

The choice $z = 0$ is arbitrary and we could have chosen $z = 1$ or $z = -1$ just as well. Or we could have let $x = 0$ and solved for y and z. The different choices would simply give different parametrizations of the same line. ■

Sometimes we want to know where a line and a plane intersect. For example, if we are looking at a flat plate and a line segment passes through it, we may be interested in knowing what portion of the line segment is hidden from our view by the plate. This application is used in computer graphics (Exercise 74).

EXAMPLE 10 Find the point where the line

$$x = \frac{8}{3} + 2t, \qquad y = -2t, \qquad z = 1 + t$$

intersects the plane $3x + 2y + 6z = 6$.

Solution The point

$$\left(\frac{8}{3} + 2t, -2t, 1 + t\right)$$

lies in the plane if its coordinates satisfy the equation of the plane, that is, if

$$\begin{aligned} 3\left(\frac{8}{3} + 2t\right) + 2(-2t) + 6(1 + t) &= 6 \\ 8 + 6t - 4t + 6 + 6t &= 6 \\ 8t &= -8 \\ t &= -1. \end{aligned}$$

The point of intersection is

$$(x, y, z)|_{t=-1} = \left(\frac{8}{3} - 2, 2, 1 - 1\right) = \left(\frac{2}{3}, 2, 0\right).$$ ■

The Distance from a Point to a Plane

If P is a point on a plane with normal $\mathbf{n}$, then the distance from any point S to the plane is the length of the vector projection of $\overrightarrow{PS}$ onto $\mathbf{n}$. That is, the distance from S to the plane is

$$d = \left|\overrightarrow{PS} \cdot \frac{\mathbf{n}}{|\mathbf{n}|}\right| \tag{6}$$

where $\mathbf{n} = A\mathbf{i} + B\mathbf{j} + C\mathbf{k}$ is normal to the plane.

EXAMPLE 11 Find the distance from $S(1, 1, 3)$ to the plane $3x + 2y + 6z = 6$.

Solution We find a point P in the plane and calculate the length of the vector projection of $\overrightarrow{PS}$ onto a vector $\mathbf{n}$ normal to the plane (Figure 10.40). The coefficients in the equation $3x + 2y + 6z = 6$ give

$$\mathbf{n} = 3\mathbf{i} + 2\mathbf{j} + 6\mathbf{k}.$$

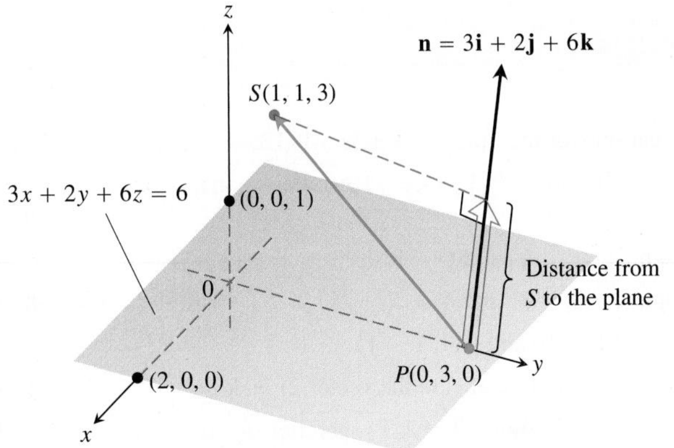

FIGURE 10.40 The distance from S to the plane is the length of the vector projection of $\overrightarrow{PS}$ onto $\mathbf{n}$ (Example 11).

The points on the plane easiest to find from the plane's equation are the intercepts. If we take P to be the y-intercept $(0, 3, 0)$, then

$$\begin{aligned}\overrightarrow{PS} &= (1-0)\mathbf{i} + (1-3)\mathbf{j} + (3-0)\mathbf{k}\\ &= \mathbf{i} - 2\mathbf{j} + 3\mathbf{k},\\ |\mathbf{n}| &= \sqrt{(3)^2 + (2)^2 + (6)^2} = \sqrt{49} = 7.\end{aligned}$$

The distance from S to the plane is

$$\begin{aligned}d &= \left|\overrightarrow{PS}\cdot\frac{\mathbf{n}}{|\mathbf{n}|}\right| \qquad \text{length of } \operatorname{proj}_{\mathbf{n}}\overrightarrow{PS}\\ &= \left|(\mathbf{i} - 2\mathbf{j} + 3\mathbf{k})\cdot\left(\frac{3}{7}\mathbf{i} + \frac{2}{7}\mathbf{j} + \frac{6}{7}\mathbf{k}\right)\right|\\ &= \left|\frac{3}{7} - \frac{4}{7} + \frac{18}{7}\right| = \frac{17}{7}.\end{aligned}$$

■

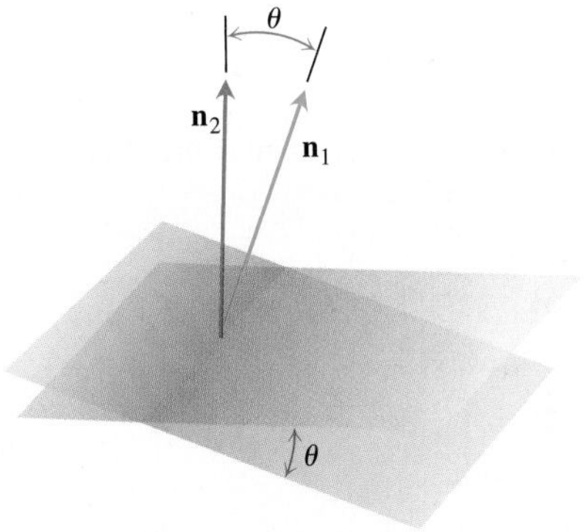

FIGURE 10.41 The angle between two planes is obtained from the angle between their normals.

Angles Between Planes

The angle between two intersecting planes is defined to be the (acute) angle between their normal vectors (Figure 10.41).

EXAMPLE 12 Find the angle between the planes $3x - 6y - 2z = 15$ and $2x + y - 2z = 5$.

Solution The vectors

$$\mathbf{n}_1 = 3\mathbf{i} - 6\mathbf{j} - 2\mathbf{k}, \qquad \mathbf{n}_2 = 2\mathbf{i} + \mathbf{j} - 2\mathbf{k}$$

are normals to the planes. The angle between them is

$$\begin{aligned}\theta &= \cos^{-1}\left(\frac{\mathbf{n}_1\cdot\mathbf{n}_2}{|\mathbf{n}_1||\mathbf{n}_2|}\right)\\ &= \cos^{-1}\left(\frac{4}{21}\right)\\ &\approx 1.38 \text{ radians.} \qquad \text{About 79 deg}\end{aligned}$$

■

EXERCISES 10.5

Find parametric equations for the lines in Exercises 1–12.

1. The line through the point $P(3, -4, -1)$ parallel to the vector $\mathbf{i} + \mathbf{j} + \mathbf{k}$
2. The line through $P(1, 2, -1)$ and $Q(-1, 0, 1)$
3. The line through $P(-2, 0, 3)$ and $Q(3, 5, -2)$
4. The line through $P(1, 2, 0)$ and $Q(1, 1, -1)$
5. The line through the origin parallel to the vector $2\mathbf{j} + \mathbf{k}$
6. The line through the point $(3, -2, 1)$ parallel to the line $x = 1 + 2t, y = 2 - t, z = 3t$
7. The line through $(1, 1, 1)$ parallel to the z-axis
8. The line through $(2, 4, 5)$ perpendicular to the plane $3x + 7y - 5z = 21$
9. The line through $(0, -7, 0)$ perpendicular to the plane $x + 2y + 2z = 13$
10. The line through $(2, 3, 0)$ perpendicular to the vectors $\mathbf{u} = \mathbf{i} + 2\mathbf{j} + 3\mathbf{k}$ and $\mathbf{v} = 3\mathbf{i} + 4\mathbf{j} + 5\mathbf{k}$
11. The x-axis
12. The z-axis

Find parametrizations for the line segments joining the points in Exercises 13–20. Draw coordinate axes and sketch each segment, indicating the direction of increasing t for your parametrization.

13. $(0, 0, 0)$, $(1, 1, 3/2)$
14. $(0, 0, 0)$, $(1, 0, 0)$
15. $(1, 0, 0)$, $(1, 1, 0)$
16. $(1, 1, 0)$, $(1, 1, 1)$
17. $(0, 1, 1)$, $(0, -1, 1)$
18. $(0, 2, 0)$, $(3, 0, 0)$
19. $(2, 0, 2)$, $(0, 2, 0)$
20. $(1, 0, -1)$, $(0, 3, 0)$

Find equations for the planes in Exercises 21–26.

21. The plane through $P_0(0, 2, -1)$ normal to $\mathbf{n} = 3\mathbf{i} - 2\mathbf{j} - \mathbf{k}$
22. The plane through $(1, -1, 3)$ parallel to the plane
$$3x + y + z = 7$$
23. The plane through $(1, 1, -1)$, $(2, 0, 2)$, and $(0, -2, 1)$
24. The plane through $(2, 4, 5)$, $(1, 5, 7)$, and $(-1, 6, 8)$
25. The plane through $P_0(2, 4, 5)$ perpendicular to the line
$$x = 5 + t, \quad y = 1 + 3t, \quad z = 4t$$
26. The plane through $A(1, -2, 1)$ perpendicular to the vector from the origin to A
27. Find the point of intersection of the lines $x = 2t + 1, y = 3t + 2, z = 4t + 3$, and $x = s + 2, y = 2s + 4, z = -4s - 1$, and then find the plane determined by these lines.
28. Find the point of intersection of the lines $x = t, y = -t + 2, z = t + 1$, and $x = 2s + 2, y = s + 3, z = 5s + 6$, and then find the plane determined by these lines.

In Exercises 29 and 30, find the plane determined by the intersecting lines.

29. $L1$: $x = -1 + t, \quad y = 2 + t, \quad z = 1 - t; \quad -\infty < t < \infty$
$L2$: $x = 1 - 4s, \quad y = 1 + 2s, \quad z = 2 - 2s; \quad -\infty < s < \infty$
30. $L1$: $x = t, \quad y = 3 - 3t, \quad z = -2 - t; \quad -\infty < t < \infty$
$L2$: $x = 1 + s, \quad y = 4 + s, \quad z = -1 + s; \quad -\infty < s < \infty$
31. Find a plane through $P_0(2, 1, -1)$ and perpendicular to the line of intersection of the planes $2x + y - z = 3, x + 2y + z = 2$.
32. Find a plane through the points $P_1(1, 2, 3), P_2(3, 2, 1)$ and perpendicular to the plane $4x - y + 2z = 7$.

In Exercises 33–38, find the distance from the point to the line.

33. $(0, 0, 12)$; $\quad x = 4t, \quad y = -2t, \quad z = 2t$
34. $(0, 0, 0)$; $\quad x = 5 + 3t, \quad y = 5 + 4t, \quad z = -3 - 5t$
35. $(2, 1, 3)$; $\quad x = 2 + 2t, \quad y = 1 + 6t, \quad z = 3$
36. $(2, 1, -1)$; $\quad x = 2t, \quad y = 1 + 2t, \quad z = 2t$
37. $(3, -1, 4)$; $\quad x = 4 - t, \quad y = 3 + 2t, \quad z = -5 + 3t$
38. $(-1, 4, 3)$; $\quad x = 10 + 4t, \quad y = -3, \quad z = 4t$

In Exercises 39–44, find the distance from the point to the plane.

39. $(2, -3, 4)$, $\quad x + 2y + 2z = 13$
40. $(0, 0, 0)$, $\quad 3x + 2y + 6z = 6$
41. $(0, 1, 1)$, $\quad 4y + 3z = -12$
42. $(2, 2, 3)$, $\quad 2x + y + 2z = 4$
43. $(0, -1, 0)$, $\quad 2x + y + 2z = 4$
44. $(1, 0, -1)$, $\quad -4x + y + z = 4$
45. Find the distance from the plane $x + 2y + 6z = 1$ to the plane $x + 2y + 6z = 10$.
46. Find the distance from the line $x = 2 + t, y = 1 + t, z = -(1/2) - (1/2)t$ to the plane $x + 2y + 6z = 10$.

Find the angles between the planes in Exercises 47 and 48.

47. $x + y = 1, \quad 2x + y - 2z = 2$
48. $5x + y - z = 10, \quad x - 2y + 3z = -1$

T Use a calculator to find the acute angles between the planes in Exercises 49–52 to the nearest hundredth of a radian.

49. $2x + 2y + 2z = 3, \quad 2x - 2y - z = 5$
50. $x + y + z = 1, \quad z = 0$ (the xy-plane)
51. $2x + 2y - z = 3, \quad x + 2y + z = 2$
52. $4y + 3z = -12, \quad 3x + 2y + 6z = 6$

In Exercises 53–56, find the point in which the line meets the plane.

53. $x = 1 - t, \quad y = 3t, \quad z = 1 + t; \quad 2x - y + 3z = 6$

54. $x = 2, \quad y = 3 + 2t, \quad z = -2 - 2t; \quad 6x + 3y - 4z = -12$

55. $x = 1 + 2t, \quad y = 1 + 5t, \quad z = 3t; \quad x + y + z = 2$

56. $x = -1 + 3t, \quad y = -2, \quad z = 5t; \quad 2x - 3z = 7$

Find parametrizations for the lines in which the planes in Exercises 57–60 intersect.

57. $x + y + z = 1, \quad x + y = 2$

58. $3x - 6y - 2z = 3, \quad 2x + y - 2z = 2$

59. $x - 2y + 4z = 2, \quad x + y - 2z = 5$

60. $5x - 2y = 11, \quad 4y - 5z = -17$

Given two lines in space, either they are parallel, or they intersect, or they are skew (imagine, for example, the flight paths of two planes in the sky). Exercises 61 and 62 each give three lines. In each exercise, determine whether the lines, taken two at a time, are parallel, intersect, or are skew. If they intersect, find the point of intersection.

61. $L1: x = 3 + 2t, y = -1 + 4t, z = 2 - t; \quad -\infty < t < \infty$

$L2: x = 1 + 4s, y = 1 + 2s, z = -3 + 4s; \quad -\infty < s < \infty$

$L3: x = 3 + 2r, y = 2 + r, z = -2 + 2r; \quad -\infty < r < \infty$

62. $L1: x = 1 + 2t, \quad y = -1 - t, \quad z = 3t; \quad -\infty < t < \infty$

$L2: x = 2 - s, \quad y = 3s, \quad z = 1 + s; \quad -\infty < s < \infty$

$L3: x = 5 + 2r, \quad y = 1 - r, \quad z = 8 + 3r; \quad -\infty < r < \infty$

63. Use Equations (3) to generate a parametrization of the line through $P(2, -4, 7)$ parallel to $\mathbf{v}_1 = 2\mathbf{i} - \mathbf{j} + 3\mathbf{k}$. Then generate another parametrization of the line using the point $P_2(-2, -2, 1)$ and the vector $\mathbf{v}_2 = -\mathbf{i} + (1/2)\mathbf{j} - (3/2)\mathbf{k}$.

64. Use the component form to generate an equation for the plane through $P_1(4, 1, 5)$ normal to $\mathbf{n}_1 = \mathbf{i} - 2\mathbf{j} + \mathbf{k}$. Then generate another equation for the same plane using the point $P_2(3, -2, 0)$ and the normal vector $\mathbf{n}_2 = -\sqrt{2}\mathbf{i} + 2\sqrt{2}\mathbf{j} - \sqrt{2}\mathbf{k}$.

65. Find the points in which the line $x = 1 + 2t, y = -1 - t, z = 3t$ meets the coordinate planes. Describe the reasoning behind your answer.

66. Find equations for the line in the plane $z = 3$ that makes an angle of $\pi/6$ rad with $\mathbf{i}$ and an angle of $\pi/3$ rad with $\mathbf{j}$. Describe the reasoning behind your answer.

67. Is the line $x = 1 - 2t, y = 2 + 5t, z = -3t$ parallel to the plane $2x + y - z = 8$? Give reasons for your answer.

68. How can you tell when two planes $A_1x + B_1y + C_1z = D_1$ and $A_2x + B_2y + C_2z = D_2$ are parallel? Perpendicular? Give reasons for your answer.

69. Find two different planes whose intersection is the line $x = 1 + t, y = 2 - t, z = 3 + 2t$. Write equations for each plane in the form $Ax + By + Cz = D$.

70. Find a plane through the origin that meets the plane M: $2x + 3y + z = 12$ in a right angle. How do you know that your plane is perpendicular to M?

71. For any nonzero numbers a, b, and c, the graph of $(x/a) + (y/b) + (z/c) = 1$ is a plane. Which planes have an equation of this form?

72. Suppose L_1 and L_2 are disjoint (nonintersecting) nonparallel lines. Is it possible for a nonzero vector to be perpendicular to both L_1 and L_2? Give reasons for your answer.

73. Perspective in computer graphics In computer graphics and perspective drawing, we need to represent objects seen by the eye in space as images on a two-dimensional plane. Suppose that the eye is at $E(x_0, 0, 0)$ as shown here and that we want to represent a point $P_1(x_1, y_1, z_1)$ as a point on the yz-plane. We do this by projecting P_1 onto the plane with a ray from E. The point P_1 will be portrayed as the point $P(0, y, z)$. The problem for us as graphics designers is to find y and z given E and P_1.

a. Write a vector equation that holds between $\overrightarrow{EP}$ and $\overrightarrow{EP_1}$. Use the equation to express y and z in terms of x_0, x_1, y_1, and z_1.

b. Test the formulas obtained for y and z in part (a) by investigating their behavior at $x_1 = 0$ and $x_1 = x_0$ and by seeing what happens as $x_0 \to \infty$. What do you find?

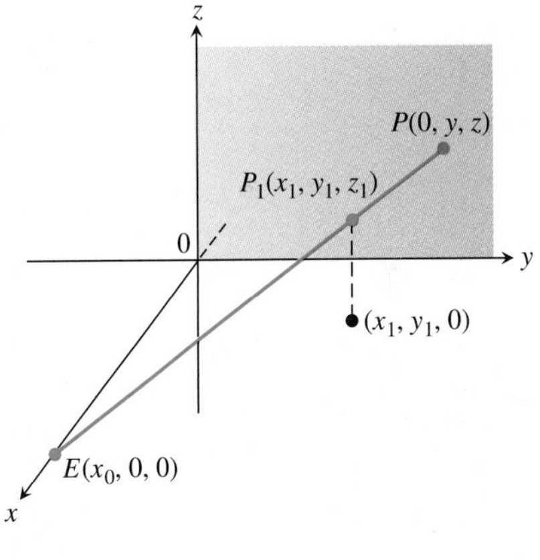

74. Hidden lines Here is another typical problem in computer graphics. Your eye is at (4, 0, 0). You are looking at a triangular plate whose vertices are at (1, 0, 1), (1, 1, 0), and (−2, 2, 2). The line segment from (1, 0, 0) to (0, 2, 2) passes through the plate. What portion of the line segment is hidden from your view by the plate? (This is an exercise in finding intersections of lines and planes.)

10.6 Cylinders and Quadric Surfaces

Up to now, we have studied two special types of surfaces: spheres and planes. In this section, we extend our inventory to include a variety of cylinders and quadric surfaces. Quadric surfaces are surfaces defined by second-degree equations in x, y, and z. Spheres are quadric surfaces, but there are others of equal interest.

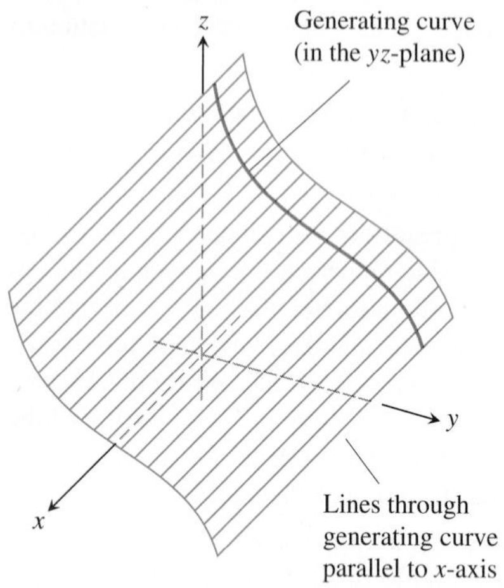

FIGURE 10.42 A cylinder and generating curve.

Cylinders

A **cylinder** is a surface that is generated by moving a straight line along a given planar curve while holding the line parallel to a given fixed line. The curve is called a **generating curve** for the cylinder (Figure 10.42). In solid geometry, where *cylinder* means *circular cylinder*, the generating curves are circles, but now we allow generating curves of any kind. The cylinder in our first example is generated by a parabola.

EXAMPLE 1 Find an equation for the cylinder made by the lines parallel to the z-axis that pass through the parabola $y = x^2, z = 0$ (Figure 10.43).

Solution The point $P_0(x_0, x_0^2, 0)$ lies on the parabola $y = x^2$ in the xy-plane. Then, for any value of z, the point $Q(x_0, x_0^2, z)$ lies on the cylinder because it lies on the line $x = x_0, y = x_0^2$ through P_0 parallel to the z-axis. Conversely, any point $Q(x_0, x_0^2, z)$ whose y-coordinate is the square of its x-coordinate lies on the cylinder because it lies on the line $x = x_0, y = x_0^2$ through P_0 parallel to the z-axis (Figure 10.43).

Regardless of the value of z, therefore, the points on the surface are the points whose coordinates satisfy the equation $y = x^2$. This makes $y = x^2$ an equation for the cylinder. Because of this, we call the cylinder "the cylinder $y = x^2$." ■

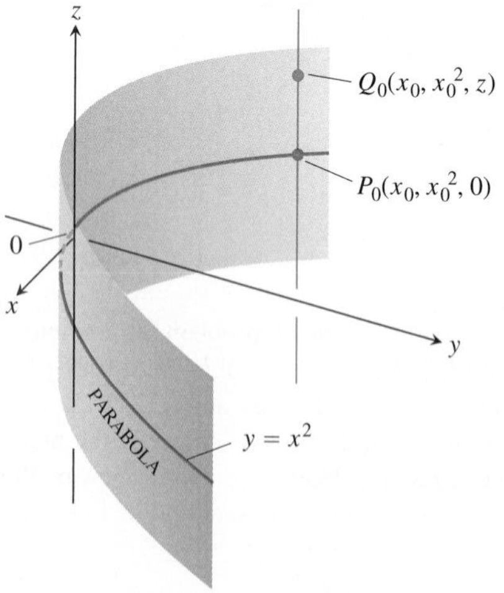

FIGURE 10.43 Every point of the cylinder in Example 1 has coordinates of the form (x_0, x_0^2, z). We call it "the cylinder $y = x^2$."

As Example 1 suggests, any curve $f(x, y) = c$ in the xy-plane defines a cylinder parallel to the z-axis whose equation is also $f(x, y) = c$. For instance, the equation $x^2 + y^2 = 1$ defines the circular cylinder made by the lines parallel to the z-axis that pass through the circle $x^2 + y^2 = 1$ in the xy-plane.

In a similar way, any curve $g(x, z) = c$ in the xz-plane defines a cylinder parallel to the y-axis whose space equation is also $g(x, z) = c$. Any curve $h(y, z) = c$ defines a cylinder parallel to the x-axis whose space equation is also $h(y, z) = c$. The axis of a cylinder need not be parallel to a coordinate axis, however.

Quadric Surfaces

A **quadric surface** is the graph in space of a second-degree equation in x, y, and z. We focus on the special equation

$$Ax^2 + By^2 + Cz^2 + Dz = E,$$

where A, B, C, D, and E are constants. The basic quadric surfaces are **ellipsoids**, **paraboloids**, **elliptical cones**, and **hyperboloids**. Spheres are special cases of ellipsoids. We present a few examples illustrating how to sketch a quadric surface, and then give a summary table of graphs of the basic types.

EXAMPLE 2 The **ellipsoid**

$$\frac{x^2}{a^2} + \frac{y^2}{b^2} + \frac{z^2}{c^2} = 1$$

(Figure 10.44) cuts the coordinate axes at $(\pm a, 0, 0)$, $(0, \pm b, 0)$, and $(0, 0, \pm c)$. It lies within the rectangular box defined by the inequalities $|x| \leq a$, $|y| \leq b$, and $|z| \leq c$. The surface is symmetric with respect to each of the coordinate planes because each variable in the defining equation is squared.

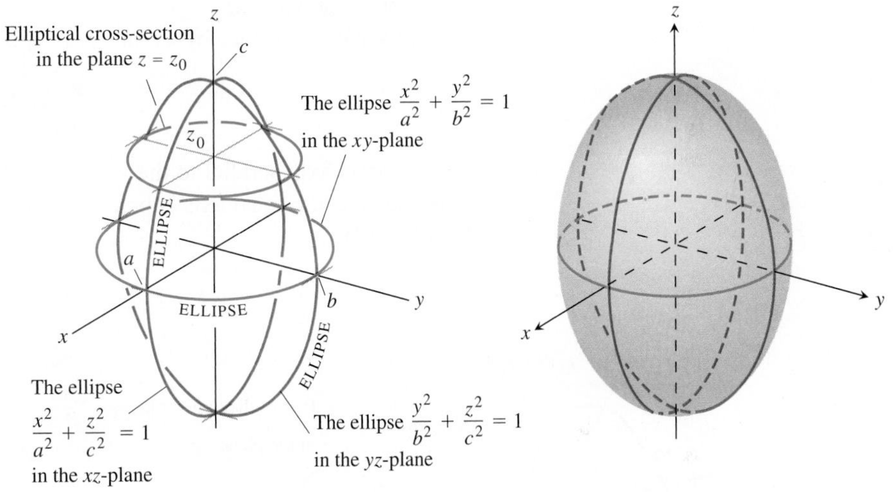

FIGURE 10.44 The ellipsoid

$$\frac{x^2}{a^2} + \frac{y^2}{b^2} + \frac{z^2}{c^2} = 1$$

in Example 2 has elliptical cross-sections in each of the three coordinate planes.

The curves in which the three coordinate planes cut the surface are ellipses. For example,

$$\frac{x^2}{a^2} + \frac{y^2}{b^2} = 1 \quad \text{when} \quad z = 0.$$

The curve cut from the surface by the plane $z = z_0$, $|z_0| < c$, is the ellipse

$$\frac{x^2}{a^2(1 - (z_0/c)^2)} + \frac{y^2}{b^2(1 - (z_0/c)^2)} = 1.$$

If any two of the semiaxes a, b, and c are equal, the surface is an **ellipsoid of revolution**. If all three are equal, the surface is a sphere. ■

EXAMPLE 3 The **hyperbolic paraboloid**

$$\frac{y^2}{b^2} - \frac{x^2}{a^2} = \frac{z}{c}, \qquad c > 0$$

has symmetry with respect to the planes $x = 0$ and $y = 0$ (Figure 10.45). The cross-sections in these planes are

$$x = 0: \quad \text{the parabola } z = \frac{c}{b^2}y^2. \tag{1}$$

$$y = 0: \quad \text{the parabola } z = -\frac{c}{a^2}x^2. \tag{2}$$

In the plane $x = 0$, the parabola opens upward from the origin. The parabola in the plane $y = 0$ opens downward.

If we cut the surface by a plane $z = z_0 > 0$, the cross-section is a hyperbola,

$$\frac{y^2}{b^2} - \frac{x^2}{a^2} = \frac{z_0}{c},$$

with its focal axis parallel to the y-axis and its vertices on the parabola in Equation (1). If z_0 is negative, the focal axis is parallel to the x-axis and the vertices lie on the parabola in Equation (2).

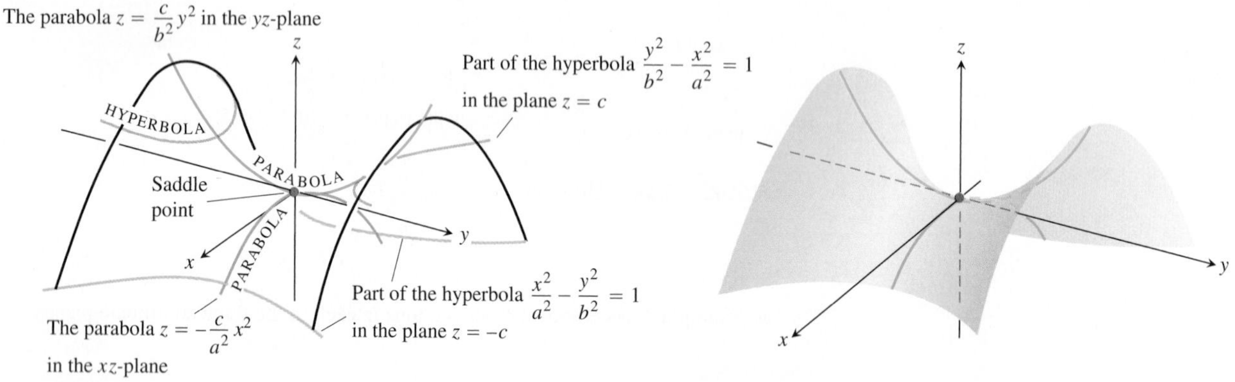

FIGURE 10.45 The hyperbolic paraboloid $(y^2/b^2) - (x^2/a^2) = z/c$, $c > 0$. The cross-sections in planes perpendicular to the z-axis above and below the xy-plane are hyperbolas. The cross-sections in planes perpendicular to the other axes are parabolas.

Near the origin, the surface is shaped like a saddle or mountain pass. To a person traveling along the surface in the yz-plane the origin looks like a minimum. To person traveling the xz-plane the origin looks like a maximum. Such a point is called a **saddle point** of a surface. We will say more about saddle points in Section 12.7. ■

Table 10.1 shows graphs of the six basic types of quadric surfaces. Each surface shown is symmetric with respect to the z-axis, but other coordinate axes can serve as well (with appropriate changes to the equation).

TABLE 10.1 Graphs of Quadric Surfaces

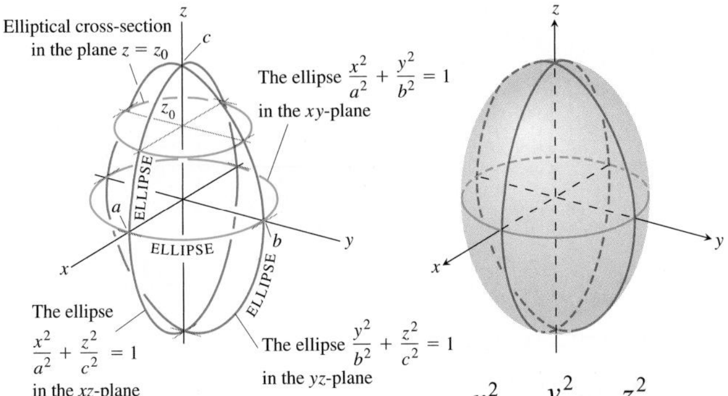

ELLIPSOID

$$\frac{x^2}{a^2} + \frac{y^2}{b^2} + \frac{z^2}{c^2} = 1$$

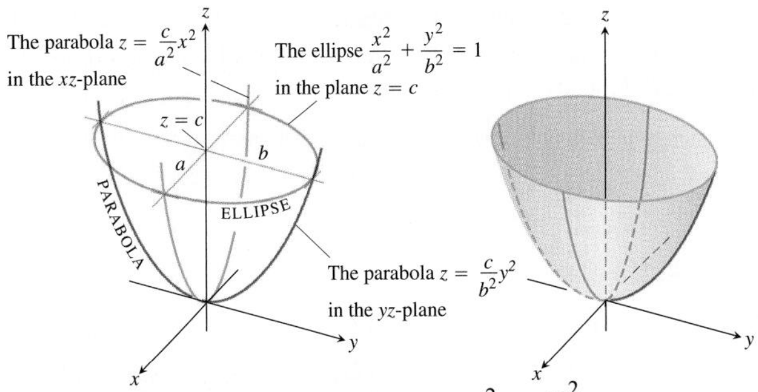

ELLIPTICAL PARABOLOID

$$\frac{x^2}{a^2} + \frac{y^2}{b^2} = \frac{z}{c}$$

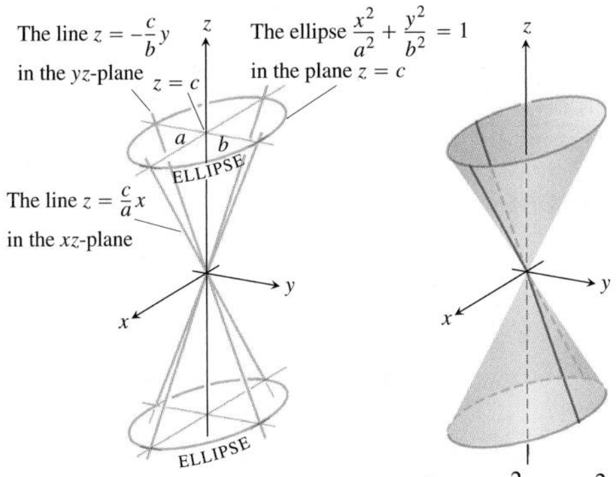

ELLIPTICAL CONE

$$\frac{x^2}{a^2} + \frac{y^2}{b^2} = \frac{z^2}{c^2}$$

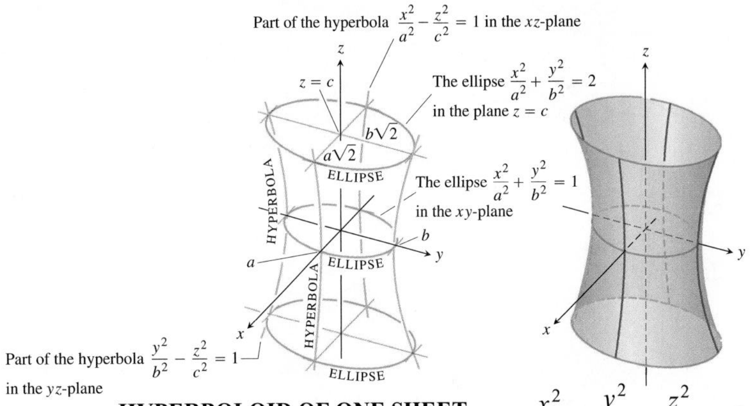

HYPERBOLOID OF ONE SHEET

$$\frac{x^2}{a^2} + \frac{y^2}{b^2} - \frac{z^2}{c^2} = 1$$

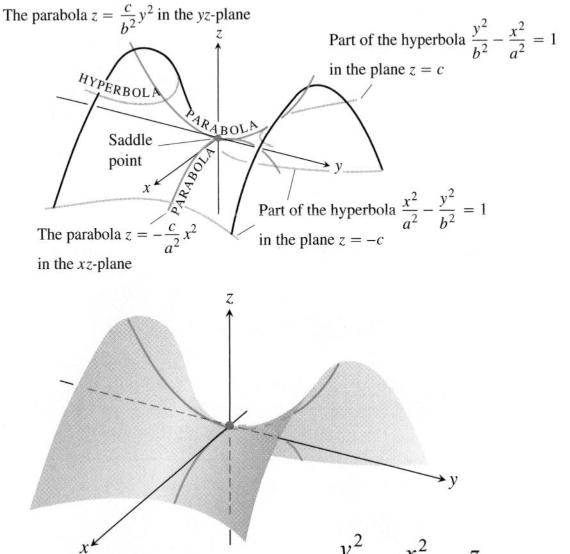

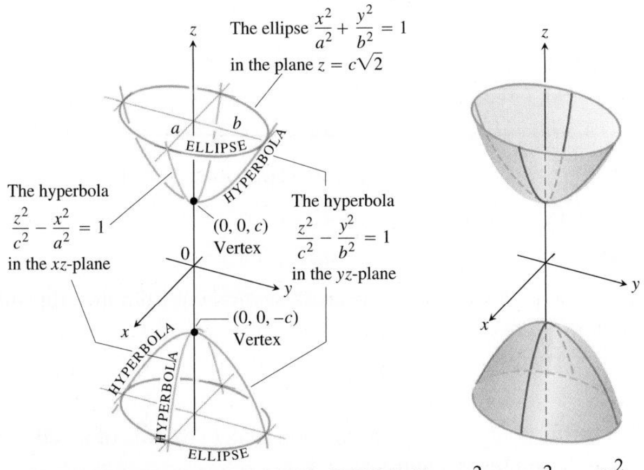

HYPERBOLOID OF TWO SHEETS

$$\frac{z^2}{c^2} - \frac{x^2}{a^2} - \frac{y^2}{b^2} = 1$$

HYPERBOLIC PARABOLOID

$$\frac{y^2}{b^2} - \frac{x^2}{a^2} = \frac{z}{c}, \quad c > 0$$

EXERCISES 10.6

In Exercises 1–12, match the equation with the surface it defines. Also, identify each surface by type (paraboloid, ellipsoid, etc.) The surfaces are labeled (a)–(l).

1. $x^2 + y^2 + 4z^2 = 10$

2. $z^2 + 4y^2 - 4x^2 = 4$

3. $9y^2 + z^2 = 16$

4. $y^2 + z^2 = x^2$

5. $x = y^2 - z^2$

6. $x = -y^2 - z^2$

7. $x^2 + 2z^2 = 8$

8. $z^2 + x^2 - y^2 = 1$

9. $x = z^2 - y^2$

10. $z = -4x^2 - y^2$

11. $x^2 + 4z^2 = y^2$

12. $9x^2 + 4y^2 + 2z^2 = 36$

a.

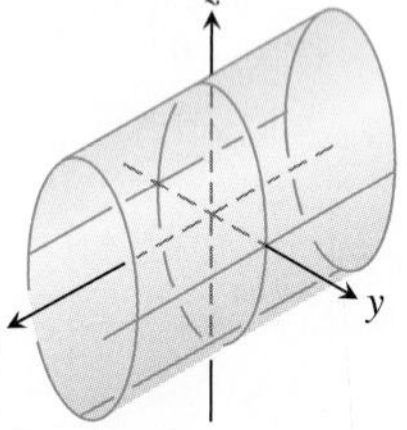

b.

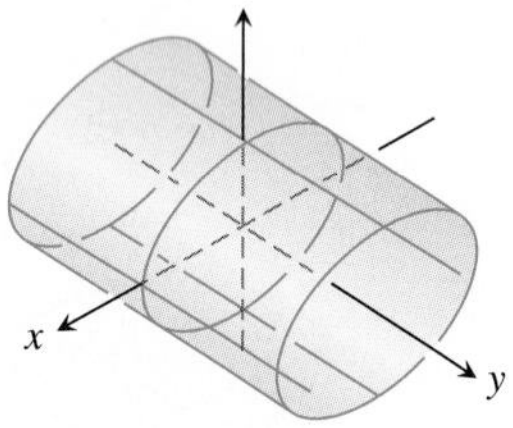

c.

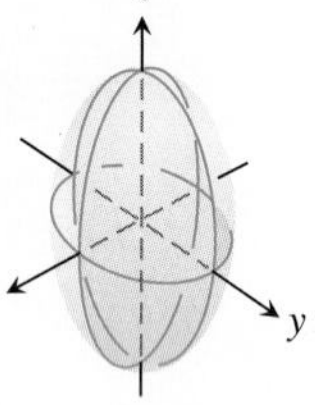

d.

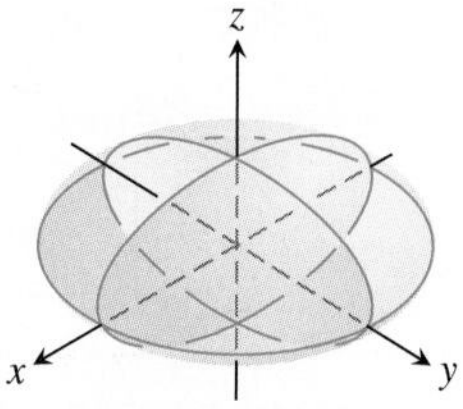

e.

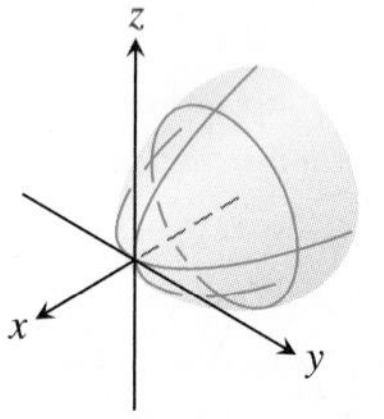

f.

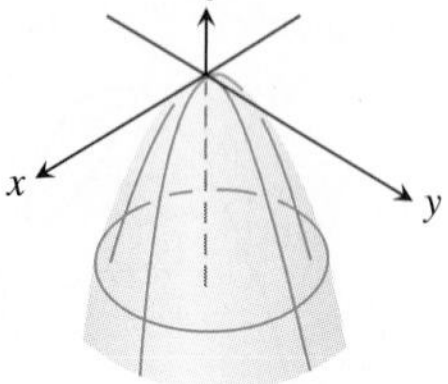

g.

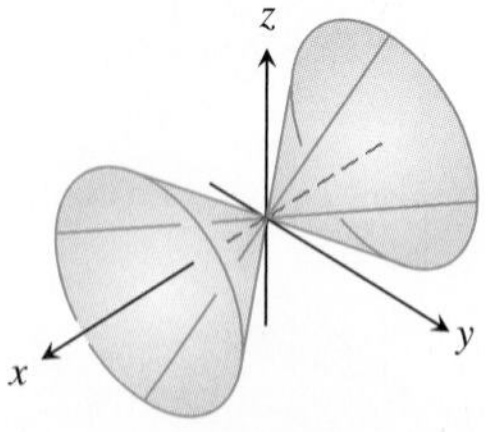

h.

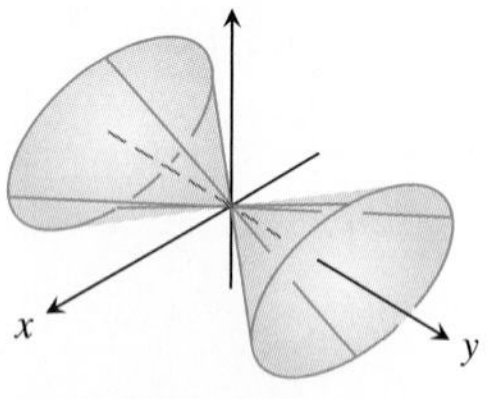

i.

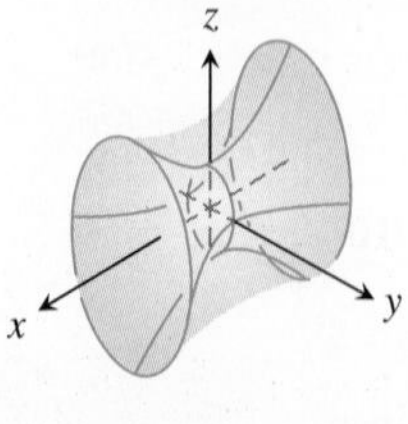

j.

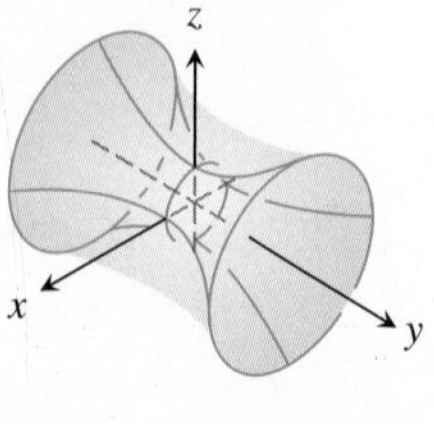

k.

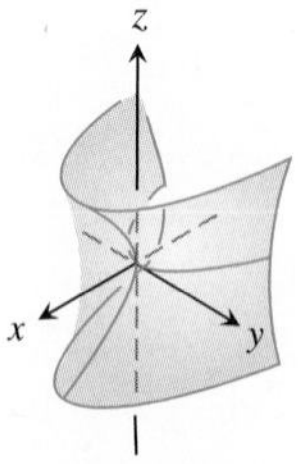

l.

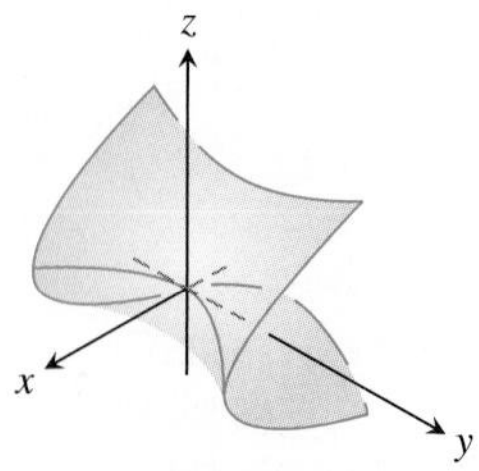

Sketch the surfaces in Exercises 13–44.

CYLINDERS

13. $x^2 + y^2 = 4$

14. $z = y^2 - 1$

15. $x^2 + 4z^2 = 16$

16. $4x^2 + y^2 = 36$

ELLIPSOIDS

17. $9x^2 + y^2 + z^2 = 9$

18. $4x^2 + 4y^2 + z^2 = 16$

19. $4x^2 + 9y^2 + 4z^2 = 36$

20. $9x^2 + 4y^2 + 36z^2 = 36$

PARABOLOIDS AND CONES

21. $z = x^2 + 4y^2$

22. $z = 8 - x^2 - y^2$

23. $x = 4 - 4y^2 - z^2$

24. $y = 1 - x^2 - z^2$

25. $x^2 + y^2 = z^2$

26. $4x^2 + 9z^2 = 9y^2$

HYPERBOLOIDS

27. $x^2 + y^2 - z^2 = 1$

28. $y^2 + z^2 - x^2 = 1$

29. $z^2 - x^2 - y^2 = 1$

30. $(y^2/4) - (x^2/4) - z^2 = 1$

HYPERBOLIC PARABOLOIDS

31. $y^2 - x^2 = z$

32. $x^2 - y^2 = z$

ASSORTED

33. $z = 1 + y^2 - x^2$

34. $4x^2 + 4y^2 = z^2$

35. $y = -(x^2 + z^2)$

36. $16x^2 + 4y^2 = 1$

37. $x^2 + y^2 - z^2 = 4$

38. $x^2 + z^2 = y$

39. $x^2 + z^2 = 1$

40. $16y^2 + 9z^2 = 4x^2$

41. $z = -(x^2 + y^2)$

42. $y^2 - x^2 - z^2 = 1$

43. $4y^2 + z^2 - 4x^2 = 4$

44. $x^2 + y^2 = z$

45. a. Express the area A of the cross-section cut from the ellipsoid

$$x^2 + \frac{y^2}{4} + \frac{z^2}{9} = 1$$

by the plane $z = c$ as a function of c. (The area of an ellipse with semiaxes a and b is πab.)

b. Use slices perpendicular to the z-axis to find the volume of the ellipsoid in part (a).

c. Now find the volume of the ellipsoid

$$\frac{x^2}{a^2} + \frac{y^2}{b^2} + \frac{z^2}{c^2} = 1.$$

Does your formula give the volume of a sphere of radius a if $a = b = c$?

46. The barrel shown here is shaped like an ellipsoid with equal pieces cut from the ends by planes perpendicular to the z-axis. The cross-sections perpendicular to the z-axis are circular. The barrel is $2h$ units high, its midsection radius is R, and its end radii are both r. Find a formula for the barrel's volume. Then check two things. First, suppose the sides of the barrel are straightened to turn the barrel into a cylinder of radius R and height $2h$. Does your formula give the cylinder's volume? Second, suppose $r = 0$ and $h = R$ so the barrel is a sphere. Does your formula give the sphere's volume?

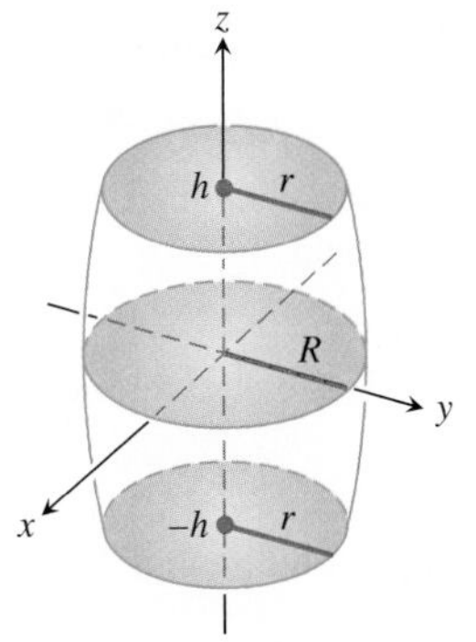

47. Show that the volume of the segment cut from the paraboloid

$$\frac{x^2}{a^2} + \frac{y^2}{b^2} = \frac{z}{c}$$

by the plane $z = h$ equals half the segment's base times its altitude.

48. a. Find the volume of the solid bounded by the hyperboloid

$$\frac{x^2}{a^2} + \frac{y^2}{b^2} - \frac{z^2}{c^2} = 1$$

and the planes $z = 0$ and $z = h, h > 0$.

b. Express your answer in part (a) in terms of h and the areas A_0 and A_h of the regions cut by the hyperboloid from the planes $z = 0$ and $z = h$.

c. Show that the volume in part (a) is also given by the formula

$$V = \frac{h}{6}(A_0 + 4A_m + A_h),$$

where A_m is the area of the region cut by the hyperboloid from the plane $z = h/2$.

T Plot the surfaces in Exercises 49–52 over the indicated domains. If you can, rotate the surface into different viewing positions.

49. $z = y^2, \quad -2 \le x \le 2, \quad -0.5 \le y \le 2$

50. $z = 1 - y^2, \quad -2 \le x \le 2, \quad -2 \le y \le 2$

51. $z = x^2 + y^2, \quad -3 \le x \le 3, \quad -3 \le y \le 3$

52. $z = x^2 + 2y^2$ over

a. $-3 \le x \le 3, \quad -3 \le y \le 3$

b. $-1 \le x \le 1, \quad -2 \le y \le 3$

c. $-2 \le x \le 2, \quad -2 \le y \le 2$

d. $-2 \le x \le 2, \quad -1 \le y \le 1$

COMPUTER EXPLORATIONS

Use a CAS to plot the surfaces in Exercises 53–58. Identify the type of quadric surface from your graph.

53. $\frac{x^2}{9} + \frac{y^2}{36} = 1 - \frac{z^2}{25}$

54. $\frac{x^2}{9} - \frac{z^2}{9} = 1 - \frac{y^2}{16}$

55. $5x^2 = z^2 - 3y^2$

56. $\frac{y^2}{16} = 1 - \frac{x^2}{9} + z$

57. $\frac{x^2}{9} - 1 = \frac{y^2}{16} + \frac{z^2}{2}$

58. $y - \sqrt{4 - z^2} = 0$

Chapter 10 Questions to Guide Your Review

1. When do directed line segments in the plane represent the same vector?
2. How are vectors added and subtracted geometrically? Algebraically?
3. How do you find a vector's magnitude and direction?
4. If a vector is multiplied by a positive scalar, how is the result related to the original vector? What if the scalar is zero? Negative?
5. Define the *dot product* (*scalar product*) of two vectors. Which algebraic laws are satisfied by dot products? Give examples. When is the dot product of two vectors equal to zero?
6. What geometric interpretation does the dot product have? Give examples.
7. What is the vector projection of a vector **u** onto a vector **v**? Give an example of a useful application of a vector projection.
8. Define the *cross product* (*vector product*) of two vectors. Which algebraic laws are satisfied by cross products, and which are not? Give examples. When is the cross product of two vectors equal to zero?
9. What geometric or physical interpretations do cross products have? Give examples.

10. What is the determinant formula for calculating the cross product of two vectors relative to the Cartesian **i**, **j**, **k**-coordinate system? Use it in an example.
11. How do you find equations for lines, line segments, and planes in space? Give examples. Can you express a line in space by a single equation? A plane?
12. How do you find the distance from a point to a line in space? From a point to a plane? Give examples.
13. What are box products? What significance do they have? How are they evaluated? Give an example.
14. How do you find equations for spheres in space? Give examples.
15. How do you find the intersection of two lines in space? A line and a plane? Two planes? Give examples.
16. What is a cylinder? Give examples of equations that define cylinders in Cartesian coordinates.
17. What are quadric surfaces? Give examples of different kinds of ellipsoids, paraboloids, cones, and hyperboloids (equations and sketches).

Chapter 10 Practice Exercises

In Exercises 1–4, let $\mathbf{u} = \langle -3, 4 \rangle$ and $\mathbf{v} = \langle 2, -5 \rangle$. Find **(a)** the component form of the vector and **(b)** its magnitude.

1. $3\mathbf{u} - 4\mathbf{v}$
2. $\mathbf{u} + \mathbf{v}$
3. $-2\mathbf{u}$
4. $5\mathbf{v}$

In Exercises 5–8, find the component form of the vector.

5. The vector obtained by rotating $\langle 0, 1 \rangle$ through an angle of $2\pi/3$ radians
6. The unit vector that makes an angle of $\pi/6$ radian with the positive x-axis
7. The vector 2 units long in the direction $4\mathbf{i} - \mathbf{j}$
8. The vector 5 units long in the direction opposite to the direction of $(3/5)\mathbf{i} + (4/5)\mathbf{j}$

Express the vectors in Exercises 9–12 in terms of their lengths and directions.

9. $\sqrt{2}\mathbf{i} + \sqrt{2}\mathbf{j}$
10. $-\mathbf{i} - \mathbf{j}$
11. Velocity vector $\mathbf{v} = (-2 \sin t)\mathbf{i} + (2 \cos t)\mathbf{j}$ when $t = \pi/2$.
12. Velocity vector $\mathbf{v} = (e^t \cos t - e^t \sin t)\mathbf{i} + (e^t \sin t + e^t \cos t)\mathbf{j}$ when $t = \ln 2$.

Express the vectors in Exercises 13 and 14 in terms of their lengths and directions.

13. $2\mathbf{i} - 3\mathbf{j} + 6\mathbf{k}$
14. $\mathbf{i} + 2\mathbf{j} - \mathbf{k}$
15. Find a vector 2 units long in the direction of $\mathbf{v} = 4\mathbf{i} - \mathbf{j} + 4\mathbf{k}$.
16. Find a vector 5 units long in the direction opposite to the direction of $\mathbf{v} = (3/5)\,\mathbf{i} + (4/5)\mathbf{k}$.

In Exercises 17 and 18, find $|\mathbf{v}|$, $|\mathbf{u}|$, $\mathbf{v}\cdot\mathbf{u}$, $\mathbf{u}\cdot\mathbf{v}$, $\mathbf{v}\times\mathbf{u}$, $\mathbf{u}\times\mathbf{v}$, $|\mathbf{v}\times\mathbf{u}|$, the angle between **v** and **u**, the scalar component of **u** in the direction of **v**, and the vector projection of **u** onto **v**.

17. $\mathbf{v} = \mathbf{i} + \mathbf{j}$
 $\mathbf{u} = 2\mathbf{i} + \mathbf{j} - 2\mathbf{k}$
18. $\mathbf{v} = \mathbf{i} + \mathbf{j} + 2\mathbf{k}$
 $\mathbf{u} = -\mathbf{i} - \mathbf{k}$

In Exercises 19 and 20, find $\text{proj}_{\mathbf{v}}\,\mathbf{u}$.

19. $\mathbf{v} = 2\mathbf{i} + \mathbf{j} - \mathbf{k}$
 $\mathbf{u} = \mathbf{i} + \mathbf{j} - 5\mathbf{k}$
20. $\mathbf{u} = \mathbf{i} - 2\mathbf{j}$
 $\mathbf{v} = \mathbf{i} + \mathbf{j} + \mathbf{k}$

In Exercises 21 and 22, draw coordinate axes and then sketch **u**, **v**, and $\mathbf{u}\times\mathbf{v}$ as vectors at the origin.

21. $\mathbf{u} = \mathbf{i}, \quad \mathbf{v} = \mathbf{i} + \mathbf{j}$
22. $\mathbf{u} = \mathbf{i} - \mathbf{j}, \quad \mathbf{v} = \mathbf{i} + \mathbf{j}$
23. If $|\mathbf{v}| = 2$, $|\mathbf{w}| = 3$, and the angle between **v** and **w** is $\pi/3$, find $|\mathbf{v} - 2\mathbf{w}|$.
24. For what value or values of a will the vectors $\mathbf{u} = 2\mathbf{i} + 4\mathbf{j} - 5\mathbf{k}$ and $\mathbf{v} = -4\mathbf{i} - 8\mathbf{j} + a\mathbf{k}$ be parallel?

In Exercises 25 and 26, find **(a)** the area of the parallelogram determined by vectors **u** and **v** and **(b)** the volume of the parallelepiped determined by the vectors **u**, **v**, and **w**.

25. $\mathbf{u} = \mathbf{i} + \mathbf{j} - \mathbf{k}, \quad \mathbf{v} = 2\mathbf{i} + \mathbf{j} + \mathbf{k}, \quad \mathbf{w} = -\mathbf{i} - 2\mathbf{j} + 3\mathbf{k}$
26. $\mathbf{u} = \mathbf{i} + \mathbf{j}, \quad \mathbf{v} = \mathbf{j}, \quad \mathbf{w} = \mathbf{i} + \mathbf{j} + \mathbf{k}$
27. Suppose that **n** is normal to a plane and that **v** is parallel to the plane. Describe how you would find a vector **n** that is both perpendicular to **v** and parallel to the plane.
28. Find a vector in the plane parallel to the line $ax + by = c$.

In Exercises 29 and 30, find the distance from the point to the line.

29. $(2, 2, 0);\ x = -t, \quad y = t, \quad z = -1 + t$
30. $(0, 4, 1);\ x = 2 + t, \quad y = 2 + t, \quad z = t$
31. Parametrize the line that passes through the point $(1, 2, 3)$ parallel to the vector $\mathbf{v} = -3\mathbf{i} + 7\mathbf{k}$.
32. Parametrize the line segment joining the points $P(1, 2, 0)$ and $Q(1, 3, -1)$.

In Exercises 33 and 34, find the distance from the point to the plane.

33. $(6, 0, -6), \quad x - y = 4$
34. $(3, 0, 10), \quad 2x + 3y + z = 2$

35. Find an equation for the plane that passes through the point $(3, -2, 1)$ normal to the vector $\mathbf{n} = 2\mathbf{i} + \mathbf{j} + \mathbf{k}$.

36. Find an equation for the plane that passes through the point $(-1, 6, 0)$ perpendicular to the line $x = -1 + t, y = 6 - 2t, z = 3t$.

In Exercises 37 and 38, find an equation for the plane through points P, Q, and R.

37. $P(1, -1, 2), \quad Q(2, 1, 3), \quad R(-1, 2, -1)$

38. $P(1, 0, 0), \quad Q(0, 1, 0), \quad R(0, 0, 1)$

39. Find the points in which the line $x = 1 + 2t, y = -1 - t, z = 3t$ meets the three coordinate planes.

40. Find the point in which the line through the origin perpendicular to the plane $2x - y - z = 4$ meets the plane $3x - 5y + 2z = 6$.

41. Find the acute angle between the planes $x = 7$ and $x + y + \sqrt{2}z = -3$.

42. Find the acute angle between the planes $x + y = 1$ and $y + z = 1$.

43. Find parametric equations for the line in which the planes $x + 2y + z = 1$ and $x - y + 2z = -8$ intersect.

44. Show that the line in which the planes

$$x + 2y - 2z = 5 \quad \text{and} \quad 5x - 2y - z = 0$$

intersect is parallel to the line

$$x = -3 + 2t, \quad y = 3t, \quad z = 1 + 4t.$$

45. The planes $3x + 6z = 1$ and $2x + 2y - z = 3$ intersect in a line.

a. Show that the planes are orthogonal.

b. Find equations for the line of intersection.

46. Find an equation for the plane that passes through the point $(1, 2, 3)$ parallel to $\mathbf{u} = 2\mathbf{i} + 3\mathbf{j} + \mathbf{k}$ and $\mathbf{v} = \mathbf{i} - \mathbf{j} + 2\mathbf{k}$.

47. Is $\mathbf{v} = 2\mathbf{i} - 4\mathbf{j} + \mathbf{k}$ related in any special way to the plane $2x + y = 5$? Give reasons for your answer.

48. The equation $\mathbf{n} \cdot \overrightarrow{P_0P} = 0$ represents the plane through P_0 normal to $\mathbf{n}$. What set does the inequality $\mathbf{n} \cdot \overrightarrow{P_0P} > 0$ represent?

49. Find the distance from the point $P(1, 4, 0)$ to the plane through $A(0, 0, 0)$, $B(2, 0, -1)$ and $C(2, -1, 0)$.

50. Find the distance from the point $(2, 2, 3)$ to the plane $2x + 3y + 5z = 0$.

51. Find a vector parallel to the plane $2x - y - z = 4$ and orthogonal to $\mathbf{i} + \mathbf{j} + \mathbf{k}$.

52. Find a unit vector orthogonal to $\mathbf{A}$ in the plane of $\mathbf{B}$ and $\mathbf{C}$ if $\mathbf{A} = 2\mathbf{i} - \mathbf{j} + \mathbf{k}$, $\mathbf{B} = \mathbf{i} + 2\mathbf{j} + \mathbf{k}$, and $\mathbf{C} = \mathbf{i} + \mathbf{j} - 2\mathbf{k}$.

53. Find a vector of magnitude 2 parallel to the line of intersection of the planes $x + 2y + z - 1 = 0$ and $x - y + 2z + 7 = 0$.

54. Find the point in which the line through the origin perpendicular to the plane $2x - y - z = 4$ meets the plane $3x - 5y + 2z = 6$.

55. Find the point in which the line through $P(3, 2, 1)$ normal to the plane $2x - y + 2z = -2$ meets the plane.

56. What angle does the line of intersection of the planes $2x + y - z = 0$ and $x + y + 2z = 0$ make with the positive x-axis?

57. The line

$$L: \quad x = 3 + 2t, \quad y = 2t, \quad z = t$$

intersects the plane $x + 3y - z = -4$ in a point P. Find the coordinates of P and find equations for the line in the plane through P perpendicular to L.

58. Show that for every real number k the plane

$$x - 2y + z + 3 + k(2x - y - z + 1) = 0$$

contains the line of intersection of the planes

$$x - 2y + z + 3 = 0 \quad \text{and} \quad 2x - y - z + 1 = 0.$$

59. Find an equation for the plane through $A(-2, 0, -3)$ and $B(1, -2, 1)$ that lies parallel to the line through $C(-2, -13/5, 26/5)$ and $D(16/5, -13/5, 0)$.

60. Is the line $x = 1 + 2t, y = -2 + 3t, z = -5t$ related in any way to the plane $-4x - 6y + 10z = 9$? Give reasons for your answer.

61. Which of the following are equations for the plane through the points $P(1, 1, -1)$, $Q(3, 0, 2)$, and $R(-2, 1, 0)$?

a. $(2\mathbf{i} - 3\mathbf{j} + 3\mathbf{k}) \cdot ((x + 2)\mathbf{i} + (y - 1)\mathbf{j} + z\mathbf{k}) = 0$

b. $x = 3 - t, \quad y = -11t, \quad z = 2 - 3t$

c. $(x + 2) + 11(y - 1) = 3z$

d. $(2\mathbf{i} - 3\mathbf{j} + 3\mathbf{k}) \times ((x + 2)\mathbf{i} + (y - 1)\mathbf{j} + z\mathbf{k}) = \mathbf{0}$

e. $(2\mathbf{i} - \mathbf{j} + 3\mathbf{k}) \times (-3\mathbf{i} + \mathbf{k}) \cdot ((x + 2)\mathbf{i} + (y - 1)\mathbf{j} + z\mathbf{k}) = 0$

62. The parallelogram shown here has vertices at $A(2, -1, 4)$, $B(1, 0, -1)$, $C(1, 2, 3)$, and D. Find

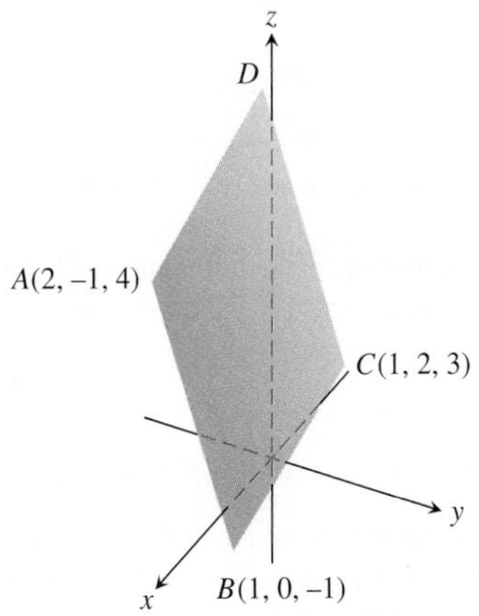

a. the coordinates of D,

b. the cosine of the interior angle at B,

c. the vector projection of $\overrightarrow{BA}$ onto $\overrightarrow{BC}$,

d. the area of the parallelogram,

e. an equation for the plane of the parallelogram,

f. the areas of the orthogonal projections of the parallelogram on the three coordinate planes.

63. Distance between lines Find the distance between the line L_1 through the points $A(1, 0, -1)$ and $B(-1, 1, 0)$ and the line L_2 through the points $C(3, 1, -1)$ and $D(4, 5, -2)$. The distance is to be measured along the line perpendicular to the two lines. First find a vector **n** perpendicular to both lines. Then project $\overrightarrow{AC}$ onto **n**.

64. (*Continuation of Exercise 63.*) Find the distance between the line through $A(4, 0, 2)$ and $B(2, 4, 1)$ and the line through $C(1, 3, 2)$ and $D(2, 2, 4)$.

Identify and sketch the surfaces in Exercises 65–76.

65. $x^2 + y^2 + z^2 = 4$

66. $x^2 + (y - 1)^2 + z^2 = 1$

67. $4x^2 + 4y^2 + z^2 = 4$

68. $36x^2 + 9y^2 + 4z^2 = 36$

69. $z = -(x^2 + y^2)$

70. $y = -(x^2 + z^2)$

71. $x^2 + y^2 = z^2$

72. $x^2 + z^2 = y^2$

73. $x^2 + y^2 - z^2 = 4$

74. $4y^2 + z^2 - 4x^2 = 4$

75. $y^2 - x^2 - z^2 = 1$

76. $z^2 - x^2 - y^2 = 1$

Chapter 10 Additional and Advanced Exercises

1. Submarine hunting Two surface ships on maneuvers are trying to determine a submarine's course and speed to prepare for an aircraft intercept. As shown here, ship A is located at $(4, 0, 0)$, whereas ship B is located at $(0, 5, 0)$. All coordinates are given in thousands of feet. Ship A locates the submarine in the direction of the vector $2\mathbf{i} + 3\mathbf{j} - (1/3)\mathbf{k}$, and ship B locates it in the direction of the vector $18\mathbf{i} - 6\mathbf{j} - \mathbf{k}$. Four minutes ago, the submarine was located at $(2, -1, -1/3)$. The aircraft is due in 20 min. Assuming that the submarine moves in a straight line at a constant speed, to what position should the surface ships direct the aircraft?

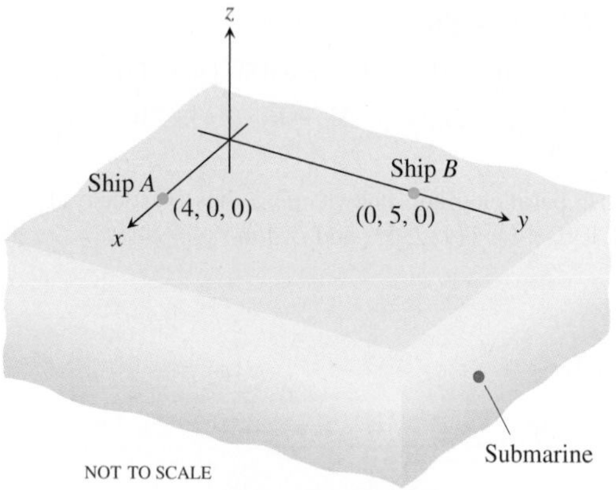

2. A helicopter rescue Two helicopters, H_1 and H_2, are traveling together. At time $t = 0$, they separate and follow different straight-line paths given by

$$H_1:\quad x = 6 + 40t, \quad y = -3 + 10t, \quad z = -3 + 2t$$

$$H_2:\quad x = 6 + 110t, \quad y = -3 + 4t, \quad z = -3 + t.$$

Time t is measured in hours and all coordinates are measured in miles. Due to system malfunctions, H_2 stops its flight at (446, 13, 1) and, in a negligible amount of time, lands at (446, 13, 0). Two hours later, H_1 is advised of this fact and heads toward H_2 at 150 mph. How long will it take H_1 to reach H_2?

3. Torque The operator's manual for the Toro® 21 in. lawnmower says "tighten the spark plug to 15 ft-lb (20.4 N · m)." If you are installing the plug with a 10.5-in. socket wrench that places the center of your hand 9 in. from the axis of the spark plug, about how hard should you pull? Answer in pounds.

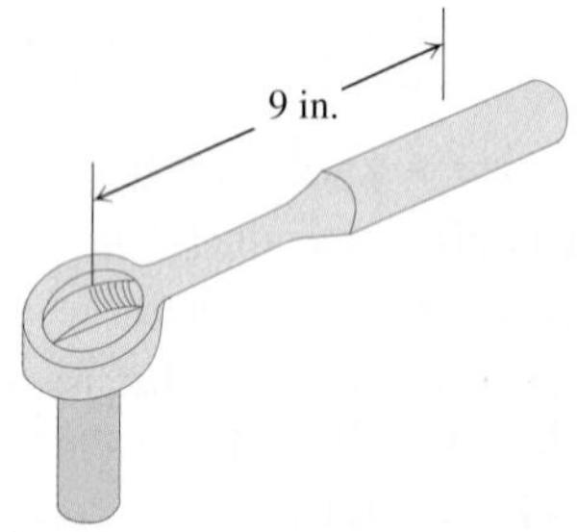

4. Rotating body The line through the origin and the point $A(1, 1, 1)$ is the axis of rotation of a right body rotating with a constant angular speed of $3/2$ rad/sec. The rotation appears to be clockwise when we look toward the origin from A. Find the velocity **v** of the point of the body that is at the position $B(1, 3, 2)$.

5. **Determinants and planes**

   a. Show that

$$\begin{vmatrix} x_1 - x & y_1 - y & z_1 - z \\ x_2 - x & y_2 - y & z_2 - z \\ x_3 - x & y_3 - y & z_3 - z \end{vmatrix} = 0$$

   is an equation for the plane through the three noncollinear points $P_1(x_1, y_1, z_1)$, $P_2(x_2, y_2, z_2)$, and $P_3(x_3, y_3, z_3)$.

   b. What set of points in space is described by the equation

$$\begin{vmatrix} x & y & z & 1 \\ x_1 & y_1 & z_1 & 1 \\ x_2 & y_2 & z_2 & 1 \\ x_3 & y_3 & z_3 & 1 \end{vmatrix} = 0?$$

6. **Determinants and lines** Show that the lines

$$x = a_1 s + b_1, y = a_2 s + b_2, z = a_3 s + b_3, -\infty < s < \infty,$$

and

$$x = c_1 t + d_1, y = c_2 t + d_2, z = c_3 t + d_3, -\infty < t < \infty,$$

intersect or are parallel if and only if

$$\begin{vmatrix} a_1 & c_1 & b_1 - d_1 \\ a_2 & c_2 & b_2 - d_2 \\ a_3 & c_3 & b_3 - d_3 \end{vmatrix} = 0.$$

7. **Parallelogram** The accompanying figure shows parallelogram $ABCD$ and the midpoint P of diagonal BD.

   a. Express $\overrightarrow{BD}$ in terms of $\overrightarrow{AB}$ and $\overrightarrow{AD}$.

   b. Express $\overrightarrow{AP}$ in terms of $\overrightarrow{AB}$ and $\overrightarrow{AD}$.

   c. Prove that P is also the midpoint of diagonal AC.

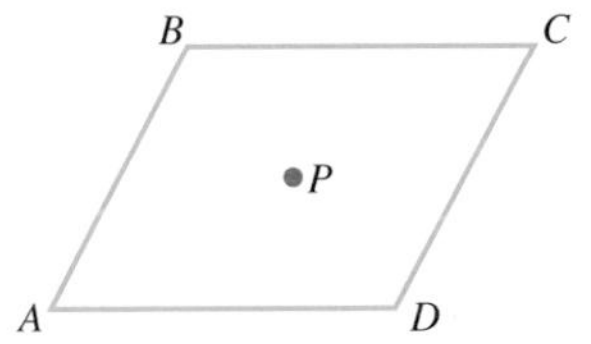

8. In the figure here, D is the midpoint of side AB of triangle ABC, and E is one-third of the way between C and B. Use vectors to prove that F is the midpoint of line segment CD.

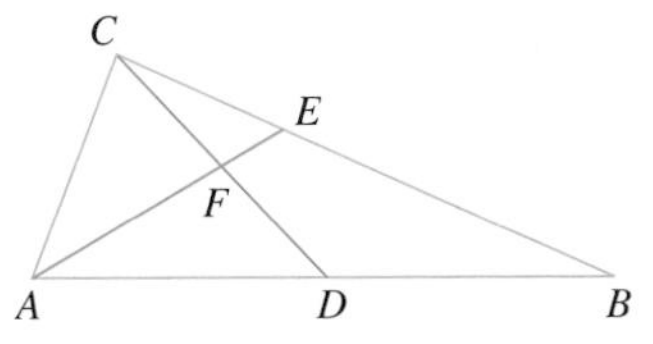

9. Use vectors to show that the distance from $P_1(x_1, y_1)$ to the line $ax + by = c$ is

$$d = \frac{|ax_1 + by_1 - c|}{\sqrt{a^2 + b^2}}.$$

10. **a.** Use vectors to show that the distance from $P_1(x_1, y_1, z_1)$ to the plane $Ax + By + Cz = D$ is

$$d = \frac{|Ax_1 + By_1 + Cz_1 - D|}{\sqrt{A^2 + B^2 + C^2}}.$$

   b. Find an equation for the sphere that is tangent to the planes $x + y + z = 3$ and $x + y + z = 9$ if the planes $2x - y = 0$ and $3x - z = 0$ pass through the center of the sphere.

11. **a.** Show that the distance between the parallel planes $Ax + By + Cz = D_1$ and $Ax + By + Cz = D_2$ is

$$d = \frac{|D_1 - D_2|}{|A\mathbf{i} + B\mathbf{j} + C\mathbf{k}|}.$$

   b. Find the distance between the planes $2x + 3y - z = 6$ and $2x + 3y - z = 12$.

   c. Find an equation for the plane parallel to the plane $2x - y + 2z = -4$ if the point $(3, 2, -1)$ is equidistant from the two planes.

   d. Write equations for the planes that lie parallel to and 5 units away from the plane $x - 2y + z = 3$.

12. Prove that four points A, B, C, and D are coplanar (lie in a common plane) if and only if $\overrightarrow{AD} \cdot (\overrightarrow{AB} \times \overrightarrow{BC}) = 0$.

13. **The projection of a vector on a plane** Let P be a plane in space and let $\mathbf{v}$ be a vector. The vector projection of $\mathbf{v}$ onto the plane P, $\text{proj}_P \mathbf{v}$, can be defined informally as follows. Suppose the sun is shining so that its rays are normal to the plane P. Then $\text{proj}_P \mathbf{v}$ is the "shadow" of $\mathbf{v}$ onto P. If P is the plane $x + 2y + 6z = 6$ and $\mathbf{v} = \mathbf{i} + \mathbf{j} + \mathbf{k}$, find $\text{proj}_P \mathbf{v}$.

14. The accompanying figure shows nonzero vectors $\mathbf{v}$, $\mathbf{w}$, and $\mathbf{z}$, with $\mathbf{z}$ orthogonal to the line L, and $\mathbf{v}$ and $\mathbf{w}$ making equal angles β with L. Assuming $|\mathbf{v}| = |\mathbf{w}|$, find $\mathbf{w}$ in terms of $\mathbf{v}$ and $\mathbf{z}$.

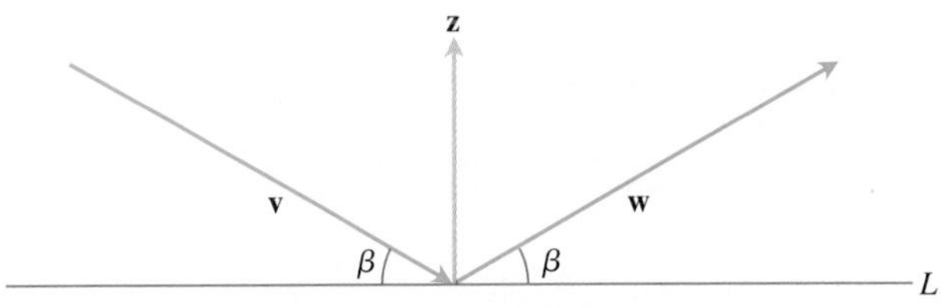

15. **Triple vector products** The *triple vector products* $(\mathbf{u} \times \mathbf{v}) \times \mathbf{w}$ and $\mathbf{u} \times (\mathbf{v} \times \mathbf{w})$ are usually not equal, although the formulas for evaluating them from components are similar:

$$(\mathbf{u} \times \mathbf{v}) \times \mathbf{w} = (\mathbf{u} \cdot \mathbf{w})\mathbf{v} - (\mathbf{v} \cdot \mathbf{w})\mathbf{u}.$$

$$\mathbf{u} \times (\mathbf{v} \times \mathbf{w}) = (\mathbf{u} \cdot \mathbf{w})\mathbf{v} - (\mathbf{u} \cdot \mathbf{v})\mathbf{w}.$$

Verify each formula for the following vectors by evaluating its two sides and comparing the results.

	$\mathbf{u}$	$\mathbf{v}$	$\mathbf{w}$
a.	$2\mathbf{i}$	$2\mathbf{j}$	$2\mathbf{k}$
b.	$\mathbf{i} - \mathbf{j} + \mathbf{k}$	$2\mathbf{i} + \mathbf{j} - 2\mathbf{k}$	$-\mathbf{i} + 2\mathbf{j} - \mathbf{k}$
c.	$2\mathbf{i} + \mathbf{j}$	$2\mathbf{i} - \mathbf{j} + \mathbf{k}$	$\mathbf{i} + 2\mathbf{k}$
d.	$\mathbf{i} + \mathbf{j} - 2\mathbf{k}$	$-\mathbf{i} - \mathbf{k}$	$2\mathbf{i} + 4\mathbf{j} - 2\mathbf{k}$

16. Cross and dot products Show that if $\mathbf{u}$, $\mathbf{v}$, $\mathbf{w}$, and $\mathbf{r}$ are any vectors, then

a. $\mathbf{u} \times (\mathbf{v} \times \mathbf{w}) + \mathbf{v} \times (\mathbf{w} \times \mathbf{u}) + \mathbf{w} \times (\mathbf{u} \times \mathbf{v}) = \mathbf{0}$

b. $\mathbf{u} \times \mathbf{v} = (\mathbf{u} \cdot \mathbf{v} \times \mathbf{i})\mathbf{i} + (\mathbf{u} \cdot \mathbf{v} \times \mathbf{j})\mathbf{j} + (\mathbf{u} \cdot \mathbf{v} \times \mathbf{k})\mathbf{k}$

c. $(\mathbf{u} \times \mathbf{v}) \cdot (\mathbf{w} \times \mathbf{r}) = \begin{vmatrix} \mathbf{u} \cdot \mathbf{w} & \mathbf{v} \cdot \mathbf{w} \\ \mathbf{u} \cdot \mathbf{r} & \mathbf{v} \cdot \mathbf{r} \end{vmatrix}.$

17. Cross and dot products Prove or disprove the formula

$$\mathbf{u} \times (\mathbf{u} \times (\mathbf{u} \times \mathbf{v})) \cdot \mathbf{w} = -|\mathbf{u}|^2 \mathbf{u} \cdot \mathbf{v} \times \mathbf{w}.$$

18. By forming the cross product of two appropriate vectors, derive the trigonometric identity

$$\sin(A - B) = \sin A \cos B - \cos A \sin B.$$

19. Use vectors to prove that

$$(a^2 + b^2)(c^2 + d^2) \geq (ac + bd)^2$$

for any four numbers a, b, c, and d. (*Hint:* Let $\mathbf{u} = a\mathbf{i} + b\mathbf{j}$ and $\mathbf{v} = c\mathbf{i} + d\mathbf{j}$.)

20. Prove that the vector $\mathbf{u} - \text{proj}_{\mathbf{v}}\,\mathbf{u}$ is orthogonal to the projection vector $\text{proj}_{\mathbf{v}}\,\mathbf{u}$ by showing their dot product is zero.

21. Show that $|\mathbf{u} + \mathbf{v}| \leq |\mathbf{u}| + |\mathbf{v}|$ for any vectors $\mathbf{u}$ and $\mathbf{v}$.

22. Show that $\mathbf{w} = |\mathbf{v}|\mathbf{u} + |\mathbf{u}|\mathbf{v}$ bisects the angle between $\mathbf{u}$ and $\mathbf{v}$.

23. Show that $|\mathbf{v}|\mathbf{u} + |\mathbf{u}|\mathbf{v}$ and $|\mathbf{v}|\mathbf{u} - |\mathbf{u}|\mathbf{v}$ are orthogonal.

24. Dot multiplication is positive definite Show that dot multiplication of vectors is *positive definite*; that is, show that $\mathbf{u} \cdot \mathbf{u} \geq 0$ for every vector $\mathbf{u}$ and that $\mathbf{u} \cdot \mathbf{u} = 0$ if and only if $\mathbf{u} = \mathbf{0}$.

APPENDICES

A.1 Real Numbers and the Real Line

This section reviews real numbers, inequalities, intervals, and absolute values.

Real Numbers

Much of calculus is based on properties of the real number system. **Real numbers** are numbers that can be expressed as decimals, such as

$$-\frac{3}{4} = -0.75000\ldots$$

$$\frac{1}{3} = 0.33333\ldots$$

$$\sqrt{2} = 1.4142\ldots$$

The dots ... in each case indicate that the sequence of decimal digits goes on forever. Every conceivable decimal expansion represents a real number, although some numbers have two representations. For instance, the infinite decimals .999... and 1.000... represent the same real number 1. A similar statement holds for any number with an infinite tail of 9's.

The real numbers can be represented geometrically as points on a number line called the **real line**.

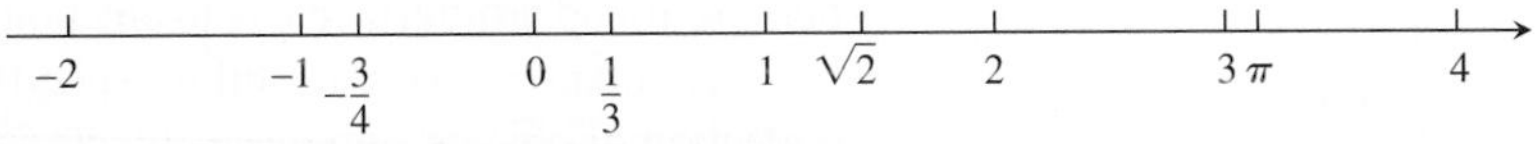

The symbol $\mathbb{R}$ denotes either the real number system or, equivalently, the real line.

The properties of the real number system fall into three categories: algebraic properties, order properties, and completeness. The **algebraic properties** say that the real numbers can be added, subtracted, multiplied, and divided (except by 0) to produce more real numbers under the usual rules of arithmetic. *You can never divide by* 0.

The **order properties** of real numbers are given in Appendix 7. The useful rules at the left can be derived from them, where the symbol $\Rightarrow$ means "implies."

Notice the rules for multiplying an inequality by a number. Multiplying by a positive number preserves the inequality; multiplying by a negative number reverses the inequality. Also, reciprocation reverses the inequality for numbers of the same sign. For example, $2 < 5$ but $-2 > -5$ and $1/2 > 1/5$.

Rules for inequalities

If a, b, and c are real numbers, then:

1. $a < b \Rightarrow a + c < b + c$
2. $a < b \Rightarrow a - c < b - c$
3. $a < b$ and $c > 0 \Rightarrow ac < bc$
4. $a < b$ and $c < 0 \Rightarrow bc < ac$
   Special case: $a < b \Rightarrow -b < -a$
5. $a > 0 \Rightarrow \frac{1}{a} > 0$
6. If a and b are both positive or both negative, then $a < b \Rightarrow \frac{1}{b} < \frac{1}{a}$

The **completeness property** of the real number system is deeper and harder to define precisely. However, the property is essential to the idea of a limit (Chapter 2). Roughly speaking, it says that there are enough real numbers to "complete" the real number line, in the sense that there are no "holes" or "gaps" in it. Many theorems of calculus would fail if the real number system were not complete. The topic is best saved for a more advanced course, but Appendix 7 hints about what is involved and how the real numbers are constructed.

We distinguish three special subsets of real numbers.

1. The **natural numbers**, namely 1, 2, 3, 4, ...
2. The **integers**, namely $0, \pm 1, \pm 2, \pm 3, \ldots$
3. The **rational numbers**, namely the numbers that can be expressed in the form of a fraction m/n, where m and n are integers and $n \neq 0$. Examples are

$$\frac{1}{3}, \quad -\frac{4}{9} = \frac{-4}{9} = \frac{4}{-9}, \quad \frac{200}{13}, \quad \text{and} \quad 57 = \frac{57}{1}.$$

The rational numbers are precisely the real numbers with decimal expansions that are either

(a) terminating (ending in an infinite string of zeros), for example,

$$\frac{3}{4} = 0.75000\ldots = 0.75 \qquad \text{or}$$

(b) eventually repeating (ending with a block of digits that repeats over and over), for example

$$\frac{23}{11} = 2.090909\ldots = 2.\overline{09}$$

The bar indicates the block of repeating digits.

A terminating decimal expansion is a special type of repeating decimal, since the ending zeros repeat.

The set of rational numbers has all the algebraic and order properties of the real numbers but lacks the completeness property. For example, there is no rational number whose square is 2; there is a "hole" in the rational line where $\sqrt{2}$ should be.

Real numbers that are not rational are called **irrational numbers**. They are characterized by having nonterminating and nonrepeating decimal expansions. Examples are π, $\sqrt{2}$, $\sqrt[3]{5}$, and $\log_{10} 3$. Since every decimal expansion represents a real number, it should be clear that there are infinitely many irrational numbers. Both rational and irrational numbers are found arbitrarily close to any point on the real line.

Set notation is very useful for specifying a particular subset of real numbers. A **set** is a collection of objects, and these objects are the **elements** of the set. If S is a set, the notation $a \in S$ means that a is an element of S, and $a \notin S$ means that a is not an element of S. If S and T are sets, then $S \cup T$ is their **union** and consists of all elements belonging either to S or T (or to both S and T). The **intersection** $S \cap T$ consists of all elements belonging to both S and T. The **empty set** $\varnothing$ is the set that contains no elements. For example, the intersection of the rational numbers and the irrational numbers is the empty set.

Some sets can be described by *listing* their elements in braces. For instance, the set A consisting of the natural numbers (or positive integers) less than 6 can be expressed as

$$A = \{1, 2, 3, 4, 5\}.$$

The entire set of integers is written as

$$\{0, \pm 1, \pm 2, \pm 3, \ldots\}.$$

Another way to describe a set is to enclose in braces a rule that generates all the elements of the set. For instance, the set

$$A = \{x \mid x \text{ is an integer and } 0 < x < 6\}$$

is the set of positive integers less than 6.

Intervals

A subset of the real line is called an **interval** if it contains at least two numbers and contains all the real numbers lying between any two of its elements. For example, the set of all real numbers x such that $x > 6$ is an interval, as is the set of all x such that $-2 \leq x \leq 5$. The set of all nonzero real numbers is not an interval; since 0 is absent, the set fails to contain every real number between -1 and 1 (for example).

Geometrically, intervals correspond to rays and line segments on the real line, along with the real line itself. Intervals of numbers corresponding to line segments are **finite intervals**; intervals corresponding to rays and the real line are **infinite intervals**.

A finite interval is said to be **closed** if it contains both of its endpoints, **half-open** if it contains one endpoint but not the other, and **open** if it contains neither endpoint. The endpoints are also called **boundary points**; they make up the interval's **boundary**. The remaining points of the interval are **interior points** and together comprise the interval's **interior**. Infinite intervals are closed if they contain a finite endpoint, and open otherwise. The entire real line $\mathbb{R}$ is an infinite interval that is both open and closed. Table A.1 summarizes the various types of intervals.

TABLE A.1 Types of intervals

Notation	Set description	Type	Picture
(a, b)	$\{x \mid a < x < b\}$	Open	
$[a, b]$	$\{x \mid a \leq x \leq b\}$	Closed	
$[a, b)$	$\{x \mid a \leq x < b\}$	Half-open	
$(a, b]$	$\{x \mid a < x \leq b\}$	Half-open	
(a, ∞)	$\{x \mid x > a\}$	Open	
$[a, \infty)$	$\{x \mid x \geq a\}$	Closed	
$(-\infty, b)$	$\{x \mid x < b\}$	Open	
$(-\infty, b]$	$\{x \mid x \leq b\}$	Closed	
$(-\infty, \infty)$	$\mathbb{R}$ (set of all real numbers)	Both open and closed	

Solving Inequalities

The process of finding the interval or intervals of numbers that satisfy an inequality in x is called **solving** the inequality.

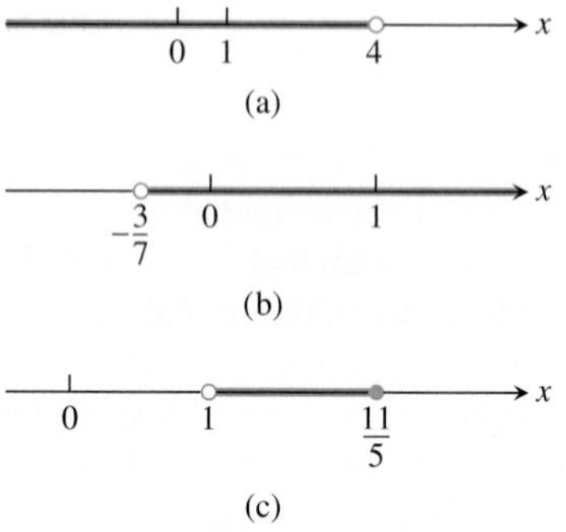

FIGURE A.1 Solution sets for the inequalities in Example 1.

EXAMPLE 1 Solve the following inequalities and show their solution sets on the real line.

(a) $2x - 1 < x + 3$ **(b)** $-\frac{x}{3} < 2x + 1$ **(c)** $\frac{6}{x-1} \geq 5$

Solution

(a)

$$\begin{aligned} 2x - 1 &< x + 3 \\ 2x &< x + 4 && \text{Add 1 to both sides.} \\ x &< 4 && \text{Subtract } x \text{ from both sides.} \end{aligned}$$

The solution set is the open interval $(-\infty, 4)$ (Figure A.1a).

(b)

$$\begin{aligned} -\frac{x}{3} &< 2x + 1 \\ -x &< 6x + 3 && \text{Multiply both sides by 3.} \\ 0 &< 7x + 3 && \text{Add } x \text{ to both sides.} \\ -3 &< 7x && \text{Subtract 3 from both sides.} \\ -\frac{3}{7} &< x && \text{Divide by 7.} \end{aligned}$$

The solution set is the open interval $(-3/7, \infty)$ (Figure A.1b).

(c) The inequality $6/(x-1) \geq 5$ can hold only if $x > 1$, because otherwise $6/(x-1)$ is undefined or negative. Therefore, $(x-1)$ is positive and the inequality will be preserved if we multiply both sides by $(x-1)$, and we have

$$\begin{aligned} \frac{6}{x-1} &\geq 5 \\ 6 &\geq 5x - 5 && \text{Multiply both sides by } (x-1). \\ 11 &\geq 5x && \text{Add 5 to both sides.} \\ \frac{11}{5} &\geq x. && \text{Or } x \leq \frac{11}{5}. \end{aligned}$$

The solution set is the half-open interval $(1, 11/5]$ (Figure A.1c). ■

Absolute Value

The **absolute value** of a number x, denoted by $|x|$, is defined by the formula

$$|x| = \begin{cases} x, & x \geq 0 \\ -x, & x < 0. \end{cases}$$

EXAMPLE 2 $|3| = 3, \quad |0| = 0, \quad |-5| = -(-5) = 5, \quad |-|a|| = |a|$ ■

Geometrically, the absolute value of x is the distance from x to 0 on the real number line. Since distances are always positive or 0, we see that $|x| \geq 0$ for every real number x,

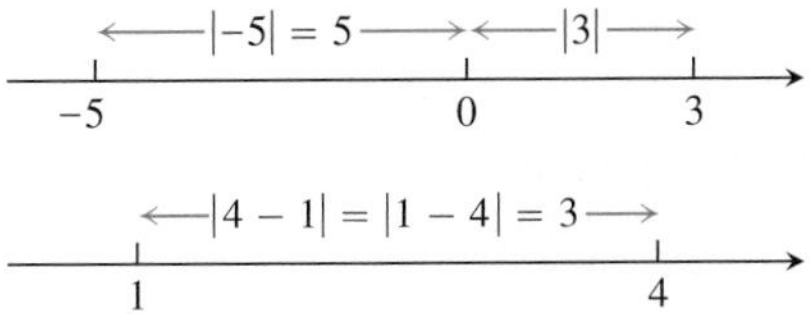

FIGURE A.2 Absolute values give distances between points on the number line.

and $|x| = 0$ if and only if $x = 0$. Also,

$$|x - y| = \text{the distance between } x \text{ and } y$$

on the real line (Figure A.2).

Since the symbol $\sqrt{a}$ always denotes the *nonnegative* square root of a, an alternate definition of $|x|$ is

$$|x| = \sqrt{x^2}.$$

It is important to remember that $\sqrt{a^2} = |a|$. Do not write $\sqrt{a^2} = a$ unless you already know that $a \geq 0$.

The absolute value has the following properties. (You are asked to prove these properties in the exercises.)

Absolute Value Properties

1. $|-a| = |a|$ — A number and its additive inverse or negative have the same absolute value.

2. $|ab| = |a||b|$ — The absolute value of a product is the product of the absolute values.

3. $\left|\dfrac{a}{b}\right| = \dfrac{|a|}{|b|}$ — The absolute value of a quotient is the quotient of the absolute values.

4. $|a + b| \leq |a| + |b|$ — The **triangle inequality**. The absolute value of the sum of two numbers is less than or equal to the sum of their absolute values.

Note that $|-a| \neq -|a|$. For example, $|-3| = 3$, whereas $-|3| = -3$. If a and b differ in sign, then $|a + b|$ is less than $|a| + |b|$. In all other cases, $|a + b|$ equals $|a| + |b|$. Absolute value bars in expressions like $|-3 + 5|$ work like parentheses: We do the arithmetic inside *before* taking the absolute value.

EXAMPLE 3

$$|-3 + 5| = |2| = 2 < |-3| + |5| = 8$$
$$|3 + 5| = |8| = |3| + |5|$$
$$|-3 - 5| = |-8| = 8 = |-3| + |-5|$$

■

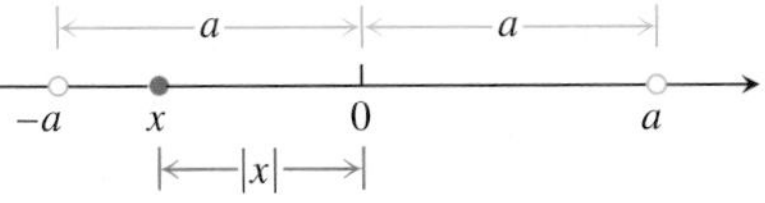

FIGURE A.3 $|x| < a$ means x lies between $-a$ and a.

Absolute values and intervals

If a is any positive number, then

5. $|x| = a \iff x = \pm a$

6. $|x| < a \iff -a < x < a$

7. $|x| > a \iff x > a$ or $x < -a$

8. $|x| \leq a \iff -a \leq x \leq a$

9. $|x| \geq a \iff x \geq a$ or $x \leq -a$

The inequality $|x| < a$ says that the distance from x to 0 is less than the positive number a. This means that x must lie between $-a$ and a, as we can see from Figure A.3.

The statements in the table are all consequences of the definition of absolute value and are often helpful when solving equations or inequalities involving absolute values.

The symbol $\iff$ is often used by mathematicians to denote the "if and only if" logical relationship. It also means "implies and is implied by."

EXAMPLE 4 Solve the equation $|2x - 3| = 7$.

Solution By Property 5, $2x - 3 = \pm 7$, so there are two possibilities:

$$2x - 3 = 7 \qquad 2x - 3 = -7 \qquad \text{Equivalent equations without absolute values}$$
$$2x = 10 \qquad 2x = -4 \qquad \text{Solve as usual.}$$
$$x = 5 \qquad x = -2$$

The solutions of $|2x - 3| = 7$ are $x = 5$ and $x = -2$. ■

EXAMPLE 5 Solve the inequality $\left|5 - \frac{2}{x}\right| < 1$.

Solution We have

$$\begin{aligned} \left|5 - \frac{2}{x}\right| < 1 &\Leftrightarrow -1 < 5 - \frac{2}{x} < 1 && \text{Property 6} \\ &\Leftrightarrow -6 < -\frac{2}{x} < -4 && \text{Subtract 5.} \\ &\Leftrightarrow 3 > \frac{1}{x} > 2 && \text{Multiply by } -\frac{1}{2}. \\ &\Leftrightarrow \frac{1}{3} < x < \frac{1}{2}. && \text{Take reciprocals.} \end{aligned}$$

Notice how the various rules for inequalities were used here. Multiplying by a negative number reverses the inequality. So does taking reciprocals in an inequality in which both sides are positive. The original inequality holds if and only if $(1/3) < x < (1/2)$. The solution set is the open interval $(1/3, 1/2)$. ■

EXERCISES A.1

1. Express $1/9$ as a repeating decimal, using a bar to indicate the repeating digits. What are the decimal representations of $2/9$? $3/9$? $8/9$? $9/9$?

2. If $2 < x < 6$, which of the following statements about x are necessarily true, and which are not necessarily true?

   a. $0 < x < 4$ b. $0 < x - 2 < 4$

   c. $1 < \frac{x}{2} < 3$ d. $\frac{1}{6} < \frac{1}{x} < \frac{1}{2}$

   e. $1 < \frac{6}{x} < 3$ f. $|x - 4| < 2$

   g. $-6 < -x < 2$ h. $-6 < -x < -2$

In Exercises 3–6, solve the inequalities and show the solution sets on the real line.

3. $-2x > 4$
4. $5x - 3 \le 7 - 3x$
5. $2x - \frac{1}{2} \ge 7x + \frac{7}{6}$
6. $\frac{4}{5}(x - 2) < \frac{1}{3}(x - 6)$

Solve the equations in Exercises 7–9.

7. $|y| = 3$
8. $|2t + 5| = 4$
9. $|8 - 3s| = \frac{9}{2}$

Solve the inequalities in Exercises 10–17, expressing the solution sets as intervals or unions of intervals. Also, show each solution set on the real line.

10. $|x| < 2$
11. $|t - 1| \le 3$
12. $|3y - 7| < 4$
13. $\left|\frac{z}{5} - 1\right| \le 1$
14. $\left|3 - \frac{1}{x}\right| < \frac{1}{2}$
15. $|2s| \ge 4$
16. $|1 - x| > 1$
17. $\left|\frac{r + 1}{2}\right| \ge 1$

Solve the inequalities in Exercises 18–21. Express the solution sets as intervals or unions of intervals and show them on the real line. Use the result $\sqrt{a^2} = |a|$ as appropriate.

18. $x^2 < 2$
19. $4 < x^2 < 9$
20. $(x - 1)^2 < 4$
21. $x^2 - x < 0$

22. Do not fall into the trap $|-a| = a$. For what real numbers a is this equation true? For what real numbers is it false?

23. Solve the equation $|x - 1| = 1 - x$.

24. A proof of the triangle inequality Give the reason justifying each of the numbered steps in the following proof of the triangle inequality.

$$
\begin{aligned}
|a + b|^2 &= (a + b)^2 && (1)\\
&= a^2 + 2ab + b^2 \\
&\le a^2 + 2|a||b| + b^2 && (2)\\
&= |a|^2 + 2|a||b| + |b|^2 && (3)\\
&= (|a| + |b|)^2 \\
|a + b| &\le |a| + |b| && (4)
\end{aligned}
$$

25. Prove that $|ab| = |a||b|$ for any numbers a and b.

26. If $|x| \le 3$ and $x > -1/2$, what can you say about x?

27. Graph the inequality $|x| + |y| \le 1$.

28. For any number a, prove that $|-a| = |a|$.

29. Let a be any positive number. Prove that $|x| > a$ if and only if $x > a$ or $x < -a$.

30. a. If b is any nonzero real number, prove that $|1/b| = 1/|b|$.

b. Prove that $\left|\dfrac{a}{b}\right| = \dfrac{|a|}{|b|}$ for any numbers a and $b \neq 0$.

A.2 Mathematical Induction

Many formulas, like

$$1 + 2 + \cdots + n = \frac{n(n + 1)}{2},$$

can be shown to hold for every positive integer n by applying an axiom called the *mathematical induction principle*. A proof that uses this axiom is called a *proof by mathematical induction* or a *proof by induction*.

The steps in proving a formula by induction are the following:

1. Check that the formula holds for $n = 1$.
2. Prove that if the formula holds for any positive integer $n = k$, then it also holds for the next integer, $n = k + 1$.

The induction axiom says that once these steps are completed, the formula holds for all positive integers n. By Step 1 it holds for $n = 1$. By Step 2 it holds for $n = 2$, and therefore by Step 2 also for $n = 3$, and by Step 2 again for $n = 4$, and so on. If the first domino falls, and the kth domino always knocks over the $(k + 1)$st when it falls, all the dominoes fall.

From another point of view, suppose we have a sequence of statements S_1, $S_2, \ldots, S_n, \ldots$, one for each positive integer. Suppose we can show that assuming any one of the statements to be true implies that the next statement in line is true. Suppose that we can also show that S_1 is true. Then we may conclude that the statements are true from S_1 on.

EXAMPLE 1 Use mathematical induction to prove that for every positive integer n,

$$1 + 2 + \cdots + n = \frac{n(n + 1)}{2}.$$

Solution We accomplish the proof by carrying out the two steps above.

1. The formula holds for $n = 1$ because

$$1 = \frac{1(1 + 1)}{2}.$$

2. If the formula holds for $n = k$, does it also hold for $n = k + 1$? The answer is yes, as we now show. If

$$1 + 2 + \cdots + k = \frac{k(k+1)}{2},$$

then

$$\begin{aligned} 1 + 2 + \cdots + k + (k+1) &= \frac{k(k+1)}{2} + (k+1) = \frac{k^2 + k + 2k + 2}{2} \\ &= \frac{(k+1)(k+2)}{2} = \frac{(k+1)((k+1)+1)}{2}. \end{aligned}$$

The last expression in this string of equalities is the expression $n(n+1)/2$ for $n = (k+1)$.

The mathematical induction principle now guarantees the original formula for all positive integers n. ■

In Example 4 of Section 5.2 we gave another proof for the formula giving the sum of the first n integers. However, proof by mathematical induction is more general. It can be used to find the sums of the squares and cubes of the first n integers (Exercises 9 and 10). Here is another example.

EXAMPLE 2 Show by mathematical induction that for all positive integers n,

$$\frac{1}{2^1} + \frac{1}{2^2} + \cdots + \frac{1}{2^n} = 1 - \frac{1}{2^n}.$$

Solution We accomplish the proof by carrying out the two steps of mathematical induction.

1. The formula holds for $n = 1$ because

$$\frac{1}{2^1} = 1 - \frac{1}{2^1}.$$

2. If

$$\frac{1}{2^1} + \frac{1}{2^2} + \cdots + \frac{1}{2^k} = 1 - \frac{1}{2^k},$$

then

$$\begin{aligned} \frac{1}{2^1} + \frac{1}{2^2} + \cdots + \frac{1}{2^k} + \frac{1}{2^{k+1}} &= 1 - \frac{1}{2^k} + \frac{1}{2^{k+1}} = 1 - \frac{1 \cdot 2}{2^k \cdot 2} + \frac{1}{2^{k+1}} \\ &= 1 - \frac{2}{2^{k+1}} + \frac{1}{2^{k+1}} = 1 - \frac{1}{2^{k+1}}. \end{aligned}$$

Thus, the original formula holds for $n = (k+1)$ whenever it holds for $n = k$.

With these steps verified, the mathematical induction principle now guarantees the formula for every positive integer n. ■

Other Starting Integers

Instead of starting at $n = 1$ some induction arguments start at another integer. The steps for such an argument are as follows.

1. Check that the formula holds for $n = n_1$ (the first appropriate integer).
2. Prove that if the formula holds for any integer $n = k \geq n_1$, then it also holds for $n = (k + 1)$.

Once these steps are completed, the mathematical induction principle guarantees the formula for all $n \geq n_1$.

EXAMPLE 3 Show that $n! > 3^n$ if n is large enough.

Solution How large is large enough? We experiment:

n	1	2	3	4	5	6	7
$n!$	1	2	6	24	120	720	5040
3^n	3	9	27	81	243	729	2187

It looks as if $n! > 3^n$ for $n \geq 7$. To be sure, we apply mathematical induction. We take $n_1 = 7$ in Step 1 and complete Step 2.

Suppose $k! > 3^k$ for some $k \geq 7$. Then

$$(k+1)! = (k+1)(k!) > (k+1)3^k > 7 \cdot 3^k > 3^{k+1}.$$

Thus, for $k \geq 7$,

$$k! > 3^k \quad \text{implies} \quad (k+1)! > 3^{k+1}.$$

The mathematical induction principle now guarantees$n! \geq 3^n$ for all $n \geq 7$. ■

EXERCISES A.2

1. Assuming that the triangle inequality $|a + b| \leq |a| + |b|$ holds for any two numbers a and b. Show that

$$|x_1 + x_2 + \cdots + x_n| \leq |x_1| + |x_2| + \cdots + |x_n|$$

for any n numbers.

2. Show that if $r \neq 1$, then

$$1 + r + r^2 + \cdots + r^n = \frac{1 - r^{n+1}}{1 - r}$$

for every positive integer n.

3. Use the Product Rule, $\frac{d}{dx}(uv) = u\frac{dv}{dx} + v\frac{du}{dx}$, and the fact that $\frac{d}{dx}(x) = 1$ to show that $\frac{d}{dx}(x^n) = nx^{n-1}$ for every positive integer n.

4. Suppose that a function $f(x)$ has the property that $f(x_1x_2) = f(x_1) + f(x_2)$ for any two positive numbers x_1 and x_2. Show that

$$f(x_1x_2\cdots x_n) = f(x_1) + f(x_2) + \cdots + f(x_n)$$

for the product of any n positive numbers $x_1, x_2, \ldots, x_n$.

5. Show that

$$\frac{2}{3^1} + \frac{2}{3^2} + \cdots + \frac{2}{3^n} = 1 - \frac{1}{3^n}$$

for all positive integers n.

6. Show that $n! > n^3$ if n is large enough.

7. Show that $2^n > n^2$ if n is large enough.

8. Show that $2^n \geq 1/8$ for $n \geq -3$.

9. Sums of squares Show that the sum of the squares of the first n positive integers is

$$\frac{n\left(n + \frac{1}{2}\right)(n + 1)}{3}.$$

10. Sums of cubes Show that the sum of the cubes of the first n positive integers is $(n(n + 1)/2)^2$.

11. Rules for finite sums Show that the following finite sum rules hold for every positive integer n. (See Section 5.2.)

a. $\sum_{k=1}^{n}(a_k + b_k) = \sum_{k=1}^{n} a_k + \sum_{k=1}^{n} b_k$

b. $\sum_{k=1}^{n}(a_k - b_k) = \sum_{k=1}^{n} a_k - \sum_{k=1}^{n} b_k$

c. $\sum_{k=1}^{n} ca_k = c \cdot \sum_{k=1}^{n} a_k$ (Any number c)

d. $\sum_{k=1}^{n} a_k = n \cdot c$ (if a_k has the constant value c)

12. Show that $|x^n| = |x|^n$ for every positive integer n and every real number x.

A.3 Lines, Circles, and Parabolas

This section reviews coordinates, lines, distance, circles, and parabolas in the plane. The notion of increment is also discussed.

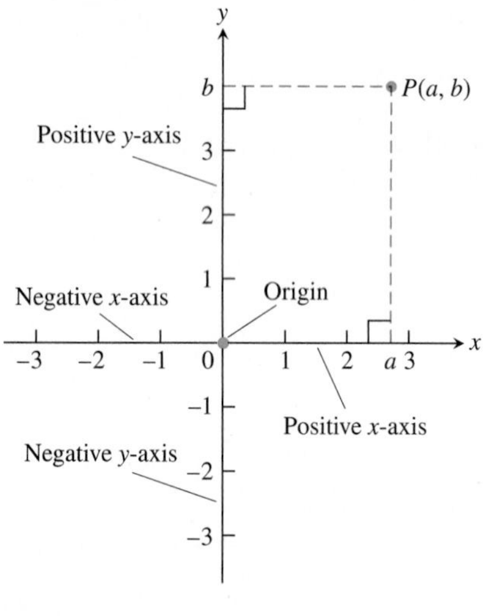

FIGURE A.4 Cartesian coordinates in the plane are based on two perpendicular axes intersecting at the origin.

Cartesian Coordinates in the Plane

In Appendix 1 we identified the points on the line with real numbers by assigning them coordinates. Points in the plane can be identified with ordered pairs of real numbers. To begin, we draw two perpendicular coordinate lines that intersect at the 0-point of each line. These lines are called **coordinate axes** in the plane. On the horizontal x-axis, numbers are denoted by x and increase to the right. On the vertical y-axis, numbers are denoted by y and increase upward (Figure A.4). Thus "upward" and "to the right" are positive directions, whereas "downward" and "to the left" are considered as negative. The **origin** O, also labeled 0, of the coordinate system is the point in the plane where x and y are both zero.

If P is any point in the plane, it can be located by exactly one ordered pair of real numbers in the following way. Draw lines through P perpendicular to the two coordinate axes. These lines intersect the axes at points with coordinates a and b (Figure A.4). The ordered pair (a, b) is assigned to the point P and is called its **coordinate pair**. The first number a is the ***x*-coordinate** (or **abscissa**) of P; the second number b is the ***y*-coordinate** (or **ordinate**) of P. The x-coordinate of every point on the y-axis is 0. The y-coordinate of every point on the x-axis is 0. The origin is the point $(0, 0)$.

Starting with an ordered pair (a, b), we can reverse the process and arrive at a corresponding point P in the plane. Often we identify P with the ordered pair and write $P(a, b)$. We sometimes also refer to "the point (a, b)" and it will be clear from the context when (a, b) refers to a point in the plane and not to an open interval on the real line. Several points labeled by their coordinates are shown in Figure A.5.

HISTORICAL BIOGRAPHY

René Descartes
(1596–1650)

This coordinate system is called the **rectangular coordinate system** or **Cartesian coordinate system** (after the sixteenth century French mathematician René Descartes).

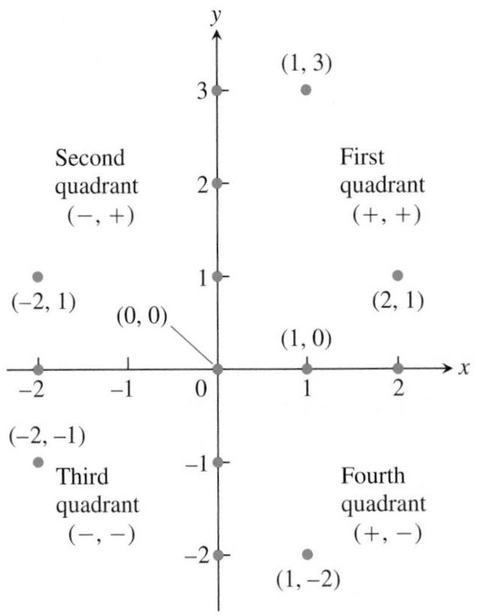

FIGURE A.5 Points labeled in the xy-coordinate or Cartesian plane. The points on the axes all have coordinate pairs but are usually labeled with single real numbers, (so (1, 0) on the x-axis is labeled as 1). Notice the coordinate sign patterns of the quadrants.

The coordinate axes of this coordinate or Cartesian plane divide the plane into four regions called **quadrants**, numbered counterclockwise as shown in Figure A.5.

The **graph** of an equation or inequality in the variables x and y is the set of all points $P(x, y)$ in the plane whose coordinates satisfy the equation or inequality. When we plot data in the coordinate plane or graph formulas whose variables have different units of measure, we do not need to use the same scale on the two axes. If we plot time vs. thrust for a rocket motor, for example, there is no reason to place the mark that shows 1 sec on the time axis the same distance from the origin as the mark that shows 1 lb on the thrust axis.

Usually when we graph functions whose variables do not represent physical measurements and when we draw figures in the coordinate plane to study their geometry and trigonometry, we try to make the scales on the axes identical. A vertical unit of distance then looks the same as a horizontal unit. As on a surveyor's map or a scale drawing, line segments that are supposed to have the same length will look as if they do and angles that are supposed to be congruent will look congruent.

Computer displays and calculator displays are another matter. The vertical and horizontal scales on machine-generated graphs usually differ, and there are corresponding distortions in distances, slopes, and angles. Circles may look like ellipses, rectangles may look like squares, right angles may appear to be acute or obtuse, and so on. We discuss these displays and distortions in greater detail in Section 1.6.

Increments and Straight Lines

When a particle moves from one point in the plane to another, the net changes in its coordinates are called *increments.* They are calculated by subtracting the coordinates of the starting point from the coordinates of the ending point. If x changes from x_1 to x_2, the **increment** in x is

$$\Delta x = x_2 - x_1 .$$

EXAMPLE 1 In going from the point $A(4, -3)$ to the point $B(2, 5)$ the increments in the x- and y-coordinates are

$$\Delta x = 2 - 4 = -2, \qquad \Delta y = 5 - (-3) = 8 .$$

From $C(5, 6)$ to $D(5, 1)$ the coordinate increments are

$$\Delta x = 5 - 5 = 0, \qquad \Delta y = 1 - 6 = -5 .$$

See Figure A.6. ■

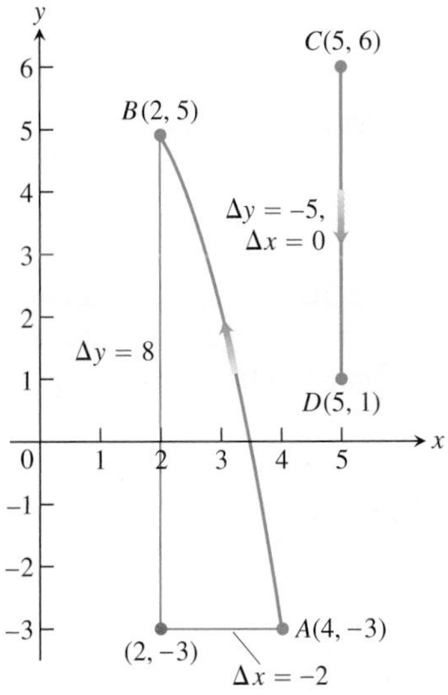

FIGURE A.6 Coordinate increments may be positive, negative, or zero (Example 1).

Given two points $P_1(x_1, y_1)$ and $P_2(x_2, y_2)$ in the plane, we call the increments $\Delta x = x_2 - x_1$ and $\Delta y = y_2 - y_1$ the **run** and the **rise**, respectively, between P_1 and P_2. Two such points always determine a unique straight line (usually called simply a line) passing through them both. We call the line P_1P_2.

Any nonvertical line in the plane has the property that the ratio

$$m = \frac{\text{rise}}{\text{run}} = \frac{\Delta y}{\Delta x} = \frac{y_2 - y_1}{x_2 - x_1}$$

has the same value for every choice of the two points $P_1(x_1, y_1)$ and $P_2(x_2, y_2)$ on the line (Figure A.7). This is because the ratios of corresponding sides for similar triangles are equal.

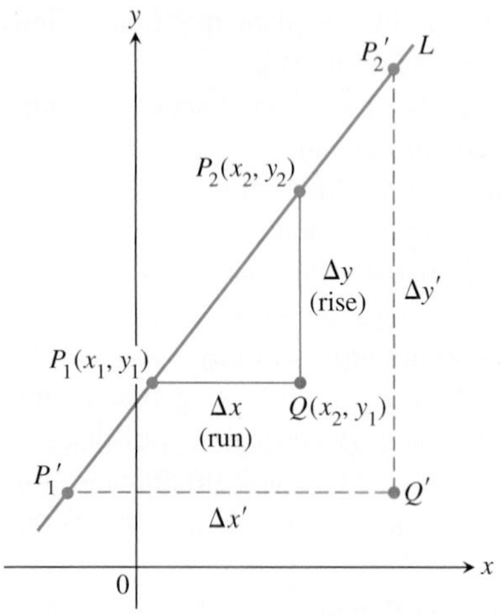

FIGURE A.7 Triangles P_1QP_2 and $P_1'Q'P_2'$ are similar, so the ratio of their sides has the same value for any two points on the line. This common value is the line's slope.

> **DEFINITION** Slope
>
> The constant
>
> $$m = \frac{\text{rise}}{\text{run}} = \frac{\Delta y}{\Delta x} = \frac{y_2 - y_1}{x_2 - x_1}$$
>
> is the **slope** of the nonvertical line P_1P_2.

The slope tells us the direction (uphill, downhill) and steepness of a line. A line with positive slope rises uphill to the right; one with negative slope falls downhill to the right (Figure A.8). The greater the absolute value of the slope, the more rapid the rise or fall. The slope of a vertical line is *undefined*. Since the run Δx is zero for a vertical line, we cannot form the slope ratio m.

The direction and steepness of a line can also be measured with an angle. The **angle of inclination** of a line that crosses the x-axis is the smallest counterclockwise angle from the x-axis to the line (Figure A.9). The inclination of a horizontal line is 0°. The inclination of a vertical line is 90°. If ϕ (the Greek letter phi) is the inclination of a line, then $0 \le \phi < 180°$.

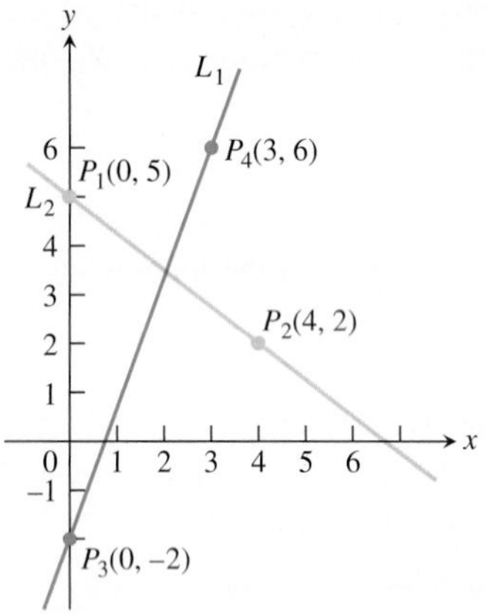

FIGURE A.8 The slope of L_1 is

$$m = \frac{\Delta y}{\Delta x} = \frac{6 - (-2)}{3 - 0} = \frac{8}{3}.$$

That is, y increases 8 units every time x increases 3 units. The slope of L_2 is

$$m = \frac{\Delta y}{\Delta x} = \frac{2 - 5}{4 - 0} = \frac{-3}{4}.$$

That is, y decreases 3 units every time x increases 4 units.

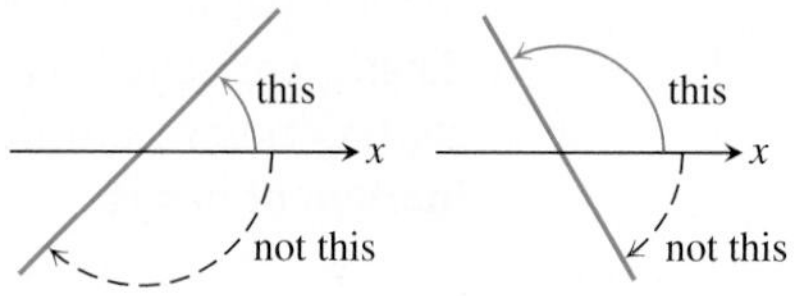

FIGURE A.9 Angles of inclination are measured counterclockwise from the x-axis.

The relationship between the slope m of a nonvertical line and the line's angle of inclination ϕ is shown in Figure A.10:

$$m = \tan \phi.$$

Straight lines have relatively simple equations. All points on the *vertical line* through the point a on the x-axis have x-coordinates equal to a. Thus, $x = a$ is an equation for the vertical line. Similarly, $y = b$ is an equation for the *horizontal line* meeting the y-axis at b. (See Figure A.11.)

We can write an equation for a nonvertical straight line L if we know its slope m and the coordinates of one point $P_1(x_1, y_1)$ on it. If $P(x, y)$ is *any* other point on L, then we can use the two points P_1 and P to compute the slope,

$$m = \frac{y - y_1}{x - x_1}$$

so that

$$y - y_1 = m(x - x_1) \qquad \text{or} \qquad y = y_1 + m(x - x_1).$$

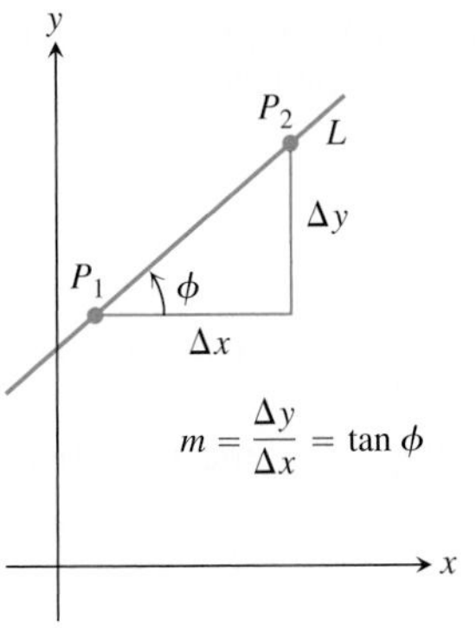

FIGURE A.10 The slope of a nonvertical line is the tangent of its angle of inclination.

> The equation
>
> $$y = y_1 + m(x - x_1)$$
>
> is the **point-slope equation** of the line that passes through the point (x_1, y_1) and has slope m.

EXAMPLE 2 Write an equation for the line through the point (2, 3) with slope $-3/2$.

Solution We substitute $x_1 = 2$, $y_1 = 3$, and $m = -3/2$ into the point-slope equation and obtain

$$y = 3 - \frac{3}{2}\left(x - 2\right), \qquad \text{or} \qquad y = -\frac{3}{2}x + 6.$$

When $x = 0$, $y = 6$ so the line intersects the y-axis at $y = 6$. ■

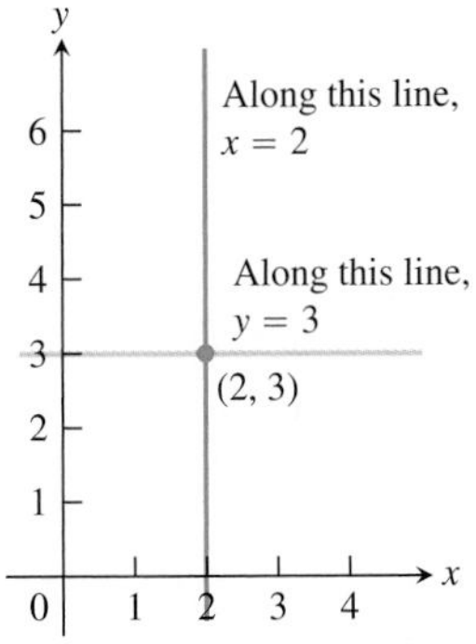

FIGURE A.11 The standard equations for the vertical and horizontal lines through (2, 3) are $x = 2$ and $y = 3$.

EXAMPLE 3 Write an equation for the line through $(-2, -1)$ and (3, 4).

Solution The line's slope is

$$m = \frac{-1 - 4}{-2 - 3} = \frac{-5}{-5} = 1.$$

We can use this slope with either of the two given points in the point-slope equation:

With $(x_1, y_1) = (-2, -1)$	**With $(x_1, y_1) = (3, 4)$**
$y = -1 + 1 \cdot (x - (-2))$	$y = 4 + 1 \cdot (x - 3)$
$y = -1 + x + 2$	$y = 4 + x - 3$
$y = x + 1$	$y = x + 1$

Same result

Either way, $y = x + 1$ is an equation for the line (Figure A.12). ■

The y-coordinate of the point where a nonvertical line intersects the y-axis is called the ***y*-intercept** of the line. Similarly, the ***x*-intercept** of a nonhorizontal line is the x-coordinate of the point where it crosses the x-axis (Figure A.13). A line with slope m and y-intercept b passes through the point $(0, b)$, so it has equation

$$y = b + m(x - 0), \qquad \text{or, more simply,} \qquad y = mx + b.$$

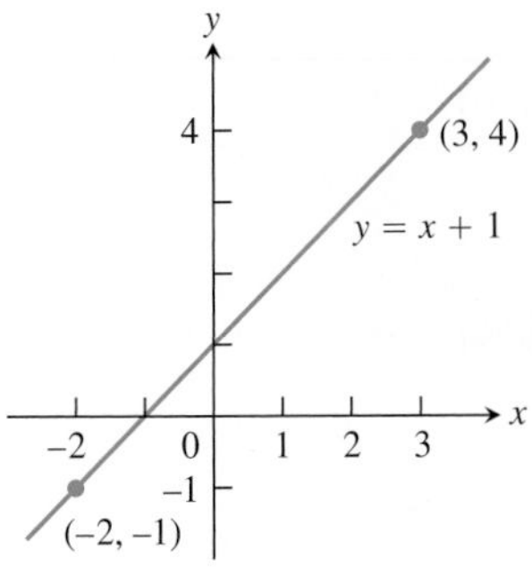

FIGURE A.12 The line in Example 3.

> The equation
>
> $$y = mx + b$$
>
> is called the **slope-intercept equation** of the line with slope m and y-intercept b.

Lines with equations of the form $y = mx$ have y-intercept 0 and so pass through the origin. Equations of lines are called **linear** equations.

The equation

$$Ax + By = C \qquad (A \text{ and } B \text{ not both } 0)$$

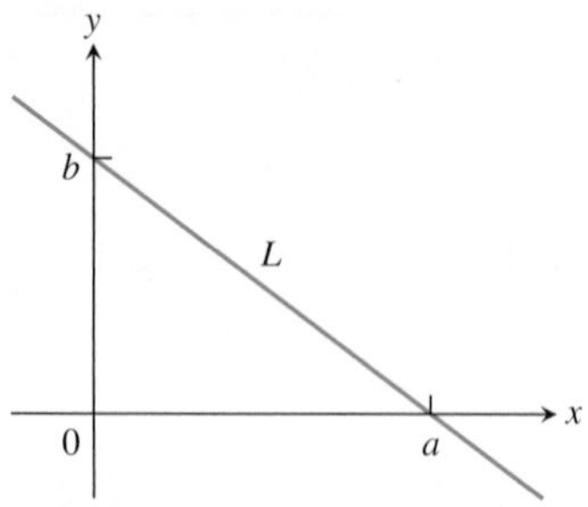

FIGURE A.13 Line L has x-intercept a and y-intercept b.

is called the **general linear equation** in x and y because its graph always represents a line and every line has an equation in this form (including lines with undefined slope).

Parallel and Perpendicular Lines

Lines that are parallel have equal angles of inclination, so they have the same slope (if they are not vertical). Conversely, lines with equal slopes have equal angles of inclination and so are parallel.

If two nonvertical lines L_1 and L_2 are perpendicular, their slopes m_1 and m_2 satisfy $m_1 m_2 = -1$, so each slope is the *negative reciprocal* of the other:

$$m_1 = -\frac{1}{m_2}, \qquad m_2 = -\frac{1}{m_1}.$$

To see this, notice by inspecting similar triangles in Figure A.14 that $m_1 = a/h$, and $m_2 = -h/a$. Hence, $m_1 m_2 = (a/h)(-h/a) = -1$.

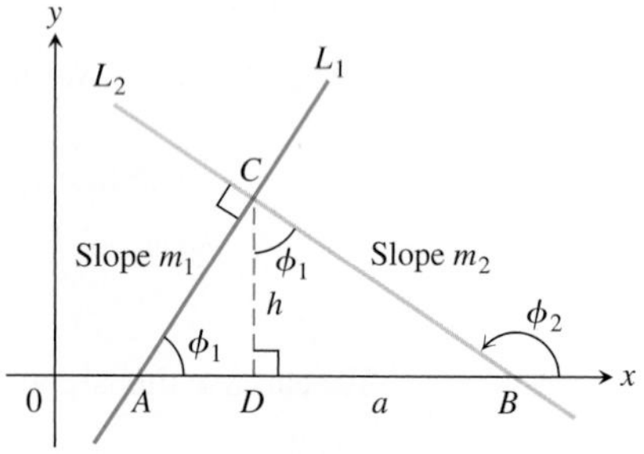

FIGURE A.14 ΔADC is similar to ΔCDB. Hence ϕ_1 is also the upper angle in ΔCDB. From the sides of ΔCDB, we read $\tan \phi_1 = a/h$.

Distance and Circles in the Plane

The distance between points in the plane is calculated with a formula that comes from the Pythagorean theorem (Figure A.15).

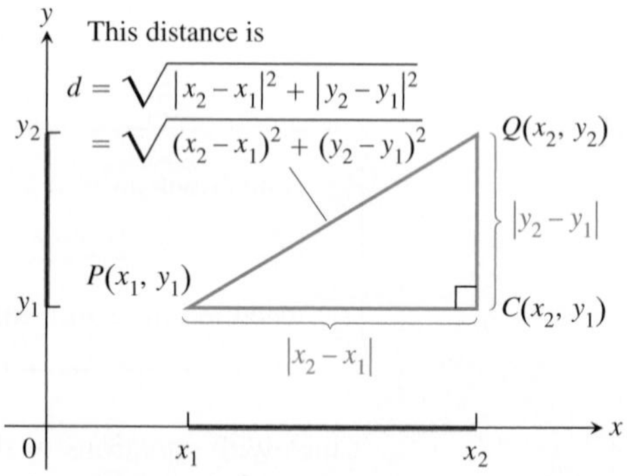

FIGURE A.15 To calculate the distance between $P(x_1, y_1)$ and $Q(x_2, y_2)$, apply the Pythagorean theorem to triangle PCQ.

Distance Formula for Points in the Plane

The distance between $P(x_1, y_1)$ and $Q(x_2, y_2)$ is

$$d = \sqrt{(\Delta x)^2 + (\Delta y)^2} = \sqrt{(x_2 - x_1)^2 + (y_2 - y_1)^2}.$$

EXAMPLE 4

(a) The distance between $P(-1, 2)$ and $Q(3, 4)$ is

$$\sqrt{(3 - (-1))^2 + (4 - 2)^2} = \sqrt{(4)^2 + (2)^2} = \sqrt{20} = \sqrt{4 \cdot 5} = 2\sqrt{5}.$$

(b) The distance from the origin to $P(x, y)$ is

$$\sqrt{(x - 0)^2 + (y - 0)^2} = \sqrt{x^2 + y^2}.$$

■

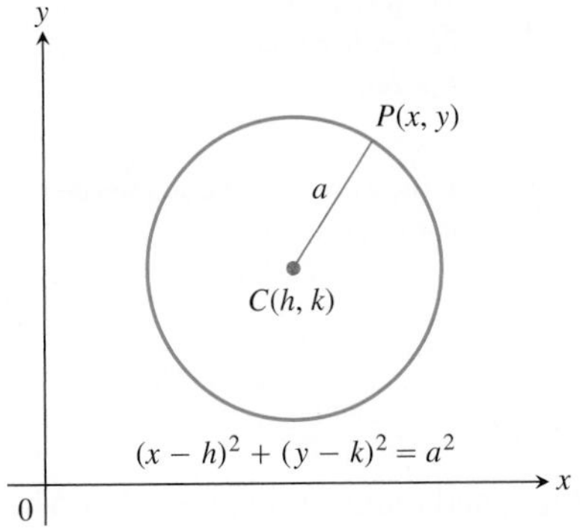

FIGURE A.16 A circle of radius a in the xy-plane, with center at (h, k).

By definition, a **circle** of radius a is the set of all points $P(x, y)$ whose distance from some center $C(h, k)$ equals a (Figure A.16). From the distance formula, P lies on the circle if and only if

$$\sqrt{(x - h)^2 + (y - k)^2} = a,$$

so

$$(x - h)^2 + (y - k)^2 = a^2. \qquad (1)$$

Equation (1) is the **standard equation** of a circle with center (h, k) and radius a. The circle of radius $a = 1$ and centered at the origin is the **unit circle** with equation

$$x^2 + y^2 = 1.$$

EXAMPLE 5

(a) The standard equation for the circle of radius 2 centered at (3, 4) is

$$(x - 3)^2 + (y - 4)^2 = 2^2 = 4.$$

(b) The circle

$$(x - 1)^2 + (y + 5)^2 = 3$$

has $h = 1$, $k = -5$, and $a = \sqrt{3}$. The center is the point $(h, k) = (1, -5)$ and the radius is $a = \sqrt{3}$.

■

If an equation for a circle is not in standard form, we can find the circle's center and radius by first converting the equation to standard form. The algebraic technique for doing so is *completing the square*.

EXAMPLE 6 Find the center and radius of the circle

$$x^2 + y^2 + 4x - 6y - 3 = 0.$$

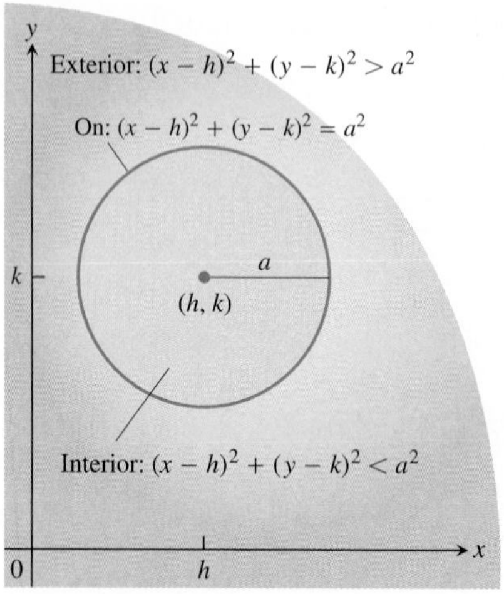

FIGURE A.17 The interior and exterior of the circle $(x-h)^2+(y-k)^2=a^2$.

Solution We convert the equation to standard form by completing the squares in x and y:

$$x^2+y^2+4x-6y-3=0$$

Start with the given equation.

$$(x^2+4x)+(y^2-6y)=3$$

Gather terms. Move the constant to the right-hand side.

$$\left(x^2+4x+\left(\frac{4}{2}\right)^2\right)+\left(y^2-6y+\left(\frac{-6}{2}\right)^2\right)=3+\left(\frac{4}{2}\right)^2+\left(\frac{-6}{2}\right)^2$$

Add the square of half the coefficient of x to each side of the equation. Do the same for y. The parenthetical expressions on the left-hand side are now perfect squares.

$$(x^2+4x+4)+(y^2-6y+9)=3+4+9$$

$$(x+2)^2+(y-3)^2=16$$

Write each quadratic as a squared linear expression.

The center is $(-2, 3)$ and the radius is $a=4$. ■

The points (x, y) satisfying the inequality

$$(x-h)^2+(y-k)^2<a^2$$

make up the **interior** region of the circle with center (h, k) and radius a (Figure A.17). The circle's **exterior** consists of the points (x, y) satisfying

$$(x-h)^2+(y-k)^2>a^2.$$

Parabolas

The geometric definition and properties of general parabolas are reviewed in Section 9.4. Here we look at parabolas arising as the graphs of equations of the form $y=ax^2+bx+c$.

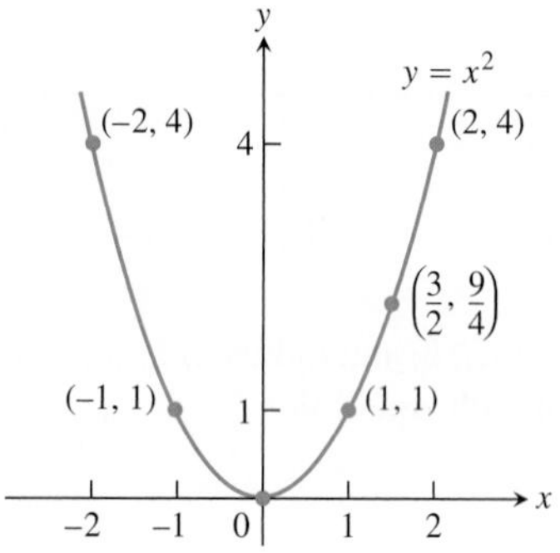

FIGURE A.18 The parabola $y=x^2$ (Example 7).

EXAMPLE 7 Consider the equation $y=x^2$. Some points whose coordinates satisfy this equation are $(0, 0)$, $(1, 1)$, $\left(\frac{3}{2}, \frac{9}{4}\right)$, $(-1, 1)$, $(2, 4)$, and $(-2, 4)$. These points (and all others satisfying the equation) make up a smooth curve called a parabola (Figure A.18). ■

The graph of an equation of the form

$$y=ax^2$$

is a **parabola** whose **axis** (axis of symmetry) is the y-axis. The parabola's **vertex** (point where the parabola and axis cross) lies at the origin. The parabola opens upward if $a>0$ and downward if $a<0$. The larger the value of $|a|$, the narrower the parabola (Figure A.19).

Generally, the graph of $y=ax^2+bx+c$ is a shifted and scaled version of the parabola $y=x^2$. We discuss shifting and scaling of graphs in more detail in Section 1.2.

The Graph of $y=ax^2+bx+c$, $a \neq 0$

The graph of the equation $y=ax^2+bx+c$, $a \neq 0$, is a parabola. The parabola opens upward if $a>0$ and downward if $a<0$. The **axis** is the line

$$x=-\frac{b}{2a}. \tag{2}$$

The **vertex** of the parabola is the point where the axis and parabola intersect. Its x-coordinate is $x=-b/2a$; its y-coordinate is found by substituting $x=-b/2a$ in the parabola's equation.

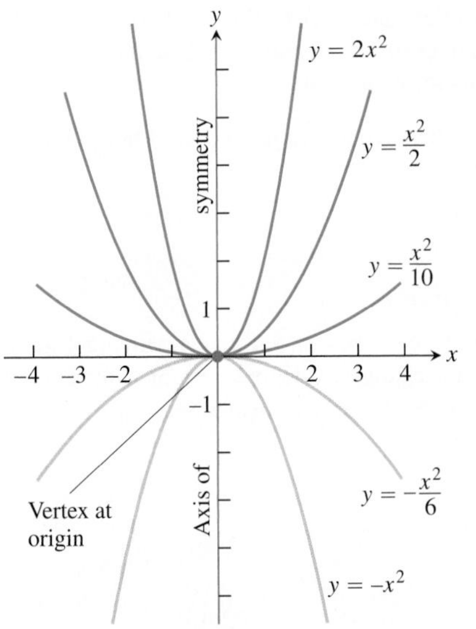

FIGURE A.19 Besides determining the direction in which the parabola $y = ax^2$ opens, the number a is a scaling factor. The parabola widens as a approaches zero and narrows as $|a|$ becomes large.

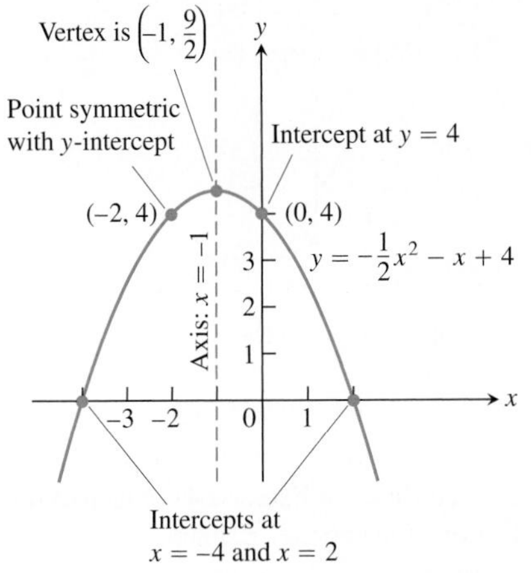

FIGURE A.20 The parabola in Example 8.

Notice that if $a = 0$, then we have $y = bx + c$ which is an equation for a line. The axis, given by Equation (2), can be found by completing the square or by using a technique we study in Section 4.1.

EXAMPLE 8 Graph the equation $y = -\frac{1}{2}x^2 - x + 4$.

Solution Comparing the equation with $y = ax^2 + bx + c$ we see that

$$a = -\frac{1}{2}, \qquad b = -1, \qquad c = 4.$$

Since $a < 0$, the parabola opens downward. From Equation (2) the axis is the vertical line

$$x = -\frac{b}{2a} = -\frac{(-1)}{2(-1/2)} = -1.$$

When $x = -1$, we have

$$y = -\frac{1}{2}(-1)^2 - (-1) + 4 = \frac{9}{2}.$$

The vertex is $(-1, 9/2)$.

The x-intercepts are where $y = 0$:

$$\begin{aligned} -\frac{1}{2}x^2 - x + 4 &= 0 \\ x^2 + 2x - 8 &= 0 \\ (x - 2)(x + 4) &= 0 \\ x = 2, \qquad x &= -4 \end{aligned}$$

We plot some points, sketch the axis, and use the direction of opening to complete the graph in Figure A.20. ■

EXERCISES A.3

In Exercises 1 and 2, a particle moves from A to B in the coordinate plane. Find the increments Δx and Δy in the particle's coordinates. Also find the distance from A to B.

1. $A(-3, 2)$, $B(-1, -2)$ **2.** $A(-3.2, -2)$, $B(-8.1, -2)$

Describe the graphs of the equations in Exercises 3 and 4.

3. $x^2 + y^2 = 1$ **4.** $x^2 + y^2 \leq 3$

Plot the points in Exercises 5 and 6 and find the slope (if any) of the line they determine. Also find the common slope (if any) of the lines perpendicular to line AB.

5. $A(-1, 2)$, $B(-2, -1)$ **6.** $A(2, 3)$, $B(-1, 3)$

In Exercises 7 and 8, find an equation for (a) the vertical line and (b) the horizontal line through the given point.

7. $(-1, 4/3)$ **8.** $\left(0, -\sqrt{2}\right)$

In Exercises 9–15, write an equation for each line described.

9. Passes through $(-1, 1)$ with slope -1

10. Passes through $(3, 4)$ and $(-2, 5)$

11. Has slope $-5/4$ and y-intercept 6

12. Passes through $(-12, -9)$ and has slope 0

13. Has y-intercept 4 and x-intercept -1

14. Passes through $(5, -1)$ and is parallel to the line $2x + 5y = 15$

15. Passes through $(4, 10)$ and is perpendicular to the line $6x - 3y = 5$.

In Exercises 16 and 17, find the line's x- and y-intercepts and use this information to graph the line.

16. $3x + 4y = 12$ **17.** $\sqrt{2}x - \sqrt{3}y = \sqrt{6}$

18. Is there anything special about the relationship between the lines $Ax + By = C_1$ and $Bx - Ay = C_2$ $(A \neq 0, B \neq 0)$? Give reasons for your answer.

19. A particle starts at $A(-2, 3)$ and its coordinates change by increments $\Delta x = 5$, $\Delta y = -6$. Find its new position.

20. The coordinates of a particle change by $\Delta x = 5$ and $\Delta y = 6$ as it moves from $A(x, y)$ to $B(3, -3)$. Find x and y.

In Exercises 21–23, find an equation for the circle with the given center $C(h, k)$ and radius a. Then sketch the circle in the xy-plane. Include the circle's center in your sketch. Also, label the circle's x- and y-intercepts, if any, with their coordinate pairs.

21. $C(0, 2), \quad a = 2$ **22.** $C(-1, 5), \quad a = \sqrt{10}$

23. $C\left(-\sqrt{3}, -2\right), \quad a = 2$

Graph the circles whose equations are given in Exercises 24–26. Label each circle's center and intercepts (if any) with their coordinate pairs.

24. $x^2 + y^2 + 4x - 4y + 4 = 0$

25. $x^2 + y^2 - 3y - 4 = 0$ **26.** $x^2 + y^2 - 4x + 4y = 0$

Graph the parabolas in Exercises 27–30. Label the vertex, axis, and intercepts in each case.

27. $y = x^2 - 2x - 3$ **28.** $y = -x^2 + 4x$

29. $y = -x^2 - 6x - 5$ **30.** $y = \frac{1}{2}x^2 + x + 4$

Describe the regions defined by the inequalities and pairs of inequalities in Exercises 31–36.

31. $x^2 + y^2 > 7$ **32.** $(x - 1)^2 + y^2 \leq 4$

33. $x^2 + y^2 > 1, \quad x^2 + y^2 < 4$

34. $x^2 + y^2 + 6y < 0, \quad y > -3$

35. Write an inequality that describes the points that lie inside the circle with center $(-2, 1)$ and radius $\sqrt{6}$.

36. Write a pair of inequalities that describe the points that lie inside or on the circle with center $(0, 0)$ and radius $\sqrt{2}$, and on or to the right of the vertical line through $(1, 0)$.

In Exercises 37–40, graph the two equations and find the points in which the graphs intersect.

37. $y = 2x, \quad x^2 + y^2 = 1$ **38.** $y - x = 1, \quad y = x^2$

39. $y = -x^2, \quad y = 2x^2 - 1$

40. $x^2 + y^2 = 1, \quad (x - 1)^2 + y^2 = 1$

41. Insulation By measuring slopes in the accompanying figure, estimate the temperature change in degrees per inch for (a) the gypsum wallboard; (b) the fiberglass insulation; (c) the wood sheathing.

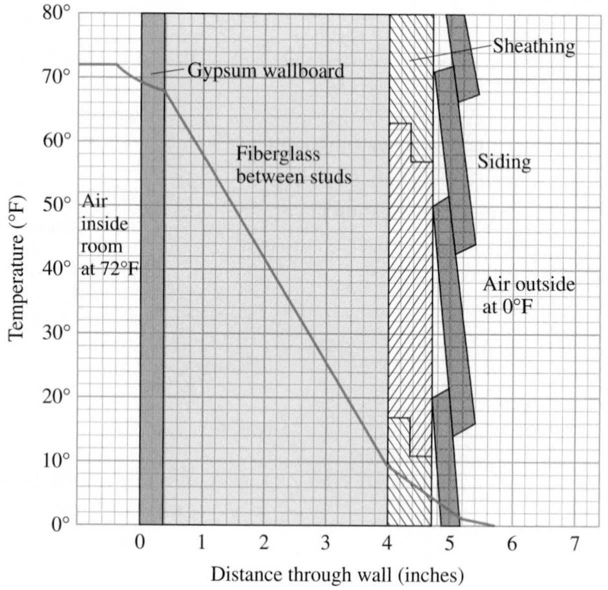

The temperature changes in the wall in Exercises 41 and 42.

42. Insulation According to the figure in Exercise 41, which of the materials is the best insulator? The poorest? Explain.

43. Pressure under water The pressure p experienced by a diver under water is related to the diver's depth d by an equation of the form $p = kd + 1$ (k a constant). At the surface, the pressure is 1 atmosphere. The pressure at 100 meters is about 10.94 atmospheres. Find the pressure at 50 meters.

44. Reflected light A ray of light comes in along the line $x + y = 1$ from the second quadrant and reflects off the x-axis (see the accompanying figure). The angle of incidence is equal to the angle of reflection. Write an equation for the line along which the departing light travels.

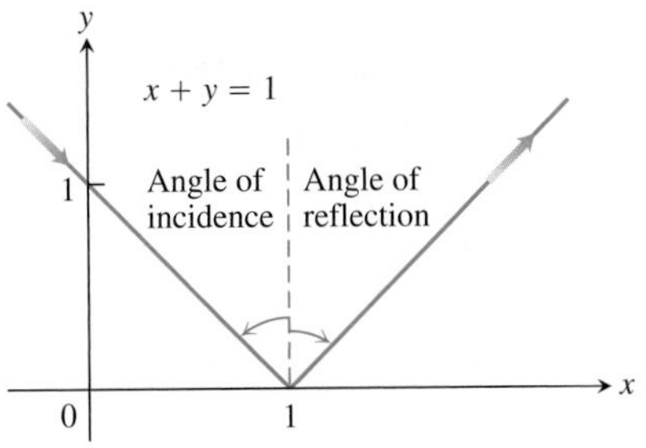

The path of the light ray in Exercise 44. Angles of incidence and reflection are measured from the perpendicular.

45. **Fahrenheit vs. Celsius** In the FC-plane, sketch the graph of the equation

$$C = \frac{5}{9}(F - 32)$$

linking Fahrenheit and Celsius temperatures. On the same graph sketch the line $C = F$. Is there a temperature at which a Celsius thermometer gives the same numerical reading as a Fahrenheit thermometer? If so, find it.

46. **The Mt. Washington Cog Railway** Civil engineers calculate the slope of roadbed as the ratio of the distance it rises or falls to the distance it runs horizontally. They call this ratio the **grade** of the roadbed, usually written as a percentage. Along the coast, commercial railroad grades are usually less than 2%. In the mountains, they may go as high as 4%. Highway grades are usually less than 5%.

    The steepest part of the Mt. Washington Cog Railway in New Hampshire has an exceptional 37.1% grade. Along this part of the track, the seats in the front of the car are 14 ft above those in the rear. About how far apart are the front and rear rows of seats?

47. By calculating the lengths of its sides, show that the triangle with vertices at the points $A(1, 2)$, $B(5, 5)$, and $C(4, -2)$ is isosceles but not equilateral.

48. Show that the triangle with vertices $A(0, 0)$, $B\left(1, \sqrt{3}\right)$, and $C(2, 0)$ is equilateral.

49. Show that the points $A(2, -1)$, $B(1, 3)$, and $C(-3, 2)$ are vertices of a square, and find the fourth vertex.

50. Three different parallelograms have vertices at $(-1, 1)$, $(2, 0)$, and $(2, 3)$. Sketch them and find the coordinates of the fourth vertex of each.

51. For what value of k is the line $2x + ky = 3$ perpendicular to the line $4x + y = 1$? For what value of k are the lines parallel?

52. **Midpoint of a line segment** Show that the point with coordinates

$$\left(\frac{x_1 + x_2}{2}, \frac{y_1 + y_2}{2}\right)$$

is the midpoint of the line segment joining $P(x_1, y_1)$ to $Q(x_2, y_2)$.

A.4 Trigonometry Formulas

Trigonometric Functions

Radian Measure

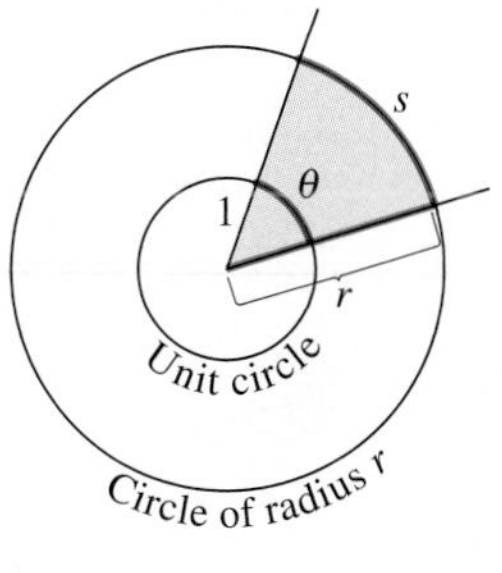

$$\frac{s}{r} = \frac{\theta}{1} = \theta \quad \text{or} \quad \theta = \frac{s}{r},$$

$180° = \pi$ radians.

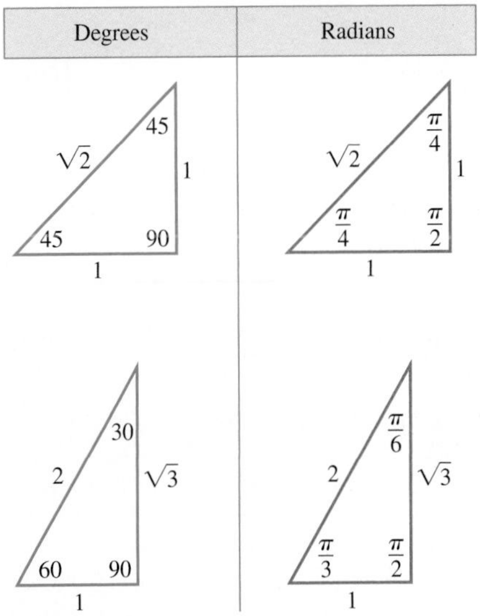

The angles of two common triangles, in degrees and radians.

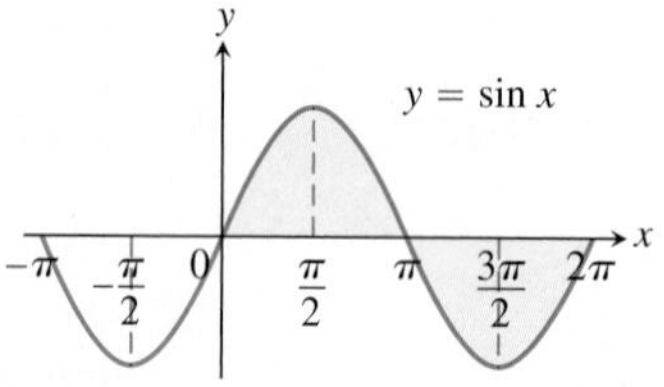

Domain: $(-\infty, \infty)$
Range: $[-1, 1]$

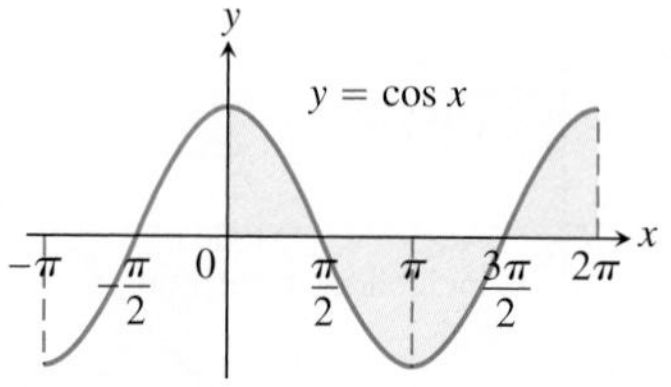

Domain: $(-\infty, \infty)$
Range: $[-1, 1]$

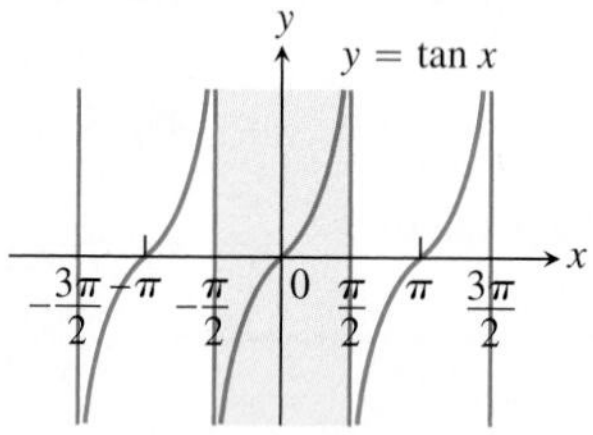

Domain: All real numbers except odd integer multiples of $\pi/2$
Range: $(-\infty, \infty)$

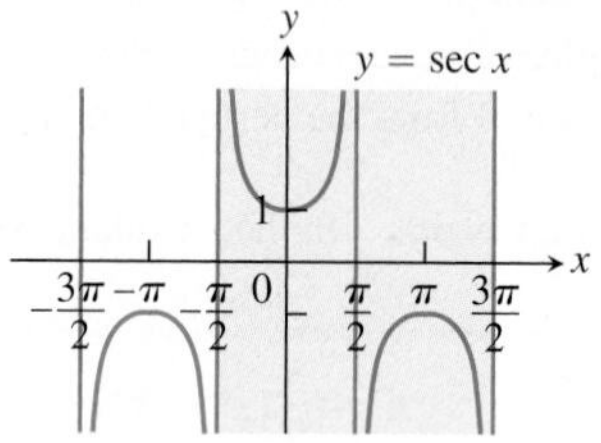

Domain: $x \neq \pm\frac{\pi}{2}, \pm\frac{3\pi}{2}, \ldots$
Range: $(-\infty, -1] \cup [1, \infty)$

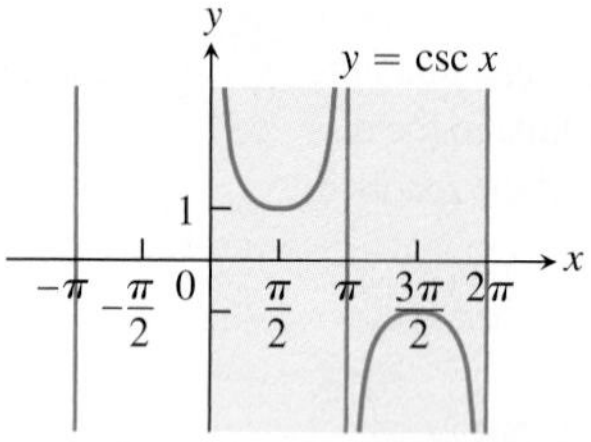

Domain: $x \neq 0, \pm\pi, \pm 2\pi, \ldots$
Range: $(-\infty, -1] \cup [1, \infty)$

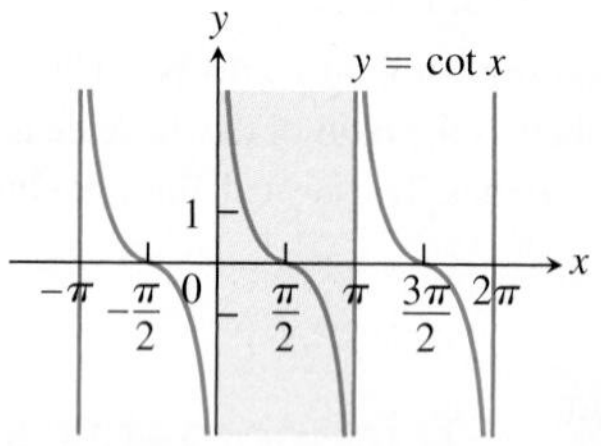

Domain: $x \neq 0, \pm\pi, \pm 2\pi, \ldots$
Range: $(-\infty, \infty)$

Trigonometry Formulas

Definitions and Fundamental Identities

Sine: $\sin\theta = \frac{y}{r} = \frac{1}{\csc\theta}$

Cosine: $\cos\theta = \frac{x}{r} = \frac{1}{\sec\theta}$

Tangent: $\tan\theta = \frac{y}{x} = \frac{1}{\cot\theta}$

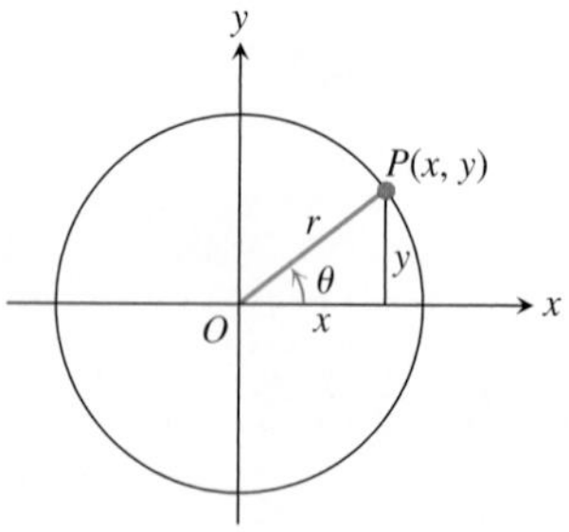

Identities

$\sin(-\theta) = -\sin\theta, \quad \cos(-\theta) = \cos\theta$

$\sin^2\theta + \cos^2\theta = 1, \quad \sec^2\theta = 1 + \tan^2\theta, \quad \csc^2\theta = 1 + \cot^2\theta$

$\sin 2\theta = 2\sin\theta\cos\theta, \quad \cos 2\theta = \cos^2\theta - \sin^2\theta$

$\cos^2\theta = \frac{1 + \cos 2\theta}{2}, \quad \sin^2\theta = \frac{1 - \cos 2\theta}{2}$

$\sin(A + B) = \sin A\cos B + \cos A\sin B$

$\sin(A - B) = \sin A\cos B - \cos A\sin B$

$$\cos(A+B) = \cos A\cos B - \sin A\sin B$$
$$\cos(A-B) = \cos A\cos B + \sin A\sin B$$
$$\tan(A+B) = \frac{\tan A + \tan B}{1 - \tan A\tan B}, \qquad \tan(A-B) = \frac{\tan A - \tan B}{1 + \tan A\tan B}$$
$$\sin\left(A - \frac{\pi}{2}\right) = -\cos A, \qquad \cos\left(A - \frac{\pi}{2}\right) = \sin A$$
$$\sin\left(A + \frac{\pi}{2}\right) = \cos A, \qquad \cos\left(A + \frac{\pi}{2}\right) = -\sin A$$
$$\sin A\sin B = \frac{1}{2}\cos(A-B) - \frac{1}{2}\cos(A+B)$$
$$\cos A\cos B = \frac{1}{2}\cos(A-B) + \frac{1}{2}\cos(A+B)$$
$$\sin A\cos B = \frac{1}{2}\sin(A-B) + \frac{1}{2}\sin(A+B)$$
$$\sin A + \sin B = 2\sin\frac{1}{2}(A+B)\cos\frac{1}{2}(A-B)$$
$$\sin A - \sin B = 2\cos\frac{1}{2}(A+B)\sin\frac{1}{2}(A-B)$$
$$\cos A + \cos B = 2\cos\frac{1}{2}(A+B)\cos\frac{1}{2}(A-B)$$
$$\cos A - \cos B = -2\sin\frac{1}{2}(A+B)\sin\frac{1}{2}(A-B)$$

A.5 Proofs of Limit Theorems

This appendix proves Theorem 1, Parts 2–5, and Theorem 4 from Section 2.2.

THEOREM 1—Limit Laws If L, M, c, and k are real numbers and

$$\lim_{x\to c} f(x) = L \quad \text{and} \quad \lim_{x\to c} g(x) = M, \quad \text{then}$$

1. *Sum Rule:* $\lim_{x\to c}\left(f(x) + g(x)\right) = L + M$
2. *Difference Rule:* $\lim_{x\to c}\left(f(x) - g(x)\right) = L - M$
3. *Product Rule:* $\lim_{x\to c}\left(f(x)\cdot g(x)\right) = L\cdot M$
4. *Constant Multiple Rule:* $\lim_{x\to c}\left(kf(x)\right) = kL$ (any number k)
5. *Quotient Rule:* $\lim_{x\to c}\frac{f(x)}{g(x)} = \frac{L}{M}$, if $M \neq 0$
6. *Power Rule:* If r and s are integers with no common factors and $s \neq 0$, then

$$\lim_{x\to c}(f(x))^{r/s} = L^{r/s}$$

provided that $L^{r/s}$ is a real number. (If s is even, we assume that $L > 0$.)

We proved the Sum Rule in Section 2.3 and the Power Rule is proved in more advanced texts. We obtain the Difference Rule by replacing $g(x)$ by $-g(x)$ and M by $-M$ in the Sum Rule. The Constant Multiple Rule is the special case $g(x) = k$ of the Product Rule. This leaves only the Product and Quotient Rules.

Proof of the Limit Product Rule We show that for any $\epsilon > 0$ there exists a $\delta > 0$ such that for all x in the intersection D of the domains of f and g,

$$0 < |x - c| < \delta \quad \Rightarrow \quad |f(x)g(x) - LM| < \epsilon.$$

Suppose then that ϵ is a positive number, and write $f(x)$ and $g(x)$ as

$$f(x) = L + (f(x) - L), \quad g(x) = M + (g(x) - M).$$

Multiply these expressions together and subtract LM:

$$\begin{aligned} f(x) \cdot g(x) - LM &= (L + (f(x) - L))(M + (g(x) - M)) - LM \\ &= LM + L(g(x) - M) + M(f(x) - L) \\ &\quad +(f(x) - L)(g(x) - M) - LM \\ &= L(g(x) - M) + M(f(x) - L) + (f(x) - L)(g(x) - M). \quad (1) \end{aligned}$$

Since f and g have limits L and M as $x \to c$, there exist positive numbers δ_1, δ_2, δ_3, and δ_4 such that for all x in D

$$\begin{aligned} 0 < |x - c| < \delta_1 \quad &\Rightarrow \quad |f(x) - L| < \sqrt{\epsilon/3} \\ 0 < |x - c| < \delta_2 \quad &\Rightarrow \quad |g(x) - M| < \sqrt{\epsilon/3} \\ 0 < |x - c| < \delta_3 \quad &\Rightarrow \quad |f(x) - L| < \epsilon/(3(1 + |M|)) \\ 0 < |x - c| < \delta_4 \quad &\Rightarrow \quad |g(x) - M| < \epsilon/(3(1 + |L|)) \end{aligned} \quad (2)$$

If we take δ to be the smallest numbers δ_1 through δ_4, the inequalities on the right-hand side of the Implications (2) will hold simultaneously for $0 < |x - c| < \delta$. Therefore, for all x in D, $0 < |x - c| < \delta$ implies

$$\begin{aligned} &|f(x) \cdot g(x) - LM| \qquad \text{Triangle inequality applied to Equation (1)} \\ &\quad \le |L||g(x) - M| + |M||f(x) - L| + |f(x) - L||g(x) - M| \\ &\quad \le (1 + |L|)|g(x) - M| + (1 + |M|)|f(x) - L| + |f(x) - L||g(x) - M| \\ &\quad < \frac{\epsilon}{3} + \frac{\epsilon}{3} + \sqrt{\frac{\epsilon}{3}}\sqrt{\frac{\epsilon}{3}} = \epsilon. \qquad \text{Values from (2)} \end{aligned}$$

This completes the proof of the Limit Product Rule. ■

Proof of the Limit Quotient Rule We show that $\lim_{x\to c}(1/g(x)) = 1/M$. We can then conclude that

$$\lim_{x\to c} \frac{f(x)}{g(x)} = \lim_{x\to c}\left(f(x) \cdot \frac{1}{g(x)}\right) = \lim_{x\to c} f(x) \cdot \lim_{x\to c} \frac{1}{g(x)} = L \cdot \frac{1}{M} = \frac{L}{M}$$

by the Limit Product Rule.

Let $\epsilon > 0$ be given. To show that $\lim_{x\to c}(1/g(x)) = 1/M$, we need to show that there exists a $\delta > 0$ such that for all x

$$0 < |x - c| < \delta \quad \Rightarrow \quad \left|\frac{1}{g(x)} - \frac{1}{M}\right| < \epsilon.$$

Since $|M| > 0$, there exists a positive number δ_1 such that for all x

$$0 < |x - c| < \delta_1 \quad \Rightarrow \quad |g(x) - M| < \frac{M}{2}. \tag{3}$$

For any numbers A and B it can be shown that $|A| - |B| \le |A - B|$ and $|B| - |A| \le |A - B|$, from which it follows that $||A| - |B|| \le |A - B|$. With $A = g(x)$ and $B = M$, this becomes

$$||g(x)| - |M|| \le |g(x) - M|,$$

which can be combined with the inequality on the right in Implication (3) to get, in turn,

$$||g(x)| - |M|| < \frac{|M|}{2}$$

$$-\frac{|M|}{2} < |g(x)| - |M| < \frac{|M|}{2}$$

$$\frac{|M|}{2} < |g(x)| < \frac{3|M|}{2}$$

$$|M| < 2|g(x)| < 3|M|$$

$$\frac{1}{|g(x)|} < \frac{2}{|M|} < \frac{3}{|g(x)|} \tag{4}$$

Therefore, $0 < |x - c| < \delta_1$ implies that

$$\left|\frac{1}{g(x)} - \frac{1}{M}\right| = \left|\frac{M - g(x)}{Mg(x)}\right| \le \frac{1}{|M|}\cdot\frac{1}{|g(x)|}\cdot|M - g(x)|$$

$$< \frac{1}{|M|}\cdot\frac{2}{|M|}\cdot|M - g(x)|. \qquad \text{Inequality (4)} \tag{5}$$

Since $(1/2)|M|^2\epsilon > 0$, there exists a number $\delta_2 > 0$ such that for all x

$$0 < |x - c| < \delta_2 \quad \Rightarrow \quad |M - g(x)| < \frac{\epsilon}{2}|M|^2. \tag{6}$$

If we take δ to be the smaller of δ_1 and δ_2, the conclusions in (5) and (6) both hold for all x such that $0 < |x - c| < \delta$. Combining these conclusions gives

$$0 < |x - c| < \delta \quad \Rightarrow \quad \left|\frac{1}{g(x)} - \frac{1}{M}\right| < \epsilon.$$

This concludes the proof of the Limit Quotient Rule. ■

> **THEOREM 4—The Sandwich Theorem** Suppose that $g(x) \le f(x) \le h(x)$ for all x in some open interval I containing c, except possibly at $x = c$ itself. Suppose also that $\lim_{x\to c} g(x) = \lim_{x\to c} h(x) = L$. Then $\lim_{x\to c} f(x) = L$.

Proof for Right-Hand Limits Suppose $\lim_{x\to c^+} g(x) = \lim_{x\to c^+} h(x) = L$. Then for any $\epsilon > 0$ there exists a $\delta > 0$ such that for all x the interval $c < x < c + \delta$ is contained in I and the inequality implies

$$L - \epsilon < g(x) < L + \epsilon \quad \text{and} \quad L - \epsilon < h(x) < L + \epsilon.$$

These inequalities combine with the inequality $g(x) \le f(x) \le h(x)$ to give

$$\begin{aligned} L - \epsilon < g(x) \le f(x) \le h(x) &< L + \epsilon, \\ L - \epsilon < f(x) &< L + \epsilon, \\ -\epsilon < f(x) - L &< \epsilon. \end{aligned}$$

Therefore, for all x, the inequality $c < x < c + \delta$ implies $|f(x) - L| < \epsilon$.

Proof for Left-Hand Limits Suppose $\lim_{x\to c^-} g(x) = \lim_{x\to c^-} h(x) = L$. Then for any $\epsilon > 0$ there exists a $\delta > 0$ such that for all x the interval $c - \delta < x < c$ is contained in I and the inequality implies

$$L - \epsilon < g(x) < L + \epsilon \quad \text{and} \quad L - \epsilon < h(x) < L + \epsilon.$$

We conclude as before that for all x, $c - \delta < x < c$ implies $|f(x) - L| < \epsilon$.

Proof for Two-Sided Limits If $\lim_{x\to c} g(x) = \lim_{x\to c} h(x) = L$, then $g(x)$ and $h(x)$ both approach L as $x \to c^+$ and as $x \to c^-$; so $\lim_{x\to c^+} f(x) = L$ and $\lim_{x\to c^-} f(x) = L$. Hence $\lim_{x\to c} f(x)$ exists and equals L. ■

EXERCISES A.5

1. Suppose that functions $f_1(x)$, $f_2(x)$, and $f_3(x)$ have limits L_1, L_2, and L_3, respectively, as $x \to c$. Show that their sum has limit $L_1 + L_2 + L_3$. Use mathematical induction (Appendix 2) to generalize this result to the sum of any finite number of functions.

2. Use mathematical induction and the Limit Product Rule in Theorem 1 to show that if functions $f_1(x), f_2(x), \dots, f_n(x)$ have limits $L_1, L_2, \dots, L_n$ as $x \to c$, then

$$\lim_{x\to c} f_1(x)f_2(x)\cdot \cdots \cdot f_n(x) = L_1 \cdot L_2 \cdot \cdots \cdot L_n.$$

3. Use the fact that $\lim_{x\to c} x = c$ and the result of Exercise 2 to show that $\lim_{x\to c} x^n = c^n$ for any integer $n > 1$.

4. **Limits of polynomials** Use the fact that $\lim_{x\to c}(k) = k$ for any number k together with the results of Exercises 1 and 3 to show that $\lim_{x\to c} f(x) = f(c)$ for any polynomial function

$$f(x) = a_n x^n + a_{n-1}x^{n-1} + \cdots + a_1 x + a_0.$$

5. **Limits of rational functions** Use Theorem 1 and the result of Exercise 4 to show that if $f(x)$ and $g(x)$ are polynomial functions and $g(c) \ne 0$, then

$$\lim_{x\to c} \frac{f(x)}{g(x)} = \frac{f(c)}{g(c)}.$$

6. **Composites of continuous functions** Figure A.21 gives the diagram for a proof that the composite of two continuous functions is continuous. Reconstruct the proof from the diagram. The statement to be proved is this: If f is continuous at $x = c$ and g is continuous at $f(c)$, then $g \circ f$ is continuous at c.

Assume that c is an interior point of the domain of f and that $f(c)$ is an interior point of the domain of g. This will make the limits involved two-sided. (The arguments for the cases that involve one-sided limits are similar.)

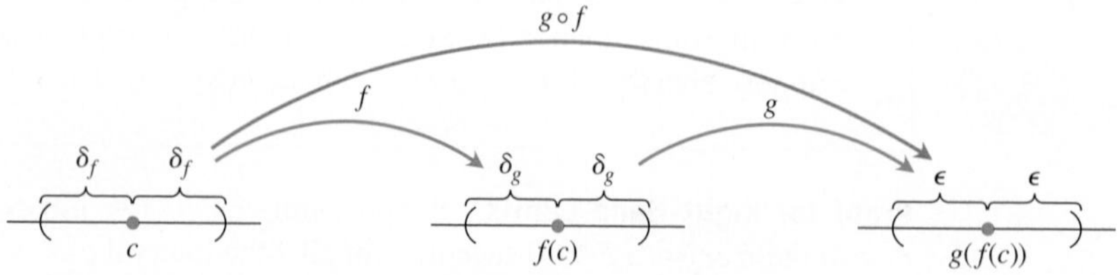

FIGURE A.21 The diagram for a proof that the composite of two continuous functions is continuous.

A.6 Commonly Occurring Limits

This appendix verifies limits (4)–(6) in Theorem 5 of Section 8.1.

Limit 4: If $|x| < 1$, $\lim_{n\to\infty} x^n = 0$ We need to show that to each $\epsilon > 0$ there corresponds an integer N so large that $|x^n| < \epsilon$ for all n greater than N. Since $\epsilon^{1/n} \to 1$, while $|x| < 1$, there exists an integer N for which $\epsilon^{1/N} > |x|$. In other words,

$$|x^N| = |x|^N < \epsilon. \tag{1}$$

This is the integer we seek because, if $|x| < 1$, then

$$|x^n| < |x^N| \quad \text{for all } n > N. \tag{2}$$

Combining (1) and (2) produces $|x^n| < \epsilon$ for all $n > N$, concluding the proof. ■

Limit 5: For any number x, $\lim_{n\to\infty}\left(1 + \frac{x}{n}\right)^n = e^x$ Let

$$a_n = \left(1 + \frac{x}{n}\right)^n.$$

Then

$$\ln a_n = \ln\left(1 + \frac{x}{n}\right)^n = n\ln\left(1 + \frac{x}{n}\right) \to x,$$

as we can see by the following application of l'Hôpital's Rule, in which we differentiate with respect to n:

$$\begin{aligned}\lim_{n\to\infty} n\ln\left(1 + \frac{x}{n}\right) &= \lim_{n\to\infty}\frac{\ln(1 + x/n)}{1/n}\\ &= \lim_{n\to\infty}\frac{\left(\dfrac{1}{1 + x/n}\right)\cdot\left(-\dfrac{x}{n^2}\right)}{-1/n^2} = \lim_{n\to\infty}\frac{x}{1 + x/n} = x.\end{aligned}$$

Apply Theorem 3, Section 8.1, with $f(x) = e^x$ to conclude that

$$\left(1 + \frac{x}{n}\right)^n = a_n = e^{\ln a_n} \to e^x.$$ ■

Limit 6: For any number x, $\lim_{n\to\infty}\frac{x^n}{n!} = 0$ Since

$$-\frac{|x|^n}{n!} \le \frac{x^n}{n!} \le \frac{|x|^n}{n!},$$

all we need to show is that $|x|^n/n! \to 0$. We can then apply the Sandwich Theorem for Sequences (Section 8.1, Theorem 2) to conclude that $x^n/n! \to 0$.

The first step in showing that $|x|^n/n! \to 0$ is to choose an integer $M > |x|$, so that $(|x|/M) < 1$. By Limit 4, just proved, we then have $(|x|/M)^n \to 0$. We then restrict our attention to values of $n > M$. For these values of n, we can write

$$\frac{|x|^n}{n!} = \frac{|x|^n}{1 \cdot 2 \cdot \cdots \cdot M \cdot \underbrace{(M+1)(M+2) \cdot \cdots \cdot n}_{(n-M) \text{ factors}}}$$

$$\leq \frac{|x|^n}{M!M^{n-M}} = \frac{|x|^n M^M}{M!M^n} = \frac{M^M}{M!}\left(\frac{|x|}{M}\right)^n.$$

Thus,

$$0 \leq \frac{|x|^n}{n!} \leq \frac{M^M}{M!}\left(\frac{|x|}{M}\right)^n.$$

Now, the constant $M^M/M!$ does not change as n increases. Thus the Sandwich Theorem tells us that $|x|^n/n! \to 0$ because $(|x|/M)^n \to 0$. ■

A.7 Theory of the Real Numbers

A rigorous development of calculus is based on properties of the real numbers. Many results about functions, derivatives, and integrals would be false if stated for functions defined only on the rational numbers. In this appendix we briefly examine some basic concepts of the theory of the reals that hint at what might be learned in a deeper, more theoretical study of calculus.

Three types of properties make the real numbers what they are. These are the **algebraic**, **order**, and **completeness** properties. The algebraic properties involve addition and multiplication, subtraction and division. They apply to rational or complex numbers as well as to the reals.

The structure of numbers is built around a set with addition and multiplication operations. The following properties are required of addition and multiplication.

A1 $a + (b + c) = (a + b) + c$ for all a, b, c.

A2 $a + b = b + a$ for all a, b, c.

A3 There is a number called "0" such that $a + 0 = a$ for all a.

A4 For each number a, there is a b such that $a + b = 0$.

M1 $a(bc) = (ab)c$ for all a, b, c.

M2 $ab = ba$ for all a, b.

M3 There is a number called "1" such that $a \cdot 1 = a$ for all a.

M4 For each nonzero a, there is a b such that $ab = 1$.

D $a(b + c) = ab + bc$ for all a, b, c.

A1 and M1 are *associative laws*, A2 and M2 are *commutativity laws*, A3 and M3 are *identity laws*, and D is the *distributive law*. Sets that have these algebraic properties are examples of **fields**, and are studied in depth in the area of theoretical mathematics called abstract algebra.

The **order** properties allow us to compare the size of any two numbers. The order properties are

O1 For any a and b, either $a \leq b$ or $b \leq a$ or both.

O2 If $a \leq b$ and $b \leq a$ then $a = b$.

O3 If $a \leq b$ and $b \leq c$ then $a \leq c$.

O4 If $a \leq b$ then $a + c \leq b + c$.

O5 If $a \leq b$ and $0 \leq c$ then $ac \leq bc$.

O3 is the *transitivity law*, and O4 and O5 relate ordering to addition and multiplication.

We can order the reals, the integers, and the rational numbers, but we cannot order the complex numbers. There is no reasonable way to decide whether a number like $i = \sqrt{-1}$ is bigger or smaller than zero. A field in which the size of any two elements can be compared as above is called an **ordered field**. Both the rational numbers and the real numbers are ordered fields, and there are many others.

We can think of real numbers geometrically, lining them up as points on a line. The **completeness property** says that the real numbers correspond to all points on the line, with no “holes” or “gaps.” The rationals, in contrast, omit points such as $\sqrt{2}$ and π, and the integers even leave out fractions like $1/2$. The reals, having the completeness property, omit no points.

What exactly do we mean by this vague idea of missing holes? To answer this we must give a more precise description of completeness. A number M is an **upper bound** for a set of numbers if all numbers in the set are smaller than or equal to M. M is a **least upper bound** if it is the smallest upper bound. For example, $M = 2$ is an upper bound for the negative numbers. So is $M = 1$, showing that 2 is not a least upper bound. The least upper bound for the set of negative numbers is $M = 0$. We define a **complete** ordered field to be one in which every nonempty set bounded above has a least upper bound.

If we work with just the rational numbers, the set of numbers less than $\sqrt{2}$ is bounded, but it does not have a rational least upper bound, since any rational upper bound M can be replaced by a slightly smaller rational number that is still larger than $\sqrt{2}$. So the rationals are not complete. In the real numbers, a set that is bounded above always has a least upper bound. The reals are a complete ordered field.

The completeness property is at the heart of many results in calculus. One example occurs when searching for a maximum value for a function on a closed interval $[a, b]$, as in Section 4.1. The function $y = x - x^3$ has a maximum value on $[0, 1]$ at the point x satisfying $1 - 3x^2 = 0$, or $x = \sqrt{1/3}$. If we limited our consideration to functions defined only on rational numbers, we would have to conclude that the function has no maximum, since $\sqrt{1/3}$ is irrational (Figure A.22). The Extreme Value Theorem (Section 4.1), which implies that continuous functions on closed intervals $[a, b]$ have a maximum value, is not true for functions defined only on the rationals.

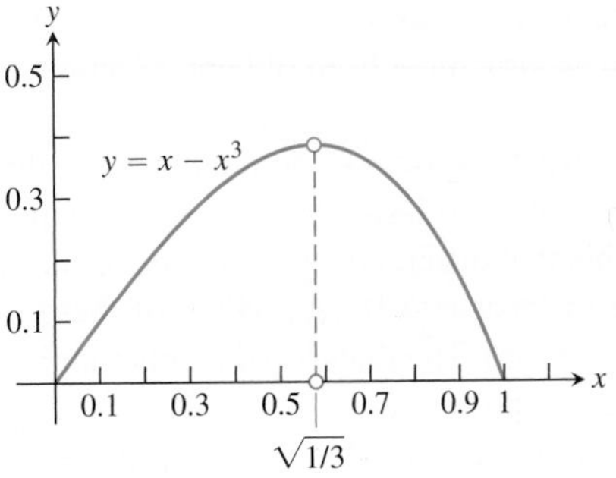

FIGURE A.22 The maximum value of $y = x - x^3$ on $[0, 1]$ occurs at the irrational number $x = \sqrt{1/3}$.

The Intermediate Value Theorem implies that a continuous function f on an interval $[a, b]$ with $f(a) < 0$ and $f(b) > 0$ must be zero somewhere in $[a, b]$. The function values cannot jump from negative to positive without there being some point x in $[a, b]$ where $f(x) = 0$. The Intermediate Value Theorem also relies on the completeness of the real numbers and is false for continuous functions defined only on the rationals. The function $f(x) = 3x^2 - 1$ has $f(0) = -1$ and $f(1) = 2$, but if we consider f only on the rational numbers, it never equals zero. The only value of x for which $f(x) = 0$ is $x = \sqrt{1/3}$, an irrational number.

We have captured the desired properties of the reals by saying that the real numbers are a complete ordered field. But we're not quite finished. Greek mathematicians in the school of Pythagoras tried to impose another property on the numbers of the real line, the condition that all numbers are ratios of integers. They learned that their effort was doomed when they discovered irrational numbers such as $\sqrt{2}$. How do we know that our efforts to specify the real numbers are not also flawed, for some unseen reason? The artist Escher drew optical illusions of spiral staircases that went up and up until they rejoined themselves at the bottom. An engineer trying to build such a staircase would find that no structure realized the plans the architect had drawn. Could it be that our design for the reals contains some subtle contradiction, and that no construction of such a number system can be made?

We resolve this issue by giving a specific description of the real numbers and verifying that the algebraic, order, and completeness properties are satisfied in this model. This is called a **construction** of the reals, and just as stairs can be built with wood, stone, or steel, there are several approaches to constructing the reals. One construction treats the reals as all the infinite decimals,

$$a.d_1d_2d_3d_4\ldots$$

In this approach a real number is an integer a followed by a sequence of decimal digits $d_1, d_2, d_3, \ldots$, each between 0 and 9. This sequence may stop, or repeat in a periodic pattern, or keep going forever with no pattern. In this form, 2.00, 0.3333333 . . . and 3.1415926535898 . . . represent three familiar real numbers. The real meaning of the dots ". . ." following these digits requires development of the theory of sequences and series, as in Chapter 8. Each real number is constructed as the limit of a sequence of rational numbers given by its finite decimal approximations. An infinite decimal is then the same as a series

$$a + \frac{d_1}{10} + \frac{d_2}{100} + \cdots.$$

This decimal construction of the real numbers is not entirely straightforward. It's easy enough to check that it gives numbers that satisfy the completeness and order properties, but verifying the algebraic properties is rather involved. Even adding or multiplying two numbers requires an infinite number of operations. Making sense of division requires a careful argument involving limits of rational approximations to infinite decimals.

A different approach was taken by Richard Dedekind (1831–1916), a German mathematician, who gave the first rigorous construction of the real numbers in 1872. Given any real number x, we can divide the rational numbers into two sets: those less than or equal to x and those greater. Dedekind cleverly reversed this reasoning and defined a real number to be a division of the rational numbers into two such sets. This seems like a strange approach, but such indirect methods of constructing new structures from old are common in theoretical mathematics.

These and other approaches can be used to construct a system of numbers having the desired algebraic, order, and completeness properties. A final issue that arises is whether all the constructions give the same thing. Is it possible that different constructions result in different number systems satisfying all the required properties? If yes, which of these is the real numbers? Fortunately, the answer turns out to be no. The reals are the only number system satisfying the algebraic, order, and completeness properties.

Confusion about the nature of the numbers and about limits caused considerable controversy in the early development of calculus. Calculus pioneers such as Newton, Leibniz, and their successors, when looking at what happens to the difference quotient

$$\frac{\Delta y}{\Delta x} = \frac{f(x + \Delta x) - f(x)}{\Delta x}$$

as each of Δy and Δx approach zero, talked about the resulting derivative being a quotient of two infinitely small quantities. These "infinitesimals," written dx and dy, were thought to be some new kind of number, smaller than any fixed number but not zero. Similarly, a definite integral was thought of as a sum of an infinite number of infinitesimals

$$f(x) \cdot dx$$

as x varied over a closed interval. While the approximating difference quotients $\Delta y/\Delta x$ were understood much as today, it was the quotient of infinitesimal quantities, rather than a limit, that was thought to encapsulate the meaning of the derivative. This way of thinking led to logical difficulties, as attempted definitions and manipulations of infinitesimals ran into contradictions and inconsistencies. The more concrete and computable difference quotients did not cause such trouble, but they were thought of merely as useful calculation tools. Difference quotients were used to work out the numerical value of the derivative and to derive general formulas for calculation, but were not considered to be at the heart of the question of what the derivative actually was. Today we realize that the logical problems associated with infinitesimals can be avoided by *defining* the derivative to be the limit of its approximating difference quotients. The ambiguities of the old approach are no longer present, and in the standard theory of calculus, infinitesimals are neither needed nor used.

A.8 The Distributive Law for Vector Cross Products

In this appendix, we prove the Distributive Law

$$\mathbf{u} \times (\mathbf{v} + \mathbf{w}) = \mathbf{u} \times \mathbf{v} + \mathbf{u} \times \mathbf{w}$$

which is Property 2 in Section 10.4.

Proof To derive the Distributive Law, we construct $\mathbf{u} \times \mathbf{v}$ a new way. We draw $\mathbf{u}$ and $\mathbf{v}$ from the common point O and construct a plane M perpendicular to $\mathbf{u}$ at O (Figure A.23). We then project $\mathbf{v}$ orthogonally onto M, yielding a vector $\mathbf{v}'$ with length $|\mathbf{v}|\sin\theta$. We rotate $\mathbf{v}'$ 90° about $\mathbf{u}$ in the positive sense to produce a vector $\mathbf{v}''$. Finally, we multiply $\mathbf{v}''$ by the length of $\mathbf{u}$. The resulting vector $|\mathbf{u}|\mathbf{v}''$ is equal to $\mathbf{u} \times \mathbf{v}$ since $\mathbf{v}''$ has the same direction as $\mathbf{u} \times \mathbf{v}$ by its construction (Figure A.23) and

$$|\mathbf{u}||\mathbf{v}''| = |\mathbf{u}||\mathbf{v}'| = |\mathbf{u}||\mathbf{v}|\sin\theta = |\mathbf{u} \times \mathbf{v}|.$$

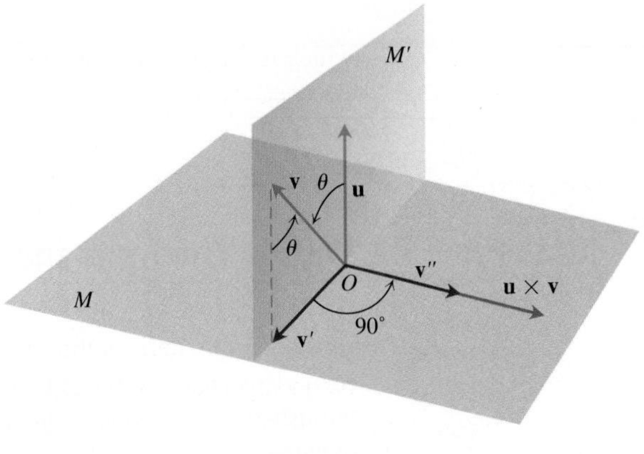

FIGURE A.23 As explained in the text, $\mathbf{u} \times \mathbf{v} = |\mathbf{u}|\mathbf{v}''$.

Now each of these three operations, namely,

1. projection onto M
2. rotation about $\mathbf{u}$ through 90°
3. multiplication by the scalar $|\mathbf{u}|$

when applied to a triangle whose plane is not parallel to $\mathbf{u}$, will produce another triangle. If we start with the triangle whose sides are $\mathbf{v}$, $\mathbf{w}$, and $\mathbf{v} + \mathbf{w}$ (Figure A.24) and apply these three steps, we successively obtain the following:

1. A triangle whose sides are $\mathbf{v}'$, $\mathbf{w}'$, and $(\mathbf{v} + \mathbf{w})'$ satisfying the vector equation

$$\mathbf{v}' + \mathbf{w}' = (\mathbf{v} + \mathbf{w})'$$

2. A triangle whose sides are $\mathbf{v}''$, $\mathbf{w}''$, and $(\mathbf{v} + \mathbf{w})''$ satisfying the vector equation

$$\mathbf{v}'' + \mathbf{w}'' = (\mathbf{v} + \mathbf{w})''$$

(the double prime on each vector has the same meaning as in Figure A.23)

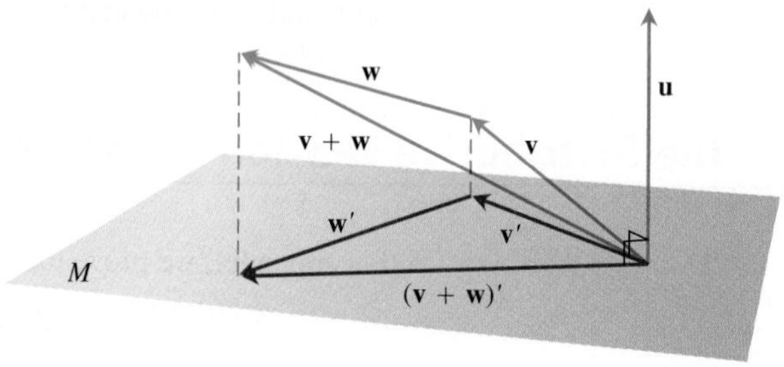

FIGURE A.24 The vectors, $\mathbf{v}$, $\mathbf{w}$, $\mathbf{v} + \mathbf{w}$, and their projections onto a plane perpendicular to $\mathbf{u}$.

3. A triangle whose sides are $|\mathbf{u}|\mathbf{v}''$, $|\mathbf{u}|\mathbf{w}''$, and $|\mathbf{u}|(\mathbf{v} + \mathbf{w})''$ satisfying the vector equation

$$|\mathbf{u}|\mathbf{v}'' + |\mathbf{u}|\mathbf{w}'' = |\mathbf{u}|(\mathbf{v} + \mathbf{w})''.$$

Substituting $|\mathbf{u}|\mathbf{v}'' = \mathbf{u} \times \mathbf{v}$, $|\mathbf{u}|\mathbf{w}'' = \mathbf{u} \times \mathbf{w}$, and $|\mathbf{u}|(\mathbf{v} + \mathbf{w})'' = \mathbf{u} \times (\mathbf{v} + \mathbf{w})$ from our discussion above into this last equation gives

$$\mathbf{u} \times \mathbf{v} + \mathbf{u} \times \mathbf{w} = \mathbf{u} \times (\mathbf{v} + \mathbf{w}),$$

which is the law we wanted to establish. ■

A.9 The Mixed Derivative Theorem and the Increment Theorem

This appendix derives the Mixed Derivative Theorem (Theorem 2, Section 12.3) and the Increment Theorem for Functions of Two Variables (Theorem 3, Section 12.3). Euler first published the Mixed Derivative Theorem in 1734, in a series of papers he wrote on hydrodynamics.

THEOREM 2—The Mixed Derivative Theorem If $f(x, y)$ and its partial derivatives f_x, f_y, f_{xy}, and f_{yx} are defined throughout an open region containing a point (a, b) and are all continuous at (a, b), then $f_{xy}(a, b) = f_{yx}(a, b)$.

Proof The equality of $f_{xy}(a, b)$ and $f_{yx}(a, b)$ can be established by four applications of the Mean Value Theorem (Theorem 4, Section 4.2). By hypothesis, the point (a, b) lies in the interior of a rectangle R in the xy-plane on which f, f_x, f_y, f_{xy}, and f_{yx} are all defined. We let h and k be the numbers such that the point $(a + h, b + k)$ also lies in R, and we consider the difference

$$\Delta = F(a + h) - F(a), \tag{1}$$

where

$$F(x) = f(x, b + k) - f(x, b). \tag{2}$$

We apply the Mean Value Theorem to F, which is continuous because it is differentiable. Then Equation (1) becomes

$$\Delta = hF'(c_1), \tag{3}$$

where c_1 lies between a and $a + h$. From Equation (2).

$$F'(x) = f_x(x, b + k) - f_x(x, b),$$

so Equation (3) becomes

$$\Delta = h[f_x(c_1, b + k) - f_x(c_1, b)]. \tag{4}$$

Now we apply the Mean Value Theorem to the function $g(y) = f_x(c_1, y)$ and have

$$g(b + k) - g(b) = kg'(d_1),$$

or

$$f_x(c_1, b + k) - f_x(c_1, b) = kf_{xy}(c_1, d_1)$$

for some d_1 between b and $b + k$. By substituting this into Equation (4), we get

$$\Delta = hkf_{xy}(c_1, d_1) \tag{5}$$

for some point (c_1, d_1) in the rectangle R' whose vertices are the four points (a, b), $(a + h, b)$, $(a + h, b + k)$, and $(a, b + k)$. (See Figure A.25.)

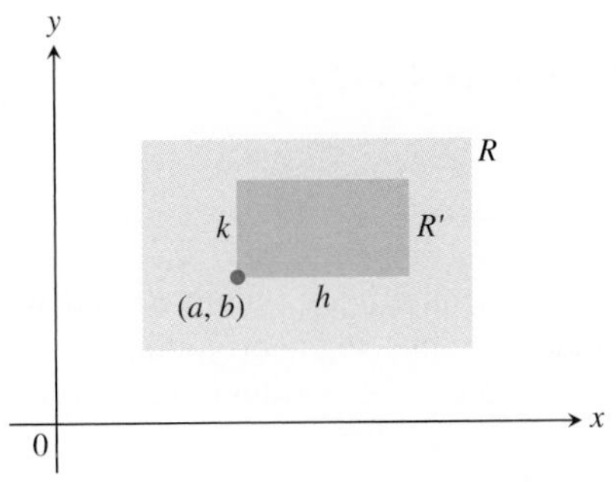

FIGURE A.25 The key to proving $f_{xy}(a, b) = f_{yx}(a, b)$ is that no matter how small R' is, f_{xy} and f_{yx} take on equal values somewhere inside R' (although not necessarily at the same point).

By substituting from Equation (2) into Equation (1), we may also write

$$\begin{aligned} \Delta &= f(a + h, b + k) - f(a + h, b) - f(a, b + k) + f(a, b) \\ &= [f(a + h, b + k) - f(a, b + k)] - [f(a + h, b) - f(a, b)] \\ &= \phi(b + k) - \phi(b), \end{aligned} \tag{6}$$

where

$$\phi(y) = f(a + h, y) - f(a, y). \tag{7}$$

The Mean Value Theorem applied to Equation (6) now gives

$$\Delta = k\phi'(d_2) \tag{8}$$

for some d_2 between b and $b + k$. By Equation (7),

$$\phi'(y) = f_y(a + h, y) - f_y(a, y). \tag{9}$$

Substituting from Equation (9) into Equation (8) gives

$$\Delta = k[f_y(a + h, d_2) - f_y(a, d_2)].$$

Finally, we apply the Mean Value Theorem to the expression in brackets and get

$$\Delta = khf_{yx}(c_2, d_2) \tag{10}$$

for some c_2 between a and $a + h$.

Together, Equations (5) and (10) show that

$$f_{xy}(c_1, d_1) = f_{yx}(c_2, d_2), \tag{11}$$

where (c_1, d_1) and (c_2, d_2) both lie in the rectangle R' (Figure A.25). Equation (11) is not quite the result we want, since it says only that f_{xy} has the same value at (c_1, d_1) that f_{yx} has at (c_2, d_2). The numbers h and k in our discussion, however, may be made as small as we wish. The hypothesis that f_{xy} and f_{yx} are both continuous at (a, b) means that $f_{xy}(c_1, d_1) = f_{xy}(a, b) + \epsilon_1$ and $f_{yx}(c_2, d_2) = f_{yx}(a, b) + \epsilon_2$, where each of $\epsilon_1, \epsilon_2 \to 0$ as both $h, k \to 0$. Hence, if we let h and $k \to 0$, we have $f_{xy}(a, b) = f_{yx}(a, b)$. ■

The equality of $f_{xy}(a, b)$ and $f_{yx}(a, b)$ can be proved with hypotheses weaker than the ones we assumed. For example, it is enough for f, f_x, and f_y to exist in R and for f_{xy} to be continuous at (a, b). Then f_{yx} will exist at (a, b) and equal f_{xy} at that point.

THEOREM 3—The Increment Theorem for Functions of Two Variables

Suppose that the first partial derivatives of $z = f(x, y)$ are defined throughout an open region R containing the point (x_0, y_0) and that f_x and f_y are continuous at (x_0, y_0). Then the change $\Delta z = f(x_0 + \Delta x, y_0 + \Delta y) - f(x_0, y_0)$ in the value of f that results from moving from (x_0, y_0) to another point $(x_0 + \Delta x, y_0 + \Delta y)$ in R satisfies an equation of the form

$$\Delta z = f_x(x_0, y_0)\Delta x + f_y(x_0, y_0)\Delta y + \epsilon_1 \Delta x + \epsilon_2 \Delta y,$$

in which each of $\epsilon_1, \epsilon_2 \to 0$ as both $\Delta x, \Delta y \to 0$.

Proof We work within a rectangle T centered at $A(x_0, y_0)$ and lying within R, and we assume that Δx and Δy are already so small that the line segment joining A to $B(x_0 + \Delta x, y_0)$ and the line segment joining B to $C(x_0 + \Delta x, y_0 + \Delta y)$ lie in the interior of T (Figure A.26).

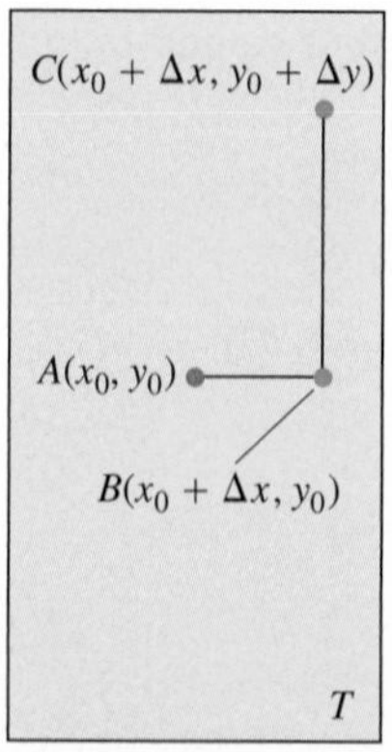

FIGURE A.26 The rectangular region T in the proof of the Increment Theorem. The figure is drawn for Δx and Δy positive, but either increment might be zero or negative.

We may think of Δz as the sum $\Delta z = \Delta z_1 + \Delta z_2$ of two increments, where

$$\Delta z_1 = f(x_0 + \Delta x, y_0) - f(x_0, y_0)$$

is the change in the value of f from A to B and

$$\Delta z_2 = f(x_0 + \Delta x, y_0 + \Delta y) - f(x_0 + \Delta x, y_0)$$

is the change in the value of f from B to C (Figure A.27).

On the closed interval of x-values joining x_0 to $x_0 + \Delta x$, the function $F(x) = f(x, y_0)$ is a differentiable (and hence continuous) function of x, with derivative

$$F'(x) = f_x(x, y_0).$$

By the Mean Value Theorem (Theorem 4, Section 4.2), there is an x-value c between x_0 and $x_0 + \Delta x$ at which

$$F(x_0 + \Delta x) - F(x_0) = F'(c)\,\Delta x$$

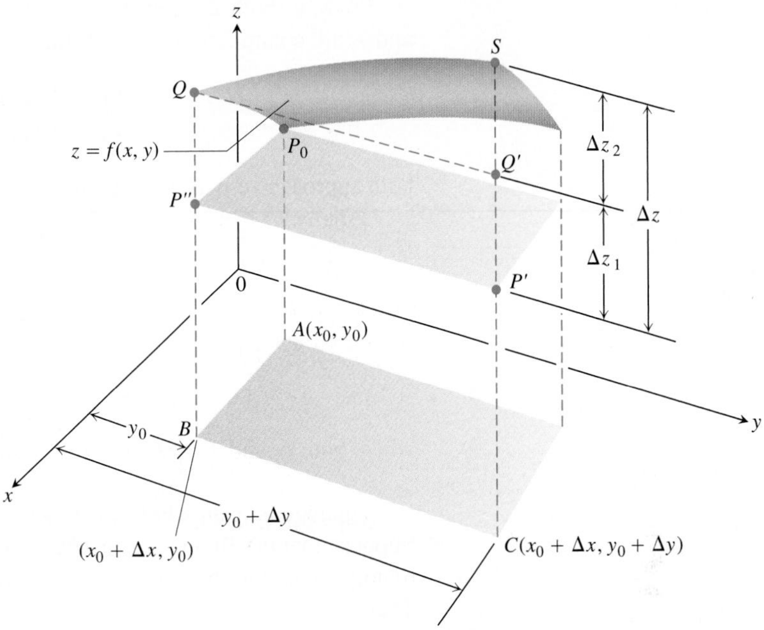

FIGURE A.27 Part of the surface $z = f(x, y)$ near $P_0(x_0, y_0, f(x_0, y_0))$. The points P_0, P', and P'' have the same height $z_0 = f(x_0, y_0)$ above the xy-plane. The change in z is $\Delta z = P'S$. The change

$$\Delta z_1 = f(x_0 + \Delta x, y_0) - f(x_0, y_0),$$

shown as $P''Q = P'Q'$, is caused by changing x from x_0 to $x_0 + \Delta x$ while holding y equal to y_0. Then, with x held equal to $x_0 + \Delta x$,

$$\Delta z_2 = f(x_0 + \Delta x, y_0 + \Delta y) - f(x_0 + \Delta x, y_0)$$

is the change in z caused by changing y_0 from $y_0 + \Delta y$, which is represented by $Q'S$? The total change in z is the sum of Δz_1 and Δz_2.

or

$$f(x_0 + \Delta x, y_0) - f(x_0, y_0) = f_x(c, y_0)\,\Delta x$$

or

$$\Delta z_1 = f_x(c, y_0)\,\Delta x. \tag{12}$$

Similarly, $G(y) = f(x_0 + \Delta x, y)$ is a differentiable (and hence continuous) function of y on the closed y-interval joining y_0 and $y_0 + \Delta y$, with derivative

$$G'(y) = f_y(x_0 + \Delta x, y).$$

Hence, there is a y-value d between y_0 and $y_0 + \Delta y$ at which

$$G(y_0 + \Delta y) - G(y_0) = G'(d)\,\Delta y$$

or

$$f(x_0 + \Delta x, y_0 + \Delta y) - f(x_0 + \Delta x, y) = f_y(x_0 + \Delta x, d)\,\Delta y$$

or

$$\Delta z_2 = f_y(x_0 + \Delta x, d)\,\Delta y. \tag{13}$$

Now, as both Δx and $\Delta y \to 0$, we know that $c \to x_0$ and $d \to y_0$. Therefore, since f_x and f_y are continuous at (x_0, y_0), the quantities

$$\begin{aligned} \epsilon_1 &= f_x(c, y_0) - f_x(x_0, y_0), \\ \epsilon_2 &= f_y(x_0 + \Delta x, d) - f_y(x_0, y_0) \end{aligned} \tag{14}$$

both approach zero as both Δx and $\Delta y \to 0$.

Finally,

$$\begin{aligned} \Delta z &= \Delta z_1 + \Delta z_2 \\ &= f_x(c, y_0)\Delta x + f_y(x_0 + \Delta x, d)\Delta y && \text{From Equations (12) and (13)} \\ &= [f_x(x_0, y_0) + \epsilon_1]\Delta x + [f_y(x_0, y_0) + \epsilon_2]\Delta y && \text{From Equation (14)} \\ &= f_x(x_0, y_0)\Delta x + f_y(x_0, y_0)\Delta y + \epsilon_1 \Delta x + \epsilon_2 \Delta y, \end{aligned}$$

where both ϵ_1 and $\epsilon_2 \to 0$ as both Δx and $\Delta y \to 0$, which is what we set out to prove. ■

Analogous results hold for functions of any finite number of independent variables. Suppose that the first partial derivatives of $w = f(x, y, z)$ are defined throughout an open region containing the point (x_0, y_0, z_0) and that f_x, f_y, and f_z are continuous at (x_0, y_0, z_0). Then

$$\begin{aligned} \Delta w &= f(x_0 + \Delta x, y_0 + \Delta y, z_0 + \Delta z) - f(x_0, y_0, z_0) \\ &= f_x \Delta x + f_y \Delta y + f_z \Delta z + \epsilon_1 \Delta x + \epsilon_2 \Delta y + \epsilon_3 \Delta z, \end{aligned} \tag{15}$$

where $\epsilon_1, \epsilon_2, \epsilon_3 \to 0$ as Δx, Δy, and $\Delta z \to 0$.

The partial derivatives f_x, f_y, f_z in Equation (15) are to be evaluated at the point (x_0, y_0, z_0).

Equation (15) can be proved by treating Δw as the sum of three increments,

$$\Delta w_1 = f(x_0 + \Delta x, y_0, z_0) - f(x_0, y_0, z_0) \tag{16}$$

$$\Delta w_2 = f(x_0 + \Delta x, y_0 + \Delta y, z_0) - f(x_0 + \Delta x, y_0, z_0) \tag{17}$$

$$\Delta w_3 = f(x_0 + \Delta x, y_0 + \Delta y, z_0 + \Delta z) - f(x_0 + \Delta x, y_0 + \Delta y, z_0), \tag{18}$$

and applying the Mean Value Theorem to each of these separately. Two coordinates remain constant and only one varies in each of these partial increments $\Delta w_1, \Delta w_2, \Delta w_3$. In Equation (17), for example, only y varies, since x is held equal to $x_0 + \Delta x$ and z is held equal to z_0. Since $f(x_0 + \Delta x, y, z_0)$ is a continuous function of y with a derivative f_y, it is subject to the Mean Value Theorem, and we have

$$\Delta w_2 = f_y(x_0 + \Delta x, y_1, z_0)\,\Delta y$$

for some y_1 between y_0 and $y_0 + \Delta y$.

ANSWERS

CHAPTER 1

Section 1.1, pp. 11–13

1. $D: (-\infty, \infty)$, $R: [1, \infty)$ **3.** $D: (0, \infty)$, $R: (0, \infty)$

5. (a) Not a function of x because some values of x have two values of y

(b) A function of x because for every x there is only one possible y

7. $A = \dfrac{\sqrt{3}}{4}x^2$, $p = 3x$ **9.** $x = \dfrac{d}{\sqrt{3}}$, $A = 2d^2$, $V = \dfrac{d^3}{3\sqrt{3}}$

11. $(-\infty, \infty)$

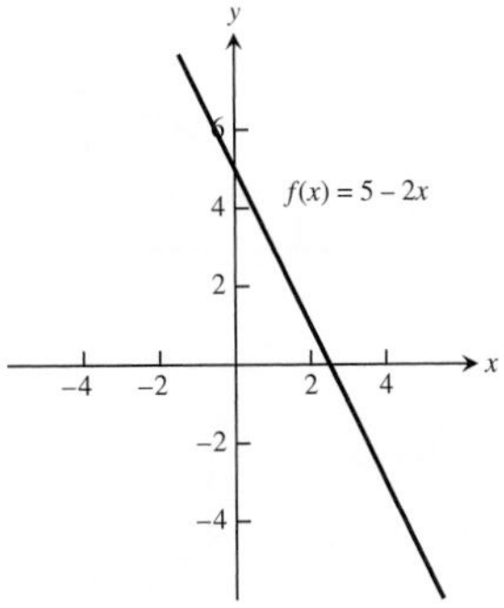

13. $(-\infty, \infty)$

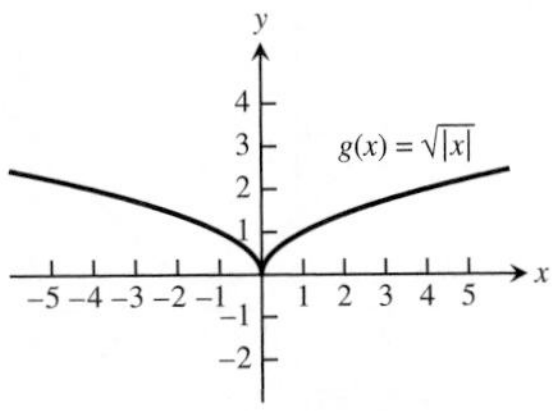

15. $(-\infty, 0) \cup (0, \infty)$

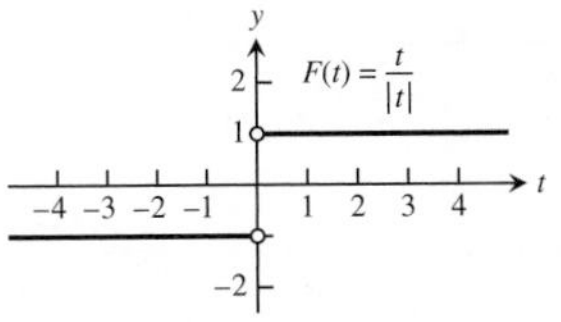

17. (a) For each positive value of x, there are two values of y.

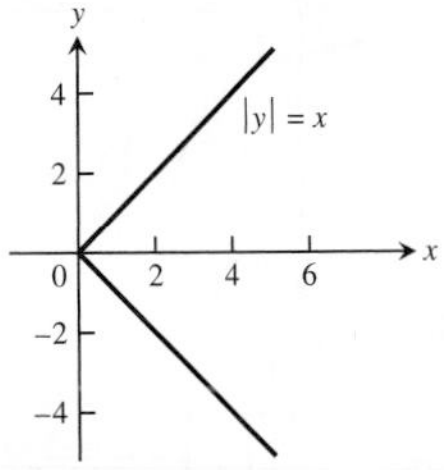

(b) For each value of $x \neq 0$, there are two values of y.

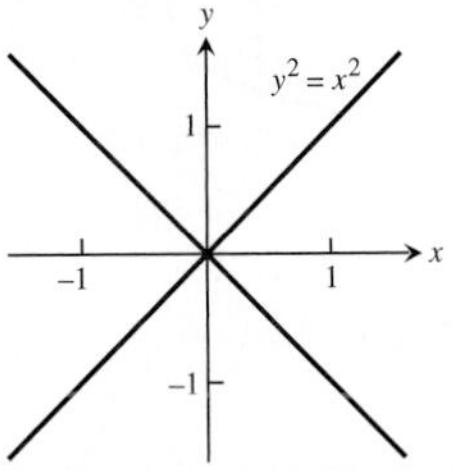

19.

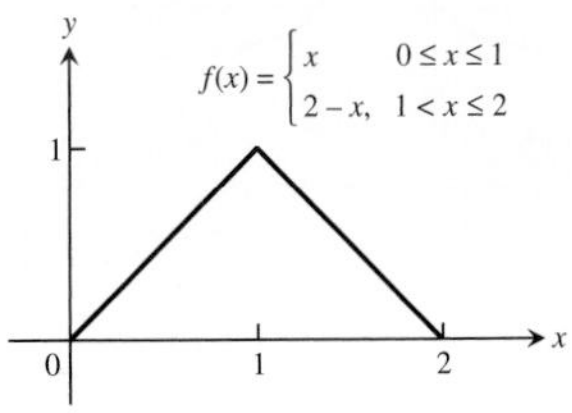

21.

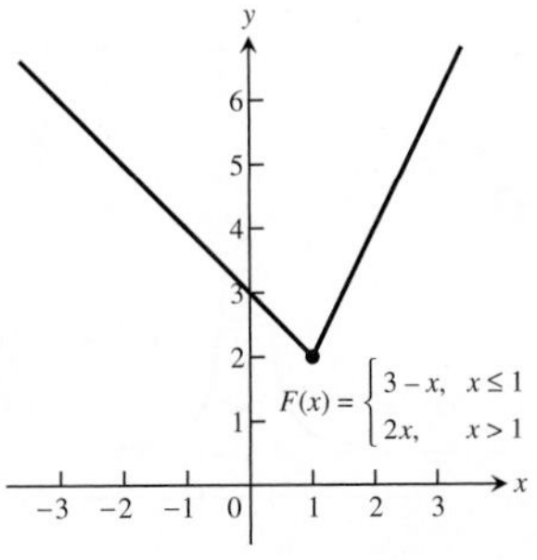

23. (a) $f(x) = \begin{cases} x, & 0 \le x \le 1 \\ -x + 2, & 1 < x \le 2 \end{cases}$

(b) $f(x) = \begin{cases} 2, & 0 \le x < 1 \\ 0, & 1 \le x < 2 \\ 2, & 2 \le x < 3 \\ 0, & 3 \le x \le 4 \end{cases}$

25. (a) $f(x) = \begin{cases} -x, & -1 \le x < 0 \\ 1, & 0 < x \le 1 \\ -\frac{1}{2}x + \frac{3}{2}, & 1 < x < 3 \end{cases}$

(b) $f(x) = \begin{cases} \frac{1}{2}x, & -2 \le x \le 0 \\ -2x + 2, & 0 < x \le 1 \\ -1, & 1 < x \le 3 \end{cases}$

27. (a) $0 \le x < 1$ **(b)** $-1 < x \le 0$ **29.** Yes

31. Symmetric about the origin

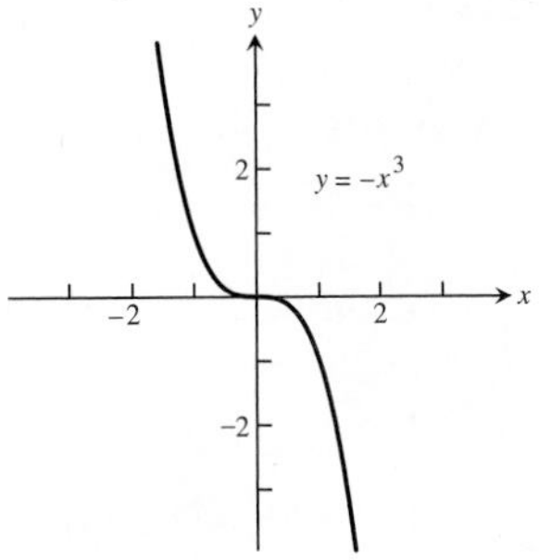

Dec. $-\infty < x < \infty$

33. Symmetric about the origin

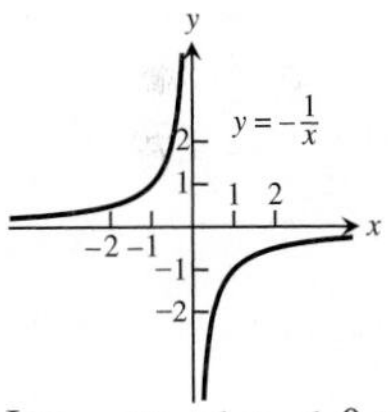

Inc. $-\infty < x < 0$ and $0 < x < \infty$

35. Symmetric about the y-axis

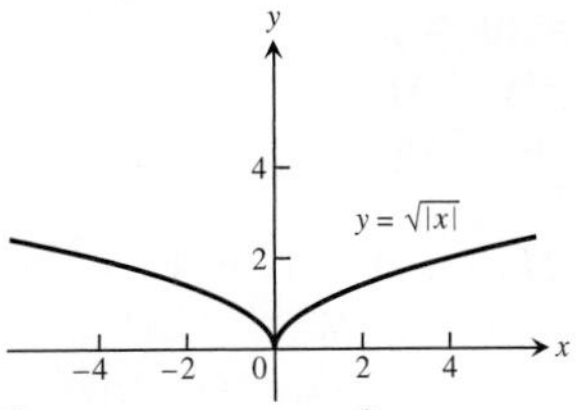

Dec. $-\infty < x \le 0$; inc. $0 \le x < \infty$

37. Symmetric about the origin

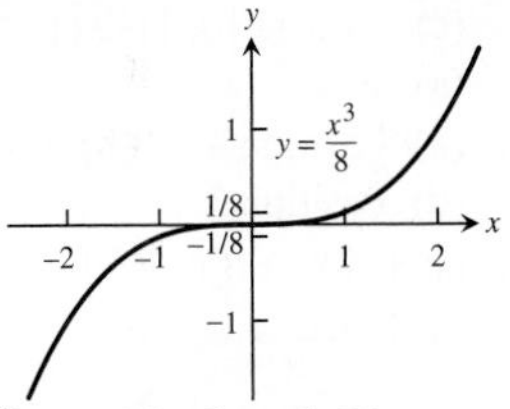

Inc. $-\infty < x < \infty$

39. No symmetry

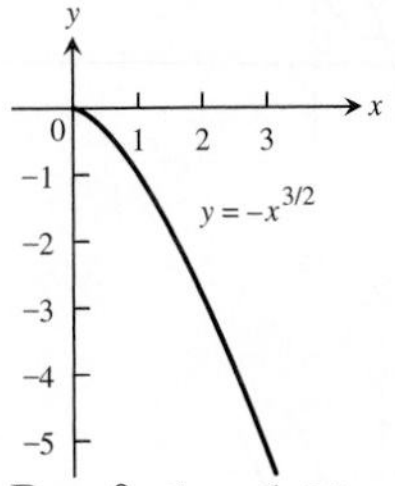

Dec. $0 \le x < \infty$

41. Symmetric about the y-axis

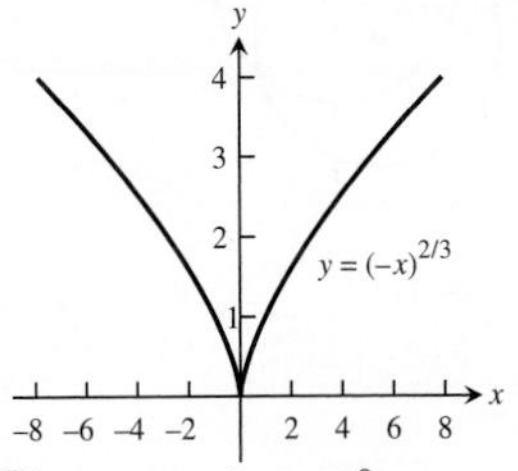

Dec. $-\infty < x \le 0$; inc. $0 \le x < \infty$

43. Even **45.** Even **47.** Odd **49.** Even **51.** Neither

53. Neither **55.** $V = x(14 - 2x)(22 - 2x)$

57. (a) h **(b)** f **(c)** g **59. (a)** $(-2, 0) \cup (4, \infty)$

Section 1.2, pp. 19–22

1. $D_f: -\infty < x < \infty,\quad D_g: x \ge 1,\quad R_f: -\infty < y < \infty,$ $R_g: y \ge 0,\quad D_{f+g} = D_{f\cdot g} = D_g,\quad R_{f+g}: y \ge 1,\quad R_{f\cdot g}: y \ge 0$

3. $D_f: -\infty < x < \infty,\quad D_g: -\infty < x < \infty,\quad R_f: y = 2,$ $R_g: y \ge 1,\quad D_{f/g}: -\infty < x < \infty,\quad R_{f/g}: 0 < y \le 2,$ $D_{g/f}: -\infty < x < \infty,\quad R_{g/f}: y \ge 1/2$

5. **(a)** 2 **(b)** 22 **(c)** $x^2 + 2$ **(d)** $x^2 + 10x + 22$ **(e)** 5 **(f)** -2 **(g)** $x + 10$ **(h)** $x^4 - 6x^2 + 6$

7. **(a)** $\dfrac{4}{x^2} - 5$ **(b)** $\dfrac{4}{x^2} - 5$ **(c)** $\left(\dfrac{4}{x} - 5\right)^2$ **(d)** $\left(\dfrac{1}{4x - 5}\right)^2$ **(e)** $\dfrac{1}{4x^2 - 5}$ **(f)** $\dfrac{1}{(4x - 5)^2}$

9. **(a)** $f(g(x))$ **(b)** $j(g(x))$ **(c)** $g(g(x))$ **(d)** $j(j(x))$ **(e)** $g(h(f(x)))$ **(f)** $h(j(f(x)))$

11.

	$g(x)$	$f(x)$	$(f \circ g)(x)$
(a)	$x - 7$	$\sqrt{x}$	$\sqrt{x - 7}$
(b)	$x + 2$	$3x$	$3x + 6$
(c)	x^2	$\sqrt{x - 5}$	$\sqrt{x^2 - 5}$
(d)	$\dfrac{x}{x - 1}$	$\dfrac{x}{x - 1}$	x
(e)	$\dfrac{1}{x - 1}$	$1 + \dfrac{1}{x}$	x
(f)	$\dfrac{1}{x}$	$\dfrac{1}{x}$	x

13. **(a)** $f(g(x)) = \sqrt{\dfrac{1}{x} + 1},\ g(f(x)) = \dfrac{1}{\sqrt{x + 1}}$

(b) $D_{f\circ g} = (-\infty, -1] \cup (0, \infty),\ D_{g\circ f} = (-1, \infty)$

(c) $R_{f\circ g} = [0, 1) \cup (1, \infty),\ R_{g\circ f} = (0, \infty)$

15. **(a)** $y = -(x + 7)^2$ **(b)** $y = -(x - 4)^2$

17. **(a)** Position 4 **(b)** Position 1 **(c)** Position 2 **(d)** Position 3

19. $(x + 2)^2 + (y + 3)^2 = 49$

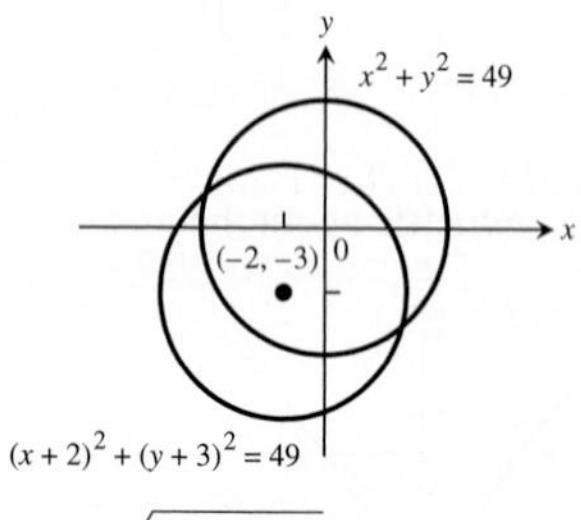

21. $y + 1 = (x + 1)^3$

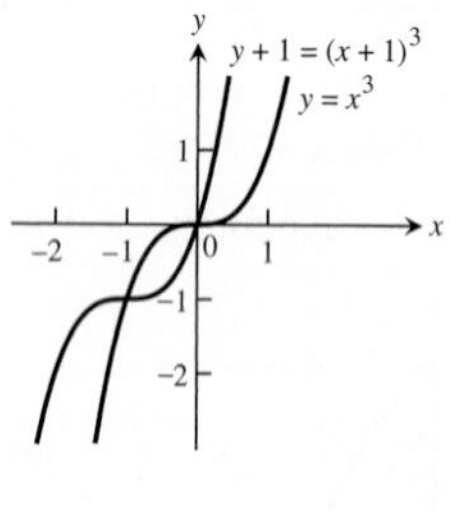

23. $y = \sqrt{x + 0.81}$

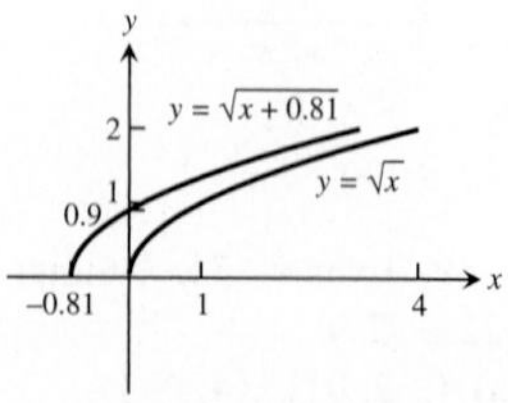

25. $y = 2x$

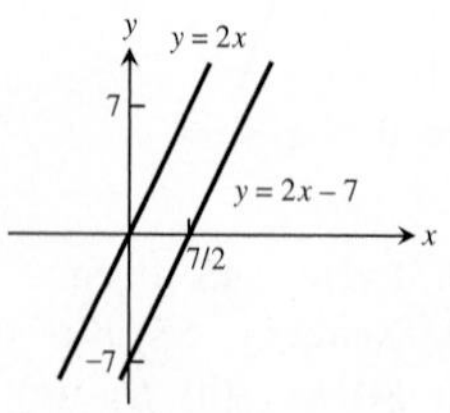

27. $y - 1 = \dfrac{1}{x - 1}$

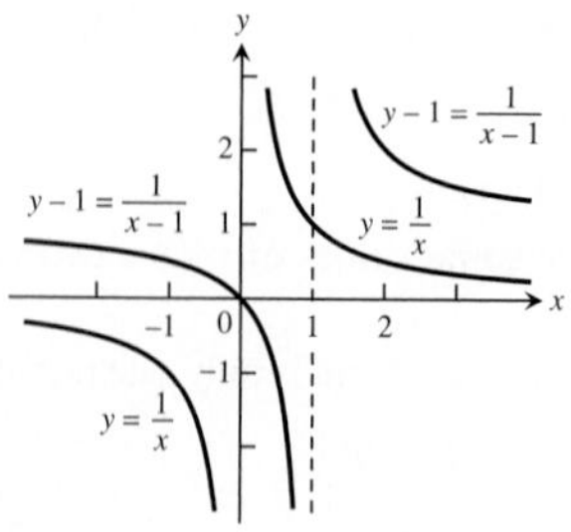

29.

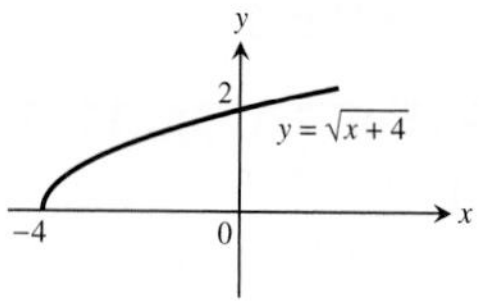

31.

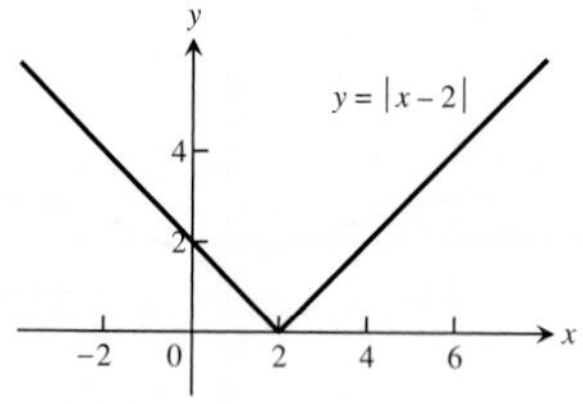

33.

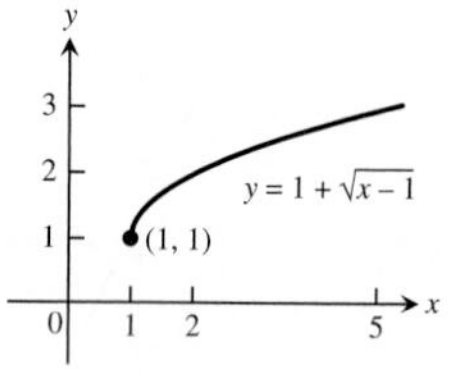

35.

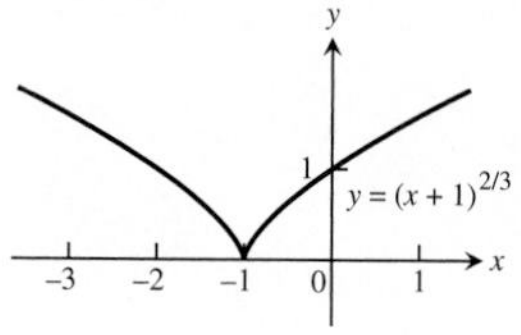

37.

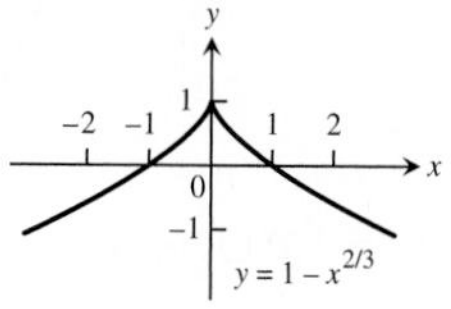

39.

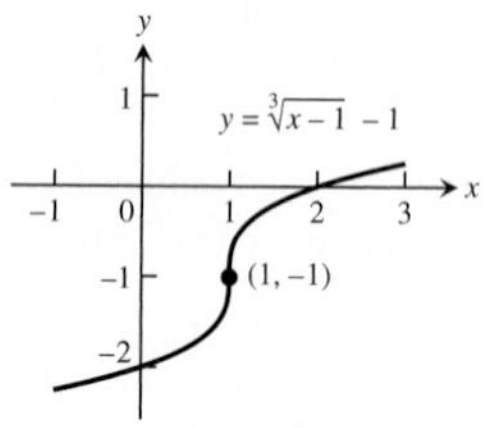

41.

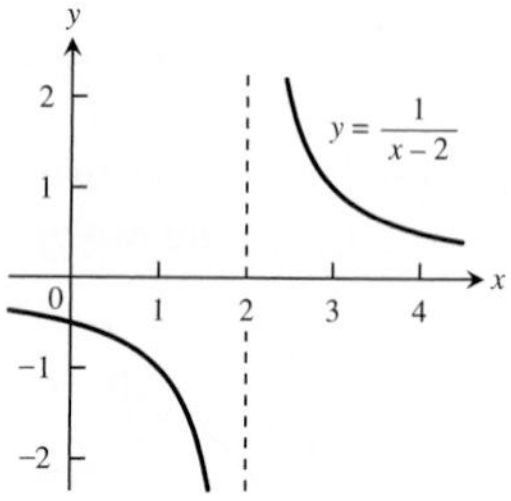

43.

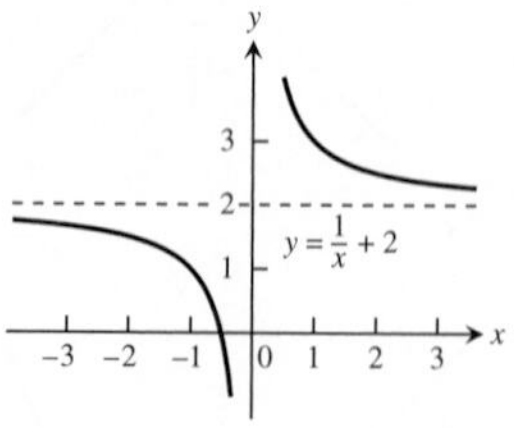

45.

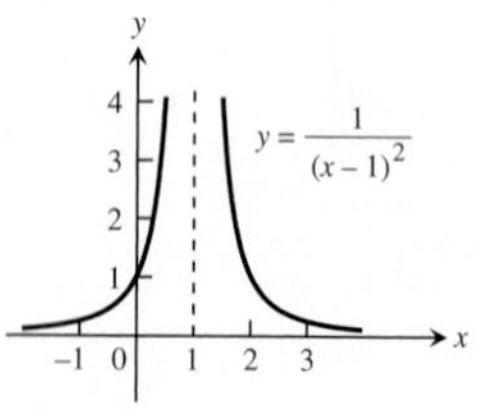

47.

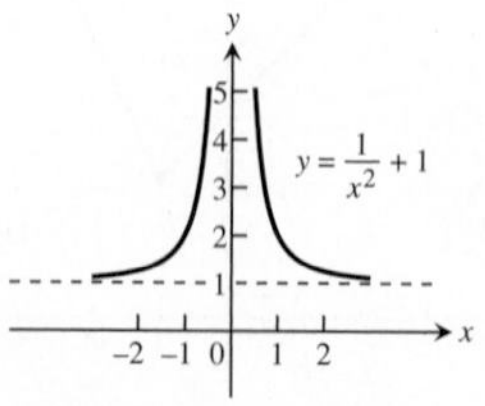

49. **(a)** $D: [0, 2], \quad R: [2, 3]$

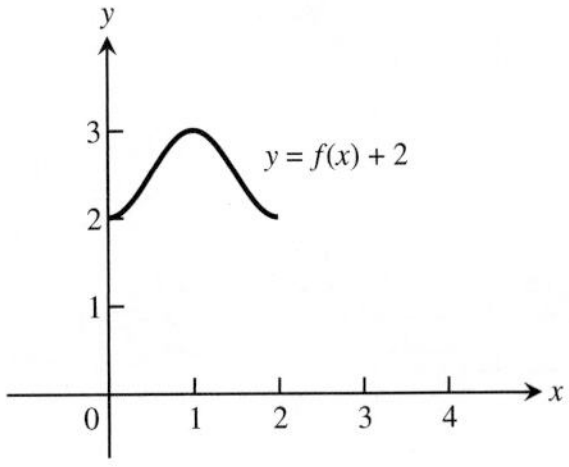

(b) $D: [0, 2], \quad R: [-1, 0]$

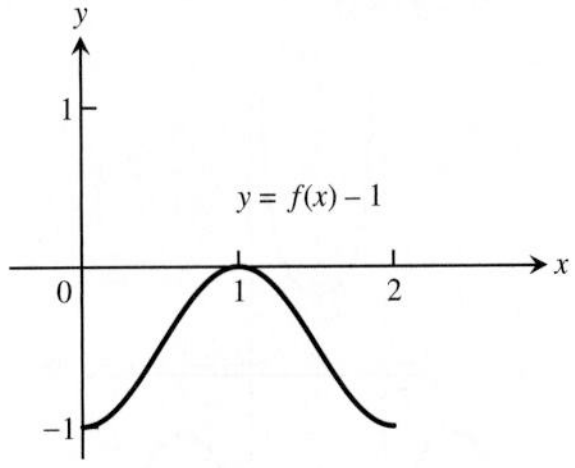

(c) $D: [0, 2], \quad R: [0, 2]$

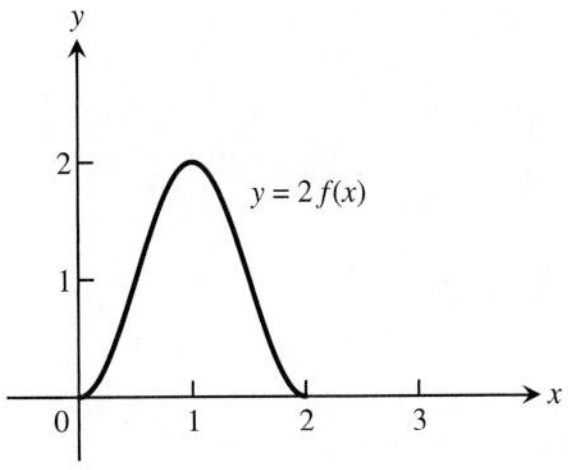

(d) $D: [0, 2], \quad R: [-1, 0]$

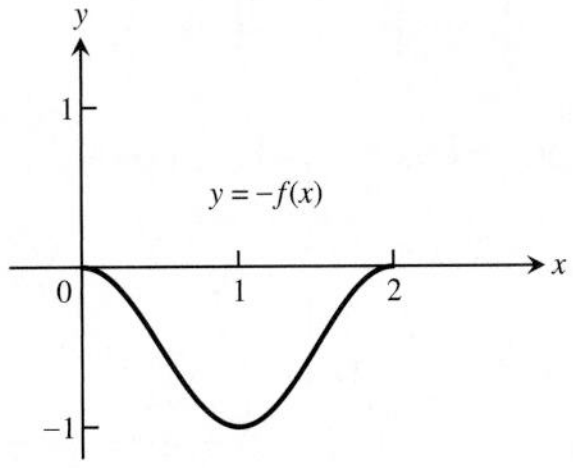

(e) $D: [-2, 0], \quad R: [0, 1]$

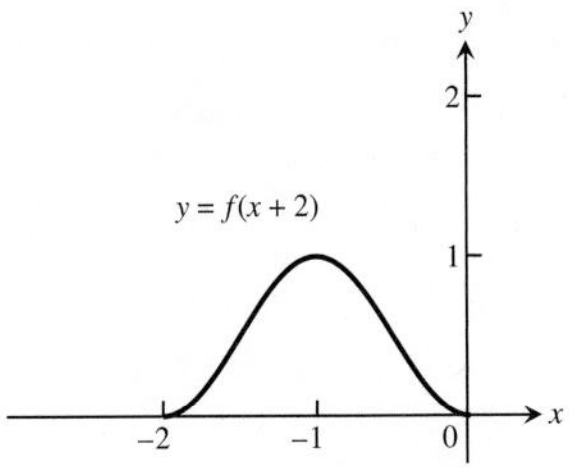

(f) $D: [1, 3], \quad R: [0, 1]$

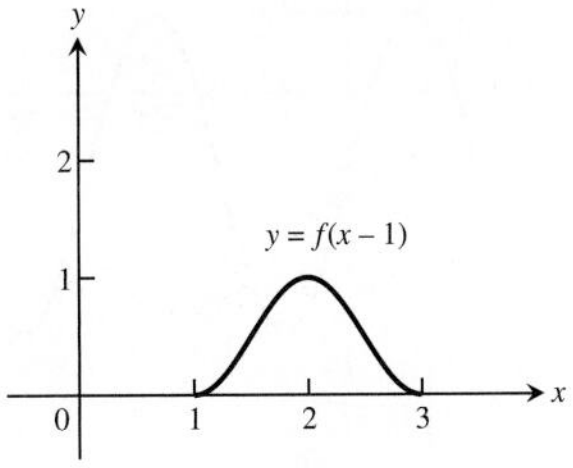

(g) $D: [-2, 0], \quad R: [0, 1]$

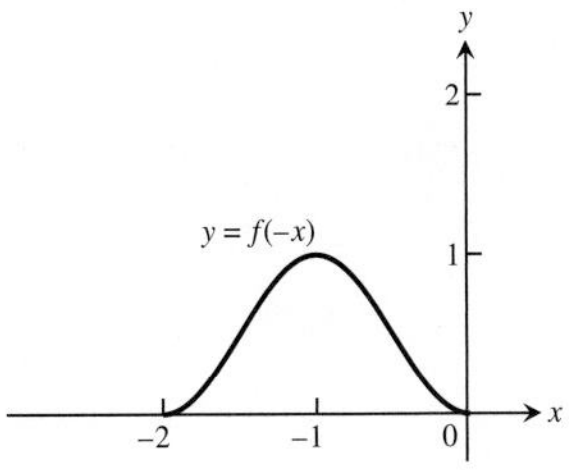

(h) $D: [-1, 1], \quad R: [0, 1]$

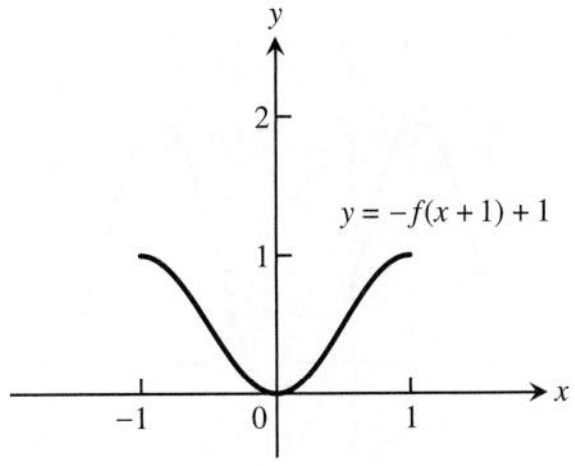

51. $y = 3x^2 - 3$ **53.** $y = \dfrac{1}{2} + \dfrac{1}{2x^2}$ **55.** $y = \sqrt{4x + 1}$

57. $y = \sqrt{4 - \dfrac{x^2}{4}}$ **59.** $y = 1 - 27x^3$

61.

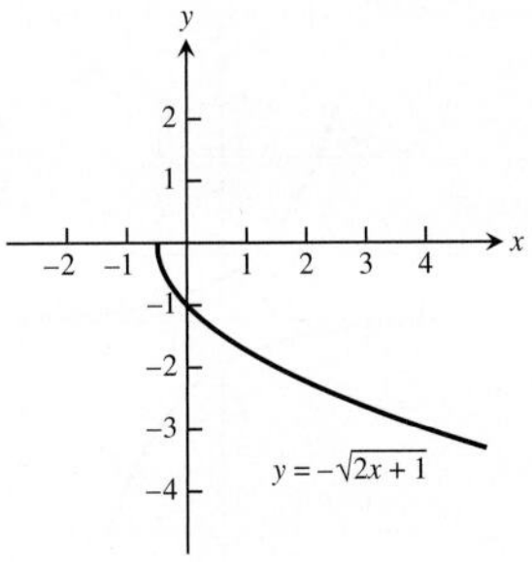

63.

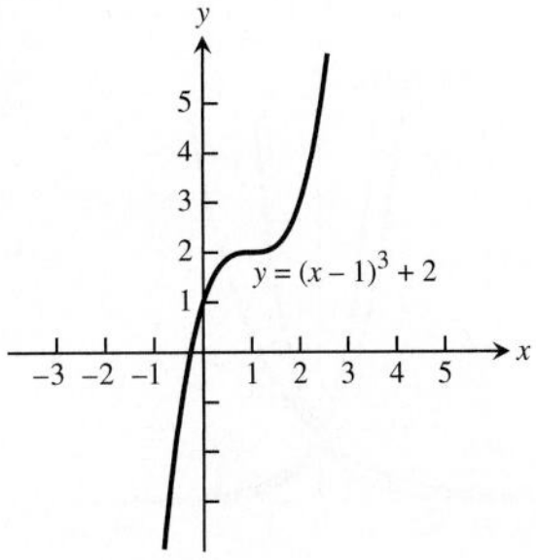

65.

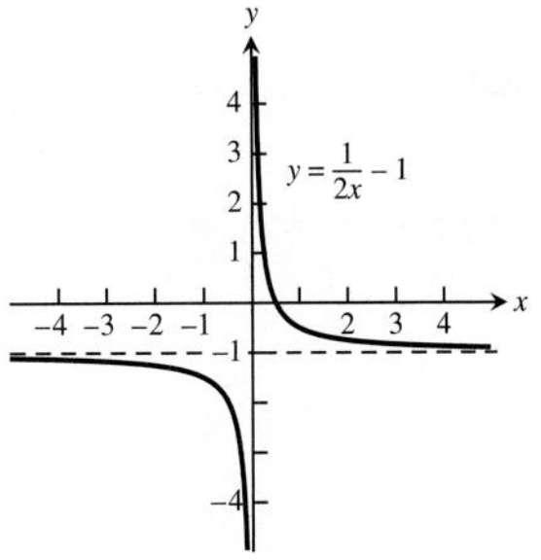

67.

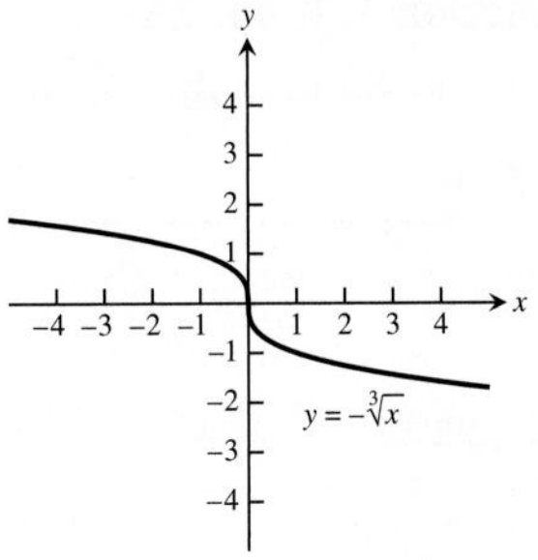

69.

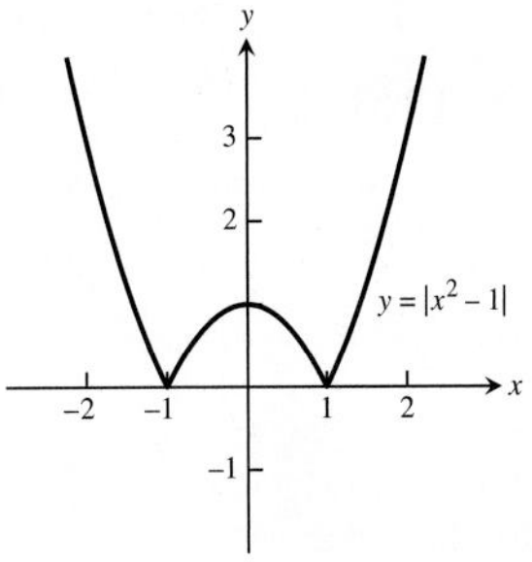

71.

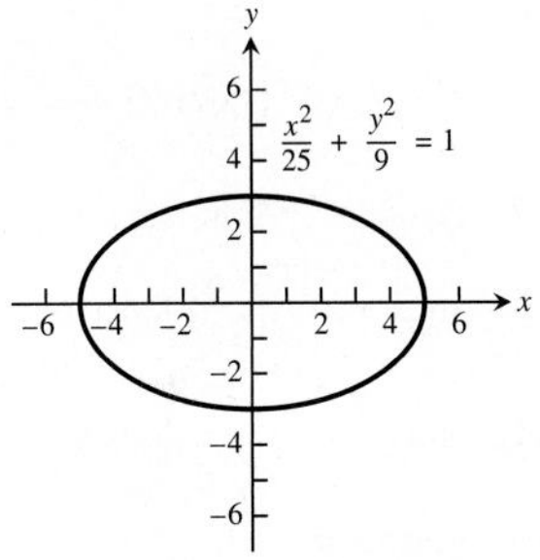

73.

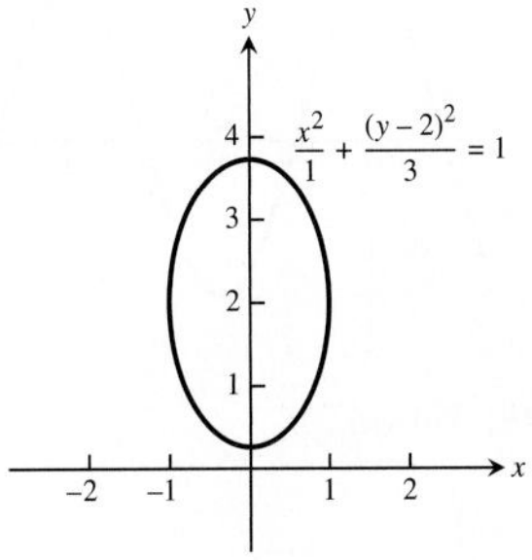

75.

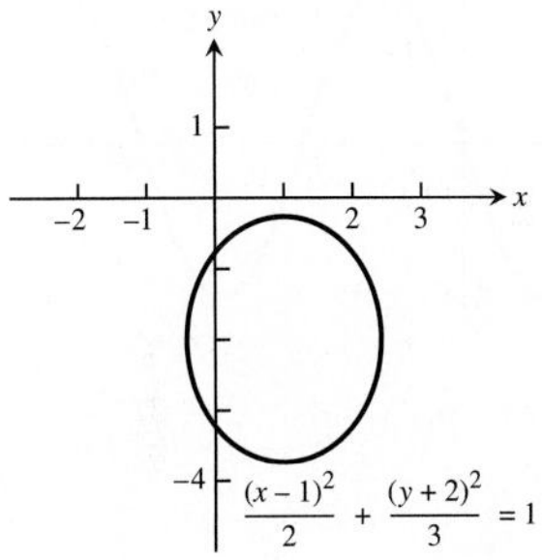

77. $\dfrac{(x + 4)^2}{16} + \dfrac{(y - 3)^2}{9} = 1$ Center: $(-4, 3)$

The major axis is the line segment between $(-8, 3)$ and $(0, 3)$.

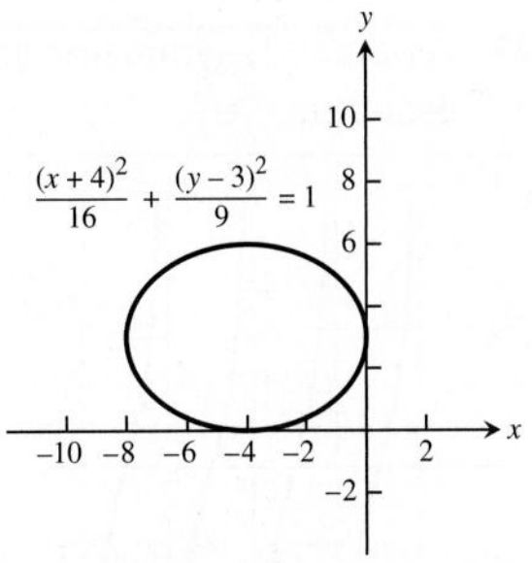

79. **(a)** Odd **(b)** Odd **(c)** Odd **(d)** Even **(e)** Even
(f) Even **(g)** Even **(h)** Even **(i)** Odd

Section 1.3, pp. 28–30

1. **(a)** 8π m **(b)** $\frac{55\pi}{9}$ m **3.** 8.4 in.

5.

θ	$-\pi$	$-2\pi/3$	0	$\pi/2$	$3\pi/4$
$\sin\theta$	0	$-\frac{\sqrt{3}}{2}$	0	1	$\frac{1}{\sqrt{2}}$
$\cos\theta$	-1	$-\frac{1}{2}$	1	0	$-\frac{1}{\sqrt{2}}$
$\tan\theta$	0	$\sqrt{3}$	0	UND	-1
$\cot\theta$	UND	$\frac{1}{\sqrt{3}}$	UND	0	-1
$\sec\theta$	-1	-2	1	UND	$-\sqrt{2}$
$\csc\theta$	UND	$-\frac{2}{\sqrt{3}}$	UND	1	$\sqrt{2}$

7. $\cos x = -4/5$, $\tan x = -3/4$

9. $\sin x = -\frac{\sqrt{8}}{3}$, $\tan x = -\sqrt{8}$

11. $\sin x = -\frac{1}{\sqrt{5}}$, $\cos x = -\frac{2}{\sqrt{5}}$

13. Period π

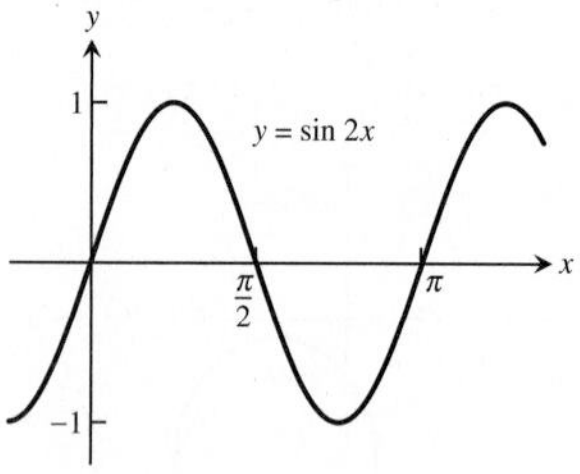

15. Period 2

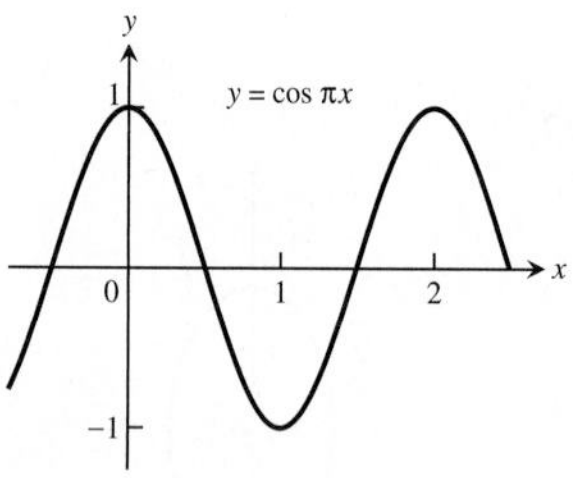

17. Period 6

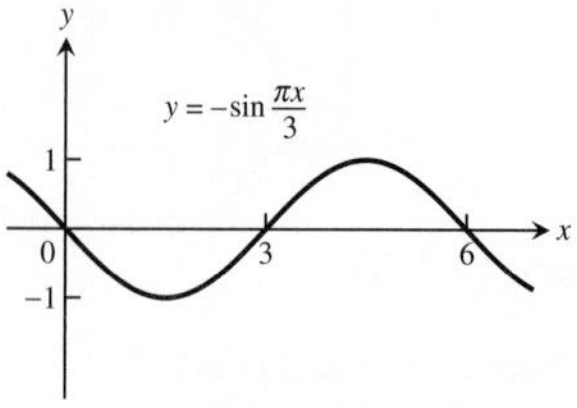

19. Period 2π

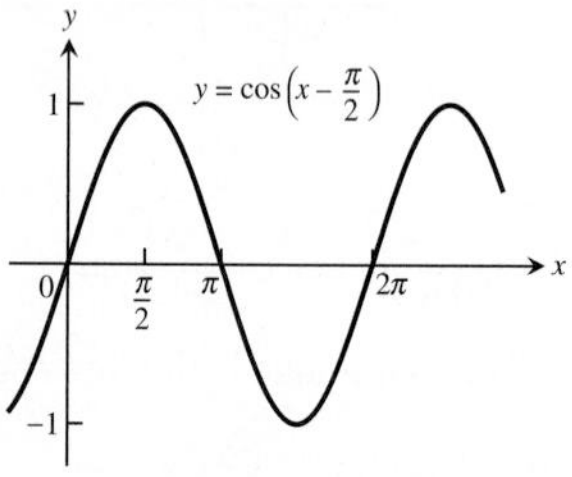

21. Period 2π

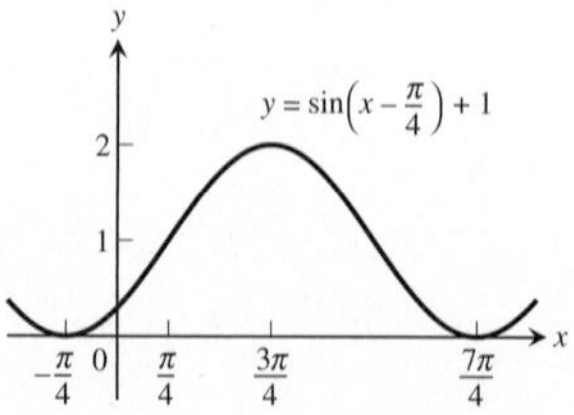

23. Period $\pi/2$, symmetric about the origin

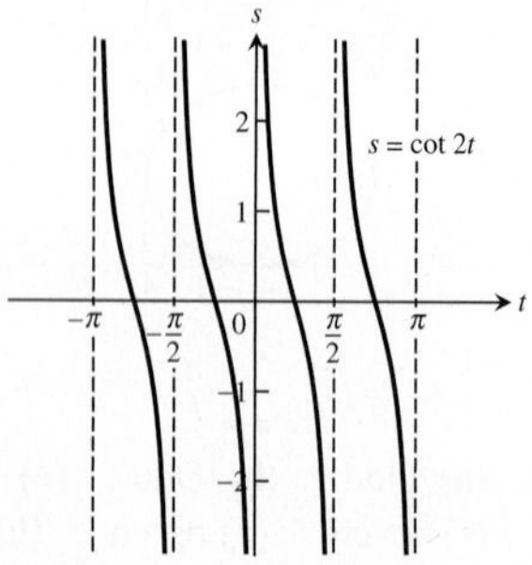

25. Period 4, symmetric about the y-axis

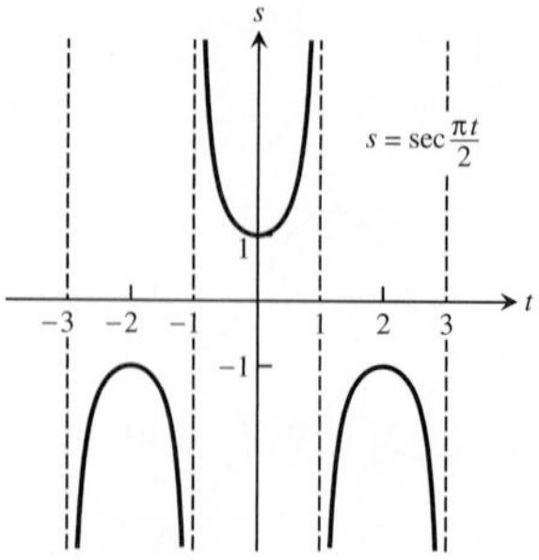

29. $D: (-\infty, \infty)$, $R: y = -1, 0, 1$

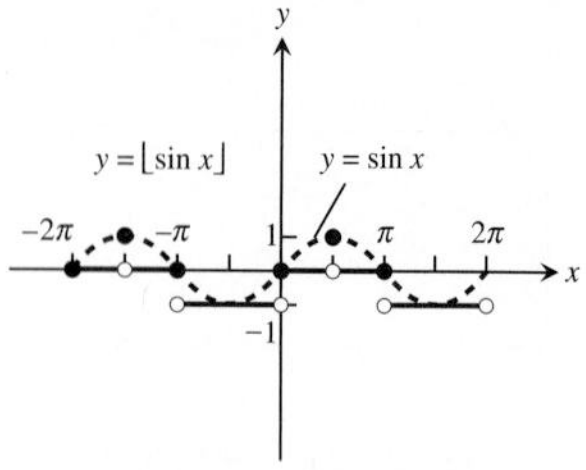

39. $-\cos x$ **41.** $-\cos x$ **43.** $\frac{\sqrt{6} + \sqrt{2}}{4}$ **45.** $\frac{\sqrt{2} + \sqrt{6}}{4}$

47. $\frac{2 + \sqrt{2}}{4}$ **49.** $\frac{2 - \sqrt{3}}{4}$ **55.** $\sqrt{7} \approx 2.65$

59. $a = 1.464$

61. $A = 2, B = 2\pi, C = -\pi, D = -1$

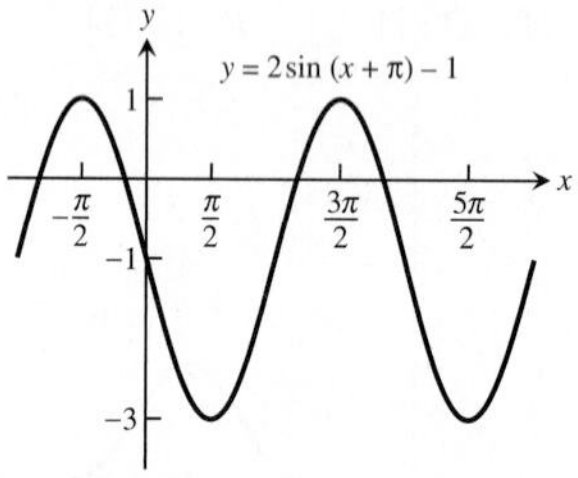

63. $A = -\frac{2}{\pi}, B = 4, C = 0, D = \frac{1}{\pi}$

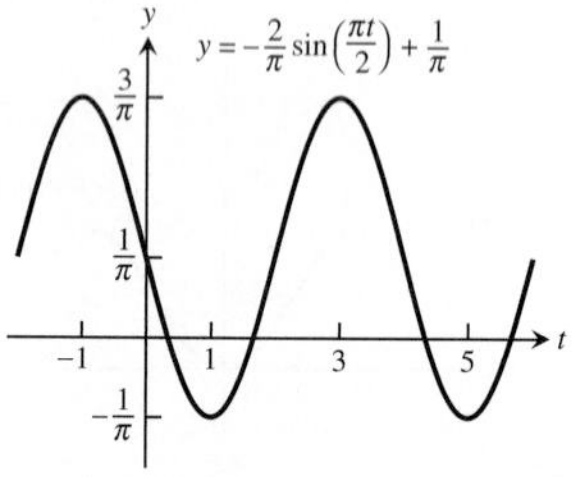

Section 1.4, pp. 35–36

1.

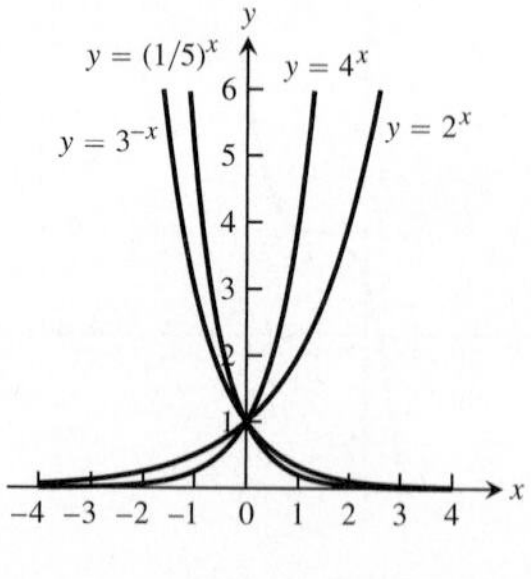

3.

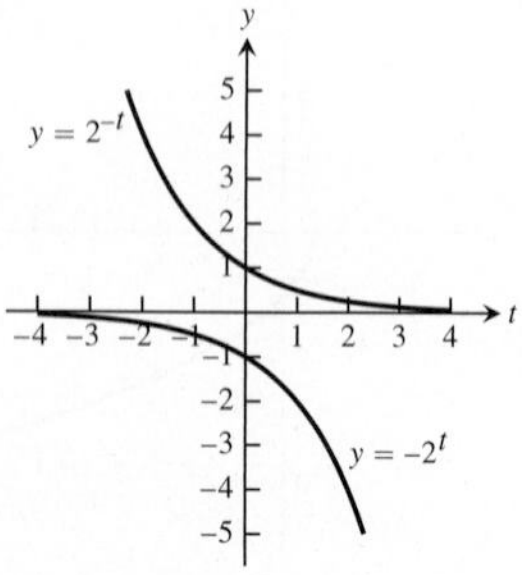

5.

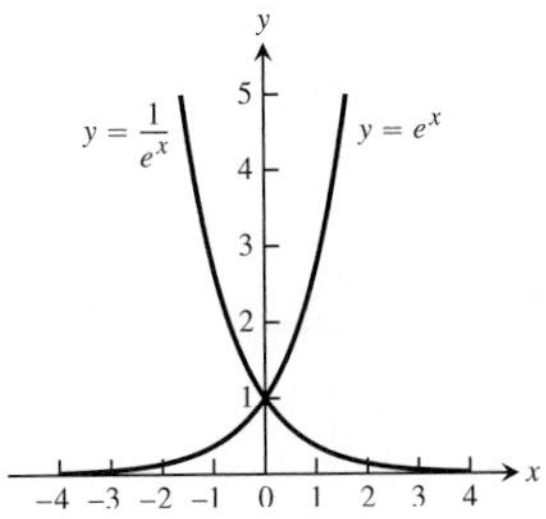

7.

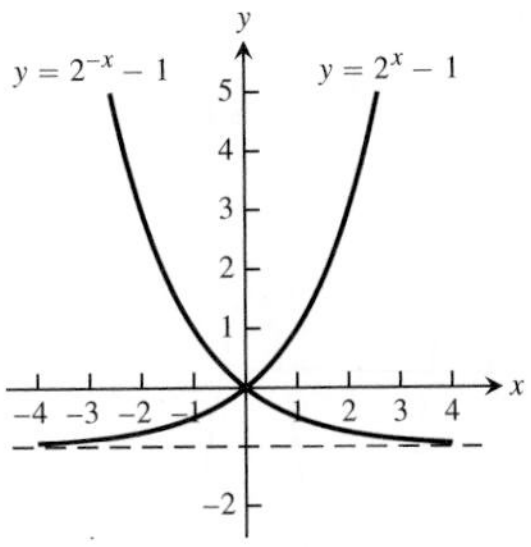

9.

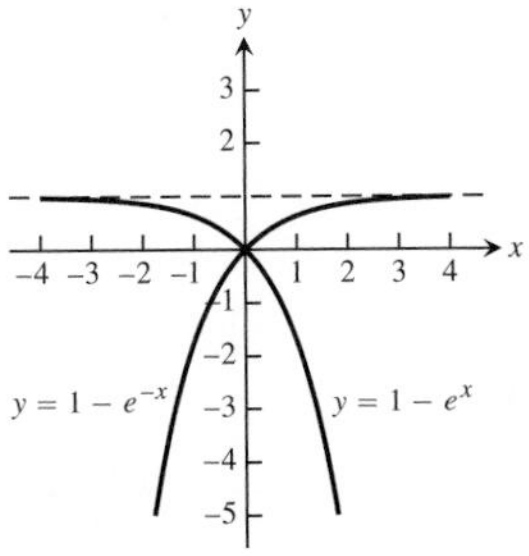

11. $16^{1/4} = 2$ **13.** $4^{1/2} = 2$ **15.** 5 **17.** $14^{\sqrt{3}}$ **19.** 4

21. Domain: $-\infty < x < \infty$
Range: $0 < y < 1/2$

23. Domain: $-\infty < t < \infty$
Range: $1 < y < \infty$

25. $x \approx 2.3219$ **27.** $x \approx -0.6309$ **29.** After 19 years

31. **(a)** $A(t) = 6.6\left(\frac{1}{2}\right)^{t/14}$ **(b)** About 38 days later

33. ≈ 11.433 years, or when interest is paid

35. $2^{48} \approx 2.815 \times 10^{14}$

Section 1.5, pp. 47–49

1. One-to-one **3.** Not one-to-one **5.** One-to-one

7. D: $(0, 1]$ R: $[0, \infty)$ **9.** D: $[-1, 1]$ R: $[-\pi/2, \pi/2]$

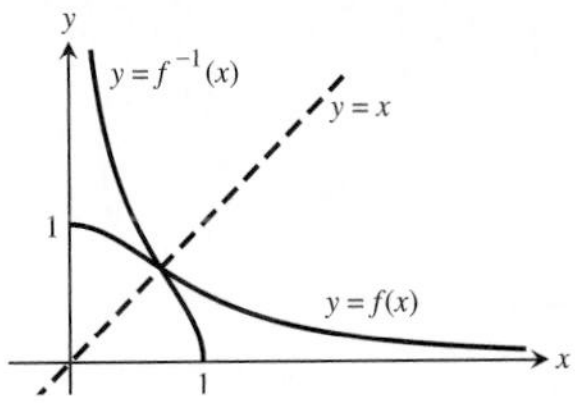

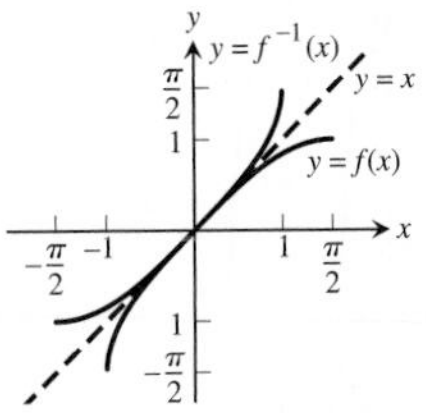

11. **(a)** Symmetric about the line $y = x$

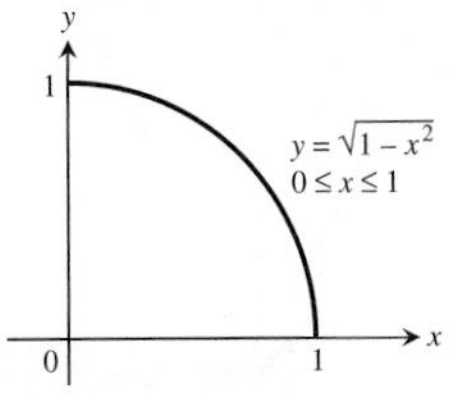

13. $f^{-1}(x) = \sqrt{x - 1}$ **15.** $f^{-1}(x) = \sqrt[3]{x + 1}$

17. $f^{-1}(x) = \sqrt{x} - 1$

19. $f^{-1}(x) = \sqrt[5]{x}$; domain: $-\infty < x < \infty$; range: $-\infty < y < \infty$

21. $f^{-1}(x) = \sqrt[3]{x - 1}$; domain: $-\infty < x < \infty$; range: $-\infty < y < \infty$

23. $f^{-1}(x) = \dfrac{1}{\sqrt{x}}$; domain: $x > 0$; range: $y > 0$

25. **(a)** $\ln 3 - 2\ln 2$ **(b)** $2(\ln 2 - \ln 3)$ **(c)** $-\ln 2$
(d) $\frac{2}{3}\ln 3$ **(e)** $\ln 3 + \frac{1}{2}\ln 2$ **(f)** $\frac{1}{2}(3\ln 3 - \ln 2)$

27. **(a)** $\ln 5$ **(b)** $\ln(x - 3)$ **(c)** $\ln(t^2)$

29. **(a)** 7.2 **(b)** $\frac{1}{x^2}$ **(c)** $\frac{x}{y}$

31. **(a)** 1 **(b)** 1 **(c)** $-x^2 - y^2$

33. e^{2t+4} **35.** $e^{5t} + 40$ **37.** $y = 2xe^x + 1$

39. **(a)** $k = \ln 2$ **(b)** $k = (1/10)\ln 2$ **(c)** $k = 1000 \ln a$

41. **(a)** $t = -10\ln 3$ **(b)** $t = -\dfrac{\ln 2}{k}$ **(c)** $t = \dfrac{\ln .4}{\ln .2}$

43. $4(\ln x)^2$

45. **(a)** 7 **(b)** $\sqrt{2}$ **(c)** 75 **(d)** 2 **(e)** 0.5 **(f)** -1

47. **(a)** $\sqrt{x}$ **(b)** x^2 **(c)** $\sin x$ **49.** **(a)** $\dfrac{\ln 3}{\ln 2}$ **(b)** 3 **(c)** 2

51. **(a)** $-\pi/6$ **(b)** $\pi/4$ **(c)** $-\pi/3$

53. **(a)** π **(b)** $\pi/2$

59. **(a)** $f^{-1}(x) = \log_2\left(\dfrac{x}{100 - x}\right)$ **(b)** $f^{-1}(x) = \log_{1.1}\left(\dfrac{x}{50 - x}\right)$

61. **(a)** Amount $= 8\left(\frac{1}{2}\right)^{t/12}$ **(b)** 36 hours

63. ≈ 44.081 years **65.** $x \approx -0.76666$

67. **(a)** $y = \ln x - 3$ **(b)** $y = \ln(x - 1)$
(c) $y = 3 + \ln(x + 1)$ **(d)** $y = \ln(x - 2) - 4$
(e) $y = \ln(-x)$ **(f)** $y = e^x$

Section 1.6, p. 54

1. d **3.** d

5. $[-3, 5]$ by $[-15, 40]$

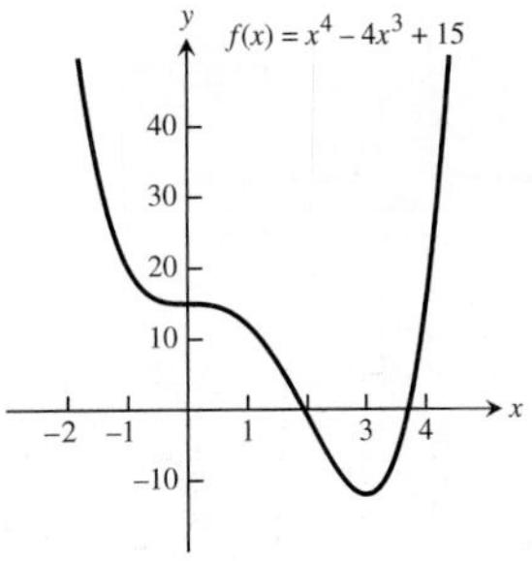

7. $[-3, 6]$ by $[-250, 50]$

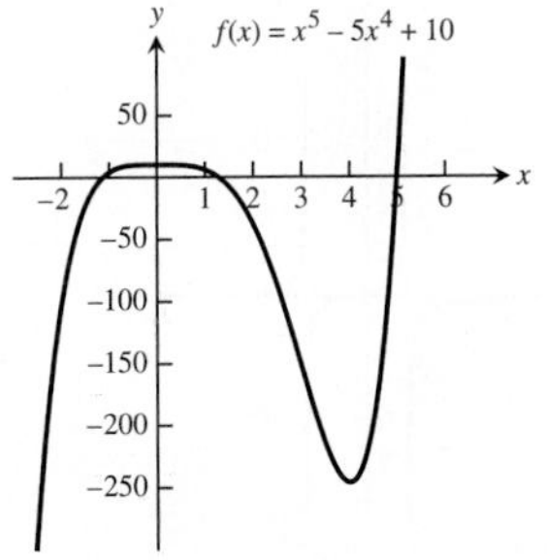

9. $[-3, 3]$ by $[-6, 6]$

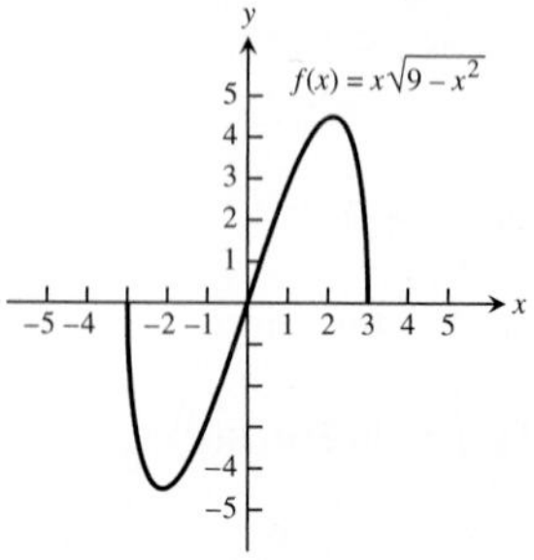

11. $[-2, 6]$ by $[-5, 4]$

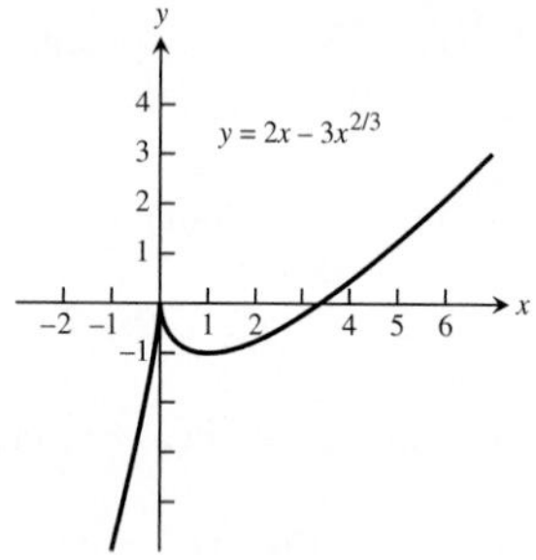

25. $\left[-\frac{\pi}{125}, \frac{\pi}{125}\right]$ by $[-1.25, 1.25]$

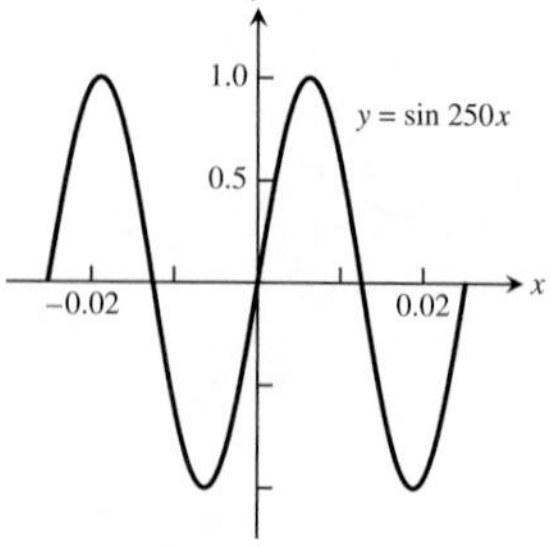

27. $[-100\pi, 100\pi]$ by $[-1.25, 1.25]$

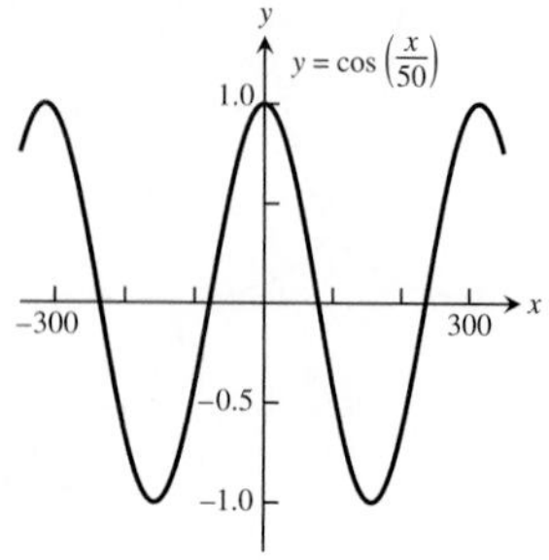

13. $[-2, 8]$ by $[-5, 10]$

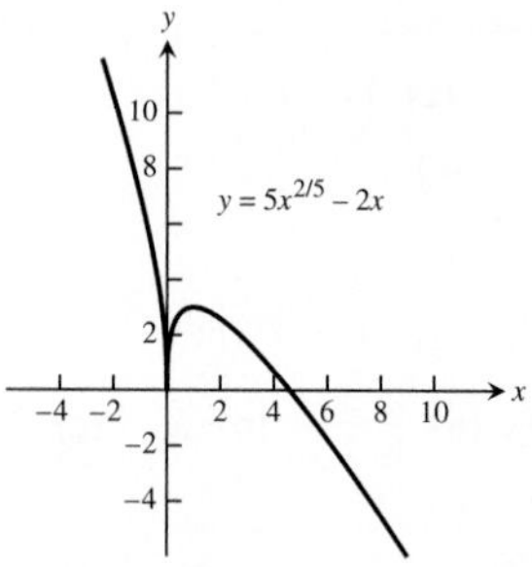

15. $[-3, 3]$ by $[0, 10]$

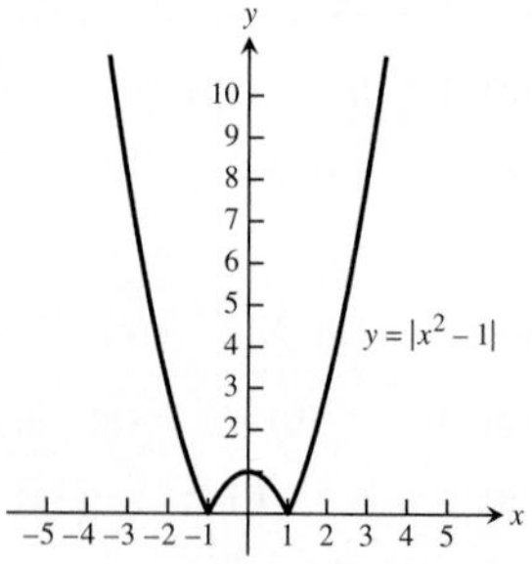

29. $\left[-\frac{\pi}{15}, \frac{\pi}{15}\right]$ by $[-0.25, 0.25]$

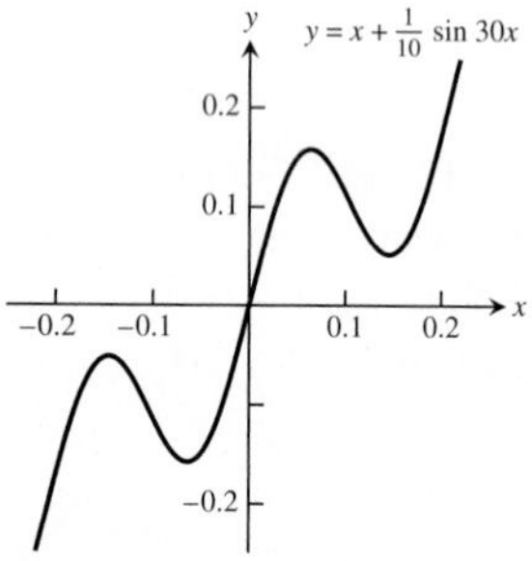

31.

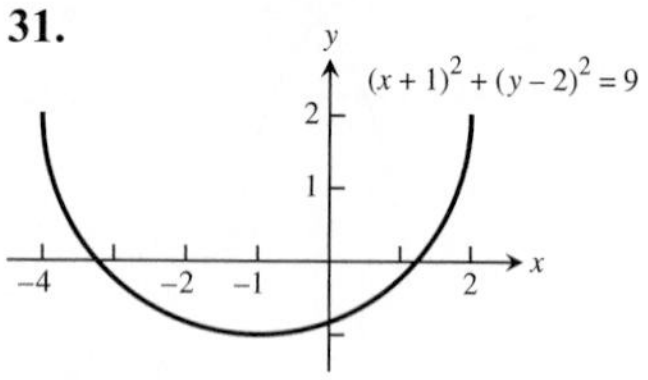

17. $[-10, 10]$ by $[-10, 10]$

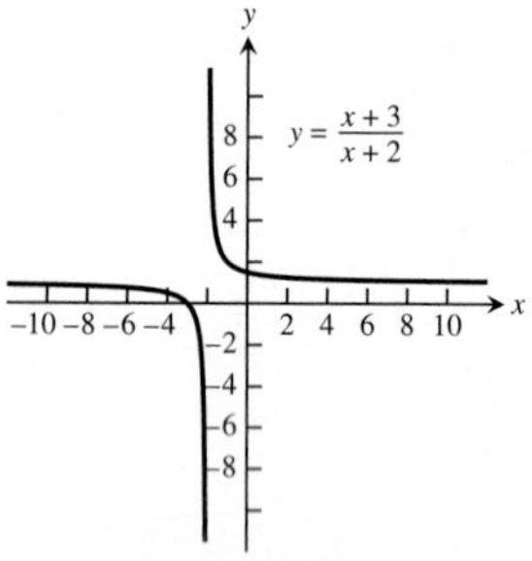

19. $[-4, 4]$ by $[0, 3]$

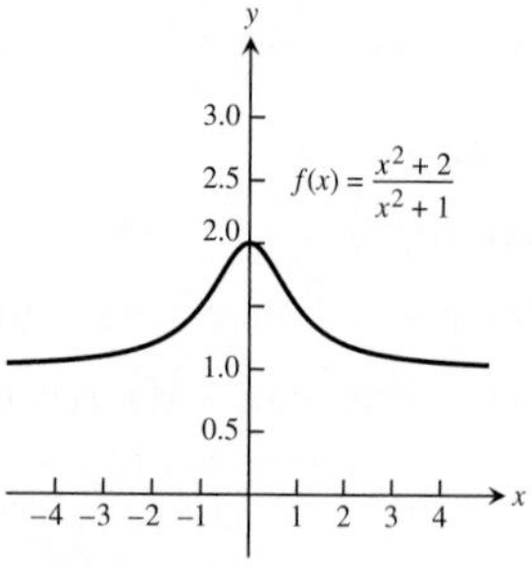

33.

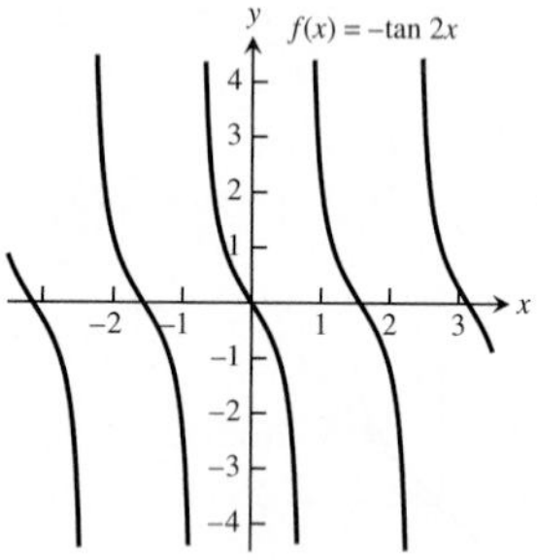

35.

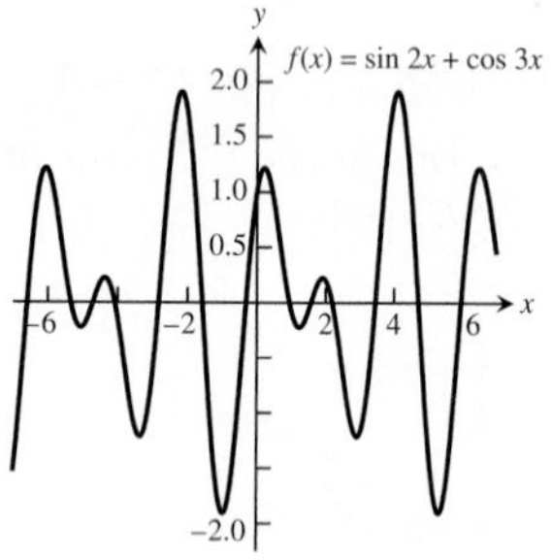

21. $[-10, 10]$ by $[-6, 6]$

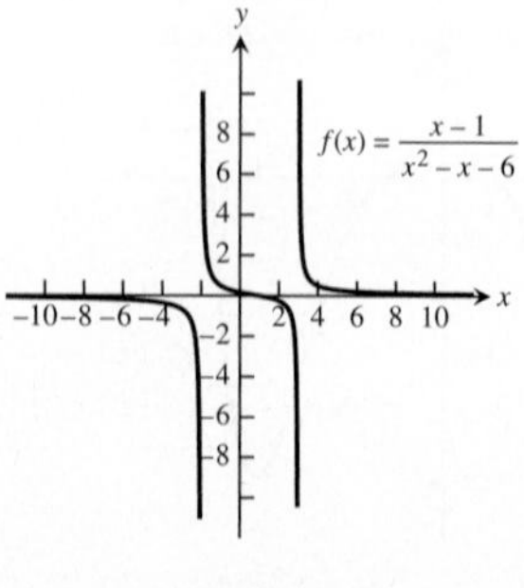

23. $[-6, 10]$ by $[-6, 6]$

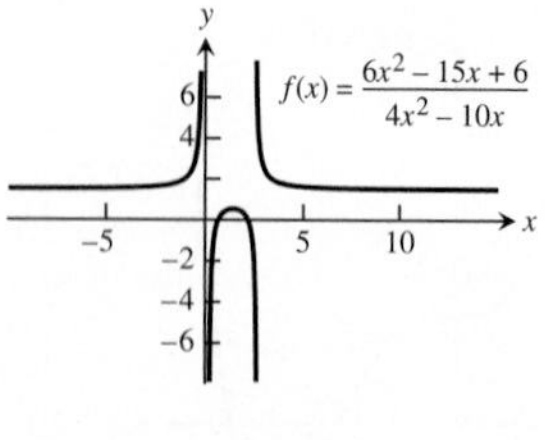

37.

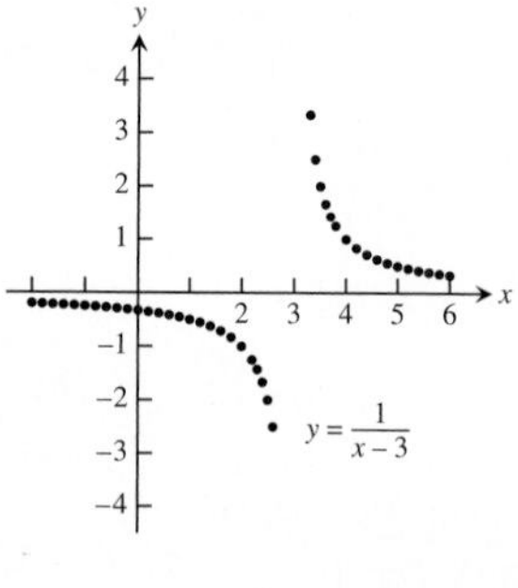

39.

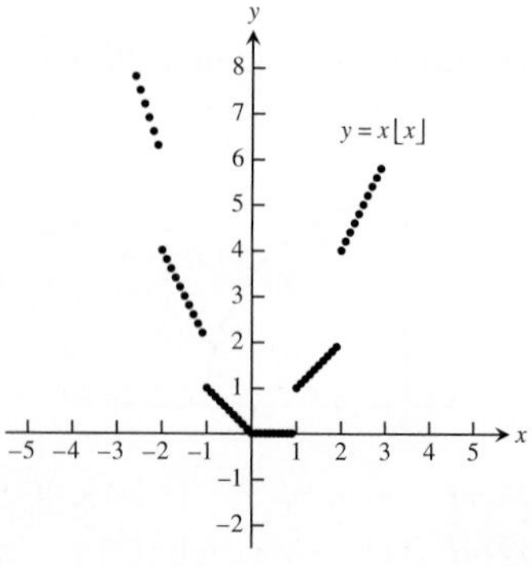

CHAPTER 2

Section 2.1, pp. 61–62

1. **(a)** 19 **(b)** 1

3. **(a)** $-\frac{4}{\pi}$ **(b)** $-\frac{3\sqrt{3}}{\pi}$ **5.** 1

7. Your estimates may not completely agree with these.

(a)

PQ_1	PQ_2	PQ_3	PQ_4
43	46	49	50

The appropriate units are m/sec.

(b) ≈ 50 m/sec or 180 km/h

9. **(a)** 4 **(b)** $y = 4x - 7$

11. **(a)** 2 **(b)** $y = 2x - 7$

13. **(a)** 12 **(b)** $y = 12x - 16$

15. **(a)** −9 **(b)** $y = -9x - 2$

17. **(a)**

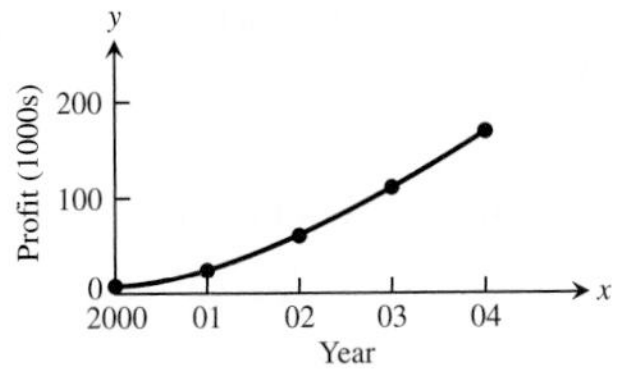

(b) ≈ \$56,000/year
(c) ≈ \$42,000/year

19. **(a)** 0.414213, 0.449489, $(\sqrt{1+h}-1)/h$ **(b)** $g(x) = \sqrt{x}$

$1 + h$	1.1	1.01	1.001	1.0001	1.00001	1.000001
$\sqrt{1+h}$	1.04880	1.004987	1.0004998	1.0000499	1.000005	1.0000005
$(\sqrt{1+h}-1)/h$	0.4880	0.4987	0.4998	0.499	0.5	0.5

(c) 0.5 **(d)** 0.5

Section 2.2, pp. 71–74

1. **(a)** Does not exist. As x approaches 1 from the right, $g(x)$ approaches 0. As x approaches 1 from the left, $g(x)$ approaches 1. There is no single number L that all the values $g(x)$ get arbitrarily close to as $x \to 1$.
(b) 1 **(c)** 0

3. **(a)** True **(b)** True **(c)** False
(d) False **(e)** False **(f)** True

[redacted]m the left, $x/|x|$ approaches −1. As x approaches 0 from the right, $x/|x|$ approaches 1. There is no single number L that the function values all get arbitrarily close to as $x \to 0$.

7. Nothing can be said. **9.** No; no; no

11. −9 **13.** 4 **15.** −8 **17.** 5/8 **19.** 5/2 **21.** 27 **23.** 16
25. 3/2 **27.** 3/2 **29.** 1/10 **31.** −7 **33.** 3/2 **35.** −1/2
37. 4/3 **39.** 1/6 **41.** 4 **43.** 1/2 **45.** 3/2 **47.** −1
49. 1 **51.** 1/3 **53.** 1

55. **(a)** Quotient Rule **(b)** Difference and Power Rules
(c) Sum and Constant Multiple Rules

57. **(a)** −10 **(b)** −20 **(c)** −1 **(d)** 5/7

59. **(a)** 4 **(b)** −21 **(c)** −12 **(d)** −7/3

61. 2 **63.** 3 **65.** $1/(2\sqrt{7})$ **67.** $\sqrt{5}$

69. **(a)** The limit is 1.

71. **(a)** $f(x) = (x^2 - 9)/(x + 3)$

x	−3.1	−3.01	−3.001	−3.0001	−3.00001	−3.000001
$f(x)$	−6.1	−6.01	−6.001	−6.0001	−6.00001	−6.000001

x	−2.9	−2.99	−2.999	−2.9999	−2.99999	−2.999999
$f(x)$	−5.9	−5.99	−5.999	−5.9999	−5.99999	−5.999999

(c) $\lim_{x\to-3} f(x) = -6$

73. **(a)** $G(x) = (x + 6)/(x^2 + 4x - 12)$

x	−5.9	−5.99	−5.999	−5.9999	−5.99999	−5.999999
$G(x)$	−.126582	−.1251564	−.1250156	−.1250015	−.1250001	−.1250000

x	−6.1	−6.01	−6.001	−6.0001	−6.00001	−6.000001
$G(x)$	−.123456	−.124843	−.124984	−.124998	−.124999	−.124999

(c) $\lim_{x\to-6} G(x) = -1/8 = -0.125$

75. **(a)** $f(x) = (x^2 - 1)/(|x| - 1)$

x	−1.1	−1.01	−1.001	−1.0001	−1.00001	−1.000001
$f(x)$	2.1	2.01	2.001	2.0001	2.00001	2.000001

x	−.9	−.99	−.999	−.9999	−.99999	−.999999
$f(x)$	1.9	1.99	1.999	1.9999	1.99999	1.999999

(c) $\lim_{x\to-1} f(x) = 2$

77. **(a)** $g(\theta) = (\sin\theta)/\theta$

θ	.1	.01	.001	.0001	.00001	.000001
$g(\theta)$	.998334	.999983	.999999	.999999	.999999	.999999

θ	−.1	−.01	−.001	−.0001	−.00001	−.000001
$g(\theta)$	.998334	.999983	.999999	.999999	.999999	.999999

$\lim_{\theta\to0} g(\theta) = 1$

79. (a) $f(x) = x^{1/(1-x)}$

x	.9	.99	.999	.9999	.99999	.999999
$f(x)$	.348678	.366032	.367695	.367861	.367877	.367879

x	1.1	1.01	1.001	1.0001	1.00001	1.000001
$f(x)$	.385543	.369711	.368063	.367897	.367881	.367878

$\lim_{x\to 1} f(x) \approx 0.36788$

81. $c = 0, 1, -1$; The limit is 0 at $c = 0$, and 1 at $c = 1, -1$.

83. 7 **85. (a)** 5 **(b)** 5

Section 2.3, pp. 80–84

1. $\delta = 2$

3. $\delta = 1/2$

5. $\delta = 1/18$

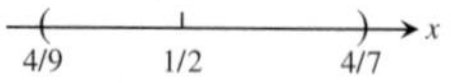

7. $\delta = 0.1$ **9.** $\delta = 7/16$ **11.** $\delta = \sqrt{5} - 2$ **13.** $\delta = 0.36$

15. $(3.99, 4.01)$, $\delta = 0.01$ **17.** $(-0.19, 0.21)$, $\delta = 0.19$

19. $(3, 15)$, $\delta = 5$ **21.** $(10/3, 5)$, $\delta = 2/3$

23. $(-\sqrt{4.5}, -\sqrt{3.5})$, $\delta = \sqrt{4.5} - 2 \approx 0.12$

25. $(\sqrt{15}, \sqrt{17})$, $\delta = \sqrt{17} - 4 \approx 0.12$

27. $\left(2 - \frac{0.03}{m}, 2 + \frac{0.03}{m}\right)$, $\delta = \frac{0.03}{m}$

29. $\left(\frac{1}{2} - \frac{c}{m}, \frac{c}{m} + \frac{1}{2}\right)$, $\delta = \frac{c}{m}$ **31.** $L = -3$, $\delta = 0.01$

33. $L = 4$, $\delta = 0.05$ **35.** $L = 4$, $\delta = 0.75$

55. [3.384, 3.387]. To be safe, the left endpoint was rounded up and the right endpoint rounded down.

59. The limit does not exist as x approaches 3.

Section 2.4, pp. 94–97

1. (a) True **(b)** True **(c)** False **(d)** True **(e)** True **(f)** True **(g)** False **(h)** False **(i)** False **(j)** False **(k)** True **(l)** False

3. (a) 2, 1 **(b)** No, $\lim_{x\to 2^+} f(x) \neq \lim_{x\to 2^-} f(x)$ **(c)** 3, 3 **(d)** Yes, 3

5. (a) No **(b)** Yes, 0 **(c)** No

7. (a)

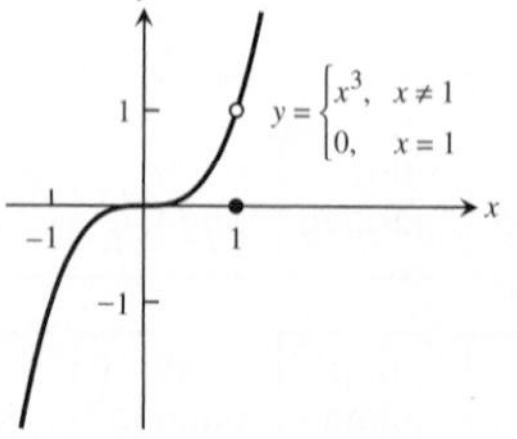

(b) 1, 1 **(c)** Yes, 1

9. (a) $D: 0 \le x \le 2, R: 0 < y \le 1$ and $y = 2$. **(b)** $(0, 1) \cup (1, 2)$ **(c)** $x = 2$ **(d)** $x = 0$

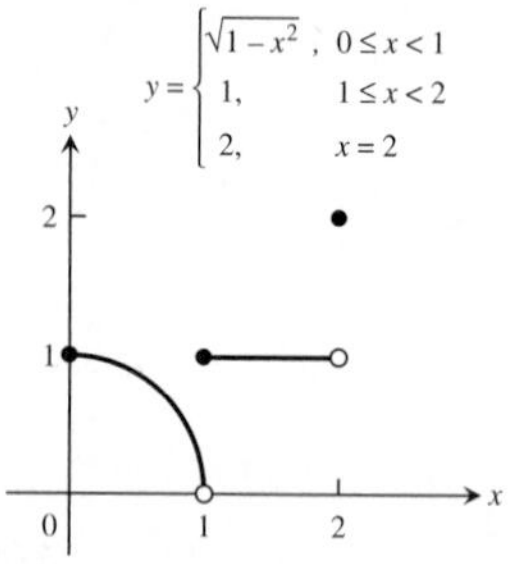

11. $\sqrt{3}$ **13.** 1 **15.** $2/\sqrt{5}$ **17. (a)** 1 **(b)** -1

19. (a) 1 **(b)** $2/3$ **21.** 1 **23.** $3/4$ **25.** 2 **27.** $1/2$

29. 2 **31.** 1 **33.** $1/2$ **35.** $3/8$ **37. (a)** -3 **(b)** -3

39. (a) $1/2$ **(b)** $1/2$ **41. (a)** $-5/3$ **(b)** $-5/3$ **43.** 0

45. -1 **47.** 0 **49.** -1 **51. (a)** $2/5$ **(b)** $2/5$

53. (a) 0 **(b)** 0 **55. (a)** 7 **(b)** 7 **57. (a)** 0 **(b)** 0

59. (a) $-2/3$ **(b)** $-2/3$ **61.** 0 **63.** 1 **65.** ∞ **73.** 1

77. $\delta = \epsilon^2$, $\lim_{x\to 5^+} \sqrt{x - 5} = 0$

81. (a) 400 **(b)** 399 **(c)** The limit does not exist.

83. 1 **85.** $3/2$ **87.** 3

Section 2.5, pp. 102–103

1. ∞ **3.** $-\infty$ **5.** $-\infty$ **7.** ∞ **9. (a)** ∞ **(b)** $-\infty$

11. ∞ **13.** ∞ **15.** $-\infty$

17. (a) ∞ **(b)** $-\infty$ **(c)** $-\infty$ **(d)** ∞

19. (a) $-\infty$ **(b)** ∞ **(c)** 0 **(d)** $3/2$

21. (a) $-\infty$ **(b)** $1/4$ **(c)** $1/4$ **(d)** $1/4$ **(e)** It will be $-\infty$.

23. (a) $-\infty$ **(b)** ∞

25. (a) ∞ **(b)** ∞ **(c)** ∞ **(d)** ∞

27.

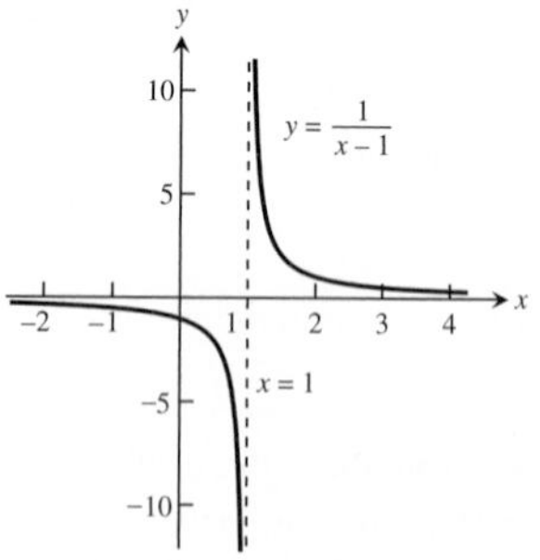

29.

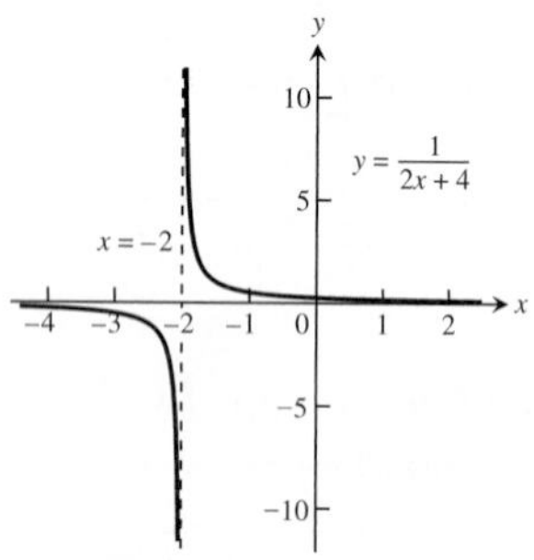

31.

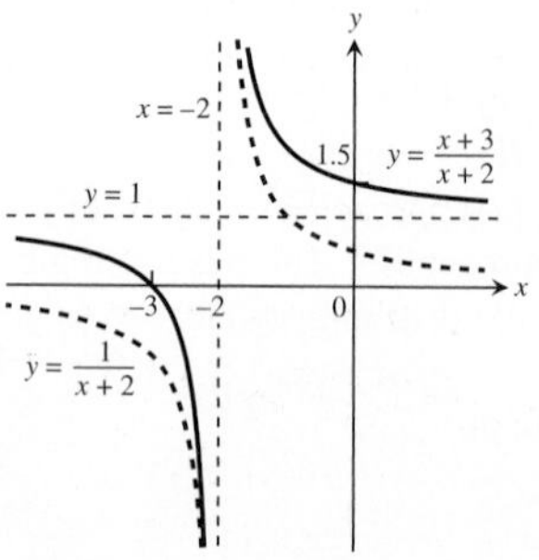

33.

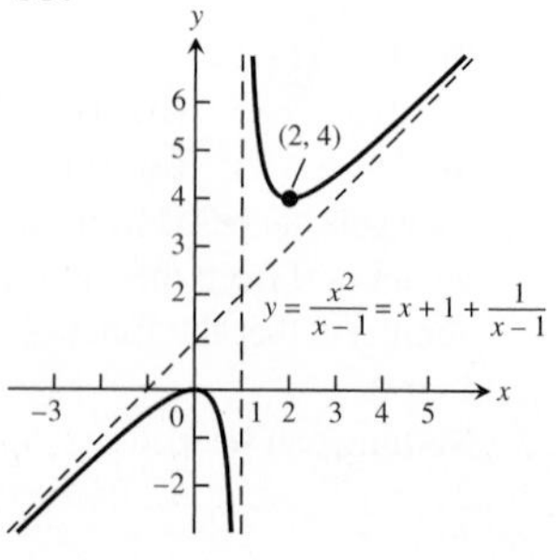

35.

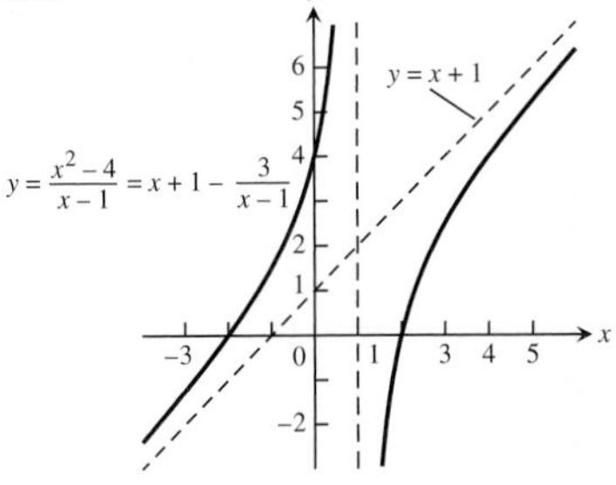

37.

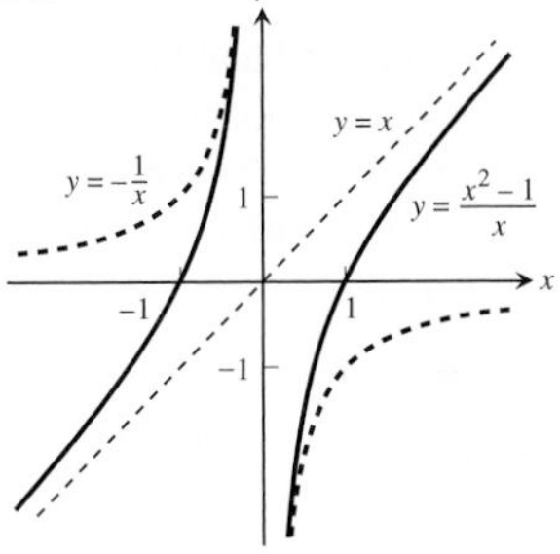

39. Here is one possibility.

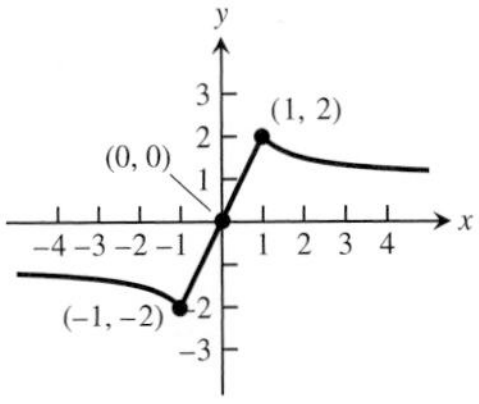

41. Here is one possibility.

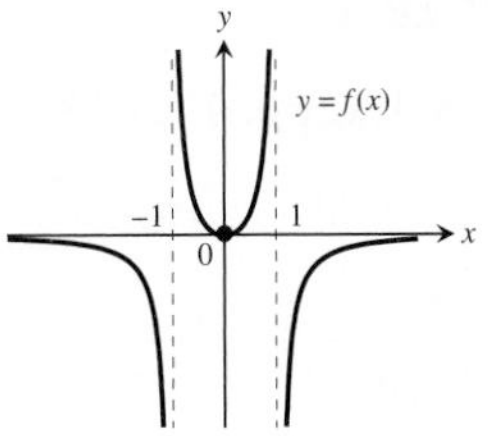

43. Here is one possibility.

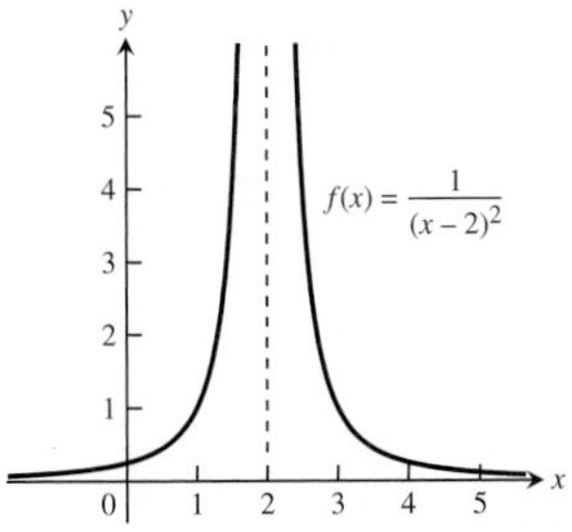

45. Here is one possibility.

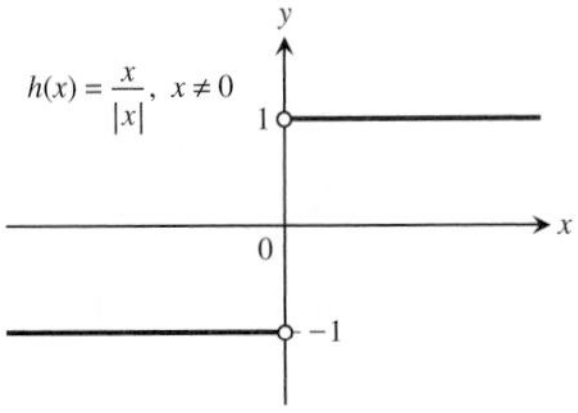

51. **(a)** For every positive real number B there exists a corresponding number $\delta > 0$ such that for all x

$$x_0 - \delta < x < x_0 \Rightarrow f(x) > B.$$

(b) For every negative real number $-B$ there exists a corresponding number $\delta > 0$ such that for all x

$$x_0 < x < x_0 + \delta \Rightarrow f(x) < -B.$$

(c) For every negative real number $-B$ there exists a corresponding number $\delta > 0$ such that for all x

$$x_0 - \delta < x < x_0 \Rightarrow f(x) < -B.$$

57.

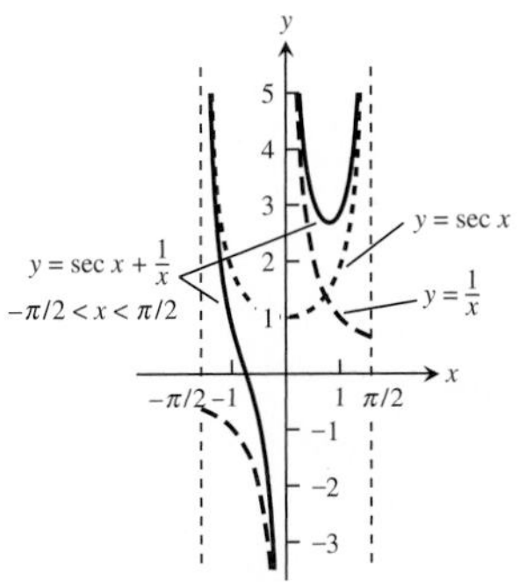

59.

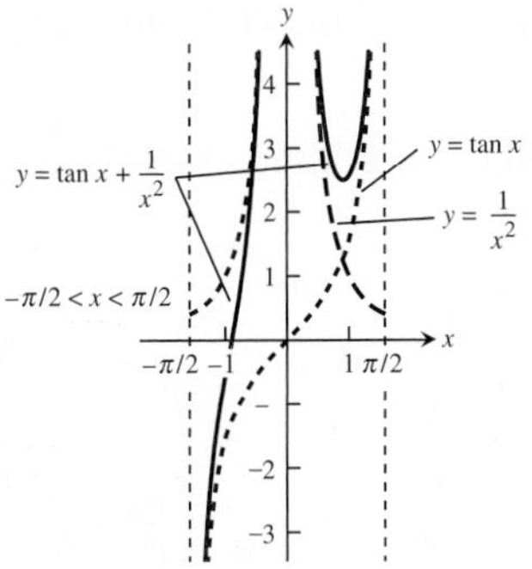

61.

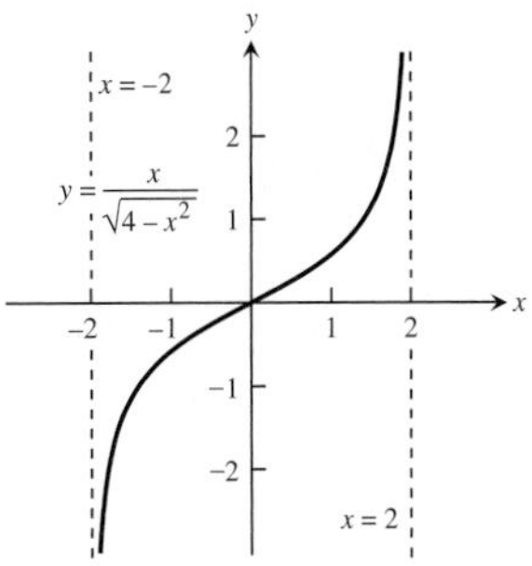

63.

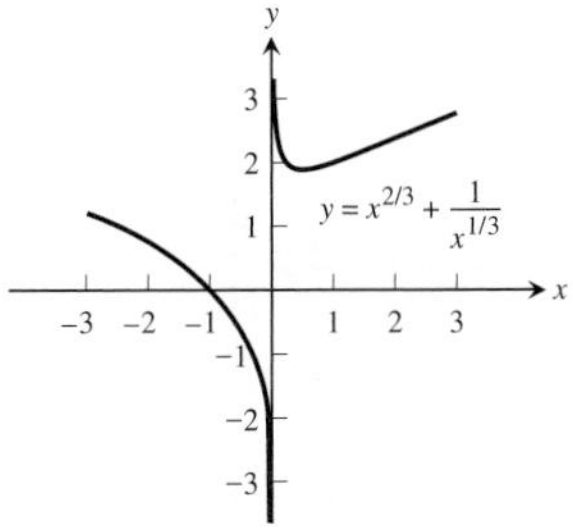

65. At ∞: ∞, at $-\infty$: 0 **67.** At ∞: 0, at $-\infty$: 0

69. **(a)** $y \to \infty$ (see the accompanying graph)

(b) $y \to \infty$ (see the accompanying graph)

(c) Cusps at $x = \pm 1$ (see the accompanying graph)

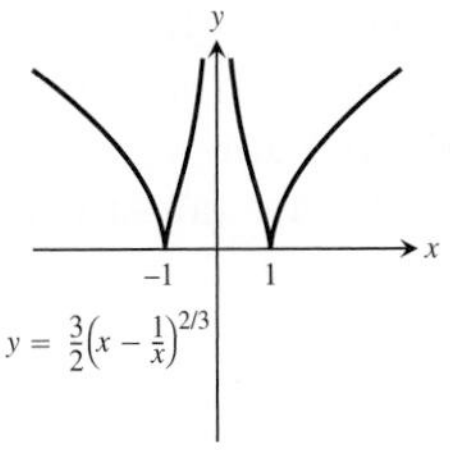

Section 2.6, pp. 113–115

1. No; discontinuous at $x = 2$; not defined at $x = 2$
3. Continuous **5.** **(a)** Yes **(b)** Yes **(c)** Yes **(d)** Yes
7. **(a)** No **(b)** No **9.** 0 **11.** 1, nonremovable; 0, removable **13.** All x except $x = 2$ **15.** All x except $x = 3, x = 1$ **17.** All x **19.** All x except $x = 0$
21. All x except $x = n\pi/2$, n any integer **23.** All x except $n\pi/2$, n an odd integer **25.** All $x \geq -3/2$ **27.** All x
29. 0; continuous at $x = \pi$ **31.** 1; continuous at $y = 1$
33. 1; continuous at $x = 0$ **35.** $g(3) = 6$ **37.** $f(1) = 3/2$
39. $a = 4/3$ **63.** $x \approx 1.8794, -1.5321, -0.3473$
65. $x \approx 1.7549$ **67.** $x \approx 3.5156$ **69.** $x \approx 0.7391$

Section 2.7, pp. 118–119

1. P_1: $m_1 = 1$, P_2: $m_2 = 5$ **3.** P_1: $m_1 = 5/2$, P_2: $m_2 = -1/2$
5. $y = 2x + 4$ **7.** $y = x + 1$

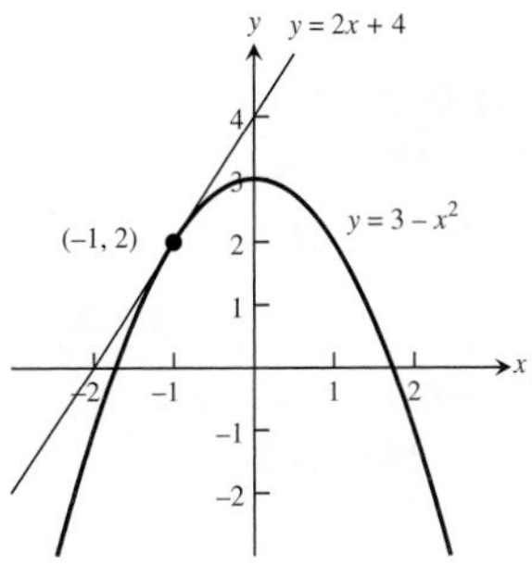

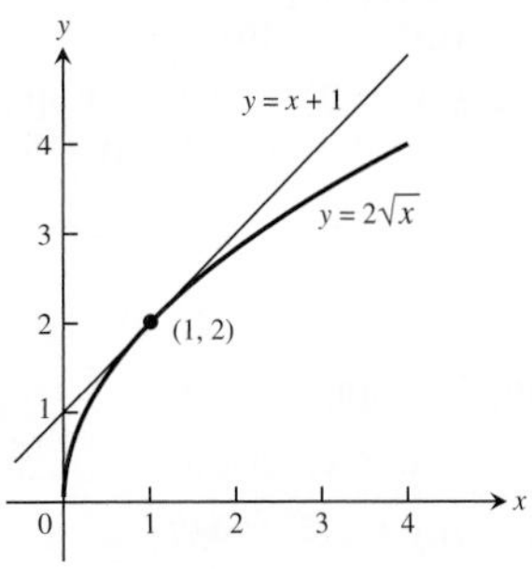

9. $y = 12x + 17$

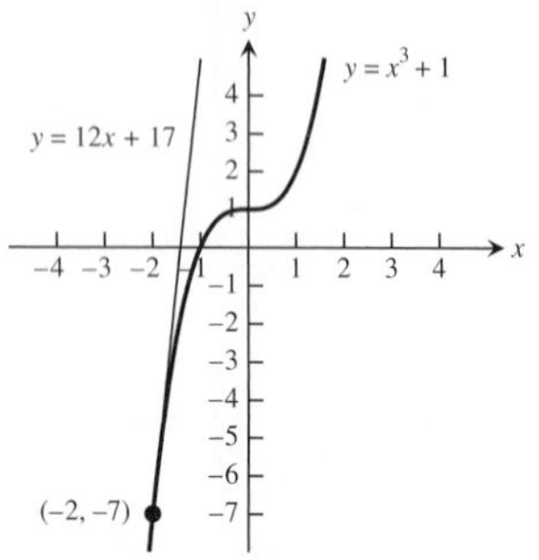

11. $m = 4, y - 5 = 4(x - 2)$
13. $m = -2, y - 3 = -2(x - 3)$
15. $m = 11, y - 6 = 11(t - 2)$
17. $m = \frac{1}{4}, y - 2 = \frac{1}{4}(x - 4)$
19. $m = -10$ **21.** $m = -1/4$ **23.** $(-2,-5)$
25. $y = -(x + 1), y = -(x - 3)$ **27.** 19.6 m/sec
29. 6π **33.** Yes **35.** Yes **37. (a)** Nowhere
39. (a) At $x = 0$ **41. (a)** Nowhere **43. (a)** At $x = 1$
45. (a) At $x = 0$

Practice Exercises, pp. 120–121

1. At $x = -1$: $\lim_{x\to -1^-} f(x) = \lim_{x\to -1^+} f(x) = 1$, so $\lim_{x\to -1} f(x) = 1 = f(-1)$; continuous at $x = -1$

At $x = 0$: $\lim_{x\to 0^-} f(x) = \lim_{x\to 0^+} f(x) = 0$, so $\lim_{x\to 0} f(x) = 0$. However, $f(0) \neq 0$, so f is discontinuous at $x = 0$. The discontinuity can be removed by redefining $f(0)$ to be 0.

At $x = 1$: $\lim_{x\to 1^-} f(x) = -1$ and $\lim_{x\to 1^+} f(x) = 1$, so $\lim_{x\to 1} f(x)$ does not exist. The function is discontinuous at $x = 1$, and the discontinuity is not removable.

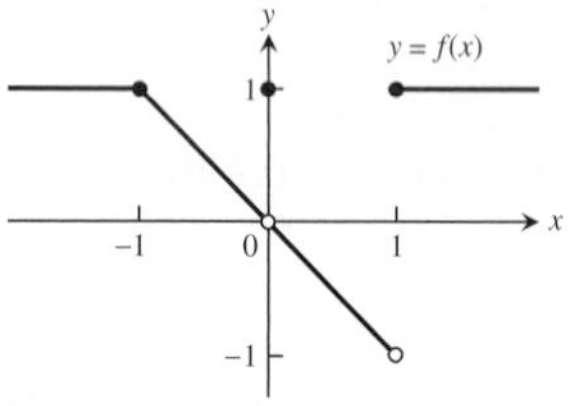

3. (a) -21 **(b)** 49 **(c)** 0 **(d)** 1 **(e)** 1 **(f)** 7 **(g)** -7 **(h)** $-\frac{1}{7}$ **5.** 4
7. (a) $(-\infty, +\infty)$ **(b)** $[0, \infty)$ **(c)** $(-\infty, 0)$ and $(0, \infty)$ **(d)** $(0, \infty)$ **9. (a)** Does not exist **(b)** 0
11. $\frac{1}{2}$ **13.** $2x$ **15.** $-\frac{1}{4}$ **17.** $\frac{2}{\pi}$ **19.** 1 **21.** $-\infty$
23. 0 **25.** 2 **27.** 0 **29.** $\frac{2}{5}$ **31.** 0 **33.** $-\infty$ **35.** 0
37. 1 **39.** 1 **41.** $-\frac{\pi}{2}$ **43.** No in both cases, because $\lim_{x\to 1} f(x)$ does not exist, and $\lim_{x\to -1} f(x)$ does not exist.
49. (b) 1.324717957

Additional and Advanced Exercises, pp. 122–124

3. 0; the left-hand limit was needed because the function is undefined for $v > c$.
5. $65 < t < 75$; within 5°F
13. (a) B **(b)** A **(c)** A **(d)** A
21. (a) $\lim_{a\to 0} r_+(a) = 0.5$, $\lim_{a\to -1^+} r_+(a) = 1$
(b) $\lim_{a\to 0} r_-(a)$ does not exist, $\lim_{a\to -1^+} r_-(a) = 1$
25. 0 **27.** 1 **29.** 4

CHAPTER 3

Section 3.1, pp. 132–134

1. $-2x, 6, 0, -2$ **3.** $-\frac{2}{t^3}, 2, -\frac{1}{4}, -\frac{2}{3\sqrt{3}}$
5. $\frac{3}{2\sqrt{3\theta}}, \frac{3}{2\sqrt{3}}, \frac{1}{2}, \frac{3}{2\sqrt{2}}$ **7.** $6x^2$ **9.** $\frac{1}{(2t + 1)^2}$
11. $\frac{-1}{2(q + 1)\sqrt{q + 1}}$ **13.** $1 - \frac{9}{x^2}, 0$ **15.** $3t^2 - 2t, 5$
17. $\frac{-4}{(x - 2)\sqrt{x - 2}}$, $y - 4 = -\frac{1}{2}(x - 6)$ **19.** 6
21. 1/8 **23.** $\frac{-1}{(x + 2)^2}$ **25.** $\frac{-1}{(x - 1)^2}$ **27.** b **29.** d
31. (a) $x = 0, 1, 4$ **(b)**

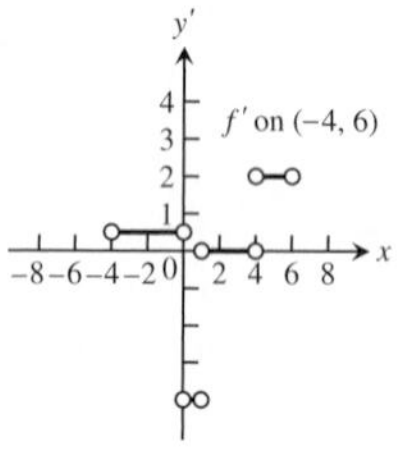

33. Since $\lim_{x\to 0^+} f'(x) = 1$ while $\lim_{x\to 0^-} f'(x) = 0$, $f(x)$ is not differentiable at $x = 0$.
35. Since $\lim_{x\to 1^+} f'(x) = 2$ while $\lim_{x\to 1^-} f'(x) = 1/2$, $f(x)$ is not differentiable at $x = 1$.
37. (a) $-3 \le x \le 2$ **(b)** None **(c)** None
39. (a) $-3 \le x < 0, 0 < x \le 3$ **(b)** None **(c)** $x = 0$
41. (a) $-1 \le x < 0, 0 < x \le 2$ **(b)** $x = 0$ **(c)** None
43. Yes, $y + 16 = -(x - 3)$ is tangent at $(3, -16)$
45. (a) $f'(0) = 0$ **(b)** $f'(0) = 0$

Section 3.2, pp. 144–146

1. $\frac{dy}{dx} = -2x, \frac{d^2y}{dx^2} = -2$
3. $\frac{ds}{dt} = 15t^2 - 15t^4, \frac{d^2s}{dt^2} = 30t - 60t^3$
5. $\frac{dy}{dx} = 4x^2 - 1 + 2e^x, \frac{d^2y}{dx^2} = 8x + 2e^x$

7. $\frac{dw}{dz} = -\frac{6}{z^3} + \frac{1}{z^2}, \frac{d^2w}{dz^2} = \frac{18}{z^4} - \frac{2}{z^3}$

9. $\frac{dy}{dx} = 12x - 10 + 10x^{-3}, \frac{d^2y}{dx^2} = 12 - 30x^{-4}$

11. $\frac{dr}{ds} = \frac{-2}{3s^3} + \frac{5}{2s^2}, \frac{d^2r}{ds^2} = \frac{2}{s^4} - \frac{5}{s^3}$

13. $y' = -5x^4 + 12x^2 - 2x - 3$

15. $y' = 3x^2 + 10x + 2 - \frac{1}{x^2}$ **17.** $y' = \frac{-19}{(3x - 2)^2}$

19. $g'(x) = \frac{x^2 + x + 4}{(x + 0.5)^2}$ **21.** $\frac{dv}{dt} = \frac{t^2 - 2t - 1}{(1 + t^2)^2}$

23. $\frac{dy}{dx} = -2e^{-x}$ **25.** $v' = -\frac{1}{x^2} + 2x^{-3/2}$

27. $\frac{dy}{dx} = 3x^2e^x + x^3e^x$ **29.** $y' = \frac{9}{4}x^{5/4}$ **31.** $\frac{ds}{dt} = 3t^{1/2}$

33. $y' = \frac{2}{7x^{5/7}} - ex^{e-1}$ **35.** $\frac{dr}{ds} = \frac{se^s - e^s}{s^2}$

37. $y' = 2x^3 - 3x - 1, y'' = 6x^2 - 3, y''' = 12x, y^{(4)} = 12,$ $y^{(n)} = 0$ for $n \geq 5$

39. $y' = 2x - 7x^{-2}, y'' = 2 + 14x^{-3}$

41. $\frac{dr}{d\theta} = 3\theta^{-4}, \frac{d^2r}{d\theta^2} = -12\theta^{-5}$

43. $\frac{dw}{dz} = 6ze^z + 3z^2e^z, \frac{d^2w}{dz^2} = 6e^z + 12ze^z + 3z^2e^z$

45. $\frac{dp}{dq} = \frac{1}{6}q + \frac{1}{6}q^{-3} + q^{-5}, \frac{d^2p}{dq^2} = \frac{1}{6} - \frac{1}{2}q^{-4} - 5q^{-6}$

47. **(a)** 13 **(b)** −7 **(c)** 7/25 **(d)** 20

49. **(a)** $y = -\frac{x}{8} + \frac{5}{4}$ **(b)** $m = -4$ at (0, 1)

(c) $y = 8x - 15, y = 8x + 17$

51. $y = 4x, y = 2$ **53.** $a = 1, b = 1, c = 0$

55. **(a)** $y = 2x + 2$ **(c)** (2, 6)

57. $P'(x) = na_nx^{n-1} + (n - 1)a_{n-1}x^{n-2} + \cdots + 2a_2x + a_1$

59. The Product Rule is then the Constant Multiple Rule, so the latter is a special case of the Product Rule.

61. **(a)** $\frac{d}{dx}(uvw) = uvw' + uv'w + u'vw$

(b) $\frac{d}{dx}(u_1u_2u_3u_4) = u_1u_2u_3u_4' + u_1u_2u_3'u_4 + u_1u_2'u_3u_4 + u_1'u_2u_3u_4$

(c) $\frac{d}{dx}(u_1 \cdots u_n) = u_1u_2 \cdots u_{n-1}u_n' + u_1u_2 \cdots u_{n-2}u_{n-1}'u_n + \cdots + u_1'u_2 \cdots u_n$

63. $\frac{dP}{dV} = -\frac{nRT}{(V - nb)^2} + \frac{2an^2}{V^3}$

Section 3.3, pp. 153–157

1. **(a)** −2 m, −1 m/sec
(b) 3 m/sec, 1 m/sec; 2 m/sec^2, 2 m/sec^2
(c) changes direction at $t = 3/2$ sec

3. **(a)** −9 m, −3 m/sec
(b) 3 m/sec, 12 m/sec; 6 m/sec^2, −12 m/sec^2
(c) no change in direction

5. **(a)** −20 m, −5 m/sec
(b) 45 m/sec, (1/5) m/sec; 140 m/sec^2, (4/25) m/sec^2
(c) no change in direction

7. **(a)** $a(1) = -6$ m/sec^2, $a(3) = 6$ m/sec^2
(b) $v(2) = 3$ m/sec **(c)** 6 m

9. Mars: ≈ 7.5 sec, Jupiter: ≈ 1.2 sec **11.** $g_s = 0.75$ m/sec^2

13. **(a)** $v = -32t, |v| = 32t$ ft/sec, $a = -32$ ft/sec^2
(b) $t \approx 3.3$ sec **(c)** $v \approx -107.0$ ft/sec

15. **(a)** $t = 2, t = 7$ **(b)** $3 \leq t \leq 6$

(c)

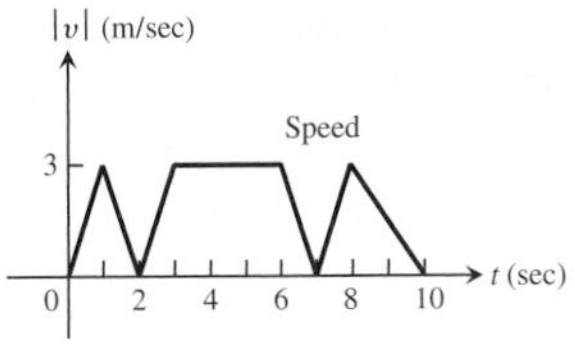

(d)

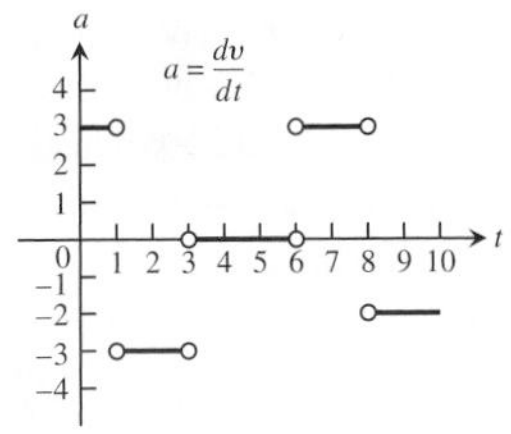

17. **(a)** 190 ft/sec **(b)** 2 sec **(c)** 8 sec, 0 ft/sec,
(d) 10.8 sec, 90 ft/sec **(e)** 2.8 sec
(f) greatest acceleration happens 2 sec after launch
(g) constant acceleration between 2 and 10.8 sec, −32 ft/sec^2

19. **(a)** $\frac{4}{7}$ sec, 280 cm/sec **(b)** 560 cm/sec, 980 cm/sec^2
(c) 29.75 flashes/sec

21. $C =$ position, $A =$ velocity, $B =$ acceleration

23. **(a)** \$110/machine **(b)** \$80 **(c)** \$79.90

25. **(a)** $b'(0) = 10^4$ bacteria/h **(b)** $b'(5) = 0$ bacteria/h
(c) $b'(10) = -10^4$ bacteria/h

27. **(a)** $\frac{dy}{dt} = \frac{t}{12} - 1$

(b) The largest value of $\frac{dy}{dt}$ is 0 m/h when $t = 12$ and the smallest value of $\frac{dy}{dt}$ is −1 m/h, when $t = 0$.

(c)

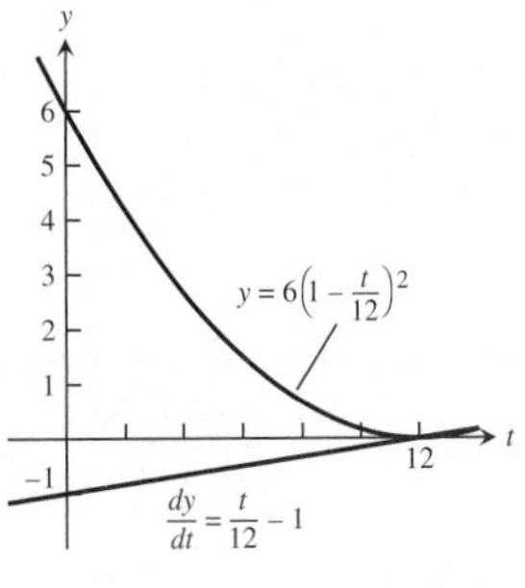

29. $t = 25$ sec $\quad D = \dfrac{6250}{9}$ m

31.

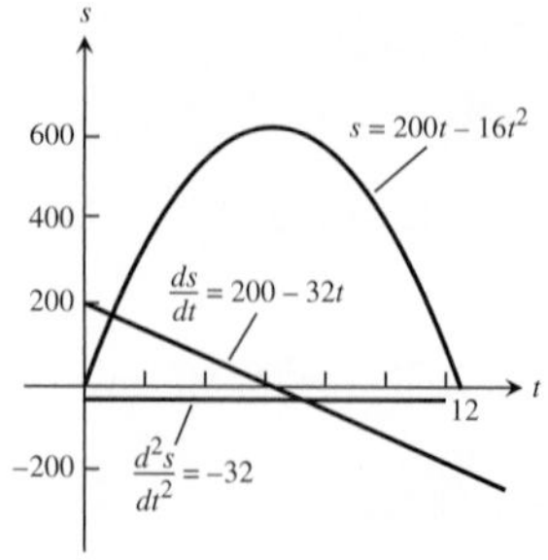

(a) $v = 0$ when $t = 6.25$ sec.
(b) $v > 0$ when $0 \le t < 6.25 \Rightarrow$ body moves up; $v < 0$ when $6.25 < t \le 12.5 \Rightarrow$ body moves down.
(c) Body changes direction at $t = 6.25$ sec.
(d) Body speeds up on $(6.25, 12.5]$ and slows down on $[0, 6.25)$.
(e) The body is moving fastest at the endpoints $t = 0$ and $t = 12.5$ when it is traveling 200 ft/sec. It's moving slowest at $t = 6.25$ when the speed is 0.
(f) When $t = 6.25$ the body is $s = 625$ m from the origin and farthest away.

33.

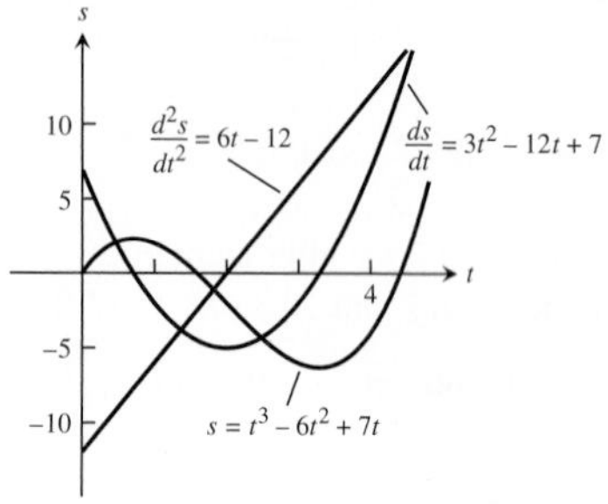

(a) $v = 0$ when $t = \dfrac{6 \pm \sqrt{15}}{3}$ sec.
(b) $v < 0$ when $\dfrac{6 - \sqrt{15}}{3} < t < \dfrac{6 + \sqrt{15}}{3} \Rightarrow$ body moves left; $v > 0$ when $0 \le t < \dfrac{6 - \sqrt{15}}{3}$ or $\dfrac{6 + \sqrt{15}}{3} < t \le 4 \Rightarrow$ body moves right.
(c) Body changes direction at $t = \dfrac{6 \pm \sqrt{15}}{3}$ sec.
(d) Body speeds up on $\left(\dfrac{6 - \sqrt{15}}{3}, 2\right) \cup \left(\dfrac{6 + \sqrt{15}}{3}, 4\right]$ and slows down on $\left[0, \dfrac{6 - \sqrt{15}}{3}\right) \cup \left(2, \dfrac{6 + \sqrt{15}}{3}\right)$.
(e) The body is moving fastest at $t = 0$ and $t = 4$ when it is moving 7 units/sec and slowest at $t = \dfrac{6 \pm \sqrt{15}}{3}$ sec.
(f) When $t = \dfrac{6 + \sqrt{15}}{3}$ the body is at position $s \approx -6.303$ units and farthest from the origin.

Section 3.4, pp. 162–164

1. $-10 - 3\sin x$ **3.** $-\csc x \cot x - \dfrac{2}{\sqrt{x}}$ **5.** 0

7. $\dfrac{-\csc^2 x}{(1 + \cot x)^2}$ **9.** $4\tan x \sec x - \csc^2 x$ **11.** $x^2 \cos x$

13. $\sec^2 t + e^{-t}$ **15.** $\dfrac{-2\csc t \cot t}{(1 - \csc t)^2}$ **17.** $-\theta(\theta\cos\theta + 2\sin\theta)$

19. $\sec\theta\csc\theta(\tan\theta - \cot\theta) = \sec^2\theta - \csc^2\theta$
21. $\sec^2 q$ **23.** $\sec^2 q$
25 **(a)** $2\csc^3 x - \csc x$ **(b)** $2\sec^3 x - \sec x$
27.

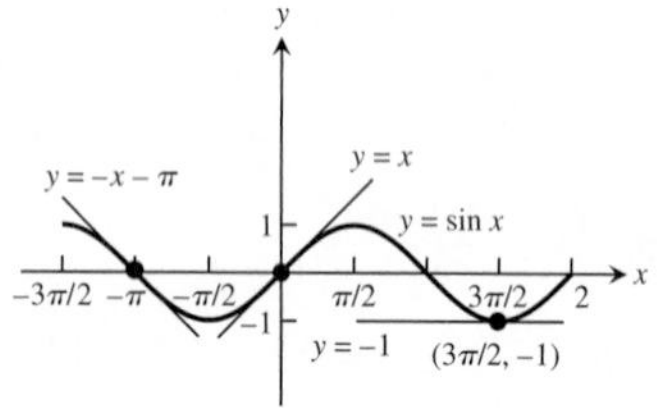

29.

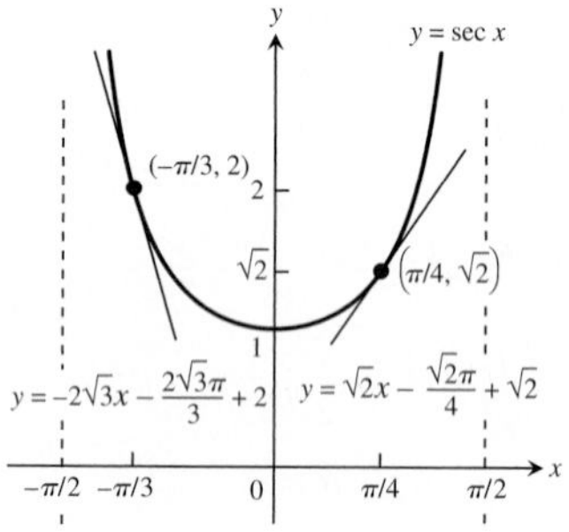

31. Yes, at $x = \pi$ **33.** No
35. $\left(-\frac{\pi}{4}, -1\right); \left(\frac{\pi}{4}, 1\right)$

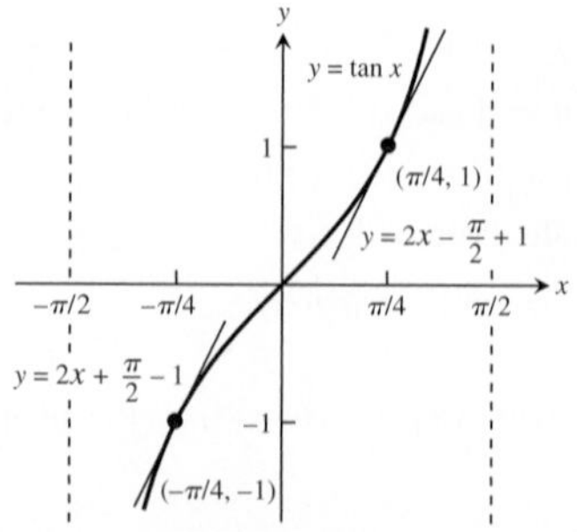

37. **(a)** $y = -x + \pi/2 + 2$ **(b)** $y = 4 - \sqrt{3}$
39. 0 **41.** -1 **43.** 0
45. $-\sqrt{2}$ m/sec, $\sqrt{2}$ m/sec, $\sqrt{2}$ m/sec^2, $\sqrt{2}$ m/sec^3
47. $c = 9$ **49.** $\sin x$

Section 3.5, pp. 173–177

1. $12x^3$ **3.** $3\cos(3x+1)$ **5.** $-\sin(\sin x)\cos x$

7. $10\sec^2(10x-5)$

9. With $u=(2x+1), y=u^5: \dfrac{dy}{dx}=\dfrac{dy}{du}\dfrac{du}{dx}=5u^4\cdot 2=10(2x+1)^4$

11. With $u=(1-(x/7)), y=u^{-7}: \dfrac{dy}{dx}=\dfrac{dy}{du}\dfrac{du}{dx}=-7u^{-8}\cdot\left(-\dfrac{1}{7}\right)=\left(1-\dfrac{x}{7}\right)^{-8}$

13. With $u=1-6x$, $y=u^{2/3}: \dfrac{dy}{dx}=\dfrac{dy}{du}\dfrac{du}{dx}=\dfrac{2}{3}u^{-1/3}\cdot(-6)=\dfrac{-4}{(1-6x)^{1/3}}$

15. With $u=\tan x, y=\sec u: \dfrac{dy}{dx}=\dfrac{dy}{du}\dfrac{du}{dx}=(\sec u\tan u)(\sec^2 x)=\sec(\tan x)\tan(\tan x)\sec^2 x$

17. With $u=\sin x, y=u^3: \dfrac{dy}{dx}=\dfrac{dy}{du}\dfrac{du}{dx}=3u^2\cos x=3\sin^2 x(\cos x)$

19. $y=e^u, u=-5x, \dfrac{dy}{dx}=-5e^{-5x}$

21. $y=e^u, u=5-7x, \dfrac{dy}{dx}=-7e^{(5-7x)}$

23. $-\dfrac{1}{2\sqrt{3-t}}$ **25.** $\dfrac{4}{\pi}(\cos 3t-\sin 5t)$ **27.** $\dfrac{\csc\theta}{\cot\theta+\csc\theta}$

29. $2x\sin^4 x+4x^2\sin^3 x\cos x+\cos^{-2}x+2x\cos^{-3}x\sin x$

31. $(3x-2)^6-\dfrac{1}{x^3\left(4-\dfrac{1}{2x^2}\right)^2}$ **33.** $\dfrac{(4x+3)^3(4x+7)}{(x+1)^4}$

35. $(1-x)e^{-x}+3e^{3x}$ **37.** $\left(\dfrac{5}{2}x^2-3x+3\right)e^{5x/2}$

39. $\sqrt{x}\sec^2(2\sqrt{x})+\tan(2\sqrt{x})$ **41.** $\dfrac{2\sin\theta}{(1+\cos\theta)^2}$

43. $h'(\theta)=-\dfrac{2}{3}(\sin 2\theta)(1+\cos 2\theta)^{-2/3}$

45. $\dfrac{dq}{dt}=\left(\dfrac{t+2}{2(t+1)^{3/2}}\right)\cos\left(\dfrac{t}{\sqrt{t+1}}\right)$ **47.** $2\theta e^{-\theta^2}\sin(e^{-\theta^2})$

49. $2\pi\sin(\pi t-2)\cos(\pi t-2)$ **51.** $\dfrac{8\sin(2t)}{(1+\cos 2t)^5}$

53. $\dfrac{dy}{dt}=-2\pi\sin(\pi t-1)\cdot\cos(\pi t-1)\cdot e^{\cos^2(\pi t-1)}$

55. $-2\cos(\cos(2t-5))(\sin(2t-5))$

57. $\left(1+\tan^4\left(\dfrac{t}{12}\right)\right)^2\left(\tan^3\left(\dfrac{t}{12}\right)\sec^2\left(\dfrac{t}{12}\right)\right)$

59. $-\dfrac{t\sin(t^2)}{\sqrt{1+\cos(t^2)}}$ **61.** $\dfrac{6}{x^3}\left(1+\dfrac{1}{x}\right)\left(1+\dfrac{2}{x}\right)$

63. $2\csc^2(3x-1)\cot(3x-1)$ **65.** $y''=2(2x^2+1)e^{x^2}$

67. $5/2$ **69.** $-\pi/4$ **71.** 0

73. **(a)** $2/3$ **(b)** $2\pi+5$ **(c)** $15-8\pi$ **(d)** $37/6$ **(e)** -1 **(f)** $\sqrt{2}/24$ **(g)** $5/32$ **(h)** $-5/(3\sqrt{17})$

75. 5

77. **(a)** 1 **(b)** 1 **79.** **(a)** $y=\pi x+2-\pi$ **(b)** $\pi/2$

81.

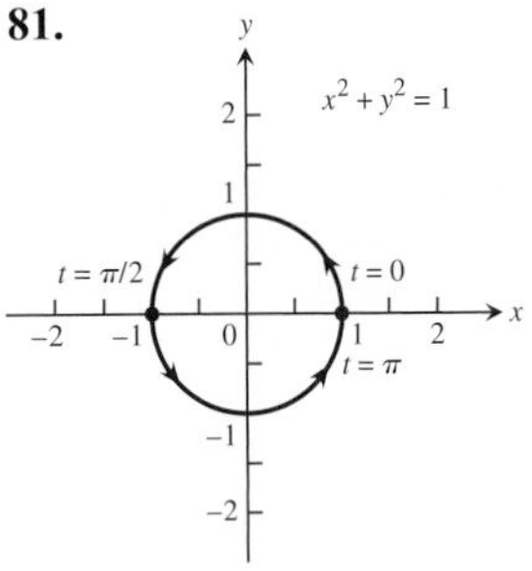

83.

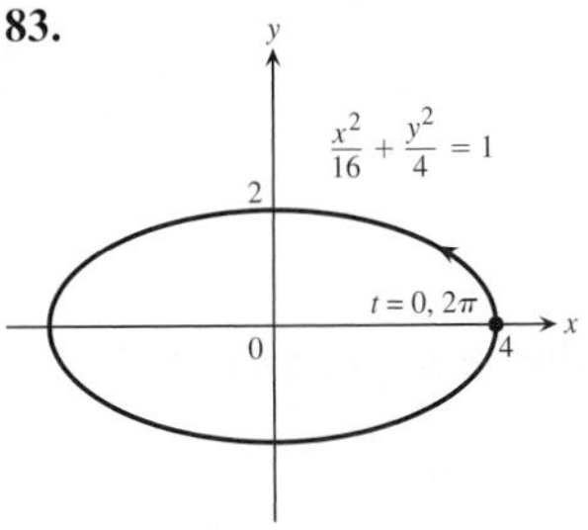

85.

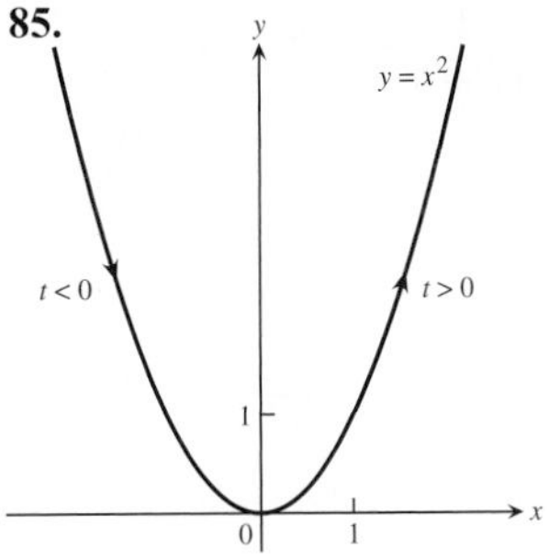

87.

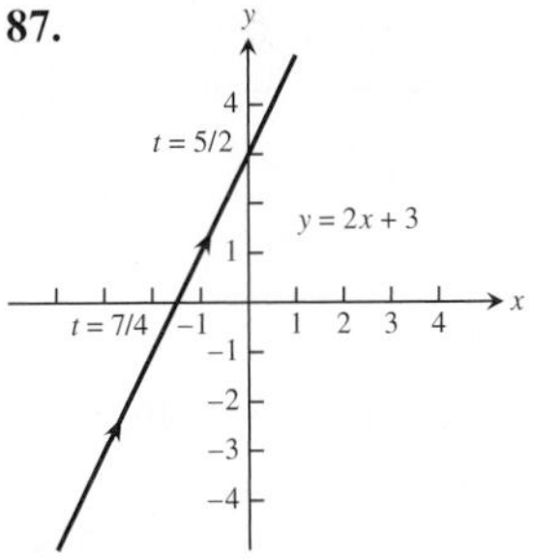

89.

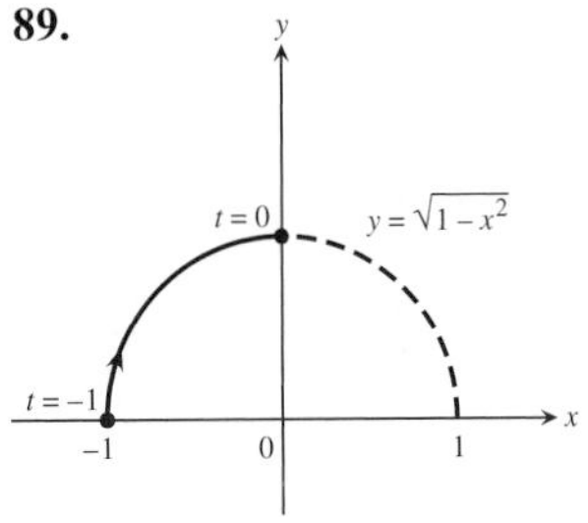

91.

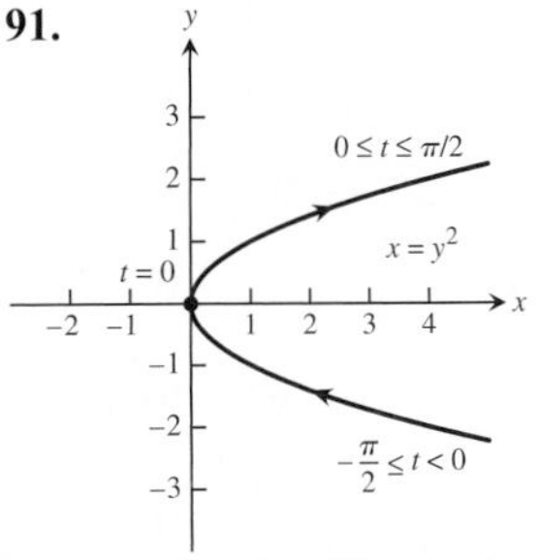

93. **(a)** $x=a\cos t, y=-a\sin t, 0\le t\le 2\pi$
(b) $x=a\cos t, y=a\sin t, 0\le t\le 2\pi$
(c) $x=a\cos t, y=-a\sin t, 0\le t\le 4\pi$
(d) $x=a\cos t, y=a\sin t, 0\le t\le 4\pi$

95. Possible answer: $x=-1+5t, y=-3+4t, 0\le t\le 1$

97. Possible answer: $x=t^2+1, y=t, t\le 0$

99. Possible answer: $x=2-3t, y=3-4t, t\ge 0$

101. $y=-x+2, \left.\dfrac{d^2y}{dx^2}\right|_{t=\pi/4}=-\sqrt{2}$

103. $y = x + \frac{1}{4}, \left.\frac{d^2y}{dx^2}\right|_{t=1/4} = -2$

105. $y = x - 4, \left.\frac{d^2y}{dx^2}\right|_{t=-1} = \frac{1}{2}$

107. $y = 2, \left.\frac{d^2y}{dx^2}\right|_{t=\pi/2} = -1$

109. It multiplies the velocity, acceleration, and jerk by 2, 4, and 8, respectively.

111. $v(6) = \frac{2}{5}$ m/sec, $a(6) = -\frac{4}{125}$ m/sec^2

121. $\left(\frac{\sqrt{2}}{2}, 1\right), y = 2x$ at $t = 0, y = -2x$ at $t = \pi$

Section 3.6, pp. 181–183

1. $\frac{-2xy - y^2}{x^2 + 2xy}$ **3.** $\frac{1 - 2y}{2x + 2y - 1}$

5. $\frac{-2x^3 + 3x^2y - xy^2 + x}{x^2y - x^3 + y}$ **7.** $\frac{1}{y(x+1)^2}$ **9.** $\cos^2 y$

11. $\frac{2e^{2x} - \cos(x + 3y)}{3\cos(x + 3y)}$ **13.** $\frac{-y^2}{y\sin\left(\frac{1}{y}\right) - \cos\left(\frac{1}{y}\right) + xy}$

15. $-\frac{\sqrt{r}}{\sqrt{\theta}}$ **17.** $\frac{-r}{\theta}$ **19.** $y' = -\frac{x}{y}, y'' = \frac{-y^2 - x^2}{y^3}$

21. $\frac{dy}{dx} = \frac{xe^{x^2} + 1}{y}, \frac{d^2y}{dx^2} = \frac{(2x^2y^2 + y^2 - 2x)e^{x^2} - x^2e^{2x^2} - 1}{y^3}$

23. $y' = \frac{\sqrt{y}}{\sqrt{y} + 1}, y'' = \frac{1}{2(\sqrt{y} + 1)^3}$

25. -2 **27.** $(-2, 1): m = -1, (-2, -1): m = 1$

29. (a) $y = \frac{7}{4}x - \frac{1}{2}$ **(b)** $y = -\frac{4}{7}x + \frac{29}{7}$

31. (a) $y = 3x + 6$ **(b)** $y = -\frac{1}{3}x + \frac{8}{3}$

33. (a) $y = \frac{6}{7}x + \frac{6}{7}$ **(b)** $y = -\frac{7}{6}x - \frac{7}{6}$

35. (a) $y = -\frac{\pi}{2}x + \pi$ **(b)** $y = \frac{2}{\pi}x - \frac{2}{\pi} + \frac{\pi}{2}$

37. (a) $y = 2\pi x - 2\pi$ **(b)** $y = -\frac{x}{2\pi} + \frac{1}{2\pi}$

39. Points: $(-\sqrt{7}, 0)$ and $(\sqrt{7}, 0)$, Slope: -2

41. $m = -1$ at $\left(\frac{\sqrt{3}}{4}, \frac{\sqrt{3}}{2}\right)$, $m = \sqrt{3}$ at $\left(\frac{\sqrt{3}}{4}, \frac{1}{2}\right)$

43. $(-3, 2): m = -\frac{27}{8}; (-3, -2): m = \frac{27}{8}; (3, 2): m = \frac{27}{8};$
$(3, -2): m = -\frac{27}{8}$

45. $-\frac{3}{16}$ **47.** -6 **49.** $(3, -1)$

53. $\frac{dy}{dx} = \frac{y^3 + 2xy}{x^2 + 3xy^2}, \frac{dx}{dy} = -\frac{x^2 + 3xy^2}{y^3 + 2xy}, \frac{dx}{dy} = \frac{1}{dy/dx}$

Section 3.7, pp. 192–193

1. (a) $f^{-1}(x) = \frac{x}{2} - \frac{3}{2}$

(b)

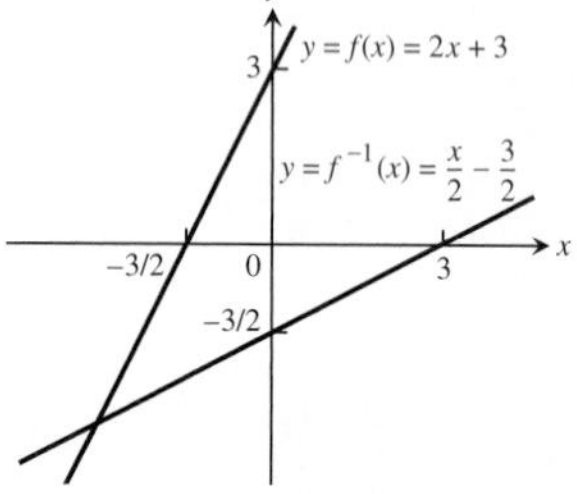

(c) $2, 1/2$

3. (a) $f^{-1}(x) = -\frac{x}{4} + \frac{5}{4}$

(b)

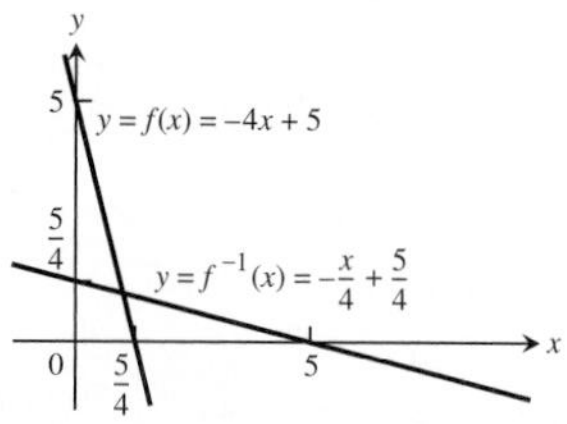

(c) $-4, -1/4$

5. (b)

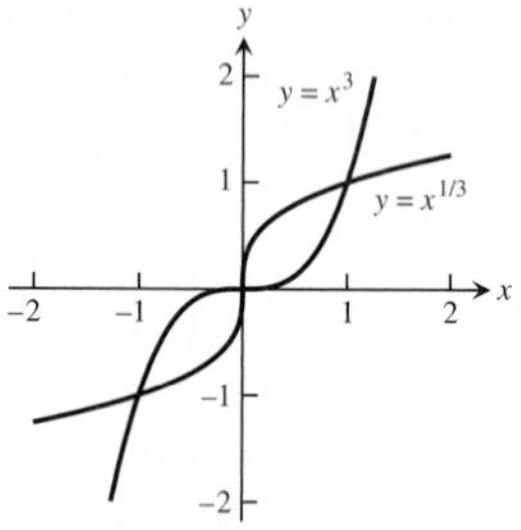

(c) Slope of f at $(1, 1): 3$; slope of g at $(1, 1)$: $1/3$; slope of f at $(-1, -1)$: 3; slope of g at $(-1, -1)$: $1/3$

(d) $y = 0$ is tangent to $y = x^3$ at $x = 0$; $x = 0$ is tangent to $y = \sqrt[3]{x}$ at $x = 0$

7. $1/9$ **9.** 3 **11.** $1/x$ **13.** $2/t$ **15.** $-1/x$ **17.** $\frac{1}{\theta + 1}$

19. $3/x$ **21.** $2(\ln t) + (\ln t)^2$ **23.** $x^3 \ln x$ **25.** $\frac{1 - \ln t}{t^2}$

27. $\frac{1}{x(1 + \ln x)^2}$ **29.** $\frac{1}{x \ln x}$ **31.** $2\cos(\ln\theta)$

33. $-\frac{3x + 2}{2x(x + 1)}$ **35.** $\frac{2}{t(1 - \ln t)^2}$ **37.** $\frac{\tan(\ln\theta)}{\theta}$

39. $\frac{10x}{x^2 + 1} + \frac{1}{2(1 - x)}$

41. $\left(\frac{1}{2}\right)\sqrt{x(x+1)}\left(\frac{1}{x}+\frac{1}{x+1}\right)=\frac{2x+1}{2\sqrt{x(x+1)}}$

43. $\left(\frac{1}{2}\right)\sqrt{\frac{t}{t+1}}\left(\frac{1}{t}-\frac{1}{t+1}\right)=\frac{1}{2\sqrt{t}\,(t+1)^{3/2}}$

45. $\sqrt{\theta+3}\,(\sin\theta)\left(\frac{1}{2(\theta+3)}+\cot\theta\right)$

47. $t(t+1)(t+2)\left[\frac{1}{t}+\frac{1}{t+1}+\frac{1}{t+2}\right]=3t^2+6t+2$

49. $\frac{\theta+5}{\theta\cos\theta}\left[\frac{1}{\theta+5}-\frac{1}{\theta}+\tan\theta\right]$

51. $\frac{x\sqrt{x^2+1}}{(x+1)^{2/3}}\left[\frac{1}{x}+\frac{x}{x^2+1}-\frac{2}{3(x+1)}\right]$

53. $\frac{1}{3}\sqrt[3]{\frac{x(x-2)}{x^2+1}}\left(\frac{1}{x}+\frac{1}{x-2}-\frac{2x}{x^2+1}\right)$ 55. $-2\tan\theta$

57. $\frac{1-t}{t}$ 59. $1/(1+e^{\theta})$ 61. $e^{\cos t}(1-t\sin t)$

63. $\frac{ye^y\cos x}{1-ye^y\sin x}$ 65. $\frac{dy}{dx}=\frac{y^2-xy\ln y}{x^2-xy\ln x}$ 67. $2^x\ln x$

69. $\left(\frac{\ln 5}{2\sqrt{s}}\right)5^{\sqrt{s}}$ 71. $\pi x^{(\pi-1)}$ 73. $\frac{1}{\theta\ln 2}$ 75. $\frac{3}{x\ln 4}$

77. $\frac{2(\ln r)}{r(\ln 2)(\ln 4)}$ 79. $\frac{-2}{(x+1)(x-1)}$

81. $\sin(\log_7\theta)+\frac{1}{\ln 7}\cos(\log_7\theta)$ 83. $\frac{1}{\ln 5}$

85. $\frac{1}{t}(\log_2 3)3^{\log_2 t}$ 87. $\frac{1}{t}$ 89. $(x+1)^x\left(\frac{x}{x+1}+\ln(x+1)\right)$

91. $(\sqrt{t})^t\left(\frac{\ln t}{2}+\frac{1}{2}\right)$ 93. $(\sin x)^x(\ln\sin x+x\cot x)$

95. $(x^{\ln x})\left(\frac{\ln x^2}{x}\right)$

Section 3.8, pp. 199–201

1. (a) $\pi/4$ (b) $-\pi/3$ (c) $\pi/6$
3. (a) $-\pi/6$ (b) $\pi/4$ (c) $-\pi/3$
5. (a) $\pi/3$ (b) $3\pi/4$ (c) $\pi/6$
7. (a) $3\pi/4$ (b) $\pi/6$ (c) $2\pi/3$
9. (a) $\pi/4$ (b) $-\pi/3$ (c) $\pi/6$
11. (a) $3\pi/4$ (b) $\pi/6$ (c) $2\pi/3$

13. $\pi/2$ 15. $\pi/2$ 17. $\pi/2$ 19. 0 21. $\frac{-2x}{\sqrt{1-x^4}}$

23. $\frac{\sqrt{2}}{\sqrt{1-2t^2}}$ 25. $\frac{1}{|2s+1|\sqrt{s^2+s}}$

27. $\frac{-2x}{(x^2+1)\sqrt{x^4+2x^2}}$ 29. $\frac{-1}{\sqrt{1-t^2}}$

31. $\frac{-1}{2\sqrt{t}\,(1+t)}$ 33. $\frac{1}{(\tan^{-1}x)(1+x^2)}$

35. $\frac{-e^t}{|e^t|\sqrt{(e^t)^2-1}}=\frac{-1}{\sqrt{e^{2t}-1}}$ 37. $\frac{-2s^n}{\sqrt{1-s^2}}$ 39. 0

41. $\sin^{-1}x$

49. (a) Defined; there is an angle whose tangent is 2.
(b) Not defined; there is no angle whose cosine is 2.

51. (a) Not defined; no angle has secant 0.
(b) Not defined; no angle has sine $\sqrt{2}$.

61. (a) Domain: all real numbers except those having the form $\frac{\pi}{2}+k\pi$ where k is an integer; range: $-\pi/2<y<\pi/2$.
(b) Domain: $-\infty<x<\infty$; range: $-\infty<y<\infty$

63. (a) Domain: $-\infty<x<\infty$; range: $0\le y\le\pi$
(b) Domain: $-1\le x\le 1$; range: $-1\le y\le 1$

65. The graphs are identical.

Section 3.9, pp. 205–209

1. $\frac{dA}{dt}=2\pi r\frac{dr}{dt}$

3. (a) $\frac{dV}{dt}=\pi r^2\frac{dh}{dt}$ (b) $\frac{dV}{dt}=2\pi hr\frac{dr}{dt}$
(c) $\frac{dV}{dt}=\pi r^2\frac{dh}{dt}+2\pi hr\frac{dr}{dt}$

5. (a) 1 volt/sec (b) $-\frac{1}{3}$ amp/sec
(c) $\frac{dR}{dt}=\frac{1}{I}\left(\frac{dV}{dt}-\frac{V}{I}\frac{dI}{dt}\right)$
(d) 3/2 ohms/sec, R is increasing.

7. (a) $\frac{ds}{dt}=\frac{x}{\sqrt{x^2+y^2}}\frac{dx}{dt}$
(b) $\frac{ds}{dt}=\frac{x}{\sqrt{x^2+y^2}}\frac{dx}{dt}+\frac{y}{\sqrt{x^2+y^2}}\frac{dy}{dt}$ (c) $\frac{dx}{dt}=-\frac{y}{x}\frac{dy}{dt}$

9. (a) $\frac{dA}{dt}=\frac{1}{2}ab\cos\theta\frac{d\theta}{dt}$
(b) $\frac{dA}{dt}=\frac{1}{2}ab\cos\theta\frac{d\theta}{dt}+\frac{1}{2}b\sin\theta\frac{da}{dt}$
(c) $\frac{dA}{dt}=\frac{1}{2}ab\cos\theta\frac{d\theta}{dt}+\frac{1}{2}b\sin\theta\frac{da}{dt}+\frac{1}{2}a\sin\theta\frac{db}{dt}$

11. (a) 14 cm^2/sec, increasing (b) 0 cm/sec, constant
(c) $-14/13$ cm/sec, decreasing

13. (a) -12 ft/sec (b) -59.5 ft^2/sec (c) -1 rad/sec

15. 20 ft/sec

17. (a) $\frac{dh}{dt}=11.19$ cm/min (b) $\frac{dr}{dt}=14.92$ cm/min

19. (a) $\frac{-1}{24\pi}$ m/min (b) $r=\sqrt{26y-y^2}$ m,
(c) $\frac{dr}{dt}=-\frac{5}{288\pi}$ m/min

21. 1 ft/min, 40π ft^2/min 23. 11 ft/sec

25. Increasing at 466/1681 L/min 27. 1 rad/sec

29. -5 m/sec **31.** -1500 ft/sec

33. $\frac{5}{72\pi}$ in./min, $\frac{10}{3}$ in.^{2}/min **35.** 7.1 in./min

37. **(a)** $-32/\sqrt{13} \approx -8.875$ ft/sec,
(b) $d\theta_1/dt = 8/65$ rad/sec, $d\theta_2/dt = -8/65$ rad/sec
(c) $d\theta_1/dt = 1/6$ rad/sec, $d\theta_2/dt = -1/6$ rad/sec

Section 3.10, pp. 218–220

1. $L(x) = 10x - 13$ **3.** $L(x) = 2$ **5.** $L(x) = x - \pi$

7. $2x$ **9.** -5 **11.** $\frac{1}{12}x + \frac{4}{3}$ **13.** $1 - x$

15. $f(0) = 1$. Also, $f'(x) = k(1+x)^{k-1}$, so $f'(0) = k$. This means the linearization at $x = 0$ is $L(x) = 1 + kx$.

17. **(a)** 1.01 **(b)** 1.003

19. $\left(3x^2 - \frac{3}{2\sqrt{x}}\right) dx$ **21.** $\frac{2 - 2x^2}{(1 + x^2)^2}\, dx$

23. $\frac{1 - y}{3\sqrt{y} + x}\, dx$ **25.** $\frac{5}{2\sqrt{x}} \cos(5\sqrt{x})\, dx$

27. $(4x^2) \sec^2\left(\frac{x^3}{3}\right) dx$

29. $\frac{3}{\sqrt{x}} (\csc(1 - 2\sqrt{x}) \cot(1 - 2\sqrt{x}))\, dx$

31. $\frac{1}{2\sqrt{x}} \cdot e^{\sqrt{x}}\, dx$ **33.** $\frac{2x}{1 + x^2}\, dx$ **35.** $\frac{2xe^{x^2}}{1 + e^{2x^2}}\, dx$

37. $\frac{-1}{\sqrt{e^{-2x} - 1}}\, dx$ **39.** **(a)** .41 **(b)** .4 **(c)** .01

41. **(a)** .231 **(b)** .2 **(c)** .031

43. **(a)** $-1/3$ **(b)** $-2/5$ **(c)** $1/15$ **45.** $dV = 4\pi r_0^2\, dr$

47. $dS = 12x_0\, dx$ **49.** $dV = 2\pi r_0 h\, dr$

51. **(a)** 0.08π m^2 **(b)** 2% **53.** $dV \approx 565.5$ in.^{3}

55. $\frac{1}{3}$% **57.** 0.05%

59. The ratio equals 37.87, so a change in the acceleration of gravity on the moon has about 38 times the effect that a change of the same magnitude has on Earth.

61. 3% **63.** 3%

67. **(a)** $L(x) = 1 + (\ln 2)x \approx 0.69x + 1$

Section 3.11, pp. 227–228

1. $\cosh x = 5/4$, $\tanh x = -3/5$, $\coth x = -5/3$, $\operatorname{sech} x = 4/5$, $\operatorname{csch} x = -4/3$

3. $\sinh x = 8/15$, $\tanh x = 8/17$, $\coth x = 17/8$, $\operatorname{sech} x = 15/17$, $\operatorname{csch} x = 15/8$

5. $x + \frac{1}{x}$ **7.** e^{5x} **9.** e^{4x} **13.** $2 \cosh \frac{x}{3}$

15. $\operatorname{sech}^2\sqrt{t} + \frac{\tanh\sqrt{t}}{\sqrt{t}}$ **17.** $\coth z$

19. $(\ln \operatorname{sech} \theta)(\operatorname{sech} \theta \tanh \theta)$ **21.** $\tanh^3 v$ **23.** 2

25. $\frac{1}{2\sqrt{x(1 + x)}}$ **27.** $\frac{1}{1 + \theta} - \tanh^{-1}\theta$

29. $\frac{1}{2\sqrt{t}} - \coth^{-1}\sqrt{t}$ **31.** $-\operatorname{sech}^{-1} x$ **33.** $\frac{\ln 2}{\sqrt{1 + \left(\frac{1}{2}\right)^{2\theta}}}$

35. $|\sec x|$ **37.** $\ln(2/3)$ **39.** $\frac{-\ln 3}{2}$ **41.** $\ln 3$

45. **(b)** $\sqrt{\frac{mg}{k}}$ **(c)** $80\sqrt{5} \approx 178.89$ ft/sec

47. **(a)** 1 **(b)** -1 **(c)** ∞ **(d)** $-\infty$
(e) 0 **(f)** 1 **(g)** ∞ **(h)** $-\infty$
(i) 0

Practice Exercises, pp. 228–233

1. $5x^4 - 0.25x + 0.25$ **3.** $3x(x - 2)$

5. $2(x + 1)(2x^2 + 4x + 1)$

7. $3(\theta^2 + \sec\theta + 1)^2 (2\theta + \sec\theta\tan\theta)$

9. $\frac{1}{2\sqrt{t}(1 + \sqrt{t})^2}$ **11.** $2 \sec^2 x \tan x$

13. $8 \cos^3(1 - 2t) \sin(1 - 2t)$

15. $5(\sec t)(\sec t + \tan t)^5$

17. $\frac{\theta\cos\theta + \sin\theta}{\sqrt{2\theta\sin\theta}}$ **19.** $\frac{\cos\sqrt{2\theta}}{\sqrt{2\theta}}$

21. $x \csc\left(\frac{2}{x}\right) + \csc\left(\frac{2}{x}\right) \cot\left(\frac{2}{x}\right)$

23. $\frac{1}{2}x^{1/2} \sec(2x)^2 \left[16 \tan(2x)^2 - x^{-2}\right]$

25. $-10x \csc^2(x^2)$ **27.** $8x^3 \sin(2x^2) \cos(2x^2) + 2x \sin^2(2x^2)$

29. $\frac{-(t + 1)}{8t^3}$ **31.** $\frac{1 - x}{(x + 1)^3}$ **33.** $\frac{-1}{2x^2\left(1 + \frac{1}{x}\right)^{1/2}}$

35. $\frac{-2\sin\theta}{(\cos\theta - 1)^2}$ **37.** $3\sqrt{2x + 1}$ **39.** $-9\left[\frac{5x + \cos 2x}{(5x^2 + \sin 2x)^{5/2}}\right]$

41. $-2e^{-x/5}$ **43.** xe^{4x} **45.** $\frac{2\sin\theta\cos\theta}{\sin^2\theta} = 2\cot\theta$

47. $\frac{2}{(\ln 2)x}$ **49.** $-8^{-t}(\ln 8)$ **51.** $18x^{2.6}$

53. $(x + 2)^{x+2}(\ln(x + 2) + 1)$ **55.** $-\frac{1}{\sqrt{1 - u^2}}$

57. $\frac{-1}{\sqrt{1 - x^2}\cos^{-1} x}$ **59.** $\tan^{-1}(t) + \frac{t}{1 + t^2} - \frac{1}{2t}$

61. $\frac{1 - z}{\sqrt{z^2 - 1}} + \sec^{-1} z$ **63.** -1 **65.** $-\frac{y + 2}{x + 3}$

67. $\frac{-3x^2 - 4y + 2}{4x - 4y^{1/3}}$ **69.** $-\frac{y}{x}$ **71.** $\frac{1}{2y(x + 1)^2}$

73. $-1/2$ **75.** y/x **77.** $\dfrac{2e^{-\tan^{-1}x}}{1+x^2}$ **79.** $\dfrac{dp}{dq} = \dfrac{6q-4p}{3p^2+4q}$

81. $\dfrac{dr}{ds} = (2r-1)(\tan 2s)$

83. (a) $\dfrac{d^2y}{dx^2} = \dfrac{-2xy^3-2x^4}{y^5}$ **(b)** $\dfrac{d^2y}{dx^2} = \dfrac{-2xy^2-1}{x^4y^3}$

85. (a) 7 **(b)** -2 **(c)** $5/12$ **(d)** $1/4$ **(e)** 12 **(f)** $9/2$ **(g)** $3/4$

87. 0 **89.** $\dfrac{3\sqrt{2}e^{\sqrt{3}/2}}{4}\cos\left(e^{\sqrt{3}/2}\right)$

91. $-\dfrac{1}{2}$ **93.** $\dfrac{-2}{(2t+1)^2}$

95. (a)

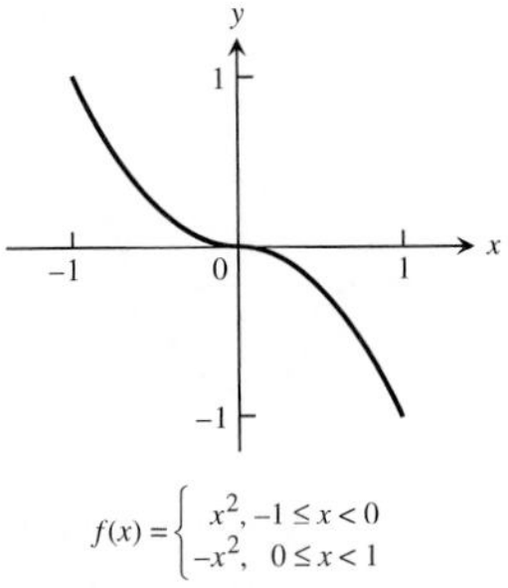

(b) Yes **(c)** Yes

97. (a)

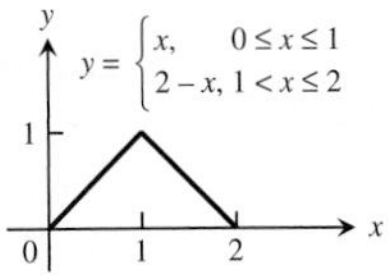

(b) Yes **(c)** No

99. $\left(\dfrac{5}{2}, \dfrac{9}{4}\right)$ and $\left(\dfrac{3}{2}, -\dfrac{1}{4}\right)$ **101.** $(-1, 27)$ and $(2, 0)$

103. (a) $(-2, 16), (3, 11)$ **(b)** $(0, 20), (1, 7)$

105.

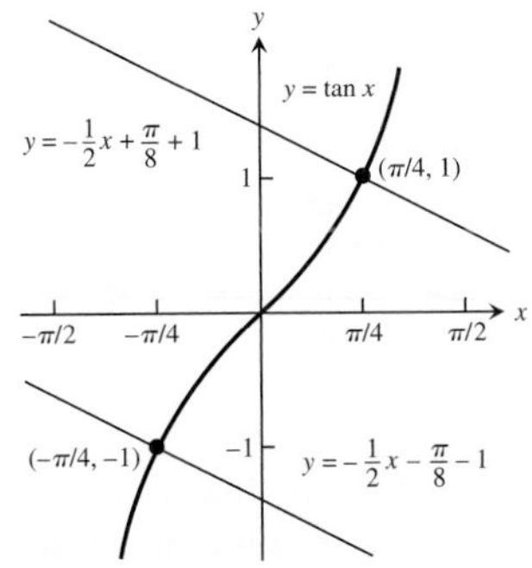

107. $\dfrac{1}{4}$ **109.** 4

111. Tangent: $y = -\dfrac{1}{4}x + \dfrac{9}{4}$, normal: $y = 4x - 2$

113. Tangent: $y = 2x - 4$, normal: $y = -\dfrac{1}{2}x + \dfrac{7}{2}$

115. Tangent: $y = -\dfrac{5}{4}x + 6$, normal: $y = \dfrac{4}{5}x - \dfrac{11}{5}$

117. $(1, 1)$: $m = -\dfrac{1}{2}$; $(1, -1)$: m not defined

119. $y = \left(\dfrac{\sqrt{3}}{2}\right)x + \dfrac{1}{4}, \dfrac{1}{4}$

121. B = graph of f, A = graph of f'

123.

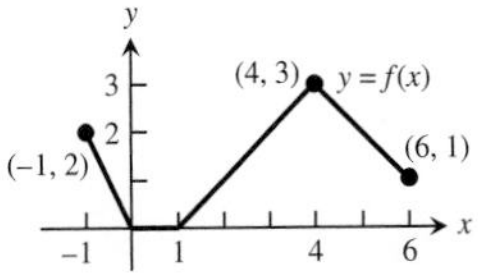

125. (a) 0, 0 **(b)** 1700 rabbits, $\approx$1400 rabbits

127. -1 **129.** $1/2$ **131.** 4 **133.** 1

137. $\dfrac{2(x^2+1)}{\sqrt{\cos 2x}}\left[\dfrac{2x}{x^2+1} + \tan 2x\right]$

139. $5\left[\dfrac{(t+1)(t-1)}{(t-2)(t+3)}\right]^5\left[\dfrac{1}{t+1} + \dfrac{1}{t-1} - \dfrac{1}{t-2} - \dfrac{1}{t+3}\right]$

141. $\dfrac{1}{\sqrt{\theta}}(\sin\theta)^{\sqrt{\theta}}\left(\dfrac{\ln\sqrt{\sin\theta}}{2} + \theta\cot\theta\right)$

143. $3\sinh 6x$ **145.** $-(\cosh y \coth y)/\sqrt{1-x^2}$

147. $(1+y^2)/(1-x^2)$ **149.** $y\,\text{csch}(\ln y)$ **151.** $|\sec x|$

153. (a) $\dfrac{dS}{dt} = (4\pi r + 2\pi h)\dfrac{dr}{dt}$ **(b)** $\dfrac{dS}{dt} = 2\pi r\dfrac{dh}{dt}$

(c) $\dfrac{dS}{dt} = (4\pi r + 2\pi h)\dfrac{dr}{dt} + 2\pi r\dfrac{dh}{dt}$

(d) $\dfrac{dr}{dt} = -\dfrac{r}{2r+h}\dfrac{dh}{dt}$

155. $-40\ \text{m}^2/\text{sec}$ **157.** 0.02 ohm/sec **159.** 22 m/sec

161. (a) $r = \dfrac{2}{5}h$ **(b)** $-\dfrac{125}{144\pi}$ ft/min

163. (a) $\dfrac{3}{5}$ km/sec or 600 m/sec **(b)** $\dfrac{18}{\pi}$ rpm

165. (a) $L(x) = 2x + \dfrac{\pi-2}{2}$

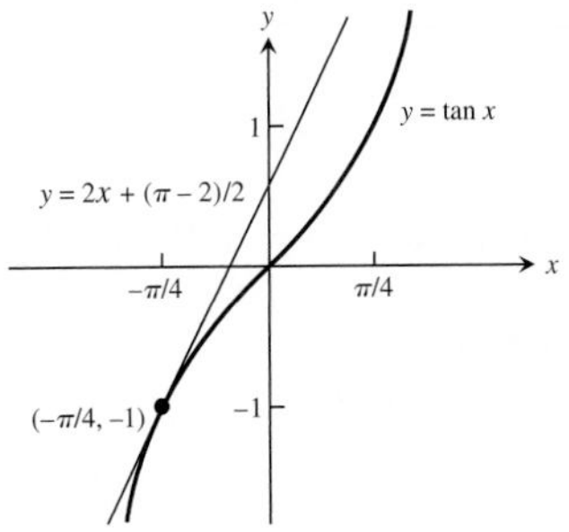

(b) $L(x) = -\sqrt{2}x + \dfrac{\sqrt{2}(4 - \pi)}{4}$

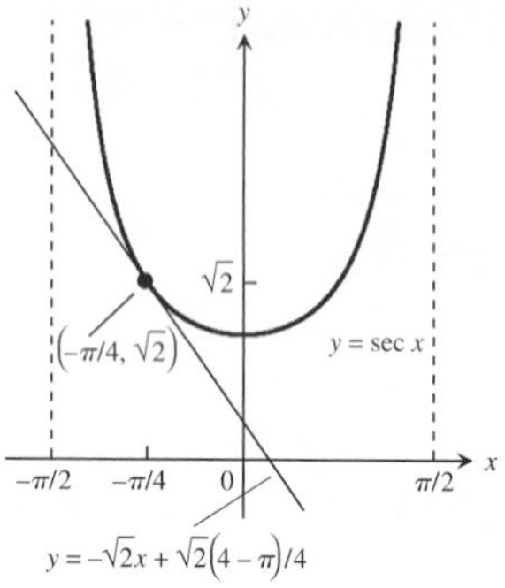

167. $L(x) = 1.5x + 0.5$ **169.** $dS = \dfrac{\pi r h_0}{\sqrt{r^2 + h_0^2}}\,dh$

171. (a) 4% **(b)** 8% **(c)** 12%

Additional and Advanced Exercises, pp. 234–236

1. (a) $\sin 2\theta = 2\sin\theta\cos\theta$; $2\cos 2\theta = 2\sin\theta(-\sin\theta) + \cos\theta(2\cos\theta)$; $2\cos 2\theta = -2\sin^2\theta + 2\cos^2\theta$; $\cos 2\theta = \cos^2\theta - \sin^2\theta$
(b) $\cos 2\theta = \cos^2\theta - \sin^2\theta$; $-2\sin 2\theta = 2\cos\theta(-\sin\theta) - 2\sin\theta(\cos\theta)$; $\sin 2\theta = \cos\theta\sin\theta + \sin\theta\cos\theta$; $\sin 2\theta = 2\sin\theta\cos\theta$

3. (a) $a = 1, b = 0, c = -\dfrac{1}{2}$ **(b)** $b = \cos a$, $c = \sin a$

5. $h = -4, k = \dfrac{9}{2}, a = \dfrac{5\sqrt{5}}{2}$

7. (a) $0.09y$ **(b)** Increasing at 1% per year

9. Answers will vary. Here is one possibility.

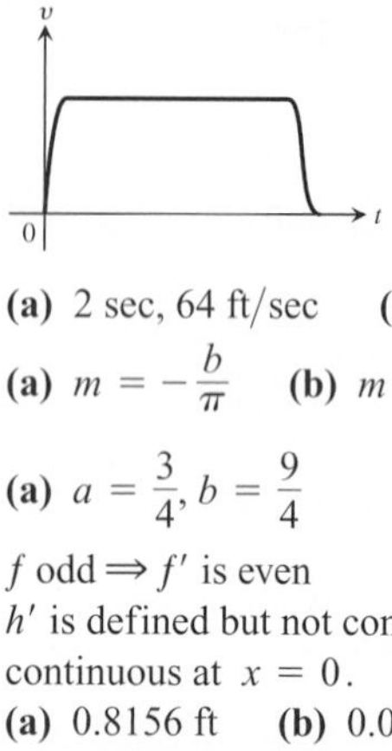

11. (a) 2 sec, 64 ft/sec **(b)** 12.31 sec, 393.85 ft

15. (a) $m = -\dfrac{b}{\pi}$ **(b)** $m = -1, b = \pi$

17. (a) $a = \dfrac{3}{4}, b = \dfrac{9}{4}$

19. f odd $\Rightarrow f'$ is even

23. h' is defined but not continuous at $x = 0$; k' is defined *and* continuous at $x = 0$.

27. (a) 0.8156 ft **(b)** 0.00613 sec
(c) It will lose about 8.83 min/day.

CHAPTER 4

Section 4.1, pp. 243–245

1. Absolute minimum at $x = c_2$; absolute maximum at $x = b$
3. Absolute maximum at $x = c$; no absolute minimum
5. Absolute minimum at $x = a$; absolute maximum at $x = c$
7. Local minimum at $(-1, 0)$; local maximum at $(1, 0)$
9. Maximum at $(0, 5)$ **11.** (c) **13.** (d)

15. Absolute maximum: -3; absolute minimum: $-19/3$

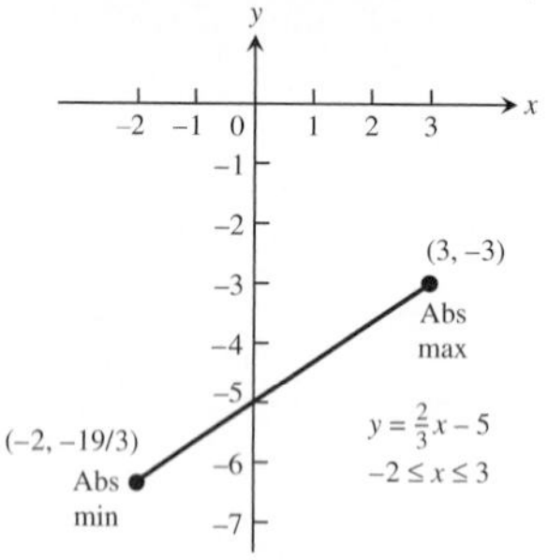

17. Absolute maximum: 3; absolute minimum: -1

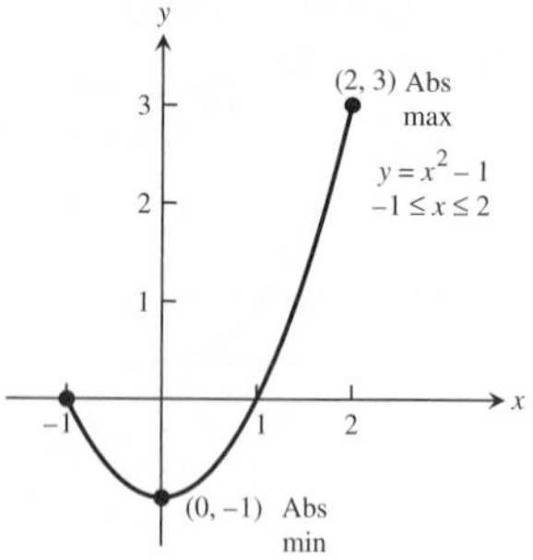

19. Absolute maximum: -0.25; absolute minimum: -4

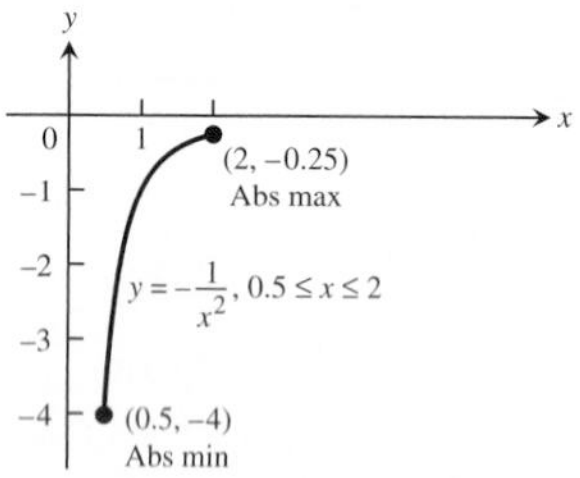

21. Absolute maximum: 2; absolute minimum: -1

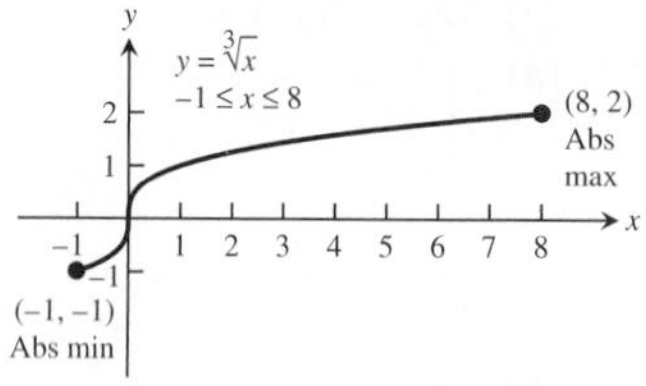

23. Absolute maximum: 2; absolute minimum: 0

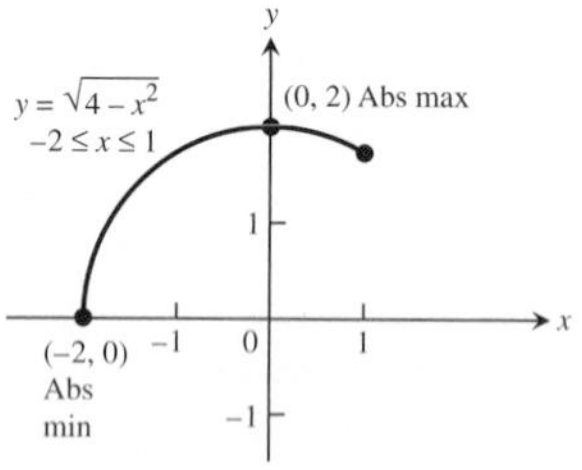

25. Absolute maximum: 1; absolute minimum: -1

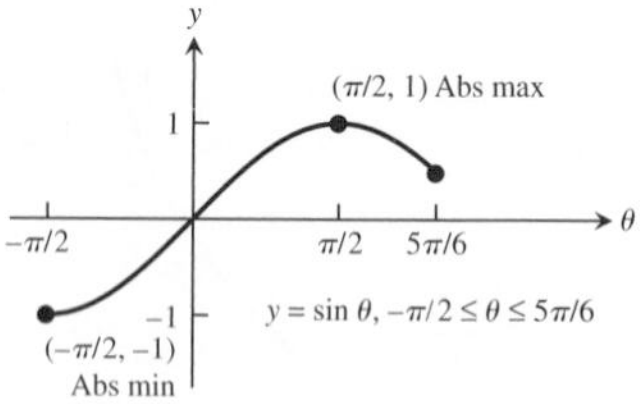

27. Absolute maximum: $2/\sqrt{3}$; absolute minimum: 1

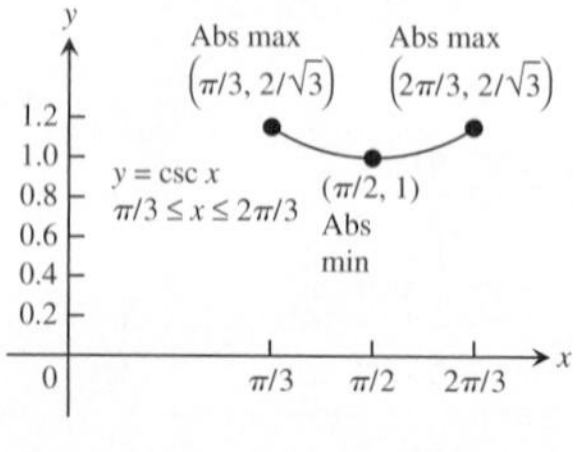

29. Absolute maximum: 2; absolute minimum: -1

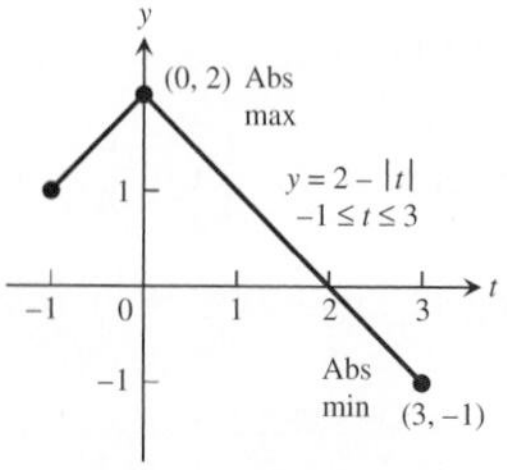

31. Absolute maximum: $1/e$; absolute minimum: $-e$

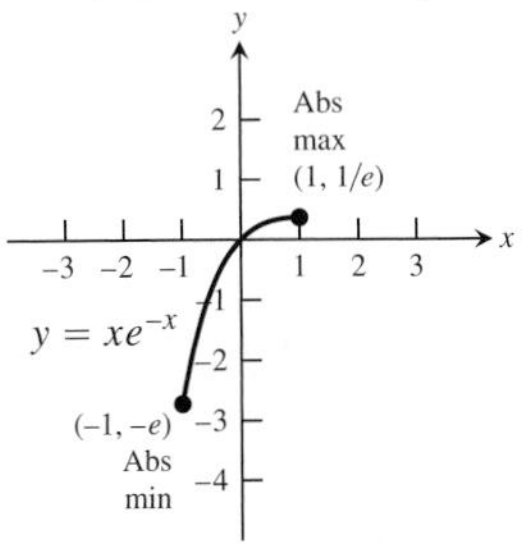

33. Absolute maximum at $(4, \frac{1}{4} + \ln 4)$; absolute minimum at $(1, 1)$

35. Increasing on $(0, 8)$, decreasing on $(-1, 0)$; absolute maximum: 16 at $x = 8$; absolute minimum: 0 at $x = 0$

37. Increasing on $(-32, 1)$; absolute maximum: 1 at $\theta = 1$; absolute minimum: -8 at $\theta = -32$

39. Minimum value is 1 at $x = 2$.

41. Local maximum at $(-2, 17)$; local minimum at $\left(\frac{4}{3}, -\frac{41}{27}\right)$

43. Minimum value is 0 at $x = -1$ and $x = 1$.

45. There is a local minimum at $(0, 1)$.

47. Maximum value is $\frac{1}{2}$ at $x = 1$; minimum value is $-\frac{1}{2}$ at $x = -1$.

49. Minimum value is 2 at $(0, 2)$.

51. Minimum value is $\frac{-1}{e}$ at $\left(\frac{1}{e}, \frac{-1}{e}\right)$

53. Maximum value is $\frac{\pi}{2}$ at $\left(0, \frac{\pi}{2}\right)$

Minimum value is 0 at $(\pm 1, 0)$

55.

Critical point	Derivative	Extremum	Value
$x = -\frac{4}{5}$	0	Local max	$\frac{12}{25} 10^{1/3} = 1.034$
$x = 0$	Undefined	Local min	0

57.

Critical point	Derivative	Extremum	Value
$x = -2$	Undefined	Local max	0
$x = -\sqrt{2}$	0	Minimum	-2
$x = \sqrt{2}$	0	Maximum	2
$x = 2$	Undefined	Local min	0

59.

Critical point	Derivative	Extremum	Value
$x = 1$	Undefined	Minimum	2

61.

Critical point	Derivative	Extremum	Value
$x = -1$	0	Maximum	5
$x = 1$	Undefined	Local min	1
$x = 3$	0	Maximum	5

63. **(a)** No
(b) The derivative is defined and nonzero for $x \neq 2$. Also, $f(2) = 0$ and $f(x) > 0$ for all $x \neq 2$.
(c) No, because $(-\infty, \infty)$ is not a closed interval.
(d) The answers are the same as parts (a) and (b) with 2 replaced by a.

65. Yes **67.** g assumes a local maximum at $-c$.

69. **(a)** Maximum value is 144 at $x = 2$.
(b) The largest volume of the box is 144 cubic units, and it occurs when $x = 2$.

71. $\frac{{v_0}^2}{2g} + s_0$

73. Maximum value is 11 at $x = 5$; minimum value is 5 on the interval $[-3, 2]$; local maximum at $(-5, 9)$.

75. Maximum value is 5 on the interval $[3, \infty)$; minimum value is -5 on the interval $(-\infty, -2]$.

Section 4.2, pp. 251–253

1. 1/2

3. $c = \pm\sqrt{1 - \frac{4}{\pi^2}} \approx \pm 0.771$

5. Does not; f is not differentiable at the interior domain point $x = 0$.

7. Does

11. **(a)**

i)

ii)

iii)

iv)

23. Yes **25.** **(a)** 4 **(b)** 3 **(c)** 3

27. **(a)** $\frac{x^2}{2} + C$ **(b)** $\frac{x^3}{3} + C$ **(c)** $\frac{x^4}{4} + C$

29. **(a)** $y = -\ln|x| + C$ **(b)** $y = x - \ln|x| + C$
(c) $y = 5x + \ln|x| + C$

31. **(a)** $-\frac{1}{2}\cos 2t + C$ **(b)** $2\sin\frac{t}{2} + C$
(c) $-\frac{1}{2}\cos 2t + 2\sin\frac{t}{2} + C$

33. $f(x) = x^2 - x$ **35.** $f(x) = 1 + \frac{e^{2x}}{2}$

37. $s = 4.9t^2 + 5t + 10$ **39.** $s = \frac{1 - \cos(\pi t)}{\pi}$

41. $s = e^t + 19t + 4$ **43.** $s = \sin(2t) - 3$

45. If $T(t)$ is the temperature of the thermometer at time t, then $T(0) = -19$ °C and $T(14) = 100$ °C. From the Mean Value Theorem, there exists a $0 < t_0 < 14$ such that $\frac{T(14) - T(0)}{14 - 0} = 8.5$ °C/sec $= T'(t_0)$, the rate at which the temperature was changing at $t = t_0$ as measured by the rising mercury on the thermometer.

47. Because its average speed was approximately 7.667 knots, and by the Mean Value Theorem, it must have been going that speed at least once during the trip.

51. The conclusion of the Mean Value Theorem yields

$$\frac{\frac{1}{b}-\frac{1}{a}}{b-a} = -\frac{1}{c^2} \Rightarrow c^2\left(\frac{a-b}{ab}\right) = a - b \Rightarrow c = \sqrt{ab}.$$

55. $f(x)$ must be zero at least once between a and b by the Intermediate Value Theorem. Now suppose that $f(x)$ is zero twice between a and b. Then, by the Mean Value Theorem, $f'(x)$ would have to be zero at least once between the two zeros of $f(x)$, but this can't be true since we are given that $f'(x) \neq 0$ on this interval. Therefore, $f(x)$ is zero once and only once between a and b.

61. $1.09999 \le f(0.1) \le 1.1$

Section 4.3, pp. 258–259

1. **(a)** 0, 1
(b) increasing on $(-\infty, 0)$ and $(1, \infty)$, decreasing on $(0, 1)$
(c) local maximum at $x = 0$, local minimum at $x = 1$

3. **(a)** $-2, 1$
(b) increasing on $(-2, 1)$ and $(1, \infty)$, decreasing on $(-\infty, -2)$
(c) no local maximum, local minimum at $x = -2$

5. **(a)** Critical point at $x = 1$
(b) increasing on $[1, \infty)$, decreasing on $(-\infty, 1]$
(c) local (and absolute) minimum at $x = 1$

7. **(a)** $-2, 0$
(b) increasing on $(-\infty, -2)$ and $(0, \infty)$, decreasing on $(-2, 0)$
(c) local maximum at $x = -2$, local minimum at $x = 0$

9. **(a)** Increasing on $(-\infty, -1.5)$, decreasing on $(-1.5, \infty)$
(b) local maximum: 5.25 at $t = -1.5$
(c) absolute maximum: 5.25 at $t = -1.5$

11. **(a)** Decreasing on $(-\infty, 0)$, increasing on $(0, 4/3)$, decreasing on $(4/3, \infty)$
(b) local minimum at $x = 0$ $(0, 0)$, local maximum at $x = 4/3$ $(4/3, 32/27)$
(c) no absolute extrema

13. **(a)** Decreasing on $(-\infty, 0)$, increasing on $(0, 1/2)$, decreasing on $(1/2, \infty)$
(b) local minimum at $\theta = 0$ $(0, 0)$, local maximum at $\theta = 1/2$ $(1/2, 1/4)$
(c) no absolute extrema

15. **(a)** Increasing on $(-\infty, \infty)$, never decreasing
(b) no local extrema
(c) no absolute extrema

17. **(a)** Increasing on $(-2, 0)$ and $(2, \infty)$, decreasing on $(-\infty, -2)$ and $(0, 2)$
(b) local maximum: 16 at $x = 0$, local minimum: 0 at $x = \pm 2$
(c) no absolute maximum; absolute minimum: 0 at $x = \pm 2$

19. **(a)** Increasing on $(-\infty, -1)$, decreasing on $(-1, 0)$, increasing on $(0, 1)$, decreasing on $(1, \infty)$
(b) local maximum at $x = \pm 1$ $(1, 0.5)$, $(-1, 0.5)$, local minimum at $x = 0$ $(0, 0)$
(c) absolute maximum: 1/2 at $x = \pm 1$; no absolute minimum

21. **(a)** Decreasing on $(-2\sqrt{2}, -2)$, increasing on $(-2, 2)$, decreasing on $(2, 2\sqrt{2})$
(b) local minima: $g(-2) = -4$, $g(2\sqrt{2}) = 0$;
local maxima: $g(-2\sqrt{2}) = 0$, $g(2) = 4$
(c) absolute maximum: 4 at $x = 2$;
absolute minimum: -4 at $x = -2$

23. **(a)** Increasing on $(-\infty, 1)$, decreasing when $1 < x < 2$, decreasing when $2 < x < 3$, discontinuous at $x = 2$, increasing on $(3, \infty)$
(b) local minimum at $x = 3$ $(3, 6)$,
local maximum at $x = 1$ $(1, 2)$
(c) no absolute extrema

25. **(a)** Increasing on $(-2, 0)$ and $(0, \infty)$, decreasing on $(-\infty, -2)$
(b) local minimum: $-6\sqrt[3]{2}$ at $x = -2$
(c) no absolute maximum; absolute minimum: $-6\sqrt[3]{2}$ at $x = -2$

27. **(a)** Increasing on $(-\infty, -2/\sqrt{7})$ and $(2/\sqrt{7}, \infty)$, decreasing on $(-2/\sqrt{7}, 0)$ and $(0, 2/\sqrt{7})$
(b) local maximum: $24\sqrt[3]{2}/7^{7/6} \approx 3.12$ at $x = -2/\sqrt{7}$;
local minimum: $-24\sqrt[3]{2}/7^{7/6} \approx -3.12$ at $x = 2/\sqrt{7}$
(c) no absolute extrema

29. **(a)** Increasing on $\left(\frac{1}{3}\ln 1/2, \infty\right)$,
decreasing on $\left(-\infty, \frac{1}{3}\ln 1/2\right)$
(b) local minimum: $\frac{3}{2^{2/3}}$ at $x = \frac{1}{3}\ln\left(\frac{1}{2}\right)$
(c) absolute minimum: $\frac{3}{2^{2/3}}$ at $x = \frac{1}{3}\ln\left(\frac{1}{2}\right)$

31. **(a)** Increasing on $\left(\frac{1}{e}, \infty\right)$, decreasing on $(0, 1/e)$
(b) local minimum: $\frac{-1}{e}$ at $x = \frac{1}{e}$
(c) absolute minimum: $\frac{-1}{e}$ at $x = \frac{1}{e}$

33. **(a)** Local maximum: 1 at $x = 1$; local minimum: 0 at $x = 2$
(b) absolute maximum: 1 at $x = 1$; no absolute minimum

35. **(a)** Local maximum: 1 at $x = 1$; local minimum: 0 at $x = 2$
(b) no absolute maximum; absolute minimum: 0 at $x = 2$

37. **(a)** Local maxima: -9 at $t = -3$ and 16 at $t = 2$; local minimum: -16 at $t = -2$
(b) absolute maximum: 16 at $t = 2$; no absolute minimum

39. **(a)** Local minimum: 0 at $x = 0$
(b) no absolute maximum; absolute minimum: 0 at $x = 0$

41. **(a)** Local minimum: $(\pi/3) - \sqrt{3}$ at $x = 2\pi/3$; local maximum: 0 at $x = 0$; local maximum: π at $x = 2\pi$

43. **(a)** Local minimum: 0 at $x = \pi/4$

45. Local maximum: 3 at $\theta = 0$; local minimum: -3 at $\theta = 2\pi$

47.

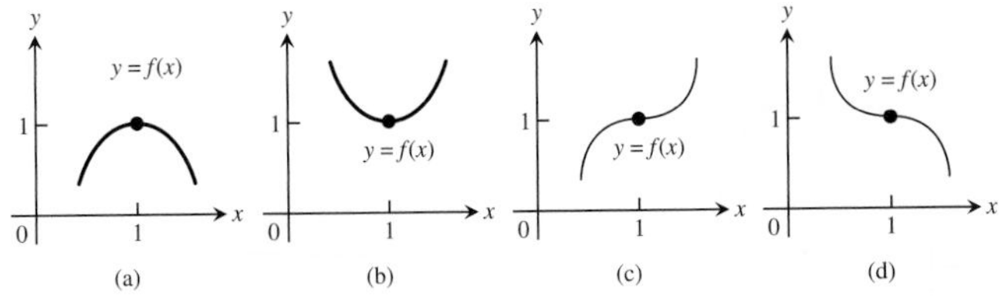

49. **(a)** **(b)**

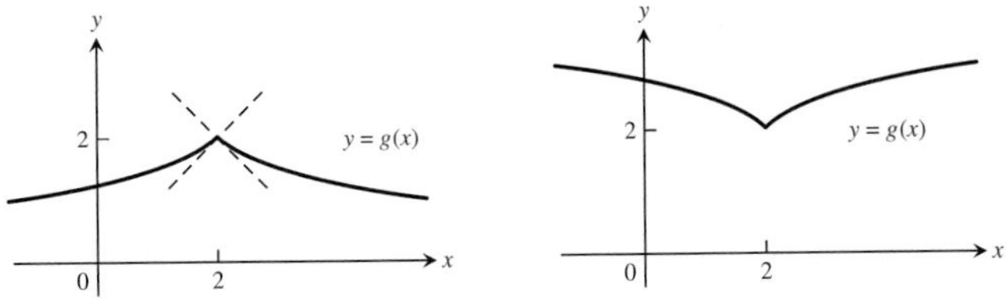

51. **(a)** Max $= 0$ at $x = 0$, min $= -\ln 2$ at $x = \pi/3$

(b) Max $= 1$ at $x = 1$, min $= \cos(\ln 2)$ at $x = \dfrac{1}{2}$ and $x = 2$.

53. Maximum: 1 at $x = 0$, minimum: $2 - 2\ln 2$ at $x = \ln 2$

55. Abs max of $1/(2e)$ assumed at $x = 1/\sqrt{e}$ **57.** Rising

61. Increasing, therefore one-to-one; $df^{-1}/dx = \dfrac{1}{9}x^{-2/3}$

63. Decreasing, therefore one-to-one; $df^{-1}/dx = -\dfrac{1}{3}x^{-2/3}$

Section 4.4, pp. 267–270

1. Local maximum: $3/2$ at $x = -1$, local minimum: -3 at $x = 2$, point of inflection at $(1/2, -3/4)$, rising on $(-\infty, -1)$ and $(2, \infty)$, falling on $(-1, 2)$, concave up on $(1/2, \infty)$, concave down on $(-\infty, 1/2)$

3. Local maximum: $3/4$ at $x = 0$, local minimum: 0 at $x = \pm 1$, points of inflection at $\left(-\sqrt{3}, \dfrac{3\sqrt[3]{4}}{4}\right)$ and $\left(\sqrt{3}, \dfrac{3\sqrt[3]{4}}{4}\right)$, rising on $(-1, 0)$ and $(1, \infty)$, falling on $(-\infty, -1)$ and $(0, 1)$, concave up on $(-\infty, -\sqrt{3})$ and $(\sqrt{3}, \infty)$, concave down on $(-\sqrt{3}, \sqrt{3})$

5. Local maxima: $-2\pi/3 + \sqrt{3}/2$ at $x = -2\pi/3$; $\dfrac{\pi}{3} + \dfrac{\sqrt{3}}{2}$ at $x = \dfrac{\pi}{3}$, local minima: $-\dfrac{\pi}{3} - \dfrac{\sqrt{3}}{2}$ at $x = -\dfrac{\pi}{3}$; $2\pi/3 - \sqrt{3}/2$ at $x = \dfrac{2\pi}{3}$, points of inflection at $(-\pi/2, -\pi/2)$, $(0, 0)$, and $(\pi/2, \pi/2)$, rising on $(-\pi/3, \pi/3)$, falling on $(-2\pi/3, -\pi/3)$ and $(\pi/3, 2\pi/3)$, concave up on $(-\pi/2, 0)$ and $(\pi/2, 2\pi/3)$, concave down on $(-2\pi/3, -\pi/2)$ and $(0, \pi/2)$

7. Local maxima: 1 at $x = -\dfrac{\pi}{2}$ and $x = \dfrac{\pi}{2}$; 0 at $x = -2\pi$ and $x = 2\pi$; local minima: -1 at $x = -\dfrac{3\pi}{2}$ and $x = \dfrac{3\pi}{2}$, 0 at $x = 0$, points of inflection at $(-\pi, 0)$ and $(\pi, 0)$, rising on $(-3\pi/2, -\pi/2)$, $(0, \pi/2)$ and $(3\pi/2, 2\pi)$, falling on $(-2\pi, -3\pi/2)$, $(-\pi/2, 0)$ and $(\pi/2, 3\pi/2)$, concave up on $(-2\pi, -\pi)$ and $(\pi, 2\pi)$, concave down on $(-\pi, 0)$ and $(0, \pi)$

9.

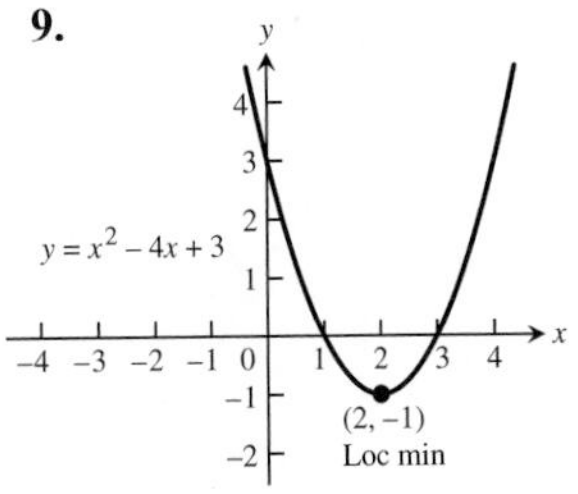

11.

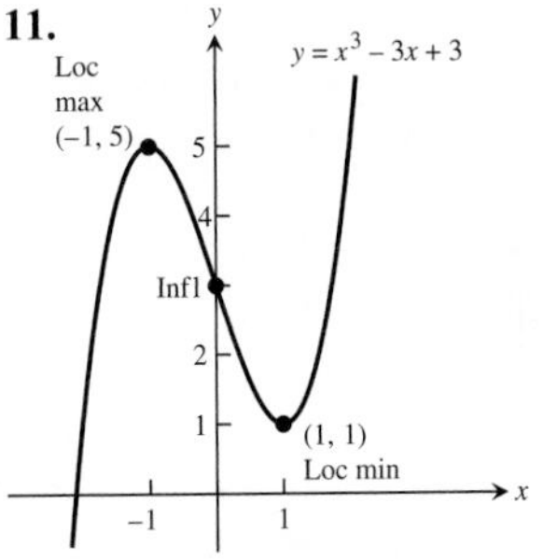

13.

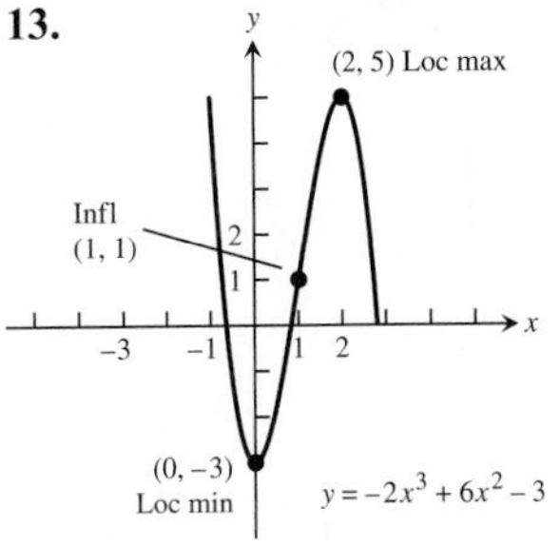

15.

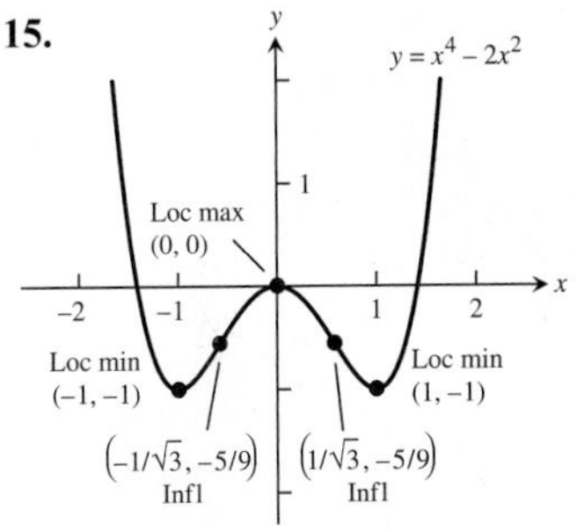

17.

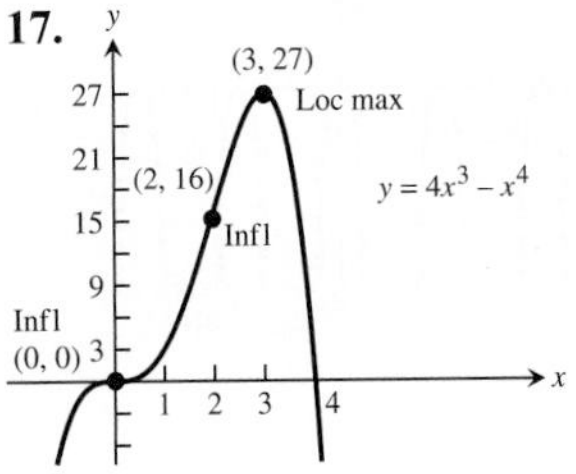

19.

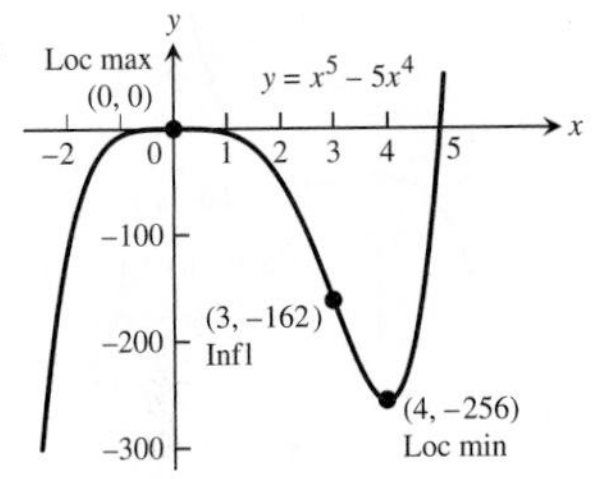

21.

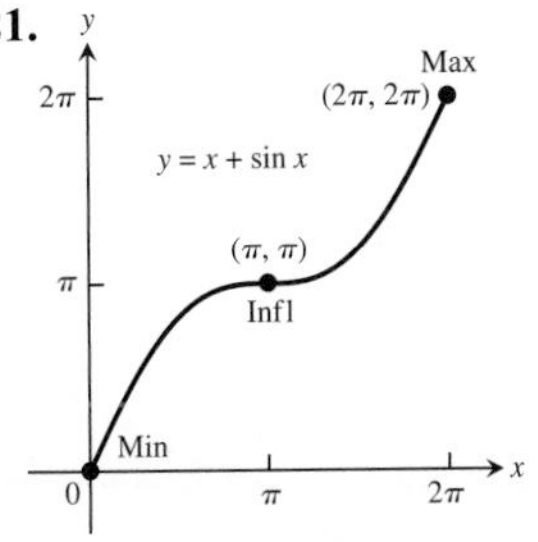

23.

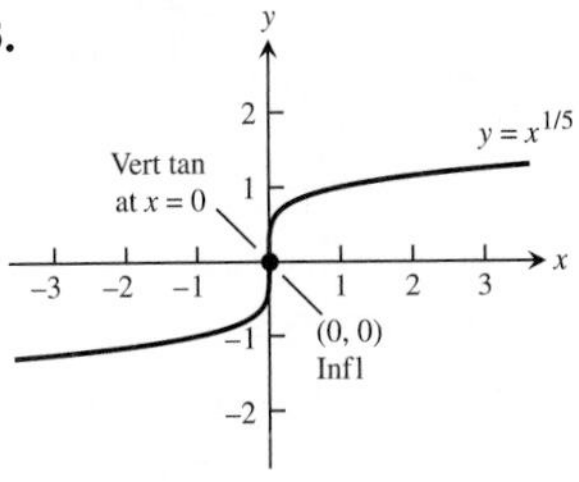

25.

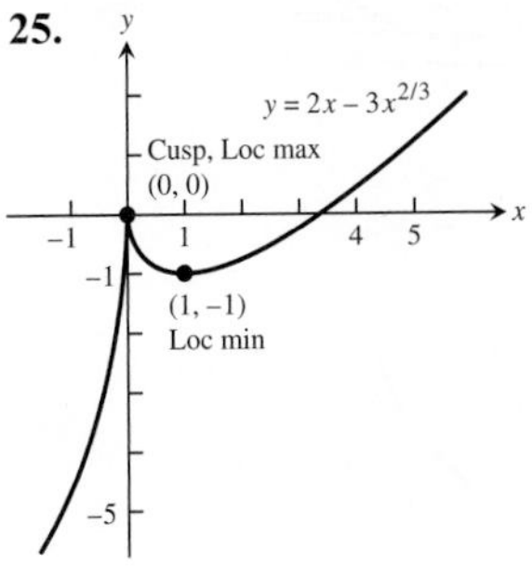

27.

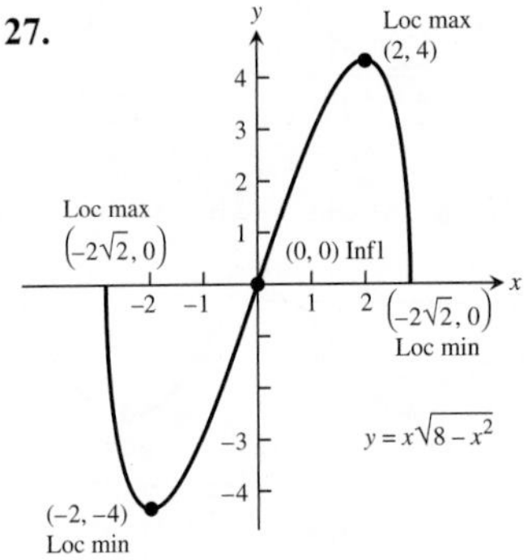

29.

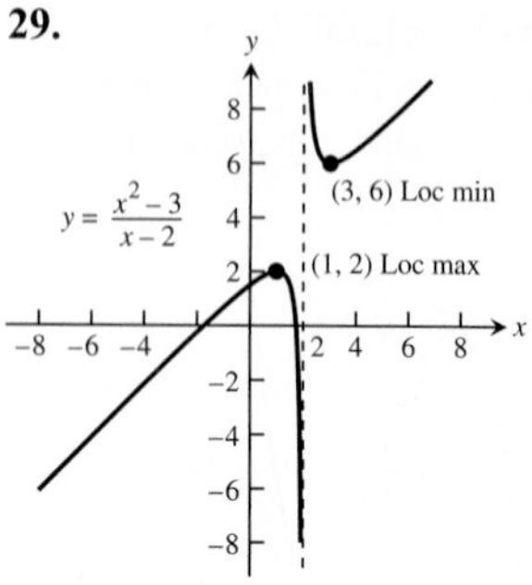

31.

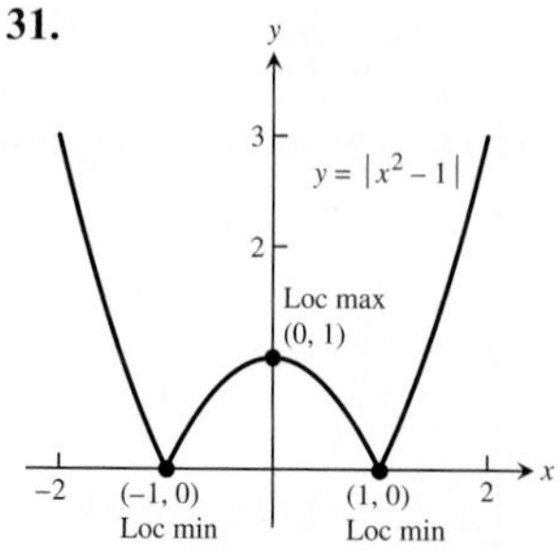

33.

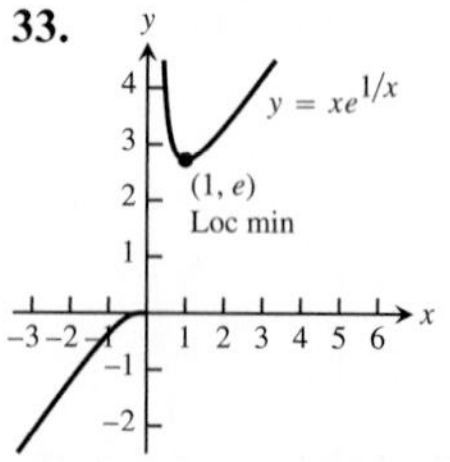

35.

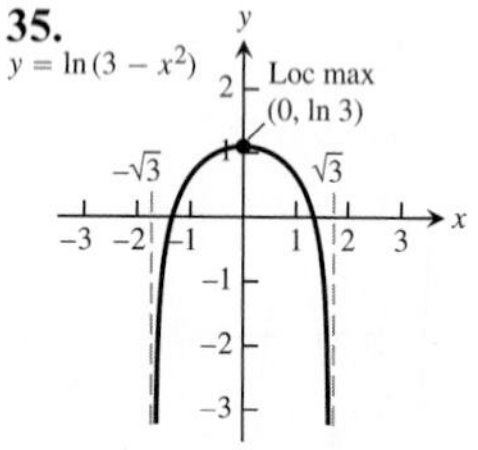

37.

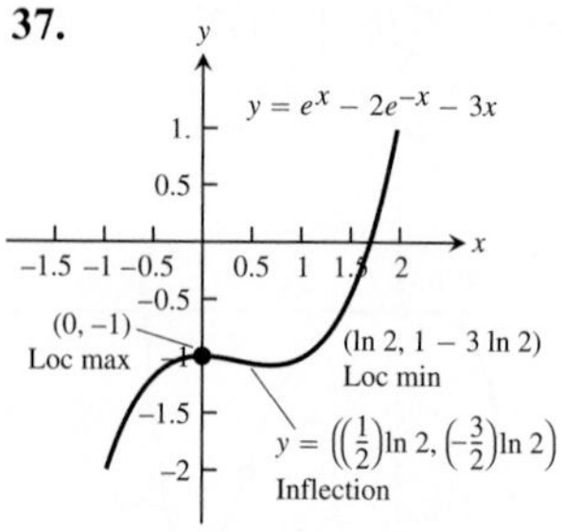

39.

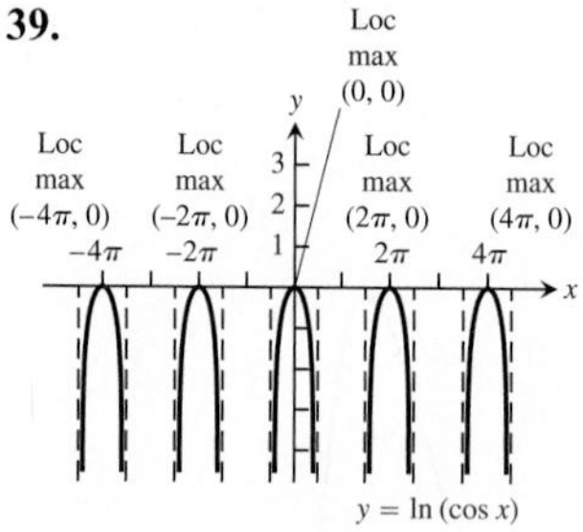

41.

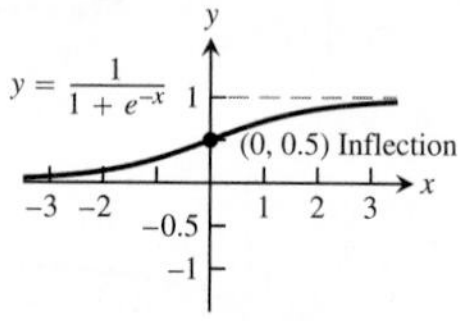

43. $y'' = 1 - 2x$

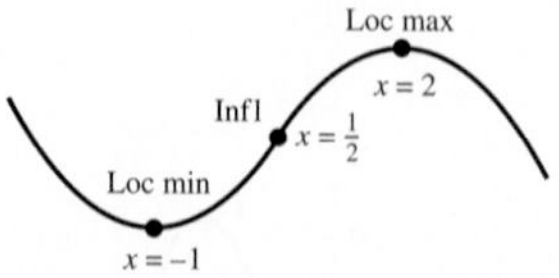

45. $y'' = 3(x - 3)(x - 1)$

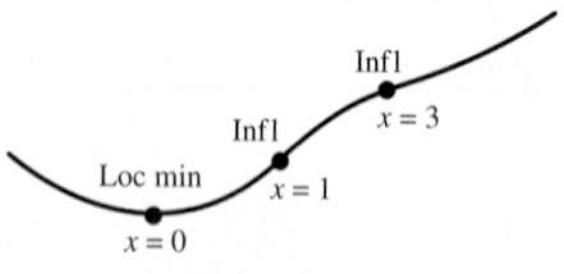

47. $y'' = 3(x - 2)(x + 2)$

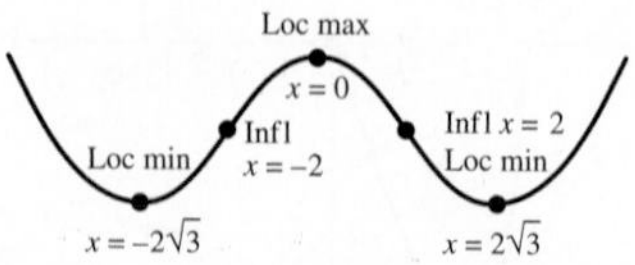

49. $y'' = 2\sec^2 x \tan x$

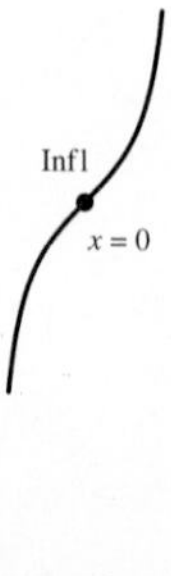

51. $y'' = -\frac{1}{2}\csc^2\frac{\theta}{2}, 0 < \theta < 2\pi$

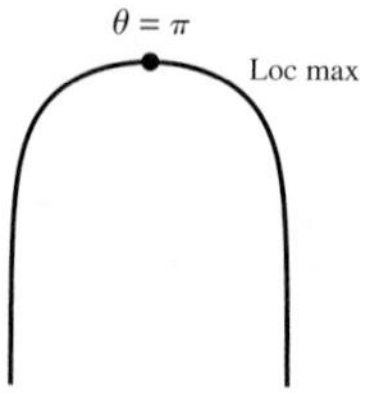

53. $y'' = 2\tan\theta\sec^2\theta, -\frac{\pi}{2} < \theta < \frac{\pi}{2}$

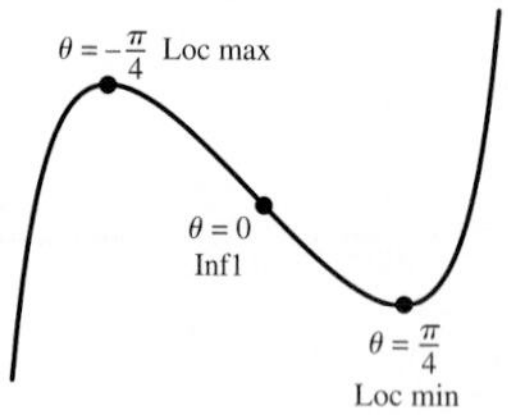

55. $y'' = -\sin t, 0 \le t \le 2\pi$

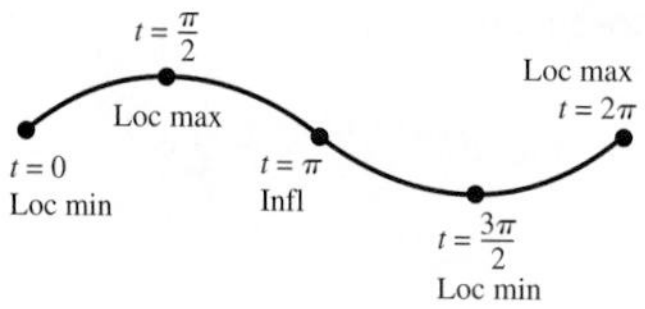

57. $y'' = -\frac{2}{3}(x + 1)^{-5/3}$

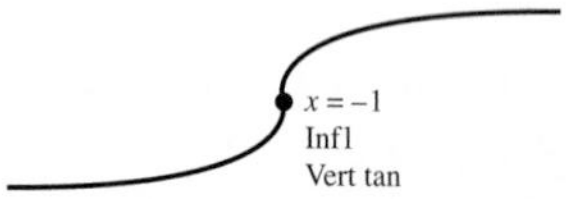

59. $y'' = \frac{1}{3}x^{-2/3} + \frac{2}{3}x^{-5/3}$

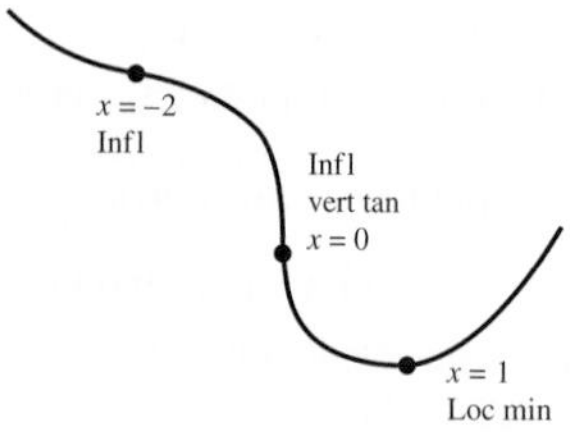

61. $y'' = \begin{cases} -2, & x < 0 \\ 2, & x > 0 \end{cases}$

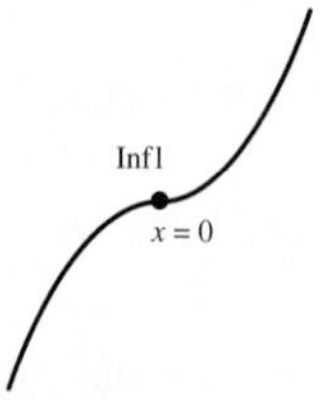

63.

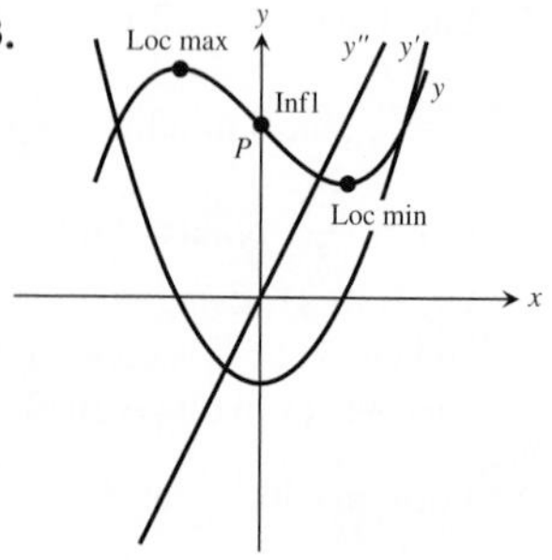

65.

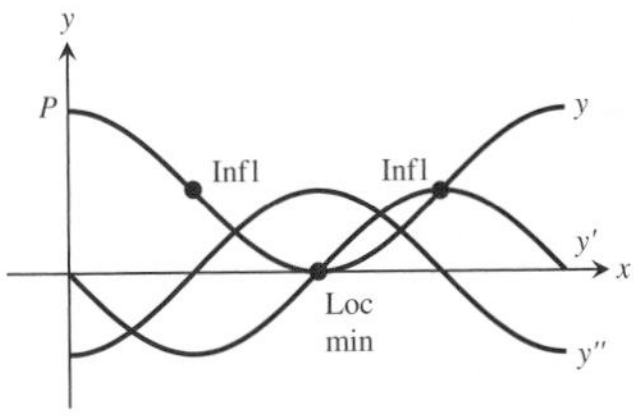

67.

Point	y'	y''
P	−	+
Q	+	0
R	+	−
S	0	−
T	−	−

69.

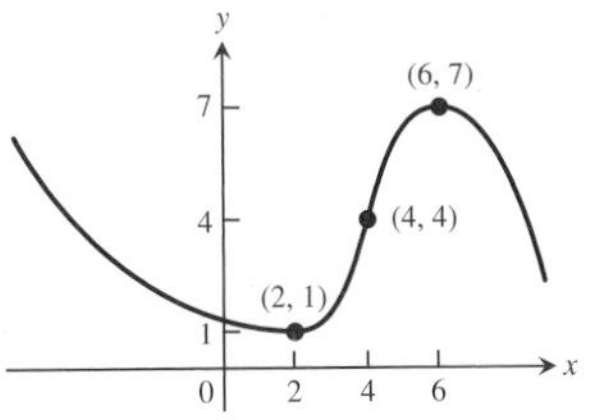

73. $\approx$ 60 thousand units

75. Local minimum at $x = 2$, inflection points at $x = 1$ and $x = 5/3$

79. $b = -3$

81. **(a)** $\left(-\dfrac{b}{2a}, \dfrac{4ac - b^2}{4a}\right)$

(b) concave up if $a > 0$, concave down if $a < 0$

85. The zeros of $y' = 0$ and $y'' = 0$ include the extrema and points of inflection, respectively. Inflection at $x = 3$, local maximum at $x = 0$, local minimum at $x = 4$.

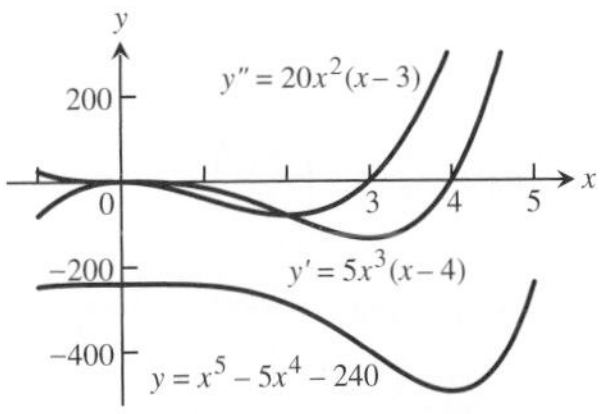

87. The zeros of $y' = 0$ and $y'' = 0$ include the extrema and points of inflection, respectively. Inflection at $x = -\sqrt[3]{2}$, local maximum at $x = -2$, local minimum at $x = 0$.

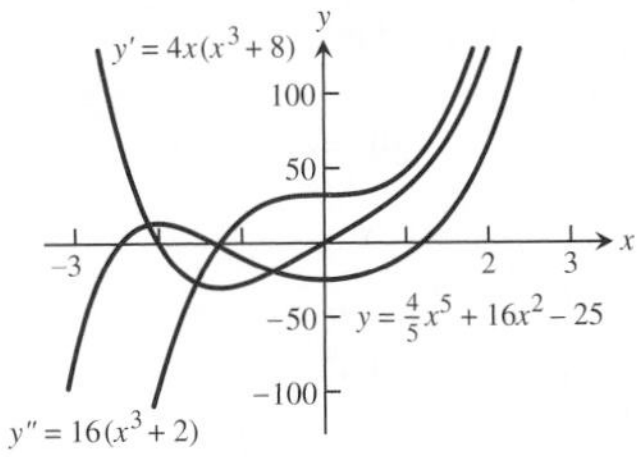

91. **(b)** $f'(x) = 3x^2 + k$; $-12k$; positive if $k < 0$, negative if $k > 0$, 0 if $k = 0$; f' has two zeros if $k < 0$, one zero if $k = 0$, no zeros if $k > 0$; that is, the sign of k controls the number of local extrema.

93. **(b)** A cusp since $\lim_{x\to 0^-} y' = \infty$ and $\lim_{x\to 0^+} y' = -\infty$

95. Yes, the graph of y' crosses through zero near -3, so y has a horizontal tangent near -3.

Section 4.5, pp. 276–282

1. 16 in., 4 in. by 4 in.

3. **(a)** $(x, 1 - x)$ **(b)** $A(x) = 2x(1 - x)$

(c) $\dfrac{1}{2}$ square units, 1 by $\dfrac{1}{2}$

5. $\dfrac{14}{3} \times \dfrac{35}{3} \times \dfrac{5}{3}$ in., $\dfrac{2450}{27}$ in.^{3} **7.** 80,000 m^2; 400 m by 200 m

9. **(a)** The optimum dimensions of the tank are 10 ft on the base edges and 5 ft deep.

(b) Minimizing the surface area of the tank minimizes its weight for a given wall thickness. The thickness of the steel walls would likely be determined by other considerations such as structural requirements.

11. 9×18 in. **13.** $\dfrac{\pi}{2}$ **15.** $h : r = 8 : \pi$

17. **(a)** $V(x) = 2x(24 - 2x)(18 - 2x)$

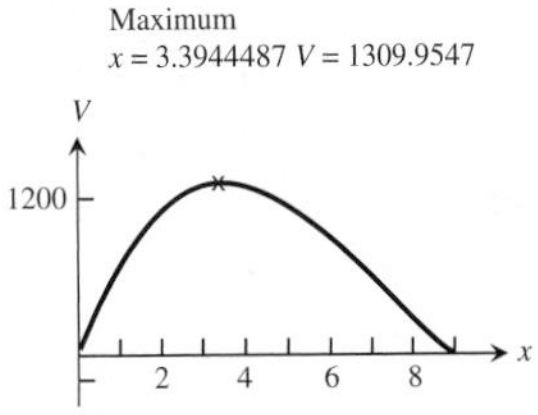

(b) Domain: $(0, 9)$

(c) Maximum volume $\approx$ 1309.95 in.^{3} when $x \approx 3.39$ in.

(d) $V'(x) = 24x^2 - 336x + 864$, so the critical point is at $x = 7 - \sqrt{13}$, which confirms the result in part (c).

(e) $x = 2$ in. or $x = 5$ in.

19. ≈ 2418.40 cm^3

21. **(a)** $h = 24$, $w = 18$

(b)

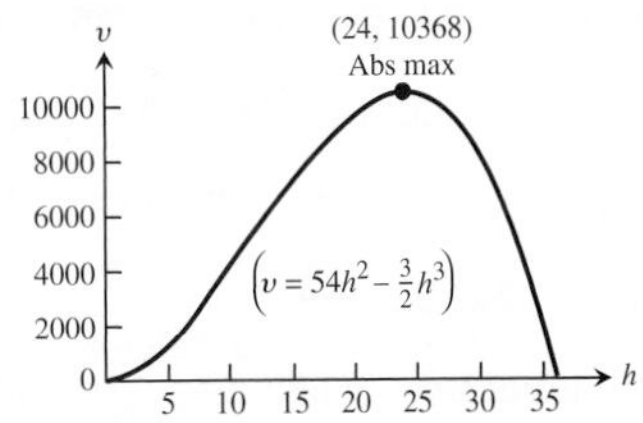

23. If r is the radius of the hemisphere, h the height of the cylinder, and V the volume, then $r = \left(\dfrac{3V}{8\pi}\right)^{1/3}$ and $h = \left(\dfrac{3V}{\pi}\right)^{1/3}$.

25. **(b)** $x = \dfrac{51}{8}$ **(c)** $L \approx 11$ in.

27. Radius $= \sqrt{2}$ m, height $= 1$ m, volume $\frac{2\pi}{3}$ m^3

31. **(a)** $v(0) = 96$ ft/sec
(b) 256 ft at $t = 3$ sec
(c) Velocity when $s = 0$ is $v(7) = -128$ ft/sec

33. ≈ 46.87 ft **35.** **(a)** $6 \times 6\sqrt{3}$ in.

37. **(a)** $10\pi \approx 31.42$ cm/sec; when $t = 0.5$ sec, 1.5 sec, 2.5 sec, 3.5 sec; $s = 0$, acceleration is 0
(b) 10 cm from rest position; speed is 0

39. $20\left(5 - \sqrt{17}\right)$ m

41. $x = \frac{a}{2}, v = \frac{ka^2}{4}$ **43.** $\frac{c}{2} + 50$

45. **(a)** $\sqrt{\frac{2km}{h}}$ **(b)** $\sqrt{\frac{2km}{h}}$

49. $M = \frac{C}{2}$ **55.** **(a)** $y = -1$

57. **(a)** The minimum distance is $\frac{\sqrt{5}}{2}$.
(b) The minimum distance is from the point (3/2, 0) to the point (1, 1) on the graph of $y = \sqrt{x}$, and this occurs at the value $x = 1$, where $D(x)$, the distance squared, has its minimum value.

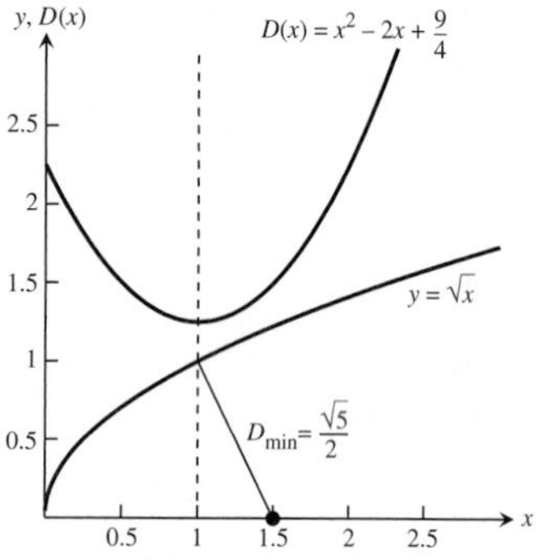

Section 4.6, pp. 289–291

1. 1/4 **3.** 5/7 **5.** 1/2 **7.** 1/4 **9.** $-23/7$ **11.** 5/7 **13.** 0

15. -16 **17.** -2 **19.** 1/4 **21.** 2 **23.** 3 **25.** -1

27. ln 3 **29.** $\frac{1}{\ln 2}$ **31.** ln 2 **33.** 1 **35.** 1/2 **37.** ln 2

39. $\cos a$ **41.** $-1/2$ **43.** -1 **45.** 1 **47.** $1/e$ **49.** 1

51. $1/e$ **53.** $e^{1/2}$ **55.** 1 **57.** 3 **59.** 1

61. (b) is correct. **63.** (d) is correct. **65.** $c = \frac{27}{10}$ **67.** -1

Section 4.7, pp. 294–295

1. $x_2 = -\frac{5}{3}, \frac{13}{21}$ **3.** $x_2 = -\frac{51}{31}, \frac{5763}{4945}$

7. x_1, and all later approximations will equal x_0.

9.

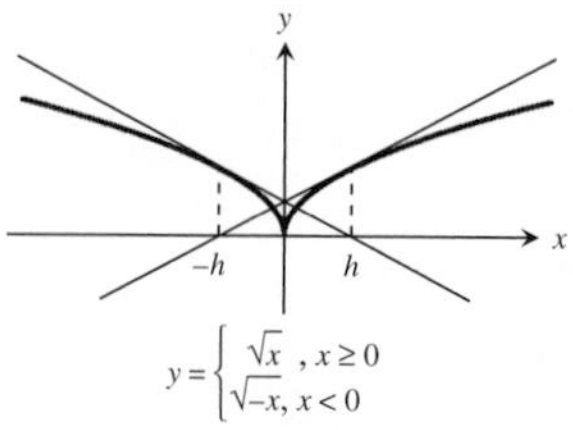

11. The points of intersection of $y = x^3$ and $y = 3x + 1$ or $y = x^3 - 3x$ and $y = 1$ have the same x-values as the roots of part (i) or the solutions of part (iv). **13.** 1.165561185

15. **(a)** Two **(b)** 0.35003501505249 and -1.0261731615301

17. $\pm 1.3065629648764, \pm 0.5411961001462$ **19.** 0, 0.53485

21. The root is 1.17951.

23. **(a)** For $x_0 = -2$ or $x_0 = -0.8$, $x_i \to -1$ as i gets large.
(b) For $x_0 = -0.5$ or $x_0 = 0.25$, $x_i \to 0$ as i gets large.
(c) For $x_0 = 0.8$ or $x_0 = 2$, $x_i \to 1$ as i gets large.
(d) For $x_0 = -\sqrt{21}/7$ or $x_0 = \sqrt{21}/7$, Newton's method does not converge. The values of x_i alternate between $-\sqrt{21}/7$ and $\sqrt{21}/7$ as i increases.

25. Answers will vary with machine speed.

Section 4.8, pp. 302–306

1. **(a)** x^2 **(b)** $\frac{x^3}{3}$ **(c)** $\frac{x^3}{3} - x^2 + x$

3. **(a)** x^{-3} **(b)** $-\frac{1}{3}x^{-3}$ **(c)** $-\frac{1}{3}x^{-3} + x^2 + 3x$

5. **(a)** $-\frac{1}{x}$ **(b)** $-\frac{5}{x}$ **(c)** $2x + \frac{5}{x}$

7. **(a)** $\sqrt{x^3}$ **(b)** $\sqrt{x}$ **(c)** $\frac{2\sqrt{x^3}}{3} + 2\sqrt{x}$

9. **(a)** $x^{2/3}$ **(b)** $x^{1/3}$ **(c)** $x^{-1/3}$

11. **(a)** $\ln x$ **(b)** $7 \ln x$ **(c)** $x - 5 \ln x$

13. **(a)** $\cos(\pi x)$ **(b)** $-3 \cos x$ **(c)** $-\frac{1}{\pi}\cos(\pi x) + \cos(3x)$

15. **(a)** $\tan x$ **(b)** $2\tan\left(\frac{x}{3}\right)$ **(c)** $-\frac{2}{3}\tan\left(\frac{3x}{2}\right)$

17. **(a)** $-\csc x$ **(b)** $\frac{1}{5}\csc(5x)$ **(c)** $2\csc\left(\frac{\pi x}{2}\right)$

19. **(a)** $\frac{1}{3}e^{3x}$ **(b)** $-e^{-x}$ **(c)** $2e^{x/2}$

21. **(a)** $\frac{1}{\ln 3}3^x$ **(b)** $\frac{-1}{\ln 2}2^{-x}$ **(c)** $\frac{1}{\ln(5/3)}\left(\frac{5}{3}\right)^x$

23. **(a)** $2\sin^{-1} x$ **(b)** $\frac{1}{2}\tan^{-1} x$ **(c)** $\frac{1}{2}\tan^{-1} 2x$

25. $\frac{x^2}{2} + x + C$ **27.** $t^3 + \frac{t^2}{4} + C$ **29.** $\frac{x^4}{2} - \frac{5x^2}{2} + 7x + C$

31. $-\frac{1}{x} - \frac{x^3}{3} - \frac{x}{3} + C$ **33.** $\frac{3}{2}x^{2/3} + C$

35. $\frac{2}{3}x^{3/2} + \frac{3}{4}x^{4/3} + C$ **37.** $4y^2 - \frac{8}{3}y^{3/4} + C$

39. $x^2 + \frac{2}{x} + C$ **41.** $2\sqrt{t} - \frac{2}{\sqrt{t}} + C$ **43.** $-2\sin t + C$

45. $-21\cos\frac{\theta}{3} + C$ **47.** $3\cot x + C$ **49.** $-\frac{1}{2}\csc\theta + C$

51. $\frac{1}{3}e^{3x} - 5e^{-x} + C$ **53.** $-e^{-x} + \frac{4^x}{\ln 4} + C$

55. $4\sec x - 2\tan x + C$ **57.** $-\frac{1}{2}\cos 2x + \cot x + C$

59. $\frac{t}{2} + \frac{\sin 4t}{8} + C$ **61.** $\ln|x| - 5\tan^{-1}x + C$

63. $\frac{3x^{(\sqrt{3}+1)}}{\sqrt{3}+1} + C$ **65.** $\tan\theta + C$ **67.** $-\cot x - x + C$

69. $-\cos\theta + \theta + C$

83. (a) Wrong: $\frac{d}{dx}\left(\frac{x^2}{2}\sin x + C\right) = \frac{2x}{2}\sin x + \frac{x^2}{2}\cos x = x\sin x + \frac{x^2}{2}\cos x$

(b) Wrong: $\frac{d}{dx}(-x\cos x + C) = -\cos x + x\sin x$

(c) Right: $\frac{d}{dx}(-x\cos x + \sin x + C) = -\cos x + x\sin x + \cos x = x\sin x$

85. (a) Wrong: $\frac{d}{dx}\left(\frac{(2x+1)^3}{3} + C\right) = \frac{3(2x+1)^2(2)}{3} = 2(2x+1)^2$

(b) Wrong: $\frac{d}{dx}((2x+1)^3 + C) = 3(2x+1)^2(2) = 6(2x+1)^2$

(c) Right: $\frac{d}{dx}((2x+1)^3 + C) = 6(2x+1)^2$

87. (b) **89.** $y = x^2 - 7x + 10$ **91.** $y = -\frac{1}{x} + \frac{x^2}{2} - \frac{1}{2}$

93. $y = 9x^{1/3} + 4$ **95.** $s = t + \sin t + 4$

97. $r = \cos(\pi\theta) - 1$ **99.** $v = \frac{1}{2}\sec t + \frac{1}{2}$

101. $v = 3\sec^{-1}t - \pi$ **103.** $y = x^2 - x^3 + 4x + 1$

105. $r = \frac{1}{t} + 2t - 2$ **107.** $y = x^3 - 4x^2 + 5$

109. $y = -\sin t + \cos t + t^3 - 1$ **111.** $y = 2x^{3/2} - 50$

113. $y = x - x^{4/3} + \frac{1}{2}$ **115.** $y = -\sin x - \cos x - 2$

117. (a) (i) 33.2 units, **(ii)** 33.2 units, **(iii)** 33.2 units **(b)** True

119. $t = 88/k, k = 16$

121. (a) $v = 10t^{3/2} - 6t^{1/2}$ **(b)** $s = 4t^{5/2} - 4t^{3/2}$

125. (a) $-\sqrt{x} + C$ **(b)** $x + C$ **(c)** $\sqrt{x} + C$ **(d)** $-x + C$ **(e)** $x - \sqrt{x} + C$ **(f)** $-x - \sqrt{x} + C$

Practice Exercises, pp. 307–311

1. No **3.** No minimum; absolute maximum: $f(1) = 16$; critical points: $x = 1$ and $11/3$

5. Absolute minimum: $g(0) = 1$; no absolute maximum; critical point $x = 0$

7. Absolute minimum: $2 - 2\ln 2$ at $x = 2$; absolute maximum 1 at $x = 1$

9. Yes, except at $x = 0$ **11.** No **15. (b)** one

17. (b) 0.8555 99677 2 **23.** Global minimum value of $\frac{1}{2}$ at $x = 2$

25. (a) $t = 0, 6, 12$ **(b)** $t = 3, 9$ **(c)** $6 < t < 12$ **(d)** $0 < t < 6$, $12 < t < 14$

27.

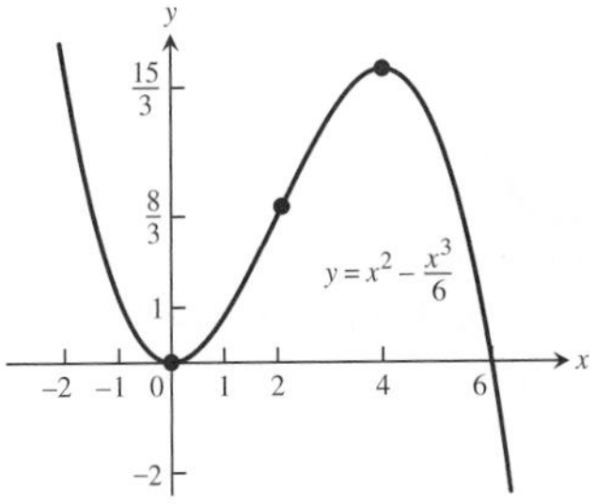

29.

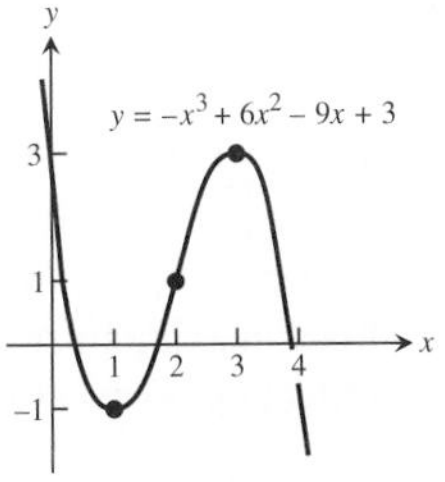

31.

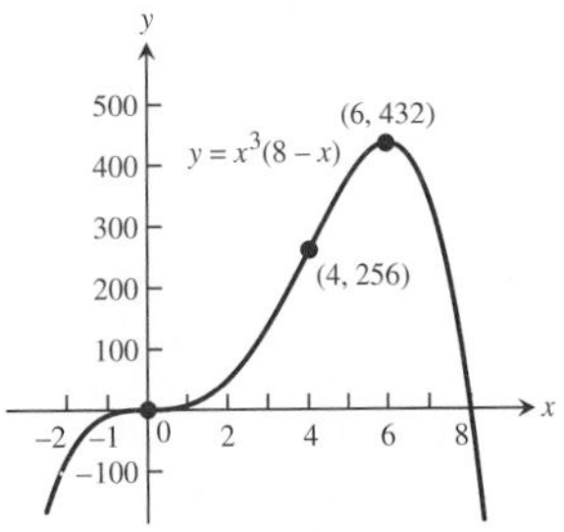

33.

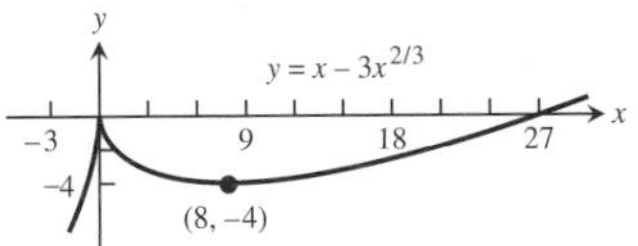

35.

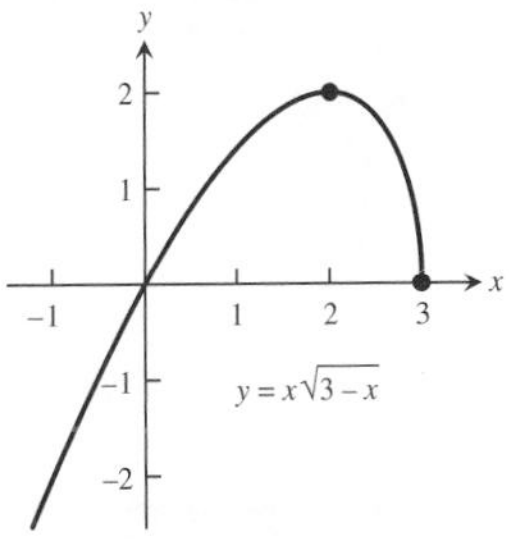

37.

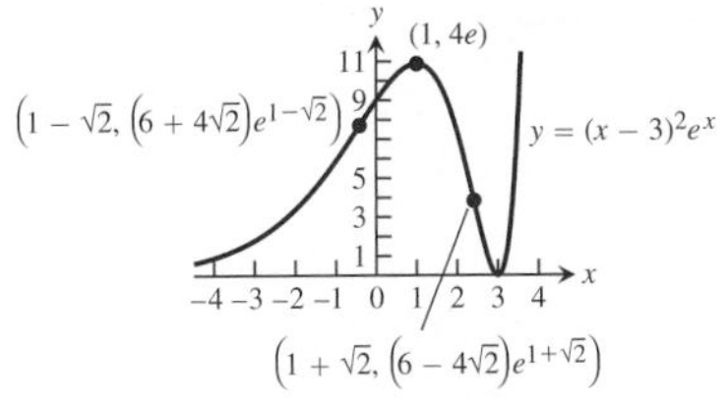

39.

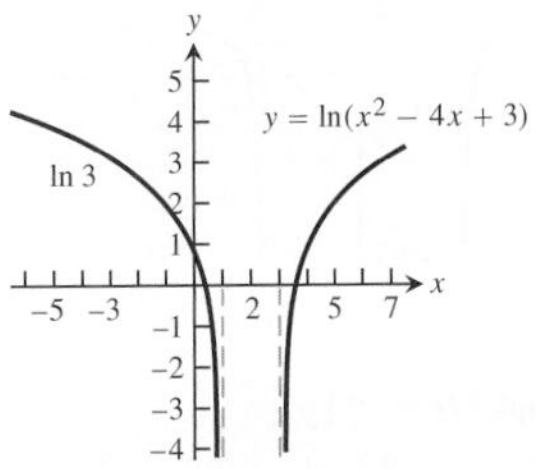

41.

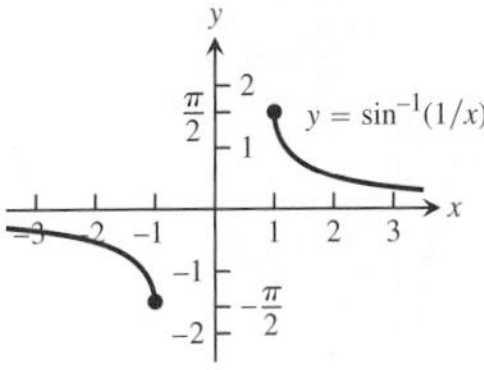

43. (a) Local maximum at $x = 4$, local minimum at $x = -4$, inflection point at $x = 0$

(b)

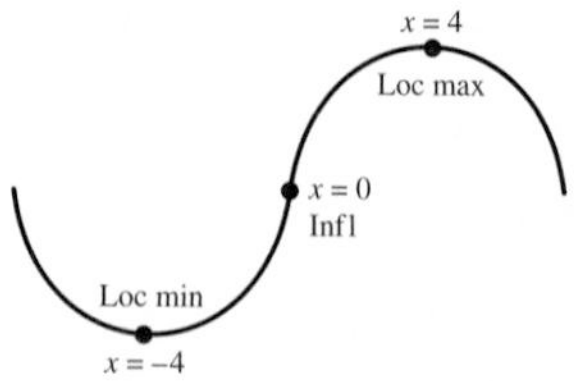

45. **(a)** Local maximum at $x = 0$, local minima at $x = -1$ and $x = 2$, inflection points at $x = (1 \pm \sqrt{7})/3$
(b)

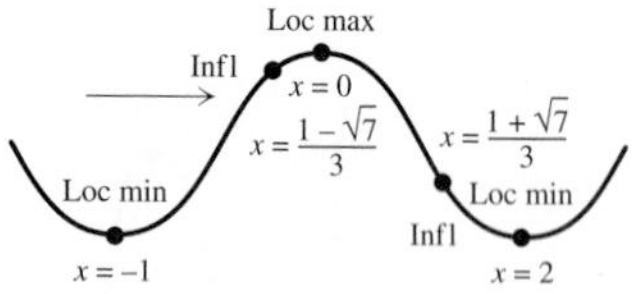

47. **(a)** Local maximum at $x = -\sqrt{2}$, local minimum at $x = \sqrt{2}$, inflection points at $x = \pm 1$ and 0
(b)

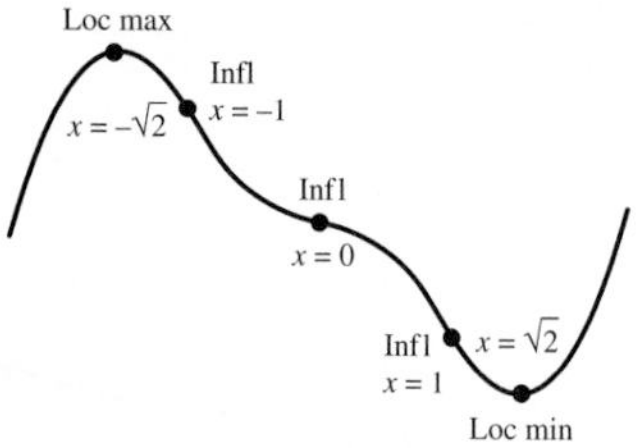

53.

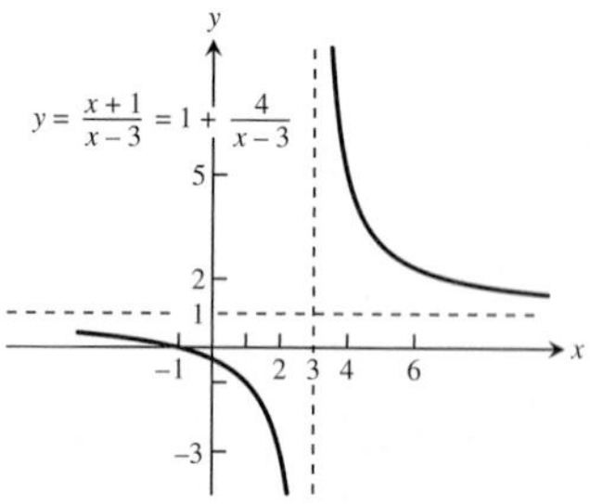

55.

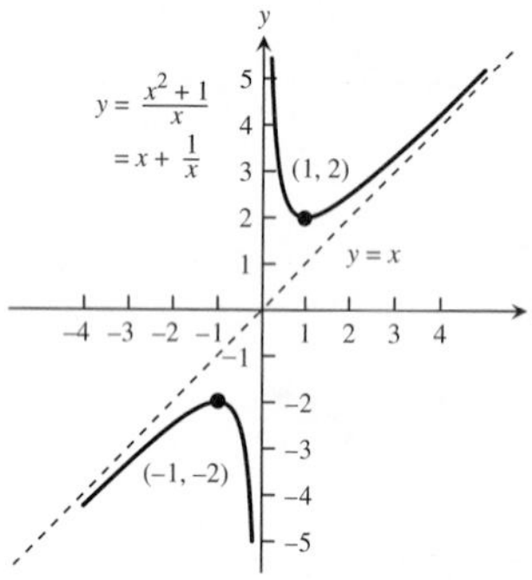

57.

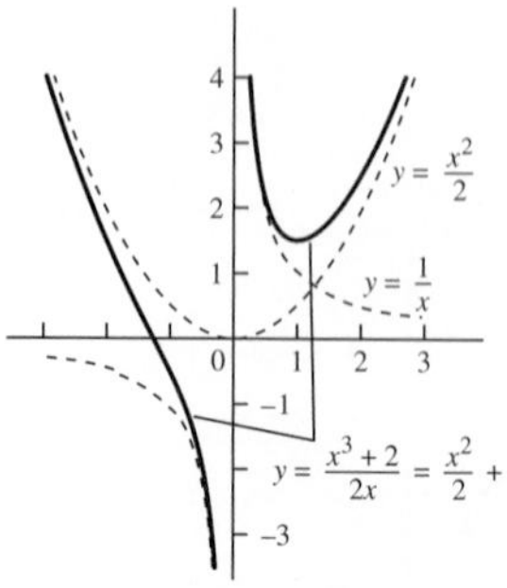

59.

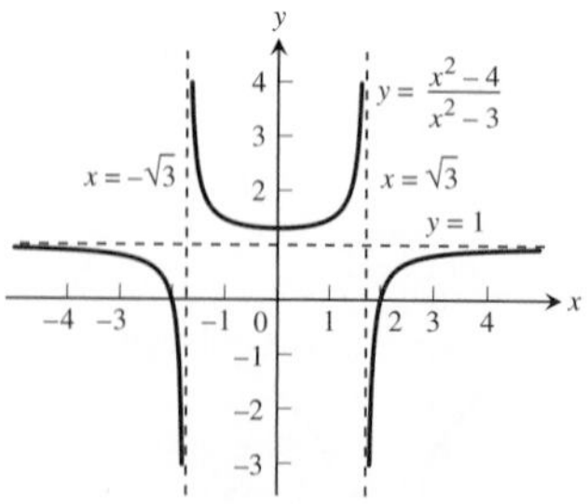

61. 5 **63.** 0 **65.** 1 **67.** 3/7 **69.** 0 **71.** 1
73. ln 10 **75.** ln 2 **77.** 5 **79.** $-\infty$ **81.** 1 **83.** e^{bk}
85. **(a)** 0, 36 **(b)** 18, 18 **87.** 54 square units
89. height = 2, radius = $\sqrt{2}$

91. $x = 5 - \sqrt{5}$ hundred ≈ 276 tires, $y = 2(5 - \sqrt{5})$ hundred ≈ 553 tires
93. Dimensions: base is 6 in. by 12 in., height = 2 in.; maximum volume = 144 in.^{3}
95. $x_5 = 2.1958\ 23345$ **97.** $\frac{x^4}{4} + \frac{5}{2}x^2 - 7x + C$
99. $2t^{3/2} - \frac{4}{t} + C$ **101.** $-\frac{1}{r + 5} + C$ **103.** $(\theta^2 + 1)^{3/2} + C$
105. $\frac{1}{3}(1 + x^4)^{3/4} + C$ **107.** $10 \tan \frac{s}{10} + C$
109. $-\frac{1}{\sqrt{2}} \csc \sqrt{2}\,\theta + C$ **111.** $\frac{1}{2}x - \sin \frac{x}{2} + C$
113. $3 \ln x - \frac{x^2}{2} + C$ **115.** $\frac{1}{2}e^t + e^{-t} + C$
117. $\frac{\theta^{2-\pi}}{2 - \pi} + C$ **119.** $\frac{3}{2} \sec^{-1}|x| + C$
121. $y = x - \frac{1}{x} - 1$ **123.** $r = 4t^{5/2} + 4t^{3/2} - 8t$
125. Yes, $\sin^{-1}(x)$ and $-\cos^{-1}(x)$ differ by the constant $\pi/2$.
127. $1/\sqrt{2}$ units long by $1/\sqrt{e}$ units high, $A = 1/\sqrt{2e} \approx 0.43$ units^2
129. Absolute maximum = 0 at $x = e/2$, absolute minimum = −0.5 at $x = 0.5$
131. $x = \pm 1$ are the critical points; $y = 1$ is a horizontal asymptote in both directions; absolute minimum value of the function is $e^{-\sqrt{2}/2}$ at $x = -1$, and absolute maximum value is $e^{\sqrt{2}/2}$ at $x = 1$.
133. **(a)** Absolute maximum of $2/e$ at $x = e^2$, inflection point $(e^{8/3}, (8/3)e^{-4/3})$, concave up on $(e^{8/3}, \infty)$, concave down on $(0, e^{8/3})$
(b) Absolute maximum of 1 at $x = 0$, inflection points $(\pm 1/\sqrt{2}, 1/\sqrt{e})$, concave up on $(-\infty, -1/\sqrt{2}) \cup (1/\sqrt{2}, \infty)$, concave down on $(-1/\sqrt{2}, 1/\sqrt{2})$
(c) Absolute maximum of 1 at $x = 0$, inflection point $(1, 2/e)$, concave up on $(1, \infty)$, concave down on $(-\infty, 1)$

Additional and Advanced Exercises, pp. 311–314

1. The function is constant on the interval.
3. The extreme points will not be at the end of an open interval.
5. **(a)** A local minimum at $x = -1$, points of inflection at $x = 0$ and $x = 2$ **(b)** A local maximum at $x = 0$ and local minima at $x = -1$ and $x = 2$, points of inflection at $x = \frac{1 \pm \sqrt{7}}{3}$
9. No **11.** $a = 1, b = 0, c = 1$ **13.** Yes
15. Drill the hole at $y = h/2$.
17. $r = \frac{RH}{2(H - R)}$ for $H > 2R$, $r = R$ if $H \le 2R$
19. **(a)** $\frac{10}{3}$ **(b)** $\frac{5}{3}$ **(c)** $\frac{1}{2}$ **(d)** 0 **(e)** $-\frac{1}{2}$ **(f)** 1 **(g)** $\frac{1}{2}$ **(h)** 3
21. **(a)** $\frac{c - b}{2e}$ **(b)** $\frac{c + b}{2}$ **(c)** $\frac{b^2 - 2bc + c^2 + 4ae}{4e}$ **(d)** $\frac{c + b + t}{2}$

23. $m_0 = 1 - \dfrac{1}{q}, m_1 = \dfrac{1}{q}$ **25.** $s = ce^{kt}$

27. (a) $k = -38.72$ **(b)** 25 ft

29. Yes, $y = x + C$ **31.** $v_0 = \dfrac{2\sqrt{2}}{3}b^{3/4}$

CHAPTER 5

Section 5.1, pp. 322–324

1. (a) 0.125 **(b)** 0.21875 **(c)** 0.625 **(d)** 0.46875
3. (a) 1.066667 **(b)** 1.283333 **(c)** 2.666667 **(d)** 2.083333
5. 0.3125, 0.328125 **7.** 1.5, 1.574603
9. (a) 87 in. **(b)** 87 in. **11. (a)** 3490 ft **(b)** 3840 ft
13. (a) 74.65 ft/sec **(b)** 45.28 ft/sec **(c)** 146.59 ft

15. $\dfrac{31}{16}$ **17.** 1

19. (a) Upper = 758 gal, lower = 543 gal
(b) Upper = 2363 gal, lower = 1693 gal
(c) ≈ 31.4 h, ≈ 32.4 h

21. (a) 2 **(b)** $2\sqrt{2} \approx 2.828$
(c) $8 \sin\left(\dfrac{\pi}{8}\right) \approx 3.061$
(d) Each area is less than the area of the circle, π. As n increases, the polygon area approaches π.

Section 5.2, pp. 331–332

1. $\dfrac{6(1)}{1+1} + \dfrac{6(2)}{2+1} = 7$

3. $\cos(1)\pi + \cos(2)\pi + \cos(3)\pi + \cos(4)\pi = 0$

5. $\sin \pi - \sin \dfrac{\pi}{2} + \sin \dfrac{\pi}{3} = \dfrac{\sqrt{3} - 2}{2}$ **7.** All of them **9.** b

11. $\sum_{k=1}^{6} k$ **13.** $\sum_{k=1}^{4} \dfrac{1}{2^k}$ **15.** $\sum_{k=1}^{5} (-1)^{k+1} \dfrac{1}{k}$

17. (a) -15 **(b)** 1 **(c)** 1 **(d)** -11 **(e)** 16
19. (a) 55 **(b)** 385 **(c)** 3025
21. -56 **23.** -73 **25.** 240 **27.** 3376

29. (a)

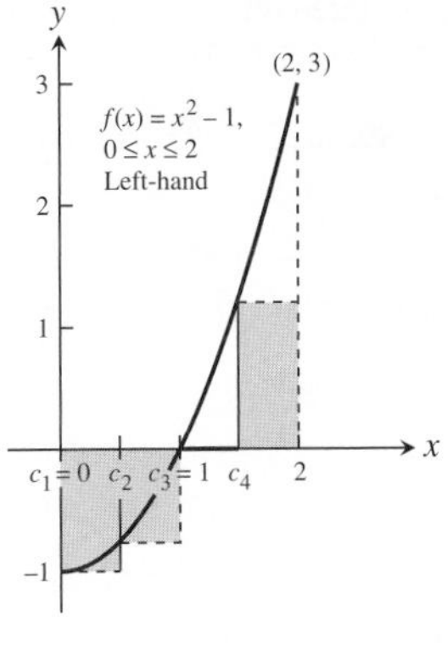

(b)

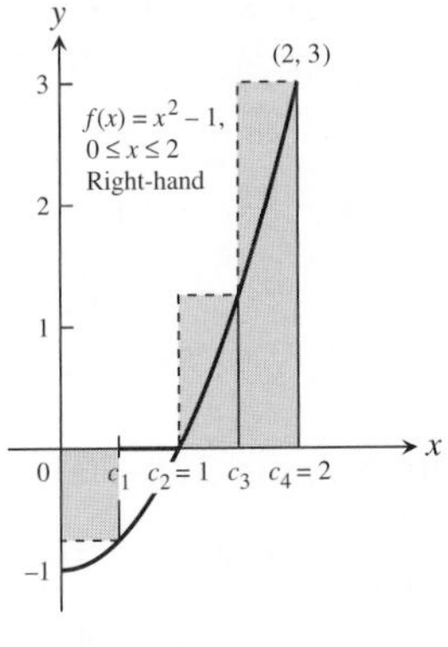

(c)

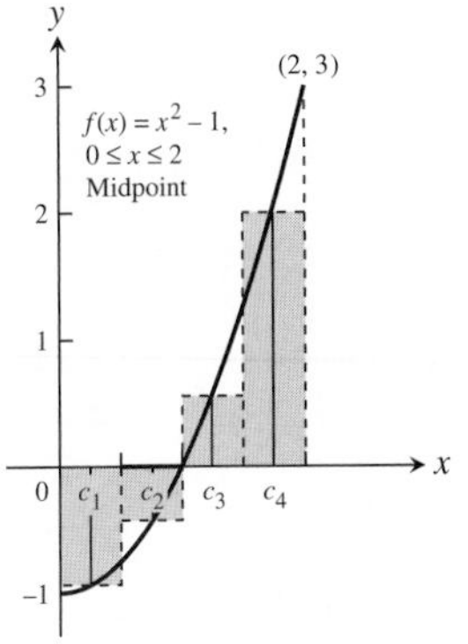

31. (a)

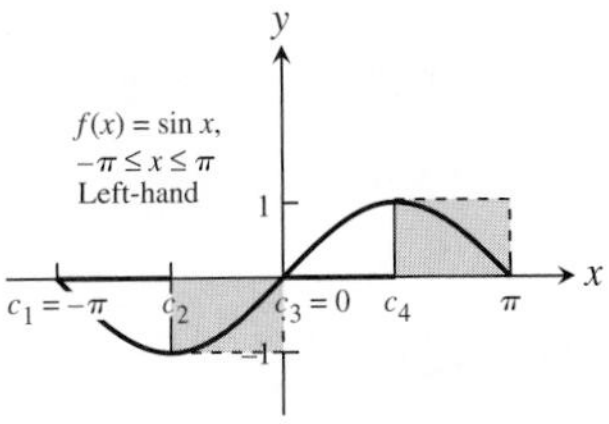

(b)

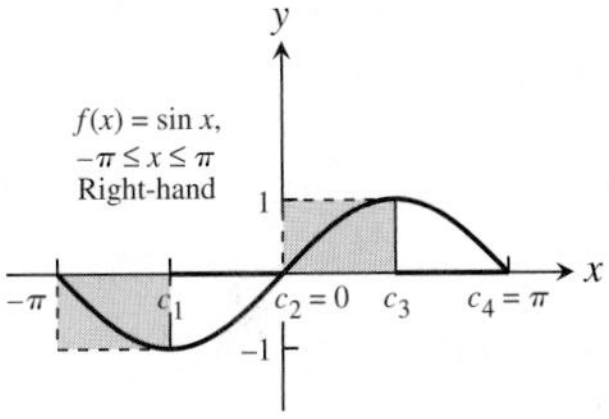

(c)

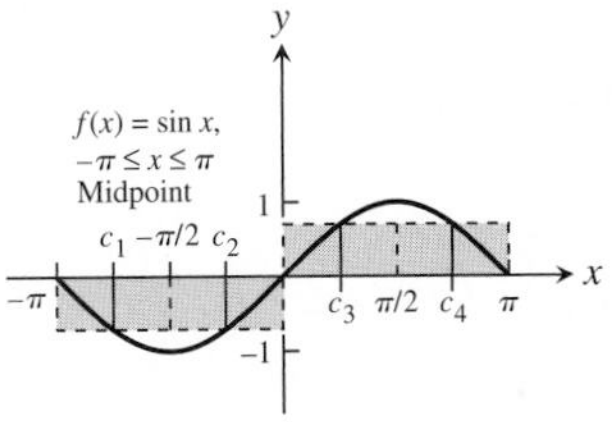

33. 1.2 **35.** $\dfrac{2}{3} + \dfrac{3n-1}{6n^2}, \dfrac{2}{3}$ **37.** $12 + \dfrac{27n+9}{2n^2}, 12$

39. $\dfrac{5}{6} + \dfrac{6n+1}{6n^2}, \dfrac{5}{6}$

Section 5.3, pp. 341–344

1. $\int_0^2 x^2\,dx$ **3.** $\int_{-7}^{5} (x^2 - 3x)\,dx$ **5.** $\int_2^3 \dfrac{1}{1-x}\,dx$

7. $\int_{-\pi/4}^{0} \sec x\,dx$

9. (a) 0 **(b)** -8 **(c)** -12 **(d)** 10 **(e)** -2 **(f)** 16
11. (a) 5 **(b)** $5\sqrt{3}$ **(c)** -5 **(d)** -5
13. (a) 4 **(b)** -4
15. Area = 21 square units
17. Area = $9\pi/2$ square units **19.** Area = 2.5 square units
21. Area = 3 square units **23.** $b^2/4$ **25.** $b^2 - a^2$ **27.** 1/2
29. $3\pi^2/2$ **31.** 7/3 **33.** 1/24 **35.** $3a^2/2$ **37.** $b/3$
39. -14 **41.** 10 **43.** -2 **45.** $-7/4$ **47.** 7 **49.** 0
51. Using n subintervals of length $\Delta x = b/n$ and right-endpoint values:

$$\text{Area} = \int_0^b 3x^2\,dx = b^3$$

53. Using n subintervals of length $\Delta x = b/n$ and right-endpoint values:

$$\text{Area} = \int_0^b 2x\,dx = b^2$$

55. $\text{av}(f) = 0$ **57.** $\text{av}(f) = -2$ **59.** $\text{av}(f) = 1$
61. (a) $\text{av}(g) = -1/2$ **(b)** $\text{av}(g) = 1$ **(c)** $\text{av}(g) = 1/4$
63. $a = 0$ and $b = 1$ maximize the integral.
65. Upper bound $= 1$, lower bound $= 1/2$
67. For example, $\int_0^1 \sin(x^2)\,dx \le \int_0^1 dx = 1$
69. $\int_a^b f(x)\,dx \ge \int_a^b 0\,dx = 0$ **71.** Upper bound $= 1/2$

Section 5.4, pp. 351–353

1. 6 **3.** 8 **5.** 1 **7.** 5/2 **9.** 2 **11.** $2\sqrt{3}$ **13.** 0
15. $-\pi/4$ **17.** $\frac{2\pi^3}{3}$ **19.** $-8/3$ **21.** $-3/4$
23. $\sqrt{2} - \sqrt[4]{8} + 1$ **25.** 16 **27.** 7/3 **29.** π
31. $\frac{1}{\pi}(4^\pi - 2^\pi)$ **33.** $\frac{1}{2}(e - 1)$ **35.** $(\cos\sqrt{x})\left(\frac{1}{2\sqrt{x}}\right)$
37. $4t^5$ **39.** $3x^2 e^{-x^3}$ **41.** $\sqrt{1 + x^2}$ **43.** $-\frac{1}{2}x^{-1/2}\sin x$
45. 1 **47.** $2xe^{(1/2)x^2}$ **49.** 1 **51.** 28/3 **53.** 1/2
55. 51/4 **57.** π **59.** $\frac{\sqrt{2\pi}}{2}$
61. d, since $y' = \frac{1}{x}$ and $y(\pi) = \int_\pi^\pi \frac{1}{t}\,dt - 3 = -3$
63. b, since $y' = \sec x$ and $y(0) = \int_0^0 \sec t\,dt + 4 = 4$
65. $y = \int_2^x \sec t\,dt + 3$ **67.** $s = \int_{t_0}^t f(x)\,dx + s_0$
69. $\frac{2}{3}bh$ **71.** \$9.00 **75.** $2x - 2$ **77.** $-3x + 5$
79. (a) True. Since f is continuous, g is differentiable by Part 1 of the Fundamental Theorem of Calculus.
(b) True: g is continuous because it is differentiable.
(c) True, since $g'(1) = f(1) = 0$.
(d) False, since $g''(1) = f'(1) > 0$.
(e) True, since $g'(1) = 0$ and $g''(1) = f'(1) > 0$.
(f) False: $g''(x) = f'(x) > 0$, so g'' never changes sign.
(g) True, since $g'(1) = f(1) = 0$ and $g'(x) = f(x)$ is an increasing function of x (because $f'(x) > 0$).

Section 5.5, pp. 358–360

1. $-\frac{1}{3}\cos 3x + C$ **3.** $\frac{1}{2}\sec 2t + C$ **5.** $-(7x - 2)^{-4} + C$
7. $-6(1 - r^3)^{1/2} + C$ **9.** $\frac{1}{3}(x^{3/2} - 1) - \frac{1}{6}\sin(2x^{3/2} - 2) + C$
11. (a) $-\frac{1}{4}(\cot^2 2\theta) + C$ **(b)** $-\frac{1}{4}(\csc^2 2\theta) + C$
13. $-\frac{1}{3}(3 - 2s)^{3/2} + C$ **15.** $\frac{2}{5}(5s + 4)^{1/2} + C$
17. $-\frac{2}{5}(1 - \theta^2)^{5/4} + C$ **19.** $(-2/(1 + \sqrt{x})) + C$
21. $\frac{1}{3}\sin(3z + 4) + C$ **23.** $\ln|\sec x| + C$
25. $\left(\frac{r^3}{18} - 1\right)^6 + C$ **27.** $-\frac{2}{3}\cos(x^{3/2} + 1) + C$
29. $\frac{1}{2\cos(2t + 1)} + C$ **31.** $-\frac{\sin^2(1/\theta)}{2} + C$
33. $-\sin\left(\frac{1}{t} - 1\right) + C$ **35.** $\frac{(s^3 + 2s^2 - 5s + 5)^2}{2} + C$
37. $\frac{2}{3}\left(1 - \frac{1}{x}\right)^{3/2} + C$ **39.** $e^{\sin x} + C$
41. $2\tan\left(e^{\sqrt{x}} + 1\right) + C$ **43.** $\ln|\ln x| + C$
45. $z - \ln(1 + e^z) + C$ **47.** $\frac{5}{6}\tan^{-1}\left(\frac{2r}{3}\right) + C$
49. $e^{\sin^{-1} x} + C$ **51.** $\frac{1}{3}(\sin^{-1} x)^3 + C$ **53.** $\ln|\tan^{-1} y| + C$
55. (a) $-\frac{6}{2 + \tan^3 x} + C$ **(b)** $-\frac{6}{2 + \tan^3 x} + C$
(c) $-\frac{6}{2 + \tan^3 x} + C$
57. $\frac{1}{6}\sin\sqrt{3(2r - 1)^2 + 6} + C$ **59.** $s = \frac{1}{2}(3t^2 - 1)^4 - 5$
61. $s = 4t - 2\sin\left(2t + \frac{\pi}{6}\right) + 9$
63. $s = \sin\left(2t - \frac{\pi}{2}\right) + 100t + 1$ **65.** 6 m

Section 5.6, pp. 366–370

1. (a) 14/3 **(b)** 2/3 **3. (a)** 1/2 **(b)** $-1/2$
5. (a) 15/16 **(b)** 0 **7. (a)** 0 **(b)** 1/8 **9. (a)** 4 **(b)** 0
11. (a) 1/6 **(b)** 1/2 **13. (a)** 0 **(b)** 0 **15.** $2\sqrt{3}$
17. 3/4 **19.** $3^{5/2} - 1$ **21.** 3 **23.** $\pi/3$ **25.** e
27. ln 3 **29.** $(\ln 2)^2$ **31.** $\frac{1}{\ln 4}$ **33.** ln 2 **35.** ln 27 **37.** π
39. $\pi/12$ **41.** $2\pi/3$ **43.** $\sqrt{3} - 1$ **45.** $-\pi/12$
47. 16/3 **49.** $2^{5/2}$ **51.** $\pi/2$ **53.** 128/15 **55.** 4/3
57. 5/6 **59.** 38/3 **61.** 49/6 **63.** 32/3 **65.** 48/5
67. 8/3 **69.** 8 **71.** 5/3 (There are three intersection points.)
73. 18 **75.** 243/8 **77.** 8/3 **79.** 2 **81.** 104/15
83. 56/15 **85.** 4 **87.** $\frac{4}{3} - \frac{4}{\pi}$ **89.** $\pi/2$ **91.** 2 **93.** 1/2
95. 1 **97.** ln 16 **99.** 2 **101.** 2 ln 5
103. (a) $(\pm\sqrt{c}, c)$ **(b)** $c = 4^{2/3}$ **(c)** $c = 4^{2/3}$
105. 11/3 **107.** 3/4 **109.** Neither **111.** $F(6) - F(2)$
113. (a) -3 **(b)** 3 **115.** $I = a/2$

Section 5.7, pp. 379–381

1. $\ln\left(\frac{2}{3}\right)$ **3.** $\ln|y^2 - 25| + C$ **5.** $\ln|6 + 3\tan t| + C$
7. $\ln(1 + \sqrt{x}) + C$ **9.** 1 **11.** $8e^{(x+1)} + C$ **13.** 2

15. $2e^{\sqrt{r}} + C$ **17.** $-e^{-t^2} + C$ **19.** $-e^{1/x} + C$

21. $\frac{1}{\pi} e^{\sec \pi t} + C$ **23.** 1 **25.** $\ln(1 + e^r) + C$ **27.** $\frac{1}{2 \ln 2}$

29. $\frac{1}{\ln 2}$ **31.** $\frac{6}{\ln 7}$ **33.** 32760 **35.** $3^{\sqrt{2}+1}$

37. $\frac{1}{\ln 10}\left(\frac{(\ln x)^2}{2}\right) + C$ **39.** $2(\ln 2)^2$ **41.** $\frac{3 \ln 2}{2}$ **43.** $\ln 10$

45. $(\ln 10) \ln|\ln x| + C$ **47.** $y = 1 - \cos(e^t - 2)$

49. $y = 2(e^{-x} + x) - 1$ **51.** $y = x + \ln|x| + 2$

53. **(b)** 0.00469

Practice Exercises, pp. 382–385

1. **(a)** about 680 ft **(b)**

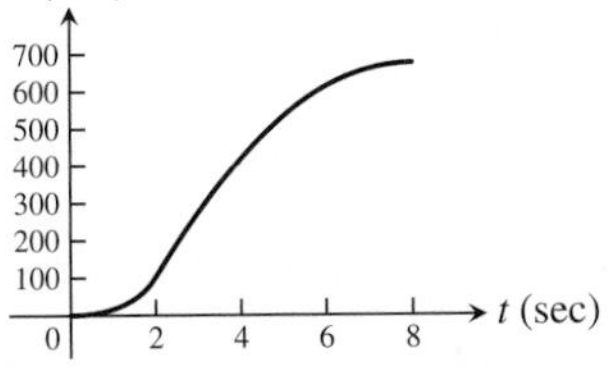

3. **(a)** $-1/2$ **(b)** 31 **(c)** 13 **(d)** 0

5. $\int_1^5 (2x - 1)^{-1/2}\, dx = 2$ **7.** $\int_{-\pi}^{0} \cos \frac{x}{2}\, dx = 2$

9. **(a)** 4 **(b)** 2 **(c)** -2 **(d)** -2π **(e)** 8/5

11. 8/3 **13.** 62 **15.** 1 **17.** 1/6 **19.** 18 **21.** 9/8

23. $\frac{\pi^2}{32} + \frac{\sqrt{2}}{2} - 1$ **25.** 4 **27.** $\frac{8\sqrt{2} - 7}{6}$

29. Min: -4, max: 0, area: 27/4 **31.** 6/5 **33.** 1

37. $y = \int_5^x \left(\frac{\sin t}{t}\right) dt - 3$ **39.** $y = \sin^{-1} x$

41. $y = \sec^{-1} x + \frac{2\pi}{3}, x > 1$ **43.** $-4(\cos x)^{1/2} + C$

45. $\theta^2 + \theta + \sin(2\theta + 1) + C$ **47.** $\frac{t^3}{3} + \frac{4}{t} + C$

49. $-\frac{1}{3} \cos(2t^{3/2}) + C$ **51.** $\tan(e^x - 7) + C$ **53.** $e^{\tan x} + C$

55. $\frac{-\ln 7}{3}$ **57.** $\ln(9/25)$ **59.** $-\frac{1}{2}(\ln x)^{-2} + C$

61. $\frac{1}{2 \ln 3}\left(3^{x^2}\right) + C$ **63.** $\frac{3}{2} \sin^{-1} 2(r - 1) + C$

65. $\frac{\sqrt{2}}{2} \tan^{-1}\left(\frac{x - 1}{\sqrt{2}}\right) + C$ **67.** $\frac{1}{4} \sec^{-1}\left|\frac{2x - 1}{2}\right| + C$

69. $e^{\sin^{-1}\sqrt{x}} + C$ **71.** $2\sqrt{\tan^{-1} y} + C$ **73.** 16

75. 2 **77.** 1 **79.** 8 **81.** $27\sqrt{3}/160$ **83.** $\pi/2$

85. $\sqrt{3}$ **87.** $6\sqrt{3} - 2\pi$ **89.** -1 **91.** 2 **93.** 1

95. $15/16 + \ln 2$ **97.** $e - 1$ **99.** 1/6 **101.** 9/14

103. $\frac{9 \ln 2}{4}$ **105.** π **107.** $\pi/\sqrt{3}$ **109.** $\sec^{-1}|2y| + C$

111. $\pi/12$ **113.** **(a)** b **(b)** b

117. **(a)** $\frac{d}{dx}(x \ln x - x + C) = x \cdot \frac{1}{x} + \ln x - 1 + 0 = \ln x$

(b) $\frac{1}{e - 1}$

119. 25°F **121.** $\sqrt{2 + \cos^3 x}$ **123.** $\frac{-6}{3 + x^4}$

125. $\frac{dy}{dx} = \frac{-2}{x} e^{\cos(2 \ln x)}$ **127.** $\frac{dy}{dx} = \frac{1}{\sqrt{1 - x^2}\sqrt{1 - 2(\sin^{-1} x)^2}}$

129. Yes **131.** $-\sqrt{1 + x^2}$

133. Cost $\approx$ \$10,899 using a lower sum estimate **135.** $1/e$ m/sec

Additional and Advanced Exercises, pp. 386–390

1. **(a)** Yes **(b)** No **5.** **(a)** 1/4 **(b)** $\sqrt[3]{12}$

7. $f(x) = \frac{x}{\sqrt{x^2 + 1}}$ **9.** $y = x^3 + 2x - 4$

11. 36/5

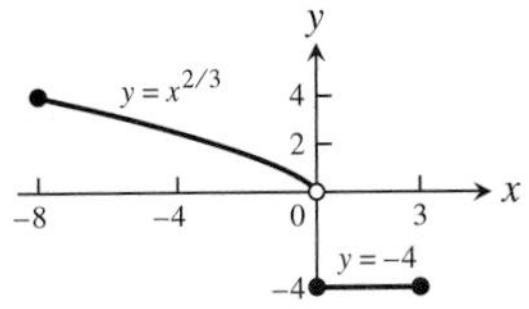

13. $\frac{1}{2} - \frac{2}{\pi}$

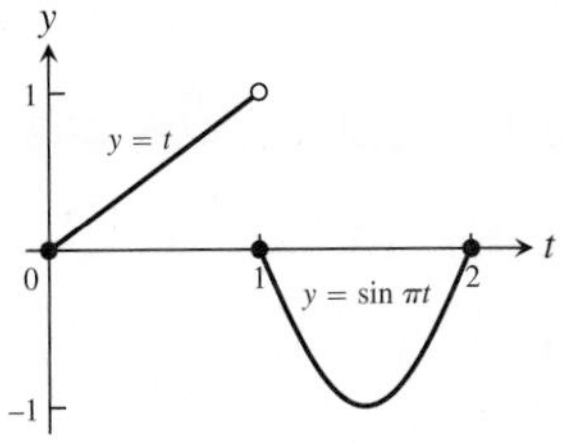

15. 13/3

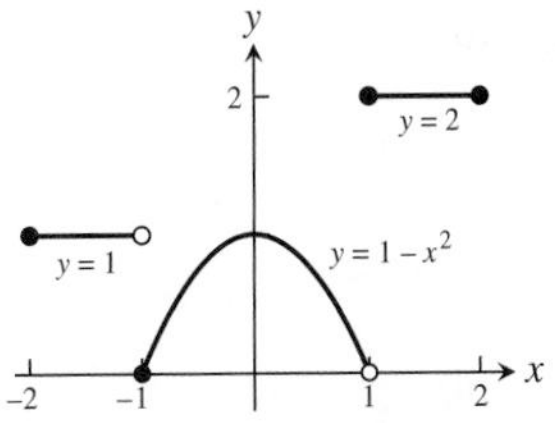

17. 1/2 **21.** **(a)** $\sinh^{-1}(\sqrt{3})$ **(b)** $\ln(\sqrt{3} + 2)$

23. **(a)** $\coth^{-1}(2) - \coth^{-1}(5/4)$ **(b)** $\left(\frac{1}{2}\right) \ln\left(\frac{1}{3}\right)$

25. **(a)** $-\operatorname{sech}^{-1}\left(\frac{12}{13}\right) + \operatorname{sech}^{-1}\left(\frac{4}{5}\right)$

(b) $-\ln\left(\frac{1 + \sqrt{1 - (12/13)^2}}{(12/13)}\right) + \ln\left(\frac{1 + \sqrt{1 - (4/5)^2}}{(4/5)}\right) =$

$-\ln\left(\frac{3}{2}\right) + \ln(2) = \ln(4/3)$

27. **(a)** 0 **(b)** 0 **29.** $\pi/2$ **31.** $\ln 2$ **33.** 1/6

35. $\int_0^1 f(x)\, dx$ **37.** **(b)** πr^2 **39.** $\frac{1}{\ln 2}, \frac{1}{2 \ln 2}, 2:1$ **41.** 2/17

43. **(a)** 0 **(b)** -1 **(c)** $-\pi$ **(d)** $x = 1$
(e) $y = 2x + 2 - \pi$ **(f)** $x = -1, x = 2$ **(g)** $[-2\pi, 0]$

47. $2/x$ **49.** $\frac{\sin 4y}{\sqrt{y}} - \frac{\sin y}{2\sqrt{y}}$ **51.** $2x \ln|x| - x \ln \frac{|x|}{\sqrt{2}}$

53. $(\sin x)/x$ **55.** 1

CHAPTER 6

Section 6.1, pp. 399–401

1. 16 **3.** $\frac{16}{3}$ **5. (a)** $2\sqrt{3}$ **(b)** 8 **7.** 8π

9. (a) $\pi^2/2$ **(b)** 2π **11. (a)** s^2h **(b)** s^2h **13.** $\frac{2\pi}{3}$

15. $4 - \pi$ **17.** $\frac{32\pi}{5}$ **19.** 36π **21.** π **23.** $\frac{\pi}{2}\left(1 - \frac{1}{e^2}\right)$

25. $\frac{\pi}{2}\ln 4$ **27.** $\pi\left(\frac{\pi}{2} + 2\sqrt{2} - \frac{11}{3}\right)$ **29.** 2π **31.** 2π

33. $4\pi\ln 4$ **35.** $\pi^2 - 2\pi$ **37.** $\frac{2\pi}{3}$ **39.** $\frac{117\pi}{5}$

41. $\pi(\pi - 2)$ **43.** $\frac{4\pi}{3}$ **45.** 8π **47.** $\frac{7\pi}{6}$

49. (a) 8π **(b)** $\frac{32\pi}{5}$ **(c)** $\frac{8\pi}{3}$ **(d)** $\frac{224\pi}{15}$

51. (a) $\frac{16\pi}{15}$ **(b)** $\frac{56\pi}{15}$ **(c)** $\frac{64\pi}{15}$

Section 6.2, pp. 406–408

1. 6π **3.** 2π **5.** $\frac{14\pi}{3}$ **7.** 8π **9.** $\frac{5\pi}{6}$ **11.** $\frac{7\pi}{15}$

13. (b) 4π **15.** $\frac{16\pi}{15}(3\sqrt{2} + 5)$ **17.** $\frac{8\pi}{3}$

19. $\frac{4\pi}{3}$ **21.** $\frac{16\pi}{3}$

23. (a) $\frac{6\pi}{5}$ **(b)** $\frac{4\pi}{5}$ **(c)** 2π **(d)** 2π

25. (a) About the x-axis: $V = \frac{2\pi}{15}$; about the y-axis: $V = \frac{\pi}{6}$
(b) About the x-axis: $V = \frac{2\pi}{15}$; about the y-axis: $V = \frac{\pi}{6}$

27. (a) $\frac{5\pi}{3}$ **(b)** $\frac{4\pi}{3}$ **(c)** 2π **(d)** $\frac{2\pi}{3}$

29. (a) $\frac{4\pi}{15}$ **(b)** $\frac{7\pi}{30}$

31. (a) $\frac{24\pi}{5}$ **(b)** $\frac{48\pi}{5}$

33. (a) $\frac{9\pi}{16}$ **(b)** $\frac{9\pi}{16}$

35. Disk: 2 integrals; washer: 2 integrals; shell: 1 integral

39. $\pi\left(1 - \frac{1}{e}\right)$

Section 6.3, pp. 413–414

1. $\frac{5\sqrt{10}}{3}$ **3.** 7 **5.** $\frac{21}{2}$ **7.** $e^3 + 2$ **9.** 12 **11.** $\frac{53}{6}$

13. $\frac{123}{32}$ **15.** $\frac{99}{8}$ **17.** $\pi/3$

19. (a) $\int_{-1}^{2}\sqrt{1 + 4x^2}\,dx$ **(c)** ≈ 6.13

21. (a) $\int_0^{\pi}\sqrt{1 + \cos^2 y}\,dy$ **(c)** ≈ 3.82

23. (a) $\int_{-1}^{3}\sqrt{1 + (y + 1)^2}\,dy$ **(c)** ≈ 9.29

25. (a) $\int_0^{\pi/6}\sec x\,dx$ **(c)** ≈ 0.55

27. Yes, $f(x) = \pm x + C$ where C is any real number.

29. (a) $y = \sqrt{x}$ from (1, 1) to (4, 2)
(b) Only one. We know the derivative of the function and the value of the function at one value of x.

31. $y = e^{x/2} - 1$ **33.** $-\ln(2)$ **35.** $e^3 - \frac{1}{e^3}$

Section 6.4, pp. 419–421

1. (a) $2\pi\int_0^{\pi/4}\tan x\sqrt{1 + \sec^4 x}\,dx$ **(c)** ≈ 3.84

3. (a) $2\pi\int_1^2 \frac{1}{y}\sqrt{1 + y^{-4}}\,dy$ **(c)** ≈ 5.02

5. (a) $2\pi\int_1^4 (3 - \sqrt{x})^2\sqrt{1 + (1 - 3x^{-1/2})^2}\,dx$ **(c)** ≈ 63.37

7. (a) $2\pi\int_0^{\pi/3}\left(\int_0^y \tan t\,dt\right)\sec y\,dy$ **(c)** ≈ 2.08

9. $4\pi\sqrt{5}$ **11.** $3\pi\sqrt{5}$ **13.** $98\pi/81$ **15.** 2π

17. $\pi(\sqrt{8} - 1)/9$ **19.** $35\pi\sqrt{5}/3$ **21.** $\pi\left(\frac{15}{16} + \ln 2\right)$

23. $253\pi/20$ **27.** Order 226.2 liters of each color.

33. $8\pi^2$ **35.** $52\pi/3$

37. $\frac{16}{3}\pi(e^{3/2} + 3e^{1/2} - 4)$ **39.** $3\pi\sqrt{5}$

Section 6.5, pp. 428–430

9. $\frac{2}{3}y^{3/2} - x^{1/2} = C$ **11.** $e^y - e^x = C$

13. $-x + 2\tan\sqrt{y} = C$ **15.** $e^{-y} + 2e^{\sqrt{x}} = C$

17. $y = \sin(x^2 + C)$

19. (a) -0.00001 **(b)** 10,536 years **(c)** 82%

21. 54.88 g **23.** 59.8 ft **25.** 2.8147498×10^{14}

27. (a) 8 years **(b)** 32.02 years

29. 15.28 years **31.** 56,562 years

35. (a) 17.5 min. **(b)** 13.26 min.

37. $-3°$C **39.** About 6658 years **41.** 41 years old

Section 6.6, pp. 433–436

1. 400 N/m **3.** 4 cm, 0.08 J

5. (a) 7238 lb/in. **(b)** 905 in.-lb, 2714 in.-lb

7. 780 J **9.** 72,900 ft-lb **13.** 160 ft-lb

15. (a) 1,497,600 ft-lb **(b)** 1 hr, 40 min
(d) At 62.26 lb/ft^3: a) 1,494,240 ft-lb b) 1 hr, 40 min
At 62.59 lb/ft^3: a) 1,502,160 ft-lb b) 1 hr, 40.1 min

17. 37,306 ft-lb **19.** 7,238,229.47 ft-lb
21. **(a)** 34,583 ft-lb **(b)** 53,483 ft-lb
23. 15,073,099.75 J
27. 85.1 ft-lb **29.** 64.6 ft-lb **31.** 110.6 ft-lb
33. 91.32 in.-oz **35.** 5.144×10^{10} J

Section 6.7, pp. 442–443

1. $\bar{x} = 0, \bar{y} = 12/5$ **3.** $\bar{x} = 1, \bar{y} = -3/5$
5. $\bar{x} = 16/105, \bar{y} = 8/15$ **7.** $\bar{x} = 0, \bar{y} = \pi/8$
9. **(a)** $\bar{x} \approx 1.44, \bar{y} \approx 0.36$
(b)

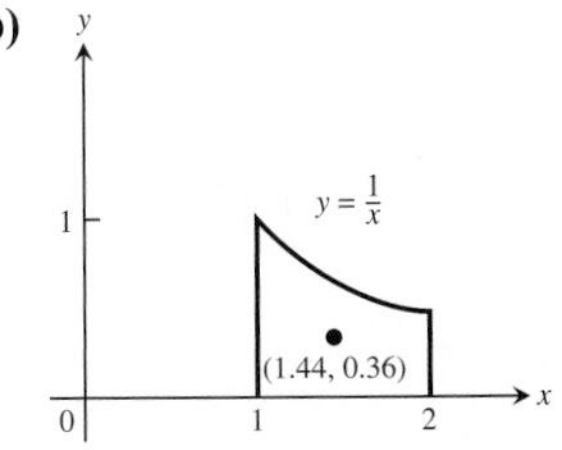

11. $\bar{x} = \dfrac{\ln 4}{\pi}, \bar{y} = 0$ **13.** $\bar{x} = 7, \bar{y} = \dfrac{\ln 16}{12}$

15. $\bar{x} = 3/2, \bar{y} = 1/2$ **17.** $\bar{x} = \dfrac{15}{\ln 16}, \bar{y} = \dfrac{3}{4 \ln 16}$

19. **(a)** $\dfrac{224\pi}{3}$ **(b)** $\bar{x} = 2, \bar{y} = 0$
(c)

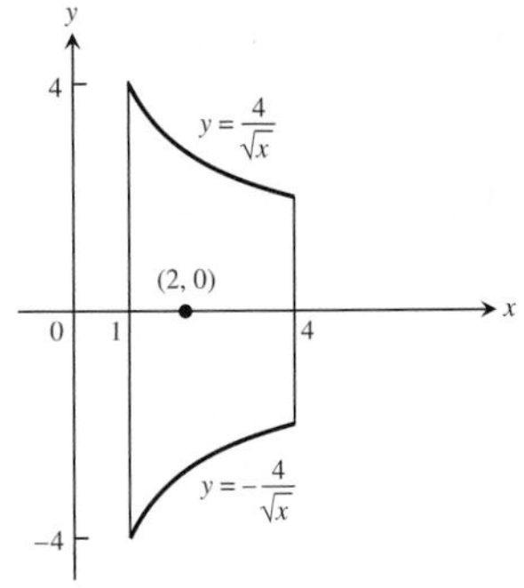

23. $\bar{x} = \bar{y} = 1/3$ **25.** $\bar{x} = a/3, \bar{y} = b/3$ **27.** $13\delta/6$

29. $\bar{x} = 0, \bar{y} = \dfrac{a\pi}{4}$

Practice Exercises, pp. 444–446

1. $\dfrac{9\pi}{280}$ **3.** π^2 **5.** $\dfrac{72\pi}{35}$
7. **(a)** 2π **(b)** π **(c)** $12\pi/5$ **(d)** $26\pi/5$
9. **(a)** 8π **(b)** $1088\pi/15$ **(c)** $512\pi/15$

11. $\pi(3\sqrt{3} - \pi)/3$ **13.** $\pi(e - 1)$ **15.** $\dfrac{28\pi}{3}$ ft³ **17.** $\dfrac{10}{3}$

19. $3 + \dfrac{1}{8}\ln 2$ **21.** 10 **23.** $\dfrac{9\pi}{2}$

25. $28\pi\sqrt{2}/3$ **27.** 4π **29.** $76\pi/3$

31. $y = \left(\tan^{-1}\left(\dfrac{x + C}{2}\right)\right)^2$ **33.** $y^2 = \sin^{-1}(2\tan x + C)$

35. $y = -2 + \ln(2 - e^{-x})$ **37.** $4x - 4\sqrt{x} + 1$
39. 18,935 years **41.** 4640 J
43. 10 ft-lb, 30 ft-lb **45.** 418,208.81 ft-lb
47. $22{,}500\pi$ ft-lb, 257 sec **49.** $\bar{x} = 0, \bar{y} = 8/5$

51. $\bar{x} = 3/2, \bar{y} = 12/5$ **53.** $\bar{x} = 9/5, \bar{y} = 11/10$

Additional and Advanced Exercises, pp. 446–447

1. $f(x) = \sqrt{\dfrac{2x - a}{\pi}}$ **3.** $f(x) = \sqrt{C^2 - 1}\,x + a$, where $C \geq 1$

5. 28/3

7. **(a)** $y = c + (y_0 - c)e^{-k(A/V)t}$
(b) Steady-state solution: $y_\infty = c$

9. $\dfrac{4h\sqrt{3mh}}{3}$

11. $\bar{x} = 0, \bar{y} = \dfrac{n}{2n + 1}$, $(0, 1/2)$

15. **(a)** $\bar{x} = \bar{y} = 4(a^2 + ab + b^2)/(3\pi(a + b))$
(b) $(2a/\pi, 2a/\pi)$

CHAPTER 7

Section 7.1, pp. 453–455

1. $-2x\cos(x/2) + 4\sin(x/2) + C$
3. $t^2\sin t + 2t\cos t - 2\sin t + C$ **5.** $\ln 4 - \dfrac{3}{4}$
7. $y\tan^{-1}(y) - \ln\sqrt{1 + y^2} + C$
9. $x\tan x + \ln|\cos x| + C$
11. $(x^3 - 3x^2 + 6x - 6)e^x + C$
13. $(x^2 - 7x + 7)e^x + C$
15. $(x^5 - 5x^4 + 20x^3 - 60x^2 + 120x - 120)e^x + C$

17. $\dfrac{\pi^2 - 4}{8}$ **19.** $\dfrac{5\pi - 3\sqrt{3}}{9}$

21. $\dfrac{1}{2}(-e^\theta\cos\theta + e^\theta\sin\theta) + C$

23. $\dfrac{e^{2x}}{13}(3\sin 3x + 2\cos 3x) + C$

25. $\dfrac{2}{3}\left(\sqrt{3s + 9}\,e^{\sqrt{3s+9}} - e^{\sqrt{3s+9}}\right) + C$

27. $\dfrac{\pi\sqrt{3}}{3} - \ln(2) - \dfrac{\pi^2}{18}$

29. $\dfrac{1}{2}[-x\cos(\ln x) + x\sin(\ln x)] + C$

31. **(a)** π **(b)** 3π **(c)** 5π **(d)** $(2n + 1)\pi$
33. $2\pi(1 - \ln 2)$ **35.** **(a)** $\pi(\pi - 2)$ **(b)** 2π

37. $\dfrac{1}{2\pi}(1 - e^{-2\pi})$ **39.** $u = x^n, dv = \cos x\,dx$
41. $u = x^n, dv = e^{ax}\,dx$ **43.** $x\sin^{-1}x + \cos(\sin^{-1}x) + C$
45. $x\sec^{-1}x - \ln\left|x + \sqrt{x^2 - 1}\right| + C$ **47.** Yes

49. **(a)** $x \sinh^{-1} x - \cosh(\sinh^{-1} x) + C$
(b) $x \sinh^{-1} x - (1 + x^2)^{1/2} + C$

Section 7.2, p. 460

1. $8/15$ **3.** $4/3$ **5.** $16/35$ **7.** 3π **9.** π **11.** 2
13. 1 **15.** 4 **17.** 2 **19.** $2\ln\left(1 + \sqrt{2}\right)$ **21.** $\sqrt{2}$
23. $2\sqrt{3} + \ln\left(2 + \sqrt{3}\right)$ **25.** $4/3$ **27.** $4/3$
29. $2(1 - \ln 2)$ **31.** $\frac{4}{3} - \ln\sqrt{3}$ **33.** $-6/5$ **35.** π
37. 0 **39.** $\dfrac{2\pi\left(\left(9\sqrt[3]{4} + 1\right)^{3/2} - 1\right)}{27}$ **41.** $\ln\left(1 + \sqrt{2}\right)$
43. $\pi^2/2$

Section 7.3, pp. 463–464

1. $\ln\left|\sqrt{9 + y^2} + y\right| + C$ **3.** $\pi/4$ **5.** $\pi/6$
7. $\frac{25}{2}\sin^{-1}\left(\frac{t}{5}\right) + \frac{t\sqrt{25 - t^2}}{2} + C$
9. $\frac{1}{2}\ln\left|\frac{2x}{7} + \frac{\sqrt{4x^2 - 49}}{7}\right| + C$
11. $7\left[\frac{\sqrt{y^2 - 49}}{7} - \sec^{-1}\left(\frac{y}{7}\right)\right] + C$ **13.** $\frac{\sqrt{x^2 - 1}}{x} + C$
15. $\frac{1}{3}(x^2 + 4)^{3/2} - 4\sqrt{x^2 + 4} + C$ **17.** $\frac{-2\sqrt{4 - w^2}}{w} + C$
19. $4\sqrt{3} - 4\pi/3$ **21.** $-\frac{x}{\sqrt{x^2 - 1}} + C$
23. $-\frac{1}{5}\left(\frac{\sqrt{1 - x^2}}{x}\right)^5 + C$ **25.** $2\tan^{-1} 2x + \frac{4x}{(4x^2 + 1)} + C$
27. $\frac{1}{3}\left(\frac{v}{\sqrt{1 - v^2}}\right)^3 + C$ **29.** $\ln 9 - \ln\left(1 + \sqrt{10}\right)$
31. $\pi/6$ **33.** $\sec^{-1}|x| + C$ **35.** $\sqrt{x^2 - 1} + C$
37. $y = 2\left[\frac{\sqrt{x^2 - 4}}{2} - \sec^{-1}\left(\frac{x}{2}\right)\right]$
39. $y = \frac{3}{2}\tan^{-1}\left(\frac{x}{2}\right) - \frac{3\pi}{8}$ **41.** $3\pi/4$

Section 7.4, pp. 469–471

1. $\frac{2}{x - 3} + \frac{3}{x - 2}$ **3.** $\frac{1}{x + 1} + \frac{3}{(x + 1)^2}$
5. $\frac{-2}{z} + \frac{-1}{z^2} + \frac{2}{z - 1}$ **7.** $1 + \frac{17}{t - 3} + \frac{-12}{t - 2}$
9. $\frac{1}{2}[\ln|1 + x| - \ln|1 - x|] + C$
11. $\frac{1}{7}\ln|(x + 6)^2(x - 1)^5| + C$ **13.** $(\ln 15)/2$
15. $-\frac{1}{2}\ln|t| + \frac{1}{6}\ln|t + 2| + \frac{1}{3}\ln|t - 1| + C$ **17.** $3\ln 2 - 2$
19. $\frac{1}{4}\ln\left|\frac{x + 1}{x - 1}\right| - \frac{x}{2(x^2 - 1)} + C$ **21.** $(\pi + 2\ln 2)/8$
23. $\tan^{-1} y - \frac{1}{y^2 + 1} + C$
25. $-(s - 1)^{-2} + (s - 1)^{-1} + \tan^{-1} s + C$
27. $\frac{-1}{\theta^2 + 2\theta + 2} + \ln(\theta^2 + 2\theta + 2) - \tan^{-1}(\theta + 1) + C$
29. $x^2 + \ln\left|\frac{x - 1}{x}\right| + C$
31. $9x + 2\ln|x| + \frac{1}{x} + 7\ln|x - 1| + C$
33. $\frac{y^2}{2} - \ln|y| + \frac{1}{2}\ln(1 + y^2) + C$ **35.** $\ln\left(\frac{e^t + 1}{e^t + 2}\right) + C$
37. $\frac{1}{5}\ln\left|\frac{\sin y - 2}{\sin y + 3}\right| + C$
39. $\frac{(\tan^{-1} 2x)^2}{4} - 3\ln|x - 2| + \frac{6}{x - 2} + C$
41. $x = \ln|t - 2| - \ln|t - 1| + \ln 2$ **43.** $x = \frac{6t}{t + 2} - 1$
45. $3\pi\ln 25$ **47.** 1.10 **49.** **(a)** $x = \frac{1000e^{4t}}{499 + e^{4t}}$ **(b)** 1.55 days

Section 7.5, pp. 476–477

1. $\frac{2}{\sqrt{3}}\left(\tan^{-1}\sqrt{\frac{x - 3}{3}}\right) + C$
3. $\sqrt{x - 2}\left(\frac{2(x - 2)}{3} + 4\right) + C$
5. $\frac{(2x - 3)^{3/2}(x + 1)}{5} + C$
7. $\frac{-\sqrt{9 - 4x}}{x} - \frac{2}{3}\ln\left|\frac{\sqrt{9 - 4x} - 3}{\sqrt{9 - 4x} + 3}\right| + C$
9. $\frac{(x + 2)(2x - 6)\sqrt{4x - x^2}}{6} + 4\sin^{-1}\left(\frac{x - 2}{2}\right) + C$
11. $-\frac{1}{\sqrt{7}}\ln\left|\frac{\sqrt{7} + \sqrt{7 + x^2}}{x}\right| + C$
13. $\sqrt{4 - x^2} - 2\ln\left|\frac{2 + \sqrt{4 - x^2}}{x}\right| + C$
15. $\frac{e^{2t}}{13}(2\cos 3t + 3\sin 3t) + C$
17. $\frac{x^2}{2}\cos^{-1}(x) + \frac{1}{4}\sin^{-1}(x) - \frac{1}{4}x\sqrt{1 - x^2} + C$
19. $\frac{x^3}{3}\tan^{-1} x - \frac{x^2}{6} + \frac{1}{6}\ln(1 + x^2) + C$
21. $-\frac{\cos 5x}{10} - \frac{\cos x}{2} + C$ **23.** $8\left[\frac{\sin(7t/2)}{7} - \frac{\sin(9t/2)}{9}\right] + C$
25. $6\sin(\theta/12) + \frac{6}{7}\sin(7\theta/12) + C$

27. $\frac{1}{2}\ln(x^2+1)+\frac{x}{2(1+x^2)}+\frac{1}{2}\tan^{-1}x+C$

29. $\left(x-\frac{1}{2}\right)\sin^{-1}\sqrt{x}+\frac{1}{2}\sqrt{x-x^2}+C$

31. $\sin^{-1}\sqrt{x}-\sqrt{x-x^2}+C$

33. $\sqrt{1-\sin^2 t}-\ln\left|\frac{1+\sqrt{1-\sin^2 t}}{\sin t}\right|+C$

35. $\ln\left|\ln y+\sqrt{3+(\ln y)^2}\right|+C$

37. $-\frac{\sin^4 2x\cos 2x}{10}-\frac{2\sin^2 2x\cos 2x}{15}-\frac{4\cos 2x}{15}+C$

39. $\frac{\sin^3 2\theta\cos^2 2\theta}{10}+\frac{\sin^3 2\theta}{15}+C$

41. $\tan^2 2x-2\ln|\sec 2x|+C$

43. $\frac{(\sec\pi x)(\tan\pi x)}{\pi}+\frac{1}{\pi}\ln|\sec\pi x+\tan\pi x|+C$

45. $\frac{-\csc^3 x\cot x}{4}-\frac{3\csc x\cot x}{8}-\frac{3}{8}\ln|\csc x+\cot x|+C$

47. $\frac{1}{2}[\sec(e^t-1)\tan(e^t-1)+$
$\ln|\sec(e^t-1)+\tan(e^t-1)|]+C$

49. $\sqrt{2}+\ln\left(\sqrt{2}+1\right)$ **51.** $\pi/3$

53. $2\pi\sqrt{3}+\pi\sqrt{2}\ln\left(\sqrt{2}+\sqrt{3}\right)$

55. $\bar{x}=4/3, \bar{y}=\ln\sqrt{2}$ **57.** 7.62 **59.** $\pi/8$ **63.** $\pi/4$

Section 7.6, pp. 484–486

1. I: (a) 1.5, 0 **(b)** 1.5, 0 **(c)** 0%
II: (a) 1.5, 0 **(b)** 1.5, 0 **(c)** 0%
3. I: (a) 2.75, 0.08 **(b)** 2.67, 0.08 **(c)** $0.0312 \approx 3\%$
II: (a) 2.67, 0 **(b)** 2.67, 0 **(c)** 0%
5. I: (a) 6.25, 0.5 **(b)** 6, 0.25 **(c)** $0.0417 \approx 4\%$
II: (a) 6, 0 **(b)** 6, 0 **(c)** 0%
7. I: (a) 0.509, 0.03125 **(b)** 0.5, 0.009 **(c)** $0.018 \approx 2\%$
II: (a) 0.5, 0.002604 **(b)** 0.5, 0.0004 **(c)** 0%
9. I: (a) 1.8961, 0.161 **(b)** 2, 0.1039 **(c)** $0.052 \approx 5\%$
II: (a) 2.0045, 0.0066 **(b)** 2, 0.00454 **(c)** 0%
11. (a) 1 **(b)** 2 **13. (a)** 116 **(b)** 2
15. (a) 283 **(b)** 2 **17. (a)** 71 **(b)** 10
19. (a) 76 **(b)** 12 **21. (a)** 82 **(b)** 8
23. 15,990 ft^3 **25.** $\approx$10.63 ft
27. (a) $\approx$0.00021 **(b)** $\approx$1.37079 **(c)** $\approx$0.015%
31. (a) $\approx$5.870 **(b)** $|E_T| \le 0.0032$
33. 21.07 in. **35.** 14.4

Section 7.7, pp. 495–497

1. $\pi/2$ **3.** 2 **5.** 6 **7.** $\pi/2$ **9.** ln 3 **11.** ln 4 **13.** 0

15. $\sqrt{3}$ **17.** π **19.** $\ln\left(1+\frac{\pi}{2}\right)$ **21.** -1 **23.** 1

25. $-1/4$ **27.** $\pi/2$ **29.** $\pi/3$ **31.** 6 **33.** ln 2
35. Diverges **37.** Converges **39.** Converges **41.** Converges
43. Diverges **45.** Converges **47.** Converges **49.** Diverges
51. Converges **53.** Converges **55.** Diverges **57.** Converges
59. Diverges **61.** Converges **63.** Converges
65. (a) Converges when $p < 1$ **(b)** Converges when $p > 1$
67. 1 **69.** 2π **71.** ln 2 **73. (b)** $\approx$0.88621
75. (a)

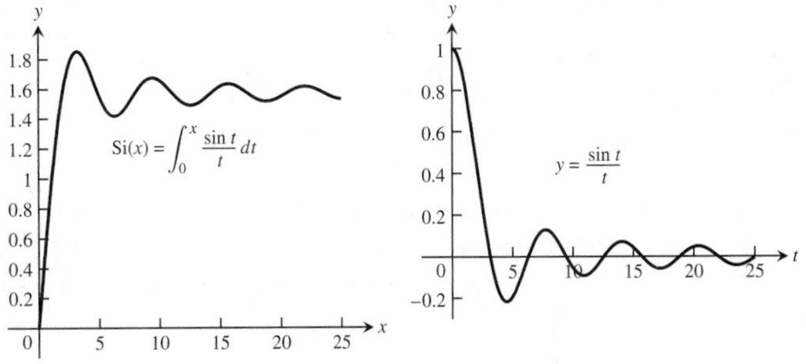

(b) $\pi/2$

77. (a)

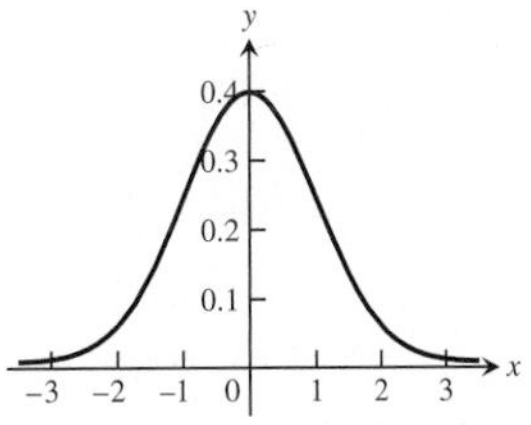

(b) $\approx$0.683, $\approx$0.954, $\approx$0.997

Practice Exercises, pp. 497–499

1. $(x+1)(\ln(x+1))-(x+1)+C$

3. $x\tan^{-1}(3x)-\frac{1}{6}\ln(1+9x^2)+C$

5. $(x+1)^2e^x-2(x+1)e^x+2e^x+C$

7. $\frac{2e^x\sin 2x}{5}+\frac{e^x\cos 2x}{5}+C$

9. $2\ln|x-2|-\ln|x-1|+C$

11. $\ln|x|-\ln|x+1|+\frac{1}{x+1}+C$

13. $-\frac{1}{3}\ln\left|\frac{\cos\theta-1}{\cos\theta+2}\right|+C$

15. $4\ln|x|-\frac{1}{2}\ln(x^2+1)+4\tan^{-1}x+C$

17. $\frac{1}{16}\ln\left|\frac{(v-2)^5(v+2)}{v^6}\right|+C$

19. $\frac{1}{2}\tan^{-1}t-\frac{\sqrt{3}}{6}\tan^{-1}\frac{t}{\sqrt{3}}+C$

21. $\frac{x^2}{2}+\frac{4}{3}\ln|x+2|+\frac{2}{3}\ln|x-1|+C$

23. $\frac{x^2}{2} - \frac{9}{2}\ln|x+3| + \frac{3}{2}\ln|x+1| + C$

25. $\frac{1}{3}\ln\left|\frac{\sqrt{x+1}-1}{\sqrt{x+1}+1}\right| + C$ **27.** $\ln|1 - e^{-s}| + C$

29. $-\sqrt{16-y^2} + C$ **31.** $-\frac{1}{2}\ln|4-x^2| + C$

33. $\ln\frac{1}{\sqrt{9-x^2}} + C$ **35.** $\frac{1}{6}\ln\left|\frac{x+3}{x-3}\right| + C$

37. $-\frac{\cos^5 x}{5} + \frac{\cos^7 x}{7} + C$ **39.** $\frac{\tan^5 x}{5} + C$

41. $\frac{\cos\theta}{2} - \frac{\cos 11\theta}{22} + C$ **43.** $4\sqrt{1-\cos(t/2)} + C$

45. At least 16 **47.** $T = \pi, S = \pi$ **49.** 25°F

51. **(a)** ≈2.42 gal **(b)** ≈24.83 mi/gal

53. $\pi/2$ **55.** 6 **57.** ln 3 **59.** 2 **61.** $\pi/6$

63. Diverges **65.** Diverges **67.** Converges

69. $\frac{2x^{3/2}}{3} - x + 2\sqrt{x} - 2\ln\left(\sqrt{x}+1\right) + C$

71. $\ln\left|\frac{\sqrt{x}}{\sqrt{x^2+1}}\right| - \frac{1}{2}\left(\frac{x}{\sqrt{x^2+1}}\right)^2 + C$

73. $-2\cot x - \ln|\csc x + \cot x| + \csc x + C$

75. $\frac{1}{12}\ln\left|\frac{3+v}{3-v}\right| + \frac{1}{6}\tan^{-1}\frac{v}{3} + C$

77. $\frac{\theta\sin(2\theta+1)}{2} + \frac{\cos(2\theta+1)}{4} + C$ **79.** $\frac{1}{4}\sec^2\theta + C$

81. $2\left(\frac{(\sqrt{2-x})^3}{3} - 2\sqrt{2-x}\right) + C$ **83.** $\tan^{-1}(y-1) + C$

85. $\frac{1}{4}\ln|z| - \frac{1}{4z} - \frac{1}{4}\left[\frac{1}{2}\ln(z^2+4) + \frac{1}{2}\tan^{-1}\left(\frac{z}{2}\right)\right] + C$

87. $-\frac{1}{4}\sqrt{9-4t^2} + C$ **89.** $\ln\left(\frac{e^t+1}{e^t+2}\right) + C$ **91.** 1/4

93. $\frac{2}{3}x^{3/2} + C$ **95.** $-\frac{1}{5}\tan^{-1}\cos(5t) + C$

97. $2\sqrt{r} - 2\ln\left(1+\sqrt{r}\right) + C$

Additional and Advanced Exercises, pp. 500–501

1. $x(\sin^{-1}x)^2 + 2(\sin^{-1}x)\sqrt{1-x^2} - 2x + C$

3. $\frac{x^2\sin^{-1}x}{2} + \frac{x\sqrt{1-x^2} - \sin^{-1}x}{4} + C$

5. $\frac{1}{2}\left(\ln\left(t - \sqrt{1-t^2}\right) - \sin^{-1}t\right) + C$

7. 0 **9.** ln(4) − 1 **11.** 1 **13.** $32\pi/35$ **15.** 2π

17. **(a)** π **(b)** $\pi(2e-5)$

19. **(b)** $\pi\left(\frac{8(\ln 2)^2}{3} - \frac{16(\ln 2)}{9} + \frac{16}{27}\right)$ **21.** $\left(\frac{e^2+1}{4}, \frac{e-2}{2}\right)$

23. $\sqrt{1+e^2} - \ln\left(\frac{\sqrt{1+e^2}}{e} + \frac{1}{e}\right) - \sqrt{2} + \ln\left(1+\sqrt{2}\right)$

25. 6 **27.** $a = \frac{1}{2}, -\frac{\ln 2}{4}$ **29.** $\frac{1}{2} < p \le 1$

CHAPTER 8

Section 8.1, pp. 511–514

1. $a_1 = 0, a_2 = -1/4, a_3 = -2/9, a_4 = -3/16$

3. $a_1 = 1, a_2 = -1/3, a_3 = 1/5, a_4 = -1/7$

5. $a_1 = 1/2, a_2 = 1/2, a_3 = 1/2, a_4 = 1/2$

7. $1, \frac{3}{2}, \frac{7}{4}, \frac{15}{8}, \frac{31}{16}, \frac{63}{32}, \frac{127}{64}, \frac{255}{128}, \frac{511}{256}, \frac{1023}{512}$

9. $2, 1, -\frac{1}{2}, -\frac{1}{4}, \frac{1}{8}, \frac{1}{16}, -\frac{1}{32}, -\frac{1}{64}, \frac{1}{128}, \frac{1}{256}$

11. 1, 1, 2, 3, 5, 8, 13, 21, 34, 55 **13.** $a_n = (-1)^{n+1}, n \ge 1$

15. $a_n = (-1)^{n+1}(n)^2, n \ge 1$ **17.** $a_n = n^2 - 1, n \ge 1$

19. $a_n = 4n - 3, n \ge 1$ **21.** $a_n = \frac{1 + (-1)^{n+1}}{2}, n \ge 1$

23. Converges, 2 **25.** Converges, −1 **27.** Converges, −5

29. Diverges **31.** Diverges **33.** Converges, 1/2

35. Converges, 0 **37.** Converges, $\sqrt{2}$ **39.** Converges, 1

41. Converges, 0 **43.** Converges, 0 **45.** Converges, 0

47. Converges, 1 **49.** Converges, e^7 **51.** Converges, 1

53. Converges, 1 **55.** Diverges **57.** Converges, 4

59. Converges, 0 **61.** Diverges **63.** Converges, e^{-1}

65. Converges, $e^{2/3}$ **67.** Converges, x $(x > 0)$

69. Converges, 0 **71.** Converges, 1 **73.** Converges, 1/2

75. Converges, $\pi/2$ **77.** Converges, 0 **79.** Converges, 0

81. Converges, 1/2 **83.** Converges, 0 **85.** $x_n = 2^{n-2}$

87. **(a)** $f(x) = x^2 - 2$, $1.414213562 \approx \sqrt{2}$

(b) $f(x) = \tan(x) - 1$, $0.7853981635 \approx \pi/4$

(c) $f(x) = e^x$, diverges

89. **(b)** 1 **97.** Nondecreasing, bounded

99. Not nondecreasing, bounded

101. Converges, nondecreasing sequence theorem

103. Converges, nondecreasing sequence theorem

105. Diverges, definition of divergence **109.** Converges

111. Converges **121.** $N = 692, a_n = \sqrt[n]{0.5}, L = 1$

123. $N = 65, a_n = (0.9)^n, L = 0$ **125.** **(b)** $\sqrt{3}$

Section 8.2, pp. 522–523

1. $s_n = \frac{2(1-(1/3)^n)}{1-(1/3)}, 3$ **3.** $s_n = \frac{1-(-1/2)^n}{1-(-1/2)}, 2/3$

5. $s_n = \frac{1}{2} - \frac{1}{n+2}, \frac{1}{2}$ **7.** $1 - \frac{1}{4} + \frac{1}{16} - \frac{1}{64} + \cdots, \frac{4}{5}$

9. $\frac{7}{4} + \frac{7}{16} + \frac{7}{64} + \cdots, \frac{7}{3}$

11. $(5+1)+\left(\frac{5}{2}+\frac{1}{3}\right)+\left(\frac{5}{4}+\frac{1}{9}\right)+\left(\frac{5}{8}+\frac{1}{27}\right)+\cdots, \frac{23}{2}$

13. $(1+1)+\left(\frac{1}{2}-\frac{1}{5}\right)+\left(\frac{1}{4}+\frac{1}{25}\right)+\left(\frac{1}{8}-\frac{1}{125}\right)+\cdots, \frac{17}{6}$

15. 1 **17.** 5 **19.** 1 **21.** $-\frac{1}{\ln 2}$ **23.** Converges, $2+\sqrt{2}$

25. Converges, 1 **27.** Diverges **29.** Converges, $\frac{e^2}{e^2-1}$

31. Converges, 2/9 **33.** Converges, 3/2 **35.** Diverges

37. Diverges **39.** Converges, $\frac{\pi}{\pi-e}$

41. $a=1, r=-x$; converges to $1/(1+x)$ for $|x|<1$

43. $a=3, r=(x-1)/2$; converges to $6/(3-x)$ for x in $(-1, 3)$

45. $|x|<\frac{1}{2}, \frac{1}{1-2x}$ **47.** $-2<x<0, \frac{1}{2+x}$

49. $x \neq (2k+1)\frac{\pi}{2}$, k an integer; $\frac{1}{1-\sin x}$

51. 23/99 **53.** 7/9 **55.** 1/15 **57.** 41333/33300

59. **(a)** $\sum_{n=-2}^{\infty}\frac{1}{(n+4)(n+5)}$ **(b)** $\sum_{n=0}^{\infty}\frac{1}{(n+2)(n+3)}$

(c) $\sum_{n=5}^{\infty}\frac{1}{(n-3)(n-2)}$

69. **(a)** $r=3/5$ **(b)** $r=-3/10$ **71.** $|r|<1, \frac{1+2r}{1-r^2}$

Section 8.3, pp. 527–528

1. Converges; geometric series, $r=\frac{1}{10}<1$

3. Diverges; $\lim_{n\to\infty}\frac{n}{n+1}=1\neq 0$ **5.** Diverges; p-series, $p<1$

7. Converges; geometric series, $r=\frac{1}{8}<1$

9. Diverges; Integral Test

11. Converges; geometric series, $r=2/3<1$

13. Diverges; Integral Test **15.** Diverges; $\lim_{n\to\infty}\frac{2^n}{n+1}\neq 0$

17. Diverges; $\lim_{n\to\infty}\left(\sqrt{n}/\ln n\right)\neq 0$

19. Diverges; geometric series, $r=\frac{1}{\ln 2}>1$

21. Converges; Integral Test **23.** Diverges; nth-Term Test

25. Converges; Integral Test **27.** Converges; Integral Test

29. Converges; Integral Test **31.** $a=1$ **33.** **(b)** About 41.55

35. True

43. **(a)** $1.20166 \le S \le 1.20253$ **(b)** $S\approx 1.2021$, error <0.0005

Section 8.4, p. 532

1. Diverges; limit comparison with $\sum\left(1/\sqrt{n}\right)$

3. Converges; compare with $\sum\left(1/2^n\right)$

5. Diverges; nth-Term Test

7. Converges; $\left(\frac{n}{3n+1}\right)^n<\left(\frac{n}{3n}\right)^n=\left(\frac{1}{3}\right)^n$

9. Diverges; direct comparison with $\sum(1/n)$

11. Converges; limit comparison with $\sum(1/n^2)$

13. Diverges; limit comparison with $\sum(1/n)$

15. Diverges; limit comparison with $\sum(1/n)$

17. Diverges; Integral Test

19. Converges; compare with $\sum(1/n^{3/2})$

21. Converges; $\frac{1}{n2^n}\le\frac{1}{2^n}$ **23.** Converges; $\frac{1}{3^{n-1}+1}<\frac{1}{3^{n-1}}$

25. Diverges; limit comparison with $\sum(1/n)$

27. Converges; compare with $\sum(1/n^2)$

29. Converges; $\frac{\tan^{-1} n}{n^{1.1}}<\frac{\pi/2}{n^{1.1}}$

31. Converges; compare with $\sum(1/n^2)$

33. Diverges; limit comparison with $\sum(1/n)$

35. Converges; limit comparison with $\sum(1/n^2)$

Section 8.5, pp. 536–537

1. Converges; Ratio Test **3.** Diverges; Ratio Test

5. Converges; Ratio Test

7. Converges; compare with $\sum(3/(1.25)^n)$

9. Diverges; $\lim_{n\to\infty}\left(1-\frac{3}{n}\right)^n=e^{-3}\neq 0$

11. Converges; compare with $\sum(1/n^2)$

13. Diverges; compare with $\sum(1/(2n))$

15. Diverges; compare with $\sum(1/n)$ **17.** Converges; Ratio Test

19. Converges; Ratio Test **21.** Converges; Ratio Test

23. Converges; Root Test

25. Converges; compare with $\sum(1/n^2)$

27. Converges; Ratio Test **29.** Diverges; Ratio Test

31. Converges; Ratio Test **33.** Converges; Ratio Test

35. Diverges; $a_n=\left(\frac{1}{3}\right)^{(1/n!)}\to 1$ **37.** Converges; Ratio Test

39. Diverges; Root Test **41.** Converges; Root Test

43. Converges; Ratio Test **47.** Yes

Section 8.6, pp. 542–543

1. Converges by Theorem 16 **3.** Diverges; $a_n \not\to 0$

5. Converges by Theorem 16 **7.** Diverges; $a_n\to 1/2$

9. Converges by Theorem 16

11. Converges absolutely. Series of absolute values is a convergent geometric series.

13. Converges conditionally. $1/\sqrt{n}\to 0$ but $\sum_{n=1}^{\infty}\frac{1}{\sqrt{n}}$ diverges.

15. Converges absolutely. Compare with $\sum_{n=1}^{\infty}(1/n^2)$.

17. Converges conditionally. $1/(n+3)\to 0$ but $\sum_{n=1}^{\infty}\frac{1}{n+3}$ diverges (compare with $\sum_{n=1}^{\infty}(1/n)$).

19. Diverges; $\frac{3+n}{5+n}\to 1$

21. Converges conditionally; $\left(\frac{1}{n^2}+\frac{1}{n}\right)\to 0$ but $(1+n)/n^2 > 1/n$

23. Converges absolutely; Ratio Test

25. Converges absolutely by Integral Test **27.** Diverges; $a_n \not\to 0$

29. Converges absolutely by the Ratio Test

31. Converges absolutely; $\frac{1}{n^2+2n+1} < \frac{1}{n^2}$

33. Converges absolutely since $\left|\frac{\cos n\pi}{n\sqrt{n}}\right| = \left|\frac{(-1)^{n+1}}{n^{3/2}}\right| = \frac{1}{n^{3/2}}$ (convergent p-series)

35. Converges absolutely by Root Test **37.** Diverges; $a_n \to \infty$

39. Converges conditionally; $\sqrt{n+1}-\sqrt{n} = 1/\left(\sqrt{n}+\sqrt{n+1}\right)\to 0$, but series of absolute values diverges (compare with $\sum\left(1/\sqrt{n}\right)$)

41. Diverges, $a_n \to 1/2 \neq 0$

43. Converges absolutely; $\operatorname{sech} n = \frac{2}{e^n+e^{-n}} = \frac{2e^n}{e^{2n}+1} < \frac{2e^n}{e^{2n}} = \frac{2}{e^n}$, a term from a convergent geometric series.

45. $|\text{Error}| < 0.2$ **47.** $|\text{Error}| < 2\times 10^{-11}$ **49.** 0.54030

51. **(a)** $a_n \geq a_{n+1}$ **(b)** $-1/2$

Section 8.7, pp. 552–553

1. **(a)** $1, -1<x<1$ **(b)** $-1<x<1$ **(c)** none

3. **(a)** $1/4, -1/2<x<0$ **(b)** $-1/2<x<0$ **(c)** none

5. **(a)** $10, -8<x<12$ **(b)** $-8<x<12$ **(c)** none

7. **(a)** $1, -1<x<1$ **(b)** $-1<x<1$ **(c)** none

9. **(a)** $3, -3\leq x\leq 3$ **(b)** $-3\leq x\leq 3$ **(c)** none

11. **(a)** ∞, for all x **(b)** for all x **(c)** none

13. **(a)** ∞, for all x **(b)** for all x **(c)** none

15. **(a)** $1, -1\leq x<1$ **(b)** $-1<x<1$ **(c)** $x=-1$

17. **(a)** $5, -8<x<2$ **(b)** $-8<x<2$ **(c)** none

19. **(a)** $3, -3<x<3$ **(b)** $-3<x<3$ **(c)** none

21. **(a)** $1, -1<x<1$ **(b)** $-1<x<1$ **(c)** none

23. **(a)** $0, x=0$ **(b)** $x=0$ **(c)** none

25. **(a)** $2, -4<x\leq 0$ **(b)** $-4<x<0$ **(c)** $x=0$

27. **(a)** $1, -1\leq x\leq 1$ **(b)** $-1\leq x\leq 1$ **(c)** none

29. **(a)** $1/4, 1\leq x\leq 3/2$ **(b)** $1\leq x\leq 3/2$ **(c)** none

31. **(a)** $1, (-1-\pi)\leq x<(1-\pi)$
(b) $(-1-\pi)<x<(1-\pi)$ **(c)** $x=-1-\pi$

33. $-1<x<3$, $4/(3+2x-x^2)$

35. $0<x<16$, $2/\left(4-\sqrt{x}\right)$

37. $-\sqrt{2}<x<\sqrt{2}$, $3/(2-x^2)$

39. $1<x<5$, $2/(x-1)$, $1<x<5$, $-2/(x-1)^2$

41. **(a)** $\cos x = 1-\frac{x^2}{2!}+\frac{x^4}{4!}-\frac{x^6}{6!}+\frac{x^8}{8!}-\frac{x^{10}}{10!}+\cdots$; converges for all x
(b) Same answer as part (c)
(c) $2x-\frac{2^3x^3}{3!}+\frac{2^5x^5}{5!}-\frac{2^7x^7}{7!}+\frac{2^9x^9}{9!}-\frac{2^{11}x^{11}}{11!}+\cdots$

43. **(a)** $\frac{x^2}{2}+\frac{x^4}{12}+\frac{x^6}{45}+\frac{17x^8}{2520}+\frac{31x^{10}}{14175}$, $-\frac{\pi}{2}<x<\frac{\pi}{2}$
(b) $1+x^2+\frac{2x^4}{3}+\frac{17x^6}{45}+\frac{62x^8}{315}+\cdots$, $-\frac{\pi}{2}<x<\frac{\pi}{2}$

Section 8.8, pp. 558–559

1. $P_0(x)=0$, $P_1(x)=x-1$, $P_2(x)=(x-1)-\frac{1}{2}(x-1)^2$,
$P_3(x)=(x-1)-\frac{1}{2}(x-1)^2+\frac{1}{3}(x-1)^3$

3. $P_0(x)=\frac{1}{2}$, $P_1(x)=\frac{1}{2}-\frac{1}{4}(x-2)$,
$P_2(x)=\frac{1}{2}-\frac{1}{4}(x-2)+\frac{1}{8}(x-2)^2$,
$P_3(x)=\frac{1}{2}-\frac{1}{4}(x-2)+\frac{1}{8}(x-2)^2-\frac{1}{16}(x-2)^3$

5. $P_0(x)=\frac{\sqrt{2}}{2}$, $P_1(x)=\frac{\sqrt{2}}{2}+\frac{\sqrt{2}}{2}\left(x-\frac{\pi}{4}\right)$,
$P_2(x)=\frac{\sqrt{2}}{2}+\frac{\sqrt{2}}{2}\left(x-\frac{\pi}{4}\right)-\frac{\sqrt{2}}{4}\left(x-\frac{\pi}{4}\right)^2$,
$P_3(x)=\frac{\sqrt{2}}{2}+\frac{\sqrt{2}}{2}\left(x-\frac{\pi}{4}\right)-\frac{\sqrt{2}}{4}\left(x-\frac{\pi}{4}\right)^2-\frac{\sqrt{2}}{12}\left(x-\frac{\pi}{4}\right)^3$

7. $P_0(x)=2$, $P_1(x)=2+\frac{1}{4}(x-4)$,
$P_2(x)=2+\frac{1}{4}(x-4)-\frac{1}{64}(x-4)^2$,
$P_3(x)=2+\frac{1}{4}(x-4)-\frac{1}{64}(x-4)^2+\frac{1}{512}(x-4)^3$

9. $\sum_{n=0}^{\infty}\frac{(-x)^n}{n!}=1-x+\frac{x^2}{2!}-\frac{x^3}{3!}+\frac{x^4}{4!}-\cdots$

11. $\sum_{n=0}^{\infty}(-1)^nx^n=1-x+x^2-x^3+\cdots$

13. $\sum_{n=0}^{\infty}\frac{(-1)^n3^{2n+1}x^{2n+1}}{(2n+1)!}$ **15.** $7\sum_{n=0}^{\infty}\frac{(-1)^nx^{2n}}{(2n)!}$ **17.** $\sum_{n=0}^{\infty}\frac{x^{2n}}{(2n)!}$

19. x^4-2x^3-5x+4

21. $8+10(x-2)+6(x-2)^2+(x-2)^3$

23. $21-36(x+2)+25(x+2)^2-8(x+2)^3+(x+2)^4$

25. $\sum_{n=0}^{\infty}(-1)^n(n+1)(x-1)^n$ **27.** $\sum_{n=0}^{\infty}\frac{e^2}{n!}(x-2)^n$

33. $L(x)=0$, $Q(x)=-x^2/2$ **35.** $L(x)=1$, $Q(x)=1+x^2/2$

37. $L(x)=x$, $Q(x)=x$

Section 8.9, pp. 567–569

1. $\sum_{n=0}^{\infty}\frac{(-5x)^n}{n!}=1-5x+\frac{5^2x^2}{2!}-\frac{5^3x^3}{3!}+\cdots$

3. $\sum_{n=0}^{\infty}\frac{5(-1)^n(-x)^{2n+1}}{(2n+1)!}=\sum_{n=0}^{\infty}\frac{5(-1)^{n+1}x^{2n+1}}{(2n+1)!}$
$=-5x+\frac{5x^3}{3!}-\frac{5x^5}{5!}+\frac{5x^7}{7!}+\cdots$

5. $\sum_{n=0}^{\infty} \frac{(-1)^n(x+1)^n}{(2n)!}$

7. $\sum_{n=0}^{\infty} \frac{x^{n+1}}{n!} = x + x^2 + \frac{x^3}{2!} + \frac{x^4}{3!} + \frac{x^5}{4!} + \cdots$

9. $\sum_{n=2}^{\infty} \frac{(-1)^n x^{2n}}{(2n)!} = \frac{x^4}{4!} - \frac{x^6}{6!} + \frac{x^8}{8!} - \frac{x^{10}}{10!} + \cdots$

11. $x - \frac{\pi^2 x^3}{2!} + \frac{\pi^4 x^5}{4!} - \frac{\pi^6 x^7}{6!} + \cdots = \sum_{n=0}^{\infty} \frac{(-1)^n \pi^{2n} x^{2n+1}}{(2n)!}$

13. $1 + \sum_{n=1}^{\infty} \frac{(-1)^n (2x)^{2n}}{2 \cdot (2n)!} =$
$1 - \frac{(2x)^2}{2 \cdot 2!} + \frac{(2x)^4}{2 \cdot 4!} - \frac{(2x)^6}{2 \cdot 6!} + \frac{(2x)^8}{2 \cdot 8!} - \cdots$

15. $x^2 \sum_{n=0}^{\infty} (2x)^n = x^2 + 2x^3 + 4x^4 + \cdots$

17. $\sum_{n=1}^{\infty} nx^{n-1} = 1 + 2x + 3x^2 + 4x^3 + \cdots$

19. $|x| < (0.06)^{1/5} < 0.56968$

21. $|\text{Error}| < (10^{-3})^3/6 < 1.67 \times 10^{-10}, \quad -10^{-3} < x < 0$

23. $|\text{Error}| < (3^{0.1})(0.1)^3/6 < 1.87 \times 10^{-4}$

25. $\frac{x^3}{3} - \frac{x^7}{7 \cdot 3!} + \frac{x^{11}}{11 \cdot 5!}$

27. **(a)** $\frac{x^2}{2} - \frac{x^4}{12}$
(b) $\frac{x^2}{2} - \frac{x^4}{3 \cdot 4} + \frac{x^6}{5 \cdot 6} - \frac{x^8}{7 \cdot 8} + \cdots + (-1)^{15} \frac{x^{32}}{31 \cdot 32}$

29. $1/2$ **31.** $-1/24$ **33.** $1/3$

35. $e^x \sin x = x + x^2 + \frac{x^3}{3} - \frac{x^5}{30} - \frac{x^6}{90} \cdots$

43. **(a)** $Q(x) = 1 + kx + \frac{k(k-1)}{2}x^2$ **(b)** for $0 \le x < 100^{-1/3}$

49. **(a)** -1 **(b)** $(1/\sqrt{2})(1+i)$ **(c)** $-i$

53. $x + x^2 + \frac{1}{3}x^3 - \frac{1}{30}x^5 \cdots$; will converge for all x

Section 8.10, p. 572

1. $1 + \frac{x}{2} - \frac{x^2}{8} + \frac{x^3}{16}$ **3.** $1 + \frac{1}{2}x + \frac{3}{8}x^2 + \frac{5}{16}x^3 + \cdots$

5. $1 - x + \frac{3x^2}{4} - \frac{x^3}{2}$ **7.** $1 - \frac{x^3}{2} + \frac{3x^6}{.8} - \frac{5x^9}{16}$

9. $1 + \frac{1}{2x} - \frac{1}{8x^2} + \frac{1}{16x^3}$

11. $(1+x)^4 = 1 + 4x + 6x^2 + 4x^3 + x^4$

13. $(1-2x)^3 = 1 - 6x + 12x^2 - 8x^3$

15. **(a)** $x + \frac{x^3}{6} + \frac{3x^5}{40} + \frac{5x^7}{112}$, radius of convergence $= 1$
(b) $\frac{\pi}{2} - x - \frac{x^3}{6} - \frac{3x^5}{40} - \frac{5x^7}{112}$

17. $1 - 2x + 3x^2 - 4x^3 + \cdots$

Practice Exercises, pp. 573–575

1. Converges to 1 **3.** Converges to -1 **5.** Diverges
7. Converges to 0 **9.** Converges to 1 **11.** Converges to e^{-5}
13. Converges to 3 **15.** Converges to ln 2 **17.** Diverges
19. $1/6$ **21.** $3/2$ **23.** $e/(e-1)$ **25.** Diverges
27. Converges conditionally **29.** Converges conditionally
31. Converges absolutely **33.** Converges absolutely
35. Converges absolutely **37.** Converges absolutely
39. Converges absolutely
41. **(a)** $3, -7 \le x < -1$ **(b)** $-7 < x < -1$ **(c)** $x = -7$
43. **(a)** $1/3, 0 \le x \le 2/3$ **(b)** $0 \le x \le 2/3$ **(c)** none
45. **(a)** ∞, for all x **(b)** for all x **(c)** none
47. **(a)** $\sqrt{3}, -\sqrt{3} < x < \sqrt{3}$ **(b)** $-\sqrt{3} < x < \sqrt{3}$
(c) none
49. **(a)** $e, -e < x < e$ **(b)** $-e < x < e$ **(c)** empty set

51. $\frac{1}{1+x}, \frac{1}{4}, \frac{4}{5}$ **53.** $\sin x, \pi, 0$ **55.** e^x, ln 2, 2 **57.** $\sum_{n=0}^{\infty} 2^n x^n$

59. $\sum_{n=0}^{\infty} \frac{(-1)^n \pi^{2n+1} x^{2n+1}}{(2n+1)!}$ **61.** $\sum_{n=0}^{\infty} \frac{(-1)^n x^{5n}}{(2n)!}$ **63.** $\sum_{n=0}^{\infty} \frac{((\pi x)/2)^n}{n!}$

65. $2 - \frac{(x+1)}{2 \cdot 1!} + \frac{3(x+1)^2}{2^3 \cdot 2!} + \frac{9(x+1)^3}{2^5 \cdot 3!} + \cdots$

67. $\frac{1}{4} - \frac{1}{4^2}(x-3) + \frac{1}{4^3}(x-3)^2 - \frac{1}{4^4}(x-3)^3$

69. 0.4849171431 **71.** ≈ 0.4872223583 **73.** $7/2$ **75.** $1/12$

77. -2 **79.** $r = -3, s = 9/2$ **81.** $2/3$

83. $\ln\left(\frac{n+1}{2n}\right)$; the series converges to $\ln\left(\frac{1}{2}\right)$.

85. **(a)** ∞ **(b)** $a = 1, \quad b = 0$ **87.** It converges.

Additional and Advanced Exercises, pp. 575–576

1. Converges; Comparison Test **3.** Diverges; nth-Term Test
5. Converges; Comparison Test **7.** Diverges; nth-Term Test

9. With $a = \pi/3$, $\cos x = \frac{1}{2} - \frac{\sqrt{3}}{2}(x - \pi/3) - \frac{1}{4}(x - \pi/3)^2 + \frac{\sqrt{3}}{12}(x - \pi/3)^3 + \cdots$

11. With $a = 0$, $e^x = 1 + x + \frac{x^2}{2!} + \frac{x^3}{3!} + \cdots$

13. With $a = 22\pi$, $\cos x = 1 - \frac{1}{2}(x - 22\pi)^2 + \frac{1}{4!}(x - 22\pi)^4 - \frac{1}{6!}(x - 22\pi)^6 + \cdots$

15. Converges, limit $= b$ **17.** $\pi/2$ **21.** $b = \pm\frac{1}{5}$

23. $a = 2, L = -7/6$ **27.** **(b)** Yes

31. **(a)** $\sum_{n=1}^{\infty} nx^{n-1}$ **(b)** 6 **(c)** $1/q$

CHAPTER 9

Section 9.1, pp. 581–582

1. a, e; b, g; c, h; d, f **3.**

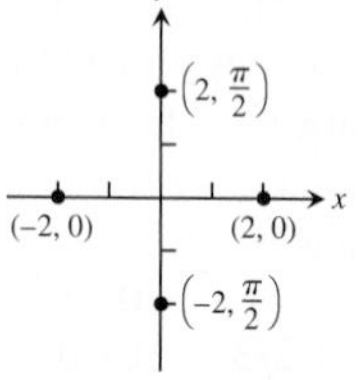

(a) $\left(2, \frac{\pi}{2} + 2n\pi\right)$ and $\left(-2, \frac{\pi}{2} + (2n + 1)\pi\right)$, n an integer

(b) $(2, 2n\pi)$ and $(-2, (2n + 1)\pi)$, n an integer

(c) $\left(2, \frac{3\pi}{2} + 2n\pi\right)$ and $\left(-2, \frac{3\pi}{2} + (2n + 1)\pi\right)$, n an integer

(d) $(2, (2n + 1)\pi)$ and $(-2, 2n\pi)$, n an integer

5. **(a)** $(3, 0)$ **(b)** $(-3, 0)$ **(c)** $\left(-1, \sqrt{3}\right)$ **(d)** $\left(1, \sqrt{3}\right)$ **(e)** $(3, 0)$ **(f)** $\left(1, \sqrt{3}\right)$ **(g)** $(-3, 0)$ **(h)** $\left(-1, \sqrt{3}\right)$

7.

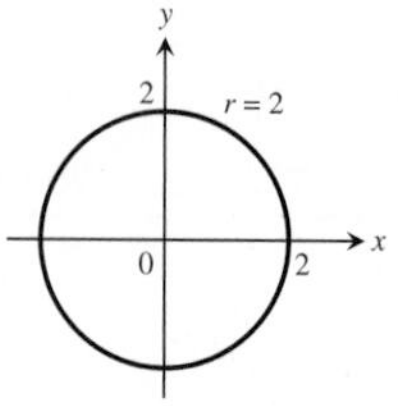

9.

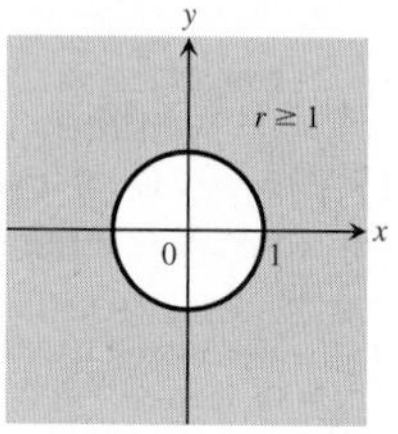

11.

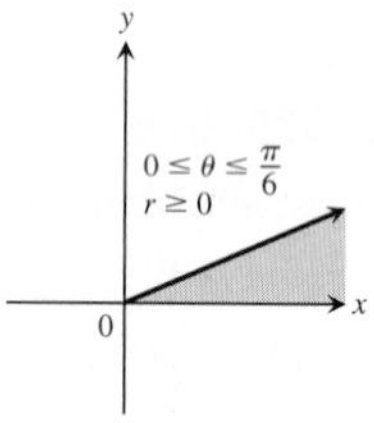

13.

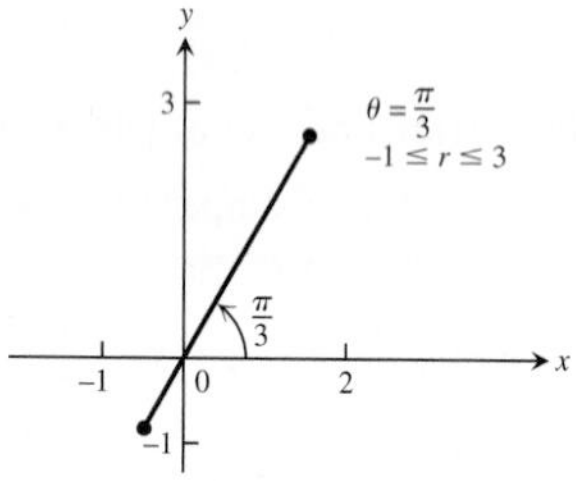

15.

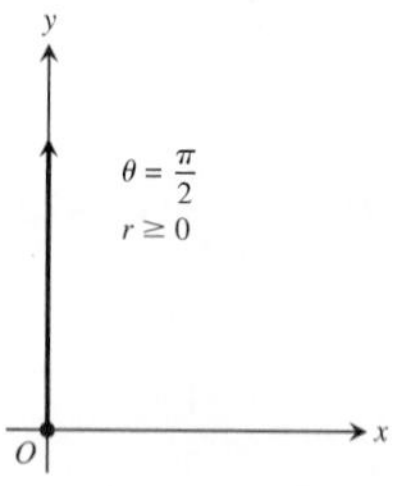

17.

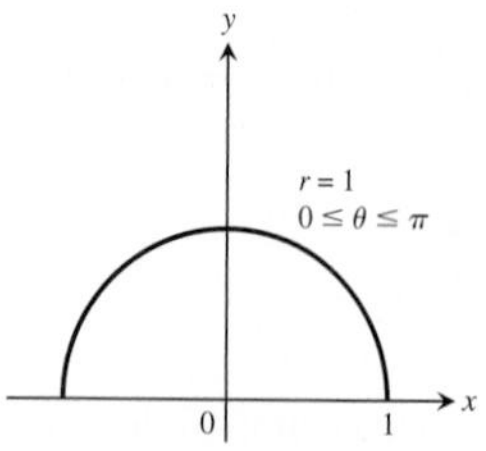

19.

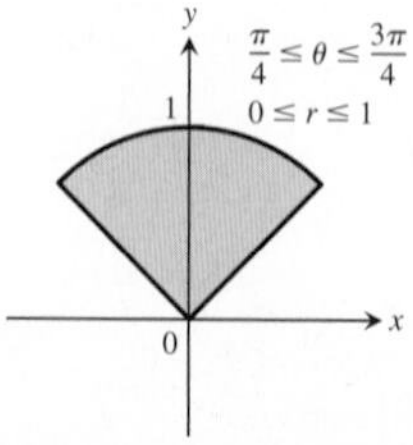

21.

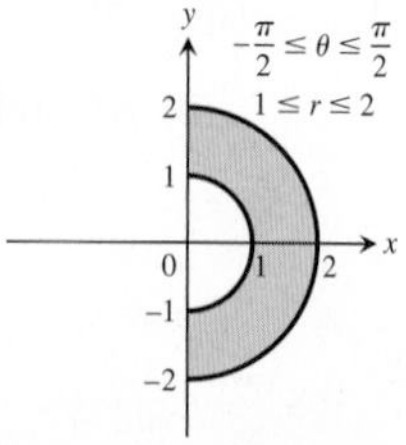

23. $x = 2$, vertical line through $(2, 0)$ **25.** $y = 0$, the x-axis

27. $y = 4$, horizontal line through $(0, 4)$

29. $x + y = 1$, line, $m = -1$, $b = 1$

31. $x^2 + y^2 = 1$, circle, $C(0, 0)$, radius 1

33. $y - 2x = 5$, line: $m = 2$, $b = 5$

35. $y^2 = x$, parabola, vertex $(0, 0)$, opens right

37. $y = e^x$, graph of natural exponential function

39. $x + y = \pm 1$, two straight lines of slope -1, y-intercepts $b = \pm 1$

41. $(x + 2)^2 + y^2 = 4$, circle, $C(-2, 0)$, radius 2

43. $x^2 + (y - 4)^2 = 16$, circle, $C(0, 4)$, radius 4

45. $(x - 1)^2 + (y - 1)^2 = 2$, circle, $C(1, 1)$, radius $\sqrt{2}$

47. $\sqrt{3}y + x = 4$ **49.** $r\cos\theta = 7$ **51.** $\theta = \pi/4$

53. $r = 2$ or $r = -2$ **55.** $4r^2\cos^2\theta + 9r^2\sin^2\theta = 36$

57. $r\sin^2\theta = 4\cos\theta$ **59.** $r = 4\sin\theta$

61. $r^2 = 6r\cos\theta - 2r\sin\theta - 6$ **63.** $(0, \theta)$, where θ is any angle

Section 9.2, pp. 585–586

1. x-axis

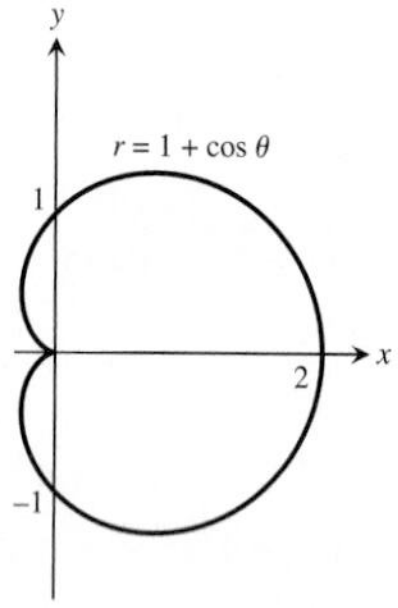

3. y-axis

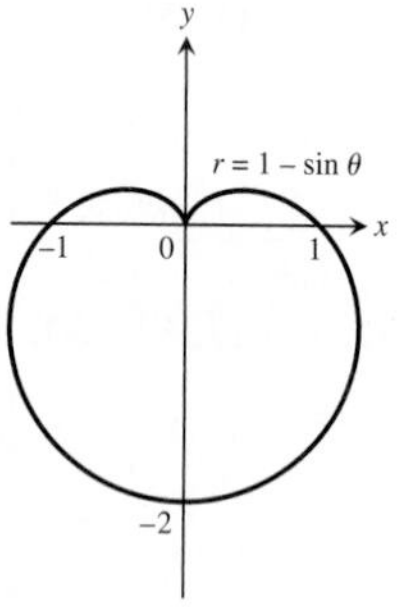

5. y-axis

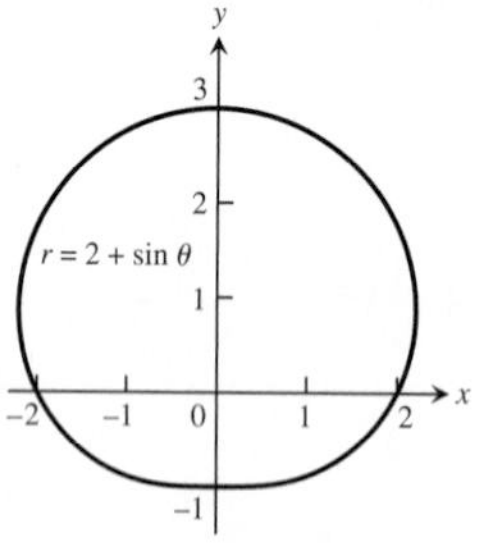

7. x-axis

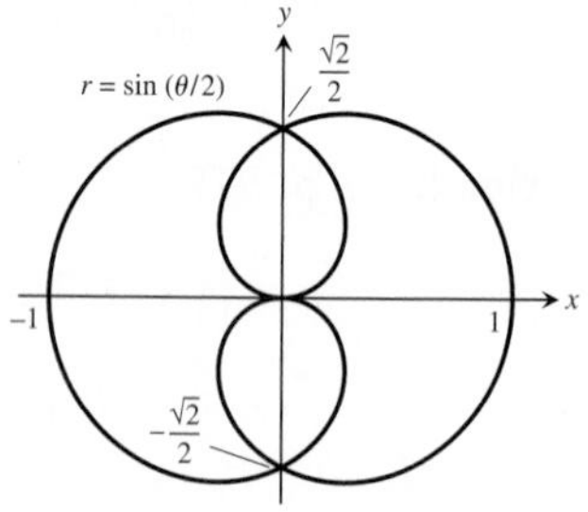

9. x-axis, y-axis, origin

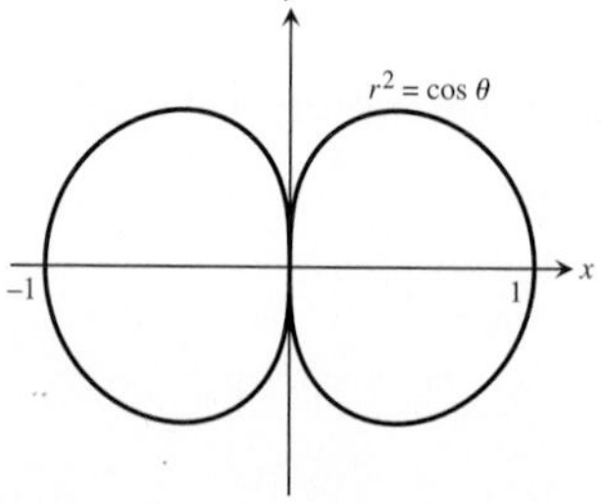

11. y-axis, x-axis, origin

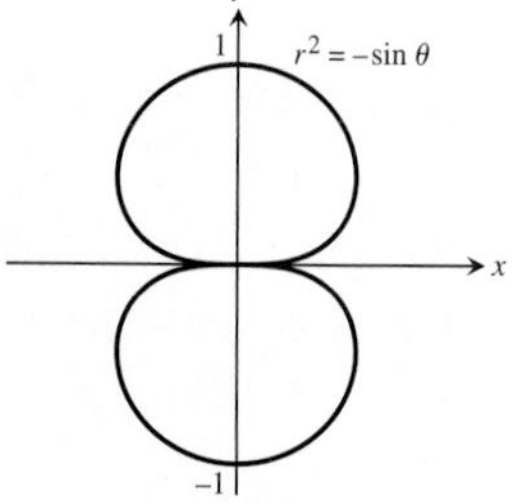

13. x-axis, y-axis, origin **15.** Origin

17. The slope at $(-1, \pi/2)$ is -1, at $(-1, -\pi/2)$ is 1.

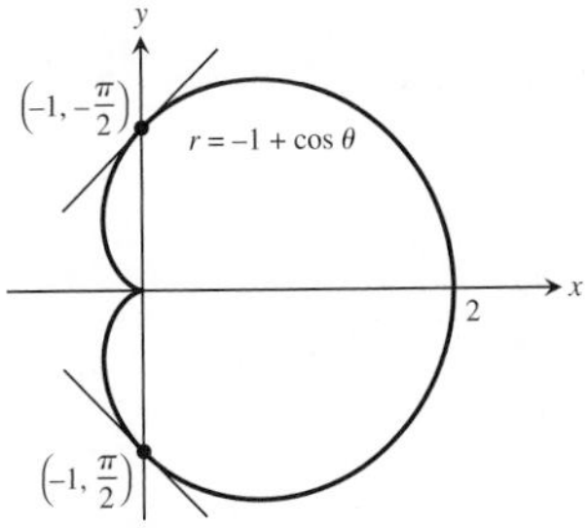

19. The slope at $(1, \pi/4)$ is -1, at $(-1, -\pi/4)$ is 1, at $(-1, 3\pi/4)$ is 1, at $(1, -3\pi/4)$ is -1.

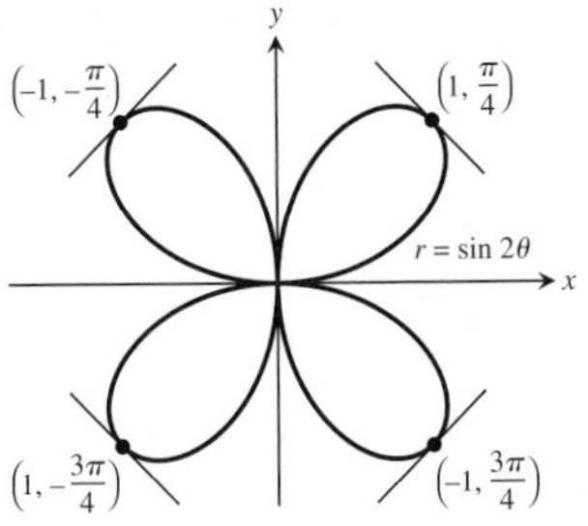

21. **(a)**

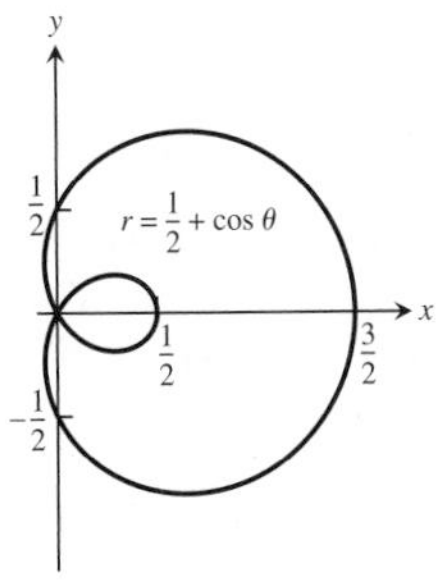

(b)

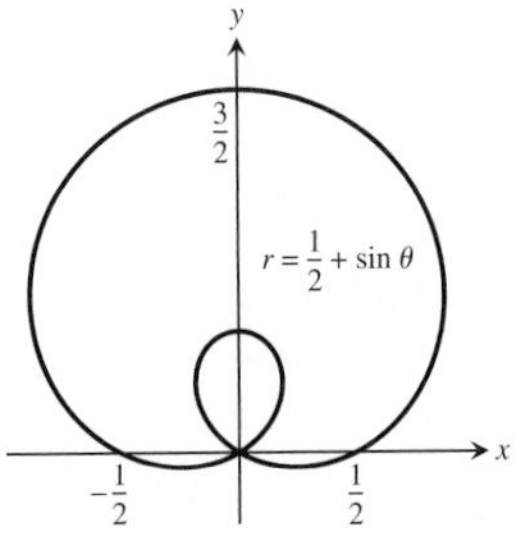

23. **(a)**

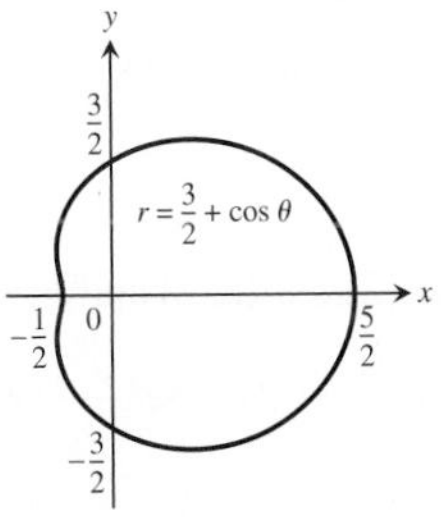

(b)

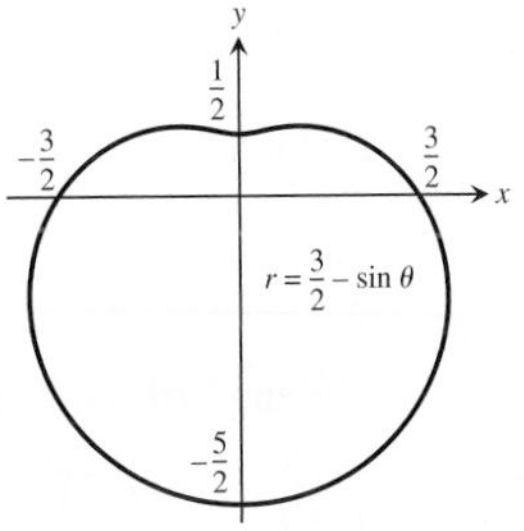

25.

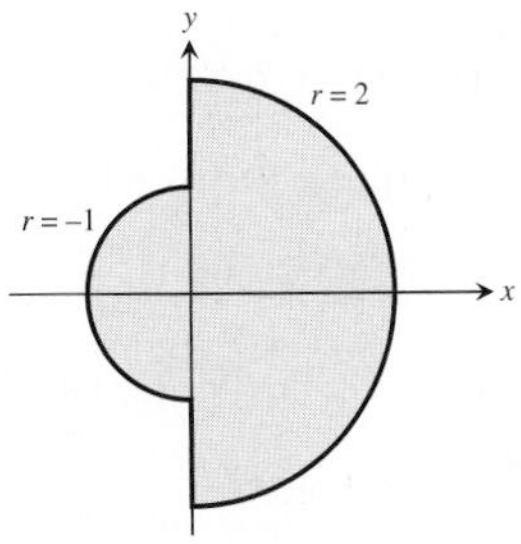

27.

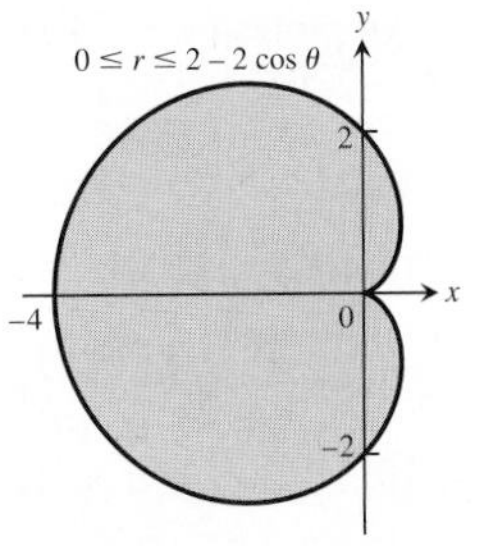

29. (a)

Section 9.3, pp. 589–590

1. 18π **3.** $\pi/8$ **5.** 2 **7.** $\dfrac{\pi}{2} - 1$ **9.** $5\pi - 8$

11. $3\sqrt{3} - \pi$ **13.** $\dfrac{\pi}{3} + \dfrac{\sqrt{3}}{2}$ **15.** **(a)** $\dfrac{3}{2} - \dfrac{\pi}{4}$ **17.** $19/3$

19. 8 **21.** $3\left(\sqrt{2} + \ln\left(1 + \sqrt{2}\right)\right)$ **23.** $\dfrac{\pi}{8} + \dfrac{3}{8}$ **25.** 2π

Section 9.4, pp. 597–599

1. $y^2 = 8x$, $F(2, 0)$, directrix: $x = -2$

3. $x^2 = -6y$, $F(0, -3/2)$, directrix: $y = 3/2$

5. $\dfrac{x^2}{4} - \dfrac{y^2}{9} = 1$, $F\left(\pm\sqrt{13}, 0\right)$, $V(\pm 2, 0)$, asymptotes: $y = \pm\dfrac{3}{2}x$

7. $\dfrac{x^2}{2} + y^2 = 1$, $F(\pm 1, 0)$, $V\left(\pm\sqrt{2}, 0\right)$

9.

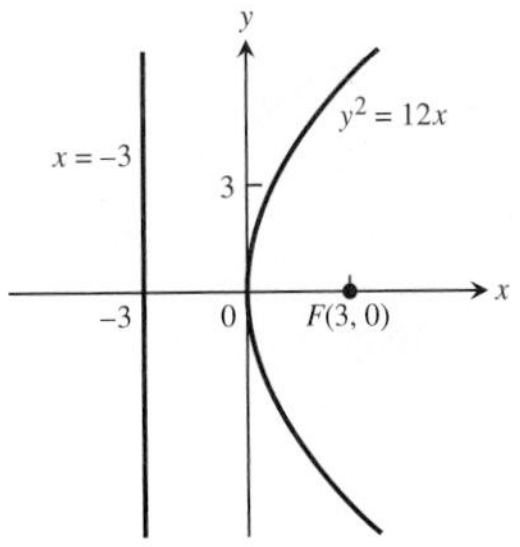

11.

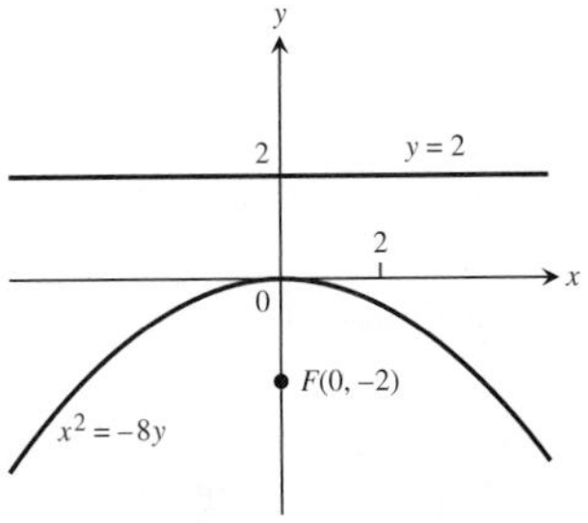

13.

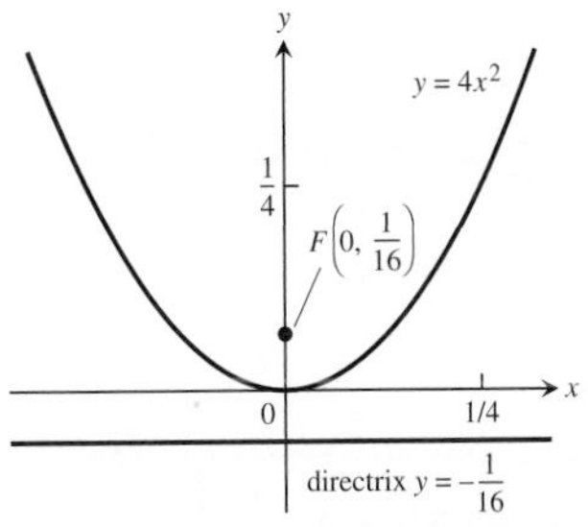

15.

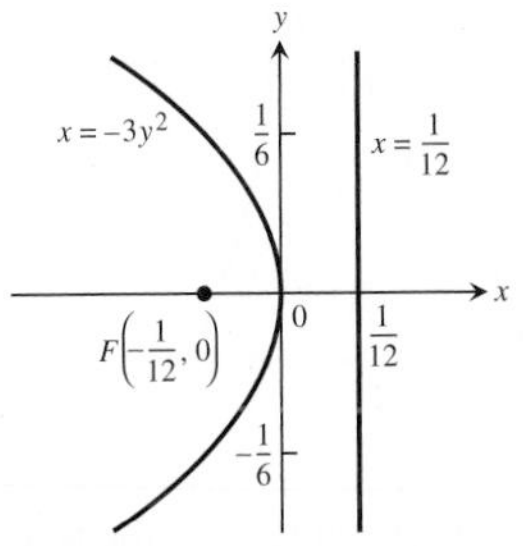

17.

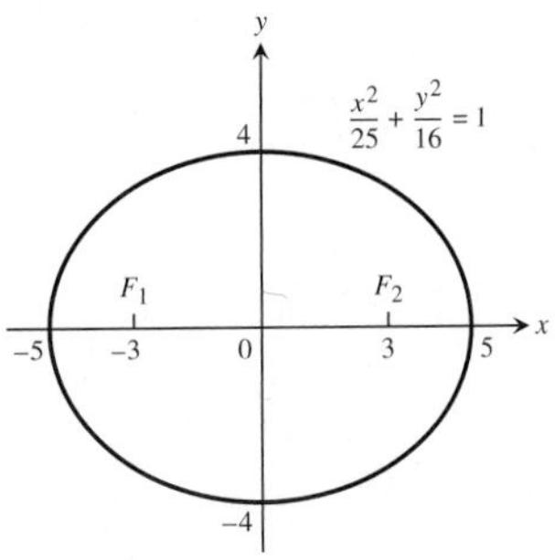

19.

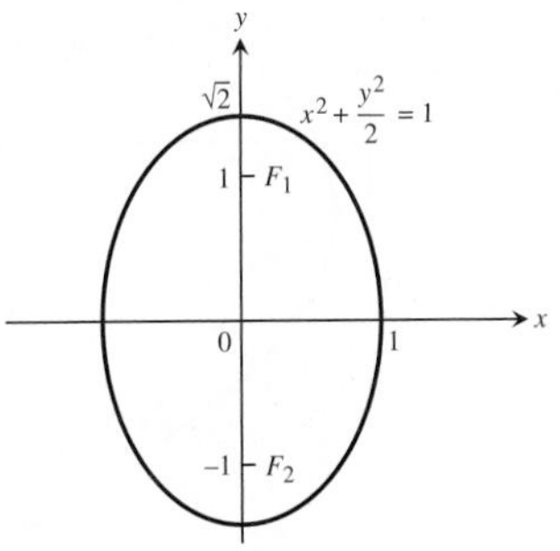

21.

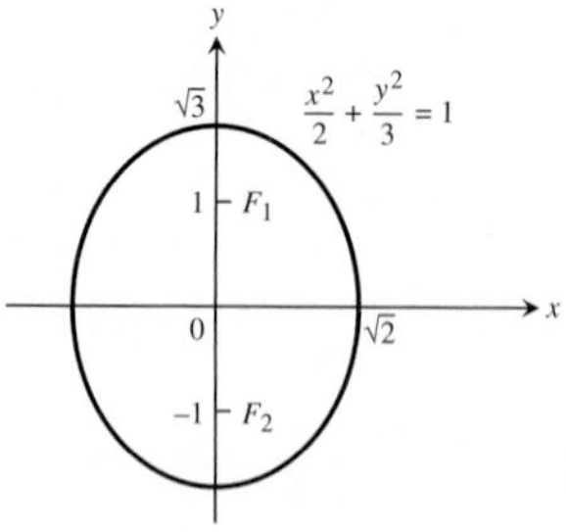

23.

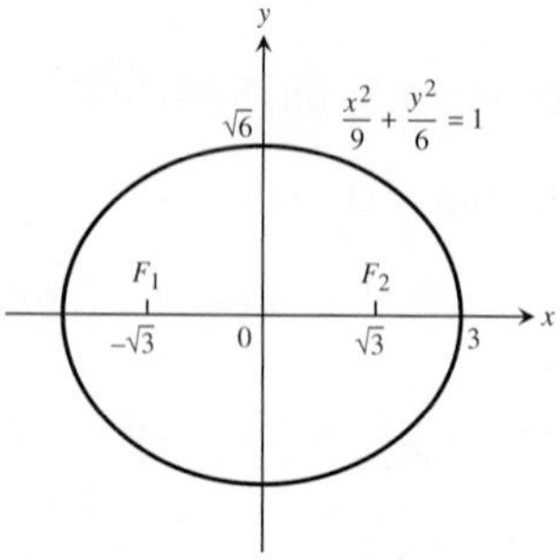

25. $\frac{x^2}{4} + \frac{y^2}{2} = 1$

27. Asymptotes: $y = \pm x$

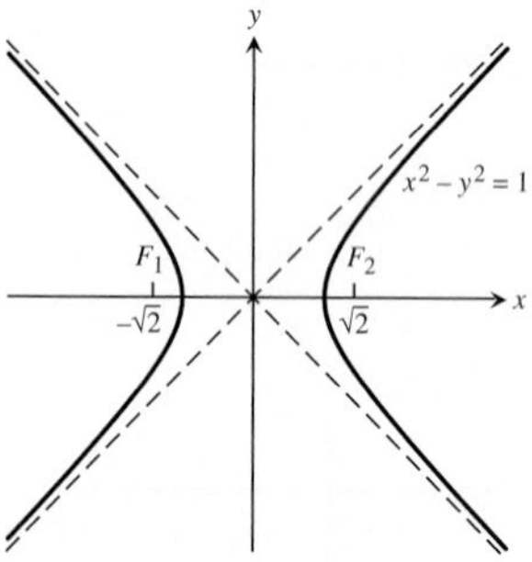

29. Asymptotes: $y = \pm x$

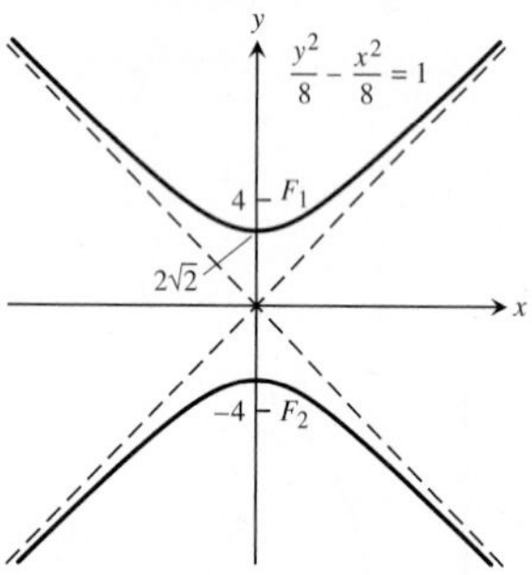

31. Asymptotes: $y = \pm 2x$

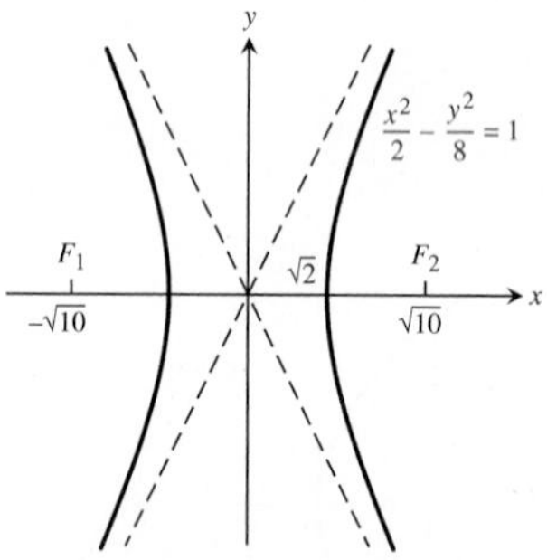

33. Asymptotes: $y = \pm\frac{x}{2}$

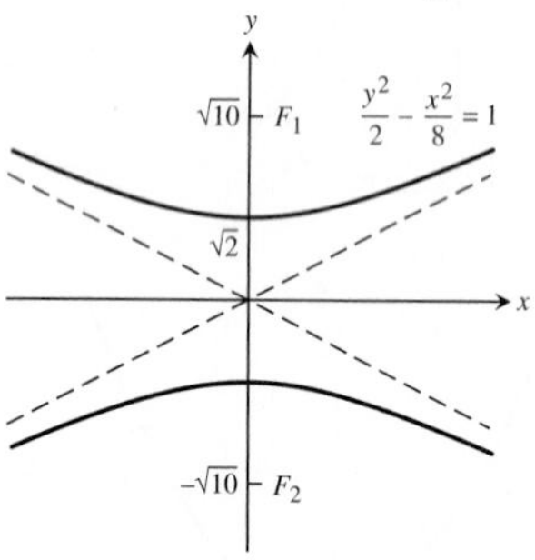

35. $y^2 - x^2 = 1$ **37.** $\frac{x^2}{9} - \frac{y^2}{16} = 1$

39. **(a)** Vertex: $(1, -2)$; focus: $(3, -2)$; directrix: $x = -1$
(b)

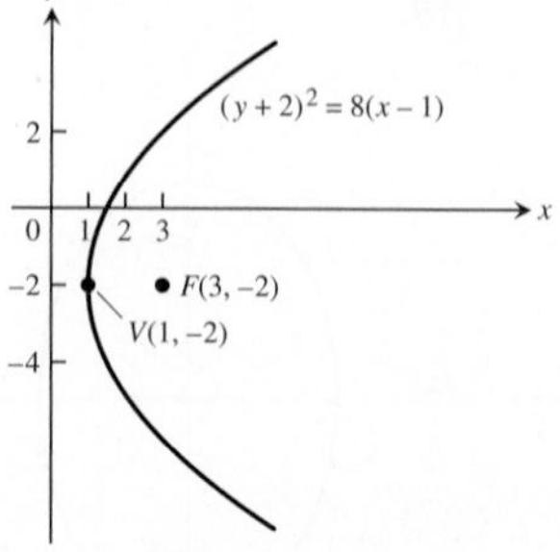

41. **(a)** Foci: $\left(4 \pm \sqrt{7}, 3\right)$; vertices: $(8, 3)$ and $(0, 3)$; center: $(4, 3)$
(b)

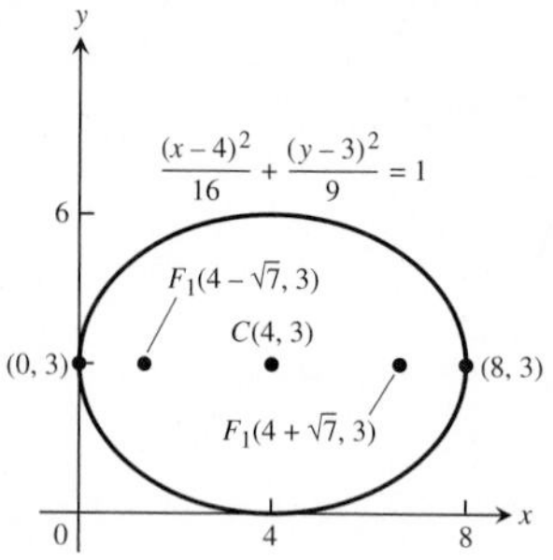

43. **(a)** Center: $(2, 0)$; foci: $(7, 0)$ and $(-3, 0)$; vertices: $(6, 0)$ and $(-2, 0)$; asymptotes: $y = \pm\frac{3}{4}(x - 2)$

(b)

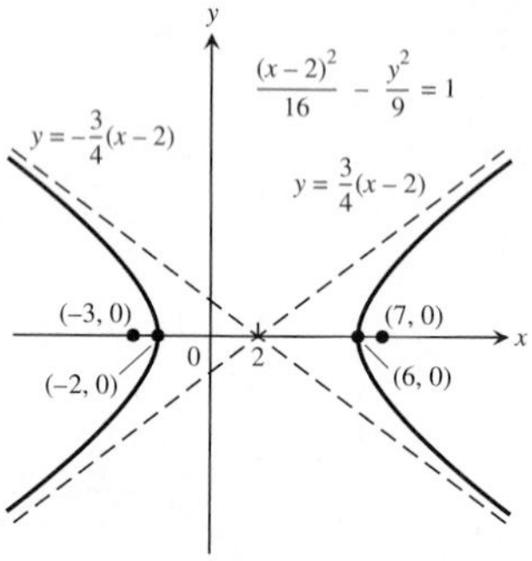

45. $(y + 3)^2 = 4(x + 2)$, $V(-2, -3)$, $F(-1, -3)$, directrix: $x = -3$

47. $(x - 1)^2 = 8(y + 7)$, $V(1, -7)$, $F(1, -5)$, directrix: $y = -9$

49. $\frac{(x + 2)^2}{6} + \frac{(y + 1)^2}{9} = 1$, $F\left(-2, \pm\sqrt{3} - 1\right)$, $V(-2, \pm 3 - 1)$, $C(-2, -1)$

51. $\frac{(x - 2)^2}{3} + \frac{(y - 3)^2}{2} = 1$, $F(3, 3)$ and $F(1, 3)$, $V\left(\pm\sqrt{3} + 2, 3\right)$, $C(2, 3)$

53. $\frac{(x - 2)^2}{4} - \frac{(y - 2)^2}{5} = 1$, $C(2, 2)$, $F(5, 2)$ and $F(-1, 2)$, $V(4, 2)$ and $V(0, 2)$; asymptotes: $(y - 2) = \pm\frac{\sqrt{5}}{2}(x - 2)$

55. $(y + 1)^2 - (x + 1)^2 = 1$, $C(-1, -1)$, $F\left(-1, \sqrt{2} - 1\right)$ and $F\left(-1, -\sqrt{2} - 1\right)$, $V(-1, 0)$ and $V(-1, -2)$; asymptotes $(y + 1) = \pm(x + 1)$

57. $C(-2, 0)$, $a = 4$ **59.** $V(-1, 1)$, $F(-1, 0)$

61. Ellipse: $\frac{(x + 2)^2}{5} + y^2 = 1$, $C(-2, 0)$, $F(0, 0)$ and $F(-4, 0)$, $V\left(\sqrt{5} - 2, 0\right)$ and $V\left(-\sqrt{5} - 2, 0\right)$

63. Ellipse: $\frac{(x - 1)^2}{2} + (y - 1)^2 = 1$, $C(1, 1)$, $F(2, 1)$ and $F(0, 1)$, $V\left(\sqrt{2} + 1, 1\right)$ and $V\left(-\sqrt{2} + 1, 1\right)$

65. Hyperbola: $(x-1)^2-(y-2)^2=1$, $C(1, 2)$, $F(1+\sqrt{2}, 2)$ and $F(1-\sqrt{2}, 2)$, $V(2, 2)$ and $V(0, 2)$; asymptotes: $(y-2)=\pm(x-1)$

67. Hyperbola: $\frac{(y-3)^2}{6}-\frac{x^2}{3}=1$, $C(0, 3)$, $F(0, 6)$ and $F(0, 0)$, $V(0, \sqrt{6}+3)$ and $V(0, -\sqrt{6}+3)$; asymptotes: $y=\sqrt{2}x+3$ or $y=-\sqrt{2}x+3$

69. (b) 1:1 **73.** Length $=2\sqrt{2}$, width $=\sqrt{2}$, area $=4$ **75.** 24π

Section 9.5, pp. 604–606

1. $e=3/5$, $F(\pm 3, 0)$, $x=\pm 25/3$
3. $e=1/\sqrt{2}$, $F(0, \pm 1)$, $y=\pm 2$
5. $e=1/\sqrt{3}$, $F(0, \pm 1)$, $y=\pm 3$
7. $e=\sqrt{3}/3$, $F(\pm\sqrt{3}, 0)$, $x=\pm 3\sqrt{3}$ **9.** $\frac{x^2}{27}+\frac{y^2}{36}=1$
11. $\frac{x^2}{4851}+\frac{y^2}{4900}=1$ **13.** $e=\frac{\sqrt{5}}{3}, \frac{x^2}{9}+\frac{y^2}{4}=1$
15. $e=1/2, \frac{x^2}{64}+\frac{y^2}{48}=1$
17. $e=\sqrt{2}$, $F(\pm\sqrt{2}, 0)$, $x=\pm 1/\sqrt{2}$
19. $e=\sqrt{2}$, $F(0, \pm 4)$, $y=\pm 2$
21. $e=\sqrt{5}$, $F(\pm\sqrt{10}, 0)$, $x=\pm 2/\sqrt{10}$
23. $e=\sqrt{5}$, $F(0, \pm\sqrt{10})$, $y=\pm 2/\sqrt{10}$
25. $y^2-\frac{x^2}{8}=1$ **27.** $x^2-\frac{y^2}{8}=1$ **29.** $r=2/(1+\cos\theta)$
31. $r=30/(1-5\sin\theta)$ **33.** $r=1/(2+\cos\theta)$
35. $r=10/(5-\sin\theta)$

37.

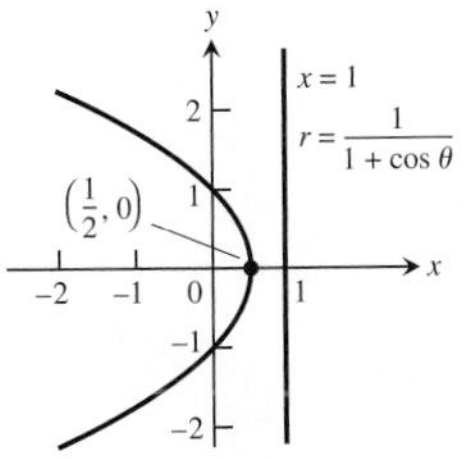

39.

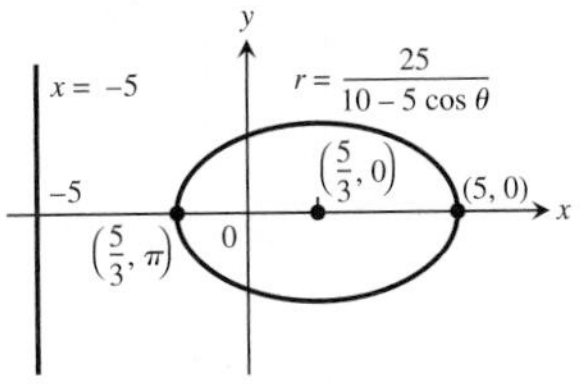

41.

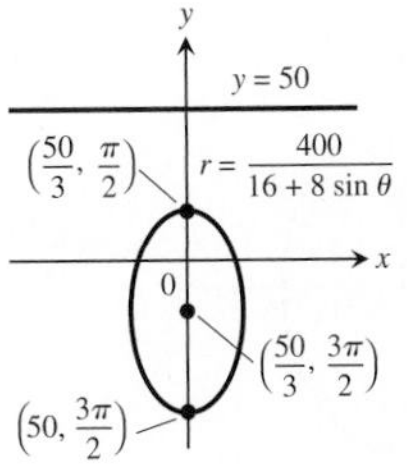

43.

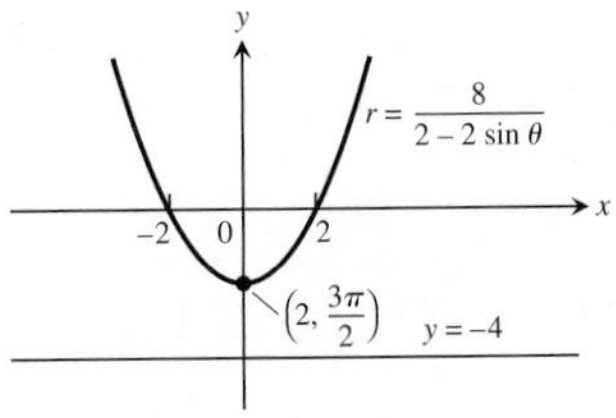

45. $y=2-x$ **47.** $y=(\sqrt{3}/3)x+2\sqrt{3}$
49. $r\cos\left(\theta-\frac{\pi}{4}\right)=3$ **51.** $r\cos\left(\theta+\frac{\pi}{2}\right)=5$
53. $C(2, 0)$, radius $=2$ **55.** $C(1, \pi)$, radius $=1$
57. $(x-6)^2+y^2=36, r=12\cos\theta$
59. $x^2+(y-5)^2=25, r=10\sin\theta$
61. $(x+1)^2+y^2=1, r=-2\cos\theta$
63. $x^2+(y+1/2)^2=1/4, r=-\sin\theta$
75. (b)

Planet	Perihelion	Aphelion
Mercury	0.3075 AU	0.4667 AU
Venus	0.7184 AU	0.7282 AU
Earth	0.9833 AU	1.0167 AU
Mars	1.3817 AU	1.6663 AU
Jupiter	4.9512 AU	5.4548 AU
Saturn	9.0210 AU	10.0570 AU
Uranus	18.2977 AU	20.0623 AU
Neptune	29.8135 AU	30.3065 AU
Pluto	29.6549 AU	49.2251 AU

77. $r=2a\sin\theta$ (a circle) **79.** $r\cos(\theta-\alpha)=p$ (a line)

Section 9.6, pp. 608–609

1.

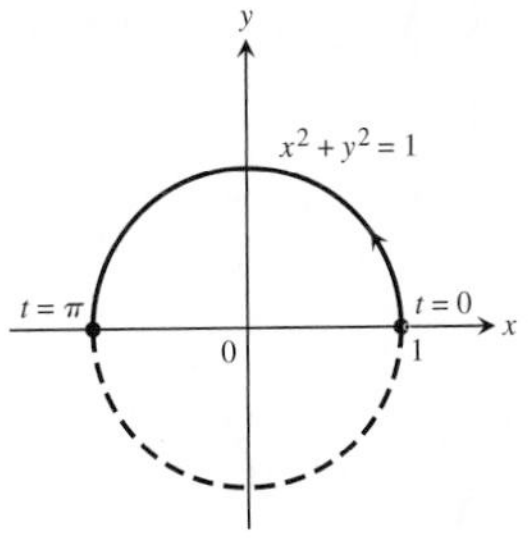

3.

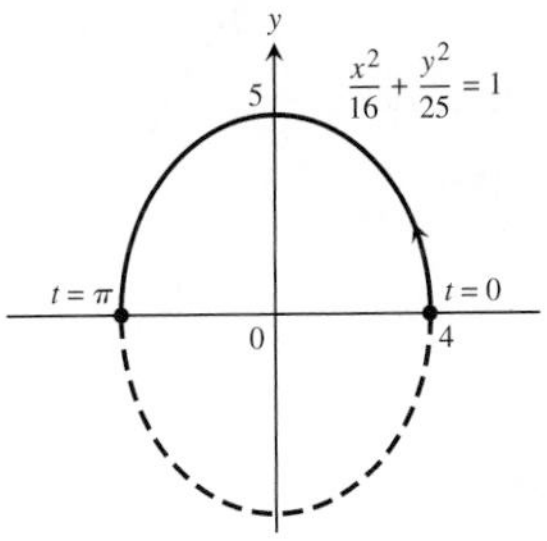

5.

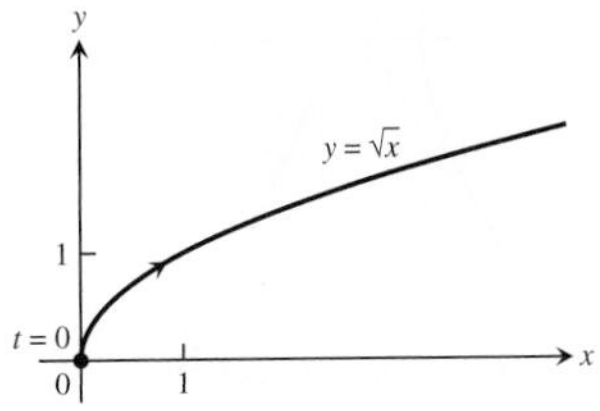

7.

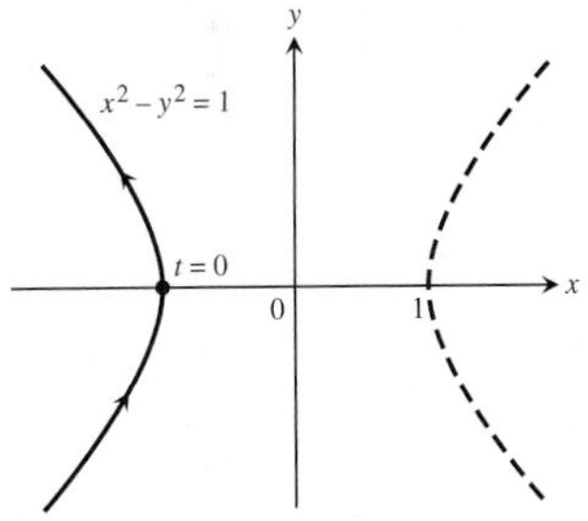

9.

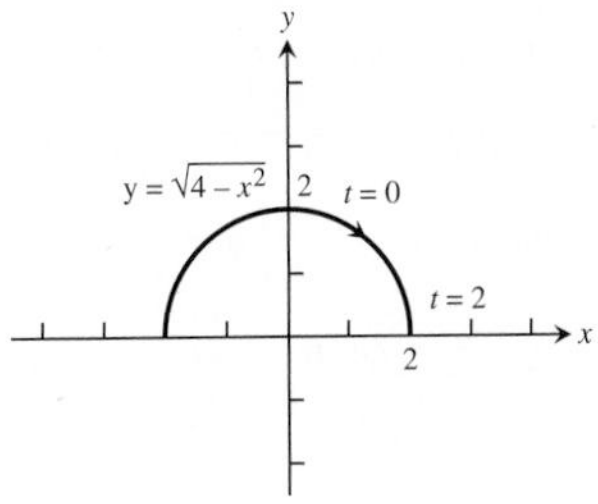

11.

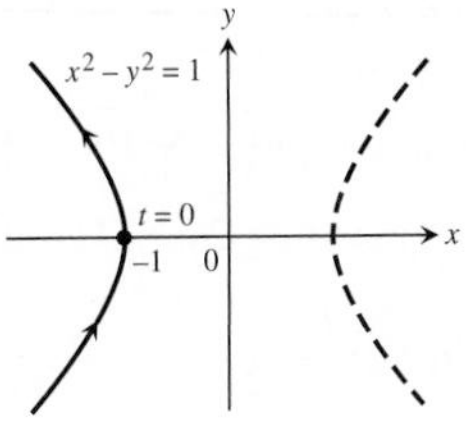

13. $x=(a-b)\cos\theta+b\cos\left(\frac{a-b}{b}\theta\right)$,
$y=(a-b)\sin\theta-b\sin\left(\frac{a-b}{b}\theta\right)$

15. $x=a\sin^2 t\tan t, y=a\sin^2 t$ **17.** $(1, 1)$

Practice Exercises, pp. 610–612

1. $y = (\sqrt{3}/3)x - 4$ **3.** $x = 2$ **5.** $y = -3/2$

7. $x^2 + (y + 2)^2 = 4$ **9.** $(x - \sqrt{2})^2 + y^2 = 2$

11. $r = -5 \sin\theta$ **13.** $r = 3\cos\theta$

15.

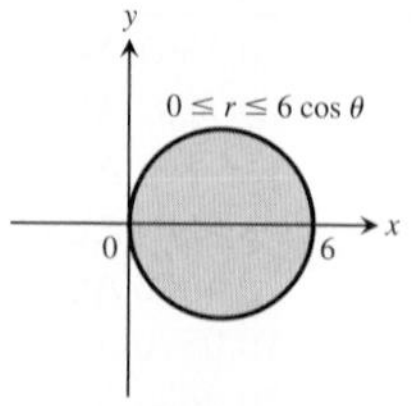

17. (d) **19.** (l) **21.** (k)

23. (i) **25.** $9\pi/2$ **27.** $2 + \pi/4$ **29.** 8 **31.** $\pi - 3$

33.

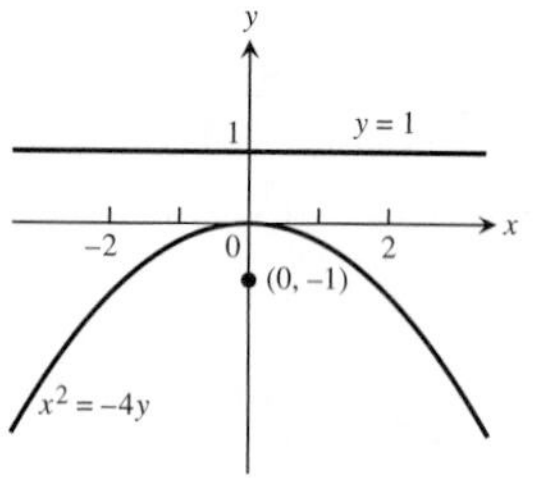

35.

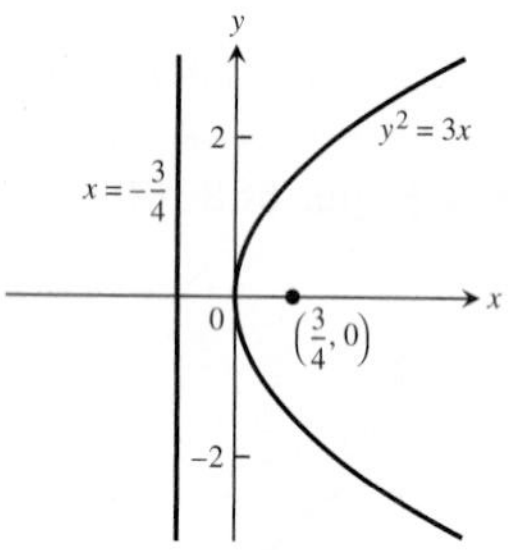

37. $e = 3/4$

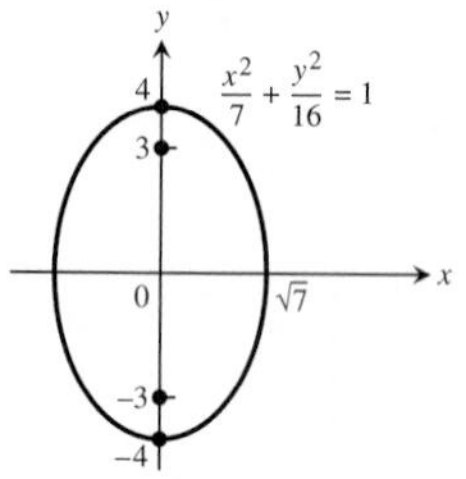

39. $e = 2$

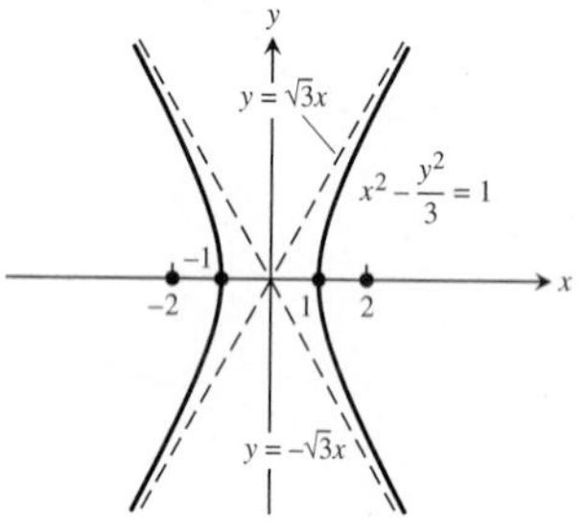

41. $(x - 2)^2 = -12(y - 3)$, $V(2, 3)$, $F(2, 0)$; directrix: $y = 6$

43. $\dfrac{(x + 3)^2}{9} + \dfrac{(y + 5)^2}{25} = 1$, $C(-3, -5)$, $V(-3, 0)$ and $V(-3, -10)$, $F(-3, -1)$ and $F(-3, -9)$

45. $\dfrac{(y - 2\sqrt{2})^2}{8} - \dfrac{(x - 2)^2}{2} = 1$, $C(2, 2\sqrt{2})$, $V(2, 4\sqrt{2})$ and $V(2, 0)$, $F(2, \sqrt{10} + 2\sqrt{2})$ and $F(2, -\sqrt{10} + 2\sqrt{2})$; asymptotes: $y = 2x - 4 + 2\sqrt{2}$ and $y = -2x + 4 + 2\sqrt{2}$

47. Hyperbola: $\dfrac{(x - 2)^2}{4} - y^2 = 1$, $F(2 \pm \sqrt{5}, 0)$, $V(2 \pm 2, 0)$, $C(2, 0)$; asymptotes: $y = \pm\dfrac{1}{2}(x - 2)$

49. Parabola: $(y - 1)^2 = -16(x + 3)$, $V(-3, 1)$, $F(-7, 1)$; directrix: $x = 1$

51. Ellipse: $\dfrac{(x + 3)^2}{16} + \dfrac{(y - 2)^2}{9} = 1$, $F(\pm\sqrt{7} - 3, 2)$, $V(\pm 4 - 3, 2)$, $C(-3, 2)$

53. Circle: $(x - 1)^2 + (y - 1)^2 = 2$, $C(1, 1)$, radius $= \sqrt{2}$

55.

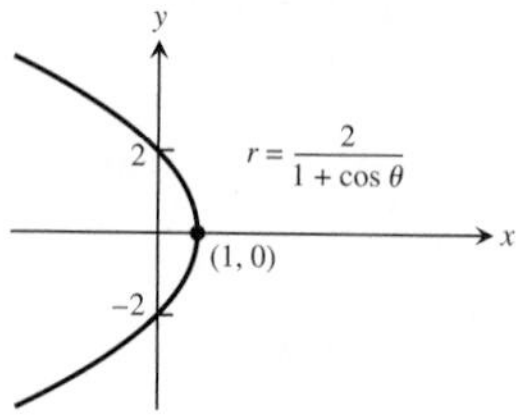

57.

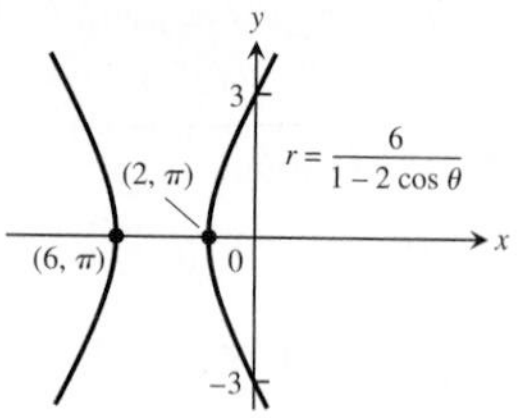

59. $r = \dfrac{4}{1 + 2\cos\theta}$ **61.** $r = \dfrac{2}{2 + \sin\theta}$

63.

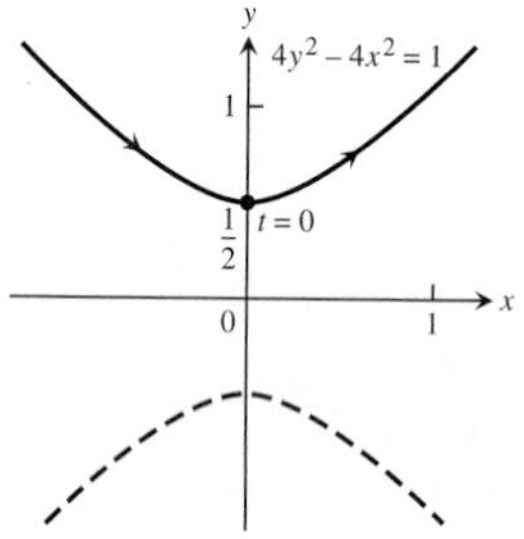

65.

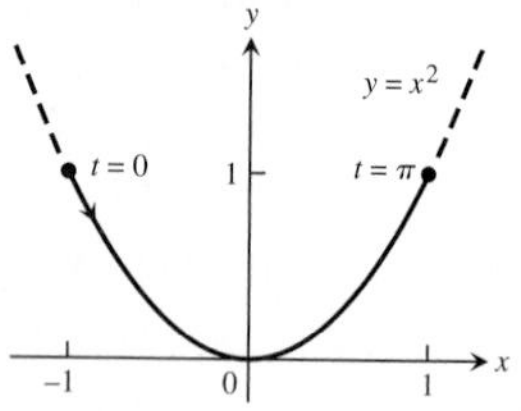

67. **(a)** 24π **(b)** 16π

Additional and Advanced Exercises, pp. 612–613

1.

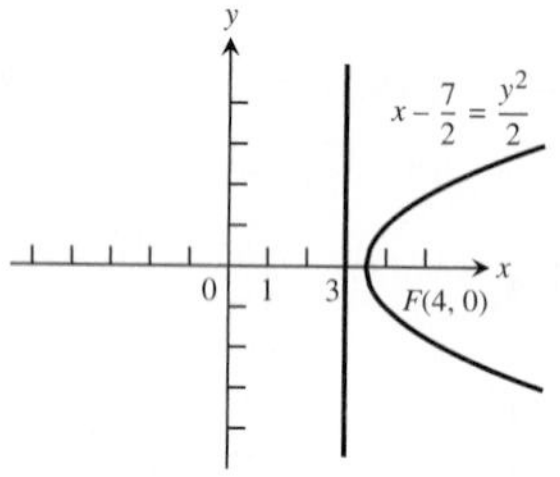

3. $3x^2 + 3y^2 - 8y + 4 = 0$ **5.** $(0, \pm 1)$

7. **(a)** $\dfrac{(y - 1)^2}{16} - \dfrac{x^2}{48} = 1$ **(b)** $\dfrac{16\left(y + \frac{3}{4}\right)^2}{25} - \dfrac{2x^2}{75} = 1$

11.

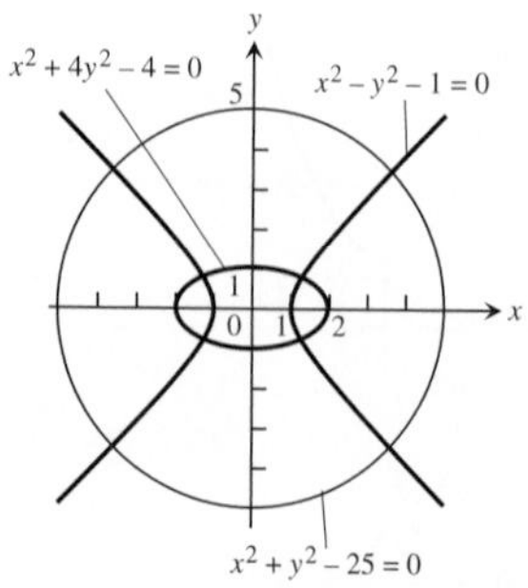

13.

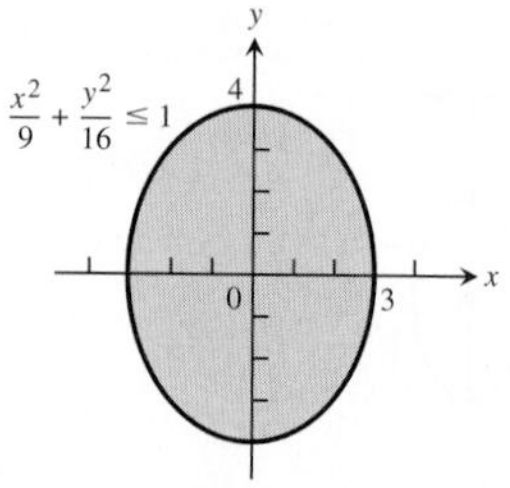

15.

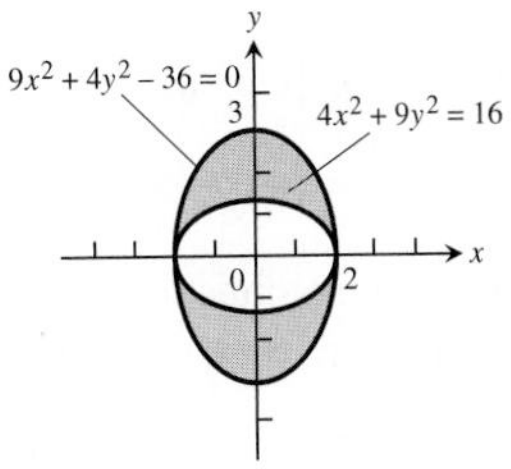

17. **(a)** $r = e^{2\theta}$ **(b)** $\dfrac{\sqrt{5}}{2}(e^{4\pi} - 1)$

19. $r = \dfrac{4}{1 + 2\cos\theta}$ **21.** $r = \dfrac{2}{2 + \sin\theta}$

23. $x = (a + b)\cos\theta - b\cos\left(\dfrac{a + b}{b}\theta\right),$

$y = (a + b)\sin\theta - b\sin\left(\dfrac{a + b}{b}\theta\right)$

27. $\pi/2$

CHAPTER 10

Section 10.1, pp. 617–618

1. The line through the point (2, 3, 0) parallel to the z-axis
3. The x-axis **5.** The circle $x^2 + y^2 = 4$ in the xy-plane
7. The circle $x^2 + z^2 = 4$ in the xz-plane
9. The circle $y^2 + z^2 = 1$ in the yz-plane
11. The circle $x^2 + y^2 = 16$ in the xy-plane
13. **(a)** The first quadrant of the xy-plane
(b) The fourth quadrant of the xy-plane
15. **(a)** The ball of radius 1 centered at the origin
(b) All points greater than 1 unit from the origin
17. **(a)** The upper hemisphere of radius 1 centered at the origin
(b) The solid upper hemisphere of radius 1 centered at the origin
19. **(a)** $x = 3$ **(b)** $y = -1$ **(c)** $z = -2$
21. **(a)** $z = 1$ **(b)** $x = 3$ **(c)** $y = -1$
23. **(a)** $x^2 + (y - 2)^2 = 4, z = 0$
(b) $(y - 2)^2 + z^2 = 4, x = 0$ **(c)** $x^2 + z^2 = 4, y = 2$
25. **(a)** $y = 3, z = -1$ **(b)** $x = 1, z = -1$ **(c)** $x = 1, y = 3$
27. $x^2 + y^2 + z^2 = 25, z = 3$ **29.** $0 \le z \le 1$ **31.** $z \le 0$
33. **(a)** $(x - 1)^2 + (y - 1)^2 + (z - 1)^2 < 1$
(b) $(x - 1)^2 + (y - 1)^2 + (z - 1)^2 > 1$
35. 3 **37.** 7 **39.** $2\sqrt{3}$ **41.** $C(-2, 0, 2), a = 2\sqrt{2}$
43. $C\left(\sqrt{2}, \sqrt{2}, -\sqrt{2}\right), a = \sqrt{2}$
45. $(x - 1)^2 + (y - 2)^2 + (z - 3)^2 = 14$
47. $(x + 2)^2 + y^2 + z^2 = 3$ **49.** $C(-2, 0, 2), a = \sqrt{8}$
51. $C\left(-\frac{1}{4}, -\frac{1}{4}, -\frac{1}{4}\right), a = \dfrac{5\sqrt{3}}{4}$
53. **(a)** $\sqrt{y^2 + z^2}$ **(b)** $\sqrt{x^2 + z^2}$ **(c)** $\sqrt{x^2 + y^2}$
55. $\sqrt{17} + \sqrt{33} + 6$

Section 10.2, pp. 626–627

1. **(a)** $\langle 9, -6\rangle$ **(b)** $3\sqrt{13}$ **3.** **(a)** $\langle 1, 3\rangle$ **(b)** $\sqrt{10}$

5. **(a)** $\langle 12, -19\rangle$ **(b)** $\sqrt{505}$ **7.** **(a)** $\left\langle \frac{1}{5}, \frac{14}{5}\right\rangle$ **(b)** $\dfrac{\sqrt{197}}{5}$

9. $\langle 1, -4\rangle$ **11.** $\langle -2, -3\rangle$ **13.** $\left\langle -\frac{1}{2}, \frac{\sqrt{3}}{2}\right\rangle$

15. $\left\langle -\frac{\sqrt{3}}{2}, -\frac{1}{2}\right\rangle$ **17.** $\langle -3\mathbf{i} + 2\mathbf{j} - \mathbf{k}\rangle$ **19.** $\langle -3\mathbf{i} + 16\mathbf{j}\rangle$

21. $\langle 3\mathbf{i} + 5\mathbf{j} - 8\mathbf{k}\rangle$

23. The vector **v** is horizontal and 1 in. long. The vectors **u** and **w** are $\frac{11}{16}$ in. long. **w** is vertical and **u** makes a 45° angle with the horizontal. All vectors must be drawn to scale.

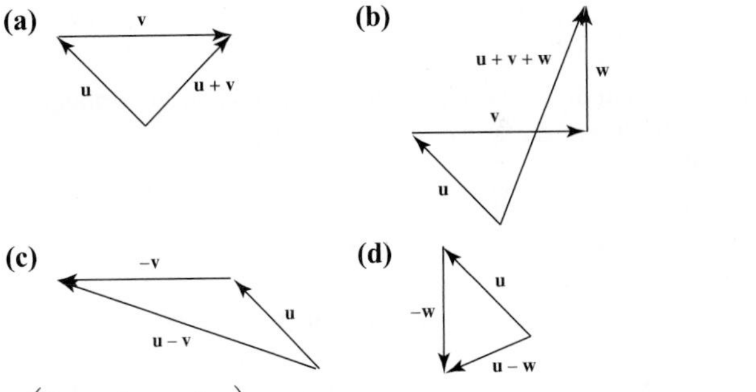

25. $3\left(\frac{2}{3}\mathbf{i} + \frac{1}{3}\mathbf{j} - \frac{2}{3}\mathbf{k}\right)$ **27.** $5(\mathbf{k})$

29. $\sqrt{\frac{1}{2}}\left(\frac{1}{\sqrt{3}}\mathbf{i} - \frac{1}{\sqrt{3}}\mathbf{j} - \frac{1}{\sqrt{3}}\mathbf{k}\right)$

31. **(a)** $2\mathbf{i}$ **(b)** $-\sqrt{3}\mathbf{k}$ **(c)** $\frac{3}{10}\mathbf{j} + \frac{2}{5}\mathbf{k}$ **(d)** $6\mathbf{i} - 2\mathbf{j} + 3\mathbf{k}$

33. $\frac{7}{13}(12\mathbf{i} - 5\mathbf{k})$

35. **(a)** $\dfrac{3}{5\sqrt{2}}\mathbf{i} + \dfrac{4}{5\sqrt{2}}\mathbf{j} - \dfrac{1}{\sqrt{2}}\mathbf{k}$ **(b)** $(1/2, 3, 5/2)$

37. **(a)** $-\dfrac{1}{\sqrt{3}}\mathbf{i} - \dfrac{1}{\sqrt{3}}\mathbf{j} - \dfrac{1}{\sqrt{3}}\mathbf{k}$ **(b)** $\left(\frac{5}{2}, \frac{7}{2}, \frac{9}{2}\right)$

39. $A(4, -3, 5)$ **41.** $a = \frac{3}{2}, b = \frac{1}{2}$ **43.** $5\sqrt{3}\mathbf{i}, 5\mathbf{j}$

45. $\approx\langle -338.095, 725.046\rangle$

47. **(a)** $(5\cos 60°, 5\sin 60°) = \left(\frac{5}{2}, \frac{5\sqrt{3}}{2}\right)$

(b) $(5\cos 60° + 10\cos 315°, 5\sin 60° + 10\sin 315°) = \left(\dfrac{5 + 10\sqrt{2}}{2}, \dfrac{5\sqrt{3} - 10\sqrt{2}}{2}\right)$

49. **(a)** $\frac{3}{2}\mathbf{i} + \frac{3}{2}\mathbf{j} - 3\mathbf{k}$ **(b)** $\mathbf{i} + \mathbf{j} - 2\mathbf{k}$ **(c)** $(2, 2, 1)$

Section 10.3, pp. 634–636

1. **(a)** $-25, 5, 5$ **(b)** -1 **(c)** -5 **(d)** $-2\mathbf{i} + 4\mathbf{j} - \sqrt{5}\mathbf{k}$

3. **(a)** $25, 15, 5$ **(b)** $\frac{1}{3}$ **(c)** $\frac{5}{3}$ **(d)** $\frac{1}{9}(10\mathbf{i} + 11\mathbf{j} - 2\mathbf{k})$

5. **(a)** $2, \sqrt{34}, \sqrt{3}$ **(b)** $\dfrac{2}{\sqrt{3}\sqrt{34}}$ **(c)** $\dfrac{2}{\sqrt{34}}$

(d) $\dfrac{1}{17}(5\mathbf{j} - 3\mathbf{k})$

7. **(a)** $10 + \sqrt{17}, \sqrt{26}, \sqrt{21}$ **(b)** $\dfrac{10 + \sqrt{17}}{\sqrt{546}}$

(c) $\dfrac{10 + \sqrt{17}}{\sqrt{26}}$ **(d)** $\dfrac{10 + \sqrt{17}}{26}(5\mathbf{i} + \mathbf{j})$

9. 0.75 rad **11.** 1.77 rad

13. Angle at $A = \cos^{-1}\left(\dfrac{1}{\sqrt{5}}\right) \approx 63.435$ degrees, angle at $B = \cos^{-1}\left(\dfrac{3}{5}\right) \approx 53.130$ degrees, angle at $C = \cos^{-1}\left(\dfrac{1}{\sqrt{5}}\right) \approx 63.435$ degrees.

17. The sum of two vectors of equal length is *always* orthogonal to their difference, as we can see from the equation $(\mathbf{v}_1 + \mathbf{v}_2) \cdot (\mathbf{v}_1 - \mathbf{v}_2) = \mathbf{v}_1 \cdot \mathbf{v}_1 + \mathbf{v}_2 \cdot \mathbf{v}_1 - \mathbf{v}_1 \cdot \mathbf{v}_2 - \mathbf{v}_2 \cdot \mathbf{v}_2 = |\mathbf{v}_1|^2 - |\mathbf{v}_2|^2 = 0$.

23. Horizontal component: ≈ 1188 ft/sec, vertical component: ≈ 167 ft/sec

25. **(a)** Since $|\cos\theta| \le 1$, we have $|\mathbf{u} \cdot \mathbf{v}| = |\mathbf{u}||\mathbf{v}||\cos\theta| \le |\mathbf{u}||\mathbf{v}|(1) = |\mathbf{u}||\mathbf{v}|$.

(b) We have equality precisely when $|\cos\theta| = 1$ or when one or both of **u** and **v** are **0**. In the case of nonzero vectors, we have equality when $\theta = 0$ or π, that is, when the vectors are parallel.

27. a

31. $x + 2y = 4$

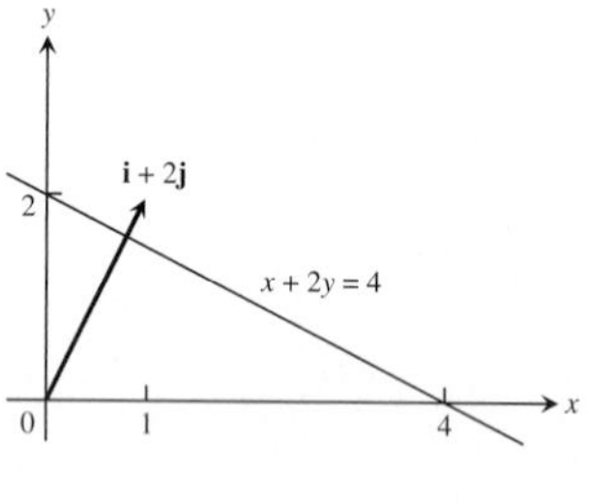

33. $-2x + y = -3$

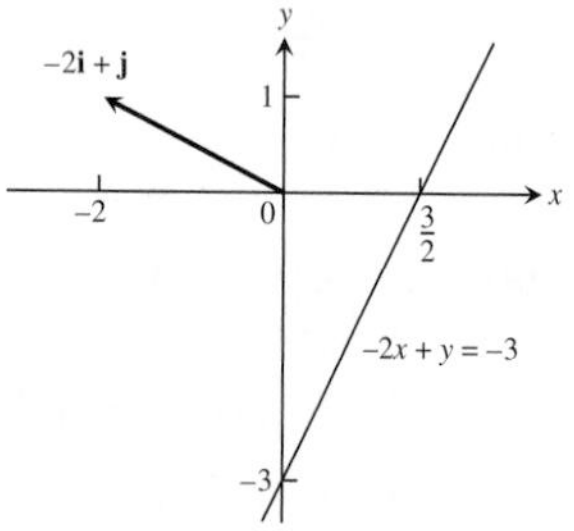

35. $x + y = -1$

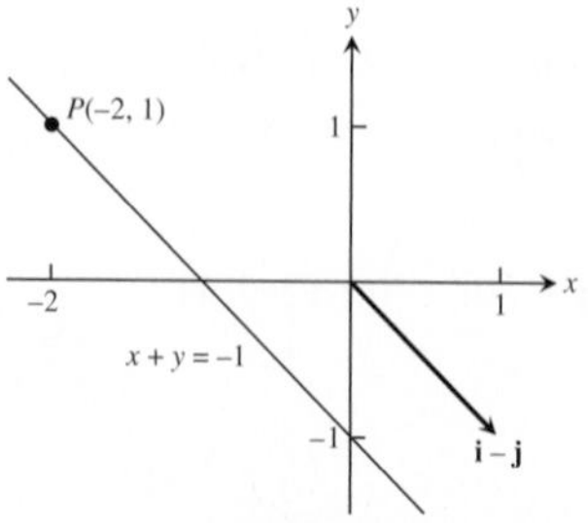

37. $2x - y = 0$

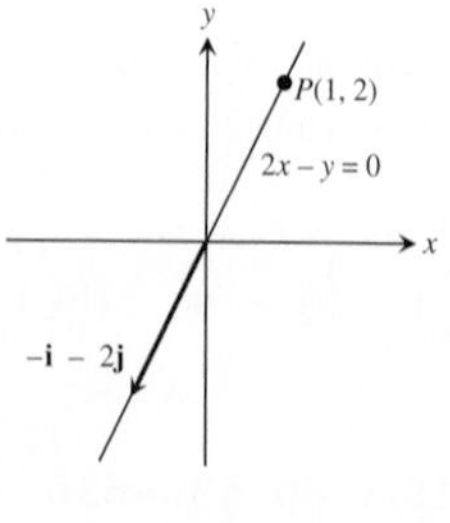

39. 5 J **41.** 3464 J **43.** $\dfrac{\pi}{4}$ **45.** $\dfrac{\pi}{6}$ **47.** 0.14

Section 10.4, pp. 641–642

1. $|\mathbf{u} \times \mathbf{v}| = 3$, direction is $\dfrac{2}{3}\mathbf{i} + \dfrac{1}{3}\mathbf{j} + \dfrac{2}{3}\mathbf{k}$; $|\mathbf{v} \times \mathbf{u}| = 3$, direction is $-\dfrac{2}{3}\mathbf{i} - \dfrac{1}{3}\mathbf{j} - \dfrac{2}{3}\mathbf{k}$

3. $|\mathbf{u} \times \mathbf{v}| = 0$, no direction; $|\mathbf{v} \times \mathbf{u}| = 0$, no direction

5. $|\mathbf{u} \times \mathbf{v}| = 6$, direction is $-\mathbf{k}$; $|\mathbf{v} \times \mathbf{u}| = 6$, direction is $\mathbf{k}$

7. $|\mathbf{u} \times \mathbf{v}| = 6\sqrt{5}$, direction is $\dfrac{1}{\sqrt{5}}\mathbf{i} - \dfrac{2}{\sqrt{5}}\mathbf{k}$; $|\mathbf{v} \times \mathbf{u}| = 6\sqrt{5}$, direction is $-\dfrac{1}{\sqrt{5}}\mathbf{i} + \dfrac{2}{\sqrt{5}}\mathbf{k}$

9.

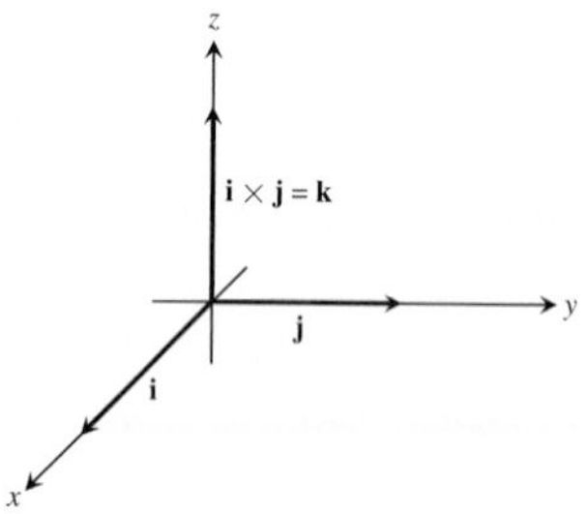

11.

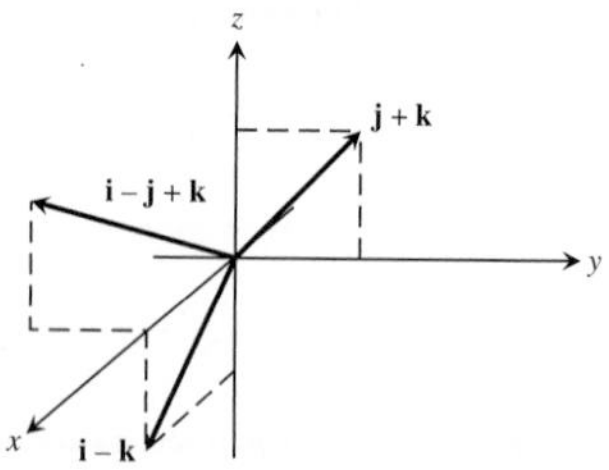

13.

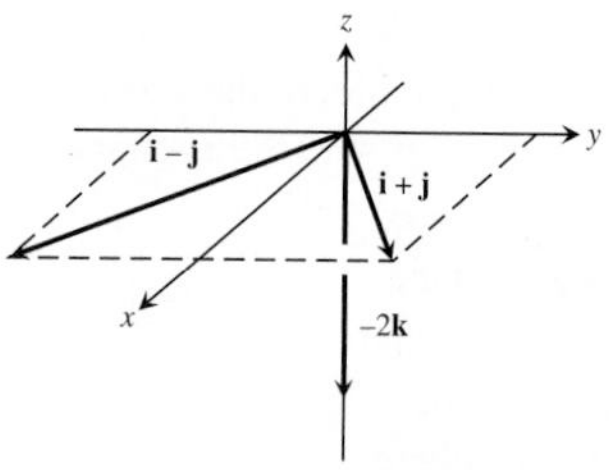

15. **(a)** $2\sqrt{6}$ **(b)** $\pm\dfrac{1}{\sqrt{6}}(2\mathbf{i} + \mathbf{j} + \mathbf{k})$

17. **(a)** $\dfrac{\sqrt{2}}{2}$ **(b)** $\pm\dfrac{1}{\sqrt{2}}(\mathbf{i} - \mathbf{j})$

19. 8 **21.** 7 **23.** **(a)** None **(b)** **u** and **w** **25.** $10\sqrt{3}$ ft-lb

27. **(a)** True **(b)** Not always true **(c)** True **(d)** True **(e)** Not always true **(f)** True **(g)** True **(h)** True

29. **(a)** $\text{proj}_{\mathbf{v}}\,\mathbf{u} = \dfrac{\mathbf{u} \cdot \mathbf{v}}{\mathbf{v} \cdot \mathbf{v}}\mathbf{v}$ **(b)** $\pm\,\mathbf{u} \times \mathbf{v}$ **(c)** $\pm\,(\mathbf{u} \times \mathbf{v}) \times \mathbf{w}$

(d) $|(\mathbf{u} \times \mathbf{v}) \cdot \mathbf{w}|$

31. **(a)** Yes **(b)** No **(c)** Yes **(d)** No

33. No, **v** need not equal **w**. For example, $\mathbf{i} + \mathbf{j} \ne -\mathbf{i} + \mathbf{j}$, but $\mathbf{i} \times (\mathbf{i} + \mathbf{j}) = \mathbf{i} \times \mathbf{i} + \mathbf{i} \times \mathbf{j} = \mathbf{0} + \mathbf{k} = \mathbf{k}$ and $\mathbf{i} \times (-\mathbf{i} + \mathbf{j}) = -\mathbf{i} \times \mathbf{i} + \mathbf{i} \times \mathbf{j} = \mathbf{0} + \mathbf{k} = \mathbf{k}$.

35. 2 **37.** 13 **39.** 11/2 **41.** 25/2

43. If $\mathbf{A} = a_1\mathbf{i} + a_2\mathbf{j}$ and $\mathbf{B} = b_1\mathbf{i} + b_2\mathbf{j}$, then

$$\mathbf{A} \times \mathbf{B} = \begin{vmatrix} \mathbf{i} & \mathbf{j} & \mathbf{k} \\ a_1 & a_2 & 0 \\ b_1 & b_2 & 0 \end{vmatrix} = \begin{vmatrix} a_1 & a_2 \\ b_1 & b_2 \end{vmatrix}\mathbf{k}$$

and the triangle's area is

$$\frac{1}{2}\left|\mathbf{A} \times \mathbf{B}\right| = \pm\frac{1}{2}\begin{vmatrix} a_1 & a_2 \\ b_1 & b_2 \end{vmatrix}.$$

The applicable sign is (+) if the acute angle from **A** to **B** runs counterclockwise in the xy-plane, and (−) if it runs clockwise.

Section 10.5, pp. 650–651

1. $x = 3 + t, y = -4 + t, z = -1 + t$

3. $x = -2 + 5t, y = 5t, z = 3 - 5t$ **5.** $x = 0, y = 2t, z = t$

7. $x = 1, y = 1, z = 1 + t$ **9.** $x = t, y = -7 + 2t, z = 2t$

11. $x = t, y = 0, z = 0$

13. $x = t, y = t, z = \frac{3}{2}t, 0 \le t \le 1$

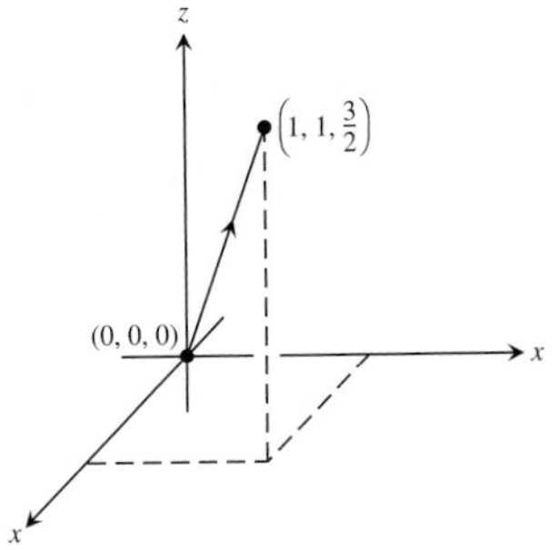

15. $x = 1, y = 1 + t, z = 0, -1 \le t \le 0$

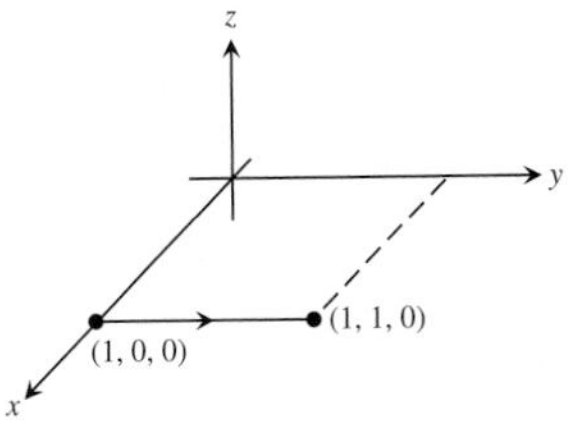

17. $x = 0, y = 1 - 2t, z = 1, 0 \le t \le 1$

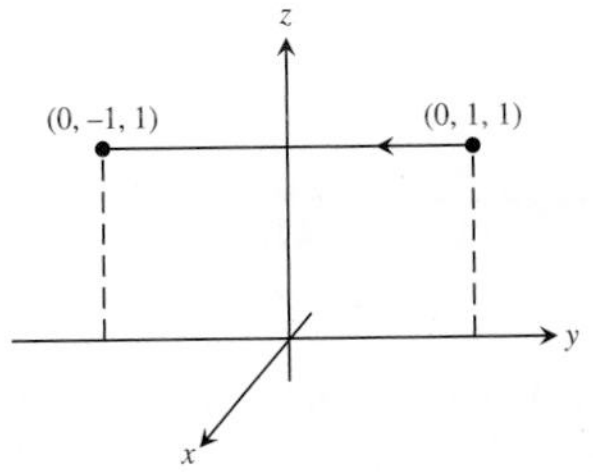

19. $x = 2 - 2t, y = 2t, z = 2 - 2t, 0 \le t \le 1$

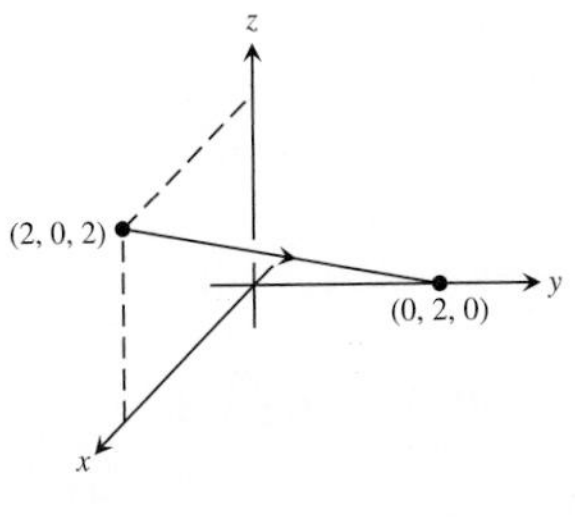

21. $3x - 2y - z = -3$ **23.** $7x - 5y - 4z = 6$

25. $x + 3y + 4z = 34$ **27.** $(1, 2, 3), -20x + 12y + z = 7$

29. $y + z = 3$ **31.** $x - y + z = 0$ **33.** $2\sqrt{30}$ **35.** 0

37. $\frac{9\sqrt{42}}{7}$ **39.** 3 **41.** 19/5 **43.** 5/3 **45.** $9/\sqrt{41}$

47. $\pi/4$ **49.** 1.76 rad **51.** 0.82 rad **53.** $\left(\frac{3}{2}, -\frac{3}{2}, \frac{1}{2}\right)$

55. (1, 1, 0) **57.** $x = 1 - t, y = 1 + t, z = -1$

59. $x = 4, y = 3 + 6t, z = 1 + 3t$

61. $L1$ intersects $L2$; $L2$ is parallel to $L3$; $L1$ and $L3$ are skew.

63. $x = 2 + 2t, y = -4 - t, z = 7 + 3t; x = -2 - t,$ $y = -2 + (1/2)t, z = 1 - (3/2)t$

65. $\left(0, -\frac{1}{2}, -\frac{3}{2}\right), (-1, 0, -3), (1, -1, 0)$

69. Many possible answers. One possibility: $x + y = 3$ and $2y + z = 7$

71. $(x/a) + (y/b) + (z/c) = 1$ describes all planes *except* those through the origin or parallel to a coordinate axis.

Section 10.6, pp. 656–657

1. **(d),** ellipsoid **3.** **(a),** cylinder **5.** **(l),** hyperbolic paraboloid

7. **(b),** cylinder **9.** **(k),** hyperbolic paraboloid **11.** **(h),** cone

13.

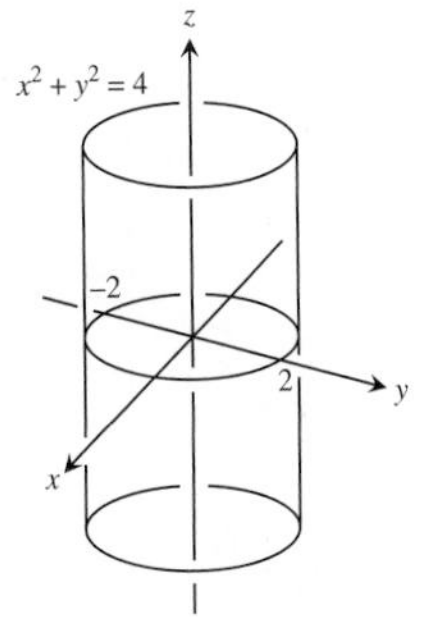

15.

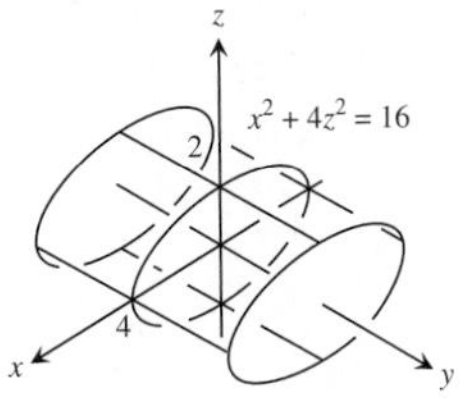

17.

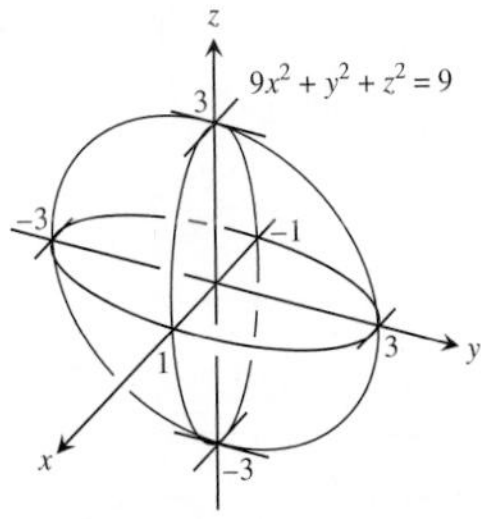

19.

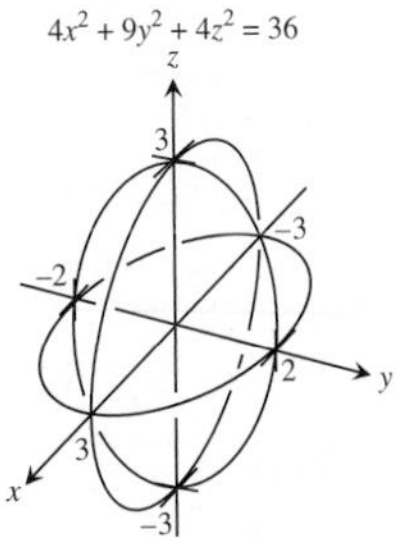

21.

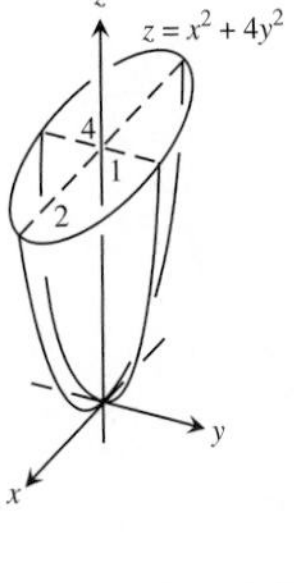

23.

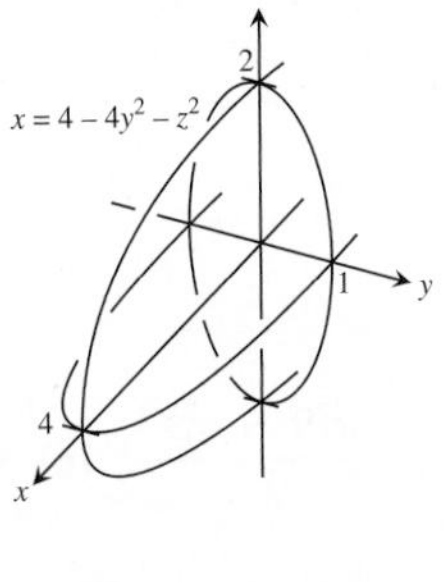

25.
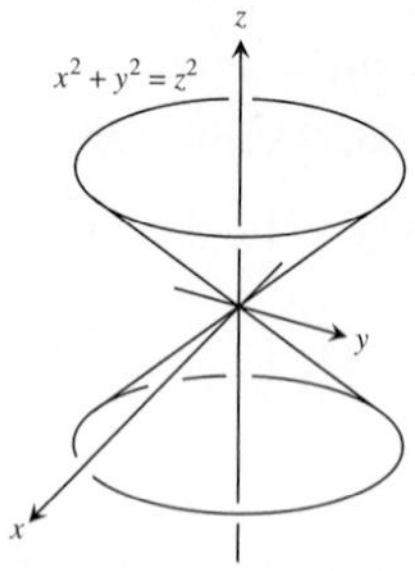

27.
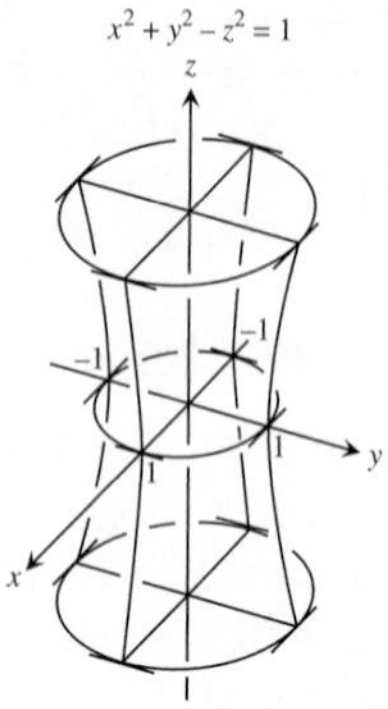

29.
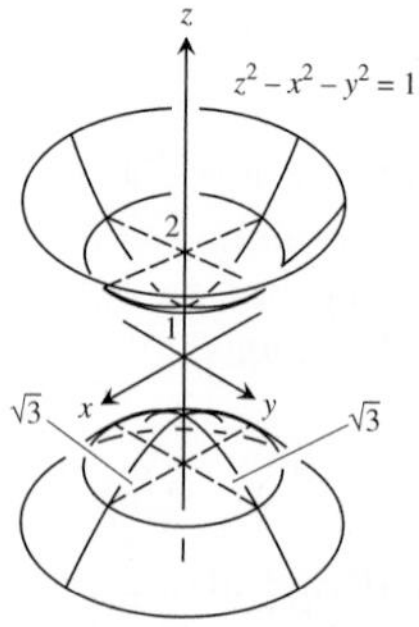

31.
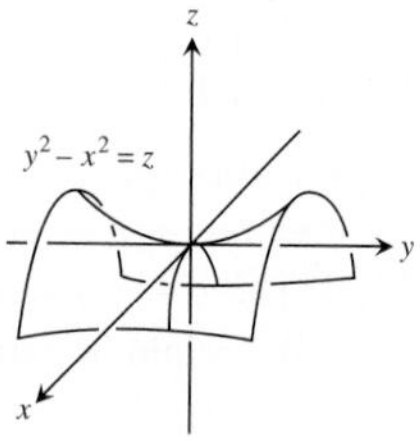

33.
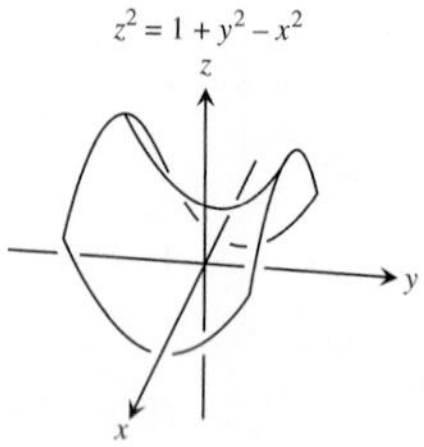

35.
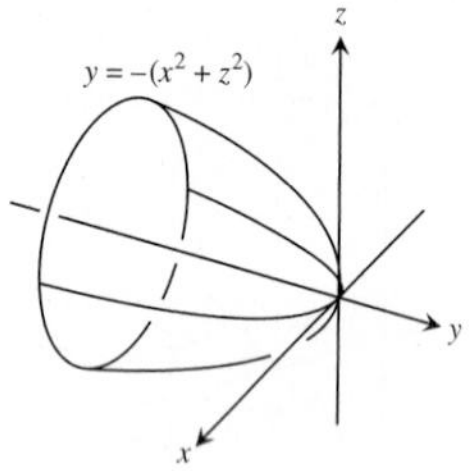

37.
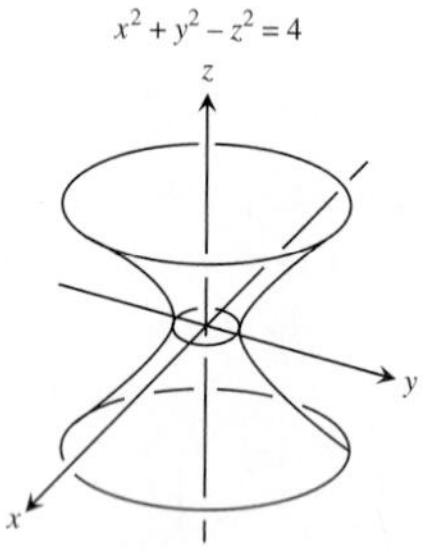

39.
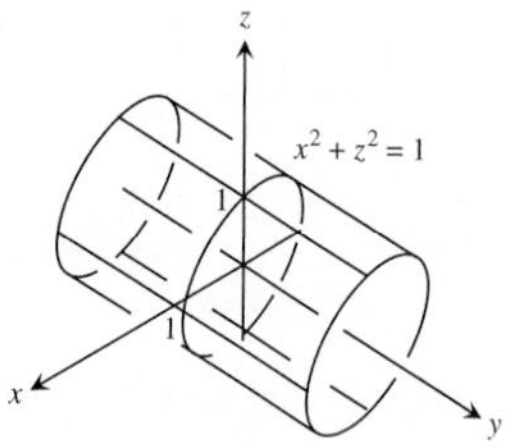

41.
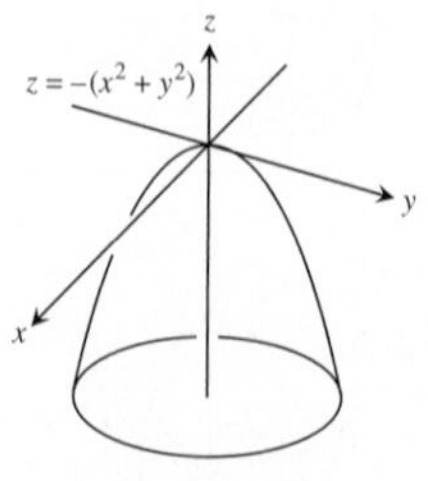

43.
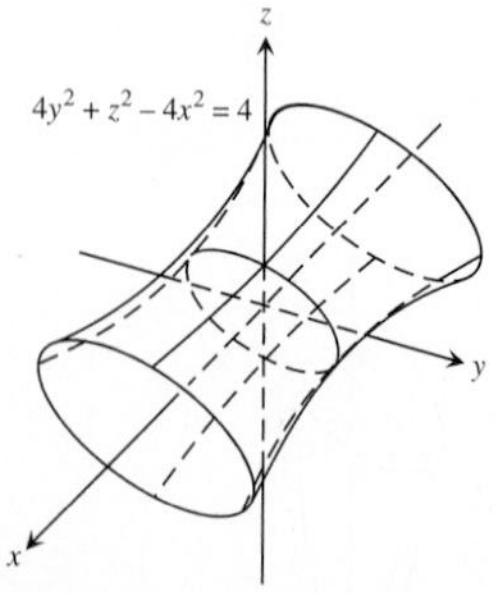

45. **(a)** $\dfrac{2\pi(9 - c^2)}{9}$ **(b)** 8π **(c)** $\dfrac{4\pi abc}{3}$

Practice Exercises, pp. 658–660

1. **(a)** $\langle -17, 32 \rangle$ **(b)** $\sqrt{1313}$
3. **(a)** $\langle 6, -8 \rangle$ **(b)** 10
5. $\left\langle -\dfrac{\sqrt{3}}{2}, -\dfrac{1}{2} \right\rangle$ [assuming counterclockwise]
7. $\left\langle \dfrac{8}{\sqrt{17}}, -\dfrac{2}{\sqrt{17}} \right\rangle$
9. Length $= 2$, direction is $\dfrac{1}{\sqrt{2}}\mathbf{i} + \dfrac{1}{\sqrt{2}}\mathbf{j}$.
11. $\mathbf{v}(\pi/2) = 2(-\mathbf{i})$
13. Length $= 7$, direction is $\dfrac{2}{7}\mathbf{i} - \dfrac{3}{7}\mathbf{j} + \dfrac{6}{7}\mathbf{k}$.
15. $\dfrac{8}{\sqrt{33}}\mathbf{i} - \dfrac{2}{\sqrt{33}}\mathbf{j} + \dfrac{8}{\sqrt{33}}\mathbf{k}$
17. $|\mathbf{v}| = \sqrt{2}, |\mathbf{u}| = 3, \mathbf{v}\cdot\mathbf{u} = \mathbf{u}\cdot\mathbf{v} = 3, \mathbf{v}\times\mathbf{u} = -2\mathbf{i} + 2\mathbf{j} - \mathbf{k}$,
$\mathbf{u}\times\mathbf{v} = 2\mathbf{i} - 2\mathbf{j} + \mathbf{k}, |\mathbf{v}\times\mathbf{u}| = 3, \theta = \cos^{-1}\left(\dfrac{1}{\sqrt{2}}\right) = \dfrac{\pi}{4}$,
$|\mathbf{u}|\cos\theta = \dfrac{3}{\sqrt{2}}$, $\text{proj}_{\mathbf{v}}\,\mathbf{u} = \dfrac{3}{2}(\mathbf{i} + \mathbf{j})$
19. $\dfrac{4}{3}(2\mathbf{i} + \mathbf{j} - \mathbf{k})$
21. $\mathbf{u}\times\mathbf{v} = \mathbf{k}$

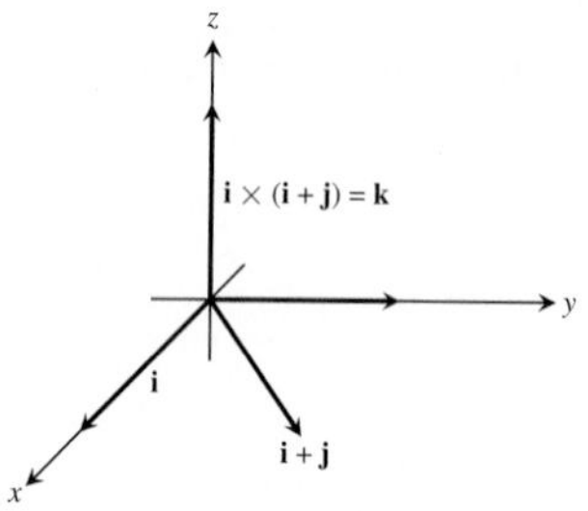

23. $2\sqrt{7}$ **25.** **(a)** $\sqrt{14}$ **(b)** 1 **29.** $\sqrt{78}/3$
31. $x = 1 - 3t, y = 2, z = 3 + 7t$ **33.** $\sqrt{2}$
35. $2x + y + z = 5$
37. $-9x + y + 7z = 4$
39. $\left(0, -\dfrac{1}{2}, -\dfrac{3}{2}\right), (-1, 0, -3), (1, -1, 0)$ **41.** $\pi/3$
43. $x = -5 + 5t, y = 3 - t, z = -3t$
45. **(b)** $x = -12t, y = 19/12 + 15t, z = 1/6 + 6t$
47. Yes; $\mathbf{v}$ is parallel to the plane.
49. 3 **51.** $-3\mathbf{j} + 3\mathbf{k}$
53. $\dfrac{2}{\sqrt{35}}\left(5\mathbf{i} - \mathbf{j} - 3\mathbf{k}\right)$
55. $\left(\dfrac{11}{9}, \dfrac{26}{9}, \dfrac{7}{9}\right)$
57. $(1, -2, -1); x = 1 - 5t, y = -2 + 3t, z = -1 + 4t$
59. $2x + 7y + 2z + 10 = 0$
61. **(a)** no **(b)** no **(c)** no **(d)** no **(e)** yes
63. $11/\sqrt{107}$

65.

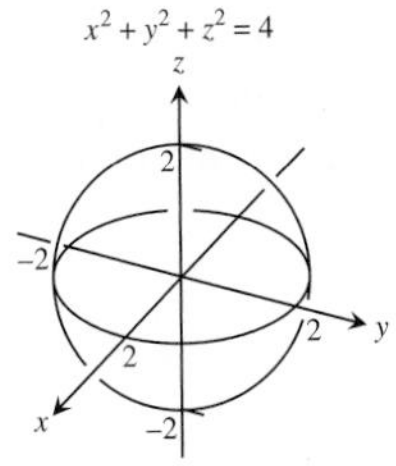

67.

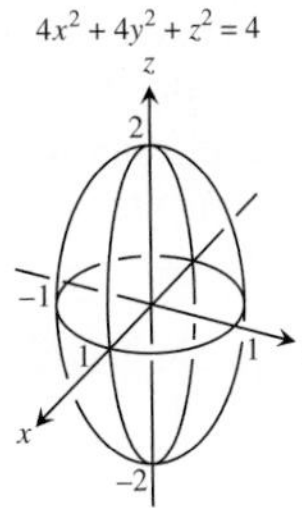

69.

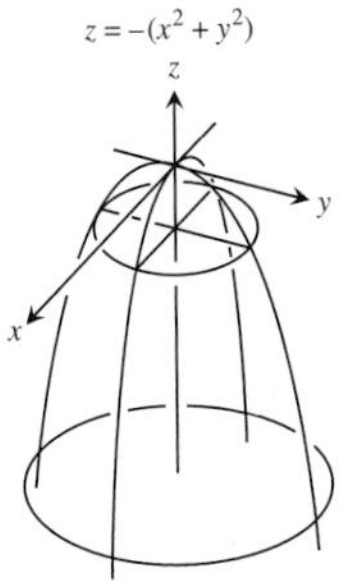

71.

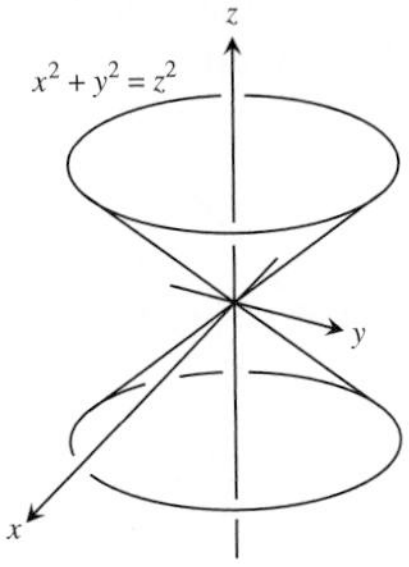

73.

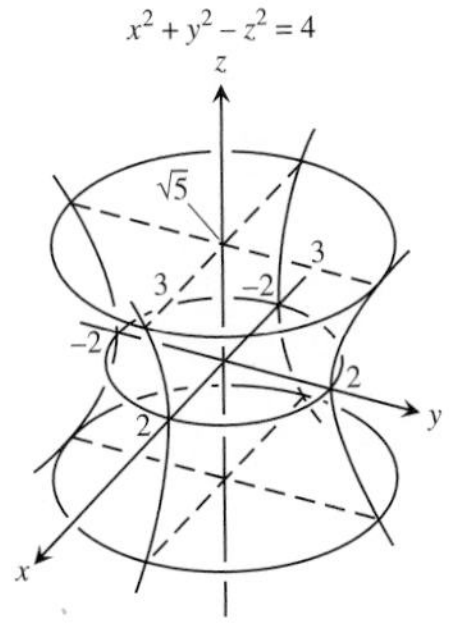

75.

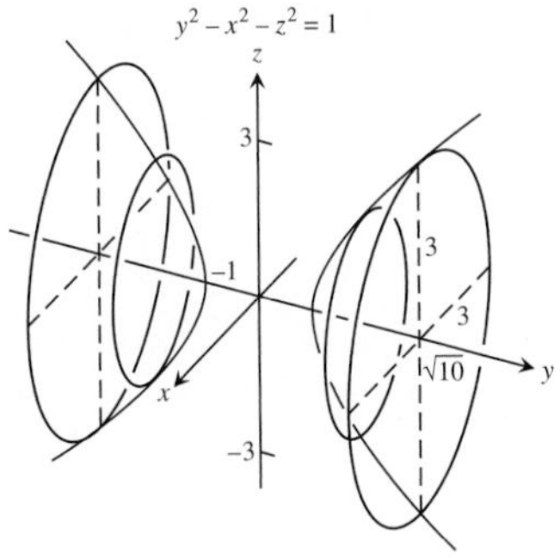

Additional and Advanced Exercises, pp. 660–662

1. $(26, 23, -1/3)$ **3.** $|\mathbf{F}| = 20$ lb

7. (a) $\overrightarrow{BD} = \overrightarrow{AD} - \overrightarrow{AB}$ **(b)** $\overrightarrow{AP} = \frac{1}{2}\overrightarrow{AB} + \frac{1}{2}\overrightarrow{AD}$

13. $\frac{32}{41}\mathbf{i} + \frac{23}{41}\mathbf{j} - \frac{13}{41}\mathbf{k}$

15. (a) $\mathbf{0}, \mathbf{0}$ **(b)** $-10\mathbf{i} - 2\mathbf{j} + 6\mathbf{k}, -9\mathbf{i} - 2\mathbf{j} + 7\mathbf{k}$
(c) $-4\mathbf{i} - 6\mathbf{j} + 2\mathbf{k}, \mathbf{i} - 2\mathbf{j} - 4\mathbf{k}$
(d) $-10\mathbf{i} - 10\mathbf{k}, -12\mathbf{i} - 4\mathbf{j} - 8\mathbf{k}$

APPENDICES

Appendix 1, pp. AP-6–AP-7

1. $0.\bar{1}, 0.\bar{2}, 0.\bar{3}, 0.\bar{8}, 0.\bar{9}$ or 1

3. $x < -2$

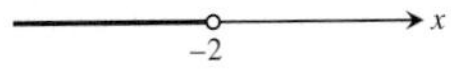

5. $x \le -\frac{1}{3}$

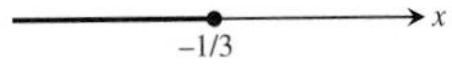

7. 3, −3 **9.** $\frac{7}{6}, \frac{25}{6}$

11. $-2 \le t \le 4$

13. $0 \le z \le 10$

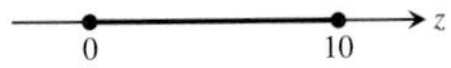

15. $(-\infty, -2] \cup [2, \infty)$

17. $(-\infty, -3] \cup [1, \infty)$

19. $(-3, -2) \cup (2, 3)$ **21.** $(0, 1)$ **23.** $(-\infty, 1]$

29. Graph of $|x| + |y| \le 1$ is the interior of "diamond-shaped" region.

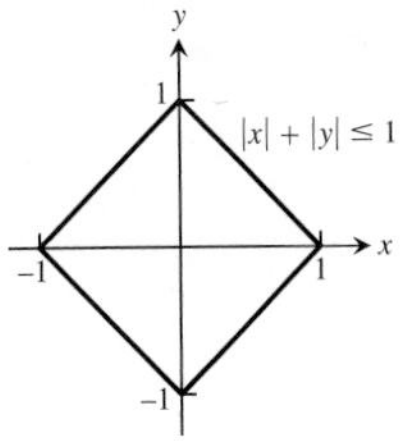

Appendix 3, pp. AP-17–AP-19

1. $2, -4; 2\sqrt{5}$ **3.** Unit circle

5. $m_{\perp} = -\frac{1}{3}$

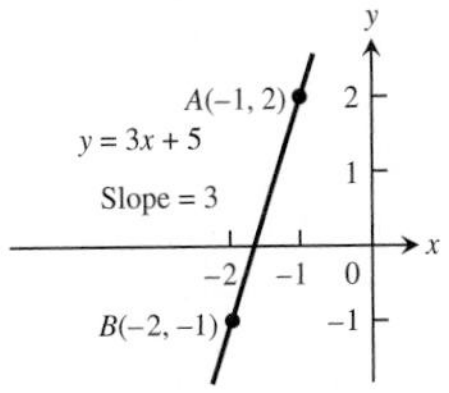

7. (a) $x = -1$ **(b)** $y = 4/3$ **9.** $y = -x$

11. $y = -\frac{5}{4}x + 6$ **13.** $y = 4x + 4$ **15.** $y = -\frac{x}{2} + 12$

17. x-intercept $= \sqrt{3}$, y-intercept $= -\sqrt{2}$

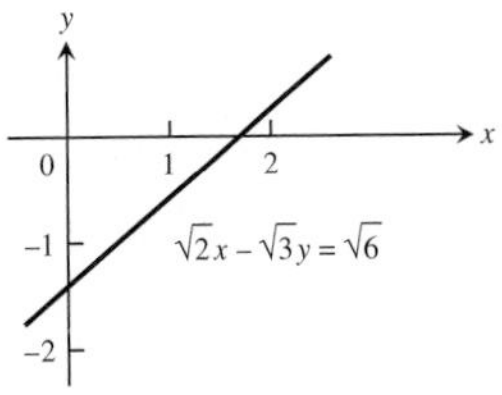

19. $(3, -3)$

21. $x^2 + (y - 2)^2 = 4$

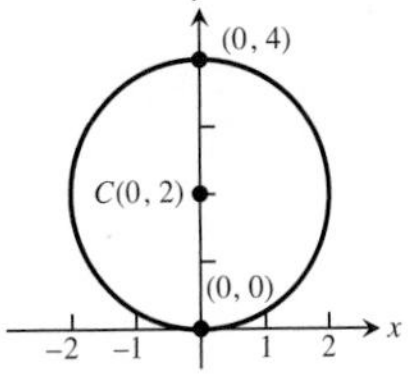

23. $(x + \sqrt{3})^2 + (y + 2)^2 = 4$

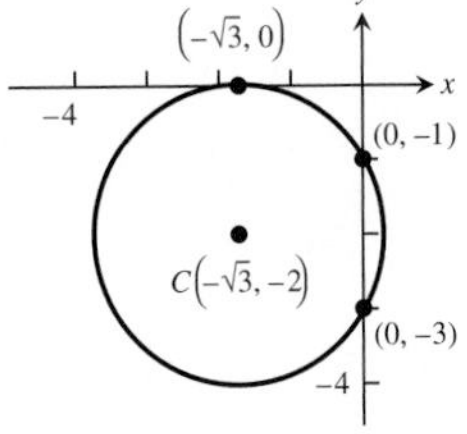

25. $x^2 + (y - 3/2)^2 = 25/4$

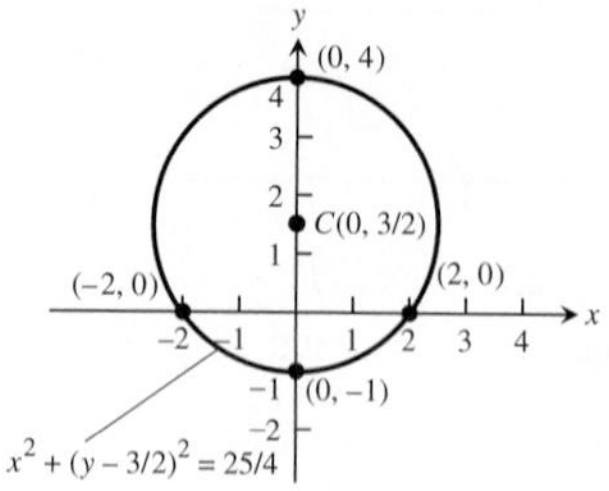

27.

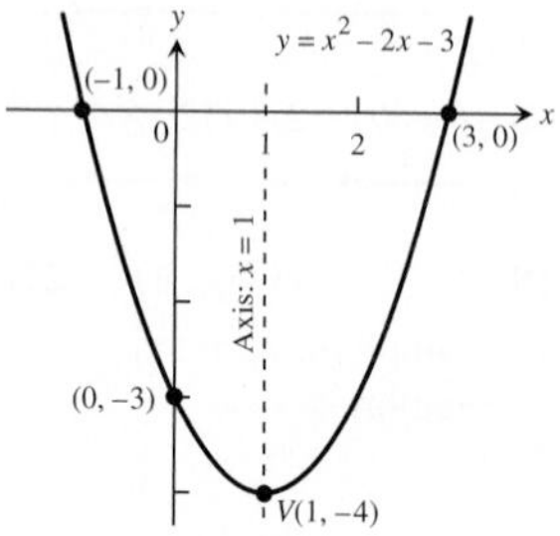

29.

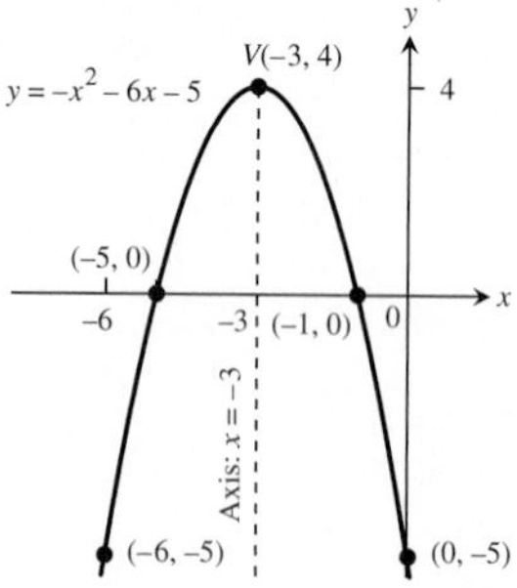

31. Exterior points of a circle of radius $\sqrt{7}$, centered at the origin

33. The washer between the circles $x^2 + y^2 = 1$ and $x^2 + y^2 = 4$ (points with distance from the origin between 1 and 2)

35. $(x + 2)^2 + (y - 1)^2 < 6$

37. $\left(\frac{1}{\sqrt{5}}, \frac{2}{\sqrt{5}}\right)$, $\left(-\frac{1}{\sqrt{5}}, -\frac{2}{\sqrt{5}}\right)$

39. $\left(-\frac{1}{\sqrt{3}}, -\frac{1}{3}\right)$, $\left(\frac{1}{\sqrt{3}}, -\frac{1}{3}\right)$

41. **(a)** ≈ -2.5 degrees/inch **(b)** ≈ -16.1 degrees/inch **(c)** ≈ -8.3 degrees/inch

43. 5.97 atm

45. Yes: $C = F = -40°$

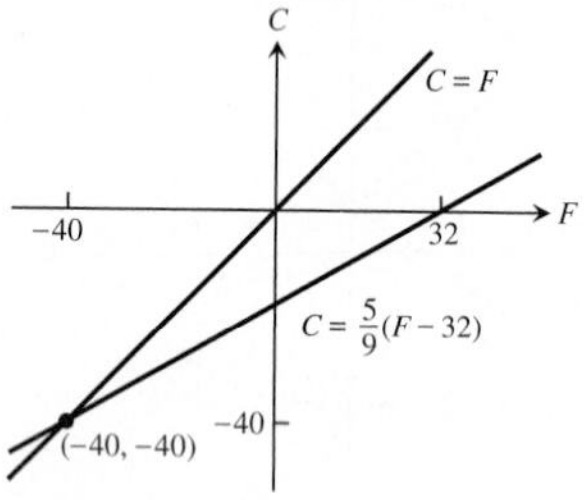

51. $k = -8, \quad k = 1/2$

INDEX

A Brief Table of Integrals

1. $\int u\,dv = uv - \int v\,du$

2. $\int a^u\,du = \frac{a^u}{\ln a} + C,\quad a \neq 1,\quad a > 0$

3. $\int \cos u\,du = \sin u + C$

4. $\int \sin u\,du = -\cos u + C$

5. $\int (ax+b)^n\,dx = \frac{(ax+b)^{n+1}}{a(n+1)} + C,\quad n \neq -1$

6. $\int (ax+b)^{-1}\,dx = \frac{1}{a}\ln|ax+b| + C$

7. $\int x(ax+b)^n\,dx = \frac{(ax+b)^{n+1}}{a^2}\left[\frac{ax+b}{n+2} - \frac{b}{n+1}\right] + C,\quad n \neq -1, -2$

8. $\int x(ax+b)^{-1}\,dx = \frac{x}{a} - \frac{b}{a^2}\ln|ax+b| + C$

9. $\int x(ax+b)^{-2}\,dx = \frac{1}{a^2}\left[\ln|ax+b| + \frac{b}{ax+b}\right] + C$

10. $\int \frac{dx}{x(ax+b)} = \frac{1}{b}\ln\left|\frac{x}{ax+b}\right| + C$

11. $\int \left(\sqrt{ax+b}\right)^n dx = \frac{2}{a}\frac{\left(\sqrt{ax+b}\right)^{n+2}}{n+2} + C,\quad n \neq -2$

12. $\int \frac{\sqrt{ax+b}}{x}\,dx = 2\sqrt{ax+b} + b\int \frac{dx}{x\sqrt{ax+b}}$

13. (a) $\int \frac{dx}{x\sqrt{ax-b}} = \frac{2}{\sqrt{b}}\tan^{-1}\sqrt{\frac{ax-b}{b}} + C$ (b) $\int \frac{dx}{x\sqrt{ax+b}} = \frac{1}{\sqrt{b}}\ln\left|\frac{\sqrt{ax+b}-\sqrt{b}}{\sqrt{ax+b}+\sqrt{b}}\right| + C$

14. $\int \frac{\sqrt{ax+b}}{x^2}\,dx = -\frac{\sqrt{ax+b}}{x} + \frac{a}{2}\int \frac{dx}{x\sqrt{ax+b}} + C$

15. $\int \frac{dx}{x^2\sqrt{ax+b}} = -\frac{\sqrt{ax+b}}{bx} - \frac{a}{2b}\int \frac{dx}{x\sqrt{ax+b}} + C$

16. $\int \frac{dx}{a^2+x^2} = \frac{1}{a}\tan^{-1}\frac{x}{a} + C$

17. $\int \frac{dx}{(a^2+x^2)^2} = \frac{x}{2a^2(a^2+x^2)} + \frac{1}{2a^3}\tan^{-1}\frac{x}{a} + C$

18. $\int \frac{dx}{a^2-x^2} = \frac{1}{2a}\ln\left|\frac{x+a}{x-a}\right| + C$

19. $\int \frac{dx}{(a^2-x^2)^2} = \frac{x}{2a^2(a^2-x^2)} + \frac{1}{4a^3}\ln\left|\frac{x+a}{x-a}\right| + C$

20. $\int \frac{dx}{\sqrt{a^2+x^2}} = \sinh^{-1}\frac{x}{a} + C = \ln\left(x + \sqrt{a^2+x^2}\right) + C$

21. $\int \sqrt{a^2+x^2}\,dx = \frac{x}{2}\sqrt{a^2+x^2} + \frac{a^2}{2}\ln\left(x + \sqrt{a^2+x^2}\right) + C$

22. $\int x^2\sqrt{a^2+x^2}\,dx = \frac{x}{8}(a^2+2x^2)\sqrt{a^2+x^2} - \frac{a^4}{8}\ln\left(x + \sqrt{a^2+x^2}\right) + C$

23. $\int \frac{\sqrt{a^2+x^2}}{x}\,dx = \sqrt{a^2+x^2} - a\ln\left|\frac{a+\sqrt{a^2+x^2}}{x}\right| + C$

24. $\int \frac{\sqrt{a^2+x^2}}{x^2}\,dx = \ln\left(x+\sqrt{a^2+x^2}\right) - \frac{\sqrt{a^2+x^2}}{x} + C$

25. $\int \frac{x^2}{\sqrt{a^2+x^2}}\,dx = -\frac{a^2}{2}\ln\left(x+\sqrt{a^2+x^2}\right) + \frac{x\sqrt{a^2+x^2}}{2} + C$

26. $\int \frac{dx}{x\sqrt{a^2+x^2}} = -\frac{1}{a}\ln\left|\frac{a+\sqrt{a^2+x^2}}{x}\right| + C$

27. $\int \frac{dx}{x^2\sqrt{a^2+x^2}} = -\frac{\sqrt{a^2+x^2}}{a^2x} + C$

28. $\int \frac{dx}{\sqrt{a^2-x^2}} = \sin^{-1}\frac{x}{a} + C$

29. $\int \sqrt{a^2-x^2}\,dx = \frac{x}{2}\sqrt{a^2-x^2} + \frac{a^2}{2}\sin^{-1}\frac{x}{a} + C$

30. $\int x^2\sqrt{a^2-x^2}\,dx = \frac{a^4}{8}\sin^{-1}\frac{x}{a} - \frac{1}{8}x\sqrt{a^2-x^2}\,(a^2-2x^2) + C$

31. $\int \frac{\sqrt{a^2-x^2}}{x}\,dx = \sqrt{a^2-x^2} - a\ln\left|\frac{a+\sqrt{a^2-x^2}}{x}\right| + C$

32. $\int \frac{\sqrt{a^2-x^2}}{x^2}\,dx = -\sin^{-1}\frac{x}{a} - \frac{\sqrt{a^2-x^2}}{x} + C$

33. $\int \frac{x^2}{\sqrt{a^2-x^2}}\,dx = \frac{a^2}{2}\sin^{-1}\frac{x}{a} - \frac{1}{2}x\sqrt{a^2-x^2} + C$

34. $\int \frac{dx}{x\sqrt{a^2-x^2}} = -\frac{1}{a}\ln\left|\frac{a+\sqrt{a^2-x^2}}{x}\right| + C$

35. $\int \frac{dx}{x^2\sqrt{a^2-x^2}} = -\frac{\sqrt{a^2-x^2}}{a^2x} + C$

36. $\int \frac{dx}{\sqrt{x^2-a^2}} = \cosh^{-1}\frac{x}{a} + C = \ln\left|x+\sqrt{x^2-a^2}\right| + C$

37. $\int \sqrt{x^2-a^2}\,dx = \frac{x}{2}\sqrt{x^2-a^2} - \frac{a^2}{2}\ln\left|x+\sqrt{x^2-a^2}\right| + C$

38. $\int \left(\sqrt{x^2-a^2}\right)^n dx = \frac{x\left(\sqrt{x^2-a^2}\right)^n}{n+1} - \frac{na^2}{n+1}\int \left(\sqrt{x^2-a^2}\right)^{n-2} dx, \quad n \neq -1$

39. $\int \frac{dx}{\left(\sqrt{x^2-a^2}\right)^n} = \frac{x\left(\sqrt{x^2-a^2}\right)^{2-n}}{(2-n)a^2} - \frac{n-3}{(n-2)a^2}\int \frac{dx}{\left(\sqrt{x^2-a^2}\right)^{n-2}}, \quad n \neq 2$

40. $\int x\left(\sqrt{x^2-a^2}\right)^n dx = \frac{\left(\sqrt{x^2-a^2}\right)^{n+2}}{n+2} + C, \quad n \neq -2$

41. $\int x^2\sqrt{x^2-a^2}\,dx = \frac{x}{8}(2x^2-a^2)\sqrt{x^2-a^2} - \frac{a^4}{8}\ln\left|x+\sqrt{x^2-a^2}\right| + C$

42. $\int \frac{\sqrt{x^2-a^2}}{x}\,dx = \sqrt{x^2-a^2} - a\sec^{-1}\left|\frac{x}{a}\right| + C$

43. $\int \frac{\sqrt{x^2-a^2}}{x^2}\,dx = \ln\left|x+\sqrt{x^2-a^2}\right| - \frac{\sqrt{x^2-a^2}}{x} + C$

44. $\int \frac{x^2}{\sqrt{x^2-a^2}}\,dx = \frac{a^2}{2}\ln\left|x+\sqrt{x^2-a^2}\right| + \frac{x}{2}\sqrt{x^2-a^2} + C$

45. $\int \frac{dx}{x\sqrt{x^2-a^2}} = \frac{1}{a}\sec^{-1}\left|\frac{x}{a}\right| + C = \frac{1}{a}\cos^{-1}\left|\frac{a}{x}\right| + C$

46. $\int \frac{dx}{x^2\sqrt{x^2-a^2}} = \frac{\sqrt{x^2-a^2}}{a^2x} + C$

47. $\displaystyle\int \frac{dx}{\sqrt{2ax - x^2}} = \sin^{-1}\left(\frac{x - a}{a}\right) + C$

48. $\displaystyle\int \sqrt{2ax - x^2}\, dx = \frac{x - a}{2}\sqrt{2ax - x^2} + \frac{a^2}{2}\sin^{-1}\left(\frac{x - a}{a}\right) + C$

49. $\displaystyle\int \left(\sqrt{2ax - x^2}\right)^n dx = \frac{(x - a)\left(\sqrt{2ax - x^2}\right)^n}{n + 1} + \frac{na^2}{n + 1}\int \left(\sqrt{2ax - x^2}\right)^{n-2} dx$

50. $\displaystyle\int \frac{dx}{\left(\sqrt{2ax - x^2}\right)^n} = \frac{(x - a)\left(\sqrt{2ax - x^2}\right)^{2-n}}{(n - 2)a^2} + \frac{n - 3}{(n - 2)a^2}\int \frac{dx}{\left(\sqrt{2ax - x^2}\right)^{n-2}}$

51. $\displaystyle\int x\sqrt{2ax - x^2}\, dx = \frac{(x + a)(2x - 3a)\sqrt{2ax - x^2}}{6} + \frac{a^3}{2}\sin^{-1}\left(\frac{x - a}{a}\right) + C$

52. $\displaystyle\int \frac{\sqrt{2ax - x^2}}{x}\, dx = \sqrt{2ax - x^2} + a\sin^{-1}\left(\frac{x - a}{a}\right) + C$

53. $\displaystyle\int \frac{\sqrt{2ax - x^2}}{x^2}\, dx = -2\sqrt{\frac{2a - x}{x}} - \sin^{-1}\left(\frac{x - a}{a}\right) + C$

54. $\displaystyle\int \frac{x\, dx}{\sqrt{2ax - x^2}} = a\sin^{-1}\left(\frac{x - a}{a}\right) - \sqrt{2ax - x^2} + C$

55. $\displaystyle\int \frac{dx}{x\sqrt{2ax - x^2}} = -\frac{1}{a}\sqrt{\frac{2a - x}{x}} + C$

56. $\displaystyle\int \sin ax\, dx = -\frac{1}{a}\cos ax + C$

57. $\displaystyle\int \cos ax\, dx = \frac{1}{a}\sin ax + C$

58. $\displaystyle\int \sin^2 ax\, dx = \frac{x}{2} - \frac{\sin 2ax}{4a} + C$

59. $\displaystyle\int \cos^2 ax\, dx = \frac{x}{2} + \frac{\sin 2ax}{4a} + C$

60. $\displaystyle\int \sin^n ax\, dx = -\frac{\sin^{n-1} ax \cos ax}{na} + \frac{n - 1}{n}\int \sin^{n-2} ax\, dx$

61. $\displaystyle\int \cos^n ax\, dx = \frac{\cos^{n-1} ax \sin ax}{na} + \frac{n - 1}{n}\int \cos^{n-2} ax\, dx$

62. **(a)** $\displaystyle\int \sin ax \cos bx\, dx = -\frac{\cos(a + b)x}{2(a + b)} - \frac{\cos(a - b)x}{2(a - b)} + C, \quad a^2 \neq b^2$

(b) $\displaystyle\int \sin ax \sin bx\, dx = \frac{\sin(a - b)x}{2(a - b)} - \frac{\sin(a + b)x}{2(a + b)} + C, \quad a^2 \neq b^2$

(c) $\displaystyle\int \cos ax \cos bx\, dx = \frac{\sin(a - b)x}{2(a - b)} + \frac{\sin(a + b)x}{2(a + b)} + C, \quad a^2 \neq b^2$

63. $\displaystyle\int \sin ax \cos ax\, dx = -\frac{\cos 2ax}{4a} + C$

64. $\displaystyle\int \sin^n ax \cos ax\, dx = \frac{\sin^{n+1} ax}{(n + 1)a} + C, \quad n \neq -1$

65. $\displaystyle\int \frac{\cos ax}{\sin ax}\, dx = \frac{1}{a}\ln|\sin ax| + C$

66. $\displaystyle\int \cos^n ax \sin ax\, dx = -\frac{\cos^{n+1} ax}{(n + 1)a} + C, \quad n \neq -1$

67. $\displaystyle\int \frac{\sin ax}{\cos ax}\, dx = -\frac{1}{a}\ln|\cos ax| + C$

68. $\int \sin^n ax \cos^m ax\,dx = -\frac{\sin^{n-1} ax \cos^{m+1} ax}{a(m+n)} + \frac{n-1}{m+n}\int \sin^{n-2} ax \cos^m ax\,dx, \quad n \neq -m \quad (\text{reduces } \sin^n ax)$

69. $\int \sin^n ax \cos^m ax\,dx = \frac{\sin^{n+1} ax \cos^{m-1} ax}{a(m+n)} + \frac{m-1}{m+n}\int \sin^n ax \cos^{m-2} ax\,dx, \quad m \neq -n \quad (\text{reduces } \cos^m ax)$

70. $\int \frac{dx}{b + c\sin ax} = \frac{-2}{a\sqrt{b^2 - c^2}} \tan^{-1}\left[\sqrt{\frac{b-c}{b+c}} \tan\left(\frac{\pi}{4} - \frac{ax}{2}\right)\right] + C, \quad b^2 > c^2$

71. $\int \frac{dx}{b + c\sin ax} = \frac{-1}{a\sqrt{c^2 - b^2}} \ln\left|\frac{c + b\sin ax + \sqrt{c^2 - b^2}\cos ax}{b + c\sin ax}\right| + C, \quad b^2 < c^2$

72. $\int \frac{dx}{1 + \sin ax} = -\frac{1}{a}\tan\left(\frac{\pi}{4} - \frac{ax}{2}\right) + C$

73. $\int \frac{dx}{1 - \sin ax} = \frac{1}{a}\tan\left(\frac{\pi}{4} + \frac{ax}{2}\right) + C$

74. $\int \frac{dx}{b + c\cos ax} = \frac{2}{a\sqrt{b^2 - c^2}} \tan^{-1}\left[\sqrt{\frac{b-c}{b+c}} \tan\frac{ax}{2}\right] + C, \quad b^2 > c^2$

75. $\int \frac{dx}{b + c\cos ax} = \frac{1}{a\sqrt{c^2 - b^2}} \ln\left|\frac{c + b\cos ax + \sqrt{c^2 - b^2}\sin ax}{b + c\cos ax}\right| + C, \quad b^2 < c^2$

76. $\int \frac{dx}{1 + \cos ax} = \frac{1}{a}\tan\frac{ax}{2} + C$

77. $\int \frac{dx}{1 - \cos ax} = -\frac{1}{a}\cot\frac{ax}{2} + C$

78. $\int x\sin ax\,dx = \frac{1}{a^2}\sin ax - \frac{x}{a}\cos ax + C$

79. $\int x\cos ax\,dx = \frac{1}{a^2}\cos ax + \frac{x}{a}\sin ax + C$

80. $\int x^n \sin ax\,dx = -\frac{x^n}{a}\cos ax + \frac{n}{a}\int x^{n-1}\cos ax\,dx$

81. $\int x^n \cos ax\,dx = \frac{x^n}{a}\sin ax - \frac{n}{a}\int x^{n-1}\sin ax\,dx$

82. $\int \tan ax\,dx = \frac{1}{a}\ln|\sec ax| + C$

83. $\int \cot ax\,dx = \frac{1}{a}\ln|\sin ax| + C$

84. $\int \tan^2 ax\,dx = \frac{1}{a}\tan ax - x + C$

85. $\int \cot^2 ax\,dx = -\frac{1}{a}\cot ax - x + C$

86. $\int \tan^n ax\,dx = \frac{\tan^{n-1} ax}{a(n-1)} - \int \tan^{n-2} ax\,dx, \quad n \neq 1$

87. $\int \cot^n ax\,dx = -\frac{\cot^{n-1} ax}{a(n-1)} - \int \cot^{n-2} ax\,dx, \quad n \neq 1$

88. $\int \sec ax\,dx = \frac{1}{a}\ln|\sec ax + \tan ax| + C$

89. $\int \csc ax\,dx = -\frac{1}{a}\ln|\csc ax + \cot ax| + C$

90. $\int \sec^2 ax\,dx = \frac{1}{a}\tan ax + C$

91. $\int \csc^2 ax\,dx = -\frac{1}{a}\cot ax + C$

92. $\int \sec^n ax\,dx = \frac{\sec^{n-2} ax \tan ax}{a(n-1)} + \frac{n-2}{n-1}\int \sec^{n-2} ax\,dx, \quad n \neq 1$

93. $\int \csc^n ax\,dx = -\frac{\csc^{n-2} ax \cot ax}{a(n-1)} + \frac{n-2}{n-1}\int \csc^{n-2} ax\,dx, \quad n \neq 1$

94. $\int \sec^n ax \tan ax\,dx = \frac{\sec^n ax}{na} + C, \quad n \neq 0$

95. $\int \csc^n ax \cot ax\,dx = -\frac{\csc^n ax}{na} + C, \quad n \neq 0$

96. $\int \sin^{-1} ax\, dx = x \sin^{-1} ax + \frac{1}{a}\sqrt{1 - a^2x^2} + C$

97. $\int \cos^{-1} ax\, dx = x \cos^{-1} ax - \frac{1}{a}\sqrt{1 - a^2x^2} + C$

98. $\int \tan^{-1} ax\, dx = x \tan^{-1} ax - \frac{1}{2a}\ln(1 + a^2x^2) + C$

99. $\int x^n \sin^{-1} ax\, dx = \frac{x^{n+1}}{n+1}\sin^{-1} ax - \frac{a}{n+1}\int \frac{x^{n+1}\, dx}{\sqrt{1 - a^2x^2}}, \quad n \neq -1$

100. $\int x^n \cos^{-1} ax\, dx = \frac{x^{n+1}}{n+1}\cos^{-1} ax + \frac{a}{n+1}\int \frac{x^{n+1}\, dx}{\sqrt{1 - a^2x^2}}, \quad n \neq -1$

101. $\int x^n \tan^{-1} ax\, dx = \frac{x^{n+1}}{n+1}\tan^{-1} ax - \frac{a}{n+1}\int \frac{x^{n+1}\, dx}{1 + a^2x^2}, \quad n \neq -1$

102. $\int e^{ax}\, dx = \frac{1}{a}e^{ax} + C$

103. $\int b^{ax}\, dx = \frac{1}{a}\frac{b^{ax}}{\ln b} + C, \quad b > 0, b \neq 1$

104. $\int xe^{ax}\, dx = \frac{e^{ax}}{a^2}(ax - 1) + C$

105. $\int x^n e^{ax}\, dx = \frac{1}{a}x^n e^{ax} - \frac{n}{a}\int x^{n-1}e^{ax}\, dx$

106. $\int x^n b^{ax}\, dx = \frac{x^n b^{ax}}{a \ln b} - \frac{n}{a \ln b}\int x^{n-1}b^{ax}\, dx, \quad b > 0, b \neq 1$

107. $\int e^{ax} \sin bx\, dx = \frac{e^{ax}}{a^2 + b^2}(a \sin bx - b \cos bx) + C$

108. $\int e^{ax} \cos bx\, dx = \frac{e^{ax}}{a^2 + b^2}(a \cos bx + b \sin bx) + C$

109. $\int \ln ax\, dx = x \ln ax - x + C$

110. $\int x^n (\ln ax)^m\, dx = \frac{x^{n+1}(\ln ax)^m}{n+1} - \frac{m}{n+1}\int x^n (\ln ax)^{m-1}\, dx, \quad n \neq -1$

111. $\int x^{-1}(\ln ax)^m\, dx = \frac{(\ln ax)^{m+1}}{m+1} + C, \quad m \neq -1$

112. $\int \frac{dx}{x \ln ax} = \ln|\ln ax| + C$

113. $\int \sinh ax\, dx = \frac{1}{a}\cosh ax + C$

114. $\int \cosh ax\, dx = \frac{1}{a}\sinh ax + C$

115. $\int \sinh^2 ax\, dx = \frac{\sinh 2ax}{4a} - \frac{x}{2} + C$

116. $\int \cosh^2 ax\, dx = \frac{\sinh 2ax}{4a} + \frac{x}{2} + C$

117. $\int \sinh^n ax\, dx = \frac{\sinh^{n-1} ax \cosh ax}{na} - \frac{n-1}{n}\int \sinh^{n-2} ax\, dx, \quad n \neq 0$

118. $\int \cosh^n ax\, dx = \frac{\cosh^{n-1} ax \sinh ax}{na} + \frac{n-1}{n}\int \cosh^{n-2} ax\, dx, \quad n \neq 0$

119. $\int x \sinh ax\, dx = \frac{x}{a}\cosh ax - \frac{1}{a^2}\sinh ax + C$

120. $\int x \cosh ax\, dx = \frac{x}{a}\sinh ax - \frac{1}{a^2}\cosh ax + C$

121. $\int x^n \sinh ax\, dx = \frac{x^n}{a}\cosh ax - \frac{n}{a}\int x^{n-1}\cosh ax\, dx$

122. $\int x^n \cosh ax\, dx = \frac{x^n}{a}\sinh ax - \frac{n}{a}\int x^{n-1}\sinh ax\, dx$

123. $\int \tanh ax\, dx = \frac{1}{a}\ln(\cosh ax) + C$

124. $\int \coth ax\, dx = \frac{1}{a}\ln|\sinh ax| + C$

125. $\int \tanh^2 ax\, dx = x - \frac{1}{a}\tanh ax + C$

126. $\int \coth^2 ax\, dx = x - \frac{1}{a}\coth ax + C$

127. $\int \tanh^n ax\, dx = -\frac{\tanh^{n-1} ax}{(n-1)a} + \int \tanh^{n-2} ax\, dx, \quad n \neq 1$

128. $\int \coth^n ax\, dx = -\frac{\coth^{n-1} ax}{(n-1)a} + \int \coth^{n-2} ax\, dx, \quad n \neq 1$

129. $\int \operatorname{sech} ax\, dx = \frac{1}{a}\sin^{-1}(\tanh ax) + C$

130. $\int \operatorname{csch} ax\, dx = \frac{1}{a}\ln\left|\tanh\frac{ax}{2}\right| + C$

131. $\int \operatorname{sech}^2 ax\, dx = \frac{1}{a}\tanh ax + C$

132. $\int \operatorname{csch}^2 ax\, dx = -\frac{1}{a}\coth ax + C$

133. $\int \operatorname{sech}^n ax\, dx = \frac{\operatorname{sech}^{n-2} ax \tanh ax}{(n-1)a} + \frac{n-2}{n-1}\int \operatorname{sech}^{n-2} ax\, dx, \quad n \neq 1$

134. $\int \operatorname{csch}^n ax\, dx = -\frac{\operatorname{csch}^{n-2} ax \coth ax}{(n-1)a} - \frac{n-2}{n-1}\int \operatorname{csch}^{n-2} ax\, dx, \quad n \neq 1$

135. $\int \operatorname{sech}^n ax \tanh ax\, dx = -\frac{\operatorname{sech}^n ax}{na} + C, \quad n \neq 0$

136. $\int \operatorname{csch}^n ax \coth ax\, dx = -\frac{\operatorname{csch}^n ax}{na} + C, \quad n \neq 0$

137. $\int e^{ax}\sinh bx\, dx = \frac{e^{ax}}{2}\left[\frac{e^{bx}}{a+b} - \frac{e^{-bx}}{a-b}\right] + C, \quad a^2 \neq b^2$

138. $\int e^{ax}\cosh bx\, dx = \frac{e^{ax}}{2}\left[\frac{e^{bx}}{a+b} + \frac{e^{-bx}}{a-b}\right] + C, \quad a^2 \neq b^2$

139. $\int_0^\infty x^{n-1}e^{-x}\, dx = \Gamma(n) = (n-1)!, \quad n > 0$

140. $\int_0^\infty e^{-ax^2}\, dx = \frac{1}{2}\sqrt{\frac{\pi}{a}}, \quad a > 0$

141. $$\int_0^{\pi/2} \sin^n x\, dx = \int_0^{\pi/2} \cos^n x\, dx = \begin{cases} \frac{1\cdot 3\cdot 5\cdot \cdots \cdot (n-1)}{2\cdot 4\cdot 6\cdot \cdots \cdot n}\cdot\frac{\pi}{2}, & \text{if } n \text{ is an even integer} \geq 2 \\ \frac{2\cdot 4\cdot 6\cdot \cdots \cdot (n-1)}{3\cdot 5\cdot 7\cdot \cdots \cdot n}, & \text{if } n \text{ is an odd integer} \geq 3 \end{cases}$$

CREDITS

Page 155, Section 3.3, photo for Exercise 19, *PSSC Physics*, 2nd ed., DC Heath & Co. with Education Development Center, Inc.; **Page 231, Figure 3.58,** NCPMF "Differentiation" by W.U. Walton et al., Project CALC, Education Development Center, Inc.; **Page 235, Chapter 3 Additional and Advanced Exercises, photo for Exercise 9,** AP/Wide World Photos; **Page 437, Figure 6.41,** *PSSC Physics*, 2nd ed., DC Heath & Co. with Education Development Center, Inc.; **Page 517, Figure 8.6,** *PSSC Physics*, 2nd ed., DC Heath & Co. with Education Development Center, Inc.; **Page 706, Figure 12.6,** Reproduced by permission from Appalachian Mountain Club; **Page 740, Figure 12.23,** Department of History, U.S. Military Academy, West Point, New York; **Page 857, Figures 14.6 and 14.7,** *NCFMF Book of Film Notes*, 1974, MIT Press with Education Development Center, Inc.; **Page 858, Figure 14.14,** InterNetwork Media, Inc., and NASA/JPL.

Trigonometry Formulas

1. Definitions and Fundamental Identities

Sine: $\sin\theta = \dfrac{y}{r} = \dfrac{1}{\csc\theta}$

Cosine: $\cos\theta = \dfrac{x}{r} = \dfrac{1}{\sec\theta}$

Tangent: $\tan\theta = \dfrac{y}{x} = \dfrac{1}{\cot\theta}$

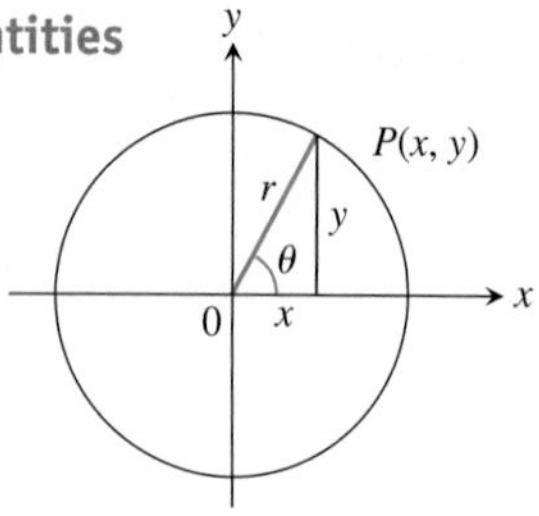

2. Identities

$\sin(-\theta) = -\sin\theta, \quad \cos(-\theta) = \cos\theta$

$\sin^2\theta + \cos^2\theta = 1, \quad \sec^2\theta = 1 + \tan^2\theta, \quad \csc^2\theta = 1 + \cot^2\theta$

$\sin 2\theta = 2\sin\theta\cos\theta, \quad \cos 2\theta = \cos^2\theta - \sin^2\theta$

$\cos^2\theta = \dfrac{1 + \cos 2\theta}{2}, \quad \sin^2\theta = \dfrac{1 - \cos 2\theta}{2}$

$\sin(A + B) = \sin A\cos B + \cos A\sin B$

$\sin(A - B) = \sin A\cos B - \cos A\sin B$

$\cos(A + B) = \cos A\cos B - \sin A\sin B$

$\cos(A - B) = \cos A\cos B + \sin A\sin B$

$\tan(A + B) = \dfrac{\tan A + \tan B}{1 - \tan A\tan B}$

$\tan(A - B) = \dfrac{\tan A - \tan B}{1 + \tan A\tan B}$

$\sin\left(A - \dfrac{\pi}{2}\right) = -\cos A, \qquad \cos\left(A - \dfrac{\pi}{2}\right) = \sin A$

$\sin\left(A + \dfrac{\pi}{2}\right) = \cos A, \qquad \cos\left(A + \dfrac{\pi}{2}\right) = -\sin A$

$\sin A\sin B = \dfrac{1}{2}\cos(A - B) - \dfrac{1}{2}\cos(A + B)$

$\cos A\cos B = \dfrac{1}{2}\cos(A - B) + \dfrac{1}{2}\cos(A + B)$

$\sin A\cos B = \dfrac{1}{2}\sin(A - B) + \dfrac{1}{2}\sin(A + B)$

$\sin A + \sin B = 2\sin\dfrac{1}{2}(A + B)\cos\dfrac{1}{2}(A - B)$

$\sin A - \sin B = 2\cos\dfrac{1}{2}(A + B)\sin\dfrac{1}{2}(A - B)$

$\cos A + \cos B = 2\cos\dfrac{1}{2}(A + B)\cos\dfrac{1}{2}(A - B)$

$\cos A - \cos B = -2\sin\dfrac{1}{2}(A + B)\sin\dfrac{1}{2}(A - B)$

Trigonometric Functions

Radian Measure

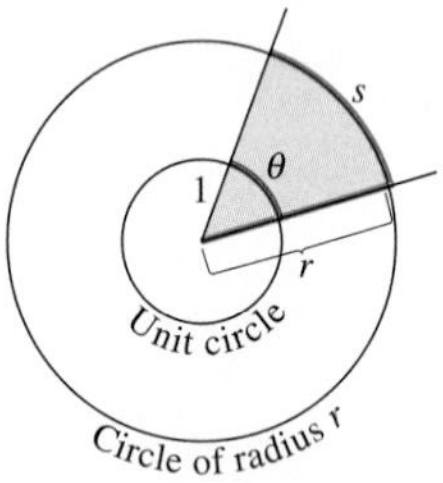

$\dfrac{s}{r} = \dfrac{\theta}{1} = \theta \quad$ or $\quad \theta = \dfrac{s}{r},$

$180° = \pi$ radians.

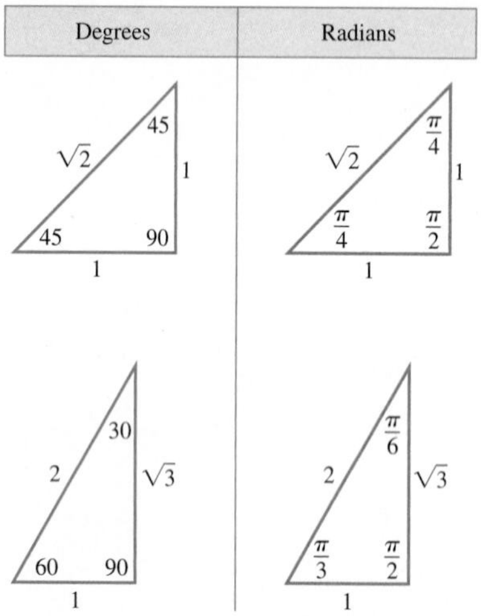

The angles of two common triangles, in degrees and radians.

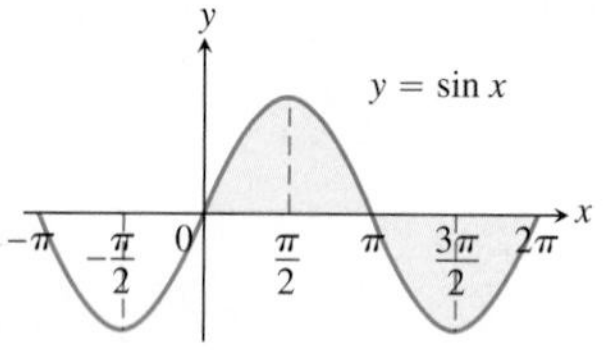

Domain: $(-\infty, \infty)$
Range: $[-1, 1]$

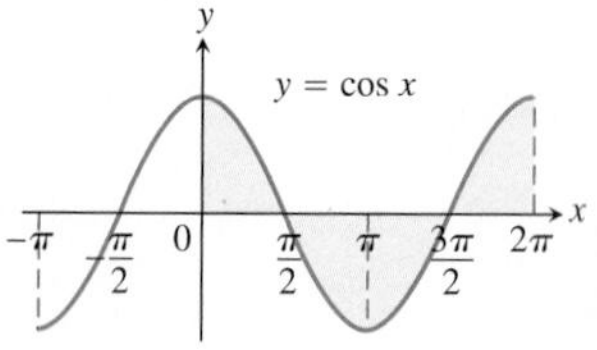

Domain: $(-\infty, \infty)$
Range: $[-1, 1]$

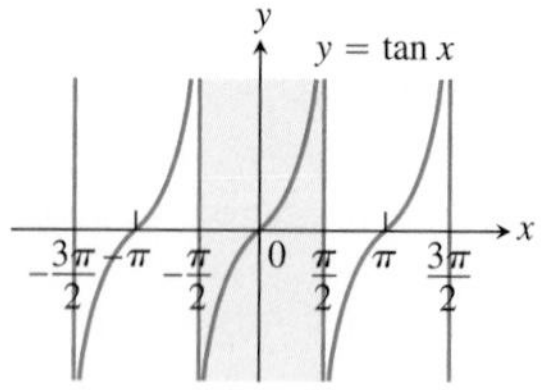

Domain: All real numbers except odd integer multiples of $\pi/2$
Range: $(-\infty, \infty)$

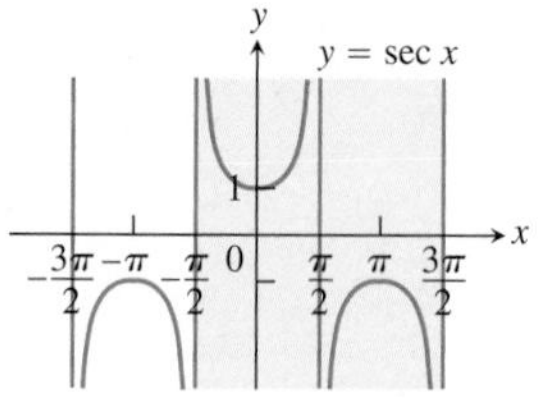

Domain: All real numbers except odd integer multiples of $\pi/2$
Range: $(-\infty, -1] \cup [1, \infty)$

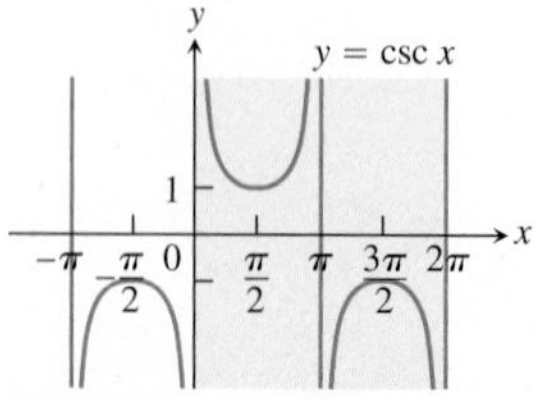

Domain: $x \neq 0, \pm\pi, \pm 2\pi, \ldots$
Range: $(-\infty, -1] \cup [1, \infty)$

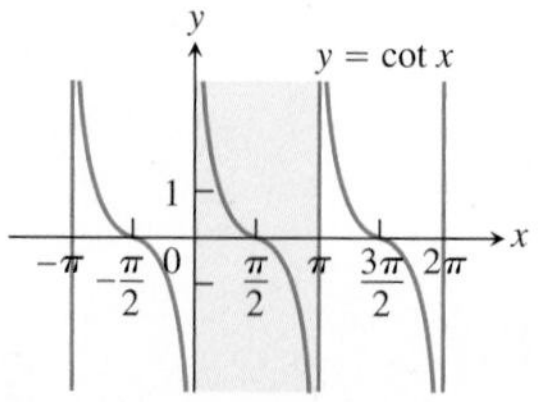

Domain: $x \neq 0, \pm\pi, \pm 2\pi, \ldots$
Range: $(-\infty, \infty)$

LIMITS

General Laws

If L, M, c, and k are real numbers and

$$\lim_{x \to c} f(x) = L \quad \text{and} \quad \lim_{x \to c} g(x) = M, \quad \text{then}$$

Sum Rule: $\lim_{x \to c} (f(x) + g(x)) = L + M$

Difference Rule: $\lim_{x \to c} (f(x) - g(x)) = L - M$

Product Rule: $\lim_{x \to c} (f(x) \cdot g(x)) = L \cdot M$

Constant Multiple Rule: $\lim_{x \to c} (k \cdot f(x)) = k \cdot L$

Quotient Rule: $\lim_{x \to c} \dfrac{f(x)}{g(x)} = \dfrac{L}{M}, \quad M \neq 0$

The Sandwich Theorem

If $g(x) \leq f(x) \leq h(x)$ in an open interval containing c, except possibly at $x = c$, and if

$$\lim_{x \to c} g(x) = \lim_{x \to c} h(x) = L,$$

then $\lim_{x \to c} f(x) = L$.

Inequalities

If $f(x) \leq g(x)$ in an open interval containing c, except possibly at $x = c$, and both limits exist, then

$$\lim_{x \to c} f(x) \leq \lim_{x \to c} g(x).$$

Continuity

If g is continuous at L and $\lim_{x \to c} f(x) = L$, then

$$\lim_{x \to c} g(f(x)) = g(L).$$

Specific Formulas

If $P(x) = a_n x^n + a_{n-1} x^{n-1} + \cdots + a_0$, then

$$\lim_{x \to c} P(x) = P(c) = a_n c^n + a_{n-1} c^{n-1} + \cdots + a_0.$$

If $P(x)$ and $Q(x)$ are polynomials and $Q(c) \neq 0$, then

$$\lim_{x \to c} \frac{P(x)}{Q(x)} = \frac{P(c)}{Q(c)}.$$

If $f(x)$ is continuous at $x = c$, then

$$\lim_{x \to c} f(x) = f(c).$$

$$\lim_{x \to 0} \frac{\sin x}{x} = 1 \quad \text{and} \quad \lim_{x \to 0} \frac{1 - \cos x}{x} = 0$$

L'Hôpital's Rule

If $f(a) = g(a) = 0$, both f' and g' exist in an open interval I containing a, and $g'(x) \neq 0$ on I if $x \neq a$, then

$$\lim_{x \to a} \frac{f(x)}{g(x)} = \lim_{x \to a} \frac{f'(x)}{g'(x)},$$

assuming the limit on the right side exists.

DIFFERENTIATION RULES

General Formulas

Assume u and v are differentiable functions of x.

Constant: $\frac{d}{dx}(c) = 0$

Sum: $\frac{d}{dx}(u + v) = \frac{du}{dx} + \frac{dv}{dx}$

Difference: $\frac{d}{dx}(u - v) = \frac{du}{dx} - \frac{dv}{dx}$

Constant Multiple: $\frac{d}{dx}(cu) = c\frac{du}{dx}$

Product: $\frac{d}{dx}(uv) = u\frac{dv}{dx} + v\frac{du}{dx}$

Quotient: $\frac{d}{dx}\left(\frac{u}{v}\right) = \frac{v\frac{du}{dx} - u\frac{dv}{dx}}{v^2}$

Power: $\frac{d}{dx}x^n = nx^{n-1}$

Chain Rule: $\frac{d}{dx}(f(g(x)) = f'(g(x)) \cdot g'(x)$

Trigonometric Functions

$\frac{d}{dx}(\sin x) = \cos x$ $\qquad$ $\frac{d}{dx}(\cos x) = -\sin x$

$\frac{d}{dx}(\tan x) = \sec^2 x$ $\qquad$ $\frac{d}{dx}(\sec x) = \sec x \tan x$

$\frac{d}{dx}(\cot x) = -\csc^2 x$ $\qquad$ $\frac{d}{dx}(\csc x) = -\csc x \cot x$

Exponential and Logarithmic Functions

$\frac{d}{dx}e^x = e^x$ $\qquad$ $\frac{d}{dx}\ln x = \frac{1}{x}$

$\frac{d}{dx}a^x = a^x \ln a$ $\qquad$ $\frac{d}{dx}(\log_a x) = \frac{1}{x \ln a}$

Inverse Trigonometric Functions

$\frac{d}{dx}(\sin^{-1} x) = \frac{1}{\sqrt{1 - x^2}}$ $\qquad$ $\frac{d}{dx}(\cos^{-1} x) = -\frac{1}{\sqrt{1 - x^2}}$

$\frac{d}{dx}(\tan^{-1} x) = \frac{1}{1 + x^2}$ $\qquad$ $\frac{d}{dx}(\sec^{-1} x) = \frac{1}{|x|\sqrt{x^2 - 1}}$

$\frac{d}{dx}(\cot^{-1} x) = -\frac{1}{1 + x^2}$ $\qquad$ $\frac{d}{dx}(\csc^{-1} x) = -\frac{1}{|x|\sqrt{x^2 - 1}}$

Hyperbolic Functions

$\frac{d}{dx}(\sinh x) = \cosh x$ $\qquad$ $\frac{d}{dx}(\cosh x) = \sinh x$

$\frac{d}{dx}(\tanh x) = \operatorname{sech}^2 x$ $\qquad$ $\frac{d}{dx}(\operatorname{sech} x) = -\operatorname{sech} x \tanh x$

$\frac{d}{dx}(\coth x) = -\operatorname{csch}^2 x$ $\qquad$ $\frac{d}{dx}(\operatorname{csch} x) = -\operatorname{csch} x \coth x$

Inverse Hyperbolic Functions

$\frac{d}{dx}(\sinh^{-1} x) = \frac{1}{\sqrt{1 + x^2}}$ $\qquad$ $\frac{d}{dx}(\cosh^{-1} x) = \frac{1}{\sqrt{x^2 - 1}}$

$\frac{d}{dx}(\tanh^{-1} x) = \frac{1}{1 - x^2}$ $\qquad$ $\frac{d}{dx}(\operatorname{sech}^{-1} x) = -\frac{1}{x\sqrt{1 - x^2}}$

$\frac{d}{dx}(\coth^{-1} x) = \frac{1}{1 - x^2}$ $\qquad$ $\frac{d}{dx}(\operatorname{csch}^{-1} x) = -\frac{1}{|x|\sqrt{1 + x^2}}$

Parametric Equations

If $x = f(t)$ and $y = g(t)$ are differentiable, then

$$y' = \frac{dy}{dx} = \frac{dy/dt}{dx/dt} \quad \text{and} \quad \frac{d^2y}{dx^2} = \frac{dy'/dt}{dx/dt}.$$

INTEGRATION RULES

General Formulas

Zero: $$\int_a^a f(x)\,dx = 0$$

Order of Integration: $$\int_b^a f(x)\,dx = -\int_a^b f(x)\,dx$$

Constant Multiples: $$\int_a^b kf(x)\,dx = k\int_a^b f(x)\,dx \qquad \text{(Any number } k\text{)}$$

$$\int_a^b -f(x)\,dx = -\int_a^b f(x)\,dx \qquad (k = -1)$$

Sums and Differences: $$\int_a^b (f(x) \pm g(x))\,dx = \int_a^b f(x)\,dx \pm \int_a^b g(x)\,dx$$

Additivity: $$\int_a^b f(x)\,dx + \int_b^c f(x)\,dx = \int_a^c f(x)\,dx$$

Max-Min Inequality: If max f and min f are the maximum and minimum values of f on $[a, b]$, then

$$\min f \cdot (b - a) \le \int_a^b f(x)\,dx \le \max f \cdot (b - a).$$

Domination: $f(x) \ge g(x)$ on $[a, b]$ implies $\int_a^b f(x)\,dx \ge \int_a^b g(x)\,dx$

$f(x) \ge 0$ on $[a, b]$ implies $\int_a^b f(x)\,dx \ge 0$

The Fundamental Theorem of Calculus

Part 1 If f is continuous on $[a, b]$, then $F(x) = \int_a^x f(t)\,dt$ is continuous on $[a, b]$ and differentiable on (a, b) and its derivative is $f(x)$;

$$F'(x) = \frac{d}{dx}\int_a^x f(t)\,dt = f(x).$$

Part 2 If f is continuous at every point of $[a, b]$ and F is any antiderivative of f on $[a, b]$, then

$$\int_a^b f(x)\,dx = F(b) - F(a).$$

Substitution in Definite Integrals

$$\int_a^b f(g(x)) \cdot g'(x)\,dx = \int_{g(a)}^{g(b)} f(u)\,du$$

Integration by Parts

$$\int_a^b f(x)g'(x)\,dx = f(x)g(x)\Big]_a^b - \int_a^b f'(x)g(x)\,dx$$